ALGEBRA

Exponents and Radicals

$$x^a x^b = x^{a+b} \qquad \frac{x^a}{x^b} = x^{a-b} \qquad x^{-a} = \frac{1}{x^a} \qquad (x^a)^b = x^{ab} \qquad \left(\frac{x}{y}\right)^a = \frac{x^a}{y^a}$$

$$x^{1/n} = \sqrt[n]{x} \qquad x^{m/n} = \sqrt[n]{x^m} = (\sqrt[n]{x})^m \qquad \sqrt[n]{xy} = \sqrt[n]{x}\sqrt[n]{y} \qquad \sqrt[n]{x/y} = \sqrt[n]{x}/\sqrt[n]{y}$$

Factoring Formulas

$a^2 - b^2 = (a - b)(a + b)$ $\qquad$ $a^2 + b^2$ does not factor over real numbers.

$a^3 - b^3 = (a - b)(a^2 + ab + b^2)$ $\qquad$ $a^3 + b^3 = (a + b)(a^2 - ab + b^2)$

$a^n - b^n = (a - b)(a^{n-1} + a^{n-2}b + a^{n-3}b^2 + \cdots + ab^{n-2} + b^{n-1})$

Binomials

$(a \pm b)^2 = a^2 \pm 2ab + b^2$

$(a \pm b)^3 = a^3 \pm 3a^2b + 3ab^2 \pm b^3$

Binomial Theorem

$$(a + b)^n = a^n + \binom{n}{1}a^{n-1}b + \binom{n}{2}a^{n-2}b^2 + \cdots + \binom{n}{n-1}ab^{n-1} + b^n,$$

where $\binom{n}{k} = \dfrac{n(n-1)(n-2)\cdots(n-k+1)}{k(k-1)(k-2)\cdots 3\cdot 2\cdot 1} = \dfrac{n!}{k!(n-k)!}$

Quadratic Formula

The solutions of $ax^2 + bx + c = 0$ are

$$x = \frac{-b \pm \sqrt{b^2 - 4ac}}{2a}.$$

GEOMETRY

Parallelogram

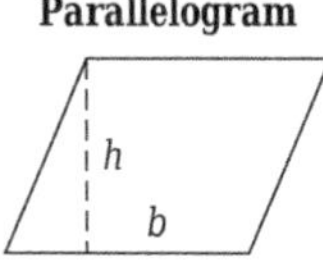

$A = bh$

Triangle

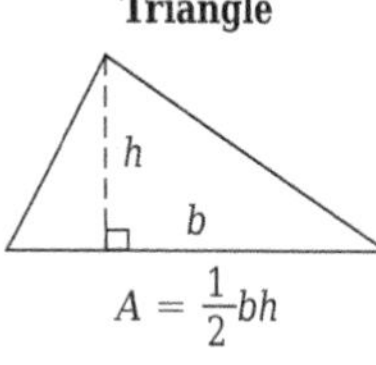

$A = \frac{1}{2}bh$

Trapezoid

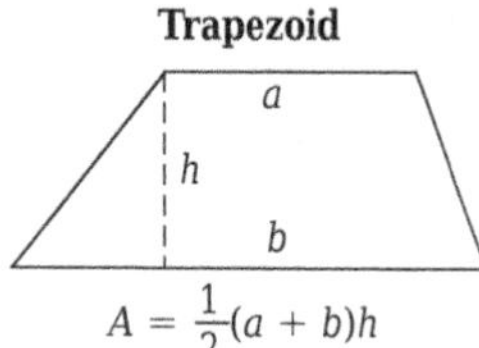

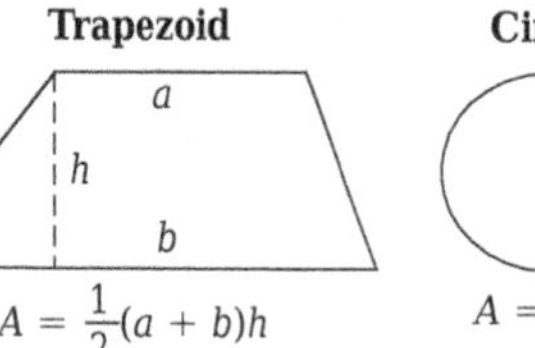

$A = \frac{1}{2}(a + b)h$

Circle / **Sector**

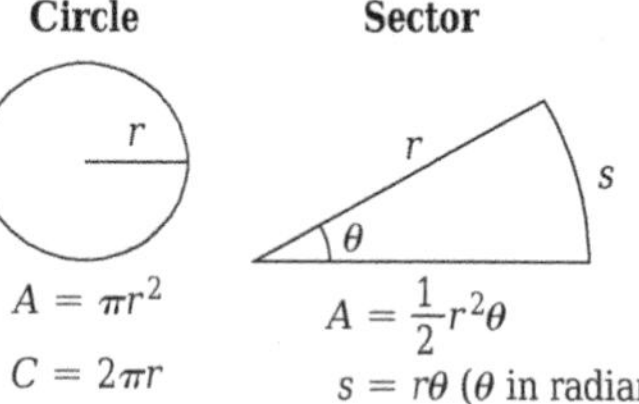

Circle: $A = \pi r^2$, $C = 2\pi r$

Sector: $A = \frac{1}{2}r^2\theta$, $s = r\theta$ (θ in radians)

Cylinder

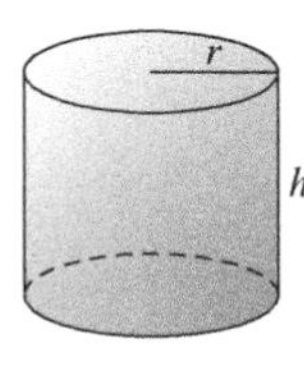

$V = \pi r^2 h$

$S = 2\pi rh$

(lateral surface area)

Cone

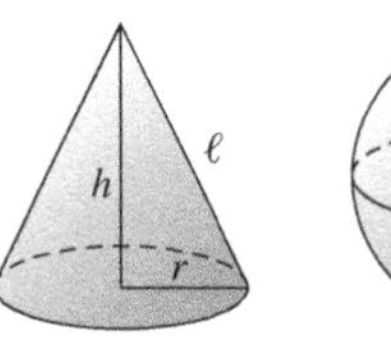

$V = \frac{1}{3}\pi r^2 h$

$S = \pi r\ell$

(lateral surface area)

Sphere

$V = \frac{4}{3}\pi r^3$

$S = 4\pi r^2$

Equations of Lines and Circles

$m = \dfrac{y_2 - y_1}{x_2 - x_1}$ — slope of line through (x_1, y_1) and (x_2, y_2)

$y - y_1 = m(x - x_1)$ — point–slope form of line through (x_1, y_1) with slope m

$y = mx + b$ — slope–intercept form of line with slope m and y-intercept $(0, b)$

$(x - h)^2 + (y - k)^2 = r^2$ — circle of radius r with center (h, k)

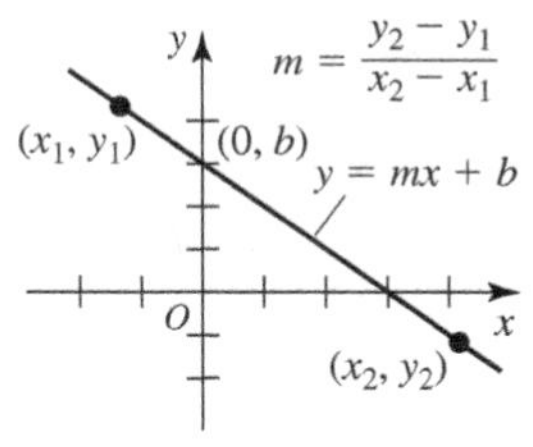

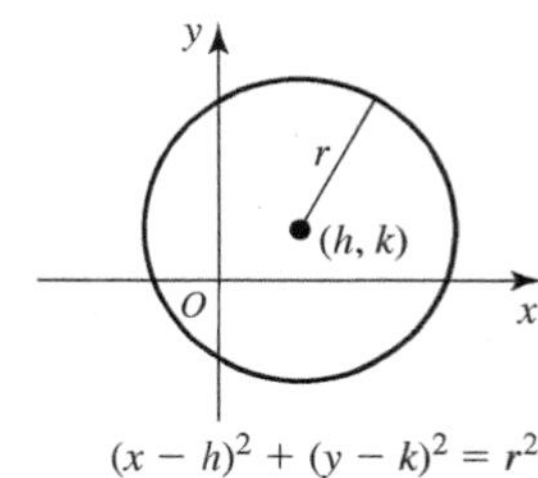

TRIGONOMETRY

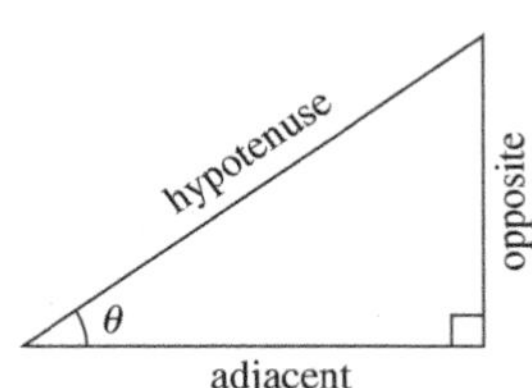

$$\cos\theta = \frac{\text{adj}}{\text{hyp}} \qquad \sin\theta = \frac{\text{opp}}{\text{hyp}} \qquad \tan\theta = \frac{\text{opp}}{\text{adj}}$$

$$\sec\theta = \frac{\text{hyp}}{\text{adj}} \qquad \csc\theta = \frac{\text{hyp}}{\text{opp}} \qquad \cot\theta = \frac{\text{adj}}{\text{opp}}$$

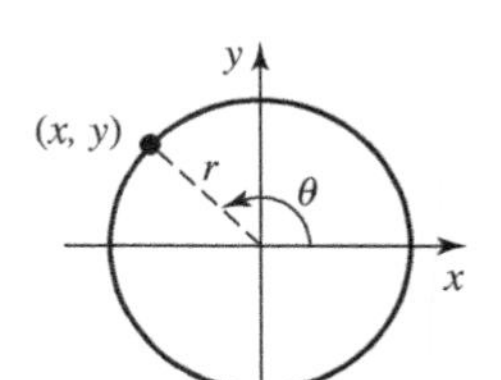

$\cos\theta = \frac{x}{r} \qquad \sec\theta = \frac{r}{x}$

$\sin\theta = \frac{y}{r} \qquad \csc\theta = \frac{r}{y}$

$\tan\theta = \frac{y}{x} \qquad \cot\theta = \frac{x}{y}$

(Continued)

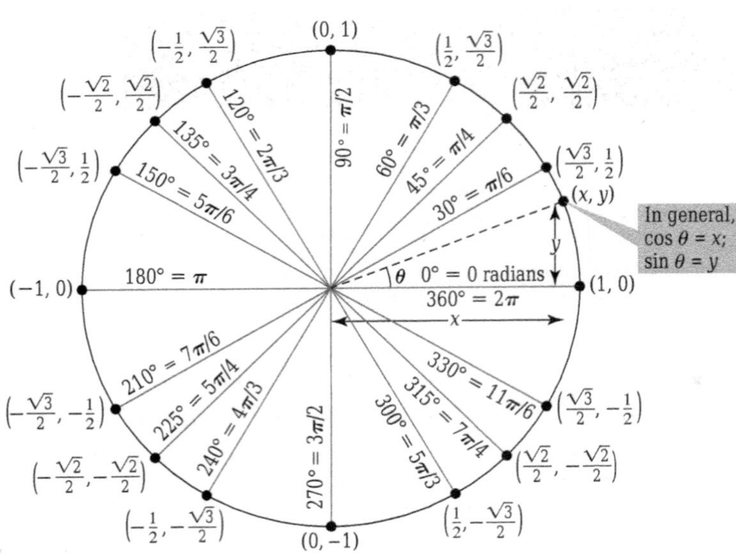

Reciprocal Identities

$$\tan\theta = \frac{\sin\theta}{\cos\theta} \quad \cot\theta = \frac{\cos\theta}{\sin\theta} \quad \sec\theta = \frac{1}{\cos\theta} \quad \csc\theta = \frac{1}{\sin\theta}$$

Pythagorean Identities

$$\sin^2\theta + \cos^2\theta = 1 \quad \tan^2\theta + 1 = \sec^2\theta \quad 1 + \cot^2\theta = \csc^2\theta$$

Sign Identities

$$\sin(-\theta) = -\sin\theta \quad \cos(-\theta) = \cos\theta \quad \tan(-\theta) = -\tan\theta$$
$$\csc(-\theta) = -\csc\theta \quad \sec(-\theta) = \sec\theta \quad \cot(-\theta) = -\cot\theta$$

Double-Angle Identities

$$\sin 2\theta = 2\sin\theta\cos\theta \qquad \cos 2\theta = \cos^2\theta - \sin^2\theta = 2\cos^2\theta - 1 = 1 - 2\sin^2\theta$$

$$\tan 2\theta = \frac{2\tan\theta}{1 - \tan^2\theta}$$

Half-Angle Formulas

$$\cos^2\theta = \frac{1 + \cos 2\theta}{2} \qquad \sin^2\theta = \frac{1 - \cos 2\theta}{2}$$

Addition Formulas

$$\sin(\alpha + \beta) = \sin\alpha\cos\beta + \cos\alpha\sin\beta \qquad \sin(\alpha - \beta) = \sin\alpha\cos\beta - \cos\alpha\sin\beta$$
$$\cos(\alpha + \beta) = \cos\alpha\cos\beta - \sin\alpha\sin\beta \qquad \cos(\alpha - \beta) = \cos\alpha\cos\beta + \sin\alpha\sin\beta$$
$$\tan(\alpha + \beta) = \frac{\tan\alpha + \tan\beta}{1 - \tan\alpha\tan\beta} \qquad \tan(\alpha - \beta) = \frac{\tan\alpha - \tan\beta}{1 + \tan\alpha\tan\beta}$$

Law of Sines

$$\frac{\sin\alpha}{a} = \frac{\sin\beta}{b} = \frac{\sin\gamma}{c}$$

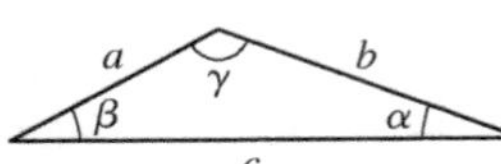

Law of Cosines

$$a^2 = b^2 + c^2 - 2bc\cos\alpha$$

Graphs of Trigonometric Functions and Their Inverses

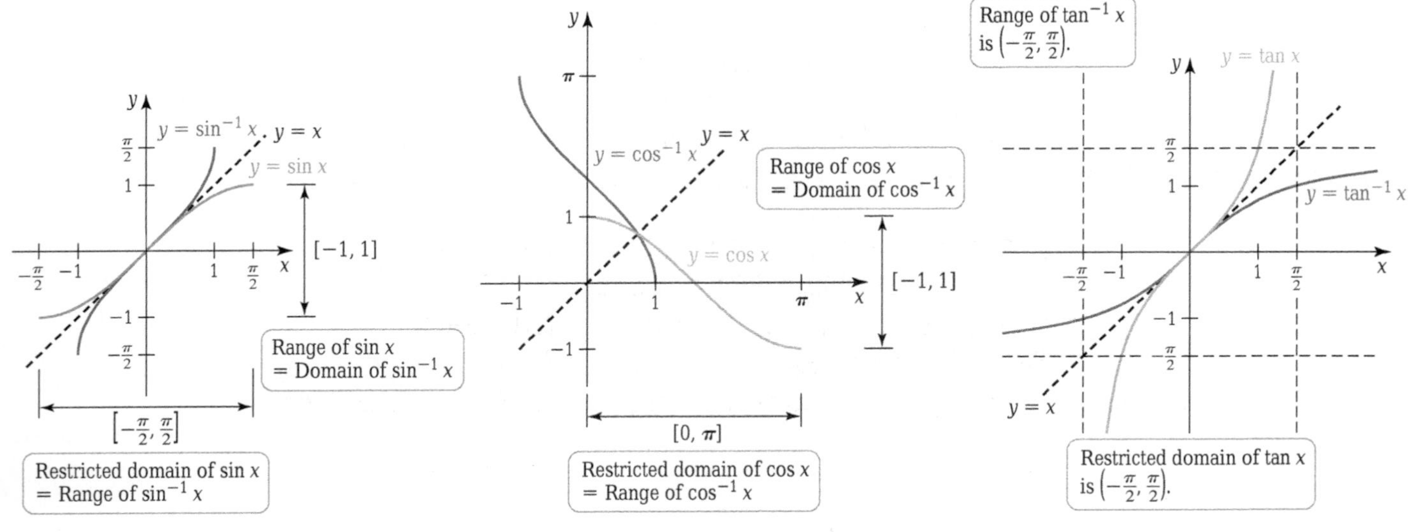

PEARSON ALWAYS LEARNING

Calculus
Early Transcendentals
Volume 2
with Student Solutions Manual

Fourth Custom Edition for the University of British Columbia

William Briggs, Lyle Cochran, and Bernard Gillett with
the assistance of Eric Schulz
Solutions Manual by Mark Woodward

Taken from:
Calculus: Early Transcendentals, Second Edition
by William Briggs, Lyle Cochran, and Bernard Gillett
with the assistance of Eric Schulz

Student Solutions Manual, Single Variable
by Mark Woodward
for *Calculus: Early Transcendentals*, Second Edition
by William L. Briggs, Lyle Cochran, and Bernard Gillett

Student Solutions Manual, Multivariable
by Mark Woodward
for *Calculus*, Second Edition and *Calculus: Early Transcendentals*, Second Edition
by William L. Briggs and Lyle Cochran, and Bernard Gillett

Cover Art: Courtesy of Photodisc/Getty Images.

Taken from:

Calculus: Early Transcendentals, Second Edition
by William Briggs, Lyle Cochran, and Bernard Gillett with the assistance of Eric Schulz

501 Boylston Street, Suite 900, Boston, MA 02116

Student Solutions Manual, Single Variable by Mark Woodward
for *Calculus: Early Transcendentals*, Second Edition
by William L. Briggs, Lyle Cochran, and Bernard Gillett

Student Solutions Manual, Multivariable by Mark Woodward
for *Calculus*, Second Edition and *Calculus: Early Transcendentals*, Second Edition
by William L. Briggs and Lyle Cochran, and Bernard Gillett

Grateful acknowledgment is made to the following source for permission to reprint material copyrighted or controlled by them:

Problem 28 and definition of continuous random variable, by Dennis D. Wackerly, William Mendenhall, and Richard L. Scheaffer, reprinted from Mathematical Statistics with Applications, Sixth Edition (2002), by permission of Duxbury Press/Cengage Learning.

Pearson Learning Solutions, 501 Boylston Street, Suite 900, Boston, MA 02116
A Pearson Education Company
www.pearsoned.com

000200010271904112

JHA/AK

ISBN 10: 1-269-92192-4
ISBN 13: 978-1-269-92192-3

2 2019

NC 10.31.2019 1721

Contents

The following is taken from *Calculus: Early Transcendentals*, Second Edition
by William Briggs, Lyle Cochran, and Bernard Gillett with the assistance of Eric Schulz

The following is taken from *Student's Solutions Manual, Single Variable* by Mark Woodward
for *Calculus: Early Transcendentals*, Second Edition by William Briggs, Lyle Cochran, and Bernard Gillett

The following is taken from *Student Solutions Manual, Multivariable* by Mark Woodward for *Calculus*, Second Edition and *Calculus: Early Transcendentals*, Second Edition by William L. Briggs and Lyle Cochran, and Bernard Gillett

Credits

Chapter opener art: Petr Vaclavek/Shutterstock

Chapter 5

Page 361, The College Mathematics Journal 32, 4 Sept. 2001. **Page 383,** Mathematics Magazine 78, 5 Dec. 2005. **Page 384,** The College Mathematics Journal 33, 5, Nov. 2002. **Page 397,** Mathematics Magazine 81, 5, Dec. 2008.

Chapter 7

Page 515, The College Mathematics Journal 32, No. 5, Nov. 2001, **Page 540,** The College Mathematics Journal, Vol. 34, No. 3 © 2003 Mathematical Association of America. Reproduced by permission. All rights reserved. **Page 550,** The College Mathematics Journal 32, No. 5, Nov. 2001. **Page 556,** The College Mathematics Journal 33, 4, Sept. 2004. **Page 562,** U.S. Energy Information Administration. **Page 562,** U.S. Energy Information Administration. **Page 563,** Collecte Localisation Satellites/Centre National d'études Spatiales/Legos. **Page 569,** U.S. Energy Information Administration. **Page 580,** P. Weidman, I. Pinelis, Comptes Rendu Méchanique 332 2004: 571–584. **Page 581,** Mathematics Magazine 59, 1, Feb. 1986. **Page 595,** Mathematics Magazine 81, No 2, Apr. 2008: 152–154.

Chapter 8

Page 639, The College Mathematics Journal 24, 5, Nov. 1993. **Page 640,** The College Mathematics Journal 30, No. 1 Jan. 1999. **Page 640,** Steve Kifowit 2006 and H. Chen, C. Kennedy, Harmonic series meets Fibonacci sequence, The College Mathematics Journal, 43 May 2012.

Chapter 11

Page 769, CALCULUS by Gilbert Strang. Copyright © 1991 Wellesley-Cambridge Press. Reprinted by permission of the author. **Pages 792, 793, and 798,** Thomas, George B.; Weir, Maurice D.; Hass, Joel; Giordano, Frank R., THOMAS'S CALCULUS, EARLY TRANSCENDENTALS, MEDIA UPGRADE, 11th, © 2008 Printed and electronically reproduced by permission of Pearson Education, Inc., Upper Saddle River, New Jersey. **Page 885,** The College Mathematics Journal 24, 5, Nov. 1993. **Page 886,** Calculus 2nd edition by George B. Thomas and Ross L. Finney. Copyright © 1994, 1990, by Addison Wesley Longman Inc. Printed and Electronically reproduced by permission of Pearson Education, Inc., Upper Saddle River, New Jersey. **Page 951,** Ira Rosenholtz, Mathematics Magazine, 1987. **Page 951,** Mathematics Magazine May 1985 and Philip Gillette, Calculus and Analytical Geometry, 2nd ed.

Chapter 12

Page 862, Thomas, George B.; Weir, Maurice D.; Hass, Joel; Giordano, Frank R., THOMAS'S CALCULUS, EARLY TRANSCENDENTALS, MEDIA UPGRADE, 11th, © 2008, Printed and Electronically reproduced by permission of Pearson Education, Inc., Upper Saddle River, New Jersey. **Page 876,** U.S. Geological Survey. **Page 881,** "Model Courtesy of COMSOL, Inc., (www.comsol.com)".

Credits

5

Integration

Chapter Preview We are now at a critical point in the calculus story. Many would argue that this chapter is the cornerstone of calculus because it explains the relationship between the two processes of calculus: differentiation and integration. We begin by explaining why finding the area of regions bounded by the graphs of functions is such an important problem in calculus. Then you will see how antiderivatives lead to definite integrals, which are used to solve the area problem. But there is more to the story. You will also see the remarkable connection between derivatives and integrals, which is expressed in the Fundamental Theorem of Calculus. In this chapter, we develop key properties of definite integrals, investigate a few of their many applications, and present the first of several powerful techniques for evaluating definite integrals.

5.1 Approximating Areas under Curves

The derivative of a function is associated with rates of change and slopes of tangent lines. We also know that antiderivatives (or indefinite integrals) reverse the derivative operation. Figure 5.1 summarizes our current understanding and raises the question: What is the geometric meaning of the integral? The following example reveals a clue.

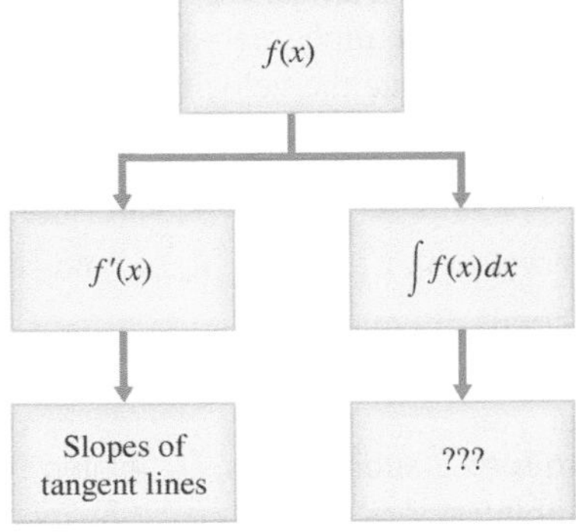

Figure 5.1

Area under a Velocity Curve

Consider an object moving along a line with a known position function. You learned in previous chapters that the slope of the line tangent to the graph of the position function at a certain time gives the velocity v at that time. We now turn the situation around. If we know the velocity function of a moving object, what can we learn about its position function?

➤ Recall from Section 3.5 that the *displacement* of an object moving along a line is the difference between its initial and final position. If the velocity of an object is positive, its displacement equals the distance traveled.

Imagine a car traveling at a constant velocity of 60 mi/hr along a straight highway over a two-hour period. The graph of the velocity function $v = 60$ on the interval $0 \le t \le 2$ is a horizontal line (Figure 5.2). The displacement of the car between $t = 0$ and $t = 2$ is found by a familiar formula:

$$\begin{aligned} \text{displacement} &= \text{rate} \cdot \text{time} \\ &= 60 \text{ mi/hr} \cdot 2 \text{ hr} = 120 \text{ mi}. \end{aligned}$$

This product is the area of the rectangle formed by the velocity curve and the t-axis between $t = 0$ and $t = 2$ (Figure 5.3). In the case of constant positive velocity, we see that the area between the velocity curve and the t-axis is the displacement of the moving object.

➤ The side lengths of the rectangle in Figure 5.3 have units mi/hr and hr. Therefore, the units of the area are mi/hr · hr = mi, which is a unit of displacement.

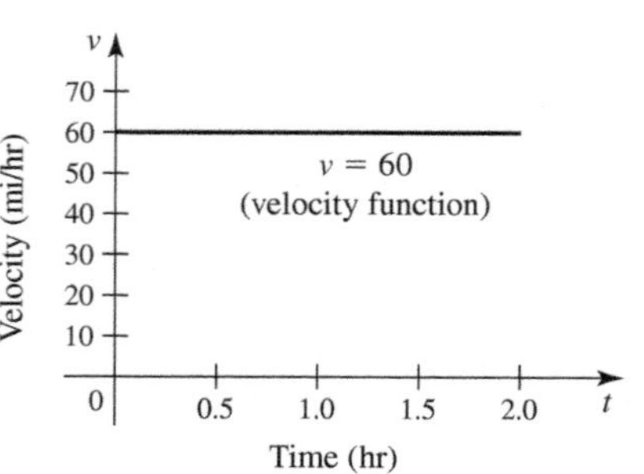

Figure 5.2

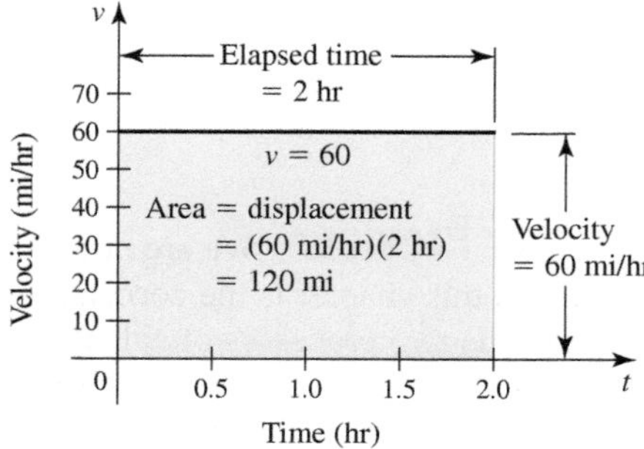

Figure 5.3

QUICK CHECK 1 What is the displacement of an object that travels at a constant velocity of 10 mi/hr for a half hour, 20 mi/hr for the next half hour, and 30 mi/hr for the next hour? ◄

Because objects do not necessarily move at a constant velocity, we first extend these ideas to positive velocities that *change* over an interval of time. One strategy is to divide the time interval into many subintervals and approximate the velocity on each subinterval with a constant velocity. Then the displacements on each subinterval are calculated and summed. This strategy produces only an approximation to the displacement; however, this approximation generally improves as the number of subintervals increases.

EXAMPLE 1 Approximating the displacement Suppose the velocity in m/s of an object moving along a line is given by the function $v = t^2$, where $0 \le t \le 8$. Approximate the displacement of the object by dividing the time interval $[0, 8]$ into n subintervals of equal length. On each subinterval, approximate the velocity with a constant equal to the value of v evaluated at the midpoint of the subinterval.

a. Begin by dividing $[0, 8]$ into $n = 2$ subintervals: $[0, 4]$ and $[4, 8]$.

b. Divide $[0, 8]$ into $n = 4$ subintervals: $[0, 2]$, $[2, 4]$, $[4, 6]$, and $[6, 8]$.

c. Divide $[0, 8]$ into $n = 8$ subintervals of equal length.

SOLUTION

a. We divide the interval $[0, 8]$ into $n = 2$ subintervals, $[0, 4]$ and $[4, 8]$, each with length 4. The velocity on each subinterval is approximated by evaluating v at the midpoint of that subinterval (Figure 5.4a).

- We approximate the velocity on $[0, 4]$ by $v(2) = 2^2 = 4$ m/s. Traveling at 4 m/s for 4 s results in a displacement of 4 m/s · 4 s = 16 m.
- We approximate the velocity on $[4, 8]$ by $v(6) = 6^2 = 36$ m/s. Traveling at 36 m/s for 4 s results in a displacement of 36 m/s · 4 s = 144 m.

Therefore, an approximation to the displacement over the entire interval $[0, 8]$ is

$$(v(2) \cdot 4 \text{ s}) + (v(6) \cdot 4 \text{ s}) = (4 \text{ m/s} \cdot 4 \text{ s}) + (36 \text{ m/s} \cdot 4 \text{ s}) = 160 \text{ m}.$$

b. With $n = 4$ (Figure 5.4b), each subinterval has length 2. The approximate displacement over the entire interval is

$$\underbrace{(1\text{ m/s}}_{v(1)}\cdot 2\text{ s}) + (\underbrace{9\text{ m/s}}_{v(3)}\cdot 2\text{ s}) + (\underbrace{25\text{ m/s}}_{v(5)}\cdot 2\text{ s}) + (\underbrace{49\text{ m/s}}_{v(7)}\cdot 2\text{ s}) = 168\text{ m}.$$

c. With $n = 8$ subintervals (Figure 5.4c), the approximation to the displacement is 170 m. In each case, the approximate displacement is the sum of the areas of the rectangles under the velocity curve.

The midpoint of each subinterval is used to approximate the velocity over that subinterval.

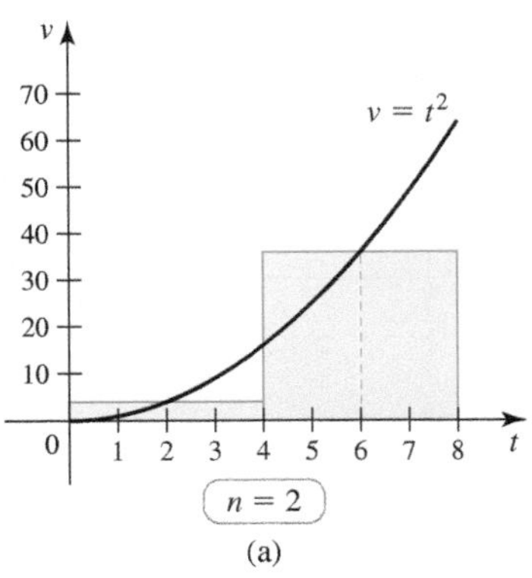

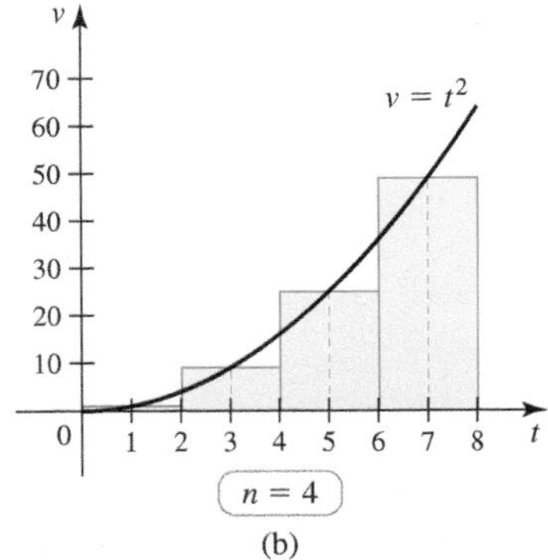

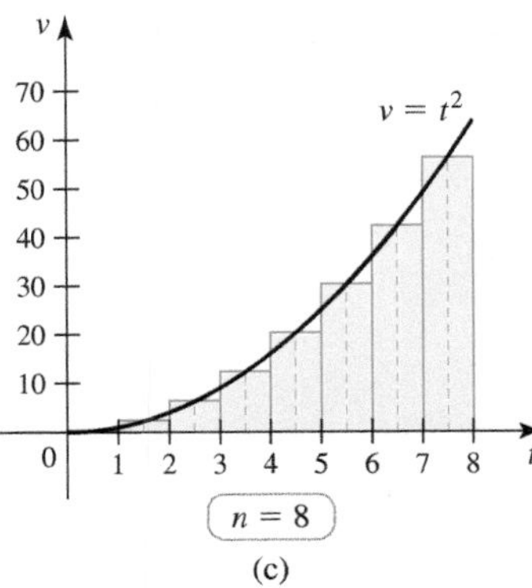

Figure 5.4

Related Exercises 9–16

QUICK CHECK 2 In Example 1, if we used $n = 32$ subintervals of equal length, what would be the length of each subinterval? Find the midpoint of the first and last subinterval.

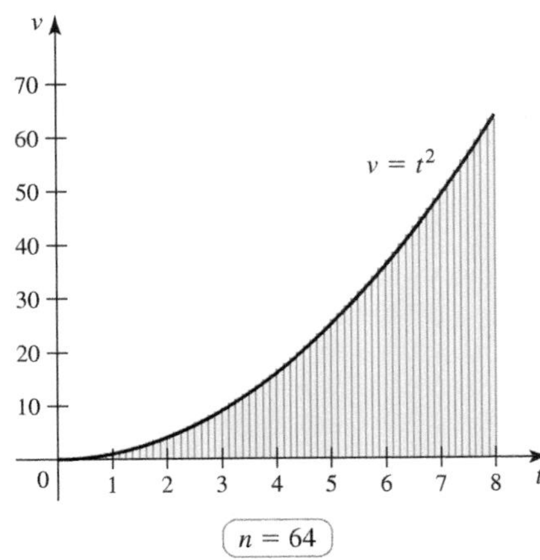

Figure 5.5

The progression in Example 1 may be continued. Larger values of n mean more rectangles; in general, more rectangles give a better fit to the region under the curve (Figure 5.5). With the help of a calculator, we can generate the approximations in Table 5.1 using $n = 1, 2, 4, 8, 16, 32$, and 64 subintervals. Observe that as n increases, the approximations appear to approach a limit of approximately 170.7 m. The limit is the exact displacement, which is represented by the area of the region under the velocity curve. This strategy of taking limits of sums is developed fully in Section 5.2.

Table 5.1 Approximations to the area under the velocity curve $v = t^2$ on $[0, 8]$

Number of subintervals	Length of each subinterval	Approximate displacement (area under curve)
1	8 s	128.0 m
2	4 s	160.0 m
4	2 s	168.0 m
8	1 s	170.0 m
16	0.5 s	170.5 m
32	0.25 s	170.625 m
64	0.125 s	170.65625 m

➤ The language "the area of the region bounded by the graph of a function" is often abbreviated as "the area under the curve."

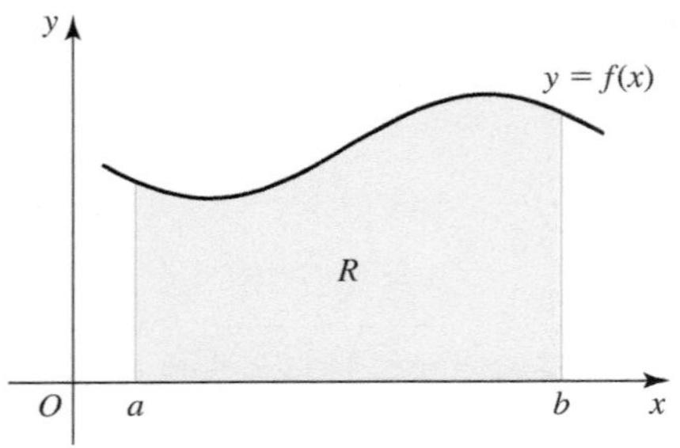

Figure 5.6

Approximating Areas by Riemann Sums

We wouldn't spend much time investigating areas under curves if the idea applied only to computing displacements from velocity curves. However, the problem of finding areas under curves arises frequently and turns out to be immensely important—as you will see in the next two chapters. For this reason, we now develop a systematic method for approximating areas under curves. Consider a function f that is continuous and nonnegative on an interval $[a, b]$. The goal is to approximate the area of the region R bounded by the graph of f and the x-axis from $x = a$ to $x = b$ (Figure 5.6). We begin by dividing the interval $[a, b]$ into n subintervals of equal length,

$$[x_0, x_1], [x_1, x_2], \ldots, [x_{n-1}, x_n],$$

where $a = x_0$ and $b = x_n$ (Figure 5.7). The length of each subinterval, denoted Δx, is found by dividing the length of the entire interval by n:

$$\Delta x = \frac{b - a}{n}.$$

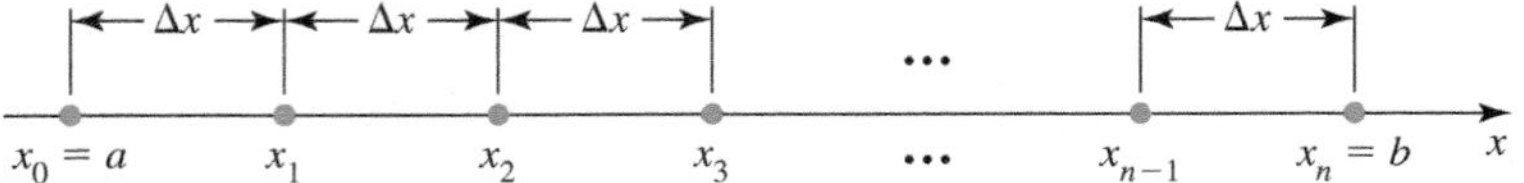

Figure 5.7

DEFINITION Regular Partition

Suppose $[a, b]$ is a closed interval containing n subintervals

$$[x_0, x_1], [x_1, x_2], \ldots, [x_{n-1}, x_n]$$

of equal length $\Delta x = \dfrac{b - a}{n}$ with $a = x_0$ and $b = x_n$. The endpoints $x_0, x_1, x_2, \ldots, x_{n-1}, x_n$ of the subintervals are called **grid points**, and they create a **regular partition** of the interval $[a, b]$. In general, the kth grid point is

$$x_k = a + k\Delta x, \text{ for } k = 0, 1, 2, \ldots, n.$$

QUICK CHECK 3 If the interval $[1, 9]$ is partitioned into 4 subintervals of equal length, what is Δx? List the grid points x_0, x_1, x_2, x_3, and x_4. ◄

In the kth subinterval $[x_{k-1}, x_k]$, we choose any point x_k^* and build a rectangle whose height is $f(x_k^*)$, the value of f at x_k^* (Figure 5.8). The area of the rectangle on the kth subinterval is

$$\text{height} \cdot \text{base} = f(x_k^*)\Delta x, \qquad \text{where } k = 1, 2, \ldots, n.$$

➤ Although the idea of integration was developed in the 17th century, it was almost 200 years later that the German mathematician Bernhard Riemann (1826–1866) worked on the mathematical theory underlying integration.

Summing the areas of the rectangles in Figure 5.8, we obtain an approximation to the area of R, which is called a **Riemann sum**:

$$f(x_1^*)\Delta x + f(x_2^*)\Delta x + \cdots + f(x_n^*)\Delta x.$$

Three notable Riemann sums are the *left*, *right*, and *midpoint Riemann sums*.

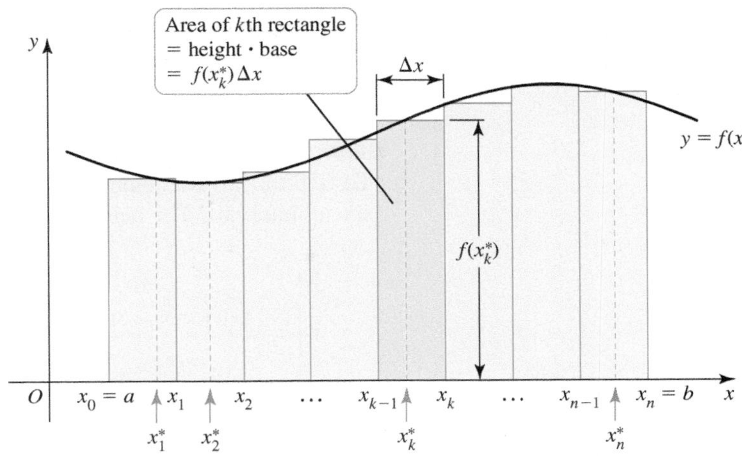

Figure 5.8

For the left Riemann sum,
$x_1^* = a + 0 \cdot \Delta x, x_2^* = a + 1 \cdot \Delta x,$
$x_3^* = a + 2 \cdot \Delta x,$
and in general, $x_k^* = a + (k - 1)\Delta x$,
for $k = 1, \ldots, n$.

For the right Riemann sum,
$x_1^* = a + 1 \cdot \Delta x, x_2^* = a + 2 \cdot \Delta x,$
$x_3^* = a + 3 \cdot \Delta x,$
and in general $x_k^* = a + k\Delta x$,
for $k = 1, \ldots, n$.

For the midpoint Riemann sum,

$$x_1^* = a + \tfrac{1}{2}\Delta x, x_2^* = a + \tfrac{3}{2}\Delta x,$$

and in general,

$$x_k^* = a + \left(k - \tfrac{1}{2}\right)\Delta x = \frac{x_k + x_{k-1}}{2},$$

for $k = 1, \ldots, n$.

DEFINITION Riemann Sum

Suppose f is defined on a closed interval $[a, b]$, which is divided into n subintervals of equal length Δx. If x_k^* is any point in the kth subinterval $[x_{k-1}, x_k]$, for $k = 1, 2, \ldots, n$, then

$$f(x_1^*)\Delta x + f(x_2^*)\Delta x + \cdots + f(x_n^*)\Delta x$$

is called a **Riemann sum** for f on $[a, b]$. This sum is called

- a **left Riemann sum** if x_k^* is the left endpoint of $[x_{k-1}, x_k]$ (Figure 5.9);
- a **right Riemann sum** if x_k^* is the right endpoint of $[x_{k-1}, x_k]$ (Figure 5.10); and
- a **midpoint Riemann sum** if x_k^* is the midpoint of $[x_{k-1}, x_k]$ (Figure 5.11), for $k = 1, 2, \ldots, n$.

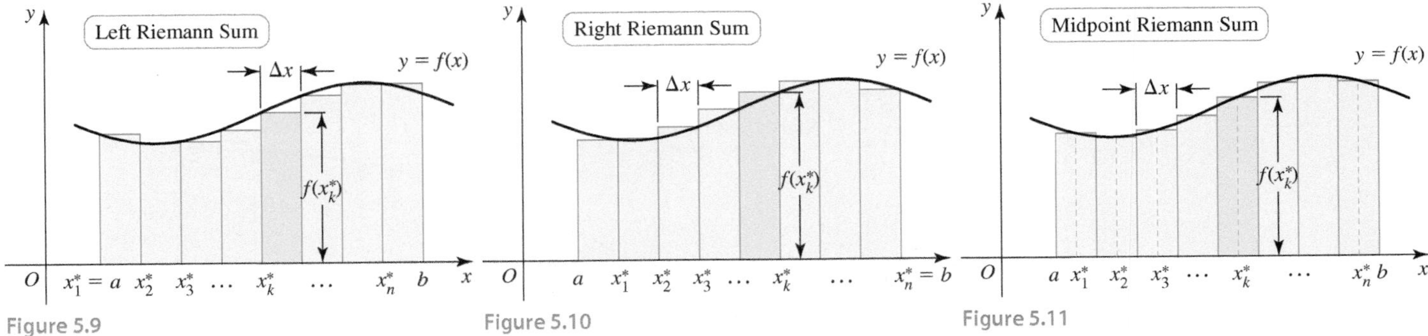

Figure 5.9

Figure 5.10

Figure 5.11

We now use this definition to approximate the area under the curve $y = \sin x$.

EXAMPLE 2 Left and right Riemann sums Let R be the region bounded by the graph of $f(x) = \sin x$ and the x-axis between $x = 0$ and $x = \pi/2$.

a. Approximate the area of R using a left Riemann sum with $n = 6$ subintervals. Illustrate the sum with the appropriate rectangles.

b. Approximate the area of R using a right Riemann sum with $n = 6$ subintervals. Illustrate the sum with the appropriate rectangles.

c. Do the area approximations in parts (a) and (b) underestimate or overestimate the actual area under the curve?

SOLUTION Dividing the interval $[a, b] = [0, \pi/2]$ into $n = 6$ subintervals means the length of each subinterval is

$$\Delta x = \frac{b - a}{n} = \frac{\pi/2 - 0}{6} = \frac{\pi}{12}.$$

a. To find the left Riemann sum, we set $x_1^*, x_2^*, \ldots, x_6^*$ equal to the left endpoints of the six subintervals. The heights of the rectangles are $f(x_k^*)$, for $k = 1, \ldots, 6$.

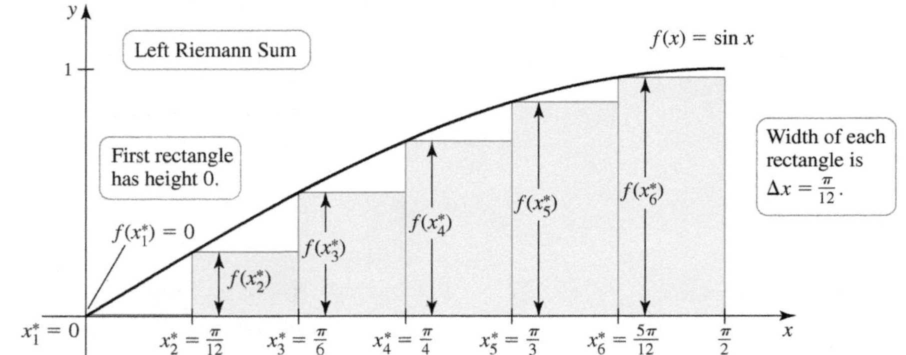

Figure 5.12

The resulting left Riemann sum (Figure 5.12) is

$$\begin{aligned} &f(x_1^*)\Delta x + f(x_2^*)\Delta x + \cdots + f(x_6^*)\Delta x \\ &= (\sin 0)\cdot\frac{\pi}{12} + \left(\sin\frac{\pi}{12}\right)\cdot\frac{\pi}{12} + \left(\sin\frac{\pi}{6}\right)\cdot\frac{\pi}{12} \\ &\quad + \left(\sin\frac{\pi}{4}\right)\cdot\frac{\pi}{12} + \left(\sin\frac{\pi}{3}\right)\cdot\frac{\pi}{12} + \left(\sin\frac{5\pi}{12}\right)\cdot\frac{\pi}{12} \\ &\approx 0.863. \end{aligned}$$

b. In a right Riemann sum, the right endpoints are used for $x_1^*, x_2^*, \ldots, x_6^*$, and the heights of the rectangles are $f(x_k^*)$, for $k = 1, \ldots, 6$.

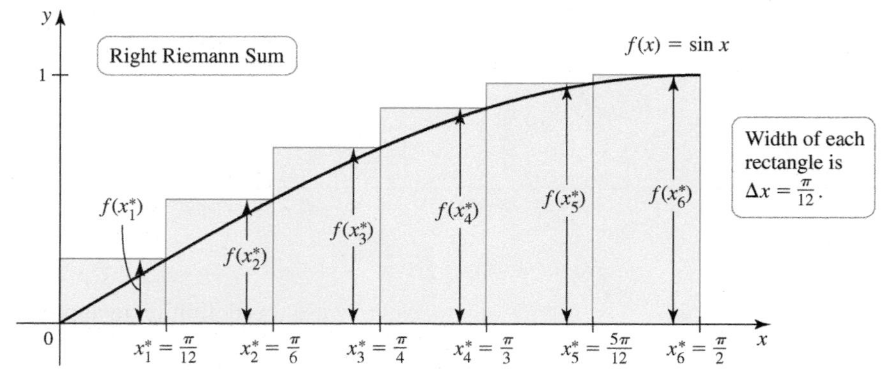

Figure 5.13

The resulting right Riemann sum (Figure 5.13) is

$$\begin{aligned} &f(x_1^*)\Delta x + f(x_2^*)\Delta x + \cdots + f(x_6^*)\Delta x \\ &= \left(\sin\frac{\pi}{12}\right)\cdot\frac{\pi}{12} + \left(\sin\frac{\pi}{6}\right)\cdot\frac{\pi}{12} + \left(\sin\frac{\pi}{4}\right)\cdot\frac{\pi}{12} \\ &\quad + \left(\sin\frac{\pi}{3}\right)\cdot\frac{\pi}{12} + \left(\sin\frac{5\pi}{12}\right)\cdot\frac{\pi}{12} + \left(\sin\frac{\pi}{2}\right)\cdot\frac{\pi}{12} \\ &\approx 1.125. \end{aligned}$$

QUICK CHECK 4 If the function in Example 2 is replaced with $f(x) = \cos x$, does the left Riemann sum or the right Riemann sum overestimate the area under the curve? ◀

c. Looking at the graphs, we see that the left Riemann sum in part (a) underestimates the actual area of R, whereas the right Riemann sum in part (b) overestimates the area of R. Therefore, the area of R is between 0.863 and 1.125. As the number of rectangles increases, these approximations improve.

Related Exercises 17–26 ◀

EXAMPLE 3 **A midpoint Riemann sum** Let R be the region bounded by the graph of $f(x) = \sin x$ and the x-axis between $x = 0$ and $x = \pi/2$. Approximate the area of R using a midpoint Riemann sum with $n = 6$ subintervals. Illustrate the sum with the appropriate rectangles.

SOLUTION The grid points and the length of the subintervals $\Delta x = \pi/12$ are the same as in Example 2. To find the midpoint Riemann sum, we set $x_1^*, x_2^*, \ldots, x_6^*$ equal to the midpoints of the subintervals. The midpoint of the first subinterval is the average of x_0 and x_1, which is

$$x_1^* = \frac{x_1 + x_0}{2} = \frac{\pi/12 + 0}{2} = \frac{\pi}{24}.$$

The remaining midpoints are also computed by averaging the two nearest grid points.

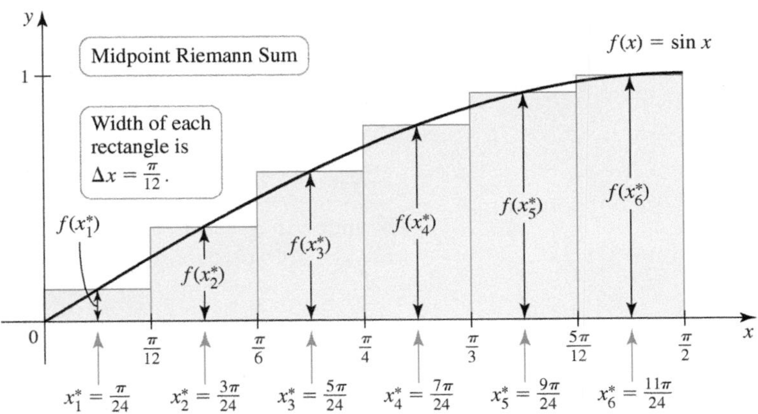

Figure 5.14

The resulting midpoint Riemann sum (Figure 5.14) is

$$\begin{aligned} &f(x_1^*)\Delta x + f(x_2^*)\Delta x + \cdots + f(x_6^*)\Delta x \\ &= \left(\sin\frac{\pi}{24}\right)\cdot\frac{\pi}{12} + \left(\sin\frac{3\pi}{24}\right)\cdot\frac{\pi}{12} + \left(\sin\frac{5\pi}{24}\right)\cdot\frac{\pi}{12} \\ &\quad + \left(\sin\frac{7\pi}{24}\right)\cdot\frac{\pi}{12} + \left(\sin\frac{9\pi}{24}\right)\cdot\frac{\pi}{12} + \left(\sin\frac{11\pi}{24}\right)\cdot\frac{\pi}{12} \\ &\approx 1.003. \end{aligned}$$

Comparing the midpoint Riemann sum (Figure 5.14) with the left (Figure 5.12) and right (Figure 5.13) Riemann sums suggests that the midpoint sum is a more accurate estimate of the area under the curve.

Related Exercises 27–34 ◀

Table 5.2

x	$f(x)$
0	1
0.5	3
1.0	4.5
1.5	5.5
2.0	6.0

EXAMPLE 4 **Riemann sums from tables** Estimate the area A under the graph of f on the interval $[0, 2]$ using left and right Riemann sums with $n = 4$, where f is continuous but known only at the points in Table 5.2.

SOLUTION With $n = 4$ subintervals on the interval $[0, 2]$, $\Delta x = 2/4 = 0.5$. Using the left endpoint of each subinterval, the left Riemann sum is

$$A \approx (f(0) + f(0.5) + f(1.0) + f(1.5))\Delta x = (1 + 3 + 4.5 + 5.5)0.5 = 7.0.$$

Using the right endpoint of each subinterval, the right Riemann sum is

$$A \approx (f(0.5) + f(1.0) + f(1.5) + f(2.0))\Delta x = (3 + 4.5 + 5.5 + 6.0)0.5 = 9.5.$$

With only five function values, these estimates of the area are necessarily crude. Better estimates are obtained by using more subintervals and more function values.

Related Exercises 35–38 ◀

Sigma (Summation) Notation

Working with Riemann sums is cumbersome with large numbers of subintervals. Therefore, we pause for a moment to introduce some notation that simplifies our work.

Sigma (or **summation**) **notation** is used to express sums in a compact way. For example, the sum $1 + 2 + 3 + \cdots + 10$ is represented in sigma notation as $\sum_{k=1}^{10} k$. Here is how the notation works. The symbol Σ (*sigma*, the Greek capital S) stands for *sum*. The **index** k takes on all integer values from the lower limit ($k = 1$) to the upper limit ($k = 10$). The expression that immediately follows Σ (the **summand**) is evaluated for each value of k, and the resulting values are summed. Here are some examples.

$$\sum_{k=1}^{99} k = 1 + 2 + 3 + \cdots + 99 = 4950 \qquad \sum_{k=1}^{n} k = 1 + 2 + \cdots + n$$

$$\sum_{k=0}^{3} k^2 = 0^2 + 1^2 + 2^2 + 3^2 = 14 \qquad \sum_{k=1}^{4} (2k + 1) = 3 + 5 + 7 + 9 = 24$$

$$\sum_{k=-1}^{2} (k^2 + k) = ((-1)^2 + (-1)) + (0^2 + 0) + (1^2 + 1) + (2^2 + 2) = 8.$$

The index in a sum is a *dummy variable*. It is internal to the sum, so it does not matter what symbol you choose as an index. For example,

$$\sum_{k=1}^{99} k = \sum_{n=1}^{99} n = \sum_{p=1}^{99} p.$$

Two properties of sums and sigma notation are useful in upcoming work. Suppose that $\{a_1, a_2, \ldots, a_n\}$ and $\{b_1, b_2, \ldots, b_n\}$ are two sets of real numbers, and suppose that c is a real number. Then we can factor multiplicative constants out of a sum:

Constant Multiple Rule $$\sum_{k=1}^{n} ca_k = c\sum_{k=1}^{n} a_k.$$

We can also split a sum into two sums:

Addition Rule $$\sum_{k=1}^{n} (a_k + b_k) = \sum_{k=1}^{n} a_k + \sum_{k=1}^{n} b_k.$$

In the coming examples and exercises, the following formulas for sums of powers of integers are essential.

➤ Formulas for $\sum_{k=1}^{n} k^p$, where p is a positive integer, have been known for centuries. The formulas for $p = 0, 1, 2,$ and 3 are relatively simple. The formulas become complicated as p increases.

THEOREM 5.1 Sums of Powers of Integers

Let n be a positive integer and c a real number.

$$\sum_{k=1}^{n} c = cn \qquad \sum_{k=1}^{n} k = \frac{n(n + 1)}{2}$$

$$\sum_{k=1}^{n} k^2 = \frac{n(n + 1)(2n + 1)}{6} \qquad \sum_{k=1}^{n} k^3 = \frac{n^2(n + 1)^2}{4}$$

Related Exercises 39–42 ◀

Riemann Sums Using Sigma Notation

With sigma notation, a Riemann sum has the convenient compact form

$$f(x_1^*)\Delta x + f(x_2^*)\Delta x + \cdots + f(x_n^*)\Delta x = \sum_{k=1}^{n} f(x_k^*)\Delta x.$$

To express left, right, and midpoint Riemann sums in sigma notation, we must identify the points x_k^*.

- For left Riemann sums, the left endpoints of the subintervals are $x_k^* = a + (k - 1)\Delta x$, for $k = 1, \ldots, n$.
- For right Riemann sums, the right endpoints of the subintervals are $x_k^* = a + k\Delta x$, for $k = 1, \ldots, n$.
- For midpoint Riemann sums, the midpoints of the subintervals are $x_k^* = a + (k - \frac{1}{2})\Delta x$, for $k = 1, \ldots, n$.

The three Riemann sums are written compactly as follows.

> DEFINITION **Left, Right, and Midpoint Riemann Sums in Sigma Notation**
>
> Suppose f is defined on a closed interval $[a, b]$, which is divided into n subintervals of equal length Δx. If x_k^* is a point in the kth subinterval $[x_{k-1}, x_k]$, for $k = 1, 2, \ldots, n$, then the **Riemann sum** for f on $[a, b]$ is $\sum_{k=1}^{n} f(x_k^*)\Delta x$. Three cases arise in practice.
>
> - **Left Riemann sum** if $x_k^* = a + (k - 1)\Delta x$
> - **Right Riemann sum** if $x_k^* = a + k\Delta x$
> - **Midpoint Riemann sum** if $x_k^* = a + (k - \frac{1}{2})\Delta x$

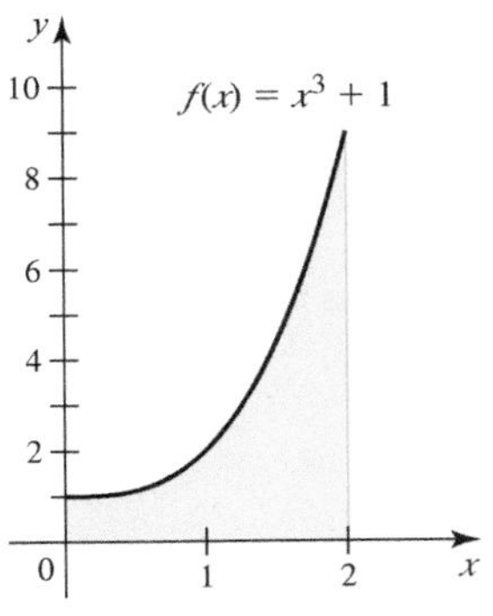

Figure 5.15

EXAMPLE 5 **Calculating Riemann sums** Evaluate the left, right, and midpoint Riemann sums for $f(x) = x^3 + 1$ between $a = 0$ and $b = 2$ using $n = 50$ subintervals. Make a conjecture about the exact area of the region under the curve (Figure 5.15).

SOLUTION With $n = 50$, the length of each subinterval is

$$\Delta x = \frac{b - a}{n} = \frac{2 - 0}{50} = \frac{1}{25} = 0.04.$$

The value of x_k^* for the left Riemann sum is

$$x_k^* = a + (k - 1)\Delta x = 0 + 0.04(k - 1) = 0.04k - 0.04,$$

for $k = 1, 2, \ldots, 50$. Therefore, the left Riemann sum, evaluated with a calculator, is

$$\sum_{k=1}^{n} f(x_k^*)\Delta x = \sum_{k=1}^{50} f(0.04k - 0.04)0.04 = 5.8416.$$

To evaluate the right Riemann sum, we let $x_k^* = a + k\Delta x = 0.04k$ and find that

$$\sum_{k=1}^{n} f(x_k^*)\Delta x = \sum_{k=1}^{50} f(0.04k)0.04 = 6.1616.$$

For the midpoint Riemann sum, we let

$$x_k^* = a + \left(k - \frac{1}{2}\right)\Delta x = 0 + 0.04\left(k - \frac{1}{2}\right) = 0.04k - 0.02.$$

The value of the sum is

$$\sum_{k=1}^{n} f(x_k^*)\,\Delta x = \sum_{k=1}^{50} f(0.04k - 0.02)0.04 = 5.9992.$$

Because f is increasing on $[0, 2]$, the left Riemann sum underestimates the area of the shaded region in Figure 5.15 and the right Riemann sum overestimates the area. Therefore, the exact area lies between 5.8416 and 6.1616. The midpoint Riemann sum usually gives the best estimate for increasing or decreasing functions.

Table 5.3 shows the left, right, and midpoint Riemann sum approximations for values of n up to 200. All three sets of approximations approach a value near 6, which is a reasonable estimate of the area under the curve. In Section 5.2, we show rigorously that the limit of all three Riemann sums as $n \to \infty$ is 6.

Table 5.3 Left, right, and midpoint Riemann sum approximations

n	L_n	R_n	M_n
20	5.61	6.41	5.995
40	5.8025	6.2025	5.99875
60	5.86778	6.13444	5.99944
80	5.90063	6.10063	5.99969
100	5.9204	6.0804	5.9998
120	5.93361	6.06694	5.99986
140	5.94306	6.05735	5.9999
160	5.95016	6.05016	5.99992
180	5.95568	6.04457	5.99994
200	5.9601	6.0401	5.99995

ALTERNATIVE SOLUTION It is worth examining another approach to Example 5. Consider the right Riemann sum given previously:

$$\sum_{k=1}^{n} f(x_k^*)\,\Delta x = \sum_{k=1}^{50} f(0.04k)0.04.$$

Rather than evaluating this sum with a calculator, we note that $f(0.04k) = (0.04k)^3 + 1$ and use the properties of sums:

$$\begin{aligned}
\sum_{k=1}^{n} f(x_k^*)\Delta x &= \sum_{k=1}^{50} \underbrace{((0.04k)^3 + 1)}_{f(x_k^*)}\underbrace{0.04}_{\Delta x} \\
&= \sum_{k=1}^{50} (0.04k)^3\,0.04 + \sum_{k=1}^{50} 1 \cdot 0.04 \qquad \textstyle\sum (a_k + b_k) = \sum a_k + \sum b_k \\
&= (0.04)^4 \sum_{k=1}^{50} k^3 + 0.04 \sum_{k=1}^{50} 1. \qquad \textstyle\sum c a_k = c \sum a_k
\end{aligned}$$

Using the summation formulas for powers of integers in Theorem 5.1, we find that

$$\sum_{k=1}^{50} 1 = 50 \quad \text{and} \quad \sum_{k=1}^{50} k^3 = \frac{50^2 \cdot 51^2}{4}.$$

Substituting the values of these sums into the right Riemann sum, its value is

$$\sum_{k=1}^{50} f(x_k^*)\,\Delta x = \frac{3851}{625} = 6.1616,$$

confirming the result given by a calculator. The idea of evaluating Riemann sums for *arbitrary* values of n is used in Section 5.2, where we evaluate the limit of the Riemann sum as $n \to \infty$.

Related Exercises 43–52 ◀

SECTION 5.1 EXERCISES

Review Questions

1. Suppose an object moves along a line at 15 m/s, for $0 \le t < 2$, and at 25 m/s, for $2 \le t \le 5$, where t is measured in seconds. Sketch the graph of the velocity function and find the displacement of the object for $0 \le t \le 5$.

2. Given the graph of the positive velocity of an object moving along a line, what is the geometrical representation of its displacement over a time interval $[a, b]$?

3. Suppose you want to approximate the area of the region bounded by the graph of $f(x) = \cos x$ and the x-axis between $x = 0$ and $x = \pi/2$. Explain a possible strategy.

4. Explain how Riemann sum approximations to the area of a region under a curve change as the number of subintervals increases.

5. Suppose the interval $[1, 3]$ is partitioned into $n = 4$ subintervals. What is the subinterval length Δx? List the grid points x_0, x_1, x_2, x_3, and x_4. Which points are used for the left, right, and midpoint Riemann sums?

6. Suppose the interval $[2, 6]$ is partitioned into $n = 4$ subintervals with grid points $x_0 = 2, x_1 = 3, x_2 = 4, x_3 = 5$, and $x_4 = 6$. Write, but do not evaluate, the left, right, and midpoint Riemann sums for $f(x) = x^2$.

7. Does a right Riemann sum underestimate or overestimate the area of the region under the graph of a function that is positive and decreasing on an interval $[a, b]$? Explain.

8. Does a left Riemann sum underestimate or overestimate the area of the region under the graph of a function that is positive and increasing on an interval $[a, b]$? Explain.

Basic Skills

9. **Approximating displacement** The velocity in ft/s of an object moving along a line is given by $v = 3t^2 + 1$ on the interval $0 \le t \le 4$.
   a. Divide the interval $[0, 4]$ into $n = 4$ subintervals, $[0, 1]$, $[1, 2]$, $[2, 3]$, and $[3, 4]$. On each subinterval, assume the object moves at a constant velocity equal to v evaluated at the midpoint of the subinterval and use these approximations to estimate the displacement of the object on $[0, 4]$ (see part (a) of the figure).
   b. Repeat part (a) for $n = 8$ subintervals (see part (b) of the figure).

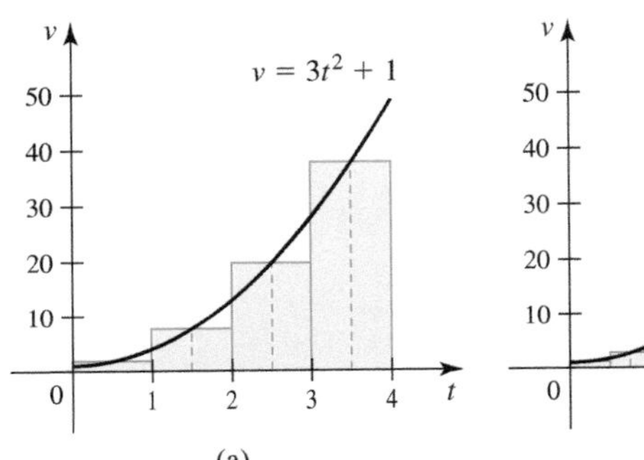

T 10. **Approximating displacement** The velocity in ft/s of an object moving along a line is given by $v = \sqrt{10t}$ on the interval $1 \le t \le 7$.
   a. Divide the time interval $[1, 7]$ into $n = 3$ subintervals, $[1, 3]$, $[3, 5]$, and $[5, 7]$. On each subinterval, assume the object moves at a constant velocity equal to v evaluated at the midpoint of the subinterval and use these approximations to estimate the displacement of the object on $[1, 7]$ (see part (a) of the figure).
   b. Repeat part (a) for $n = 6$ subintervals (see part (b) of the figure).

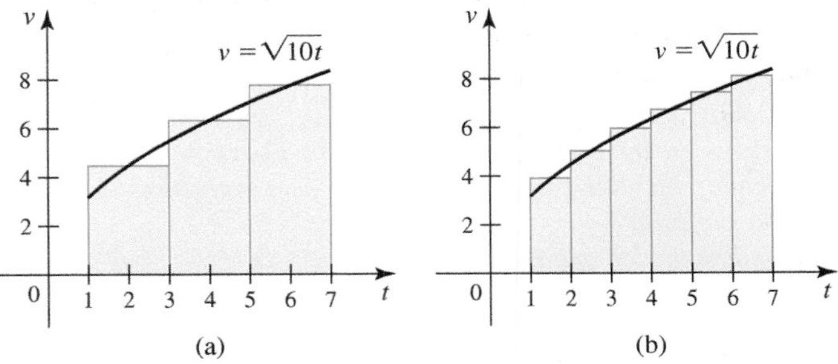

11–16. Approximating displacement *The velocity of an object is given by the following functions on a specified interval. Approximate the displacement of the object on this interval by subdividing the interval into n subintervals. Use the left endpoint of each subinterval to compute the height of the rectangles.*

11. $v = 2t + 1$ (m/s), for $0 \le t \le 8$; $n = 2$

T 12. $v = e^t$ (m/s), for $0 \le t \le 3$; $n = 3$

13. $v = \dfrac{1}{2t + 1}$ (m/s), for $0 \le t \le 8$; $n = 4$

14. $v = t^2/2 + 4$ (ft/s), for $0 \le t \le 12$; $n = 6$

T 15. $v = 4\sqrt{t + 1}$ (mi/hr), for $0 \le t \le 15$; $n = 5$

16. $v = \dfrac{t + 3}{6}$ (m/s), for $0 \le t \le 4$; $n = 4$

17–18. Left and right Riemann sums *Use the figures to calculate the left and right Riemann sums for f on the given interval and for the given value of n.*

17. $f(x) = x + 1$ on $[1, 6]$; $n = 5$

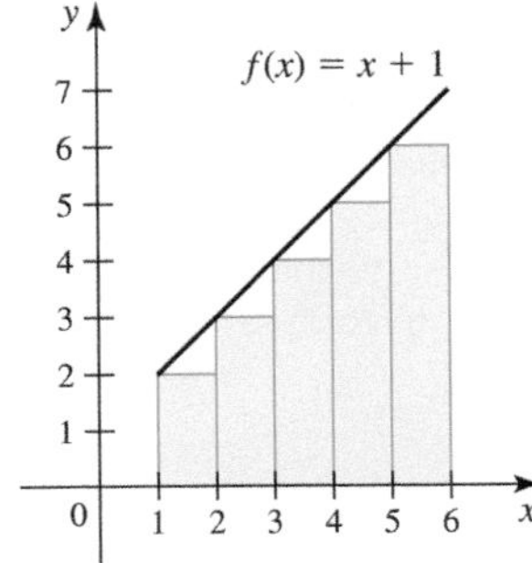

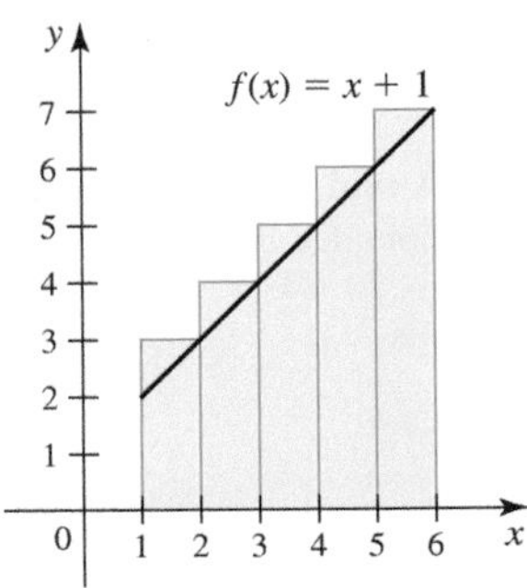

18. $f(x) = \frac{1}{x}$ on $[1, 5]$; $n = 4$

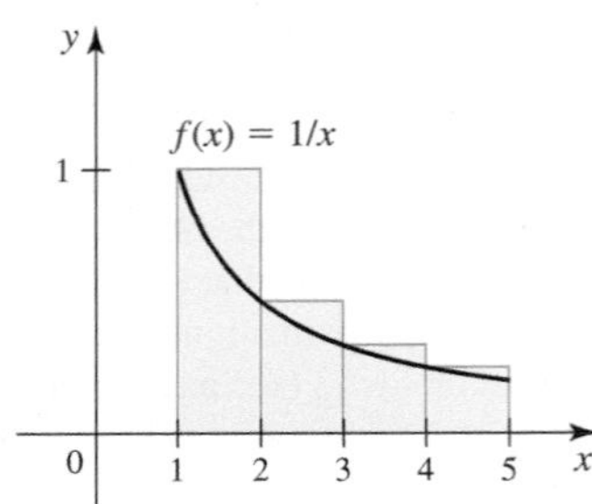

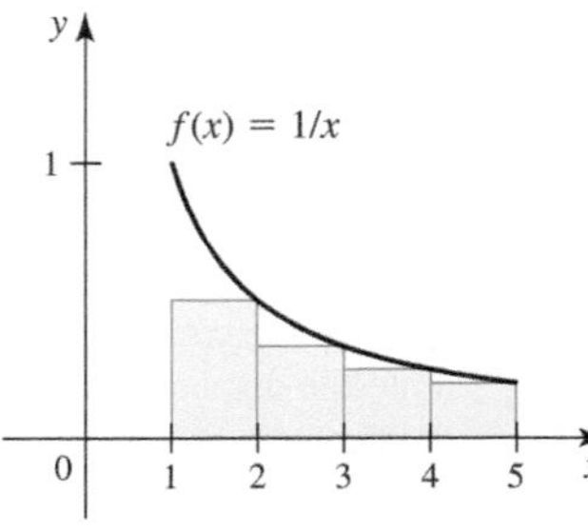

19–26. Left and right Riemann sums *Complete the following steps for the given function, interval, and value of n.*

a. Sketch the graph of the function on the given interval.
b. Calculate Δx and the grid points $x_0, x_1, \ldots, x_n$.
c. Illustrate the left and right Riemann sums. Then determine which Riemann sum underestimates and which sum overestimates the area under the curve.
d. Calculate the left and right Riemann sums.

19. $f(x) = x + 1$ on $[0, 4]$; $n = 4$

20. $f(x) = 9 - x$ on $[3, 8]$; $n = 5$

21. $f(x) = \cos x$ on $[0, \pi/2]$; $n = 4$

T **22.** $f(x) = \sin^{-1}(x/3)$ on $[0, 3]$; $n = 6$

23. $f(x) = x^2 - 1$ on $[2, 4]$; $n = 4$

24. $f(x) = 2x^2$ on $[1, 6]$; $n = 5$

T **25.** $f(x) = e^{x/2}$ on $[1, 4]$; $n = 6$

T **26.** $f(x) = \ln 4x$ on $[1, 3]$; $n = 5$

27. A midpoint Riemann sum Approximate the area of the region bounded by the graph of $f(x) = 100 - x^2$ and the x-axis on $[0, 10]$ with $n = 5$ subintervals. Use the midpoint of each subinterval to determine the height of each rectangle (see figure).

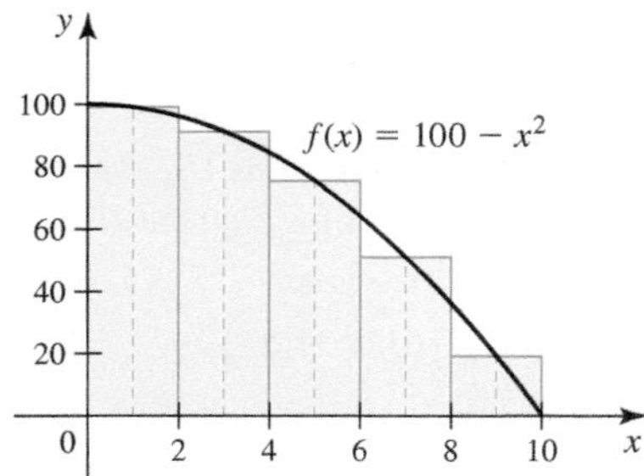

T **28. A midpoint Riemann sum** Approximate the area of the region bounded by the graph of $f(t) = \cos(t/2)$ and the t-axis on $[0, \pi]$ with $n = 4$ subintervals. Use the midpoint of each subinterval to determine the height of each rectangle (see figure).

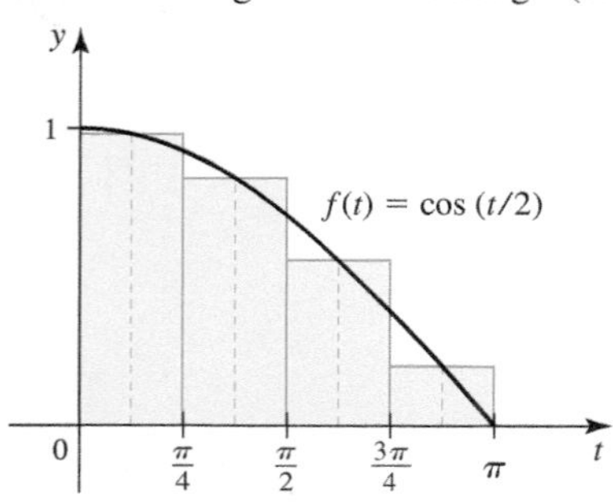

29–34. Midpoint Riemann sums *Complete the following steps for the given function, interval, and value of n.*

a. Sketch the graph of the function on the given interval.
b. Calculate Δx and the grid points $x_0, x_1, \ldots, x_n$.
c. Illustrate the midpoint Riemann sum by sketching the appropriate rectangles.
d. Calculate the midpoint Riemann sum.

29. $f(x) = 2x + 1$ on $[0, 4]$; $n = 4$

T **30.** $f(x) = 2\cos^{-1} x$ on $[0, 1]$; $n = 5$

T **31.** $f(x) = \sqrt{x}$ on $[1, 3]$; $n = 4$

32. $f(x) = x^2$ on $[0, 4]$; $n = 4$

33. $f(x) = \frac{1}{x}$ on $[1, 6]$; $n = 5$

34. $f(x) = 4 - x$ on $[-1, 4]$; $n = 5$

35–36. Riemann sums from tables *Evaluate the left and right Riemann sums for f over the given interval for the given value of n.*

35. $n = 4$; $[0, 2]$

x	0	0.5	1	1.5	2
$f(x)$	5	3	2	1	1

36. $n = 8$; $[1, 5]$

x	1	1.5	2	2.5	3	3.5	4	4.5	5
$f(x)$	0	2	3	2	2	1	0	2	3

37. Displacement from a table of velocities The velocities (in mi/hr) of an automobile moving along a straight highway over a two-hour period are given in the following table.

t (hr)	0	0.25	0.5	0.75	1	1.25	1.5	1.75	2
v (mi/hr)	50	50	60	60	55	65	50	60	70

a. Sketch a smooth curve passing through the data points.
b. Find the midpoint Riemann sum approximation to the displacement on $[0, 2]$ with $n = 2$ and $n = 4$.

38. Displacement from a table of velocities The velocities (in m/s) of an automobile moving along a straight freeway over a four-second period are given in the following table.

t (s)	0	0.5	1	1.5	2	2.5	3	3.5	4
v (m/s)	20	25	30	35	30	30	35	40	40

a. Sketch a smooth curve passing through the data points.
b. Find the midpoint Riemann sum approximation to the displacement on $[0, 4]$ with $n = 2$ and $n = 4$ subintervals.

39. Sigma notation Express the following sums using sigma notation. (Answers are not unique.)

a. $1 + 2 + 3 + 4 + 5$
b. $4 + 5 + 6 + 7 + 8 + 9$
c. $1^2 + 2^2 + 3^2 + 4^2$
d. $1 + \frac{1}{2} + \frac{1}{3} + \frac{1}{4}$

40. Sigma notation Express the following sums using sigma notation. (Answers are not unique.)

a. $1 + 3 + 5 + 7 + \cdots + 99$
b. $4 + 9 + 14 + \cdots + 44$
c. $3 + 8 + 13 + \cdots + 63$
d. $\frac{1}{1 \cdot 2} + \frac{1}{2 \cdot 3} + \frac{1}{3 \cdot 4} + \cdots + \frac{1}{49 \cdot 50}$

41. Sigma notation Evaluate the following expressions.

a. $\sum_{k=1}^{10} k$
b. $\sum_{k=1}^{6} (2k + 1)$
c. $\sum_{k=1}^{4} k^2$
d. $\sum_{n=1}^{5} (1 + n^2)$
e. $\sum_{m=1}^{3} \frac{2m + 2}{3}$
f. $\sum_{j=1}^{3} (3j - 4)$
g. $\sum_{p=1}^{5} (2p + p^2)$
h. $\sum_{n=0}^{4} \sin \frac{n\pi}{2}$

T **42. Evaluating sums** Evaluate the following expressions by two methods.

(i) Use Theorem 5.1. (ii) Use a calculator.

a. $\sum_{k=1}^{45} k$
b. $\sum_{k=1}^{45} (5k - 1)$
c. $\sum_{k=1}^{75} 2k^2$
d. $\sum_{n=1}^{50} (1 + n^2)$
e. $\sum_{m=1}^{75} \frac{2m + 2}{3}$
f. $\sum_{j=1}^{20} (3j - 4)$
g. $\sum_{p=1}^{35} (2p + p^2)$
h. $\sum_{n=0}^{40} (n^2 + 3n - 1)$

T **43–46. Riemann sums for larger values of** n *Complete the following steps for the given function f and interval.*

a. For the given value of n, use sigma notation to write the left, right, and midpoint Riemann sums. Then evaluate each sum using a calculator.

b. Based on the approximations found in part (a), estimate the area of the region bounded by the graph of f and the x-axis on the interval.

43. $f(x) = \sqrt{x}$ on $[0, 4]$; $n = 40$

44. $f(x) = x^2 + 1$ on $[-1, 1]$; $n = 50$

45. $f(x) = x^2 - 1$ on $[2, 7]$; $n = 75$

46. $f(x) = \cos 2x$ on $[0, \pi/4]$; $n = 60$

T **47–52. Approximating areas with a calculator** *Use a calculator and right Riemann sums to approximate the area of the given region. Present your calculations in a table showing the approximations for* $n = 10, 30, 60,$ *and* 80 *subintervals. Comment on whether your approximations appear to approach a limit.*

47. The region bounded by the graph of $f(x) = 4 - x^2$ and the x-axis on the interval $[-2, 2]$

48. The region bounded by the graph of $f(x) = x^2 + 1$ and the x-axis on the interval $[0, 2]$

49. The region bounded by the graph of $f(x) = 2 - 2 \sin x$ and the x-axis on the interval $[-\pi/2, \pi/2]$

50. The region bounded by the graph of $f(x) = 2^x$ and the x-axis on the interval $[1, 2]$

51. The region bounded by the graph of $f(x) = \ln x$ and the x-axis on the interval $[1, e]$

52. The region bounded by the graph of $f(x) = \sqrt{x + 1}$ and the x-axis on the interval $[0, 3]$

Further Explorations

53. Explain why or why not Determine whether the following statements are true and give an explanation or counterexample.

a. Consider the linear function $f(x) = 2x + 5$ and the region bounded by its graph and the x-axis on the interval $[3, 6]$. Suppose the area of this region is approximated using midpoint Riemann sums. Then the approximations give the exact area of the region for any number of subintervals.

b. A left Riemann sum always overestimates the area of a region bounded by a positive increasing function and the x-axis on an interval $[a, b]$.

c. For an increasing or decreasing nonconstant function on an interval $[a, b]$ and a given value of n, the value of the midpoint Riemann sum always lies between the values of the left and right Riemann sums.

T **54. Riemann sums for a semicircle** Let $f(x) = \sqrt{1 - x^2}$.

a. Show that the graph of f is the upper half of a circle of radius 1 centered at the origin.

b. Estimate the area between the graph of f and the x-axis on the interval $[-1, 1]$ using a midpoint Riemann sum with $n = 25$.

c. Repeat part (b) using $n = 75$ rectangles.

d. What happens to the midpoint Riemann sums on $[-1, 1]$ as $n \to \infty$?

T **55–58. Sigma notation for Riemann sums** *Use sigma notation to write the following Riemann sums. Then evaluate each Riemann sum using Theorem 5.1 or a calculator.*

55. The right Riemann sum for $f(x) = x + 1$ on $[0, 4]$ with $n = 50$

56. The left Riemann sum for $f(x) = e^x$ on $[0, \ln 2]$ with $n = 40$

57. The midpoint Riemann sum for $f(x) = x^3$ on $[3, 11]$ with $n = 32$

58. The midpoint Riemann sum for $f(x) = 1 + \cos \pi x$ on $[0, 2]$ with $n = 50$

59–62. Identifying Riemann sums *Fill in the blanks with right or midpoint, an interval, and a value of n. In some cases, more than one answer may work.*

59. $\sum_{k=1}^{4} f(1 + k) \cdot 1$ is a ______ Riemann sum for f on the interval [___, ___] with $n =$ ______.

60. $\sum_{k=1}^{4} f(2 + k) \cdot 1$ is a ______ Riemann sum for f on the interval [___, ___] with $n =$ ______.

61. $\sum_{k=1}^{4} f(1.5 + k) \cdot 1$ is a ______ Riemann sum for f on the interval [___, ___] with $n =$ ______.

62. $\sum_{k=1}^{8} f\left(1.5 + \frac{k}{2}\right) \cdot \frac{1}{2}$ is a ______ Riemann sum for f on the interval [___, ___] with $n =$ ______.

63. Approximating areas Estimate the area of the region bounded by the graph of $f(x) = x^2 + 2$ and the x-axis on $[0, 2]$ in the following ways.

a. Divide $[0, 2]$ into $n = 4$ subintervals and approximate the area of the region using a left Riemann sum. Illustrate the solution geometrically.

b. Divide $[0, 2]$ into $n = 4$ subintervals and approximate the area of the region using a midpoint Riemann sum. Illustrate the solution geometrically.

c. Divide $[0, 2]$ into $n = 4$ subintervals and approximate the area of the region using a right Riemann sum. Illustrate the solution geometrically.

64. Approximating area from a graph Approximate the area of the region bounded by the graph (see figure) and the x-axis by dividing the interval $[0, 6]$ into $n = 3$ subintervals. Use a left and right Riemann sum to obtain two different approximations.

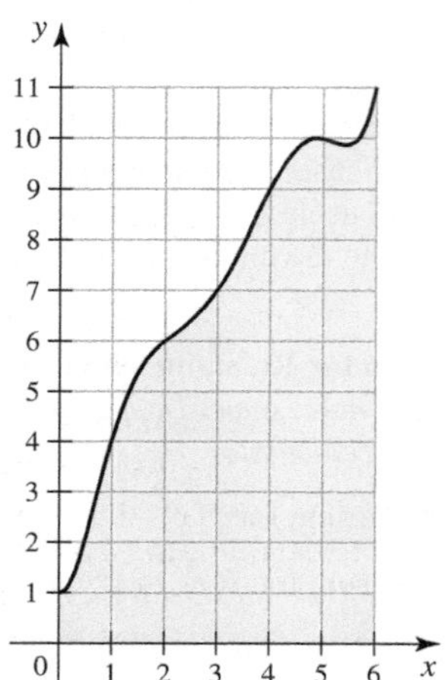

65. Approximating area from a graph Approximate the area of the region bounded by the graph (see figure) and the x-axis by dividing the interval $[1, 7]$ into $n = 6$ subintervals. Use a left and right Riemann sum to obtain two different approximations.

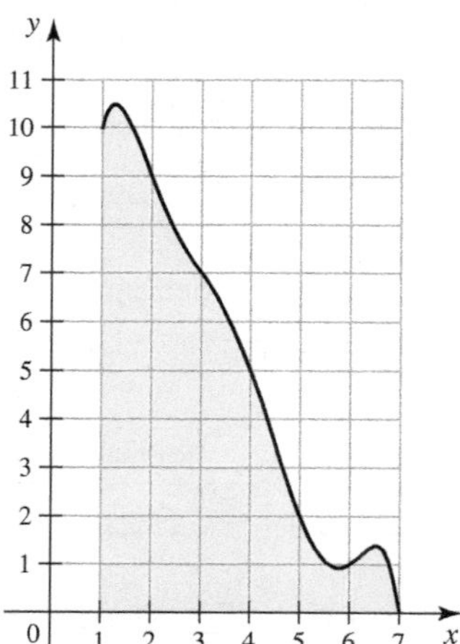

Applications

66. Displacement from a velocity graph Consider the velocity function for an object moving along a line (see figure).

a. Describe the motion of the object over the interval $[0, 6]$.

b. Use geometry to find the displacement of the object between $t = 0$ and $t = 3$.

c. Use geometry to find the displacement of the object between $t = 3$ and $t = 5$.

d. Assuming that the velocity remains 30 m/s, for $t \geq 4$, find the function that gives the displacement between $t = 0$ and any time $t \geq 5$.

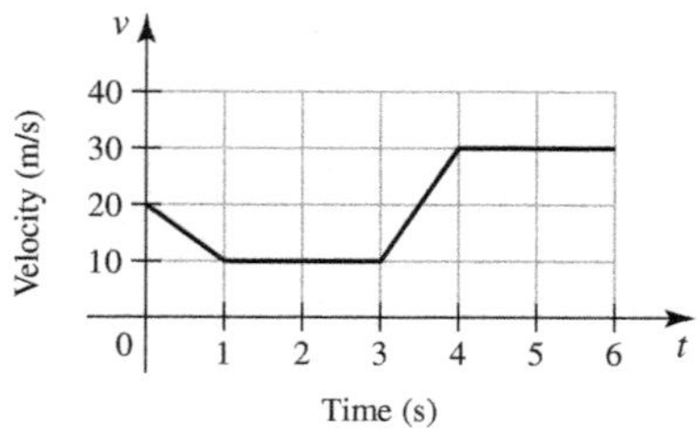

67. Displacement from a velocity graph Consider the velocity function for an object moving along a line (see figure).

a. Describe the motion of the object over the interval $[0, 6]$.

b. Use geometry to find the displacement of the object between $t = 0$ and $t = 2$.

c. Use geometry to find the displacement of the object between $t = 2$ and $t = 5$.

d. Assuming that the velocity remains 10 m/s, for $t \geq 5$, find the function that gives the displacement between $t = 0$ and any time $t \geq 5$.

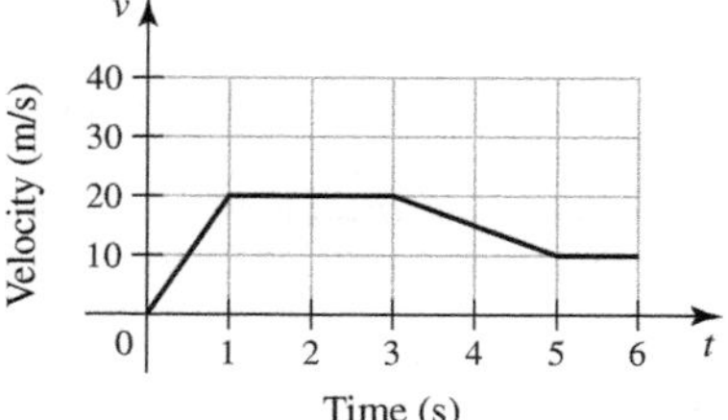

68. Flow rates Suppose a gauge at the outflow of a reservoir measures the flow rate of water in units of ft^3/hr. In Chapter 6, we show that the total amount of water that flows out of the reservoir is the area under the flow rate curve. Consider the flow-rate function shown in the figure.

a. Find the amount of water (in units of ft^3) that flows out of the reservoir over the interval $[0, 4]$.

b. Find the amount of water that flows out of the reservoir over the interval $[8, 10]$.

c. Does more water flow out of the reservoir over the interval $[0, 4]$ or $[4, 6]$?

d. Show that the units of your answer are consistent with the units of the variables on the axes.

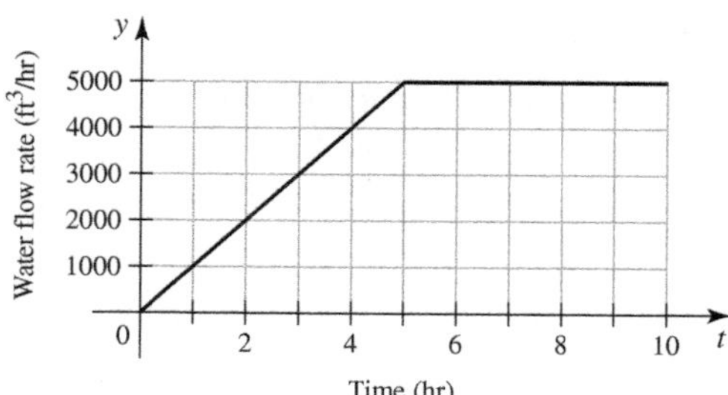

69. Mass from density A thin 10-cm rod is made of an alloy whose density varies along its length according to the function shown in the figure. Assume density is measured in units of g/cm.

In Chapter 6, we show that the mass of the rod is the area under the density curve.

a. Find the mass of the left half of the rod ($0 \le x \le 5$).
b. Find the mass of the right half of the rod ($5 \le x \le 10$).
c. Find the mass of the entire rod ($0 \le x \le 10$).
d. Find the point along the rod at which it will balance (called the center of mass).

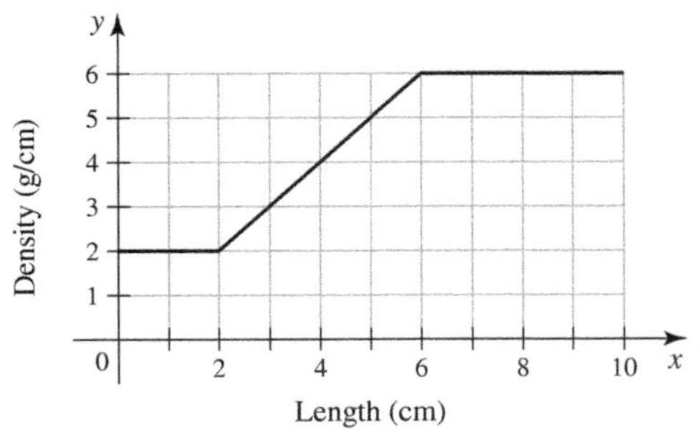

70–71. Displacement from velocity *The following functions describe the velocity of a car (in mi/hr) moving along a straight highway for a 3-hr interval. In each case, find the function that gives the displacement of the car over the interval* $[0, t]$*, where* $0 \le t \le 3$.

70. $v(t) = \begin{cases} 40 & \text{if } 0 \le t \le 1.5 \\ 50 & \text{if } 1.5 < t \le 3 \end{cases}$

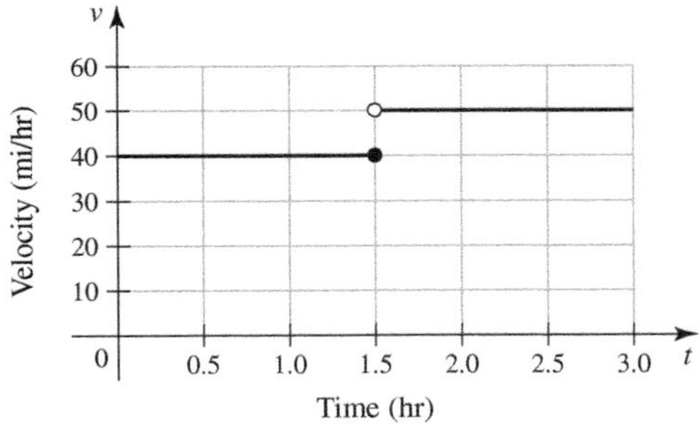

71. $v(t) = \begin{cases} 30 & \text{if } 0 \le t \le 2 \\ 50 & \text{if } 2 < t \le 2.5 \\ 44 & \text{if } 2.5 < t \le 3 \end{cases}$

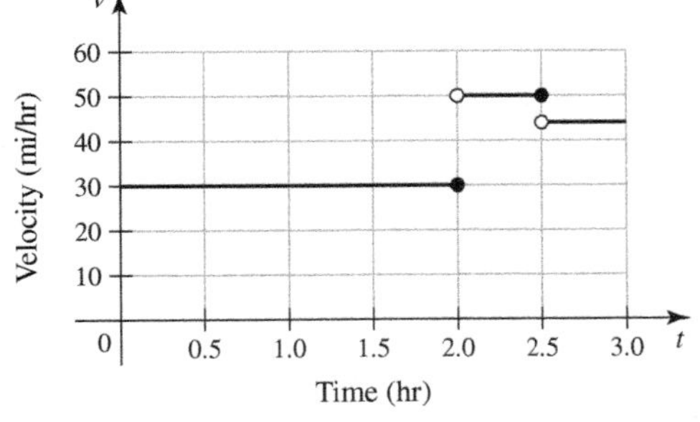

T **72–75. Functions with absolute value** *Use a calculator and the method of your choice to approximate the area of the following regions. Present your calculations in a table, showing approximations using* $n = 16, 32,$ *and* 64 *subintervals. Comment on whether your approximations appear to approach a limit.*

72. The region bounded by the graph of $f(x) = |25 - x^2|$ and the x-axis on the interval $[0, 10]$

73. The region bounded by the graph of $f(x) = |x(x^2 - 1)|$ and the x-axis on the interval $[-1, 1]$

74. The region bounded by the graph of $f(x) = |\cos 2x|$ and the x-axis on the interval $[0, \pi]$

75. The region bounded by the graph of $f(x) = |1 - x^3|$ and the x-axis on the interval $[-1, 2]$

Additional Exercises

76. Riemann sums for constant functions Let $f(x) = c$, where $c > 0$, be a constant function on $[a, b]$. Prove that any Riemann sum for any value of n gives the exact area of the region between the graph of f and the x-axis on $[a, b]$.

77. Riemann sums for linear functions Assume that the linear function $f(x) = mx + c$ is positive on the interval $[a, b]$. Prove that the midpoint Riemann sum with any value of n gives the exact area of the region between the graph of f and the x-axis on $[a, b]$.

78. Shape of the graph for left Riemann sums Suppose a left Riemann sum is used to approximate the area of the region bounded by the graph of a positive function and the x-axis on the interval $[a, b]$. Fill in the following table to indicate whether the resulting approximation underestimates or overestimates the exact area in the four cases shown. Use a sketch to explain your reasoning in each case.

	Increasing on $[a, b]$	**Decreasing on $[a, b]$**
Concave up on $[a, b]$		
Concave down on $[a, b]$		

79. Shape of the graph for right Riemann sums Suppose a right Riemann sum is used to approximate the area of the region bounded by the graph of a positive function and the x-axis on the interval $[a, b]$. Fill in the following table to indicate whether the resulting approximation underestimates or overestimates the exact area in the four cases shown. Use a sketch to explain your reasoning in each case.

	Increasing on $[a, b]$	**Decreasing on $[a, b]$**
Concave up on $[a, b]$		
Concave down on $[a, b]$		

QUICK CHECK ANSWERS

1. 45 mi **2.** 0.25, 0.125, 7.875
3. $\Delta x = 2$; $\{1, 3, 5, 7, 9\}$
4. The left sum overestimates the area. ◀

5.2 Definite Integrals

We introduced Riemann sums in Section 5.1 as a way to approximate the area of a region bounded by a curve $y = f(x)$ and the x-axis on an interval $[a, b]$. In that discussion, we assumed f to be nonnegative on the interval. Our next task is to discover the geometric meaning of Riemann sums when f is negative on some or all of $[a, b]$. Once this matter is settled, we proceed to the main event of this section, which is to define the *definite integral*. With definite integrals, the approximations given by Riemann sums become exact.

Net Area

How do we interpret Riemann sums when f is negative at some or all points of $[a, b]$? The answer follows directly from the Riemann sum definition.

EXAMPLE 1 **Interpreting Riemann sums** Evaluate and interpret the following Riemann sums for $f(x) = 1 - x^2$ on the interval $[a, b]$ with n equally spaced subintervals.

a. A midpoint Riemann sum with $[a, b] = [1, 3]$ and $n = 4$

b. A left Riemann sum with $[a, b] = [0, 3]$ and $n = 6$

SOLUTION

a. The length of each subinterval is $\Delta x = \dfrac{b - a}{n} = \dfrac{3 - 1}{4} = 0.5$. So the grid points are

$$x_0 = 1, \quad x_1 = 1.5, \quad x_2 = 2, \quad \text{and} \quad x_3 = 2.5, \quad \text{and} \quad x_4 = 3.$$

To compute the midpoint Riemann sum, we evaluate f at the midpoints of the subintervals, which are

$$x_1^* = 1.25, \quad x_2^* = 1.75, \quad x_3^* = 2.25, \quad \text{and} \quad x_4^* = 2.75.$$

The resulting midpoint Riemann sum is

$$\begin{aligned}\sum_{k=1}^{n} f(x_k^*)\,\Delta x &= \sum_{k=1}^{4} f(x_k^*)(0.5)\\ &= f(1.25)(0.5) + f(1.75)(0.5) + f(2.25)(0.5) + f(2.75)(0.5)\\ &= (-0.5625 - 2.0625 - 4.0625 - 6.5625)0.5\\ &= -6.625.\end{aligned}$$

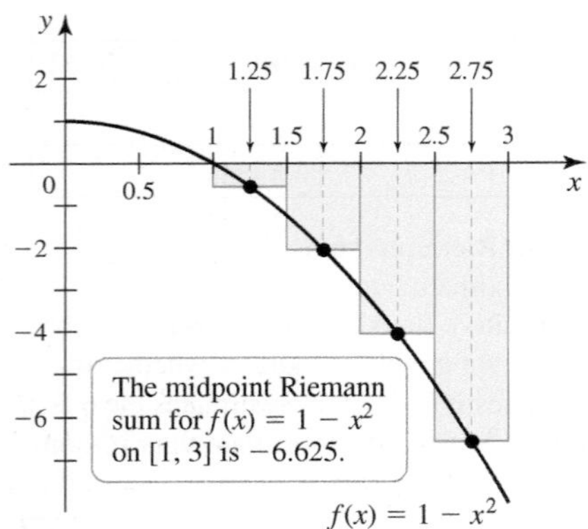

Figure 5.16

All values of $f(x_k^*)$ are negative, so the Riemann sum is also negative. Because area is always a nonnegative quantity, this Riemann sum does not approximate the area of the region between the curve and the x-axis on $[1, 3]$. Notice, however, that the values of $f(x_k^*)$ are the *negative* of the heights of the corresponding rectangles (Figure 5.16). Therefore, the Riemann sum approximates the *negative* of the area of the region bounded by the curve.

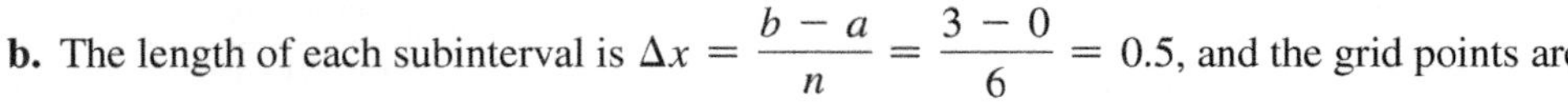

b. The length of each subinterval is $\Delta x = \dfrac{b - a}{n} = \dfrac{3 - 0}{6} = 0.5$, and the grid points are

$$x_0 = 0, \quad x_1 = 0.5, \quad x_2 = 1, \quad x_3 = 1.5, \quad x_4 = 2, \quad x_5 = 2.5, \quad \text{and} \quad x_6 = 3.$$

To calculate the left Riemann sum, we set $x_1^*, x_2^*, \ldots, x_6^*$ equal to the left endpoints of the subintervals:

$$x_1^* = 0, \quad x_2^* = 0.5, \quad x_3^* = 1, \quad x_4^* = 1.5, \quad x_5^* = 2, \quad \text{and} \quad x_6^* = 2.5.$$

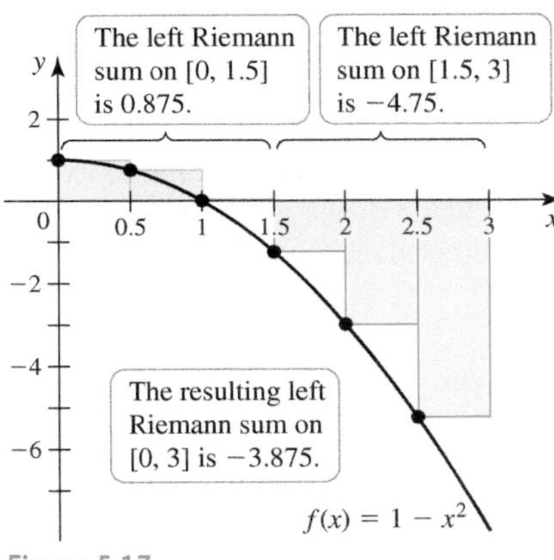

Figure 5.17

The resulting left Riemann sum is

$$\begin{aligned}\sum_{k=1}^{n} f(x_k^*)\Delta x &= \sum_{k=1}^{6} f(x_k^*)(0.5)\\ &= (\underbrace{f(0) + f(0.5) + f(1)}_{\text{nonnegative contribution}} + \underbrace{f(1.5) + f(2) + f(2.5)}_{\text{negative contribution}})0.5\\ &= (1 + 0.75 + 0 - 1.25 - 3 - 5.25)0.5\\ &= -3.875.\end{aligned}$$

In this case, the values of $f(x_k^*)$ are nonnegative for $k = 1, 2$, and 3, and negative for $k = 4, 5$, and 6 (Figure 5.17). Where f is positive, we get positive contributions to the Riemann sum, and where f is negative, we get negative contributions to the sum.

Related Exercises 11–20 ◀

Let's recap what we learned in Example 1. On intervals where $f(x) < 0$, Riemann sums approximate the *negative* of the area of the region bounded by the curve (Figure 5.18).

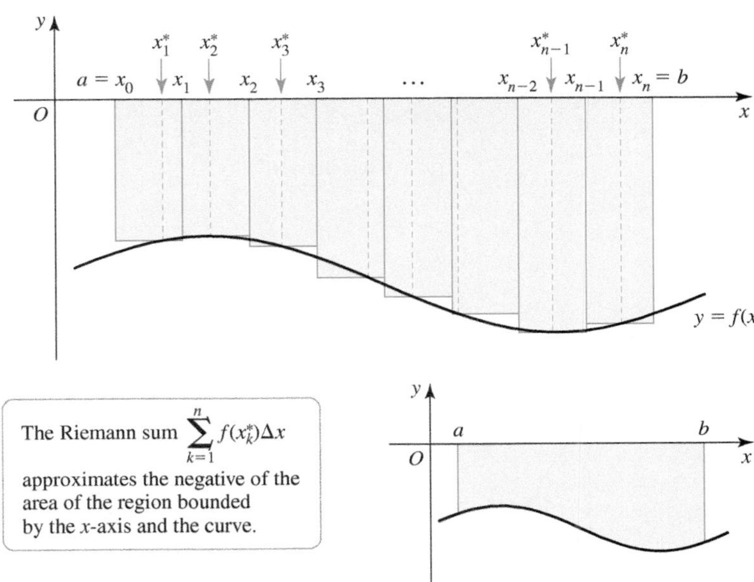

Figure 5.18

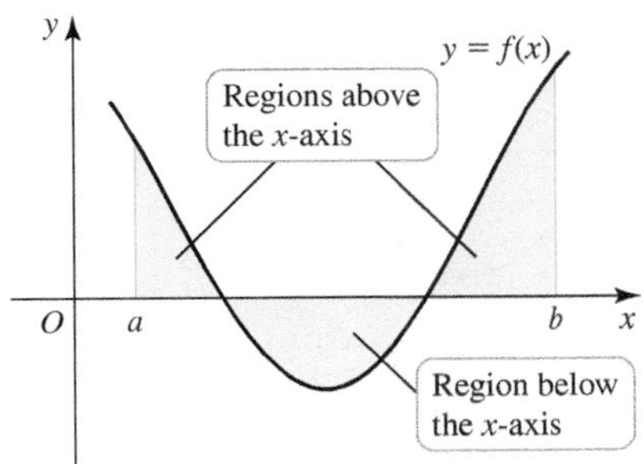

Figure 5.19

In the more general case that f is positive on only part of $[a, b]$, we get positive contributions to the sum where f is positive and negative contributions to the sum where f is negative. In this case, Riemann sums approximate the area of the regions that lie above the x-axis *minus* the area of the regions that lie *below* the x-axis (Figure 5.19). This difference between the positive and negative contributions is called the *net area*; it can be positive, negative, or zero.

➤ Net area suggests the difference between positive and negative contributions much like net change or net profit. Some texts use the term **signed area** for net area.

DEFINITION Net Area

Consider the region R bounded by the graph of a continuous function f and the x-axis between $x = a$ and $x = b$. The **net area** of R is the sum of the areas of the parts of R that lie above the x-axis *minus* the sum of the areas of the parts of R that lie below the x-axis on $[a, b]$.

QUICK CHECK 1 Suppose $f(x) = -5$. What is the net area of the region bounded by the graph of f and the x-axis on the interval $[1, 5]$? Make a sketch of the function and the region. ◀

QUICK CHECK 2 Sketch a continuous function f that is positive over the interval $[0, 1)$ and negative over the interval $(1, 2]$, such that the net area of the region bounded by the graph of f and the x-axis on $[0, 2]$ is zero. ◂

The Definite Integral

Riemann sums for f on $[a, b]$ give *approximations* to the net area of the region bounded by the graph of f and the x-axis between $x = a$ and $x = b$, where $a < b$. How can we make these approximations exact? If f is continuous on $[a, b]$, it is reasonable to expect the Riemann sum approximations to approach the exact value of the net area as the number of subintervals $n \to \infty$ and as the length of the subintervals $\Delta x \to 0$ (Figure 5.20). In terms of limits, we write

$$\text{net area} = \lim_{n\to\infty} \sum_{k=1}^{n} f(x_k^*)\,\Delta x.$$

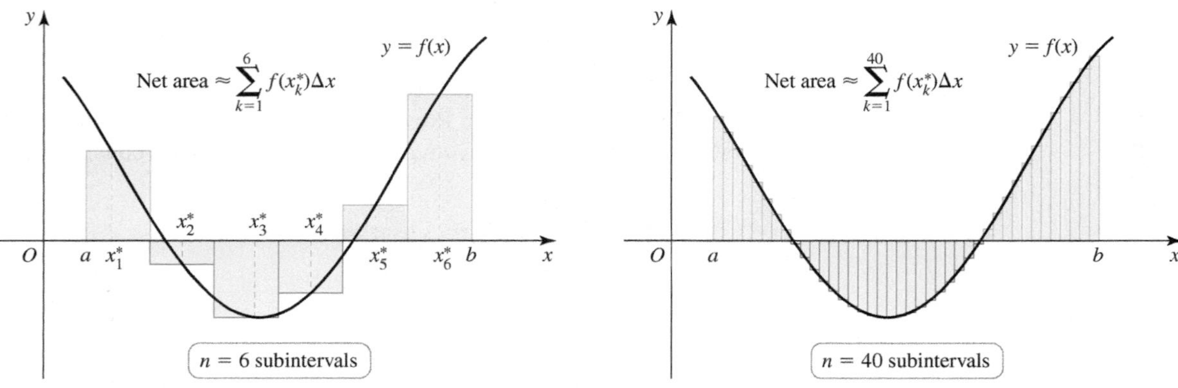

As the number of subintervals n increases, the Riemann sums approach the net area of the region between the curve $y = f(x)$ and the x-axis on $[a, b]$.

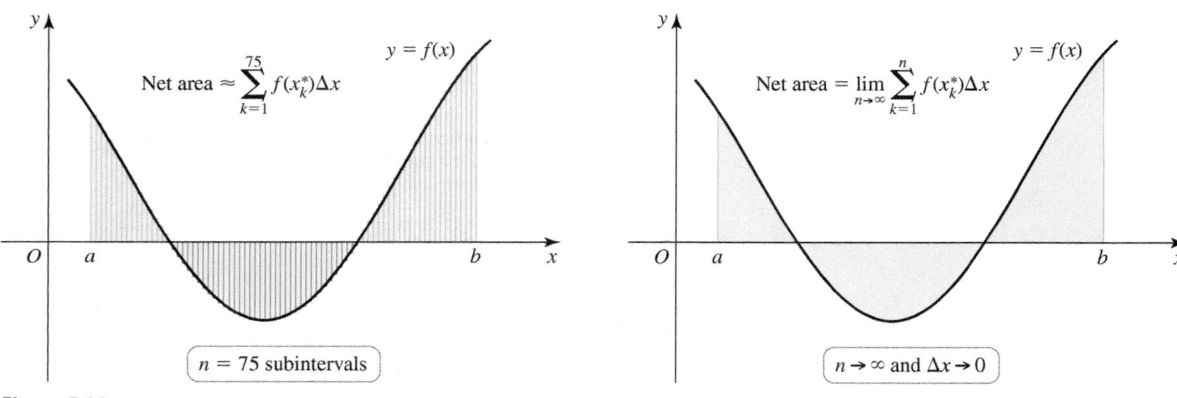

Figure 5.20

The Riemann sums we have used so far involve regular partitions in which the subintervals have the same length Δx. We now introduce partitions of $[a, b]$ in which the lengths of the subintervals are not necessarily equal. A **general partition** of $[a, b]$ consists of the n subintervals

$$[x_0, x_1], [x_1, x_2], \ldots, [x_{n-1}, x_n],$$

where $x_0 = a$ and $x_n = b$. The length of the kth subinterval is $\Delta x_k = x_k - x_{k-1}$, for $k = 1, \ldots, n$. We let x_k^* be any point in the subinterval $[x_{k-1}, x_k]$. This general partition is used to define the *general Riemann sum*.

> **DEFINITION General Riemann Sum**
>
> Suppose $[x_0, x_1], [x_1, x_2], \ldots, [x_{n-1}, x_n]$ are subintervals of $[a, b]$ with
>
> $$a = x_0 < x_1 < x_2 < \cdots < x_{n-1} < x_n = b.$$
>
> Let Δx_k be the length of the subinterval $[x_{k-1}, x_k]$ and let x_k^* be any point in $[x_{k-1}, x_k]$, for $k = 1, 2, \ldots, n$.
>
> 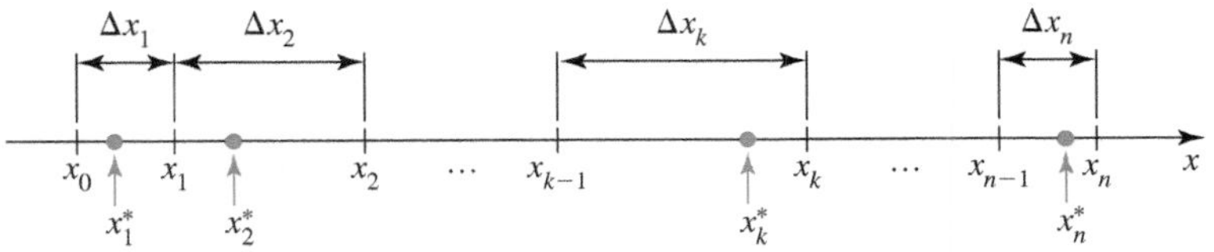
>
>
> If f is defined on $[a, b]$, the sum
>
> $$\sum_{k=1}^{n} f(x_k^*)\,\Delta x_k = f(x_1^*)\,\Delta x_1 + f(x_2^*)\,\Delta x_2 + \cdots + f(x_n^*)\,\Delta x_n$$
>
> is called a **general Riemann sum for f on $[a, b]$**.

As was the case for regular Riemann sums, if we choose x_k^* to be the left endpoint of $[x_{k-1}, x_k]$, for $k = 1, 2, \ldots, n$, then the general Riemann sum is a left Riemann sum. Similarly, if we choose x_k^* to be the right endpoint $[x_{k-1}, x_k]$, for $k = 1, 2, \ldots, n$, then the general Riemann sum is a right Riemann sum, and if we choose x_k^* to be the midpoint of the interval $[x_{k-1}, x_k]$, for $k = 1, 2, \ldots, n$, then the general Riemann sum is a midpoint Riemann sum.

Now consider the limit of $\sum_{k=1}^{n} f(x_k^*)\,\Delta x_k$ as $n \to \infty$ and as *all* the $\Delta x_k \to 0$. We let Δ denote the largest value of Δx_k; that is, $\Delta = \max\{\Delta x_1, \Delta x_2, \ldots, \Delta x_n\}$. Observe that if $\Delta \to 0$, then $\Delta x_k \to 0$, for $k = 1, 2, \ldots, n$. For the limit $\lim_{\Delta \to 0} \sum_{k=1}^{n} f(x_k^*)\Delta x_k$ to exist, it must have the same value over all general partitions of $[a, b]$ and for all choices of x_k^* on a partition.

➤ Note that $\Delta \to 0$ forces all $\Delta x_k \to 0$, which forces $n \to \infty$. Therefore, it suffices to write $\Delta \to 0$ in the limit.

> **DEFINITION Definite Integral**
>
> A function f defined on $[a, b]$ is **integrable** on $[a, b]$ if $\lim_{\Delta \to 0} \sum_{k=1}^{n} f(x_k^*)\Delta x_k$ exists and is unique over all partitions of $[a, b]$ and all choices of x_k^* on a partition. This limit is the **definite integral of f from a to b**, which we write
>
> $$\int_a^b f(x)\,dx = \lim_{\Delta \to 0} \sum_{k=1}^{n} f(x_k^*)\Delta x_k.$$

When the limit defining the definite integral of f exists, it equals the net area of the region bounded by the graph of f and the x-axis on $[a, b]$. It is imperative to remember that the indefinite integral $\int f(x)\,dx$ is a family of functions of x (the antiderivatives of f) and that the definite integral $\int_a^b f(x)\,dx$ is a real number (the net area of a region).

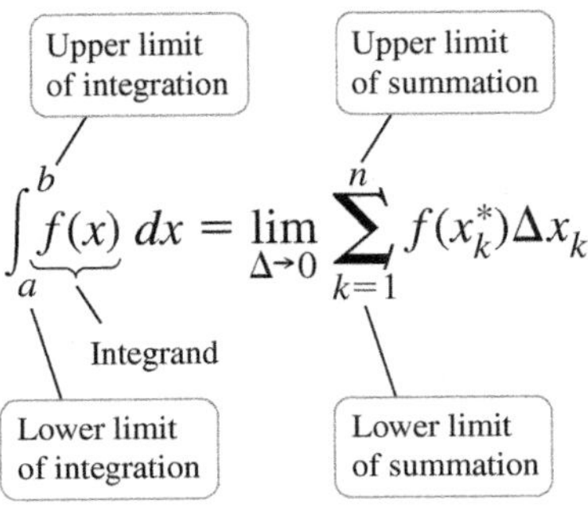

Figure 5.21

Notation The notation for the definite integral requires some explanation. There is a direct match between the notation on either side of the equation in the definition (Figure 5.21). In the limit as $\Delta \to 0$, the finite sum, denoted Σ, becomes a sum with an infinite number of terms, denoted $\int$. The integral sign $\int$ is an elongated S for sum. The **limits of integration**, a and b, and the limits of summation also match: The lower limit in the sum,

$k = 1$, corresponds to the left endpoint of the interval, $x = a$, and the upper limit in the sum, $k = n$, corresponds to the right endpoint of the interval, $x = b$. The function under the integral sign is called the **integrand**. Finally, the differential dx in the integral (which corresponds to Δx_k in the sum) is an essential part of the notation; it tells us that the **variable of integration** is x.

The variable of integration is a dummy variable that is completely internal to the integral. It does not matter what the variable of integration is called, as long as it does not conflict with other variables that are in use. Therefore, the integrals in Figure 5.22 all have the same meaning.

➤ For Leibniz, who introduced this notation in 1675, dx represented the width of an infinitesimally thin rectangle and $f(x)\,dx$ represented the area of such a rectangle. He used $\int_a^b f(x)\,dx$ to denote the sum of these areas from a to b.

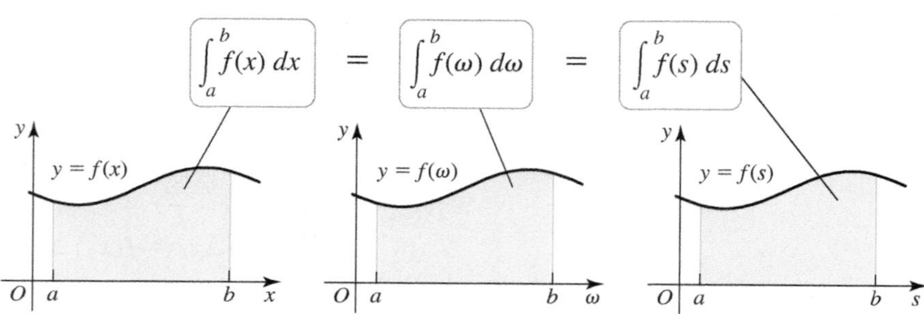

Figure 5.22

The strategy of slicing a region into smaller parts, summing the results from the parts, and taking a limit is used repeatedly in calculus and its applications. We call this strategy the **slice-and-sum method**. It often results in a Riemann sum whose limit is a definite integral.

Evaluating Definite Integrals

➤ A function f is bounded on an interval I if there is a number M such that $|f(x)| < M$ for all x in I.

Most of the functions encountered in this text are integrable (see Exercise 83 for an exception). In fact, if f is continuous on $[a, b]$ or if f is bounded on $[a, b]$ with a finite number of discontinuities, then f is integrable on $[a, b]$. The proof of this result goes beyond the scope of this text.

> **THEOREM 5.2 Integrable Functions**
> If f is continuous on $[a, b]$ or bounded on $[a, b]$ with a finite number of discontinuities, then f is integrable on $[a, b]$.

Net area $= \int_a^b f(x)\,dx$
= area above x-axis (Regions 1 and 3)
− area below x-axis (Region 2)

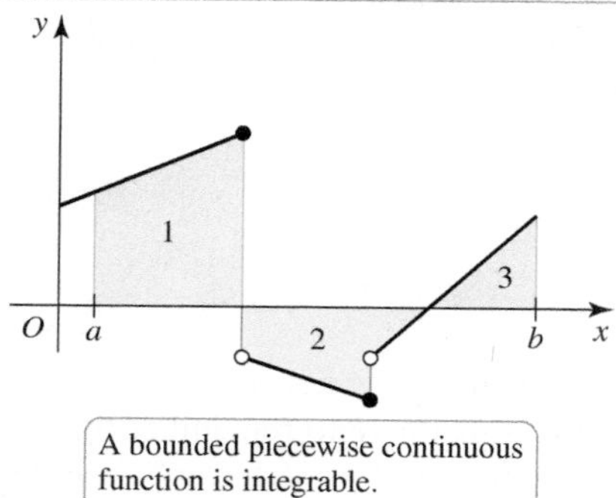

Figure 5.23

When f is continuous on $[a, b]$, we have seen that the definite integral $\int_a^b f(x)\,dx$ is the net area bounded by the graph of f and the x-axis on $[a, b]$. Figure 5.23 illustrates how the idea of net area carries over to piecewise continuous functions (Exercises 76–80).

QUICK CHECK 3 Graph $f(x) = x$ and use geometry to evaluate $\int_{-1}^{1} x\,dx$. ◄

EXAMPLE 2 Identifying the limit of a sum Assume that

$$\lim_{\Delta \to 0} \sum_{k=1}^{n} (3x_k^{*2} + 2x_k^* + 1)\Delta x_k$$

is the limit of a Riemann sum for a function f on $[1, 3]$. Identify the function f and express the limit as a definite integral. What does the definite integral represent geometrically?

SOLUTION By comparing the sum $\sum_{k=1}^{n} (3x_k^{*2} + 2x_k^* + 1)\Delta x_k$ to the general Riemann sum $\sum_{k=1}^{n} f(x_k^*)\Delta x_k$, we see that $f(x) = 3x^2 + 2x + 1$. Because f is a polynomial, it is continuous on $[1, 3]$ and is, therefore, integrable on $[1, 3]$. It follows that

$$\lim_{\Delta \to 0} \sum_{k=1}^{n} (3x_k^{*2} + 2x_k^* + 1)\,\Delta x_k = \int_1^3 (3x^2 + 2x + 1)\,dx.$$

Because f is positive on $[1, 3]$, the definite integral $\int_1^3 (3x^2 + 2x + 1)\,dx$ is the area of the region bounded by the curve $y = 3x^2 + 2x + 1$ and the x-axis on $[1, 3]$ (Figure 5.24).

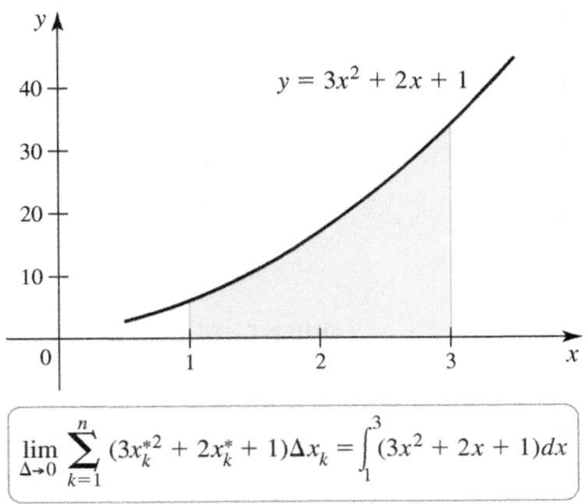

Figure 5.24

Related Exercises 21–24 ◄

Figure 5.25

➤ **A trapezoid and its area** When $a = 0$, we get the area of a triangle. When $a = b$, we get the area of a rectangle.

$A = \frac{1}{2}h(a + b)$

EXAMPLE 3 Evaluating definite integrals using geometry Use familiar area formulas to evaluate the following definite integrals.

a. $\displaystyle\int_2^4 (2x + 3)\,dx$ **b.** $\displaystyle\int_1^6 (2x - 6)\,dx$ **c.** $\displaystyle\int_3^4 \sqrt{1 - (x - 3)^2}\,dx$

SOLUTION To evaluate these definite integrals geometrically, a sketch of the corresponding region is essential.

a. The definite integral $\int_2^4 (2x + 3)\,dx$ is the area of the trapezoid bounded by the x-axis and the line $y = 2x + 3$ from $x = 2$ to $x = 4$ (Figure 5.25). The width of its base is 2 and the lengths of its two parallel sides are $f(2) = 7$ and $f(4) = 11$. Using the area formula for a trapezoid, we have

$$\int_2^4 (2x + 3)\,dx = \frac{1}{2}\cdot 2(11 + 7) = 18.$$

b. A sketch shows that the regions bounded by the line $y = 2x - 6$ and the x-axis are triangles (Figure 5.26). The area of the triangle on the interval $[1, 3]$ is $\frac{1}{2}\cdot 2\cdot 4 = 4$. Similarly, the area of the triangle on $[3, 6]$ is $\frac{1}{2}\cdot 3\cdot 6 = 9$. The definite integral is the net area of the entire region, which is the area of the triangle above the x-axis minus the area of the triangle below the x-axis:

$$\int_1^6 (2x - 6)\,dx = \text{net area} = 9 - 4 = 5.$$

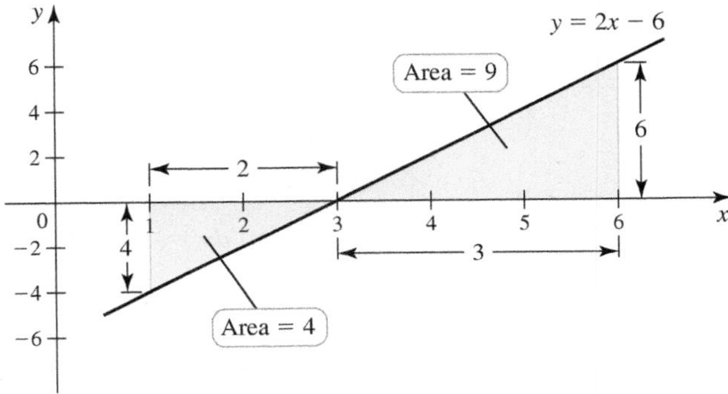

Figure 5.26

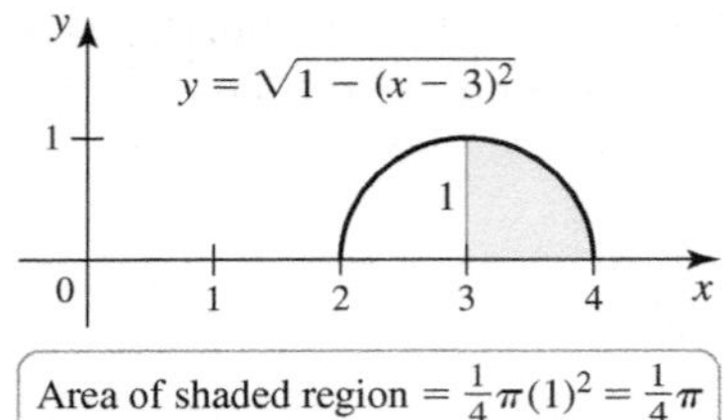

Figure 5.27

c. We first let $y = \sqrt{1 - (x - 3)^2}$ and observe that $y \geq 0$ when $2 \leq x \leq 4$. Squaring both sides leads to the equation $(x - 3)^2 + y^2 = 1$, whose graph is a circle of radius 1 centered at (3, 0). Because $y \geq 0$, the graph of $y = \sqrt{1 - (x - 3)^2}$ is the upper half of the circle. It follows that the integral $\int_3^4 \sqrt{1 - (x - 3)^2}\, dx$ is the area of a quarter circle of radius 1 (Figure 5.27). Therefore,

$$\int_3^4 \sqrt{1 - (x - 3)^2}\, dx = \frac{1}{4}\pi(1)^2 = \frac{\pi}{4}.$$

Related Exercises 25–32 ◀

QUICK CHECK 4 Let $f(x) = 5$ and use geometry to evaluate $\int_1^3 f(x)\, dx$. What is the value of $\int_a^b c\, dx$, where c is a real number? ◀

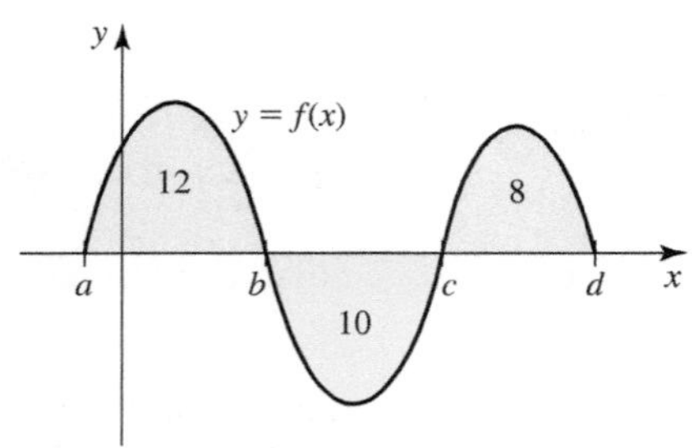

Figure 5.28

EXAMPLE 4 Definite integrals from graphs Figure 5.28 shows the graph of a function f with the areas of the regions bounded by its graph and the x-axis given. Find the values of the following definite integrals.

a. $\int_a^b f(x)\, dx$ **b.** $\int_b^c f(x)\, dx$ **c.** $\int_a^c f(x)\, dx$ **d.** $\int_b^d f(x)\, dx$

SOLUTION

a. Because f is positive on $[a, b]$, the value of the definite integral is the area of the region between the graph and the x-axis on $[a, b]$; that is, $\int_a^b f(x)\, dx = 12$.

b. Because f is negative on $[b, c]$, the value of the definite integral is the negative of the area of the corresponding region; that is, $\int_b^c f(x)\, dx = -10$.

c. The value of the definite integral is the area of the region on $[a, b]$ (where f is positive) minus the area of the region on $[b, c]$ (where f is negative). Therefore, $\int_a^c f(x)\, dx = 12 - 10 = 2$.

d. Reasoning as in part (c), we have $\int_b^d f(x)\, dx = -10 + 8 = -2$.

Related Exercises 33–40 ◀

Properties of Definite Integrals

Recall that the definite integral $\int_a^b f(x)\, dx$ was defined assuming that $a < b$. There are, however, occasions when it is necessary to reverse the limits of integration. If f is integrable on $[a, b]$, we define

$$\int_b^a f(x)\, dx = -\int_a^b f(x)\, dx.$$

In other words, reversing the limits of integration changes the sign of the integral.

Another fundamental property of integrals is that if we integrate from a point to itself, then the length of the interval of integration is zero, which means the definite integral is also zero.

DEFINITION Reversing Limits and Identical Limits of Integration

Suppose f is integrable on $[a, b]$.

1. $\int_b^a f(x)\, dx = -\int_a^b f(x)\, dx$ **2.** $\int_a^a f(x)\, dx = 0$

QUICK CHECK 5 Evaluate $\int_a^b f(x)\, dx + \int_b^a f(x)\, dx$ assuming f is integrable on $[a, b]$. ◀

Integral of a Sum Definite integrals possess other properties that often simplify their evaluation. Assume f and g are integrable on $[a, b]$. The first property states that their sum $f + g$ is integrable on $[a, b]$ and the integral of their sum is the sum of their integrals:

$$\int_a^b (f(x) + g(x))\, dx = \int_a^b f(x)\, dx + \int_a^b g(x)\, dx.$$

We prove this property assuming that f and g are continuous. In this case, $f + g$ is continuous and, therefore, integrable. We then have

$$\begin{aligned}
\int_a^b (f(x) + g(x))\, dx &= \lim_{\Delta \to 0} \sum_{k=1}^{n} (f(x_k^*) + g(x_k^*))\Delta x_k && \text{Definition of definite integral} \\
&= \lim_{\Delta \to 0} \left(\sum_{k=1}^{n} f(x_k^*)\Delta x_k + \sum_{k=1}^{n} g(x_k^*)\Delta x_k \right) && \text{Split into two finite sums.} \\
&= \lim_{\Delta \to 0} \sum_{k=1}^{n} f(x_k^*)\Delta x_k + \lim_{\Delta \to 0} \sum_{k=1}^{n} g(x_k^*)\Delta x_k && \text{Split into two limits.} \\
&= \int_a^b f(x)\, dx + \int_a^b g(x)\, dx. && \text{Definition of definite integral}
\end{aligned}$$

Constants in Integrals Another property of definite integrals is that constants can be factored out of the integral. If f is integrable on $[a, b]$ and c is a constant, then cf is integrable on $[a, b]$ and

$$\int_a^b cf(x)\, dx = c\int_a^b f(x)\, dx.$$

The justification for this property (Exercise 81) is based on the fact that for finite sums,

$$\sum_{k=1}^{n} cf(x_k^*)\Delta x_k = c\sum_{k=1}^{n} f(x_k^*)\Delta x_k.$$

Integrals over Subintervals If the point p lies between a and b, then the integral on $[a, b]$ may be split into two integrals. As shown in Figure 5.29, we have the property

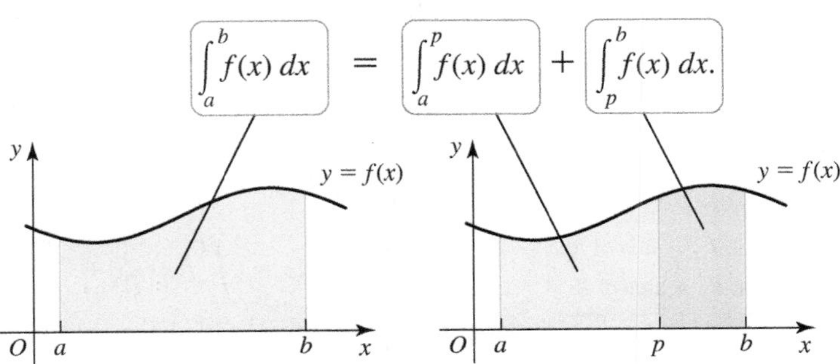

Figure 5.29

It is surprising that this property also holds when p lies outside the interval $[a, b]$. For example, if $a < b < p$ and f is integrable on $[a, p]$, then it follows (Figure 5.30) that

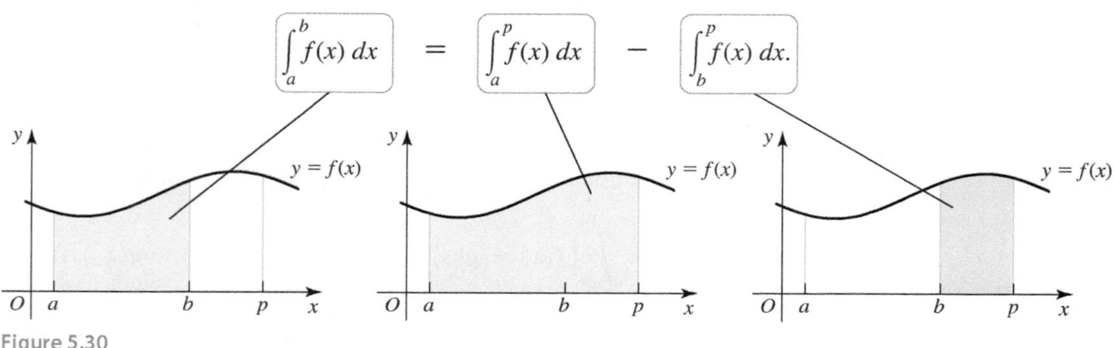

Figure 5.30

Because $\int_p^b f(x)\,dx = -\int_b^p f(x)\,dx$, we have the original property:

$$\int_a^b f(x)\,dx = \int_a^p f(x)\,dx + \int_p^b f(x)\,dx.$$

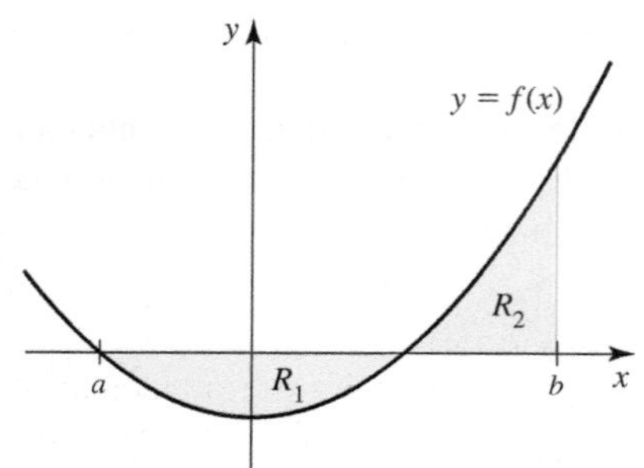

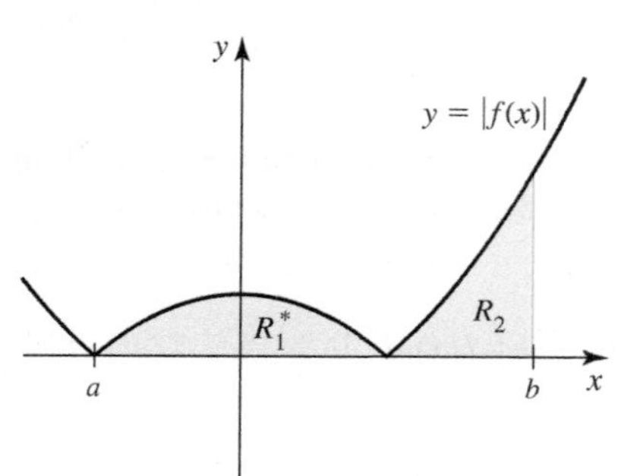

$\int_a^b |f(x)|\,dx$ = area of R_1^* + area of R_2
= area of R_1 + area of R_2

Figure 5.31

Integrals of Absolute Values Finally, how do we interpret $\int_a^b |f(x)|\,dx$, the integral of the absolute value of an integrable function? The graphs f and $|f|$ are shown in Figure 5.31. The integral $\int_a^b |f(x)|\,dx$ gives the area of regions R_1^* and R_2. But R_1 and R_1^* have the same area; therefore, $\int_a^b |f(x)|\,dx$ also gives the area of R_1 and R_2. The conclusion is that $\int_a^b |f(x)|\,dx$ is the area of the entire region (above and below the x-axis) that lies between the graph of f and the x-axis on $[a, b]$.

All these properties will be used frequently in upcoming work. It's worth collecting them in one table (Table 5.4).

Table 5.4 Properties of definite integrals

Let f and g be integrable functions on an interval that contains a, b, and p.

1. $\displaystyle\int_a^a f(x)\,dx = 0$ Definition
2. $\displaystyle\int_b^a f(x)\,dx = -\int_a^b f(x)\,dx$ Definition
3. $\displaystyle\int_a^b (f(x) + g(x))\,dx = \int_a^b f(x)\,dx + \int_a^b g(x)\,dx$
4. $\displaystyle\int_a^b cf(x)\,dx = c\int_a^b f(x)\,dx$ For any constant c
5. $\displaystyle\int_a^b f(x)\,dx = \int_a^p f(x)\,dx + \int_p^b f(x)\,dx$

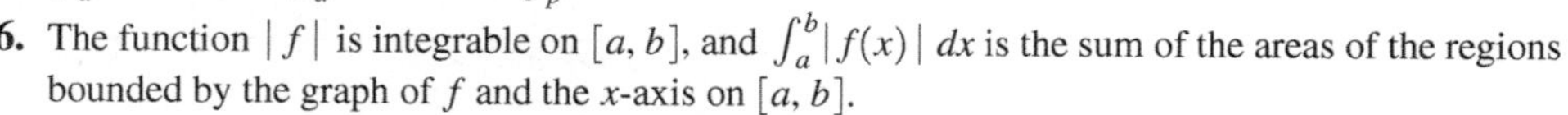

6. The function $|f|$ is integrable on $[a, b]$, and $\int_a^b |f(x)|\,dx$ is the sum of the areas of the regions bounded by the graph of f and the x-axis on $[a, b]$.

EXAMPLE 5 Properties of integrals Assume that $\int_0^5 f(x)\,dx = 3$ and $\int_0^7 f(x)\,dx = -10$. Evaluate the following integrals, if possible.

a. $\int_0^7 2f(x)\,dx$ **b.** $\int_5^7 f(x)\,dx$ **c.** $\int_5^0 f(x)\,dx$ **d.** $\int_7^0 6f(x)\,dx$ **e.** $\int_0^7 |f(x)|\,dx$

SOLUTION

a. By Property 4 of Table 5.4,

$$\int_0^7 2f(x)\,dx = 2\int_0^7 f(x)\,dx = 2\cdot(-10) = -20.$$

b. By Property 5 of Table 5.4, $\int_0^7 f(x)\,dx = \int_0^5 f(x)\,dx + \int_5^7 f(x)\,dx$. Therefore,

$$\int_5^7 f(x)\,dx = \int_0^7 f(x)\,dx - \int_0^5 f(x)\,dx = -10 - 3 = -13.$$

c. By Property 2 of Table 5.4,

$$\int_5^0 f(x)\,dx = -\int_0^5 f(x)\,dx = -3.$$

d. Using Properties 2 and 4 of Table 5.4, we have

$$\int_7^0 6f(x)\,dx = -\int_0^7 6f(x)\,dx = -6\int_0^7 f(x)\,dx = (-6)(-10) = 60.$$

e. This integral cannot be evaluated without knowing the intervals on which f is positive and negative. It could have any value greater than or equal to 10.

Related Exercises 41–46 ◀

QUICK CHECK 6 Evaluate $\int_{-1}^2 x\,dx$ and $\int_{-1}^2 |x|\,dx$ using geometry. ◀

Evaluating Definite Integrals Using Limits

In Example 3, we used area formulas for trapezoids, triangles, and circles to evaluate definite integrals. Regions bounded by more general functions have curved boundaries for which conventional geometrical methods do not work. At the moment, the only way to handle such integrals is to appeal to the definition of the definite integral and the summation formulas given in Theorem 5.1.

We know that if f is integrable on $[a, b]$, then $\int_a^b f(x)\,dx = \lim_{\Delta\to 0}\sum_{k=1}^{n} f(x_k^*)\Delta x_k$, for any partition of $[a, b]$ and any points x_k^*. To simplify these calculations, we use equally spaced grid points and right Riemann sums. That is, for each value of n, we let $\Delta x_k = \Delta x = \dfrac{b-a}{n}$ and $x_k^* = a + k\,\Delta x$, for $k = 1, 2, \ldots, n$. Then as $n \to \infty$ and $\Delta \to 0$,

$$\int_a^b f(x)\,dx = \lim_{\Delta\to 0}\sum_{k=1}^{n} f(x_k^*)\Delta x_k = \lim_{n\to\infty}\sum_{k=1}^{n} f(a + k\Delta x)\Delta x.$$

EXAMPLE 6 **Evaluating definite integrals** Find the value of $\int_0^2 (x^3 + 1)\,dx$ by evaluating a right Riemann sum and letting $n \to \infty$.

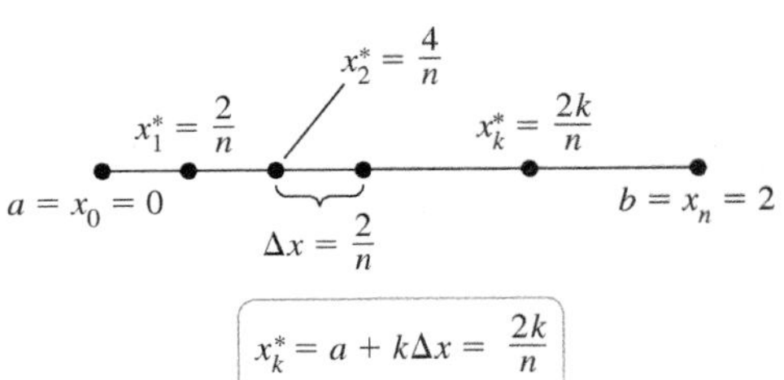

SOLUTION Based on approximations found in Example 5, Section 5.1, we conjectured that the value of this integral is 6. To verify this conjecture, we now evaluate the integral exactly. The interval $[a, b] = [0, 2]$ is divided into n subintervals of length $\Delta x = \dfrac{b-a}{n} = \dfrac{2}{n}$, which produces the grid points

$$x_k^* = a + k\Delta x = 0 + k\cdot\frac{2}{n} = \frac{2k}{n}, \qquad \text{for } k = 1, 2, \ldots, n.$$

Letting $f(x) = x^3 + 1$, the right Riemann sum is

$$\begin{aligned}\sum_{k=1}^{n} f(x_k^*)\Delta x &= \sum_{k=1}^{n}\left(\left(\frac{2k}{n}\right)^3 + 1\right)\frac{2}{n} \\ &= \frac{2}{n}\sum_{k=1}^{n}\left(\frac{8k^3}{n^3} + 1\right) && \sum_{k=1}^{n} ca_k = c\sum_{k=1}^{n} a_k \\ &= \frac{2}{n}\left(\frac{8}{n^3}\sum_{k=1}^{n} k^3 + \sum_{k=1}^{n} 1\right) && \sum_{k=1}^{n}(a_k + b_k) = \sum_{k=1}^{n} a_k + \sum_{k=1}^{n} b_k \\ &= \frac{2}{n}\left(\frac{8}{n^3}\left(\frac{n^2(n+1)^2}{4}\right) + n\right) && \sum_{k=1}^{n} k^3 = \frac{n^2(n+1)^2}{4} \text{ and } \sum_{k=1}^{n} 1 = n; \text{ Theorem 5.1} \\ &= \frac{4(n^2 + 2n + 1)}{n^2} + 2. && \text{Simplify.}\end{aligned}$$

➤ An analogous calculation could be done using left Riemann sums or midpoint Riemann sums.

Now we evaluate $\int_0^2 (x^3 + 1)\,dx$ by letting $n \to \infty$ in the Riemann sum:

$$\begin{aligned}\int_0^2 (x^3 + 1)\,dx &= \lim_{n\to\infty}\sum_{k=1}^{n} f(x_k^*)\Delta x \\ &= \lim_{n\to\infty}\left(\frac{4(n^2 + 2n + 1)}{n^2} + 2\right) \\ &= 4\underbrace{\lim_{n\to\infty}\left(\frac{n^2 + 2n + 1}{n^2}\right)}_{1} + \lim_{n\to\infty} 2 \\ &= 4(1) + 2 = 6.\end{aligned}$$

Therefore, $\int_0^2 (x^3 + 1)\,dx = 6$, confirming our conjecture in Example 5, Section 5.1.

Related Exercises 47–52 ◄

The Riemann sum calculations in Example 6 are tedious even if f is a simple function. For polynomials of degree 4 and higher, the calculations are more challenging, and for rational and transcendental functions, advanced mathematical results are needed. The next section introduces more efficient methods for evaluating definite integrals.

SECTION 5.2 EXERCISES

Review Questions

1. What does net area measure?
2. What is the geometric meaning of a definite integral if the integrand changes sign on the interval of integration?
3. Under what conditions does the net area of a region equal the area of a region? When does the net area of a region differ from the area of a region?
4. Suppose that $f(x) < 0$ on the interval $[a, b]$. Using Riemann sums, explain why the definite integral $\int_a^b f(x)\,dx$ is negative.
5. Use graphs to evaluate $\int_0^{2\pi} \sin x\,dx$ and $\int_0^{2\pi} \cos x\,dx$.
6. Explain how the notation for Riemann sums, $\sum_{k=1}^{n} f(x_k^*)\Delta x$, corresponds to the notation for the definite integral, $\int_a^b f(x)\,dx$.
7. Give a geometrical explanation of why $\int_a^a f(x)\,dx = 0$.
8. Use Table 5.4 to rewrite $\int_1^6 (2x^3 - 4x)\,dx$ as the difference of two integrals.
9. Use geometry to find a formula for $\int_0^a x\,dx$, in terms of a.
10. If f is continuous on $[a, b]$ and $\int_a^b |f(x)|\,dx = 0$, what can you conclude about f?

Basic Skills

11–14. Approximating net area *The following functions are negative on the given interval.*

a. Sketch the function on the given interval.

b. Approximate the net area bounded by the graph of f and the x-axis on the interval using a left, right, and midpoint Riemann sum with $n = 4$.

11. $f(x) = -2x - 1$ on $[0, 4]$

T 12. $f(x) = -4 - x^3$ on $[3, 7]$

T 13. $f(x) = \sin 2x$ on $[\pi/2, \pi]$

T 14. $f(x) = x^3 - 1$ on $[-2, 0]$

T 15–20. Approximating net area *The following functions are positive and negative on the given interval.*

a. Sketch the function on the given interval.
b. Approximate the net area bounded by the graph of f and the x-axis on the interval using a left, right, and midpoint Riemann sum with $n = 4$.
c. Use the sketch in part (a) to show which intervals of $[a, b]$ *make positive and negative contributions to the net area.*

15. $f(x) = 4 - 2x$ on $[0, 4]$

16. $f(x) = 8 - 2x^2$ on $[0, 4]$

17. $f(x) = \sin 2x$ on $[0, 3\pi/4]$

18. $f(x) = x^3$ on $[-1, 2]$

19. $f(x) = \tan^{-1}(3x - 1)$ on $[0, 1]$

20. $f(x) = xe^{-x}$ on $[-1, 1]$

21–24. Identifying definite integrals as limits of sums *Consider the following limits of Riemann sums for a function f on* $[a, b]$. *Identify f and express the limit as a definite integral.*

21. $\lim_{\Delta \to 0} \sum_{k=1}^{n} (x_k^{*2} + 1)\Delta x_k$ on $[0, 2]$

22. $\lim_{\Delta \to 0} \sum_{k=1}^{n} (4 - x_k^{*2})\Delta x_k$ on $[-2, 2]$

23. $\lim_{\Delta \to 0} \sum_{k=1}^{n} x_k^* \ln x_k^* \Delta x_k$ on $[1, 2]$

24. $\lim_{\Delta \to 0} \sum_{k=1}^{n} |x_k^{*2} - 1|\Delta x_k$ on $[-2, 2]$

25–32. Net area and definite integrals *Use geometry (not Riemann sums) to evaluate the following definite integrals. Sketch a graph of the integrand, show the region in question, and interpret your result.*

25. $\int_0^4 (8 - 2x)\,dx$

26. $\int_{-4}^{2} (2x + 4)\,dx$

27. $\int_{-1}^{2} (-|x|)\,dx$

28. $\int_0^2 (1 - x)\,dx$

29. $\int_0^4 \sqrt{16 - x^2}\,dx$

30. $\int_{-1}^{3} \sqrt{4 - (x - 1)^2}\,dx$

31. $\int_0^4 f(x)\,dx$, where $f(x) = \begin{cases} 5 & \text{if } x \le 2 \\ 3x - 1 & \text{if } x > 2 \end{cases}$

32. $\int_1^{10} g(x)\,dx$, where $g(x) = \begin{cases} 4x & \text{if } 0 \le x \le 2 \\ -8x + 16 & \text{if } 2 < x \le 3 \\ -8 & \text{if } x > 3 \end{cases}$

33–36. Net area from graphs *The figure shows the areas of regions bounded by the graph of f and the x-axis. Evaluate the following integrals.*

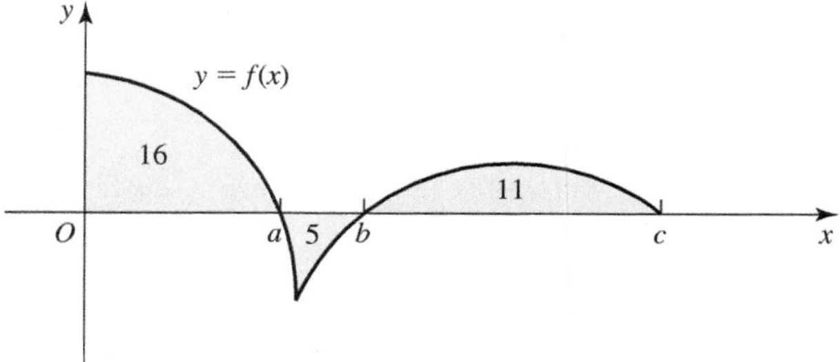

33. $\int_0^a f(x)\,dx$

34. $\int_0^b f(x)\,dx$

35. $\int_a^c f(x)\,dx$

36. $\int_0^c f(x)\,dx$

37–40. Net area from graphs *The accompanying figure shows four regions bounded by the graph of* $y = x \sin x$: R_1, R_2, R_3, *and* R_4, *whose areas are* $1, \pi - 1, \pi + 1$, *and* $2\pi - 1$, *respectively. (We verify these results later in the text.) Use this information to evaluate the following integrals.*

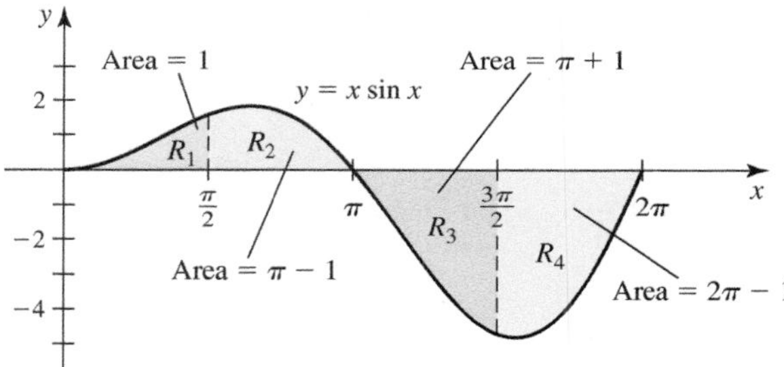

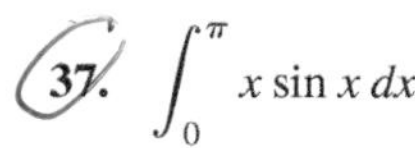

37. $\int_0^{\pi} x \sin x\,dx$

38. $\int_0^{3\pi/2} x \sin x\,dx$

39. $\int_0^{2\pi} x \sin x\,dx$

40. $\int_{\pi/2}^{2\pi} x \sin x\,dx$

41. Properties of integrals Use only the fact that $\int_0^4 3x(4 - x)\,dx = 32$ and the definitions and properties of integrals to evaluate the following integrals, if possible.

a. $\int_4^0 3x(4 - x)\,dx$

b. $\int_0^4 x(x - 4)\,dx$

c. $\int_4^0 6x(4 - x)\,dx$

d. $\int_0^8 3x(4 - x)\,dx$

42. Properties of integrals Suppose $\int_1^4 f(x)\,dx = 8$ and $\int_1^6 f(x)\,dx = 5$. Evaluate the following integrals.

a. $\int_1^4 (-3f(x))\,dx$

b. $\int_1^4 3f(x)\,dx$

c. $\int_6^4 12f(x)\,dx$

d. $\int_4^6 3f(x)\,dx$

43. Properties of integrals Suppose $\int_0^3 f(x)\,dx = 2$, $\int_3^6 f(x)\,dx = -5$, and $\int_3^6 g(x)\,dx = 1$. Evaluate the following integrals.

a. $\int_0^3 5f(x)\,dx$ b. $\int_3^6 (-3g(x))\,dx$

c. $\int_3^6 (3f(x) - g(x))\,dx$ d. $\int_6^3 (f(x) + 2g(x))\,dx$

44. Properties of integrals Suppose $f(x) \geq 0$ on $[0, 2]$, $f(x) \leq 0$ on $[2, 5]$, $\int_0^2 f(x)\,dx = 6$, and $\int_2^5 f(x)\,dx = -8$. Evaluate the following integrals.

a. $\int_0^5 f(x)\,dx$ b. $\int_0^5 |f(x)|\,dx$

c. $\int_2^5 4|f(x)|\,dx$ d. $\int_0^5 (f(x) + |f(x)|)\,dx$

45–46. Using properties of integrals *Use the value of the first integral I to evaluate the two given integrals.*

45. $I = \int_0^1 (x^3 - 2x)\,dx = -\frac{3}{4}$

a. $\int_0^1 (4x - 2x^3)\,dx$ b. $\int_1^0 (2x - x^3)\,dx$

46. $\int_0^{\pi/2} (2\sin\theta - \cos\theta)\,d\theta$

a. $\int_0^{\pi/2} (2\sin\theta - \cos\theta)\,d\theta$ b. $\int_{\pi/2}^0 (4\cos\theta - 8\sin\theta)\,d\theta$

47–52. Limits of sums *Use the definition of the definite integral to evaluate the following definite integrals. Use right Riemann sums and Theorem 5.1.*

47. $\int_0^2 (2x + 1)\,dx$ **48.** $\int_1^5 (1 - x)\,dx$

49. $\int_3^7 (4x + 6)\,dx$ **50.** $\int_0^2 (x^2 - 1)\,dx$

51. $\int_1^4 (x^2 - 1)\,dx$ **52.** $\int_0^2 4x^3\,dx$

Further Explorations

53. Explain why or why not Determine whether the following statements are true and give an explanation or counterexample.

a. If f is a constant function on the interval $[a, b]$, then the right and left Riemann sums give the exact value of $\int_a^b f(x)\,dx$, for any positive integer n.

b. If f is a linear function on the interval $[a, b]$, then a midpoint Riemann sum gives the exact value of $\int_a^b f(x)\,dx$, for any positive integer n.

c. $\int_0^{2\pi/a} \sin ax\,dx = \int_0^{2\pi/a} \cos ax\,dx = 0$. (*Hint:* Graph the functions and use properties of trigonometric functions.)

d. If $\int_a^b f(x)\,dx = \int_b^a f(x)\,dx$, then f is a constant function.

e. Property 4 of Table 5.4 implies that $\int_a^b xf(x)\,dx = x\int_a^b f(x)\,dx$.

T 54–57. Approximating definite integrals *Complete the following steps for the given integral and the given value of n.*

a. Sketch the graph of the integrand on the interval of integration.

b. Calculate Δx and the grid points $x_0, x_1, \ldots, x_n$, assuming a regular partition.

c. Calculate the left and right Riemann sums for the given value of n.

d. Determine which Riemann sum (left or right) underestimates the value of the definite integral and which overestimates the value of the definite integral.

54. $\int_0^2 (x^2 - 2)\,dx;\ n = 4$ **55.** $\int_3^6 (1 - 2x)\,dx;\ n = 6$

56. $\int_0^{\pi/2} \cos x\,dx;\ n = 4$ **57.** $\int_1^7 \frac{1}{x}\,dx;\ n = 6$

T 58–62. Approximating definite integrals with a calculator *Consider the following definite integrals.*

a. Write the left and right Riemann sums in sigma notation, for $n = 20, 50,$ and 100. Then evaluate the sums using a calculator.

b. Based on your answers to part (a), make a conjecture about the value of the definite integral.

58. $\int_4^9 3\sqrt{x}\,dx$ **59.** $\int_0^1 (x^2 + 1)\,dx$

60. $\int_1^e \ln x\,dx$ **61.** $\int_0^1 \cos^{-1} x\,dx$

62. $\int_{-1}^1 \pi\cos\left(\frac{\pi x}{2}\right) dx$

T 63–66. Midpoint Riemann sums with a calculator *Consider the following definite integrals.*

a. Write the midpoint Riemann sum in sigma notation for an arbitrary value of n.

b. Evaluate each sum using a calculator with $n = 20, 50,$ and 100. Use these values to estimate the value of the integral.

63. $\int_1^4 2\sqrt{x}\,dx$ **64.** $\int_{-1}^2 \sin\left(\frac{\pi x}{4}\right) dx$

65. $\int_0^4 (4x - x^2)\,dx$ **66.** $\int_0^{1/2} \sin^{-1} x\,dx$

67. More properties of integrals Consider two functions f and g on $[1, 6]$ such that $\int_1^6 f(x)\,dx = 10$, $\int_1^6 g(x)\,dx = 5$, $\int_4^6 f(x)\,dx = 5$, and $\int_1^4 g(x)\,dx = 2$. Evaluate the following integrals.

a. $\int_1^4 3f(x)\,dx$ b. $\int_1^6 (f(x) - g(x))\,dx$

c. $\int_1^4 (f(x) - g(x))\,dx$ d. $\int_4^6 (g(x) - f(x))\,dx$

e. $\int_4^6 8g(x)\,dx$ f. $\int_4^1 2f(x)\,dx$

68–71. Area versus net area *Graph the following functions. Then use geometry (not Riemann sums) to find the area and the net area of the region described.*

68. The region between the graph of $y = 4x - 8$ and the x-axis, for $-4 \le x \le 8$

69. The region between the graph of $y = -3x$ and the x-axis, for $-2 \le x \le 2$

70. The region between the graph of $y = 3x - 6$ and the x-axis, for $0 \le x \le 6$

71. The region between the graph of $y = 1 - |x|$ and the x-axis, for $-2 \le x \le 2$

72–75. Area by geometry *Use geometry to evaluate the following integrals.*

72. $\int_{-2}^3 |x + 1|\,dx$ 73. $\int_1^6 |2x - 4|\,dx$

74. $\int_1^6 (3x - 6)\,dx$ 75. $\int_{-6}^4 \sqrt{24 - 2x - x^2}\,dx$

Additional Exercises

76. **Integrating piecewise continuous functions** Suppose f is continuous on the intervals $[a, p]$ and $(p, b]$, where $a < p < b$, with a finite jump at p. Form a uniform partition on the interval $[a, p]$ with n grid points and another uniform partition on the interval $[p, b]$ with m grid points, where p is a grid point of both partitions. Write a Riemann sum for $\int_a^b f(x)\,dx$ and separate it into two pieces for $[a, p]$ and $[p, b]$. Explain why $\int_a^b f(x)\,dx = \int_a^p f(x)\,dx + \int_p^b f(x)\,dx$.

77–78. Integrating piecewise continuous functions *Use geometry and the result of Exercise 76 to evaluate the following integrals.*

77. $\int_0^{10} f(x)\,dx$, where $f(x) = \begin{cases} 2 & \text{if } 0 \le x \le 5 \\ 3 & \text{if } 5 < x \le 10 \end{cases}$

78. $\int_1^6 f(x)\,dx$, where $f(x) = \begin{cases} 2x & \text{if } 1 \le x < 4 \\ 10 - 2x & \text{if } 4 \le x \le 6 \end{cases}$

79–80. Integrating piecewise continuous functions *Recall that the* floor function $\lfloor x \rfloor$ *is the greatest integer less than or equal to x and that the* ceiling function $\lceil x \rceil$ *is the least integer greater than or equal to x. Use the result of Exercise 76 and the graphs to evaluate the following integrals.*

79. $\int_1^5 x\lfloor x \rfloor\,dx$

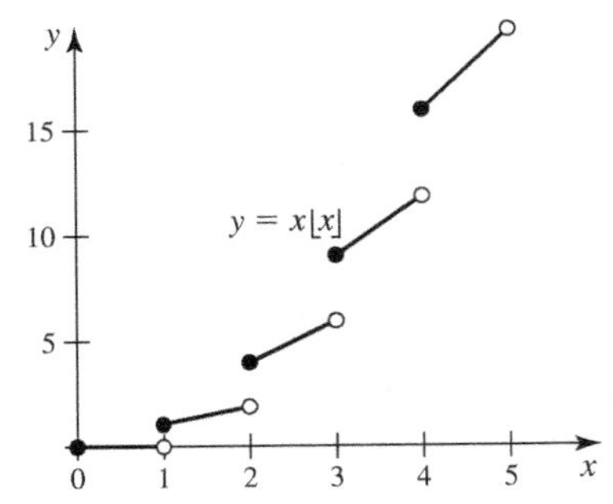

80. $\int_0^4 \frac{x}{\lceil x \rceil}\,dx$

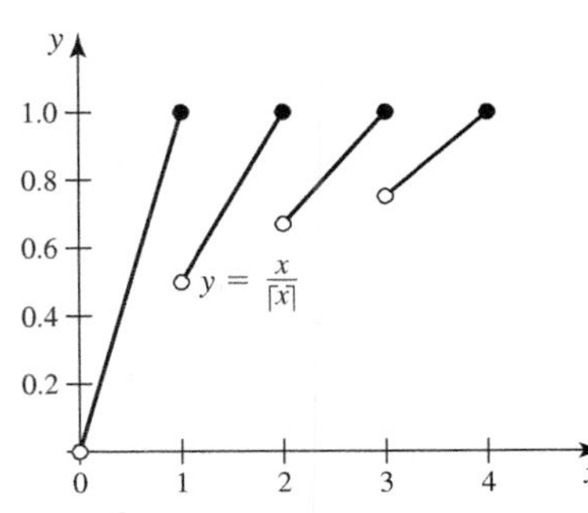

81. **Constants in integrals** Use the definition of the definite integral to justify the property $\int_a^b cf(x)\,dx = c\int_a^b f(x)\,dx$, where f is continuous and c is a real number.

82. **Zero net area** If $0 < c < d$, then find the value of b (in terms of c and d) for which $\int_c^d (x + b)\,dx = 0$.

83. **A nonintegrable function** Consider the function defined on $[0, 1]$ such that $f(x) = 1$ if x is a rational number and $f(x) = 0$ if x is irrational. This function has an infinite number of discontinuities, and the integral $\int_0^1 f(x)\,dx$ does not exist. Show that the right, left, and midpoint Riemann sums on *regular* partitions with n subintervals equal 1 for all n. (*Hint:* Between any two real numbers lie a rational and an irrational number.)

84. **Powers of x by Riemann sums** Consider the integral $I(p) = \int_0^1 x^p\,dx$, where p is a positive integer.

a. Write the left Riemann sum for the integral with n subintervals.

b. It is a fact (proved by the 17th-century mathematicians Fermat and Pascal) that $\lim_{n\to\infty} \frac{1}{n}\sum_{k=0}^{n-1}\left(\frac{k}{n}\right)^p = \frac{1}{p+1}$. Use this fact to evaluate $I(p)$.

85. **An exact integration formula** Evaluate $\int_a^b \frac{dx}{x^2}$, where $0 < a < b$, using the definition of the definite integral and the following steps.

a. Assume $\{x_0, x_1, \ldots, x_n\}$ is a partition of $[a, b]$ with $\Delta x_k = x_k - x_{k-1}$, for $k = 1, 2, \ldots, n$. Show that $x_{k-1} \le \sqrt{x_{k-1}x_k} \le x_k$, for $k = 1, 2, \ldots, n$.

b. Show that $\frac{1}{x_{k-1}} - \frac{1}{x_k} = \frac{\Delta x_k}{x_{k-1}x_k}$, for $k = 1, 2, \ldots, n$.

c. Simplify the general Riemann sum for $\int_a^b \frac{dx}{x^2}$ using $\bar{x}_k^* = \sqrt{x_{k-1}x_k}$.

d. Conclude that $\int_a^b \frac{dx}{x^2} = \frac{1}{a} - \frac{1}{b}$.

(*Source: The College Mathematics Journal,* 32, 4, Sep 2001)

QUICK CHECK ANSWERS

1. -20 **2.** $f(x) = 1 - x$ is one possibility. **3.** 0 **4.** 10; $c(b - a)$ **5.** 0 **6.** $\frac{3}{2}; \frac{5}{2}$ ◄

5.3 Fundamental Theorem of Calculus

Evaluating definite integrals using limits of Riemann sums, as described in Section 5.2, is usually not possible or practical. Fortunately, there is a powerful and practical method for evaluating definite integrals, which is developed in this section. Along the way, we discover the inverse relationship between differentiation and integration, expressed in the most important result of calculus, the Fundamental Theorem of Calculus. The first step in this process is to introduce *area functions* (first seen in Section 1.2).

Area Functions

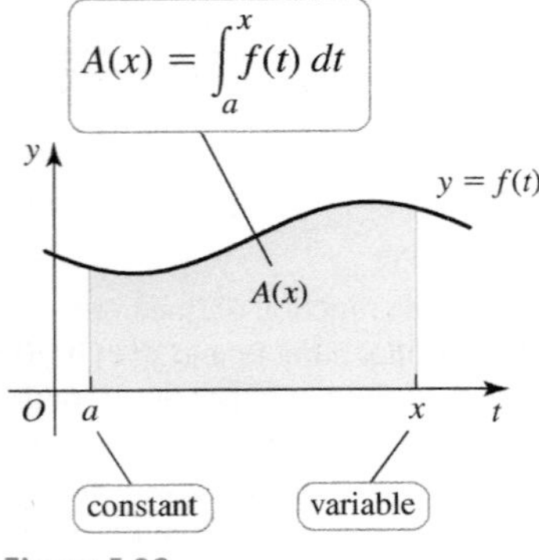

Figure 5.32

The concept of an area function is crucial to the discussion about the connection between derivatives and integrals. We start with a continuous function $y = f(t)$ defined for $t \geq a$, where a is a fixed number. The *area function* for f with left endpoint a is denoted $A(x)$; it gives the net area of the region bounded by the graph of f and the t-axis between $t = a$ and $t = x$ (Figure 5.32). The net area of this region is also given by the definite integral

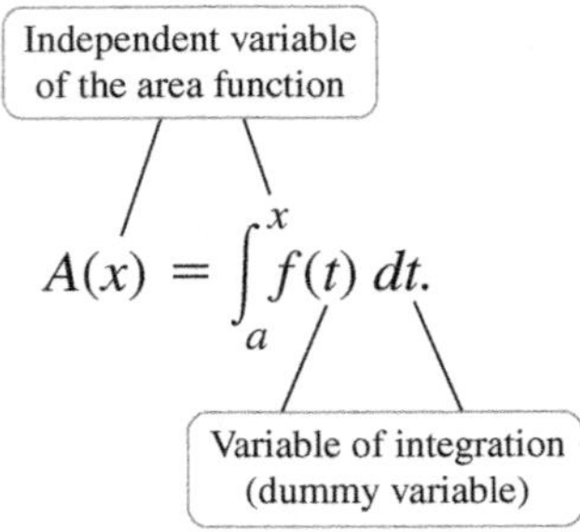

> Suppose you want to devise a function A whose value is the sum of the first n positive integers, $1 + 2 + \cdots + n$. The most compact way to write this function is $A(n) = \sum_{k=1}^{n} k$, for $n \geq 1$. In this function, n is the independent variable of the function A, and k, which is internal to the sum, is a dummy variable. This function involving a sum is analogous to an area function involving an integral.

Notice that x is the upper limit of the integral *and* the independent variable of the area function: As x changes, so does the net area under the curve. Because the symbol x is already in use as the independent variable for A, we must choose another symbol for the variable of integration. Any symbol—except x—can be used because it is a *dummy variable*; we have chosen t as the integration variable.

Figure 5.33 gives a general view of how an area function is generated. Suppose that f is a continuous function and a is a fixed number. Now choose a point $b > a$. The net area

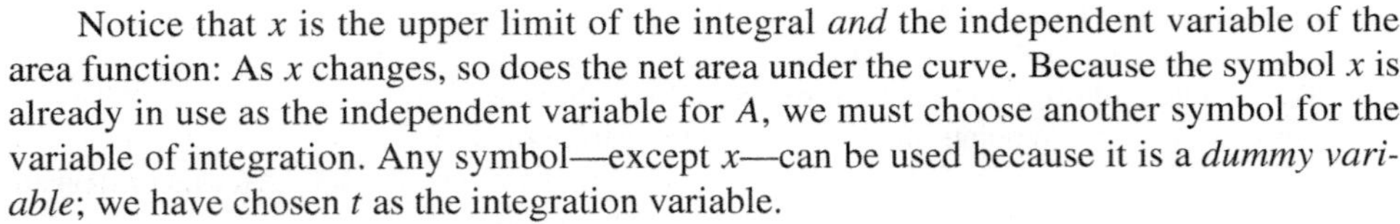

> Notice that t is the independent variable when we plot f and x is the independent variable when we plot A.

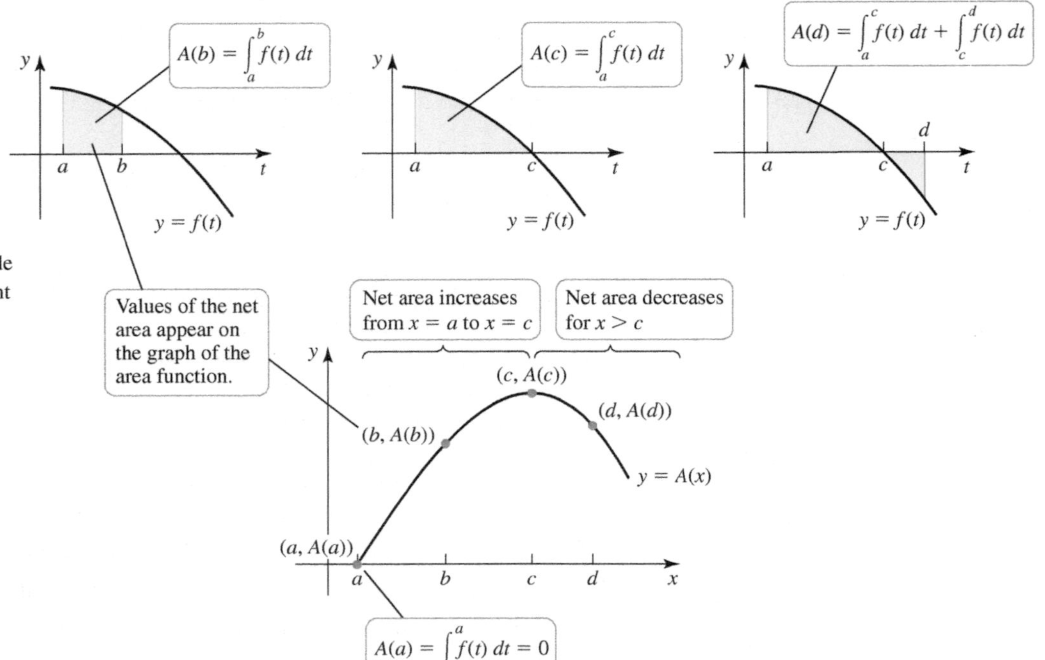

Figure 5.33

of the region between the graph of f and the t-axis on the interval $[a, b]$ is $A(b)$. Moving the right endpoint to $(c, 0)$ or $(d, 0)$ produces different regions with net areas $A(c)$ and $A(d)$, respectively. In general, if $x > a$ is a variable point, then $A(x) = \int_a^x f(t)\,dt$ is the net area of the region between the graph of f and the t-axis on the interval $[a, x]$.

Figure 5.33 shows how $A(x)$ varies with respect to x. Notice that $A(a) = \int_a^a f(t)\,dt = 0$. Then for $x > a$, the net area increases for $x < c$, at which point $f(c) = 0$. For $x > c$, the function f is negative, which produces a negative contribution to the area function. As a result, the area function decreases for $x > c$.

> **DEFINITION Area Function**
>
> Let f be a continuous function, for $t \geq a$. The **area function for f with left endpoint a** is
>
> $$A(x) = \int_a^x f(t)\,dt,$$
>
> where $x \geq a$. The area function gives the net area of the region bounded by the graph of f and the t-axis on the interval $[a, x]$.

The following two examples illustrate the idea of area functions.

EXAMPLE 1 Comparing area functions The graph of f is shown in Figure 5.34 with areas of various regions marked. Let $A(x) = \int_{-1}^x f(t)\,dt$ and $F(x) = \int_3^x f(t)\,dt$ be two area functions for f (note the different left endpoints). Evaluate the following area functions.

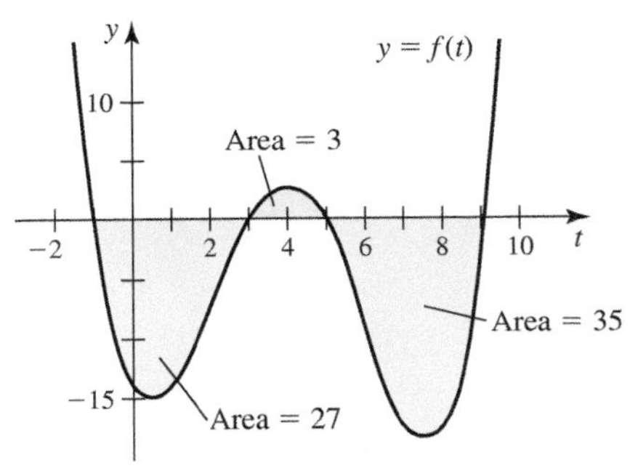

Figure 5.34

a. $A(3)$ and $F(3)$ **b.** $A(5)$ and $F(5)$ **c.** $A(9)$ and $F(9)$

SOLUTION

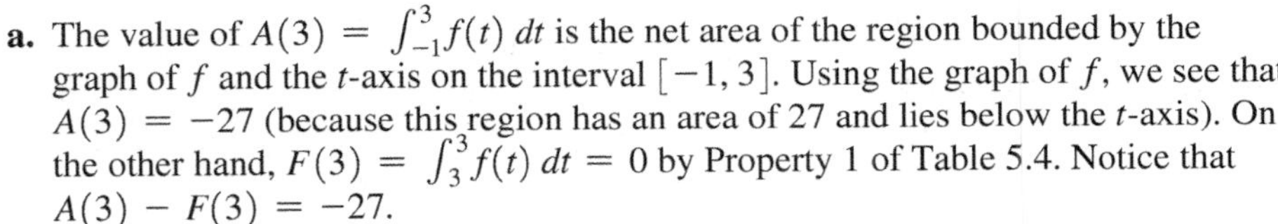

a. The value of $A(3) = \int_{-1}^3 f(t)\,dt$ is the net area of the region bounded by the graph of f and the t-axis on the interval $[-1, 3]$. Using the graph of f, we see that $A(3) = -27$ (because this region has an area of 27 and lies below the t-axis). On the other hand, $F(3) = \int_3^3 f(t)\,dt = 0$ by Property 1 of Table 5.4. Notice that $A(3) - F(3) = -27$.

b. The value of $A(5) = \int_{-1}^5 f(t)\,dt$ is found by subtracting the area of the region that lies below the t-axis on $[-1, 3]$ from the area of the region that lies above the t-axis on $[3, 5]$. Therefore, $A(5) = 3 - 27 = -24$. Similarly, $F(5)$ is the net area of the region bounded by the graph of f and the t-axis on the interval $[3, 5]$; therefore, $F(5) = 3$. Notice that $A(5) - F(5) = -27$.

c. Reasoning as in parts (a) and (b), we see that $A(9) = -27 + 3 - 35 = -59$ and $F(9) = 3 - 35 = -32$. As before, observe that $A(9) - F(9) = -27$.

Related Exercises 11–12 ◀

Example 1 illustrates the important fact (to be explained shortly) that two area functions of the same function differ by a constant; in Example 1, the constant is -27.

QUICK CHECK 1 In Example 1, let $B(x)$ be the area function for f with left endpoint 5. Evaluate $B(5)$ and $B(9)$. ◀

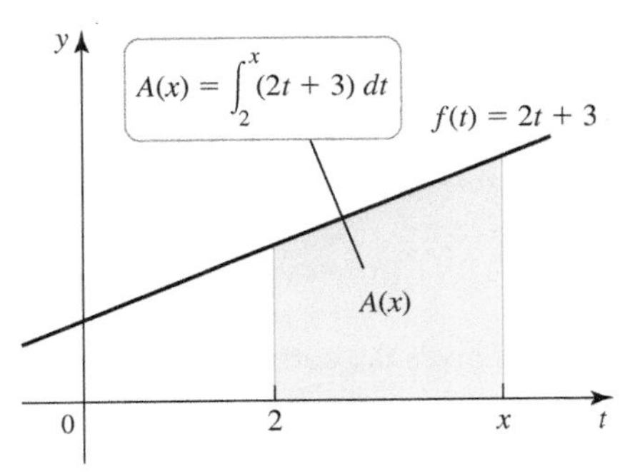

Figure 5.35

EXAMPLE 2 Area of a trapezoid Consider the trapezoid bounded by the line $f(t) = 2t + 3$ and the t-axis from $t = 2$ to $t = x$ (Figure 5.35). The area function $A(x) = \int_2^x f(t)\,dt$ gives the area of the trapezoid, for $x \geq 2$.

a. Evaluate $A(2)$. **b.** Evaluate $A(5)$.

c. Find and graph the area function $y = A(x)$, for $x \geq 2$.

d. Compare the derivative of A to f.

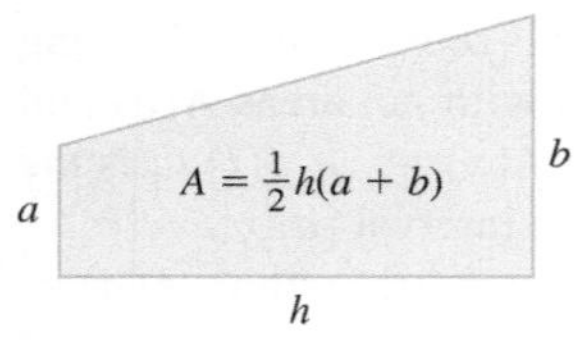

Figure 5.36

SOLUTION

a. By Property 1 of Table 5.4, $A(2) = \int_2^2 (2t + 3)\,dt = 0$.

b. Notice that $A(5)$ is the area of the trapezoid (Figure 5.35) bounded by the line $y = 2t + 3$ and the t-axis on the interval $[2, 5]$. Using the area formula for a trapezoid (Figure 5.36), we find that

$$A(5) = \int_2^5 (2t + 3)\,dt = \frac{1}{2}\underbrace{(5 - 2)}_{\text{distance between parallel sides}} \cdot \underbrace{(f(2) + f(5))}_{\text{sum of parallel side lengths}} = \frac{1}{2}\cdot 3(7 + 13) = 30.$$

c. Now the right endpoint of the base is a variable $x \geq 2$ (Figure 5.37). The distance between the parallel sides of the trapezoid is $x - 2$. By the area formula for a trapezoid, the area of this trapezoid for any $x \geq 2$ is

$$\begin{aligned} A(x) &= \frac{1}{2}\underbrace{(x - 2)}_{\text{distance between parallel sides}} \cdot \underbrace{(f(2) + f(x))}_{\text{sum of parallel side lengths}} \\ &= \frac{1}{2}(x - 2)(7 + 2x + 3) \\ &= (x - 2)(x + 5) \\ &= x^2 + 3x - 10. \end{aligned}$$

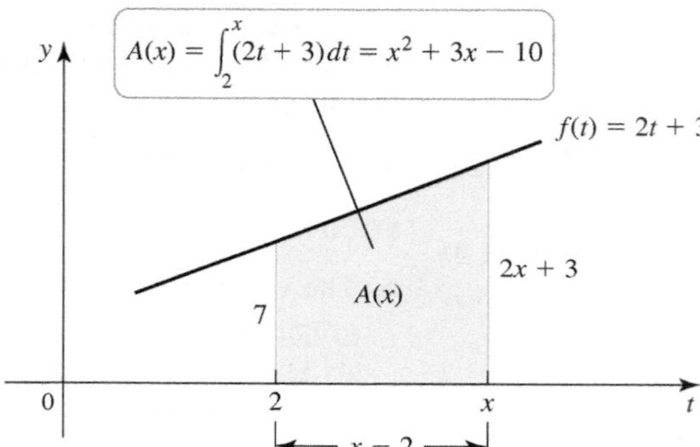

Figure 5.37

Expressing the area function in terms of an integral with a variable upper limit we have

$$A(x) = \int_2^x (2t + 3)\,dt = x^2 + 3x - 10.$$

Because the line $f(t) = 2t + 3$ is above the t-axis, for $t \geq 2$, the area function $A(x) = x^2 + 3x - 10$ is an increasing function of x with $A(2) = 0$ (Figure 5.38).

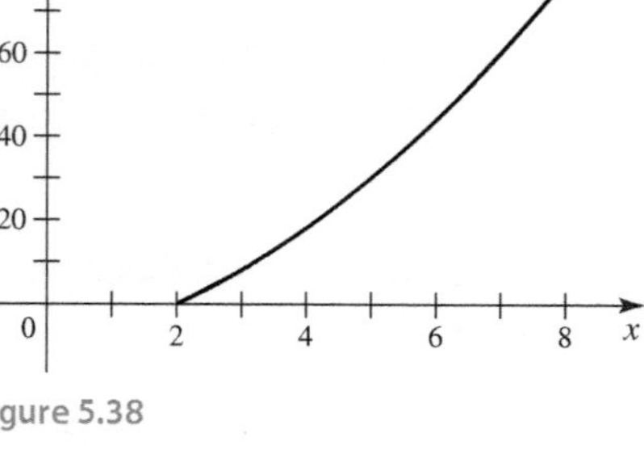

Figure 5.38

d. Differentiating the area function, we find that

$$A'(x) = \frac{d}{dx}(x^2 + 3x - 10) = 2x + 3 = f(x).$$

Therefore, $A'(x) = f(x)$, or equivalently, the area function A is an antiderivative of f. We soon show that this relationship is not an accident; it is the first part of the Fundamental Theorem of Calculus.

Related Exercises 13–22 ◀

➤ Recall that if $A'(x) = f(x)$, then f is the derivative of A; equivalently, A is an antiderivative of f.

QUICK CHECK 2 Verify that the area function in Example 2c gives the correct area when $x = 6$ and $x = 10$. ◀

Fundamental Theorem of Calculus

Example 2 suggests that the area function A for a linear function f is an antiderivative of f; that is, $A'(x) = f(x)$. Our goal is to show that this conjecture holds for more general functions. Let's start with an intuitive argument; a formal proof is given at the end of the section.

Assume that f is a continuous function defined on an interval $[a, b]$. As before, $A(x) = \int_a^x f(t)\,dt$ is the area function for f with a left endpoint a: It gives the net area of the region bounded by the graph of f and the t-axis on the interval $[a, x]$, for $x \geq a$. Figure 5.39 is the key to the argument.

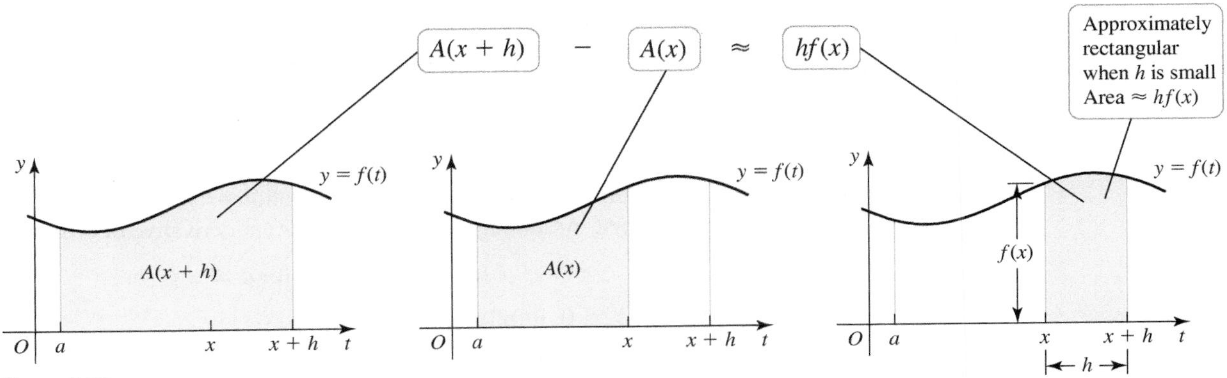

Figure 5.39

Note that with $h > 0$, $A(x + h)$ is the net area of the region whose base is the interval $[a, x + h]$ and $A(x)$ is the net area of the region whose base is the interval $[a, x]$. So the difference $A(x + h) - A(x)$ is the net area of the region whose base is the interval $[x, x + h]$. If h is small, the region in question is nearly rectangular with a base of length h and a height $f(x)$. Therefore, the net area of this region is

$$A(x + h) - A(x) \approx hf(x).$$

Dividing by h, we have

$$\frac{A(x + h) - A(x)}{h} \approx f(x).$$

➤ Recall that

$$f'(x) = \lim_{h \to 0} \frac{f(x + h) - f(x)}{h}.$$

If the function f is replaced with A, then

$$A'(x) = \lim_{h \to 0} \frac{A(x + h) - A(x)}{h}.$$

An analogous argument can be made with $h < 0$. Now observe that as h tends to zero, this approximation improves. In the limit as $h \to 0$, we have

$$\underbrace{\lim_{h \to 0} \frac{A(x + h) - A(x)}{h}}_{A'(x)} = \underbrace{\lim_{h \to 0} f(x)}_{f(x)}.$$

We see that indeed $A'(x) = f(x)$. Because $A(x) = \int_a^x f(t)\,dt$, the result can also be written

$$A'(x) = \frac{d}{dx}\underbrace{\int_a^x f(t)\,dt}_{A(x)} = f(x),$$

which says that the derivative of the integral of f is f. This conclusion is the first part of the Fundamental Theorem of Calculus.

> **THEOREM 5.3 (PART 1) Fundamental Theorem of Calculus**
> If f is continuous on $[a, b]$, then the area function
>
> $$A(x) = \int_a^x f(t)\,dt, \quad \text{for} \quad a \le x \le b,$$
>
> is continuous on $[a, b]$ and differentiable on (a, b). The area function satisfies $A'(x) = f(x)$. Equivalently,
>
> $$A'(x) = \frac{d}{dx}\int_a^x f(t)\,dt = f(x),$$
>
> which means that the area function of f is an antiderivative of f on $[a, b]$.

Given that A is an antiderivative of f on $[a, b]$, it is one short step to a powerful method for evaluating definite integrals. Remember (Section 4.9) that any two antiderivatives of f differ by a constant. Assuming that F is any other antiderivative of f on $[a, b]$, we have

$$F(x) = A(x) + C, \text{ for } a \le x \le b.$$

Noting that $A(a) = 0$, it follows that

$$F(b) - F(a) = (A(b) + C) - (A(a) + C) = A(b).$$

Writing $A(b)$ in terms of a definite integral leads to the remarkable result

$$A(b) = \int_a^b f(x)\,dx = F(b) - F(a).$$

We have shown that to evaluate a definite integral of f, we

- find any antiderivative of f, which we call F; and
- compute $F(b) - F(a)$, the difference in the values of F between the upper and lower limits of integration.

This process is the essence of the second part of the Fundamental Theorem of Calculus.

> **THEOREM 5.3 (PART 2) Fundamental Theorem of Calculus**
> If f is continuous on $[a, b]$ and F is any antiderivative of f on $[a, b]$, then
>
> $$\int_a^b f(x)\,dx = F(b) - F(a).$$

It is customary and convenient to denote the difference $F(b) - F(a)$ by $F(x)\big|_a^b$. Using this shorthand, the Fundamental Theorem is summarized in Figure 5.40.

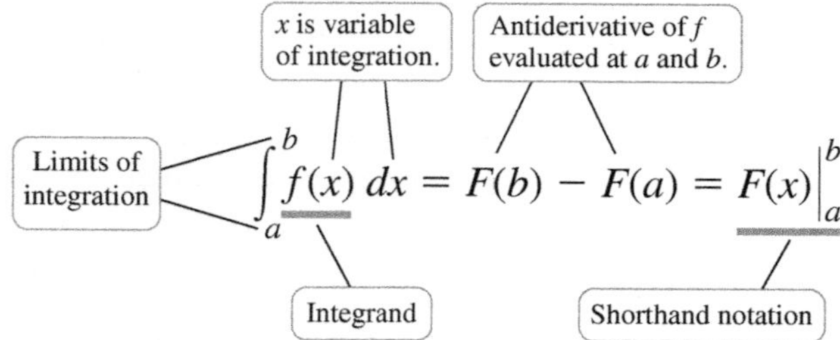

Figure 5.40

QUICK CHECK 3 Evaluate $\left(\dfrac{x}{x+1}\right)\Bigg|_1^2$. ◄

The Inverse Relationship between Differentiation and Integration It is worth pausing to observe that the two parts of the Fundamental Theorem express the inverse relationship between differentiation and integration. Part 1 of the Fundamental Theorem says

$$\frac{d}{dx}\int_a^x f(t)\,dt = f(x),$$

or the derivative of the integral of f is f itself.

Noting that f is an antiderivative of f', Part 2 of the Fundamental Theorem says

$$\int_a^b f'(x)\,dx = f(b) - f(a),$$

QUICK CHECK 4 Explain why f is an antiderivative of f'. ◄

or the definite integral of the derivative of f is given in terms of f evaluated at two points. In other words, the integral "undoes" the derivative.

This last relationship is important because it expresses the integral as an *accumulation* operation. Suppose we know the rate of change of f (which is f') on an interval $[a, b]$. The Fundamental Theorem says that we can integrate (that is, sum or accumulate) the rate of change over that interval and the result is simply the difference in f evaluated at the endpoints. You will see this accumulation property used many times in the next chapter. Now let's use the Fundamental Theorem to evaluate definite integrals.

EXAMPLE 3 **Evaluating definite integrals** Evaluate the following definite integrals using the Fundamental Theorem of Calculus, Part 2. Interpret each result geometrically.

a. $\displaystyle\int_0^{10} (60x - 6x^2)\,dx$ **b.** $\displaystyle\int_0^{2\pi} 3\sin x\,dx$ **c.** $\displaystyle\int_{1/16}^{1/4} \frac{\sqrt{t} - 1}{t}\,dt$

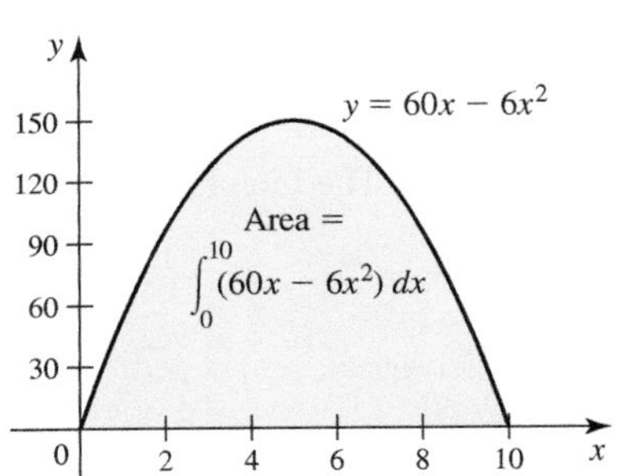

Figure 5.41

SOLUTION

a. Using the antiderivative rules of Section 4.9, an antiderivative of $60x - 6x^2$ is $30x^2 - 2x^3$. By the Fundamental Theorem, the value of the definite integral is

$$\begin{aligned}\int_0^{10} (60x - 6x^2)\,dx &= (30x^2 - 2x^3)\Big|_0^{10} && \text{Fundamental Theorem}\\ &= (30\cdot 10^2 - 2\cdot 10^3) - (30\cdot 0^2 - 2\cdot 0^3) && \text{Evaluate at } x = 10 \text{ and } x = 0.\\ &= (3000 - 2000) - 0\\ &= 1000. && \text{Simplify.}\end{aligned}$$

Because f is positive on $[0, 10]$, the definite integral $\int_0^{10}(60x - 6x^2)\,dx$ is the area of the region between the graph of f and the x-axis on the interval $[0, 10]$ (Figure 5.41).

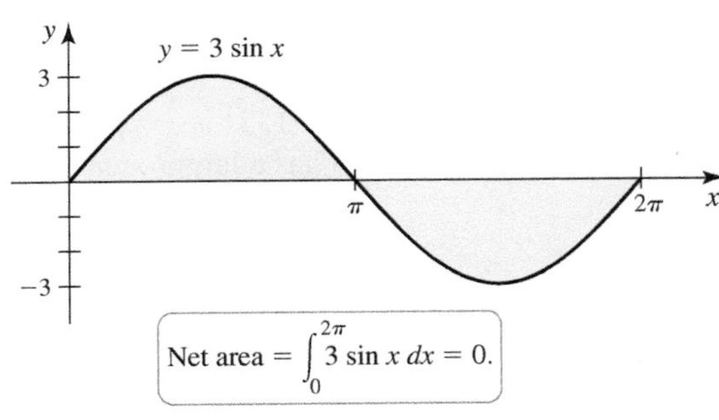

Figure 5.42

b. As shown in Figure 5.42, the region bounded by the graph of $f(x) = 3\sin x$ and the x-axis on $[0, 2\pi]$ consists of two parts, one above the x-axis and one below the x-axis. By the symmetry of f, these two regions have the same area, so the definite integral over $[0, 2\pi]$ is zero. Let's confirm this fact. An antiderivative of $f(x) = 3\sin x$ is $-3\cos x$. Therefore, the value of the definite integral is

$$\begin{aligned}\int_0^{2\pi} 3\sin x\,dx &= -3\cos x\Big|_0^{2\pi} && \text{Fundamental Theorem}\\ &= (-3\cos(2\pi)) - (-3\cos(0)) && \text{Substitute.}\\ &= -3 - (-3) = 0. && \text{Simplify.}\end{aligned}$$

c. Although the variable of integration is t, rather than x, we proceed as in parts (a) and (b) after simplifying the integrand:

$$\frac{\sqrt{t} - 1}{t} = \frac{1}{\sqrt{t}} - \frac{1}{t}.$$

➤ We know that

$$\frac{d}{dt}(t^{1/2}) = \frac{1}{2}t^{-1/2}.$$

Therefore, $\int \frac{1}{2}t^{-1/2}\,dt = t^{1/2} + C$

and $\int \frac{dt}{\sqrt{t}} = \int t^{-1/2}\,dt = 2t^{1/2} + C.$

Finding antiderivatives with respect to t and applying the Fundamental Theorem, we have

$$\begin{aligned}
\int_{1/16}^{1/4} \frac{\sqrt{t} - 1}{t}\,dt &= \int_{1/16}^{1/4}\left(t^{-1/2} - \frac{1}{t}\right)dt && \text{Simplify the integrand.}\\
&= \left(2t^{1/2} - \ln|t|\right)\Big|_{1/16}^{1/4} && \text{Fundamental Theorem}\\
&= \left(2\left(\frac{1}{4}\right)^{1/2} - \ln\frac{1}{4}\right) - \left(2\left(\frac{1}{16}\right)^{1/2} - \ln\frac{1}{16}\right) && \text{Evaluate.}\\
&= 1 - \ln\frac{1}{4} - \frac{1}{2} + \ln\frac{1}{16} && \text{Simplify.}\\
&= \frac{1}{2} - \ln 4 \approx -0.8863.
\end{aligned}$$

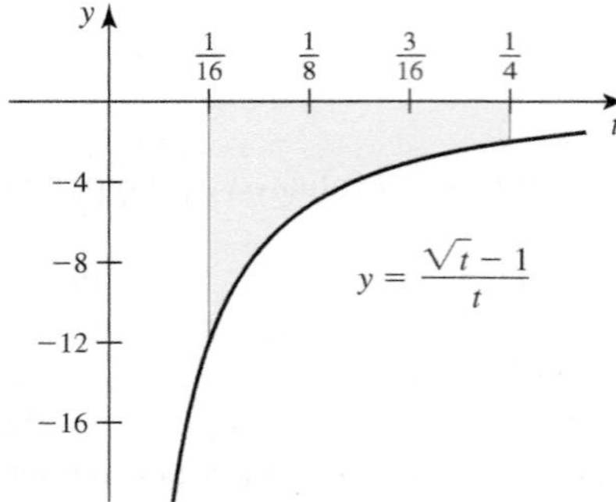

Figure 5.43

The definite integral is negative because the graph of f lies below the t-axis (Figure 5.43). *Related Exercises 23–50* ◀

EXAMPLE 4 Net areas and definite integrals The graph of $f(x) = 6x(x + 1)(x - 2)$ is shown in Figure 5.44. The region R_1 is bounded by the curve and the x-axis on the interval $[-1, 0]$, and R_2 is bounded by the curve and the x-axis on the interval $[0, 2]$.

a. Find the *net area* of the region between the curve and the x-axis on $[-1, 2]$.

b. Find the *area* of the region between the curve and the x-axis on $[-1, 2]$.

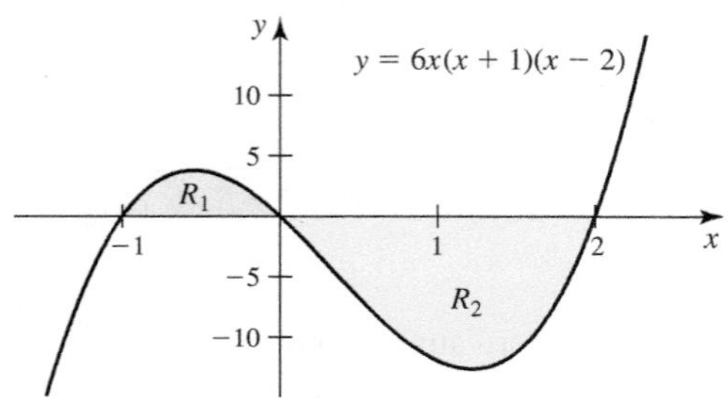

Figure 5.44

SOLUTION

a. The net area of the region is given by a definite integral. The integrand f is first expanded to find an antiderivative:

$$\begin{aligned}
\int_{-1}^{2} f(x)\,dx &= \int_{-1}^{2}(6x^3 - 6x^2 - 12x)\,dx. && \text{Expand } f.\\
&= \left(\frac{3}{2}x^4 - 2x^3 - 6x^2\right)\Big|_{-1}^{2} && \text{Fundamental Theorem}\\
&= -\frac{27}{2}. && \text{Simplify.}
\end{aligned}$$

The net area of the region between the curve and the x-axis on $[-1, 2]$ is $-\frac{27}{2}$, which is the area of R_1 *minus* the area of R_2 (Figure 5.44). Because R_2 has a larger area than R_1, the net area is negative.

b. The region R_1 lies above the x-axis, so its area is

$$\int_{-1}^{0}(6x^3 - 6x^2 - 12x)\,dx = \left(\frac{3}{2}x^4 - 2x^3 - 6x^2\right)\Big|_{-1}^{0} = \frac{5}{2}.$$

The region R_2 lies below the x-axis, so its net area is negative:

$$\int_{0}^{2}(6x^3 - 6x^2 - 12x)\,dx = \left(\frac{3}{2}x^4 - 2x^3 - 6x^2\right)\Big|_{0}^{2} = -16.$$

Therefore, the *area* of R_2 is $-(-16) = 16$. The combined area of R_1 and R_2 is $\frac{5}{2} + 16 = \frac{37}{2}$. We could also find the area of this region directly by evaluating $\int_{-1}^{2}|f(x)|\,dx$. *Related Exercises 51–60* ◀

Examples 3 and 4 make use of Part 2 of the Fundamental Theorem, which is the most potent tool for evaluating definite integrals. The remaining examples illustrate the use of the equally important Part 1 of the Fundamental Theorem.

EXAMPLE 5 **Derivatives of integrals** Use Part 1 of the Fundamental Theorem to simplify the following expressions.

a. $\dfrac{d}{dx}\displaystyle\int_1^x \sin^2 t\,dt$ **b.** $\dfrac{d}{dx}\displaystyle\int_x^5 \sqrt{t^2+1}\,dt$ **c.** $\dfrac{d}{dx}\displaystyle\int_0^{x^2} \cos t^2\,dt$

SOLUTION

a. Using Part 1 of the Fundamental Theorem, we see that

$$\frac{d}{dx}\int_1^x \sin^2 t\,dt = \sin^2 x.$$

b. To apply Part 1 of the Fundamental Theorem, the variable must appear in the upper limit. Therefore, we use the fact that $\int_a^b f(t)\,dt = -\int_b^a f(t)\,dt$ and then apply the Fundamental Theorem:

$$\frac{d}{dx}\int_x^5 \sqrt{t^2+1}\,dt = -\frac{d}{dx}\int_5^x \sqrt{t^2+1}\,dt = -\sqrt{x^2+1}.$$

c. The upper limit of the integral is not x, but a function of x. Therefore, the function to be differentiated is a composite function, which requires the Chain Rule. We let $u = x^2$ to produce

$$y = g(u) = \int_0^u \cos t^2\,dt.$$

By the Chain Rule,

$$\frac{d}{dx}\int_0^{x^2} \cos t^2\,dt = \frac{dy}{dx} = \frac{dy}{du}\frac{du}{dx} \qquad \text{Chain Rule}$$

$$= \left(\frac{d}{du}\int_0^u \cos t^2\,dt\right)(2x) \qquad \text{Substitute for } g\text{; note that } u'(x) = 2x.$$

$$= (\cos u^2)(2x) \qquad \text{Fundamental Theorem}$$

$$= 2x\cos x^4. \qquad \text{Substitute } u = x^2.$$

Related Exercises 61–68 ◀

➤ Example 5c illustrates one case of Leibniz's Rule:

$$\frac{d}{dx}\int_a^{g(x)} f(t)\,dt = f(g(x))g'(x).$$

EXAMPLE 6 **Working with area functions** Consider the function f shown in Figure 5.45 and its area function $A(x) = \int_0^x f(t)\,dt$, for $0 \le x \le 17$. Assume that the four regions R_1, R_2, R_3, and R_4 have the same area. Based on the graph of f, do the following.

a. Find the zeros of A on $[0, 17]$.

b. Find the points on $[0, 17]$ at which A has local maxima or local minima.

c. Sketch a graph of A, for $0 \le x \le 17$.

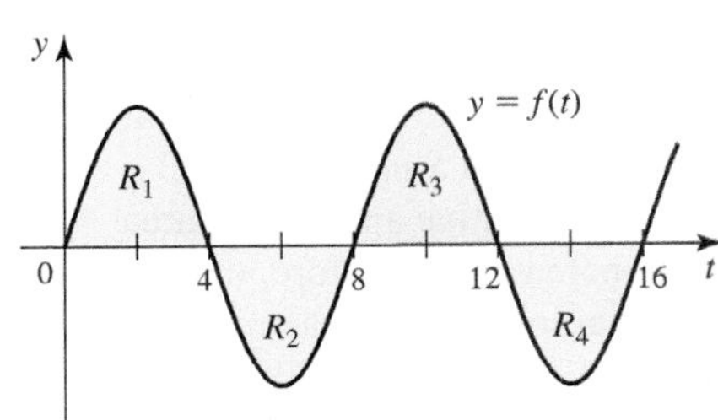

Figure 5.45

SOLUTION

a. The area function $A(x) = \int_0^x f(t)\,dt$ gives the net area bounded by the graph of f and the t-axis on the interval $[0, x]$ (Figure 5.46a). Therefore, $A(0) = \int_0^0 f(t)\,dt = 0$. Because R_1 and R_2 have the same area but lie on opposite sides of the t-axis, it follows that $A(8) = \int_0^8 f(t)\,dt = 0$. Similarly, $A(16) = \int_0^{16} f(t)\,dt = 0$. Therefore, the zeros of A are $x = 0$, 8, and 16.

b. Observe that the function f is positive, for $0 < t < 4$, which implies that $A(x)$ increases as x increases from 0 to 4 (Figure 5.46b). Then as x increases from 4 to 8, $A(x)$ decreases because f is negative, for $4 < t < 8$ (Figure 5.46c). Similarly, $A(x)$ increases as x increases from $x = 8$ to $x = 12$ (Figure 5.46d) and decreases from $x = 12$ to $x = 16$. By the First Derivative Test, A has local minima at $x = 8$ and $x = 16$ and local maxima at $x = 4$ and $x = 12$ (Figure 5.46e).

➤ Recall that local extrema occur only at interior points of the domain.

c. Combining the observations in parts (a) and (b) leads to a qualitative sketch of A (Figure 5.46e). Note that $A(x) \geq 0$, for all $x \geq 0$. It is not possible to determine function values (y-coordinates) on the graph of A.

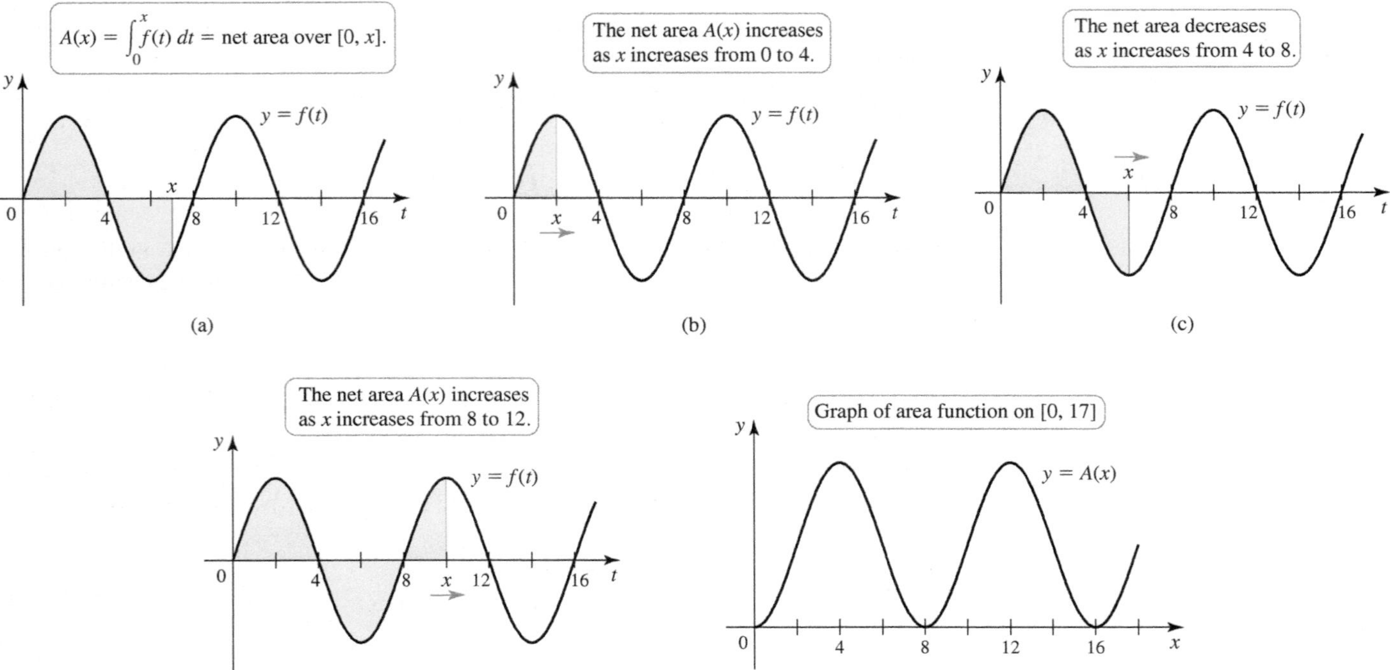

Figure 5.46

Related Exercises 69–80 ◀

EXAMPLE 7 **The sine integral function** Let

$$g(t) = \begin{cases} \dfrac{\sin t}{t} & \text{if } t > 0 \\ 1 & \text{if } t = 0. \end{cases}$$

Graph the *sine integral function* $S(x) = \int_0^x g(t)\,dt$, for $x \geq 0$.

SOLUTION Notice that S is an area function for g. The independent variable of S is x, and t has been chosen as the (dummy) variable of integration. A good way to start is by graphing the integrand g (Figure 5.47a). The function oscillates with a decreasing amplitude with $g(0) = 1$. Beginning with $S(0) = 0$, the area function S increases until $x = \pi$ because g is positive on $(0, \pi)$. However, on $(\pi, 2\pi)$, g is negative and the net area decreases. On $(2\pi, 3\pi)$, g is positive again, so S again increases. Therefore, the graph of S has alternating local maxima and minima. Because the amplitude of g decreases, each maximum of S is less than the previous maximum and each minimum of S is greater than the previous minimum (Figure 5.47b). Determining the exact value of S at these maxima and minima is difficult.

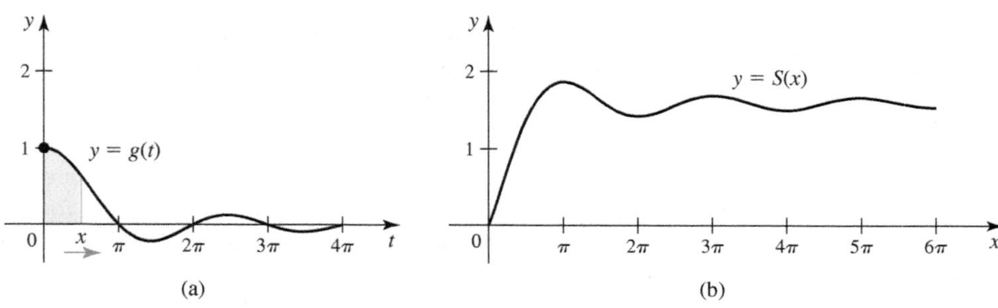

Figure 5.47

Appealing to Part 1 of the Fundamental Theorem, we find that

$$S'(x) = \frac{d}{dx}\int_0^x g(t)\,dt = \frac{\sin x}{x}, \text{ for } x > 0.$$

➤ Note that

$$\lim_{x\to\infty} S'(x) = \lim_{x\to\infty} g(x) = 0.$$

As anticipated, the derivative of S changes sign at integer multiples of π. Specifically, S' is positive and S increases on the intervals $(0, \pi)$, $(2\pi, 3\pi)$, $\ldots$, $(2n\pi, (2n + 1)\pi)$, $\ldots$, while S' is negative and S decreases on the remaining intervals. Clearly, S has local maxima at $x = \pi, 3\pi, 5\pi, \ldots$, and it has local minima at $x = 2\pi, 4\pi, 6\pi, \ldots$.

One more observation is helpful. It can be shown that although S oscillates for increasing x, its graph gradually flattens out and approaches a horizontal asymptote. (Finding the exact value of this horizontal asymptote is challenging; see Exercise 111.) Assembling all these observations, the graph of the sine integral function emerges (Figure 5.47b).

Related Exercises 81–84 ◄

We conclude this section with a formal proof of the Fundamental Theorem of Calculus.

Proof of the Fundamental Theorem: Let f be continuous on $[a, b]$ and let A be the area function for f with left endpoint a. The first step is to prove that A is differentiable on (a, b) and $A'(x) = f(x)$, which is Part 1 of the Fundamental Theorem. The proof of Part 2 then follows.

Step 1. We assume that $a < x < b$ and use the definition of the derivative,

$$A'(x) = \lim_{h\to 0} \frac{A(x + h) - A(x)}{h}.$$

First assume that $h > 0$. Using Figure 5.48 and Property 5 of Table 5.4, we have

$$A(x + h) - A(x) = \int_a^{x+h} f(t)\,dt - \int_a^x f(t)\,dt = \int_x^{x+h} f(t)\,dt.$$

That is, $A(x + h) - A(x)$ is the net area of the region bounded by the curve on the interval $[x, x + h]$.

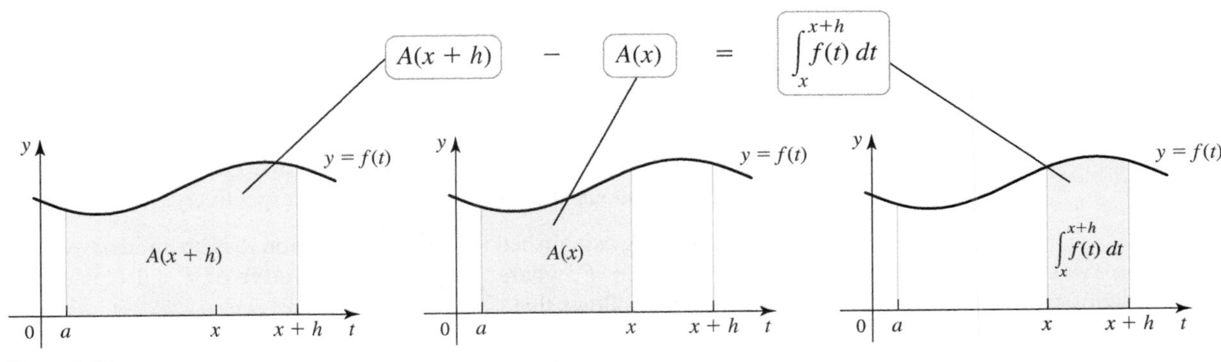

Figure 5.48

➤ The quantities m and M exist for any $h > 0$; however, their values depend on h.

Let m and M be the minimum and maximum values of f on $[x, x + h]$, respectively, which exist by the continuity of f. Suppose $x = t_0 < t_1 < t_2 < \ldots < t_n = x + h$ is a general partition of $[x, x + h]$ and let $\sum_{k=1}^{n} f(t_k^*)\Delta t_k$ be a corresponding general Riemann sum, where $\Delta t_k = t_k - t_{k-1}$. Because $m \le f(t) \le M$ on $[x, x + h]$, it follows that

$$\underbrace{\sum_{k=1}^{n} m\Delta t_k}_{mh} \le \sum_{k=1}^{n} f(t_k^*)\Delta t_k \le \underbrace{\sum_{k=1}^{n} M\Delta t_k}_{Mh}$$

or

$$mh \le \sum_{k=1}^{n} f(t_k^*)\Delta t_k \le Mh.$$

We have used the facts that $\sum_{k=1}^{n} m\Delta t_k = m\sum_{k=1}^{n} \Delta t_k = mh$ and similarly, $\sum_{k=1}^{n} M\Delta t_k = Mh$. Notice that these inequalities hold for every Riemann sum for f on $[x, x + h]$; that is, for all partitions and for all n. Therefore, we are justified in taking the limit as $n \to \infty$ across these inequalities to obtain

$$\lim_{n\to\infty} mh \le \underbrace{\lim_{n\to\infty} \sum_{k=1}^{n} f(t_k^*)\Delta t_k}_{\int_x^{x+h} f(t)\,dt} \le \lim_{n\to\infty} Mh.$$

Evaluating each of these three limits results in

$$mh \le \underbrace{\int_x^{x+h} f(t)\,dt}_{A(x+h)-A(x)} \le Mh.$$

Substituting for the integral, we find that

$$mh \le A(x + h) - A(x) \le Mh.$$

Dividing these inequalities by $h > 0$, we have

$$m \le \frac{A(x + h) - A(x)}{h} \le M.$$

The case $h < 0$ is handled similarly and leads to the same conclusion.

We now take the limit as $h \to 0$ across these inequalities. As $h \to 0$, m and M approach $f(x)$, because f is continuous at x. At the same time, as $h \to 0$, the quotient that is sandwiched between m and M approaches $A'(x)$:

$$\underbrace{\lim_{h\to 0} m}_{f(x)} = \underbrace{\lim_{h\to 0} \frac{A(x + h) - A(x)}{h}}_{A'(x)} = \underbrace{\lim_{h\to 0} M}_{f(x)}.$$

By the Squeeze Theorem (Theorem 2.5), we conclude that $A'(x)$ exists and A is differentiable for $a < x < b$. Furthermore, $A'(x) = f(x)$. Finally, because A is differentiable on (a, b), A is continuous on (a, b) by Theorem 3.1. Exercise 116 shows that A is also right- and left-continuous at the endpoints a and b, respectively.

➤ Once again we use an important fact: Two antiderivatives of the same function differ by a constant.

Step 2. Having established that the area function A is an antiderivative of f, we know that $F(x) = A(x) + C$, where F is any antiderivative of f and C is a constant. Noting that $A(a) = 0$, it follows that

$$F(b) - F(a) = (A(b) + C) - (A(a) + C) = A(b).$$

Writing $A(b)$ in terms of a definite integral, we have

$$A(b) = \int_a^b f(x)\,dx = F(b) - F(a),$$

which is Part 2 of the Fundamental Theorem. ◄

SECTION 5.3 EXERCISES

Review Questions

1. Suppose A is an area function of f. What is the relationship between f and A?

2. Suppose F is an antiderivative of f and A is an area function of f. What is the relationship between F and A?

3. Explain in words and write mathematically how the Fundamental Theorem of Calculus is used to evaluate definite integrals.

4. Let $f(x) = c$, where c is a positive constant. Explain why an area function of f is an increasing function.

5. The linear function $f(x) = 3 - x$ is decreasing on the interval $[0, 3]$. Is the area function for f (with left endpoint 0) increasing or decreasing on the interval $[0, 3]$? Draw a picture and explain.

6. Evaluate $\int_0^2 3x^2\,dx$ and $\int_{-2}^2 3x^2\,dx$.

7. Explain in words and express mathematically the inverse relationship between differentiation and integration as given by Part 1 of the Fundamental Theorem of Calculus.

8. Why can the constant of integration be omitted from the antiderivative when evaluating a definite integral?

9. Evaluate $\dfrac{d}{dx}\displaystyle\int_a^x f(t)\,dt$ and $\dfrac{d}{dx}\displaystyle\int_a^b f(t)\,dt$, where a and b are constants.

10. Explain why $\int_a^b f'(x)\,dx = f(b) - f(a)$.

Basic Skills

11. **Area functions** The graph of f is shown in the figure. Let $A(x) = \int_{-2}^x f(t)\,dt$ and $F(x) = \int_4^x f(t)\,dt$ be two area functions for f. Evaluate the following area functions.

    a. $A(-2)$ b. $F(8)$ c. $A(4)$ d. $F(4)$ e. $A(8)$

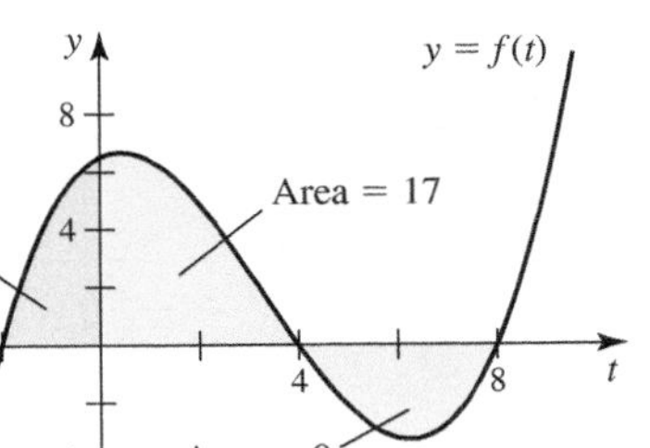

12. **Area functions** The graph of f is shown in the figure. Let $A(x) = \int_0^x f(t)\,dt$ and $F(x) = \int_2^x f(t)\,dt$ be two area functions for f. Evaluate the following area functions.

    a. $A(2)$ b. $F(5)$ c. $A(0)$ d. $F(8)$
    e. $A(8)$ f. $A(5)$ g. $F(2)$

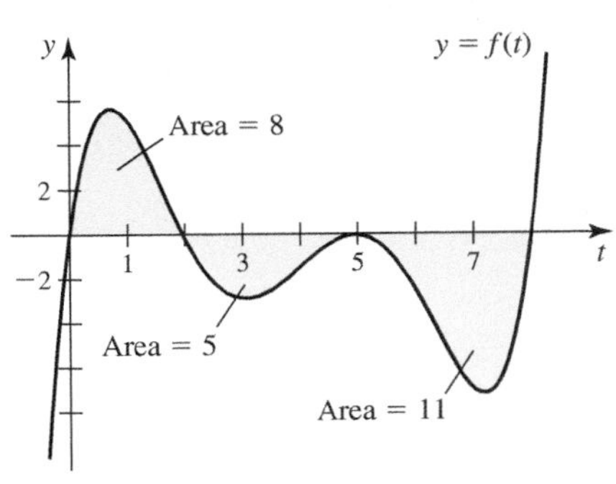

13–16. Area functions for constant functions *Consider the following functions f and real numbers a (see figure).*

a. Find and graph the area function $A(x) = \int_a^x f(t)\,dt$ for f.
b. Verify that $A'(x) = f(x)$.

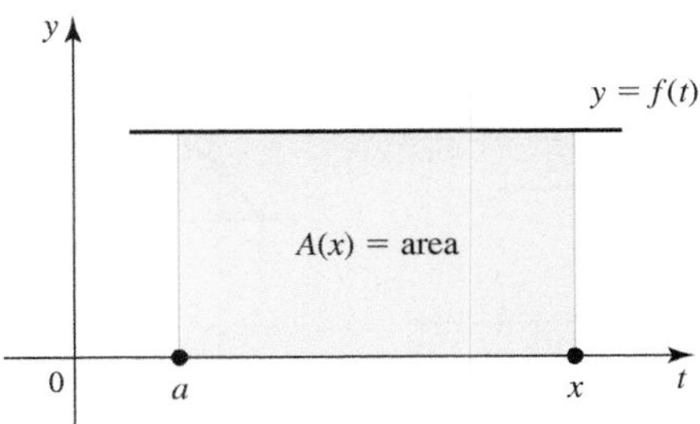

13. $f(t) = 5,\ a = 0$

14. $f(t) = 10,\ a = 4$

15. $f(t) = 5,\ a = -5$

16. $f(t) = 2,\ a = -3$

17. **Area functions for the same linear function** Let $f(t) = t$ and consider the two area functions $A(x) = \int_0^x f(t)\,dt$ and $F(x) = \int_2^x f(t)\,dt$.
    a. Evaluate $A(2)$ and $A(4)$. Then use geometry to find an expression for $A(x)$, for $x \geq 0$.
    b. Evaluate $F(4)$ and $F(6)$. Then use geometry to find an expression for $F(x)$, for $x \geq 2$.
    c. Show that $A(x) - F(x)$ is a constant and that $A'(x) = F'(x) = f(x)$.

18. **Area functions for the same linear function** Let $f(t) = 2t - 2$ and consider the two area functions $A(x) = \int_1^x f(t)\,dt$ and $F(x) = \int_4^x f(t)\,dt$.
    a. Evaluate $A(2)$ and $A(3)$. Then use geometry to find an expression for $A(x)$, for $x \geq 1$.
    b. Evaluate $F(5)$ and $F(6)$. Then use geometry to find an expression for $F(x)$, for $x \geq 4$.
    c. Show that $A(x) - F(x)$ is a constant and that $A'(x) = F'(x) = f(x)$.

19–22. Area functions for linear functions *Consider the following functions f and real numbers a (see figure).*

a. Find and graph the area function $A(x) = \int_a^x f(t)\,dt$.
b. Verify that $A'(x) = f(x)$.

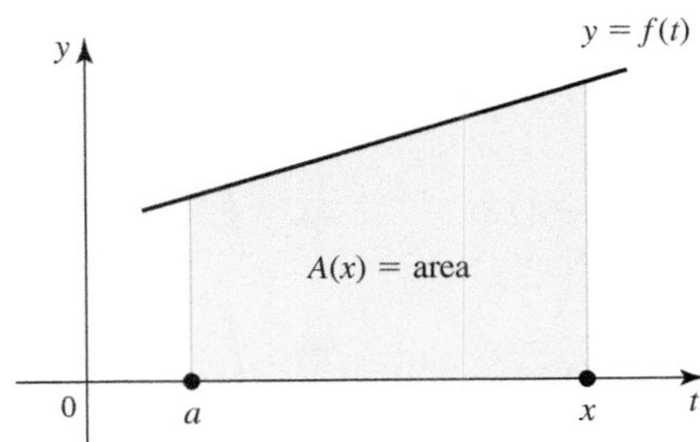

19. $f(t) = t + 5,\ a = -5$

20. $f(t) = 2t + 5,\ a = 0$

21. $f(t) = 3t + 1,\ a = 2$

22. $f(t) = 4t + 2,\ a = 0$

23–24. Definite integrals *Evaluate the following integrals using the Fundamental Theorem of Calculus. Explain why your result is consistent with the figure.*

23. $\int_0^1 (x^2 - 2x + 3)\,dx$

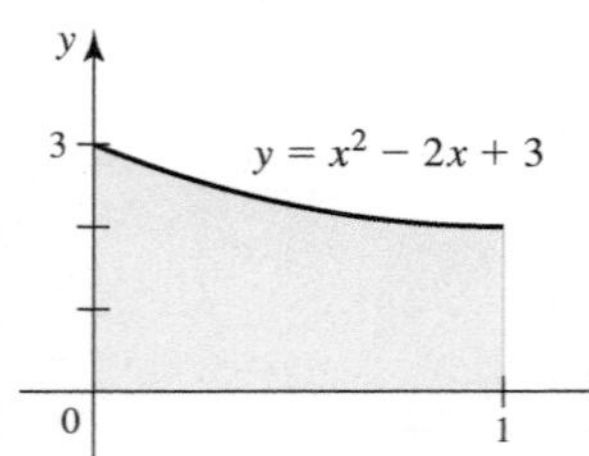

24. $\int_{-\pi/4}^{7\pi/4} (\sin x + \cos x)\,dx$

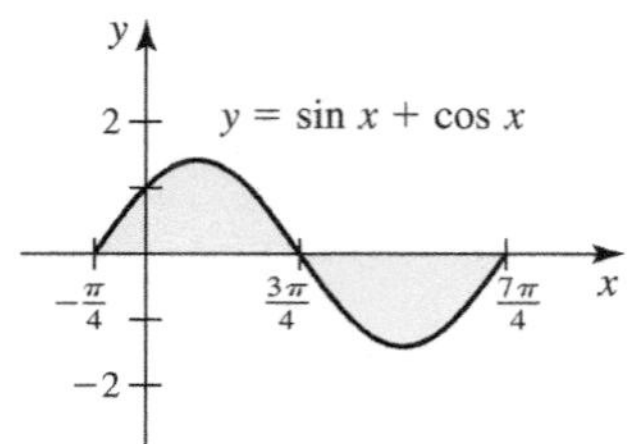

25–28. Definite integrals *Evaluate the following integrals using the Fundamental Theorem of Calculus. Sketch the graph of the integrand and shade the region whose net area you have found.*

25. $\int_{-2}^{3} (x^2 - x - 6)\,dx$

26. $\int_0^1 (x - \sqrt{x})\,dx$

27. $\int_0^5 (x^2 - 9)\,dx$

28. $\int_{1/2}^{2} \left(1 - \frac{1}{x^2}\right) dx$

29–50. Definite integrals *Evaluate the following integrals using the Fundamental Theorem of Calculus.*

29. $\int_0^2 4x^3\,dx$

30. $\int_0^2 (3x^2 + 2x)\,dx$

31. $\int_0^1 (x + \sqrt{x})\,dx$

32. $\int_0^{\pi/4} 2\cos x\,dx$

33. $\int_1^9 \frac{2}{\sqrt{x}}\,dx$

34. $\int_4^9 \frac{2 + \sqrt{t}}{t}\,dt$

35. $\int_{-2}^{2} (x^2 - 4)\,dx$

36. $\int_0^{\ln 8} e^x\,dx$

37. $\int_{1/2}^{1} (x^{-3} - 8)\,dx$

38. $\int_0^4 x(x - 2)(x - 4)\,dx$

39. $\int_0^{\pi/4} \sec^2\theta\,d\theta$

40. $\int_0^{1/2} \frac{dx}{\sqrt{1 - x^2}}$

41. $\int_{-2}^{-1} x^{-3}\,dx$

42. $\int_0^{\pi} (1 - \sin x)\,dx$

43. $\int_1^4 (1 - x)(x - 4)\,dx$

44. $\int_{-\pi/2}^{\pi/2} (\cos x - 1)\,dx$

45. $\int_1^2 \frac{3}{t}\,dt$

46. $\int_4^9 \frac{x - \sqrt{x}}{x^3}\,dx$

47. $\int_0^{\pi/8} \cos 2x\,dx$

48. $\int_0^1 10e^{2x}\,dx$

49. $\int_1^{\sqrt{3}} \frac{dx}{1 + x^2}$

50. $\int_{\pi/16}^{\pi/8} 8\csc^2 4x\,dx$

51–54. Areas *Find (i) the net area and (ii) the area of the following regions. Graph the function and indicate the region in question.*

51. The region bounded by $y = x^{1/2}$ and the x-axis between $x = 1$ and $x = 4$

52. The region above the x-axis bounded by $y = 4 - x^2$

53. The region below the x-axis bounded by $y = x^4 - 16$

54. The region bounded by $y = 6\cos x$ and the x-axis between $x = -\pi/2$ and $x = \pi$

55–60. Areas of regions *Find the area of the region bounded by the graph of f and the x-axis on the given interval.*

55. $f(x) = x^2 - 25$ on $[2, 4]$

56. $f(x) = x^3 - 1$ on $[-1, 2]$

57. $f(x) = \frac{1}{x}$ on $[-2, -1]$

58. $f(x) = x(x + 1)(x - 2)$ on $[-1, 2]$

59. $f(x) = \sin x$ on $[-\pi/4, 3\pi/4]$

60. $f(x) = \cos x$ on $[\pi/2, \pi]$

61–68. Derivatives of integrals *Simplify the following expressions.*

61. $\frac{d}{dx}\int_3^x (t^2 + t + 1)\,dt$

62. $\frac{d}{dx}\int_0^x e^t\,dt$

63. $\frac{d}{dx}\int_2^{x^3} \frac{dp}{p^2}$

64. $\frac{d}{dx}\int_{x^2}^{10} \frac{dz}{z^2 + 1}$

65. $\frac{d}{dx}\int_x^1 \sqrt{t^4 + 1}\,dt$

66. $\frac{d}{dx}\int_x^0 \frac{dp}{p^2 + 1}$

67. $\frac{d}{dx}\int_{-x}^{x} \sqrt{1 + t^2}\,dt$

68. $\frac{d}{dx}\int_{e^x}^{e^{2x}} \ln t^2\,dt$

69. **Matching functions with area functions** Match the functions f, whose graphs are given in a–d, with the area functions $A(x) = \int_0^x f(t)\,dt$, whose graphs are given in A–D.

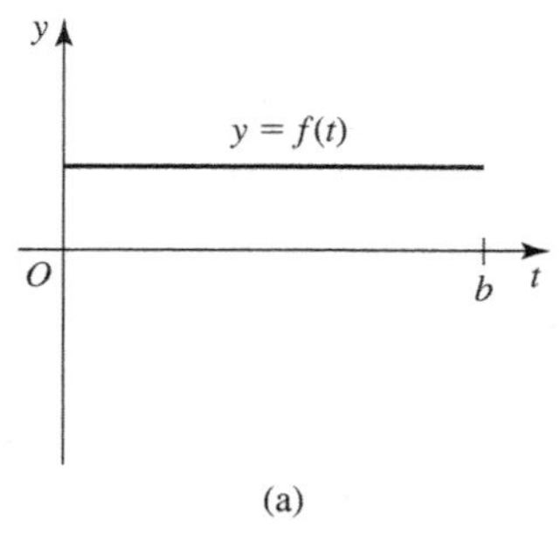

(a)

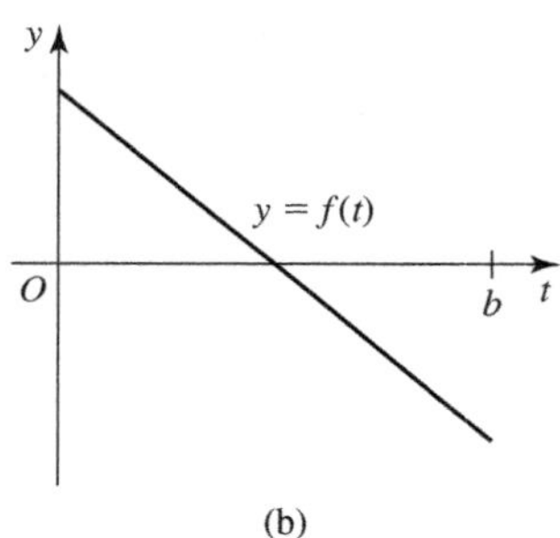

(b)

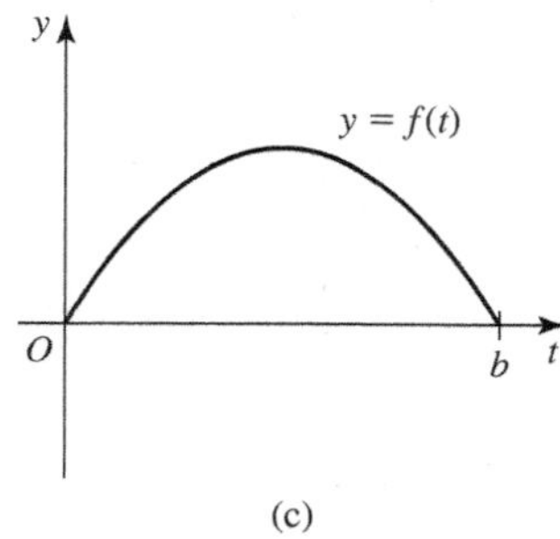

(c)

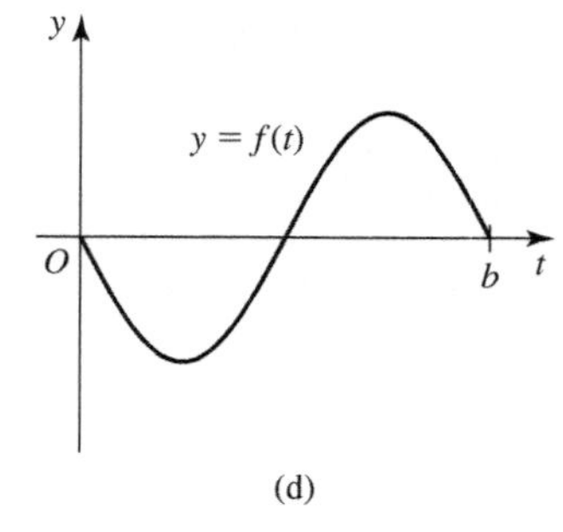

(d)

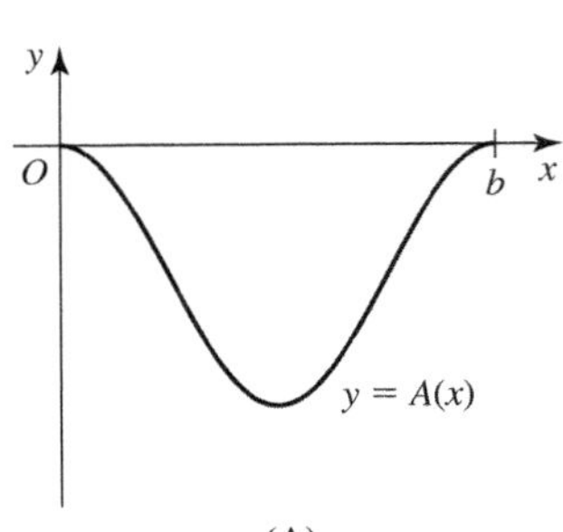

(A)

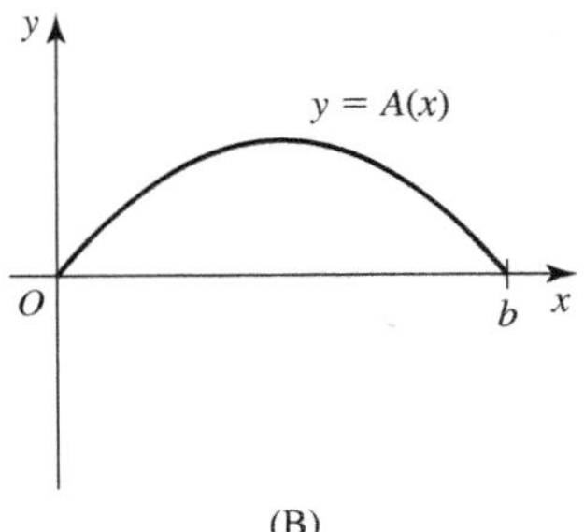

(B)

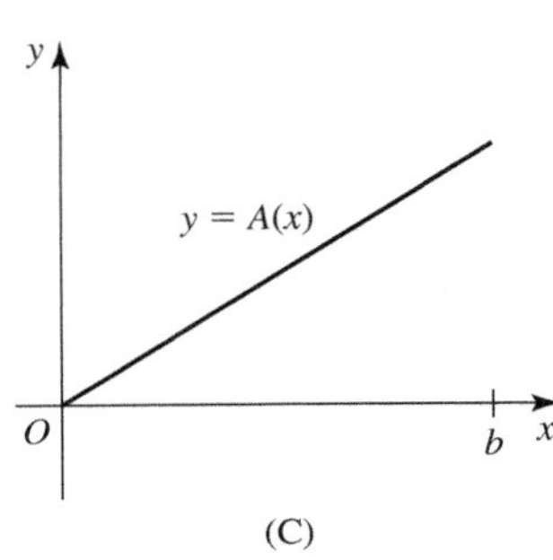

(C)

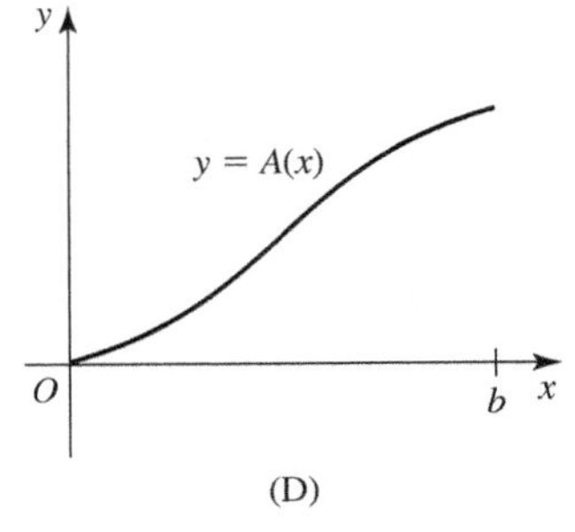

(D)

70–73. Working with area functions *Consider the function f and its graph.*

a. *Estimate the zeros of the area function $A(x) = \int_0^x f(t)\,dt$, for $0 \le x \le 10$.*

b. *Estimate the points (if any) at which A has a local maximum or minimum.*

c. *Sketch a graph of A, for $0 \le x \le 10$, without a scale on the y-axis.*

70.

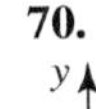

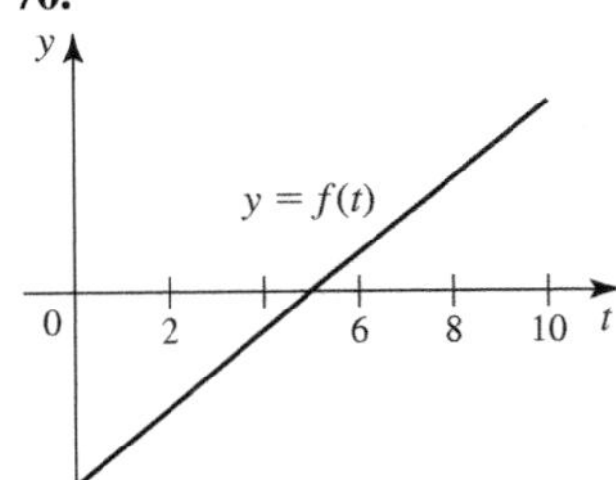

71.

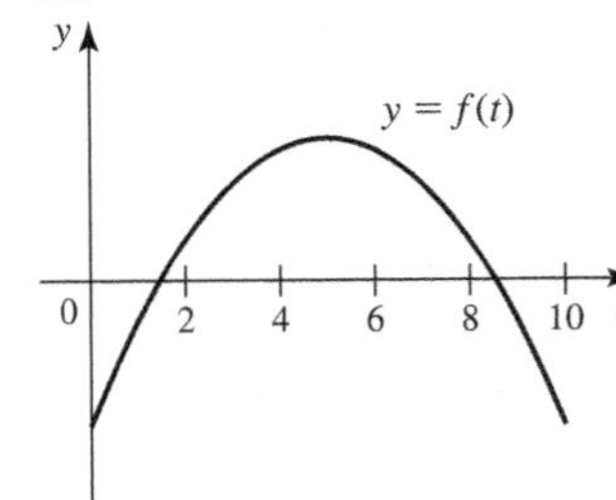

72.

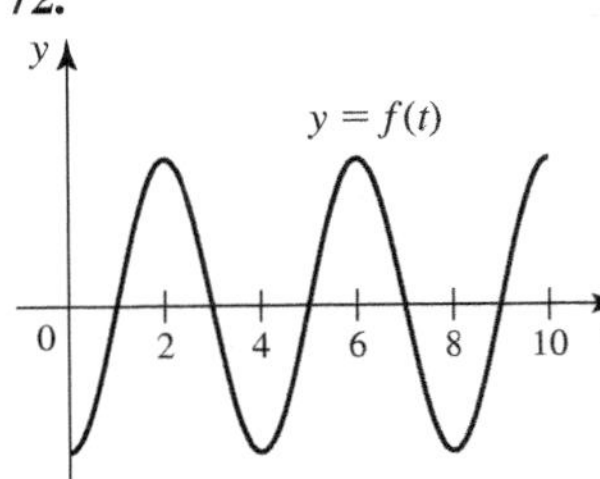

73.

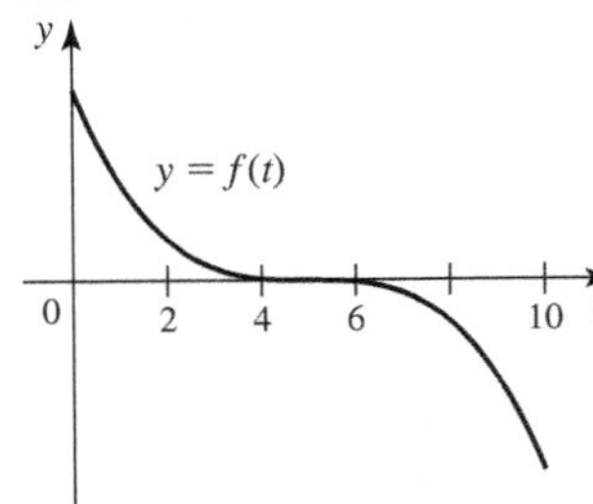

74. Area functions from graphs The graph of f is given in the figure. Let $A(x) = \int_0^x f(t)\,dt$ and evaluate $A(1)$, $A(2)$, $A(4)$, and $A(6)$.

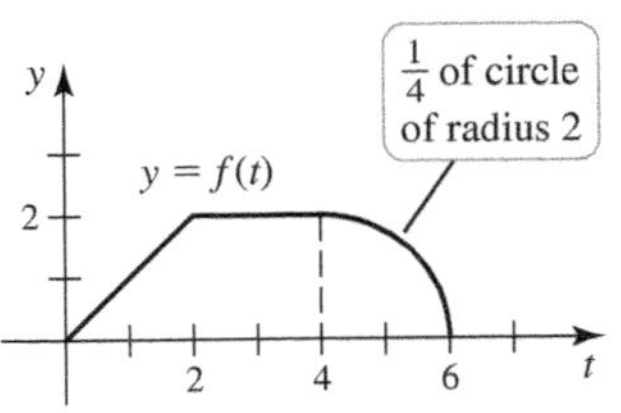

75. Area functions from graphs The graph of f is given in the figure. Let $A(x) = \int_0^x f(t)\,dt$ and evaluate $A(2)$, $A(5)$, $A(8)$, and $A(12)$.

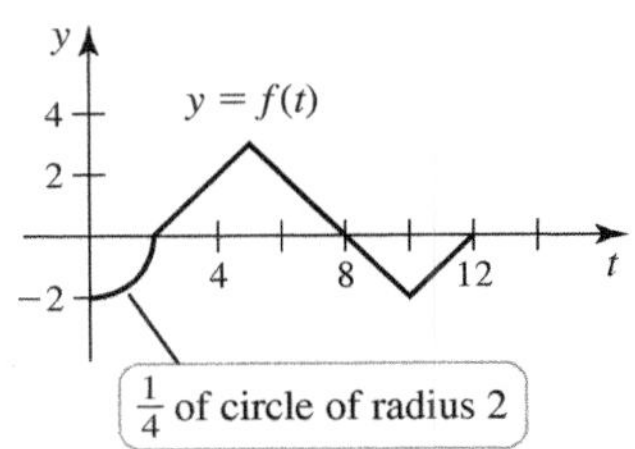

76–80. Working with area functions *Consider the function f and the points a, b, and c.*

a. *Find the area function $A(x) = \int_a^x f(t)\,dt$ using the Fundamental Theorem.*

b. *Graph f and A.*

c. *Evaluate A(b) and A(c). Interpret the results using the graphs of part (b).*

76. $f(x) = \sin x$; $a = 0, b = \pi/2, c = \pi$

77. $f(x) = e^x$; $a = 0, b = \ln 2, c = \ln 4$

78. $f(x) = -12x(x-1)(x-2)$; $a = 0, b = 1, c = 2$

79. $f(x) = \cos \pi x$; $a = 0, b = \frac{1}{2}, c = 1$

80. $f(x) = \dfrac{1}{x}$; $a = 1, b = 4, c = 6$

T **81–84. Functions defined by integrals** *Consider the function g, which is given in terms of a definite integral with a variable upper limit.*

a. *Graph the integrand.*

b. *Calculate g′(x).*

c. *Graph g, showing all your work and reasoning.*

81. $g(x) = \displaystyle\int_0^x \sin^2 t\,dt$

82. $g(x) = \displaystyle\int_0^x (t^2 + 1)\,dt$

83. $g(x) = \displaystyle\int_0^x \sin(\pi t^2)\,dt$ (a Fresnel integral)

84. $g(x) = \displaystyle\int_0^x \cos(\pi\sqrt{t})\,dt$

Further Explorations

85. Explain why or why not Determine whether the following statements are true and give an explanation or counterexample.

a. Suppose that f is a positive decreasing function, for $x > 0$. Then the area function $A(x) = \int_0^x f(t)\,dt$ is an increasing function of x.

b. Suppose that f is a negative increasing function, for $x > 0$. Then the area function $A(x) = \int_0^x f(t)\,dt$ is a decreasing function of x.

c. The functions $p(x) = \sin 3x$ and $q(x) = 4 \sin 3x$ are antiderivatives of the same function.

d. If $A(x) = 3x^2 - x - 3$ is an area function for f, then $B(x) = 3x^2 - x$ is also an area function for f.

e. $\dfrac{d}{dx}\displaystyle\int_a^b f(t)\,dt = 0.$

86–94. Definite integrals *Evaluate the following definite integrals using the Fundamental Theorem of Calculus.*

86. $\frac{1}{2}\int_0^{\ln 2} e^x\,dx$ **87.** $\int_1^4 \frac{x-2}{\sqrt{x}}\,dx$ **88.** $\int_1^2 \left(\frac{2}{s} - \frac{4}{s^3}\right) ds$

89. $\int_0^{\pi/3} \sec x \tan x\,dx$ **90.** $\int_{\pi/4}^{\pi/2} \csc^2\theta\,d\theta$ **91.** $\int_1^8 \sqrt[3]{y}\,dy$

92. $\int_{\sqrt{2}}^2 \frac{dx}{x\sqrt{x^2-1}}$ **93.** $\int_1^2 \frac{z^2+4}{z}\,dz$ **94.** $\int_0^{\sqrt{3}} \frac{3\,dx}{9+x^2}$

T **95–98. Areas of regions** *Find the area of the region R bounded by the graph of f and the x-axis on the given interval. Graph f and show the region R.*

95. $f(x) = 2 - |x|$ on $[-2, 4]$

96. $f(x) = (1 - x^2)^{-1/2}$ on $[-1/2, \sqrt{3}/2]$

97. $f(x) = x^4 - 4$ on $[1, 4]$ **98.** $f(x) = x^2(x - 2)$ on $[-1, 3]$

99–102. Derivatives and integrals *Simplify the given expressions.*

99. $\int_3^8 f'(t)\,dt$, where f' is continuous on $[3, 8]$

100. $\frac{d}{dx}\int_0^{x^2} \frac{dt}{t^2+4}$ **101.** $\frac{d}{dx}\int_0^{\cos x} (t^4 + 6)\,dt$

102. $\frac{d}{dx}\int_x^1 e^{t^2}\,dt$ **103.** $\frac{d}{dt}\left(\int_1^t \frac{3}{x}\,dx - \int_{t^2}^1 \frac{3}{x}\,dx\right)$

104. $\frac{d}{dt}\left(\int_0^t \frac{dx}{1+x^2} + \int_0^{1/t} \frac{dx}{1+x^2}\right)$

Additional Exercises

105. Zero net area Consider the function $f(x) = x^2 - 4x$.

a. Graph f on the interval $x \ge 0$.
b. For what value of $b > 0$ is $\int_0^b f(x)\,dx = 0$?
c. In general, for the function $f(x) = x^2 - ax$, where $a > 0$, for what value of $b > 0$ (as a function of a) is $\int_0^b f(x)\,dx = 0$?

106. Cubic zero net area Consider the graph of the cubic $y = x(x - a)(x - b)$, where $0 < a < b$. Verify that the graph bounds a region above the x-axis, for $0 < x < a$, and bounds a region below the x-axis, for $a < x < b$. What is the relationship between a and b if the areas of these two regions are equal?

107. Maximum net area What value of $b > -1$ maximizes the integral

$$\int_{-1}^b x^2(3 - x)\,dx?$$

108. Maximum net area Graph the function $f(x) = 8 + 2x - x^2$ and determine the values of a and b that maximize the value of the integral

$$\int_a^b (8 + 2x - x^2)\,dx.$$

109. An integral equation Use the Fundamental Theorem of Calculus, Part 1, to find the function f that satisfies the equation

$$\int_0^x f(t)\,dt = 2\cos x + 3x - 2.$$

Verify the result by substitution into the equation.

110. Max/min of area functions Suppose f is continuous on $[0, \infty)$ and $A(x)$ is the net area of the region bounded by the graph of f and the t-axis on $[0, x]$. Show that the local maxima and minima of A occur at the zeros of f. Verify this fact with the function $f(x) = x^2 - 10x$.

T **111. Asymptote of sine integral** Use a calculator to approximate

$$\lim_{x\to\infty} S(x) = \lim_{x\to\infty} \int_0^x \frac{\sin t}{t}\,dt,$$

where S is the sine integral function (see Example 7). Explain your reasoning.

112. Sine integral Show that the sine integral $S(x) = \int_0^x \frac{\sin t}{t}\,dt$ satisfies the (differential) equation $xS'(x) + 2S''(x) + xS'''(x) = 0$.

113. Fresnel integral Show that the Fresnel integral $S(x) = \int_0^x \sin t^2\,dt$ satisfies the (differential) equation

$$(S'(x))^2 + \left(\frac{S''(x)}{2x}\right)^2 = 1.$$

114. Variable integration limits Evaluate $\frac{d}{dx}\int_{-x}^x (t^2 + t)\,dt$. (*Hint:* Separate the integral into two pieces.)

115. Discrete version of the Fundamental Theorem In this exercise, we work with a discrete problem and show why the relationship $\int_a^b f'(x)\,dx = f(b) - f(a)$ makes sense. Suppose we have a set of equally spaced grid points

$$\{a = x_0 < x_1 < x_2 < \dots < x_{n-1} < x_n = b\},$$

where the distance between any two grid points is Δx. Suppose also that at each grid point x_k, a function value $f(x_k)$ is defined, for $k = 0, \dots, n$.

a. We now replace the integral with a sum and replace the derivative with a difference quotient. Explain why $\int_a^b f'(x)\,dx$ is analogous to $\sum_{k=1}^n \underbrace{\frac{f(x_k) - f(x_{k-1})}{\Delta x}}_{\approx f'(x_k)} \Delta x$.
b. Simplify the sum in part (a) and show that it is equal to $f(b) - f(a)$.
c. Explain the correspondence between the integral relationship and the summation relationship.

116. Continuity at the endpoints Assume that f is continuous on $[a, b]$ and let A be the area function for f with left endpoint a. Let m^* and M^* be the absolute minimum and maximum values of f on $[a, b]$, respectively.

a. Prove that $m^*(x - a) \le A(x) \le M^*(x - a)$ for all x in $[a, b]$. Use this result and the Squeeze Theorem to show that A is continuous from the right at $x = a$.
b. Prove that $m^*(b - x) \le A(b) - A(x) \le M^*(b - x)$ for all x in $[a, b]$. Use this result to show that A is continuous from the left at $x = b$.

QUICK CHECK ANSWERS

1. $0, -35$ **2.** $A(6) = 44$; $A(10) = 120$ **3.** $\frac{2}{3} - \frac{1}{2} = \frac{1}{6}$
4. If f is differentiated, we get f'. Therefore, f is an antiderivative of f'. ◄

5.4 Working with Integrals

With the Fundamental Theorem of Calculus in hand, we may begin an investigation of integration and its applications. In this section, we discuss the role of symmetry in integrals, we use the slice-and-sum strategy to define the average value of a function, and we explore a theoretical result called the Mean Value Theorem for Integrals.

Integrating Even and Odd Functions

Symmetry appears throughout mathematics in many different forms, and its use often leads to insights and efficiencies. Here we use the symmetry of a function to simplify integral calculations.

Section 1.1 introduced the symmetry of even and odd functions. An **even function** satisfies the property $f(-x) = f(x)$, which means that its graph is symmetric about the y-axis (Figure 5.49a). Examples of even functions are $f(x) = \cos x$ and $f(x) = x^n$, where n is an even integer. An **odd function** satisfies the property $f(-x) = -f(x)$, which means that its graph is symmetric about the origin (Figure 5.49b). Examples of odd functions are $f(x) = \sin x$ and $f(x) = x^n$, where n is an odd integer.

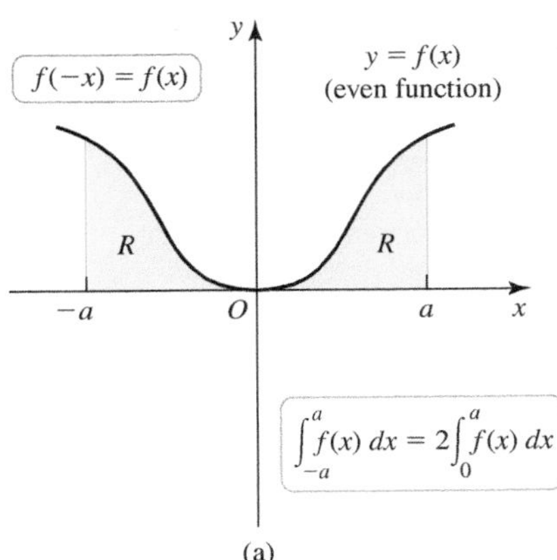

(a)

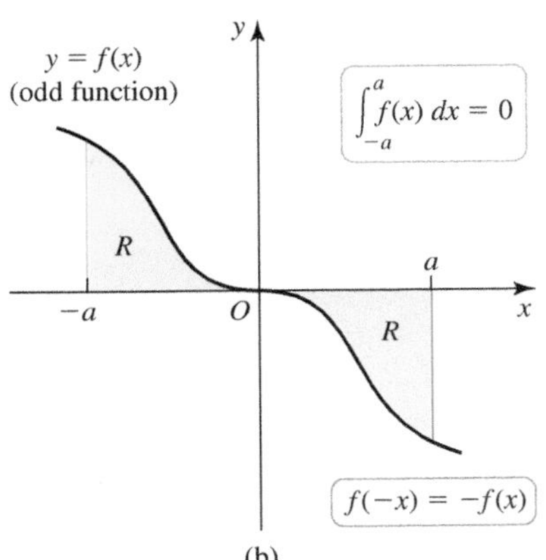

(b)

Figure 5.49

Special things happen when we integrate even and odd functions on intervals centered at the origin. First suppose f is an even function and consider $\int_{-a}^{a} f(x)\,dx$. From Figure 5.49a, we see that the integral of f on $[-a, 0]$ equals the integral of f on $[0, a]$. Therefore, the integral on $[-a, a]$ is twice the integral on $[0, a]$, or

$$\int_{-a}^{a} f(x)\,dx = 2\int_{0}^{a} f(x)\,dx.$$

On the other hand, suppose f is an odd function and consider $\int_{-a}^{a} f(x)\,dx$. As shown in Figure 5.49b, the integral on the interval $[-a, 0]$ is the negative of the integral on $[0, a]$. Therefore, the integral on $[-a, a]$ is zero, or

$$\int_{-a}^{a} f(x)\,dx = 0.$$

We summarize these results in the following theorem.

> **THEOREM 5.4 Integrals of Even and Odd Functions**
> Let a be a positive real number and let f be an integrable function on the interval $[-a, a]$.
> - If f is even, $\int_{-a}^{a} f(x)\,dx = 2\int_{0}^{a} f(x)\,dx$.
> - If f is odd, $\int_{-a}^{a} f(x)\,dx = 0$.

QUICK CHECK 1 If f and g are both even functions, is the product fg even or odd? Use the facts that $f(-x) = f(x)$ and $g(-x) = g(x)$. ◄

The following example shows how symmetry can simplify integration.

EXAMPLE 1 Integrating symmetric functions Evaluate the following integrals using symmetry arguments.

a. $\int_{-2}^{2} (x^4 - 3x^3)\,dx$ **b.** $\int_{-\pi/2}^{\pi/2} (\cos x - 4\sin^3 x)\,dx$

SOLUTION

a. Note that $x^4 - 3x^3$ is neither odd nor even so Theorem 5.4 cannot be applied directly. However, we can split the integral and then use symmetry:

$$\int_{-2}^{2}(x^4 - 3x^3)\,dx = \int_{-2}^{2} x^4\,dx - 3\underbrace{\int_{-2}^{2} x^3\,dx}_{0} \quad \text{Properties 3 and 4 of Table 5.4}$$

$$= 2\int_0^2 x^4\,dx - 0 \quad x^4 \text{ is even; } x^3 \text{ is odd.}$$

$$= 2\left(\frac{x^5}{5}\right)\Big|_0^2 \quad \text{Fundamental Theorem}$$

$$= 2\left(\frac{32}{5}\right) = \frac{64}{5}. \quad \text{Simplify.}$$

Notice how the odd-powered term of the integrand is eliminated by symmetry. Integration of the even-powered term is simplified because the lower limit is zero.

➤ There are a couple of ways to see that $\sin^3 x$ is an odd function. Its graph is symmetric about the origin, indicating that $\sin^3(-x) = -\sin^3 x$. Or by analogy, take an odd power of x and raise it to an odd power. For example, $(x^5)^3 = x^{15}$, which is odd. See Exercises 53–56 for direct proofs of symmetry in composite functions.

b. The $\cos x$ term is an even function, so it can be integrated on the interval $[0, \pi/2]$. What about $\sin^3 x$? It is an odd function raised to an odd power, which results in an odd function; its integral on $[-\pi/2, \pi/2]$ is zero. Therefore,

$$\int_{-\pi/2}^{\pi/2}(\cos x - 4\sin^3 x)\,dx = 2\int_0^{\pi/2}\cos x\,dx - 0 \quad \text{Symmetry}$$

$$= 2\sin x\Big|_0^{\pi/2} \quad \text{Fundamental Theorem}$$

$$= 2(1 - 0) = 2. \quad \text{Simplify.}$$

Related Exercises 7–20 ◀

Average Value of a Function

If five people weigh 155, 143, 180, 105, and 123 lb, their average (mean) weight is

$$\frac{155 + 143 + 180 + 105 + 123}{5} = 141.2 \text{ lb.}$$

This idea generalizes quite naturally to functions. Consider a function f that is continuous on $[a, b]$. Using a regular partition $x_0 = a, x_1, x_2, \ldots, x_n = b$ with $\Delta x = \dfrac{b - a}{n}$, we select a point x_k^* in each subinterval and compute $f(x_k^*)$, for $k = 1, \ldots, n$. The values of $f(x_k^*)$ may be viewed as a sampling of f on $[a, b]$. The average of these function values is

$$\frac{f(x_1^*) + f(x_2^*) + \cdots + f(x_n^*)}{n}.$$

Noting that $n = \dfrac{b - a}{\Delta x}$, we write the average of the n sample values as the Riemann sum

$$\frac{f(x_1^*) + f(x_2^*) + \cdots + f(x_n^*)}{(b - a)/\Delta x} = \frac{1}{b - a}\sum_{k=1}^{n} f(x_k^*)\Delta x.$$

Now suppose we increase n, taking more and more samples of f, while Δx decreases to zero. The limit of this sum is a definite integral that gives the average value $\bar{f}$ on $[a, b]$:

$$\bar{f} = \frac{1}{b - a}\lim_{n\to\infty}\sum_{k=1}^{n} f(x_k^*)\Delta x$$

$$= \frac{1}{b - a}\int_a^b f(x)\,dx.$$

This definition of the average value of a function is analogous to the definition of the average of a finite set of numbers.

> **DEFINITION Average Value of a Function**
> The average value of an integrable function f on the interval $[a, b]$ is
> $$\bar{f} = \frac{1}{b - a}\int_a^b f(x)\,dx.$$

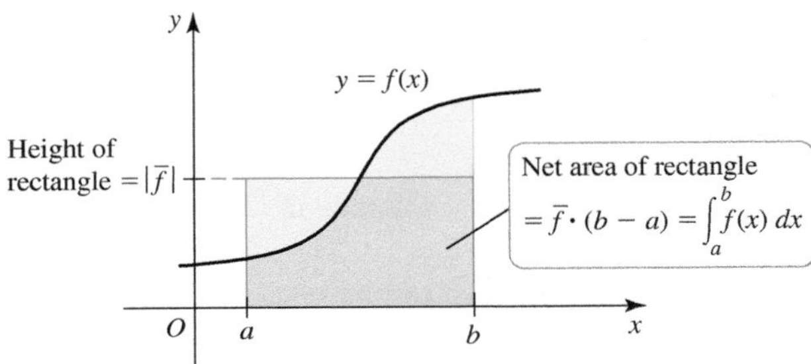

Figure 5.50

The average value of a function f on an interval $[a, b]$ has a clear geometrical interpretation. Multiplying both sides of the definition of average value by $(b - a)$, we have

$$\underbrace{(b - a)\bar{f}}_{\text{net area of rectangle}} = \underbrace{\int_a^b f(x)\,dx}_{\text{net area of region bounded by curve}}.$$

We see that $|\bar{f}|$ is the height of a rectangle with base $[a, b]$, and that rectangle has the same net area as the region bounded by the graph of f on the interval $[a, b]$ (Figure 5.50). Note that $\bar{f}$ may be zero or negative.

QUICK CHECK 2 What is the average value of a constant function on an interval? What is the average value of an odd function on an interval $[-a, a]$? ◄

EXAMPLE 2 Average elevation A hiking trail has an elevation given by

$$f(x) = 60x^3 - 650x^2 + 1200x + 4500,$$

where f is measured in feet above sea level and x represents horizontal distance along the trail in miles, with $0 \le x \le 5$. What is the average elevation of the trail?

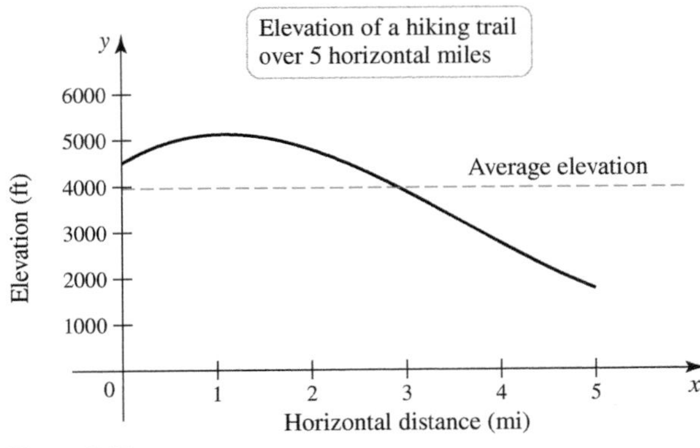

Figure 5.51

SOLUTION The trail ranges between elevations of about 2000 and 5000 ft (Figure 5.51). If we let the endpoints of the trail correspond to the horizontal distances $a = 0$ and $b = 5$, the average elevation of the trail in feet is

$$\begin{aligned}\bar{f} &= \frac{1}{5}\int_0^5 (60x^3 - 650x^2 + 1200x + 4500)\,dx \\ &= \frac{1}{5}\left(60\frac{x^4}{4} - 650\frac{x^3}{3} + 1200\frac{x^2}{2} + 4500x\right)\Bigg|_0^5 && \text{Fundamental Theorem} \\ &= 3958\tfrac{1}{3}. && \text{Simplify.}\end{aligned}$$

The average elevation of the trail is slightly less than 3960 ft.

Related Exercises 21–34 ◄

Mean Value Theorem for Integrals

➤ Compare this statement to that of the Mean Value Theorem for Derivatives: There is at least one point c in (a, b) such that $f'(c)$ equals the average slope of f.

The average value of a function brings us close to an important theoretical result. The Mean Value Theorem for Integrals says that if f is continuous on $[a, b]$, then there is at least one point c in the interval (a, b) such that $f(c)$ equals the average value of f on

(a, b). In other words, the horizontal line $y = \bar{f}$ intersects the graph of f for some point c in (a, b) (Figure 5.52). If f were not continuous, such a point might not exist.

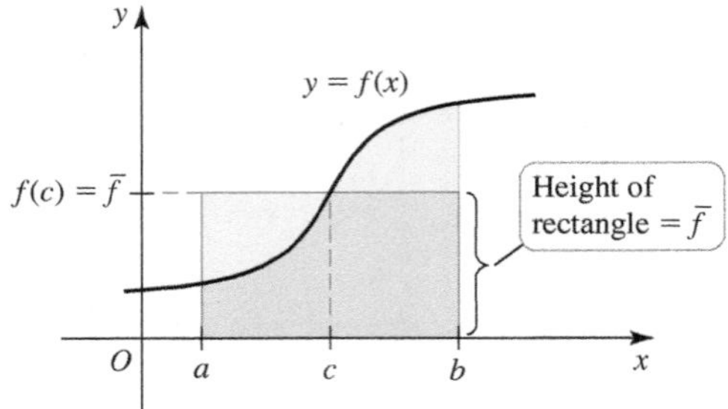

Figure 5.52

➤ Theorem 5.5 guarantees a point c in the open interval (a, b) at which f equals its average value. However, f may also equal its average value at an endpoint of that interval.

THEOREM 5.5 Mean Value Theorem for Integrals
Let f be continuous on the interval $[a, b]$. There exists a point c in (a, b) such that

$$f(c) = \bar{f} = \frac{1}{b-a}\int_a^b f(t)\,dt.$$

Proof: We begin by letting $F(x) = \int_a^x f(t)\,dt$ and noting that F is continuous on $[a, b]$ and differentiable on (a, b) (by Theorem 5.3, Part 1). We now apply the Mean Value Theorem for derivatives (Theorem 4.9) to F and conclude that there exists at least one point c in (a, b) such that

$$\underbrace{F'(c)}_{f(c)} = \frac{F(b) - F(a)}{b - a}.$$

By Theorem 5.3, Part 1, we know that $F'(c) = f(c)$, and by Theorem 5.3, Part 2, we know that

$$F(b) - F(a) = \int_a^b f(t)\,dt.$$

Combining these observations, we have

$$f(c) = \frac{1}{b-a}\int_a^b f(t)\,dt,$$

where c is a point in (a, b). ◄

➤ A more general form of the Mean Value Theorem states that if f and g are continuous on $[a, b]$ with $g(x) \ge 0$ on $[a, b]$, then there exists a number c in (a, b) such that

$$\int_a^b f(x)g(x)\,dx = f(c)\int_a^b g(x)\,dx.$$

QUICK CHECK 3 Explain why $f(x) = 0$ for at least one point of (a, b) if f is continuous and $\int_a^b f(x)\,dx = 0$. ◄

EXAMPLE 3 Average value equals function value Find the point(s) on the interval $(0, 1)$ at which $f(x) = 2x(1 - x)$ equals its average value on $[0, 1]$.

SOLUTION The average value of f on $[0, 1]$ is

$$\bar{f} = \frac{1}{1-0}\int_0^1 2x(1-x)\,dx = \left(x^2 - \frac{2}{3}x^3\right)\Big|_0^1 = \frac{1}{3}.$$

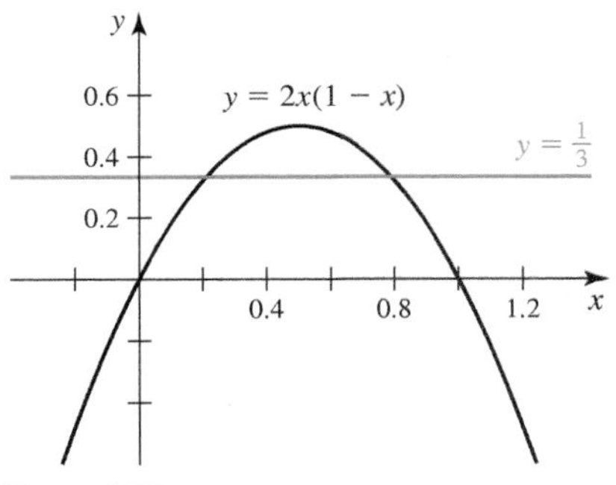

Figure 5.53

We must find the points on $(0, 1)$ at which $f(x) = \frac{1}{3}$ (Figure 5.53). Using the quadratic formula, the two solutions of $f(x) = 2x(1 - x) = \frac{1}{3}$ are

$$\frac{1 - \sqrt{1/3}}{2} \approx 0.211 \quad \text{and} \quad \frac{1 + \sqrt{1/3}}{2} \approx 0.789.$$

These two points are located symmetrically on either side of $x = \frac{1}{2}$. The two solutions, 0.211 and 0.789, are the same for $f(x) = ax(1 - x)$ for any nonzero value of a (Exercise 57).

Related Exercises 35–40 ◀

SECTION 5.4 EXERCISES

Review Questions

1. If f is an odd function, why is $\int_{-a}^{a} f(x)\,dx = 0$?
2. If f is an even function, why is $\int_{-a}^{a} f(x)\,dx = 2\int_{0}^{a} f(x)\,dx$?
3. Is x^{12} an even or odd function? Is $\sin x^2$ an even or odd function?
4. Explain how to find the average value of a function on an interval $[a, b]$ and why this definition is analogous to the definition of the average of a set of numbers.
5. Explain the statement that a continuous function on an interval $[a, b]$ equals its average value at some point on (a, b).
6. Sketch the function $y = x$ on the interval $[0, 2]$ and let R be the region bounded by $y = x$ and the x-axis on $[0, 2]$. Now sketch a rectangle in the first quadrant whose base is $[0, 2]$ and whose area equals the area of R.

Basic Skills

7–16. Symmetry in integrals *Use symmetry to evaluate the following integrals.*

7. $\displaystyle\int_{-2}^{2} x^9\,dx$

8. $\displaystyle\int_{-200}^{200} 2x^5\,dx$

9. $\displaystyle\int_{-2}^{2} (3x^8 - 2)\,dx$

10. $\displaystyle\int_{-\pi/4}^{\pi/4} \cos x\,dx$

11. $\displaystyle\int_{-2}^{2} (x^9 - 3x^5 + 2x^2 - 10)\,dx$

12. $\displaystyle\int_{-\pi/2}^{\pi/2} 5\sin x\,dx$

13. $\displaystyle\int_{-10}^{10} \frac{x}{\sqrt{200 - x^2}}\,dx$

14. $\displaystyle\int_{-\pi/2}^{\pi/2} (\cos 2x + \cos x \sin x - 3\sin x^5)\,dx$

15. $\displaystyle\int_{-\pi/4}^{\pi/4} \sin^5 x\,dx$

16. $\displaystyle\int_{-1}^{1} (1 - |x|)\,dx$

17–20. Symmetry and definite integrals *Use symmetry to evaluate the following integrals. Draw a figure to interpret your result.*

17. $\displaystyle\int_{-\pi}^{\pi} \sin x\,dx$

18. $\displaystyle\int_{0}^{2\pi} \cos x\,dx$

19. $\displaystyle\int_{0}^{\pi} \cos x\,dx$

20. $\displaystyle\int_{0}^{2\pi} \sin x\,dx$

21–30. Average values *Find the average value of the following functions on the given interval. Draw a graph of the function and indicate the average value.*

21. $f(x) = x^3$ on $[-1, 1]$
22. $f(x) = x^2 + 1$ on $[-2, 2]$
23. $f(x) = \dfrac{1}{x^2 + 1}$ on $[-1, 1]$
24. $f(x) = \cos 2x$ on $[-\frac{\pi}{4}, \frac{\pi}{4}]$
25. $f(x) = 1/x$ on $[1, e]$
26. $f(x) = e^{2x}$ on $[0, \ln 2]$
27. $f(x) = \cos x$ on $[-\frac{\pi}{2}, \frac{\pi}{2}]$
28. $f(x) = x(1 - x)$ on $[0, 1]$
29. $f(x) = x^n$ on $[0, 1]$, for any positive integer n
30. $f(x) = x^{1/n}$ on $[0, 1]$, for any positive integer n
31. **Average distance on a parabola** What is the average distance between the parabola $y = 30x(20 - x)$ and the x-axis on the interval $[0, 20]$?
32. T **Average elevation** The elevation of a path is given by $f(x) = x^3 - 5x^2 + 30$, where x measures horizontal distances. Draw a graph of the elevation function and find its average value, for $0 \le x \le 4$.
33. **Average height of an arch** The height of an arch above the ground is given by the function $y = 10\sin x$, for $0 \le x \le \pi$. What is the average height of the arch above the ground?
34. **Average height of a wave** The surface of a water wave is described by $y = 5(1 + \cos x)$, for $-\pi \le x \le \pi$, where $y = 0$ corresponds to a trough of the wave (see figure). Find the average height of the wave above the trough on $[-\pi, \pi]$.

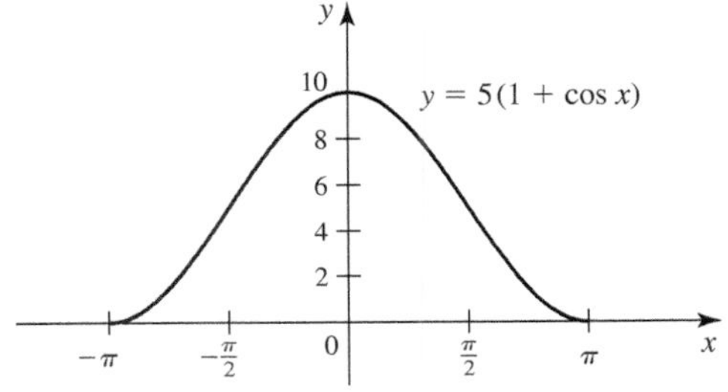

T 35–40. Mean Value Theorem for Integrals *Find or approximate all points at which the given function equals its average value on the given interval.*

35. $f(x) = 8 - 2x$ on $[0, 4]$ **36.** $f(x) = e^x$ on $[0, 2]$

37. $f(x) = 1 - x^2/a^2$ on $[0, a]$, where a is a positive real number

38. $f(x) = \frac{\pi}{4} \sin x$ on $[0, \pi]$ **39.** $f(x) = 1 - |x|$ on $[-1, 1]$

40. $f(x) = 1/x$ on $[1, 4]$

Further Explorations

41. Explain why or why not Determine whether the following statements are true and give an explanation or counterexample.

a. If f is symmetric about the line $x = 2$, then $\int_0^4 f(x)\,dx = 2\int_0^2 f(x)\,dx$.

b. If f has the property $f(a + x) = -f(a - x)$, for all x, where a is a constant, then $\int_{a-2}^{a+2} f(x)\,dx = 0$.

c. The average value of a linear function on an interval $[a, b]$ is the function value at the midpoint of $[a, b]$.

d. Consider the function $f(x) = x(a - x)$ on the interval $[0, a]$, for $a > 0$. Its average value on $[0, a]$ is $\frac{1}{2}$ of its maximum value.

42–45. Symmetry in integrals *Use symmetry to evaluate the following integrals.*

42. $\int_{-\pi/4}^{\pi/4} \tan x\,dx$ **43.** $\int_{-\pi/4}^{\pi/4} \sec^2 x\,dx$

44. $\int_{-2}^{2} (1 - |x|^3)\,dx$ **45.** $\int_{-2}^{2} \frac{x^3 - 4x}{x^2 + 1}\,dx$

Applications

46. Root mean square The root mean square (or RMS) is another measure of average value, often used with oscillating functions (for example, sine and cosine functions that describe the current, voltage, or power in an alternating circuit). The RMS of a function f on the interval $[0, T]$ is

$$\bar{f}_{\text{RMS}} = \sqrt{\frac{1}{T}\int_0^T f(t)^2\,dt}\,.$$

Compute the RMS of $f(t) = A \sin(\omega t)$, where A and ω are positive constants and T is any integer multiple of the period of f, which is $2\pi/\omega$.

47. Gateway Arch The Gateway Arch in St. Louis is 630 ft high and has a 630-ft base. Its shape can be modeled by the parabola

$$y = 630\left(1 - \left(\frac{x}{315}\right)^2\right).$$

Find the average height of the arch above the ground.

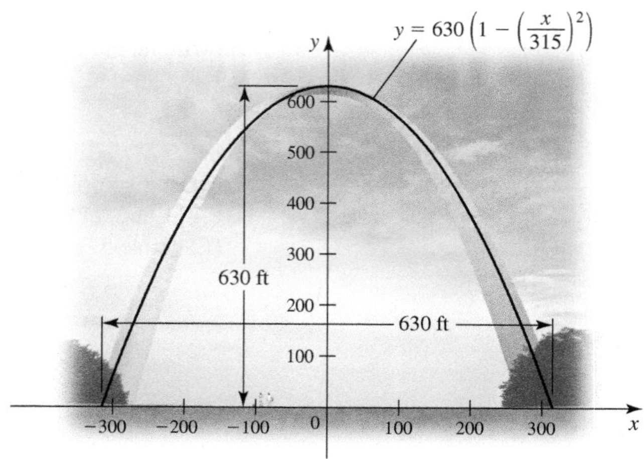

48. Another Gateway Arch Another description of the Gateway Arch is

$$y = 1260 - 315(e^{0.00418x} + e^{-0.00418x}),$$

where the base of the arch is $[-315, 315]$ and x and y are measured in feet. Find the average height of the arch above the ground.

49. Planetary orbits The planets orbit the Sun in elliptical orbits with the Sun at one focus (see Section 10.4 for more on ellipses). The equation of an ellipse whose dimensions are $2a$ in the x-direction and $2b$ in the y-direction is $\frac{x^2}{a^2} + \frac{y^2}{b^2} = 1$.

a. Let d^2 denote the square of the distance from a planet to the center of the ellipse at $(0, 0)$. Integrate over the interval $[-a, a]$ to show that the average value of d^2 is $(a^2 + 2b^2)/3$.

b. Show that in the case of a circle ($a = b = R$), the average value in part (a) is R^2.

c. Assuming $0 < b < a$, the coordinates of the Sun are $(\sqrt{a^2 - b^2}, 0)$. Let D^2 denote the square of the distance from the planet to the Sun. Integrate over the interval $[-a, a]$ to show that the average value of D^2 is $(4a^2 - b^2)/3$.

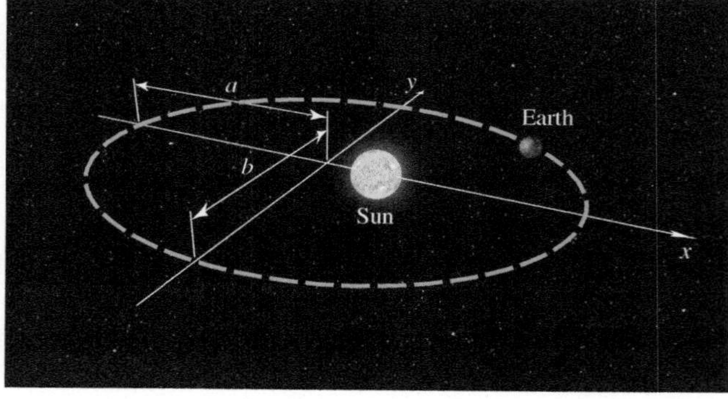

Additional Exercises

50. Comparing a sine and a quadratic function Consider the functions $f(x) = \sin x$ and $g(x) = \dfrac{4}{\pi^2}x(\pi - x)$.

a. Carefully graph f and g on the same set of axes. Verify that both functions have a single local maximum on the interval $[0, \pi]$ and that they have the same maximum value on $[0, \pi]$.
b. On the interval $[0, \pi]$, which is true: $f(x) \geq g(x)$, $g(x) \geq f(x)$, or neither?
c. Compute and compare the average values of f and g on $[0, \pi]$.

51. Using symmetry Suppose f is an even function and

$$\int_{-8}^{8} f(x)\,dx = 18.$$

a. Evaluate $\displaystyle\int_{0}^{8} f(x)\,dx$ b. Evaluate $\displaystyle\int_{-8}^{8} xf(x)\,dx$

52. Using symmetry Suppose f is an odd function, $\displaystyle\int_{0}^{4} f(x)\,dx = 3$, and $\displaystyle\int_{0}^{8} f(x)\,dx = 9$.

a. Evaluate $\displaystyle\int_{-4}^{8} f(x)\,dx$ b. Evaluate $\displaystyle\int_{-8}^{4} f(x)\,dx$

53–56. Symmetry of composite functions *Prove that the integrand is either even or odd. Then give the value of the integral or show how it can be simplified. Assume that f and g are even functions and p and q are odd functions.*

53. $\displaystyle\int_{-a}^{a} f(g(x))\,dx$ **54.** $\displaystyle\int_{-a}^{a} f(p(x))\,dx$

55. $\displaystyle\int_{-a}^{a} p(g(x))\,dx$ **56.** $\displaystyle\int_{-a}^{a} p(q(x))\,dx$

57. Average value with a parameter Consider the function $f(x) = ax(1 - x)$ on the interval $[0, 1]$, where a is a positive real number.

a. Find the average value of f as a function of a.
b. Find the points at which the value of f equals its average value and prove that they are independent of a.

58. Square of the average For what polynomials f is it true that the square of the average value of f equals the average value of the square of f over all intervals $[a, b]$?

59. Problems of antiquity Several calculus problems were solved by Greek mathematicians long before the discovery of calculus. The following problems were solved by Archimedes using methods that predated calculus by 2000 years.

a. Show that the area of a segment of a parabola is $\frac{4}{3}$ that of its inscribed triangle of greatest area. In other words, the area bounded by the parabola $y = a^2 - x^2$ and the x-axis is $\frac{4}{3}$ the area of the triangle with vertices $(\pm a, 0)$ and $(0, a^2)$. Assume that $a > 0$ but is unspecified.
b. Show that the area bounded by the parabola $y = a^2 - x^2$ and the x-axis is $\frac{2}{3}$ the area of the rectangle with vertices $(\pm a, 0)$ and $(\pm a, a^2)$. Assume that $a > 0$ but is unspecified.

60. Unit area sine curve Find the value of c such that the region bounded by $y = c \sin x$ and the x-axis on the interval $[0, \pi]$ has area 1.

61. Unit area cubic Find the value of $c > 0$ such that the region bounded by the cubic $y = x(x - c)^2$ and the x-axis on the interval $[0, c]$ has area 1.

62. Unit area

a. Consider the curve $y = 1/x$, for $x \geq 1$. For what value of $b > 0$ does the region bounded by this curve and the x-axis on the interval $[1, b]$ have an area of 1?
b. Consider the curve $y = 1/x^p$, where $x \geq 1$, and $p < 2$ with $p \neq 1$. For what value of b (as a function of p) does the region bounded by this curve and the x-axis on the interval $[1, b]$ have unit area?
c. Is $b(p)$ in part (b) an increasing or decreasing function of p? Explain.

63. A sine integral by Riemann sums Consider the integral $I = \int_0^{\pi/2} \sin x\,dx$.

a. Write the left Riemann sum for I with n subintervals.
b. Show that $\displaystyle\lim_{\theta\to 0} \theta\left(\frac{\cos\theta + \sin\theta - 1}{2(1 - \cos\theta)}\right) = 1.$
c. It is a fact that $\displaystyle\sum_{k=0}^{n-1} \sin\left(\frac{\pi k}{2n}\right) = \frac{\cos\left(\frac{\pi}{2n}\right) + \sin\left(\frac{\pi}{2n}\right) - 1}{2\left(1 - \cos\left(\frac{\pi}{2n}\right)\right)}.$

Use this fact and part (b) to evaluate I by taking the limit of the Riemann sum as $n \to \infty$.

64. Alternate definitions of means Consider the function

$$f(t) = \frac{\int_a^b x^{t+1}\,dx}{\int_a^b x^t\,dx}.$$

Show that the following means can be defined in terms of f.

a. Arithmetic mean: $f(0) = \dfrac{a + b}{2}$
b. Geometric mean: $f\left(-\dfrac{3}{2}\right) = \sqrt{ab}$
c. Harmonic mean: $f(-3) = \dfrac{2ab}{a + b}$
d. Logarithmic mean: $f(-1) = \dfrac{b - a}{\ln b - \ln a}$

(*Source: Mathematics Magazine* 78, 5, Dec 2005)

65. Symmetry of powers Fill in the following table with either **even** or **odd**, and prove each result. Assume n is a nonnegative integer and f^n means the nth power of f.

	f is even	*f* is odd
***n* is even**	f^n is _____	f^n is _____
***n* is odd**	f^n is _____	f^n is _____

66. **Average value of the derivative** Suppose that f' is a continuous function for all real numbers. Show that the average value of the derivative on an interval $[a, b]$ is $\overline{f'} = \dfrac{f(b) - f(a)}{b - a}$. Interpret this result in terms of secant lines.

67. **Symmetry about a point** A function f is symmetric about a point (c, d) if whenever $(c - x, d - y)$ is on the graph, then so is $(c + x, d + y)$. Functions that are symmetric about a point (c, d) are easily integrated on an interval with midpoint c.
    - **a.** Show that if f is symmetric about (c, d) and $a > 0$, then $\int_{c-a}^{c+a} f(x)\,dx = 2af(c) = 2ad$.
    - **b.** Graph the function $f(x) = \sin^2 x$ on the interval $[0, \pi/2]$ and show that the function is symmetric about the point $(\frac{\pi}{4}, \frac{1}{2})$.
    - **c.** Using only the graph of f (and no integration), show that $\int_0^{\pi/2} \sin^2 x\,dx = \frac{\pi}{4}$. (See the Guided Project *Symmetry in Integrals*.)

68. **Bounds on an integral** Suppose f is continuous on $[a, b]$ with $f''(x) > 0$ on the interval. It can be shown that

$$(b - a)f\left(\frac{a + b}{2}\right) \leq \int_a^b f(x)\,dx \leq (b - a)\frac{f(a) + f(b)}{2}.$$

- **a.** Assuming f is nonnegative on $[a, b]$, draw a figure to illustrate the geometric meaning of these inequalities. Discuss your conclusions.
- **b.** Divide these inequalities by $(b - a)$ and interpret the resulting inequalities in terms of the average value of f on $[a, b]$.

69. **Generalizing the Mean Value Theorem for Integrals** Suppose f and g are continuous on $[a, b]$ and let

$$h(x) = (x - b)\int_a^x f(t)\,dt + (x - a)\int_x^b g(t)\,dt.$$

- **a.** Use Rolle's theorem to show that there is a number c in (a, b) such that

$$\int_a^c f(t)\,dt + \int_c^b g(t)\,dt = f(c)(b - c) + g(c)(c - a),$$

which is a generalization of the Mean Value Theorem for Integrals.
- **b.** Show that there a number c in (a, b) such that $\int_a^x f(t)\,dt = f(c)(b - c)$.
- **c.** Use a sketch to interpret part (b) geometrically.
- **d.** Use the result of part (a) to give an alternate proof of the Mean Value Theorem for Integrals.

(*Source: The College Mathematics Journal,* 33, 5, Nov 2002)

QUICK CHECK ANSWERS

1. $f(-x)g(-x) = f(x)g(x)$; therefore, fg is even. **2.** The average value is the constant; the average value is 0. **3.** The average value is zero on the interval; by the Mean Value Theorem for Integrals, $f(x) = 0$ at some point on the interval. ◄

5.5 Substitution Rule

Given just about any differentiable function, with enough know-how and persistence, you can compute its derivative. But the same cannot be said of antiderivatives. Many functions, even relatively simple ones, do not have antiderivatives that can be expressed in terms of familiar functions. Examples are $\sin x^2$, $(\sin x)/x$, and x^x. The immediate goal of this section is to enlarge the family of functions for which we can find antiderivatives. This campaign resumes in Chapter 7, where additional integration methods are developed.

Indefinite Integrals

One way to find new antiderivative rules is to start with familiar derivative rules and work backward. When applied to the Chain Rule, this strategy leads to the Substitution Rule. A few examples illustrate the technique.

EXAMPLE 1 **Antiderivatives by trial and error** Find $\int \cos 2x\,dx$.

SOLUTION The closest familiar indefinite integral related to this problem is

➤ We assume C is an arbitrary constant without stating so each time it appears.

$$\int \cos x\,dx = \sin x + C,$$

which is true because

$$\frac{d}{dx}(\sin x + C) = \cos x.$$

Therefore, we might *incorrectly* conclude that the indefinite integral of $\cos 2x$ is $\sin 2x + C$. However, by the Chain Rule,

$$\frac{d}{dx}(\sin 2x + C) = 2\cos 2x \neq \cos 2x.$$

Note that $\sin 2x$ fails to be an antiderivative of $\cos 2x$ by a multiplicative factor of 2. A small adjustment corrects this problem. Let's try $\frac{1}{2}\sin 2x$:

$$\frac{d}{dx}\left(\frac{1}{2}\sin 2x\right) = \frac{1}{2}\cdot 2\cos 2x = \cos 2x.$$

It works! So we have

$$\int \cos 2x\,dx = \frac{1}{2}\sin 2x + C.$$

Related Exercises 9–12

The trial-and-error approach of Example 1 is impractical for complicated integrals. To develop a systematic method, consider a composite function $F(g(x))$, where F is an antiderivative of f; that is, $F' = f$. Using the Chain Rule to differentiate the composite function $F(g(x))$, we find that

$$\frac{d}{dx}\big(F(g(x))\big) = \underbrace{F'(g(x))}_{f(g(x))}g'(x) = f(g(x))g'(x).$$

This equation says that $F(g(x))$ is an antiderivative of $f(g(x))g'(x)$, which is written

$$\int f(g(x))g'(x)\,dx = F(g(x)) + C, \qquad (1)$$

where F is any antiderivative of f.

Why is this approach called the *Substitution Rule* (or *Change of Variables Rule*)? In the composite function $f(g(x))$ in equation (1), we identify the "inner function" as $u = g(x)$, which implies that $du = g'(x)\,dx$. Making this identification, the integral in equation (1) is written

> You can call the new variable anything you want because it is just another variable of integration. Typically, u is the standard choice for the new variable.

$$\int \underbrace{f(g(x))}_{f(u)}\underbrace{g'(x)dx}_{du} = \int f(u)\,du = F(u) + C.$$

We see that the integral $\int f(g(x))g'(x)\,dx$ with respect to x is replaced with a new integral $\int f(u)du$ with respect to the new variable u. In other words, we have substituted the new variable u for the old variable x. Of course, if the new integral with respect to u is no easier to find than the original integral, then the change of variables has not helped. The Substitution Rule requires plenty of practice until certain patterns become familiar.

THEOREM 5.6 Substitution Rule for Indefinite Integrals

Let $u = g(x)$, where g' is continuous on an interval, and let f be continuous on the corresponding range of g. On that interval,

$$\int f(g(x))g'(x)\,dx = \int f(u)\,du.$$

In practice, Theorem 5.6 is applied using the following procedure.

PROCEDURE Substitution Rule (Change of Variables)

1. Given an indefinite integral involving a composite function $f(g(x))$, identify an inner function $u = g(x)$ such that a constant multiple of $g'(x)$ appears in the integrand.
2. Substitute $u = g(x)$ and $du = g'(x)\,dx$ in the integral.
3. Evaluate the new indefinite integral with respect to u.
4. Write the result in terms of x using $u = g(x)$.

Disclaimer: Not all integrals yield to the Substitution Rule.

EXAMPLE 2 Perfect substitutions Use the Substitution Rule to find the following indefinite integrals. Check your work by differentiating.

a. $\int 2(2x + 1)^3\,dx$ **b.** $\int 10e^{10x}\,dx$

SOLUTION

a. We identify $u = 2x + 1$ as the inner function of the composite function $(2x + 1)^3$. Therefore, we choose the new variable $u = 2x + 1$, which implies that $\frac{du}{dx} = 2$, or $du = 2\,dx$. Notice that $du = 2\,dx$ appears as a factor in the integrand. The change of variables looks like this:

$$\int \underbrace{(2x + 1)^3}_{u^3} \cdot \underbrace{2\,dx}_{du} = \int u^3\,du \qquad \text{Substitute } u = 2x + 1,\ du = 2\,dx.$$

$$= \frac{u^4}{4} + C \qquad \text{Antiderivative}$$

$$= \frac{(2x + 1)^4}{4} + C. \qquad \text{Replace } u \text{ with } 2x + 1.$$

➤ Use the Chain Rule to check that $\frac{d}{dx}\left(\frac{(2x + 1)^4}{4} + C\right) = 2(2x + 1)^3$.

Notice that the final step uses $u = 2x + 1$ to return to the original variable.

b. The composite function e^{10x} has the inner function $u = 10x$, which implies that $du = 10\,dx$. The change of variables appears as

$$\int \underbrace{e^{10x}}_{e^u}\,\underbrace{10\,dx}_{du} = \int e^u\,du \qquad \text{Substitute } u = 10x,\ du = 10\,dx.$$

$$= e^u + C \qquad \text{Antiderivative}$$

$$= e^{10x} + C. \qquad \text{Replace } u \text{ with } 10x.$$

In checking, we see that $\frac{d}{dx}(e^{10x} + C) = e^{10x} \cdot 10 = 10e^{10x}$.

Related Exercises 13–16 ◄

QUICK CHECK 1 Find a new variable u so that $\int 4x^3(x^4 + 5)^{10}\,dx = \int u^{10}\,du$. ◄

Most substitutions are not perfect. The remaining examples show more typical situations that require introducing a constant factor.

EXAMPLE 3 Introducing a constant Find the following indefinite integrals.

a. $\int x^4(x^5 + 6)^9\,dx$ **b.** $\int \cos^3 x \sin x\,dx$

SOLUTION

a. The inner function of the composite function $(x^5 + 6)^9$ is $x^5 + 6$ and its derivative $5x^4$ also appears in the integrand (up to a multiplicative factor). Therefore, we use the substitution $u = x^5 + 6$, which implies that $du = 5x^4\,dx$, or $x^4\,dx = \frac{1}{5}\,du$. By the Substitution Rule,

$$\int \underbrace{(x^5 + 6)^9}_{u^9}\underbrace{x^4\,dx}_{\frac{1}{5}du} = \int u^9 \cdot \frac{1}{5}\,du \qquad \text{Substitute } u = x^5 + 6,\ du = 5x^4\,dx \Rightarrow x^4\,dx = \frac{1}{5}\,du.$$

$$= \frac{1}{5}\int u^9\,du \qquad \int cf(x)\,dx = c\int f(x)\,dx$$

$$= \frac{1}{5}\cdot\frac{u^{10}}{10} + C \qquad \text{Antiderivative}$$

$$= \frac{1}{50}(x^5 + 6)^{10} + C. \qquad \text{Replace } u \text{ with } x^5 + 6.$$

b. The integrand can be written as $(\cos x)^3 \sin x$. The inner function in the composition $(\cos x)^3$ is $\cos x$, which suggests the substitution $u = \cos x$. Note that $du = -\sin x\,dx$ or $\sin x\,dx = -du$. The change of variables appears as

$$\int \underbrace{\cos^3 x}_{u^3}\,\underbrace{\sin x\,dx}_{-du} = -\int u^3\,du \qquad \text{Substitute } u = \cos x,\ du = -\sin x\,dx.$$

$$= -\frac{u^4}{4} + C \qquad \text{Antiderivative}$$

$$= -\frac{\cos^4 x}{4} + C. \qquad \text{Replace } u \text{ with } \cos x.$$

Related Exercises 17–32 ◄

QUICK CHECK 2 In Example 3a, explain why the same substitution would not work as well for the integral $\int x^3(x^5 + 6)^9\,dx$. ◄

Sometimes the choice for a u-substitution is not so obvious *or* more than one u-substitution works. The following example illustrates both of these points.

EXAMPLE 4 Variations on the substitution method Find $\int \frac{x}{\sqrt{x + 1}}\,dx$.

SOLUTION

Substitution 1 The composite function $\sqrt{x + 1}$ suggests the new variable $u = x + 1$. You might doubt whether this choice will work because $du = dx$, which leaves the x in the numerator of the integrand unaccounted for. But let's proceed. Letting $u = x + 1$, we have $x = u - 1$, $du = dx$, and

$$\int \frac{x}{\sqrt{x + 1}}\,dx = \int \frac{u - 1}{\sqrt{u}}\,du \qquad \text{Substitute } u = x + 1,\ du = dx.$$

$$= \int \left(\sqrt{u} - \frac{1}{\sqrt{u}}\right) du \qquad \text{Rewrite integrand.}$$

$$= \int (u^{1/2} - u^{-1/2})\,du. \qquad \text{Fractional powers}$$

We integrate each term individually and then return to the original variable x:

$$\int (u^{1/2} - u^{-1/2})\, du = \frac{2}{3}u^{3/2} - 2u^{1/2} + C \quad \text{Antiderivatives}$$

$$= \frac{2}{3}(x+1)^{3/2} - 2(x+1)^{1/2} + C \quad \text{Replace } u \text{ with } x+1.$$

$$= \frac{2}{3}(x+1)^{1/2}(x-2) + C. \quad \text{Factor out } (x+1)^{1/2} \text{ and simplify.}$$

➤ In Substitution 2, you could also use the fact that

$$u'(x) = \frac{1}{2\sqrt{x+1}},$$

which implies

$$du = \frac{1}{2\sqrt{x+1}}\, dx.$$

Substitution 2 Another possible substitution is $u = \sqrt{x+1}$. Now $u^2 = x + 1$, $x = u^2 - 1$, and $dx = 2u\, du$. Making these substitutions leads to

$$\int \frac{x}{\sqrt{x+1}}\, dx = \int \frac{u^2-1}{u} 2u\, du \quad \text{Substitute } u = \sqrt{x+1}, x = u^2 - 1.$$

$$= 2\int (u^2 - 1)\, du \quad \text{Simplify the integrand.}$$

$$= 2\left(\frac{u^3}{3} - u\right) + C \quad \text{Antiderivatives}$$

$$= \frac{2}{3}(x+1)^{3/2} - 2(x+1)^{1/2} + C \quad \text{Replace } u \text{ with } \sqrt{x+1}.$$

$$= \frac{2}{3}(x+1)^{1/2}(x-2) + C. \quad \text{Factor out } (x+1)^{1/2} \text{ and simplify.}$$

Observe that the same indefinite integral is found using either substitution.

Related Exercises 33–38 ◀

Definite Integrals

The Substitution Rule is also used for definite integrals; in fact, there are two ways to proceed.

- You may use the Substitution Rule to find an antiderivative F and then use the Fundamental Theorem to evaluate $F(b) - F(a)$.
- Alternatively, once you have changed variables from x to u, you also may change the limits of integration and complete the integration with respect to u. Specifically, if $u = g(x)$, the lower limit $x = a$ is replaced with $u = g(a)$ and the upper limit $x = b$ is replaced with $u = g(b)$.

The second option tends to be more efficient, and we use it whenever possible. This approach is summarized in the following theorem, which is then applied to several definite integrals.

THEOREM 5.7 Substitution Rule for Definite Integrals
Let $u = g(x)$, where g' is continuous on $[a, b]$, and let f be continuous on the range of g. Then

$$\int_a^b f(g(x))g'(x)\, dx = \int_{g(a)}^{g(b)} f(u)\, du.$$

EXAMPLE 5 Definite integrals Evaluate the following integrals.

a. $\displaystyle\int_0^2 \frac{dx}{(x+3)^3}$ **b.** $\displaystyle\int_0^4 \frac{x}{x^2+1}\, dx$ **c.** $\displaystyle\int_0^{\pi/2} \sin^4 x \cos x\, dx$

SOLUTION

➤ When the integrand has the form $f(ax + b)$, the substitution $u = ax + b$ is often effective.

a. Let the new variable be $u = x + 3$ and then $du = dx$. Because we have changed the variable of integration from x to u, the limits of integration must also be expressed in terms of u. In this case,

$$x = 0 \text{ implies } u = 0 + 3 = 3, \quad \text{Lower limit}$$
$$x = 2 \text{ implies } u = 2 + 3 = 5. \quad \text{Upper limit}$$

The entire integration is carried out as follows:

$$\begin{aligned}\int_0^2 \frac{dx}{(x+3)^3} &= \int_3^5 u^{-3}\,du && \text{Substitute } u = x + 3,\ du = dx.\\ &= -\frac{u^{-2}}{2}\bigg|_3^5 && \text{Fundamental Theorem}\\ &= -\frac{1}{2}(5^{-2} - 3^{-2}) = \frac{8}{225}. && \text{Simplify.}\end{aligned}$$

b. Notice that a multiple of the derivative of the denominator appears in the numerator; therefore, we let $u = x^2 + 1$, which implies that $du = 2x\,dx$, or $x\,dx = \frac{1}{2}\,du$. Changing limits of integration,

$$x = 0 \text{ implies } u = 0 + 1 = 1, \quad \text{Lower limit}$$
$$x = 4 \text{ implies } u = 4^2 + 1 = 17. \quad \text{Upper limit}$$

Changing variables, we have

$$\begin{aligned}\int_0^4 \frac{x}{x^2+1}\,dx &= \frac{1}{2}\int_1^{17} u^{-1}\,du && \text{Substitute } u = x^2 + 1,\ du = 2x\,dx.\\ &= \frac{1}{2}\ln|u|\bigg|_1^{17} && \text{Fundamental Theorem}\\ &= \frac{1}{2}(\ln 17 - \ln 1) && \text{Simplify.}\\ &= \frac{1}{2}\ln 17 \approx 1.417. && \ln 1 = 0\end{aligned}$$

c. Let $u = \sin x$, which implies that $du = \cos x\,dx$. The lower limit of integration becomes $u = 0$ and the upper limit becomes $u = 1$. Changing variables, we have

$$\begin{aligned}\int_0^{\pi/2} \sin^4 x \cos x\,dx &= \int_0^1 u^4\,du && u = \sin x,\ du = \cos x\,dx\\ &= \left(\frac{u^5}{5}\right)\bigg|_0^1 = \frac{1}{5}. && \text{Fundamental Theorem}\end{aligned}$$

Related Exercises 39–52 ◀

The Substitution Rule enables us to find two standard integrals that appear frequently in practice, $\int \sin^2 x\,dx$ and $\int \cos^2 x\,dx$. These integrals are handled using the identities

$$\sin^2 x = \frac{1 - \cos 2x}{2} \quad \text{and} \quad \cos^2 x = \frac{1 + \cos 2x}{2}.$$

EXAMPLE 6 **Integral of $\cos^2 \theta$** Evaluate $\displaystyle\int_0^{\pi/2} \cos^2 \theta \, d\theta$.

SOLUTION Working with the indefinite integral first, we use the identity for $\cos^2 \theta$:

$$\int \cos^2 \theta \, d\theta = \int \frac{1 + \cos 2\theta}{2} \, d\theta = \frac{1}{2}\int d\theta + \frac{1}{2}\int \cos 2\theta \, d\theta.$$

➤ See Exercise 102 for a generalization of Example 6. Trigonometric integrals involving powers of $\sin x$ and $\cos x$ are explored in greater detail in Section 7.3.

The change of variables $u = 2\theta$ (or Table 4.9) is now used for the second integral, and we have

$$\begin{aligned}\int \cos^2 \theta \, d\theta &= \frac{1}{2}\int d\theta + \frac{1}{2}\int \cos 2\theta \, d\theta \\ &= \frac{1}{2}\int d\theta + \frac{1}{2}\cdot\frac{1}{2}\int \cos u \, du \qquad u = 2\theta,\ du = 2\,d\theta \\ &= \frac{\theta}{2} + \frac{1}{4}\sin 2\theta + C. \qquad \text{Evaluate integrals; } u = 2\theta.\end{aligned}$$

Using the Fundamental Theorem of Calculus, the value of the definite integral is

$$\begin{aligned}\int_0^{\pi/2} \cos^2 \theta \, d\theta &= \left(\frac{\theta}{2} + \frac{1}{4}\sin 2\theta\right)\Bigg|_0^{\pi/2} \\ &= \left(\frac{\pi}{4} + \frac{1}{4}\sin \pi\right) - \left(0 + \frac{1}{4}\sin 0\right) = \frac{\pi}{4}.\end{aligned}$$

Related Exercises 53–60 ◀

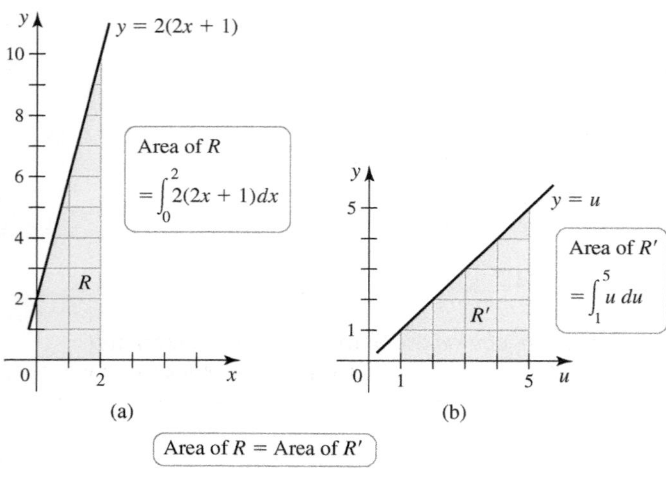

Figure 5.54

Geometry of Substitution

The Substitution Rule has a geometric interpretation. To keep matters simple, consider the integral $\int_0^2 2(2x + 1)\, dx$. The graph of the integrand $y = 2(2x + 1)$ on the interval $[0, 2]$ is shown in Figure 5.54a, along with the region R whose area is given by the integral. The change of variables $u = 2x + 1$, $du = 2\,dx$, $u(0) = 1$, and $u(2) = 5$ leads to the new integral

$$\int_0^2 2(2x + 1)\, dx = \int_1^5 u \, du.$$

Figure 5.54b also shows the graph of the new integrand $y = u$ on the interval $[1, 5]$ and the region R' whose area is given by the new integral. You can check that the areas of R and R' are equal. An analogous interpretation may be given to more complicated integrands and substitutions.

QUICK CHECK 3 Changes of variables occur frequently in mathematics. For example, suppose you want to solve the equation $x^4 - 13x^2 + 36 = 0$. If you use the substitution $u = x^2$, what is the new equation that must be solved for u? What are the roots of the original equation? ◀

SECTION 5.5 EXERCISES

Review Questions

1. On which derivative rule is the Substitution Rule based?
2. Why is the Substitution Rule referred to as a change of variables?
3. The composite function $f(g(x))$ consists of an inner function g and an outer function f. If an integrand includes $f(g(x))$, which function is often a likely choice for a new variable u?
4. Find a suitable substitution for evaluating $\int \tan x \sec^2 x \, dx$ and explain your choice.
5. When using a change of variables $u = g(x)$ to evaluate the definite integral $\int_a^b f(g(x))g'(x)\, dx$, how are the limits of integration transformed?
6. If the change of variables $u = x^2 - 4$ is used to evaluate the definite integral $\int_2^4 f(x)\, dx$, what are the new limits of integration?
7. Find $\int \cos^2 x \, dx$.
8. What identity is needed to find $\int \sin^2 x \, dx$?

Basic Skills

9–12. Trial and error *Find an antiderivative of the following functions by trial and error. Check your answer by differentiating.*

9. $f(x) = (x + 1)^{12}$

10. $f(x) = e^{3x+1}$

11. $f(x) = \sqrt{2x + 1}$

12. $f(x) = \cos(2x + 5)$

13–16. Substitution given *Use the given substitution to find the following indefinite integrals. Check your answer by differentiating.*

13. $\int 2x(x^2 + 1)^4\,dx,\ u = x^2 + 1$

14. $\int 8x \cos(4x^2 + 3)\,dx,\ u = 4x^2 + 3$

15. $\int \sin^3 x \cos x\,dx,\ u = \sin x$

16. $\int (6x + 1)\sqrt{3x^2 + x}\,dx,\ u = 3x^2 + x$

17–32. Indefinite integrals *Use a change of variables to find the following indefinite integrals. Check your work by differentiating.*

17. $\int 2x(x^2 - 1)^{99}\,dx$

18. $\int xe^{x^2}\,dx$

19. $\int \frac{2x^2}{\sqrt{1 - 4x^3}}\,dx$

20. $\int \frac{(\sqrt{x} + 1)^4}{2\sqrt{x}}\,dx$

21. $\int (x^2 + x)^{10}(2x + 1)\,dx$

22. $\int \frac{1}{10x - 3}\,dx$

23. $\int x^3(x^4 + 16)^6\,dx$

24. $\int \sin^{10}\theta \cos\theta\,d\theta$

25. $\int \frac{dx}{\sqrt{1 - 9x^2}}$

26. $\int x^9 \sin x^{10}\,dx$

27. $\int (x^6 - 3x^2)^4(x^5 - x)\,dx$

28. $\int \frac{x}{x - 2}\,dx$ (*Hint:* Let $u = x - 2$.)

29. $\int \frac{dx}{1 + 4x^2}$

30. $\int \frac{3}{1 + 25y^2}\,dy$

31. $\int \frac{2}{x\sqrt{4x^2 - 1}}\,dx,\ x > \frac{1}{2}$

32. $\int \frac{8x + 6}{2x^2 + 3x}\,dx$

33–38. Variations on the substitution method *Find the following integrals.*

33. $\int \frac{x}{\sqrt{x - 4}}\,dx$

34. $\int \frac{y^2}{(y + 1)^4}\,dy$

35. $\int \frac{x}{\sqrt[3]{x + 4}}\,dx$

36. $\int \frac{e^x - e^{-x}}{e^x + e^{-x}}\,dx$

37. $\int x\sqrt[3]{2x + 1}\,dx$

38. $\int (z + 1)\sqrt{3z + 2}\,dz$

39–52. Definite integrals *Use a change of variables to evaluate the following definite integrals.*

39. $\int_0^1 2x(4 - x^2)\,dx$

40. $\int_0^2 \frac{2x}{(x^2 + 1)^2}\,dx$

41. $\int_0^{\pi/2} \sin^2\theta \cos\theta\,d\theta$

42. $\int_0^{\pi/4} \frac{\sin x}{\cos^2 x}\,dx$

43. $\int_{-1}^2 x^2 e^{x^3+1}\,dx$

44. $\int_0^4 \frac{p}{\sqrt{9 + p^2}}\,dp$

45. $\int_{\pi/4}^{\pi/2} \frac{\cos x}{\sin^2 x}\,dx$

46. $\int_0^{\pi/4} \frac{\sin\theta}{\cos^3\theta}\,d\theta$

47. $\int_{2/(5\sqrt{3})}^{2/5} \frac{dx}{x\sqrt{25x^2 - 1}}$

48. $\int_0^3 \frac{v^2 + 1}{\sqrt{v^3 + 3v + 4}}\,dv$

49. $\int_0^4 \frac{x}{x^2 + 1}\,dx$

50. $\int_0^{1/4} \frac{x}{\sqrt{1 - 16x^2}}\,dx$

51. $\int_{1/3}^{1/\sqrt{3}} \frac{4}{9x^2 + 1}\,dx$

52. $\int_0^{\ln 4} \frac{e^x}{3 + 2e^x}\,dx$

53–60. Integrals with $\sin^2 x$ and $\cos^2 x$ *Evaluate the following integrals.*

53. $\int_{-\pi}^{\pi} \cos^2 x\,dx$

54. $\int \sin^2 x\,dx$

55. $\int \sin^2\left(\theta + \frac{\pi}{6}\right)d\theta$

56. $\int_0^{\pi/4} \cos^2 8\theta\,d\theta$

57. $\int_{-\pi/4}^{\pi/4} \sin^2 2\theta\,d\theta$

58. $\int x\cos^2(x^2)\,dx$

59. $\int_0^{\pi/6} \frac{\sin 2y}{\sin^2 y + 2}\,dy$ (*Hint:* $\sin 2y = 2\sin y \cos y$.)

60. $\int_0^{\pi/2} \sin^4\theta\,d\theta$

Further Explorations

61. **Explain why or why not** Determine whether the following statements are true and give an explanation or counterexample. Assume that f, f', and f'' are continuous functions for all real numbers.

a. $\int f(x)f'(x)\,dx = \frac{1}{2}(f(x))^2 + C.$

b. $\int (f(x))^n f'(x)\,dx = \frac{1}{n + 1}(f(x))^{n+1} + C,\ n \neq -1.$

c. $\int \sin 2x\,dx = 2\int \sin x\,dx.$

d. $\int (x^2 + 1)^9\,dx = \frac{(x^2 + 1)^{10}}{10} + C.$

e. $\int_a^b f'(x)f''(x)\,dx = f'(b) - f'(a).$

62–78. Additional integrals *Use a change of variables to evaluate the following integrals.*

62. $\int \sec 4w \tan 4w \, dw$

63. $\int \sec^2 10x \, dx$

64. $\int (\sin^5 x + 3\sin^3 x - \sin x) \cos x \, dx$

65. $\int \frac{\csc^2 x}{\cot^3 x} \, dx$

66. $\int (x^{3/2} + 8)^5 \sqrt{x} \, dx$

67. $\int \sin x \sec^8 x \, dx$

68. $\int \frac{e^{2x}}{e^{2x} + 1} \, dx$

69. $\int_0^1 x\sqrt{1 - x^2} \, dx$

70. $\int_1^{e^2} \frac{\ln p}{p} \, dp$

71. $\int_2^3 \frac{x}{\sqrt[3]{x^2 - 1}} \, dx$

72. $\int_0^{6/5} \frac{dx}{25x^2 + 36}$

73. $\int_0^2 x^3 \sqrt{16 - x^4} \, dx$

74. $\int_{-1}^1 (x - 1)(x^2 - 2x)^7 \, dx$

75. $\int_{-\pi}^0 \frac{\sin x}{2 + \cos x} \, dx$

76. $\int_0^1 \frac{(v + 1)(v + 2)}{2v^3 + 9v^2 + 12v + 36} \, dv$

77. $\int_1^2 \frac{4}{9x^2 + 6x + 1} \, dx$

78. $\int_0^{\pi/4} e^{\sin^2 x} \sin 2x \, dx$

79–82. Areas of regions *Find the area of the following regions.*

79. The region bounded by the graph of $f(x) = x \sin x^2$ and the x-axis between $x = 0$ and $x = \sqrt{\pi}$

80. The region bounded by the graph of $f(\theta) = \cos\theta \sin\theta$ and the θ-axis between $\theta = 0$ and $\theta = \pi/2$

81. The region bounded by the graph of $f(x) = (x - 4)^4$ and the x-axis between $x = 2$ and $x = 6$

82. The region bounded by the graph of $f(x) = \frac{x}{\sqrt{x^2 - 9}}$ and the x-axis between $x = 4$ and $x = 5$

83. **Morphing parabolas** The family of parabolas $y = (1/a) - x^2/a^3$, where $a > 0$, has the property that for $x \geq 0$, the x-intercept is $(a, 0)$ and the y-intercept is $(0, 1/a)$. Let $A(a)$ be the area of the region in the first quadrant bounded by the parabola and the x-axis. Find $A(a)$ and determine whether it is an increasing, decreasing, or constant function of a.

84. **Substitutions** Suppose that f is an even function with $\int_0^8 f(x)\,dx = 9$. Evaluate each integral.

  a. $\int_{-1}^1 x f(x^2) \, dx$ **b.** $\int_{-2}^2 x^2 f(x^3) \, dx$

85. **Substitutions** Suppose that p is a nonzero real number and f is an odd integrable function with $\int_0^1 f(x)\,dx = \pi$. Evaluate each integral.

  a. $\int_0^{\pi/(2p)} \cos px \, f(\sin px) \, dx$

  b. $\int_{-\pi/2}^{\pi/2} \cos x \, f(\sin x) \, dx$

Applications

T 86. **Periodic motion** An object moves along a line with a velocity in m/s given by $v(t) = 8\cos(\pi t/6)$. Its initial position is $s(0) = 0$.

  a. Graph the velocity function.
  b. As discussed in Chapter 6, the position of the object is given by $s(t) = \int_0^t v(y)\,dy$, for $t \geq 0$. Find the position function, for $t \geq 0$.
  c. What is the period of the motion—that is, starting at any point, how long does it take the object to return to that position?

87. **Population models** The population of a culture of bacteria has a growth rate given by $p'(t) = \frac{200}{(t + 1)^r}$ bacteria per hour, for $t \geq 0$, where $r > 1$ is a real number. In Chapter 6 it is shown that the increase in the population over the time interval $[0, t]$ is given by $\int_0^t p'(s)\,ds$. (Note that the growth rate decreases in time, reflecting competition for space and food.)

  a. Using the population model with $r = 2$, what is the increase in the population over the time interval $0 \leq t \leq 4$?
  b. Using the population model with $r = 3$, what is the increase in the population over the time interval $0 \leq t \leq 6$?
  c. Let ΔP be the increase in the population over a fixed time interval $[0, T]$. For fixed T, does ΔP increase or decrease with the parameter r? Explain.
  d. A lab technician measures an increase in the population of 350 bacteria over the 10-hr period $[0, 10]$. Estimate the value of r that best fits this data point.
  e. Looking ahead: Use the population model in part (b) to find the increase in population over the time interval $[0, T]$, for any $T > 0$. If the culture is allowed to grow indefinitely $(T \to \infty)$, does the bacteria population increase without bound? Or does it approach a finite limit?

88. **Average distance on a triangle** Consider the right triangle with vertices $(0, 0)$, $(0, b)$, and $(a, 0)$, where $a > 0$ and $b > 0$. Show that the average vertical distance from points on the x-axis to the hypotenuse is $b/2$, for all $a > 0$.

T 89. **Average value of sine functions** Use a graphing utility to verify that the functions $f(x) = \sin kx$ have a period of $2\pi/k$, where $k = 1, 2, 3, \ldots$. Equivalently, the first "hump" of $f(x) = \sin kx$ occurs on the interval $[0, \pi/k]$. Verify that the average value of the first hump of $f(x) = \sin kx$ is independent of k. What is the average value?

Additional Exercises

90. **Looking ahead: Integrals of $\tan x$ and $\cot x$** Use a change of variables to verify each integral.

  a. $\int \tan x \, dx = -\ln|\cos x| + C = \ln|\sec x| + C$
  b. $\int \cot x \, dx = \ln|\sin x| + C$

91. **Looking ahead: Integrals of $\sec x$ and $\csc x$**

  a. Multiply the numerator and denominator of $\sec x$ by $\sec x + \tan x$; then use a change of variables to show that

$$\int \sec x \, dx = \ln|\sec x + \tan x| + C.$$

  b. Use a change of variables to show that

$$\int \csc x \, dx = -\ln|\csc x + \cot x| + C.$$

92. Equal areas The area of the shaded region under the curve $y = 2 \sin 2x$ in (a) equals the area of the shaded region under the curve $y = \sin x$ in (b). Explain why this is true without computing areas.

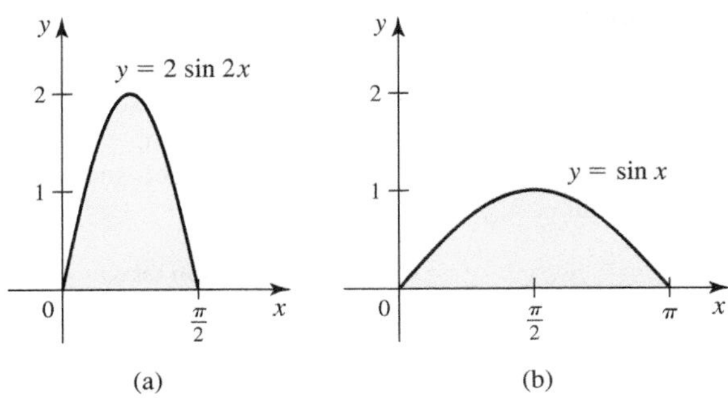

93. Equal areas The area of the shaded region under the curve $y = \dfrac{(\sqrt{x} - 1)^2}{2\sqrt{x}}$ on the interval $[4, 9]$ in (a) equals the area of the shaded region under the curve $y = x^2$ on the interval $[1, 2]$ in (b). Without computing areas, explain why.

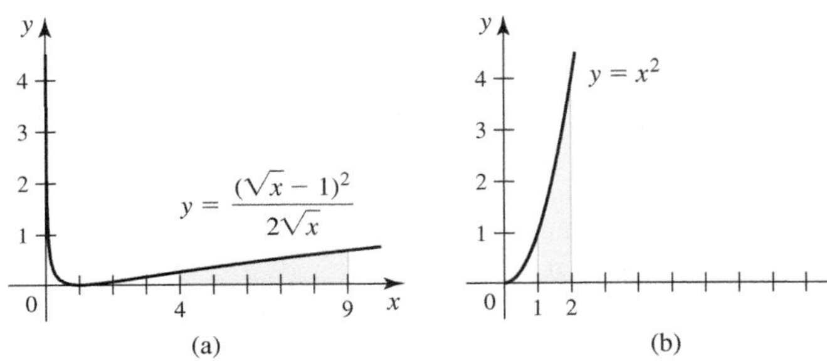

94–98. General results *Evaluate the following integrals in which the function f is unspecified. Note that $f^{(p)}$ is the pth derivative of f and f^p is the pth power of f. Assume f and its derivatives are continuous for all real numbers.*

94. $\displaystyle\int (5f^3(x) + 7f^2(x) + f(x))f'(x)\,dx$

95. $\displaystyle\int_1^2 (5f^3(x) + 7f^2(x) + f(x))f'(x)\,dx$, where $f(1) = 4$, $f(2) = 5$

96. $\displaystyle\int_0^1 f'(x)f''(x)\,dx$, where $f'(0) = 3$ and $f'(1) = 2$

97. $\displaystyle\int (f^{(p)}(x))^n f^{(p+1)}(x)\,dx$, where p is a positive integer, $n \neq -1$

98. $\displaystyle\int 2(f^2(x) + 2f(x))f(x)f'(x)\,dx$

99–101. More than one way *Occasionally, two different substitutions do the job. Use each substitution to evaluate the following integrals.*

99. $\displaystyle\int_0^1 x\sqrt{x + a}\,dx;\ a > 0 \qquad (u = \sqrt{x + a} \text{ and } u = x + a)$

100. $\displaystyle\int_0^1 x\sqrt[p]{x + a}\,dx;\ a > 0 \qquad (u = \sqrt[p]{x + a} \text{ and } u = x + a)$

101. $\displaystyle\int \sec^3\theta \tan\theta\,d\theta \qquad (u = \cos\theta \text{ and } u = \sec\theta)$

102. $\sin^2 ax$ and $\cos^2 ax$ integrals Use the Substitution Rule to prove that

$$\int \sin^2 ax\,dx = \frac{x}{2} - \frac{\sin(2ax)}{4a} + C \quad \text{and}$$
$$\int \cos^2 ax\,dx = \frac{x}{2} + \frac{\sin(2ax)}{4a} + C.$$

103. Integral of $\sin^2 x \cos^2 x$ Consider the integral $I = \int \sin^2 x \cos^2 x\,dx$.

a. Find I using the identity $\sin 2x = 2 \sin x \cos x$.
b. Find I using the identity $\cos^2 x = 1 - \sin^2 x$.
c. Confirm that the results in parts (a) and (b) are consistent and compare the work involved in each method.

104. Substitution: shift Perhaps the simplest change of variables is the shift or translation given by $u = x + c$, where c is a real number.

a. Prove that shifting a function does not change the net area under the curve, in the sense that

$$\int_a^b f(x + c)\,dx = \int_{a+c}^{b+c} f(u)\,du.$$

b. Draw a picture to illustrate this change of variables in the case that $f(x) = \sin x$, $a = 0$, $b = \pi$, and $c = \pi/2$.

105. Substitution: scaling Another change of variables that can be interpreted geometrically is the scaling $u = cx$, where c is a real number. Prove and interpret the fact that

$$\int_a^b f(cx)\,dx = \frac{1}{c}\int_{ac}^{bc} f(u)\,du.$$

Draw a picture to illustrate this change of variables in the case that $f(x) = \sin x$, $a = 0$, $b = \pi$, and $c = \frac{1}{2}$.

106–109. Multiple substitutions *If necessary, use two or more substitutions to find the following integrals.*

106. $\displaystyle\int x \sin^4 x^2 \cos x^2\,dx$ (*Hint:* Begin with $u = x^2$, then use $v = \sin u$.)

107. $\displaystyle\int \frac{dx}{\sqrt{1 + \sqrt{1 + x}}}$ (*Hint:* Begin with $u = \sqrt{1 + x}$.)

108. $\displaystyle\int_0^1 x\sqrt{1 - \sqrt{x}}\,dx$

109. $\displaystyle\int_0^1 \sqrt{x - x\sqrt{x}}\,dx$

110. $\displaystyle\int \tan^{10} 4x \sec^2 4x\,dx$ (*Hint:* Begin with $u = 4x$.)

111. $\displaystyle\int_0^{\pi/2} \frac{\cos\theta \sin\theta}{\sqrt{\cos^2\theta + 16}}\,d\theta$ (*Hint:* Begin with $u = \cos\theta$.)

QUICK CHECK ANSWERS

1. $u = x^4 + 5$ **2.** With $u = x^5 + 6$, we have $du = 5x^4$, and x^4 does not appear in the integrand. **3.** New equation: $u^2 - 13u + 36 = 0$; roots: $x = \pm 2, \pm 3$ ◄

CHAPTER 5 REVIEW EXERCISES

1. **Explain why or why not** Determine whether the following statements are true and give an explanation or counterexample. Assume f and f' are continuous functions for all real numbers.
   a. If $A(x) = \int_a^x f(t)\,dt$ and $f(t) = 2t - 3$, then A is a quadratic function.
   b. Given an area function $A(x) = \int_a^x f(t)\,dt$ and an antiderivative F of f, it follows that $A'(x) = F(x)$.
   c. $\int_a^b f'(x)\,dx = f(b) - f(a)$.
   d. If f is continuous on $[a, b]$ and $\int_a^b |f(x)|\,dx = 0$, then $f(x) = 0$ on $[a, b]$.
   e. If the average value of f on $[a, b]$ is zero, then $f(x) = 0$ on $[a, b]$.
   f. $\int_a^b (2f(x) - 3g(x))\,dx = 2\int_a^b f(x)\,dx + 3\int_b^a g(x)\,dx$.
   g. $\int f'(g(x))g'(x)\,dx = f(g(x)) + C$.

2. **Velocity to displacement** An object travels on the x-axis with a velocity given by $v(t) = 2t + 5$, for $0 \le t \le 4$.
   a. How far does the object travel, for $0 \le t \le 4$?
   b. What is the average value of v on the interval $[0, 4]$?
   c. True or false: The object would travel as far as in part (a) if it traveled at its average velocity (a constant), for $0 \le t \le 4$.

3. **Area by geometry** Use geometry to evaluate the following definite integrals, where the graph of f is given in the figure.
   a. $\displaystyle\int_0^4 f(x)\,dx$
   b. $\displaystyle\int_6^4 f(x)\,dx$
   c. $\displaystyle\int_5^7 f(x)\,dx$
   d. $\displaystyle\int_0^7 f(x)\,dx$

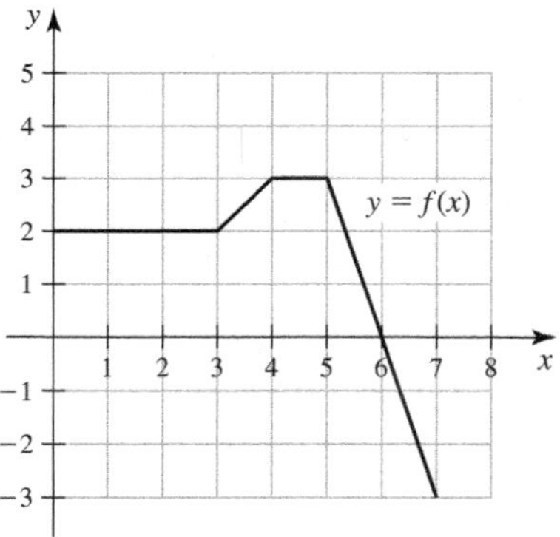

4. **Displacement by geometry** Use geometry to find the displacement of an object moving along a line for the time intervals (*i*) $0 \le t \le 5$, (*ii*) $3 \le t \le 7$, and (*iii*) $0 \le t \le 8$, where the graph of its velocity $v = g(t)$ is given in the figure.

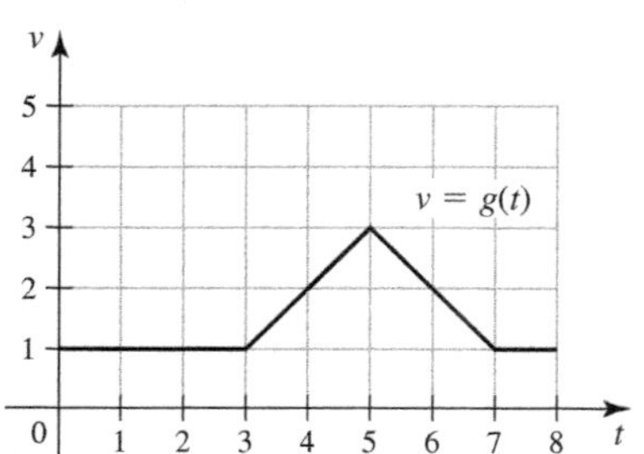

5. **Area by geometry** Use geometry to evaluate $\int_0^4 \sqrt{8x - x^2}\,dx$. (*Hint:* Complete the square.)

6. **Bagel output** The manager of a bagel bakery collects the following production rate data (in bagels per minute) at seven different times during the morning. Estimate the total number of bagels produced between 6:00 and 7:30 A.M., using a left and right Riemann sum.

Time of day (A.M.)	Production rate (bagels/min)
6:00	45
6:15	60
6:30	75
6:45	60
7:00	50
7:15	40
7:30	30

7. **Integration by Riemann sums** Consider the integral $\int_1^4 (3x - 2)\,dx$.
   a. Evaluate the right Riemann sum for the integral with $n = 3$.
   b. Use summation notation to express the right Riemann sum in terms of a positive integer n.
   c. Evaluate the definite integral by taking the limit as $n \to \infty$ of the Riemann sum of part (b).
   d. Confirm the result of part (c) by graphing $y = 3x - 2$ and using geometry to evaluate the integral. Then evaluate $\int_1^4 (3x - 2)\,dx$ with the Fundamental Theorem of Calculus.

8–11. Limit definition of the definite integral *Use the limit definition of the definite integral with right Riemann sums and a regular partition to evaluate the following definite integrals. Use the Fundamental Theorem of Calculus to check your answer.*

8. $\displaystyle\int_0^1 (4x - 2)\,dx$

9. $\displaystyle\int_0^2 (x^2 - 4)\,dx$

10. $\displaystyle\int_1^2 (3x^2 + x)\,dx$

11. $\displaystyle\int_0^4 (x^3 - x)\,dx$

12. **Evaluating Riemann sums** Consider the function $f(x) = 3x + 4$ on the interval $[3, 7]$. Show that the midpoint Riemann sum with $n = 4$ gives the exact area of the region bounded by the graph.

13. **Sum to integral** Evaluate the following limit by identifying the integral that it represents:

$$\lim_{n\to\infty} \sum_{k=1}^{n} \left(\left(\frac{4k}{n} \right)^5 + 1 \right) \left(\frac{4}{n} \right).$$

14. **Area function by geometry** Use geometry to find the area $A(x)$ that is bounded by the graph of $f(t) = 2t - 4$ and the t-axis between the point $(2, 0)$ and the variable point $(x, 0)$, where $x \ge 2$. Verify that $A'(x) = f(x)$.

15–30. Evaluating integrals *Evaluate the following integrals.*

15. $\int_{-2}^{2} (3x^4 - 2x + 1)\, dx$

16. $\int \cos 3x\, dx$

17. $\int_0^2 (x + 1)^3\, dx$

18. $\int_0^1 (4x^{21} - 2x^{16} + 1)\, dx$

19. $\int (9x^8 - 7x^6)\, dx$

20. $\int_{-2}^{2} e^{4x+8}\, dx$

21. $\int_0^1 \sqrt{x}(\sqrt{x} + 1)\, dx$

22. $\int \frac{y^2}{y^3 + 27}\, dy$

23. $\int_0^1 \frac{dx}{\sqrt{4 - x^2}}$

24. $\int y^2(3y^3 + 1)^4\, dy$

25. $\int_0^3 \frac{x}{\sqrt{25 - x^2}}\, dx$

26. $\int x \sin x^2 \cos^8 x^2\, dx$

27. $\int_0^{\pi} \sin^2 5\theta\, d\theta$

28. $\int_0^{\pi} (1 - \cos^2 3\theta)\, d\theta$

29. $\int_2^3 \frac{x^2 + 2x - 2}{x^3 + 3x^2 - 6x}\, dx$

30. $\int_0^{\ln 2} \frac{e^x}{1 + e^{2x}}\, dx$

31–34. Area of regions *Compute the area of the region bounded by the graph of f and the x-axis on the given interval. You may find it useful to sketch the region.*

31. $f(x) = 16 - x^2$ on $[-4, 4]$

32. $f(x) = x^3 - x$ on $[-1, 0]$

33. $f(x) = 2\sin(x/4)$ on $[0, 2\pi]$

34. $f(x) = 1/(x^2 + 1)$ on $[-1, \sqrt{3}]$

35–36. Area versus net area *Find (i) the net area and (ii) the area of the region bounded by the graph of f and the x-axis on the given interval. You may find it useful to sketch the region.*

35. $f(x) = x^4 - x^2$ on $[-1, 1]$

36. $f(x) = x^2 - x$ on $[0, 3]$

37. Symmetry properties Suppose that $\int_0^4 f(x)\, dx = 10$ and $\int_0^4 g(x)\, dx = 20$. Furthermore, suppose that f is an even function and g is an odd function. Evaluate the following integrals.

a. $\int_{-4}^{4} f(x)\, dx$

b. $\int_{-4}^{4} 3g(x)\, dx$

c. $\int_{-4}^{4} (4f(x) - 3g(x))\, dx$

d. $\int_0^1 8x f(4x^2)\, dx$

e. $\int_{-2}^{2} 3x f(x)\, dx$

38. Properties of integrals The figure shows the areas of regions bounded by the graph of f and the x-axis. Evaluate the following integrals.

a. $\int_a^c f(x)\, dx$

b. $\int_b^d f(x)\, dx$

c. $\int_c^b 2f(x)\, dx$

d. $\int_a^d 4f(x)\, dx$

e. $\int_a^b 3f(x)\, dx$

f. $\int_b^d 2f(x)\, dx$

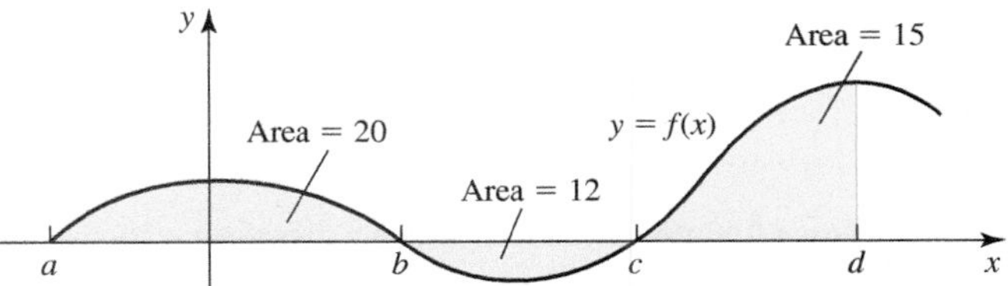

39–44. Properties of integrals *Suppose that* $\int_1^4 f(x)\, dx = 6$, $\int_1^4 g(x)\, dx = 4$, *and* $\int_3^4 f(x)\, dx = 2$. *Evaluate the following integrals or state that there is not enough information.*

39. $\int_1^4 3f(x)\, dx$

40. $-\int_4^1 2f(x)\, dx$

41. $\int_1^4 (3f(x) - 2g(x))\, dx$

42. $\int_1^4 f(x)g(x)\, dx$

43. $\int_1^3 \frac{f(x)}{g(x)}\, dx$

44. $\int_4^1 (f(x) - g(x))\, dx$

45. Displacement from velocity A particle moves along a line with a velocity given by $v(t) = 5\sin \pi t$ starting with an initial position $s(0) = 0$. Find the displacement of the particle between $t = 0$ and $t = 2$, which is given by $s(t) = \int_0^2 v(t)\, dt$. Find the distance traveled by the particle during this interval, which is $\int_0^2 |v(t)|\, dt$.

46. Average height A baseball is launched into the outfield on a parabolic trajectory given by $y = 0.01x(200 - x)$. Find the average height of the baseball over the horizontal extent of its flight.

47. Average values Integration is not needed.

a. Find the average value of f shown in the figure on the interval $[1, 6]$ and then find the point(s) c in $(1, 6)$ guaranteed to exist by the Mean Value Theorem for Integrals.

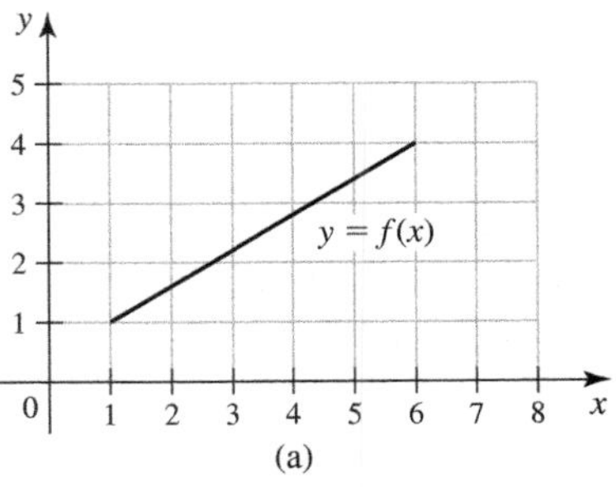

(a)

b. Find the average value of f shown in the figure on the interval $[2, 6]$ and then find the point(s) c in $(2, 6)$ guaranteed to exist by the Mean Value Theorem for Integrals.

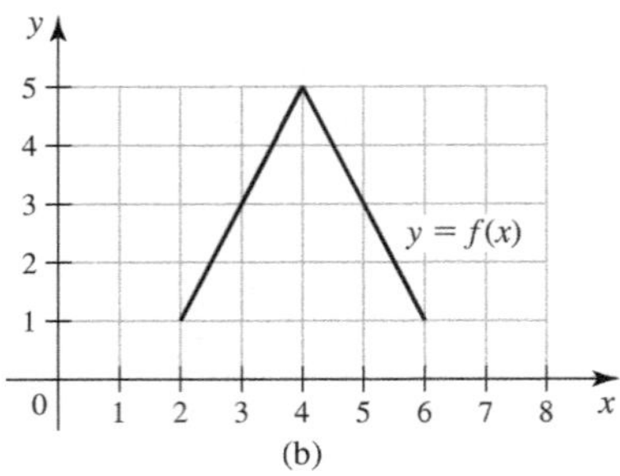

(b)

48. An unknown function The function f satisfies the equation $3x^4 - 48 = \int_2^x f(t)\,dt$. Find f and check your answer by substitution.

49. An unknown function Assume f' is continuous on $[2, 4]$, $\int_1^2 f'(2x)\,dx = 10$, and $f(2) = 4$. Evaluate $f(4)$.

50. Function defined by an integral Let $H(x) = \int_0^x \sqrt{4 - t^2}\,dt$, for $-2 \le x \le 2$.

a. Evaluate $H(0)$.
b. Evaluate $H'(1)$.
c. Evaluate $H'(2)$.
d. Use geometry to evaluate $H(2)$.
e. Find the value of s such that $H(x) = sH(-x)$.

51. Function defined by an integral Make a graph of the function $f(x) = \int_1^x \frac{dt}{t}$, for $x \ge 1$. Be sure to include all of the evidence you used to arrive at the graph.

52. Identifying functions Match the graphs A, B, and C in the figure with the functions $f(x)$, $f'(x)$, and $\int_0^x f(t)\,dt$.

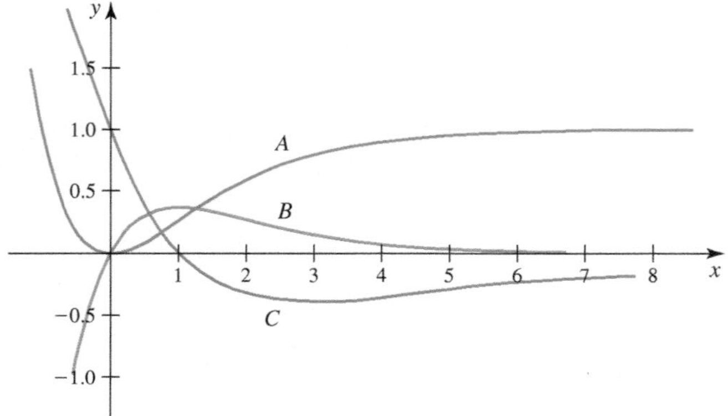

53. Ascent rate of a scuba diver Divers who ascend too quickly in the water risk *decompression illness.* A common recommendation for a maximum rate of ascent is 30 feet/minute with a 5-minute safety stop 15 feet below the surface of the water. Suppose that a diver ascends to the surface in 8 minutes according to the velocity function

$$v(t) = \begin{cases} 30 & \text{if } 0 \le t \le 2 \\ 0 & \text{if } 2 < t \le 7 \\ 15 & \text{if } 7 < t \le 8. \end{cases}$$

a. Graph the velocity function v.
b. Compute the area under the velocity curve.
c. Interpret the physical meaning of the area under the velocity curve.

54. Area functions Consider the graph of the continuous function f in the figure and let $F(x) = \int_0^x f(t)\,dt$ and $G(x) = \int_1^x f(t)\,dt$.

Assume the graph consists of a line segment from $(0, -2)$ to $(2, 2)$ and two quarter circles of radius 2.

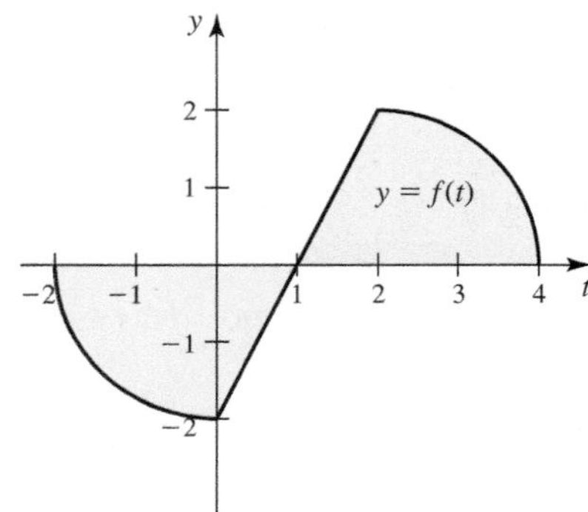

a. Evaluate $F(2)$, $F(-2)$, and $F(4)$.
b. Evaluate $G(-2)$, $G(0)$, and $G(4)$.
c. Explain why there is a constant C such that $F(x) = G(x) + C$, for $-2 \le x \le 4$. Fill in the blank with a number: $F(x) = G(x) +$ _____, for $-2 \le x \le 4$.

55–56. Area functions and the Fundamental Theorem *Consider the function*

$$f(t) = \begin{cases} t & \text{if } -2 \le t < 0 \\ \dfrac{t^2}{2} & \text{if } 0 \le t \le 2 \end{cases}$$

and its graph shown below.

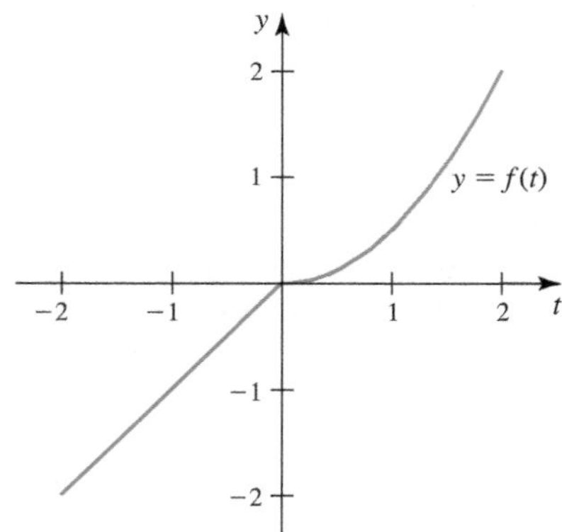

Let $F(x) = \int_{-1}^x f(t)\,dt$ and $G(x) = \int_{-2}^x f(t)\,dt$.

55. a. Evaluate $F(-2)$ and $F(2)$.
b. Use the Fundamental Theorem to find an expression for $F'(x)$, for $-2 \le x < 0$.
c. Use the Fundamental Theorem to find an expression for $F'(x)$, for $0 \le x \le 2$.
d. Evaluate $F'(-1)$ and $F'(1)$. Interpret these values.
e. Evaluate $F''(-1)$ and $F''(1)$.
f. Find a constant C such that $F(x) = G(x) + C$.

56. **a.** Evaluate $G(-1)$ and $G(1)$.
b. Use the Fundamental Theorem to find an expression for $G'(x)$, for $-2 \le x < 0$.
c. Use the Fundamental Theorem to find an expression for $G'(x)$, for $0 \le x \le 2$.
d. Evaluate $G'(0)$ and $G'(1)$. Interpret these values.
e. Find a constant C such that $F(x) = G(x) + C$.

57–58. Limits with integrals *Evaluate the following limits.*

57. $\lim\limits_{x\to 2} \dfrac{\int_2^x e^{t^2}\,dt}{x-2}$

58. $\lim\limits_{x\to 1} \dfrac{\int_1^{x^2} e^{t^3}\,dt}{x-1}$

59. **Geometry of integrals** Without evaluating the integrals, explain why the following statement is true for positive integers n:

$$\int_0^1 x^n\,dx + \int_0^1 \sqrt[n]{x}\,dx = 1.$$

60. **Change of variables** Use the change of variables $u^3 = x^2 - 1$ to evaluate the integral $\int_1^3 x\sqrt[3]{x^2-1}\,dx$.

61. **Inverse tangent integral** Prove that for nonzero constants a and b, $\displaystyle\int \frac{dx}{a^2x^2+b^2} = \frac{1}{ab}\tan^{-1}\left(\frac{ax}{b}\right) + C.$

62–67. Additional integrals *Evaluate the following integrals.*

62. $\displaystyle\int \frac{\sin 2x}{1+\cos^2 x}\,dx$ (*Hint*: $\sin 2x = 2\sin x\cos x$.)

63. $\displaystyle\int \frac{1}{x^2}\sin\frac{1}{x}\,dx$

64. $\displaystyle\int \frac{(\tan^{-1} x)^5}{1+x^2}\,dx$

65. $\displaystyle\int \frac{dx}{(\tan^{-1} x)(1+x^2)}$

66. $\displaystyle\int \frac{\sin^{-1} x}{\sqrt{1-x^2}}\,dx$

67. $\displaystyle\int \frac{e^x - e^{-x}}{e^x + e^{-x}}\,dx$

68. **Area with a parameter** Let $a > 0$ be a real number and consider the family of functions $f(x) = \sin ax$ on the interval $[0, \pi/a]$.
a. Graph f, for $a = 1, 2, 3$.
b. Let $g(a)$ be the area of the region bounded by the graph of f and the x-axis on the interval $[0, \pi/a]$. Graph g for $0 < a < \infty$. Is g an increasing function, a decreasing function, or neither?

69. **Equivalent equations** Explain why if a function u satisfies the equation $u(x) + 2\int_0^x u(t)\,dt = 10$, then it also satisfies the equation $u'(x) + 2u(x) = 0$. Is it true that if u satisfies the second equation, then it satisfies the first equation?

T 70. **Area function properties** Consider the function $f(t) = t^2 - 5t + 4$ and the area function $A(x) = \int_0^x f(t)\,dt$.
a. Graph f on the interval $[0, 6]$.
b. Compute and graph A on the interval $[0, 6]$.
c. Show that the local extrema of A occur at the zeros of f.
d. Give a geometrical and analytical explanation for the observation in part (c).
e. Find the approximate zeros of A, other than 0, and call them x_1 and x_2, where $x_1 < x_2$.
f. Find b such that the area bounded by the graph of f and the t-axis on the interval $[0, t_1]$ equals the area bounded by the graph of f and the t-axis on the interval $[t_1, b]$.
g. If f is an integrable function and $A(x) = \int_a^x f(t)\,dt$, is it always true that the local extrema of A occur at the zeros of f? Explain.

71. **Function defined by an integral**
Let $f(x) = \int_0^x (t-1)^{15}(t-2)^9\,dt$.
a. Find the intervals on which f is increasing and the intervals on which f is decreasing.
b. Find the intervals on which f is concave up and the intervals on which f is concave down.
c. For what values of x does f have local minima? Local maxima?
d. Where are the inflection points of f?

72. **Exponential inequalities** Sketch a graph of $f(t) = e^t$ on an arbitrary interval $[a, b]$. Use the graph and compare areas of regions to prove that

$$e^{(a+b)/2} < \frac{e^b - e^a}{b-a} < \frac{e^a + e^b}{2}.$$

(*Source: Mathematics Magazine* 81, 5, Dec 2008)

Chapter 5 Guided Projects

Applications of the material in this chapter and related topics can be found in the following Guided Projects. For additional information, see the Preface.

- Limits of sums
- Distribution of wealth
- Symmetry in integrals

7

Integration Techniques

Chapter Preview In this chapter, we return to integration methods and present a variety of new strategies that supplement the substitution (or change of variables) method. The new techniques introduced here are integration by parts, trigonometric substitution, and partial fractions. Taken altogether, these *analytical methods* (pencil-and-paper methods) greatly enlarge the collection of integrals that we can evaluate. Nevertheless, it is important to recognize that these methods are limited because many integrals do not yield to them. For this reason, we also introduce table-based methods, which are used to evaluate many indefinite integrals, and computer-based methods for approximating definite integrals. The discussion then turns to integrals that have either infinite integrands or infinite intervals of integration. These integrals, called *improper integrals*, offer surprising results and have many practical applications. The chapter closes with an introductory survey of differential equations, a vast topic that has a central place in both the theory and applications of mathematics.

7.1 Basic Approaches

Before plunging into new integration techniques, we devote this section to two practical goals. The first is to review what you learned about the substitution method in Section 5.5. The other is to introduce several basic simplifying procedures that are worth keeping in mind for any integral that you might be working on. Table 7.1 will remind you of some frequently used indefinite integrals.

➤ Table 7.1 is similar to Tables 4.9 and 4.10 in Section 4.9. It is a subset of the table of integrals at the back of the book.

Table 7.1 Basic Integration Formulas

1. $\displaystyle\int k\,dx = kx + C, k \text{ real}$	**2.** $\displaystyle\int x^p\,dx = \frac{x^{p+1}}{p+1} + C,\ p \neq -1 \text{ real}$
3. $\displaystyle\int \cos ax\,dx = \frac{1}{a}\sin ax + C$	**4.** $\displaystyle\int \sin ax\,dx = -\frac{1}{a}\cos ax + C$
5. $\displaystyle\int \sec^2 ax\,dx = \frac{1}{a}\tan ax + C$	**6.** $\displaystyle\int \csc^2 ax\,dx = -\frac{1}{a}\cot ax + C$
7. $\displaystyle\int \sec ax \tan ax\,dx = \frac{1}{a}\sec ax + C$	**8.** $\displaystyle\int \csc ax \cot ax\,dx = -\frac{1}{a}\csc ax + C$
9. $\displaystyle\int e^{ax}\,dx = \frac{1}{a}e^{ax} + C$	**10.** $\displaystyle\int \frac{dx}{x} = \ln\lvert x\rvert + C$
11. $\displaystyle\int \frac{dx}{\sqrt{a^2 - x^2}} = \sin^{-1}\frac{x}{a} + C$	**12.** $\displaystyle\int \frac{dx}{a^2 + x^2} = \frac{1}{a}\tan^{-1}\frac{x}{a} + C$
13. $\displaystyle\int \frac{dx}{x\sqrt{x^2 - a^2}} = \frac{1}{a}\sec^{-1}\left\lvert\frac{x}{a}\right\rvert + C, a > 0$	

➤ A common choice for a change of variables is a linear term of the form $ax + b$.

EXAMPLE 1 **Substitution review** Evaluate $\int_{-1}^{2} \frac{dx}{3 + 2x}$.

SOLUTION The expression $3 + 2x$ suggests the change of variables $u = 3 + 2x$, which implies that $du = 2\,dx$. Note that when $x = -1$, $u = 1$, and when $x = 2$, $u = 7$. The substitution may now be done:

$$\int_{-1}^{2} \frac{dx}{3 + 2x} = \int_{1}^{7} \frac{1}{u} \underbrace{\frac{du}{2}}_{dx} = \frac{1}{2} \ln |u| \Big|_{1}^{7} = \frac{1}{2} \ln 7.$$

Related Exercises 7–14 ◄

QUICK CHECK 1 What change of variable would you use for the integral $\int (6 + 5x)^8\,dx$? ◄

➤ Example 2 shows the useful technique of multiplying the integrand by 1. In this case, $1 = \frac{e^x}{e^x}$. The idea is used again in Example 6.

EXAMPLE 2 **Subtle substitution** Evaluate $\int \frac{dx}{e^x + e^{-x}}$.

SOLUTION In this case, we see nothing in Table 7.1 that resembles the given integral. In a spirit of trial and error, we multiply numerator and denominator of the integrand by e^x:

$$\int \frac{dx}{e^x + e^{-x}} = \int \frac{e^x}{e^{2x} + 1}\,dx. \quad e^x \cdot e^x = e^{2x}$$

This form of the integrand suggests the substitution $u = e^x$, which implies that $du = e^x\,dx$. Making these substitutions, the integral becomes

$$\int \frac{e^x}{e^{2x} + 1}\,dx = \int \frac{du}{u^2 + 1} \quad \text{Substitute } u = e^x,\ du = e^x\,dx.$$
$$= \tan^{-1} u + C \quad \text{Table 7.1}$$
$$= \tan^{-1} e^x + C. \quad u = e^x$$

Related Exercises 15–22 ◄

EXAMPLE 3 **Split up fractions** Evaluate $\int \frac{\cos x + \sin^3 x}{\sec x}\,dx$.

SOLUTION Don't overlook the opportunity to split a fraction into two or more fractions. In this case, the integrand is simplified in a useful way:

$$\int \frac{\cos x + \sin^3 x}{\sec x}\,dx = \int \frac{\cos x}{\sec x}\,dx + \int \frac{\sin^3 x}{\sec x}\,dx \quad \text{Split fraction.}$$
$$= \int \cos^2 x\,dx + \int \sin^3 x \cos x\,dx. \quad \sec x = \frac{1}{\cos x}$$

➤ Half-angle formulas

$$\cos^2 x = \frac{1 + \cos 2x}{2}$$
$$\sin^2 x = \frac{1 - \cos 2x}{2}$$

The first of the resulting integrals is evaluated using a half-angle formula (Example 6 of Section 5.5). In the second integral, the substitution $u = \sin x$ is used:

$$\int \frac{\cos x + \sin^3 x}{\sec x}\,dx = \int \cos^2 x\,dx + \int \sin^3 x \cos x\,dx$$
$$= \int \frac{1 + \cos 2x}{2}\,dx + \int \sin^3 x \cos x\,dx \quad \text{Half-angle formula}$$
$$= \frac{1}{2}\int dx + \frac{1}{2}\int \cos 2x\,dx + \int u^3\,du \quad u = \sin x,\ du = \cos x\,dx$$
$$= \frac{x}{2} + \frac{1}{4}\sin 2x + \frac{1}{4}\sin^4 x + C. \quad \text{Evaluate integrals.}$$

Related Exercises 23–28 ◄

QUICK CHECK 2 Explain how to simplify the integrand of $\int \frac{x^3 + \sqrt{x}}{x^{3/2}}\,dx$ before integrating. ◄

EXAMPLE 4 **Division with rational functions** Evaluate $\int \frac{x^2 + 2x - 1}{x + 4}\,dx$.

SOLUTION When integrating rational functions (polynomials in the numerator and denominator), check to see whether the function is *improper* (the degree of the numerator is greater than or equal to the degree of the denominator). In this example, we have an improper rational function, and long division is used to simplify it. The integration is done as follows:

➤
$$\begin{array}{r} x - 2 \\ x + 4\overline{)x^2 + 2x - 1} \\ \underline{x^2 + 4x} \\ -2x - 1 \\ \underline{-2x - 8} \\ 7 \end{array}$$

$$\int \frac{x^2 + 2x - 1}{x + 4}\,dx = \int (x - 2)\,dx + \int \frac{7}{x + 4}\,dx \quad \text{Long division}$$

$$= \frac{x^2}{2} - 2x + 7\ln|x + 4| + C. \quad \text{Evaluate integrals.}$$

Related Exercises 29–32 ◄

QUICK CHECK 3 Explain how to simplify the integrand of $\int \frac{x + 1}{x - 1}\,dx$ before integrating. ◄

EXAMPLE 5 **Complete the square** Evaluate $\int \frac{dx}{\sqrt{-x^2 - 8x - 7}}$.

SOLUTION We don't see an integral in Table 7.1 that looks like the given integral, so some preliminary work is needed. In this case, the key is to complete the square on the polynomial in the denominator. We find that

$$\begin{aligned} -x^2 - 8x - 7 &= -(x^2 + 8x + 7) \\ &= -(x^2 + 8x \underbrace{+ 16 - 16}_{\text{add and subtract 16}} + 7) && \text{Complete the square.} \\ &= -((x + 4)^2 - 9) && \text{Factor and combine terms.} \\ &= 9 - (x + 4)^2. && \text{Rearrange terms.} \end{aligned}$$

After a change of variables, the integral is recognizable:

$$\begin{aligned} \int \frac{dx}{\sqrt{-7 - 8x - x^2}} &= \int \frac{dx}{\sqrt{9 - (x + 4)^2}} && \text{Complete the square.} \\ &= \int \frac{du}{\sqrt{9 - u^2}} && u = x + 4,\ du = dx \\ &= \sin^{-1}\frac{u}{3} + C && \text{Table 7.1} \\ &= \sin^{-1}\left(\frac{x + 4}{3}\right) + C. && \text{Replace } u \text{ with } x + 4. \end{aligned}$$

Related Exercises 33–36 ◄

QUICK CHECK 4 Express $x^2 + 6x + 16$ in terms of a perfect square. ◄

EXAMPLE 6 **Multiply by 1** Evaluate $\int \frac{dx}{1 + \cos x}$.

SOLUTION The key to evaluating this integral is admittedly not obvious, and the trick works only on special integrals. The idea is to multiply the integrand by 1, but the challenge is finding the appropriate representation of 1. In this case, we use

$$1 = \frac{1 - \cos x}{1 - \cos x}.$$

The integral is evaluated as follows:

$$\begin{aligned}
\int \frac{dx}{1+\cos x} &= \int \frac{1}{1+\cos x}\cdot\frac{1-\cos x}{1-\cos x}\,dx && \text{Multiply by 1.}\\
&= \int \frac{1-\cos x}{1-\cos^2 x}\,dx && \text{Simplify.}\\
&= \int \frac{1-\cos x}{\sin^2 x}\,dx && 1-\cos^2 x=\sin^2 x\\
&= \int \frac{1}{\sin^2 x}\,dx - \int \frac{\cos x}{\sin^2 x}\,dx && \text{Split up the fraction.}\\
&= \int \csc^2 x\,dx - \int \csc x\cot x\,dx && \csc x=\frac{1}{\sin x},\ \cot x=\frac{\cos x}{\sin x}\\
&= -\cot x + \csc x + C. && \text{Integrate using Table 7.1.}
\end{aligned}$$

Related Exercises 37–40 ◀

The techniques illustrated in this section are designed to transform or simplify an integrand before you apply a specific method. In fact, these ideas may help you recognize the best method to use. Keep them in mind as you learn new integration methods and improve your integration skills.

SECTION 7.1 EXERCISES

Review Questions

1. What change of variables would you use for the integral $\int (4-7x)^{-6}\,dx$?
2. Before integrating, how would you rewrite the integrand of $\int (x^4+2)^2\,dx$?
3. What trigonometric identity is useful in evaluating $\int \sin^2 x\,dx$?
4. Describe a first step in integrating $\int \frac{x^3-2x+4}{x-1}\,dx$.
5. Describe a first step in integrating $\int \frac{10}{x^2-4x+5}\,dx$.
6. Describe a first step in integrating $\int \frac{x^{10}-2x^4+10x^2+1}{3x^3}\,dx$.

Basic Skills

7–14. Substitution Review *Evaluate the following integrals.*

7. $\int \frac{dx}{(3-5x)^4}$
8. $\int (9x-2)^{-3}\,dx$
9. $\int_0^{3\pi/8} \sin\left(2x-\frac{\pi}{4}\right)dx$
10. $\int e^{3-4x}\,dx$
11. $\int \frac{\ln 2x}{x}\,dx$
12. $\int_{-5}^{0} \frac{dx}{\sqrt{4-x}}$
13. $\int \frac{e^x}{e^x+1}\,dx$
14. $\int \frac{e^{2\sqrt{y}+1}}{\sqrt{y}}\,dy$

15–22. Subtle substitutions *Evaluate the following integrals.*

15. $\int \frac{e^x}{e^x-2e^{-x}}\,dx$
16. $\int \frac{e^{2z}}{e^{2z}-4e^{-z}}\,dz$
17. $\int_1^{e^2} \frac{\ln^2(x^2)}{x}\,dx$
18. $\int \frac{\sin^3 x}{\cos^5 x}\,dx$
19. $\int \frac{\cos^4 x}{\sin^6 x}\,dx$
20. $\int_0^2 \frac{x(3x+2)}{\sqrt{x^3+x^2+4}}\,dx$
21. $\int \frac{dx}{x^{-1}+1}$
22. $\int \frac{dy}{y^{-1}+y^{-3}}$

23–28. Splitting fractions *Evaluate the following integrals.*

23. $\int \frac{x+2}{x^2+4}\,dx$
24. $\int_4^9 \frac{x^{5/2}-x^{1/2}}{x^{3/2}}\,dx$
25. $\int \frac{\sin t+\tan t}{\cos^2 t}\,dt$
26. $\int \frac{4+e^{-2x}}{e^{3x}}\,dx$
27. $\int \frac{2-3x}{\sqrt{1-x^2}}\,dx$
28. $\int \frac{3x+1}{\sqrt{4-x^2}}\,dx$

29–32. Division with rational functions *Evaluate the following integrals.*

29. $\int \frac{x+2}{x+4}\,dx$
30. $\int_2^4 \frac{x^2+2}{x-1}\,dx$
31. $\int \frac{t^3-2}{t+1}\,dt$
32. $\int \frac{6-x^4}{x^2+4}\,dx$

33–36. Completing the square *Evaluate the following integrals.*

33. $\displaystyle\int \frac{dx}{x^2 - 2x + 10}$

34. $\displaystyle\int_0^2 \frac{x}{x^2 + 4x + 8}\,dx$

35. $\displaystyle\int \frac{d\theta}{\sqrt{27 - 6\theta - \theta^2}}$

36. $\displaystyle\int \frac{x}{x^4 + 2x^2 + 1}\,dx$

37–40. Multiply by 1 *Evaluate the following integrals.*

37. $\displaystyle\int \frac{d\theta}{1 + \sin\theta}$

38. $\displaystyle\int \frac{1 - x}{1 - \sqrt{x}}\,dx$

39. $\displaystyle\int \frac{dx}{\sec x - 1}$

40. $\displaystyle\int \frac{d\theta}{1 - \csc\theta}$

Further Explorations

41. **Explain why or why not** Determine whether the following statements are true and give an explanation or counterexample.
   a. $\displaystyle\int \frac{3}{x^2 + 4}\,dx = \int \frac{3}{x^2}\,dx + \int \frac{3}{4}\,dx.$
   b. Long division simplifies the evaluation of the integral $\displaystyle\int \frac{x^3 + 2}{3x^4 + x}\,dx.$
   c. $\displaystyle\int \frac{dx}{\sin x + 1} = \ln|\sin x + 1| + C.$
   d. $\displaystyle\int \frac{dx}{e^x} = \ln e^x + C.$

42–54. Miscellaneous integrals *Use the approaches discussed in this section to evaluate the following integrals.*

42. $\displaystyle\int_4^9 \frac{dx}{1 - \sqrt{x}}$

43. $\displaystyle\int_{-1}^0 \frac{x}{x^2 + 2x + 2}\,dx$

44. $\displaystyle\int_0^1 \sqrt{1 + \sqrt{x}}\,dx$

45. $\displaystyle\int \sin x \sin 2x\,dx$

46. $\displaystyle\int_0^{\pi/2} \sqrt{1 + \cos 2x}\,dx$

47. $\displaystyle\int \frac{dx}{x^{1/2} + x^{3/2}}$

48. $\displaystyle\int_0^1 \frac{dp}{4 - \sqrt{p}}$

49. $\displaystyle\int \frac{x - 2}{x^2 + 6x + 13}\,dx$

50. $\displaystyle\int_0^{\pi/4} 3\sqrt{1 + \sin 2x}\,dx$

51. $\displaystyle\int \frac{e^x}{e^{2x} + 2e^x + 1}\,dx$

52. $\displaystyle\int_0^{\pi/8} \sqrt{1 - \cos 4x}\,dx$

53. $\displaystyle\int_1^3 \frac{2}{x^2 + 2x + 1}\,dx$

54. $\displaystyle\int_0^2 \frac{2}{s^3 + 3s^2 + 3s + 1}\,ds$

55. **Different substitutions**
   a. Evaluate $\int \tan x \sec^2 x\,dx$ using the substitution $u = \tan x$.
   b. Evaluate $\int \tan x \sec^2 x\,dx$ using the substitution $u = \sec x$.
   c. Reconcile the results in parts (a) and (b).

56. **Different methods**
   a. Evaluate $\int \cot x \csc^2 x\,dx$ using the substitution $u = \cot x$.
   b. Evaluate $\int \cot x \csc^2 x\,dx$ using the substitution $u = \csc x$.
   c. Reconcile the results in parts (a) and (b).

57. **Different methods**
   a. Evaluate $\displaystyle\int \frac{x^2}{x + 1}\,dx$ using the substitution $u = x + 1$.
   b. Evaluate $\displaystyle\int \frac{x^2}{x + 1}\,dx$ after first performing long division on the integrand.
   c. Reconcile the results in parts (a) and (b).

58. **Different substitutions**
   a. Show that $\displaystyle\int \frac{dx}{\sqrt{x - x^2}} = \sin^{-1}(2x - 1) + C$ using either $u = 2x - 1$ or $u = x - \frac{1}{2}$.
   b. Show that $\displaystyle\int \frac{dx}{\sqrt{x - x^2}} = 2\sin^{-1}\sqrt{x} + C$ using $u = \sqrt{x}$.
   c. Prove the identity $2\sin^{-1}\sqrt{x} - \sin^{-1}(2x - 1) = \frac{\pi}{2}$.

   (*Source: The College Mathematics Journal* 32, 5, Nov 2001)

Applications

59. **Area of a region between curves** Find the area of the region bounded by the curves $y = \dfrac{x^2}{x^3 - 3x}$ and $y = \dfrac{1}{x^3 - 3x}$ on the interval $[2, 4]$.

60. **Area of a region between curves** Find the area of the entire region bounded by the curves $y = \dfrac{x^3}{x^2 + 1}$ and $y = \dfrac{8x}{x^2 + 1}$.

61. **Volumes of solids** Consider the region R bounded by the graph of $f(x) = \sqrt{x^2 + 1}$ and the x-axis on the interval $[0, 2]$.
   a. Find the volume of the solid formed when R is revolved about the x-axis.
   b. Find the volume of the solid formed when R is revolved about the y-axis.

62. **Volumes of solids** Consider the region R bounded by the graph of $f(x) = \dfrac{1}{x + 2}$ and the x-axis on the interval $[0, 3]$.
   a. Find the volume of the solid formed when R is revolved about the x-axis.
   b. Find the volume of the solid formed when R is revolved about the y-axis.

63. **Arc length** Find the length of the curve $y = x^{5/4}$ on the interval $[0, 1]$. (*Hint:* Write the arc length integral and let $u^2 = 1 + \left(\frac{5}{4}\right)^2\sqrt{x}$.)

64. **Surface area** Find the area of the surface generated when the region bounded by the graph of $y = e^x + \frac{1}{4}e^{-x}$ on the interval $[0, \ln 2]$ is revolved about the x-axis.

65. **Surface area** Let $f(x) = \sqrt{x + 1}$. Find the area of the surface generated when the region bounded by the graph of f on the interval $[0, 1]$ is revolved about the x-axis.

66. **Skydiving** A skydiver in free fall subject to gravitational acceleration and air resistance has a velocity given by $v(t) = v_T\left(\frac{e^{at} - 1}{e^{at} + 1}\right)$, where v_T is the terminal velocity and $a > 0$ is a physical constant. Find the distance that the skydiver falls after t seconds, which is $d(t) = \int_0^t v(y)\,dy$.

QUICK CHECK ANSWERS

1. Let $u = 6 + 5x$. **2.** Write the integrand as $x^{3/2} + x^{-1}$. **3.** Use long division to write the integrand as $1 + \frac{2}{x - 1}$. **4.** $(x + 3)^2 + 7$ ◄

7.2 Integration by Parts

The Substitution Rule (Section 5.5) arises when we reverse the Chain Rule for derivatives. In this section, we employ a similar strategy and reverse the Product Rule for derivatives. The result is an integration technique called *integration by parts*. To illustrate the importance of integration by parts, consider the indefinite integrals

$$\int e^x\,dx = e^x + C \quad \text{and} \quad \int xe^x\,dx = ?$$

The first integral is an elementary integral that we have already encountered. The second integral is only slightly different—and yet, the appearance of the product xe^x in the integrand makes this integral (at the moment) impossible to evaluate. Integration by parts is ideally suited for evaluating integrals of *products* of functions.

Integration by Parts for Indefinite Integrals

Given two differentiable functions u and v, the Product Rule states that

$$\frac{d}{dx}(u(x)v(x)) = u'(x)v(x) + u(x)v'(x).$$

By integrating both sides, we can write this rule in terms of an indefinite integral:

$$u(x)v(x) = \int (u'(x)v(x) + u(x)v'(x))\,dx.$$

Rearranging this expression in the form

$$\int u(x)\underbrace{v'(x)\,dx}_{dv} = u(x)v(x) - \int v(x)\underbrace{u'(x)\,dx}_{du}$$

leads to the basic relationship for *integration by parts*. It is expressed compactly by noting that $du = u'(x)\,dx$ and $dv = v'(x)\,dx$. Suppressing the independent variable x, we have

$$\int u\,dv = uv - \int v\,du.$$

The integral $\int u\,dv$ is viewed as the given integral, and we use integration by parts to express it in terms of a new integral $\int v\,du$. The technique is successful if the new integral can be evaluated.

> **Integration by Parts**
>
> Suppose that u and v are differentiable functions. Then
>
> $$\int u\,dv = uv - \int v\,du.$$

➤ The integration by parts calculation may be done without including the constant of integration—as long as it is included in the final result.

EXAMPLE 1 Integration by parts Evaluate $\int xe^x\,dx$.

SOLUTION The presence of *products* in the integrand often suggests integration by parts. We split the product xe^x into two factors, one of which must be identified as u and the other as dv (the latter always includes the differential dx). Powers of x are *often* good choices for u. The choice for dv should be easy to integrate. In this case, the choices $u = x$ and $dv = e^x\,dx$ are advisable. It follows that $du = dx$. The relationship $dv = e^x\,dx$ means that v is an antiderivative of e^x, which implies $v = e^x$. A table is helpful for organizing these calculations.

➤ The arrows in the table show how to combine factors in the integration by parts formula. The first arrow indicates the product uv; the second arrow indicates the integrand $v\,du$.

Functions in original integral	$u = x$	$dv = e^x\,dx$
Functions in new integral	$du = dx$	$v = e^x$

The integration by parts rule is now applied:

$$\int \underbrace{x}_{u}\,\underbrace{e^x\,dx}_{dv} = \underbrace{x}_{u}\,\underbrace{e^x}_{v} - \int \underbrace{e^x}_{v}\,\underbrace{dx}_{du}.$$

The original integral $\int xe^x\,dx$ has been replaced with the integral of e^x, which is easier to evaluate: $\int e^x\,dx = e^x + C$. The entire procedure looks like this:

$$\int xe^x\,dx = xe^x - \int e^x\,dx \quad \text{Integration by parts}$$
$$= xe^x - e^x + C. \quad \text{Evaluate the new integral.}$$

Related Exercises 7–22 ◀

➤ To make the table, first write the functions in the original integral:

$u =$ ______, $dv =$ ______.

Then find the functions in the new integral by differentiating u and integrating dv:

$du =$ ______, $v =$ ______.

EXAMPLE 2 Integration by parts Evaluate $\int x \sin x\,dx$.

SOLUTION Remembering that powers of x are often a good choice for u, we form the following table.

$u = x$	$dv = \sin x\,dx$
$du = dx$	$v = -\cos x$

Applying integration by parts, we have

$$\int \underbrace{x}_{u}\,\underbrace{\sin x\,dx}_{dv} = \underbrace{x}_{u}\,\underbrace{(-\cos x)}_{v} - \int \underbrace{(-\cos x)}_{v}\,\underbrace{dx}_{du} \quad \text{Integration by parts}$$
$$= -x\cos x + \sin x + C. \quad \text{Evaluate } \int \cos x\,dx = \sin x.$$

Related Exercises 7–22 ◀

QUICK CHECK 1 What are the best choices for u and dv in evaluating $\int x\cos x\,dx$? ◀

In general, integration by parts works when we can easily integrate the choice for dv and when the new integral is easier to evaluate than the original. Integration by parts is often used for integrals of the form $\int x^n f(x)\,dx$, where n is a positive integer. Such integrals generally require the repeated use of integration by parts, as shown in the following example.

EXAMPLE 3 Repeated use of integration by parts

a. Evaluate $\int x^2 e^x\,dx$.

b. How would you evaluate $\int x^n e^x\,dx$, where n is a positive integer?

SOLUTION

a. The factor x^2 is a good choice for u, leaving $dv = e^x\,dx$. We then have

$u = x^2$	$dv = e^x\,dx$
$du = 2x\,dx$	$v = e^x$

$$\int \underbrace{x^2}_{u}\,\underbrace{e^x\,dx}_{dv} = \underbrace{x^2}_{u}\,\underbrace{e^x}_{v} - \int \underbrace{e^x}_{v}\,\underbrace{2x\,dx}_{du}.$$

Notice that the new integral on the right side is simpler than the original integral because the power of x has been reduced by one. In fact, the new integral was evaluated in Example 1. Therefore, after using integration by parts twice, we have

$$\int x^2e^x\,dx = x^2e^x - 2\int xe^x\,dx \quad \text{Integration by parts}$$

$$= x^2e^x - 2(xe^x - e^x) + C \quad \text{Result of Example 1}$$

$$= e^x(x^2 - 2x + 2) + C. \quad \text{Simplify.}$$

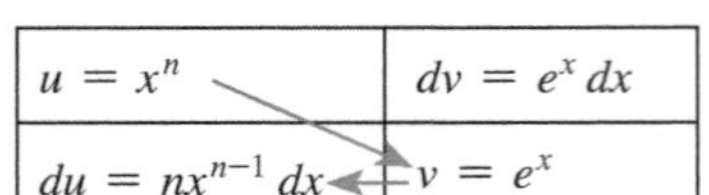

$u = x^n$	$dv = e^x\,dx$
$du = nx^{n-1}\,dx$	$v = e^x$

b. We now let $u = x^n$ and $dv = e^x\,dx$. The integration takes the form

$$\int x^ne^x\,dx = x^ne^x - n\int x^{n-1}e^x\,dx.$$

➤ An integral identity in which the power of a variable is reduced is called a **reduction formula**. Other examples of reduction formulas are explored in Exercises 44–47.

We see that integration by parts reduces the power of the variable in the integrand. The integral in part (a) with $n = 2$ requires two uses of integration by parts. You can probably anticipate that evaluating the integral $\int x^ne^x\,dx$ requires n applications of integration by parts to reach the integral $\int e^x\,dx$, which is easily evaluated.

Related Exercises 23–30 ◄

➤ In Example 4, we could also use $u = \sin x$ and $dv = e^{2x}\,dx$. In general, some trial and error may be required when using integration by parts. Effective choices come with practice.

EXAMPLE 4 Repeated use of integration by parts Evaluate $\int e^{2x}\sin x\,dx$.

SOLUTION The integrand consists of a product, which suggests integration by parts. In this case, there is no obvious choice for u and dv, so let's try the following choices.

$u = e^{2x}$	$dv = \sin x\,dx$
$du = 2e^{2x}\,dx$	$v = -\cos x$

The integral then becomes

$$\int e^{2x}\sin x\,dx = -e^{2x}\cos x + 2\int e^{2x}\cos x\,dx. \tag{1}$$

➤ When using integration by parts, the acronym LIPET may help. If the integrand is the product of two or more functions, choose u to be the first function type that appears in the list

Logarithmic, **I**nverse trigonometric, **P**olynomial, **E**xponential, **T**rigonometric.

The original integral has been expressed in terms of a new integral, $\int e^{2x}\cos x\,dx$, which is no easier to evaluate than the original integral. It is tempting to start over with a new choice of u and dv, but a little persistence pays off. Suppose we evaluate $\int e^{2x}\cos x\,dx$ using integration by parts with the following choices.

$u = e^{2x}$	$dv = \cos x\,dx$
$du = 2e^{2x}\,dx$	$v = \sin x$

Integrating by parts, we have

$$\int e^{2x}\cos x\,dx = e^{2x}\sin x - 2\int e^{2x}\sin x\,dx. \tag{2}$$

Now observe that equation (2) contains the original integral, $\int e^{2x}\sin x\,dx$. Substituting the result of equation (2) into equation (1), we find that

➤ To solve for $\int e^{2x}\sin x\,dx$ in the equation $\int e^{2x}\sin x\,dx = -e^{2x}\cos x + 2e^{2x}\sin x - 4\int e^{2x}\sin x\,dx$, add $4\int e^{2x}\sin x\,dx$ to both sides of the equation and then divide both sides by 5.

$$\int e^{2x}\sin x\,dx = -e^{2x}\cos x + 2\int e^{2x}\cos x\,dx$$

$$= -e^{2x}\cos x + 2\left(e^{2x}\sin x - 2\int e^{2x}\sin x\,dx\right) \quad \text{Substitute for } \int e^{2x}\cos x\,dx.$$

$$= -e^{2x}\cos x + 2e^{2x}\sin x - 4\int e^{2x}\sin x\,dx. \quad \text{Simplify.}$$

Now it is a matter of solving for $\int e^{2x}\sin x\,dx$ and including the constant of integration:

$$\int e^{2x}\sin x\,dx = \frac{1}{5}e^{2x}(2\sin x - \cos x) + C.$$

Related Exercises 23–30 ◄

Integration by Parts for Definite Integrals

Integration by parts with definite integrals presents two options. You can use the method outlined in Examples 1–4 to find an antiderivative and then evaluate it at the upper and lower limits of integration. Alternatively, the limits of integration can be incorporated directly into the integration by parts process. With the second approach, integration by parts for definite integrals has the following form.

> Integration by parts for definite integrals still has the form
>
> $$\int u\,dv = uv - \int v\,du.$$
>
> However, both definite integrals must be written with respect to x.

Integration by Parts for Definite Integrals

Let u and v be differentiable. Then

$$\int_a^b u(x)v'(x)\,dx = u(x)v(x)\Big|_a^b - \int_a^b v(x)u'(x)\,dx.$$

EXAMPLE 5 A definite integral Evaluate $\int_1^2 \ln x\,dx$.

SOLUTION This example is instructive because the integrand does not appear to be a product. The key is to view the integrand as the product $(\ln x)(1\,dx)$. Then the following choices are plausible.

$u = \ln x$	$dv = dx$
$du = \frac{1}{x}\,dx$	$v = x$

Using integration by parts, we have

$$\begin{aligned}
\int_1^2 \underbrace{\ln x}_{u}\,\underbrace{dx}_{dv} &= \big(\underbrace{(\ln x)}_{u}\,\underbrace{x}_{v}\big)\Big|_1^2 - \int_1^2 \underbrace{x}_{v}\,\underbrace{\frac{1}{x}\,dx}_{du} && \text{Integration by parts}\\
&= (x\ln x - x)\Big|_1^2 && \text{Integrate and simplify.}\\
&= (2\ln 2 - 0) - (2 - 1) && \text{Evaluate.}\\
&= 2\ln 2 - 1 \approx 0.386. && \text{Simplify.}
\end{aligned}$$

Related Exercises 31–38 ◀

In Example 5, we evaluated a definite integral of $\ln x$. The corresponding indefinite integral can be added to our list of integration formulas.

QUICK CHECK 2 Verify by differentiation that $\int \ln x\,dx = x\ln x - x + C$. ◀

Integral of ln x

$$\int \ln x\,dx = x\ln x - x + C$$

We now apply integration by parts to a familiar geometry problem.

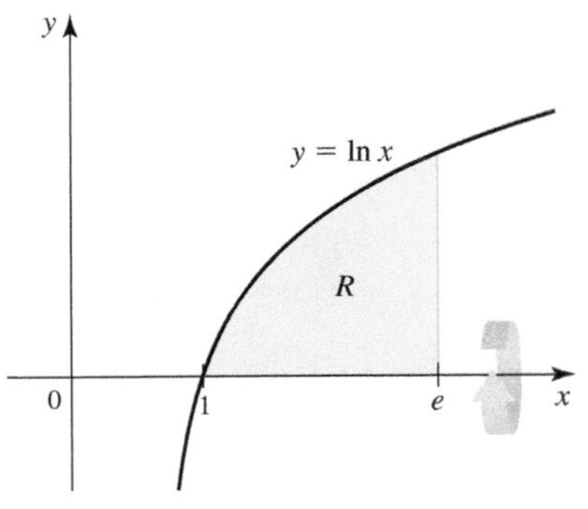

Figure 7.1

EXAMPLE 6 Solids of revolution Let R be the region bounded by $y = \ln x$, the x-axis, and the line $x = e$ (Figure 7.1). Find the volume of the solid that is generated when the region R is revolved about the x-axis.

SOLUTION Revolving R about the x-axis generates a solid whose volume is computed with the disk method (Section 6.3). Its volume is

$$V = \int_1^e \pi(\ln x)^2\,dx.$$

We integrate by parts with the following assignments.

$u = (\ln x)^2$	$dv = dx$
$du = \frac{2 \ln x}{x}\, dx$	$v = x$

➤ Recall that if $f(x) \geq 0$ on $[a, b]$ and the region bounded by the graph of f and the x-axis on $[a, b]$ is revolved about the x-axis, then the volume of the solid generated is $V = \int_a^b \pi f(x)^2\, dx$.

The integration is carried out as follows, using the indefinite integral of $\ln x$ just given:

$$V = \int_1^e \pi (\ln x)^2\, dx \qquad \text{Disk method}$$

$$= \pi \left(\underbrace{(\ln x)^2}_{u} \underbrace{x}_{v} \Big|_1^e - \int_1^e \underbrace{x}_{v} \underbrace{\frac{2 \ln x}{x}\, dx}_{du} \right) \qquad \text{Integration by parts}$$

$$= \pi \left(x(\ln x)^2 \Big|_1^e - 2 \int_1^e \ln x\, dx \right) \qquad \text{Simplify.}$$

$$= \pi \left(x(\ln x)^2 \Big|_1^e - 2(x \ln x - x) \Big|_1^e \right) \qquad \int \ln x\, dx = x \ln x - x + C$$

$$= \pi(e(\ln e)^2 - 2e \ln e + 2e - 2). \qquad \text{Evaluate and simplify.}$$

$$= \pi(e - 2) \approx 2.257 \qquad \text{Simplify.}$$

Related Exercises 39–42 ◄

QUICK CHECK 3 How many times do you need to integrate by parts to reduce $\int_1^e (\ln x)^6\, dx$ to an integral of $\ln x$? ◄

SECTION 7.2 EXERCISES

Review Questions

1. On which derivative rule is integration by parts based?
2. How would you choose dv when evaluating $\int x^n e^{ax}\, dx$ using integration by parts?
3. How would you choose u when evaluating $\int x^n \cos ax\, dx$ using integration by parts?
4. Explain how integration by parts is used to evaluate a definite integral.
5. What type of integrand is a good candidate for integration by parts?
6. What choices for u and dv simplify $\int \tan^{-1} x\, dx$?

Basic Skills

7–22. Integration by parts *Evaluate the following integrals.*

7. $\int x \cos x\, dx$
8. $\int x \sin 2x\, dx$
9. $\int te^t\, dt$
10. $\int 2xe^{3x}\, dx$
11. $\int \frac{x}{\sqrt{x+1}}\, dx$
12. $\int se^{-2s}\, ds$
13. $\int x^2 \ln x^3\, dx$
14. $\int \theta \sec^2 \theta\, d\theta$
15. $\int x^2 \ln x\, dx$
16. $\int x \ln x\, dx$
17. $\int \frac{\ln x}{x^{10}}\, dx$
18. $\int \sin^{-1} x\, dx$
19. $\int \tan^{-1} x\, dx$
20. $\int x \sec^{-1} x\, dx,\ x \geq 1$
21. $\int x \sin x \cos x\, dx$
22. $\int x \tan^{-1} x^2\, dx$

23–30. Repeated integration by parts *Evaluate the following integrals.*

23. $\int t^2 e^{-t}\, dt$
24. $\int e^{3x} \cos 2x\, dx$
25. $\int e^{-x} \sin 4x\, dx$
26. $\int x^2 \ln^2 x\, dx$
27. $\int e^x \cos x\, dx$
28. $\int e^{-2\theta} \sin 6\theta\, d\theta$
29. $\int x^2 \sin 2x\, dx$
30. $\int x^2 e^{4x}\, dx$

31–38. Definite integrals *Evaluate the following definite integrals.*

31. $\int_0^{\pi} x \sin x\, dx$
32. $\int_1^e \ln 2x\, dx$
33. $\int_0^{\pi/2} x \cos 2x\, dx$
34. $\int_0^{\ln 2} xe^x\, dx$
35. $\int_1^{e^2} x^2 \ln x\, dx$
36. $\int_0^{1/\sqrt{2}} y \tan^{-1} y^2\, dy$
37. $\int_{1/2}^{\sqrt{3}/2} \sin^{-1} y\, dy$
38. $\int_{2/\sqrt{3}}^{2} z \sec^{-1} z\, dz$

39–42. Volumes of solids *Find the volume of the solid that is generated when the given region is revolved as described.*

39. The region bounded by $f(x) = e^{-x}$, $x = \ln 2$, and the coordinate axes is revolved about the y-axis.

40. The region bounded by $f(x) = \sin x$ and the x-axis on $[0, \pi]$ is revolved about the y-axis.

41. The region bounded by $f(x) = x \ln x$ and the x-axis on $[1, e^2]$ is revolved about the x-axis.

42. The region bounded by $f(x) = e^{-x}$ and the x-axis on $[0, \ln 2]$ is revolved about the line $x = \ln 2$.

Further Explorations

43. **Explain why or why not** Determine whether the following statements are true and give an explanation or counterexample.

a. $\int uv'\,dx = \left(\int u\,dx\right)\left(\int v'\,dx\right)$.

b. $\int uv'\,dx = uv - \int vu'\,dx$.

c. $\int v\,du = uv - \int u\,dv$.

44–47. Reduction formulas *Use integration by parts to derive the following reduction formulas.*

44. $\int x^n e^{ax}\,dx = \frac{x^n e^{ax}}{a} - \frac{n}{a}\int x^{n-1}e^{ax}\,dx$, for $a \neq 0$

45. $\int x^n \cos ax\,dx = \frac{x^n \sin ax}{a} - \frac{n}{a}\int x^{n-1}\sin ax\,dx$, for $a \neq 0$

46. $\int x^n \sin ax\,dx = -\frac{x^n \cos ax}{a} + \frac{n}{a}\int x^{n-1}\cos ax\,dx$, for $a \neq 0$

47. $\int \ln^n x\,dx = x\ln^n x - n\int \ln^{n-1} x\,dx$

48–51. Applying reduction formulas *Use the reduction formulas in Exercises 44–47 to evaluate the following integrals.*

48. $\int x^2 e^{3x}\,dx$

49. $\int x^2 \cos 5x\,dx$

50. $\int x^3 \sin x\,dx$

51. $\int \ln^4 x\,dx$

52–53. Integrals involving $\int \ln x\,dx$ *Use a substitution to reduce the following integrals to $\int \ln u\,du$. Then evaluate the resulting integral.*

52. $\int (\cos x)\ln(\sin x)\,dx$

53. $\int (\sec^2 x)\ln(\tan x + 2)\,dx$

54. **Two methods**

a. Evaluate $\int x \ln x^2\,dx$ using the substitution $u = x^2$ and evaluating $\int \ln u\,du$.

b. Evaluate $\int x \ln x^2\,dx$ using integration by parts.

c. Verify that your answers to parts (a) and (b) are consistent.

55. **Logarithm base b** Prove that

$$\int \log_b x\,dx = \frac{1}{\ln b}(x \ln x - x) + C.$$

56. **Two integration methods** Evaluate $\int \sin x \cos x\,dx$ using integration by parts. Then evaluate the integral using a substitution. Reconcile your answers.

57. **Combining two integration methods** Evaluate $\int \cos \sqrt{x}\,dx$ using a substitution followed by integration by parts.

58. **Combining two integration methods** Evaluate $\int_0^{\pi^2/4} \sin \sqrt{x}\,dx$ using a substitution followed by integration by parts.

59. **Function defined as an integral** Find the arc length of the function $f(x) = \int_e^x \sqrt{\ln^2 t - 1}\,dt$ on $[e, e^3]$.

60. **A family of exponentials** The curves $y = xe^{-ax}$ are shown in the figure for $a = 1, 2,$ and 3.

a. Find the area of the region bounded by $y = xe^{-x}$ and the x-axis on the interval $[0, 4]$.

b. Find the area of the region bounded by $y = xe^{-ax}$ and the x-axis on the interval $[0, 4]$, where $a > 0$.

c. Find the area of the region bounded by $y = xe^{-ax}$ and the x-axis on the interval $[0, b]$. Because this area depends on a and b, we call it $A(a, b)$, where $a > 0$ and $b > 0$.

d. Use part (c) to show that $A(1, \ln b) = 4A(2, (\ln b)/2)$.

e. Does this pattern continue? Is it true that $A(1, \ln b) = a^2 A(a, (\ln b)/a)$?

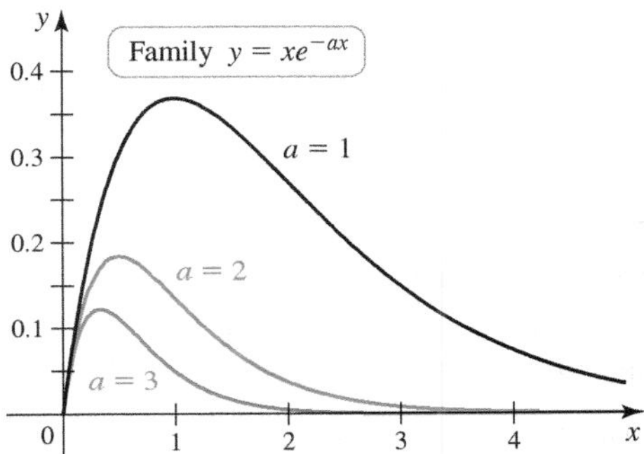

61. **Solid of revolution** Find the volume of the solid generated when the region bounded by $y = \cos x$ and the x-axis on the interval $[0, \pi/2]$ is revolved about the y-axis.

62. **Between the sine and inverse sine** Find the area of the region bounded by the curves $y = \sin x$ and $y = \sin^{-1} x$ on the interval $[0, \frac{1}{2}]$.

63. **Comparing volumes** Let R be the region bounded by $y = \sin x$ and the x-axis on the interval $[0, \pi]$. Which is greater, the volume of the solid generated when R is revolved about the x-axis or the volume of the solid generated when R is revolved about the y-axis?

64. **Log integrals** Use integration by parts to show that for $m \neq -1$,

$$\int x^m \ln x\,dx = \frac{x^{m+1}}{m+1}\left(\ln x - \frac{1}{m+1}\right) + C$$

and for $m = -1$,

$$\int \frac{\ln x}{x}\,dx = \frac{1}{2}\ln^2 x + C.$$

65. **A useful integral**

a. Use integration by parts to show that if f' is continuous,

$$\int xf'(x)\,dx = xf(x) - \int f(x)\,dx.$$

b. Use part (a) to evaluate $\int xe^{3x}\,dx$.

66. Integrating inverse functions Assume that f has an inverse on its domain.

a. Let $y = f^{-1}(x)$ and show that

$$\int f^{-1}(x)\,dx = \int y f'(y)\,dy.$$

b. Use part (a) to show that

$$\int f^{-1}(x)\,dx = yf(y) - \int f(y)\,dy.$$

c. Use the result of part (b) to evaluate $\int \ln x\,dx$ (express the result in terms of x).

d. Use the result of part (b) to evaluate $\int \sin^{-1} x\,dx$.

e. Use the result of part (b) to evaluate $\int \tan^{-1} x\,dx$.

67. Integral of $\sec^3 x$ Use integration by parts to show that

$$\int \sec^3 x\,dx = \frac{1}{2}\sec x \tan x + \frac{1}{2}\int \sec x\,dx.$$

68. Two useful exponential integrals Use integration by parts to derive the following formulas for real numbers a and b.

$$\int e^{ax}\sin bx\,dx = \frac{e^{ax}(a\sin bx - b\cos bx)}{a^2 + b^2} + C$$

$$\int e^{ax}\cos bx\,dx = \frac{e^{ax}(a\cos bx + b\sin bx)}{a^2 + b^2} + C$$

Applications

T 69. Oscillator displacements Suppose a mass on a spring that is slowed by friction has the position function $s(t) = e^{-t}\sin t$.

a. Graph the position function. At what times does the oscillator pass through the position $s = 0$?

b. Find the average value of the position on the interval $[0, \pi]$.

c. Generalize part (b) and find the average value of the position on the interval $[n\pi, (n + 1)\pi]$, for $n = 0, 1, 2, \ldots$.

d. Let a_n be the absolute value of the average position on the intervals $[n\pi, (n + 1)\pi]$, for $n = 0, 1, 2, \ldots$. Describe the pattern in the numbers $a_0, a_1, a_2, \ldots$.

Additional Exercises

70. Find the error Suppose you evaluate $\int \frac{dx}{x}$ using integration by parts. With $u = 1/x$ and $dv = dx$, you find that $du = -1/x^2\,dx$, $v = x$, and

$$\int \frac{dx}{x} = \left(\frac{1}{x}\right)x - \int x\left(-\frac{1}{x^2}\right)dx = 1 + \int \frac{dx}{x}.$$

You conclude that $0 = 1$. Explain the problem with the calculation.

71. Tabular integration Consider the integral $\int f(x)g(x)\,dx$, where f and g are sufficiently "smooth" to allow repeated differentiation and integration, respectively. Let G_k represent the result of calculating k indefinite integrals of g, where the constants of integration are omitted.

a. Show that integration by parts, when applied to $\int f(x)g(x)dx$ with the choices $u = f(x)$ and $dv = g(x)dx$, leads to $\int f(x)g(x)dx = f(x)G_1(x) - \int f'(x)G_1(x)dx$.

This formula can be remembered by utilizing the following table, where a right arrow represents a product of functions on the right side of the integration by parts formula, and a left arrow represents the *integral* of a product of functions (also appearing on the right side of the formula). Explain the significance of the signs associated with the arrows.

f and its derivatives	g and its integrals
$f(x)$ ↘ +	$g(x)$
$f'(x)$ ← −	$G_1(x)$

b. Perform integration by parts again on $\int f'(x)G_1(x)dx$ (from part (a)) with the choices $u = f'(x)$ and $dv = G_1(x)$ to show that $\int f(x)g(x)dx = f(x)G_1(x) - f'(x)G_2(x) + \int f''(x)G_2(x)dx$. Explain the connection between this integral formula and the following table, paying close attention to the signs attached to the arrows.

f and its derivatives	g and its integrals
$f(x)$ ↘ +	$g(x)$
$f'(x)$ ↘ −	$G_1(x)$
$f''(x)$ ← +	$G_2(x)$

c. Continue the pattern established in parts (a) and (b) and integrate by parts a third time. Write the integral formula that results from three applications of integration by parts, and construct the associated *tabular integration* table (include signs of the arrows).

d. The tabular integration table from part (c) is easily extended to allow for as many steps as necessary in the integration-by-parts process. Evaluate $\int x^2 e^{0.5x}dx$ by constructing an appropriate table, and explain why the process terminates after four rows of the table have been filled in.

e. Use tabular integration to evaluate $\int x^3 \cos x\,dx$. How many rows of the table are necessary? Why?

f. Explain why tabular integration is particularly suited to integrals of the form $\int p_n(x)g(x)\,dx$, where p_n is a polynomial of degree $n > 0$ (and where, as before, we assume g is easily integrated as many times as necessary).

72. Practice with tabular integration Evaluate the following integrals using tabular integration (refer to Exercise 71).

a. $\int x^4 e^x dx$

b. $\int 7xe^{3x}dx$

c. $\int_{-1}^{0} 2x^2\sqrt{x + 1}\,dx$

d. $\int (x^3 - 2x)\sin 2x\,dx$

e. $\int \frac{2x^2 - 3x}{(x - 1)^3}\,dx$

f. $\int \frac{x^2 + 3x + 4}{\sqrt[3]{2x + 1}}\,dx$

g. Why doesn't tabular integration work well when applied to $\int \frac{x}{\sqrt{1 - x^2}}\,dx$? Evaluate this integral using a different method.

73. Tabular integration extended Refer to Exercise 71.

a. The following table shows the method of tabular integration applied to $\int e^x \cos x\, dx$. Use the table to express $\int e^x \cos x\, dx$ in terms of the sum of functions and an indefinite integral.

f and its derivatives		g and its integrals
e^x	+	$\cos x$
e^x	−	$\sin x$
e^x	+	$-\cos x$

b. Solve the equation in part (a) for $\int e^x \cos x\, dx$.

c. Evaluate $\int e^{-2x} \sin 3x\, dx$ by applying the idea from parts (a) and (b).

74. Integrating derivatives Use integration by parts to show that if f' is continuous on $[a, b]$, then

$$\int_a^b f(x) f'(x)\, dx = \frac{1}{2}\left(f(b)^2 - f(a)^2\right).$$

75. An identity Show that if f has a continuous second derivative on $[a, b]$ and $f'(a) = f'(b) = 0$, then

$$\int_a^b x f''(x)\, dx = f(a) - f(b).$$

76. An identity Show that if f and g have continuous second derivatives and $f(0) = f(1) = g(0) = g(1) = 0$, then

$$\int_0^1 f''(x) g(x)\, dx = \int_0^1 f(x) g''(x)\, dx.$$

77. Possible and impossible integrals Let $I_n = \int x^n e^{-x^2}\, dx$, where n is a nonnegative integer.

a. $I_0 = \int e^{-x^2}\, dx$ cannot be expressed in terms of elementary functions. Evaluate I_1.

b. Use integration by parts to evaluate I_3.

c. Use integration by parts and the result of part (b) to evaluate I_5.

d. Show that, in general, if n is odd, then $I_n = -\frac{1}{2} e^{-x^2} p_{n-1}(x)$, where p_{n-1} is a polynomial of degree $n - 1$.

e. Argue that if n is even, then I_n cannot be expressed in terms of elementary functions.

78. Looking ahead (to Chapter 9) Suppose that a function f has derivatives of all orders near $x = 0$. By the Fundamental Theorem of Calculus,

$$f(x) - f(0) = \int_0^x f'(t)\, dt.$$

a. Evaluate the integral using integration by parts to show that

$$f(x) = f(0) + x f'(0) + \int_0^x f''(t)(x - t)\, dt.$$

b. Show that integrating by parts n times gives

$$f(x) = f(0) + x f'(0) + \frac{1}{2!} x^2 f''(0) + \cdots + \frac{1}{n!} x^n f^{(n)}(0)$$
$$+ \frac{1}{n!} \int_0^x f^{(n+1)}(t)(x - t)^n\, dt + \cdots.$$

This expression, called the *Taylor series* for f at $x = 0$, is revisited in Chapter 9.

QUICK CHECK ANSWERS

1. Let $u = x$ and $dv = \cos x\, dx$.
2. $\frac{d}{dx}(x \ln x - x + C) = \ln x$
3. Integration by parts must be applied five times. ◄

7.3 Trigonometric Integrals

At the moment, our inventory of integrals involving trigonometric functions is rather limited. For example, we can integrate $\sin ax$ and $\cos ax$, where a is a constant, but missing from the list are integrals of $\tan ax$, $\cot ax$, $\sec ax$, and $\csc ax$. It turns out that integrals of powers of trigonometric functions, such as $\int \cos^5 x\, dx$ and $\int \cos^2 x \sin^4 x\, dx$, are also important. The goal of this section is to develop techniques for evaluating integrals involving trigonometric functions. These techniques are indispensable when we encounter *trigonometric substitutions* in the next section.

➤ Some of the techniques described in this section also work for negative powers of trigonometric functions.

Integrating Powers of $\sin x$ or $\cos x$

Two strategies are employed when evaluating integrals of the form $\int \sin^m x\, dx$ or $\int \cos^n x\, dx$, where m and n are positive integers. Both strategies use trigonometric identities to recast the integrand, as shown in the first example.

EXAMPLE 1 **Powers of sine or cosine** Evaluate the following integrals.

a. $\int \cos^5 x\, dx$ **b.** $\int \sin^4 x\, dx$

> Pythagorean identities:
> $\cos^2 x + \sin^2 x = 1$
> $1 + \tan^2 x = \sec^2 x$
> $\cot^2 x + 1 = \csc^2 x$

SOLUTION

a. Integrals involving odd powers of $\cos x$ (or $\sin x$) are most easily evaluated by splitting off a single factor of $\cos x$ (or $\sin x$). In this case, we rewrite $\cos^5 x$ as $\cos^4 x \cdot \cos x$. Notice that $\cos^4 x$ can be written in terms of $\sin x$ using the identity $\cos^2 x = 1 - \sin^2 x$. The result is an integrand that readily yields to the substitution $u = \sin x$:

$$
\begin{aligned}
\int \cos^5 x\, dx &= \int \cos^4 x \cdot \cos x\, dx && \text{Split off } \cos x. \\
&= \int (1 - \sin^2 x)^2 \cdot \cos x\, dx && \text{Pythagorean identity} \\
&= \int (1 - u^2)^2\, du && \text{Let } u = \sin x;\ du = \cos x\, dx. \\
&= \int (1 - 2u^2 + u^4)\, du && \text{Expand.} \\
&= u - \frac{2}{3}u^3 + \frac{1}{5}u^5 + C && \text{Integrate.} \\
&= \sin x - \frac{2}{3}\sin^3 x + \frac{1}{5}\sin^5 x + C. && \text{Replace } u \text{ with } \sin x.
\end{aligned}
$$

> The half-angle formulas for $\sin^2 x$ and $\cos^2 x$ are easily confused. Use the phrase "sine is minus" to remember that a minus sign is associated with the half-angle formula for $\sin^2 x$, whereas a positive sign is used for $\cos^2 x$.

b. With even positive powers of $\sin x$ or $\cos x$, we use the half-angle formulas

$$\sin^2 x = \frac{1 - \cos 2x}{2} \quad \text{and} \quad \cos^2 x = \frac{1 + \cos 2x}{2}$$

to reduce the powers in the integrand:

$$
\begin{aligned}
\int \sin^4 x\, dx &= \int \Bigg(\underbrace{\frac{1 - \cos 2x}{2}}_{\sin^2 x}\Bigg)^2 dx && \text{Half-angle formula} \\
&= \frac{1}{4}\int (1 - 2\cos 2x + \cos^2 2x)\, dx. && \text{Expand the integrand.}
\end{aligned}
$$

Using the half-angle formula for $\cos^2 2x$, the evaluation may be completed:

$$
\begin{aligned}
\int \sin^4 x\, dx &= \frac{1}{4}\int \Bigg(1 - 2\cos 2x + \underbrace{\frac{1 + \cos 4x}{2}}_{\cos^2 2x}\Bigg) dx && \text{Half-angle formula} \\
&= \frac{1}{4}\int \left(\frac{3}{2} - 2\cos 2x + \frac{1}{2}\cos 4x\right) dx && \text{Simplify.} \\
&= \frac{3x}{8} - \frac{1}{4}\sin 2x + \frac{1}{32}\sin 4x + C. && \text{Evaluate the integrals.}
\end{aligned}
$$

Related Exercises 9–14 ◄

QUICK CHECK 1 Evaluate $\int \sin^3 x\, dx$ by splitting off a factor of $\sin x$, rewriting $\sin^2 x$ in terms of $\cos x$, and using an appropriate u-substitution. ◄

Integrating Products of Powers of $\sin x$ and $\cos x$

We now consider integrals of the form $\int \sin^m x \cos^n x\, dx$. If m is an odd, positive integer, we split off a factor of $\sin x$ and write the remaining even power of $\sin x$ in terms of cosine functions. This step prepares the integrand for the substitution $u = \cos x$, and the resulting integral is readily evaluated. A similar strategy is used when n is an odd, positive integer.

If both m and n are even positive integers, the half-angle formulas are used to transform the integrand into a polynomial in $\cos 2x$, each of whose terms can be integrated, as shown in Example 2.

EXAMPLE 2 **Products of sine and cosine** Evaluate the following integrals.

a. $\int \sin^4 x \cos^2 x\, dx$ **b.** $\int \sin^3 x \cos^{-2} x\, dx$

SOLUTION

a. When both powers are even positive integers, the half-angle formulas are used:

$$\int \sin^4 x \cos^2 x\, dx = \int \underbrace{\left(\frac{1-\cos 2x}{2}\right)^2}_{\sin^2 x}\underbrace{\left(\frac{1+\cos 2x}{2}\right)}_{\cos^2 x} dx \qquad \text{Half-angle formulas}$$

$$= \frac{1}{8}\int (1 - \cos 2x - \cos^2 2x + \cos^3 2x)\, dx. \qquad \text{Expand.}$$

The third term in the integrand is rewritten with a half-angle formula. For the last term, a factor of $\cos 2x$ is split off, and the resulting even power of $\cos 2x$ is written in terms of $\sin 2x$ to prepare for a u-substitution:

$$\int \sin^4 x \cos^2 x\, dx =$$

$$\frac{1}{8}\int \left(1 - \cos 2x - \overbrace{\left(\frac{1+\cos 4x}{2}\right)}^{\cos^2 2x}\right) dx + \frac{1}{8}\int \overbrace{(1 - \sin^2 2x)}^{\cos^2 2x} \cdot \cos 2x\, dx.$$

Finally, the integrals are evaluated, using the substitution $u = \sin 2x$ for the second integral. After simplification, we find that

$$\int \sin^4 x \cos^2 x\, dx = \frac{1}{16}x - \frac{1}{64}\sin 4x - \frac{1}{48}\sin^3 2x + C.$$

b. When at least one power is odd and positive, the following approach works:

$$\int \sin^3 x \cos^{-2} x\, dx = \int \sin^2 x \cos^{-2} x \cdot \sin x\, dx \qquad \text{Split off } \sin x.$$

$$= \int (1 - \cos^2 x)\cos^{-2} x \cdot \sin x\, dx \qquad \text{Pythagorean identity}$$

$$= -\int (1 - u^2)\, u^{-2}\, du \qquad u = \cos x;\ du = -\sin x\, dx$$

$$= \int (1 - u^{-2})\, du = u + \frac{1}{u} + C \qquad \text{Evaluate the integral.}$$

$$= \cos x + \sec x + C. \qquad \text{Replace } u \text{ with } \cos x.$$

Related Exercises 15–24 ◄

QUICK CHECK 2 What strategy would you use to evaluate $\int \sin^3 x \cos^3 x\, dx$? ◄

Table 7.2 summarizes the techniques used to evaluate integrals of the form $\int \sin^m x \cos^n x\, dx$.

➤ If both m and n are odd, you may split off $\sin x$ or $\cos x$; both choices are effective.

Table 7.2

$\int \sin^m x \cos^n x\, dx$	**Strategy**
m odd and positive, n real	Split off $\sin x$, rewrite the resulting even power of $\sin x$ in terms of $\cos x$, and then use $u = \cos x$.
n odd and positive, m real	Split off $\cos x$, rewrite the resulting even power of $\cos x$ in terms of $\sin x$, and then use $u = \sin x$.
m and n both even, nonnegative integers	Use half-angle formulas to transform the integrand into a polynomial in $\cos 2x$ and apply the preceding strategies once again to powers of $\cos 2x$ greater than 1.

Reduction Formulas

Evaluating an integral such as $\int \sin^8 x\, dx$ using the method of Example 1b is tedious, at best. For this reason, *reduction formulas* have been developed to ease the workload. A reduction formula equates an integral involving a power of a function with another integral in which the power is reduced; several reduction formulas were encountered in Exercises 44–47 of Section 7.2. Here are some frequently used reduction formulas for trigonometric integrals.

Reduction Formulas

Assume n is a positive integer.

1. $$\int \sin^n x\, dx = -\frac{\sin^{n-1} x \cos x}{n} + \frac{n-1}{n}\int \sin^{n-2} x\, dx$$

2. $$\int \cos^n x\, dx = \frac{\cos^{n-1} x \sin x}{n} + \frac{n-1}{n}\int \cos^{n-2} x\, dx$$

3. $$\int \tan^n x\, dx = \frac{\tan^{n-1} x}{n-1} - \int \tan^{n-2} x\, dx,\ n \neq 1$$

4. $$\int \sec^n x\, dx = \frac{\sec^{n-2} x \tan x}{n-1} + \frac{n-2}{n-1}\int \sec^{n-2} x\, dx,\ n \neq 1$$

Formulas 1, 3, and 4 are derived in Exercises 64–66. The derivation of formula 2 is similar to that of formula 1.

EXAMPLE 3 **Powers of $\tan x$** Evaluate $\int \tan^4 x\, dx$.

SOLUTION Reduction formula 3 gives

$$\int \tan^4 x\, dx = \frac{1}{3}\tan^3 x - \underbrace{\int \tan^2 x\, dx}_{\text{use (3) again}}$$

$$= \frac{1}{3}\tan^3 x - \Big(\tan x - \int \underbrace{\tan^0 x}_{=1}\, dx\Big)$$

$$= \frac{1}{3}\tan^3 x - \tan x + x + C.$$

An alternative solution uses the identity $\tan^2 x = \sec^2 x - 1$:

$$\int \tan^4 x\,dx = \int \tan^2 x\,\underbrace{(\sec^2 x - 1)}_{\tan^2 x}\,dx$$

$$= \int \tan^2 x \sec^2 x\,dx - \int \tan^2 x\,dx.$$

The substitution $u = \tan x$, $du = \sec^2 x\,dx$ is used in the first integral, and the identity $\tan^2 x = \sec^2 x - 1$ is used again in the second integral:

$$\int \tan^4 x\,dx = \int \underbrace{\tan^2 x}_{u^2}\,\underbrace{\sec^2 x\,dx}_{du} - \int \tan^2 x\,dx$$

$$= \int u^2\,du - \int (\sec^2 x - 1)\,dx \qquad \text{Substitution and identity}$$

$$= \frac{u^3}{3} - \tan x + x + C \qquad \text{Evaluate integrals.}$$

$$= \frac{1}{3}\tan^3 x - \tan x + x + C. \qquad u = \tan x$$

Related Exercises 25–30 ◀

Note that for odd powers of $\tan x$ and $\sec x$, the use of reduction formula 3 or 4 will eventually lead to $\int \tan x\,dx$ or $\int \sec x\,dx$. Theorem 7.1 gives these integrals, along with the integrals of $\cot x$ and $\csc x$.

THEOREM 7.1 Integrals of $\tan x$, $\cot x$, $\sec x$, and $\csc x$

$$\int \tan x\,dx = -\ln|\cos x| + C = \ln|\sec x| + C \qquad \int \cot x\,dx = \ln|\sin x| + C$$

$$\int \sec x\,dx = \ln|\sec x + \tan x| + C \qquad \int \csc x\,dx = -\ln|\csc x + \cot x| + C$$

Proof: In the first integral, $\tan x$ is expressed as the ratio of $\sin x$ and $\cos x$ to prepare for a standard substitution:

$$\int \tan x\,dx = \int \frac{\sin x}{\cos x}\,dx$$

$$= -\int \frac{1}{u}\,du \qquad u = \cos x;\ du = -\sin x\,dx$$

$$= -\ln|u| + C = -\ln|\cos x| + C.$$

Using properties of logarithms, the integral can also be written

$$\int \tan x\,dx = -\ln|\cos x| + C = \ln|(\cos x)^{-1}| + C = \ln|\sec x| + C.$$

To integrate sec x, we utilize the technique of multiplying by 1 introduced in Section 7.1:

$$\int \sec x\,dx = \int \sec x \cdot \underbrace{\frac{\sec x + \tan x}{\sec x + \tan x}}_{1}\,dx \quad \text{Multiply integrand by 1.}$$

$$= \int \frac{\sec^2 x + \sec x \tan x}{\sec x + \tan x}\,dx \quad \text{Expand numerator.}$$

$$= \int \frac{du}{u} \quad u = \sec x + \tan x;\ du = (\sec^2 x + \sec x \tan x)\,dx$$

$$= \ln|u| + C \quad \text{Integrate.}$$

$$= \ln|\sec x + \tan x| + C. \quad u = \sec x + \tan x$$

Derivations of the remaining integrals are left to Exercises 46–47.

Integrating Products of Powers of tan x and sec x

Integrals of the form $\int \tan^m x \sec^n x\,dx$ are evaluated using methods analogous to those used for $\int \sin^m x \cos^n x\,dx$. For example, if n is an even positive integer, we split off a factor of $\sec^2 x$ and write the remaining even power of sec x in terms of tan x. This step prepares the integral for the substitution $u = \tan x$. If m is odd and positive, we split off a factor of sec x tan x (the derivative of sec x), which prepares the integral for the substitution $u = \sec x$. If m is even and n is odd, the integrand is expressed as a polynomial in sec x, each of whose terms is handled by a reduction formula. Example 4 illustrates these techniques.

EXAMPLE 4 **Products of tan x and sec x** Evaluate the following integrals.

a. $\int \tan^3 x \sec^4 x\,dx$ **b.** $\int \tan^2 x \sec x\,dx$

SOLUTION

a. With an even power of sec x, we split off a factor of $\sec^2 x$ and prepare the integral for the substitution $u = \tan x$:

$$\int \tan^3 x \sec^4 x\,dx = \int \tan^3 x \sec^2 x \cdot \sec^2 x\,dx$$

$$= \int \tan^3 x\,(\tan^2 x + 1) \cdot \sec^2 x\,dx \quad \sec^2 x = \tan^2 x + 1$$

$$= \int u^3 (u^2 + 1)\,du \quad u = \tan x;\ du = \sec^2 x\,dx$$

$$= \frac{1}{6}\tan^6 x + \frac{1}{4}\tan^4 x + C. \quad \text{Evaluate; } u = \tan x.$$

Because the integrand also has an odd power of tan x, an alternative solution is to split off a factor of sec x tan x and prepare the integral for the substitution $u = \sec x$:

$$\int \tan^3 x \sec^4 x\,dx = \int \underbrace{\tan^2 x}_{\sec^2 x - 1} \sec^3 x \cdot \sec x \tan x\,dx$$

$$= \int (\sec^2 x - 1) \sec^3 x \cdot \sec x \tan x\,dx$$

$$= \int (u^2 - 1)\,u^3\,du \quad u = \sec x;\ du = \sec x \tan x\,dx$$

$$= \frac{1}{6}\sec^6 x - \frac{1}{4}\sec^4 x + C. \quad \text{Evaluate; } u = \sec x.$$

➤ In Example 4a, the two methods produce results that look different, but are equivalent. This is common when evaluating trigonometric integrals. For instance, evaluate $\int \sin^4 x\,dx$ using reduction formula 1, and compare your answer to

$$\frac{3x}{8} - \frac{1}{4}\sin 2x + \frac{1}{32}\sin 4x + C,$$

the solution found in Example 1b.

The apparent difference in the two solutions given here is reconciled by using the identity $1 + \tan^2 x = \sec^2 x$ to transform the second result into the first, the only difference being an additive constant, which is part of C.

b. In this case, we write the even power of $\tan x$ in terms of $\sec x$:

$$\int \tan^2 x \sec x\, dx = \int (\sec^2 x - 1) \sec x\, dx \qquad \tan^2 x = \sec^2 x - 1$$

$$= \int \sec^3 x\, dx - \int \sec x\, dx$$

$$= \overbrace{\frac{1}{2} \sec x \tan x + \frac{1}{2}\int \sec x\, dx}^{\text{reduction formula 4}} - \int \sec x\, dx$$

$$= \frac{1}{2} \sec x \tan x - \frac{1}{2} \ln |\sec x + \tan x| + C. \qquad \text{Add secant integrals; use Theorem 7.1.}$$

Related Exercises 31–44 ◄

Table 7.3 summarizes the methods used to integrate $\int \tan^m x \sec^n x\, dx$. Analogous techniques are used for $\int \cot^m x \csc^n x\, dx$.

Table 7.3

$\int \tan^m x \sec^n x\, dx$	**Strategy**
n even	Split off $\sec^2 x$, rewrite the remaining even power of $\sec x$ in terms of $\tan x$, and use $u = \tan x$.
m odd	Split off $\sec x \tan x$, rewrite the remaining even power of $\tan x$ in terms of $\sec x$, and use $u = \sec x$.
m even and n odd	Rewrite the even power of $\tan x$ in terms of $\sec x$ to produce a polynomial in $\sec x$; apply reduction formula 4 to each term.

SECTION 7.3 EXERCISES

Review Questions

1. State the half-angle identities used to integrate $\sin^2 x$ and $\cos^2 x$.
2. State the three Pythagorean identities.
3. Describe the method used to integrate $\sin^3 x$.
4. Describe the method used to integrate $\sin^m x \cos^n x$, for m even and n odd.
5. What is a reduction formula?
6. How would you evaluate $\int \cos^2 x \sin^3 x\, dx$?
7. How would you evaluate $\int \tan^{10} x \sec^2 x\, dx$?
8. How would you evaluate $\int \sec^{12} x \tan x\, dx$?

Basic Skills

9–14. Integrals of sin x or cos x *Evaluate the following integrals.*

9. $\int \sin^2 x\, dx$
10. $\int \sin^3 x\, dx$
11. $\int \cos^3 x\, dx$
12. $\int \cos^4 2\theta\, d\theta$
13. $\int \sin^5 x\, dx$
14. $\int \cos^3 20x\, dx$

15–24. Integrals of sin x and cos x *Evaluate the following integrals.*

15. $\int \sin^2 x \cos^2 x\, dx$
16. $\int \sin^3 x \cos^5 x\, dx$
17. $\int \sin^3 x \cos^2 x\, dx$
18. $\int \sin^2 \theta \cos^5 \theta\, d\theta$
19. $\int \cos^3 x \sqrt{\sin x}\, dx$
20. $\int \sin^3 \theta \cos^{-2} \theta\, d\theta$
21. $\int \sin^5 x \cos^{-2} x\, dx$
22. $\int \sin^{-3/2} x \cos^3 x\, dx$
23. $\int \sin^2 x \cos^4 x\, dx$
24. $\int \sin^3 x \cos^{3/2} x\, dx$

25–30. Integrals of tan x or cot x *Evaluate the following integrals.*

25. $\int \tan^2 x\, dx$
26. $\int 6 \sec^4 x\, dx$
27. $\int \cot^4 x\, dx$
28. $\int \tan^3 \theta\, d\theta$
29. $\int 20 \tan^6 x\, dx$
30. $\int \cot^5 3x\, dx$

31–44. Integrals involving $\tan x$ and $\sec x$ *Evaluate the following integrals.*

31. $\int 10 \tan^9 x \sec^2 x\, dx$

32. $\int \tan^9 x \sec^4 x\, dx$

33. $\int \tan x \sec^3 x\, dx$

34. $\int \sqrt{\tan x} \sec^4 x\, dx$

35. $\int \tan^3 4x\, dx$

36. $\int \frac{\sec^2 x}{\tan^5 x}\, dx$

37. $\int \sec^2 x \tan^{1/2} x\, dx$

38. $\int \sec^{-2} x \tan^3 x\, dx$

39. $\int \frac{\csc^4 x}{\cot^2 x}\, dx$

40. $\int \csc^{10} x \cot x\, dx$

41. $\int_0^{\pi/4} \sec^4 \theta\, d\theta$

42. $\int \tan^5 \theta \sec^4 \theta\, d\theta$

43. $\int_{\pi/6}^{\pi/3} \cot^3 \theta\, d\theta$

44. $\int_0^{\pi/4} \tan^3 \theta \sec^2 \theta\, d\theta$

Further Explorations

45. **Explain why or why not** Determine whether the following statements are true and give an explanation or counterexample.
    a. If m is a positive integer, then $\int_0^{\pi} \cos^{2m+1} x\, dx = 0$.
    b. If m is a positive integer, then $\int_0^{\pi} \sin^m x\, dx = 0$.

46–47. Integrals of $\cot x$ and $\csc x$

46. Use a change of variables to prove that $\int \cot x\, dx = \ln |\sin x| + C$.

47. Prove that $\int \csc x\, dx = -\ln |\csc x + \cot x| + C$. (*Hint:* See the proof of Theorem 7.1.)

48. **Comparing areas** The region R_1 is bounded by the graph of $y = \tan x$ and the x-axis on the interval $[0, \pi/3]$. The region R_2 is bounded by the graph of $y = \sec x$ and the x-axis on the interval $[0, \pi/6]$. Which region has the greater area?

49. **Region between curves** Find the area of the region bounded by the graphs of $y = \tan x$ and $y = \sec x$ on the interval $[0, \pi/4]$.

50–57. Additional integrals *Evaluate the following integrals.*

50. $\int_0^{\sqrt{\pi/2}} x \sin^3 (x^2)\, dx$

51. $\int \frac{\sec^4 (\ln \theta)}{\theta}\, d\theta$

52. $\int_{\pi/6}^{\pi/2} \frac{dy}{\sin y}$

53. $\int_{-\pi/3}^{\pi/3} \sqrt{\sec^2 \theta - 1}\, d\theta$

54. $\int_{-\pi/4}^{\pi/4} \tan^3 x \sec^2 x\, dx$

55. $\int_0^{\pi} (1 - \cos 2x)^{3/2}\, dx$

56. $\int \csc^{10} x \cot^3 x\, dx$

57. $\int e^x \sec (e^x + 1)\, dx$

58–61. Square roots *Evaluate the following integrals.*

58. $\int_{-\pi/4}^{\pi/4} \sqrt{1 + \cos 4x}\, dx$

59. $\int_0^{\pi/2} \sqrt{1 - \cos 2x}\, dx$

60. $\int_0^{\pi/8} \sqrt{1 - \cos 8x}\, dx$

61. $\int_0^{\pi/4} (1 + \cos 4x)^{3/2}\, dx$

62. **Sine football** Find the volume of the solid generated when the region bounded by the graph of $y = \sin x$ and the x-axis on the interval $[0, \pi]$ is revolved about the x-axis.

63. **Arc length** Find the length of the curve $y = \ln (\sec x)$, for $0 \le x \le \pi/4$.

64. **A sine reduction formula** Use integration by parts to obtain a reduction formula for positive integers n:
$$\int \sin^n x\, dx = -\sin^{n-1} x \cos x + (n - 1) \int \sin^{n-2} x \cos^2 x\, dx.$$
Then use an identity to obtain the reduction formula
$$\int \sin^n x\, dx = -\frac{\sin^{n-1} x \cos x}{n} + \frac{n-1}{n} \int \sin^{n-2} x\, dx.$$
Use this reduction formula to evaluate $\int \sin^6 x\, dx$.

65. **A tangent reduction formula** Prove that for positive integers $n \neq 1$,
$$\int \tan^n x\, dx = \frac{\tan^{n-1} x}{n-1} - \int \tan^{n-2} x\, dx.$$
Use the formula to evaluate $\int_0^{\pi/4} \tan^3 x\, dx$.

66. **A secant reduction formula** Prove that for positive integers $n \neq 1$,
$$\int \sec^n x\, dx = \frac{\sec^{n-2} x \tan x}{n-1} + \frac{n-2}{n-1} \int \sec^{n-2} x\, dx.$$
(*Hint:* Integrate by parts with $u = \sec^{n-2} x$ and $dv = \sec^2 x\, dx$.)

Applications

67–71. Integrals of the form $\int \sin mx \cos nx\, dx$ *Use the following three identities to evaluate the given integrals.*

$$\sin mx \sin nx = \frac{1}{2}\left(\cos ((m - n)x) - \cos ((m + n)x)\right)$$
$$\sin mx \cos nx = \frac{1}{2}\left(\sin ((m - n)x) + \sin ((m + n)x)\right)$$
$$\cos mx \cos nx = \frac{1}{2}\left(\cos ((m - n)x) + \cos ((m + n)x)\right)$$

67. $\int \sin 3x \cos 7x\, dx$

68. $\int \sin 5x \sin 7x\, dx$

69. $\int \sin 3x \sin 2x\, dx$

70. $\int \cos x \cos 2x\, dx$

71. Prove the following **orthogonality relations** (which are used to generate *Fourier series*). Assume m and n are integers with $m \neq n$.
    a. $\int_0^{\pi} \sin mx \sin nx\, dx = 0$
    b. $\int_0^{\pi} \cos mx \cos nx\, dx = 0$
    c. $\int_0^{\pi} \sin mx \cos nx\, dx = 0$, for $|m + n|$ even

72. Mercator map projection The Mercator map projection was proposed by the Flemish geographer Gerardus Mercator (1512–1594). The stretching factor of the Mercator map as a function of the latitude θ is given by the function

$$G(\theta) = \int_0^\theta \sec x\, dx.$$

Graph G, for $0 \le \theta < \pi/2$. (See the Guided Project *Mercator projections* for a derivation of this integral.)

Additional Exercises

73. Exploring powers of sine and cosine

a. Graph the functions $f_1(x) = \sin^2 x$ and $f_2(x) = \sin^2 2x$ on the interval $[0, \pi]$. Find the area under these curves on $[0, \pi]$.

b. Graph a few more of the functions $f_n(x) = \sin^2 nx$ on the interval $[0, \pi]$, where n is a positive integer. Find the area under these curves on $[0, \pi]$. Comment on your observations.

c. Prove that $\int_0^\pi \sin^2(nx)\, dx$ has the same value for all positive integers n.

d. Does the conclusion of part (c) hold if sine is replaced with cosine?

e. Repeat parts (a), (b), and (c) with $\sin^2 x$ replaced with $\sin^4 x$. Comment on your observations.

f. Challenge problem: Show that for $m = 1, 2, 3, \ldots,$

$$\int_0^\pi \sin^{2m} x\, dx = \int_0^\pi \cos^{2m} x\, dx = \pi \cdot \frac{1\cdot 3\cdot 5\cdots(2m-1)}{2\cdot 4\cdot 6\cdots 2m}.$$

QUICK CHECK ANSWERS

1. $\frac{1}{3}\cos^3 x - \cos x + C$ **2.** Write $\int \sin^3 x \cos^3 x\, dx = \int \sin^2 x \cos^3 x \sin x\, dx = \int (1 - \cos^2 x)\cos^3 x \sin x\, dx$. Then use the substitution $u = \cos x$. Or begin by writing $\int \sin^3 x \cos^3 x\, dx = \int \sin^3 x \cos^2 x \cos x\, dx$. ◄

7.4 Trigonometric Substitutions

In Example 4 of Section 6.5, we wrote the arc length integral for the segment of the parabola $y = x^2$ on the interval $[0, 2]$ as

$$\int_0^2 \sqrt{1 + 4x^2}\, dx = \int_0^2 2\sqrt{\tfrac{1}{4} + x^2}\, dx.$$

At the time, we did not have the analytical methods needed to evaluate this integral. The difficulty with $\int_0^2 \sqrt{1 + 4x^2}\, dx$ is that the square root of a sum (or difference) of two squares is not easily simplified. On the other hand, the square root of a product of two squares is easily simplified: $\sqrt{A^2B^2} = |AB|$. If we could somehow replace $1 + 4x^2$ with a product of squares, this integral might be easier to evaluate. The goal of this section is to introduce techniques that transform sums of squares $a^2 + x^2$ (and the difference of squares $a^2 - x^2$ and $x^2 - a^2$) into products of squares.

➤ To understand how a sum of squares is rewritten as a product of squares, think of the Pythagorean Theorem: $a^2 + b^2 = c^2$. A rearrangement of this theorem leads to the standard substitution for integrals involving the difference of squares $a^2 - x^2$. The term $\sqrt{a^2 - x^2}$ is the length of one side of a right triangle whose hypotenuse has length a and whose other side has length x. Labeling one acute angle θ, we see that $x = a\sin\theta$.

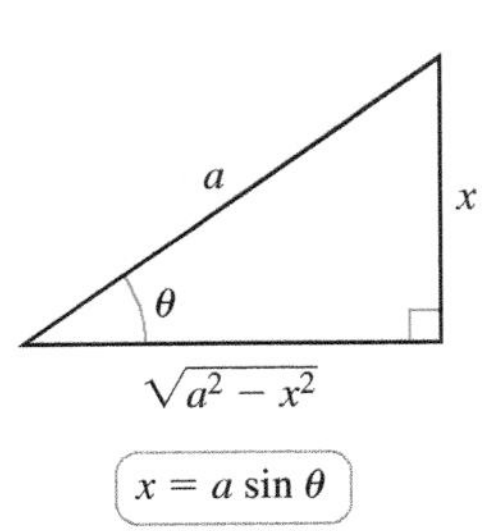

$x = a \sin\theta$

Integrals similar to the arc length integral for the parabola arise in many different situations. For example, electrostatic, magnetic, and gravitational forces obey an inverse square law (their strength is proportional to $1/r^2$, where r is a distance). Computing these force fields in two dimensions leads to integrals such as $\int \frac{dx}{\sqrt{x^2 + a^2}}$ or $\int \frac{dx}{(x^2 + a^2)^{3/2}}$. It turns out that integrals containing the terms $a^2 \pm x^2$ or $x^2 - a^2$, where a is a constant, can be simplified using somewhat unexpected substitutions involving trigonometric functions. The new integrals produced by these substitutions are often trigonometric integrals of the variety studied in the preceding section.

Integrals Involving $a^2 - x^2$

Suppose you are faced with an integral whose integrand contains the term $a^2 - x^2$, where a is a positive constant. Observe what happens when x is replaced with $a \sin\theta$:

$$\begin{aligned} a^2 - x^2 &= a^2 - (a\sin\theta)^2 && \text{Replace } x \text{ with } a\sin\theta. \\ &= a^2 - a^2\sin^2\theta && \text{Simplify.} \\ &= a^2(1 - \sin^2\theta) && \text{Factor.} \\ &= a^2\cos^2\theta. && 1 - \sin^2\theta = \cos^2\theta \end{aligned}$$

QUICK CHECK 1 Use a substitution of the form $x = a \sin\theta$ to transform $9 - x^2$ into a product. ◄

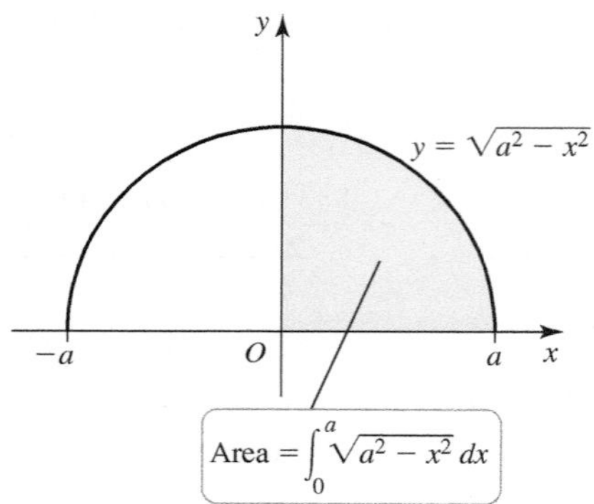

Figure 7.2

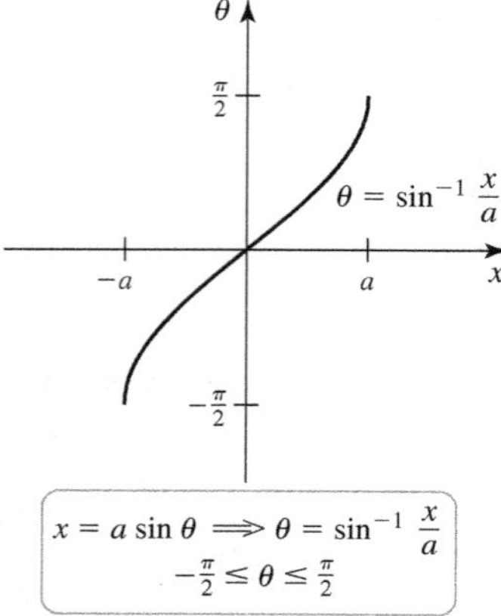

Figure 7.3

➤ The key identities for integrating $\sin^2\theta$ and $\cos^2\theta$ are

$$\sin^2\theta = \frac{1 - \cos 2\theta}{2} \quad\text{and}$$

$$\cos^2\theta = \frac{1 + \cos 2\theta}{2}.$$

This calculation shows that the substitution $x = a\sin\theta$ turns the difference $a^2 - x^2$ into the product $a^2\cos^2\theta$. The resulting integral—now with respect to θ—is often easier to evaluate than the original integral. The details of this procedure are spelled out in the following examples.

EXAMPLE 1 **Area of a circle** Verify that the area of a circle of radius a is πa^2.

SOLUTION The function $f(x) = \sqrt{a^2 - x^2}$ describes the upper half of a circle centered at the origin with radius a (Figure 7.2). The region under this curve on the interval $[0, a]$ is a quarter-circle. Therefore, the area of the full circle is $4\int_0^a \sqrt{a^2 - x^2}\,dx$.

Because the integrand contains the expression $a^2 - x^2$, we use the trigonometric substitution $x = a\sin\theta$. As with all substitutions, the differential associated with the substitution must be computed:

$$x = a\sin\theta \quad\text{implies that}\quad dx = a\cos\theta\,d\theta.$$

The substitution $x = a\sin\theta$ can also be written $\theta = \sin^{-1}(x/a)$, where $-\pi/2 \le \theta \le \pi/2$ (Figure 7.3). Notice that the new variable θ plays the role of an angle. Replacing x with $a\sin\theta$ in the integrand, we have

$$\begin{aligned}
\sqrt{a^2 - x^2} &= \sqrt{a^2 - (a\sin\theta)^2} && \text{Replace } x \text{ with } a\sin\theta.\\
&= \sqrt{a^2(1 - \sin^2\theta)} && \text{Factor.}\\
&= \sqrt{a^2\cos^2\theta} && 1 - \sin^2\theta = \cos^2\theta\\
&= |a\cos\theta| && \sqrt{x^2} = |x|\\
&= a\cos\theta. && a > 0,\ \cos\theta \ge 0, \text{ for } -\frac{\pi}{2} \le \theta \le \frac{\pi}{2}
\end{aligned}$$

We also change the limits of integration: When $x = 0$, $\theta = \sin^{-1} 0 = 0$; when $x = a$, $\theta = \sin^{-1}(a/a) = \sin^{-1} 1 = \pi/2$. Making these substitutions, the integral is evaluated as follows:

$$\begin{aligned}
4\int_0^a \sqrt{a^2 - x^2}\,dx &= 4\int_0^{\pi/2} \underbrace{a\cos\theta}_{\substack{\text{integrand}\\\text{simplified}}} \cdot \underbrace{a\cos\theta\,d\theta}_{dx} && x = a\sin\theta,\ dx = a\cos\theta\,d\theta\\
&= 4a^2\int_0^{\pi/2} \cos^2\theta\,d\theta && \text{Simplify.}\\
&= 4a^2\left(\frac{\theta}{2} + \frac{\sin 2\theta}{4}\right)\Bigg|_0^{\pi/2} && \cos^2\theta = \frac{1 + \cos 2\theta}{2}\\
&= 4a^2\left(\left(\frac{\pi}{4} + 0\right) - (0 + 0)\right) = \pi a^2. && \text{Simplify.}
\end{aligned}$$

A similar calculation (Exercise 66) gives the area of an ellipse.

Related Exercises 7–16 ◄

EXAMPLE 2 **Sine substitution** Evaluate $\displaystyle\int \frac{dx}{(16 - x^2)^{3/2}}$.

SOLUTION The factor $16 - x^2$ has the form $a^2 - x^2$ with $a = 4$, so we use the substitution $x = 4\sin\theta$. It follows that $dx = 4\cos\theta\,d\theta$. We now simplify $(16 - x^2)^{3/2}$:

$$\begin{aligned}
(16 - x^2)^{3/2} &= (16 - (4\sin\theta)^2)^{3/2} && \text{Substitute } x = 4\sin\theta.\\
&= (16(1 - \sin^2\theta))^{3/2} && \text{Factor.}\\
&= (16\cos^2\theta)^{3/2} && 1 - \sin^2\theta = \cos^2\theta\\
&= 64\cos^3\theta. && \text{Simplify.}
\end{aligned}$$

Replacing the factors $(16 - x^2)^{3/2}$ and dx of the original integral with appropriate expressions in θ, we have

$$\int \frac{\overbrace{dx}^{4\cos\theta\,d\theta}}{\underbrace{(16 - x^2)^{3/2}}_{64\cos^3\theta}} = \int \frac{4\cos\theta}{64\cos^3\theta}\,d\theta$$

$$= \frac{1}{16}\int \frac{d\theta}{\cos^2\theta}$$

$$= \frac{1}{16}\int \sec^2\theta\,d\theta \quad \text{Simplify.}$$

$$= \frac{1}{16}\tan\theta + C. \quad \text{Evaluate the integral.}$$

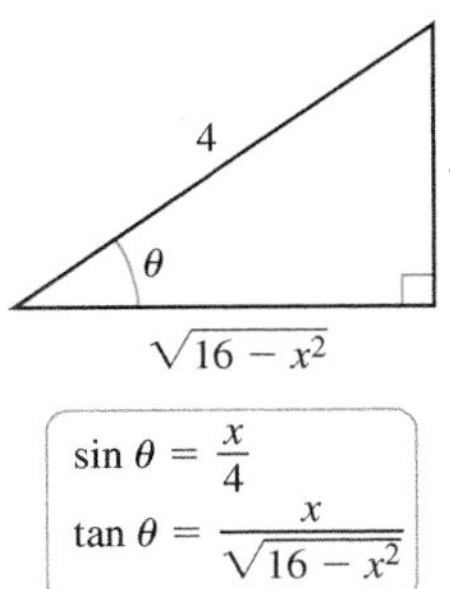

Figure 7.4

The final step is to express this result in terms of x. In many integrals, this step is most easily done with a reference triangle showing the relationship between x and θ. Figure 7.4 shows a right triangle with an angle θ and with the sides labeled such that $x = 4\sin\theta$ (or $\sin\theta = x/4$). Using this triangle, we see that $\tan\theta = \dfrac{x}{\sqrt{16 - x^2}}$, which implies that

$$\int \frac{dx}{(16 - x^2)^{3/2}} = \frac{1}{16}\tan\theta + C = \frac{x}{16\sqrt{16 - x^2}} + C.$$

Related Exercises 7–16 ◄

Integrals Involving $a^2 + x^2$ or $x^2 - a^2$

The additional trigonometric substitutions involving tangent and secant use a procedure similar to that used for the sine substitution. Figure 7.5 and Table 7.4 summarize the three basic trigonometric substitutions for real numbers $a > 0$.

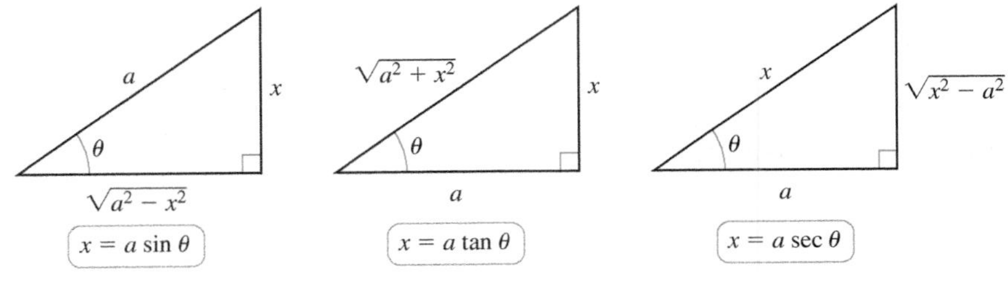

Figure 7.5

Table 7.4

The Integral Contains . . .	Corresponding Substitution	Useful Identity
$a^2 - x^2$	$x = a\sin\theta,\ -\frac{\pi}{2} \le \theta \le \frac{\pi}{2}$, for $\lvert x\rvert \le a$	$a^2 - a^2\sin^2\theta = a^2\cos^2\theta$
$a^2 + x^2$	$x = a\tan\theta,\ -\frac{\pi}{2} < \theta < \frac{\pi}{2}$	$a^2 + a^2\tan^2\theta = a^2\sec^2\theta$
$x^2 - a^2$	$x = a\sec\theta,\ \begin{cases} 0 \le \theta < \frac{\pi}{2}, \text{ for } x \ge a \\ \frac{\pi}{2} < \theta \le \pi, \text{ for } x \le -a \end{cases}$	$a^2\sec^2\theta - a^2 = a^2\tan^2\theta$

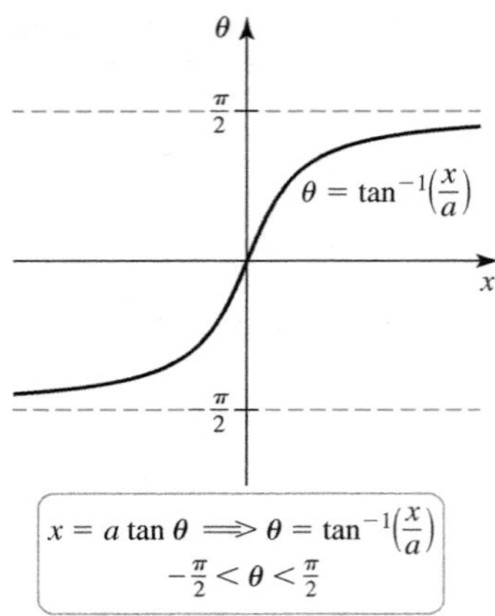

Figure 7.6

In order for the tangent substitution $x = a\tan\theta$ to be well defined, the angle θ must be restricted to the interval $-\pi/2 < \theta < \pi/2$, which is the range of $\tan^{-1}(x/a)$ (Figure 7.6). On this interval, $\sec\theta > 0$ and with $a > 0$, it is valid to write

$$\sqrt{a^2 + x^2} = \sqrt{a^2 + (a\tan\theta)^2} = \sqrt{a^2\underbrace{(1 + \tan^2\theta)}_{\sec^2\theta}} = a\sec\theta.$$

With the secant substitution, there is a technicality. As discussed in Section 1.4, $\theta = \sec^{-1}(x/a)$ is defined for $x \ge a$, in which case $0 \le \theta < \pi/2$, *and* for $x \le -a$, in which case $\pi/2 < \theta \le \pi$ (Figure 7.7). These restrictions on θ must be treated carefully when simplifying integrands with a factor of $\sqrt{x^2 - a^2}$. Because $\tan\theta$ is positive in the first quadrant but negative in the second, we have

$$\sqrt{x^2 - a^2} = \sqrt{a^2\underbrace{(\sec^2\theta - 1)}_{\tan^2\theta}} = |a\tan\theta| = \begin{cases} a\tan\theta & \text{if } 0 \le \theta < \dfrac{\pi}{2} \\ -a\tan\theta & \text{if } \dfrac{\pi}{2} < \theta \le \pi. \end{cases}$$

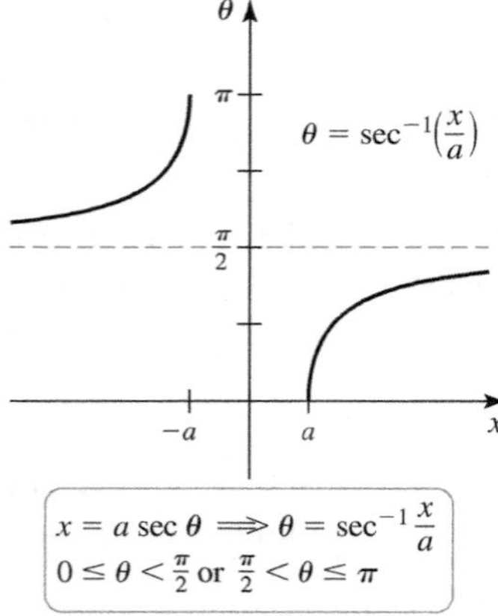

Figure 7.7

When evaluating a definite integral, you should check the limits of integration to see which of these two cases applies. For indefinite integrals, a piecewise formula is often needed, unless a restriction on the variable is given in the problem (see Exercises 85–88).

QUICK CHECK 2 What change of variables would you use for these integrals?

a. $\displaystyle\int \frac{x^2}{\sqrt{x^2 + 9}}\,dx$ **b.** $\displaystyle\int \frac{3}{x\sqrt{16 - x^2}}\,dx$? ◀

EXAMPLE 3 **Arc length of a parabola** Evaluate $\int_0^2 \sqrt{1 + 4x^2}\,dx$, the arc length of the segment of the parabola $y = x^2$ on $[0, 2]$.

SOLUTION Removing a factor of 4 from the square root, we have

$$\int_0^2 \sqrt{1 + 4x^2}\,dx = 2\int_0^2 \sqrt{\tfrac{1}{4} + x^2}\,dx = 2\int_0^2 \sqrt{\left(\tfrac{1}{2}\right)^2 + x^2}\,dx.$$

The integrand contains the expression $a^2 + x^2$, with $a = \frac{1}{2}$, which suggests the substitution $x = \frac{1}{2}\tan\theta$. It follows that $dx = \frac{1}{2}\sec^2\theta\,d\theta$, and

$$\sqrt{\left(\tfrac{1}{2}\right)^2 + x^2} = \sqrt{\left(\tfrac{1}{2}\right)^2 + \left(\tfrac{1}{2}\tan\theta\right)^2} = \frac{1}{2}\sqrt{\underbrace{1 + \tan^2\theta}_{\sec^2\theta}} = \frac{1}{2}\sec\theta.$$

➤ Because we are evaluating a definite integral, we could change the limits of integration to $\theta = 0$ and $\theta = \tan^{-1} 4$. However, $\tan^{-1} 4$ is not a standard angle, so it is easier to express the antiderivative in terms of x and use the original limits of integration.

Setting aside the limits of integration for the moment, we compute the antiderivative:

$$2\int \sqrt{\left(\tfrac{1}{2}\right)^2 + x^2}\,dx = 2\int \tfrac{1}{2}\sec\theta\,\underbrace{\tfrac{1}{2}\sec^2\theta\,d\theta}_{dx} \qquad x = \tfrac{1}{2}\tan\theta,\ dx = \tfrac{1}{2}\sec^2\theta\,d\theta$$

$$= \frac{1}{2}\int \sec^3\theta\,d\theta \qquad \text{Simplify.}$$

$$= \frac{1}{4}\left(\sec\theta\tan\theta + \ln|\sec\theta + \tan\theta|\right) + C. \qquad \text{Reduction formula 4, Section 7.3}$$

Using a reference triangle (Figure 7.8), we express the antiderivative in terms of the original variable x and evaluate the definite integral:

$$2\int_0^2 \sqrt{\left(\tfrac{1}{2}\right)^2 + x^2}\,dx = \frac{1}{4}\left(\underbrace{\sqrt{1 + 4x^2}}_{\sec\theta}\,\underbrace{2x}_{\tan\theta} + \ln\left|\underbrace{\sqrt{1 + 4x^2}}_{\sec\theta} + \underbrace{2x}_{\tan\theta}\right|\right)\Bigg|_0^2 \qquad \tan\theta = 2x,\ \sec\theta = \sqrt{1 + 4x^2}$$

$$= \frac{1}{4}\left(4\sqrt{17} + \ln\left(\sqrt{17} + 4\right)\right) \approx 4.65.$$

Related Exercises 17–56 ◀

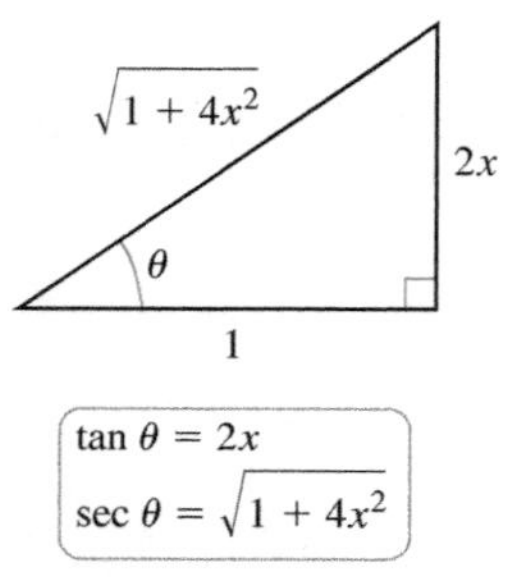

Figure 7.8

QUICK CHECK 3 The integral $\int \frac{dx}{a^2 + x^2} = \frac{1}{a}\tan^{-1}\frac{x}{a} + C$ is given in Section 4.9. Verify this result with the appropriate trigonometric substitution. ◄

EXAMPLE 4 Another tangent substitution Evaluate $\int \frac{dx}{(1 + x^2)^2}$.

SOLUTION The factor $1 + x^2$ suggests the substitution $x = \tan\theta$. It follows that $\theta = \tan^{-1} x$, $dx = \sec^2\theta\, d\theta$, and

$$(1 + x^2)^2 = (\underbrace{1 + \tan^2\theta}_{\sec^2\theta})^2 = \sec^4\theta.$$

Substituting these factors leads to

$$\int \frac{dx}{(1 + x^2)^2} = \int \frac{\sec^2\theta}{\sec^4\theta}\, d\theta \qquad x = \tan\theta,\ dx = \sec^2\theta\, d\theta$$

$$= \int \cos^2\theta\, d\theta \qquad \text{Simplify.}$$

$$= \frac{\theta}{2} + \frac{\sin 2\theta}{4} + C. \qquad \text{Integrate } \cos^2\theta = \frac{1 + \cos 2\theta}{2}.$$

The final step is to return to the original variable x. The first term $\theta/2$ is replaced with $\frac{1}{2}\tan^{-1} x$. The second term involving $\sin 2\theta$ requires the identity $\sin 2\theta = 2\sin\theta\cos\theta$. The reference triangle (Figure 7.9) tells us that

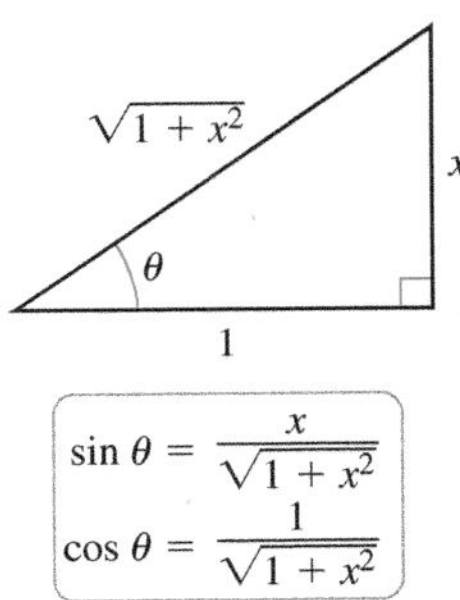

$\sin\theta = \frac{x}{\sqrt{1 + x^2}}$

$\cos\theta = \frac{1}{\sqrt{1 + x^2}}$

Figure 7.9

$$\frac{1}{4}\sin 2\theta = \frac{1}{2}\sin\theta\cos\theta = \frac{1}{2}\cdot\frac{x}{\sqrt{1 + x^2}}\cdot\frac{1}{\sqrt{1 + x^2}} = \frac{x}{2(1 + x^2)}.$$

The integration can now be completed:

$$\int \frac{dx}{(1 + x^2)^2} = \frac{\theta}{2} + \frac{\sin 2\theta}{4} + C$$

$$= \frac{1}{2}\tan^{-1} x + \frac{x}{2(1 + x^2)} + C.$$

Related Exercises 17–56 ◄

EXAMPLE 5 Multiple approaches Evaluate the integral $\int \frac{dx}{\sqrt{x^2 + 4}}$.

SOLUTION Our goal is to show that several different methods lead to the same end.

Solution 1: The term $x^2 + 4$ suggests the substitution $x = 2\tan\theta$, which implies that $dx = 2\sec^2\theta\, d\theta$ and

$$\sqrt{x^2 + 4} = \sqrt{4\tan^2\theta + 4} = \sqrt{4(\tan^2\theta + 1)} = 2\sqrt{\sec^2\theta} = 2\sec\theta.$$

Making these substitutions, the integral becomes

$$\int \frac{dx}{\sqrt{x^2 + 4}} = \int \frac{2\sec^2\theta}{2\sec\theta}\, d\theta = \int \sec\theta\, d\theta = \ln|\sec\theta + \tan\theta| + C.$$

To express the indefinite integral in terms of x, notice that with $x = 2\tan\theta$, we have

$$\tan\theta = \frac{x}{2} \quad\text{and}\quad \sec\theta = \sqrt{\tan^2\theta + 1} = \frac{1}{2}\sqrt{x^2 + 4}.$$

Therefore,

$$\int \frac{dx}{\sqrt{x^2+4}} = \ln|\sec\theta + \tan\theta| + C$$

$$= \ln\left|\frac{1}{2}\sqrt{x^2+4} + \frac{x}{2}\right| + C \qquad \text{Substitute for } \sec\theta \text{ and } \tan\theta.$$

$$= \ln\left(\frac{1}{2}(\sqrt{x^2+4} + x)\right) + C \qquad \text{Factor; } \sqrt{x^2+4} + x > 0.$$

$$= \ln\frac{1}{2} + \ln(\sqrt{x^2+4} + x) + C \qquad \ln ab = \ln a + \ln b$$

$$= \ln(\sqrt{x^2+4} + x) + C. \qquad \text{Absorb constant in } C.$$

Solution 2: Using Theorem 6.12 of Section 6.10, we see that

$$\int \frac{dx}{\sqrt{x^2+4}} = \sinh^{-1}\frac{x}{2} + C.$$

By Theorem 6.10 of Section 6.10, we also know that

$$\sinh^{-1}\frac{x}{2} = \ln\left(\frac{x}{2} + \sqrt{\left(\frac{x}{2}\right)^2 + 1}\right) = \ln\left(\frac{1}{2}(\sqrt{x^2+4} + x)\right),$$

which leads to the same result as in Solution 1.

Solution 3: Yet another approach is to use the substitution $x = 2\sinh t$, which implies that $dx = 2\cosh t\,dt$ and

$$\sqrt{x^2+4} = \sqrt{4\sinh^2 t + 4} = \sqrt{4(\sinh^2 t + 1)} = 2\sqrt{\cosh^2 t} = 2\cosh t.$$

The original integral now becomes

$$\int \frac{dx}{\sqrt{x^2+4}} = \int \frac{2\cosh t}{2\cosh t}\,dt = \int dt = t + C.$$

Because $x = 2\sinh t$, we have $t = \sinh^{-1}\frac{x}{2}$, which, by Theorem 6.10, leads to the result found in Solution 2.

This example shows that some integrals may be evaluated by more than one method. With practice, you will learn to identify the best method for a given integral.

Related Exercises 17–56 ◄

➤ Recall that to complete the square with $x^2 + bx + c$, you add and subtract $(b/2)^2$ to the expression, and then factor to form a perfect square. You could also make the single substitution $x + 2 = 3\sec\theta$ in Example 6.

EXAMPLE 6 A secant substitution Evaluate $\displaystyle\int_1^4 \frac{\sqrt{x^2+4x-5}}{x+2}\,dx.$

SOLUTION This example illustrates a useful preliminary step first encountered in Section 7.1. The integrand does not contain any of the patterns in Table 7.4 that suggest a trigonometric substitution. Completing the square does, however, lead to one of those patterns. Noting that $x^2 + 4x - 5 = (x+2)^2 - 9$, we change variables with $u = x + 2$ and write the integral as

$$\int_1^4 \frac{\sqrt{x^2+4x-5}}{x+2}\,dx = \int_1^4 \frac{\sqrt{(x+2)^2-9}}{x+2}\,dx \qquad \text{Complete the square.}$$

$$= \int_3^6 \frac{\sqrt{u^2-9}}{u}\,du. \qquad u = x+2,\ du = dx \text{ Change limits of integration.}$$

➤ The substitution $u = 3\sec\theta$ can be rewritten as $\theta = \sec^{-1}(u/3)$. Because $u \ge 3$ in the integral $\int_3^6 \frac{\sqrt{u^2-9}}{u}\,du$, we have $0 \le \theta < \frac{\pi}{2}$.

This new integral calls for the secant substitution $u = 3\sec\theta$ (where $0 \le \theta < \pi/2$), which implies that $du = 3\sec\theta\tan\theta\,d\theta$ and $\sqrt{u^2-9} = 3\tan\theta$. We also change the limits of integration: When $u = 3$, $\theta = 0$, and when $u = 6$, $\theta = \pi/3$. The complete integration can now be done:

$$\int_1^4 \frac{\sqrt{x^2+4x-5}}{x+2}\,dx = \int_3^6 \frac{\sqrt{u^2-9}}{u}\,du \qquad u = x+2,\ du = dx$$

$$= \int_0^{\pi/3} \frac{3\tan\theta}{3\sec\theta}\,3\sec\theta\tan\theta\,d\theta \qquad u = 3\sec\theta,\ du = 3\sec\theta\tan\theta\,d\theta$$

$$= 3\int_0^{\pi/3} \tan^2\theta\,d\theta \qquad \text{Simplify.}$$

$$= 3\int_0^{\pi/3} (\sec^2\theta - 1)\,d\theta \qquad \tan^2\theta = \sec^2\theta - 1$$

$$= 3(\tan\theta - \theta)\Big|_0^{\pi/3} \qquad \text{Evaluate integrals.}$$

$$= 3\sqrt{3} - \pi. \qquad \text{Simplify.}$$

Related Exercises 17–56 ◄

SECTION 7.4 EXERCISES

Review Questions

1. What change of variables is suggested by an integral containing $\sqrt{x^2-9}$?
2. What change of variables is suggested by an integral containing $\sqrt{x^2+36}$?
3. What change of variables is suggested by an integral containing $\sqrt{100-x^2}$?
4. If $x = 4\tan\theta$, express $\sin\theta$ in terms of x.
5. If $x = 2\sin\theta$, express $\cot\theta$ in terms of x.
6. If $x = 8\sec\theta$, express $\tan\theta$ in terms of x.

Basic Skills

7–16. Sine substitution *Evaluate the following integrals.*

7. $\int_0^{5/2} \frac{dx}{\sqrt{25-x^2}}$
8. $\int_0^{3/2} \frac{dx}{(9-x^2)^{3/2}}$
9. $\int_5^{10} \sqrt{100-x^2}\,dx$
10. $\int_0^{\sqrt{2}} \frac{x^2}{\sqrt{4-x^2}}\,dx$
11. $\int_0^{1/2} \frac{x^2}{\sqrt{1-x^2}}\,dx$
12. $\int_{1/2}^{1} \frac{\sqrt{1-x^2}}{x^2}\,dx$
13. $\int \frac{dx}{(16-x^2)^{1/2}}$
14. $\int \sqrt{36-t^2}\,dt$
15. $\int \frac{\sqrt{9-x^2}}{x}\,dx$
16. $\int (36-9x^2)^{-3/2}\,dx$

17–46. Trigonometric substitutions *Evaluate the following integrals.*

17. $\int \sqrt{64-x^2}\,dx$
18. $\int \frac{dx}{\sqrt{x^2-49}},\ x > 7$
19. $\int \frac{dx}{(1-x^2)^{3/2}}$
20. $\int \frac{dx}{(1+x^2)^{3/2}}$
21. $\int \frac{dx}{x^2\sqrt{x^2+9}}$
22. $\int \frac{dt}{t^2\sqrt{9-t^2}}$
23. $\int \frac{dx}{\sqrt{36-x^2}}$
24. $\int \frac{dx}{\sqrt{16+4x^2}}$
25. $\int \frac{dx}{\sqrt{x^2-81}},\ x > 9$
26. $\int \frac{dx}{\sqrt{1-2x^2}}$
27. $\int \frac{dx}{(1+4x^2)^{3/2}}$
28. $\int \frac{dx}{(x^2-36)^{3/2}},\ x > 6$
29. $\int \frac{x^2}{\sqrt{16-x^2}}\,dx$
30. $\int \frac{dx}{(81+x^2)^2}$
31. $\int \frac{\sqrt{x^2-9}}{x}\,dx,\ x > 3$
32. $\int \sqrt{9-4x^2}\,dx$
33. $\int \frac{x^2}{\sqrt{4+x^2}}\,dx$
34. $\int \frac{\sqrt{4x^2-1}}{x^2}\,dx,\ x > \frac{1}{2}$
35. $\int \frac{dx}{\sqrt{3-2x-x^2}}$
36. $\int \frac{y^4}{1+y^2}\,dy$
37. $\int \frac{\sqrt{9x^2-25}}{x^3}\,dx,\ x > \frac{5}{3}$
38. $\int \frac{\sqrt{9-x^2}}{x^2}\,dx$
39. $\int \frac{x^2}{(25+x^2)^2}\,dx$
40. $\int \frac{dx}{x^2\sqrt{9x^2-1}},\ x > \frac{1}{3}$
41. $\int \frac{x^2}{(100-x^2)^{3/2}}\,dx$
42. $\int \frac{dx}{x^3\sqrt{x^2-100}},\ x > 10$
43. $\int \frac{x^3}{(81-x^2)^2}\,dx$
44. $\int \frac{dx}{x^3\sqrt{x^2-1}},\ x > 1$

45. $\displaystyle\int \frac{dx}{x(x^2 - 1)^{3/2}},\ x > 1$

46. $\displaystyle\int \frac{x^3}{(x^2 - 16)^{3/2}}\,dx,\ x < -4$

47–56. Evaluating definite integrals *Evaluate the following definite integrals.*

47. $\displaystyle\int_0^1 \frac{dx}{\sqrt{x^2 + 16}}$

48. $\displaystyle\int_{8\sqrt{2}}^{16} \frac{dx}{\sqrt{x^2 - 64}}$

49. $\displaystyle\int_{1/\sqrt{3}}^{1} \frac{dx}{x^2\sqrt{1 + x^2}}$

50. $\displaystyle\int_1^{\sqrt{2}} \frac{dx}{x^2\sqrt{4 - x^2}}$

51. $\displaystyle\int_0^{1/\sqrt{3}} \sqrt{x^2 + 1}\,dx$

52. $\displaystyle\int_{\sqrt{2}}^{2} \frac{\sqrt{x^2 - 1}}{x}\,dx$

53. $\displaystyle\int_0^{1/3} \frac{dx}{(9x^2 + 1)^{3/2}}$

54. $\displaystyle\int_{10/\sqrt{3}}^{10} \frac{dy}{\sqrt{y^2 - 25}}$

55. $\displaystyle\int_{4/\sqrt{3}}^{4} \frac{dx}{x^2(x^2 - 4)}$

56. $\displaystyle\int_6^{6\sqrt{3}} \frac{z^2}{(z^2 + 36)^2}\,dz$

Further Explorations

57. **Explain why or why not** Determine whether the following statements are true and give an explanation or counterexample.
   a. If $x = 4\tan\theta$, then $\csc\theta = 4/x$.
   b. The integral $\int_1^2 \sqrt{1 - x^2}\,dx$ does not have a finite real value.
   c. The integral $\int_1^2 \sqrt{x^2 - 1}\,dx$ does not have a finite real value.
   d. The integral $\displaystyle\int \frac{dx}{x^2 + 4x + 9}$ cannot be evaluated using a trigonometric substitution.

58–65. Completing the square *Evaluate the following integrals.*

58. $\displaystyle\int \frac{dx}{x^2 - 6x + 34}$

59. $\displaystyle\int \frac{dx}{x^2 + 6x + 18}$

60. $\displaystyle\int \frac{du}{2u^2 - 12u + 36}$

61. $\displaystyle\int \frac{x^2 - 2x + 1}{\sqrt{x^2 - 2x + 10}}\,dx$

62. $\displaystyle\int \frac{x^2 + 2x + 4}{\sqrt{x^2 - 4x}}\,dx,\ x > 4$

63. $\displaystyle\int \frac{x^2 - 8x + 16}{(9 + 8x - x^2)^{3/2}}\,dx$

64. $\displaystyle\int_1^4 \frac{dt}{t^2 - 2t + 10}$

65. $\displaystyle\int_{1/2}^{(\sqrt{2}+3)/(2\sqrt{2})} \frac{dx}{8x^2 - 8x + 11}$

66. **Area of an ellipse** The upper half of the ellipse centered at the origin with axes of length $2a$ and $2b$ is described by $y = \frac{b}{a}\sqrt{a^2 - x^2}$ (see figure). Find the area of the ellipse in terms of a and b.

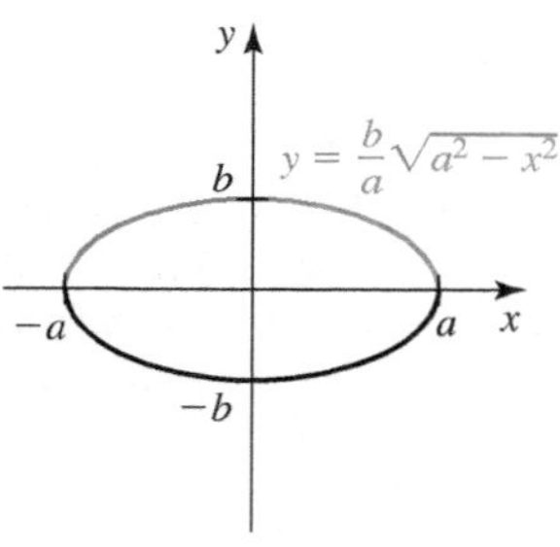

67. **Area of a segment of a circle** Use two approaches to show that the area of a cap (or segment) of a circle of radius r subtended by an angle θ (see figure) is given by

$$A_{\text{seg}} = \frac{1}{2}r^2(\theta - \sin\theta).$$

   a. Find the area using geometry (no calculus).
   b. Find the area using calculus.

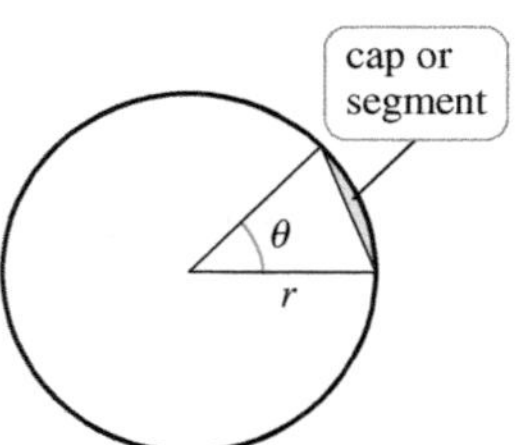

68. **Area of a lune** A lune is a crescent-shaped region bounded by the arcs of two circles. Let C_1 be a circle of radius 4 centered at the origin. Let C_2 be a circle of radius 3 centered at the point $(2, 0)$. Find the area of the lune (shaded in the figure) that lies inside C_1 and outside C_2.

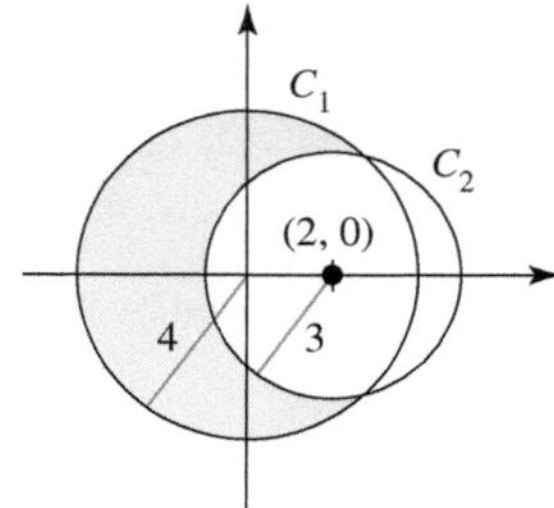

69. **Area and volume** Consider the function $f(x) = (9 + x^2)^{-1/2}$ and the region R on the interval $[0, 4]$ (see figure).
   a. Find the area of R.
   b. Find the volume of the solid generated when R is revolved about the x-axis.
   c. Find the volume of the solid generated when R is revolved about the y-axis.

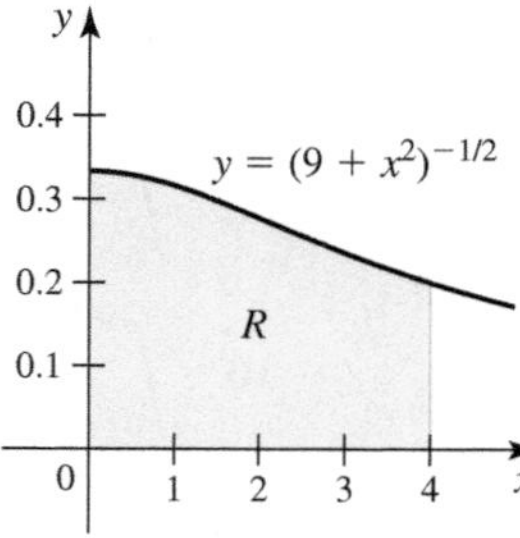

T 70. **Area of a region** Graph the function $f(x) = (16 + x^2)^{-3/2}$ and find the area of the region bounded by the curve and the x-axis on the interval $[0, 3]$.

71. **Arc length of a parabola** Find the length of the curve $y = ax^2$ from $x = 0$ to $x = 10$, where $a > 0$ is a real number.

72. **Computing areas** On the interval $[0, 2]$, the graphs of $f(x) = x^2/3$ and $g(x) = x^2(9 - x^2)^{-1/2}$ have similar shapes.
   a. Find the area of the region bounded by the graph of f and the x-axis on the interval $[0, 2]$.
   b. Find the area of the region bounded by the graph of g and the x-axis on the interval $[0, 2]$.
   c. Which region has greater area?

T **73–75. Using the integral of $\sec^3 u$** *By reduction formula 4 in Section 7.3,*

$$\int \sec^3 u \, du = \frac{1}{2}(\sec u \tan u + \ln|\sec u + \tan u|) + C.$$

Graph the following functions and find the area under the curve on the given interval.

73. $f(x) = (9 - x^2)^{-2}$, $\left[0, \frac{3}{2}\right]$

74. $f(x) = (4 + x^2)^{1/2}$, $[0, 2]$

75. $f(x) = (x^2 - 25)^{1/2}$, $[5, 10]$

76–77. Asymmetric integrands *Evaluate the following integrals. Consider completing the square.*

76. $\displaystyle\int \frac{dx}{\sqrt{(x-1)(3-x)}}$

77. $\displaystyle\int_{2+\sqrt{2}}^{4} \frac{dx}{\sqrt{(x-1)(x-3)}}$

78. **Clever substitution** Evaluate $\displaystyle\int \frac{dx}{1 + \sin x + \cos x}$ using the substitution $x = 2\tan^{-1}\theta$. The identities $\sin x = 2 \sin\frac{x}{2}\cos\frac{x}{2}$ and $\cos x = \cos^2\frac{x}{2} - \sin^2\frac{x}{2}$ are helpful.

Applications

79. **A torus (doughnut)** Find the volume of the solid torus formed when the circle of radius 4 centered at $(0, 6)$ is revolved about the x-axis.

80. **Bagel wars** Bob and Bruce bake bagels (shaped like tori). They both make bagels that have an inner radius of 0.5 in and an outer radius of 2.5 in. Bob plans to increase the volume of his bagels by decreasing the inner radius by 20% (leaving the outer radius unchanged). Bruce plans to increase the volume of his bagels by increasing the outer radius by 20% (leaving the inner radius unchanged). Whose new bagels will have the greater volume? Does this result depend on the size of the original bagels? Explain.

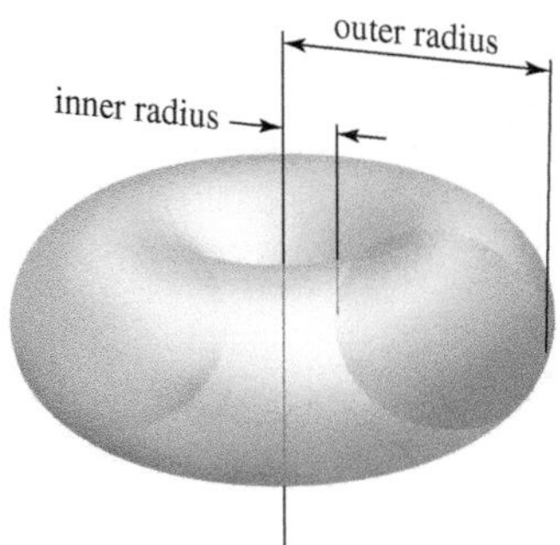

81. **Electric field due to a line of charge** A total charge of Q is distributed uniformly on a line segment of length $2L$ along the y-axis (see figure). The x-component of the electric field at a point $(a, 0)$ is given by

$$E_x(a) = \frac{kQa}{2L}\int_{-L}^{L} \frac{dy}{(a^2 + y^2)^{3/2}},$$

where k is a physical constant and $a > 0$.
   a. Confirm that $E_x(a) = \dfrac{kQ}{a\sqrt{a^2 + L^2}}$.
   b. Letting $\rho = Q/2L$ be the charge density on the line segment, show that if $L \to \infty$, then $E_x(a) = 2k\rho/a$.

(See the Guided Project *Electric field integrals* for a derivation of this and other similar integrals.)

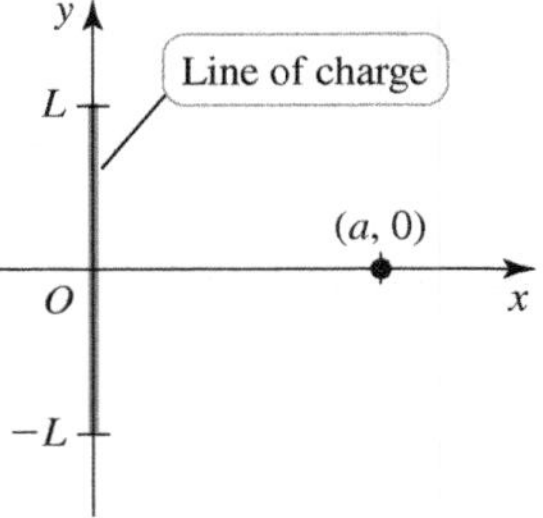

82. **Magnetic field due to current in a straight wire** A long, straight wire of length $2L$ on the y-axis carries a current I. According to the Biot-Savart Law, the magnitude of the magnetic field due to the current at a point $(a, 0)$ is given by

$$B(a) = \frac{\mu_0 I}{4\pi}\int_{-L}^{L} \frac{\sin\theta}{r^2}\,dy,$$

where μ_0 is a physical constant, $a > 0$, and θ, r, and y are related as shown in the figure.
   a. Show that the magnitude of the magnetic field at $(a, 0)$ is $B(a) = \dfrac{\mu_0 IL}{2\pi a\sqrt{a^2 + L^2}}$.
   b. What is the magnitude of the magnetic field at $(a, 0)$ due to an infinitely long wire $(L \to \infty)$?

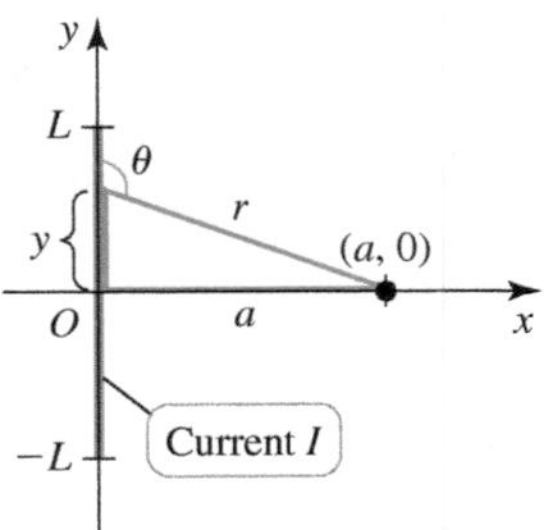

83. **Fastest descent time** The cycloid is the curve traced by a point on the rim of a rolling wheel. Imagine a wire shaped like an inverted cycloid (see figure). A bead sliding down this wire without friction has some remarkable properties. Among all wire shapes, the

cycloid is the shape that produces the fastest descent time (see the Guided Project *The amazing cycloid* for more about the *brachistochrone property*). It can be shown that the descent time between any two points $0 \le a < b \le \pi$ on the curve is

$$\text{descent time} = \int_a^b \sqrt{\frac{1 - \cos t}{g(\cos a - \cos t)}}\,dt,$$

where g is the acceleration due to gravity, $t = 0$ corresponds to the top of the wire, and $t = \pi$ corresponds to the lowest point on the wire.

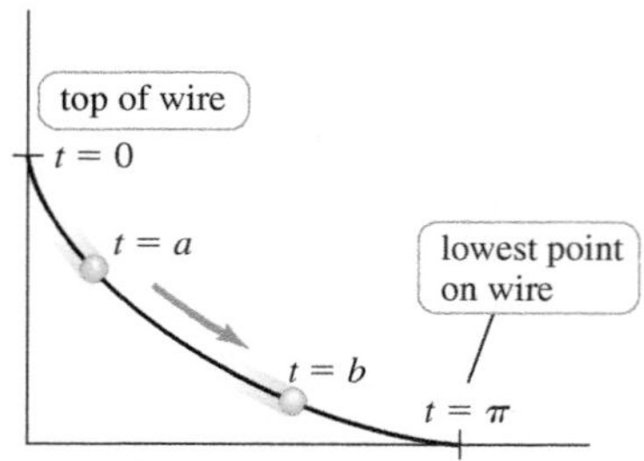

a. Find the descent time on the interval $[a, b]$ by making the substitution $u = \cos t$.

b. Show that when $b = \pi$, the descent time is the same for all values of a; that is, the descent time to the bottom of the wire is the same for all starting points.

T 84. Maximum path length of a projectile (Adapted from Putnam Exam 1940) A projectile is launched from the ground with an initial speed V at an angle θ from the horizontal. Assume that the x-axis is the horizontal ground and y is the height above the ground. Neglecting air resistance and letting g be the acceleration due to gravity, it can be shown that the trajectory of the projectile is given by

$$y = -\frac{1}{2}kx^2 + y_{\text{max}}, \quad \text{where } k = \frac{g}{(V\cos\theta)^2}$$

$$\text{and } y_{\text{max}} = \frac{(V\sin\theta)^2}{2g}.$$

a. Note that the high point of the trajectory occurs at $(0, y_{\text{max}})$. If the projectile is on the ground at $(-a, 0)$ and $(a, 0)$, what is a?

b. Show that the length of the trajectory (arc length) is $2\int_0^a \sqrt{1 + k^2x^2}\,dx$.

c. Evaluate the arc length integral and express your result in terms of V, g, and θ.

d. For a fixed value of V and g, show that the launch angle θ that maximizes the length of the trajectory satisfies $(\sin\theta)\ln(\sec\theta + \tan\theta) = 1$.

e. Use a graphing utility to approximate the optimal launch angle.

Additional Exercises

85–88. Care with the secant substitution *Recall that the substitution $x = a\sec\theta$ implies either $x \ge a$ (in which case $0 \le \theta < \pi/2$ and $\tan\theta \ge 0$) or $x \le -a$ (in which case $\pi/2 < \theta \le \pi$ and $\tan\theta \le 0$).*

85. Show that $\displaystyle\int \frac{dx}{x\sqrt{x^2 - 1}} =$

$$\begin{cases} \sec^{-1}x + C = \tan^{-1}\sqrt{x^2 - 1} + C & \text{if } x > 1 \\ -\sec^{-1}x + C = -\tan^{-1}\sqrt{x^2 - 1} + C & \text{if } x < -1. \end{cases}$$

86. Evaluate for $\displaystyle\int \frac{\sqrt{x^2 - 1}}{x^3}\,dx$, for $x > 1$ and for $x < -1$.

T 87. Graph the function $f(x) = \dfrac{\sqrt{x^2 - 9}}{x}$ and consider the region bounded by the curve and the x-axis on $[-6, -3]$. Then evaluate $\displaystyle\int_{-6}^{-3} \frac{\sqrt{x^2 - 9}}{x}\,dx$. Be sure the result is consistent with the graph.

T 88. Graph the function $f(x) = \dfrac{1}{x\sqrt{x^2 - 36}}$ on its domain. Then find the area of the region R_1 bounded by the curve and the x-axis on $[-12, -12/\sqrt{3}]$ and the area of the region R_2 bounded by the curve and the x-axis on $[12/\sqrt{3}, 12]$. Be sure your results are consistent with the graph.

89. Visual proof Let $F(x) = \int_0^x \sqrt{a^2 - t^2}\,dt$. The figure shows that $F(x)$ = area of sector OAB + area of triangle OBC.

a. Use the figure to prove that

$$F(x) = \frac{a^2\sin^{-1}(x/a)}{2} + \frac{x\sqrt{a^2 - x^2}}{2}.$$

b. Conclude that

$$\int \sqrt{a^2 - x^2}\,dx = \frac{a^2\sin^{-1}(x/a)}{2} + \frac{x\sqrt{a^2 - x^2}}{2} + C.$$

(*Source: The College Mathematics Journal* 34, 3, May 2003)

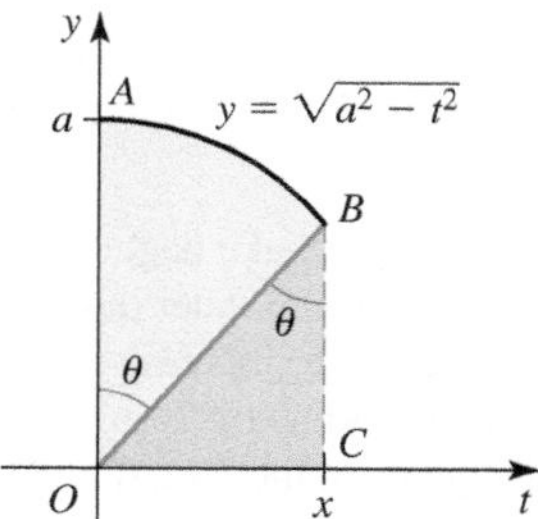

QUICK CHECK ANSWERS

1. Use $x = 3\sin\theta$ to obtain $9\cos^2\theta$. **2.** (a) Use $x = 3\tan\theta$. (b) Use $x = 4\sin\theta$. **3.** Let $x = a\tan\theta$, so that $dx = a\sec^2\theta\,d\theta$. The new integral is $\displaystyle\int \frac{a\sec^2\theta\,d\theta}{a^2(1 + \tan^2\theta)} = \frac{1}{a}\int d\theta = \frac{1}{a}\theta + C = \frac{1}{a}\tan^{-1}\frac{x}{a} + C.$ ◀

7.5 Partial Fractions

Later in this chapter, we will see that finding the velocity of a skydiver requires evaluating an integral of the form $\int \frac{dv}{a - bv^2}$ and finding the population of a species that is limited in size involves an integral of the form $\int \frac{dP}{aP(1 - bP)}$, where a and b are constants in both cases. These integrals have the common feature that their integrands are rational functions. Similar integrals result from modeling mechanical and electrical networks. The goal of this section is to introduce the *method of partial fractions* for integrating rational functions. When combined with standard and trigonometric substitutions (Section 7.4), this method allows us (in principle) to integrate any rational function.

➤ Recall that a rational function has the form p/q, where p and q are polynomials.

Method of Partial Fractions

Given a function such as

$$f(x) = \frac{1}{x - 2} + \frac{2}{x + 4},$$

it is a straightforward task to find a common denominator and write the equivalent expression

$$f(x) = \frac{(x + 4) + 2(x - 2)}{(x - 2)(x + 4)} = \frac{3x}{(x - 2)(x + 4)} = \frac{3x}{x^2 + 2x - 8}.$$

The purpose of partial fractions is to reverse this process. Given a rational function that is difficult to integrate, the method of partial fractions produces an equivalent function that is much easier to integrate.

Rational function		**Partial fraction decomposition**
$\frac{3x}{x^2 + 2x - 8}$	*method of partial fractions* ⟶	$\frac{1}{x - 2} + \frac{2}{x + 4}$
Difficult to integrate		**Easy to integrate**
$\int \frac{3x}{x^2 + 2x - 8}\,dx$		$\int \left(\frac{1}{x - 2} + \frac{2}{x + 4}\right) dx$

QUICK CHECK 1 Find an antiderivative of $f(x) = \frac{1}{x - 2} + \frac{2}{x + 4}$. ◄

The Key Idea Working with the same function, $f(x) = \frac{3x}{(x - 2)(x + 4)}$, our objective is to write it in the form

$$\frac{A}{x - 2} + \frac{B}{x + 4},$$

where A and B are constants to be determined. This expression is called the **partial fraction decomposition** of the original function; in this case, it has two terms, one for each factor in the denominator of the original function.

➤ Notice that the numerator of the original rational function does not affect the form of the partial fraction decomposition. The constants A and B are called *undetermined coefficients*.

The constants A and B are determined using the condition that the original function f and its partial fraction decomposition must be equal for all values of x in the domain of f; that is,

$$\frac{3x}{(x - 2)(x + 4)} = \frac{A}{x - 2} + \frac{B}{x + 4}. \quad (1)$$

➤ This step requires that $x \neq 2$ and $x \neq -4$; both values are outside the domain of f.

Multiplying both sides of equation (1) by $(x - 2)(x + 4)$ gives

$$3x = A(x + 4) + B(x - 2).$$

Collecting like powers of x results in

$$3x = (A + B)x + (4A - 2B). \tag{2}$$

If equation (2) is to hold for all values of x, then

- the coefficients of x^1 on both sides of the equation must be equal, and
- the coefficients of x^0 (that is, the constants) on both sides of the equation must be equal.

$$3x + 0 = (A + B)x + (4A - 2B)$$

These observations lead to two equations for A and B.

Equate coefficients of x^1: $\quad 3 = A + B$

Equate coefficients of x^0: $\quad 0 = 4A - 2B$

The first equation says that $A = 3 - B$. Substituting $A = 3 - B$ into the second equation gives the equation $0 = 4(3 - B) - 2B$. Solving for B, we find that $6B = 12$, or $B = 2$. The value of A now follows; we have $A = 3 - B = 1$.

Substituting these values of A and B into equation (1), the partial fraction decomposition is

$$\frac{3x}{(x - 2)(x + 4)} = \frac{1}{x - 2} + \frac{2}{x + 4}.$$

Simple Linear Factors

➤ Like an ordinary fraction, a rational function is said to be in **reduced form** if the numerator and denominator have no common factors and it is said to be **proper** if the degree of the numerator is less than the degree of the denominator.

The previous calculation illustrates the method of partial fractions with **simple linear factors**, meaning the denominator of the original function consists only of linear factors of the form $(x - r)$, which appear to the first power and no higher power. Here is the general procedure for this case.

PROCEDURE Partial Fractions with Simple Linear Factors

Suppose $f(x) = p(x)/q(x)$, where p and q are polynomials with no common factors and with the degree of p less than the degree of q. Assume that q is the product of simple linear factors. The partial fraction decomposition is obtained as follows.

Step 1. **Factor the denominator q** in the form $(x - r_1)(x - r_2) \cdots (x - r_n)$, where $r_1, \ldots, r_n$ are real numbers.

Step 2. **Partial fraction decomposition** Form the partial fraction decomposition by writing

$$\frac{p(x)}{q(x)} = \frac{A_1}{(x - r_1)} + \frac{A_2}{(x - r_2)} + \cdots + \frac{A_n}{(x - r_n)}.$$

Step 3. **Clear denominators** Multiply both sides of the equation in Step 2 by $q(x) = (x - r_1)(x - r_2) \cdots (x - r_n)$, which produces conditions for $A_1, \ldots, A_n$.

Step 4. **Solve for coefficients** Equate like powers of x in Step 3 to solve for the undetermined coefficients $A_1, \ldots, A_n$.

QUICK CHECK 2 If the denominator of a reduced proper rational function is $(x - 1)(x + 5)(x - 10)$, what is the general form of its partial fraction decomposition? ◄

EXAMPLE 1 **Integrating with partial fractions**

a. Find the partial fraction decomposition for $f(x) = \dfrac{3x^2 + 7x - 2}{x^3 - x^2 - 2x}$.

b. Evaluate $\int f(x)\, dx$.

SOLUTION

a. The partial fraction decomposition is done in four steps.

Step 1: Factoring the denominator, we find that

$$x^3 - x^2 - 2x = x(x + 1)(x - 2),$$

in which only simple linear factors appear.

Step 2: The partial fraction decomposition has one term for each factor in the denominator:

$$\frac{3x^2 + 7x - 2}{x(x + 1)(x - 2)} = \frac{A}{x} + \frac{B}{x + 1} + \frac{C}{x - 2}. \qquad (3)$$

➤ You can call the undetermined coefficients $A_1, A_2, A_3, \ldots$ or $A, B, C, \ldots$. The latter choice avoids subscripts.

The goal is to find the undetermined coefficients A, B, and C.

Step 3: We multiply both sides of equation (3) by $x(x + 1)(x - 2)$:

$$\begin{aligned} 3x^2 + 7x - 2 &= A(x + 1)(x - 2) + Bx(x - 2) + Cx(x + 1) \\ &= (A + B + C)x^2 + (-A - 2B + C)x - 2A. \end{aligned}$$

Step 4: We now equate coefficients of x^2, x^1, and x^0 on both sides of the equation in Step 3.

$$\begin{aligned} &\text{Equate coefficients of } x^2: & A + B + C &= 3 \\ &\text{Equate coefficients of } x^1: & -A - 2B + C &= 7 \\ &\text{Equate coefficients of } x^0: & -2A &= -2 \end{aligned}$$

The third equation implies that $A = 1$, which is substituted into the first two equations to give

$$B + C = 2 \quad \text{and} \quad -2B + C = 8.$$

Solving for B and C, we conclude that $A = 1$, $B = -2$, and $C = 4$. Substituting the values of A, B, and C into equation (3), the partial fraction decomposition is

$$f(x) = \frac{1}{x} - \frac{2}{x + 1} + \frac{4}{x - 2}.$$

b. Integration is now straightforward:

$$\begin{aligned} \int \frac{3x^2 + 7x - 2}{x^3 - x^2 - 2x}\, dx &= \int \left(\frac{1}{x} - \frac{2}{x + 1} + \frac{4}{x - 2} \right) dx && \text{Partial fractions} \\ &= \ln|x| - 2\ln|x + 1| + 4\ln|x - 2| + K && \text{Integrate; arbitrary constant } K. \\ &= \ln \frac{|x|(x - 2)^4}{(x + 1)^2} + K. && \text{Properties of logarithms} \end{aligned}$$

Related Exercises 5–26 ◄

A Shortcut (Convenient Values) Solving for more than three unknown coefficients in a partial fraction decomposition may be difficult. In the case of simple linear factors, a shortcut saves work. In Example 1, Step 3 led to the equation

$$3x^2 + 7x - 2 = A(x + 1)(x - 2) + Bx(x - 2) + Cx(x + 1).$$

➤ In cases other than simple linear factors, the shortcut can be used to determine some, but not all the coefficients, which reduces the work required to find the remaining coefficients. A modified shortcut can be utilized to find all the coefficients; see the margin note next to Example 3.

Because this equation holds for *all* values of x, it must hold for any particular value of x. By choosing values of x judiciously, it is easy to solve for A, B, and C. For example, setting $x = 0$ in this equation results in $-2 = -2A$, or $A = 1$. Setting $x = -1$ results in $-6 = 3B$, or $B = -2$, and setting $x = 2$ results in $24 = 6C$, or $C = 4$. In each case, we choose a value of x that eliminates all but one term on the right side of the equation.

EXAMPLE 2 Using the shortcut

a. Find the partial fraction decomposition for $f(x) = \dfrac{3x^2 + 2x + 5}{(x-1)(x^2 - x - 20)}$.

b. Evaluate $\displaystyle\int_2^4 f(x)\,dx$.

SOLUTION

a. We use four steps to obtain the partial fraction decomposition.

Step 1: Factoring the denominator of f results in $(x-1)(x-5)(x+4)$, so the integrand has three simple linear factors.

Step 2: We form the partial fraction decomposition with one term for each factor in the denominator:

$$\frac{3x^2 + 2x + 5}{(x-1)(x-5)(x+4)} = \frac{A}{x-1} + \frac{B}{x-5} + \frac{C}{x+4}. \quad (4)$$

The goal is to find the undetermined coefficients A, B, and C.

Step 3: We now multiply both sides of equation (4) by $(x-1)(x-5)(x+4)$:

$$3x^2 + 2x + 5 = A(x-5)(x+4) + B(x-1)(x+4) + C(x-1)(x-5). \quad (5)$$

Step 4: The shortcut is now used to determine A, B, and C. Substituting $x = 1, 5$, and -4 in equation (5) allows us to solve directly for the coefficients:

$$\text{Letting } x = 1 \Rightarrow 10 = -20A + 0 \cdot B + 0 \cdot C \Rightarrow A = -\frac{1}{2};$$

$$\text{Letting } x = 5 \Rightarrow 90 = 0 \cdot A + 36B + 0 \cdot C \Rightarrow B = \frac{5}{2};$$

$$\text{Letting } x = -4 \Rightarrow 45 = 0 \cdot A + 0 \cdot B + 45C \Rightarrow C = 1.$$

Substituting the values of A, B, and C into equation (4) gives the partial fraction decomposition

$$f(x) = -\frac{1/2}{x-1} + \frac{5/2}{x-5} + \frac{1}{x+4}.$$

b. We now carry out the integration.

$$\int_2^4 f(x)dx = \int_2^4 \left(-\frac{1/2}{x-1} + \frac{5/2}{x-5} + \frac{1}{x+4}\right)dx \qquad \text{Partial fractions}$$

$$= \left(-\frac{1}{2}\ln|x-1| + \frac{5}{2}\ln|x-5| + \ln|x+4|\right)\bigg|_2^4 \qquad \text{Integrate.}$$

$$= -\frac{1}{2}\ln 3 + \frac{5}{2}\underbrace{\ln 1}_{0} + \ln 8 - \left(-\frac{1}{2}\underbrace{\ln 1}_{0} + \frac{5}{2}\ln 3 + \ln 6\right) \qquad \text{Evaluate.}$$

$$= -3\ln 3 + \ln 8 - \ln 6 \qquad \text{Simplify.}$$

$$= \ln\frac{4}{81} \approx -3.008 \qquad \text{Log properties}$$

Related Exercises 5–26 ◀

Repeated Linear Factors

➤ *Simple* means the factor is raised to the first power; *repeated* means the factor is raised to an integer power greater than 1.

The preceding discussion relies on the assumption that the denominator of the rational function can be factored into simple linear factors of the form $(x - r)$. But what about denominators such as $x^2(x - 3)$ or $(x + 2)^2(x - 4)^3$, in which linear factors are raised to integer powers greater than 1? In these cases we have *repeated linear factors*, and a modification to the previous procedure must be made.

Here is the modification: Suppose the factor $(x - r)^m$ appears in the denominator, where $m > 1$ is an integer. Then there must be a partial fraction for each power of $(x - r)$ up to and including the mth power. For example, if $x^2(x - 3)^4$ appears in the denominator, then the partial fraction decomposition includes the terms

➤ Think of x^2 as the repeated linear factor $(x - 0)^2$.

$$\frac{A}{x} + \frac{B}{x^2} + \frac{C}{(x-3)} + \frac{D}{(x-3)^2} + \frac{E}{(x-3)^3} + \frac{F}{(x-3)^4}.$$

The rest of the partial fraction procedure remains the same, although the amount of work increases as the number of coefficients increases.

PROCEDURE Partial Fractions for Repeated Linear Factors

Suppose the repeated linear factor $(x - r)^m$ appears in the denominator of a proper rational function in reduced form. The partial fraction decomposition has a partial fraction for each power of $(x - r)$ up to and including the mth power; that is, the partial fraction decomposition contains the sum

$$\frac{A_1}{(x-r)} + \frac{A_2}{(x-r)^2} + \frac{A_3}{(x-r)^3} + \cdots + \frac{A_m}{(x-r)^m},$$

where $A_1, \ldots, A_m$ are constants to be determined.

EXAMPLE 3 Integrating with repeated linear factors Evaluate $\int f(x)\,dx$, where $f(x) = \dfrac{5x^2 - 3x + 2}{x^3 - 2x^2}$.

SOLUTION The denominator factors as $x^3 - 2x^2 = x^2(x - 2)$, so it has one simple linear factor $(x - 2)$ and one repeated linear factor x^2. The partial fraction decomposition has the form

$$\frac{5x^2 - 3x + 2}{x^2(x-2)} = \frac{A}{x} + \frac{B}{x^2} + \frac{C}{(x-2)}.$$

Multiplying both sides of the partial fraction decomposition by $x^2(x - 2)$, we find

$$\begin{aligned} 5x^2 - 3x + 2 &= Ax(x-2) + B(x-2) + Cx^2 \\ &= (A + C)x^2 + (-2A + B)x - 2B. \end{aligned}$$

The coefficients A, B, and C are determined by equating the coefficients of x^2, x^1, and x^0.

➤ The shortcut can be used to obtain two of the three coefficients easily. Choosing $x = 0$ allows B to be determined. Choosing $x = 2$ determines C. To find A, any other value of x may be substituted.

Equate coefficients of x^2: $A + C = 5$

Equate coefficients of x^1: $-2A + B = -3$

Equate coefficients of x^0: $-2B = 2$

Solving these three equations in three unknowns results in the solution $A = 1$, $B = -1$, and $C = 4$. When A, B, and C are substituted, the partial fraction decomposition is

$$f(x) = \frac{1}{x} - \frac{1}{x^2} + \frac{4}{x-2}.$$

Integration is now straightforward:

$$\int \frac{5x^2 - 3x + 2}{x^3 - 2x^2}\,dx = \int \left(\frac{1}{x} - \frac{1}{x^2} + \frac{4}{x - 2}\right) dx \qquad \text{Partial fractions}$$

$$= \ln|x| + \frac{1}{x} + 4\ln|x - 2| + K \qquad \text{Integrate; arbitrary constant } K.$$

$$= \frac{1}{x} + \ln\left(|x|(x - 2)^4\right) + K. \qquad \text{Properties of logarithms}$$

Related Exercises 27–37 ◀

QUICK CHECK 3 State the form of the partial fraction decomposition of the reduced proper rational function $p(x)/q(x)$ if $q(x) = x^2(x - 3)^2(x - 1)$. ◀

Irreducible Quadratic Factors

➤ The quadratic $ax^2 + bx + c$ has no real roots and cannot be factored over the real numbers if $b^2 - 4ac < 0$.

By the Fundamental Theorem of Algebra, we know that a polynomial with real-valued coefficients can be written as the product of linear factors of the form $x - r$ and *irreducible quadratic factors* of the form $ax^2 + bx + c$, where r, a, b, and c are real numbers. By irreducible, we mean that $ax^2 + bx + c$ cannot be factored over the real numbers. For example, the polynomial

$$x^9 + 4x^8 + 6x^7 + 34x^6 + 64x^5 - 84x^4 - 287x^3 - 500x^2 - 354x - 180$$

factors as

$$\underbrace{(x - 2)}_{\text{linear factor}}\underbrace{(x + 3)^2}_{\text{repeated linear factor}}\underbrace{(x^2 - 2x + 10)}_{\text{irreducible quadratic factor}}\underbrace{(x^2 + x + 1)^2}_{\text{repeated irreducible quadratic factor}}.$$

In this factored form, we see linear factors (simple and repeated) and irreducible quadratic factors (simple and repeated).

With irreducible quadratic factors, two cases must be considered: simple and repeated factors. Simple quadratic factors are examined in the following examples, and repeated quadratic factors (which generally involve long computations) are explored in the exercises.

PROCEDURE Partial Fractions with Simple Irreducible Quadratic Factors

Suppose a simple irreducible factor $ax^2 + bx + c$ appears in the denominator of a proper rational function in reduced form. The partial fraction decomposition contains a term of the form

$$\frac{Ax + B}{ax^2 + bx + c},$$

where A and B are unknown coefficients to be determined.

EXAMPLE 4 Setting up partial fractions Give the appropriate form of the partial fraction decomposition for the following functions.

a. $\dfrac{x^2 + 1}{x^4 - 4x^3 - 32x^2}$ **b.** $\dfrac{10}{(x - 2)^2(x^2 + 2x + 2)}$

SOLUTION

a. The denominator factors as $x^2(x^2 - 4x - 32) = x^2(x - 8)(x + 4)$. Therefore, x is a repeated linear factor, and $(x - 8)$ and $(x + 4)$ are simple linear factors. The required form of the decomposition is

$$\frac{A}{x} + \frac{B}{x^2} + \frac{C}{x - 8} + \frac{D}{x + 4}.$$

We see that the factor $x^2 - 4x - 32$ is quadratic, but it can be factored as $(x - 8)(x + 4)$, so it is not irreducible.

➤ In Example 4b, the factor $(x - 2)^2$ cannot be treated as an irreducible quadratic factor; it is a repeated linear factor.

b. The denominator is already fully factored. The quadratic factor $x^2 + 2x + 2$ cannot be factored using real numbers; therefore, it is irreducible. The form of the decomposition is

$$\frac{A}{x-2} + \frac{B}{(x-2)^2} + \frac{Cx + D}{x^2 + 2x + 2}.$$

Related Exercises 38–41 ◀

EXAMPLE 5 **Integrating with partial fractions** Evaluate

$$\int \frac{7x^2 - 13x + 13}{(x-2)(x^2 - 2x + 3)}\,dx.$$

SOLUTION The appropriate form of the partial fraction decomposition is

$$\frac{7x^2 - 13x + 13}{(x-2)(x^2 - 2x + 3)} = \frac{A}{x-2} + \frac{Bx + C}{x^2 - 2x + 3}.$$

Note that the irreducible quadratic factor requires $Bx + C$ in the numerator of the second fraction. Multiplying both sides of this equation by $(x - 2)(x^2 - 2x + 3)$ leads to

$$\begin{aligned} 7x^2 - 13x + 13 &= A(x^2 - 2x + 3) + (Bx + C)(x - 2) \\ &= (A + B)x^2 + (-2A - 2B + C)x + (3A - 2C). \end{aligned}$$

Equating coefficients of equal powers of x results in the equations

$$A + B = 7, \qquad -2A - 2B + C = -13, \quad \text{and} \quad 3A - 2C = 13.$$

Solving this system of equations gives $A = 5, B = 2$, and $C = 1$; therefore, the original integral can be written as

$$\int \frac{7x^2 - 13x + 13}{(x-2)(x^2 - 2x + 3)}\,dx = \int \frac{5}{x-2}\,dx + \int \frac{2x + 1}{x^2 - 2x + 3}\,dx.$$

Let's work on the second (more difficult) integral. The substitution $u = x^2 - 2x + 3$ would work if $du = (2x - 2)\,dx$ appeared in the numerator. For this reason, we write the numerator as $2x + 1 = (2x - 2) + 3$ and split the integral:

$$\int \frac{2x + 1}{x^2 - 2x + 3}\,dx = \int \frac{2x - 2}{x^2 - 2x + 3}\,dx + \int \frac{3}{x^2 - 2x + 3}\,dx.$$

Assembling all the pieces, we have

$$\begin{aligned} &\int \frac{7x^2 - 13x + 13}{(x-2)(x^2 - 2x + 3)}\,dx \\ &= \int \frac{5}{x-2}\,dx + \underbrace{\int \frac{2x - 2}{x^2 - 2x + 3}\,dx}_{\text{let } u = x^2 - 2x + 3} + \underbrace{\int \frac{3}{x^2 - 2x + 3}\,dx}_{(x-1)^2 + 2} \\ &= 5 \ln|x - 2| + \ln|x^2 - 2x + 3| + \frac{3}{\sqrt{2}} \tan^{-1}\left(\frac{x-1}{\sqrt{2}}\right) + K \qquad \text{Integrate.} \\ &= \ln|(x - 2)^5(x^2 - 2x + 3)| + \frac{3}{\sqrt{2}} \tan^{-1}\left(\frac{x-1}{\sqrt{2}}\right) + K. \qquad \text{Property of logarithms} \end{aligned}$$

To evaluate the last integral $\int \frac{3}{x^2 - 2x + 3}\,dx$, we completed the square in the denominator and used the substitution $u = x - 1$ to produce $3 \int \frac{du}{u^2 + 2}$, which is a standard form.

Related Exercises 42–50 ◀

Long Division The preceding discussion of partial fraction decomposition assumes that $f(x) = p(x)/q(x)$ is a proper rational function. If this is not the case and we are faced with an improper rational function f, we divide the denominator into the numerator and express f in two parts. One part will be a polynomial, and the other will be a proper rational function. For example, given the function

$$f(x) = \frac{2x^3 + 11x^2 + 28x + 33}{x^2 - x - 6},$$

we perform long division.

$$\begin{array}{r} 2x \;+\; 13 \qquad\qquad\quad \\ x^2 - x - 6 \overline{\big)\, 2x^3 + 11x^2 + 28x + 33} \\ \underline{2x^3 - \;\; 2x^2 - 12x \qquad} \\ 13x^2 + 40x + 33 \\ \underline{13x^2 - 13x - 78} \\ 53x + 111 \end{array}$$

QUICK CHECK 4 What is the result of simplifying $\frac{x}{x + 1}$ by long division?

It follows that

$$f(x) = \underbrace{2x + 13}_{\text{polynomial; easy to integrate}} + \underbrace{\frac{53x + 111}{x^2 - x - 6}}_{\text{apply partial fraction decomposition}}.$$

The first piece is easily integrated, and the second piece now qualifies for the methods described in this section.

SUMMARY Partial Fraction Decompositions

Let $f(x) = p(x)/q(x)$ be a proper rational function in reduced form. Assume the denominator q has been factored completely over the real numbers and m is a positive integer.

1. **Simple linear factor** A factor $x - r$ in the denominator requires the partial fraction $\frac{A}{x - r}$.

2. **Repeated linear factor** A factor $(x - r)^m$ with $m > 1$ in the denominator requires the partial fractions

$$\frac{A_1}{(x - r)} + \frac{A_2}{(x - r)^2} + \frac{A_3}{(x - r)^3} + \cdots + \frac{A_m}{(x - r)^m}.$$

3. **Simple irreducible quadratic factor** An irreducible factor $ax^2 + bx + c$ in the denominator requires the partial fraction

$$\frac{Ax + B}{ax^2 + bx + c}.$$

4. **Repeated irreducible quadratic factor** (See Exercises 83–86.) An irreducible factor $(ax^2 + bx + c)^m$ with $m > 1$ in the denominator requires the partial fractions

$$\frac{A_1x + B_1}{ax^2 + bx + c} + \frac{A_2x + B_2}{(ax^2 + bx + c)^2} + \cdots + \frac{A_mx + B_m}{(ax^2 + bx + c)^m}.$$

SECTION 7.5 EXERCISES

Review Questions

1. What kinds of functions can be integrated using partial fraction decomposition?

2. Give an example of each of the following.
   a. A simple linear factor
   b. A repeated linear factor
   c. A simple irreducible quadratic factor
   d. A repeated irreducible quadratic factor

3. What term(s) should appear in the partial fraction decomposition of a proper rational function with each of the following?
   a. A factor of $x - 3$ in the denominator
   b. A factor of $(x - 4)^3$ in the denominator
   c. A factor of $x^2 + 2x + 6$ in the denominator

4. What is the first step in integrating $\dfrac{x^2 + 2x - 3}{x + 1}$?

Basic Skills

5–12. Setting up partial fraction decomposition *Give the partial fraction decomposition for the following functions.*

5. $\dfrac{2}{x^2 - 2x - 8}$

6. $\dfrac{x - 9}{x^2 - 3x - 18}$

7. $\dfrac{5x - 7}{x^2 - 3x + 2}$

8. $\dfrac{11x - 10}{x^2 - x}$

9. $\dfrac{x^2}{x^3 - 16x}, x \neq 0$

10. $\dfrac{x^2 - 3x}{x^3 - 3x^2 - 4x}, x \neq 0$

11. $\dfrac{x + 2}{x^3 - 3x^2 + 2x}$

12. $\dfrac{x^2 - 4x + 11}{(x - 3)(x - 1)(x + 1)}$

13–26. Simple linear factors *Evaluate the following integrals.*

13. $\displaystyle\int \frac{3}{(x - 1)(x + 2)}\,dx$

14. $\displaystyle\int \frac{8}{(x - 2)(x + 6)}\,dx$

15. $\displaystyle\int \frac{6}{x^2 - 1}\,dx$

16. $\displaystyle\int_0^1 \frac{dt}{t^2 - 9}$

17. $\displaystyle\int_{-1}^2 \frac{5x}{x^2 - x - 6}\,dx$

18. $\displaystyle\int \frac{21x^2}{x^3 - x^2 - 12x}\,dx$

19. $\displaystyle\int \frac{10x}{x^2 - 2x - 24}\,dx$

20. $\displaystyle\int \frac{y + 1}{y^3 + 3y^2 - 18y}\,dy$

21. $\displaystyle\int \frac{6x^2}{x^4 - 5x^2 + 4}\,dx$

22. $\displaystyle\int \frac{4x - 2}{x^3 - x}\,dx$

23. $\displaystyle\int \frac{x^2 + 12x - 4}{x^3 - 4x}\,dx$

24. $\displaystyle\int \frac{z^2 + 20z - 15}{z^3 + 4z^2 - 5z}\,dz$

25. $\displaystyle\int \frac{dx}{x^4 - 10x^2 + 9}$

26. $\displaystyle\int_0^5 \frac{2}{x^2 - 4x - 32}\,dx$

27–37. Repeated linear factors *Evaluate the following integrals.*

27. $\displaystyle\int \frac{81}{x^3 - 9x^2}\,dx$

28. $\displaystyle\int \frac{16x^2}{(x - 6)(x + 2)^2}\,dx$

29. $\displaystyle\int_{-1}^1 \frac{x}{(x + 3)^2}\,dx$

30. $\displaystyle\int \frac{dx}{x^3 - 2x^2 - 4x + 8}$

31. $\displaystyle\int \frac{2}{x^3 + x^2}\,dx$

32. $\displaystyle\int_1^2 \frac{2}{t^3(t + 1)}\,dt$

33. $\displaystyle\int \frac{x - 5}{x^2(x + 1)}\,dx$

34. $\displaystyle\int \frac{x^2}{(x - 2)^3}\,dx$

35. $\displaystyle\int \frac{x^2 - x}{(x - 2)(x - 3)^2}\,dx$

36. $\displaystyle\int \frac{12y - 8}{y^4 - 2y^2 + 1}\,dy$

37. $\displaystyle\int \frac{x^2 - 4}{x^3 - 2x^2 + x}\,dx$

38–41. Setting up partial fraction decompositions *Give the appropriate form of the partial fraction decomposition for the following functions.*

38. $\dfrac{2}{x(x^2 - 6x + 9)}$

39. $\dfrac{20x}{(x - 1)^2(x^2 + 1)}$

40. $\dfrac{x^2}{x^3(x^2 + 1)}$

41. $\dfrac{2x^2 + 3}{(x^2 - 8x + 16)(x^2 + 3x + 4)}$

42–50. Simple irreducible quadratic factors *Evaluate the following integrals.*

42. $\displaystyle\int \frac{8(x^2 + 4)}{x(x^2 + 8)}\,dx$

43. $\displaystyle\int \frac{x^2 + x + 2}{(x + 1)(x^2 + 1)}\,dx$

44. $\displaystyle\int \frac{x^2 + 3x + 2}{x(x^2 + 2x + 2)}\,dx$

45. $\displaystyle\int \frac{2x^2 + 5x + 5}{(x + 1)(x^2 + 2x + 2)}\,dx$

46. $\displaystyle\int \frac{z + 1}{z(z^2 + 4)}\,dz$

47. $\displaystyle\int \frac{20x}{(x - 1)(x^2 + 4x + 5)}\,dx$

48. $\displaystyle\int \frac{2x + 1}{x^2 + 4}\,dx$

49. $\displaystyle\int \frac{x^2}{x^3 - x^2 + 4x - 4}\,dx$

50. $\displaystyle\int \frac{dy}{(y^2 + 1)(y^2 + 2)}$

Further Explorations

51. **Explain why or why not** Determine whether the following statements are true and give an explanation or counterexample.
   a. To evaluate $\displaystyle\int \frac{4x^6}{x^4 + 3x^2}\,dx$, the first step is to find the partial fraction decomposition of the integrand.
   b. The easiest way to evaluate $\displaystyle\int \frac{6x + 1}{3x^2 + x}\,dx$ is with a partial fraction decomposition of the integrand.
   c. The rational function $f(x) = \dfrac{1}{x^2 - 13x + 42}$ has an irreducible quadratic denominator.
   d. The rational function $f(x) = \dfrac{1}{x^2 - 13x + 43}$ has an irreducible quadratic denominator.

T **52–55. Areas of regions** *Find the area of the following regions.*

52. The region bounded by the curve $y = x/(1 + x)$, the x-axis, and the line $x = 4$

53. The region bounded by the curve $y = 10/(x^2 - 2x - 24)$, the x-axis, and the lines $x = -2$ and $x = 2$

54. The region bounded by the curves $y = 1/x$, $y = x/(3x + 4)$, and the line $x = 10$

55. The region bounded by the curve $y = \dfrac{x^2 - 4x - 4}{x^2 - 4x - 5}$ and the x-axis

56–61. Volumes of solids *Find the volume of the following solids.*

56. The region bounded by $y = 1/(x + 1)$, $y = 0$, $x = 0$, and $x = 2$ is revolved about the y-axis.

57. The region bounded by $y = x/(x + 1)$, the x-axis, and $x = 4$ is revolved about the x-axis.

58. The region bounded by $y = (1 - x^2)^{-1/2}$ and $y = 4$ is revolved about the x-axis.

59. The region bounded by $y = \dfrac{1}{\sqrt{x(3 - x)}}$, $y = 0$, $x = 1$, and $x = 2$ is revolved about the x-axis.

60. The region bounded by $y = \dfrac{1}{\sqrt{4 - x^2}}$, $y = 0$, $x = -1$, and $x = 1$ is revolved about the x-axis.

61. The region bounded by $y = 1/(x + 2)$, $y = 0$, $x = 0$, and $x = 3$ is revolved about the line $x = -1$.

62. What's wrong? Why are there no constants A and B satisfying

$$\frac{x^2}{(x - 4)(x + 5)} = \frac{A}{x - 4} + \frac{B}{x + 5}?$$

63–74. Preliminary steps *The following integrals require a preliminary step such as long division or a change of variables before using the method of partial fractions. Evaluate these integrals.*

63. $\displaystyle\int \frac{dx}{1 + e^x}$

64. $\displaystyle\int \frac{x^4 + 1}{x^3 + 9x}\,dx$

65. $\displaystyle\int \frac{3x^2 + 4x - 6}{x^2 - 3x + 2}\,dx$

66. $\displaystyle\int \frac{2z^3 + z^2 - 6z + 7}{z^2 + z - 6}\,dz$

67. $\displaystyle\int \frac{dt}{2 + e^t}$

68. $\displaystyle\int \frac{dx}{e^x + e^{2x}}$

69. $\displaystyle\int \frac{\sec t}{1 + \sin t}\,dt$

70. $\displaystyle\int \sqrt{e^x + 1}\,dx$ (*Hint:* Let $u = \sqrt{e^x + 1}$.)

71. $\displaystyle\int \frac{e^x}{(e^x - 1)(e^x + 2)}\,dx$

72. $\displaystyle\int \frac{\cos\theta}{(\sin^3\theta - 4\sin\theta)}\,d\theta$

73. $\displaystyle\int \frac{dx}{(e^x + e^{-x})^2}$

74. $\displaystyle\int \frac{dy}{y(\sqrt{a} - \sqrt{y})}$, for $a > 0$. (*Hint:* Let $u = \sqrt{y}$.)

75. Another form of $\displaystyle\int \sec x\,dx$.

a. Verify the identity $\sec x = \dfrac{\cos x}{1 - \sin^2 x}$.

b. Use the identity in part (a) to verify that

$$\int \sec x\,dx = \frac{1}{2}\ln\left|\frac{1 + \sin x}{1 - \sin x}\right| + C.$$

(*Source: The College Mathematics Journal* 32, 5, Nov 2001)

76–81. Fractional powers *Use the indicated substitution to convert the given integral to an integral of a rational function. Evaluate the resulting integral.*

76. $\displaystyle\int \frac{dx}{x - \sqrt[3]{x}}$; $x = u^3$

77. $\displaystyle\int \frac{dx}{\sqrt[4]{x + 2} + 1}$; $x + 2 = u^4$

78. $\displaystyle\int \frac{dx}{x\sqrt{1 + 2x}}$; $1 + 2x = u^2$

79. $\displaystyle\int \frac{dx}{\sqrt{x} + \sqrt[3]{x}}$; $x = u^6$

80. $\displaystyle\int \frac{dx}{x - \sqrt[4]{x}}$; $x = u^4$

81. $\displaystyle\int \frac{dx}{\sqrt{1 + \sqrt{x}}}$; $x = (u^2 - 1)^2$

T **82. Arc length of the natural logarithm** Consider the curve $y = \ln x$.

a. Find the length of the curve from $x = 1$ to $x = a$ and call it $L(a)$. (*Hint:* The change of variables $u = \sqrt{x^2 + 1}$ allows evaluation by partial fractions.)

b. Graph $L(a)$.

c. As a increases, $L(a)$ increases as what power of a?

83–86. Repeated quadratic factors *Refer to the summary box (Partial Fraction Decompositions) and evaluate the following integrals.*

83. $\displaystyle\int \frac{2}{x(x^2 + 1)^2}\,dx$

84. $\displaystyle\int \frac{dx}{(x + 1)(x^2 + 2x + 2)^2}$

85. $\displaystyle\int \frac{x}{(x - 1)(x^2 + 2x + 2)^2}\,dx$

86. $\displaystyle\int \frac{x^3 + 1}{x(x^2 + x + 1)^2}\,dx$

87. Two methods Evaluate $\displaystyle\int \frac{dx}{x^2 - 1}$, for $x > 1$, in two ways: using partial fractions and a trigonometric substitution. Reconcile your two answers.

88–94. Rational functions of trigonometric functions *An integrand with trigonometric functions in the numerator and denominator can often be converted to a rational integrand using the substitution* $u = \tan(x/2)$ *or equivalently* $x = 2\tan^{-1} u$. *The following relations are used in making this change of variables.*

$$A: dx = \frac{2}{1+u^2}\,du \quad B: \sin x = \frac{2u}{1+u^2} \quad C: \cos x = \frac{1-u^2}{1+u^2}$$

88. Verify relation A by differentiating $x = 2\tan^{-1} u$. Verify relations B and C using a right-triangle diagram and the double-angle formulas

$$\sin x = 2 \sin \frac{x}{2} \cos \frac{x}{2} \text{ and } \cos x = 2\cos^2 \frac{x}{2} - 1.$$

89. Evaluate $\displaystyle\int \frac{dx}{1 + \sin x}$.

90. Evaluate $\displaystyle\int \frac{dx}{2 + \cos x}$.

91. Evaluate $\displaystyle\int \frac{dx}{1 - \cos x}$.

92. Evaluate $\displaystyle\int \frac{dx}{1 + \sin x + \cos x}$.

93. Evaluate $\displaystyle\int_0^{\pi/2} \frac{d\theta}{\cos\theta + \sin\theta}$.

94. Evaluate $\displaystyle\int_0^{\pi/3} \frac{\sin\theta}{1 - \sin\theta}\,d\theta$.

Applications

95. Three start-ups Three cars, A, B, and C, start from rest and accelerate along a line according to the following velocity functions:

$$v_A(t) = \frac{88t}{t+1}, \quad v_B(t) = \frac{88t^2}{(t+1)^2}, \quad \text{and} \quad v_C(t) = \frac{88t^2}{t^2+1}.$$

a. Which car travels farthest on the interval $0 \le t \le 1$?

b. Which car travels farthest on the interval $0 \le t \le 5$?

c. Find the position functions for each car assuming that each car starts at the origin.

d. Which car ultimately gains the lead and remains in front?

T **96. Skydiving** A skydiver has a downward velocity given by

$$v(t) = V_T\left(\frac{1 - e^{-2gt/V_T}}{1 + e^{-2gt/V_T}}\right),$$

where $t = 0$ is the instant the skydiver starts falling, $g \approx 9.8 \text{ m/s}^2$ is the acceleration due to gravity, and V_T is the terminal velocity of the skydiver.

a. Evaluate $v(0)$ and $\lim_{t\to\infty} v(t)$ and interpret these results.

b. Graph the velocity function.

c. Verify by integration that the position function is given by

$$s(t) = V_T t + \frac{V_T^2}{g} \ln\left(\frac{1 + e^{-2gt/V_T}}{2}\right),$$

where $s'(t) = v(t)$ and $s(0) = 0$.

d. Graph the position function.

(See the Guided Project *Terminal velocity* for more details on free fall and terminal velocity.)

Additional Exercises

97. $\boldsymbol{\pi < \frac{22}{7}}$ One of the earliest approximations to π is $\frac{22}{7}$. Verify that $0 < \displaystyle\int_0^1 \frac{x^4(1-x)^4}{1+x^2}\,dx = \frac{22}{7} - \pi$. Why can you conclude that $\pi < \frac{22}{7}$?

98. Challenge Show that with the change of variables $u = \sqrt{\tan x}$, the integral $\int \sqrt{\tan x}\,dx$ can be converted to an integral amenable to partial fractions. Evaluate $\int_0^{\pi/4} \sqrt{\tan x}\,dx$.

QUICK CHECK ANSWERS

1. $\ln|x - 2| + 2\ln|x + 4| = \ln|(x - 2)(x + 4)^2|$

2. $A/(x - 1) + B/(x + 5) + C/(x - 10)$

3. $A/x + B/x^2 + C/(x - 3) + D/(x - 3)^2 + E/(x - 1)$

4. $1 - \dfrac{1}{x+1}$ ◀

7.6 Other Integration Strategies

The integration methods studied so far—various substitutions, integration by parts, and partial fractions—are examples of *analytical methods*; they are done with pencil and paper, and they give exact results. While many important integrals can be evaluated with analytical methods, many more integrals lie beyond their reach. For example, the following integrals cannot be evaluated in terms of familiar functions:

$$\int e^{x^2}\,dx, \quad \int \sin x^2\,dx, \quad \int \frac{\sin x}{x}\,dx, \quad \int \frac{e^{-x}}{x}\,dx, \quad \text{and} \quad \int \ln(\ln x)\,dx.$$

The next two sections survey alternative strategies for evaluating integrals when standard analytical methods do not work. These strategies fall into three categories.

1. **Tables of integrals** The endpapers of this text contain a table of many standard integrals. Because these integrals were evaluated analytically, using tables is considered an analytical method. Tables of integrals also contain reduction formulas like those discussed in Sections 7.2 and 7.3.
2. **Symbolic methods** Computer algebra systems have sophisticated algorithms to evaluate difficult integrals. Many definite and indefinite integrals can be evaluated exactly using these symbolic methods.

3. **Numerical methods** The value of a definite integral can be approximated accurately using numerical methods introduced in the next section. *Numerical* means that these methods compute numbers rather than manipulate symbols. Computers and calculators often have built-in functions to carry out numerical calculations.

Figure 7.10 is a chart of the various integration strategies and how they are related.

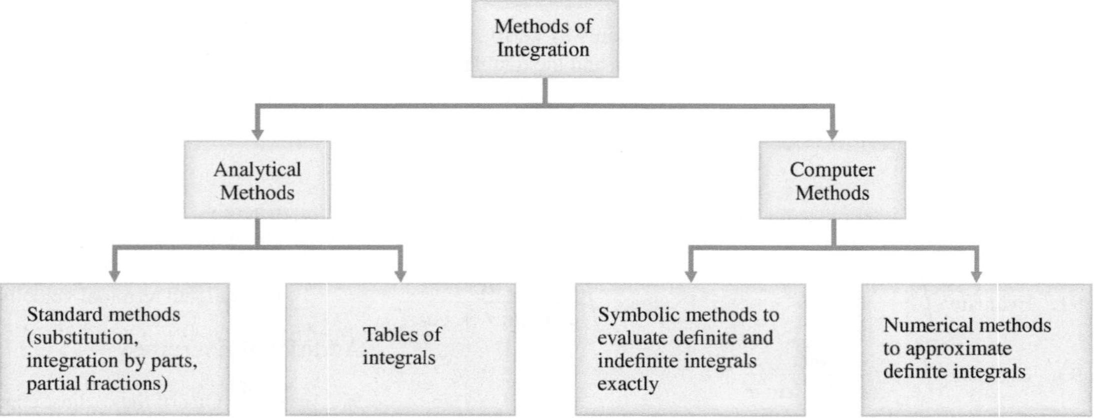

Figure 7.10

➤ A short table of integrals is found at the end of the book. Longer tables of integrals are found online and in venerable collections such as the *CRC Mathematical Tables* and *Handbook of Mathematical Functions*, by Abramowitz and Stegun.

Using Tables of Integrals

Given a specific integral, you *may* be able to find the identical integral in a table of integrals. More likely, some preliminary work is needed to convert the given integral into one that appears in a table. Most tables give only indefinite integrals, although some tables include special definite integrals. The following examples illustrate various ways in which tables of integrals are used.

EXAMPLE 1 **Using tables of integrals** Evaluate the integral $\int \frac{dx}{x\sqrt{2x - 9}}$.

SOLUTION It is worth noting that this integral may be evaluated with the change of variables $u^2 = 2x - 9$. Alternatively, a table of integrals includes the integral

$$\int \frac{dx}{x\sqrt{ax - b}} = \frac{2}{\sqrt{b}} \tan^{-1} \sqrt{\frac{ax - b}{b}} + C, \quad \text{where} \quad b > 0,$$

which matches the given integral. Letting $a = 2$ and $b = 9$, we find that

$$\int \frac{dx}{x\sqrt{2x - 9}} = \frac{2}{\sqrt{9}} \tan^{-1} \sqrt{\frac{2x - 9}{9}} + C = \frac{2}{3} \tan^{-1} \frac{\sqrt{2x - 9}}{3} + C.$$

Related Exercises 5–22 ◀

➤ Letting $u^2 = 2x - 9$, we have $u\,du = dx$ and $x = \frac{1}{2}(u^2 + 9)$. Therefore,

$$\int \frac{dx}{x\sqrt{2x - 9}} = 2 \int \frac{du}{u^2 + 9}.$$

EXAMPLE 2 **Preliminary work** Evaluate $\int \sqrt{x^2 + 6x}\, dx$.

SOLUTION Most tables of integrals do not include this integral. The nearest integral you are likely to find is $\int \sqrt{x^2 \pm a^2}\, dx$. The given integral can be put into this form by completing the square and using a substitution:

$$x^2 + 6x = x^2 + 6x + 9 - 9 = (x + 3)^2 - 9.$$

With the change of variables $u = x + 3$, the evaluation appears as follows:

$$\int \sqrt{x^2 + 6x}\, dx = \int \sqrt{(x+3)^2 - 9}\, dx \quad \text{Complete the square.}$$

$$= \int \sqrt{u^2 - 9}\, du \quad u = x + 3,\ du = dx$$

$$= \frac{u}{2}\sqrt{u^2 - 9} - \frac{9}{2}\ln\left|u + \sqrt{u^2 - 9}\right| + C \quad \text{Table of integrals}$$

$$= \frac{x+3}{2}\sqrt{(x+3)^2 - 9} - \frac{9}{2}\ln\left|x + 3 + \sqrt{(x+3)^2 - 9}\right| + C \quad \text{Replace } u \text{ with } x + 3.$$

$$= \frac{x+3}{2}\sqrt{x^2 + 6x} - \frac{9}{2}\ln\left|x + 3 + \sqrt{x^2 + 6x}\right| + C. \quad \text{Simplify.}$$

Related Exercises 23–38 ◀

EXAMPLE 3 Using tables of integrals for area Find the area of the region bounded by the curve $y = \frac{1}{1 + \sin x}$ and the x-axis between $x = 0$ and $x = \pi$.

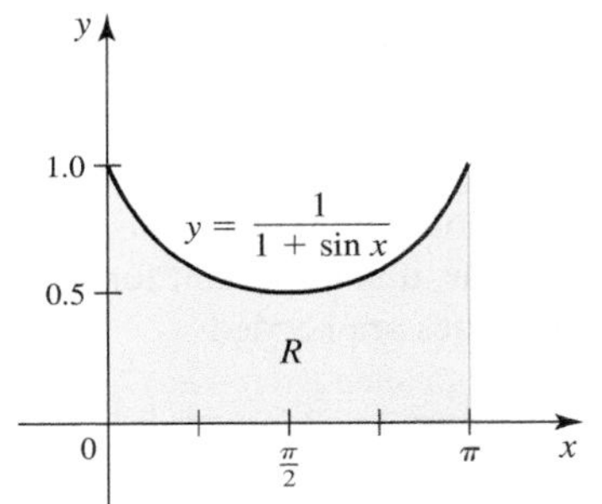

Figure 7.11

SOLUTION The region in question (Figure 7.11) lies entirely above the x-axis, so its area is $\int_0^{\pi} \frac{dx}{1 + \sin x}$. A matching integral in a table of integrals is

$$\int \frac{dx}{1 + \sin ax} = -\frac{1}{a}\tan\left(\frac{\pi}{4} - \frac{ax}{2}\right) + C.$$

Evaluating the definite integral with $a = 1$, we have

$$\int_0^{\pi} \frac{dx}{1 + \sin x} = -\tan\left(\frac{\pi}{4} - \frac{x}{2}\right)\bigg|_0^{\pi} = -\tan\left(-\frac{\pi}{4}\right) - \left(-\tan\frac{\pi}{4}\right) = 2.$$

Related Exercises 39–46 ◀

QUICK CHECK 1 Use the result of Example 3 to evaluate $\int_0^{\pi/2} \frac{dx}{1 + \sin x}$. ◀

Symbolic Methods

Computer algebra systems evaluate many integrals exactly using symbolic methods, and they approximate many definite integrals using numerical methods. Different software packages may produce different results for the same indefinite integral, but ultimately, they must agree. The discussion that follows does not rely on one particular computer algebra system. Rather, it illustrates results from different systems and shows some of the idiosyncrasies of using a computer algebra system.

QUICK CHECK 2 Using one computer algebra system, it was found that $\int \sin x \cos x\, dx = \frac{1}{2}\sin^2 x + C$; using another computer algebra system, it was found that $\int \sin x \cos x\, dx = -\frac{1}{2}\cos^2 x + C$. Reconcile the two answers. ◀

➤ Most computer algebra systems do not include the constant of integration after evaluating an indefinite integral. But it should always be included when reporting a result.

EXAMPLE 4 Apparent discrepancies Evaluate $\int \frac{dx}{\sqrt{e^x + 1}}$ using tables and a computer algebra system.

SOLUTION Using one particular computer algebra system, we find that

$$\int \frac{dx}{\sqrt{e^x + 1}} = -2 \tanh^{-1} \sqrt{e^x + 1} + C,$$

where $\tanh^{-1}$ is the *inverse hyperbolic tangent* function (Section 6.10). However, we can obtain a result in terms of more familiar functions by first using the substitution $u = e^x$, which implies that $du = e^x\,dx$ or $dx = du/e^x = du/u$. The integral becomes

$$\int \frac{dx}{\sqrt{e^x + 1}} = \int \frac{du}{u\sqrt{u + 1}}.$$

➤ Recall that the *hyperbolic tangent* is defined as

$$\tanh x = \frac{e^x - e^{-x}}{e^x + e^{-x}}.$$

Its inverse is the *inverse hyperbolic tangent*, written $\tanh^{-1} x$.

Using a computer algebra system again, we obtain

$$\begin{aligned}\int \frac{dx}{\sqrt{e^x + 1}} = \int \frac{du}{u\sqrt{u + 1}} &= \ln(\sqrt{1 + u} - 1) - \ln(\sqrt{1 + u} + 1)\\ &= \ln(\sqrt{1 + e^x} - 1) - \ln(\sqrt{1 + e^x} + 1).\end{aligned}$$

➤ Some computer algebra systems use $\log x$ for $\ln x$.

A table of integrals leads to a third equivalent form of the integral:

$$\begin{aligned}\int \frac{dx}{\sqrt{e^x + 1}} = \int \frac{du}{u\sqrt{u + 1}} &= \ln\left(\frac{\sqrt{u + 1} - 1}{\sqrt{u + 1} + 1}\right) + C\\ &= \ln\left(\frac{\sqrt{e^x + 1} - 1}{\sqrt{e^x + 1} + 1}\right) + C.\end{aligned}$$

Often the difference between two results is a few steps of algebra or a trigonometric identity. In this case, the final two results are reconciled using logarithm properties. This example illustrates that computer algebra systems generally do not include constants of integration and may omit absolute values when logarithms appear. It is important for the user to determine whether integration constants and absolute values are needed.

Related Exercises 47–62 ◀

QUICK CHECK 3 Using partial fractions, we know that $\int \frac{dx}{x(x + 1)} = \ln\left|\frac{x}{x + 1}\right| + C.$ Using a computer algebra system, we find that $\int \frac{dx}{x(x + 1)} = \ln x - \ln(x + 1)$. What is wrong with the result from the computer algebra system? ◀

EXAMPLE 5 **Symbolic versus numerical integration** Use a computer algebra system to evaluate $\int_0^1 \sin x^2\,dx$.

SOLUTION Sometimes a computer algebra system gives the exact value of an integral in terms of an unfamiliar function, or it may not be able to evaluate the integral exactly. For example, one particular computer algebra system returns the result

$$\int_0^1 \sin x^2\,dx = \sqrt{\frac{\pi}{2}}\,S\left(\sqrt{\frac{2}{\pi}}\right),$$

where S is known as the *Fresnel integral function* $\left(S(x) = \int_0^x \sin\left(\frac{\pi t^2}{2}\right) dt\right)$. However, if the computer algebra system is instructed to approximate the integral, the result is

$$\int_0^1 \sin x^2\,dx \approx 0.3102683017,$$

which is an excellent approximation.

Related Exercises 47–62 ◀

SECTION 7.6 EXERCISES

Review Questions

1. Give some examples of analytical methods for evaluating integrals.
2. Does a computer algebra system give an exact result for an indefinite integral? Explain.
3. Why might an integral found in a table differ from the same integral evaluated by a computer algebra system?
4. Is a reduction formula an analytical method or a numerical method? Explain.

Basic Skills

5–22. Table lookup integrals *Use a table of integrals to determine the following indefinite integrals.*

5. $\int \cos^{-1} x\,dx$
6. $\int \sin 3x \cos 2x\,dx$
7. $\int \frac{dx}{\sqrt{x^2+16}}$
8. $\int \frac{dx}{\sqrt{x^2-25}}$
9. $\int \frac{3u}{2u+7}\,du$
10. $\int \frac{dy}{y(2y+9)}$
11. $\int \frac{dx}{1-\cos 4x}$
12. $\int \frac{dx}{x\sqrt{81-x^2}}$
13. $\int \frac{x}{\sqrt{4x+1}}\,dx$
14. $\int t\sqrt{4t+12}\,dt$
15. $\int \frac{dx}{\sqrt{9x^2-100}},\ x > \frac{10}{3}$
16. $\int \frac{dx}{225-16x^2}$
17. $\int \frac{dx}{(16+9x^2)^{3/2}}$
18. $\int \sqrt{4x^2-9}\,dx,\ x > \frac{3}{2}$
19. $\int \frac{dx}{x\sqrt{144-x^2}}$
20. $\int \frac{dv}{v(v^2+8)}$
21. $\int \ln^2 x\,dx$
22. $\int x^2 e^{5x}\,dx$

23–38. Preliminary work *Use a table of integrals to determine the following indefinite integrals. These integrals require preliminary work, such as completing the square or changing variables, before they can be found in a table.*

23. $\int \sqrt{x^2+10x}\,dx,\ x > 0$
24. $\int \sqrt{x^2-8x}\,dx,\ x > 8$
25. $\int \frac{dx}{x^2+2x+10}$
26. $\int \sqrt{x^2-4x+8}\,dx$
27. $\int \frac{dx}{x(x^{10}+1)}$
28. $\int \frac{dt}{t(t^8-256)}$
29. $\int \frac{dx}{\sqrt{x^2-6x}},\ x > 6$
30. $\int \frac{dx}{\sqrt{x^2+10x}},\ x > 0$
31. $\int \frac{e^x}{\sqrt{e^{2x}+4}}\,dx$
32. $\int \frac{\sqrt{\ln^2 x+4}}{x}\,dx$
33. $\int \frac{\cos x}{\sin^2 x+2\sin x}\,dx$
34. $\int \frac{\cos^{-1}\sqrt{x}}{\sqrt{x}}\,dx$
35. $\int \frac{\tan^{-1} x^3}{x^4}\,dx$
36. $\int \frac{e^{3t}}{\sqrt{4+e^{2t}}}\,dt$
37. $\int \frac{(\ln x)\sin^{-1}(\ln x)}{x}\,dx$
38. $\int \frac{dt}{\sqrt{1+4e^t}}$

39–46. Geometry problems *Use a table of integrals to solve the following problems.*

39. Find the length of the curve $y = x^2/4$ on the interval $[0, 8]$.
40. Find the length of the curve $y = x^{3/2} + 8$ on the interval $[0, 2]$.
41. Find the length of the curve $y = e^x$ on the interval $[0, \ln 2]$.
42. The region bounded by the graph of $y = x^2\sqrt{\ln x}$ and the x-axis on the interval $[1, e]$ is revolved about the x-axis. What is the volume of the solid that is formed?
43. The region bounded by the graph of $y = \frac{1}{\sqrt{x+4}}$ and the x-axis on the interval $[0, 12]$ is revolved about the y-axis. What is the volume of the solid that is formed?
44. Find the area of the region bounded by the graph of $y = \frac{1}{\sqrt{x^2-2x+2}}$ and the x-axis between $x = 0$ and $x = 3$.
45. The region bounded by the graphs of $y = \pi/2$, $y = \sin^{-1} x$, and the y-axis is revolved about the y-axis. What is the volume of the solid that is formed?
46. The graphs of $f(x) = \frac{2}{x^2+1}$ and $g(x) = \frac{7}{4\sqrt{x^2+1}}$ are shown in the figure. Which is greater, the average value of f or that of g on the interval $[-1, 1]$?

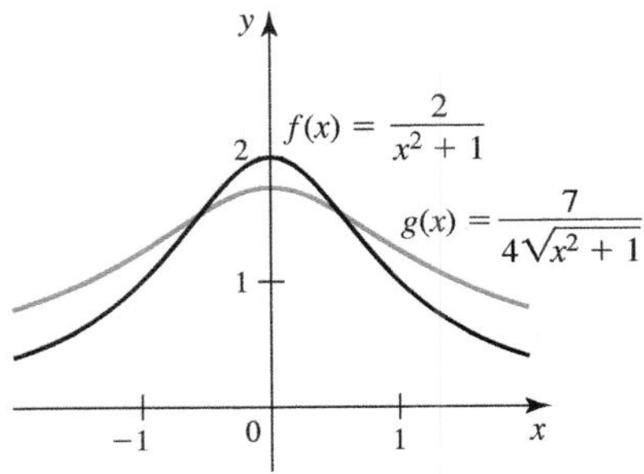

T 47–54. Indefinite integrals *Use a computer algebra system to evaluate the following indefinite integrals. Assume that a is a positive real number.*

47. $\int \frac{x}{\sqrt{2x+3}}\,dx$
48. $\int \sqrt{4x^2+36}\,dx$
49. $\int \tan^2 3x\,dx$
50. $\int (a^2-t^2)^{-2}\,dt$
51. $\int \frac{(x^2-a^2)^{3/2}}{x}\,dx$
52. $\int \frac{dx}{x(a^2-x^2)^2}$
53. $\int (a^2-x^2)^{3/2}\,dx$
54. $\int (y^2+a^2)^{-5/2}\,dy$

T 55–62. Definite integrals *Use a computer algebra system to evaluate the following definite integrals. In each case, find an exact value of the integral (obtained by a symbolic method) and find an approximate value (obtained by a numerical method). Compare the results.*

55. $\int_{2/3}^{4/5} x^8\,dx$

56. $\int_0^{\pi/2} \cos^6 x\,dx$

57. $\int_0^4 (9 + x^2)^{3/2}\,dx$

58. $\int_{1/2}^1 \frac{\sin^{-1} x}{x}\,dx$

59. $\int_0^{\pi/2} \frac{dt}{1 + \tan^2 t}$

60. $\int_0^{2\pi} \frac{dt}{(4 + 2\sin t)^2}$

61. $\int_0^1 (\ln x)\ln(1 + x)\,dx$

62. $\int_0^{\pi/4} \ln(1 + \tan x)\,dx$

Further Explorations

63. Explain why or why not Determine whether the following statements are true and give an explanation or counterexample.

a. It is possible that a computer algebra system says $\int \frac{dx}{x(x-1)} = \ln(x-1) - \ln x$ and a table of integrals says $\int \frac{dx}{x(x-1)} = \ln\left|\frac{x-1}{x}\right| + C$.

b. A computer algebra system working in symbolic mode could give the result $\int_0^1 x^8\,dx = \frac{1}{9}$, and a computer algebra system working in approximate (numerical) mode could give the result $\int_0^1 x^8\,dx = 0.11111111$.

64. Apparent discrepancy Three different computer algebra systems give the following results:

$$\int \frac{dx}{x\sqrt{x^4 - 1}} = \frac{1}{2}\cos^{-1}\sqrt{x^{-4}} = \frac{1}{2}\cos^{-1} x^{-2} = \frac{1}{2}\tan^{-1}\sqrt{x^4 - 1}.$$

Explain how they can all be correct.

65. Reconciling results Using one computer algebra system, it was found that $\int \frac{dx}{1 + \sin x} = \frac{\sin x - 1}{\cos x}$, and using another computer algebra system, it was found that $\int \frac{dx}{1 + \sin x} = \frac{2\sin(x/2)}{\cos(x/2) + \sin(x/2)}$. Reconcile the two answers.

66. Apparent discrepancy Resolve the apparent discrepancy between

$$\int \frac{dx}{x(x-1)(x+2)} = \frac{1}{6}\ln\frac{(x-1)^2|x+2|}{|x|^3} + C \quad \text{and}$$

$$\int \frac{dx}{x(x-1)(x+2)} = \frac{\ln|x-1|}{3} + \frac{\ln|x+2|}{6} - \frac{\ln|x|}{2} + C.$$

67–70. Reduction formulas *Use the reduction formulas in a table of integrals to evaluate the following integrals.*

67. $\int x^3 e^{2x}\,dx$

68. $\int p^2 e^{-3p}\,dp$

69. $\int \tan^4 3y\,dy$

70. $\int \sec^4 4t\,dt$

T 71–74. Double table lookup *The following integrals may require more than one table lookup. Evaluate the integrals using a table of integrals; then check your answer with a computer algebra system.*

71. $\int x\sin^{-1} 2x\,dx$

72. $\int 4x\cos^{-1} 10x\,dx$

73. $\int \frac{\tan^{-1} x}{x^2}\,dx$

74. $\int \frac{\sin^{-1} ax}{x^2}\,dx,\ a > 0$

75. Evaluating an integral without the Fundamental Theorem of Calculus Evaluate $\int_0^{\pi/4} \ln(1 + \tan x)\,dx$ using the following steps.

a. If f is integrable on $[0, b]$, use substitution to show that

$$\int_0^b f(x)\,dx = \int_0^{b/2} (f(x) + f(b - x))\,dx.$$

b. Use part (a) and the identity $\tan(\alpha + \beta) = \frac{\tan\alpha + \tan\beta}{1 - \tan\alpha\tan\beta}$ to evaluate $\int_0^{\pi/4} \ln(1 + \tan x)\,dx$.
(*Source: The College Mathematics Journal* 33, 4, Sep 2004)

76. Two integration approaches Evaluate $\int \cos(\ln x)\,dx$ two different ways:

a. Use tables after first using the substitution $u = \ln x$.

b. Use integration by parts twice to verify your answer to part (a).

Applications

T 77. Period of a pendulum Consider a pendulum of length L meters swinging only under the influence of gravity. Suppose the pendulum starts swinging with an initial displacement of θ_0 radians (see figure). The period (time to complete one full cycle) is given by

$$T = \frac{4}{\omega}\int_0^{\pi/2} \frac{d\varphi}{\sqrt{1 - k^2\sin^2\varphi}},$$

where $\omega^2 = g/L$, $g \approx 9.8\ \text{m/s}^2$ is the acceleration due to gravity, and $k^2 = \sin^2(\theta_0/2)$. Assume $L = 9.8$ m, which means $\omega = 1\ \text{s}^{-1}$.

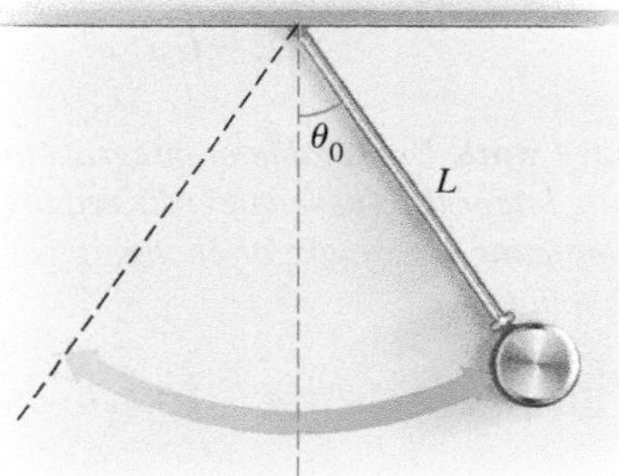

a. Use a computer algebra system to find the period of the pendulum for $\theta_0 = 0.1, 0.2, \ldots, 0.9, 1.0$ rad.

b. For small values of θ_0, the period should be approximately 2π seconds. For what values of θ_0 are your computed values within 10% of 2π (relative error less than 0.1)?

Additional Exercises

T 78. Arc length of a parabola Let $L(c)$ be the length of the parabola $f(x) = x^2$ from $x = 0$ to $x = c$, where $c \geq 0$ is a constant.

a. Find an expression for L and graph the function.
b. Is L concave up or concave down on $[0, \infty)$?
c. Show that as c becomes large and positive, the arc length function increases as c^2; that is, $L(c) \approx kc^2$, where k is a constant.

79–82. Deriving formulas *Evaluate the following integrals. Assume a and b are real numbers and n is an integer.*

79. $\displaystyle\int \frac{x}{ax+b}\,dx$ (Use $u = ax + b$.)

80. $\displaystyle\int \frac{x}{\sqrt{ax+b}}\,dx$ (Use $u^2 = ax + b$.)

81. $\int x(ax+b)^n\,dx$ (Use $u = ax + b$.)

82. $\int x^n \sin^{-1} x\,dx$ (Use integration by parts.)

T 83. Powers of sine and cosine It can be shown that

$$\int_0^{\pi/2} \sin^n x\,dx = \int_0^{\pi/2} \cos^n x\,dx = \begin{cases} \dfrac{1\cdot 3\cdot 5\cdots(n-1)}{2\cdot 4\cdot 6\cdots n}\cdot\dfrac{\pi}{2} & \text{if } n \geq 2 \text{ is an even integer} \\ \dfrac{2\cdot 4\cdot 6\cdots(n-1)}{3\cdot 5\cdot 7\cdots n} & \text{if } n \geq 3 \text{ is an odd integer.} \end{cases}$$

a. Use a computer algebra system to confirm this result for $n = 2, 3, 4$, and 5.
b. Evaluate the integrals with $n = 10$ and confirm the result.
c. Using graphing and/or symbolic computation, determine whether the values of the integrals increase or decrease as n increases.

T 84. A remarkable integral It is a fact that $\displaystyle\int_0^{\pi/2} \frac{dx}{1+\tan^m x} = \frac{\pi}{4}$ for *all* real numbers m.

a. Graph the integrand for $m = -2, -3/2, -1, -1/2, 0, 1/2, 1, 3/2$, and 2, and explain geometrically how the area under the curve on the interval $[0, \pi/2]$ remains constant as m varies.
b. Use a computer algebra system to confirm that the integral is constant for all m.

QUICK CHECK ANSWERS

1. 1 **2.** Because $\sin^2 x = 1 - \cos^2 x$, the two results differ by a constant, which can be absorbed in the arbitrary constant C. **3.** The second result agrees with the first for $x > 0$ after using $\ln a - \ln b = \ln(a/b)$. The second result should have absolute values and an arbitrary constant. ◀

7.7 Numerical Integration

Situations arise in which the analytical methods we have developed so far cannot be used to evaluate a definite integral. For example, an integrand may not have an obvious antiderivative (such as $\cos x^2$ and $1/\ln x$), or perhaps the value of the integrand is known only at a finite set of points, which makes finding an antiderivative impossible.

When analytical methods fail, we often turn to *numerical methods*, which are typically done on a calculator or computer. These methods do not produce exact values of definite integrals, but they provide approximations that are generally quite accurate. Many calculators, software packages, and computer algebra systems have built-in numerical integration methods. In this section, we explore some of these methods.

Absolute and Relative Error

Because numerical methods do not typically produce exact results, we should be concerned about the accuracy of approximations, which leads to the ideas of *absolute* and *relative error.*

> Because the exact solution is usually not known, the goal in practice is to estimate the maximum size of the error.

DEFINITION Absolute and Relative Error

Suppose c is a computed numerical solution to a problem having an exact solution x. There are two common measures of the error in c as an approximation to x:

$$\textbf{absolute error} = |c - x|$$

and

$$\textbf{relative error} = \frac{|c - x|}{|x|} \quad (\text{if } x \neq 0).$$

EXAMPLE 1 **Absolute and relative error** The ancient Greeks used $\frac{22}{7}$ to approximate the value of π. Determine the absolute and relative error in this approximation to π.

SOLUTION Letting $c = \frac{22}{7}$ be the approximate value of $x = \pi$, we find that

$$\text{absolute error} = \left|\frac{22}{7} - \pi\right| \approx 0.00126$$

and

$$\text{relative error} = \frac{|22/7 - \pi|}{|\pi|} \approx 0.000402 \approx 0.04\%.$$

Related Exercises 7–10 ◀

Midpoint Rule

Many numerical integration methods are based on the ideas that underlie Riemann sums; these methods approximate the net area of regions bounded by curves. A typical problem is shown in Figure 7.12, where we see a function f defined on an interval $[a, b]$. The goal is to approximate the value of $\int_a^b f(x)\,dx$. As with Riemann sums, we first partition the interval $[a, b]$ into n subintervals of equal length $\Delta x = (b - a)/n$. This partition establishes $n + 1$ grid points

$$x_0 = a, \quad x_1 = a + \Delta x, \quad x_2 = a + 2\Delta x, \ldots, \quad x_k = a + k\Delta x, \ldots, \quad x_n = b.$$

The kth subinterval is $[x_{k-1}, x_k]$, for $k = 1, 2, \ldots, n$.

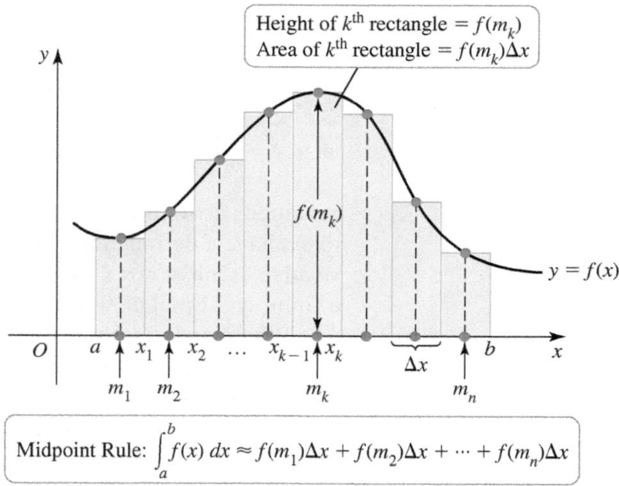

Figure 7.12

The Midpoint Rule approximates the region under the curve using rectangles. The bases of the rectangles have width Δx. The height of the kth rectangle is $f(m_k)$, where $m_k = (x_{k-1} + x_k)/2$ is the midpoint of the kth subinterval (Figure 7.12). Therefore, the net area of the kth rectangle is $f(m_k)\Delta x$.

Let $M(n)$ be the Midpoint Rule approximation to the integral using n rectangles. Summing the net areas of the rectangles, we have

➤ If $f(m_k) < 0$ for some k, then the net area of the corresponding rectangle is negative, which makes a negative contribution to the approximation (Section 5.2).

$$\begin{aligned}\int_a^b f(x)\,dx &\approx M(n) \\ &= f(m_1)\Delta x + f(m_2)\Delta x + \cdots + f(m_n)\Delta x \\ &= \sum_{k=1}^{n} f\left(\frac{x_{k-1} + x_k}{2}\right)\Delta x.\end{aligned}$$

Just as with Riemann sums, the Midpoint Rule approximations to $\int_a^b f(x)\,dx$ generally improve as n increases.

➤ The Midpoint Rule is a midpoint Riemann sum, introduced in Section 5.1.

> **DEFINITION Midpoint Rule**
>
> Suppose f is defined and integrable on $[a, b]$. The **Midpoint Rule approximation** to $\int_a^b f(x)\,dx$ using n equally spaced subintervals on $[a, b]$ is
>
> $$M(n) = f(m_1)\Delta x + f(m_2)\Delta x + \cdots + f(m_n)\Delta x$$
> $$= \sum_{k=1}^{n} f\left(\frac{x_{k-1} + x_k}{2}\right)\Delta x,$$
>
> where $\Delta x = (b - a)/n$, $x_k = a + k\Delta x$, and $m_k = (x_{k-1} + x_k)/2$ is the midpoint of $[x_{k-1}, x_k]$, for $k = 1, \ldots, n$.

QUICK CHECK 1 To apply the Midpoint Rule on the interval $[3, 11]$ with $n = 4$, at what points must the integrand be evaluated? ◄

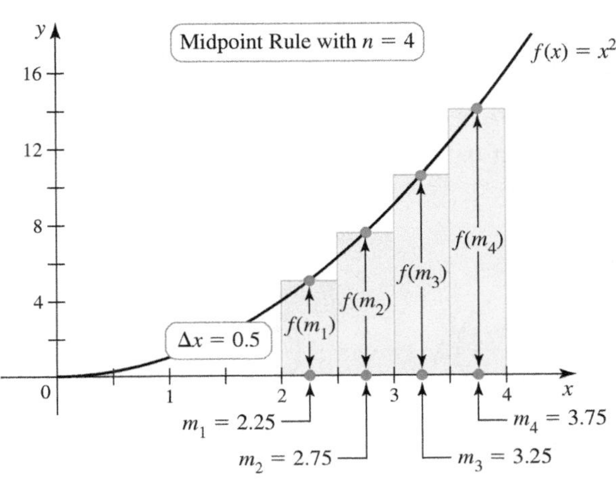

Figure 7.13

EXAMPLE 2 Applying the Midpoint Rule Approximate $\int_2^4 x^2\,dx$ using the Midpoint Rule with $n = 4$ and $n = 8$ subintervals.

SOLUTION With $a = 2$, $b = 4$, and $n = 4$ subintervals, the length of each subinterval is $\Delta x = (b - a)/n = 2/4 = 0.5$. The grid points are

$$x_0 = 2, \quad x_1 = 2.5, \quad x_2 = 3, \quad x_3 = 3.5, \quad \text{and} \quad x_4 = 4.$$

The integrand must be evaluated at the midpoints (Figure 7.13)

$$m_1 = 2.25, \quad m_2 = 2.75, \quad m_3 = 3.25, \quad \text{and} \quad m_4 = 3.75.$$

With $f(x) = x^2$ and $n = 4$, the Midpoint Rule approximation is

$$\begin{aligned} M(4) &= f(m_1)\Delta x + f(m_2)\Delta x + f(m_3)\Delta x + f(m_4)\Delta x \\ &= (m_1^2 + m_2^2 + m_3^2 + m_4^2)\Delta x \\ &= (2.25^2 + 2.75^2 + 3.25^2 + 3.75^2)\cdot 0.5 \\ &= 18.625. \end{aligned}$$

The exact area of the region is $\frac{56}{3}$, so this Midpoint Rule approximation has an absolute error of

$$|18.625 - 56/3| \approx 0.0417$$

and a relative error of

$$\left|\frac{18.625 - 56/3}{56/3}\right| \approx 0.00223 = 0.223\%.$$

Using $n = 8$ subintervals, the midpoint approximation is

$$M(8) = \sum_{k=1}^{8} f(m_k)\Delta x = 18.65625,$$

which has an absolute error of about 0.0104 and a relative error of about 0.0558%. We see that increasing n and using more rectangles decreases the error in the approximations.

Related Exercises 11–14 ◄

The Trapezoid Rule

Another numerical method for estimating $\int_a^b f(x)\,dx$ is the Trapezoid Rule, which uses the same partition of the interval $[a, b]$ described for the Midpoint Rule. Instead of approximating the region under the curve by rectangles, the Trapezoid Rule uses (what else?) trapezoids. The bases of the trapezoids have length Δx. The sides of the kth

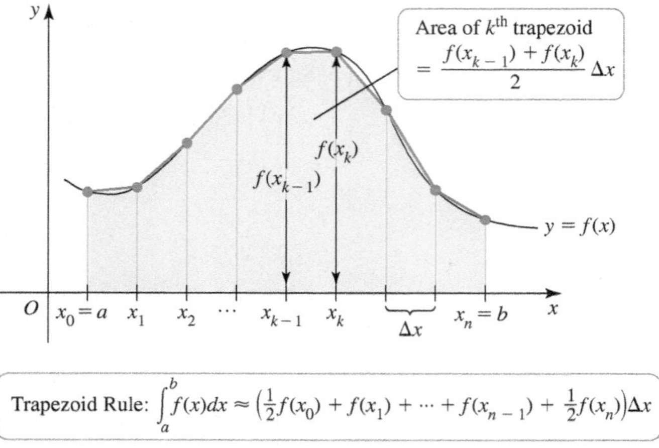

Figure 7.14

➤ This derivation of the Trapezoid Rule assumes that f is nonnegative on $[a, b]$. However, the same argument can be used if f is negative on all or part of $[a, b]$. In fact, the argument illustrates how negative contributions to the net area arise when f is negative.

Area of a trapezoid

a $\quad$ b $\quad$ h

$\text{Area} = h\left(\frac{a+b}{2}\right)$

trapezoid have lengths $f(x_{k-1})$ and $f(x_k)$, for $k = 1, 2, \ldots, n$ (Figure 7.14). Therefore, the net area of the kth trapezoid is $\left(\dfrac{f(x_{k-1}) + f(x_k)}{2}\right)\Delta x$.

Letting $T(n)$ be the Trapezoid Rule approximation to the integral using n subintervals, we have

$$\begin{aligned}\int_a^b f(x)\,dx &\approx T(n)\\ &= \underbrace{\left(\frac{f(x_0) + f(x_1)}{2}\right)\Delta x}_{\text{area of first trapezoid}} + \underbrace{\left(\frac{f(x_1) + f(x_2)}{2}\right)\Delta x}_{\text{area of second trapezoid}} + \cdots + \underbrace{\left(\frac{f(x_{n-1}) + f(x_n)}{2}\right)\Delta x}_{\text{area of } n\text{th trapezoid}}\\ &= \left(\frac{f(x_0)}{2} + \underbrace{\frac{f(x_1)}{2} + \frac{f(x_1)}{2}}_{f(x_1)} + \cdots + \underbrace{\frac{f(x_{n-1})}{2} + \frac{f(x_{n-1})}{2}}_{f(x_{n-1})} + \frac{f(x_n)}{2}\right)\Delta x\\ &= \left(\frac{f(x_0)}{2} + \underbrace{f(x_1) + \cdots + f(x_{n-1})}_{\sum_{k=1}^{n-1} f(x_k)} + \frac{f(x_n)}{2}\right)\Delta x.\end{aligned}$$

As with the Midpoint Rule, the Trapezoid Rule approximations generally improve as n increases.

QUICK CHECK 2 Does the Trapezoid Rule underestimate or overestimate the value of $\int_0^4 x^2 dx$? ◄

> **DEFINITION Trapezoid Rule**
>
> Suppose f is defined and integrable on $[a, b]$. The **Trapezoid Rule approximation** to $\int_a^b f(x)\,dx$ using n equally spaced subintervals on $[a, b]$ is
>
> $$T(n) = \left(\frac{1}{2}f(x_0) + \sum_{k=1}^{n-1} f(x_k) + \frac{1}{2}f(x_n)\right)\Delta x,$$
>
> where $\Delta x = (b - a)/n$ and $x_k = a + k\Delta x$, for $k = 0, 1, \ldots, n$.

EXAMPLE 3 **Applying the Trapezoid Rule** Approximate $\int_2^4 x^2\,dx$ using the Trapezoid Rule with $n = 4$ subintervals.

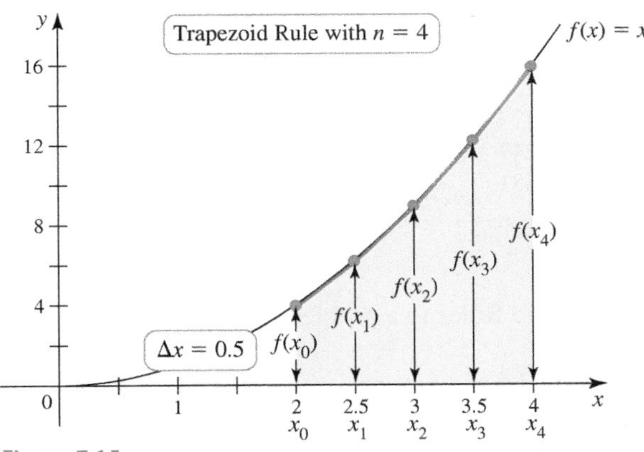

Figure 7.15

SOLUTION As in Example 2, the grid points are

$$x_0 = 2, \quad x_1 = 2.5, \quad x_2 = 3, \quad x_3 = 3.5, \quad \text{and} \quad x_4 = 4.$$

With $f(x) = x^2$ and $n = 4$, the Trapezoid Rule approximation is

$$\begin{aligned} T(4) &= \tfrac{1}{2}f(x_0)\Delta x + f(x_1)\Delta x + f(x_2)\Delta x + f(x_3)\Delta x + \tfrac{1}{2}f(x_4)\Delta x \\ &= \left(\tfrac{1}{2}x_0^2 + x_1^2 + x_2^2 + x_3^2 + \tfrac{1}{2}x_4^2\right)\Delta x \\ &= \left(\tfrac{1}{2}\cdot 2^2 + 2.5^2 + 3^2 + 3.5^2 + \tfrac{1}{2}\cdot 4^2\right)\cdot 0.5 \\ &= 18.75. \end{aligned}$$

Figure 7.15 shows the approximation with $n = 4$ trapezoids. The exact area of the region is $56/3$, so the Trapezoid Rule approximation has an absolute error of about 0.0833 and a relative error of approximately 0.00446, or 0.446%. Increasing n decreases this error.

Related Exercises 15–18 ◀

EXAMPLE 4 **Errors in the Midpoint and Trapezoid Rules** Given that

$$\int_0^1 xe^{-x}\,dx = 1 - 2e^{-1},$$

find the absolute errors in the Midpoint Rule and Trapezoid Rule approximations to the integral with $n = 4, 8, 16, 32, 64$, and 128 subintervals.

SOLUTION Because the exact value of the integral is known (which does *not* happen in practice), we can compute the error in various approximations. For example, if $n = 16$, then

$$\Delta x = \frac{1}{16} \quad \text{and} \quad x_k = \frac{k}{16}, \quad \text{for } k = 0, 1, \ldots, n.$$

Using sigma notation and a calculator, we have

$$M(16) = \sum_{k=1}^{\overbrace{16}^{n}} f\left(\frac{\overbrace{(k-1)/16}^{x_{k-1}} + \overbrace{k/16}^{x_k}}{2}\right)\overbrace{\frac{1}{16}}^{\Delta x} = \sum_{k=1}^{16} f\left(\frac{2k-1}{32}\right)\frac{1}{16} \approx 0.26440383609318$$

and

$$T(16) = \left(\frac{1}{2}\underbrace{f(0)}_{x_0 = a} + \sum_{k=1}^{\overbrace{15}^{n-1}} \underbrace{f(k/16)}_{x_k} + \frac{1}{2}\underbrace{f(1)}_{x_{16} = b}\right)\frac{1}{16} \approx 0.26391564480235.$$

The absolute error in the Midpoint Rule approximation with $n = 16$ is $|M(16) - (1 - 2e^{-1})| \approx 0.000163$. The absolute error in the Trapezoid Rule approximation with $n = 16$ is $|T(16) - (1 - 2e^{-1})| \approx 0.000325$.

The Midpoint Rule and Trapezoid Rule approximations to the integral, together with the associated absolute errors, are shown in Table 7.5 for various values of n. Notice that as n increases, the errors in both methods decrease, as expected. With $n = 128$ subintervals, the approximations $M(128)$ and $T(128)$ agree to four decimal places. Based on these approximations, a good approximation to the integral is 0.2642. The way in which the errors decrease is also worth noting. If you look carefully at both error columns in Table 7.5, you will see that each time n is doubled (or Δx is halved), the error decreases by a factor of approximately 4.

Table 7.5

n	$M(n)$	$T(n)$	Error in $M(n)$	Error in $T(n)$
4	0.26683456310319	0.25904504019141	0.00259	0.00520
8	0.26489148795740	0.26293980164730	0.000650	0.00130
16	0.26440383609318	0.26391564480235	0.000163	0.000325
32	0.26428180513718	0.26415974044777	0.0000407	0.0000814
64	0.26425129001915	0.26422077279247	0.0000102	0.0000203
128	0.26424366077837	0.26423603140581	0.00000254	0.00000509

Related Exercises 19–26 ◀

QUICK CHECK 3 Compute the approximate factor by which the error decreases in Table 7.5 between $T(16)$ and $T(32)$, and between $T(32)$ and $T(64)$. ◀

We now apply the Midpoint and Trapezoid Rules to a problem with real data.

EXAMPLE 5 World oil production Table 7.6 and Figure 7.16 show data for the rate of world crude oil production (in billions of barrels/yr) over a 16-year period. If the rate of oil production is given by the (assumed to be integrable) function R, then the total amount of oil produced in billions of barrels over the time period $a \le t \le b$ is $Q = \int_a^b R(t)\,dt$ (Section 6.1). Use the Midpoint and Trapezoid Rules to approximate the total oil produced between 1995 and 2011.

Table 7.6

Year	World Crude Oil Production (billions barrels/yr)
1995	21.9
1996	22.3
1997	23.0
1998	23.7
1999	24.5
2000	23.7
2001	25.2
2002	24.8
2003	24.5
2004	25.2
2005	25.9
2006	26.3
2007	27.0
2008	26.9
2009	26.4
2010	27.0
2011	27.0

(*Source*: U.S. Energy Information Administration)

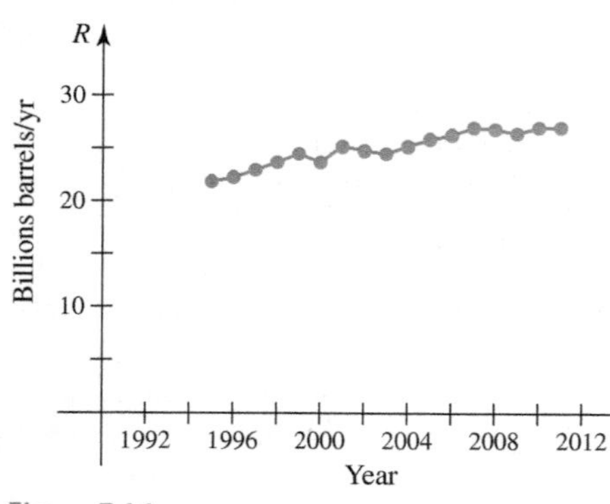

Figure 7.16
(*Source:* U.S. Energy Information Administration)

SOLUTION For convenience, let $t = 0$ represent 1995 and $t = 16$ represent 2011. We let $R(t)$ be the rate of oil production in the year corresponding to t (for example, $R(6) = 25.2$ is the rate in 2001). The goal is to approximate $Q = \int_0^{16} R(t)\,dt$. If we use $n = 4$ subintervals, then $\Delta t = 4$ yr. The resulting Midpoint and Trapezoid Rule approximations (in billions of barrels) are

$$\begin{aligned} Q \approx M(4) &= (R(2) + R(6) + R(10) + R(14))\Delta t \\ &= (23.0 + 25.2 + 25.9 + 26.4)4 \\ &= 402.0 \end{aligned}$$

and

$$\begin{aligned} Q \approx T(4) &= \left(\frac{1}{2}R(0) + R(4) + R(8) + R(12) + \frac{1}{2}R(16)\right)\Delta t \\ &= \left(\frac{1}{2}\cdot 21.9 + 24.5 + 24.5 + 27.0 + \frac{1}{2}\cdot 27.0\right)4 \\ &= 401.8. \end{aligned}$$

The two methods give reasonable agreement. Using $n = 8$ subintervals, with $\Delta t = 2$ yr, similar calculations give the approximations

$$Q \approx M(8) = 399.8 \quad \text{and} \quad Q \approx T(8) = 401.9.$$

The given data do not allow us to compute the next Midpoint Rule approximation $M(16)$. However, we can compute the next Trapezoid Rule approximation $T(16)$, and here is a good way to do it. If $T(n)$ and $M(n)$ are known, then the next Trapezoid Rule approximation is (Exercise 62)

$$T(2n) = \frac{T(n) + M(n)}{2}.$$

Using this identity, we find that

$$T(16) = \frac{T(8) + M(8)}{2} = \frac{401.9 + 399.8}{2} \approx 400.9.$$

Based on these calculations, the best approximation to the total oil produced between 1995 and 2011 is 400.9 billion barrels.

Related Exercises 27–30 ◀

The Midpoint and Trapezoid Rules, as well as left and right Riemann sums, can be applied to problems in which data are given on a nonuniform grid (that is, the lengths of the subintervals vary). In the case of the Trapezoid Rule, the net areas of the approximating trapezoids must be computed individually and then summed, as shown in the next example.

EXAMPLE 6 **Net change in sea level** Table 7.7 lists rates of change $s'(t)$ in global sea level $s(t)$ in various years from 1995 ($t = 0$) to 2011 ($t = 16$), with rates of change reported in mm/yr.

Table 7.7

t (years from 1995)	0 (1995)	3 (1998)	5 (2000)	7 (2002)	8 (2003)	12 (2007)	14 (2009)	16 (2011)
$s'(t)$ (mm/yr)	0.51	5.19	4.39	2.21	5.24	0.63	4.19	2.38

(*Source:* Collecte Localisation Satellites/Centre national d'études spatiales/Legos)

➤ The rate of change in sea level varies from one location on Earth to the next; sea level also varies seasonally and is influenced by ocean currents. The data in Table 7.7 reflect approximate rates of change at the beginning of each year listed, averaged over the entire globe.

a. Assuming s' is continuous on $[0, 16]$, explain how a definite integral can be used to find the net change in sea level from 1995 to 2011; then write the definite integral.

b. Use the data in Table 7.7 and generalize the Trapezoid Rule to estimate the value of the integral from part (a).

SOLUTION

a. The net change in any quantity Q over the interval $[a, b]$ is $Q(b) - Q(a)$ (Section 6.1). When the rate of change Q' is known, the net change in Q is found by integrating Q' over the same interval; that is,

$$\text{net change in } Q = Q(b) - Q(a) = \int_a^b Q'(t)\,dt. \quad \text{Fundamental Theorem}$$

Therefore, the net change in sea level from 1995 to 2011 is $\int_0^{16} s'(t)\,dt$.

b. The values from Table 7.7 are plotted in Figure 7.17, accompanied by seven trapezoids whose area approximates $\int_0^{16} s'(t)\,dt$. Notice that the grid points (the t-values in Table 7.7) do not form a regular partition of the interval $[0, 16]$. Therefore, we must generalize the standard Trapezoid Rule and compute the area of each trapezoid separately.

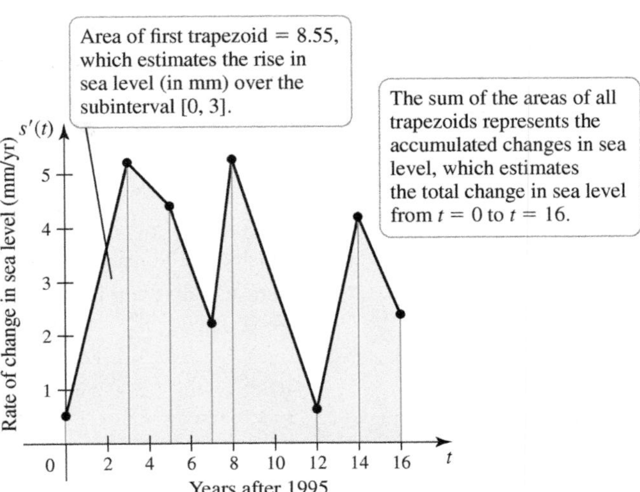

Figure 7.17

Focusing on the first trapezoid over the subinterval $[0, 3]$, we find that its area is

$$\underbrace{\text{area of first trapezoid}}_{A=\frac{1}{2}(b_1+b_2)h} = \frac{1}{2}\cdot\underbrace{(s'(0) + s'(3))}_{\text{measured in mm/yr}}\cdot\underbrace{3}_{\text{yr}} = \frac{1}{2}\cdot(0.51 + 5.19)\cdot 3 = 8.55.$$

Because s' is measured in mm/yr and t is measured in yr, the area of this trapezoid (8.55) is interpreted as the approximate net change in sea level from 1995 to 1998, measured in mm. As we add new trapezoid areas to the ongoing sum that approximates $\int_0^{16} s'(t)\,dt$, the changes in sea level accumulate, resulting in the total change in sea level on $[0, 16]$. The sum of the areas of all seven trapezoids is

$$\underbrace{\frac{1}{2}(s'(0) + s'(3))\cdot 3}_{\text{first trapezoid}} + \underbrace{\frac{1}{2}(s'(3) + s'(5))\cdot 2}_{\text{second trapezoid...}} + \frac{1}{2}(s'(5) + s'(7))\cdot 2 + \frac{1}{2}(s'(7) + s'(8))\cdot 1$$

$$+ \frac{1}{2}(s'(8) + s'(12))\cdot 4 + \frac{1}{2}(s'(12) + s'(14))\cdot 2 + \underbrace{\frac{1}{2}(s'(14) + s'(16))\cdot 2}_{\text{...last trapezoid}} = 51.585.$$

We conclude that an estimate of the rise in sea level from 1995 to 2011 is 51.585 mm.

Related Exercises 31–34 ◄

Simpson's Rule

An improvement over the Midpoint Rule and the Trapezoid Rule results when the graph of f is approximated with curves rather than line segments. Let's return to the partition used by the Midpoint and Trapezoid Rules, but now suppose we work with three neighboring points on the curve $y = f(x)$, say $(x_0, f(x_0))$, $(x_1, f(x_1))$, and $(x_2, f(x_2))$. These three points determine a *parabola*, and it is easy to find the net area bounded by the parabola on the interval $[x_0, x_2]$. When this idea is applied to every group of three consecutive points along the interval of integration, the result is *Simpson's Rule*. With n subintervals, Simpson's Rule is denoted $S(n)$ and is given by

$$\int_a^b f(x)\,dx \approx S(n)$$

$$= (f(x_0) + 4f(x_1) + 2f(x_2) + 4f(x_3) + \cdots + 2f(x_{n-2}) + 4f(x_{n-1}) + f(x_n))\frac{\Delta x}{3}.$$

Notice that apart from the first and last terms, the coefficients alternate between 4 and 2; *n must be an even integer* for this rule to apply.

DEFINITION Simpson's Rule

Suppose f is defined and integrable on $[a, b]$ and $n \geq 2$ is an even integer. The **Simpson's Rule approximation** to $\int_a^b f(x)\,dx$ using n equally spaced subintervals on $[a, b]$ is

$$S(n) = (f(x_0) + 4f(x_1) + 2f(x_2) + 4f(x_3) + \cdots + 4f(x_{n-1}) + f(x_n))\frac{\Delta x}{3},$$

where n is an even integer, $\Delta x = (b - a)/n$, and $x_k = a + k\Delta x$, for $k = 0, 1, \ldots, n$.

You can use the formula for Simpson's Rule given above; but here is an easier way. If you already have the Trapezoid Rule approximations $T(n)$ and $T(2n)$, the next Simpson's Rule approximation follows immediately with a simple calculation (Exercise 64):

$$S(2n) = \frac{4T(2n) - T(n)}{3}.$$

EXAMPLE 7 Errors in the Trapezoid Rule and Simpson's Rule Given that $\int_0^1 xe^{-x}\,dx = 1 - 2e^{-1}$, find the absolute errors in the Trapezoid Rule and Simpson's Rule approximations to the integral with $n = 8, 16, 32, 64$, and 128 subintervals.

SOLUTION Because the shortcut formula for Simpson's Rule is based on values generated by the Trapezoid Rule, it is best to calculate the Trapezoid Rule approximations first. The second column of Table 7.8 shows the Trapezoid Rule approximations computed in Example 4. Having a column of Trapezoid Rule approximations, the corresponding Simpson's Rule approximations are easily found. For example, if $n = 4$, we have

$$S(8) = \frac{4T(8) - T(4)}{3} \approx 0.26423805546593.$$

The table also shows the absolute errors in the approximations. The Simpson's Rule errors decrease more rapidly than the Trapezoid Rule errors. By careful inspection, you will see that the Simpson's Rule errors decrease with a clear pattern: Each time n is doubled (or Δx is halved), the errors decrease by a factor of approximately 16, which makes Simpson's Rule a more accurate method.

Table 7.8

n	$T(n)$	$S(n)$	Error in $T(n)$	Error in $S(n)$
4	0.25904504019141		0.00520	
8	0.26293980164730	0.26423805546593	0.00130	0.00000306
16	0.26391564480235	0.26424092585404	0.000325	0.000000192
32	0.26415974044777	0.26424110566291	0.0000814	0.0000000120
64	0.26422077279247	0.26424111690738	0.0000203	0.000000000750
128	0.26423603140581	0.26424111761026	0.00000509	0.0000000000469

Related Exercises 35–42 ◀

QUICK CHECK 4 Compute the approximate factor by which the error decreases in Table 7.8 between $S(16)$ and $S(32)$ and between $S(32)$ and $S(64)$.

Errors in Numerical Integration

A detailed analysis of the errors in the three methods we have discussed goes beyond the scope of the book. We state without proof the standard error theorems for the methods and note that Examples 3, 4, and 6 are consistent with these results.

➤ Because $\Delta x = \frac{b-a}{n}$, the error bounds in Theorem 7.2 can also be written as

$$E_M \le \frac{k(b-a)^3}{24n^2},$$

$$E_T \le \frac{k(b-a)^3}{12n^2}, \text{ and}$$

$$E_S \le \frac{K(b-a)^5}{180n^4}.$$

THEOREM 7.2 Errors in Numerical Integration
Assume that f'' is continuous on the interval $[a, b]$ and that k is a real number such that $|f''(x)| \le k$, for all x in $[a, b]$. The absolute errors in approximating the integral $\int_a^b f(x)\,dx$ by the Midpoint Rule and Trapezoid Rule with n subintervals satisfy the inequalities

$$E_M \le \frac{k(b-a)}{24}(\Delta x)^2 \quad \text{and} \quad E_T \le \frac{k(b-a)}{12}(\Delta x)^2,$$

respectively, where $\Delta x = (b-a)/n$.

Assume that $f^{(4)}$ is continuous on the interval $[a, b]$ and that K is a real number such that $|f^{(4)}(x)| \le K$ on $[a, b]$. The absolute error in approximating the integral $\int_a^b f(x)\,dx$ by Simpson's Rule with n subintervals satisfies the inequality

$$E_S \le \frac{K(b-a)}{180}(\Delta x)^4.$$

The absolute errors associated with the Midpoint Rule and Trapezoid Rule are proportional to $(\Delta x)^2$. So if Δx is reduced by a factor of 2, the errors decrease roughly by a factor of 4, as shown in Example 4. Simpson's Rule is a more accurate method; its error is proportional to $(\Delta x)^4$, which means that if Δx is reduced by a factor of 2, the errors decrease roughly by a factor of 16, as shown in Example 6. Computing both the Trapezoid Rule and Simpson's Rule together, as shown in Example 6, is a powerful method that produces accurate approximations with relatively little work.

SECTION 7.7 EXERCISES

Review Questions

1. If the interval $[4, 18]$ is partitioned into $n = 28$ subintervals of equal length, what is Δx?
2. Explain geometrically how the Midpoint Rule is used to approximate a definite integral.
3. Explain geometrically how the Trapezoid Rule is used to approximate a definite integral.
4. If the Midpoint Rule is used on the interval $[-1, 11]$ with $n = 3$ subintervals, at what x-coordinates is the integrand evaluated?
5. If the Trapezoid Rule is used on the interval $[-1, 9]$ with $n = 5$ subintervals, at what x-coordinates is the integrand evaluated?
6. State how to compute the Simpson's Rule approximation $S(2n)$ if the Trapezoid Rule approximations $T(2n)$ and $T(n)$ are known.

Basic Skills

T **7–10. Absolute and relative error** *Compute the absolute and relative errors in using c to approximate x.*

7. $x = \pi$; $c = 3.14$
8. $x = \sqrt{2}$; $c = 1.414$
9. $x = e$; $c = 2.72$
10. $x = e$; $c = 2.718$

T **11–14. Midpoint Rule approximations** *Find the indicated Midpoint Rule approximations to the following integrals.*

11. $\int_2^{10} 2x^2\,dx$ using $n = 1, 2,$ and 4 subintervals
12. $\int_1^{9} x^3\,dx$ using $n = 1, 2,$ and 4 subintervals
13. $\int_0^{1} \sin \pi x\,dx$ using $n = 6$ subintervals
14. $\int_0^{1} e^{-x}\,dx$ using $n = 8$ subintervals

T **15–18. Trapezoid Rule approximations** *Find the indicated Trapezoid Rule approximations to the following integrals.*

15. $\int_2^{10} 2x^2\,dx$ using $n = 2, 4,$ and 8 subintervals
16. $\int_1^{9} x^3\,dx$ using $n = 2, 4,$ and 8 subintervals
17. $\int_0^{1} \sin \pi x\,dx$ using $n = 6$ subintervals
18. $\int_0^{1} e^{-x}\,dx$ using $n = 8$ subintervals

T 19. **Midpoint Rule, Trapezoid Rule, and relative error** Find the Midpoint and Trapezoid Rule approximations to $\int_0^1 \sin \pi x\,dx$ using $n = 25$ subintervals. Compute the relative error of each approximation.

T 20. **Midpoint Rule, Trapezoid Rule, and relative error** Find the Midpoint and Trapezoid Rule approximations to $\int_0^1 e^{-x}\,dx$ using $n = 50$ subintervals. Compute the relative error of each approximation.

T **21–26. Comparing the Midpoint and Trapezoid Rules** *Apply the Midpoint and Trapezoid Rules to the following integrals. Make a table similar to Table 7.5 showing the approximations and errors for n = 4, 8, 16, and 32. The exact values of the integrals are given for computing the error.*

21. $\int_1^5 (3x^2 - 2x)\,dx = 100$
22. $\int_{-2}^6 \left(\frac{x^3}{16} - x\right) dx = 4$
23. $\int_0^{\pi/4} 3 \sin 2x\,dx = \frac{3}{2}$
24. $\int_1^e \ln x\,dx = 1$
25. $\int_0^{\pi} \sin x \cos 3x\,dx = 0$
26. $\int_0^8 e^{-2x}\,dx = \frac{1 - e^{-16}}{2}$

T **27–30. Temperature data** *Hourly temperature data for Boulder, Colorado, San Francisco, California, Nantucket, Massachusetts, and Duluth, Minnesota, over a 12 hr period on the same day of January are shown in the figure. Assume that these data are taken from a continuous temperature function T(t). The average temperature over the 12-hr period is* $\bar{T} = \frac{1}{12}\int_0^{12} T(t)\,dt$.

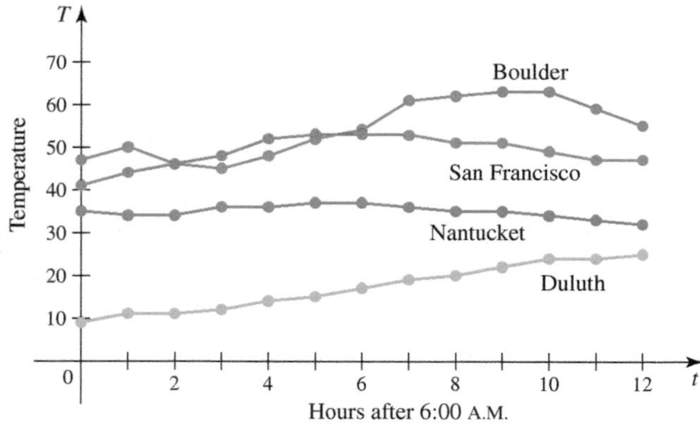

t	0	1	2	3	4	5	6	7	8	9	10	11	12
B	47	50	46	45	48	52	54	61	62	63	63	59	55
SF	41	44	46	48	52	53	53	53	51	51	49	47	47
N	35	34	34	36	36	37	37	36	35	35	34	33	32
D	9	11	11	12	14	15	17	19	20	22	24	24	25

27. Find an accurate approximation to the average temperature over the 12-hr period for Boulder. State your method.

28. Find an accurate approximation to the average temperature over the 12-hr period for San Francisco. State your method.

29. Find an accurate approximation to the average temperature over the 12-hr period for Nantucket. State your method.

30. Find an accurate approximation to the average temperature over the 12-hr period for Duluth. State your method.

31–34. Nonuniform grids *Use the indicated methods to solve the following problems with nonuniform grids.*

31. A curling iron is plugged into an outlet at time $t = 0$. Its temperature T in degrees Fahrenheit, assumed to be a continuous function that is strictly increasing and concave down on $0 \le t \le 120$, is given at various times (in seconds) in the table.

t (seconds)	0	20	45	60	90	110	120
$T(t)$ (°F)	70	130	200	239	311	355	375

a. Approximate $\frac{1}{120}\int_0^{120} T(t)\,dt$ in three ways: using a left Riemann sum, a right Riemann sum, and the Trapezoid Rule. Interpret the value of $\frac{1}{120}\int_0^{120} T(t)\,dt$ in the context of this problem.

b. Which of the estimates made in part (a) overestimates the value of $\frac{1}{120}\int_0^{120} T(t)\,dt$? Underestimates? Justify your answers with a simple sketch of the sums you computed.

c. Evaluate and interpret $\int_0^{120} T'(t)\,dt$ in the context of this problem.

32. Approximating integrals The function f is twice differentiable on $(-\infty, \infty)$. Values of f at various points on $[0, 20]$ are given in the table.

x	0	4	7	12	14	18	20
$f(x)$	3	0	−2	−1	2	4	7

a. Approximate $\int_0^{20} f(x)\,dx$ in three ways: using a left Riemann sum, a right Riemann sum, and the Trapezoid Rule.

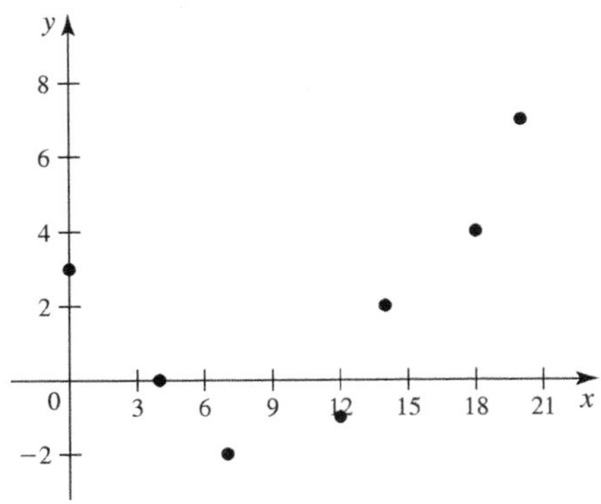

b. A scatterplot of the data in the table is provided in the figure. Use the scatterplot to illustrate each of the approximations in part (a) by sketching appropriate rectangles for the Riemann sums and by sketching trapezoids for the Trapezoid Rule approximation.

c. Evaluate $\int_4^{12} (3f'(x) + 2)\,dx$.

33. A hot-air balloon is launched from an elevation of 5400 ft above sea level. As it rises, its vertical velocity is computed using a device (called a *variometer*) that measures the change in atmospheric pressure. The vertical velocities at selected times are shown in the table (with units of ft/min).

t (min)	0	1	1.5	3	3.5	4	5
Velocity (ft/min)	0	100	120	150	110	90	80

a. Use the Trapezoid Rule to estimate the elevation of the balloon after five minutes. Remember that the balloon starts at an elevation of 5400 ft.

b. Use a right Riemann sum to estimate the elevation of the balloon after five minutes.

c. A polynomial that fits the data reasonably well is

$$g(t) = 3.49t^3 - 43.21t^2 + 142.43t - 1.75.$$

Estimate the elevation of the balloon after five minutes using this polynomial.

34. A piece of wood paneling must be cut in the shape shown in the figure. The coordinates of several points on its curved surface are also shown (with units of inches).

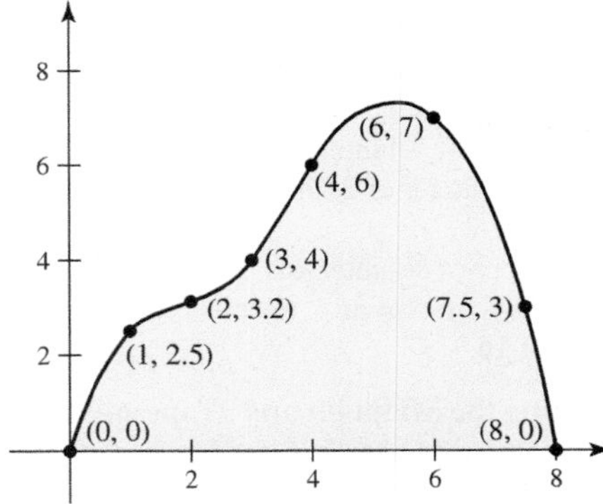

a. Estimate the surface area of the paneling using the Trapezoid Rule.

b. Estimate the surface area of the paneling using a left Riemann sum.

c. Could two identical pieces be cut from a 9-in by 9-in piece of wood? Answer carefully.

T **35–38. Trapezoid Rule and Simpson's Rule** *Consider the following integrals and the given values of n.*

a. Find the Trapezoid Rule approximations to the integral using n and 2n subintervals.

b. Find the Simpson's Rule approximation to the integral using 2n subintervals. It is easiest to obtain Simpson's Rule approximations from the Trapezoid Rule approximations, as in Example 7.

c. Compute the absolute errors in the Trapezoid Rule and Simpson's Rule with 2n subintervals.

35. $\int_0^1 e^{2x}\,dx;\ n = 25$

36. $\int_0^2 x^4\,dx;\ n = 30$

37. $\int_1^e \frac{dx}{x};\ n = 50$

38. $\int_0^{\pi/4} \frac{dx}{1 + x^2};\ n = 64$

T 39–42. Simpson's Rule *Apply Simpson's Rule to the following integrals. It is easiest to obtain the Simpson's Rule approximations from the Trapezoid Rule approximations, as in Example 7. Make a table similar to Table 7.8 showing the approximations and errors for n = 4, 8, 16, and 32. The exact values of the integrals are given for computing the error.*

39. $\int_0^4 (3x^5 - 8x^3)\,dx = 1536$

40. $\int_1^e \ln x\,dx = 1$

41. $\int_0^\pi e^{-t}\sin t\,dt = \frac{1}{2}(e^{-\pi} + 1)$

42. $\int_0^6 3e^{-3x}\,dx = 1 - e^{-18} \approx 1.000000$

Further Explorations

43. **Explain why or why not** Determine whether the following statements are true and give an explanation or counterexample.
    a. The Trapezoid Rule is exact when used to approximate the definite integral of a linear function.
    b. If the number of subintervals used in the Midpoint Rule is increased by a factor of 3, the error is expected to decrease by a factor of 8.
    c. If the number of subintervals used in the Trapezoid Rule is increased by a factor of 4, the error is expected to decrease by a factor of 16.

T 44–47. Comparing the Midpoint and Trapezoid Rules *Compare the errors in the Midpoint and Trapezoid Rules with n = 4, 8, 16, and 32 subintervals when they are applied to the following integrals (with their exact values given).*

44. $\int_0^{\pi/2} \sin^6 x\,dx = \frac{5\pi}{32}$

45. $\int_0^{\pi/2} \cos^9 x\,dx = \frac{128}{315}$

46. $\int_0^1 (8x^7 - 7x^8)\,dx = \frac{2}{9}$

47. $\int_0^\pi \ln(5 + 3\cos x)\,dx = \pi \ln \frac{9}{2}$

T 48–51. Using Simpson's Rule *Approximate the following integrals using Simpson's Rule. Experiment with values of n to ensure that the error is less than 10^{-3}.*

48. $\int_0^{2\pi} \frac{dx}{(5 + 3\sin x)^2} = \frac{5\pi}{32}$

49. $\int_0^\pi \frac{4\cos x}{5 - 4\cos x}\,dx = \frac{2\pi}{3}$

50. $\int_0^\pi \ln(2 + \cos x)\,dx = \pi \ln\left(\frac{2 + \sqrt{3}}{2}\right)$

51. $\int_0^\pi \sin 6x \cos 3x\,dx = \frac{4}{9}$

Applications

T 52. Period of a pendulum A standard pendulum of length L swinging under only the influence of gravity (no resistance) has a period of

$$T = \frac{4}{\omega}\int_0^{\pi/2} \frac{d\varphi}{\sqrt{1 - k^2\sin^2\varphi}},$$

where $\omega^2 = g/L$, $k^2 = \sin^2(\theta_0/2)$, $g \approx 9.8\ \text{m/s}^2$ is the acceleration due to gravity, and θ_0 is the initial angle from which the pendulum is released (in radians). Use numerical integration to approximate the period of a pendulum with $L = 1$ m that is released from an angle of $\theta_0 = \pi/4$ rad.

T 53. Arc length of an ellipse The length of an ellipse with axes of length $2a$ and $2b$ is

$$\int_0^{2\pi} \sqrt{a^2\cos^2 t + b^2\sin^2 t}\,dt.$$

Use numerical integration and experiment with different values of n to approximate the length of an ellipse with $a = 4$ and $b = 8$.

T 54. Sine integral The theory of diffraction produces the sine integral function $\text{Si}(x) = \int_0^x \frac{\sin t}{t}\,dt$. Use the Midpoint Rule to approximate Si (1) and Si (10). (Recall that $\lim_{x\to 0}(\sin x)/x = 1$.) Experiment with the number of subintervals until you obtain approximations that have an error less than 10^{-3}. A rule of thumb is that if two successive approximations differ by less than 10^{-3}, then the error is usually less than 10^{-3}.

T 55. Normal distribution of heights The heights of U.S. men are normally distributed with a mean of 69 inches and a standard deviation of 3 inches. This means that the fraction of men with a height between a and b (with $a < b$) inches is given by the integral

$$\frac{1}{3\sqrt{2\pi}}\int_a^b e^{-((x-69)/3)^2/2}\,dx.$$

What percentage of American men are between 66 and 72 inches tall? Use the method of your choice and experiment with the number of subintervals until you obtain successive approximations that differ by less than 10^{-3}.

T **56. Normal distribution of movie lengths** A recent study revealed that the lengths of U.S. movies are normally distributed with a mean of 110 minutes and a standard deviation of 22 minutes. This means that the fraction of movies with lengths between a and b minutes (with $a < b$) is given by the integral

$$\frac{1}{22\sqrt{2\pi}}\int_a^b e^{-((x-110)/22)^2/2}\,dx.$$

What percentage of U.S. movies are between 1 hr and 1.5 hr long (60–90 min)?

T **57. U.S. oil produced and imported** The figure shows the rate at which U.S. oil was produced and imported between 1920 and 2005 in units of millions of barrels per day. The total amount of oil produced or imported is given by the area of the region under the corresponding curve. Be careful with units because both days and years are used in this data set.

a. Use numerical integration to estimate the amount of U.S. oil produced between 1940 and 2000. Use the method of your choice and experiment with values of n.

b. Use numerical integration to estimate the amount of oil imported between 1940 and 2000. Use the method of your choice and experiment with values of n.

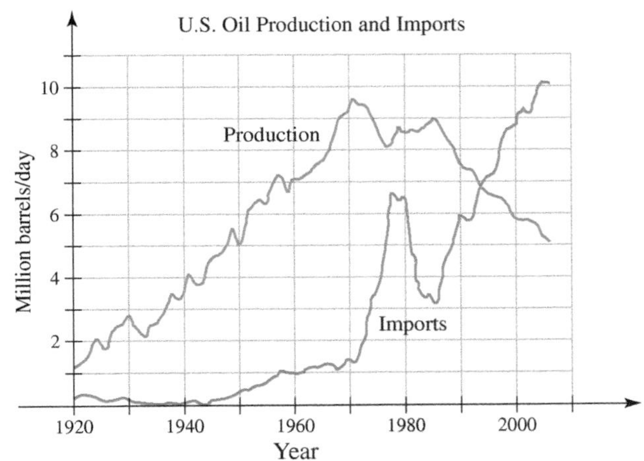

(*Source:* U.S. Energy Information Administration)

Additional Exercises

T **58. Estimating error** Refer to Theorem 7.2 and let $f(x) = e^{x^2}$.

a. Find a Trapezoid Rule approximation to $\int_0^1 e^{x^2}\,dx$ using $n = 50$ subintervals.

b. Calculate $f''(x)$.

c. Explain why $|f''(x)| < 18$ on $[0, 1]$, given that $e < 3$.

d. Use Theorem 7.2 to find an upper bound on the absolute error in the estimate found in part (a).

T **59. Estimating error** Refer to Theorem 7.2 and let $f(x) = \sin e^x$.

a. Find a Trapezoid Rule approximation to $\int_0^1 \sin e^x\,dx$ using $n = 40$ subintervals.

b. Calculate $f''(x)$.

c. Explain why $|f''(x)| < 6$ on $[0, 1]$, given that $e < 3$. (*Hint:* Graph f''.)

d. Find an upper bound on the absolute error in the estimate found in part (a) using Theorem 7.2.

60. Exact Trapezoid Rule Prove that the Trapezoid Rule is exact (no error) when approximating the definite integral of a linear function.

61. Exact Simpson's Rule

a. Use Simpson's Rule to approximate $\int_0^4 x^3\,dx$ using two subintervals ($n = 2$); compare the approximation to the value of the integral.

b. Use Simpson's Rule to approximate $\int_0^4 x^3\,dx$ using four subintervals ($n = 4$); compare the approximation to the value of the integral.

c. Use the error bound associated with Simpson's Rule given in Theorem 7.2 to explain why the approximations in parts (a) and (b) give the exact value of the integral.

d. Use Theorem 7.2 to explain why a Simpson's Rule approximation using any (even) number of subintervals gives the exact value of $\int_a^b f(x)\,dx$, where $f(x)$ is a polynomial of degree 3 or less.

62. Shortcut for the Trapezoid Rule Given a Midpoint Rule approximation $M(n)$ and a Trapezoid Rule approximation $T(n)$ for a continuous function on $[a, b]$ with n subintervals, show that $T(2n) = (T(n) + M(n))/2$.

63. Trapezoid Rule and concavity Suppose f is positive and its first two derivatives are continuous on $[a, b]$. If f'' is positive on $[a, b]$, then is a Trapezoid Rule estimate of $\int_a^b f(x)\,dx$ an underestimate or overestimate of the integral? Justify your answer using Theorem 7.2 and an illustration.

64. Shortcut for Simpson's Rule Using the notation of the text, prove that $S(2n) = \dfrac{4T(2n) - T(n)}{3}$, for $n \geq 1$.

T **65. Another Simpson's Rule formula** Another Simpson's Rule formula is $S(2n) = \dfrac{2M(n) + T(n)}{3}$, for $n \geq 1$. Use this rule to estimate $\int_1^e 1/x\,dx$ using $n = 10$ subintervals.

QUICK CHECK ANSWERS

1. 4, 6, 8, 10 **2.** Overestimates **3.** 4 and 4 **4.** 16 and 16 ◄

7.8 Improper Integrals

The definite integrals we have encountered so far involve finite-valued functions and finite intervals of integration. In this section, you will see that definite integrals can sometimes be evaluated when these conditions are not met. Here is an example. The energy required to launch a rocket from the surface of Earth ($R = 6370$ km from the center of Earth) to an altitude H is given by an integral of the form $\int_R^{R+H} k/x^2\,dx$, where k is a constant that includes the mass of the rocket, the mass of Earth, and the gravitational constant. This integral may be evaluated for any finite altitude $H > 0$. Now suppose that the aim is to launch the rocket to an arbitrarily large altitude H so that it escapes Earth's gravitational field. The energy required is given by the preceding integral as $H \to \infty$, which we write $\int_R^{\infty} k/x^2\,dx$. This integral is an example of an *improper integral*, and it has a finite value (which explains why it is possible to launch rockets to outer space). For historical reasons, the term *improper integral* is used for cases in which

- the interval of integration is infinite, or
- the integrand is unbounded on the interval of integration.

In this section, we explore improper integrals and their many uses.

Infinite Intervals

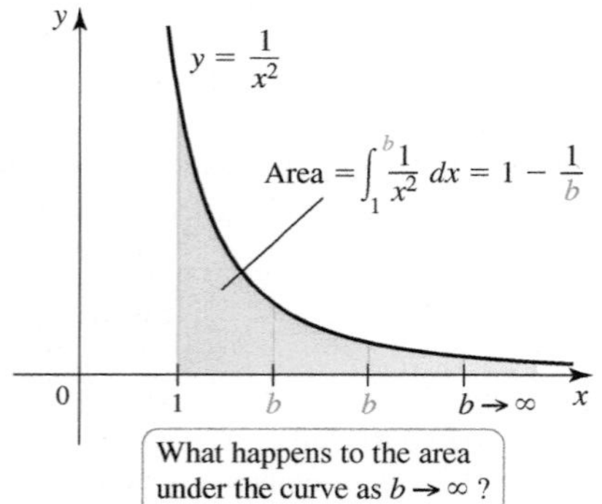

Figure 7.18

A simple example illustrates what can happen when integrating a function over an infinite interval. Consider the integral $\displaystyle\int_1^b \frac{1}{x^2}\,dx$, for any real number $b > 1$. As shown in Figure 7.18, this integral gives the area of the region bounded by the curve $y = x^{-2}$ and the x-axis between $x = 1$ and $x = b$. In fact, the value of the integral is

$$\int_1^b \frac{1}{x^2}\,dx = -\frac{1}{x}\bigg|_1^b = 1 - \frac{1}{b}.$$

For example, if $b = 2$, the area under the curve is $\frac{1}{2}$; if $b = 3$, the area under the curve is $\frac{2}{3}$. In general, as b increases, the area under the curve increases.

Now let's ask what happens to the area as b becomes arbitrarily large. Letting $b \to \infty$, the area of the region under the curve is

$$\lim_{b\to\infty}\left(1 - \frac{1}{b}\right) = 1.$$

We have discovered, surprising as it may seem, a curve of *infinite* length that bounds a region with *finite* area (1 square unit).

We express this result as

$$\int_1^{\infty} \frac{1}{x^2}\,dx = 1,$$

which is an improper integral because ∞ appears in the upper limit. In general, to evaluate $\int_a^{\infty} f(x)\,dx$, we first integrate over a finite interval $[a, b]$ and then let $b \to \infty$. Similar procedures are used to evaluate $\int_{-\infty}^{b} f(x)\,dx$ and $\int_{-\infty}^{\infty} f(x)\,dx$.

➤ Doubly infinite integrals (Case 3 in the definition) must be evaluated as two independent limits and not as

$$\int_{-\infty}^{\infty} f(x)\,dx = \lim_{b\to\infty}\int_{-b}^{b} f(x)\,dx.$$

DEFINITION Improper Integrals over Infinite Intervals

1. If f is continuous on $[a, \infty)$, then

$$\int_a^{\infty} f(x)\,dx = \lim_{b\to\infty}\int_a^b f(x)\,dx.$$

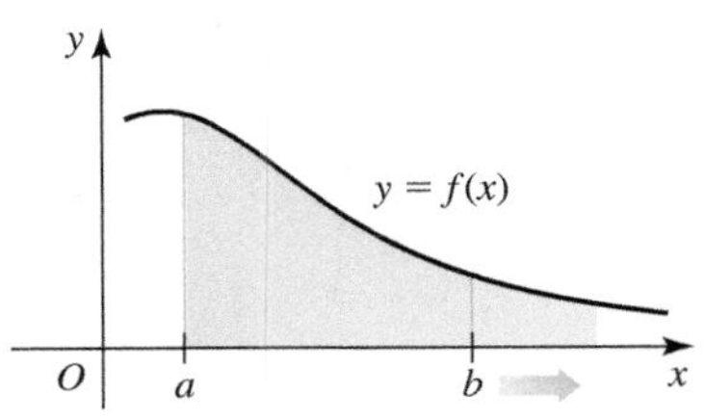

2. If f is continuous on $(-\infty, b]$, then

$$\int_{-\infty}^{b} f(x)\,dx = \lim_{a\to-\infty}\int_a^b f(x)\,dx.$$

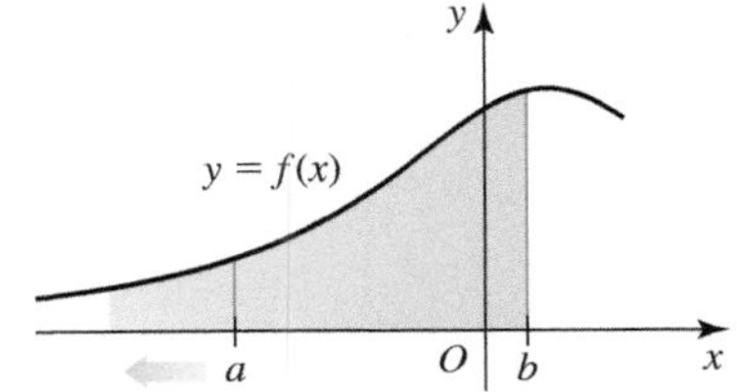

3. If f is continuous on $(-\infty, \infty)$, then

$$\int_{-\infty}^{\infty} f(x)\,dx = \lim_{a\to-\infty}\int_a^c f(x)\,dx + \lim_{b\to\infty}\int_c^b f(x)\,dx,$$

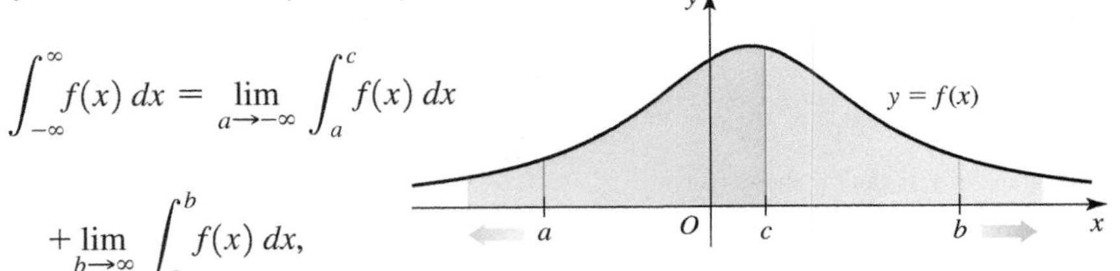

where c is any real number.

If the limits in cases 1–3 exist, then the improper integrals **converge**; otherwise, they **diverge**.

EXAMPLE 1 Infinite intervals Evaluate each integral.

a. $\displaystyle\int_0^{\infty} e^{-3x}\,dx$ **b.** $\displaystyle\int_{-\infty}^{\infty} \frac{dx}{1+x^2}$

SOLUTION

a. Using the definition of the improper integral, we have

$$\int_0^{\infty} e^{-3x}\,dx = \lim_{b\to\infty}\int_0^b e^{-3x}\,dx \quad \text{Definition of improper integral}$$

$$= \lim_{b\to\infty}\left(-\frac{1}{3}e^{-3x}\right)\Big|_0^b \quad \text{Evaluate the integral.}$$

$$= \lim_{b\to\infty}\frac{1}{3}(1 - e^{-3b}) \quad \text{Simplify.}$$

$$= \frac{1}{3}\Big(1 - \underbrace{\lim_{b\to\infty}\frac{1}{e^{3b}}}_{\text{equals } 0}\Big) = \frac{1}{3}. \quad \text{Evaluate the limit; } e^{-3b} = \frac{1}{e^{3b}}.$$

In this case, the limit exists, so the integral converges and the region under the curve has a finite area of $\frac{1}{3}$ (Figure 7.19).

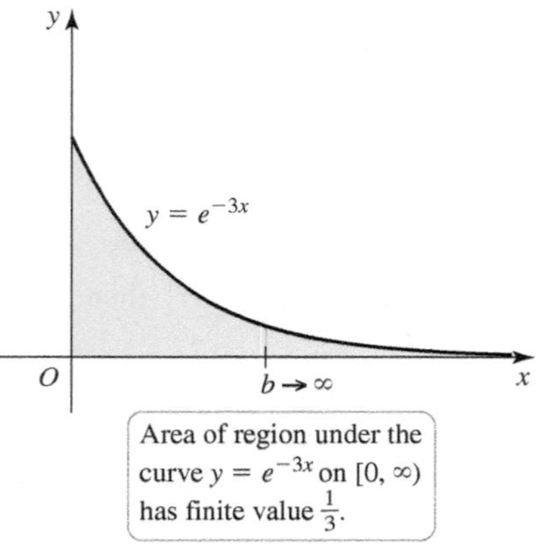

Area of region under the curve $y = e^{-3x}$ on $[0, \infty)$ has finite value $\frac{1}{3}$.

Figure 7.19

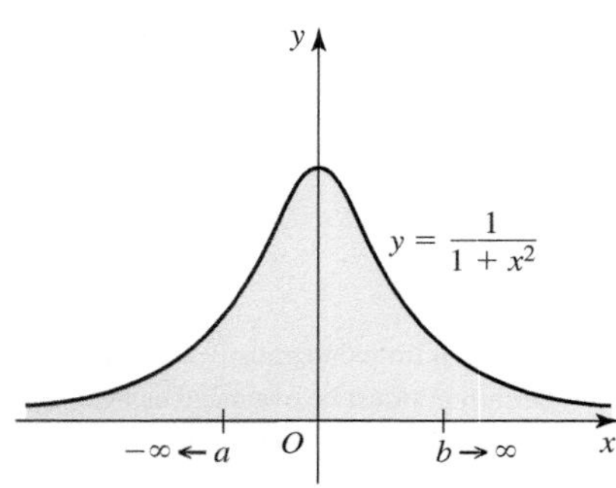

Area of region under the curve $y = \frac{1}{1 + x^2}$ on $(-\infty, \infty)$ has finite value π.

Figure 7.20

➤ Recall that

$$\int \frac{dx}{a^2 + x^2} = \frac{1}{a}\tan^{-1}\frac{x}{a} + C.$$

The graph of $y = \tan^{-1} x$ shows that

$\lim_{x\to\infty} \tan^{-1} x = \frac{\pi}{2}$ and $\lim_{x\to-\infty} \tan^{-1} x = -\frac{\pi}{2}$.

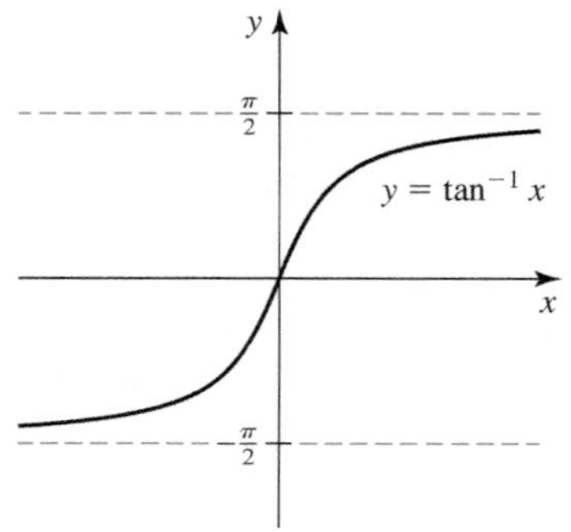

b. Using the definition of the improper integral, we choose $c = 0$ and write

$$\int_{-\infty}^{\infty} \frac{dx}{1 + x^2} = \lim_{a\to-\infty} \int_a^c \frac{dx}{1 + x^2} + \lim_{b\to\infty} \int_c^b \frac{dx}{1 + x^2} \quad \text{Definition of improper integral}$$

$$= \lim_{a\to-\infty} \tan^{-1} x \Big|_a^0 + \lim_{b\to\infty} \tan^{-1} x \Big|_0^b \quad \text{Evaluate integral; } c = 0.$$

$$= \lim_{a\to-\infty} (0 - \tan^{-1} a) + \lim_{b\to\infty} (\tan^{-1} b - 0) \quad \text{Simplify.}$$

$$= \frac{\pi}{2} + \frac{\pi}{2} = \pi. \quad \text{Evaluate limits.}$$

The same result is obtained with any value of the intermediate point c; therefore, the value of the integral is π (Figure 7.20).

Related Exercises 5–28 ◄

QUICK CHECK 1 The function $f(x) = 1 + x^{-1}$ decreases to 1 as $x \to \infty$. Does $\int_1^{\infty} f(x)\,dx$ exist? ◄

EXAMPLE 2 The family $f(x) = 1/x^p$ Consider the family of functions $f(x) = 1/x^p$, where p is a real number. For what values of p does $\int_1^{\infty} f(x)\,dx$ converge?

➤ Recall that for $p \neq 1$,

$$\int \frac{1}{x^p}\,dx = \int x^{-p}\,dx = \frac{x^{-p+1}}{-p + 1} + C = \frac{x^{1-p}}{1 - p} + C.$$

SOLUTION For $p > 0$, the functions $f(x) = 1/x^p$ approach zero as $x \to \infty$, with larger values of p giving greater rates of decrease (Figure 7.21). Assuming $p \neq 1$, the integral is evaluated as follows:

$$\int_1^{\infty} \frac{1}{x^p}\,dx = \lim_{b\to\infty} \int_1^b x^{-p}\,dx \quad \text{Definition of improper integral}$$

$$= \frac{1}{1 - p} \lim_{b\to\infty} \left(x^{1-p} \Big|_1^b \right) \quad \text{Evaluate the integral on a finite interval.}$$

$$= \frac{1}{1 - p} \lim_{b\to\infty} (b^{1-p} - 1). \quad \text{Simplify.}$$

It is easiest to consider three cases.

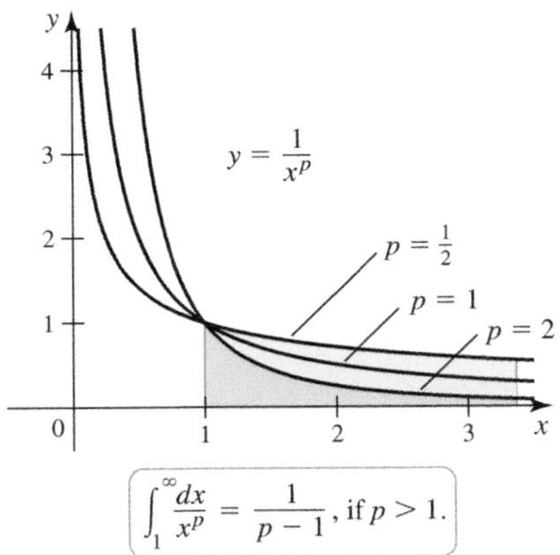

Figure 7.21

Case 1: If $p > 1$, then $p - 1 > 0$, and $b^{1-p} = 1/b^{p-1}$ approaches 0 as $b \to \infty$. Therefore, the integral converges and its value is

$$\int_1^\infty \frac{1}{x^p}\,dx = \frac{1}{1-p}\lim_{b\to\infty}(\underbrace{b^{1-p}}_{\text{approaches } 0} - 1) = \frac{1}{p-1}.$$

Case 2: If $p < 1$, then $1 - p > 0$, and the integral diverges:

$$\int_1^\infty \frac{1}{x^p}\,dx = \frac{1}{1-p}\lim_{b\to\infty}(\underbrace{b^{1-p}}_{\text{arbitrarily large}} - 1) = \infty.$$

Case 3: If $p = 1$, then $\int_1^\infty \frac{1}{x}\,dx = \lim_{b\to\infty} \ln b = \infty$, so the integral diverges.

In summary, $\int_1^\infty \frac{1}{x^p}\,dx = \frac{1}{p-1}$ if $p > 1$, and the integral diverges if $p \le 1$.

Related Exercises 5–28 ◀

➤ Example 2 is important in the study of infinite series in Chapter 8. It shows that a continuous function f must do more than simply decrease to zero for its integral on $[a, \infty)$ to converge; it must decrease to zero *sufficiently fast.*

QUICK CHECK 2 Use the result of Example 2 to evaluate $\int_1^\infty \frac{1}{x^4}\,dx$. ◀

EXAMPLE 3 Solids of revolution Let R be the region bounded by the graph of $y = x^{-1}$ and the x-axis, for $x \ge 1$.

a. What is the volume of the solid generated when R is revolved about the x-axis?

b. What is the surface area of the solid generated when R is revolved about the x-axis?

c. What is the volume of the solid generated when R is revolved about the y-axis?

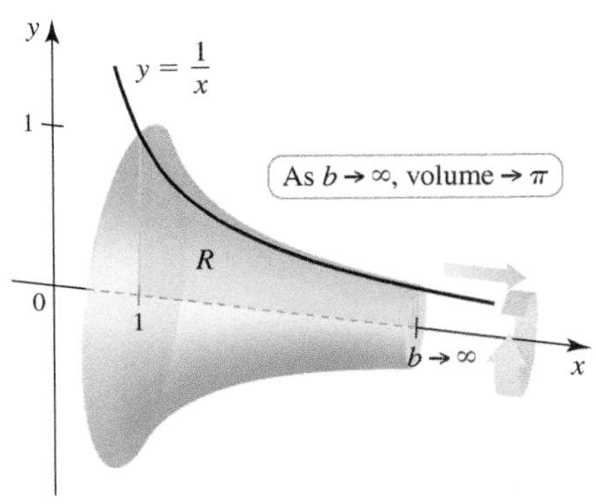

Figure 7.22

SOLUTION

a. The region in question and the corresponding solid of revolution are shown in Figure 7.22. We use the disk method (Section 6.3) over the interval $[1, b]$ and then let $b \to \infty$:

$$\begin{aligned} \text{Volume} &= \int_1^\infty \pi(f(x))^2\,dx && \text{Disk method} \\ &= \pi \lim_{b\to\infty} \int_1^b \frac{1}{x^2}\,dx && \text{Definition of improper integral} \\ &= \pi \lim_{b\to\infty} \left(1 - \frac{1}{b}\right) = \pi. && \text{Evaluate the integral.} \end{aligned}$$

The improper integral exists, and the solid has a volume of π cubic units.

b. Using the results of Section 6.6, the area of the surface generated on the interval $[1, b]$, where $b > 1$, is

$$\int_1^b 2\pi f(x)\sqrt{1 + f'(x)^2}\,dx.$$

The area of the surface generated on the interval $[1, \infty)$ is found by letting $b \to \infty$:

$$\text{surface area} = 2\pi \lim_{b\to\infty} \int_1^b f(x)\sqrt{1 + f'(x)^2}\,dx \quad \text{Surface area formula; let } b \to \infty.$$

$$= 2\pi \lim_{b\to\infty} \int_1^b \frac{1}{x}\sqrt{1 + \left(-\frac{1}{x^2}\right)^2}\,dx \quad \text{Substitute } f \text{ and } f'.$$

$$= 2\pi \lim_{b\to\infty} \int_1^b \frac{1}{x^3}\sqrt{1 + x^4}\,dx. \quad \text{Simplify.}$$

➤ The integral in Example 3b can be evaluated directly by using the substitution $u = x^2$ and then consulting a table of integrals.

Notice that on the interval of integration $x \geq 1$, we have $\sqrt{1 + x^4} > \sqrt{x^4} = x^2$, which means that

$$\frac{1}{x^3}\sqrt{1 + x^4} > \frac{x^2}{x^3} = \frac{1}{x}.$$

Therefore, for all b with $1 < b < \infty$,

$$\text{surface area} = 2\pi \int_1^b \frac{1}{x^3}\sqrt{1 + x^4}\,dx > 2\pi \int_1^b \frac{1}{x}\,dx.$$

➤ The solid in Examples 3a and 3b is called *Gabriel's horn* or *Torricelli's trumpet*. We have shown—quite remarkably—that it has finite volume and infinite surface area.

Because $2\pi \lim_{b\to\infty} \int_1^b \frac{1}{x}\,dx = \infty$ (by Example 2), the preceding inequality implies that $2\pi \lim_{b\to\infty} \int_1^b \frac{1}{x^3}\sqrt{1 + x^4}\,dx = \infty$. Therefore, the integral diverges and the surface area of the solid is infinite.

➤ Recall that if $f(x) > 0$ on $[a, b]$ and the region bounded by the graph of f and the x-axis on $[a, b]$ is revolved about the y-axis, the volume of the solid generated is

$$V = \int_a^b 2\pi x f(x)\,dx.$$

c. The region in question and the corresponding solid of revolution are shown in Figure 7.23. Using the shell method (Section 6.4) on the interval $[1, b)$ and letting $b \to \infty$, the volume is given by

$$\text{Volume} = \int_1^\infty 2\pi x f(x)\,dx \quad \text{Shell method}$$

$$= 2\pi \int_1^\infty 1\,dx \quad f(x) = x^{-1}$$

$$= 2\pi \lim_{b\to\infty} \int_1^b 1\,dx \quad \text{Definition of improper integral}$$

$$= 2\pi \lim_{b\to\infty} (b - 1) \quad \text{Evaluate the integral over a finite interval.}$$

$$= \infty. \quad \text{The improper integral diverges.}$$

Revolving the region R about the y-axis, the volume of the solid is infinite.

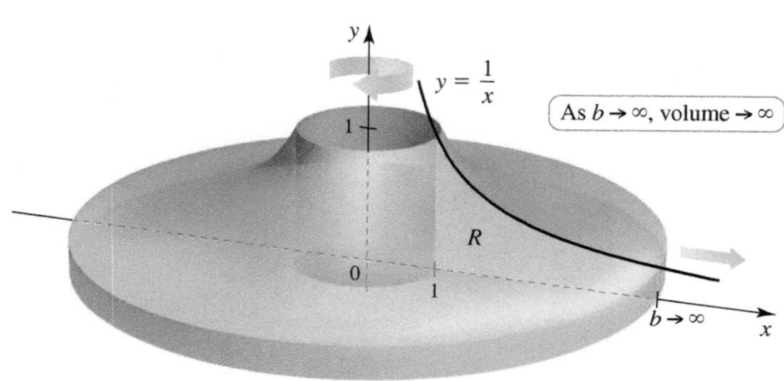

Figure 7.23

Related Exercises 29–34 ◀

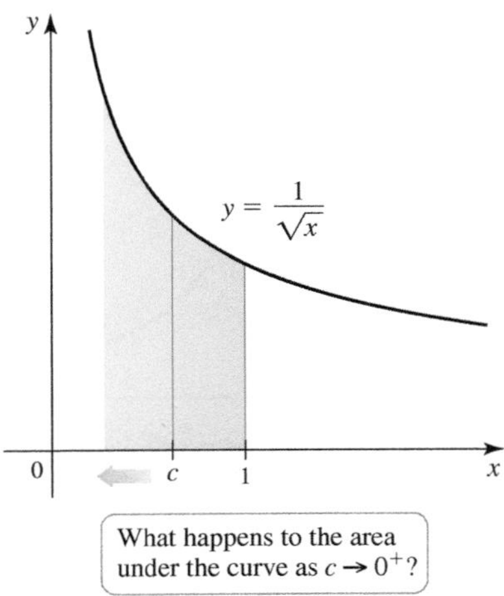

Figure 7.24

Unbounded Integrands

Improper integrals also occur when the integrand becomes infinite somewhere on the interval of integration. Consider the function $f(x) = 1/\sqrt{x}$ (Figure 7.24). Let's examine the area of the region bounded by the graph of f between $x = 0$ and $x = 1$. Notice that f is not defined at $x = 0$, and it increases without bound as $x \to 0^+$.

The idea here is to replace the lower limit 0 with a nearby positive number c and then consider the integral $\int_c^1 \frac{dx}{\sqrt{x}}$, where $0 < c < 1$. We find that

$$\int_c^1 \frac{dx}{\sqrt{x}} = 2\sqrt{x}\Big|_c^1 = 2(1 - \sqrt{c}).$$

To find the area of the region under the curve over the interval $(0, 1]$, we let $c \to 0^+$. The resulting area, which we denote $\int_0^1 \frac{dx}{\sqrt{x}}$, is

$$\lim_{c \to 0^+} \int_c^1 \frac{dx}{\sqrt{x}} = \lim_{c \to 0^+} 2(1 - \sqrt{c}) = 2.$$

Once again, we have a surprising result: Although the region in question has a boundary curve with infinite length, the area of the region is finite.

➤ The functions $f(x) = 1/x^p$ are unbounded at $x = 0$, for $p > 0$. It can be shown (Exercise 74) that

$$\int_0^1 \frac{dx}{x^p} = \frac{1}{1 - p},$$

provided $p < 1$. Otherwise, the integral diverges.

QUICK CHECK 3 Explain why the one-sided limit $c \to 0^+$ (instead of a two-sided limit) must be used in the previous calculation. ◀

The preceding example shows that if a function is unbounded at a point c, it may be possible to integrate that function over an interval that contains c. The point c may occur at either endpoint or at an interior point of the interval of integration.

DEFINITIONS Improper Integrals with an Unbounded Integrand

1. Suppose f is continuous on $(a, b]$ with $\lim_{x \to a^+} f(x) = \pm\infty$. Then

$$\int_a^b f(x)\,dx = \lim_{c \to a^+} \int_c^b f(x)\,dx.$$

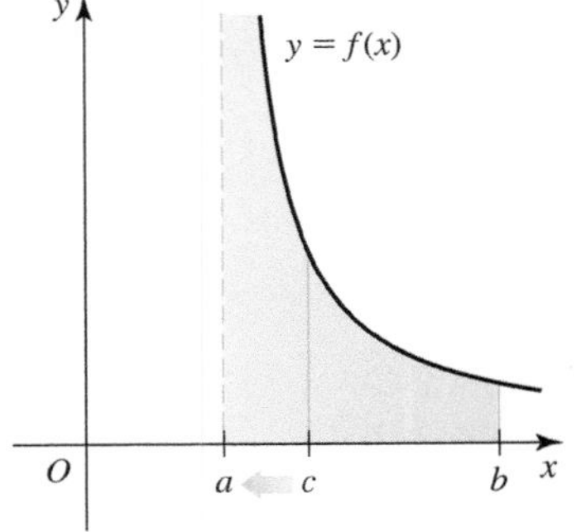

2. Suppose f is continuous on $[a, b)$ with $\lim_{x \to b^-} f(x) = \pm\infty$. Then

$$\int_a^b f(x)\,dx = \lim_{c \to b^-} \int_a^c f(x)\,dx.$$

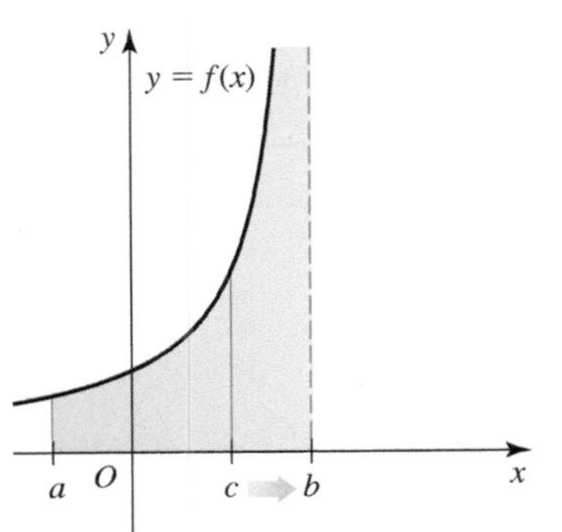

3. Suppose f is continuous on $[a, b]$ except at the interior point p where f is unbounded. Then

$$\int_a^b f(x)\,dx = \lim_{c \to p^-} \int_a^c f(x)\,dx + \lim_{d \to p^+} \int_d^b f(x)\,dx.$$

If the limits in cases 1–3 exist, then the improper integrals **converge**; otherwise, they **diverge**.

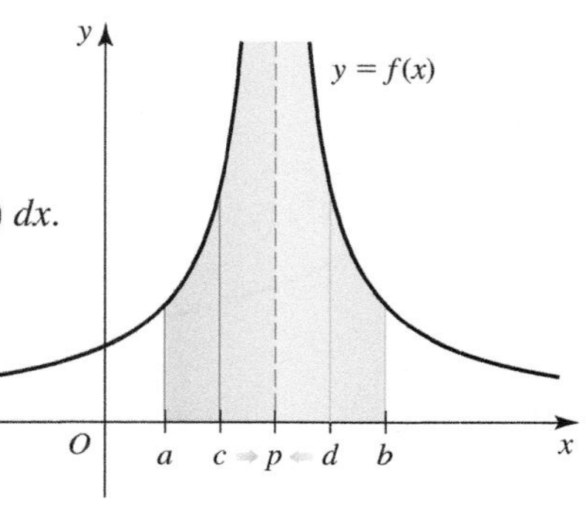

EXAMPLE 4 **Infinite integrand** Find the area of the region R between the graph of $f(x) = \dfrac{1}{\sqrt{9 - x^2}}$ and the x-axis on the interval $(-3, 3)$ (if it exists).

SOLUTION The integrand is even and has vertical asymptotes at $x = \pm 3$ (Figure 7.25). By symmetry, the area of R is given by

➤ Recall that

$$\int \frac{dx}{\sqrt{a^2 - x^2}} = \sin^{-1}\frac{x}{a} + C.$$

$$\int_{-3}^{3} \frac{1}{\sqrt{9 - x^2}}\,dx = 2\int_0^3 \frac{1}{\sqrt{9 - x^2}}\,dx,$$

assuming these improper integrals exist. Because the integrand is unbounded at $x = 3$, we replace the upper limit with c, evaluate the resulting integral, and then let $c \to 3^-$:

$$2\int_0^3 \frac{dx}{\sqrt{9 - x^2}} = 2\lim_{c \to 3^-} \int_0^c \frac{dx}{\sqrt{9 - x^2}} \qquad \text{Definition of improper integral}$$

$$= 2\lim_{c \to 3^-} \sin^{-1}\frac{x}{3}\Big|_0^c \qquad \text{Evaluate the integral.}$$

$$= 2\lim_{c \to 3^-}\Big(\underbrace{\sin^{-1}\frac{c}{3}}_{\text{approaches } \pi/2} - \underbrace{\sin^{-1} 0}_{\text{equals } 0}\Big). \qquad \text{Simplify.}$$

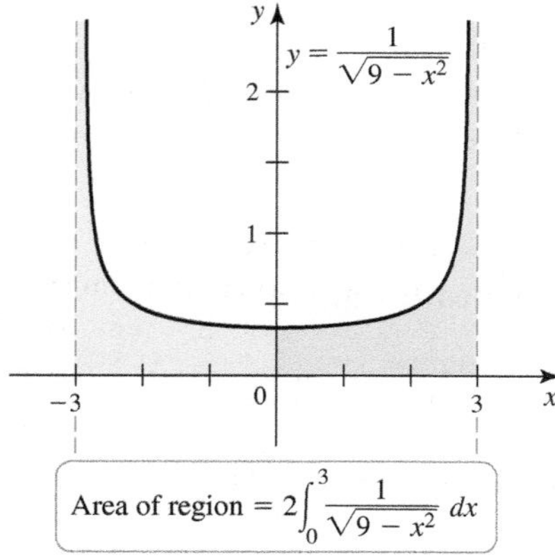

Figure 7.25

Note that as $c \to 3^-$, $\sin^{-1}(c/3) \to \sin^{-1} 1 = \pi/2$. Therefore, the area of R is

$$2\int_0^3 \frac{1}{\sqrt{9 - x^2}}\,dx = 2\left(\frac{\pi}{2} - 0\right) = \pi.$$

Related Exercises 35–56 ◀

EXAMPLE 5 **Infinite integrand at an interior point** Evaluate $\displaystyle\int_1^{10} \frac{dx}{(x - 2)^{1/3}}$.

SOLUTION The integrand is unbounded at $x = 2$, which is an interior point of the interval of integration (Figure 7.26). We split the interval into two subintervals and evaluate an improper integral on each subinterval:

$$\int_1^{10} \frac{dx}{(x - 2)^{1/3}} = \lim_{a \to 2^-} \int_1^a \frac{dx}{(x - 2)^{1/3}} + \lim_{b \to 2^+} \int_b^{10} \frac{dx}{(x - 2)^{1/3}} \qquad \text{Definition of improper integral}$$

$$= \lim_{a \to 2^-} \frac{3}{2}(x - 2)^{2/3}\Big|_1^a + \lim_{b \to 2^+} \frac{3}{2}(x - 2)^{2/3}\Big|_b^{10} \qquad \text{Evaluate integrals.}$$

Figure 7.26

➤ We interpret the result of 9/2 from Example 5 as the net area bounded by the curve $y = 1/(x-2)^{1/3}$ over the interval [1, 10].

$$= \frac{3}{2}\left(\lim_{a\to 2^-}(a-2)^{2/3} - (1-2)^{2/3}\right)$$

$$+\frac{3}{2}\left((10-2)^{2/3} - \lim_{b\to 2^+}(b-2)^{2/3}\right) \quad \text{Simplify.}$$

$$= \frac{3}{2}\left(0 - (-1)^{2/3} + 8^{2/3} - 0\right) = \frac{9}{2}. \quad \text{Evaluate limits.}$$

Related Exercises 35–56 ◀

We close with one of many practical uses of improper integrals.

EXAMPLE 6 Bioavailability The most efficient way to deliver a drug to its intended target site is to administer it intravenously (directly into the blood). If a drug is administered any other way (for example, by injection, orally, by nasal inhalant, or by skin patch), then some of the drug is typically lost due to absorption before it gets to the blood. By definition, the bioavailability of a drug measures the effectiveness of a nonintravenous method compared to the intravenous method. The bioavailability of intravenous dosing is 100%.

Let the functions $C_i(t)$ and $C_o(t)$ give the concentration of a drug in the blood, for times $t \ge 0$, using intravenous and oral dosing, respectively. (These functions can be determined through clinical experiments.) Assuming the same amount of drug is initially administered by both methods, the bioavailability for an oral dose is defined to be

$$F = \frac{\text{AUC}_o}{\text{AUC}_i} = \frac{\int_0^\infty C_o(t)\,dt}{\int_0^\infty C_i(t)\,dt},$$

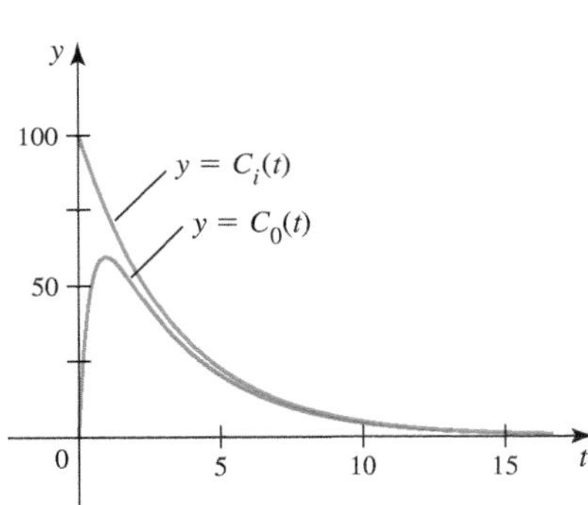

Figure 7.27

where AUC is used in the pharmacology literature to mean *area under the curve*.

Suppose the concentration of a certain drug in the blood in mg/L when given intravenously is $C_i(t) = 100e^{-0.3t}$, where $t \ge 0$ is measured in hours. Suppose also that the concentration of the same drug when delivered orally is $C_o(t) = 90(e^{-0.3t} - e^{-2.5t})$ (Figure 7.27). Find the bioavailability of the drug.

SOLUTION Evaluating the integrals of the concentration functions, we find that

$$\text{AUC}_i = \int_0^\infty C_i(t)\,dt = \int_0^\infty 100e^{-0.3t}\,dt$$

$$= \lim_{b\to\infty}\int_0^b 100e^{-0.3t}\,dt \quad \text{Improper integral}$$

$$= \lim_{b\to\infty}\frac{1000}{3}(1 - \underbrace{e^{-0.3b}}_{\text{approaches zero}}) \quad \text{Evaluate the integral.}$$

$$= \frac{1000}{3}. \quad \text{Evaluate the limit.}$$

Similarly,

$$\begin{aligned} \text{AUC}_o &= \int_0^\infty C_o(t)\,dt = \int_0^\infty 90(e^{-0.3t} - e^{-2.5t})\,dt \\ &= \lim_{b\to\infty} \int_0^b 90(e^{-0.3t} - e^{-2.5t})\,dt && \text{Improper integral} \\ &= \lim_{b\to\infty} \big(300(1 - \underbrace{e^{-0.3b}}_{\text{approaches zero}}) - 36(1 - \underbrace{e^{-2.5b}}_{\text{approaches zero}})\big) && \text{Evaluate the integral.} \\ &= 264. && \text{Evaluate the limit.} \end{aligned}$$

Therefore, the bioavailability is $F = 264/(1000/3) = 0.792$, which means oral administration of the drug is roughly 80% as effective as intravenous dosing. Notice that F is the ratio of the areas under the two curves on the interval $[0, \infty)$.

Related Exercises 57–60 ◀

SECTION 7.8 EXERCISES

Review Questions

1. What are the two general ways in which an improper integral may occur?
2. Explain how to evaluate $\int_a^\infty f(x)\,dx$.
3. Explain how to evaluate $\int_0^1 x^{-1/2}\,dx$.
4. For what values of p does $\int_1^\infty x^{-p}\,dx$ converge?

Basic Skills

5–28. Infinite intervals of integration *Evaluate the following integrals or state that they diverge.*

5. $\int_1^\infty x^{-2}\,dx$
6. $\int_0^\infty \frac{dx}{(x+1)^3}$
7. $\int_{-\infty}^0 e^x\,dx$
8. $\int_1^\infty 2^{-x}\,dx$
9. $\int_2^\infty \frac{dx}{\sqrt{x}}$
10. $\int_{-\infty}^0 \frac{dx}{\sqrt[3]{2-x}}$
11. $\int_0^\infty e^{-2x}\,dx$
12. $\int_{4/\pi}^\infty \frac{1}{x^2}\sec^2\left(\frac{1}{x}\right)dx$
13. $\int_0^\infty e^{-ax}\,dx,\ a > 0$
14. $\int_2^\infty \frac{dy}{y\ln y}$
15. $\int_{e^2}^\infty \frac{dx}{x\ln^p x},\ p > 1$
16. $\int_0^\infty \frac{p}{\sqrt[5]{p^2+1}}\,dp$
17. $\int_{-\infty}^\infty xe^{-x^2}\,dx$
18. $\int_0^\infty \cos x\,dx$
19. $\int_2^\infty \frac{\cos(\pi/x)}{x^2}\,dx$
20. $\int_{-\infty}^\infty \frac{dx}{x^2+2x+5}$
21. $\int_0^\infty \frac{e^u}{e^{2u}+1}\,du$
22. $\int_{-\infty}^a \sqrt{e^x}\,dx,\ a$ real
23. $\int_1^\infty \frac{dv}{v(v+1)}$
24. $\int_1^\infty \frac{dx}{x^2(x+1)}$
25. $\int_1^\infty \frac{3x^2+1}{x^3+x}\,dx$
26. $\int_1^\infty \frac{1}{z^2}\sin\frac{\pi}{z}\,dz$
27. $\int_2^\infty \frac{dx}{(x+2)^2}$
28. $\int_1^\infty \frac{\tan^{-1}s}{s^2+1}\,ds$

29–34. Volumes on infinite intervals *Find the volume of the described solid of revolution or state that it does not exist.*

29. The region bounded by $f(x) = x^{-2}$ and the x-axis on the interval $[1, \infty)$ is revolved about the x-axis.
30. The region bounded by $f(x) = (x^2+1)^{-1/2}$ and the x-axis on the interval $[2, \infty)$ is revolved about the x-axis.
31. The region bounded by $f(x) = \sqrt{\frac{x+1}{x^3}}$ and the x-axis on the interval $[1, \infty)$ is revolved about the x-axis.
32. The region bounded by $f(x) = (x+1)^{-3}$ and the x-axis on the interval $[0, \infty)$ is revolved about the y-axis.
33. The region bounded by $f(x) = \frac{1}{\sqrt{x}\ln x}$ and the x-axis on the interval $[2, \infty)$ is revolved about the x-axis.
34. The region bounded by $f(x) = \frac{\sqrt{x}}{\sqrt[3]{x^2+1}}$ and the x-axis on the interval $[0, \infty)$ is revolved about the x-axis.

35–50. Integrals with unbounded integrands *Evaluate the following integrals or state that they diverge.*

35. $\int_0^8 \frac{dx}{\sqrt[3]{x}}$
36. $\int_0^{\pi/2} \tan\theta\,d\theta$
37. $\int_1^2 \frac{dx}{\sqrt{x-1}}$
38. $\int_{-3}^1 \frac{dx}{(2x+6)^{2/3}}$
39. $\int_0^{\pi/2} \sec x\tan x\,dx$
40. $\int_3^4 \frac{dz}{(z-3)^{3/2}}$
41. $\int_0^1 \frac{e^{\sqrt{x}}}{\sqrt{x}}\,dx$
42. $\int_0^{\ln 3} \frac{e^y}{(e^y-1)^{2/3}}\,dy$

43. $\int_0^1 \frac{x^3}{x^4 - 1}\,dx$

44. $\int_1^\infty \frac{dx}{\sqrt[3]{x - 1}}$

45. $\int_0^{10} \frac{dx}{\sqrt[4]{10 - x}}$

46. $\int_1^{11} \frac{dx}{(x - 3)^{2/3}}$

47. $\int_{-1}^1 \ln y^2\,dy$

48. $\int_{-2}^6 \frac{dx}{\sqrt{|x - 2|}}$

49. $\int_{-2}^2 \frac{dp}{\sqrt{4 - p^2}}$

50. $\int_0^9 \frac{dx}{(x - 1)^{1/3}}$

51–56. Volumes with infinite integrands *Find the volume of the described solid of revolution or state that it does not exist.*

51. The region bounded by $f(x) = (x - 1)^{-1/4}$ and the x-axis on the interval $(1, 2]$ is revolved about the x-axis.

52. The region bounded by $f(x) = (x^2 - 1)^{-1/4}$ and the x-axis on the interval $(1, 2]$ is revolved about the y-axis.

53. The region bounded by $f(x) = (4 - x)^{-1/3}$ and the x-axis on the interval $[0, 4)$ is revolved about the y-axis.

54. The region bounded by $f(x) = (x + 1)^{-3/2}$ and the x-axis on the interval $(-1, 1]$ is revolved about the line $y = -1$.

55. The region bounded by $f(x) = \tan x$ and the x-axis on the interval $[0, \pi/2)$ is revolved about the x-axis.

56. The region bounded by $f(x) = -\ln x$ and the x-axis on the interval $(0, 1]$ is revolved about the x-axis.

57. **Bioavailability** When a drug is given intravenously, the concentration of the drug in the blood is $C_i(t) = 250e^{-0.08t}$, for $t \geq 0$. When the same drug is given orally, the concentration of the drug in the blood is $C_o(t) = 200(e^{-0.08t} - e^{-1.8t})$, for $t \geq 0$. Compute the bioavailability of the drug.

58. **Draining a pool** Water is drained from a swimming pool at a rate given by $R(t) = 100\,e^{-0.05t}$ gal/hr. If the drain is left open indefinitely, how much water drains from the pool?

59. **Maximum distance** An object moves on a line with velocity $v(t) = 10/(t + 1)^2$ mi/hr, for $t \geq 0$. What is the maximum distance the object can travel?

60. **Depletion of oil reserves** Suppose that the rate at which a company extracts oil is given by $r(t) = r_0 e^{-kt}$, where $r_0 = 10^7$ barrels/yr and $k = 0.005\text{ yr}^{-1}$. Suppose also the estimate of the total oil reserve is 2×10^9 barrels. If the extraction continues indefinitely, will the reserve be exhausted?

Further Explorations

61. **Explain why or why not** Determine whether the following statements are true and give an explanation or counterexample.

a. If f is continuous and $0 < f(x) < g(x)$ on the interval $[0, \infty)$, and $\int_0^\infty g(x)\,dx = M < \infty$, then $\int_0^\infty f(x)\,dx$ exists.

b. If $\lim_{x\to\infty} f(x) = 1$, then $\int_0^\infty f(x)\,dx$ exists.

c. If $\int_0^1 x^{-p}\,dx$ exists, then $\int_0^1 x^{-q}\,dx$ exists, where $q > p$.

d. If $\int_1^\infty x^{-p}\,dx$ exists, then $\int_1^\infty x^{-q}\,dx$ exists, where $q > p$.

e. $\int_1^\infty \frac{dx}{x^{3p+2}}$ exists, for $p > -\frac{1}{3}$.

62. **Incorrect calculation** What is wrong with this calculation?

$$\int_{-1}^1 \frac{dx}{x} = \ln|x|\Big|_{-1}^1 = \ln 1 - \ln 1 = 0$$

63. **Using symmetry** Use symmetry to evaluate the following integrals.

a. $\int_{-\infty}^\infty e^{-|x|}\,dx$ b. $\int_{-\infty}^\infty \frac{x^3}{1 + x^8}\,dx$

64. **Integral with a parameter** For what values of p does the integral $\int_2^\infty \frac{dx}{x \ln^p x}$ exist and what is its value (in terms of p)?

T 65. **Improper integrals by numerical methods** Use the Trapezoid Rule (Section 7.7) to approximate $\int_0^R e^{-x^2}\,dx$ with $R = 2, 4$, and 8. For each value of R, take $n = 4, 8, 16$, and 32, and compare approximations with successive values of n. Use these approximations to approximate $I = \int_0^\infty e^{-x^2}\,dx$.

66–68. Integration by parts *Use integration by parts to evaluate the following integrals.*

66. $\int_0^\infty xe^{-x}\,dx$

67. $\int_0^1 x \ln x\,dx$

68. $\int_1^\infty \frac{\ln x}{x^2}\,dx$

T 69. **A close comparison** Graph the integrands and then evaluate and compare the values of $\int_0^\infty xe^{-x^2}\,dx$ and $\int_0^\infty x^2 e^{-x^2}\,dx$.

70. **Area between curves** Let R be the region bounded by the graphs of $y = x^{-p}$ and $y = x^{-q}$, for $x \geq 1$, where $q > p > 1$. Find the area of R.

71. **Area between curves** Let R be the region bounded by the graphs of $y = e^{-ax}$ and $y = e^{-bx}$, for $x \geq 0$, where $a > b > 0$. Find the area of R.

72. **An area function** Let $A(a)$ denote the area of the region bounded by $y = e^{-ax}$ and the x-axis on the interval $[0, \infty)$. Graph the function $A(a)$, for $0 < a < \infty$. Describe how the area of the region decreases as the parameter a increases.

T 73. **Regions bounded by exponentials** Let $a > 0$ and let R be the region bounded by the graph of $y = e^{-ax}$ and the x-axis on the interval $[b, \infty)$.

a. Find $A(a, b)$, the area of R as a function of a and b.

b. Find the relationship $b = g(a)$ such that $A(a, b) = 2$.

c. What is the minimum value of b (call it b^*) such that when $b > b^*$, $A(a, b) = 2$ for some value of $a > 0$?

74. **The family $f(x) = 1/x^p$ revisited** Consider the family of functions $f(x) = 1/x^p$, where p is a real number. For what values of p does the integral $\int_0^1 f(x)\,dx$ exist? What is its value?

75. **When is the volume finite?** Let R be the region bounded by the graph of $f(x) = x^{-p}$ and the x-axis, for $0 < x \leq 1$.

a. Let S be the solid generated when R is revolved about the x-axis. For what values of p is the volume of S finite?

b. Let S be the solid generated when R is revolved about the y-axis. For what values of p is the volume of S finite?

76. **When is the volume finite?** Let R be the region bounded by the graph of $f(x) = x^{-p}$ and the x-axis, for $x \geq 1$.

a. Let S be the solid generated when R is revolved about the x-axis. For what values of p is the volume of S finite?

b. Let S be the solid generated when R is revolved about the y-axis. For what values of p is the volume of S finite?

T 77–80. Numerical methods *Use numerical methods or a calculator to approximate the following integrals as closely as possible. The exact value of each integral is given.*

77. $\int_0^{\pi/2} \ln(\sin x)\, dx = \int_0^{\pi/2} \ln(\cos x)\, dx = -\frac{\pi \ln 2}{2}$

78. $\int_0^{\infty} \frac{\sin^2 x}{x^2}\, dx = \frac{\pi}{2}$

79. $\int_0^{\infty} \ln\left(\frac{e^x + 1}{e^x - 1}\right) dx = \frac{\pi^2}{4}$

80. $\int_0^{1} \frac{\ln x}{1 + x}\, dx = -\frac{\pi^2}{12}$

Applications

81. **Perpetual annuity** Imagine that today you deposit \$$B$ in a savings account that earns interest at a rate of $p\%$ per year compounded continuously (Section 6.9). The goal is to draw an income of \$$I$ per year from the account forever. The amount of money that must be deposited is $B = I\int_0^{\infty} e^{-rt}\, dt$, where $r = p/100$. Suppose you find an account that earns 12% interest annually and you wish to have an income from the account of \$5000 per year. How much must you deposit today?

82. **Draining a tank** Water is drained from a 3000-gal tank at a rate that starts at 100 gal/hr and decreases continuously by 5%/hr. If the drain is left open indefinitely, how much water drains from the tank? Can a full tank be emptied at this rate?

83. **Decaying oscillations** Let $a > 0$ and b be real numbers. Use integration to confirm the following identities. (See Exercise 68 of Section 7.2)

 a. $\int_0^{\infty} e^{-ax} \cos bx\, dx = \frac{a}{a^2 + b^2}$

 b. $\int_0^{\infty} e^{-ax} \sin bx\, dx = \frac{b}{a^2 + b^2}$

84. **Electronic chips** Suppose the probability that a particular computer chip fails after a hours of operation is $0.00005\int_a^{\infty} e^{-0.00005t}\, dt$.

 a. Find the probability that the computer chip fails after 15,000 hr of operation.

 b. Of the chips that are still operating after 15,000 hr, what fraction of these will operate for at least another 15,000 hr?

 c. Evaluate $0.00005\int_0^{\infty} e^{-0.00005t}\, dt$ and interpret its meaning.

85. **Average lifetime** The average time until a computer chip fails (see Exercise 84) is $0.00005\int_0^{\infty} te^{-0.00005t}\, dt$. Find this value.

86. **The Eiffel Tower property** Let R be the region between the curves $y = e^{-cx}$ and $y = -e^{-cx}$ on the interval $[a, \infty)$, where $a \geq 0$ and $c > 0$. The center of mass of R is located at $(\bar{x}, 0)$, where $\bar{x} = \frac{\int_a^{\infty} xe^{-cx}\, dx}{\int_a^{\infty} e^{-cx}\, dx}$. (The profile of the Eiffel Tower is modeled by the two exponential curves; see the Guided Project *The exponential Eiffel Tower*.)

 a. For $a = 0$ and $c = 2$, sketch the curves that define R and find the center of mass of R. Indicate the location of the center of mass.

 b. With $a = 0$ and $c = 2$, find equations of the lines tangent to the curves at the points corresponding to $x = 0$.

 c. Show that the tangent lines intersect at the center of mass.

 d. Show that this same property holds for any $a \geq 0$ and any $c > 0$; that is, the tangent lines to the curves $y = \pm e^{-cx}$ at $x = a$ intersect at the center of mass of R.

 (*Source:* P. Weidman and I. Pinelis, *Comptes Rendu Mechanique*, 332, 571–584, 2004)

87. **Escape velocity and black holes** The work required to launch an object from the surface of Earth to outer space is given by $W = \int_R^{\infty} F(x)\, dx$, where $R = 6370$ km is the approximate radius of Earth, $F(x) = GMm/x^2$ is the gravitational force between Earth and the object, G is the gravitational constant, M is the mass of Earth, m is the mass of the object, and $GM = 4 \times 10^{14}\ \text{m}^3/\text{s}^2$.

 a. Find the work required to launch an object in terms of m.

 b. What escape velocity v_e is required to give the object a kinetic energy $\frac{1}{2}mv_e^2$ equal to W?

 c. The French scientist Laplace anticipated the existence of black holes in the 18th century with the following argument: If a body has an escape velocity that equals or exceeds the speed of light, $c = 300{,}000$ km/s, then light cannot escape the body and it cannot be seen. Show that such a body has a radius $R \leq 2GM/c^2$. For Earth to be a black hole, what would its radius need to be?

88. **Adding a proton to a nucleus** The nucleus of an atom is positively charged because it consists of positively charged protons and uncharged neutrons. To bring a free proton toward a nucleus, a repulsive force $F(r) = kqQ/r^2$ must be overcome, where $q = 1.6 \times 10^{-19}$ C (coulombs) is the charge on the proton, $k = 9 \times 10^9\ \text{N-m}^2/\text{C}^2$, Q is the charge on the nucleus, and r is the distance between the center of the nucleus and the proton. Find the work required to bring a free proton (assumed to be a point mass) from a large distance ($r \to \infty$) to the edge of a nucleus that has a charge $Q = 50q$ and a radius of 6×10^{-11} m.

T 89. **Gaussians** An important function in statistics is the Gaussian (or normal distribution, or bell-shaped curve), $f(x) = e^{-ax^2}$.

 a. Graph the Gaussian for $a = 0.5$, 1, and 2.

 b. Given that $\int_{-\infty}^{\infty} e^{-ax^2}\, dx = \sqrt{\frac{\pi}{a}}$, compute the area under the curves in part (a).

 c. Complete the square to evaluate $\int_{-\infty}^{\infty} e^{-(ax^2 + bx + c)}\, dx$, where $a > 0$, b, and c are real numbers.

90–94. Laplace transforms *A powerful tool in solving problems in engineering and physics is the Laplace transform. Given a function $f(t)$, the Laplace transform is a new function $F(s)$ defined by*

$$F(s) = \int_0^{\infty} e^{-st} f(t)\, dt,$$

where we assume that s is a positive real number. For example, to find the Laplace transform of $f(t) = e^{-t}$, the following improper integral is evaluated:

$$F(s) = \int_0^{\infty} e^{-st} e^{-t}\, dt = \int_0^{\infty} e^{-(s+1)t}\, dt = \frac{1}{s + 1}.$$

Verify the following Laplace transforms, where a is a real number.

90. $f(t) = 1 \longrightarrow F(s) = \frac{1}{s}$

91. $f(t) = e^{at} \longrightarrow F(s) = \frac{1}{s - a}$

92. $f(t) = t \longrightarrow F(s) = \frac{1}{s^2}$

93. $f(t) = \sin at \longrightarrow F(s) = \dfrac{a}{s^2 + a^2}$

94. $f(t) = \cos at \longrightarrow F(s) = \dfrac{s}{s^2 + a^2}$

Additional Exercises

95. **Improper integrals** Evaluate the following improper integrals (Putnam Exam, 1939).

a. $\displaystyle\int_1^3 \frac{dx}{\sqrt{(x-1)(3-x)}}$ b. $\displaystyle\int_1^\infty \frac{dx}{e^{x+1} + e^{3-x}}$

96. **A better way** Compute $\int_0^1 \ln x\, dx$ using integration by parts. Then explain why $-\int_0^\infty e^{-x}\, dx$ (an easier integral) gives the same result.

97. **Competing powers** For what values of $p > 0$ is
$$\int_0^\infty \frac{dx}{x^p + x^{-p}} < \infty?$$

98. **Gamma function** The gamma function is defined by $\Gamma(p) = \int_0^\infty x^{p-1}e^{-x}\, dx$, for p not equal to zero or a negative integer.

a. Use the reduction formula
$$\int_0^\infty x^p e^{-x}\, dx = p\int_0^\infty x^{p-1}e^{-x}\, dx, \text{ for } p = 1, 2, 3, \ldots$$
to show that $\Gamma(p+1) = p!$ (p factorial).

b. Use the substitution $x = u^2$ and the fact that $\displaystyle\int_0^\infty e^{-u^2}\, du = \frac{\sqrt{\pi}}{2}$ to show that $\Gamma\left(\frac{1}{2}\right) = \sqrt{\pi}$.

99. **Many methods needed** Show that $\displaystyle\int_0^\infty \frac{\sqrt{x}\ln x}{(1+x)^2}\, dx = \pi$ in the following steps.

a. Integrate by parts with $u = \sqrt{x}\ln x$.

b. Change variables by letting $y = 1/x$.

c. Show that $\displaystyle\int_0^1 \frac{\ln x}{\sqrt{x}(1+x)}\, dx = -\int_1^\infty \frac{\ln x}{\sqrt{x}(1+x)}\, dx$ (and that both integrals converge). Conclude that
$$\int_0^\infty \frac{\ln x}{\sqrt{x}(1+x)}\, dx = 0.$$

d. Evaluate the remaining integral using the change of variables $z = \sqrt{x}$.

(*Source: Mathematics Magazine* 59, 1, Feb 1986)

100. **Riemann sums to integrals** Show that $L = \displaystyle\lim_{n\to\infty}\left(\frac{1}{n}\ln n! - \ln n\right) = -1$ in the following steps.

a. Note that $n! = n(n-1)(n-2)\cdots 1$ and use $\ln(ab) = \ln a + \ln b$ to show that
$$L = \lim_{n\to\infty}\left(\left(\frac{1}{n}\sum_{k=1}^n \ln k\right) - \ln n\right)$$
$$= \lim_{n\to\infty}\frac{1}{n}\sum_{k=1}^n \ln\frac{k}{n}.$$

b. Identify the limit of this sum as a Riemann sum for $\int_0^1 \ln x\, dx$. Integrate this improper integral by parts and reach the desired conclusion.

101–102. Improper integrals and l'Hôpital's Rule *Evaluate the following integrals.*

101. $\displaystyle\int_0^a x^x(\ln x + 1)\, dx, a > 0$ 102. $\displaystyle\int_0^\infty x^{-x}(\ln x + 1)\, dx$

QUICK CHECK ANSWERS

1. The integral diverges. $\displaystyle\lim_{b\to\infty}\int_1^b (1 + x^{-1})\, dx = \lim_{b\to\infty}(x + \ln x)\Big|_1^b$ does not exist. **2.** $\frac{1}{3}$ **3.** c must approach 0 through values in the interval of integration $(0, 1)$. Therefore, $c \to 0^+$. ◀

7.9 Introduction to Differential Equations

If you had to demonstrate the utility of mathematics to a skeptic, a convincing way would be to cite *differential equations*. This vast subject lies at the heart of mathematical modeling and is used in engineering, the natural and biological sciences, economics, management, and finance. Differential equations rely heavily on calculus, and they are usually studied in advanced courses that follow calculus. Nevertheless, you have now seen enough calculus to understand a brief survey of differential equations and appreciate their power.

An Overview

If you studied Section 4.9 or 6.1, then you saw a preview of differential equations. Given the *derivative* of a function (for example, a velocity or some other rate of change), these two sections show how to find the function itself by integration. This process amounts to solving a differential equation.

More generally, a differential equation involves an unknown function and its derivatives. The unknown in a differential equation is not a number (as in an algebraic equation), but rather *a function.* Examples of differential equations are

$$\text{(A) } y''(x) + 16y = 0, \quad \text{(B) } \frac{dy}{dx} + 4y = \cos x, \quad \text{(C) } y'(t) = 0.1y(100 - y).$$

In each case, the goal is to find solutions of the equation—that is, functions y that satisfy the equation. Just to be clear about what we mean by a solution, consider equation (A). If we substitute $y = \cos 4x$ and $y'' = -16 \cos 4x$ into this equation, we find that

$$\underbrace{-16 \cos 4x}_{y''} + \underbrace{16 \cos 4x}_{16y} = 0,$$

which implies that $y = \cos 4x$ is a solution of the equation. You should verify that $y = C \cos 4x$ is also a solution for any real number C (as is $y = C \sin 4x$). Let's begin by verifying that given functions are solutions of a differential equation.

EXAMPLE 1 **Verifying solutions** Consider the exponential growth equation $y'(t) = 2.5y$.

a. Show by substitution that the exponential function $y = 10e^{2.5t}$ is a solution of the differential equation.

b. Show by substitution that the function $y = Ce^{2.5t}$ is a solution of the same differential equation, for *any* constant C.

SOLUTION

a. We differentiate $y = 10e^{2.5t}$ to obtain $y'(t) = 2.5 \cdot 10e^{2.5t}$. Now observe that

$$y'(t) = \underbrace{2.5 \cdot 10e^{2.5t}}_{y'(t)} = 2.5 \cdot \underbrace{10e^{2.5t}}_{y(t)} = 2.5y.$$

Therefore, the function $y = 10e^{2.5t}$ satisfies the equation $y'(t) = 2.5y$.

b. Duplicating the calculation of part (a) with 10 replaced with an arbitrary constant C, we find that

$$y'(t) = \underbrace{2.5 \cdot Ce^{2.5t}}_{y'(t)} = 2.5 \cdot \underbrace{Ce^{2.5t}}_{y(t)} = 2.5y.$$

The functions $y = Ce^{2.5t}$ also satisfy the equation, where C is an arbitrary constant.

Related Exercises 9–12 ◀

The basic terminology associated with differential equations is helpful. The **order** of a differential equation is the highest order appearing on a derivative in the equation. For example, the equations $y' + 4y = \cos x$ and $y' = 0.1y(100 - y)$ are first order, and $y'' + 16y = 0$ is second order.

➤ A *linear* differential equation cannot have terms such as y^2, yy', or $\sin y$, where y is the unknown function.

Linear differential equations (first- and second-order) have the form

$$\underbrace{y'(x) + p(x)y(x) = f(x)}_{\text{first-order}} \quad \text{and} \quad \underbrace{y''(x) + p(x)y'(x) + q(x)y(x) = f(x),}_{\text{second-order}}$$

where p, q, and f are given functions that depend only on the independent variable x. Of the equations on p. 581, (A) and (B) are linear, but (C) is **nonlinear** (because the right side contains y^2).

➤ The term *initial condition* originates with equations in which the independent variable is *time.* In such problems, the initial state of the system (for example, position and velocity) is specified at some initial time (often $t = 0$). We use the term *initial condition* whenever information about the solution is given at a single point.

A differential equation is often accompanied by **initial conditions** that specify the values of y, and possibly its derivatives, at a particular point. In general, an nth-order equation requires n initial conditions. A differential equation, together with the appropriate number of initial conditions, is called an **initial value problem.** A typical first-order initial value problem has the form

$$y'(t) = f(t, y) \quad \text{Differential equation}$$
$$y(0) = A, \quad \text{Initial condition}$$

where A is given and f is a given expression that involves t and/or y.

EXAMPLE 2 **Solution of an initial value problem** Consider the differential equation in Example 1. Find the solution of the initial value problem

$$y'(t) = 2.5y \quad \text{Differential equation}$$
$$y(0) = 3.2. \quad \text{Initial condition}$$

SOLUTION By Example lb, functions of the form $y = Ce^{2.5t}$ satisfy the differential equation $y'(t) = 2.5y$, where C is an arbitrary constant. We now use the initial condition $y(0) = 3.2$ to determine the arbitrary constant C. Noting that $y(0) = Ce^{2.5 \cdot 0} = C$, the condition $y(0) = 3.2$ implies that $C = 3.2$.

Therefore, $y = 3.2e^{2.5t}$ is the solution of the initial value problem. Figure 7.28 shows the family of curves $y = Ce^{2.5t}$ for several different values of the constant C. It also shows the function $y = 3.2e^{2.5t}$ highlighted in red, which is the solution of the initial value problem.

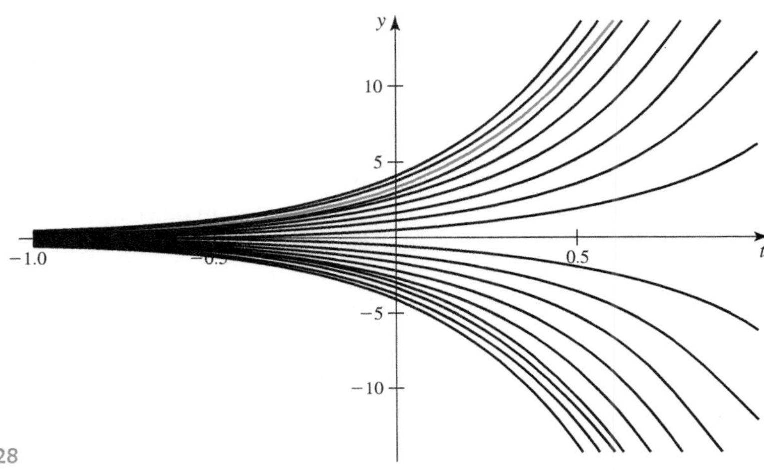

Figure 7.28

Related Exercises 13–16

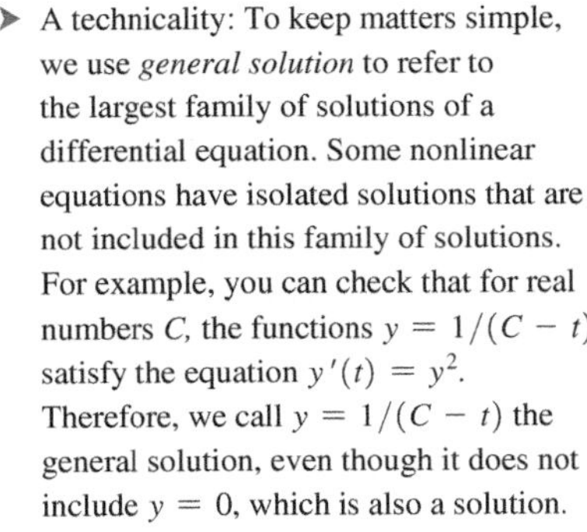
➤ A technicality: To keep matters simple, we use *general solution* to refer to the largest family of solutions of a differential equation. Some nonlinear equations have isolated solutions that are not included in this family of solutions. For example, you can check that for real numbers C, the functions $y = 1/(C - t)$ satisfy the equation $y'(t) = y^2$. Therefore, we call $y = 1/(C - t)$ the general solution, even though it does not include $y = 0$, which is also a solution.

➤ The two integrals in the calculation of Example 3 both produce an arbitrary constant of integration. These two constants may be combined as one arbitrary constant.

Solving a first-order differential equation requires integration—you must "undo" the derivative $y'(t)$ to find $y(t)$. One integration introduces one arbitrary constant, which generates an entire family of solutions. Solving an nth-order differential equation typically requires n integrations, each of which introduces an arbitrary constant; again, the result is a family of solutions. For any differential equation, the largest family of solutions, generated by arbitrary constants, is called the **general solution.** For instance, in Example 1, we found the general solution $y = Ce^{2.5t}$.

EXAMPLE 3 **An initial value problem** Solve the initial value problem

$$y'(t) = 10e^{-t/2}, \qquad y(0) = 4.$$

SOLUTION Notice that the right side of the equation depends only on t. The solution is found by integrating both sides of the differential equation with respect to t:

$$\underbrace{\int y'(t)\,dt}_{y(t)} = \int 10e^{-t/2}\,dt \quad \text{Integrate both sides with respect to } t.$$

$$y = -20e^{-t/2} + C. \quad \text{Evaluate integrals; } y(t) \text{ is an antiderivative of } y'(t).$$

We have found the general solution, which involves one arbitrary constant. To determine its value, we use the initial condition by substituting $t = 0$ and $y = 4$ into the general solution:

$$y(0) = (-20e^{-t/2} + C)\big|_{t=0} = -20 + C = 4 \Rightarrow C = 24.$$

Therefore, the solution of the initial value problem is $y = -20e^{-t/2} + 24$ (Figure 7.29). You should check that this function satisfies both the differential equation and the initial condition.

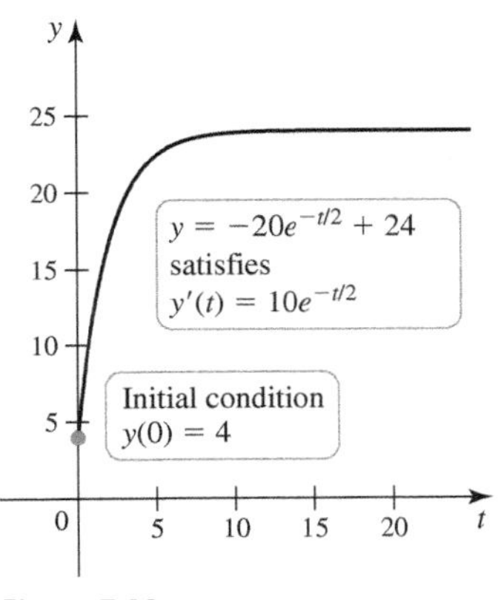

Figure 7.29

Related Exercises 17–20

QUICK CHECK 1 What is the order of the equation in Example 3? Is it linear or nonlinear? ◄

In Examples 2 and 3, we found solutions to initial value problems without worrying about whether there might be other solutions. Once we find a solution to an initial value problem, how can we be sure there aren't other solutions? More generally, given a particular initial value problem, how do we know whether a solution exists and whether it is unique?

These theoretical questions are handled by powerful *existence and uniqueness theorems* whose proofs are presented in advanced courses. Here is an informal statement of an existence and uniqueness theorem for the type of initial value problems encountered in this section:

The solution of the general first-order initial value problem

$$y'(t) = f(t, y), y(a) = A$$

exists and is unique in some region that contains the point (a, A) provided f is a "well-behaved" function in that region.

The technical challenges arise in defining *well-behaved* in the most general way possible. The initial value problems we consider in this section satisfy the conditions of this theorem and can be assumed to have unique solutions.

A First-Order Linear Differential Equation

In Section 6.9, we studied functions that exhibit exponential growth or decay. Such functions have the property that their rate of change at a particular point is proportional to the function value at that point. In other words, these functions satisfy a first-order differential equation of the form $y'(t) = ky$, where k is a real number. You should verify by substitution that the function $y = Ce^{kt}$ is the general solution of this equation, where C is an arbitrary constant.

➤ The solution of the equation $y'(t) = ky$ is $y = Ce^{kt}$, so it models exponential growth when $k > 0$ and exponential decay when $k < 0$.

Now let's generalize and consider the first-order linear equation $y'(t) = ky + b$, where k and b are real numbers. Solutions of this equation have a wide range of behavior (depending on the values of k and b), and the equation itself has many modeling applications. Specifically, the terms of the equation have the following meaning:

$$\underbrace{y'(t)}_{\text{rate of change of } y} = \underbrace{ky}_{\text{natural growth or decay rate of } y} + \underbrace{b.}_{\text{growth of decay rate due to external effects}}$$

For example, if y represents the number of fish in a hatchery, then ky (with $k > 0$) models exponential growth in the fish population, in the absence of other factors, and $b < 0$ is the harvesting rate at which the population is depleted. As another example, if y represents the amount of a drug in the blood, then ky (with $k < 0$) models exponential decay of the drug through the kidneys, and $b > 0$ is the rate at which the drug is added to the blood intravenously. We can give an explicit solution for the equation $y'(t) = ky + b$.

We begin by dividing both sides of the equation $y'(t) = ky + b$ by $ky + b$, which gives

$$\frac{y'(t)}{ky + b} = 1.$$

Because the goal is to determine y from $y'(t)$, we integrate both sides of this equation with respect to t:

$$\int \frac{y'(t)}{ky + b}\,dt = \int dt.$$

The factor $y'(t)\,dt$ on the left side is simply dy. Making this substitution and evaluating the integrals, we have

$$\int \frac{dy}{ky + b} = \int dt \quad \text{or} \quad \frac{1}{k}\ln|ky + b| = t + C.$$

➤ The arbitrary constant of integration needs to be included in only one of the integrals.

For the moment, we assume that $ky + b \geq 0$, or equivalently $y \geq -b/k$, so the absolute value may be removed. Multiplying through by k, exponentiating both sides of the equation, and solving for y gives the solution $y = Ce^{kt} - b/k$. In the process of solving for y, we have successively redefined C; for example, if C is arbitrary, then kC and e^C are also arbitrary. You can also show that if $ky + b < 0$, or $y < -b/k$, then the same solution results.

➤ The equation $y'(t) = ky + b$ is one of many first-order linear differential equations. If k and b are functions of t, the equation is still first-order linear.

Solution of a First-Order Linear Differential Equation

The general solution of the first-order linear equation $y'(t) = ky + b$, where k and b are specified real numbers, is $y = Ce^{kt} - b/k$, where C is an arbitrary constant. Given an initial condition, the value of C may be determined.

QUICK CHECK 2 Verify by substitution that $y = Ce^{kt} - b/k$ is a solution of $y'(t) = ky + b$. ◄

EXAMPLE 4 **An initial value problem for drug dosing** A drug is administered to a patient through an intravenous line at a rate of 6 mg/hr. The drug has a half-life that corresponds to a rate constant of 0.03/hr (Section 6.9). Let $y(t)$ be the amount of drug in the blood for $t \geq 0$. Solve the following initial value problem and interpret the solution.

$$\begin{aligned} &\text{Differential equation:} \quad && y'(t) = -0.03y + 6 \\ &\text{Initial condition:} && y(0) = 0 \end{aligned}$$

SOLUTION The equation has the form $y'(t) = ky + b$, where $k = -0.03$ and $b = 6$. Therefore, the general solution is $y(t) = Ce^{-0.03t} + 200$. To determine the value of C for this particular problem, we substitute $y(0) = 0$ into the general solution. We find that $y(0) = C + 200 = 0$, which implies that $C = -200$. Therefore, the solution of the initial value problem is

$$y = -200e^{-0.03t} + 200 = 200(1 - e^{-0.03t}).$$

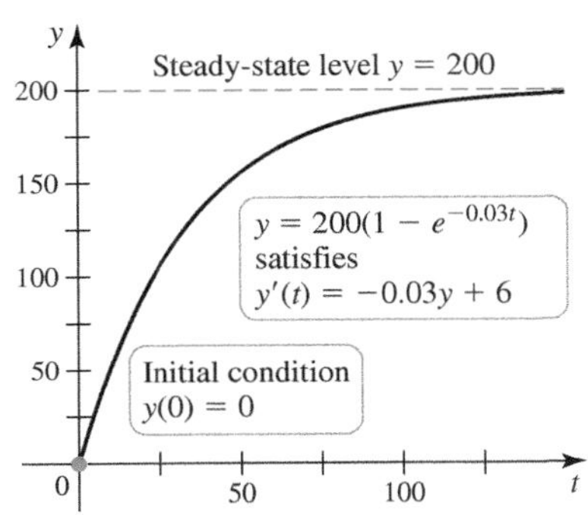

Figure 7.30

The graph of the solution (Figure 7.30) reveals an important fact: Though the amount of drug in the blood increases, it approaches a steady-state level of

$$\lim_{t\to\infty} y(t) = \lim_{t\to\infty} (200(1 - e^{-0.03t})) = 200 \text{ mg}.$$

Related Exercises 21–30 ◄

QUICK CHECK 3 What is the solution of $y'(t) = 3y(t) + 6$ with the initial condition $y(0) = 14$? ◄

Separable First-Order Differential Equations

The most general first-order differential equation has the form $y'(t) = F(t, y)$, where F is an expression that involves t and/or y. We have a *chance* of solving such an equation if it can be written in the form

$$g(y)\, y'(t) = h(t),$$

in which the terms that involve y appear on one side of the equation *separated* from the terms that involve t. An equation that can be written in this form is said to be **separable**.

The solution of the linear equation $y'(t) = ky + b$ presented above is a specific example of the method for solving separable differential equations. In general, we solve the separable equation $g(y)\, y'(t) = h(t)$ by integrating both sides of the equation with respect to t.

$$\int g(y) \underbrace{y'(t)\, dt}_{dy} = \int h(t)\, dt \quad \text{Integrate both sides.}$$

$$\int g(y)\, dy = \int h(t)\, dt \quad \text{Change of variables on the left side}$$

➤ The result of this change of variables is that the left side of the equation is integrated with respect to y and the right side is integrated with respect to t. With this justification, this shortcut is permissible and is often taken.

A change of variables on the left side of the equation leaves us with two integrals to evaluate, one with respect to y and one with respect to t. Finding a solution depends on evaluating these integrals.

QUICK CHECK 4 Write $y'(t) = (t^2 + 1)/y^3$ in separated form. ◄

EXAMPLE 5 **A separable equation** Find the function that satisfies the initial value problem

$$\frac{dy}{dx} = y^2 e^{-x}, \qquad y(0) = \frac{1}{2}.$$

SOLUTION The equation can be written in separable form by dividing both sides of the equation by y^2 to give $y'(x)/y^2 = e^{-x}$. We now integrate both sides of the equation with respect to x and evaluate the resulting integrals.

$$\int \frac{1}{y^2} \underbrace{y'(x)\,dx}_{dy} = \int e^{-x}\,dx$$

$$\int \frac{dy}{y^2} = \int e^{-x}\,dx \quad \text{Change of variables on the left side}$$

$$-\frac{1}{y} = -e^{-x} + C \quad \text{Evaluate the integrals.}$$

Solving for y gives the general solution

$$y = \frac{1}{e^{-x} - C}.$$

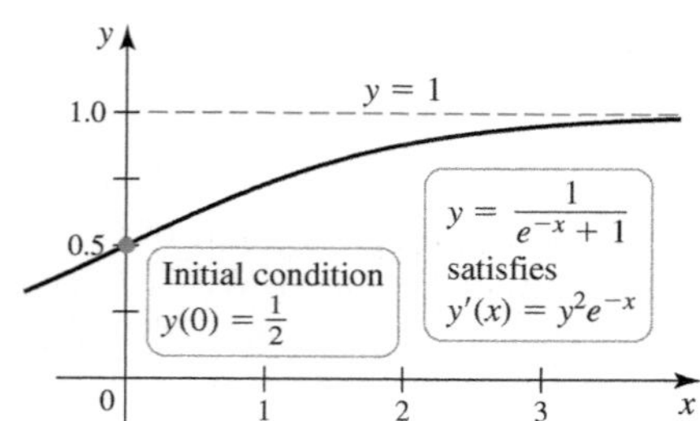

Figure 7.31

The initial condition $y(0) = \frac{1}{2}$ implies that

$$y(0) = \frac{1}{e^0 - C} = \frac{1}{1 - C} = \frac{1}{2}.$$

Solving for C gives $C = -1$, so the solution of the initial value problem is $y = \dfrac{1}{e^{-x} + 1}$. The solution (Figure 7.31) has a graph that passes through $(0, \frac{1}{2})$ and rises to approach the asymptote $y = 1$ (because $\displaystyle\lim_{x\to\infty} \frac{1}{e^{-x} + 1} = 1$).

Related Exercises 31–40 ◀

➤ The logistic equation is used to describe the population of many different species as well as the spread of rumors and epidemics (Exercises 41–42).

EXAMPLE 6 **Logistic population growth** Fifty fruit flies are in a large container at the beginning of an experiment. Let $P(t)$ be the number of fruit flies in the container t days later. At first, the population grows exponentially, but due to limited space and food supply, the growth rate decreases and the population is prevented from growing without bound. This experiment can be modeled by the *logistic equation*

$$\frac{dP}{dt} = 0.1P\left(1 - \frac{P}{300}\right)$$

together with the initial condition $P(0) = 50$. Solve this initial value problem.

SOLUTION We see that the equation is separable by writing it in the form

$$\frac{1}{P\left(1 - \frac{P}{300}\right)} \cdot \frac{dP}{dt} = 0.1.$$

Integrating both sides with respect to t leads to the equation

$$\int \frac{1}{P\left(1 - \frac{P}{300}\right)}\,dP = \underbrace{\int 0.1\,dt.}_{0.1t + C} \tag{1}$$

The integral on the right side of equation (1) is $\int 0.1\,dt = 0.1t + C$. Because the integrand on the left side is a rational function in P, we use partial fractions. You should verify that

$$\frac{1}{P\left(1 - \frac{P}{300}\right)} = \frac{300}{P(300 - P)} = \frac{1}{P} + \frac{1}{300 - P},$$

and therefore,

$$\int \frac{1}{P\left(1 - \frac{P}{300}\right)}\, dP = \int \left(\frac{1}{P} + \frac{1}{300 - P}\right) dP = \ln\left|\frac{P}{300 - P}\right| + C.$$

Equation (1) now becomes

$$\ln\left|\frac{P}{300 - P}\right| = 0.1t + C. \tag{2}$$

➤ Notice again that two constants of integration have been combined into one.

The final step is to solve for P, which is tangled up inside the logarithm. To simplify matters, we assume that if the initial population $P(0)$ is between 0 and 300, then $0 < P(t) < 300$ for all $t > 0$. This assumption (which can be verified independently) allows us to remove the absolute value on the left side of equation (2).

Using the initial condition $P(0) = 50$ and solving for C (Exercise 68), we find that $C = -\ln 5$. Solving for P, the solution of the initial value problem is

$$P = \frac{300}{1 + 5e^{-0.1t}}.$$

➤ It is always a good idea to check that the final solution satisfies the initial condition. In this case, $P(0) = 50$.

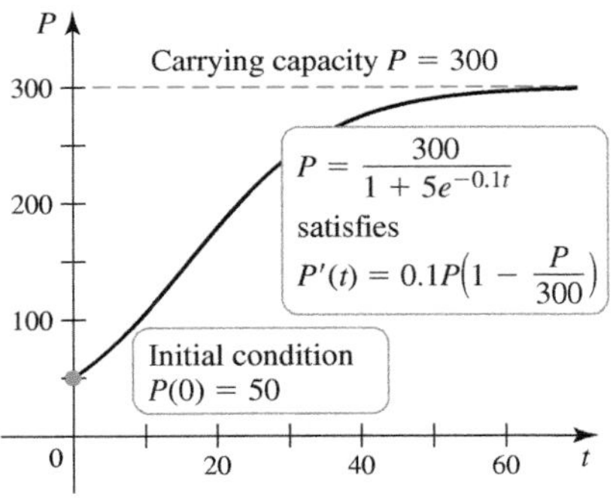

Figure 7.32

The graph of the solution shows that the population increases, but not without bound (Figure 7.32). Instead, it approaches a steady state value of

$$\lim_{t\to\infty} P(t) = \lim_{t\to\infty} \frac{300}{1 + 5e^{-0.1t}} = 300,$$

which is the maximum population that the environment (space and food supply) can sustain. This steady-state population is called the **carrying capacity**.

Related Exercises 41–42 ◄

Direction Fields

The geometry of first-order differential equations is beautifully displayed using *direction fields*. Consider the general first-order differential equation $y'(t) = F(t, y)$, where F is a given expression involving t and/or y. A solution of this equation has the property that at each point (t, y) of the solution curve, the slope of the curve is $F(t, y)$. A **direction field** is simply a picture that shows the slope of the solution at selected points of the ty-plane.

For example, consider the equation $y'(t) = y^2e^{-t}$. We choose a regular grid of points in the ty-plane, and at each point (t, y), we make a small line segment with slope y^2e^{-t}. The line segment at a point P gives the slope of the solution curve that passes through P (Figure 7.33). For example, along the t-axis ($y = 0$), the slopes of the line segments are $F(t, 0) = 0$. And along the y-axis ($t = 0$), the slopes of the line segments are $F(0, y) = y^2$.

➤ Drawing direction fields by hand can be tedious. It's best to use a calculator or software.

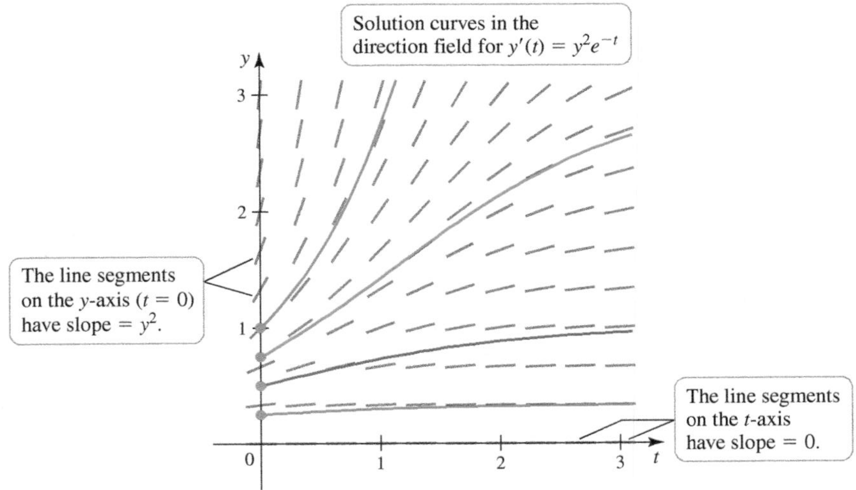

Figure 7.33

Now suppose an initial condition $y(a) = A$ is given. We start at the point (a, A) in the direction field and sketch a curve in the positive t-direction that follows the flow of the direction field. At each point of the solution curve, the slope matches the direction field. A different initial condition gives a different solution curve (Figure 7.33). The collection of solution curves for several different initial conditions is a representation of the general solution of the equation.

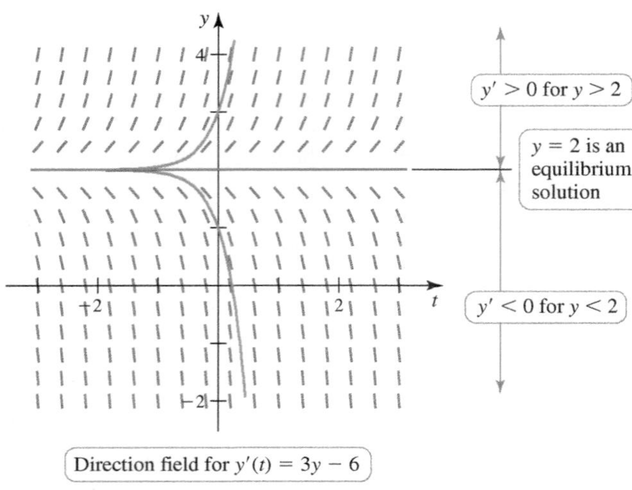

Figure 7.34

EXAMPLE 7 Direction field for a linear equation Sketch the direction field for the first-order linear equation $y'(t) = 3y - 6$. For what initial conditions at $t = 0$ are the solutions increasing? Decreasing?

SOLUTION Notice that $y'(t) = 0$ when $y = 2$. Therefore, the direction field has horizontal line segments when $y = 2$. The line $y = 2$ corresponds to an *equilibrium solution*, a solution that is constant in time: If the initial condition is $y(0) = 2$, then the solution is $y = 2$ for $t \geq 0$.

We also see that $y'(t) > 0$ when $y > 2$. Therefore, the direction field has small line segments with positive slopes above the line $y = 2$. When $y < 2$, $y'(t) < 0$, which means the direction field has small line segments with negative slopes below the line $y = 2$ (Figure 7.34).

The direction field shows that if the initial condition satisfies $y(0) > 2$, the resulting solution increases for $t \geq 0$. If the initial condition satisfies $y(0) < 2$, the resulting solution decreases for $t \geq 0$.

Related Exercises 43–48 ◀

QUICK CHECK 5 In Example 7, describe the behavior of the solution that results from the initial condition (a) $y(-1) = 3$ and (b) $y(-2) = 0$. ◀

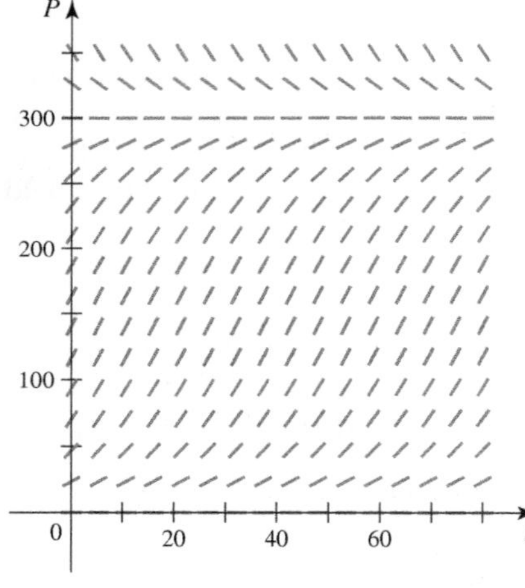

Figure 7.35

➤ The constant solutions $P = 0$ and $P = 300$ are equilibrium solutions. The solution $P = 0$ is an *unstable* equilibrium because nearby solution curves move away from $P = 0$. By contrast, the solution $P = 300$ is a stable equilibrium because nearby solution curves are attracted to $P = 300$.

EXAMPLE 8 Direction field for the logistic equation Consider the logistic equation of Example 6,

$$\frac{dP}{dt} = 0.1P\left(1 - \frac{P}{300}\right) \quad \text{for} \quad t \geq 0,$$

and its direction field (Figure 7.35). Sketch the solution curves corresponding to each of the initial conditions $y(0) = 50$, $y(0) = 150$, and $y(0) = 350$.

SOLUTION A few preliminary observations are useful. Because P represents a population, we assume that $P \geq 0$.

- Notice that $\frac{dP}{dt} = 0$ when $P = 0$ or $P = 300$. Therefore, if the initial population is $P = 0$ or $P = 300$, then $\frac{dP}{dt} = 0$ for all $t \geq 0$, and the solution is constant. For this reason, the direction field has horizontal line segments when $P = 0$ and $P = 300$.
- The equation implies that $dP/dt > 0$ when $0 < P < 300$. Therefore, the direction field has positive slopes, and the solutions are increasing for $t \geq 0$ and $0 < P < 300$.
- The equation also implies that $dP/dt < 0$ when $P > 300$. Therefore, the direction field has negative slopes, and the solutions are decreasing for $t \geq 0$ and $P > 300$.

Figure 7.36 shows the direction field with three solution curves corresponding to three different initial conditions. The horizontal line $P = 300$ corresponds to the carrying capacity of the population. We see that if the initial population is less than 300, the resulting solution increases to the carrying capacity from below. If the initial population is greater than 300, the resulting solution decreases to the carrying capacity from above.

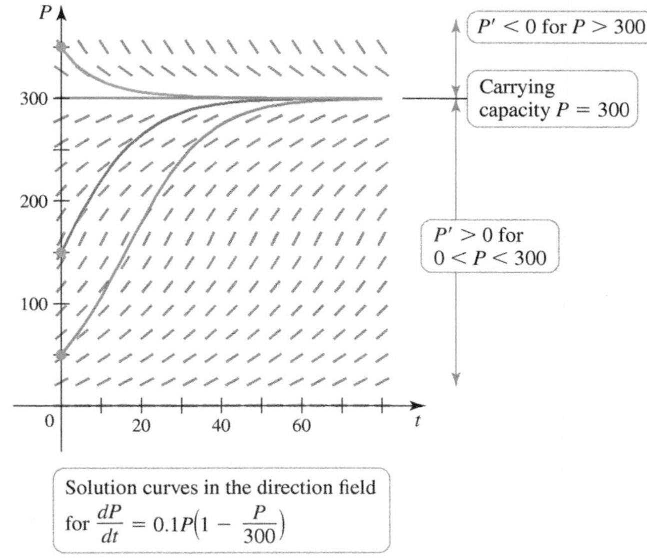

Figure 7.36

Related Exercises 43–48 ◀

Direction fields are useful for at least two reasons. As shown in Example 7, a direction field provides valuable qualitative information about the solutions of a differential equation *without solving the equation*. In addition, it turns out that direction fields are the basis for many computer-based methods for approximating solutions of a differential equation. The computer begins with the initial condition and advances the solution in small steps, always following the direction field at each time step.

SECTION 7.9 EXERCISES

Review Questions

1. What is the order of $y''(t) + 9y(t) = 10$?

2. Is $y''(t) + 9y(t) = 10$ linear or nonlinear?

3. How many arbitrary constants appear in the general solution of $y''(t) + 9y(t) = 10$?

4. If the general solution of a differential equation is $y = Ce^{-3t} + 10$, what is the solution that satisfies the initial condition $y(0) = 5$?

5. What is a separable first-order differential equation?

6. Is the equation $t^2y'(t) = (t + 4)/y^2$ separable?

7. Explain how to solve a separable differential equation of the form $g(y)\,y'(t) = h(t)$.

8. Explain how to sketch the direction field of the equation $y'(t) = F(t, y)$, where F is given.

Basic Skills

9–12. Verifying general solutions *Verify that the given function y is a solution of the differential equation that follows it. Assume that C, C_1, and C_2 are arbitrary constants.*

9. $y = Ce^{-5t}$; $y'(t) + 5y = 0$

10. $y = Ct^{-3}$; $ty'(t) + 3y = 0$

11. $y = C_1 \sin 4t + C_2 \cos 4t$; $y''(t) + 16y = 0$

12. $y = C_1e^{-x} + C_2e^{x}$; $y''(x) - y = 0$

13–16. Verifying solutions of initial value problems *Verify that the given function y is a solution of the initial value problem that follows it.*

13. $y = 16e^{2t} - 10$; $y'(t) - 2y = 20$, $y(0) = 6$

14. $y = 8t^6 - 3$; $ty'(t) - 6y = 18$, $y(1) = 5$

15. $y = -3 \cos 3t$; $y''(t) + 9y = 0$, $y(0) = -3$, $y'(0) = 0$

16. $y = \frac{1}{4}(e^{2x} - e^{-2x})$; $y''(x) - 4y = 0$, $y(0) = 0$, $y'(0) = 1$

17–20. Warm-up initial value problems *Solve the following problems.*

17. $y'(t) = 3t^2 - 4t + 10$, $y(0) = 20$

18. $\dfrac{dy}{dt} = 8e^{-4t} + 1$, $y(0) = 5$

19. $y'(t) = (2t^2 + 4)/t$, $y(1) = 2$

20. $\dfrac{dy}{dx} = 3 \cos 2x + 2 \sin 3x$, $y(\pi/2) = 8$

21–24. First-order linear equations *Find the general solution of the following equations.*

21. $y'(t) = 3y - 4$

22. $\dfrac{dy}{dx} = -y + 2$

23. $y'(x) = -2y - 4$

24. $\dfrac{dy}{dt} = 2y + 6$

25–28. Initial value problems *Solve the following problems.*

25. $y'(t) = 3y - 6,\ y(0) = 9$

26. $\dfrac{dy}{dx} = -y + 2,\ y(0) = -2$

27. $y'(t) = -2y - 4,\ y(0) = 0$

28. $\dfrac{du}{dx} = 2u + 6,\ u(1) = 6$

T 29. Intravenous drug dosing The amount of drug in the blood of a patient (in mg) due to an intravenous line is governed by the initial value problem

$$y'(t) = -0.02y + 3, \quad y(0) = 0 \qquad \text{for } t \geq 0,$$

where t is measured in hours.

a. Find and graph the solution of the initial value problem.
b. What is the steady-state level of the drug?
c. When does the drug level reach 90% of the steady-state value?

T 30. Fish harvesting A fish hatchery has 500 fish at time $t = 0$, when harvesting begins at a rate of b fish/yr, where $b > 0$. The fish population is modeled by the initial value problem

$$y'(t) = 0.1y - b, \quad y(0) = 500 \qquad \text{for } t \geq 0,$$

where t is measured in years.

a. Find the fish population for $t \geq 0$ in terms of the harvesting rate b.
b. Graph the solution in the case that $b = 40$ fish/yr. Describe the solution.
c. Graph the solution in the case that $b = 60$ fish/yr. Describe the solution.

31–34. Separable differential equations *Find the general solution of the following equations.*

31. $\dfrac{dy}{dt} = \dfrac{3t^2}{y}$

32. $\dfrac{dy}{dx} = y(x^2 + 1)$, where $y > 0$

33. $y'(t) = e^{y/2} \sin t$

34. $x^2 \dfrac{dw}{dx} = \sqrt{w}(3x + 1)$

35–40. Separable differential equations *Determine whether the following equations are separable. If so, solve the given initial value problem.*

35. $\dfrac{dy}{dt} = ty + 2,\ y(1) = 2$

36. $y'(t) = y(4t^3 + 1),\ y(0) = 4$

37. $y'(t) = \dfrac{e^t}{2y},\ y(\ln 2) = 1$

38. $(\sec x)\, y'(x) = y^3,\ y(0) = 3$

39. $\dfrac{dy}{dx} = e^{x-y},\ y(0) = \ln 3$

40. $y'(t) = 2e^{3y-t},\ y(0) = 0$

T 41. Logistic equation for a population A community of hares on an island has a population of 50 when observations begin at $t = 0$. The population for $t \geq 0$ is modeled by the initial value problem

$$\frac{dP}{dt} = 0.08P\left(1 - \frac{P}{200}\right), \qquad P(0) = 50.$$

a. Find and graph the solution of the initial value problem.
b. What is the steady-state population?

T 42. Logistic equation for an epidemic When an infected person is introduced into a closed and otherwise healthy community, the number of people who become infected with the disease (in the absence of any intervention) may be modeled by the logistic equation

$$\frac{dP}{dt} = kP\left(1 - \frac{P}{A}\right), \qquad P(0) = P_0,$$

where k is a positive infection rate, A is the number of people in the community, and P_0 is the number of infected people at $t = 0$. The model assumes no recovery or intervention.

a. Find the solution of the initial value problem in terms of k, A, and P_0.
b. Graph the solution in the case that $k = 0.025$, $A = 300$, and $P_0 = 1$.
c. For fixed values of k and A, describe the long-term behavior of the solutions for any P_0 with $0 < P_0 < A$.

43–44. Direction fields *A differential equation and its direction field are given. Sketch a graph of the solution that results with each initial condition.*

43. $y'(t) = \dfrac{t^2}{y^2 + 1}$,
$y(0) = -2$ and
$y(-2) = 0$

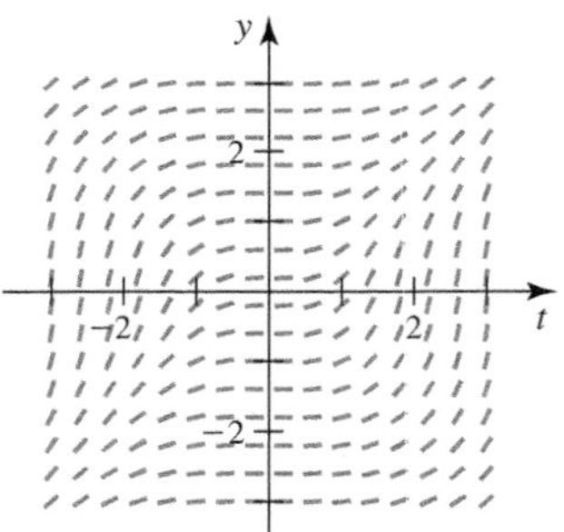

44. $y'(t) = \dfrac{\sin t}{y}$,
$y(-2) = -2$ and
$y(-2) = 2$

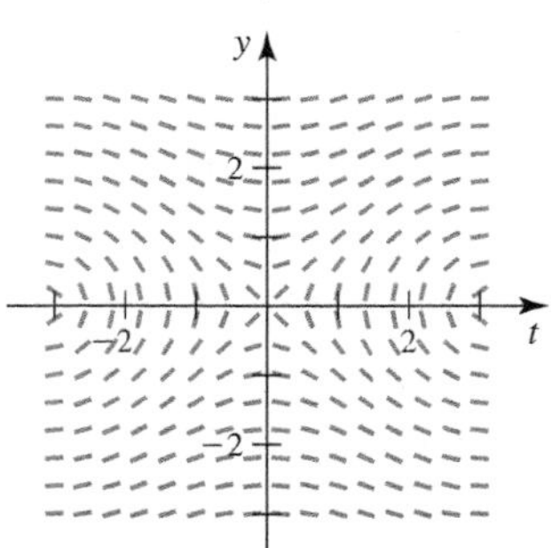

45. Matching direction fields Match equations a–d with the direction fields A–D.

a. $y'(t) = t/2$
b. $y'(t) = y/2$
c. $y'(t) = (t^2 + y^2)/2$
d. $y'(t) = y/t$

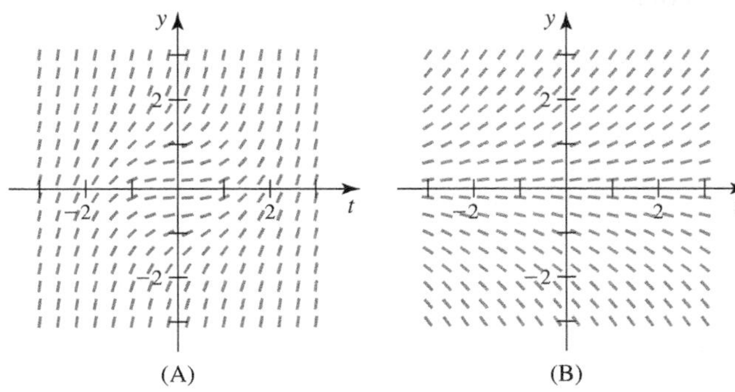

(A) (B)

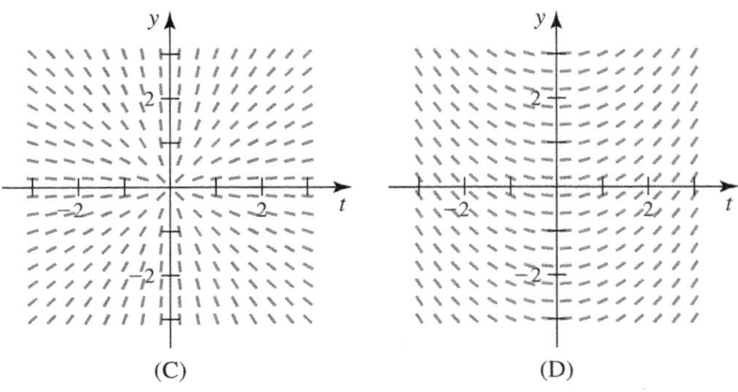

(C) (D)

46–48. Sketching direction fields *Use the window $[-2, 2] \times [-2, 2]$ to sketch a direction field for the following equations. Then sketch the solution curve that corresponds to the given initial condition.*

46. $y'(t) = y - 3,\ y(0) = 1$

47. $y'(x) = \sin x,\ y(-2) = 2$

48. $y'(t) = \sin y,\ y(-2) = \frac{1}{2}$

Further Explorations

49. Explain why or why not Determine whether the following statements are true and give an explanation or counterexample.

a. The general solution of $y'(t) = 20y$ is $y = e^{20t}$.
b. The functions $y = 2e^{-2t}$ and $y = 10e^{-2t}$ do not both satisfy the differential equation $y' + 2y = 0$.
c. The equation $y'(t) = ty + 2y + 2t + 4$ is not separable.
d. A solution of $y'(t) = 2\sqrt{y}$ is $y = (t + 1)^2$.

50–55. Equilibrium solutions *A differential equation of the form $y'(t) = F(y)$ is said to be* ***autonomous*** *(the function F depends only on y). The constant function $y = y_0$ is an equilibrium solution of the equation provided $F(y_0) = 0$ (because then $y'(t) = 0$, and the solution remains constant for all t). Note that equilibrium solutions correspond to horizontal line segments in the direction field. Note also that for autonomous equations, the direction field is independent of t. Consider the following equations.*

a. *Find all equilibrium solutions.*
b. *Sketch the direction field on either side of the equilibrium solutions for $t \geq 0$.*
c. *Sketch the solution curve that corresponds to the initial condition $y(0) = 1$.*

50. $y'(t) = 2y + 4$

51. $y'(t) = y^2$

52. $y'(t) = y(2 - y)$

53. $y'(t) = y(y - 3)$

54. $y'(t) = \sin y$

55. $y'(t) = y(y - 3)(y + 2)$

56–59. Solving initial value problems *Solve the following problems using the method of your choice.*

56. $u'(t) = 4u - 2,\ u(0) = 4$

57. $\dfrac{dp}{dt} = \dfrac{p + 1}{t^2},\ p(1) = 3$

58. $\dfrac{dz}{dx} = \dfrac{z^2}{1 + x^2},\ z(0) = \dfrac{1}{6}$

59. $w'(t) = 2t\cos^2 w,\ w(0) = \pi/4$

60. Optimal harvesting rate Let $y(t)$ be the population of a species that is being harvested. Consider the harvesting model $y'(t) = 0.008y - h$, $y(0) = y_0$, where $h > 0$ is the annual harvesting rate and y_0 is the initial population of the species.

a. If $y_0 = 2000$, what harvesting rate should be used to maintain a constant population of $y = 2000$ for $t \geq 0$?
b. If the harvesting rate is $h = 200$/year, what initial population ensures a constant population for $t \geq 0$?

Applications

T **61. Logistic equation for spread of rumors** Sociologists model the spread of rumors using logistic equations. The key assumption is that at any given time, a fraction y of the population, where $0 \leq y \leq 1$, knows the rumor, while the remaining fraction $1 - y$ does not. Furthermore, the rumor spreads by interactions between those who know the rumor and those who do not. The number of such interactions is proportional to $y(1 - y)$. Therefore, the equation that models the spread of the rumor is $y'(t) = ky(1 - y)$, where k is a positive real number. The fraction of people who initially know the rumor is $y(0) = y_0$, where $0 < y_0 < 1$.

a. Solve this initial value problem and give the solution in terms of k and y_0.
b. Assume $k = 0.3$ weeks^{-1} and graph the solution for $y_0 = 0.1$ and $y_0 = 0.7$.
c. Describe and interpret the long-term behavior of the rumor function for any $0 < y_0 < 1$.

T **62. Free fall** An object in free fall may be modeled by assuming that the only forces at work are the gravitational force and resistance (friction due to the medium in which the object falls). By Newton's second law (mass $\times$ acceleration $=$ the sum of the external forces), the velocity of the object satisfies the differential equation

$$\underbrace{m}_{\text{mass}} \cdot \underbrace{v'(t)}_{\text{acceleration}} = \underbrace{mg + f(v)}_{\text{external forces}},$$

where f is a function that models the resistance and the positive direction is downward. One common assumption (often used for motion in air) is that $f(v) = -kv^2$, where $k > 0$ is a drag coefficient.

a. Show that the equation can be written in the form $v'(t) = g - av^2$, where $a = k/m$.
b. For what (positive) value of v is $v'(t) = 0$? (This equilibrium solution is called the **terminal velocity**.)
c. Find the solution of this separable equation assuming $v(0) = 0$ and $0 < v(t)^2 < g/a$, for $t \geq 0$.
d. Graph the solution found in part (c) with $g = 9.8\ \text{m/s}^2$, $m = 1$ kg, and $k = 0.1$ kg/m, and verify that the terminal velocity agrees with the value found in part (b).

T **63. Free fall** Using the background given in Exercise 62, assume the resistance is given by $f(v) = -Rv$, where $R > 0$ is a drag coefficient (an assumption often made for a heavy medium such as water or oil).

a. Show that the equation can be written in the form $v'(t) = g - bv$, where $b = R/m$.
b. For what (positive) value of v is $v'(t) = 0$? (This equilibrium solution is called the **terminal velocity**.)
c. Find the solution of this separable equation assuming $v(0) = 0$ and $0 < v < g/b$.
d. Graph the solution found in part (c) with $g = 9.8\text{ m/s}^2$, $m = 1$ kg, and $R = 0.1$ kg/s, and verify that the terminal velocity agrees with the value found in part (b).

T **64. Torricelli's Law** An open cylindrical tank initially filled with water drains through a hole in the bottom of the tank according to Torricelli's Law (see figure). If $h(t)$ is the depth of water in the tank for $t \geq 0$, then Torricelli's Law implies $h'(t) = 2k\sqrt{h}$, where k is a constant that includes the acceleration due to gravity, the radius of the tank, and the radius of the drain. Assume that the initial depth of the water is $h(0) = H$.

a. Find the general solution of the equation.
b. Find the solution in the case that $k = 0.1$ and $H = 0.5$ m.
c. In general, how long does it take the tank to drain in terms of k and H?

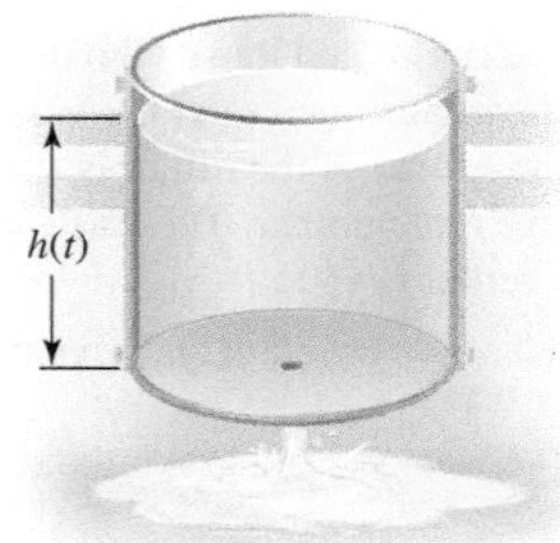

T **65. Chemical rate equations** The reaction of chemical compounds can often be modeled by differential equations. Let $y(t)$ be the concentration of a substance in reaction for $t \geq 0$ (typical units of y are moles/L). The change in the concentration of the substance, under appropriate conditions, is $\dfrac{dy}{dt} = -ky^n$, where $k > 0$ is a rate constant and the positive integer n is the order of the reaction.

a. Show that for a first-order reaction $(n = 1)$, the concentration obeys an exponential decay law.
b. Solve the initial value problem for a second-order reaction $(n = 2)$ assuming $y(0) = y_0$.
c. Graph and compare the concentration for a first-order and second-order reaction with $k = 0.1$ and $y_0 = 1$.

T **66. Tumor growth** The growth of cancer tumors may be modeled by the Gompertz growth equation. Let $M(t)$ be the mass of the tumor for $t \geq 0$. The relevant initial value problem is

$$\frac{dM}{dt} = -aM\ln\frac{M}{K}, \qquad M(0) = M_0,$$

where a and K are positive constants and $0 < M_0 < K$.

a. Graph the growth rate function $R(M) = -aM\ln\dfrac{M}{K}$ assuming $a = 1$ and $K = 4$. For what values of M is the growth rate positive? For what value of M is the growth rate a maximum?
b. Solve the initial value problem and graph the solution for $a = 1$, $K = 4$, and $M_0 = 1$. Describe the growth pattern of the tumor. Is the growth unbounded? If not, what is the limiting size of the tumor?
c. In the general equation, what is the meaning of K?

T **67. Endowment model** An endowment is an investment account in which the balance ideally remains constant and withdrawals are made on the interest earned by the account. Such an account may be modeled by the initial value problem $B'(t) = aB - m$ for $t \geq 0$, with $B(0) = B_0$. The constant a reflects the annual interest rate, m is the annual rate of withdrawal, and B_0 is the initial balance in the account.

a. Solve the initial value problem with $a = 0.05$, $m = \$1000/\text{yr}$, and $B_0 = \$15{,}000$. Does the balance in the account increase or decrease?
b. If $a = 0.05$ and $B_0 = \$50{,}000$, what is the annual withdrawal rate m that ensures a constant balance in the account? What is the constant balance?

Additional Exercises

68. Solution of the logistic equation Consider the solution of the logistic equation in Example 6.

a. From the general solution $\ln\left|\dfrac{P}{300 - P}\right| = 0.1t + C$, show that the initial condition $P(0) = 50$ implies that $C = -\ln 5$.
b. Solve for P and show that $P = \dfrac{300}{1 + 5e^{-0.1t}}$.

69. Direction field analysis Consider the general first-order initial value problem $y'(t) = ay + b$, $y(0) = y_0$, for $t \geq 0$, where a, b, and y_0 are real numbers.

a. Explain why $y = -b/a$ is an equilibrium solution and corresponds to horizontal line segments in the direction field.
b. Draw a representative direction field in the case that $a > 0$. Show that if $y_0 > -b/a$, then the solution increases for $t \geq 0$ and if $y_0 < -b/a$, then the solution decreases for $t \geq 0$.
c. Draw a representative direction field in the case that $a < 0$. Show that if $y_0 > -b/a$, then the solution decreases for $t \geq 0$ and if $y_0 < -b/a$, then the solution increases for $t \geq 0$.

70. Concavity of solutions Consider the logistic equation

$$P'(t) = 0.1P\left(1 - \frac{P}{300}\right), \text{ for } t \geq 0,$$

with $P(0) > 0$. Show that the solution curve is concave down for $150 < P < 300$ and concave up for $0 < P < 150$ and $P > 300$.

QUICK CHECK ANSWERS

1. The equation is first order and linear. **3.** The solution is $y(t) = 16e^{3t} - 2$. **4.** $y^3y'(t) = t^2 + 1$ **5. a.** Solution increases for $t \geq -1$. **b.** Solution decreases for $t \geq -2$. ◄

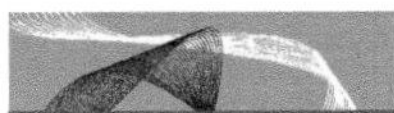

CHAPTER 7 REVIEW EXERCISES

1. **Explain why or why not** Determine whether the following statements are true and give an explanation or counterexample.
   a. The integral $\int x^2 e^{2x}\,dx$ can be evaluated using integration by parts.
   b. To evaluate the integral $\int \frac{dx}{\sqrt{x^2 - 100}}$ analytically, it is best to use partial fractions.
   c. One computer algebra system produces $\int 2\sin x\cos x\,dx = \sin^2 x$. Another computer algebra system produces $\int 2\sin x\cos x\,dx = -\cos^2 x$. One computer algebra system is wrong (apart from a missing constant of integration).
   d. $\int 2\sin x\cos x\,dx = -\frac{1}{2}\cos 2x + C$.
   e. The best approach to evaluating $\int \frac{x^3 + 1}{3x^2}\,dx$ is to use the change of variables $u = x^3 + 1$.

2–7. Basic integration techniques *Use the methods introduced in Section 7.1 to evaluate the following integrals.*

2. $\int \cos\left(\frac{x}{2} + \frac{\pi}{3}\right) dx$
3. $\int \frac{3x}{\sqrt{x + 4}}\,dx$
4. $\int \frac{2 - \sin 2\theta}{\cos^2 2\theta}\,d\theta$
5. $\int_{-2}^{1} \frac{3}{x^2 + 4x + 13}\,dx$
6. $\int \frac{x^3 + 3x^2 + 1}{x^3 + 1}\,dx$
7. $\int \frac{\sqrt{t - 1}}{2t}\,dt$ (*Hint:* Let $u = \sqrt{t - 1}$.)

8–11. Integration by parts *Use integration by parts to evaluate the following integrals.*

8. $\int_{-1}^{\ln 2} \frac{3t}{e^t}\,dt$
9. $\int \frac{x}{2\sqrt{x + 2}}\,dx$
10. $\int x\tan^{-1} x\,dx$
11. $\int x\sinh x\,dx$

12–17. Trigonometric integrals *Evaluate the following trigonometric integrals.*

12. $\int_{\pi}^{2\pi} \cot\frac{x}{3}\,dx$
13. $\int_0^{\pi/4} \cos^5 2x\sin^2 2x\,dx$
14. $\int \tan^3\theta\,d\theta$
15. $\int \frac{\sin^4 t}{\cos^6 t}\,dt$
16. $\int \csc^2 x\cot x\,dx$
17. $\int \tan^3\theta\sec^3\theta\,d\theta$

18–21. Trigonometric substitutions *Evaluate the following integrals using a trigonometric substitution.*

18. $\int \frac{\sqrt{1 - x^2}}{x}\,dx$
19. $\int_{\sqrt{2}}^{2} \frac{\sqrt{x^2 - 1}}{x}\,dx$
20. $\int \frac{w^3}{\sqrt{4 - w^2}}\,dw$
21. $\int \frac{x^3}{\sqrt{x^2 + 4}}\,dx$

22–25. Partial fractions *Use partial fractions to evaluate the following integrals.*

22. $\int \frac{8x + 5}{2x^2 + 3x + 1}\,dx$
23. $\int \frac{2x^2 + 7x + 4}{x^3 + 2x^2 + 2x}\,dx$
24. $\int_{-1/2}^{1/2} \frac{u^2 + 1}{u^2 - 1}\,du$
25. $\int \frac{3x^3 + 4x^2 + 6x}{(x + 1)^2(x^2 + 4)}\,dx$

26–29. Table of integrals *Use a table of integrals to evaluate the following integrals.*

26. $\int x(2x + 3)^5\,dx$
27. $\int \frac{dx}{x\sqrt{4x - 6}}$
28. $\int_0^{\pi/2} \frac{d\theta}{1 + \sin 2\theta}$
29. $\int \sec^5 x\,dx$

30–31. Approximations *Use a computer algebra system to approximate the value of the following integrals.*

30. $\int_1^{\sqrt{e}} x^3\ln^3 x\,dx$
31. $\int_{-1}^{1} e^{-2x^2}\,dx$

T 32. **Errors in numerical integration** Let $I = \int_{-1}^{2}(x^7 - 3x^5 - x^2 + \frac{7}{8})\,dx$ and note that $I = 0$.
   a. Complete the following table with Trapezoid Rule $(T(n))$ and Midpoint Rule $(M(n))$ approximations to I for various values of n.
   b. Fill in the error columns with the absolute errors in the approximations in part (a).
   c. How do the errors in $T(n)$ decrease as n doubles in size?
   d. How do the errors in $M(n)$ decrease as n doubles in size?

n	$T(n)$	$M(n)$	Abs error in $T(n)$	Abs error in $M(n)$
4				
8				
16				
32				
64				

T 33. **Numerical integration methods** Let $I = \int_0^3 x^2\,dx = 9$ and consider the Trapezoid Rule $(T(n))$ and the Midpoint Rule $(M(n))$ approximations to I.
   a. Compute $T(6)$ and $M(6)$.
   b. Compute $T(12)$ and $M(12)$.

34–37. Improper integrals *Evaluate the following integrals.*

34. $\int_{-\infty}^{-1} \frac{dx}{(x - 1)^4}$
35. $\int_0^{\infty} xe^{-x}\,dx$
36. $\int_0^{\pi} \sec^2 x\,dx$
37. $\int_0^3 \frac{dx}{\sqrt{9 - x^2}}$

38–63. Miscellaneous Integrals *Evaluate the following integrals analytically.*

38. $\int \frac{x^2 - 4}{x + 4}\, dx$

39. $\int \frac{d\theta}{1 + \cos\theta}$

40. $\int x^2 \cos x\, dx$

41. $\int e^x \sin x\, dx$

42. $\int_1^e x^2 \ln x\, dx$

43. $\int \cos^2 4\theta\, d\theta$

44. $\int \sin 3x \cos^6 3x\, dx$

45. $\int \sec^5 z \tan z\, dz$

46. $\int_0^{\pi/2} \cos^4 x\, dx$

47. $\int_0^{\pi/6} \sin^5 \theta\, d\theta$

48. $\int \tan^4 u\, du$

49. $\int \frac{dx}{\sqrt{4 - x^2}}$

50. $\int \frac{dx}{\sqrt{9x^2 - 25}},\ x > \frac{5}{3}$

51. $\int \frac{dy}{y^2\sqrt{9 - y^2}}$

52. $\int_0^{\sqrt{3}/2} \frac{x^2}{(1 - x^2)^{3/2}}\, dx$

53. $\int_0^{\sqrt{3}/2} \frac{4}{9 + 4x^2}\, dx$

54. $\int \frac{(1 - u^2)^{5/2}}{u^8}\, du$

55. $\int \operatorname{sech}^2 x \sinh x\, dx$

56. $\int x^2 \cosh x\, dx$

57. $\int_0^{\ln(\sqrt{3}+2)} \frac{\cosh x}{\sqrt{4 - \sinh^2 x}}\, dx$

58. $\int \sinh^{-1} x\, dx$

59. $\int \frac{dx}{x^2 - 2x - 15}$

60. $\int \frac{dx}{x^3 - 2x^2}$

61. $\int_0^1 \frac{dy}{(y + 1)(y^2 + 1)}$

62. $\int_0^\infty \frac{6x}{1 + x^6}\, dx$

63. $\int_0^2 \frac{dx}{\sqrt[3]{|x - 1|}}$

64–69. Preliminary work *Make a change of variables or use an algebra step before evaluating the following integrals.*

64. $\int_{-1}^1 \frac{dx}{x^2 + 2x + 5}$

65. $\int \frac{dx}{x^2 - x - 2}$

66. $\int \frac{3x^2 + x - 3}{x^2 - 1}\, dx$

67. $\int \frac{2x^2 - 4x}{x^2 - 4}\, dx$

68. $\int_{1/12}^{1/4} \frac{dx}{\sqrt{x}(1 + 4x)}$

69. $\int \frac{e^{2t}}{(1 + e^{4t})^{3/2}}\, dt$

70. **Three ways** Evaluate $\int \frac{dx}{4 - x^2}$ using (i) partial fractions, (ii) a trigonometric substitution, and (iii) Theorem 6.12 (Section 6.10). Then show that the results are consistent.

71–74. Volumes *The region R is bounded by the curve $y = \ln x$ and the x-axis on the interval $[1, e]$. Find the volume of the solid that is generated when R is revolved in the following ways.*

71. About the x-axis

72. About the y-axis

73. About the line $x = 1$

74. About the line $y = 1$

75. **Comparing volumes** Let R be the region bounded by the graph of $y = \sin x$ and the x-axis on the interval $[0, \pi]$. Which is greater, the volume of the solid generated when R is revolved about the x-axis or the y-axis?

76. **Comparing areas** Show that the area of the region bounded by the graph of $y = ae^{-ax}$ and the x-axis on the interval $[0, \infty)$ is the same for all values of $a > 0$.

T 77. **Zero log integral** It is evident from the graph of $y = \ln x$ that for every real number a with $0 < a < 1$, there is a unique real number $b = g(a)$ with $b > 1$, such that $\int_a^b \ln x\, dx = 0$ (the net area bounded by the graph of $y = \ln x$ on $[a, b]$ is 0).

a. Approximate $b = g(\frac{1}{2})$.
b. Approximate $b = g(\frac{1}{3})$.
c. Find the equation satisfied by all pairs of numbers (a, b) such that $b = g(a)$.
d. Is g an increasing or decreasing function of a? Explain.

78. **Arc length** Find the length of the curve $y = \ln x$ on the interval $[1, e^2]$.

79. **Average velocity** Find the average velocity of a projectile whose velocity over the interval $0 \le t \le \pi$ is given by $v(t) = 10 \sin 3t$.

80. **Comparing distances** Starting at the same time and place ($t = 0$ and $s = 0$), the velocity of car A (in mi/hr) is given by $u(t) = 40/(t + 1)$ and the velocity of car B (in mi/hr) is given by $v(t) = 40e^{-t/2}$.

a. After $t = 2$ hr, which car has traveled farther?
b. After $t = 3$ hr, which car has traveled farther?
c. If allowed to travel indefinitely ($t \to \infty$), which car will travel a finite distance?

81. **Traffic flow** When data from a traffic study are fitted to a curve, the flow rate of cars past a point on a highway is approximated by $R(t) = 800te^{-t/2}$ cars/hr. How many cars pass the measuring site during the time interval $0 \le t \le 4$?

T 82. **Comparing integrals** Graph the functions $f(x) = \pm 1/x^2$, $g(x) = (\cos x)/x^2$, and $h(x) = (\cos^2 x)/x^2$. Without evaluating integrals and knowing that $\int_1^\infty f(x)\, dx$ has a finite value, determine whether $\int_1^\infty g(x)\, dx$ and $\int_1^\infty h(x)\, dx$ have finite values.

83. **A family of logarithm integrals** Let $I(p) = \int_1^e \frac{\ln x}{x^p}\, dx$, where p is a real number.

a. Find an expression for $I(p)$, for all real values of p.
b. Evaluate $\lim_{p\to\infty} I(p)$ and $\lim_{p\to-\infty} I(p)$.
c. For what value of p is $I(p) = 1$?

84. **Arc length** Find the length of the curve

$$y = \frac{x}{2}\sqrt{3 - x^2} + \frac{3}{2}\sin^{-1}\frac{x}{\sqrt{3}} \text{ from } x = 0 \text{ to } x = 1.$$

T 85. **Best approximation** Let $I = \int_0^1 \frac{x^2 - x}{\ln x}\, dx$. Use any method you choose to find a good approximation to I. You may use the facts that $\lim_{x\to 0^+} \frac{x^2 - x}{\ln x} = 0$ and $\lim_{x\to 1} \frac{x^2 - x}{\ln x} = 1$.

T 86. **Numerical integration** Use a calculator to determine the integer n that satisfies $\int_0^{1/2} \frac{\ln(1 + 2x)}{x}\, dx = \frac{\pi^2}{n}$.

T **87. Numerical integration** Use a calculator to determine the integer n that satisfies $\int_0^1 \frac{\sin^{-1}x}{x}\,dx = \frac{\pi \ln 2}{n}$.

88. Two worthy integrals

a. Let $I(a) = \int_0^\infty \frac{dx}{(1 + x^a)(1 + x^2)}$, where a is a real number. Evaluate $I(a)$ and show that its value is independent of a. (*Hint:* Split the integral into two integrals over $[0, 1]$ and $[1, \infty)$; then use a change of variables to convert the second integral into an integral over $[0, 1]$.)

b. Let f be any positive continuous function on $[0, \pi/2]$. Evaluate $\int_0^{\pi/2} \frac{f(\cos x)}{f(\cos x) + f(\sin x)}\,dx$. (*Hint:* Use the identity $\cos(\pi/2 - x) = \sin x$.)

(*Source: Mathematics Magazine* 81, 2, Apr 2008)

T **89. Comparing volumes** Let R be the region bounded by $y = \ln x$, the x-axis, and the line $x = a$, where $a > 1$.

a. Find the volume $V_1(a)$ of the solid generated when R is revolved about the x-axis (as a function of a).

b. Find the volume $V_2(a)$ of the solid generated when R is revolved about the y-axis (as a function of a).

c. Graph V_1 and V_2. For what values of $a > 1$ is $V_1(a) > V_2(a)$?

90. Equal volumes

a. Let R be the region bounded by the graph of $f(x) = x^{-p}$ and the x-axis, for $x \geq 1$. Let V_1 and V_2 be the volumes of the solids generated when R is revolved about the x-axis and the y-axis, respectively, if they exist. For what values of p (if any) is $V_1 = V_2$?

b. Repeat part (a) on the interval $(0, 1]$.

91. Equal volumes Let R_1 be the region bounded by the graph of $y = e^{-ax}$ and the x-axis on the interval $[0, b]$ where $a > 0$ and $b > 0$. Let R_2 be the region bounded by the graph of $y = e^{-ax}$ and the x-axis on the interval $[b, \infty)$. Let V_1 and V_2 be the volumes of the solids generated when R_1 and R_2 are revolved about the x-axis. Find and graph the relationship between a and b for which $V_1 = V_2$.

92–96. Initial value problems *Solve the following initial value problems.*

92. $y'(t) + 3y = 0, y(0) = 6$

93. $y'(t) = 2y + 4,\ y(0) = 8$

94. $\frac{dy}{dt} = \frac{2ty}{\ln y},\ y(2) = e$

95. $y'(t) = \frac{t + 1}{2ty},\ y(1) = 4$

96. $\frac{dy}{dt} = \sqrt{y}\sin t,\ y(0) = 4$

97. Limit of a solution Evaluate $\lim_{t\to\infty} y(t)$, where y is the solution of the initial value problem $y'(t) = \frac{\sec y}{t^2}, y(1) = 0$.

98–100. Sketching direction fields *Use the window* $[-2, 2] \times [-2, 2]$ *to sketch a direction field for the given differential equation. Then sketch the solution curve that corresponds to the given initial condition.*

98. $y'(t) = 3y - 6,\ y(0) = 1$

99. $y'(t) = t^2,\ y(-1) = -1$

100. $y'(t) = y - t,\ y(-2) = \frac{1}{2}$

T **101. Enzyme kinetics** The consumption of a substrate in a reaction involving an enzyme is often modeled using Michaelis-Menton kinetics, which involves the initial value problem $\frac{ds}{dt} = -\frac{Qs}{K + s}$, $s(0) = s_0$, where $s(t)$ is the amount of substrate present at time $t \geq 0$, and Q and K are positive constants. Solve the initial value problem with $Q = 10, K = 5$, and $s_0 = 50$. Notice that the solution can be expressed explicitly only with t as a function of s. Graph the solution and describe how s behaves as $t \to \infty$. (See the Guided Project *Enzyme kinetics*.)

102. Investment model An investment account, which earns interest and has regular deposits, can be modeled by the initial value problem $B'(t) = aB + m$ for $t \geq 0$, with $B(0) = B_0$. The constant a reflects the monthly interest rate, m is the rate of monthly deposits, and B_0 is the initial balance in the account. Solve the initial value problem with $a = 0.005$, $m =$ \$100/month, and $B_0 =$ \$100. After how many months does the account have a balance of \$7500?

Chapter 7 Guided Projects

Applications of the material in this chapter and related topics can be found in the following Guided Projects. For additional information, see the Preface.

- Cooling coffee
- Euler's method for differential equations
- Terminal velocity
- A pursuit problem
- How long will your iPod last?
- Simpson's rule
- Predator-prey models
- Period of the pendulum
- Logistic growth
- Mercator projections

8

Sequences and Infinite Series

Chapter Preview This chapter covers topics that lie at the foundation of calculus—indeed, at the foundation of mathematics. The first task is to make a clear distinction between a *sequence* and an *infinite series*. A sequence is an ordered *list* of numbers, $a_1, a_2, \ldots$, while an infinite series is a *sum* of numbers, $a_1 + a_2 + \cdots$. The idea of convergence to a limit is important for both sequences and series, but convergence is analyzed differently in the two cases. To determine limits of sequences, we use the same tools used for limits of functions at infinity. Convergence of infinite series is a different matter, and we develop the required methods in this chapter. The study of infinite series begins with *geometric series*, which have theoretical importance and are used to answer many practical questions (When is your auto loan paid off? How much antibiotic is in your blood if you take three pills per day?). We then present several tests that are used to determine whether series with positive terms converge. Finally, alternating series, whose terms alternate in sign, are discussed in anticipation of power series in the next chapter.

8.1 An Overview

To understand sequences and series, you must understand how they differ and how they are related. The purposes of this opening section are to introduce sequences and series in concrete terms, and to illustrate both their differences and their relationships with each other.

➤ Keeping with common practice, the terms *series* and *infinite series* are used interchangeably throughout this chapter.

Examples of Sequences

Consider the following *list* of numbers:

$$\{1, 4, 7, 10, 13, 16, \ldots\}.$$

Each number in the list is obtained by adding 3 to the previous number in the list. With this rule, we could extend the list indefinitely.

➤ The dots (. . . , an ellipsis) after the last number of a sequence mean that the list continues indefinitely.

This list is an example of a *sequence*, where each number in the sequence is called a **term** of the sequence. We denote sequences in any of the following forms:

$$\{a_1, a_2, a_3, \ldots, a_n, \ldots\}, \qquad \{a_n\}_{n=1}^{\infty}, \quad \text{or} \quad \{a_n\}.$$

The subscript n that appears in a_n is called an **index**, and it indicates the order of terms in the sequence. The choice of a starting index is arbitrary, but sequences usually begin with $n = 0$ or $n = 1$.

The sequence $\{1, 4, 7, 10, \ldots\}$ can be defined in two ways. First, we have the rule that each term of the sequence is 3 more than the previous term; that is, $a_2 = a_1 + 3$, $a_3 = a_2 + 3$, $a_4 = a_3 + 3$, and so forth. In general, we see that

$$a_1 = 1 \quad \text{and} \quad a_{n+1} = a_n + 3, \qquad \text{for } n = 1, 2, 3, \ldots.$$

This way of defining a sequence is called a *recurrence relation* (or an *implicit formula*). It specifies the initial term of the sequence (in this case, $a_1 = 1$) and gives a general rule for computing the next term of the sequence from previous terms. For example, if you know a_{100}, the recurrence relation can be used to find a_{101}.

Suppose instead you want to find a_{147} directly without computing the first 146 terms of the sequence. The first four terms of the sequence can be written

$$a_1 = 1 + (3 \cdot 0), \qquad a_2 = 1 + (3 \cdot 1), \qquad a_3 = 1 + (3 \cdot 2), \qquad a_4 = 1 + (3 \cdot 3).$$

Observe the pattern: The nth term of the sequence is 1 plus 3 multiplied by $n - 1$, or

$$a_n = 1 + 3(n - 1) = 3n - 2, \qquad \text{for } n = 1, 2, 3, \ldots.$$

QUICK CHECK 1 Find a_{10} for the sequence $\{1, 4, 7, 10, \ldots\}$ using the recurrence relation and then again using the explicit formula for the nth term. ◂

With this *explicit formula*, the nth term of the sequence is determined directly from the value of n. For example, with $n = 147$,

$$\underbrace{a_{147}}_{n} = 3 \cdot \underbrace{147}_{n} - 2 = 439.$$

➤ When defined by an explicit formula $a_n = f(n)$, it is evident that sequences are functions. The domain is generally a subset of the nonnegative integers, and one real number a_n is assigned to each integer n in the domain.

DEFINITION Sequence

A **sequence** $\{a_n\}$ is an ordered list of numbers of the form

$$\{a_1, a_2, a_3, \ldots, a_n, \ldots\}.$$

A sequence may be generated by a **recurrence relation** of the form $a_{n+1} = f(a_n)$, for $n = 1, 2, 3, \ldots$, where a_1 is given. A sequence may also be defined with an **explicit formula** of the form $a_n = f(n)$, for $n = 1, 2, 3, \ldots$.

EXAMPLE 1 **Explicit formulas** Use the explicit formula for $\{a_n\}_{n=1}^{\infty}$ to write the first four terms of each sequence. Sketch a graph of the sequence.

a. $a_n = \dfrac{1}{2^n}$ **b.** $a_n = \dfrac{(-1)^n n}{n^2 + 1}$

SOLUTION

a. Substituting $n = 1, 2, 3, 4, \ldots$ into the explicit formula $a_n = \dfrac{1}{2^n}$, we find that the terms of the sequence are

$$\left\{\frac{1}{2}, \frac{1}{2^2}, \frac{1}{2^3}, \frac{1}{2^4}, \ldots\right\} = \left\{\frac{1}{2}, \frac{1}{4}, \frac{1}{8}, \frac{1}{16}, \ldots\right\}.$$

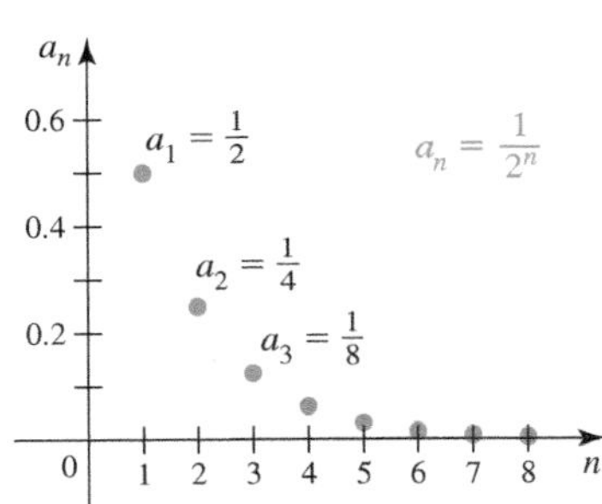

Figure 8.1

The graph of a sequence is the graph of a function that is defined only on a set of integers. In this case, we plot the coordinate pairs (n, a_n), for $n = 1, 2, 3, \ldots$, resulting in a graph consisting of individual points. The graph of the sequence $a_n = \dfrac{1}{2^n}$ suggests that the terms of this sequence approach 0 as n increases (Figure 8.1).

b. Substituting $n = 1, 2, 3, 4, \ldots$ into the explicit formula, the terms of the sequence are

$$\left\{\frac{(-1)^1(1)}{1^2 + 1}, \frac{(-1)^2 2}{2^2 + 1}, \frac{(-1)^3 3}{3^2 + 1}, \frac{(-1)^4 4}{4^2 + 1}, \ldots\right\} = \left\{-\frac{1}{2}, \frac{2}{5}, -\frac{3}{10}, \frac{4}{17}, \ldots\right\}.$$

➤ The "switch" $(-1)^n$ is used frequently to alternate the signs of the terms of sequences and series.

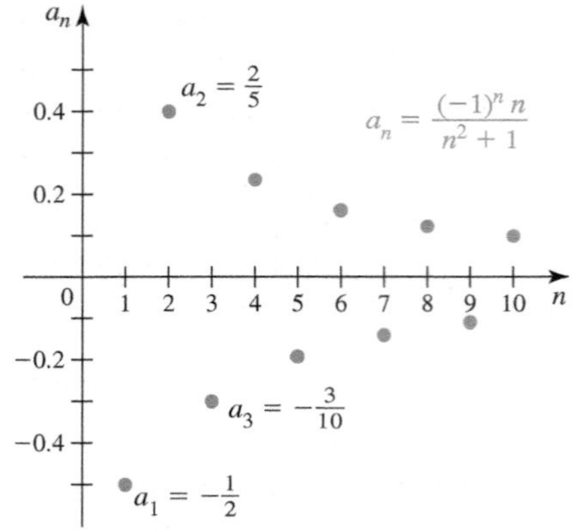

Figure 8.2

From the graph (Figure 8.2), we see that the terms of the sequence alternate in sign and appear to approach 0 as n increases.

Related Exercises 9–16 ◀

EXAMPLE 2 **Recurrence relations** Use the recurrence relation for $\{a_n\}_{n=1}^{\infty}$ to write the first four terms of the sequences

$$a_{n+1} = 2a_n + 1, a_1 = 1 \quad \text{and} \quad a_{n+1} = 2a_n + 1, a_1 = -1.$$

SOLUTION Notice that the recurrence relation is the same for the two sequences; only the first term differs. The first four terms of each of the sequences are as follows.

n	a_n with $a_1 = 1$	a_n with $a_1 = -1$
1	$a_1 = 1$ (given)	$a_1 = -1$ (given)
2	$a_2 = 2a_1 + 1 = 2 \cdot 1 + 1 = 3$	$a_2 = 2a_1 + 1 = 2(-1) + 1 = -1$
3	$a_3 = 2a_2 + 1 = 2 \cdot 3 + 1 = 7$	$a_3 = 2a_2 + 1 = 2(-1) + 1 = -1$
4	$a_4 = 2a_3 + 1 = 2 \cdot 7 + 1 = 15$	$a_4 = 2a_3 + 1 = 2(-1) + 1 = -1$

We see that the terms of the first sequence increase without bound, while all terms of the second sequence are -1. Clearly, the initial term of the sequence may determine the behavior of the entire sequence.

Related Exercises 17–22 ◀

QUICK CHECK 2 Find an explicit formula for the sequence $\{1, 3, 7, 15, \dots\}$ (Example 2). ◀

EXAMPLE 3 **Working with sequences** Consider the following sequences.

a. $\{a_n\} = \{-2, 5, 12, 19, \dots\}$ **b.** $\{b_n\} = \{3, 6, 12, 24, 48, \dots\}$

(i) Find the next two terms of the sequence.
(ii) Find a recurrence relation that generates the sequence.
(iii) Find an explicit formula for the nth term of the sequence.

SOLUTION

a. (i) Each term is obtained by adding 7 to its predecessor. The next two terms are $19 + 7 = 26$ and $26 + 7 = 33$.

(ii) Because each term is seven more than its predecessor, a recurrence relation is

$$a_{n+1} = a_n + 7, a_0 = -2, \qquad \text{for } n = 0, 1, 2, \dots.$$

➤ In Example 3, we chose the starting index $n = 0$. Other choices are possible.

(iii) Notice that $a_0 = -2, a_1 = -2 + (1 \cdot 7)$, and $a_2 = -2 + (2 \cdot 7)$, so an explicit formula is

$$a_n = 7n - 2, \qquad \text{for } n = 0, 1, 2, \dots.$$

b. (i) Each term is obtained by multiplying its predecessor by 2. The next two terms are $48 \cdot 2 = 96$ and $96 \cdot 2 = 192$.

(ii) Because each term is two times its predecessor, a recurrence relation is

$$a_{n+1} = 2a_n, a_0 = 3, \qquad \text{for } n = 0, 1, 2, \dots.$$

(iii) To obtain an explicit formula, note that $a_0 = 3, a_1 = 3(2^1)$, and $a_2 = 3(2^2)$. In general,

$$a_n = 3(2^n), \qquad \text{for } n = 0, 1, 2, \dots.$$

Related Exercises 23–30 ◀

Limit of a Sequence

Perhaps the most important question about a sequence is this: If you go farther and farther out in the sequence, $a_{100}, \ldots, a_{10,000}, \ldots, a_{100,000}, \ldots$, how do the terms of the sequence behave? Do they approach a specific number, and if so, what is that number? Or do they grow in magnitude without bound? Or do they wander around with or without a pattern?

The long-term behavior of a sequence is described by its **limit**. The limit of a sequence is defined rigorously in the next section. For now, we work with an informal definition.

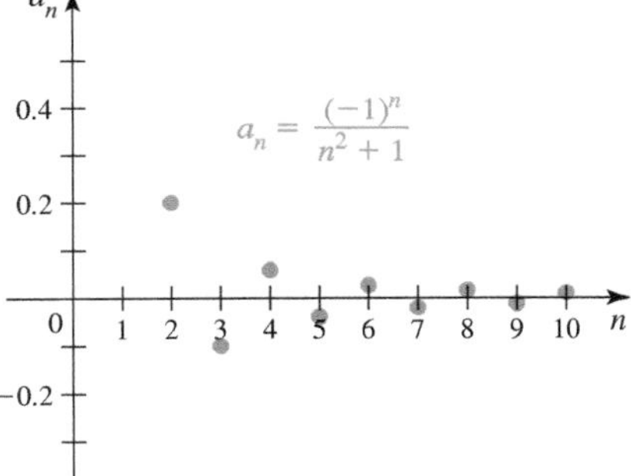

Figure 8.3

> DEFINITION **Limit of a Sequence**
>
> If the terms of a sequence $\{a_n\}$ approach a unique number L as n increases—that is, if a_n can be made arbitrarily close to L by taking n sufficiently large—then we say $\lim_{n\to\infty} a_n = L$ exists, and the sequence **converges** to L. If the terms of the sequence do not approach a single number as n increases, the sequence has no limit, and the sequence **diverges**.

EXAMPLE 4 **Limits of sequences** Write the first four terms of each sequence. If you believe the sequence converges, make a conjecture about its limit. If the sequence appears to diverge, explain why.

a. $\left\{\dfrac{(-1)^n}{n^2+1}\right\}_{n=1}^{\infty}$ Explicit formula

b. $\{\cos n\pi\}_{n=1}^{\infty}$ Explicit formula

c. $\{a_n\}_{n=1}^{\infty}$, where $a_{n+1} = -2a_n$, $a_1 = 1$ Recurrence relation

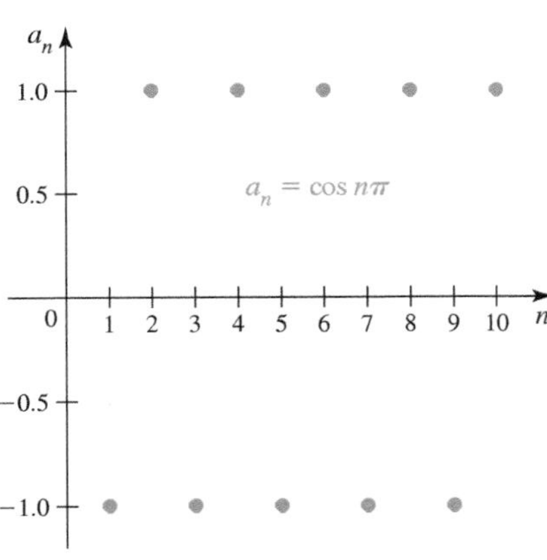

Figure 8.4

SOLUTION

a. Beginning with $n = 1$, the first four terms of the sequence are

$$\left\{\frac{(-1)^1}{1^2+1}, \frac{(-1)^2}{2^2+1}, \frac{(-1)^3}{3^2+1}, \frac{(-1)^4}{4^2+1}, \ldots\right\} = \left\{-\frac{1}{2}, \frac{1}{5}, -\frac{1}{10}, \frac{1}{17}, \ldots\right\}.$$

The terms decrease in magnitude and approach zero with alternating signs. The limit appears to be 0 (Figure 8.3).

b. The first four terms of the sequence are

$$\{\cos \pi, \cos 2\pi, \cos 3\pi, \cos 4\pi, \ldots\} = \{-1, 1, -1, 1, \ldots\}.$$

In this case, the terms of the sequence alternate between -1 and $+1$, and never approach a single value. Therefore, the sequence diverges (Figure 8.4).

c. The first four terms of the sequence are

$$\{1, -2a_1, -2a_2, -2a_3, \ldots\} = \{1, -2, 4, -8, \ldots\}.$$

Because the magnitudes of the terms increase without bound, the sequence diverges (Figure 8.5).

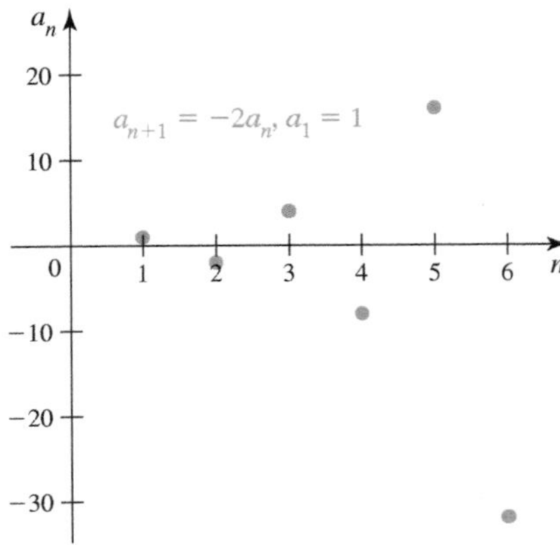

Figure 8.5

Related Exercises 31–40 ◄

EXAMPLE 5 **Limit of a sequence** Enumerate and graph the terms of the following sequence, and make a conjecture about its limit.

$$a_n = \frac{4n^3}{n^3+1}, \quad \text{for } n = 1, 2, 3, \ldots. \quad \text{Explicit formula}$$

SOLUTION The first 14 terms of the sequence $\{a_n\}$ are tabulated in Table 8.1 and graphed in Figure 8.6. The terms appear to approach 4.

Table 8.1

n	a_n	n	a_n
1	2.000	8	3.992
2	3.556	9	3.995
3	3.857	10	3.996
4	3.938	11	3.997
5	3.968	12	3.998
6	3.982	13	3.998
7	3.988	14	3.999

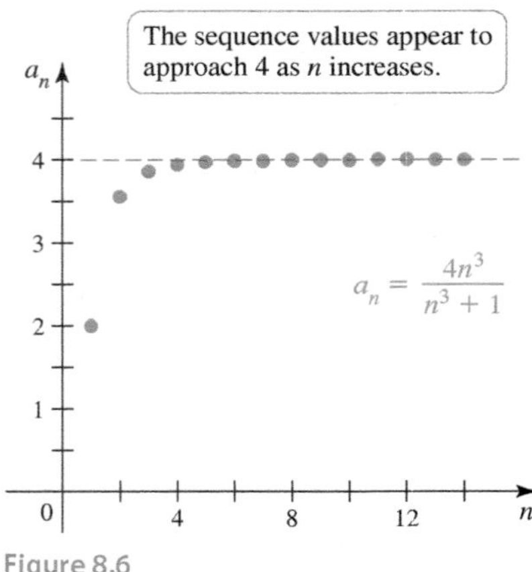

Figure 8.6

Related Exercises 41–54 ◀

EXAMPLE 6 **A bouncing ball** A basketball tossed straight up in the air reaches a high point and falls to the floor. Each time the ball bounces on the floor it rebounds to 0.8 of its previous height. Let h_n be the high point after the nth bounce, with the initial height being $h_0 = 20$ ft.

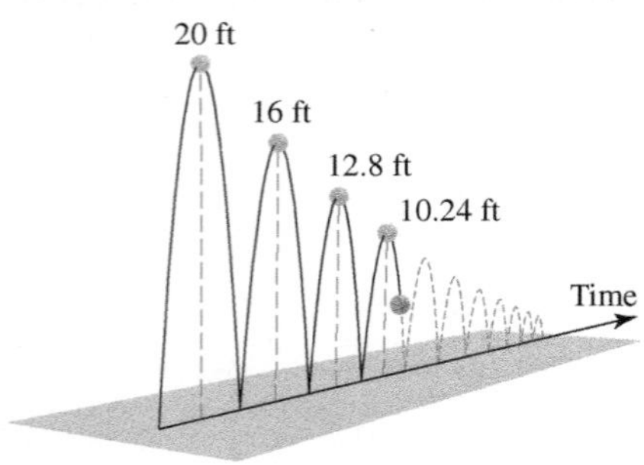

Figure 8.7

a. Find a recurrence relation and an explicit formula for the sequence $\{h_n\}$.

b. What is the high point after the 10th bounce? after the 20th bounce?

c. Speculate on the limit of the sequence $\{h_n\}$.

SOLUTION

a. We first write and graph the heights of the ball for several bounces using the rule that each height is 0.8 of the previous height (Figure 8.7). For example, we have

$$\begin{aligned} h_0 &= 20 \text{ ft}, \\ h_1 &= 0.8\, h_0 = 16 \text{ ft}, \\ h_2 &= 0.8\, h_1 = 0.8^2\, h_0 = 12.80 \text{ ft}, \\ h_3 &= 0.8\, h_2 = 0.8^3\, h_0 = 10.24 \text{ ft, and} \\ h_4 &= 0.8\, h_3 = 0.8^4\, h_0 \approx 8.19 \text{ ft}. \end{aligned}$$

Each number in the list is 0.8 of the previous number. Therefore, the recurrence relation for the sequence of heights is

$$h_{n+1} = 0.8\, h_n, \quad h_0 = 20, \qquad \text{for } n = 0, 1, 2, 3, \ldots.$$

To find an explicit formula for the nth term, note that

$$h_1 = h_0 \cdot 0.8, \quad h_2 = h_0 \cdot 0.8^2, \quad h_3 = h_0 \cdot 0.8^3, \quad \text{and} \quad h_4 = h_0 \cdot 0.8^4.$$

In general, we have

$$h_n = h_0 \cdot 0.8^n = 20 \cdot 0.8^n, \qquad \text{for } n = 0, 1, 2, 3, \ldots,$$

which is an explicit formula for the terms of the sequence.

b. Using the explicit formula for the sequence, we see that after $n = 10$ bounces, the next height is

$$h_{10} = 20 \cdot 0.8^{10} \approx 2.15 \text{ ft}.$$

After $n = 20$ bounces, the next height is

$$h_{20} = 20 \cdot 0.8^{20} \approx 0.23 \text{ ft}.$$

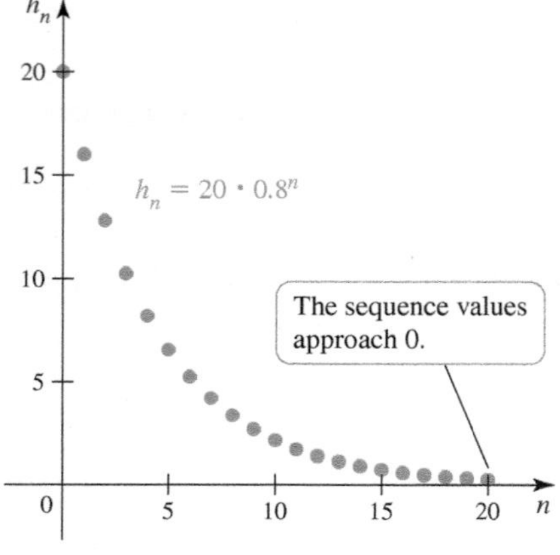

Figure 8.8

c. The terms of the sequence (Figure 8.8) appear to decrease and approach 0. A reasonable conjecture is that $\lim_{n\to\infty} h_n = 0$.

Related Exercises 55–58 ◀

Infinite Series and the Sequence of Partial Sums

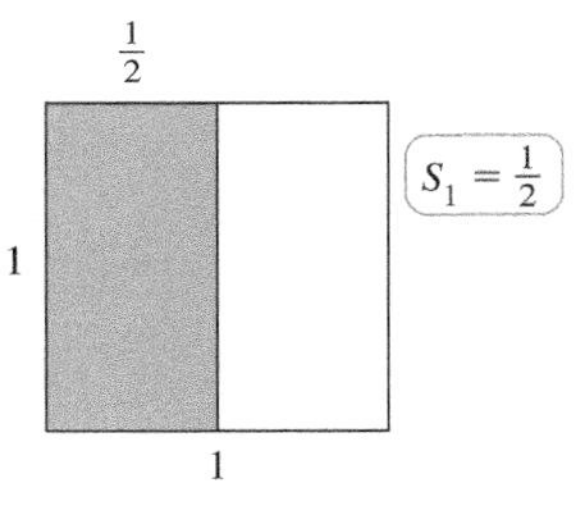

An infinite series can be viewed as a *sum* of an infinite set of numbers; it has the form

$$a_1 + a_2 + \cdots + a_n + \cdots,$$

where the terms of the series, $a_1, a_2, \ldots$, are real numbers. We first answer the question: How is it possible to sum an infinite set of numbers and produce a finite number? Here is an informative example.

Consider a unit square (sides of length 1) that is subdivided as shown in Figure 8.9. We let S_n be the area of the colored region in the nth figure of the progression. The area of the colored region in the first figure is

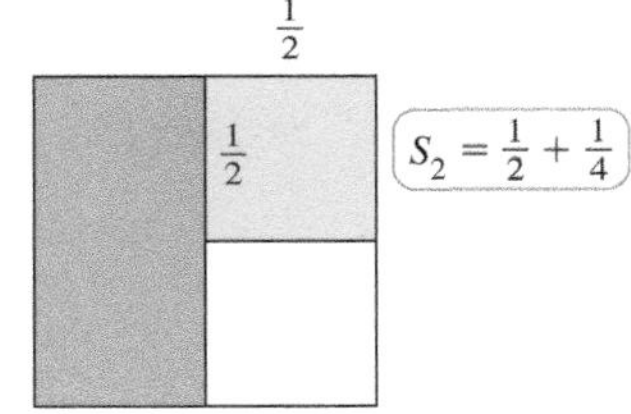

$$S_1 = \frac{1}{2} \cdot 1 = \frac{1}{2}. \qquad \frac{1}{2} = \frac{2^1 - 1}{2^1}$$

The area of the colored region in the second figure is S_1 plus the area of the smaller blue square, which is $\frac{1}{2} \cdot \frac{1}{2} = \frac{1}{4}$. Therefore,

$$S_2 = \frac{1}{2} + \frac{1}{4} = \frac{3}{4}. \qquad \frac{3}{4} = \frac{2^2 - 1}{2^2}$$

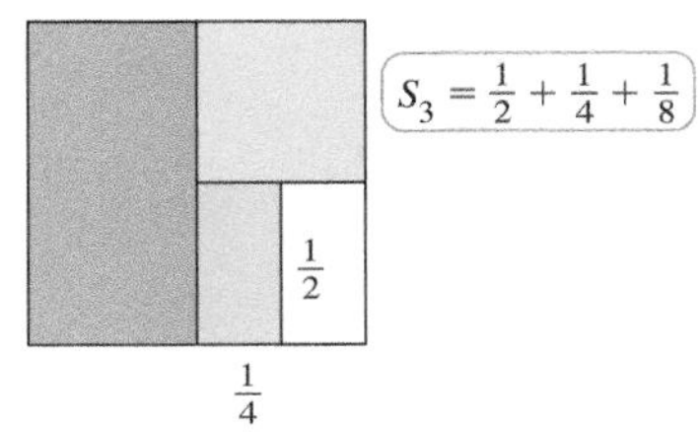

The area of the colored region in the third figure is S_2 plus the area of the smaller green rectangle, which is $\frac{1}{2} \cdot \frac{1}{4} = \frac{1}{8}$. Therefore,

$$S_3 = \frac{1}{2} + \frac{1}{4} + \frac{1}{8} = \frac{7}{8}. \qquad \frac{7}{8} = \frac{2^3 - 1}{2^3}$$

Continuing in this manner, we find that

$$S_n = \frac{1}{2} + \frac{1}{4} + \frac{1}{8} + \cdots + \frac{1}{2^n} = \frac{2^n - 1}{2^n}.$$

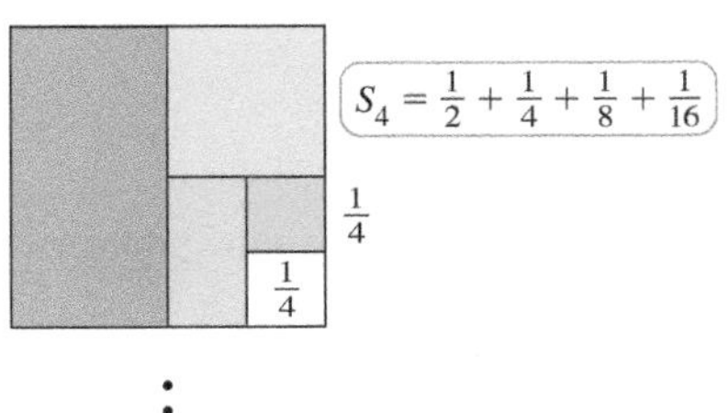

If this process is continued indefinitely, the area of the colored region S_n approaches the area of the unit square, which is 1. So it is plausible that

$$\lim_{n\to\infty} S_n = \underbrace{\frac{1}{2} + \frac{1}{4} + \frac{1}{8} + \cdots}_{\text{sum continues indefinitely}} = 1.$$

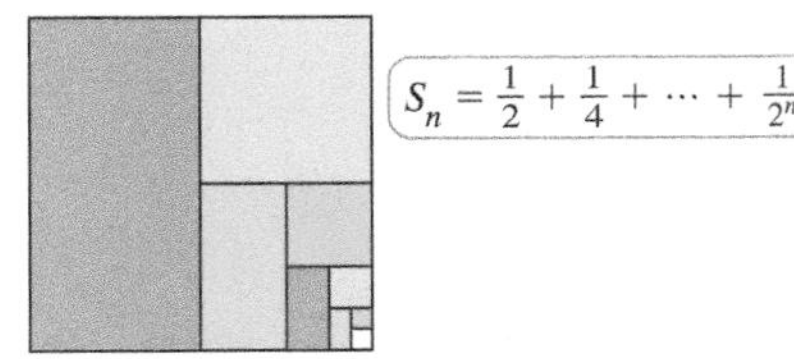

Figure 8.9

The explicit formula $S_n = \dfrac{2^n - 1}{2^n}$ can be analyzed to verify our assertion that $\lim_{n\to\infty} S_n = 1$; we turn to that task in Section 8.2.

This example shows that it is possible to sum an infinite set of numbers and obtain a finite number—in this case, the sum is 1. The sequence $\{S_n\}$ generated in this example is extremely important. It is called a *sequence of partial sums*, and its limit is the value of the infinite series $\frac{1}{2} + \frac{1}{4} + \frac{1}{8} + \cdots$. The idea of a sequence of partial sums is illustrated by the decimal expansion of 1.

EXAMPLE 7 **Working with series** Consider the infinite series

$$0.9 + 0.09 + 0.009 + 0.0009 + \cdots,$$

where each term of the sum is $\frac{1}{10}$ of the previous term.

a. Find the sum of the first one, two, three, and four terms of the series.

b. What value would you assign to the infinite series $0.9 + 0.09 + 0.009 + \cdots$?

SOLUTION

a. Let S_n denote the sum of the first n terms of the given series. Then

$$\begin{aligned} S_1 &= 0.9, \\ S_2 &= 0.9 + 0.09 = 0.99, \\ S_3 &= 0.9 + 0.09 + 0.009 = 0.999, \text{ and} \\ S_4 &= 0.9 + 0.09 + 0.009 + 0.0009 = 0.9999. \end{aligned}$$

b. The sums $S_1, S_2, \ldots, S_n$ form a sequence $\{S_n\}$, which is a sequence of partial sums. As more and more terms are included, the values of S_n approach 1. Therefore, a reasonable conjecture for the value of the series is 1:

$$\underbrace{\underbrace{\underbrace{0.9}_{S_1 = 0.9} + 0.09}_{S_2 = 0.99} + 0.009}_{S_3 = 0.999} + 0.0009 + \cdots = 1.$$

Related Exercises 59–62 ◀

QUICK CHECK 3 Reasoning as in Example 7, what is the value of $0.3 + 0.03 + 0.003 + \cdots$? ◀

➤ Recall the summation notation introduced in Chapter 5: $\sum_{k=1}^{n} a_k$ means $a_1 + a_2 + \cdots + a_n$.

The nth term of the sequence is

$$S_n = \underbrace{0.9 + 0.09 + 0.009 + \cdots + 0.0\ldots09}_{n \text{ terms}} = \sum_{k=1}^{n} 9 \cdot 0.1^k.$$

We observed that $\lim_{n \to \infty} S_n = 1$. For this reason, we write

$$\lim_{n \to \infty} S_n = \lim_{n \to \infty} \underbrace{\sum_{k=1}^{n} 9 \cdot 0.1^k}_{S_n} = \underbrace{\sum_{k=1}^{\infty} 9 \cdot 0.1^k}_{\text{new object}} = 1.$$

By letting $n \to \infty$, a new mathematical object $\sum_{k=1}^{\infty} 9 \cdot 0.1^k$ is created. It is an infinite series, and its value is the *limit* of the sequence of partial sums.

➤ The term *series* is used for historical reasons. When you see *series*, you should think *sum*.

DEFINITION Infinite Series

Given a sequence $\{a_1, a_2, a_3, \ldots\}$, the sum of its terms

$$a_1 + a_2 + a_3 + \cdots = \sum_{k=1}^{\infty} a_k$$

is called an **infinite series**. The **sequence of partial sums** $\{S_n\}$ associated with this series has the terms

$$\begin{aligned} S_1 &= a_1 \\ S_2 &= a_1 + a_2 \\ S_3 &= a_1 + a_2 + a_3 \\ &\vdots \\ S_n &= a_1 + a_2 + a_3 + \cdots + a_n = \sum_{k=1}^{n} a_k, \quad \text{for } n = 1, 2, 3, \ldots. \end{aligned}$$

If the sequence of partial sums $\{S_n\}$ has a limit L, the infinite series **converges** to that limit, and we write

$$\sum_{k=1}^{\infty} a_k = \lim_{n \to \infty} \underbrace{\sum_{k=1}^{n} a_k}_{S_n} = \lim_{n \to \infty} S_n = L.$$

If the sequence of partial sums diverges, the infinite series also **diverges**.

QUICK CHECK 4 Do the series $\sum_{k=1}^{\infty} 1$ and $\sum_{k=1}^{\infty} k$ converge or diverge? ◀

EXAMPLE 8 **Sequence of partial sums** Consider the infinite series

$$\sum_{k=1}^{\infty} \frac{1}{k(k+1)}.$$

a. Find the first four terms of the sequence of partial sums.

b. Find an expression for S_n and make a conjecture about the value of the series.

SOLUTION

a. The sequence of partial sums can be evaluated explicitly:

$$S_1 = \sum_{k=1}^{1} \frac{1}{k(k+1)} = \frac{1}{2},$$

$$S_2 = \sum_{k=1}^{2} \frac{1}{k(k+1)} = \frac{1}{2} + \frac{1}{6} = \frac{2}{3},$$

$$S_3 = \sum_{k=1}^{3} \frac{1}{k(k+1)} = \frac{1}{2} + \frac{1}{6} + \frac{1}{12} = \frac{3}{4}, \text{ and}$$

$$S_4 = \sum_{k=1}^{4} \frac{1}{k(k+1)} = \frac{1}{2} + \frac{1}{6} + \frac{1}{12} + \frac{1}{20} = \frac{4}{5}.$$

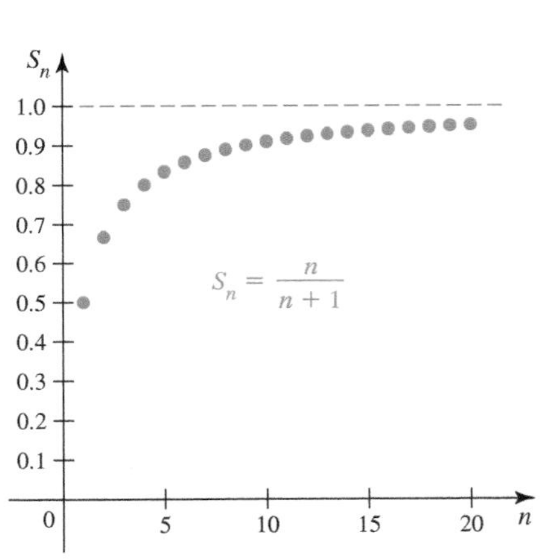

Figure 8.10

b. Based on the pattern in the sequence of partial sums, a reasonable conjecture is that $S_n = \frac{n}{n+1}$, for $n = 1, 2, 3, \ldots$, which produces the sequence $\left\{\frac{1}{2}, \frac{2}{3}, \frac{3}{4}, \frac{4}{5}, \frac{5}{6}, \ldots\right\}$ (Figure 8.10). Because $\lim_{n\to\infty} \frac{n}{n+1} = 1$, we claim that

$$\sum_{k=1}^{\infty} \frac{1}{k(k+1)} = \lim_{n\to\infty} S_n = 1.$$

Related Exercises 63–66 ◄

QUICK CHECK 5 Find the first four terms of the sequence of partial sums for the series $\sum_{k=1}^{\infty} (-1)^k k$. Does the series converge or diverge? ◄

Summary

This section features three key ideas to keep in mind.

- A *sequence* $\{a_1, a_2, \ldots, a_n, \ldots\}$ is an ordered *list* of numbers.
- An *infinite series* $\sum_{k=1}^{\infty} a_k = a_1 + a_2 + a_3 + \cdots$ is a *sum* of numbers.
- A *sequence of partial sums* $\{S_1, S_2, S_3, \ldots\}$, where $S_n = a_1 + a_2 + \cdots + a_n$, is used to evaluate the series $\sum_{k=1}^{\infty} a_k$.

For sequences, we ask about the behavior of the individual terms as we go out farther and farther in the list; that is, we ask about $\lim_{n\to\infty} a_n$. For infinite series, we examine the sequence of partial sums related to the series. If the sequence of partial sums $\{S_n\}$ has a limit, then the infinite series $\sum_{k=1}^{\infty} a_k$ converges to that limit. If the sequence of partial sums does not have a limit, the infinite series diverges.

Table 8.2 shows the correspondences between sequences/series and functions, and between summation and integration. For a sequence, the index n plays the role of the independent variable and takes on integer values; the terms of the sequence $\{a_n\}$ correspond to the dependent variable.

With sequences $\{a_n\}$, the idea of accumulation corresponds to summation, whereas with functions, accumulation corresponds to integration. A finite sum is analogous to integrating a function over a finite interval. An infinite series is analogous to integrating a function over an infinite interval.

Table 8.2

	Sequences/Series	Functions
Independent variable	n	x
Dependent variable	a_n	$f(x)$
Domain	Integers e.g., $n = 1, 2, 3, \ldots$	Real numbers e.g., $\{x: x \geq 1\}$
Accumulation	Sums	Integrals
Accumulation over a finite interval	$\sum_{k=1}^{n} a_k$	$\int_1^n f(x)\,dx$
Accumulation over an infinite interval	$\sum_{k=1}^{\infty} a_k$	$\int_1^{\infty} f(x)\,dx$

SECTION 8.1 EXERCISES

Review Questions

1. Define *sequence* and give an example.
2. Suppose the sequence $\{a_n\}$ is defined by the explicit formula $a_n = 1/n$, for $n = 1, 2, 3, \ldots$. Write out the first five terms of the sequence.
3. Suppose the sequence $\{a_n\}$ is defined by the recurrence relation $a_{n+1} = na_n$, for $n = 1, 2, 3, \ldots$, where $a_1 = 1$. Write out the first five terms of the sequence.
4. Define *finite sum* and give an example.
5. Define *infinite series* and give an example.
6. Given the series $\sum_{k=1}^{\infty} k$, evaluate the first four terms of its sequence of partial sums $S_n = \sum_{k=1}^{n} k$.
7. The terms of a sequence of partial sums are defined by $S_n = \sum_{k=1}^{n} k^2$, for $n = 1, 2, 3, \ldots$. Evaluate the first four terms of the sequence.
8. Consider the infinite series $\sum_{k=1}^{\infty} \frac{1}{k}$. Evaluate the first four terms of the sequence of partial sums.

Basic Skills

9–16. Explicit formulas *Write the first four terms of the sequence* $\{a_n\}_{n=1}^{\infty}$.

9. $a_n = 1/10^n$
10. $a_n = 3n + 1$
11. $a_n = \dfrac{(-1)^n}{2^n}$
12. $a_n = 2 + (-1)^n$
13. $a_n = \dfrac{2^{n+1}}{2^n + 1}$
14. $a_n = n + 1/n$
15. $a_n = 1 + \sin(\pi n/2)$
16. $a_n = 2n^2 - 3n + 1$

17–22. Recurrence relations *Write the first four terms of the sequence* $\{a_n\}$ *defined by the following recurrence relations.*

17. $a_{n+1} = 2a_n;\ a_1 = 2$
18. $a_{n+1} = a_n/2;\ a_1 = 32$
19. $a_{n+1} = 3a_n - 12;\ a_1 = 10$
20. $a_{n+1} = a_n^2 - 1;\ a_1 = 1$
21. $a_{n+1} = 3a_n^2 + n + 1;\ a_1 = 0$
22. $a_{n+1} = a_n + a_{n-1};\ a_1 = 1, a_0 = 1$

23–30. Working with sequences *Several terms of a sequence $\{a_n\}_{n=1}^{\infty}$ are given.*

a. *Find the next two terms of the sequence.*
b. *Find a recurrence relation that generates the sequence (supply the initial value of the index and the first term of the sequence).*
c. *Find an explicit formula for the nth term of the sequence.*

23. $\left\{1, \frac{1}{2}, \frac{1}{4}, \frac{1}{8}, \frac{1}{16}, \ldots\right\}$

24. $\{1, -2, 3, -4, 5, \ldots\}$

25. $\{-5, 5, -5, 5, \ldots\}$

26. $\{2, 5, 8, 11, \ldots\}$

27. $\{1, 2, 4, 8, 16, \ldots\}$

28. $\{1, 4, 9, 16, 25, \ldots\}$

29. $\{1, 3, 9, 27, 81, \ldots\}$

30. $\{64, 32, 16, 8, 4, \ldots\}$

31–40. Limits of sequences *Write the terms a_1, a_2, a_3, and a_4 of the following sequences. If the sequence appears to converge, make a conjecture about its limit. If the sequence diverges, explain why.*

31. $a_n = 10^n - 1;\ n = 1, 2, 3, \ldots$

32. $a_n = n^4 + 1;\ n = 1, 2, 3, \ldots$

33. $a_n = \frac{1}{10^n};\ n = 1, 2, 3, \ldots$

34. $a_{n+1} = \frac{a_n}{10};\ a_0 = 1$

35. $a_n = \frac{(-1)^n}{2^n};\ n = 1, 2, 3, \ldots$

36. $a_n = 1 - 10^{-n};\ n = 1, 2, 3, \ldots$

37. $a_{n+1} = 1 + \frac{a_n}{2};\ a_0 = 2$

38. $a_{n+1} = 1 - \frac{a_n}{2};\ a_0 = \frac{2}{3}$

T **39.** $a_{n+1} = \frac{a_n}{11} + 50;\ a_0 = 50$

40. $a_{n+1} = 10a_n - 1;\ a_0 = 0$

T **41–46. Explicit formulas for sequences** *Consider the formulas for the following sequences. Using a calculator, make a table with at least ten terms and determine a plausible value for the limit of the sequence or state that the sequence diverges.*

41. $a_n = \cot^{-1} 2^n;\ n = 1, 2, 3, \ldots$

42. $a_n = 2\tan^{-1}(1000n);\ n = 1, 2, 3, \ldots$

43. $a_n = n^2 - n;\ n = 1, 2, 3, \ldots$

44. $a_n = \frac{100n - 1}{10n};\ n = 1, 2, 3, \ldots$

45. $a_n = \frac{5^n}{5^n + 1};\ n = 1, 2, 3, \ldots$

46. $a_n = 2^n \sin(2^{-n});\ n = 1, 2, 3, \ldots$

47–48. Limits from graphs *Consider the following sequences.*

a. *Find the first four terms of the sequence.*
b. *Based on part (a) and the figure, determine a plausible limit of the sequence.*

47. $a_n = 2 + 2^{-n};\ n = 1, 2, 3, \ldots$

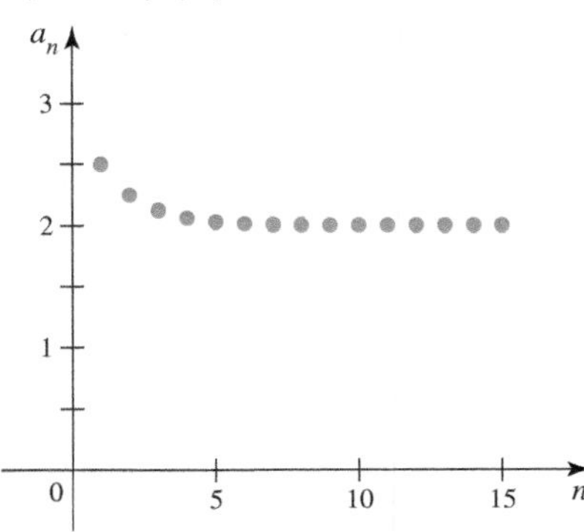

48. $a_n = \frac{n^2}{n^2 - 1};\ n = 2, 3, 4, \ldots$

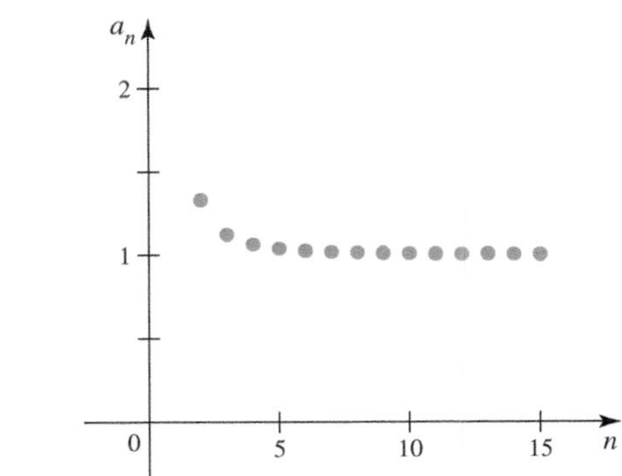

T **49–54. Recurrence relations** *Consider the following recurrence relations. Using a calculator, make a table with at least ten terms and determine a plausible limit of the sequence or state that the sequence diverges.*

49. $a_{n+1} = \frac{1}{2}a_n + 2;\ a_0 = 3$

50. $a_n = \frac{1}{4}a_{n-1} - 3;\ a_0 = 1$

51. $a_{n+1} = 2a_n + 1;\ a_0 = 0$

52. $a_{n+1} = \frac{a_n}{10} + 3;\ a_0 = 10$

53. $a_{n+1} = \frac{1}{2}\sqrt{a_n} + 3;\ a_0 = 1000$

54. $a_{n+1} = \sqrt{1 + a_n};\ a_0 = 1$

55–58. Heights of bouncing balls *A ball is thrown upward to a height of h_0 meters. After each bounce, the ball rebounds to a fraction r of its previous height. Let h_n be the height after the nth bounce. Consider the following values of h_0 and r.*

a. *Find the first four terms of the sequence of heights $\{h_n\}$.*
b. *Find an explicit formula for the nth term of the sequence $\{h_n\}$.*

55. $h_0 = 20,\ r = 0.5$

56. $h_0 = 10,\ r = 0.9$

57. $h_0 = 30,\ r = 0.25$

58. $h_0 = 20,\ r = 0.75$

59–62. Sequences of partial sums *For the following infinite series, find the first four terms of the sequence of partial sums. Then make a conjecture about the value of the infinite series.*

59. $0.3 + 0.03 + 0.003 + \cdots$

60. $0.6 + 0.06 + 0.006 + \cdots$

61. $4 + 0.9 + 0.09 + 0.009 + \cdots$

62. $1 + \frac{1}{2} + \frac{1}{4} + \frac{1}{8} + \cdots$

T **63–66. Formulas for sequences of partial sums** *Consider the following infinite series.*

a. Find the first four terms of the sequence of partial sums.
b. Use the results of part (a) to find a formula for S_n.
c. Find the value of the series.

63. $\sum_{k=1}^{\infty} \frac{2}{(2k-1)(2k+1)}$ **64.** $\sum_{k=1}^{\infty} \frac{1}{2^k}$

65. $\sum_{k=1}^{\infty} \frac{1}{4k^2-1}$ **66.** $\sum_{k=1}^{\infty} \frac{2}{3^k}$

Further Explorations

67. Explain why or why not Determine whether the following statements are true and give an explanation or counterexample.

a. The sequence of partial sums for the series $1 + 2 + 3 + \cdots$ is $\{1, 3, 6, 10, \ldots\}$.
b. If a sequence of positive numbers converges, then the terms of the sequence must decrease in size.
c. If the terms of the sequence $\{a_n\}$ are positive and increasing, then the sequence of partial sums for the series $\sum_{k=1}^{\infty} a_k$ diverges.

T **68–69. Distance traveled by bouncing balls** *A ball is thrown upward to a height of h_0 meters. After each bounce, the ball rebounds to a fraction r of its previous height. Let h_n be the height after the nth bounce and let S_n be the total distance the ball has traveled at the moment of the nth bounce.*

a. Find the first four terms of the sequence $\{S_n\}$.
b. Make a table of 20 terms of the sequence $\{S_n\}$ and determine a plausible value for the limit of $\{S_n\}$.

68. $h_0 = 20$, $r = 0.5$

69. $h_0 = 20$, $r = 0.75$

70–77. Sequences of partial sums *Consider the following infinite series.*

a. Write out the first four terms of the sequence of partial sums.
b. Estimate the limit of $\{S_n\}$ or state that it does not exist.

70. $\sum_{k=1}^{\infty} \cos \pi k$ **71.** $\sum_{k=1}^{\infty} 9(0.1)^k$

72. $\sum_{k=1}^{\infty} 1.5^k$ **73.** $\sum_{k=1}^{\infty} 3^{-k}$

74. $\sum_{k=1}^{\infty} k$ **75.** $\sum_{k=1}^{\infty} (-1)^k$

76. $\sum_{k=1}^{\infty} (-1)^k k$ **77.** $\sum_{k=1}^{\infty} \frac{3}{10^k}$

Applications

T **78–81. Practical sequences** *Consider the following situations that generate a sequence.*

a. Write out the first five terms of the sequence.
b. Find an explicit formula for the terms of the sequence.
c. Find a recurrence relation that generates the sequence.
d. Using a calculator or a graphing utility, estimate the limit of the sequence or state that it does not exist.

78. Population growth When a biologist begins a study, a colony of prairie dogs has a population of 250. Regular measurements reveal that each month the prairie dog population increases by 3%. Let p_n be the population (rounded to whole numbers) at the end of the nth month, where the initial population is $p_0 = 250$.

79. Radioactive decay A material transmutes 50% of its mass to another element every 10 years due to radioactive decay. Let M_n be the mass of the radioactive material at the end of the nth decade, where the initial mass of the material is $M_0 = 20$ g.

80. Consumer Price Index The Consumer Price Index (the CPI is a measure of the U.S. cost of living) is given a base value of 100 in the year 1984. Assume the CPI has increased by an average of 3% per year since 1984. Let c_n be the CPI n years after 1984, where $c_0 = 100$.

81. Drug elimination Jack took a 200-mg dose of a painkiller at midnight. Every hour, 5% of the drug is washed out of his bloodstream. Let d_n be the amount of drug in Jack's blood n hours after the drug was taken, where $d_0 = 200$ mg.

T **82. A square root finder** A well-known method for approximating $\sqrt{c}$ for a positive real number c consists of the following recurrence relation (based on Newton's method; see Section 4.8). Let $a_0 = c$ and

$$a_{n+1} = \frac{1}{2}\left(a_n + \frac{c}{a_n}\right), \quad \text{for } n = 0, 1, 2, 3, \ldots.$$

a. Use this recurrence relation to approximate $\sqrt{10}$. How many terms of the sequence are needed to approximate $\sqrt{10}$ with an error less than 0.01? How many terms of the sequence are needed to approximate $\sqrt{10}$ with an error less than 0.0001? (To compute the error, assume a calculator gives the exact value.)
b. Use this recurrence relation to approximate $\sqrt{c}$, for $c = 2, 3, \ldots, 10$. Make a table showing the number of terms of the sequence needed to approximate $\sqrt{c}$ with an error less than 0.01.

QUICK CHECK ANSWERS

1. $a_{10} = 28$ **2.** $a_n = 2^n - 1$, $n = 1, 2, 3, \ldots$ **3.** $0.33333\ldots = \frac{1}{3}$ **4.** Both diverge. **5.** $S_1 = -1$, $S_2 = 1$, $S_3 = -2$, $S_4 = 2$; the series diverges. ◄

8.2 Sequences

The previous section sets the stage for an in-depth investigation of sequences and infinite series. This section is devoted to sequences, and the remainder of the chapter deals with series.

Limit of a Sequence and Limit Laws

A fundamental question about sequences concerns the behavior of the terms as we go out farther and farther in the sequence. For example, in the sequence

$$\{a_n\}_{n=0}^{\infty} = \left\{\frac{1}{n^2+1}\right\}_{n=0}^{\infty} = \left\{1, \frac{1}{2}, \frac{1}{5}, \frac{1}{10}, \ldots\right\},$$

the terms remain positive and decrease to 0. We say that this sequence converges and its limit is 0, written $\lim_{n\to\infty} a_n = 0$. Similarly, the terms of the sequence

$$\{b_n\}_{n=1}^{\infty} = \left\{(-1)^n \frac{n(n+1)}{2}\right\}_{n=1}^{\infty} = \{-1, 3, -6, 10, \ldots\}$$

increase in magnitude and do not approach a unique value as n increases. In this case, we say that the sequence diverges.

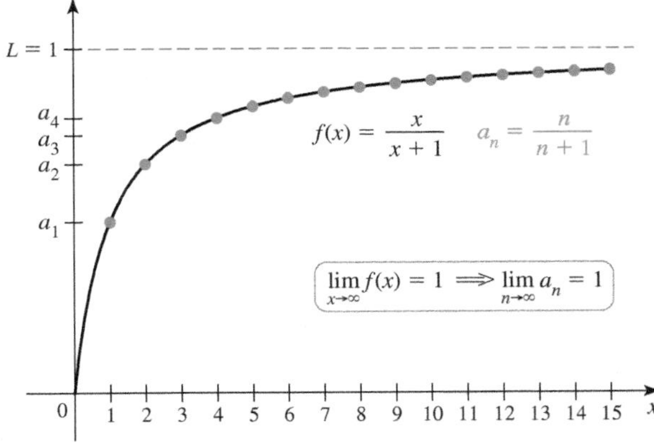

Figure 8.11

Limits of sequences are really no different from limits at infinity of functions except that the variable n assumes only integer values as $n \to \infty$. This idea works as follows.

Given a sequence $\{a_n\}$, we define a function f such that $f(n) = a_n$ for all indices n. For example, if $a_n = n/(n+1)$, then we let $f(x) = x/(x+1)$. By the methods of Section 2.5, we know that $\lim_{x\to\infty} f(x) = 1$; because the terms of the sequence lie on the graph of f, it follows that $\lim_{n\to\infty} a_n = 1$ (Figure 8.11). This reasoning is the basis of the following theorem.

➤ The converse of Theorem 8.1 is not true. For example, if $a_n = \cos 2\pi n$, then $\lim_{n\to\infty} a_n = 1$, but $\lim_{x\to\infty} \cos 2\pi x$ does not exist.

THEOREM 8.1 Limits of Sequences from Limits of Functions

Suppose f is a function such that $f(n) = a_n$ for all positive integers n. If $\lim_{x\to\infty} f(x) = L$, then the limit of the sequence $\{a_n\}$ is also L.

Because of the correspondence between limits of sequences and limits of functions at infinity, we have the following properties that are analogous to those for functions given in Theorem 2.3.

➤ The limit of a sequence $\{a_n\}$ is determined by the terms in the *tail* of the sequence—the terms with large values of n. If the sequences $\{a_n\}$ and $\{b_n\}$ differ in their first 100 terms but have identical terms for $n > 100$, then they have the same limit. For this reason, the initial index of a sequence (for example, $n = 0$ or $n = 1$) is often not specified.

THEOREM 8.2 Limit Laws for Sequences

Assume that the sequences $\{a_n\}$ and $\{b_n\}$ have limits A and B, respectively. Then

1. $\lim_{n\to\infty} (a_n \pm b_n) = A \pm B$
2. $\lim_{n\to\infty} ca_n = cA$, where c is a real number
3. $\lim_{n\to\infty} a_n b_n = AB$
4. $\lim_{n\to\infty} \frac{a_n}{b_n} = \frac{A}{B}$, provided $B \neq 0$.

EXAMPLE 1 **Limits of sequences** Determine the limits of the following sequences.

a. $a_n = \dfrac{3n^3}{n^3 + 1}$ **b.** $b_n = \left(\dfrac{n+5}{n}\right)^n$ **c.** $c_n = n^{1/n}$

SOLUTION

a. A function with the property that $f(n) = a_n$ is $f(x) = \dfrac{3x^3}{x^3 + 1}$. Dividing numerator and denominator by x^3 (or appealing to Theorem 2.7), we find that $\lim_{x\to\infty} f(x) = 3$. (Alternatively, we can apply l'Hôpital's Rule and obtain the same result.) We conclude that $\lim_{n\to\infty} a_n = 3$.

b. The limit

$$\lim_{n\to\infty} b_n = \lim_{n\to\infty}\left(\frac{n+5}{n}\right)^n = \lim_{n\to\infty}\left(1 + \frac{5}{n}\right)^n$$

has the indeterminate form 1^∞. Recall that for this limit (Section 4.7), we first evaluate

$$L = \lim_{n\to\infty} \ln\left(1 + \frac{5}{n}\right)^n = \lim_{n\to\infty} n \ln\left(1 + \frac{5}{n}\right),$$

and then, if L exists, $\lim_{n\to\infty} b_n = e^L$. Using l'Hôpital's Rule for the indeterminate form $0/0$, we have

➤ When using l'Hôpital's Rule, it is customary to treat n as a continuous variable and differentiate with respect to n, rather than write the sequence as a function of x, as was done in Example 1a.

$$L = \lim_{n\to\infty} n \ln\left(1 + \frac{5}{n}\right) = \lim_{n\to\infty}\frac{\ln(1 + (5/n))}{1/n} \qquad \text{Indeterminate form } 0/0$$

$$= \lim_{n\to\infty}\frac{\dfrac{1}{1 + (5/n)}\left(-\dfrac{5}{n^2}\right)}{-1/n^2} \qquad \text{L'Hôpital's Rule}$$

$$= \lim_{n\to\infty}\frac{5}{1 + (5/n)} = 5. \qquad \text{Simplify; } 5/n \to 0 \text{ as } n \to \infty.$$

Because $\lim_{n\to\infty} b_n = e^L = e^5$, we have $\lim_{n\to\infty}\left(\dfrac{5+n}{n}\right)^n = e^5$.

➤ For a review of l'Hôpital's Rule, see Section 4.7, where we showed that $\lim_{x\to\infty}\left(1 + \dfrac{a}{x}\right)^x = e^a$.

c. The limit has the indeterminate form ∞^0, so we first evaluate $L = \lim_{n\to\infty} \ln n^{1/n} = \lim_{n\to\infty}\dfrac{\ln n}{n}$; if L exists, then $\lim_{n\to\infty} c_n = e^L$. Using either l'Hôpital's Rule or the relative growth rates in Section 4.7, we find that $L = 0$. Therefore, $\lim_{n\to\infty} c_n = e^0 = 1$.

Related Exercises 9–34 ◀

Terminology for Sequences

We now introduce some terminology for sequences that is similar to that used for functions. The following terms are used to describe sequences $\{a_n\}$.

DEFINITIONS **Terminology for Sequences**

$\{a_n\}$ is **increasing** if $a_{n+1} > a_n$; for example, $\{0, 1, 2, 3, \dots\}$.

$\{a_n\}$ is **nondecreasing** if $a_{n+1} \geq a_n$; for example, $\{1, 1, 2, 2, 3, 3, \dots\}$.

$\{a_n\}$ is **decreasing** if $a_{n+1} < a_n$; for example, $\{2, 1, 0, -1, \dots\}$.

$\{a_n\}$ is **nonincreasing** if $a_{n+1} \leq a_n$; for example, $\{0, -1, -1, -2, -2, -3, -3, \dots\}$.

$\{a_n\}$ is **monotonic** if it is either nonincreasing or nondecreasing (it moves in one direction).

$\{a_n\}$ is **bounded** if there is number M such that $|a_n| \leq M$, for all relevant values of n.

➤ Because an increasing sequence is, by definition, nondecreasing, it is also monotonic. Similarly, a decreasing sequence is monotonic.

For example, the sequence

$$\{a_n\} = \left\{1 - \frac{1}{n}\right\}_{n=1}^{\infty} = \left\{0, \frac{1}{2}, \frac{2}{3}, \frac{3}{4}, \ldots\right\}$$

satisfies $|a_n| \leq 1$, for $n \geq 1$, and it terms are increasing in size. Therefore, the sequence is bounded and increasing; it is also monotonic (Figure 8.12). The sequence

$$\{a_n\} = \left\{1 + \frac{1}{n}\right\}_{n=1}^{\infty} = \left\{2, \frac{3}{2}, \frac{4}{3}, \frac{5}{4}, \ldots\right\}$$

satisfies $|a_n| \leq 2$, for $n \geq 1$, and it terms are decreasing in size. Therefore, the sequence is bounded and decreasing; it is also monotonic (Figure 8.12).

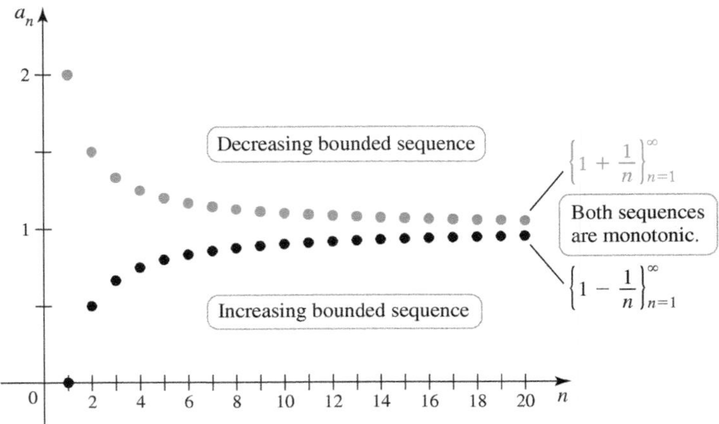

Figure 8.12

QUICK CHECK 1 Classify the following sequences as bounded, monotonic, or neither.

a. $\left\{\frac{1}{2}, \frac{3}{4}, \frac{7}{8}, \frac{15}{16}, \ldots\right\}$

b. $\left\{1, -\frac{1}{2}, \frac{1}{4}, -\frac{1}{8}, \frac{1}{16}, \ldots\right\}$

c. $\{1, -2, 3, -4, 5, \ldots\}$

d. $\{1, 1, 1, 1, \ldots\}$ ◀

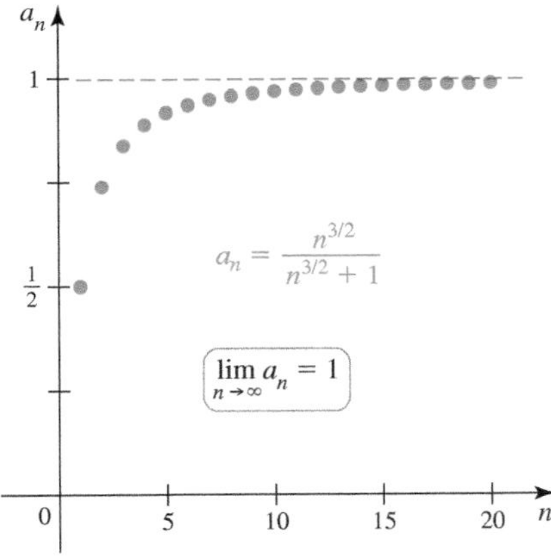

Figure 8.13

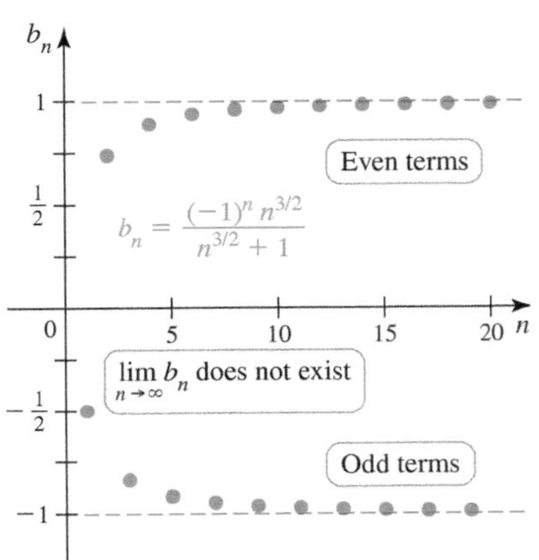

Figure 8.14

EXAMPLE 2 Limits of sequences and graphing Compare and contrast the behavior of $\{a_n\}$ and $\{b_n\}$ as $n \to \infty$.

a. $a_n = \dfrac{n^{3/2}}{n^{3/2} + 1}$ **b.** $b_n = \dfrac{(-1)^n n^{3/2}}{n^{3/2} + 1}$

SOLUTION

a. The terms of $\{a_n\}$ are positive, increasing, and bounded (Figure 8.13). Dividing the numerator and denominator of a_n by $n^{3/2}$, we see that

$$\lim_{n\to\infty} a_n = \lim_{n\to\infty} \frac{n^{3/2}}{n^{3/2} + 1} = \lim_{n\to\infty} \frac{1}{1 + \underbrace{\frac{1}{n^{3/2}}}_{\text{approaches 0 as } n \to \infty}} = 1.$$

b. The terms of the bounded sequence $\{b_n\}$ alternate in sign. Using the result of part (a), it follows that the even terms form an increasing sequence that approaches 1 and the odd terms form a decreasing sequence that approaches -1 (Figure 8.14). Therefore, the sequence diverges, illustrating the fact that the presence of $(-1)^n$ may significantly alter the behavior of a sequence.

Related Exercises 35–44 ◀

Geometric Sequences

Geometric sequences have the property that each term is obtained by multiplying the previous term by a fixed constant, called the **ratio**. They have the form $\{r^n\}$ or $\{ar^n\}$, where the ratio r and $a \neq 0$ are real numbers.

EXAMPLE 3 **Geometric sequences** Graph the following sequences and discuss their behavior.

a. $\{0.75^n\}$ **b.** $\{(-0.75)^n\}$ **c.** $\{1.15^n\}$ **d.** $\{(-1.15)^n\}$

SOLUTION

a. When a number less than 1 in magnitude is raised to increasing powers, the resulting numbers decrease to zero. The sequence $\{0.75^n\}$ converges to zero and is monotonic (Figure 8.15).

b. Note that $\{(-0.75)^n\} = \{(-1)^n 0.75^n\}$. Observe also that the factor $(-1)^n$ oscillates between 1 and -1, while 0.75^n decreases to zero as n increases. Therefore, the sequence oscillates and converges to zero (Figure 8.16).

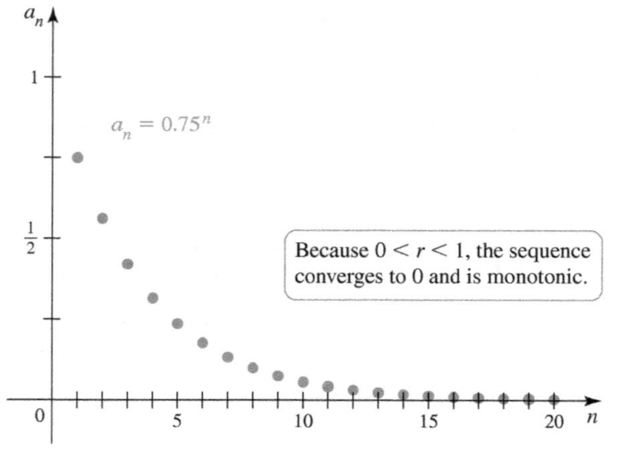

Figure 8.15

Because $(-r)^n = (-1)^n r^n$ and $0 < r < 1$, the sequence oscillates *and* converges to 0.

$a_n = (-0.75)^n$

Figure 8.16

c. When a number greater than 1 in magnitude is raised to increasing powers, the resulting numbers increase in magnitude. The terms of the sequence $\{1.15^n\}$ are positive and increase without bound. In this case, the sequence diverges and is monotonic (Figure 8.17).

d. We write $\{(-1.15)^n\} = \{(-1)^n 1.15^n\}$ and observe that $(-1)^n$ oscillates between 1 and -1, while 1.15^n increases without bound as n increases. The terms of the sequence increase in magnitude without bound and alternate in sign. In this case, the sequence oscillates and diverges (Figure 8.18).

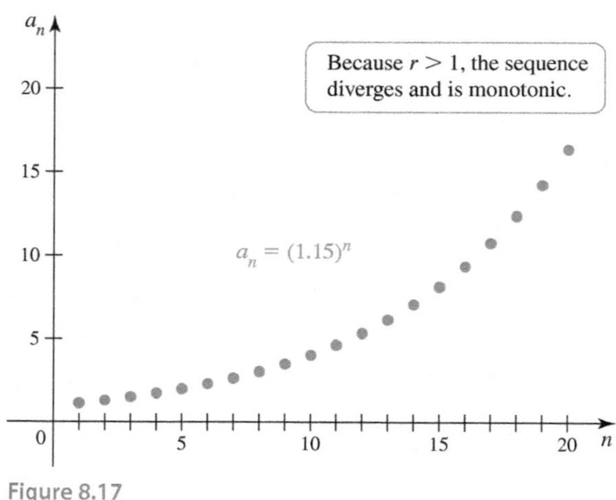

Figure 8.17

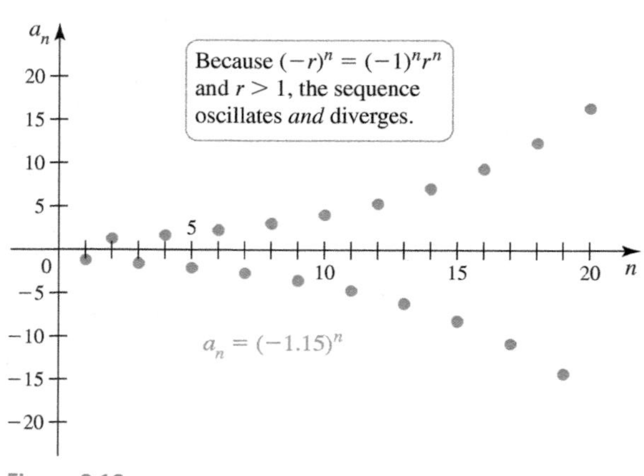

Figure 8.18

Related Exercises 45–52 ◄

QUICK CHECK 2 Describe the behavior of $\{r^n\}$ in the cases $r = -1$ and $r = 1$. ◄

The results of Example 3 and Quick Check 2 are summarized in the following theorem.

> **THEOREM 8.3 Geometric Sequences**
> Let r be a real number. Then
>
> $$\lim_{n\to\infty} r^n = \begin{cases} 0 & \text{if } |r| < 1 \\ 1 & \text{if } r = 1 \\ \text{does not exist} & \text{if } r \le -1 \text{ or } r > 1. \end{cases}$$
>
> If $r > 0$, then $\{r^n\}$ is a monotonic sequence. If $r < 0$, then $\{r^n\}$ oscillates.
>
> 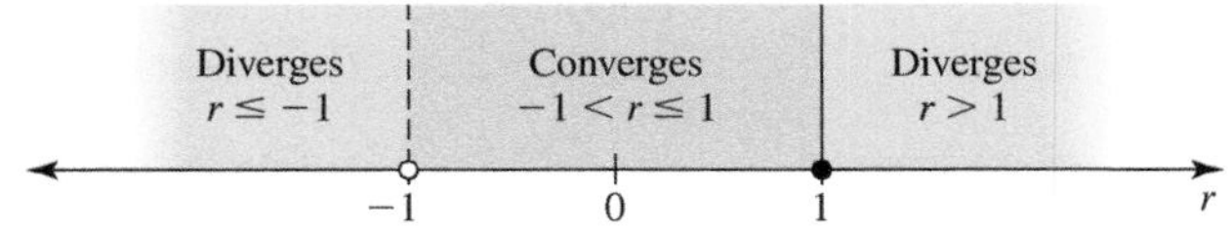
>

The previous examples show that a sequence may display any of the following behaviors:

- It may converge to a single value, which is the limit of the sequence.
- Its terms may increase in magnitude without bound (either with one sign or with mixed signs), in which case the sequence diverges.
- Its terms may remain bounded but settle into an oscillating pattern in which the terms approach two or more values; in this case, the sequence diverges.

Not illustrated in the preceding examples is one other type of behavior: The terms of a sequence may remain bounded, but wander chaotically forever without a pattern. In this case, the sequence also diverges (see the Guided Project *Chaos!*)

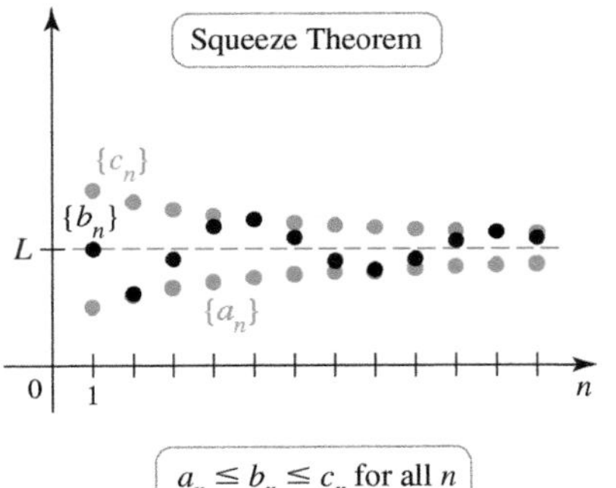

Figure 8.19

The Squeeze Theorem

We cite two theorems that are used to evaluate limits and to establish that limits exist. The first theorem is a direct analog of the Squeeze Theorem from Section 2.3.

> **THEOREM 8.4 Squeeze Theorem for Sequences**
> Let $\{a_n\}$, $\{b_n\}$, and $\{c_n\}$ be sequences with $a_n \le b_n \le c_n$ for all integers n greater than some index N. If $\lim_{n\to\infty} a_n = \lim_{n\to\infty} c_n = L$, then $\lim_{n\to\infty} b_n = L$ (Figure 8.19).

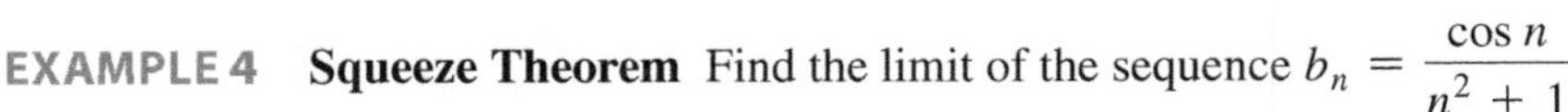

EXAMPLE 4 Squeeze Theorem Find the limit of the sequence $b_n = \dfrac{\cos n}{n^2+1}$.

SOLUTION The goal is to find two sequences $\{a_n\}$ and $\{c_n\}$ whose terms lie below and above the terms of the given sequence $\{b_n\}$. Note that $-1 \le \cos n \le 1$, for all n. Therefore,

$$\underbrace{-\frac{1}{n^2+1}}_{a_n} \le \underbrace{\frac{\cos n}{n^2+1}}_{b_n} \le \underbrace{\frac{1}{n^2+1}}_{c_n}.$$

Letting $a_n = -\dfrac{1}{n^2+1}$ and $c_n = \dfrac{1}{n^2+1}$, we have $a_n \le b_n \le c_n$, for $n \ge 1$. Furthermore, $\lim_{n\to\infty} a_n = \lim_{n\to\infty} c_n = 0$. By the Squeeze Theorem, $\lim_{n\to\infty} b_n = 0$ (Figure 8.20).

Related Exercises 53–58 ◄

Figure 8.20

Bounded Monotonic Sequence Theorem

Suppose you pour a cup of hot coffee and put it on your desk to cool. Assume that every minute you measure the temperature of the coffee to create a sequence of temperature readings $\{T_1, T_2, T_3, \ldots\}$. This sequence has two notable properties: First, the terms of the sequence are decreasing (because the coffee is cooling); and second, the sequence is bounded below (because the temperature of the coffee cannot be less than the temperature of the surrounding room). In fact, if the measurements continue indefinitely, the sequence of temperatures converges to the temperature of the room. This example illustrates an important theorem that characterizes convergent sequences in terms of boundedness and monotonicity. The theorem is easy to believe, but its proof is beyond the scope of this text.

> **THEOREM 8.5 Bounded Monotonic Sequences**
> A bounded monotonic sequence converges.

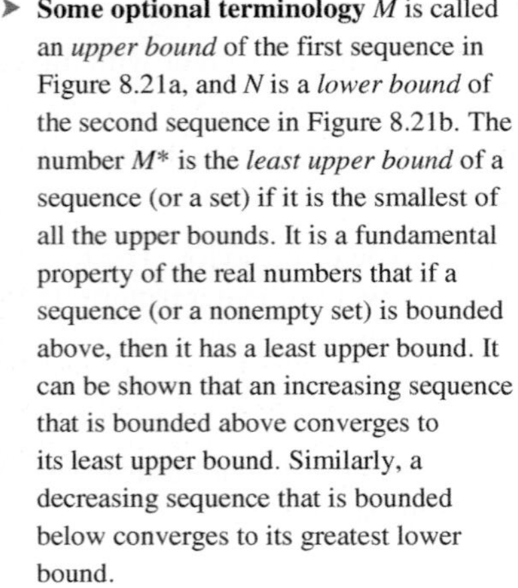

➤ **Some optional terminology** M is called an *upper bound* of the first sequence in Figure 8.21a, and N is a *lower bound* of the second sequence in Figure 8.21b. The number M^* is the *least upper bound* of a sequence (or a set) if it is the smallest of all the upper bounds. It is a fundamental property of the real numbers that if a sequence (or a nonempty set) is bounded above, then it has a least upper bound. It can be shown that an increasing sequence that is bounded above converges to its least upper bound. Similarly, a decreasing sequence that is bounded below converges to its greatest lower bound.

Figure 8.21 shows the two cases of this theorem. In the first case, we see a nondecreasing sequence, all of whose terms are less than M. It must converge to a limit less than or equal to M. Similarly, a nonincreasing sequence, all of whose terms are greater than N, must converge to a limit greater than or equal to N.

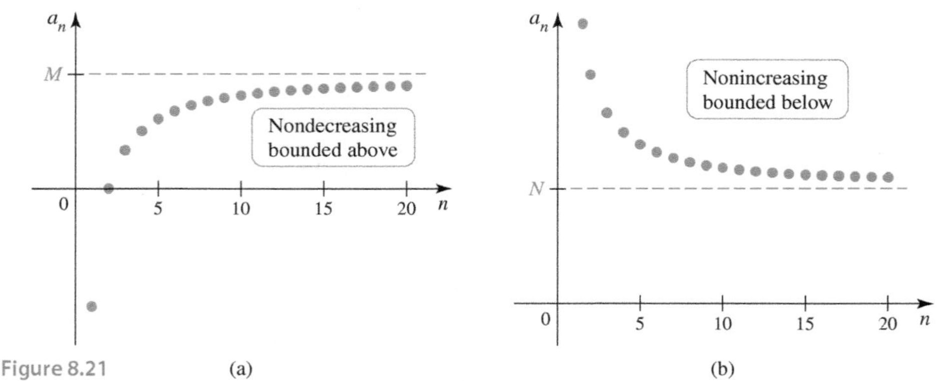

Figure 8.21 (a) (b)

An Application: Recurrence Relations

➤ Most drugs decay exponentially in the bloodstream and have a characteristic half-life assuming that the drug absorbs quickly into the blood.

EXAMPLE 5 Sequences for drug doses Suppose your doctor prescribes a 100-mg dose of an antibiotic to be taken every 12 hours. Furthermore, the drug is known to have a half-life of 12 hours; that is, every 12 hours half of the drug in your blood is eliminated.

a. Find the sequence that gives the amount of drug in your blood immediately after each dose.

b. Use a graph to propose the limit of this sequence; that is, in the long run, how much drug do you have in your blood?

c. Find the limit of the sequence directly.

SOLUTION

a. Let d_n be the amount of drug in the blood immediately following the nth dose, where $n = 1, 2, 3, \ldots$ and $d_1 = 100$ mg. We want to write a recurrence relation that gives the amount of drug in the blood after the $(n + 1)$st dose (d_{n+1}) in terms of the amount of drug after the nth dose (d_n). In the 12 hours between the nth dose and the $(n + 1)$st dose, half of the drug in the blood is eliminated *and* another 100 mg of drug is added. So we have

$$d_{n+1} = 0.5\,d_n + 100, \qquad \text{for } n = 1, 2, 3, \ldots, \text{ with } d_1 = 100,$$

which is the recurrence relation for the sequence $\{d_n\}$.

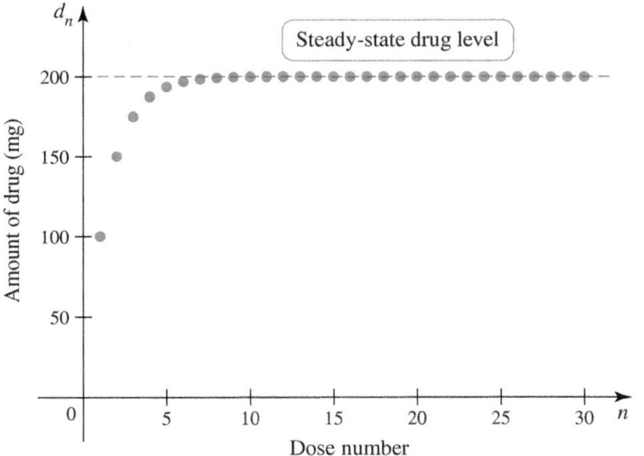

Figure 8.22

b. We see from Figure 8.22 that after about 10 doses (5 days) the amount of antibiotic in the blood is close to 200 mg, and—importantly for your body—it never exceeds 200 mg.

c. The graph of part (b) gives evidence that the terms of the sequence are increasing and bounded (Exercise 96). By the Bounded Monotonic Sequence Theorem, the sequence has a limit; therefore, $\lim_{n\to\infty} d_n = L$ and $\lim_{n\to\infty} d_{n+1} = L$. We now take the limit of both sides of the recurrence relation:

$$d_{n+1} = 0.5\,d_n + 100 \qquad \text{Recurrence relation}$$

$$\underbrace{\lim_{n\to\infty} d_{n+1}}_{L} = 0.5\underbrace{\lim_{n\to\infty} d_n}_{L} + \lim_{n\to\infty} 100 \qquad \text{Limits of both sides}$$

$$L = 0.5L + 100. \qquad \text{Substitute } L.$$

Solving for L, the steady-state drug level is $L = 200$.

Related Exercises 59–62 ◄

QUICK CHECK 3 If a drug has the same half-life as in Example 5, (i) how would the steady-state level of drug in the blood change if the regular dose were 150 mg instead of 100 mg? (ii) How would the steady-state level change if the dosing interval were 6 hr instead of 12 hr? ◄

Growth Rates of Sequences

All the hard work we did in Section 4.7 to establish the relative growth rates of functions is now applied to sequences. Here is the question: Given two nondecreasing sequences of positive terms $\{a_n\}$ and $\{b_n\}$, which sequence grows faster as $n \to \infty$? As with functions, to compare growth rates, we evaluate $\lim_{n\to\infty} a_n/b_n$. If $\lim_{n\to\infty} a_n/b_n = 0$, then $\{b_n\}$ grows faster than $\{a_n\}$. If $\lim_{n\to\infty} a_n/b_n = \infty$, then $\{a_n\}$ grows faster than $\{b_n\}$.

Using the results of Section 4.7, we immediately arrive at the following ranking of growth rates of sequences as $n \to \infty$, with positive real numbers p, q, r, s, and $b > 1$:

$$\{\ln^q n\} \ll \{n^p\} \ll \{n^p \ln^r n\} \ll \{n^{p+s}\} \ll \{b^n\} \ll \{n^n\}.$$

➤ $0! = 1$ (by definition)
$1! = 1$
$2! = 2\cdot 1! = 2$
$3! = 3\cdot 2! = 6$
$4! = 4\cdot 3! = 24$
$5! = 5\cdot 4! = 120$
$6! = 6\cdot 5! = 720$

As before, the notation $\{a_n\} \ll \{b_n\}$ means $\{b_n\}$ *grows faster than* $\{a_n\}$ as $n \to \infty$. Another important sequence that should be added to the list is the **factorial sequence** $\{n!\}$, where $n! = n(n-1)(n-2)\cdots 2\cdot 1$. Where does the factorial sequence $\{n!\}$ appear in the list? The following argument provides some intuition. Notice that

$$n^n = \underbrace{n\cdot n\cdot n \cdots n}_{n \text{ factors}}, \qquad \text{whereas}$$

$$n! = \underbrace{n\cdot(n-1)\cdot(n-2)\cdots 2\cdot 1}_{n \text{ factors}}.$$

The nth term of both sequences involves the product of n factors; however, the factors of $n!$ decrease, while the factors of n^n are the same. Based on this observation, we claim that $\{n^n\}$ grows faster than $\{n!\}$, and we have the ordering $\{n!\} \ll \{n^n\}$. But where does $\{n!\}$ appear in the list relative to $\{b^n\}$? Again, some intuition is gained by noting that

$$b^n = \underbrace{b\cdot b\cdot b \cdots b}_{n \text{ factors}}, \qquad \text{whereas}$$

$$n! = \underbrace{n\cdot(n-1)\cdot(n-2)\cdots 2\cdot 1}_{n \text{ factors}}.$$

The nth term of both sequences involves a product of n factors; however, the factors of b^n remain constant as n increases, while the factors of $n!$ increase with n. So we claim that $\{n!\}$ grows faster than $\{b^n\}$. This conjecture is supported by computation, although the outcome of the race may not be immediately evident if b is large (Exercise 91).

> **THEOREM 8.6 Growth Rates of Sequences**
> The following sequences are ordered according to increasing growth rates as $n \to \infty$; that is, if $\{a_n\}$ appears before $\{b_n\}$ in the list, then $\lim_{n\to\infty} \frac{a_n}{b_n} = 0$ and $\lim_{n\to\infty} \frac{b_n}{a_n} = \infty$:
> $$\{\ln^q n\} \ll \{n^p\} \ll \{n^p \ln^r n\} \ll \{n^{p+s}\} \ll \{b^n\} \ll \{n!\} \ll \{n^n\}.$$
> The ordering applies for positive real numbers p, q, r, s, and $b > 1$.

QUICK CHECK 4 Which sequence grows faster: $\{\ln n\}$ or $\{n^{1.1}\}$? What is $\lim_{n\to\infty} \frac{n^{1,000,000}}{e^n}$? ◀

It is worth noting that the rankings in Theorem 8.6 do not change if a sequence is multiplied by a positive constant (Exercise 104).

EXAMPLE 6 Convergence and growth rates Compare growth rates of sequences to determine whether the following sequences converge.

a. $\left\{\frac{\ln n^{10}}{0.00001n}\right\}$ **b.** $\left\{\frac{n^8 \ln n}{n^{8.001}}\right\}$ **c.** $\left\{\frac{n!}{10^n}\right\}$

SOLUTION

a. Because $\ln n^{10} = 10 \ln n$, the sequence in the numerator is a constant multiple of the sequence $\{\ln n\}$. Similarly, the sequence in the denominator is a constant multiple of the sequence $\{n\}$. By Theorem 8.6, $\{n\}$ grows faster than $\{\ln n\}$ as $n \to \infty$; therefore, the sequence $\left\{\frac{\ln n^{10}}{0.00001n}\right\}$ converges to zero.

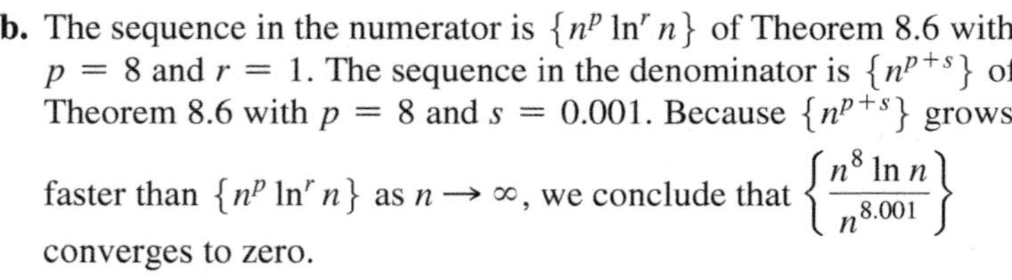

b. The sequence in the numerator is $\{n^p \ln^r n\}$ of Theorem 8.6 with $p = 8$ and $r = 1$. The sequence in the denominator is $\{n^{p+s}\}$ of Theorem 8.6 with $p = 8$ and $s = 0.001$. Because $\{n^{p+s}\}$ grows faster than $\{n^p \ln^r n\}$ as $n \to \infty$, we conclude that $\left\{\frac{n^8 \ln n}{n^{8.001}}\right\}$ converges to zero.

c. Using Theorem 8.6, we see that $n!$ grows faster than any exponential function as $n \to \infty$. Therefore, $\lim_{n\to\infty} \frac{n!}{10^n} = \infty$, and the sequence diverges. Figure 8.23 gives a visual comparison of the growth rates of $\{n!\}$ and $\{10^n\}$. Because these sequences grow so quickly, we plot the logarithm of the terms. The exponential sequence $\{10^n\}$ dominates the factorial sequence $\{n!\}$ until $n = 25$ terms. At that point, the factorial sequence overtakes the exponential sequence.

Related Exercises 63–68 ◀

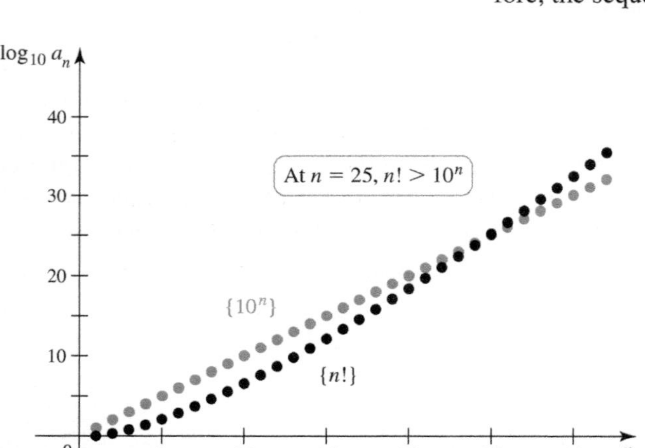

Figure 8.23

Formal Definition of a Limit of a Sequence

As with limits of functions, there is a formal definition of the limit of a sequence.

> **DEFINITION Limit of a Sequence**
>
> The sequence $\{a_n\}$ converges to L provided the terms of a_n can be made arbitrarily close to L by taking n sufficiently large. More precisely, $\{a_n\}$ has the unique limit L if given any $\varepsilon > 0$, it is possible to find a positive integer N (depending only on ε) such that
>
> $$|a_n - L| < \varepsilon \qquad \text{whenever } n > N.$$
>
> If the **limit of a sequence** is L, we say the sequence **converges** to L, written
>
> $$\lim_{n\to\infty} a_n = L.$$
>
> A sequence that does not converge is said to **diverge**.

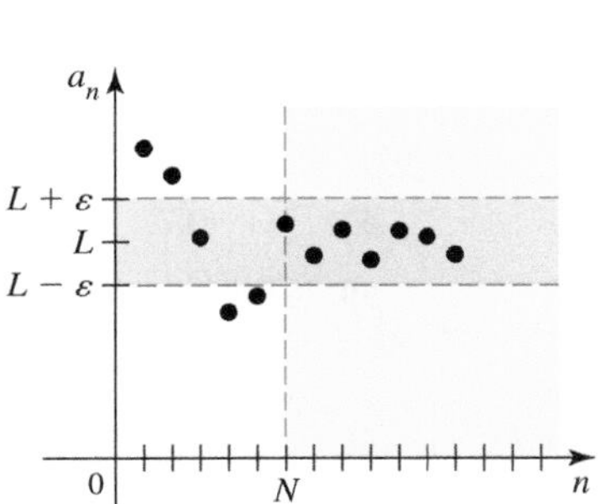

Figure 8.24

The formal definition of the limit of a convergent sequence is interpreted in much the same way as the limit at infinity of a function. Given a small tolerance $\varepsilon > 0$, how far out in the sequence must you go so that all succeeding terms are within ε of the limit L (Figure 8.24)? Given *any* value of $\varepsilon > 0$ (no matter how small), you must find a value of N such that all terms beyond a_N are within ε of L.

EXAMPLE 7 Limits using the formal definition Consider the claim that $\lim_{n\to\infty} a_n = \lim_{n\to\infty} \frac{n}{n-1} = 1.$

a. Given $\varepsilon = 0.01$, find a value of N that satisfies the conditions of the limit definition.

b. Prove that $\lim_{n\to\infty} a_n = 1.$

SOLUTION

a. We must find an integer N such that $|a_n - 1| < \varepsilon = 0.01$ whenever $n > N$. This condition can be written

$$|a_n - 1| = \left|\frac{n}{n-1} - 1\right| = \left|\frac{1}{n-1}\right| < 0.01.$$

Noting that $n > 1$, the absolute value can be removed. The condition on n becomes $n - 1 > 1/0.01 = 100$, or $n > 101$. Therefore, we take $N = 101$ or any larger number. This means that $|a_n - 1| < 0.01$ whenever $n > 101$.

b. Given *any* $\varepsilon > 0$, we must find a value of N (depending on ε) that guarantees $|a_n - 1| = \left|\frac{n}{n-1} - 1\right| < \varepsilon$ whenever $n > N$. For $n > 1$, the inequality $\left|\frac{n}{n-1} - 1\right| < \varepsilon$ implies that

$$\left|\frac{n}{n-1} - 1\right| = \frac{1}{n-1} < \varepsilon.$$

Solving for n, we find that $\frac{1}{n-1} < \varepsilon$ or $n - 1 > \frac{1}{\varepsilon}$ or $n > \frac{1}{\varepsilon} + 1$. Therefore, given a tolerance $\varepsilon > 0$, we must look beyond a_N in the sequence, where $N \geq \frac{1}{\varepsilon} + 1$, to be sure that the terms of the sequence are within ε of the limit 1. Because we can provide a value of N for *any* $\varepsilon > 0$, the limit exists and equals 1.

Related Exercises 69–74 ◀

➤ In general, $1/\varepsilon + 1$ is not an integer, so N should be the least integer greater than $1/\varepsilon + 1$ or any larger integer.

SECTION 8.2 EXERCISES

Review Questions

1. Give an example of a nonincreasing sequence with a limit.
2. Give an example of a nondecreasing sequence without a limit.
3. Give an example of a bounded sequence that has a limit.
4. Give an example of a bounded sequence without a limit.
5. For what values of r does the sequence $\{r^n\}$ converge? Diverge?
6. Explain how the methods used to find the limit of a function as $x \to \infty$ are used to find the limit of a sequence.
7. Compare the growth rates of $\{n^{100}\}$ and $\{e^{n/100}\}$ as $n \to \infty$.
8. Explain how two sequences that differ only in their first ten terms can have the same limit.

Basic Skills

9–34. Limits of sequences *Find the limit of the following sequences or determine that the limit does not exist.*

9. $\left\{\frac{n^3}{n^4+1}\right\}$
10. $\left\{\frac{n^{12}}{3n^{12}+4}\right\}$
11. $\left\{\frac{3n^3-1}{2n^3+1}\right\}$
12. $\left\{\frac{2e^n+1}{e^n}\right\}$
13. $\left\{\frac{3^{n+1}+3}{3^n}\right\}$
14. $\left\{\frac{k}{\sqrt{9k^2+1}}\right\}$
15. $\{\tan^{-1} n\}$
16. $\{\sqrt{n^2+1}-n\}$
17. $\left\{\frac{\tan^{-1} n}{n}\right\}$
18. $\{n^{2/n}\}$
19. $\left\{\left(1+\frac{2}{n}\right)^n\right\}$
20. $\left\{\left(\frac{n}{n+5}\right)^n\right\}$
21. $\left\{\sqrt{\left(1+\frac{1}{2n}\right)^n}\right\}$
22. $\left\{\left(1+\frac{4}{n}\right)^{3n}\right\}$
23. $\left\{\frac{n}{e^n+3n}\right\}$
24. $\left\{\frac{\ln(1/n)}{n}\right\}$
25. $\left\{\left(\frac{1}{n}\right)^{1/n}\right\}$
26. $\left\{\left(1-\frac{4}{n}\right)^n\right\}$
27. $\{b_n\}$, where $b_n = \begin{cases} n/(n+1) & \text{if } n \le 5000 \\ ne^{-n} & \text{if } n > 5000 \end{cases}$
28. $\{\ln(n^3+1) - \ln(3n^3+10n)\}$
29. $\{\ln \sin(1/n) + \ln n\}$
30. $\{n(1-\cos(1/n))\}$
31. $\left\{n \sin \frac{6}{n}\right\}$
32. $\left\{\frac{(-1)^n}{n}\right\}$
33. $\left\{\frac{(-1)^n n}{n+1}\right\}$
34. $\left\{\frac{(-1)^{n+1} n^2}{2n^3+n}\right\}$

T **35–44. Limits of sequences and graphing** *Find the limit of the following sequences or determine that the limit does not exist. Verify your result with a graphing utility.*

35. $a_n = \sin \frac{n\pi}{2}$
36. $a_n = \frac{(-1)^n n}{n+1}$
37. $a_n = \frac{\sin(n\pi/3)}{\sqrt{n}}$
38. $a_n = \frac{3^n}{3^n+4^n}$
39. $a_n = 1 + \cos \frac{1}{n}$
40. $a_n = \frac{e^{-n}}{2\sin(e^{-n})}$
41. $a_n = e^{-n} \cos n$
42. $a_n = \frac{\ln n}{n^{1.1}}$
43. $a_n = (-1)^n \sqrt[n]{n}$
44. $a_n = \cot\left(\frac{n\pi}{2n+2}\right)$

45–52. Geometric sequences *Determine whether the following sequences converge or diverge, and state whether they are monotonic or whether they oscillate. Give the limit when the sequence converges.*

45. $\{0.2^n\}$
46. $\{1.2^n\}$
47. $\{(-0.7)^n\}$
48. $\{5(-1.01)^n\}$
49. $\{1.00001^n\}$
50. $\{2^{n+1}3^{-n}\}$
51. $\{(-2.5)^n\}$
52. $\{100(-0.003)^n\}$

53–58. Squeeze Theorem *Find the limit of the following sequences or state that they diverge.*

53. $\left\{\frac{\cos n}{n}\right\}$
54. $\left\{\frac{\sin 6n}{5n}\right\}$
55. $\left\{\frac{\sin n}{2^n}\right\}$
56. $\left\{\frac{\cos(n\pi/2)}{\sqrt{n}}\right\}$
57. $\left\{\frac{2\tan^{-1} n}{n^3+4}\right\}$
58. $\left\{\frac{n \sin^3(n\pi/2)}{n+1}\right\}$

T 59. **Periodic dosing** Many people take aspirin on a regular basis as a preventive measure for heart disease. Suppose a person takes 80 mg of aspirin every 24 hours. Assume also that aspirin has a half-life of 24 hours; that is, every 24 hours, half of the drug in the blood is eliminated.

a. Find a recurrence relation for the sequence $\{d_n\}$ that gives the amount of drug in the blood after the nth dose, where $d_1 = 80$.
b. Using a calculator, determine the limit of the sequence. In the long run, how much drug is in the person's blood?
c. Confirm the result of part (b) by finding the limit of $\{d_n\}$ directly.

T 60. **A car loan** Marie takes out a \$20,000 loan for a new car. The loan has an annual interest rate of 6% or, equivalently, a monthly interest rate of 0.5%. Each month, the bank adds interest to the loan balance (the interest is always 0.5% of the current balance), and then Marie makes a \$200 payment to reduce the loan balance. Let B_n be the loan balance immediately after the nth payment, where $B_0 = \$20{,}000$.

a. Write the first five terms of the sequence $\{B_n\}$.
b. Find a recurrence relation that generates the sequence $\{B_n\}$.
c. Determine how many months are needed to reduce the loan balance to zero.

T 61. **A savings plan** James begins a savings plan in which he deposits \$100 at the beginning of each month into an account that earns 9% interest annually or, equivalently, 0.75% per month. To be clear, on the first day of each month, the bank adds 0.75% of the current balance as interest, and then James deposits \$100. Let B_n be the balance in the account after the nth deposit, where $B_0 = \$0$.

a. Write the first five terms of the sequence $\{B_n\}$.
b. Find a recurrence relation that generates the sequence $\{B_n\}$.
c. How many months are needed to reach a balance of \$5000?

62. Diluting a solution A tank is filled with 100 L of a 40% alcohol solution (by volume). You repeatedly perform the following operation: Remove 2 L of the solution from the tank and replace them with 2 L of 10% alcohol solution.

a. Let C_n be the concentration of the solution in the tank after the nth replacement, where $C_0 = 40\%$. Write the first five terms of the sequence $\{C_n\}$.
b. After how many replacements does the alcohol concentration reach 15%?
c. Determine the limiting (steady-state) concentration of the solution that is approached after many replacements.

63–68. Growth rates of sequences *Use Theorem 8.6 to find the limit of the following sequences or state that they diverge.*

63. $\left\{\frac{n!}{n^n}\right\}$
64. $\left\{\frac{3^n}{n!}\right\}$
65. $\left\{\frac{n^{10}}{\ln^{20} n}\right\}$
66. $\left\{\frac{n^{10}}{\ln^{1000} n}\right\}$
67. $\left\{\frac{n^{1000}}{2^n}\right\}$
68. $\left\{\frac{e^{n/10}}{2^n}\right\}$

69–74. Formal proofs of limits *Use the formal definition of the limit of a sequence to prove the following limits.*

69. $\lim_{n\to\infty} \frac{1}{n} = 0$
70. $\lim_{n\to\infty} \frac{1}{n^2} = 0$
71. $\lim_{n\to\infty} \frac{3n^2}{4n^2 + 1} = \frac{3}{4}$
72. $\lim_{n\to\infty} b^{-n} = 0$, for $b > 1$
73. $\lim_{n\to\infty} \frac{cn}{bn + 1} = \frac{c}{b}$, for real numbers $b > 0$ and $c > 0$
74. $\lim_{n\to\infty} \frac{n}{n^2 + 1} = 0$

Further Explorations

75. **Explain why or why not** Determine whether the following statements are true and give an explanation or counterexample.

a. If $\lim_{n\to\infty} a_n = 1$ and $\lim_{n\to\infty} b_n = 3$, then $\lim_{n\to\infty} \frac{b_n}{a_n} = 3$.
b. If $\lim_{n\to\infty} a_n = 0$ and $\lim_{n\to\infty} b_n = \infty$, then $\lim_{n\to\infty} a_n b_n = 0$.
c. The convergent sequences $\{a_n\}$ and $\{b_n\}$ differ in their first 100 terms, but $a_n = b_n$, for $n > 100$. It follows that $\lim_{n\to\infty} a_n = \lim_{n\to\infty} b_n$.
d. If $\{a_n\} = \left\{1, \frac{1}{2}, \frac{1}{3}, \frac{1}{4}, \frac{1}{5}, \ldots\right\}$ and $\{b_n\} = \left\{1, 0, \frac{1}{2}, 0, \frac{1}{3}, 0, \frac{1}{4}, 0, \ldots\right\}$, then $\lim_{n\to\infty} a_n = \lim_{n\to\infty} b_n$.
e. If the sequence $\{a_n\}$ converges, then the sequence $\{(-1)^n a_n\}$ converges.
f. If the sequence $\{a_n\}$ diverges, then the sequence $\{0.000001\, a_n\}$ diverges.

76–77. Reindexing *Express each sequence $\{a_n\}_{n=1}^{\infty}$ as an equivalent sequence of the form $\{b_n\}_{n=3}^{\infty}$.*

76. $\{2n + 1\}_{n=1}^{\infty}$
77. $\{n^2 + 6n - 9\}_{n=1}^{\infty}$

78–85. More sequences *Evaluate the limit of the following sequences or state that the limit does not exist.*

78. $a_n = \int_1^n x^{-2}\, dx$
79. $a_n = \frac{75^{n-1}}{99^n} + \frac{5^n \sin n}{8^n}$
80. $a_n = \tan^{-1}\left(\frac{10n}{10n + 4}\right)$
81. $a_n = \cos(0.99^n) + \frac{7^n + 9^n}{63^n}$
82. $a_n = \frac{4^n + 5n!}{n! + 2^n}$
83. $a_n = \frac{6^n + 3^n}{6^n + n^{100}}$
84. $a_n = \frac{n^8 + n^7}{n^7 + n^8 \ln n}$
85. $a_n = \frac{7^n}{n^7 5^n}$

86–90. Sequences by recurrence relations *Consider the following sequences defined by a recurrence relation. Use a calculator, analytical methods, and/or graphing to make a conjecture about the limit of the sequence or state that the sequence diverges.*

86. $a_{n+1} = \frac{1}{2}a_n + 2;\ a_0 = 5$
87. $a_{n+1} = 2a_n(1 - a_n);\ a_0 = 0.3$
88. $a_{n+1} = \frac{1}{2}(a_n + 2/a_n);\ a_0 = 2$
89. $a_{n+1} = 4a_n(1 - a_n);\ a_0 = 0.5$
90. $a_{n+1} = \sqrt{2 + a_n};\ a_0 = 1$

91. **Crossover point** The sequence $\{n!\}$ ultimately grows faster than the sequence $\{b^n\}$, for any $b > 1$, as $n \to \infty$. However, b^n is generally greater than $n!$ for small values of n. Use a calculator to determine the smallest value of n such that $n! > b^n$ for each of the cases $b = 2$, $b = e$, and $b = 10$.

Applications

92. **Fish harvesting** A fishery manager knows that her fish population naturally increases at a rate of 1.5% per month, while 80 fish are harvested each month. Let F_n be the fish population after the nth month, where $F_0 = 4000$ fish.

a. Write out the first five terms of the sequence $\{F_n\}$.
b. Find a recurrence relation that generates the sequence $\{F_n\}$.
c. Does the fish population decrease or increase in the long run?
d. Determine whether the fish population decreases or increases in the long run if the initial population is 5500 fish.
e. Determine the initial fish population F_0 below which the population decreases.

93. **The hungry heifer** A heifer weighing 200 lb today gains 5 lb per day with a food cost of 45¢/day. The price for heifers is 65¢/lb today but is falling 1¢/day.

a. Let h_n be the profit in selling the heifer on the nth day, where $h_0 = (200\text{ lb}) \cdot (\$0.65/\text{lb}) = \$130$. Write out the first 10 terms of the sequence $\{h_n\}$.
b. How many days after today should the heifer be sold to maximize the profit?

94. **Sleep model** After many nights of observation, you notice that if you oversleep one night, you tend to undersleep the following night, and vice versa. This pattern of compensation is described by the relationship

$$x_{n+1} = \frac{1}{2}(x_n + x_{n-1}), \quad \text{for } n = 1, 2, 3, \ldots,$$

where x_n is the number of hours of sleep you get on the nth night and $x_0 = 7$ and $x_1 = 6$ are the number of hours of sleep on the first two nights, respectively.

a. Write out the first six terms of the sequence $\{x_n\}$ and confirm that the terms alternately increase and decrease.
b. Show that the explicit formula

$$x_n = \frac{19}{3} + \frac{2}{3}\left(-\frac{1}{2}\right)^n, \text{ for } n \geq 0,$$

generates the terms of the sequence in part (a).
c. What is the limit of the sequence?

T 95. Calculator algorithm The CORDIC (COordinate Rotation DIgital Calculation) algorithm is used by most calculators to evaluate trigonometric and logarithmic functions. An important number in the CORDIC algorithm, called the *aggregate constant*, is given by the infinite product $\prod_{n=0}^{\infty} \frac{2^n}{\sqrt{1+2^{2n}}}$, where $\prod_{n=0}^{N} a_n$ represents the product $a_0 \cdot a_1 \cdots a_N$.

This infinite product is the limit of the sequence

$$\left\{\prod_{n=0}^{0} \frac{2^n}{\sqrt{1+2^{2n}}}, \prod_{n=0}^{1} \frac{2^n}{\sqrt{1+2^{2n}}}, \prod_{n=0}^{2} \frac{2^n}{\sqrt{1+2^{2n}}}, \ldots\right\}.$$

Estimate the value of the aggregate constant. (See the Guided Project *CORDIC algorithms: How your calculator works.*)

Additional Exercises

96. Bounded monotonic proof Use mathematical induction to prove that the drug dose sequence in Example 5,

$$d_{n+1} = 0.5d_n + 100, d_1 = 100, \quad \text{for } n = 1, 2, 3, \ldots,$$

is bounded and monotonic.

T 97. Repeated square roots Consider the expression $\sqrt{1 + \sqrt{1 + \sqrt{1 + \sqrt{1 + \cdots}}}}$, where the process continues indefinitely.

a. Show that this expression can be built in steps using the recurrence relation $a_0 = 1, a_{n+1} = \sqrt{1 + a_n}$, for $n = 0, 1, 2, 3, \ldots$. Explain why the value of the expression can be interpreted as $\lim_{n\to\infty} a_n$, provided the limit exists.
b. Evaluate the first five terms of the sequence $\{a_n\}$.
c. Estimate the limit of the sequence. Compare your estimate with $(1 + \sqrt{5})/2$, a number known as the *golden mean*.
d. Assuming the limit exists, use the method of Example 5 to determine the limit exactly.
e. Repeat the preceding analysis for the expression $\sqrt{p + \sqrt{p + \sqrt{p + \sqrt{p + \cdots}}}}$, where $p > 0$. Make a table showing the approximate value of this expression for various values of p. Does the expression seem to have a limit for all positive values of p?

T 98. A sequence of products Find the limit of the sequence

$$\{a_n\}_{n=2}^{\infty} = \left\{\left(1 - \frac{1}{2}\right)\left(1 - \frac{1}{3}\right) \cdots \left(1 - \frac{1}{n}\right)\right\}_{n=2}^{\infty}.$$

T 99. Continued fractions The expression

$$1 + \cfrac{1}{1 + \cfrac{1}{1 + \cfrac{1}{1 + \cfrac{1}{1 + \ddots}}}},$$

where the process continues indefinitely, is called a *continued fraction*.

a. Show that this expression can be built in steps using the recurrence relation $a_0 = 1, a_{n+1} = 1 + 1/a_n$, for $n = 0, 1, 2, 3, \ldots$. Explain why the value of the expression can be interpreted as $\lim_{n\to\infty} a_n$, provided the limit exists.
b. Evaluate the first five terms of the sequence $\{a_n\}$.
c. Using computation and/or graphing, estimate the limit of the sequence.
d. Assuming the limit exists, use the method of Example 5 to determine the limit exactly. Compare your estimate with $(1 + \sqrt{5})/2$, a number known as the *golden mean.*
e. Assuming the limit exists, use the same ideas to determine the value of

$$a + \cfrac{b}{a + \cfrac{b}{a + \cfrac{b}{a + \cfrac{b}{a + \ddots}}}},$$

where a and b are positive real numbers.

T 100. Tower of powers For a positive real number p, the tower of exponents $p^{p^{p^{\cdot^{\cdot}}}}$ continues indefinitely and the expression is ambiguous. The tower could be built from the top as the limit of the sequence $\{p^p, (p^p)^p, ((p^p)^p)^p, \ldots\}$, in which case the sequence is defined recursively as

$$a_{n+1} = a_n^p \text{ (building from the top)}, \tag{1}$$

where $a_1 = p^p$. The tower could also be built from the bottom as the limit of the sequence $\{p^p, p^{(p^p)}, p^{(p^{(p^p)})}, \ldots\}$, in which case the sequence is defined recursively as

$$a_{n+1} = p^{a_n} \text{ (building from the bottom)}, \tag{2}$$

where again $a_1 = p^p$.

a. Estimate the value of the tower with $p = 0.5$ by building from the top. That is, use tables to estimate the limit of the sequence defined recursively by (1) with $p = 0.5$. Estimate the maximum value of $p > 0$ for which the sequence has a limit.
b. Estimate the value of the tower with $p = 1.2$ by building from the bottom. That is, use tables to estimate the limit of the sequence defined recursively by (2) with $p = 1.2$. Estimate the maximum value of $p > 1$ for which the sequence has a limit.

T 101. Fibonacci sequence The famous Fibonacci sequence was proposed by Leonardo Pisano, also known as Fibonacci, in about A.D. 1200 as a model for the growth of rabbit populations. It is given by the recurrence relation $f_{n+1} = f_n + f_{n-1}$, for $n = 1, 2, 3, \ldots$, where $f_0 = 1, f_1 = 1$. Each term of the sequence is the sum of its two predecessors.

a. Write out the first ten terms of the sequence.
b. Is the sequence bounded?
c. Estimate or determine $\varphi = \lim_{n\to\infty} \frac{f_{n+1}}{f_n}$, the ratio of the successive terms of the sequence. Provide evidence that $\varphi = (1 + \sqrt{5})/2$, a number known as the *golden mean.*
d. Use induction to verify the remarkable result that

$$f_n = \frac{1}{\sqrt{5}}(\varphi^n - (-1)^n \varphi^{-n}).$$

102. Arithmetic-geometric mean Pick two positive numbers a_0 and b_0 with $a_0 > b_0$, and write out the first few terms of the two sequences $\{a_n\}$ and $\{b_n\}$:

$$a_{n+1} = \frac{a_n + b_n}{2}, \qquad b_{n+1} = \sqrt{a_n b_n}, \qquad \text{for } n = 0, 1, 2 \ldots.$$

(Recall that the arithmetic mean $A = (p + q)/2$ and the geometric mean $G = \sqrt{pq}$ of two positive numbers p and q satisfy $A \geq G$.)

a. Show that $a_n > b_n$ for all n.
b. Show that $\{a_n\}$ is a decreasing sequence and $\{b_n\}$ is an increasing sequence.
c. Conclude that $\{a_n\}$ and $\{b_n\}$ converge.
d. Show that $a_{n+1} - b_{n+1} < (a_n - b_n)/2$ and conclude that $\lim_{n\to\infty} a_n = \lim_{n\to\infty} b_n$. The common value of these limits is called the arithmetic-geometric mean of a_0 and b_0, denoted $\text{AGM}(a_0, b_0)$.
e. Estimate AGM(12, 20). Estimate Gauss' constant $1/\text{AGM}(1, \sqrt{2})$.

103. The hailstone sequence Here is a fascinating (unsolved) problem known as the hailstone problem (or the Ulam Conjecture or the Collatz Conjecture). It involves sequences in two different ways. First, choose a positive integer N and call it a_0. This is the *seed* of a sequence. The rest of the sequence is generated as follows: For $n = 0, 1, 2, \ldots$

$$a_{n+1} = \begin{cases} a_n/2 & \text{if } a_n \text{ is even} \\ 3a_n + 1 & \text{if } a_n \text{ is odd.} \end{cases}$$

However, if $a_n = 1$ for any n, then the sequence terminates.

a. Compute the sequence that results from the seeds $N = 2, 3, 4, \ldots, 10$. You should verify that in all these cases, the sequence eventually terminates. The hailstone conjecture (still unproved) states that for all positive integers N, the sequence terminates after a finite number of terms.
b. Now define the hailstone sequence $\{H_k\}$, which is the number of terms needed for the sequence $\{a_n\}$ to terminate starting with a seed of k. Verify that $H_2 = 1$, $H_3 = 7$, and $H_4 = 2$.
c. Plot as many terms of the hailstone sequence as is feasible. How did the sequence get its name? Does the conjecture appear to be true?

104. Prove that if $\{a_n\} \ll \{b_n\}$ (as used in Theorem 8.6), then $\{ca_n\} \ll \{db_n\}$, where c and d are positive real numbers.

105. Convergence proof Consider the sequence defined by $a_{n+1} = \sqrt{3a_n}$, $a_1 = \sqrt{3}$, for $n \ge 1$.
a. Show that $\{a_n\}$ is increasing.
b. Show that $\{a_n\}$ is bounded between 0 and 3.
c. Explain why $\lim_{n\to\infty} a_n$ exists.
d. Find $\lim_{n\to\infty} a_n$.

T 106–110. Comparing sequences *In the following exercises, two sequences are given, one of which initially has smaller values, but eventually "overtakes" the other sequence. Find the sequence with the larger growth rate and the value of n at which it overtakes the other sequence.*

106. $a_n = \sqrt{n}$ and $b_n = 2 \ln n$, $n \ge 3$

107. $a_n = e^{n/2}$ and $b_n = n^5$, $n \ge 2$

108. $a_n = n^{1.001}$ and $b_n = \ln n^{10}$, $n \ge 1$

109. $a_n = n!$ and $b_n = n^{0.7n}$, $n \ge 2$

110. $a_n = n^{10}$ and $b_n = n^9 \ln^3 n$, $n \ge 7$

T 111. Comparing sequences with a parameter For what values of a does the sequence $\{n!\}$ grow faster than the sequence $\{n^{an}\}$? (*Hint:* Stirling's formula is useful: $n! \approx \sqrt{2\pi n}\, n^n e^{-n}$, for large values of n.)

QUICK CHECK ANSWERS

1. a. Bounded, monotonic; **b.** Bounded, not monotonic; **c.** Not bounded, not monotonic; **d.** Bounded, monotonic (both nonincreasing and nondecreasing) **2.** If $r = -1$, the sequence is $\{-1, 1, -1, 1, \ldots\}$, the terms alternate in sign, and the sequence diverges. If $r = 1$, the sequence is $\{1, 1, 1, 1, \ldots\}$, the terms are constant, and the sequence converges to 1. **3.** Both changes would increase the steady-state level of drug. **4.** $\{n^{1.1}\}$ grows faster; the limit is 0. ◄

8.3 Infinite Series

➤ The sequence of partial sums may be visualized nicely as follows:

$$\underbrace{\underbrace{\underbrace{a_1}_{S_1} + a_2}_{S_2} + a_3}_{S_3} + a_4 + \cdots$$

We begin our discussion of infinite series with *geometric series*. These series arise more frequently than any other infinite series, they are used in many practical problems, and they illustrate all the essential features of infinite series in general. First let's summarize some important ideas from Section 8.1.

Recall that every infinite series $\sum_{k=1}^{\infty} a_k$ has a sequence of partial sums:

$$S_1 = a_1, \qquad S_2 = a_1 + a_2, \qquad S_3 = a_1 + a_2 + a_3,$$

and in general, $S_n = \sum_{k=1}^{n} a_k$, for $n = 1, 2, 3, \ldots$.

If the sequence of partial sums $\{S_n\}$ converges—that is, if $\lim_{n\to\infty} S_n = L$—then the value of the infinite series is also L. If the sequence of partial sums diverges, then the infinite series also diverges.

In summary, to evaluate an infinite series, it is necessary to determine a formula for the sequence of partial sums $\{S_n\}$ and then find its limit. This procedure can be carried out with the series that we discuss in this section: geometric series and telescoping series.

Geometric Sums and Series

➤ Geometric *sequences* have the form $\{r^k\}$ or $\{ar^k\}$. Geometric *sums* and *series* have the form $\sum r^k$ or $\sum ar^k$.

As a preliminary step to geometric series, we study geometric sums, which are *finite sums* in which each term in the sum is a constant multiple of the previous term. A **geometric sum** with n terms has the form

$$S_n = a + ar + ar^2 + \cdots + ar^{n-1} = \sum_{k=0}^{n-1} ar^k,$$

where $a \neq 0$ and r are real numbers; r is called the **ratio** of the sum and a is its first term. For example, the geometric sum with $r = 0.1$, $a = 0.9$, and $n = 4$ is

$$0.9 + 0.09 + 0.009 + 0.0009 = 0.9(1 + 0.1 + 0.01 + 0.001)$$
$$= \sum_{k=0}^{3} 0.9(0.1^k).$$

QUICK CHECK 1 Which of the following sums are not geometric sums?

a. $\sum_{k=0}^{10} \left(\frac{1}{2}\right)^k$ **b.** $\sum_{k=0}^{20} \frac{1}{k}$

c. $\sum_{k=0}^{30} (2k + 1)$ ◄

Our goal is to find a formula for the value of the geometric sum

$$S_n = a + ar + ar^2 + \cdots + ar^{n-1}, \tag{1}$$

for any values of $a \neq 0$, r, and the positive integer n. Doing so requires a clever maneuver. The first step is to multiply both sides of equation (1) by the ratio r:

$$rS_n = r(a + ar + ar^2 + ar^3 + \cdots + ar^{n-1})$$
$$= ar + ar^2 + ar^3 + \cdots + ar^{n-1} + ar^n. \tag{2}$$

➤ The notation $\sum_{k=0}^{\infty} ar^k$ appears to have an undefined first term when $r = 0$. The notation is understood to mean $a + ar + ar^2 + \cdots$ and therefore, the series has a value of a when $r = 0$.

We now subtract equation (2) from equation (1). Notice how most of the terms on the right sides of these equations cancel, leaving

$$S_n - rS_n = a - ar^n.$$

Assuming $r \neq 1$ and solving for S_n results in a general formula for the value of a geometric sum:

$$S_n = a\frac{1 - r^n}{1 - r}. \tag{3}$$

Having dealt with geometric sums, it is a short step to *geometric series*. We simply note that the geometric sums $S_n = \sum_{k=0}^{n-1} ar^k$ form the sequence of partial sums for the geometric series $\sum_{k=0}^{\infty} ar^k$. The value of the geometric series is the limit of its sequence of partial sums (provided it exists). Using equation (3), we have

QUICK CHECK 2 Verify that the geometric sum formula gives the correct result for the sums $1 + \frac{1}{2}$ and $\frac{1}{2} + \frac{1}{4} + \frac{1}{8}$. ◄

$$\underbrace{\sum_{k=0}^{\infty} ar^k}_{\text{geometric series}} = \lim_{n\to\infty} \underbrace{\sum_{k=0}^{n-1} ar^k}_{\text{geometric sum } S_n} = \lim_{n\to\infty} a\frac{1 - r^n}{1 - r}.$$

To compute this limit, we must examine the behavior of r^n as $n \to \infty$. Recall from our work with geometric sequences (Section 8.2) that

$$\lim_{n\to\infty} r^n = \begin{cases} 0 & \text{if } |r| < 1 \\ 1 & \text{if } r = 1 \\ \text{does not exist} & \text{if } r \leq -1 \text{ or } r > 1. \end{cases}$$

Case 1: $|r| < 1$ Because $\lim_{n\to\infty} r^n = 0$, we have

$$\lim_{n\to\infty} S_n = \lim_{n\to\infty} a\frac{1 - r^n}{1 - r} = a\frac{1 - \overbrace{\lim_{n\to\infty} r^n}^{0}}{1 - r} = \frac{a}{1 - r}.$$

In the case that $|r| < 1$, the geometric series *converges* to $\dfrac{a}{1 - r}$.

Case 2: $|r| > 1$ In this case, $\lim_{n\to\infty} r^n$ does not exist, so $\lim_{n\to\infty} S_n$ does not exist and the series *diverges.*

Case 3: $|r| = 1$ If $r = 1$, then the geometric series is $\sum_{k=0}^{\infty} a = a + a + a + \cdots$, which diverges. If $r = -1$, the geometric series is $a\sum_{k=0}^{\infty}(-1)^k = a - a + a - \cdots$, which also diverges (because the sequence of partial sums oscillates between 0 and a). We summarize these results in Theorem 8.7.

QUICK CHECK 3 Evaluate $\frac{1}{2} + \frac{1}{4} + \frac{1}{8} + \frac{1}{16} + \cdots$. ◀

THEOREM 8.7 Geometric Series

Let $a \neq 0$ and r be real numbers. If $|r| < 1$, then $\sum_{k=0}^{\infty} ar^k = \frac{a}{1-r}$. If $|r| \geq 1$, then the series diverges.

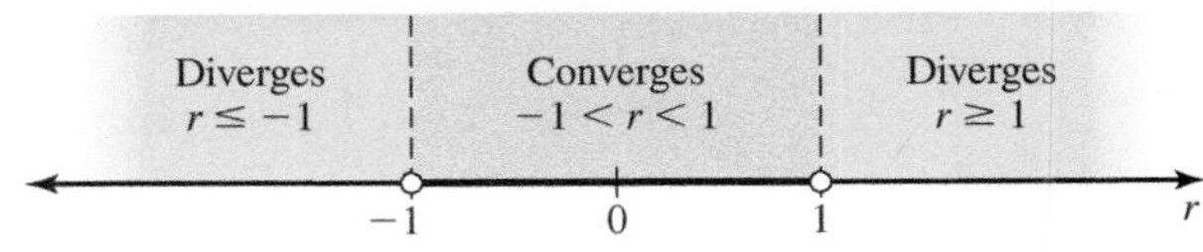

QUICK CHECK 4 Explain why $\sum_{k=0}^{\infty} 0.2^k$ converges and why $\sum_{k=0}^{\infty} 2^k$ diverges. ◀

EXAMPLE 1 Geometric series Evaluate the following geometric series or state that the series diverges.

a. $\sum_{k=0}^{\infty} 1.1^k$ **b.** $\sum_{k=0}^{\infty} e^{-k}$ **c.** $\sum_{k=2}^{\infty} 3(-0.75)^k$

SOLUTION

a. The ratio of this geometric series is $r = 1.1$. Because $|r| \geq 1$, the series diverges.

b. Note that $e^{-k} = \frac{1}{e^k} = \left(\frac{1}{e}\right)^k$. Therefore, the ratio of the series is $r = \frac{1}{e}$, and its first term is $a = 1$. Because $|r| < 1$, the series converges and its value is

$$\sum_{k=0}^{\infty} e^{-k} = \sum_{k=0}^{\infty}\left(\frac{1}{e}\right)^k = \frac{1}{1-(1/e)} = \frac{e}{e-1} \approx 1.582.$$

c. Writing out the first few terms of the series is helpful:

➤ The series in Example 1c is called an *alternating series* because the terms alternate in sign. Such series are discussed in detail in Section 8.6.

$$\sum_{k=2}^{\infty} 3(-0.75)^k = \underbrace{3(-0.75)^2}_{a} + \underbrace{3(-0.75)^3}_{ar} + \underbrace{3(-0.75)^4}_{ar^2} + \cdots.$$

We see that the first term of the series is $a = 3(-0.75)^2$ and that the ratio of the series is $r = -0.75$. Because $|r| < 1$, the series converges, and its value is

$$\sum_{k=2}^{\infty} 3(-0.75)^k = \underbrace{\frac{3(-0.75)^2}{1-(-0.75)}}_{\frac{a}{1-r}} = \frac{27}{28}.$$

Related Exercises 7–40 ◀

EXAMPLE 2 **Decimal expansions as geometric series** Write $1.0\overline{35} = 1.0353535...$ as a geometric series and express its value as a fraction.

SOLUTION Notice that the decimal part of this number is a convergent geometric series with $a = 0.035$ and $r = 0.01$:

$$1.0353535\ldots = 1 + \underbrace{0.035 + 0.00035 + 0.0000035 + \cdots}_{\text{geometric series with } a = 0.035 \text{ and } r = 0.01}.$$

Evaluating the series, we have

$$1.0353535\ldots = 1 + \frac{a}{1-r} = 1 + \frac{0.035}{1 - 0.01} = 1 + \frac{35}{990} = \frac{205}{198}.$$

Related Exercises 41–54 ◀

Telescoping Series

With geometric series, we carried out the entire evaluation process by finding a formula for the sequence of partial sums and evaluating the limit of the sequence. Not many infinite series can be subjected to this sort of analysis. With another class of series, called **telescoping series**, it can also be done. Here is an example.

EXAMPLE 3 **Telescoping series** Evaluate the following series.

a. $\displaystyle\sum_{k=1}^{\infty}\left(\frac{1}{3^k} - \frac{1}{3^{k+1}}\right)$ **b.** $\displaystyle\sum_{k=1}^{\infty}\frac{1}{k(k+1)}$

SOLUTION

a. The nth term of the sequence of partial sums is

$$\begin{aligned} S_n &= \sum_{k=1}^{n}\left(\frac{1}{3^k} - \frac{1}{3^{k+1}}\right) = \left(\frac{1}{3} - \frac{1}{3^2}\right) + \left(\frac{1}{3^2} - \frac{1}{3^3}\right) + \cdots + \left(\frac{1}{3^n} - \frac{1}{3^{n+1}}\right) \\ &= \frac{1}{3} + \underbrace{\left(-\frac{1}{3^2} + \frac{1}{3^2}\right)}_{0} + \cdots + \underbrace{\left(-\frac{1}{3^n} + \frac{1}{3^n}\right)}_{0} - \frac{1}{3^{n+1}} \quad \text{Regroup terms.} \\ &= \frac{1}{3} - \frac{1}{3^{n+1}}. \quad \text{Simplify.} \end{aligned}$$

Observe that the interior terms of the sum cancel (or telescope), leaving a simple expression for S_n. Taking the limit, we find that

$$\sum_{k=1}^{\infty}\left(\frac{1}{3^k} - \frac{1}{3^{k+1}}\right) = \lim_{n\to\infty} S_n = \lim_{n\to\infty}\left(\frac{1}{3} - \underbrace{\frac{1}{3^{n+1}}}_{\to 0}\right) = \frac{1}{3}.$$

➤ See Section 7.5 for a review of partial fractions.

b. Using the method of partial fractions, the sequence of partial sums is

$$S_n = \sum_{k=1}^{n}\frac{1}{k(k+1)} = \sum_{k=1}^{n}\left(\frac{1}{k} - \frac{1}{k+1}\right).$$

Writing out this sum, we see that

$$\begin{aligned} S_n &= \left(1 - \frac{1}{2}\right) + \left(\frac{1}{2} - \frac{1}{3}\right) + \left(\frac{1}{3} - \frac{1}{4}\right) + \cdots + \left(\frac{1}{n} - \frac{1}{n+1}\right) \\ &= 1 + \underbrace{\left(-\frac{1}{2} + \frac{1}{2}\right)}_{0} + \underbrace{\left(-\frac{1}{3} + \frac{1}{3}\right)}_{0} + \cdots + \underbrace{\left(-\frac{1}{n} + \frac{1}{n}\right)}_{0} - \frac{1}{n+1} \\ &= 1 - \frac{1}{n+1}. \end{aligned}$$

Again, the sum telescopes and all the interior terms cancel. The result is a simple formula for the nth term of the sequence of partial sums. The value of the series is

$$\sum_{k=1}^{\infty} \frac{1}{k(k+1)} = \lim_{n\to\infty} S_n = \lim_{n\to\infty}\left(1 - \frac{1}{n+1}\right) = 1.$$

Related Exercises 55–68 ◀

SECTION 8.3 EXERCISES

Review Questions

1. What is the defining characteristic of a geometric series? Give an example.
2. What is the difference between a geometric sum and a geometric series?
3. What is meant by the *ratio* of a geometric series?
4. Does a geometric sum always have a finite value?
5. Does a geometric series always have a finite value?
6. What is the condition for convergence of the geometric series $\sum_{k=0}^{\infty} ar^k$?

Basic Skills

7–18. Geometric sums *Evaluate each geometric sum.*

7. $\sum_{k=0}^{8} 3^k$
T 8. $\sum_{k=0}^{10} \left(\frac{1}{4}\right)^k$
T 9. $\sum_{k=0}^{20} \left(\frac{2}{5}\right)^{2k}$
10. $\sum_{k=4}^{12} 2^k$
T 11. $\sum_{k=0}^{9} \left(-\frac{3}{4}\right)^k$
T 12. $\sum_{k=1}^{5} (-2.5)^k$
13. $\sum_{k=0}^{6} \pi^k$
T 14. $\sum_{k=1}^{10} \left(\frac{4}{7}\right)^k$
15. $\sum_{k=0}^{20} (-1)^k$
16. $1 + \frac{2}{3} + \frac{4}{9} + \frac{8}{27}$
T 17. $\frac{1}{4} + \frac{1}{12} + \frac{1}{36} + \frac{1}{108} + \cdots + \frac{1}{2916}$
T 18. $\frac{1}{5} + \frac{3}{25} + \frac{9}{125} + \cdots + \frac{243}{15{,}625}$

19–34. Geometric series *Evaluate each geometric series or state that it diverges.*

19. $\sum_{k=0}^{\infty} \left(\frac{1}{4}\right)^k$
20. $\sum_{k=0}^{\infty} \left(\frac{3}{5}\right)^k$
21. $\sum_{k=0}^{\infty} 0.9^k$
22. $1 + \frac{2}{7} + \frac{2^2}{7^2} + \frac{2^3}{7^3} + \cdots$
23. $1 + 1.01 + 1.01^2 + 1.01^3 + \cdots$
24. $1 + \frac{1}{\pi} + \frac{1}{\pi^2} + \frac{1}{\pi^3} + \cdots$
25. $\sum_{k=1}^{\infty} e^{-2k}$
26. $\sum_{m=2}^{\infty} \frac{5}{2^m}$
27. $\sum_{k=1}^{\infty} 2^{-3k}$
28. $\sum_{k=3}^{\infty} \frac{3 \cdot 4^k}{7^k}$
29. $\sum_{k=4}^{\infty} \frac{1}{5^k}$
30. $\sum_{k=0}^{\infty} \left(\frac{4}{3}\right)^{-k}$
31. $1 + \frac{e}{\pi} + \frac{e^2}{\pi^2} + \frac{e^3}{\pi^3} + \cdots$
32. $\frac{1}{16} + \frac{3}{64} + \frac{9}{256} + \frac{27}{1024} + \cdots$
33. $\sum_{k=0}^{\infty} \left(\frac{1}{4}\right)^k 5^{3-k}$
T 34. $\sum_{k=2}^{\infty} \left(\frac{3}{8}\right)^{3k}$

35–40. Geometric series with alternating signs *Evaluate each geometric series or state that it diverges.*

35. $\sum_{k=0}^{\infty} \left(-\frac{9}{10}\right)^k$
36. $\sum_{k=1}^{\infty} \left(-\frac{2}{3}\right)^k$
37. $3\sum_{k=0}^{\infty} (-\pi)^{-k}$
38. $\sum_{k=1}^{\infty} (-e)^{-k}$
39. $\sum_{k=2}^{\infty} (-0.15)^k$
40. $\sum_{k=1}^{\infty} 3\left(-\frac{1}{8}\right)^{3k}$

41–54. Decimal expansions *Write each repeating decimal first as a geometric series and then as a fraction (a ratio of two integers).*

41. $0.\overline{3} = 0.333\ldots$
42. $0.\overline{6} = 0.666\ldots$
43. $0.\overline{1} = 0.111\ldots$
44. $0.\overline{5} = 0.555\ldots$
45. $0.\overline{09} = 0.090909\ldots$
46. $0.\overline{27} = 0.272727\ldots$
47. $0.\overline{037} = 0.037037\ldots$
48. $0.\overline{027} = 0.027027\ldots$
49. $0.\overline{12} = 0.121212\ldots$
50. $1.\overline{25} = 1.252525\ldots$
51. $0.\overline{456} = 0.456456456\ldots$
52. $1.00\overline{39} = 1.00393939\ldots$
53. $0.00\overline{952} = 0.00952952\ldots$
54. $5.12\overline{83} = 5.12838383\ldots$

55–68. Telescoping series *For the following telescoping series, find a formula for the nth term of the sequence of partial sums $\{S_n\}$. Then evaluate $\lim_{n\to\infty} S_n$ to obtain the value of the series or state that the series diverges.*

55. $\sum_{k=1}^{\infty} \left(\frac{1}{k+1} - \frac{1}{k+2}\right)$
56. $\sum_{k=1}^{\infty} \left(\frac{1}{k+2} - \frac{1}{k+3}\right)$
57. $\sum_{k=1}^{\infty} \frac{1}{(k+6)(k+7)}$
58. $\sum_{k=0}^{\infty} \frac{1}{(3k+1)(3k+4)}$
59. $\sum_{k=3}^{\infty} \frac{4}{(4k-3)(4k+1)}$
60. $\sum_{k=3}^{\infty} \frac{2}{(2k-1)(2k+1)}$
61. $\sum_{k=1}^{\infty} \ln \frac{k+1}{k}$
62. $\sum_{k=1}^{\infty} (\sqrt{k+1} - \sqrt{k})$

63. $\displaystyle\sum_{k=1}^{\infty} \frac{1}{(k+p)(k+p+1)}$, where p is a positive integer

64. $\displaystyle\sum_{k=1}^{\infty} \frac{1}{(ak+1)(ak+a+1)}$, where a is a positive integer

65. $\displaystyle\sum_{k=1}^{\infty} \left(\frac{1}{\sqrt{k+1}} - \frac{1}{\sqrt{k+3}}\right)$

66. $\displaystyle\sum_{k=0}^{\infty} \left(\sin\left(\frac{(k+1)\pi}{2k+1}\right) - \sin\left(\frac{k\pi}{2k-1}\right)\right)$

67. $\displaystyle\sum_{k=0}^{\infty} \frac{1}{16k^2 + 8k - 3}$

68. $\displaystyle\sum_{k=1}^{\infty} (\tan^{-1}(k+1) - \tan^{-1} k)$

Further Explorations

69. Explain why or why not Determine whether the following statements are true and give an explanation or counterexample.

a. $\displaystyle\sum_{k=1}^{\infty} \left(\frac{\pi}{e}\right)^{-k}$ is a convergent geometric series.

b. If a is a real number and $\displaystyle\sum_{k=12}^{\infty} a^k$ converges, then $\displaystyle\sum_{k=1}^{\infty} a^k$ converges.

c. If the series $\displaystyle\sum_{k=1}^{\infty} a^k$ converges and $|a| < |b|$, then the series $\displaystyle\sum_{k=1}^{\infty} b^k$ converges.

d. Viewed as a function of r, the series $1 + r^2 + r^3 + \cdots$ takes on all values in the interval $\left(\frac{1}{2}, \infty\right)$.

e. Viewed as a function of r, the series $\displaystyle\sum_{k=1}^{\infty} r^k$ takes on all values in the interval $\left(-\frac{1}{2}, \infty\right)$.

70–73. Evaluating series *Evaluate each series or state that it diverges.*

70. $\displaystyle\sum_{k=1}^{\infty} (\sin^{-1}(1/k) - \sin^{-1}(1/(k+1)))$

71. $\displaystyle\sum_{k=1}^{\infty} \frac{(-2)^k}{3^{k+1}}$

72. $\displaystyle\sum_{k=1}^{\infty} \frac{\pi^k}{e^{k+1}}$

73. $\displaystyle\sum_{k=2}^{\infty} \frac{\ln((k+1)k^{-1})}{(\ln k)\ln(k+1)}$

74. Evaluating an infinite series two ways Evaluate the series $\displaystyle\sum_{k=1}^{\infty} \left(\frac{1}{2^k} - \frac{1}{2^{k+1}}\right)$ two ways.

a. Use a telescoping series argument.

b. Use a geometric series argument after first simplifying $\dfrac{1}{2^k} - \dfrac{1}{2^{k+1}}$.

75. Evaluating an infinite series two ways Evaluate the series $\displaystyle\sum_{k=1}^{\infty} \left(\frac{4}{3^k} - \frac{4}{3^{k+1}}\right)$ two ways.

a. Use a telescoping series argument.

b. Use a geometric series argument after first simplifying $\dfrac{4}{3^k} - \dfrac{4}{3^{k+1}}$.

76. Zeno's paradox The Greek philosopher Zeno of Elea (who lived about 450 B.C.) invented many paradoxes, the most famous of which tells of a race between the swift warrior Achilles and a tortoise. Zeno argued

> *The slower when running will never be overtaken by the quicker; for that which is pursuing must first reach the point from which that which is fleeing started, so that the slower must necessarily always be some distance ahead.*

In other words, by giving the tortoise a head start, Achilles will never overtake the tortoise because every time Achilles reaches the point where the tortoise was, the tortoise has moved ahead. Resolve this paradox by assuming that Achilles gives the tortoise a 1-mi head start and runs 5 mi/hr to the tortoise's 1 mi/hr. How far does Achilles run before he overtakes the tortoise, and how long does it take?

77. Archimedes' quadrature of the parabola The Greeks solved several calculus problems almost 2000 years before the discovery of calculus. One example is Archimedes' calculation of the area of the region R bounded by a segment of a parabola, which he did using the "method of exhaustion." As shown in the figure, the idea was to fill R with an infinite sequence of triangles. Archimedes began with an isosceles triangle inscribed in the parabola, with area A_1, and proceeded in stages, with the number of new triangles doubling at each stage. He was able to show (the key to the solution) that at each stage, the area of a new triangle is $\frac{1}{8}$ of the area of a triangle at the previous stage; for example, $A_2 = \frac{1}{8}A_1$, and so forth. Show, as Archimedes did, that the area of R is $\frac{4}{3}$ times the area of A_1.

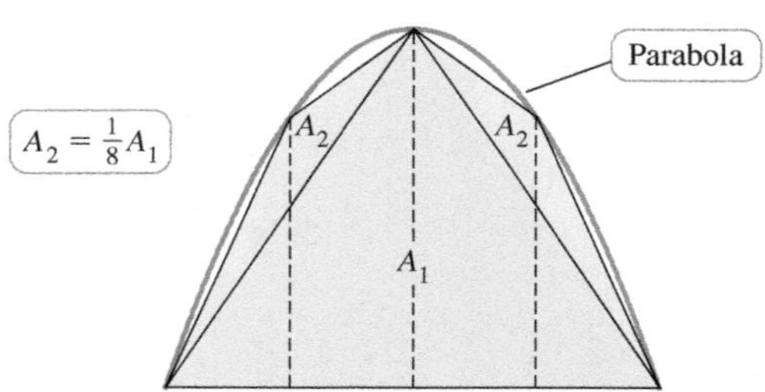

78. Value of a series

a. Evaluate the series

$$\sum_{k=1}^{\infty} \frac{3^k}{(3^{k+1}-1)(3^k-1)}.$$

b. For what values of a does the series

$$\sum_{k=1}^{\infty} \frac{a^k}{(a^{k+1}-1)(a^k-1)}$$

converge, and in those cases, what is its value?

Applications

T 79. House loan Suppose you take out a home mortgage for \$180,000 at a monthly interest rate of 0.5%. If you make payments of \$1000/month, after how many months will the loan balance be zero? Estimate the answer by graphing the sequence of loan balances and then obtain an exact answer using infinite series.

T 80. Car loan Suppose you borrow \$20,000 for a new car at a monthly interest rate of 0.75%. If you make payments of \$600/month, after how many months will the loan balance be zero? Estimate the answer by graphing the sequence of loan balances and then obtain an exact answer using infinite series.

81. Fish harvesting A fishery manager knows that her fish population naturally increases at a rate of 1.5% per month. At the end of each month, 120 fish are harvested. Let F_n be the fish population after the nth month, where $F_0 = 4000$ fish. Assume that this process continues indefinitely. Use infinite series to find the long-term (steady-state) population of the fish.

82. Periodic doses Suppose that you take 200 mg of an antibiotic every 6 hr. The half-life of the drug is 6 hr (the time it takes for half of the drug to be eliminated from your blood). Use infinite series to find the long-term (steady-state) amount of antibiotic in your blood.

83. China's one-son policy In 1978, in an effort to reduce population growth, China instituted a policy that allows only one child per family. One unintended consequence has been that, because of a cultural bias toward sons, China now has many more young boys than girls. To solve this problem, some people have suggested replacing the one-child policy with a one-son policy: A family may have children until a boy is born. Suppose that the one-son policy were implemented and that natural birth rates remained the same (half boys and half girls). Using geometric series, compare the total number of children under the two policies.

84. Double glass An insulated window consists of two parallel panes of glass with a small spacing between them. Suppose that each pane reflects a fraction p of the incoming light and transmits the remaining light. Considering all reflections of light between the panes, what fraction of the incoming light is ultimately transmitted by the window? Assume the amount of incoming light is 1.

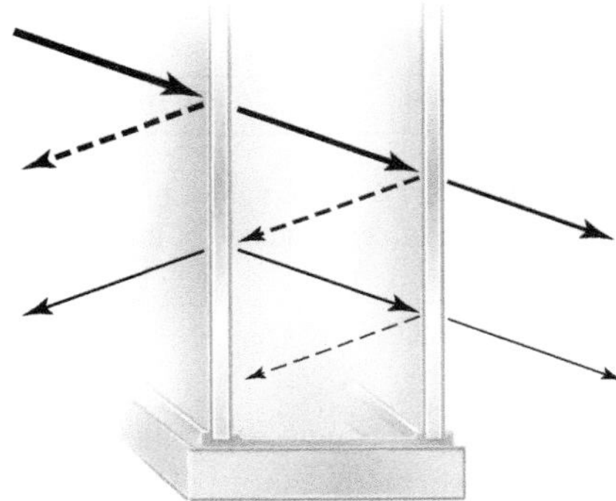

85. Bouncing ball for time Suppose a rubber ball, when dropped from a given height, returns to a fraction p of that height. In the absence of air resistance, a ball dropped from a height h requires $\sqrt{2h/g}$ seconds to fall to the ground, where $g \approx 9.8\ \text{m/s}^2$ is the acceleration due to gravity. The time taken to bounce *up* to a given height equals the time to fall from that height to the ground. How long does it take a ball dropped from 10 m to come to rest?

86. Multiplier effect Imagine that the government of a small community decides to give a total of $\$W$, distributed equally, to all its citizens. Suppose that each month each citizen saves a fraction p of his or her new wealth and spends the remaining $1 - p$ in the community. Assume no money leaves or enters the community, and all the spent money is redistributed throughout the community.

a. If this cycle of saving and spending continues for many months, how much money is ultimately spent? Specifically, by what factor is the initial investment of $\$W$ increased (in terms of p)? Economists refer to this increase in the investment as the *multiplier effect.*

b. Evaluate the limits $p \rightarrow 0$ and $p \rightarrow 1$, and interpret their meanings.

(See the Guided Project *Economic stimulus packages* for more on stimulus packages.)

87. Snowflake island fractal The fractal called the *snowflake island* (or *Koch island*) is constructed as follows: Let I_0 be an equilateral triangle with sides of length 1. The figure I_1 is obtained by replacing the middle third of each side of I_0 with a new outward equilateral triangle with sides of length $1/3$ (see figure). The process is repeated where I_{n+1} is obtained by replacing the middle third of each side of I_n with a new outward equilateral triangle with sides of length $1/3^{n+1}$. The limiting figure as $n \rightarrow \infty$ is called the snowflake island.

a. Let L_n be the perimeter of I_n. Show that $\lim_{n\rightarrow\infty} L_n = \infty$.

b. Let A_n be the area of I_n. Find $\lim_{n\rightarrow\infty} A_n$. It exists!

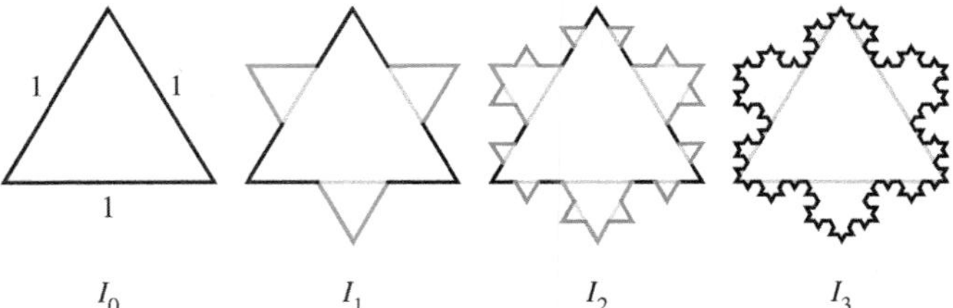

Additional Exercises

88. Decimal expansions

a. Consider the number 0.555555. . . , which can be viewed as the series $5\sum_{k=1}^{\infty} 10^{-k}$. Evaluate the geometric series to obtain a rational value of 0.555555. . . .

b. Consider the number 0.54545454. . . , which can be represented by the series $54\sum_{k=1}^{\infty} 10^{-2k}$. Evaluate the geometric series to obtain a rational value of the number.

c. Now generalize parts (a) and (b). Suppose you are given a number with a decimal expansion that repeats in cycles of length p, say, $n_1, n_2, \ldots, n_p$, where $n_1, \ldots, n_p$ are integers between 0 and 9. Explain how to use geometric series to obtain a rational form for $0.\overline{n_1 n_2 \cdots n_p}$.

d. Try the method of part (c) on the number $0.\overline{123456789} = 0.123456789123456789\ldots$.

e. Prove that $0.\overline{9} = 1$.

89. Remainder term Consider the geometric series $S = \sum_{k=0}^{\infty} r^k$, which has the value $1/(1 - r)$ provided $|r| < 1$. Let

$S_n = \sum_{k=0}^{n-1} r^k = \frac{1 - r^n}{1 - r}$ be the sum of the first n terms.

The magnitude of the remainder R_n is the error in approximating S by S_n. Show that

$$R_n = S - S_n = \frac{r^n}{1 - r}.$$

90–93. Comparing remainder terms *Use Exercise 89 to determine how many terms of each series are needed so that the partial sum is within 10^{-6} of the value of the series (that is, to ensure $|R_n| < 10^{-6}$).*

90. **a.** $\sum_{k=0}^{\infty} 0.6^k$ **b.** $\sum_{k=0}^{\infty} 0.15^k$

91. **a.** $\sum_{k=0}^{\infty} (-0.8)^k$ **b.** $\sum_{k=0}^{\infty} 0.2^k$

92. **a.** $\sum_{k=0}^{\infty} 0.72^k$ **b.** $\sum_{k=0}^{\infty} (-0.25)^k$

93. **a.** $\sum_{k=0}^{\infty} \left(\frac{1}{\pi}\right)^k$ **b.** $\sum_{k=0}^{\infty} \left(\frac{1}{e}\right)^k$

94. Functions defined as series Suppose a function f is defined by the geometric series $f(x) = \sum_{k=0}^{\infty} x^k$.

a. Evaluate $f(0), f(0.2), f(0.5), f(1)$, and $f(1.5)$, if possible.
b. What is the domain of f?

95. Functions defined as series Suppose a function f is defined by the geometric series $f(x) = \sum_{k=0}^{\infty} (-1)^k x^k$.

a. Evaluate $f(0), f(0.2), f(0.5), f(1)$, and $f(1.5)$, if possible.
b. What is the domain of f?

96. Functions defined as series Suppose a function f is defined by the geometric series $f(x) = \sum_{k=0}^{\infty} x^{2k}$.

a. Evaluate $f(0), f(0.2), f(0.5), f(1)$, and $f(1.5)$, if possible.
b. What is the domain of f?

97. Series in an equation For what values of x does the geometric series

$$f(x) = \sum_{k=0}^{\infty} \left(\frac{1}{1 + x}\right)^k$$

converge? Solve $f(x) = 3$.

98. Bubbles Imagine a stack of hemispherical soap bubbles with decreasing radii $r_1 = 1, r_2, r_3, \ldots$ (see figure). Let h_n be the distance between the diameters of bubble n and bubble $n + 1$, and let H_n be the total height of the stack with n bubbles.

a. Use the Pythagorean theorem to show that in a stack with n bubbles, $h_1^2 = r_1^2 - r_2^2$, $h_2^2 = r_2^2 - r_3^2$, and so forth. Note that for the last bubble $h_n = r_n$.
b. Use part (a) to show that the height of a stack with n bubbles is

$$H_n = \sqrt{r_1^2 - r_2^2} + \sqrt{r_2^2 - r_3^2} + \cdots + \sqrt{r_{n-1}^2 - r_n^2} + r_n.$$

c. The height of a stack of bubbles depends on how the radii decrease. Suppose that $r_1 = 1, r_2 = a, r_3 = a^2, \ldots, r_n = a^{n-1}$, where $0 < a < 1$ is a fixed real number. In terms of a, find the height H_n of a stack with n bubbles.
d. Suppose the stack in part (c) is extended indefinitely ($n \to \infty$). In terms of a, how high would the stack be?
e. Challenge problem: Fix n and determine the sequence of radii $r_1, r_2, r_3, \ldots, r_n$ that maximizes H_n, the height of the stack with n bubbles.

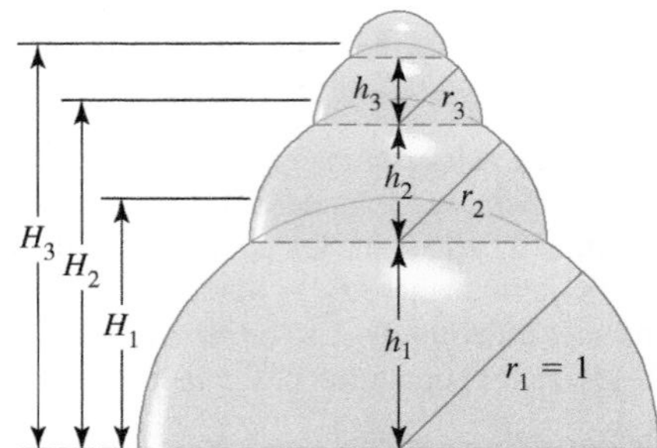

99. Values of the geometric series Consider the geometric series $f(r) = \sum_{k=0}^{\infty} r^k$, where $|r| < 1$.

a. Fill in the following table that shows the value of the series $f(r)$ for various values of r.

r	−0.9	−0.7	−0.5	−0.2	0	0.2	0.5	0.7	0.9
$f(r)$									

b. Graph f, for $|r| < 1$.
c. Evaluate $\lim_{r \to 1^-} f(r)$ and $\lim_{r \to -1^+} f(r)$.

100. Convergence rates Consider series $S = \sum_{k=0}^{\infty} r^k$, where $|r| < 1$, and its sequence of partial sums $S_n = \sum_{k=0}^{n} r^k$.

a. Complete the following table showing the smallest value of n, calling it $N(r)$, such that $|S - S_n| < 10^{-4}$, for various values of r. For example, with $r = 0.5$ and $S = 2$, we find that $|S - S_{13}| = 1.2 \times 10^{-4}$ and $|S - S_{14}| = 6.1 \times 10^{-5}$. Therefore, $N(0.5) = 14$.

r	−0.9	−0.7	−0.5	−0.2	0	0.2	0.5	0.7	0.9
$N(r)$							14		

b. Make a graph of $N(r)$ for the values of r in part (a).
c. How does the rate of convergence of the geometric series depend on r?

QUICK CHECK ANSWERS

1. b and c **2.** Using the formula, the values are $\frac{3}{2}$ and $\frac{7}{8}$. **3.** 1 **4.** The first converges because $|r| = 0.2 < 1$; the second diverges because $|r| = 2 > 1$. ◄

8.4 The Divergence and Integral Tests

With geometric series and telescoping series, the sequence of partial sums can be found and its limit can be evaluated (when it exists). Unfortunately, it is difficult or impossible to find an explicit formula for the sequence of partial sums for most infinite series. Therefore, it is difficult to obtain the exact value of most convergent series.

In light of these observations, we now shift our focus and ask a simple *yes* or *no* question: Given an infinite series, does it converge? If the answer is *no*, the series diverges and there are no more questions to ask. If the answer is *yes*, the series converges and it may be possible to estimate its value.

The Divergence Test

One of the simplest and most useful tests determines whether an infinite series *diverges*. Though our focus in this section and the next is on series with positive terms, the Divergence Test applies to series with arbitrary terms.

> **THEOREM 8.8 Divergence Test**
> If Σa_k converges, then $\lim_{k\to\infty} a_k = 0$. Equivalently, if $\lim_{k\to\infty} a_k \neq 0$, then the series diverges.

Important note: Theorem 8.8 cannot be used to conclude that a series converges.

Proof: Let $\{S_n\}$ be the sequence of partial sums for the series Σa_k. Assuming the series converges, it has a finite value, call it S, where

$$S = \lim_{n\to\infty} S_n = \lim_{n\to n} S_{n-1}.$$

Note that $S_n - S_{n-1} = a_n$. Therefore,

$$\lim_{n\to\infty} a_n = \lim_{n\to\infty} (S_n - S_{n-1}) = S - S = 0;$$

that is, $\lim_{n\to\infty} a_n = 0$ (which implies $\lim_{k\to\infty} a_k = 0$; Figure 8.25). The second part of the test follows immediately because it is the *contrapositive* of the first part (see margin note). ◄

➤ If the statement *if p, then q* is true, then its contrapositive, *if (not q), then (not p)*, is also true. However its converse, *if q, then p*, is not necessarily true. Try it out on the true statement, *if I live in Paris, then I live in France.*

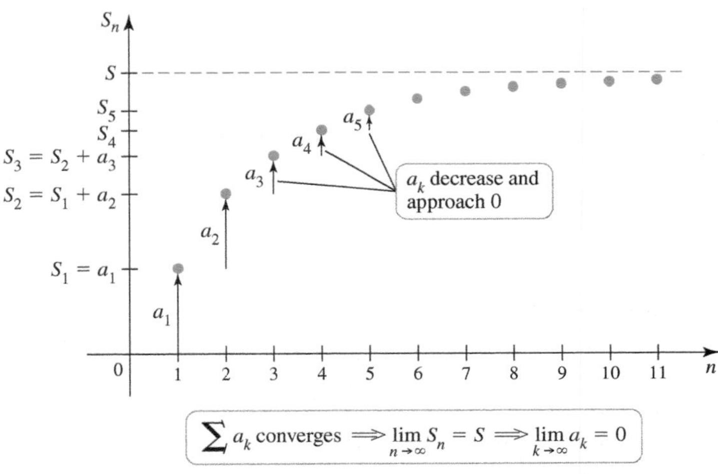

Figure 8.25

EXAMPLE 1 **Using the Divergence Test** Determine whether the following series diverge or state that the Divergence Test is inconclusive.

a. $\displaystyle\sum_{k=0}^{\infty} \frac{k}{k+1}$ **b.** $\displaystyle\sum_{k=1}^{\infty} \frac{1+3^k}{2^k}$ **c.** $\displaystyle\sum_{k=1}^{\infty} \frac{1}{k}$ **d.** $\displaystyle\sum_{k=1}^{\infty} \frac{1}{k^2}$

SOLUTION By the Divergence Test, if $\lim_{k\to\infty} a_k \neq 0$, then the series $\sum a_k$ diverges.

a. $\displaystyle\lim_{k\to\infty} a_k = \lim_{k\to\infty} \frac{k}{k+1} = 1 \neq 0$

The terms of the series do not approach zero, so the series diverges by the Divergence Test.

b.
$$\lim_{k\to\infty} a_k = \lim_{k\to\infty} \frac{1+3^k}{2^k}$$
$$= \lim_{k\to\infty} \Big(\underbrace{2^{-k}}_{\to 0} + \underbrace{\left(\frac{3}{2}\right)^k}_{\to\infty}\Big) \quad \text{Simplify.}$$
$$= \infty$$

In this case, $\lim_{k\to\infty} a_k \neq 0$, so the corresponding series $\displaystyle\sum_{k=1}^{\infty} \frac{1+3^k}{2^k}$ diverges by the Divergence Test.

c. $\displaystyle\lim_{k\to\infty} a_k = \lim_{k\to\infty} \frac{1}{k} = 0$

In this case, the terms of the series approach zero, so the Divergence Test is inconclusive. Remember, the Divergence Test cannot be used to prove that a series converges.

QUICK CHECK 1 Apply the Divergence Test to the geometric series $\sum r^k$. For what values of r does the series diverge? ◀

d. $\displaystyle\lim_{k\to\infty} a_k = \lim_{k\to\infty} \frac{1}{k^2} = 0$

As in part (c), the terms of the series approach 0, so the Divergence Test is inconclusive.

Related Exercises 9–18 ◀

To summarize: If the terms a_k of a given series do *not* approach zero as $k \to \infty$, then the series diverges. Unfortunately, the test is easy to misuse. It's tempting to conclude that if the terms of the series approach zero, then the series converges. However, look again at the series in Examples 1(c) and 1(d). Although it is true that $\lim_{k\to\infty} a_k = 0$ for both series, we will soon discover that one of them converges while the other diverges. We cannot tell which behavior to expect based only on the observation that $\lim_{k\to\infty} a_k = 0$.

The Harmonic Series

We now look at an example with a surprising result. Consider the infinite series

$$\sum_{k=1}^{\infty} \frac{1}{k} = 1 + \frac{1}{2} + \frac{1}{3} + \frac{1}{4} + \frac{1}{5} + \cdots,$$

a famous series known as the **harmonic series**. Does it converge? As explained in Example 1(c), this question cannot be answered by the Divergence Test, despite the fact that $\lim_{k\to\infty} \frac{1}{k} = 0$. Suppose instead you try to answer the convergence question by writing out the terms of the sequence of partial sums:

$$S_1 = 1, \qquad S_2 = 1 + \frac{1}{2} = \frac{3}{2},$$
$$S_3 = 1 + \frac{1}{2} + \frac{1}{3} = \frac{11}{6}, \qquad S_4 = 1 + \frac{1}{2} + \frac{1}{3} + \frac{1}{4} = \frac{25}{12},$$

and in general,

$$S_n = \sum_{k=1}^{n} \frac{1}{k} = 1 + \frac{1}{2} + \frac{1}{3} + \frac{1}{4} + \cdots + \frac{1}{n}.$$

There is no obvious pattern in this sequence, and in fact, no simple explicit formula for S_n exists; so we analyze the sequence numerically. Have a look at the first 200 terms of the sequence of partial sums shown in Figure 8.26. What do you think—does the series converge? The terms of the sequence of partial sums increase, but at a decreasing rate. They could approach a limit or they could increase without bound.

Computing additional terms of the sequence of partial sums does not provide conclusive evidence. Table 8.3 shows that the sum of the first million terms is less than 15; the sum of the first 10^{40} terms—an unimaginably large number of terms—is less than 100. This is a case in which computation alone is not sufficient to determine whether a series converges. We need another way to determine whether the series converges.

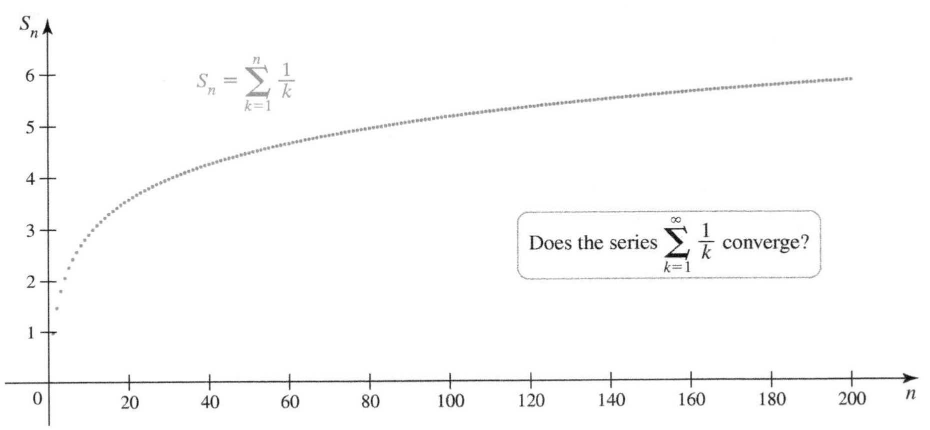

Figure 8.26

Table 8.3

n	S_n	n	S_n
10^3	≈ 7.49	10^{10}	≈ 23.60
10^4	≈ 9.79	10^{20}	≈ 46.63
10^5	≈ 12.09	10^{30}	≈ 69.65
10^6	≈ 14.39	10^{40}	≈ 92.68

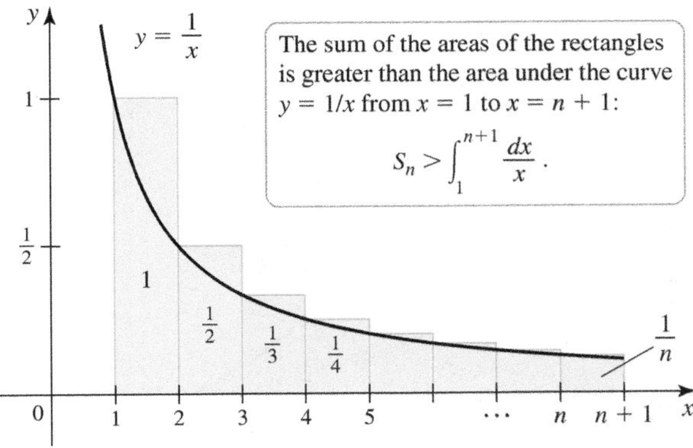

Figure 8.27

➤ Recall that $\int \frac{dx}{x} = \ln |x| + C$. In Section 7.8, we showed that $\int_1^{\infty} \frac{dx}{x^p}$ diverges for $p \leq 1$. Therefore, $\int_1^{\infty} \frac{dx}{x}$ diverges.

Observe that the nth term of the sequence of partial sums,

$$S_n = \sum_{k=1}^{n} \frac{1}{k} = 1 + \frac{1}{2} + \frac{1}{3} + \frac{1}{4} + \cdots + \frac{1}{n},$$

is represented geometrically by a left Riemann sum of the function $y = \frac{1}{x}$ on the interval $[1, n + 1]$ (Figure 8.27). This fact follows by noticing that the areas of the rectangles, from left to right, are $1, \frac{1}{2}, \ldots,$ and $\frac{1}{n}$. Comparing the sum of the areas of these n rectangles with the area under the curve, we see that $S_n > \int_1^{n+1} \frac{dx}{x}$. We know that $\int_1^{n+1} \frac{dx}{x} = \ln (n + 1)$ increases without bound as n increases. Because S_n exceeds $\int_1^{n+1} \frac{dx}{x}$, S_n also increases without bound; therefore, $\lim_{n \to \infty} S_n = \infty$ and the harmonic series $\sum_{k=1}^{\infty} \frac{1}{k}$ diverges. This argument justifies the following theorem.

THEOREM 8.9 Harmonic Series

The harmonic series $\sum_{k=1}^{\infty} \frac{1}{k} = 1 + \frac{1}{2} + \frac{1}{3} + \frac{1}{4} + \frac{1}{5} + \cdots$ diverges—even though the terms of the series approach zero.

The ideas used to demonstrate that the harmonic series diverges are now used to prove a new and powerful convergence test. This test and those presented in Section 8.5 apply only to series with positive terms.

The Integral Test

The fact that infinite series are sums and that integrals are limits of sums suggests a connection between series and integrals. The Integral Test exploits this connection.

THEOREM 8.10 Integral Test

Suppose f is a continuous, positive, decreasing function, for $x \geq 1$, and let $a_k = f(k)$, for $k = 1, 2, 3, \ldots$. Then

$$\sum_{k=1}^{\infty} a_k \quad \text{and} \quad \int_1^{\infty} f(x)\,dx$$

either both converge or both diverge. In the case of convergence, the value of the integral is *not* equal to the value of the series.

➤ The Integral Test also applies if the terms of the series a_k are decreasing for $k > N$ for some finite number $N > 1$. The proof can be modified to account for this situation.

Proof: By comparing the shaded regions in Figure 8.28, it follows that

$$\sum_{k=2}^{n} a_k < \int_1^{n} f(x)\,dx < \sum_{k=1}^{n-1} a_k. \tag{1}$$

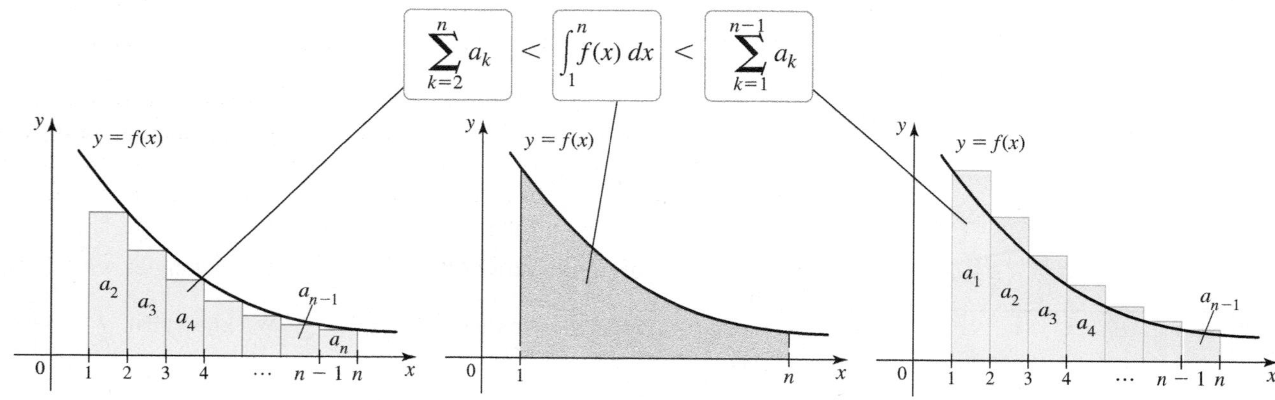

Figure 8.28

The proof must demonstrate two results: If the improper integral $\int_1^{\infty} f(x)\,dx$ has a finite value, then the infinite series converges, *and* if the infinite series converges, then the improper integral has a finite value. First suppose that the improper integral $\int_1^\infty f(x)\,dx$ has a finite value, say I. We have

$$\begin{aligned}\sum_{k=1}^{n} a_k &= a_1 + \sum_{k=2}^{n} a_k && \text{Separate the first term of the series.}\\ &< a_1 + \int_1^n f(x)\,dx && \text{Left inequality in expression (1)}\\ &< a_1 + \int_1^\infty f(x)\,dx && f \text{ is positive, so } \int_1^n f(x)\,dx < \int_1^\infty f(x)\,dx.\\ &= a_1 + I.\end{aligned}$$

➤ In this proof, we rely twice on the Bounded Monotonic Sequence Theorem of Section 8.2: A bounded monotonic sequence converges.

This argument implies that the terms of the sequence of partial sums $S_n = \sum_{k=1}^{n} a_k$ are bounded above by $a_1 + I$. Because $\{S_n\}$ is also increasing (the series consists of positive terms), the sequence of partial sums converges, which means the series $\sum_{k=1}^{\infty} a_k$ converges (to a value less than or equal to $a_1 + I$).

Now suppose the infinite series $\sum_{k=1}^{\infty} a_k$ converges and has a value S. We have

$$\begin{aligned}\int_1^n f(x)\,dx &< \sum_{k=1}^{n-1} a_k && \text{Right inequality in expression (1)}\\ &< \sum_{k=1}^{\infty} a_k && \text{Terms } a_k \text{ are positive.}\\ &= S. && \text{Value of infinite series}\end{aligned}$$

➤ An extended version of this proof can be used to show that, in fact, $\int_1^\infty f(x)\,dx < \sum_{k=1}^{\infty} a_k$ (strict inequality) in all cases.

We see that the sequence $\left\{\int_1^n f(x)\,dx\right\}$ is increasing (because $f(x) > 0$) and bounded above by a fixed number S. Therefore, the improper integral $\int_1^\infty f(x)\,dx = \lim_{n\to\infty} \int_1^n f(x)\,dx$ has a finite value (less than or equal to S).

We have shown that if $\int_1^\infty f(x)\,dx$ is finite, then $\sum a_k$ converges and vice versa. The same inequalities imply that $\int_1^\infty f(x)\,dx$ and $\sum a_k$ also diverge together. ◄

The Integral Test is used to determine *whether* a series converges or diverges. For this reason, adding or subtracting a few terms in the series *or* changing the lower limit of integration to another finite point does not change the outcome of the test. Therefore, the test depends on neither the lower index of the series nor the lower limit of the integral.

EXAMPLE 2 **Applying the Integral Test** Determine whether the following series converge.

a. $\displaystyle\sum_{k=1}^{\infty} \frac{k}{k^2+1}$ **b.** $\displaystyle\sum_{k=3}^{\infty} \frac{1}{\sqrt{2k-5}}$ **c.** $\displaystyle\sum_{k=0}^{\infty} \frac{1}{k^2+4}$

SOLUTION

a. The function associated with this series is $f(x) = x/(x^2+1)$, which is positive, for $x \geq 1$. We must also show that the terms of the series are decreasing beyond some fixed term of the series. The first few terms of the series are $\left\{\frac{1}{2}, \frac{2}{5}, \frac{3}{10}, \frac{4}{17}, \ldots\right\}$, and it appears that the terms are decreasing. When the decreasing property is difficult to confirm, one approach is to use derivatives to show that the associated function is decreasing. In this case, we have

$$f'(x) = \frac{d}{dx}\left(\frac{x}{x^2+1}\right) = \underbrace{\frac{x^2+1-2x^2}{(x^2+1)^2}}_{\text{Quotient Rule}} = \frac{1-x^2}{(x^2+1)^2}.$$

For $x > 1, f'(x) < 0$, which implies that the function and the terms of the series are decreasing. The integral that determines convergence is

$$\int_1^{\infty} \frac{x}{x^2+1}\,dx = \lim_{b\to\infty} \int_1^b \frac{x}{x^2+1}\,dx \qquad \text{Definition of improper integral}$$

$$= \lim_{b\to\infty} \frac{1}{2} \ln (x^2+1)\Big|_1^b \qquad \text{Evaluate integral.}$$

$$= \frac{1}{2} \lim_{b\to\infty} (\ln (b^2+1) - \ln 2) \qquad \text{Simplify.}$$

$$= \infty. \qquad \lim_{b\to\infty} \ln (b^2+1) = \infty$$

Because the integral diverges, the series diverges.

b. The Integral Test may be modified to accommodate initial indices other than $k = 1$. The terms of this series decrease, for $k \geq 3$. In this case, the relevant integral is

$$\int_3^{\infty} \frac{dx}{\sqrt{2x-5}} = \lim_{b\to\infty} \int_3^b \frac{dx}{\sqrt{2x-5}} \qquad \text{Definition of improper integral}$$

$$= \lim_{b\to\infty} \sqrt{2x-5}\Big|_3^b \qquad \text{Evaluate integral.}$$

$$= \infty. \qquad \lim_{b\to\infty} \sqrt{2b-5} = \infty$$

Because the integral diverges, the series also diverges.

c. The terms of the series are positive and decrease, for $k \geq 0$. The relevant integral is

$$\int_0^{\infty} \frac{dx}{x^2+4} = \lim_{b\to\infty} \int_0^b \frac{dx}{x^2+4} \qquad \text{Definition of improper integral}$$

$$= \lim_{b\to\infty} \frac{1}{2} \tan^{-1} \frac{x}{2}\Big|_0^b \qquad \text{Evaluate integral.}$$

$$= \frac{1}{2} \underbrace{\lim_{b\to\infty} \tan^{-1} \frac{b}{2}}_{\frac{\pi}{2}} - \tan^{-1} 0 \qquad \text{Simplify.}$$

$$= \frac{\pi}{4}. \qquad \tan^{-1} x \to \frac{\pi}{2}, \text{ as } x \to \infty.$$

Because the integral is finite (equivalently, it converges), the infinite series also converges $\left(\text{but not to } \frac{\pi}{4}\right)$.

Related Exercises 19–28 ◀

The p-Series

The Integral Test is used to prove Theorem 8.11, which addresses the convergence of an entire family of infinite series known as the *p-series.*

> **THEOREM 8.11 Convergence of the p-Series**
>
> The **p-series** $\sum_{k=1}^{\infty} \frac{1}{k^p}$ converges for $p > 1$ and diverges for $p \leq 1$.

Proof: To apply the Integral Test, observe that the terms of the given series are positive and decreasing, for $p > 0$. The function associated with the series is $f(x) = \frac{1}{x^p}$. The relevant integral is $\int_1^\infty \frac{dx}{x^p}$. Appealing to Example 2 in Section 7.8, recall that this improper integral converges for $p > 1$ and diverges for $p \leq 1$. Therefore, by the Integral Test, the p-series $\sum_{k=1}^{\infty} \frac{1}{k^p}$ converges for $p > 1$ and diverges for $0 < p \leq 1$. For $p \leq 0$, the series diverges by the Divergence Test. ◀

QUICK CHECK 2 Which of the following series are p-series, and which series converge?

a. $\sum_{k=1}^{\infty} k^{-0.8}$ **b.** $\sum_{k=1}^{\infty} 2^{-k}$ **c.** $\sum_{k=10}^{\infty} k^{-4}$ ◀

EXAMPLE 3 **Using the p-series test** Determine whether the following series converge or diverge.

a. $\sum_{k=1}^{\infty} k^{-3}$ **b.** $\sum_{k=1}^{\infty} \frac{1}{\sqrt[4]{k^3}}$ **c.** $\sum_{k=4}^{\infty} \frac{1}{(k-1)^2}$

SOLUTION

a. Because $\sum_{k=1}^{\infty} k^{-3} = \sum_{k=1}^{\infty} \frac{1}{k^3}$ is a p-series with $p = 3$, it converges by Theorem 8.11.

b. This series is a p-series with $p = \frac{3}{4}$. By Theorem 8.11, it diverges.

c. The series

$$\sum_{k=4}^{\infty} \frac{1}{(k-1)^2} = \sum_{k=3}^{\infty} \frac{1}{k^2} = \frac{1}{3^2} + \frac{1}{4^2} + \frac{1}{5^2} + \cdots$$

is a convergent p-series ($p = 2$) without the first two terms. As we prove shortly, adding or removing a finite number of terms does not affect the convergence of a series. Therefore, the given series converges.

Related Exercises 29–34 ◀

Estimating the Value of Infinite Series

The Integral Test is powerful in its own right, but it comes with an added bonus. It can be used to estimate the value of a convergent series with positive terms. We define the **remainder** to be the error in approximating a convergent series by the sum of its first n terms; that is,

$$R_n = \underbrace{\sum_{k=1}^{\infty} a_k}_{\text{value of series}} - \underbrace{\sum_{k=1}^{n} a_k}_{\text{approximation based on first } n \text{ terms}} = a_{n+1} + a_{n+2} + a_{n+3} + \cdots.$$

The remainder consists of the *tail* of the series—those terms beyond a_n. For series with positive terms, the remainder is positive.

QUICK CHECK 3 If Σa_k is a convergent series of positive terms, why is $R_n > 0$? ◀

We now argue much as we did in the proof of the Integral Test. Let f be a continuous, positive, decreasing function such that $f(k) = a_k$, for all relevant k. From Figure 8.29, we see that $\int_{n+1}^{\infty} f(x)\,dx < R_n$.

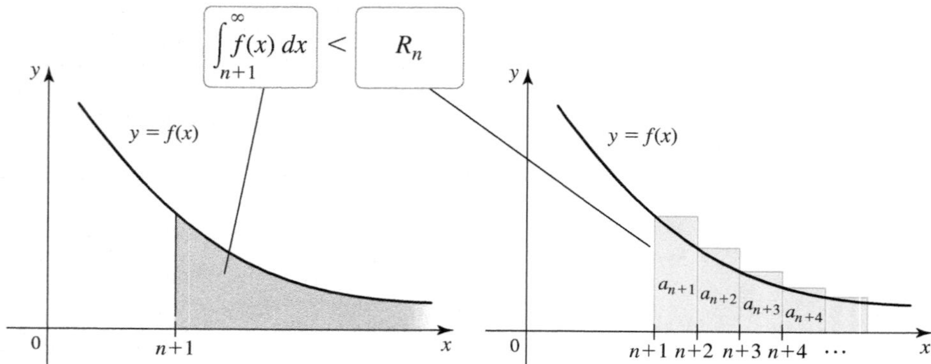

Figure 8.29

Similarly, Figure 8.30 shows that $R_n < \int_n^{\infty} f(x)\,dx$.

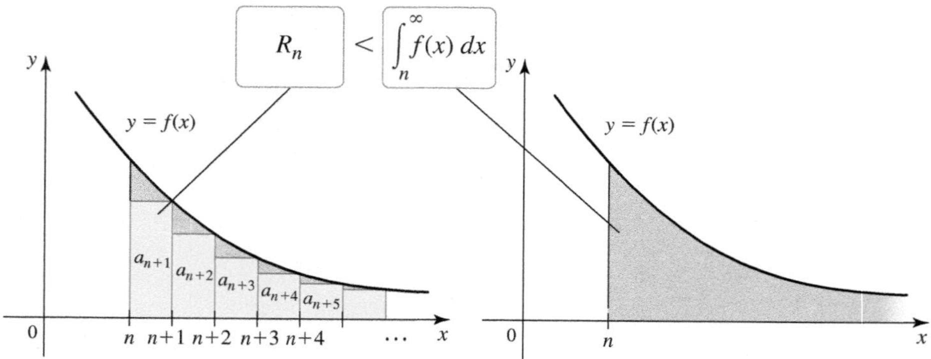

Figure 8.30

Combining these two inequalities, the remainder is squeezed between two integrals:

$$\int_{n+1}^{\infty} f(x)\,dx < R_n < \int_n^{\infty} f(x)\,dx. \qquad (2)$$

If the integrals can be evaluated, this result provides an estimate of the remainder.

There is, however, another equally useful way to express this result. Notice that the value of the series is

$$S = \sum_{k=1}^{\infty} a_k = \underbrace{\sum_{k=1}^{n} a_k}_{S_n} + R_n,$$

which is the sum of the first n terms S_n and the remainder R_n. Adding S_n to each term of (2), we have

$$\underbrace{S_n + \int_{n+1}^{\infty} f(x)\,dx}_{L_n} < \underbrace{\sum_{k=1}^{\infty} a_k}_{S_n + R_n = S} < \underbrace{S_n + \int_n^{\infty} f(x)\,dx.}_{U_n}$$

These inequalities can be abbreviated as $L_n < S < U_n$, where S is the exact value of the series, and L_n and U_n are lower and upper bounds for S, respectively. If the integrals in these bounds can be evaluated, it is straightforward to compute S_n (by summing the first n terms of the series) and to compute both L_n and U_n.

THEOREM 8.12 Estimating Series with Positive Terms

Let f be a continuous, positive, decreasing function, for $x \geq 1$, and let $a_k = f(k)$, for $k = 1, 2, 3, \ldots$. Let $S = \sum_{k=1}^{\infty} a_k$ be a convergent series and let $S_n = \sum_{k=1}^{n} a_k$ be the sum of the first n terms of the series. The remainder $R_n = S - S_n$ satisfies

$$R_n < \int_n^{\infty} f(x)\, dx.$$

Furthermore, the exact value of the series is bounded as follows:

$$S_n + \int_{n+1}^{\infty} f(x)\, dx < \sum_{k=1}^{\infty} a_k < S_n + \int_n^{\infty} f(x)\, dx.$$

EXAMPLE 4 Approximating a *p*-series

a. How many terms of the convergent p-series $\sum_{k=1}^{\infty} \frac{1}{k^2}$ must be summed to obtain an approximation that is within 10^{-3} of the exact value of the series?

b. Find an approximation to the series using 50 terms of the series.

SOLUTION The function associated with this series is $f(x) = 1/x^2$.

a. Using the bound on the remainder, we have

$$R_n < \int_n^{\infty} f(x)\, dx = \int_n^{\infty} \frac{dx}{x^2} = \frac{1}{n}.$$

To ensure that $R_n < 10^{-3}$, we must choose n so that $1/n < 10^{-3}$, which implies that $n > 1000$. In other words, we must sum at least 1001 terms of the series to be sure that the remainder is less than 10^{-3}.

b. Using the bounds on the series, we have $L_n < S < U_n$, where S is the exact value of the series, and

$$L_n = S_n + \int_{n+1}^{\infty} \frac{dx}{x^2} = S_n + \frac{1}{n+1} \quad \text{and} \quad U_n = S_n + \int_n^{\infty} \frac{dx}{x^2} = S_n + \frac{1}{n}.$$

➤ The values of p-series with even values of p are generally known. For example, with $p = 2$, the series converges to $\pi^2/6$ (a proof is outlined in Exercise 66); with $p = 4$, the series converges to $\pi^4/90$. The values of p-series with odd values of p are not known.

Therefore, the series is bounded as follows:

$$S_n + \frac{1}{n+1} < S < S_n + \frac{1}{n},$$

where S_n is the sum of the first n terms. Using a calculator to sum the first 50 terms of the series, we find that $S_{50} \approx 1.625133$. The exact value of the series is in the interval

$$S_{50} + \frac{1}{50+1} < S < S_{50} + \frac{1}{50},$$

or $1.644741 < S < 1.645133$. Taking the average of these two bounds as our approximation of S, we find that $S \approx 1.644937$. This estimate is better than simply using S_{50}. Figure 8.31a shows the lower and upper bounds, L_n and U_n, respectively, for $n = 1, 2, \ldots, 50$. Figure 8.31b shows these bounds on an enlarged scale for $n = 50, 51, \ldots, 100$. These figures illustrate how the exact value of the series is squeezed into a narrowing interval as n increases.

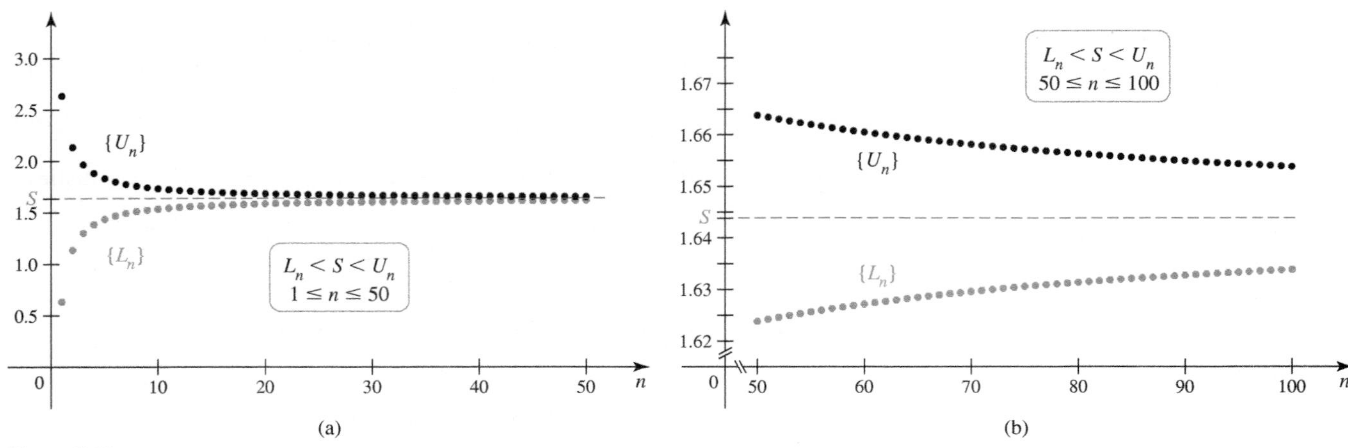

Figure 8.31

Related Exercises 35–42 ◄

Properties of Convergent Series

We close this section with several properties that are useful in upcoming work. The notation Σa_k, without initial and final values of k, is used to refer to a general infinite series whose terms may be positive or negative (or both).

> The **leading terms** of an infinite series are those at the beginning with a small index. The **tail** of an infinite series consists of the terms at the "end" of the series with a large and increasing index. The convergence or divergence of an infinite series depends on the tail of the series, while the value of a convergent series is determined primarily by the leading terms.

THEOREM 8.13 Properties of Convergent Series

1. Suppose Σa_k converges to A and c is a real number. The series $\Sigma c a_k$ converges, and $\Sigma c a_k = c \Sigma a_k = cA$.
2. Suppose Σa_k converges to A and Σb_k converges to B. The series $\Sigma (a_k \pm b_k)$ converges, and $\Sigma (a_k \pm b_k) = \Sigma a_k \pm \Sigma b_k = A \pm B$.
3. If M is a positive integer, then $\sum_{k=1}^{\infty} a_k$ and $\sum_{k=M}^{\infty} a_k$ either both converge or both diverge. In general, *whether* a series converges does not depend on a finite number of terms added to or removed from the series. However, the *value* of a convergent series does change if nonzero terms are added or removed.

Proof: These properties are proved using properties of finite sums and limits of sequences. To prove Property 1, assume that $\sum_{k=1}^{\infty} a_k$ converges to A and note that

$$\begin{aligned}
\sum_{k=1}^{\infty} c a_k &= \lim_{n\to\infty} \sum_{k=1}^{n} c a_k && \text{Definition of infinite series} \\
&= \lim_{n\to\infty} c \sum_{k=1}^{n} a_k && \text{Property of finite sums} \\
&= c \lim_{n\to\infty} \sum_{k=1}^{n} a_k && \text{Property of limits} \\
&= c \sum_{k=1}^{\infty} a_k && \text{Definition of infinite series} \\
&= cA. && \text{Value of the series}
\end{aligned}$$

Property 2 is proved in a similar way (Exercise 62).

Property 3 follows by noting that for finite sums with $1 < M < n$,

$$\sum_{k=M}^{n} a_k = \sum_{k=1}^{n} a_k - \sum_{k=1}^{M-1} a_k.$$

Letting $n \to \infty$ in this equation and assuming that $\sum_{k=1}^{\infty} a_k = A$, it follows that

$$\sum_{k=M}^{\infty} a_k = \underbrace{\sum_{k=1}^{\infty} a_k}_{A} - \underbrace{\sum_{k=1}^{M-1} a_k}_{\text{finite number}}.$$

QUICK CHECK 4 Explain why if $\sum_{k=1}^{\infty} a_k$ converges, then the series $\sum_{k=5}^{\infty} a_k$ (with a different starting index) also converges. Do the two series have the same value? ◄

Because the right side has a finite value, $\sum_{k=M}^{\infty} a_k$ converges. Similarly, if $\sum_{k=M}^{\infty} a_k$ converges, then $\sum_{k=1}^{\infty} a_k$ converges. By an analogous argument, if one of these series diverges, then the other series diverges. ◄

Use caution when applying Theorem 8.13. For example, you can write

$$\sum_{k=2}^{\infty} \frac{1}{k(k-1)} = \sum_{k=2}^{\infty} \left(\frac{1}{k-1} - \frac{1}{k} \right)$$

and then recognize a telescoping series (that converges to 1). An *incorrect* application of Theorem 8.13 would be to write

$$\sum_{k=2}^{\infty} \left(\frac{1}{k-1} - \frac{1}{k} \right) = \underbrace{\sum_{k=2}^{\infty} \frac{1}{k-1}}_{\text{diverges}} - \underbrace{\sum_{k=2}^{\infty} \frac{1}{k}}_{\text{diverges}} \qquad \text{This is } \textit{incorrect}!$$

and then conclude that the original series diverges. Neither $\sum_{k=2}^{\infty} \frac{1}{k-1}$ nor $\sum_{k=2}^{\infty} \frac{1}{k}$ converges; therefore, Property 2 of Theorem 8.13 does not apply.

EXAMPLE 5 **Using properties of series** Evaluate the infinite series

$$S = \sum_{k=1}^{\infty} \left(5\left(\frac{2}{3}\right)^k - \frac{2^{k-1}}{7^k} \right).$$

SOLUTION We examine the two series $\sum_{k=1}^{\infty} 5\left(\frac{2}{3}\right)^k$ and $\sum_{k=1}^{\infty} \frac{2^{k-1}}{7^k}$ individually. The first series is a geometric series and is evaluated using the methods of Section 8.3. Its first few terms are

$$\sum_{k=1}^{\infty} 5\left(\frac{2}{3}\right)^k = 5\left(\frac{2}{3}\right) + 5\left(\frac{2}{3}\right)^2 + 5\left(\frac{2}{3}\right)^3 + \cdots.$$

The first term of the series is $a = 5\left(\frac{2}{3}\right)$ and the ratio is $r = \frac{2}{3} < 1$; therefore,

$$\sum_{k=1}^{\infty} 5\left(\frac{2}{3}\right)^k = \frac{a}{1-r} = \frac{5\left(\frac{2}{3}\right)}{1-\frac{2}{3}} = 10.$$

Writing out the first few terms of the second series, we see that it, too, is a geometric series:

$$\sum_{k=1}^{\infty} \frac{2^{k-1}}{7^k} = \frac{1}{7} + \frac{2}{7^2} + \frac{2^2}{7^3} + \cdots.$$

The first term is $a = \frac{1}{7}$ and the ratio is $r = \frac{2}{7} < 1$; therefore,

$$\sum_{k=1}^{\infty} \frac{2^{k-1}}{7^k} = \frac{a}{1-r} = \frac{\frac{1}{7}}{1-\frac{2}{7}} = \frac{1}{5}.$$

Both series converge. By Property 2 of Theorem 8.13, we combine the two series and have $S = 10 - \frac{1}{5} = \frac{49}{5}$.

Related Exercises 43–50 ◀

QUICK CHECK 5 For a series with positive terms, explain why the sequence of partial sums $\{S_n\}$ is an increasing sequence. ◀

SECTION 8.4 EXERCISES

Review Questions

1. If we know that $\lim_{k\to\infty} a_k = 1$, then what can we say about $\sum_{k=1}^{\infty} a_k$?
2. Is it true that if the terms of a series of positive terms decrease to zero, then the series converges? Explain using an example.
3. Can the Integral Test be used to determine whether a series diverges?
4. For what values of p does the series $\sum_{k=1}^{\infty} \frac{1}{k^p}$ converge? For what values of p does it diverge?
5. For what values of p does the series $\sum_{k=10}^{\infty} \frac{1}{k^p}$ converge (initial index is 10)? For what values of p does it diverge?
6. Explain why the sequence of partial sums for a series with positive terms is an increasing sequence.
7. Define the remainder of an infinite series.
8. If a series of positive terms converges, does it follow that the remainder R_n must decrease to zero as $n \to \infty$? Explain.

Basic Skills

9–18. Divergence Test *Use the Divergence Test to determine whether the following series diverge or state that the test is inconclusive.*

9. $\sum_{k=0}^{\infty} \frac{k}{2k+1}$
10. $\sum_{k=1}^{\infty} \frac{k}{k^2+1}$
11. $\sum_{k=2}^{\infty} \frac{k}{\ln k}$
12. $\sum_{k=1}^{\infty} \frac{k^2}{2^k}$
13. $\sum_{k=0}^{\infty} \frac{1}{1000+k}$
14. $\sum_{k=1}^{\infty} \frac{k^3}{k^3+1}$
15. $\sum_{k=2}^{\infty} \frac{\sqrt{k}}{\ln^{10} k}$
16. $\sum_{k=1}^{\infty} \frac{\sqrt{k^2+1}}{k}$
17. $\sum_{k=1}^{\infty} k^{1/k}$
18. $\sum_{k=1}^{\infty} \frac{k^3}{k!}$

19–28. Integral Test *Use the Integral Test to determine the convergence or divergence of the following series, or state that the test does not apply.*

19. $\sum_{k=2}^{\infty} \frac{1}{e^k}$
20. $\sum_{k=1}^{\infty} \frac{k}{\sqrt{k^2+4}}$
21. $\sum_{k=1}^{\infty} ke^{-2k^2}$
22. $\sum_{k=1}^{\infty} \frac{1}{\sqrt[3]{k+10}}$
23. $\sum_{k=0}^{\infty} \frac{1}{\sqrt{k+8}}$
24. $\sum_{k=2}^{\infty} \frac{1}{k(\ln k)^2}$
25. $\sum_{k=1}^{\infty} \frac{k}{e^k}$
26. $\sum_{k=3}^{\infty} \frac{1}{k(\ln k)\ln \ln k}$
27. $\sum_{k=1}^{\infty} \frac{|\sin k|}{k^2}$
28. $\sum_{k=1}^{\infty} \frac{k}{(k^2+1)^3}$

29–34. *p*-series *Determine the convergence or divergence of the following series.*

29. $\sum_{k=1}^{\infty} \frac{1}{k^{10}}$
30. $\sum_{k=2}^{\infty} \frac{k^e}{k^\pi}$
31. $\sum_{k=3}^{\infty} \frac{1}{(k-2)^4}$
32. $\sum_{k=1}^{\infty} 2k^{-3/2}$
33. $\sum_{k=1}^{\infty} \frac{1}{\sqrt[3]{k}}$
34. $\sum_{k=1}^{\infty} \frac{1}{\sqrt[3]{27k^2}}$

T **35–42. Remainders and estimates** *Consider the following convergent series.*

a. *Find an upper bound for the remainder in terms of n.*
b. *Find how many terms are needed to ensure that the remainder is less than 10^{-3}.*
c. *Find lower and upper bounds (L_n and U_n, respectively) on the exact value of the series.*
d. *Find an interval in which the value of the series must lie if you approximate it using ten terms of the series.*

35. $\sum_{k=1}^{\infty} \frac{1}{k^6}$
36. $\sum_{k=1}^{\infty} \frac{1}{k^8}$
37. $\sum_{k=1}^{\infty} \frac{1}{3^k}$
38. $\sum_{k=2}^{\infty} \frac{1}{k(\ln k)^2}$
39. $\sum_{k=1}^{\infty} \frac{1}{k^{3/2}}$
40. $\sum_{k=1}^{\infty} e^{-k}$
41. $\sum_{k=1}^{\infty} \frac{1}{k^3}$
42. $\sum_{k=1}^{\infty} ke^{-k^2}$

43–50. Properties of series *Use the properties of infinite series to evaluate the following series.*

43. $\sum_{k=1}^{\infty} \frac{4}{12^k}$
44. $\sum_{k=2}^{\infty} 3e^{-k}$
45. $\sum_{k=0}^{\infty} \left(3\left(\frac{2}{5}\right)^k - 2\left(\frac{5}{7}\right)^k\right)$
46. $\sum_{k=1}^{\infty} \left(2\left(\frac{3}{5}\right)^k + 3\left(\frac{4}{9}\right)^k\right)$
47. $\sum_{k=1}^{\infty} \left(\frac{1}{3}\left(\frac{5}{6}\right)^k + \frac{3}{5}\left(\frac{7}{9}\right)^k\right)$
48. $\sum_{k=0}^{\infty} \left(\frac{1}{2}(0.2)^k + \frac{3}{2}(0.8)^k\right)$
49. $\sum_{k=1}^{\infty} \left(\left(\frac{1}{6}\right)^k + \left(\frac{1}{3}\right)^{k-1}\right)$
50. $\sum_{k=0}^{\infty} \frac{2-3^k}{6^k}$

Further Explorations

51. Explain why or why not Determine whether the following statements are true and give an explanation or counterexample.

a. If $\sum_{k=1}^{\infty} a_k$ converges, then $\sum_{k=10}^{\infty} a_k$ converges.

b. If $\sum_{k=1}^{\infty} a_k$ diverges, then $\sum_{k=10}^{\infty} a_k$ diverges.

c. If $\sum a_k$ converges, then $\sum (a_k + 0.0001)$ also converges.

d. If $\sum p^k$ diverges, then $\sum (p + 0.001)^k$ diverges, for a fixed real number p.

e. If $\sum k^{-p}$ converges, then $\sum k^{-p+0.001}$ converges.

f. If $\lim_{k\to\infty} a_k = 0$, then $\sum a_k$ converges.

52–57. Choose your test *Determine whether the following series converge or diverge.*

52. $\sum_{k=1}^{\infty} \sqrt{\frac{k+1}{k}}$

53. $\sum_{k=1}^{\infty} \frac{1}{(3k+1)(3k+4)}$

54. $\sum_{k=0}^{\infty} \frac{10}{k^2+9}$

55. $\sum_{k=1}^{\infty} \frac{k}{\sqrt{k^2+1}}$

56. $\sum_{k=1}^{\infty} \frac{2^k+3^k}{4^k}$

57. $\sum_{k=1}^{\infty} \frac{4}{k(\ln k)^2}$

58. Log p-series Consider the series $\sum_{k=2}^{\infty} \frac{1}{k(\ln k)^p}$, where p is a real number.

a. Use the Integral Test to determine the values of p for which this series converges.

b. Does this series converge faster for $p = 2$ or $p = 3$? Explain.

59. Loglog p-series Consider the series $\sum_{k=3}^{\infty} \frac{1}{k(\ln k)(\ln \ln k)^p}$, where p is a real number.

a. For what values of p does this series converge?

b. Which of the following series converges faster? Explain.

$$\sum_{k=2}^{\infty} \frac{1}{k(\ln k)^2} \quad \text{or} \quad \sum_{k=3}^{\infty} \frac{1}{k(\ln k)(\ln \ln k)^2}?$$

60. Find a series Find a series that

a. converges faster than $\sum \frac{1}{k^2}$ but slower than $\sum \frac{1}{k^3}$.

b. Diverges faster than $\sum \frac{1}{k}$ but slower than $\sum \frac{1}{\sqrt{k}}$.

c. Converges faster than $\sum \frac{1}{k \ln^2 k}$ but slower than $\sum \frac{1}{k^2}$.

Additional Exercises

61. A divergence proof Give an argument similar to that given in the text for the harmonic series to show that $\sum_{k=1}^{\infty} \frac{1}{\sqrt{k}}$ diverges.

62. Properties proof Use the ideas in the proof of Property 1 of Theorem 8.13 to prove Property 2 of Theorem 8.13.

63. Property of divergent series Prove that if $\sum a_k$ diverges, then $\sum ca_k$ also diverges, where $c \neq 0$ is a constant.

64. Prime numbers The prime numbers are those positive integers that are divisible by only 1 and themselves (for example, 2, 3, 5, 7, 11, 13, . . .). A celebrated theorem states that the sequence of prime numbers $\{p_k\}$ satisfies $\lim_{k\to\infty} p_k/(k \ln k) = 1$. Show that $\sum_{k=2}^{\infty} \frac{1}{k \ln k}$ diverges, which implies that the series $\sum_{k=1}^{\infty} \frac{1}{p_k}$ diverges.

T 65. The zeta function The Riemann zeta function is the subject of extensive research and is associated with several renowned unsolved problems. It is defined by $\zeta(x) = \sum_{k=1}^{\infty} \frac{1}{k^x}$. When x is a real number, the zeta function becomes a p-series. For even positive integers p, the value of $\zeta(p)$ is known exactly. For example,

$$\sum_{k=1}^{\infty} \frac{1}{k^2} = \frac{\pi^2}{6}, \quad \sum_{k=1}^{\infty} \frac{1}{k^4} = \frac{\pi^4}{90}, \quad \text{and} \quad \sum_{k=1}^{\infty} \frac{1}{k^6} = \frac{\pi^6}{945}, \ldots.$$

Use the estimation techniques described in the text to approximate $\zeta(3)$ and $\zeta(5)$ (whose values are not known exactly) with a remainder less than 10^{-3}.

66. Showing that $\sum_{k=1}^{\infty} \frac{1}{k^2} = \frac{\pi^2}{6}$ In 1734, Leonhard Euler informally proved that $\sum_{k=1}^{\infty} \frac{1}{k^2} = \frac{\pi^2}{6}$. An elegant proof is outlined here that uses the inequality

$$\cot^2 x < \frac{1}{x^2} < 1 + \cot^2 x \quad \left(\text{provided that } 0 < x < \frac{\pi}{2}\right)$$

and the identity

$$\sum_{k=1}^{n} \cot^2 k\theta = \frac{n(2n-1)}{3}, \text{ for } n = 1, 2, 3, \ldots, \text{ where } \theta = \frac{\pi}{2n+1}.$$

a. Show that $\sum_{k=1}^{n} \cot^2 k\theta < \frac{1}{\theta^2} \sum_{k=1}^{n} \frac{1}{k^2} < n + \sum_{k=1}^{n} \cot^2 k\theta$.

b. Use the inequality in part (a) to show that

$$\frac{n(2n-1)\pi^2}{3(2n+1)^2} < \sum_{k=1}^{n} \frac{1}{k^2} < \frac{n(2n+2)\pi^2}{3(2n+1)^2}.$$

c. Use the Squeeze Theorem to conclude that $\sum_{k=1}^{\infty} \frac{1}{k^2} = \frac{\pi^2}{6}$.

(*Source: The College Mathematics Journal*, 24, 5, Nov 1993)

67. Reciprocals of odd squares Assume that $\sum_{k=1}^{\infty} \frac{1}{k^2} = \frac{\pi^2}{6}$ (Exercises 65 and 66) and that the terms of this series may be rearranged without changing the value of the series. Determine the sum of the reciprocals of the squares of the odd positive integers.

T 68. Shifted p-series Consider the sequence $\{F_n\}$ defined by

$$F_n = \sum_{k=1}^{\infty} \frac{1}{k(k+n)},$$

for $n = 0, 1, 2, \ldots$. When $n = 0$, the series is a p-series, and we have $F_0 = \pi^2/6$ (Exercises 65 and 66).

a. Explain why $\{F_n\}$ is a decreasing sequence.

b. Plot $\{F_n\}$, for $n = 1, 2, \ldots, 20$.

c. Based on your experiments, make a conjecture about $\lim_{n\to\infty} F_n$.

69. A sequence of sums Consider the sequence $\{x_n\}$ defined for $n = 1, 2, 3, \ldots$ by

$$x_n = \sum_{k=n+1}^{2n} \frac{1}{k} = \frac{1}{n+1} + \frac{1}{n+2} + \cdots + \frac{1}{2n}.$$

a. Write out the terms x_1, x_2, x_3.

b. Show that $\frac{1}{2} \leq x_n < 1$, for $n = 1, 2, 3, \ldots$.

c. Show that x_n is the right Riemann sum for $\int_1^2 \frac{dx}{x}$ using n subintervals.

d. Conclude that $\lim_{n\to\infty} x_n = \ln 2$.

T 70. The harmonic series and Euler's constant

a. Sketch the function $f(x) = 1/x$ on the interval $[1, n + 1]$, where n is a positive integer. Use this graph to verify that

$$\ln(n+1) < 1 + \frac{1}{2} + \frac{1}{3} + \cdots + \frac{1}{n} < 1 + \ln n.$$

b. Let S_n be the sum of the first n terms of the harmonic series, so part (a) says $\ln(n+1) < S_n < 1 + \ln n$. Define the new sequence $\{E_n\}$ by

$$E_n = S_n - \ln(n+1), \quad \text{for } n = 1, 2, 3, \ldots.$$

Show that $E_n > 0$, for $n = 1, 2, 3, \ldots$.

c. Using a figure similar to that used in part (a), show that

$$\frac{1}{n+1} > \ln(n+2) - \ln(n+1).$$

d. Use parts (a) and (c) to show that $\{E_n\}$ is an increasing sequence $(E_{n+1} > E_n)$.

e. Use part (a) to show that $\{E_n\}$ is bounded above by 1.

f. Conclude from parts (d) and (e) that $\{E_n\}$ has a limit less than or equal to 1. This limit is known as **Euler's constant** and is denoted γ (the Greek lowercase gamma).

g. By computing terms of $\{E_n\}$, estimate the value of γ and compare it to the value $\gamma \approx 0.5772$. (It has been conjectured that γ is irrational.)

h. The preceding arguments show that the sum of the first n terms of the harmonic series satisfy $S_n \approx 0.5772 + \ln(n+1)$. How many terms must be summed for the sum to exceed 10?

71. Stacking dominoes Consider a set of identical dominoes that are 2 inches long. The dominoes are stacked on top of each other with their long edges aligned so that each domino overhangs the one beneath it *as far as possible* (see figure).

a. If there are n dominoes in the stack, what is the *greatest* distance that the top domino can be made to overhang the bottom domino? (*Hint:* Put the nth domino beneath the previous $n - 1$ dominoes.)

b. If we allow for infinitely many dominoes in the stack, what is the greatest distance that the top domino can be made to overhang the bottom domino?

72. Gabriel's wedding cake Consider a wedding cake of infinite height, each layer of which is a right circular cylinder of height 1. The bottom layer of the cake has a radius of 1, the second layer has a radius of $1/2$, the third layer has a radius of $1/3$, and the nth layer has a radius of $1/n$ (see figure).

a. To determine how much frosting is needed to cover the cake, find the area of the lateral (vertical) sides of the wedding cake. What is the area of the horizontal surfaces of the cake?

b. Determine the volume of the cake. (*Hint:* Use the result of Exercise 66.)

c. Comment on your answers to parts (a) and (b).

(*Source: The College Mathematics Journal*, 30, 1, Jan 1999)

73. The harmonic series and the Fibonacci sequence The Fibonacci sequence $\{1, 1, 2, 3, 5, 8, 13, \ldots\}$ is generated by the recurrence relation

$$f_{n+1} = f_n + f_{n-1}, \text{ for } n = 1, 2, 3, \ldots, \text{ where } f_0 = 1, f_1 = 1.$$

a. It can be shown that the sequence of ratios of successive terms of the sequence $\left\{\frac{f_{n+1}}{f_n}\right\}$ has a limit φ. Divide both sides of the recurrence relation by f_n, take the limit as $n \to \infty$, and show that $\varphi = \lim_{n\to\infty} \frac{f_{n+1}}{f_n} = \frac{1+\sqrt{5}}{2} \approx 1.618$.

b. Show that $\lim_{n\to\infty} \frac{f_{n-1}}{f_{n+1}} = 1 - \frac{1}{\varphi} \approx 0.382$.

c. Now consider the harmonic series and group terms as follows:

$$\sum_{k=1}^{\infty} \frac{1}{k} = 1 + \frac{1}{2} + \frac{1}{3} + \underbrace{\left(\frac{1}{4} + \frac{1}{5}\right)}_{\text{2 terms}} + \underbrace{\left(\frac{1}{6} + \frac{1}{7} + \frac{1}{8}\right)}_{\text{3 terms}} + \underbrace{\left(\frac{1}{9} + \cdots + \frac{1}{13}\right)}_{\text{5 terms}} + \cdots.$$

With the Fibonacci sequence in mind, show that

$$\sum_{k=1}^{\infty} \frac{1}{k} \geq 1 + \frac{1}{2} + \frac{1}{3} + \frac{2}{5} + \frac{3}{8} + \frac{5}{13} + \cdots = 1 + \sum_{k=1}^{\infty} \frac{f_{k-1}}{f_{k+1}}.$$

d. Use part (b) to conclude that the harmonic series diverges.

(*Source*: *The College Mathematics Journal*, 43, May 2012)

QUICK CHECK ANSWERS

1. The series diverges for $|r| \geq 1$. **2. a.** Divergent p-series **b.** Convergent geometric series **c.** Convergent p-series **3.** The remainder is $R_n = a_{n+1} + a_{n+2} + \cdots$, which consists of positive numbers. **4.** Removing a finite number of terms does not change whether the series converges. It generally changes the value of the series. **5.** Given the nth term of the sequence of partial sums S_n, the next term is obtained by adding a positive number. So $S_{n+1} > S_n$, which means the sequence is increasing. ◄

8.5 The Ratio, Root, and Comparison Tests

We now consider several additional convergence tests for series with positive terms: the Ratio Test, the Root Test, and two comparison tests. The Ratio Test is used frequently throughout the next chapter, and comparison tests are valuable when no other test works. As in Section 8.4, these tests determine *whether* an infinite series converges, but they do not establish the value of the series.

The Ratio Test

The Integral Test is powerful, but limited, because it requires evaluating integrals. For example, the series $\sum 1/k!$, with a factorial term, cannot be handled by the Integral Test. The next test significantly enlarges the set of infinite series that we can analyze.

> In words, the Ratio Test says the limit of the ratio of successive terms of the series must be less than 1 for convergence of the series.

THEOREM 8.14 Ratio Test

Let $\sum a_k$ be an infinite series with positive terms and let $r = \lim_{k\to\infty} \frac{a_{k+1}}{a_k}$.

1. If $0 \le r < 1$, the series converges.
2. If $r > 1$ (including $r = \infty$), the series diverges.
3. If $r = 1$, the test is inconclusive.

> See Appendix B for a formal proof of Theorem 8.14.

Proof (outline): The idea behind the proof provides insight. Let's assume that the limit r exists. Then as k gets large and the ratio a_{k+1}/a_k approaches r, we have $a_{k+1} \approx ra_k$. Therefore, as one goes farther and farther out in the series, it behaves like

$$\begin{aligned} a_k + a_{k+1} + a_{k+2} + \cdots &\approx a_k + ra_k + r^2a_k + r^3a_k + \cdots \\ &= a_k(1 + r + r^2 + r^3 + \cdots). \end{aligned}$$

The tail of the series, which determines whether the series converges, behaves like a geometric series with ratio r. We know that if $0 \le r < 1$, the geometric series converges, and if $r > 1$, the series diverges, which is the conclusion of the Ratio Test. ◀

EXAMPLE 1 Using the Ratio Test Use the Ratio Test to determine whether the following series converge.

a. $\sum_{k=1}^{\infty} \frac{10^k}{k!}$ **b.** $\sum_{k=1}^{\infty} \frac{k^k}{k!}$ **c.** $\sum_{k=1}^{\infty} e^{-k}(k^2 + 4)$

> Recall that
> $$k! = k \cdot (k-1) \cdots 2 \cdot 1.$$
> Therefore,
> $$(k+1)! = (k+1)\underbrace{k(k-1)\cdots 1}_{k!} = (k+1)k!.$$

SOLUTION In each case, the limit of the ratio of successive terms is determined.

a. $$\begin{aligned} r = \lim_{k\to\infty} \frac{a_{k+1}}{a_k} &= \lim_{k\to\infty} \frac{10^{k+1}/(k+1)!}{10^k/k!} && \text{Substitute } a_{k+1} \text{ and } a_k. \\ &= \lim_{k\to\infty} \frac{10^{k+1}}{10^k} \cdot \frac{k!}{(k+1)k!} && \text{Invert and multiply.} \\ &= \lim_{k\to\infty} \frac{10}{k+1} = 0 && \text{Simplify and evaluate the limit.} \end{aligned}$$

Because $r = 0 < 1$, the series converges by the Ratio Test.

$$\textbf{b. } r = \lim_{k\to\infty} \frac{a_{k+1}}{a_k} = \lim_{k\to\infty} \frac{(k+1)^{k+1}/(k+1)!}{k^k/k!} \quad \text{Substitute } a_{k+1} \text{ and } a_k.$$

$$= \lim_{k\to\infty} \left(\frac{k+1}{k}\right)^k \quad \text{Simplify.}$$

$$= \lim_{k\to\infty} \left(1 + \frac{1}{k}\right)^k = e \quad \text{Simplify and evaluate the limit.}$$

➤ Recall from Section 4.7 that $\lim_{k\to\infty} \left(1 + \frac{1}{k}\right)^k = e \approx 2.718$.

Because $r = e > 1$, the series diverges by the Ratio Test. Alternatively, we could have noted that $\lim_{k\to\infty} k^k/k! = \infty$ (Theorem 8.6) and used the Divergence Test to reach the same conclusion.

$$\textbf{c. } r = \lim_{k\to\infty} \frac{a_{k+1}}{a_k} = \lim_{k\to\infty} \frac{e^{-(k+1)}((k+1)^2 + 4)}{e^{-k}(k^2+4)} \quad \text{Substitute } a_{k+1} \text{ and } a_k.$$

$$= \lim_{k\to\infty} \frac{e^{-k}e^{-1}(k^2 + 2k + 5)}{e^{-k}(k^2+4)} \quad \text{Simplify.}$$

$$= e^{-1} \underbrace{\lim_{k\to\infty} \frac{k^2 + 2k + 5}{k^2 + 1}}_{1} \quad \text{Simplify.}$$

$$= e^{-1}$$

Because $e^{-1} = \frac{1}{e} < 1$, the series converges by the Ratio Test.

Related Exercises 9–18 ◄

QUICK CHECK 1 Evaluate $10!/9!$, $(k+2)!/k!$, and $k!/(k+1)!$ ◄

The Ratio Test is conclusive for many series. Nevertheless, observe what happens when the Ratio Test is applied to the harmonic series $\sum_{k=1}^{\infty} \frac{1}{k}$:

$$r = \lim_{k\to\infty} \frac{a_{k+1}}{a_k} = \lim_{k\to\infty} \frac{1/(k+1)}{1/k} = \lim_{k\to\infty} \frac{k}{k+1} = 1,$$

➤ At the end of this section, we offer guidelines to help you to decide which convergence test is best suited for a given series.

which means the test is inconclusive. We know the harmonic series diverges, yet the Ratio Test cannot be used to establish this fact. Like all the convergence tests presented so far, the Ratio Test works only for certain classes of series. For this reason, it is useful to present a few additional convergence tests.

QUICK CHECK 2 Verify that the Ratio Test is inconclusive for $\sum_{k=1}^{\infty} \frac{1}{k^2}$. What test could be applied to show that $\sum_{k=1}^{\infty} \frac{1}{k^2}$ converges? ◄

The Root Test

Occasionally a series arises for which the preceding tests are difficult to apply. In these situations, the Root Test may be the tool that is needed.

THEOREM 8.15 Root Test
Let $\sum a_k$ be an infinite series with nonnegative terms and let $\rho = \lim_{k\to\infty} \sqrt[k]{a_k}$.

1. If $0 \le \rho < 1$, the series converges.
2. If $\rho > 1$ (including $\rho = \infty$), the series diverges.
3. If $\rho = 1$, the test is inconclusive.

Proof (outline): Assume that the limit ρ exists. If k is large, we have $\rho \approx \sqrt[k]{a_k}$ or $a_k \approx \rho^k$. For large values of k, the tail of the series, which determines whether a series converges, behaves like

$$a_k + a_{k+1} + a_{k+2} + \cdots \approx \rho^k + \rho^{k+1} + \rho^{k+2} + \cdots.$$

➤ See Appendix B for a formal proof of Theorem 8.15.

Therefore, the tail of the series is approximately a geometric series with ratio ρ. If $0 \le \rho < 1$, the geometric series converges, and if $\rho > 1$, the series diverges, which is the conclusion of the Root Test. ◀

EXAMPLE 2 **Using the Root Test** Use the Root Test to determine whether the following series converge.

a. $\displaystyle\sum_{k=1}^{\infty}\left(\frac{4k^2 - 3}{7k^2 + 6}\right)^k$ **b.** $\displaystyle\sum_{k=1}^{\infty}\frac{2^k}{k^{10}}$

SOLUTION

a. The required limit is

$$\rho = \lim_{k\to\infty}\sqrt[k]{\left(\frac{4k^2 - 3}{7k^2 + 6}\right)^k} = \lim_{k\to\infty}\frac{4k^2 - 3}{7k^2 + 6} = \frac{4}{7}.$$

Because $0 \le \rho < 1$, the series converges by the Root Test.

b. In this case,

$$\rho = \lim_{k\to\infty}\sqrt[k]{\frac{2^k}{k^{10}}} = \lim_{k\to\infty}\frac{2}{k^{10/k}} = \lim_{k\to\infty}\frac{2}{(k^{1/k})^{10}} = 2. \quad \lim_{k\to\infty} k^{1/k} = 1$$

Because $\rho > 1$, the series diverges by the Root Test.

We could have used the Ratio Test for both series in this example, but the Root Test is easier to apply in each case. In part (b), the Divergence Test leads to the same conclusion.

Related Exercises 19–26 ◀

The Comparison Test

Tests that use known series to test unknown series are called *comparison tests*. The first test is the Basic Comparison Test or simply the Comparison Test.

➤ Whether a series converges depends on the behavior of terms in the tail (large values of the index). So the inequalities $0 < a_k \le b_k$ and $0 < b_k \le a_k$ need not hold for all terms of the series. They must hold for all $k > N$ for some positive integer N.

THEOREM 8.16 **Comparison Test**
Let Σa_k and Σb_k be series with positive terms.

1. If $0 < a_k \le b_k$ and Σb_k converges, then Σa_k converges.
2. If $0 < b_k \le a_k$ and Σb_k diverges, then Σa_k diverges.

Proof: Assume that Σb_k converges, which means that Σb_k has a finite value B. The sequence of partial sums for Σa_k satisfies

$$S_n = \sum_{k=1}^{n} a_k \le \sum_{k=1}^{n} b_k \quad a_k \le b_k$$

$$< \sum_{k=1}^{\infty} b_k \quad \text{Positive terms are added to a finite sum.}$$

$$= B. \quad \text{Value of series}$$

Therefore, the sequence of partial sums for Σa_k is increasing and bounded above by B. By the Bounded Monotonic Sequence Theorem (Theorem 8.5), the sequence of partial sums of Σa_k has a limit, which implies that Σa_k converges. The second case of the theorem is proved in a similar way. ◀

The Comparison Test can be illustrated with graphs of sequences of partial sums. Consider the series

$$\sum_{k=1}^{\infty} a_k = \sum_{k=1}^{\infty} \frac{1}{k^2 + 10} \quad \text{and} \quad \sum_{k=1}^{\infty} b_k = \sum_{k=1}^{\infty} \frac{1}{k^2}.$$

Because $\frac{1}{k^2 + 10} < \frac{1}{k^2}$, it follows that $a_k < b_k$, for $k \geq 1$. Furthermore, Σb_k is a convergent p-series. By the Comparison Test, we conclude that Σa_k also converges (Figure 8.32). The second case of the Comparison Test is illustrated with the series

$$\sum_{k=4}^{\infty} a_k = \sum_{k=4}^{\infty} \frac{1}{\sqrt{k} - 3} \quad \text{and} \quad \sum_{k=4}^{\infty} b_k = \sum_{k=4}^{\infty} \frac{1}{\sqrt{k}}.$$

Now $\frac{1}{\sqrt{k}} < \frac{1}{\sqrt{k} - 3}$, for $k \geq 4$. Therefore, $b_k < a_k$, for $k \geq 4$. Because Σb_k is a divergent p-series, by the Comparison Test, Σa_k also diverges. Figure 8.33 shows that the sequence of partial sums for Σa_k lies above the sequence of partial sums for Σb_k. Because the sequence of partial sums for Σb_k diverges, the sequence of partial sums for Σa_k also diverges.

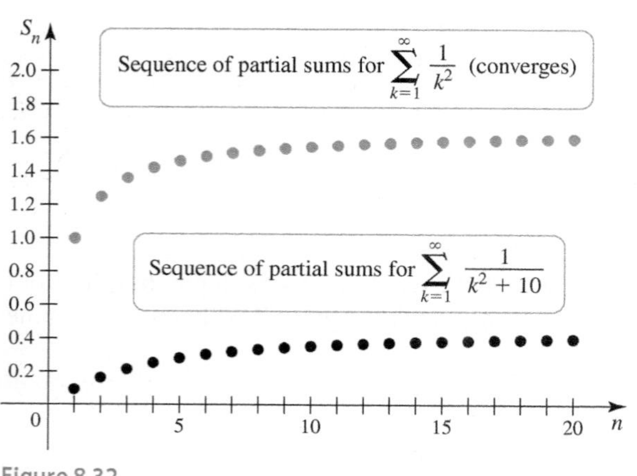

Figure 8.32

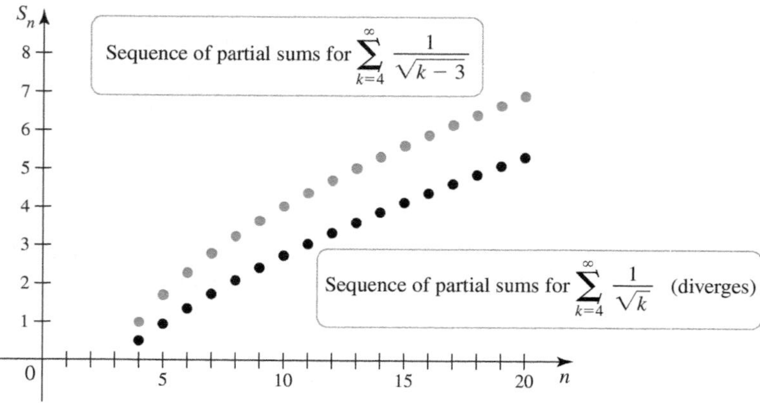

Figure 8.33

The key in using the Comparison Test is finding an appropriate comparison series. Plenty of practice will enable you to spot patterns and choose good comparison series.

EXAMPLE 3 Using the Comparison Test Determine whether the following series converge.

a. $\displaystyle\sum_{k=1}^{\infty} \frac{k^3}{2k^4 - 1}$ **b.** $\displaystyle\sum_{k=2}^{\infty} \frac{\ln k}{k^3}$

SOLUTION In using comparison tests, it's helpful to get a feel for how the terms of the given series are decreasing. If they are not decreasing, the series diverges.

➤ If Σa_k diverges, then $\Sigma c a_k$ also diverges for any constant $c \neq 0$ (Exercise 63 of Section 8.4).

a. As we go farther and farther out in this series ($k \rightarrow \infty$), the terms behave like

$$\frac{k^3}{2k^4 - 1} \approx \frac{k^3}{2k^4} = \frac{1}{2k}.$$

So a reasonable choice for a comparison series is the divergent series $\sum \frac{1}{2k}$. We must now show that the terms of the given series are *greater* than the terms of the comparison series. It is done by noting that $2k^4 - 1 < 2k^4$. Inverting both sides, we have

$$\frac{1}{2k^4 - 1} > \frac{1}{2k^4}, \quad \text{which implies that} \quad \frac{k^3}{2k^4 - 1} > \frac{k^3}{2k^4} = \frac{1}{2k}.$$

Because $\sum \frac{1}{2k}$ diverges, case (2) of the Comparison Test implies that the given series also diverges.

b. We note that $\ln k < k$, for $k \geq 2$, and then divide by k^3:

$$\frac{\ln k}{k^3} < \frac{k}{k^3} = \frac{1}{k^2}.$$

Therefore, an appropriate comparison series is the convergent p-series $\sum \frac{1}{k^2}$. Because $\sum \frac{1}{k^2}$ converges, the given series converges.

Related Exercises 27–38 ◀

QUICK CHECK 3 Explain why it is difficult to use the divergent series $\Sigma 1/k$ as a comparison series to test $\Sigma 1/(k + 1)$. ◀

The Limit Comparison Test

The Comparison Test should be tried if there is an obvious comparison series and the necessary inequality is easily established. Notice, however, that if the series in Example 3a were $\sum_{k=1}^{\infty} \frac{k^3}{2k^4 + 10}$ instead of $\sum_{k=1}^{\infty} \frac{k^3}{2k^4 - 1}$, then the comparison to the series $\sum \frac{1}{2k}$ would not work. Rather than fiddling with inequalities, it is often easier to use a more refined test called the *Limit Comparison Test.*

THEOREM 8.17 Limit Comparison Test
Let Σa_k and Σb_k be series with positive terms and let

$$\lim_{k \to \infty} \frac{a_k}{b_k} = L.$$

1. If $0 < L < \infty$ (that is, L is a finite positive number), then Σa_k and Σb_k either both converge or both diverge.
2. If $L = 0$ and Σb_k converges, then Σa_k converges.
3. If $L = \infty$ and Σb_k diverges, then Σa_k diverges.

QUICK CHECK 4 For case (1) of the Limit Comparison Test, we must have $0 < L < \infty$. Why can either a_k or b_k be chosen as the known comparison series? That is, why can L be the limit of a_k/b_k or b_k/a_k? ◀

➤ Recall that $|x| < a$ is equivalent to $-a < x < a$.

Proof (Case 1): Recall the definition of $\lim_{k \to \infty} \frac{a_k}{b_k} = L$: Given any $\varepsilon > 0$, $\left|\frac{a_k}{b_k} - L\right| < \varepsilon$ provided k is sufficiently large. In this case, let's take $\varepsilon = L/2$. It then follows that for sufficiently large k, $\left|\frac{a_k}{b_k} - L\right| < \frac{L}{2}$, or (removing the absolute value) $-\frac{L}{2} < \frac{a_k}{b_k} - L < \frac{L}{2}$. Adding L to all terms in these inequalities, we have

$$\frac{L}{2} < \frac{a_k}{b_k} < \frac{3L}{2}.$$

These inequalities imply that for sufficiently large k,

$$\frac{Lb_k}{2} < a_k < \frac{3Lb_k}{2}.$$

We see that the terms of Σa_k are sandwiched between multiples of the terms of Σb_k. By the Comparison Test, it follows that the two series converge or diverge together. Cases (2) and (3) ($L = 0$ and $L = \infty$, respectively) are treated in Exercise 81. ◀

EXAMPLE 4 **Using the Limit Comparison Test** Determine whether the following series converge.

a. $\displaystyle\sum_{k=1}^{\infty} \frac{5k^4 - 2k^2 + 3}{2k^6 - k + 5}$ **b.** $\displaystyle\sum_{k=1}^{\infty} \frac{\ln k}{k^2}$.

SOLUTION In both cases, we must find a comparison series whose terms behave like the terms of the given series as $k \to \infty$.

a. As $k \to \infty$, a rational function behaves like the ratio of the leading (highest-power) terms. In this case, as $k \to \infty$,

$$\frac{5k^4 - 2k^2 + 3}{2k^6 - k + 5} \approx \frac{5k^4}{2k^6} = \frac{5}{2k^2}.$$

Therefore, a reasonable comparison series is the convergent p-series $\displaystyle\sum_{k=1}^{\infty} \frac{1}{k^2}$ (the factor of $5/2$ does not affect whether the given series converges). Having chosen a comparison series, we compute the limit L:

$$L = \lim_{k\to\infty} \frac{(5k^4 - 2k^2 + 3)/(2k^6 - k + 5)}{1/k^2} \quad \text{Ratio of terms of series}$$

$$= \lim_{k\to\infty} \frac{k^2(5k^4 - 2k^2 + 3)}{2k^6 - k + 5} \quad \text{Simplify.}$$

$$= \lim_{k\to\infty} \frac{5k^6 - 2k^4 + 3k^2}{2k^6 - k + 5} = \frac{5}{2}. \quad \text{Simplify and evaluate the limit.}$$

We see that $0 < L < \infty$; therefore, the given series converges.

b. Why is this series interesting? We know that $\displaystyle\sum_{k=1}^{\infty} \frac{1}{k^2}$ converges and that $\displaystyle\sum_{k=1}^{\infty} \frac{1}{k}$ diverges. The given series $\displaystyle\sum_{k=1}^{\infty} \frac{\ln k}{k^2}$ is "between" these two series. This observation suggests that we use either $\displaystyle\sum_{k=1}^{\infty} \frac{1}{k^2}$ or $\displaystyle\sum_{k=1}^{\infty} \frac{1}{k}$ as a comparison series. In the first case, letting $a_k = \ln k/k^2$ and $b_k = 1/k^2$, we find that

$$L = \lim_{k\to\infty} \frac{a_k}{b_k} = \lim_{k\to\infty} \frac{\ln k/k^2}{1/k^2} = \lim_{k\to\infty} \ln k = \infty.$$

Case (3) of the Limit Comparison Test does not apply here because the comparison series $\displaystyle\sum_{k=1}^{\infty} \frac{1}{k^2}$ converges; we can reach the conclusion of case (3) only when the comparison series *diverges*.

If, instead, we use the comparison series $\sum b_k = \sum \frac{1}{k}$, then

$$L = \lim_{k\to\infty} \frac{a_k}{b_k} = \lim_{k\to\infty} \frac{\ln k/k^2}{1/k} = \lim_{k\to\infty} \frac{\ln k}{k} = 0.$$

Case (2) of the Limit Comparison Test does not apply here because the comparison series $\displaystyle\sum_{k=1}^{\infty} \frac{1}{k}$ diverges; case (2) is conclusive only when the comparison series *converges*.

With a bit more cunning, the Limit Comparison Test becomes conclusive. A series that lies "between" $\sum_{k=1}^{\infty} \frac{1}{k^2}$ and $\sum_{k=1}^{\infty} \frac{1}{k}$ is the convergent p-series $\sum_{k=1}^{\infty} \frac{1}{k^{3/2}}$; we try it as a comparison series. Letting $a_k = \ln k/k^2$ and $b_k = 1/k^{3/2}$, we find that

$$L = \lim_{k\to\infty} \frac{a_k}{b_k} = \lim_{k\to\infty} \frac{\ln k/k^2}{1/k^{3/2}} = \lim_{k\to\infty} \frac{\ln k}{\sqrt{k}} = 0.$$

(This limit is evaluated using l'Hôpital's Rule or by recalling that $\ln k$ grows more slowly than any positive power of k.) Now case (2) of the Limit Comparison Test applies; the comparison series $\sum \frac{1}{k^{3/2}}$ converges, so the given series converges.

Related Exercises 27–38 ◄

Guidelines for Choosing a Test

We close by outlining a procedure that puts the various convergence tests in perspective. Here is a reasonable course of action when testing a series of positive terms $\sum a_k$ for convergence.

1. Begin with the Divergence Test. If you show that $\lim_{k\to\infty} a_k \neq 0$, then the series diverges and your work is finished. The order of growth rates of sequences given in Section 8.2 is useful for evaluating $\lim_{k\to\infty} a_k$. (Recall that the Divergence Test also applies to series with arbitrary terms.)
2. Is the series a special series? Recall the convergence properties for the following series.
   - Geometric series: $\sum ar^k$ converges for $|r| < 1$ and diverges for $|r| \geq 1$ $(a \neq 0)$.
   - p-series: $\sum \frac{1}{k^p}$ converges for $p > 1$ and diverges for $p \leq 1$.
   - Check also for a telescoping series.
3. If the general kth term of the series looks like a function you can integrate, then try the Integral Test.
4. If the general kth term of the series involves $k!$, k^k, or a^k, where a is a constant, the Ratio Test is advisable. Series with k in an exponent may yield to the Root Test.
5. If the general kth term of the series is a rational function of k (or a root of a rational function), use the Comparison or the Limit Comparison Test with the families of series given in Step 2 as comparison series.

These guidelines will help, but in the end, convergence tests are mastered through practice. It's your turn.

SECTION 8.5 EXERCISES

Review Questions

1. Explain how the Ratio Test works.
2. Explain how the Root Test works.
3. Explain how the Limit Comparison Test works.
4. What is the first test you should use in analyzing the convergence of a series?
5. What test is advisable if a series of positive terms involves a factorial term?
6. What tests are best for the series $\sum a_k$ when a_k is a rational function of k?
7. Explain why, with a series of positive terms, the sequence of partial sums is an increasing sequence.
8. Do the tests discussed in this section tell you the value of the series? Explain.

Basic Skills

9–18. The Ratio Test *Use the Ratio Test to determine whether the following series converge.*

9. $\sum_{k=1}^{\infty} \frac{1}{k!}$ **10.** $\sum_{k=1}^{\infty} \frac{2^k}{k!}$ **11.** $\sum_{k=1}^{\infty} \frac{k^2}{4^k}$ **12.** $\sum_{k=1}^{\infty} \frac{k^k}{2^k}$

13. $\sum_{k=1}^{\infty} ke^{-k}$ **14.** $\sum_{k=1}^{\infty} \frac{k^k}{k!}$ **15.** $\sum_{k=1}^{\infty} \frac{2^k}{k^{99}}$ **16.** $\sum_{k=1}^{\infty} \frac{k^6}{k!}$

17. $\sum_{k=1}^{\infty} \frac{(k!)^2}{(2k)!}$

18. $2 + \frac{4}{16} + \frac{8}{81} + \frac{16}{256} + \cdots$

19–26. The Root Test *Use the Root Test to determine whether the following series converge.*

19. $\sum_{k=1}^{\infty}\left(\frac{10k^3+k}{9k^3+k+1}\right)^k$

20. $\sum_{k=1}^{\infty}\left(\frac{2k}{k+1}\right)^k$

21. $\sum_{k=1}^{\infty}\frac{k^2}{2^k}$

22. $\sum_{k=1}^{\infty}\left(1+\frac{3}{k}\right)^{k^2}$

23. $\sum_{k=1}^{\infty}\left(\frac{k}{k+1}\right)^{2k^2}$

24. $\sum_{k=1}^{\infty}\left(\frac{1}{\ln(k+1)}\right)^k$

25. $1+\left(\frac{1}{2}\right)^2+\left(\frac{1}{3}\right)^3+\left(\frac{1}{4}\right)^4+\cdots$

26. $\sum_{k=1}^{\infty}\frac{k}{e^k}$

27–38. Comparison tests *Use the Comparison Test or Limit Comparison Test to determine whether the following series converge.*

27. $\sum_{k=1}^{\infty}\frac{1}{k^2+4}$

28. $\sum_{k=1}^{\infty}\frac{k^2+k-1}{k^4+4k^2-3}$

29. $\sum_{k=1}^{\infty}\frac{k^2-1}{k^3+4}$

30. $\sum_{k=1}^{\infty}\frac{0.0001}{k+4}$

31. $\sum_{k=1}^{\infty}\frac{1}{k^{3/2}+1}$

32. $\sum_{k=1}^{\infty}\sqrt{\frac{k}{k^3+1}}$

33. $\sum_{k=1}^{\infty}\frac{\sin(1/k)}{k^2}$

34. $\sum_{k=1}^{\infty}\frac{1}{3^k-2^k}$

35. $\sum_{k=1}^{\infty}\frac{1}{2k-\sqrt{k}}$

36. $\sum_{k=1}^{\infty}\frac{1}{k\sqrt{k+2}}$

37. $\sum_{k=1}^{\infty}\frac{\sqrt[3]{k^2+1}}{\sqrt{k^3+2}}$

38. $\sum_{k=2}^{\infty}\frac{1}{(k\ln k)^2}$

Further Explorations

39. **Explain why or why not** Determine whether the following statements are true and give an explanation or counterexample.

a. Suppose that $0 < a_k < b_k$. If Σa_k converges, then Σb_k converges.

b. Suppose that $0 < a_k < b_k$. If Σa_k diverges, then Σb_k diverges.

c. Suppose $0 < b_k < c_k < a_k$. If Σa_k converges, then Σb_k and Σc_k converge.

d. The Ratio Test is always inconclusive when applied to Σa_k, where a_k is a rational function of k.

40–69. Choose your test *Use the test of your choice to determine whether the following series converge.*

40. $\left(\frac{1}{2}\right)^2+\left(\frac{2}{3}\right)^3+\left(\frac{3}{4}\right)^4+\cdots$

41. $\sum_{k=1}^{\infty}\left(1+\frac{2}{k}\right)^k$

42. $\sum_{k=1}^{\infty}\left(\frac{k^2}{2k^2+1}\right)^k$

43. $\sum_{k=1}^{\infty}\frac{k^{100}}{(k+1)!}$

44. $\sum_{k=1}^{\infty}\frac{\sin^2 k}{k^2}$

45. $\sum_{k=1}^{\infty}(\sqrt[k]{k}-1)^{2k}$

46. $\sum_{k=1}^{\infty}\frac{2^k}{e^k-1}$

47. $\sum_{k=1}^{\infty}\frac{k^2+2k+1}{3k^2+1}$

48. $\sum_{k=1}^{\infty}\frac{1}{5^k-1}$

49. $\sum_{k=3}^{\infty}\frac{1}{\ln k}$

50. $\sum_{k=3}^{\infty}\frac{1}{5^k-3^k}$

51. $\sum_{k=1}^{\infty}\frac{1}{\sqrt{k^3-k+1}}$

52. $\sum_{k=1}^{\infty}\frac{(k!)^3}{(3k)!}$

53. $\sum_{k=1}^{\infty}\left(\frac{1}{k}+2^{-k}\right)$

54. $\sum_{k=2}^{\infty}\frac{5\ln k}{k}$

55. $\sum_{k=1}^{\infty}\frac{2^k k!}{k^k}$

56. $\sum_{k=1}^{\infty}\left(1-\frac{1}{k}\right)^{k^2}$

57. $\sum_{k=1}^{\infty}\frac{k^8}{k^{11}+3}$

58. $\sum_{k=1}^{\infty}\frac{1}{(1+p)^k},\ p>0$

59. $\sum_{k=1}^{\infty}\frac{1}{k^{1+p}},\ p>0$

60. $\sum_{k=2}^{\infty}\frac{1}{k^2\ln k}$

61. $\sum_{k=1}^{\infty}\ln\left(\frac{k+2}{k+1}\right)$

62. $\sum_{k=1}^{\infty}k^{-1/k}$

63. $\sum_{k=2}^{\infty}\frac{1}{k^{\ln k}}$

64. $\sum_{k=1}^{\infty}\sin^2\frac{1}{k}$

65. $\sum_{k=1}^{\infty}\tan\frac{1}{k}$

66. $\sum_{k=2}^{\infty}100k^{-k}$

67. $\frac{1}{1\cdot 3}+\frac{1}{3\cdot 5}+\frac{1}{5\cdot 7}+\cdots$

68. $\frac{1}{2^2}+\frac{2}{3^2}+\frac{3}{4^2}+\cdots$

69. $\frac{1}{1!}+\frac{4}{2!}+\frac{9}{3!}+\frac{16}{4!}+\cdots$

70–77. Convergence parameter *Find the values of the parameter $p > 0$ for which the following series converge.*

70. $\sum_{k=2}^{\infty}\frac{1}{(\ln k)^p}$

71. $\sum_{k=2}^{\infty}\frac{\ln k}{k^p}$

72. $\sum_{k=2}^{\infty}\frac{1}{k(\ln k)(\ln\ln k)^p}$

73. $\sum_{k=2}^{\infty}\left(\frac{\ln k}{k}\right)^p$

74. $\sum_{k=0}^{\infty}\frac{k!\,p^k}{(k+1)^k}$ (*Hint:* Stirling's formula is useful: $k! \approx \sqrt{2\pi k}\,k^k e^{-k}$ for large k.)

75. $\sum_{k=1}^{\infty}\frac{kp^k}{k+1}$

76. $\sum_{k=1}^{\infty}\ln\left(\frac{k}{k+1}\right)^p$

77. $\sum_{k=1}^{\infty}\left(1-\frac{p}{k}\right)^k$

78. **Series of squares** Prove that if Σa_k is a convergent series of positive terms, then the series Σa_k^2 also converges.

79. **Geometric series revisited** We know from Section 8.3 that the geometric series Σar^k $(a \neq 0)$ converges if $0 < r < 1$ and diverges if $r > 1$. Prove these facts using the Integral Test, the Ratio Test, and the Root Test. Now consider all values of r. What can be determined about the geometric series using the Divergence Test?

80. **Two sine series** Determine whether the following series converge.

a. $\sum_{k=1}^{\infty}\sin\frac{1}{k}$

b. $\sum_{k=1}^{\infty}\frac{1}{k}\sin\frac{1}{k}$

Additional Exercises

81. **Limit Comparison Test proof** Use the proof of case (1) of the Limit Comparison Test (Theorem 8.17) to prove cases (2) and (3).

82–87. A glimpse ahead to power series *Use the Ratio Test to determine the values of $x \geq 0$ for which each series converges.*

82. $\sum_{k=1}^{\infty}\frac{x^k}{k!}$

83. $\sum_{k=1}^{\infty}x^k$

84. $\sum_{k=1}^{\infty}\frac{x^k}{k}$

85. $\sum_{k=1}^{\infty} \frac{x^k}{k^2}$

86. $\sum_{k=1}^{\infty} \frac{x^{2k}}{k^2}$

87. $\sum_{k=1}^{\infty} \frac{x^k}{2^k}$

88. Infinite products An infinite product $P = a_1 a_2 a_3 \ldots$, which is denoted $\prod_{k=1}^{\infty} a_k$, is the limit of the *sequence of partial products* $\{a_1, a_1 a_2, a_1 a_2 a_3, \ldots\}$. Assume that $a_k > 0$ for all k.

a. Show that the infinite product converges (which means its sequence of partial products converges) provided the series $\sum_{k=1}^{\infty} \ln a_k$ converges.

b. Consider the infinite product

$$P = \prod_{k=2}^{\infty} \left(1 - \frac{1}{k^2}\right) = \frac{3}{4} \cdot \frac{8}{9} \cdot \frac{15}{16} \cdot \frac{24}{25} \cdots.$$

Write out the first few terms of the sequence of partial products,

$$P_n = \prod_{k=2}^{n} \left(1 - \frac{1}{k^2}\right)$$

(for example, $P_2 = \frac{3}{4}$, $P_3 = \frac{2}{3}$). Write out enough terms to determine the value of $P = \lim_{n\to\infty} P_n$.

c. Use the results of parts (a) and (b) to evaluate the series

$$\sum_{k=2}^{\infty} \ln\left(1 - \frac{1}{k^2}\right).$$

89. Infinite products *Use the ideas of Exercise 88 to evaluate the following infinite products.*

a. $\prod_{k=0}^{\infty} e^{1/2^k} = e \cdot e^{1/2} \cdot e^{1/4} \cdot e^{1/8} \cdots$

b. $\prod_{k=2}^{\infty} \left(1 - \frac{1}{k}\right) = \frac{1}{2} \cdot \frac{2}{3} \cdot \frac{3}{4} \cdot \frac{4}{5} \cdots$

90. An early limit Working in the early 1600s, the mathematicians Wallis, Pascal, and Fermat were calculating the area of the region under the curve $y = x^p$ between $x = 0$ and $x = 1$, where p is a positive integer. Using arguments that predated the Fundamental Theorem of Calculus, they were able to prove that

$$\lim_{n\to\infty} \frac{1}{n} \sum_{k=0}^{n-1} \left(\frac{k}{n}\right)^p = \frac{1}{p+1}.$$

Use what you know about Riemann sums and integrals to verify this limit.

91. Stirling's formula Complete the following steps to find the values of $p > 0$ for which the series $\sum_{k=1}^{\infty} \frac{1 \cdot 3 \cdot 5 \cdots (2k-1)}{p^k k!}$ converges.

a. Use the Ratio Test to show that $\sum_{k=1}^{\infty} \frac{1 \cdot 3 \cdot 5 \cdots (2k-1)}{p^k k!}$ converges for $p > 2$.

b. Use Stirling's formula, $k! \approx \sqrt{2\pi k}\, k^k e^{-k}$ for large k, to determine whether the series converges when $p = 2$. (*Hint:* $1 \cdot 3 \cdot 5 \cdots (2k-1) = \frac{1 \cdot 2 \cdot 3 \cdot 4 \cdot 5 \cdot 6 \cdots (2k-1)2k}{2 \cdot 4 \cdot 6 \cdots 2k}$.) (See the Guided Project *Stirling's formula and n!* for more on this topic.)

QUICK CHECK ANSWERS

1. 10; $(k+2)(k+1)$; $1/(k+1)$ **2.** The Integral Test or p-series with $p = 2$ **3.** To use the Comparison Test, we would need to show that $1/(k+1) > 1/k$, which is not true. **4.** If $\lim_{k\to\infty} \frac{a_k}{b_k} = L$ for $0 < L < \infty$, then $\lim_{k\to\infty} \frac{b_k}{a_k} = \frac{1}{L}$, where $0 < 1/L < \infty$. ◄

8.6 Alternating Series

Our previous discussion focused on infinite series with positive terms, which is certainly an important part of the entire subject. But there are many interesting series with terms of mixed sign. For example, the series

$$1 + \frac{1}{2} - \frac{1}{3} - \frac{1}{4} + \frac{1}{5} + \frac{1}{6} - \frac{1}{7} - \frac{1}{8} + \cdots$$

has the pattern that two positive terms are followed by two negative terms and vice versa. Clearly, infinite series could have endless sign patterns, so we need to restrict our attention.

Fortunately, the simplest sign pattern is also the most important. We consider **alternating series** in which the signs strictly alternate, as in the series

$$\sum_{k=1}^{\infty} \frac{(-1)^{k+1}}{k} = 1 - \frac{1}{2} + \frac{1}{3} - \frac{1}{4} + \frac{1}{5} - \frac{1}{6} + \frac{1}{7} - \frac{1}{8} + \cdots.$$

The factor $(-1)^{k+1}$ (or $(-1)^k$) has the pattern $\{\ldots, 1, -1, 1, -1, \ldots\}$ and provides the alternating signs.

Alternating Harmonic Series

Let's see what is different about alternating series by working with the series $\sum_{k=1}^{\infty} \frac{(-1)^{k+1}}{k}$, which is called the **alternating harmonic series**. Recall that this series *without* the alternating signs, $\sum_{k=1}^{\infty} \frac{1}{k}$, is the *divergent* harmonic series. So an immediate question is whether the presence of alternating signs affects the convergence of a series.

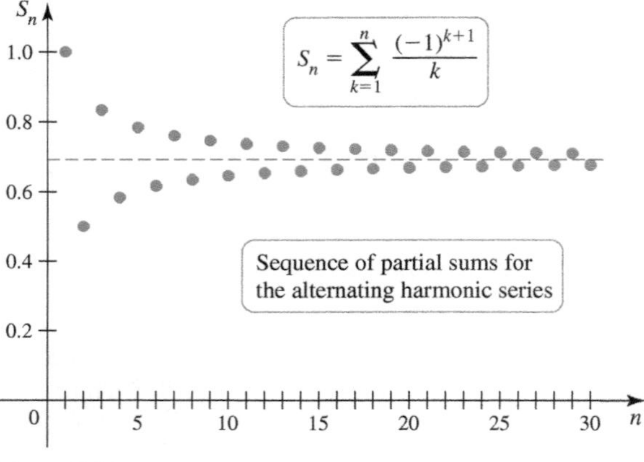

Figure 8.34

We investigate this question by looking at the sequence of partial sums for the series. In this case, the first four terms of the sequence of partial sums are

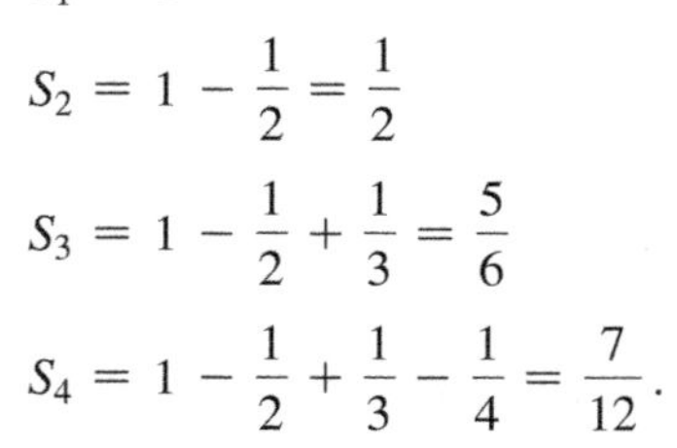

$$S_1 = 1$$
$$S_2 = 1 - \frac{1}{2} = \frac{1}{2}$$
$$S_3 = 1 - \frac{1}{2} + \frac{1}{3} = \frac{5}{6}$$
$$S_4 = 1 - \frac{1}{2} + \frac{1}{3} - \frac{1}{4} = \frac{7}{12}.$$

Plotting the first 30 terms of the sequence of partial sums results in Figure 8.34, which has several noteworthy features.

- The terms of the sequence of partial sums appear to converge to a limit; if they do, it means that, while the harmonic series diverges, the *alternating* harmonic series converges. We will soon learn that taking a divergent series with positive terms and making it an alternating series *may* turn it into a convergent series.
- For series with *positive* terms, the sequence of partial sums is necessarily an increasing sequence. Because the terms of an alternating series alternate in sign, the sequence of partial sums is not increasing (Figure 8.34).
- For the alternating harmonic series, the odd terms of the sequence of partial sums form a decreasing sequence and the even terms form an increasing sequence. As a result, the limit of the sequence of partial sums lies between any two consecutive terms of the sequence.

QUICK CHECK 1 Write out the first few terms of the sequence of partial sums for the alternating series $1 - 2 + 3 - 4 + 5 - 6 + \cdots$. Does this series appear to converge or diverge? ◄

Alternating Series Test

➤ Depending on the sign of the first term of the series, an alternating series may be written with $(-1)^k$ or $(-1)^{k+1}$.

We now consider alternating series in general, which are written $\sum(-1)^{k+1}a_k$, where $a_k > 0$. With the exception of the Divergence Test, none of the convergence tests for series with positive terms applies to alternating series. The fortunate news is that one test works for most alternating series—and it is easy to use.

➤ Recall that the Divergence Test of Section 8.4 applies to all series: If the terms of *any* series (including an alternating series) do not tend to zero, then the series diverges.

THEOREM 8.18 Alternating Series Test
The alternating series $\sum(-1)^{k+1}a_k$ converges provided

1. the terms of the series are nonincreasing in magnitude ($0 < a_{k+1} \le a_k$, for k greater than some index N) and
2. $\lim_{k\to\infty} a_k = 0$.

There is potential for confusion here. *For series of positive terms,* $\lim_{k\to\infty} a_k = 0$ ***does not*** *imply convergence. For alternating series with nonincreasing terms,* $\lim_{k\to\infty} a_k = 0$ ***does*** *imply convergence.*

Proof: The proof is short and instructive; it relies on Figure 8.35. We consider an alternating series in the form

$$\sum_{k=1}^{\infty}(-1)^{k+1}a_k = a_1 - a_2 + a_3 - a_4 + \cdots.$$

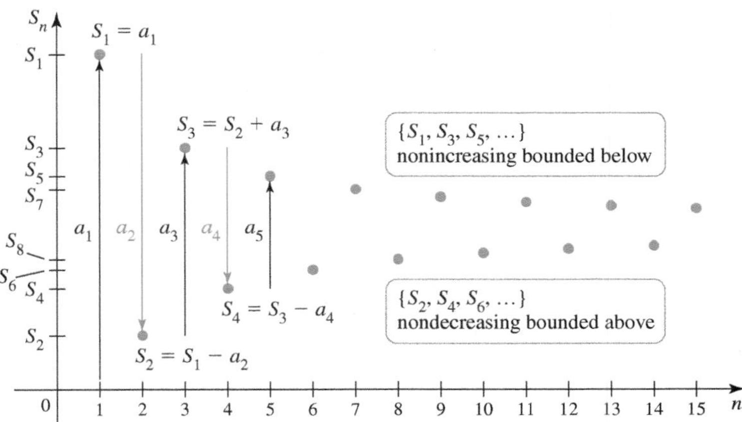

Figure 8.35

Because the terms of the series are nonincreasing in magnitude, the even terms of the sequence of partial sums $\{S_{2k}\} = \{S_2, S_4, \ldots\}$ form a nondecreasing sequence that is bounded above by S_1. By the Bounded Monotonic Sequence Theorem (Section 8.2), this sequence has a limit; call it L. Similarly, the odd terms of the sequence of partial sums $\{S_{2k-1}\} = \{S_1, S_3, \ldots\}$ form a nonincreasing sequence that is bounded below by S_2. By the Bounded Monotonic Sequence Theorem, this sequence also has a limit; call it L'. At the moment, we cannot conclude that $L = L'$. However, notice that $S_{2k} = S_{2k-1} - a_{2k}$. By the condition that $\lim_{k\to\infty} a_k = 0$, it follows that

$$\underbrace{\lim_{k\to\infty} S_{2k}}_{L} = \underbrace{\lim_{k\to\infty} S_{2k-1}}_{L'} - \underbrace{\lim_{k\to\infty} a_{2k}}_{0},$$

or $L = L'$. Therefore, the sequence of partial sums converges to a (unique) limit and the corresponding alternating series converges to that limit. ◄

Now we can confirm that the alternating harmonic series $\sum_{k=1}^{\infty}\frac{(-1)^{k+1}}{k}$ converges.

This fact follows immediately from the Alternating Series Test because the terms $a_k = \frac{1}{k}$ decrease and $\lim_{k\to\infty} a_k = 0$.

➤ $\sum_{k=1}^{\infty}\frac{1}{k}$
- Diverges
- Partial sums increase.

$\sum_{k=1}^{\infty}\frac{(-1)^{k+1}}{k}$
- Converges
- Partial sums bound the series above and below.

THEOREM 8.19 Alternating Harmonic Series

The alternating harmonic series $\sum_{k=1}^{\infty}\frac{(-1)^{k+1}}{k} = 1 - \frac{1}{2} + \frac{1}{3} - \frac{1}{4} + \frac{1}{5} - \cdots$ converges (even though the harmonic series $\sum_{k=1}^{\infty}\frac{1}{k} = 1 + \frac{1}{2} + \frac{1}{3} + \frac{1}{4} + \frac{1}{5} + \cdots$ diverges).

QUICK CHECK 2 Explain why the value of a convergent alternating series, with terms that are nonincreasing in magnitude, is trapped between successive terms of the sequence of partial sums. ◄

EXAMPLE 1 **Alternating Series Test** Determine whether the following series converge or diverge.

a. $\sum_{k=1}^{\infty} \frac{(-1)^{k+1}}{k^2}$ **b.** $2 - \frac{3}{2} + \frac{4}{3} - \frac{5}{4} + \cdots$ **c.** $\sum_{k=2}^{\infty} \frac{(-1)^k \ln k}{k}$

SOLUTION

a. The terms of this series decrease in magnitude, for $k \geq 1$. Furthermore,

$$\lim_{k\to\infty} a_k = \lim_{k\to\infty} \frac{1}{k^2} = 0.$$

Therefore, the series converges.

b. The magnitudes of the terms of this series are $a_k = \frac{k+1}{k} = 1 + \frac{1}{k}$. While these terms decrease, they approach 1, not 0, as $k \to \infty$. By the Divergence Test, the series diverges.

c. The first step is to show that the terms decrease in magnitude after some fixed term of the series. One way to proceed is to look at the function $f(x) = \frac{\ln x}{x}$, which generates the terms of the series. By the Quotient Rule, $f'(x) = \frac{1 - \ln x}{x^2}$. The fact that $f'(x) < 0$, for $x > e$, implies that the terms $\frac{\ln k}{k}$ decrease, for $k \geq 3$. As long as the terms of the series decrease for all k greater than some fixed integer, the first condition of the test is met. Furthermore, using l'Hôpital's Rule or the fact that $\{\ln k\}$ increases more slowly than $\{k\}$ (Section 8.2), we see that

$$\lim_{k\to\infty} a_k = \lim_{k\to\infty} \frac{\ln k}{k} = 0.$$

The conditions of the Alternating Series Test are met and the series converges.

Related Exercises 11–28 ◀

Remainders in Alternating Series

Recall that if a series converges to a value S, then the remainder is $R_n = S - S_n$, where S_n is the sum of the first n terms of the series. The magnitude of the remainder is the *absolute error* in approximating S by S_n.

An upper bound on the magnitude of the remainder in an alternating series arises from the following observation: When the terms are nonincreasing in magnitude, the value of the series is always trapped between successive terms of the sequence of partial sums. Therefore, as shown in Figure 8.36,

$$|R_n| = |S - S_n| \leq |S_{n+1} - S_n| = a_{n+1}.$$

This argument justifies the following theorem.

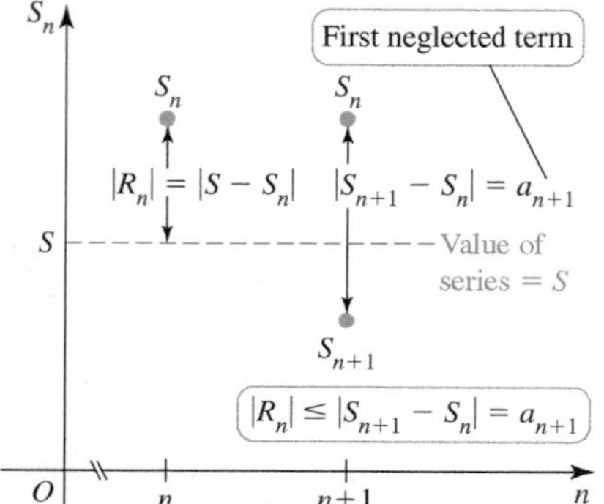

Figure 8.36

THEOREM 8.20 **Remainder in Alternating Series**

Let $\sum_{k=1}^{\infty} (-1)^{k+1} a_k$ be a convergent alternating series with terms that are nonincreasing in magnitude. Let $R_n = S - S_n$ be the remainder in approximating the value of that series by the sum of its first n terms. Then $|R_n| \leq a_{n+1}$. In other words, the magnitude of the remainder is less than or equal to the magnitude of the first neglected term.

EXAMPLE 2 Remainder in an alternating series

a. In turns out that $\ln 2 = 1 - \frac{1}{2} + \frac{1}{3} - \frac{1}{4} + \cdots = \sum_{k=1}^{\infty} \frac{(-1)^{k+1}}{k}$. How many terms of the series are required to approximate ln 2 with an error less than 10^{-6}? The exact value of the series is given but is not needed to answer the question.

b. Consider the series $-1 + \frac{1}{2!} - \frac{1}{3!} + \frac{1}{4!} - \cdots = \sum_{k=1}^{\infty} \frac{(-1)^k}{k!}$. Find an upper bound for the magnitude of the error in approximating the value of the series (which is $e^{-1} - 1$) with $n = 9$ terms.

SOLUTION Notice that both series meet the conditions of Theorem 8.20.

a. The series is expressed as the sum of the first n terms plus the remainder:

$$\sum_{k=1}^{\infty} \frac{(-1)^{k+1}}{k} = \underbrace{1 - \frac{1}{2} + \frac{1}{3} - \frac{1}{4} + \cdots + \frac{(-1)^{n+1}}{n}}_{S_n = \text{ the sum of the first } n \text{ terms}} + \underbrace{\frac{(-1)^{n+2}}{n+1}}_{|R_n| = |S - S_n| \text{ is less than the magnitude of this term}} + \cdots.$$

In magnitude, the remainder is less than or equal to the magnitude of the $(n + 1)$st term:

$$|R_n| = |S - S_n| \le a_{n+1} = \frac{1}{n+1}.$$

To ensure that the error is less than 10^{-6}, we require that

$$a_{n+1} = \frac{1}{n+1} < 10^{-6}, \quad \text{or} \quad n + 1 > 10^6.$$

Therefore, it takes 1 million terms of the series to approximate ln 2 with an error less than 10^{-6}.

b. The series may be expressed as the sum of the first nine terms plus the remainder:

$$\sum_{k=1}^{\infty} \frac{(-1)^k}{k!} = \underbrace{-1 + \frac{1}{2!} - \frac{1}{3!} + \cdots - \frac{1}{9!}}_{S_9 = \text{ sum of first 9 terms}} + \underbrace{\frac{1}{10!}}_{|R_9| = |S - S_9| \text{ is less than this term}} - \cdots.$$

The error committed when using the first nine terms to approximate the value of the series satisfies

$$|R_9| = |S - S_9| \le a_{10} = \frac{1}{10!} \approx 2.8 \times 10^{-7}.$$

Therefore, the error is no greater than 2.8×10^{-7}. As a check, the difference between the sum of the first nine terms, $\sum_{k=1}^{9} \frac{(-1)^k}{k!} \approx -0.632120811$, and the exact value, $S = e^{-1} - 1 \approx -0.632120559$, is approximately 2.5×10^{-7}. Therefore, the actual error satisfies the bound given by Theorem 8.20.

Related Exercises 29–44 ◀

QUICK CHECK 3 Compare and comment on the speed of convergence of the two series in the previous example. Why does one series converge more rapidly than the other? ◀

Absolute and Conditional Convergence

In this final segment, some terminology is introduced that is needed in Chapter 9. We now let the notation $\sum a_k$ denote any series—a series of positive terms, an alternating series, or even a more general infinite series.

Look again at the convergent alternating harmonic series $\sum(-1)^{k+1}/k$. The corresponding series of positive terms, $\sum 1/k$, is the divergent harmonic series. In contrast, we saw in Example 1a that the alternating series $\sum(-1)^{k+1}/k^2$ converges, and the corresponding p-series of positive terms $\sum 1/k^2$ also converges. These examples illustrate that removing the alternating signs in a convergent series *may* or *may not* result in a convergent series. The terminology that we now introduce distinguishes these cases.

> DEFINITION **Absolute and Conditional Convergence**
> If $\sum |a_k|$ converges, then $\sum a_k$ **converges absolutely**. If $\sum |a_k|$ diverges and $\sum a_k$ converges, then $\sum a_k$ **converges conditionally**.

The series $\sum(-1)^{k+1}/k^2$ is an example of an absolutely convergent series because the series of absolute values,

$$\sum_{k=1}^{\infty}\left|\frac{(-1)^{k+1}}{k^2}\right| = \sum_{k=1}^{\infty}\frac{1}{k^2},$$

is a convergent p-series. In this case, removing the alternating signs in the series does *not* affect its convergence.

On the other hand, the convergent alternating harmonic series $\sum(-1)^{k+1}/k$ has the property that the corresponding series of absolute values,

$$\sum_{k=1}^{\infty}\left|\frac{(-1)^{k+1}}{k}\right| = \sum_{k=1}^{\infty}\frac{1}{k},$$

does *not* converge. In this case, removing the alternating signs in the series *does* affect convergence, so this series does not converge absolutely. Instead, we say it *converges conditionally*. A convergent series (such as $\sum(-1)^{k+1}/k$) may not converge absolutely. However, if a series converges absolutely, then it converges.

> THEOREM 8.21 **Absolute Convergence Implies Convergence**
> If $\sum |a_k|$ converges, then $\sum a_k$ converges (absolute convergence implies convergence). Equivalently, if $\sum a_k$ diverges, then $\sum |a_k|$ diverges.

Proof: Because $|a_k| = a_k$ or $|a_k| = -a_k$, it follows that $0 \le a_k + |a_k| \le 2|a_k|$. By assumption, $\sum |a_k|$ converges, which, in turn, implies that $2\sum |a_k|$ converges. Using the Comparison Test and the inequality $0 \le a_k + |a_k| \le 2|a_k|$, it follows that $\sum(a_k + |a_k|)$ converges. Now note that

$$\sum a_k = \sum(a_k + |a_k| - |a_k|) = \underbrace{\sum(a_k + |a_k|)}_{\text{converges}} - \underbrace{\sum |a_k|}_{\text{converges}}.$$

We see that $\sum a_k$ is the sum of two convergent series, so it also converges. The second statement of the theorem is logically equivalent to the first statement. ◄

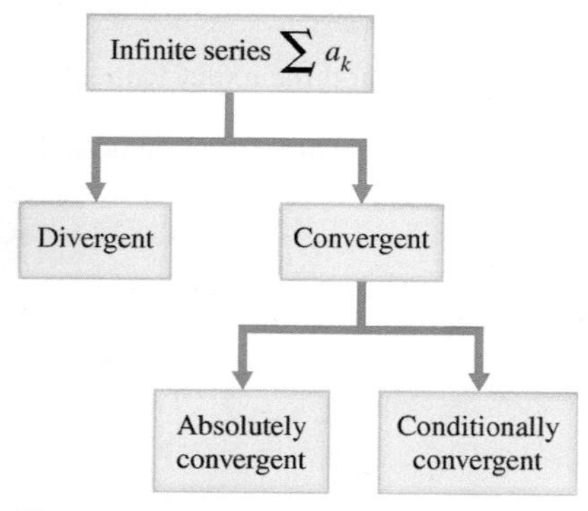

Figure 8.37

Figure 8.37 gives an overview of absolute and conditional convergence. It shows the universe of all infinite series, split first according to whether they converge or diverge. Convergent series are further divided between absolutely and conditionally convergent series.

Here are a few more consequences of these definitions.

- The distinction between absolute and conditional convergence is relevant only for series of mixed sign, which includes alternating series. If a series of positive terms converges, it converges absolutely; conditional convergence does not apply.
- To test for absolute convergence, we test the series $\sum |a_k|$, which is a series of positive terms. Therefore, the convergence tests of Sections 8.4 and 8.5 (for positive-term series) are used to determine absolute convergence.

QUICK CHECK 4 Explain why a convergent series of positive terms converges absolutely. ◀

EXAMPLE 3 **Absolute and conditional convergence** Determine whether the following series diverge, converge absolutely, or converge conditionally.

a. $\displaystyle\sum_{k=1}^{\infty} \frac{(-1)^{k+1}}{\sqrt{k}}$ **b.** $\displaystyle\sum_{k=1}^{\infty} \frac{(-1)^{k+1}}{\sqrt{k^3}}$ **c.** $\displaystyle\sum_{k=1}^{\infty} \frac{\sin k}{k^2}$ **d.** $\displaystyle\sum_{k=1}^{\infty} \frac{(-1)^k k}{k+1}$

SOLUTION

a. We examine the series of absolute values,

$$\sum_{k=1}^{\infty} \left| \frac{(-1)^{k+1}}{\sqrt{k}} \right| = \sum_{k=1}^{\infty} \frac{1}{\sqrt{k}},$$

which is a divergent p-series (with $p = \frac{1}{2} < 1$). Therefore, the given alternating series does not converge absolutely. To determine whether the series converges conditionally, we look at the original series—with alternating signs. The magnitude of the terms of this series decrease with $\lim_{k\to\infty} 1/\sqrt{k} = 0$, so by the Alternating Series Test, the series converges. Because this series converges, but not absolutely, it converges conditionally.

b. To assess absolute convergence, we look at the series of absolute values,

$$\sum_{k=1}^{\infty} \left| \frac{(-1)^{k+1}}{\sqrt{k^3}} \right| = \sum_{k=1}^{\infty} \frac{1}{k^{3/2}},$$

which is a convergent p-series (with $p = \frac{3}{2} > 1$). Therefore, the original alternating series converges absolutely (and by Theorem 8.21 it converges).

c. The terms of this series do not strictly alternate sign (the first few signs are $+++---$), so the Alternating Series Test does not apply. Because $|\sin k| \leq 1$, the terms of the series of absolute values satisfy

$$\left| \frac{\sin k}{k^2} \right| = \frac{|\sin k|}{k^2} \leq \frac{1}{k^2}.$$

The series $\sum \frac{1}{k^2}$ is a convergent p-series. Therefore, by the Comparison Test, the series $\sum \left| \frac{\sin k}{k^2} \right|$ converges, which implies that the series $\sum \frac{\sin k}{k^2}$ converges absolutely (and by Theorem 8.21 it converges).

d. Notice that $\lim_{k\to\infty} k/(k+1) = 1$. The terms of the series do not tend to zero, and by the Divergence Test, the series diverges.

Related Exercises 45–56 ◀

We close the chapter with the summary of tests and series shown in Table 8.4.

Table 8.4 Special Series and Convergence Tests

Series or Test	Form of Series	Condition for Convergence	Condition for Divergence	Comments
Geometric series	$\sum_{k=0}^{\infty} ar^k, a \neq 0$	$\lvert r \rvert < 1$	$\lvert r \rvert \geq 1$	If $\lvert r \rvert < 1$, then $\sum_{k=0}^{\infty} ar^k = \frac{a}{1-r}$.
Divergence Test	$\sum_{k=1}^{\infty} a_k$	Does not apply	$\lim_{k\to\infty} a_k \neq 0$	Cannot be used to prove convergence
Integral Test	$\sum_{k=1}^{\infty} a_k$, where $a_k = f(k)$ and f is continuous, positive, and decreasing	$\int_1^{\infty} f(x)\,dx$ converges.	$\int_1^{\infty} f(x)\,dx$ diverges.	The value of the integral is not the value of the series.
p-series	$\sum_{k=1}^{\infty} \frac{1}{k^p}$	$p > 1$	$p \leq 1$	Useful for comparison tests
Ratio Test	$\sum_{k=1}^{\infty} a_k$, where $a_k > 0$	$\lim_{k\to\infty} \frac{a_{k+1}}{a_k} < 1$	$\lim_{k\to\infty} \frac{a_{k+1}}{a_k} > 1$	Inconclusive if $\lim_{k\to\infty} \frac{a_{k+1}}{a_k} = 1$
Root Test	$\sum_{k=1}^{\infty} a_k$, where $a_k \geq 0$	$\lim_{k\to\infty} \sqrt[k]{a_k} < 1$	$\lim_{k\to\infty} \sqrt[k]{a_k} > 1$	Inconclusive if $\lim_{k\to\infty} \sqrt[k]{a_k} = 1$
Comparison Test	$\sum_{k=1}^{\infty} a_k$, where $a_k > 0$	$0 < a_k \leq b_k$ and $\sum_{k=1}^{\infty} b_k$ converges.	$0 < b_k \leq a_k$ and $\sum_{k=1}^{\infty} b_k$ diverges	$\sum_{k=1}^{\infty} a_k$ is given; you supply $\sum_{k=1}^{\infty} b_k$.
Limit Comparison Test	$\sum_{k=1}^{\infty} a_k$, where $a_k > 0, b_k > 0$	$0 \leq \lim_{k\to\infty} \frac{a_k}{b_k} < \infty$ and $\sum_{k=1}^{\infty} b_k$ converges.	$\lim_{k\to\infty} \frac{a_k}{b_k} > 0$ and $\sum_{k=1}^{\infty} b_k$ diverges.	$\sum_{k=1}^{\infty} a_k$ is given; you supply $\sum_{k=1}^{\infty} b_k$.
Alternating Series Test	$\sum_{k=1}^{\infty} (-1)^k a_k$, where $a_k > 0, 0 < a_{k+1} \leq a_k$	$\lim_{k\to\infty} a_k = 0$	$\lim_{k\to\infty} a_k \neq 0$	Remainder R_n satisfies $\lvert R_n \rvert \leq a_{n+1}$
Absolute Convergence	$\sum_{k=1}^{\infty} a_k$, a_k arbitrary	$\sum_{k=1}^{\infty} \lvert a_k \rvert$ converges		Applies to arbitrary series

SECTION 8.6 EXERCISES

Review Questions

1. Explain why the sequence of partial sums for an alternating series is not an increasing sequence.
2. Describe how to apply the Alternating Series Test.
3. Why does the value of a converging alternating series with terms that are nonincreasing in magnitude lie between any two consecutive terms of its sequence of partial sums?
4. Suppose an alternating series with terms that are nonincreasing in magnitude converges to a value L. Explain how to estimate the remainder that occurs when the series is terminated after n terms.
5. Explain why the magnitude of the remainder in an alternating series (with terms that are nonincreasing in magnitude) is less than or equal to the magnitude of the first neglected term.
6. Give an example of a convergent alternating series that fails to converge absolutely.
7. Is it possible for a series of positive terms to converge conditionally? Explain.
8. Why does absolute convergence imply convergence?
9. Is it possible for an alternating series to converge absolutely but not conditionally?
10. Give an example of a series that converges conditionally but not absolutely.

Basic Skills

11–28. Alternating Series Test *Determine whether the following series converge.*

11. $\displaystyle\sum_{k=0}^{\infty} \frac{(-1)^k}{2k+1}$

12. $\displaystyle\sum_{k=1}^{\infty} \frac{(-1)^k}{\sqrt{k}}$

13. $\displaystyle\sum_{k=1}^{\infty} \frac{(-1)^k k}{3k+2}$

14. $\displaystyle\sum_{k=1}^{\infty} (-1)^k \left(1+\frac{1}{k}\right)^k$

15. $\displaystyle\sum_{k=1}^{\infty} \frac{(-1)^{k+1}}{k^3}$

16. $\displaystyle\sum_{k=0}^{\infty} \frac{(-1)^k}{k^2+10}$

17. $\displaystyle\sum_{k=1}^{\infty} (-1)^{k+1} \frac{k^2}{k^3+1}$

18. $\displaystyle\sum_{k=2}^{\infty} (-1)^k \frac{\ln k}{k^2}$

19. $\displaystyle\sum_{k=2}^{\infty} (-1)^k \frac{k^2-1}{k^2+3}$

20. $\displaystyle\sum_{k=0}^{\infty} \left(-\frac{1}{5}\right)^k$

21. $\displaystyle\sum_{k=2}^{\infty} (-1)^k \left(1+\frac{1}{k}\right)$

22. $\displaystyle\sum_{k=1}^{\infty} \frac{\cos \pi k}{k^2}$

23. $\displaystyle\sum_{k=1}^{\infty} (-1)^{k+1} \frac{k^{10}+2k^5+1}{k(k^{10}+1)}$

24. $\displaystyle\sum_{k=2}^{\infty} \frac{(-1)^k}{k \ln^2 k}$

25. $\displaystyle\sum_{k=1}^{\infty} (-1)^{k+1} k^{1/k}$

26. $\displaystyle\sum_{k=1}^{\infty} (-1)^{k+1} \frac{k!}{k^k}$

27. $\displaystyle\sum_{k=0}^{\infty} \frac{(-1)^k}{\sqrt{k^2+4}}$

28. $\displaystyle\sum_{k=1}^{\infty} (-1)^k k \sin \frac{1}{k}$

T 29–38. Remainders in alternating series *Determine how many terms of the following convergent series must be summed to be sure that the remainder is less than 10^{-4} in magnitude. Although you do not need it, the exact value of the series is given in each case.*

29. $\displaystyle\ln 2 = \sum_{k=1}^{\infty} \frac{(-1)^{k+1}}{k}$

30. $\displaystyle\frac{1}{e} = \sum_{k=0}^{\infty} \frac{(-1)^k}{k!}$

31. $\displaystyle\frac{\pi}{4} = \sum_{k=0}^{\infty} \frac{(-1)^k}{2k+1}$

32. $\displaystyle\frac{\pi^2}{12} = \sum_{k=1}^{\infty} \frac{(-1)^{k+1}}{k^2}$

33. $\displaystyle\frac{7\pi^4}{720} = \sum_{k=1}^{\infty} \frac{(-1)^{k+1}}{k^4}$

34. $\displaystyle\frac{\pi^3}{32} = \sum_{k=0}^{\infty} \frac{(-1)^k}{(2k+1)^3}$

35. $\displaystyle\frac{\pi\sqrt{3}}{9} + \frac{\ln 2}{3} = \sum_{k=0}^{\infty} \frac{(-1)^k}{3k+1}$

36. $\displaystyle\frac{31\pi^6}{30{,}240} = \sum_{k=1}^{\infty} \frac{(-1)^{k+1}}{k^6}$

37. $\displaystyle\pi = \sum_{k=0}^{\infty} \frac{(-1)^k}{4^k}\left(\frac{2}{4k+1} + \frac{2}{4k+2} + \frac{1}{4k+3}\right)$

38. $\displaystyle\frac{\pi\sqrt{3}}{9} - \frac{\ln 2}{3} = \sum_{k=0}^{\infty} \frac{(-1)^k}{3k+2}$

T 39–44. Estimating infinite series *Estimate the value of the following convergent series with an absolute error less than 10^{-3}.*

39. $\displaystyle\sum_{k=1}^{\infty} \frac{(-1)^k}{k^5}$

40. $\displaystyle\sum_{k=1}^{\infty} \frac{(-1)^k}{(2k+1)^3}$

41. $\displaystyle\sum_{k=1}^{\infty} \frac{(-1)^k k}{k^2+1}$

42. $\displaystyle\sum_{k=1}^{\infty} \frac{(-1)^k k}{k^4+1}$

43. $\displaystyle\sum_{k=1}^{\infty} \frac{(-1)^k}{k^k}$

44. $\displaystyle\sum_{k=1}^{\infty} \frac{(-1)^{k+1}}{(2k+1)!}$

45–56. Absolute and conditional convergence *Determine whether the following series converge absolutely, converge conditionally, or diverge.*

45. $\displaystyle\sum_{k=1}^{\infty} \frac{(-1)^k}{k^{2/3}}$

46. $\displaystyle\sum_{k=1}^{\infty} \frac{(-1)^k}{\sqrt{k}}$

47. $\displaystyle\sum_{k=1}^{\infty} \frac{(-1)^{k+1}}{k^{3/2}}$

48. $\displaystyle\sum_{k=1}^{\infty} \left(-\frac{1}{3}\right)^k$

49. $\displaystyle\sum_{k=1}^{\infty} \frac{\cos k}{k^3}$

50. $\displaystyle\sum_{k=1}^{\infty} \frac{(-1)^k k^2}{\sqrt{k^6+1}}$

51. $\displaystyle\sum_{k=1}^{\infty} (-1)^k \tan^{-1} k$

52. $\displaystyle\sum_{k=1}^{\infty} (-1)^k e^{-k}$

53. $\displaystyle\sum_{k=1}^{\infty} \frac{(-1)^k k}{2k+1}$

54. $\displaystyle\sum_{k=2}^{\infty} \frac{(-1)^k}{\ln k}$

55. $\displaystyle\sum_{k=1}^{\infty} \frac{(-1)^k \tan^{-1} k}{k^3}$

56. $\displaystyle\sum_{k=1}^{\infty} \frac{(-1)^{k+1} e^k}{(k+1)!}$

Further Explorations

57. **Explain why or why not** Determine whether the following statements are true and give an explanation or counterexample.
    a. A series that converges must converge absolutely.
    b. A series that converges absolutely must converge.
    c. A series that converges conditionally must converge.
    d. If $\sum a_k$ diverges, then $\sum |a_k|$ diverges.
    e. If $\sum a_k^2$ converges, then $\sum a_k$ converges.
    f. If $a_k > 0$ and $\sum a_k$ converges, then $\sum a_k^2$ converges.
    g. If $\sum a_k$ converges conditionally, then $\sum |a_k|$ diverges.

58. **Alternating Series Test** Show that the series
$$\frac{1}{3} - \frac{2}{5} + \frac{3}{7} - \frac{4}{9} + \cdots = \sum_{k=1}^{\infty} (-1)^{k+1} \frac{k}{2k+1}$$
diverges. Which condition of the Alternating Series Test is not satisfied?

59. **Alternating p-series** Given that $\displaystyle\sum_{k=1}^{\infty} \frac{1}{k^2} = \frac{\pi^2}{6}$, show that $\displaystyle\sum_{k=1}^{\infty} \frac{(-1)^{k+1}}{k^2} = \frac{\pi^2}{12}$. (Assume the result of Exercise 63.)

60. **Alternating p-series** Given that $\displaystyle\sum_{k=1}^{\infty} \frac{1}{k^4} = \frac{\pi^4}{90}$, show that $\displaystyle\sum_{k=1}^{\infty} \frac{(-1)^{k+1}}{k^4} = \frac{7\pi^4}{720}$. (Assume the result of Exercise 63.)

61. **Geometric series** In Section 8.3, we established that the geometric series $\sum r^k$ converges provided $|r| < 1$. Notice that if $-1 < r < 0$, the geometric series is also an alternating series. Use the Alternating Series Test to show that for $-1 < r < 0$, the series $\sum r^k$ converges.

T 62. **Remainders in alternating series** Given any infinite series $\sum a_k$, let $N(r)$ be the number of terms of the series that must be summed to guarantee that the remainder is less than 10^{-r} in magnitude, where r is a positive integer.
    a. Graph the function $N(r)$ for the three alternating p-series $\displaystyle\sum_{k=1}^{\infty} \frac{(-1)^{k+1}}{k^p}$, for $p = 1, 2,$ and 3. Compare the three graphs and discuss what they mean about the rates of convergence of the three series.
    b. Carry out the procedure of part (a) for the series $\displaystyle\sum_{k=1}^{\infty} \frac{(-1)^{k+1}}{k!}$ and compare the rates of convergence of all four series.

Additional Exercises

63. **Rearranging series** It can be proved that if a series converges absolutely, then its terms may be summed in any order without changing the value of the series. However, if a series converges conditionally, then the value of the series depends on the order of summation. For example, the (conditionally convergent) alternating harmonic series has the value

$$1 - \frac{1}{2} + \frac{1}{3} - \frac{1}{4} + \cdots = \ln 2.$$

Show that by rearranging the terms (so the sign pattern is $++-$),

$$1 + \frac{1}{3} - \frac{1}{2} + \frac{1}{5} + \frac{1}{7} - \frac{1}{4} + \cdots = \frac{3}{2} \ln 2.$$

64. **A better remainder** Suppose an alternating series $\sum(-1)^k a_k$, with terms that are nonincreasing in magnitude, converges to S and the sum of the first n terms of the series is S_n. Suppose also that the difference between the magnitudes of consecutive terms decreases with k. It can be shown that for $n \geq 1$,

$$\left| S - \left(S_n + \frac{(-1)^{n+1} a_{n+1}}{2} \right) \right| \leq \frac{1}{2} \left| a_{n+1} - a_{n+2} \right|.$$

a. Interpret this inequality and explain why it is a better approximation to S than S_n.

b. For the following series, determine how many terms of the series are needed to approximate its exact value with an error less than 10^{-6} using both S_n and the method explained in part (a).

(i) $\displaystyle\sum_{k=1}^{\infty} \frac{(-1)^k}{k}$ (ii) $\displaystyle\sum_{k=2}^{\infty} \frac{(-1)^k}{k \ln k}$ (iii) $\displaystyle\sum_{k=2}^{\infty} \frac{(-1)^k}{\sqrt{k}}$

65. **A fallacy** Explain the fallacy in the following argument.

Let $x = 1 + \frac{1}{3} + \frac{1}{5} + \frac{1}{7} + \cdots$ and $y = \frac{1}{2} + \frac{1}{4} + \frac{1}{6} + \frac{1}{8} + \cdots$. It follows that $2y = x + y$, which implies that $x = y$. On the other hand,

$$x - y = \underbrace{\left(1 - \frac{1}{2}\right)}_{>0} + \underbrace{\left(\frac{1}{3} - \frac{1}{4}\right)}_{>0} + \underbrace{\left(\frac{1}{5} - \frac{1}{6}\right)}_{>0} + \cdots > 0$$

is a sum of positive terms, so $x > y$. Therefore, we have shown that $x = y$ and $x > y$.

66. **Conditions of the Alternating Series Test** Consider the alternating series

$$\sum_{k=1}^{\infty} (-1)^{k+1} a_k, \text{ where } a_k = \begin{cases} \dfrac{4}{k+1}, & \text{if } k \text{ is odd} \\ \dfrac{2}{k}, & \text{if } k \text{ is even} \end{cases}$$

a. Write out the first ten terms of the series, group them in pairs, and show that the even partial sums of the series form the (divergent) harmonic series.

b. Show that $\lim_{k \to \infty} a_k = 0$.

c. Explain why the series diverges even though the terms of the series approach zero.

QUICK CHECK ANSWERS

1. $1, -1, 2, -2, 3, -3, \ldots$; series diverges. **2.** The even terms of the sequence of partial sums approach the value of the series from one side; the odd terms of the sequence of partial sums approach the value of the series from the other side. **3.** The second series with $k!$ in the denominators converges much more quickly than the first series because $k!$ increases much faster than k as $k \to \infty$. **4.** If a series has positive terms, the series of absolute values is the same as the series itself. ◀

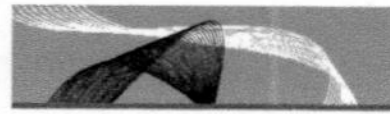

CHAPTER 8 REVIEW EXERCISES

1. **Explain why or why not** Determine whether the following statements are true and give an explanation or counterexample.

a. The terms of the sequence $\{a_n\}$ increase in magnitude, so the limit of the sequence does not exist.

b. The terms of the series $\sum 1/\sqrt{k}$ approach zero, so the series converges.

c. The terms of the sequence of partial sums of the series $\sum a_k$ approach $\frac{5}{2}$, so the infinite series converges to $\frac{5}{2}$.

d. An alternating series that converges absolutely must converge conditionally.

e. The sequence $a_n = \dfrac{n^2}{n^2 + 1}$ converges.

f. The sequence $a_n = \dfrac{(-1)^n n^2}{n^2 + 1}$ converges.

g. The series $\displaystyle\sum_{k=1}^{\infty} \frac{k^2}{k^2 + 1}$ converges.

h. The sequence of partial sums associated with the series $\displaystyle\sum_{k=1}^{\infty} \frac{1}{k^2 + 1}$ converges.

2–10. Limits of sequences *Evaluate the limit of the sequence or state that it does not exist.*

2. $a_n = \dfrac{n^2 + 4}{\sqrt{4n^4 + 1}}$

3. $a_n = \dfrac{8^n}{n!}$

4. $a_n = \left(1 + \dfrac{3}{n}\right)^{2n}$

5. $a_n = \sqrt[n]{n}$

6. $a_n = n - \sqrt{n^2 - 1}$

7. $a_n = \left(\dfrac{1}{n}\right)^{1/\ln n}$

8. $a_n = \sin \dfrac{\pi n}{6}$

9. $a_n = \dfrac{(-1)^n}{0.9^n}$

10. $a_n = \tan^{-1} n$

11. **Sequence of partial sums** Consider the series

$$\sum_{k=1}^{\infty} \frac{1}{k(k+2)} = \frac{1}{2} \sum_{k=1}^{\infty} \left(\frac{1}{k} - \frac{1}{k+2} \right).$$

a. Write the first four terms of the sequence of partial sums $S_1, \ldots, S_4$.

b. Write the nth term of the sequence of partial sums S_n.

c. Find $\lim_{n \to \infty} S_n$ and evaluate the series.

12–20. Evaluating series *Evaluate the following infinite series or state that the series diverges.*

12. $\sum_{k=1}^{\infty}\left(\frac{9}{10}\right)^k$

13. $\sum_{k=1}^{\infty}3(1.001)^k$

14. $\sum_{k=0}^{\infty}\left(-\frac{1}{5}\right)^k$

15. $\sum_{k=1}^{\infty}\frac{1}{k(k+1)}$

16. $\sum_{k=2}^{\infty}\left(\frac{1}{\sqrt{k}}-\frac{1}{\sqrt{k-1}}\right)$

17. $\sum_{k=1}^{\infty}\left(\frac{3}{3k-2}-\frac{3}{3k+1}\right)$

18. $\sum_{k=1}^{\infty}4^{-3k}$

19. $\sum_{k=1}^{\infty}\frac{2^k}{3^{k+2}}$

20. $\sum_{k=0}^{\infty}\left(\left(\frac{1}{3}\right)^k-\left(\frac{2}{3}\right)^{k+1}\right)$

21. **Sequences of partial sums** The sequences of partial sums for three series are shown in the figures. Assume that the pattern in the sequences continues as $n \to \infty$.

a. Does it appear that series A converges? If so, what is its (approximate) value?

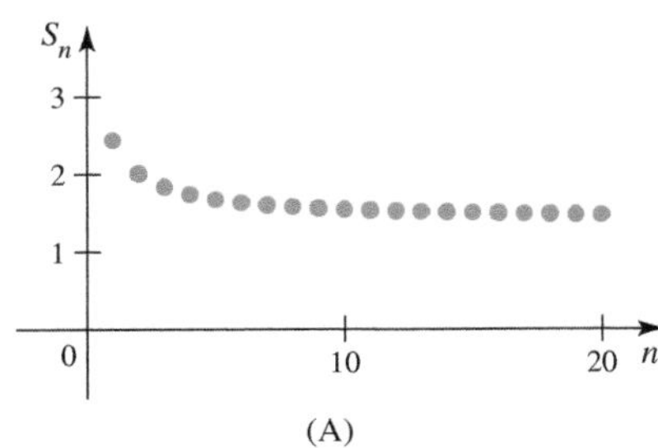

(A)

b. What can you conclude about the convergence or divergence of series B?

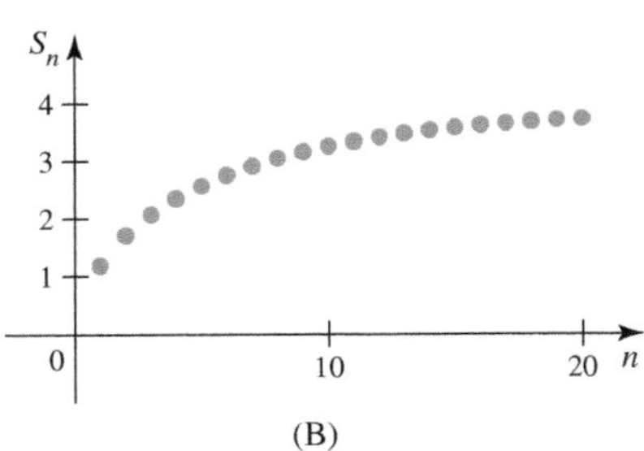

(B)

c. Does it appear that series C converges? If so, what is its (approximate) value?

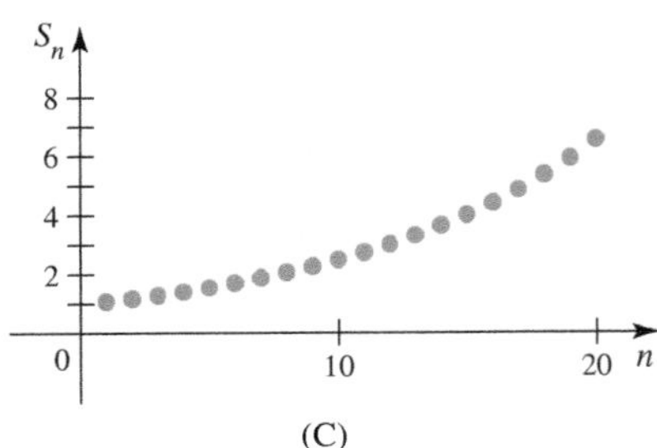

(C)

22–42. Convergence or divergence *Use a convergence test of your choice to determine whether the following series converge or diverge.*

22. $\sum_{k=1}^{\infty}\frac{2}{k^{3/2}}$

23. $\sum_{k=1}^{\infty}k^{-2/3}$

24. $\sum_{k=1}^{\infty}\frac{2k^2+1}{\sqrt{k^3+2}}$

25. $\sum_{k=1}^{\infty}\frac{2^k}{e^k}$

26. $\sum_{k=1}^{\infty}\left(\frac{k}{k+3}\right)^{2k}$

27. $\sum_{k=1}^{\infty}\frac{2^k k!}{k^k}$

28. $\sum_{k=1}^{\infty}\frac{1}{\sqrt{k}\sqrt{k+1}}$

29. $\sum_{k=1}^{\infty}\frac{3}{2+e^k}$

30. $\sum_{k=1}^{\infty}k\sin\frac{1}{k}$

31. $\sum_{k=1}^{\infty}\frac{\sqrt[3]{k}}{k^3}$

32. $\sum_{k=1}^{\infty}\frac{1}{1+\ln k}$

33. $\sum_{k=1}^{\infty}k^5e^{-k}$

34. $\sum_{k=4}^{\infty}\frac{2}{k^2-10}$

35. $\sum_{k=1}^{\infty}\frac{\ln k^2}{k^2}$

36. $\sum_{k=1}^{\infty}ke^{-k}$

37. $\sum_{k=0}^{\infty}\frac{2\cdot 4^k}{(2k+1)!}$

38. $\sum_{k=0}^{\infty}\frac{9^k}{(2k)!}$

39. $\sum_{k=1}^{\infty}\frac{\coth k}{k}$

40. $\sum_{k=1}^{\infty}\frac{1}{\sinh k}$

41. $\sum_{k=1}^{\infty}\tanh k$

42. $\sum_{k=0}^{\infty}\operatorname{sech} k$

43–50. Alternating series *Determine whether the following series converge or diverge. In the case of convergence, state whether the convergence is conditional or absolute.*

43. $\sum_{k=2}^{\infty}\frac{(-1)^k}{k^2-1}$

44. $\sum_{k=1}^{\infty}\frac{(-1)^{k+1}(k^2+4)}{2k^2+1}$

45. $\sum_{k=1}^{\infty}(-1)^k ke^{-k}$

46. $\sum_{k=1}^{\infty}\frac{(-1)^k}{\sqrt{k^2+1}}$

47. $\sum_{k=1}^{\infty}\frac{(-1)^{k+1}10^k}{k!}$

48. $\sum_{k=2}^{\infty}\frac{(-1)^k}{k\ln k}$

49. $\sum_{k=1}^{\infty}\frac{(-2)^{k+1}}{k^2}$

50. $\sum_{k=0}^{\infty}\frac{(-1)^k}{e^k+e^{-k}}$

51. **Sequences versus series**

a. Find the limit of the sequence $\left\{\left(-\frac{4}{5}\right)^k\right\}$.

b. Evaluate $\sum_{k=0}^{\infty}\left(-\frac{4}{5}\right)^k$.

52. **Sequences versus series**

a. Find the limit of the sequence $\left\{\frac{1}{k}-\frac{1}{k+1}\right\}$.

b. Evaluate $\sum_{k=1}^{\infty}\left(\frac{1}{k}-\frac{1}{k+1}\right)$.

53–56. Sequences versus series

53. Give an example (if possible) of a sequence $\{a_k\}$ that converges, while the series $\sum_{k=1}^{\infty}a_k$ diverges.

54. Give an example (if possible) of a series $\sum_{k=1}^{\infty}a_k$ that converges, while the sequence $\{a_k\}$ diverges.

55. a. Does the sequence $\left\{\frac{k}{k+1}\right\}$ converge? Why or why not?

b. Does the series $\sum_{k=1}^{\infty}\frac{k}{k+1}$ converge? Why or why not?

56. Is it true that the geometric sequence $\{r^k\}$ converges if and only if the geometric series $\sum_{k=1}^{\infty}r^k$ converges?

57. **Partial sums** Let S_n be the nth partial sum of $\sum_{k=1}^{\infty}a_k = 8$. Find $\lim_{k\to\infty}a_k$ and $\lim_{n\to\infty}S_n$.

T **58. Remainder term** Let R_n be the remainder associated with $\sum_{k=1}^{\infty} \frac{1}{k^5}$. Find an upper bound for R_n (in terms of n). How many terms of the series must be summed to approximate the series with an error less than 10^{-4}?

59. Conditional p-series Find the values of p for which $\sum_{k=1}^{\infty} \frac{(-1)^k}{k^p}$ converges conditionally.

60. Logarithmic p-series Show that the series $\sum_{k=2}^{\infty} \frac{1}{k(\ln k)^p}$ converges provided $p > 1$.

T **61. Error in a finite sum** Approximate the series $\sum_{k=1}^{\infty} \frac{1}{5^k}$ by evaluating the first 20 terms. Compute an upper bound for the error in the approximation.

T **62. Error in a finite sum** Approximate the series $\sum_{k=1}^{\infty} \frac{1}{k^5}$ by evaluating the first 20 terms. Compute an upper bound for the error in the approximation.

T **63. Error in a finite alternating sum** How many terms of the series $\sum_{k=1}^{\infty} \frac{(-1)^{k+1}}{k^4}$ must be summed to ensure that the error is less than 10^{-8}?

64. Equations involving series Solve the following equations for x.

a. $\sum_{k=0}^{\infty} e^{kx} = 2$ b. $\sum_{k=0}^{\infty} (3x)^k = 4$

c. $\sum_{k=1}^{\infty} \left(\frac{x}{kx - \frac{x}{2}} - \frac{x}{kx + \frac{x}{2}} \right) = 6$

65. Building a tunnel—first scenario A crew of workers is constructing a tunnel through a mountain. Understandably, the rate of construction decreases because rocks and earth must be removed a greater distance as the tunnel gets longer. Suppose that each week the crew digs 0.95 of the distance it dug the previous week. In the first week, the crew constructed 100 m of tunnel.

a. How far does the crew dig in 10 weeks? 20 weeks? N weeks?
b. What is the longest tunnel the crew can build at this rate?

66. Building a tunnel—second scenario As in Exercise 65, a crew of workers is constructing a tunnel. The time required to dig 100 m increases by 10% each week, starting with 1 week to dig the first 100 m. Can the crew complete a 1.5-km (1500-m) tunnel in 30 weeks? Explain.

67. Pages of circles On page 1 of a book, there is one circle of radius 1. On page 2, there are two circles of radius $\frac{1}{2}$. On page n, there are 2^{n-1} circles of radius 2^{-n+1}.

a. What is the sum of the areas of the circles on page n of the book?
b. Assuming the book continues indefinitely ($n \to \infty$), what is the sum of the areas of all the circles in the book?

T **68. Sequence on a calculator** Let $\{x_n\}$ be generated by the recurrence relation $x_0 = 1$ and $x_{n+1} = x_n + \cos x_n$, for $n = 0, 1, 2, \ldots$. Use a calculator (in radian mode) to generate as many terms of the sequence $\{x_n\}$ needed to find the integer p such that $\lim_{n \to \infty} x_n = \pi/p$.

69. A savings plan Suppose that you open a savings account by depositing \$100. The account earns interest at an annual rate of 3% per year (0.25% per month). At the end of each month, you earn interest on the current balance, and then you deposit \$100. Let B_n be the balance at the beginning of the nth month, where $B_0 = \$100$.

a. Find a recurrence relation for the sequence $\{B_n\}$.
b. Find an explicit formula that gives B_n, for $n = 0, 1, 2, 3, \ldots$.

70. Sequences of integrals Find the limits of the sequences $\{a_n\}$ and $\{b_n\}$.

a. $a_n = \int_0^1 x^n\,dx,\ n \geq 1$ b. $b_n = \int_1^n \frac{dx}{x^p},\ p > 1, n \geq 1$

71. Sierpinski triangle The fractal called the *Sierpinski triangle* is the limit of a sequence of figures. Starting with the equilateral triangle with sides of length 1, an inverted equilateral triangle with sides of length $\frac{1}{2}$ is removed. Then, three inverted equilateral triangles with sides of length $\frac{1}{4}$ are removed from this figure (see figure). The process continues in this way. Let T_n be the total area of the removed triangles after stage n of the process. The area of an equilateral triangle with side length L is $A = \sqrt{3}L^2/4$.

a. Find T_1 and T_2, the total area of the removed triangles after stages 1 and 2, respectively.
b. Find T_n, for $n = 1, 2, 3, \ldots$.
c. Find $\lim_{n \to \infty} T_n$.
d. What is the area of the original triangle that remains as $n \to \infty$?

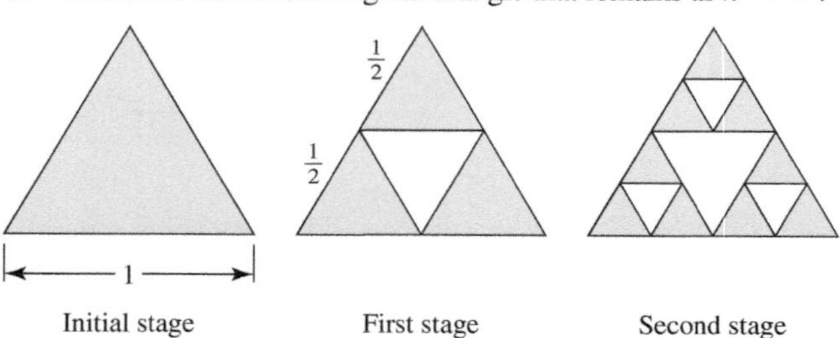

72. Max sine sequence Let $a_n = \max \{\sin 1, \sin 2, \ldots, \sin n\}$, for $n = 1, 2, 3, \ldots$, where max $\{\ldots\}$ denotes the maximum element of the set. Does $\{a_n\}$ converge? If so, make a conjecture about the limit.

Chapter 8 Guided Projects

Applications of the material in this chapter and related topics can be found in the following Guided Projects. For additional information, see the Preface.

- Chaos!
- Financial matters
- Periodic drug dosing
- Economic stimulus packages
- The mathematics of loans
- Archimedes' approximation to π
- Exact values of infinite series
- Conditional convergence in a crystal lattice

9

Power Series

Chapter Preview Until now, you have worked with infinite series consisting of real numbers. In this chapter, we make a seemingly small, but significant, change by considering infinite series whose terms include powers of a variable. With this change, an infinite series becomes a *power series*. One of the most fundamental ideas in all of calculus is that functions can be represented by power series. As a first step toward this result, we look at approximating functions using polynomials. The transition from polynomials to power series is then straightforward, and we learn how to represent the familiar functions of mathematics in terms of power series called *Taylor series*. The remainder of the chapter is devoted to the properties and many uses of Taylor series.

9.1 Approximating Functions with Polynomials

Power series provide a way to represent familiar functions and to define new functions. For this reason, power series—like sets and functions—are among the most fundamental entities in mathematics.

What Is a Power Series?

A *power series* is an infinite series of the form

$$\sum_{k=0}^{\infty} c_k x^k = \underbrace{c_0 + c_1 x + c_2 x^2 + \cdots + c_n x^n}_{n\text{th-degree polynomial}} + \underbrace{c_{n+1} x^{n+1} + \cdots}_{\text{terms continue}},$$

or, more generally,

$$\sum_{k=0}^{\infty} c_k (x-a)^k = \underbrace{c_0 + c_1 (x-a) + \cdots + c_n (x-a)^n}_{n\text{th-degree polynomial}} + \underbrace{c_{n+1}(x-a)^{n+1} + \cdots}_{\text{terms continue}},$$

where the *center* of the series a and the coefficients c_k are constants. This type of series is called a power series because it consists of powers of x or $(x - a)$.

Viewed another way, a power series is built up from polynomials of increasing degree, as shown in the following progression.

$$\left.\begin{array}{l}\text{Degree 0: } c_0 \\ \text{Degree 1: } c_0 + c_1 x \\ \text{Degree 2: } c_0 + c_1 x + c_2 x^2 \\ \quad\vdots \qquad \vdots \qquad \vdots \\ \text{Degree } n\text{: } c_0 + c_1 x + c_2 x^2 + \cdots + c_n x^n = \displaystyle\sum_{k=0}^{n} c_k x^k \end{array}\right\} \text{Polynomials}$$

$$\vdots \qquad \vdots \qquad \vdots$$

$$c_0 + c_1 x + c_2 x^2 + \cdots + c_n x^n + \cdots = \sum_{k=0}^{\infty} c_k x^k \;\Big\}\; \text{Power series}$$

According to this perspective, a power series is a "super-polynomial." Therefore, we begin our exploration of power series by using polynomials to approximate functions.

Polynomial Approximation

An important observation motivates our work. To evaluate a polynomial $\left(\text{say, } f(x) = x^8 - 4x^5 + \frac{1}{2}\right)$, all we need is arithmetic—addition, subtraction, multiplication, and division. However, algebraic functions $\left(\text{say, } f(x) = \sqrt[3]{x^4 - 1}\right)$ and the trigonometric, logarithmic, and exponential functions usually cannot be evaluated exactly using arithmetic. Therefore, it makes practical sense to use the simplest of functions, polynomials, to approximate more complicated functions.

Linear and Quadratic Approximation

In Section 4.5, you learned that if a function f is differentiable at a point a, then it can be approximated near a by its tangent line, which is the linear approximation to f at the point a. The linear approximation at a is given by

$$y - f(a) = f'(a)(x - a) \quad \text{or} \quad y = f(a) + f'(a)(x - a).$$

Because the linear approximation is a first-degree polynomial, we name it p_1:

$$p_1(x) = f(a) + f'(a)(x - a).$$

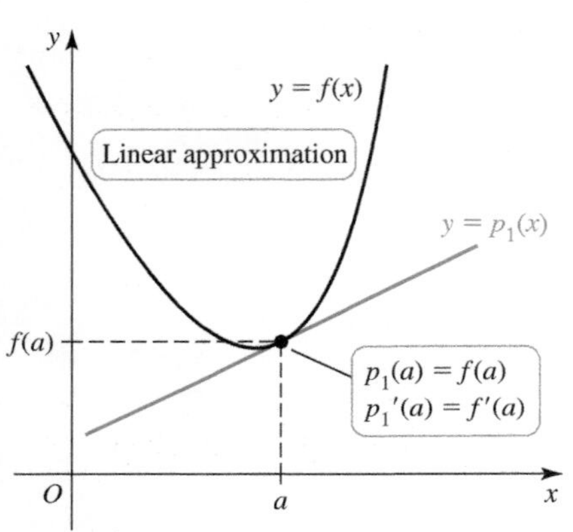

Figure 9.1

This polynomial has some important properties: It matches f in *value* and in *slope* at a. In other words (Figure 9.1),

$$p_1(a) = f(a) \quad \text{and} \quad p_1'(a) = f'(a).$$

Linear approximation works well if f has a fairly constant slope near a. However, if f has a lot of curvature near a, then the tangent line may not provide an accurate approximation. To remedy this situation, we create a quadratic approximating polynomial by adding one new term to the linear polynomial. Denoting this new polynomial p_2, we let

$$p_2(x) = \underbrace{f(a) + f'(a)(x - a)}_{p_1(x)} + \underbrace{c_2(x - a)^2}_{\text{quadratic term}}.$$

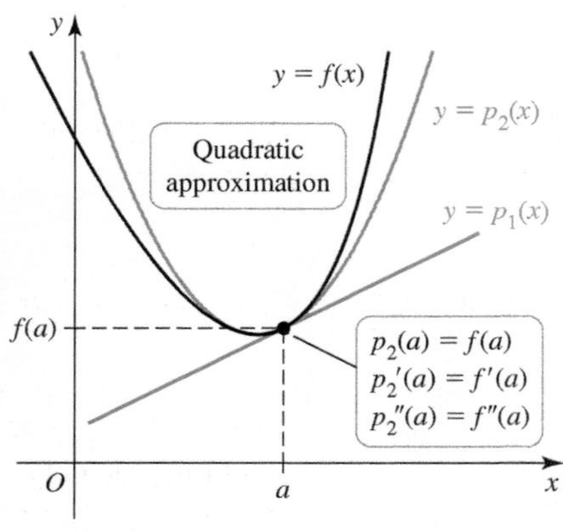

Figure 9.2

➤ Matching concavity (second derivatives) ensures that the graph of p_2 bends in the same direction as the graph of f at a.

The new term consists of a coefficient c_2 that must be determined and a quadratic factor $(x - a)^2$.

To determine c_2 and to ensure that p_2 is a good approximation to f near the point a, we require that p_2 agree with f in value, slope, and concavity at a; that is, p_2 must satisfy the matching conditions

$$p_2(a) = f(a), \quad p_2'(a) = f'(a), \quad \text{and} \quad p_2''(a) = f''(a),$$

where we assume that f and its first and second derivatives exist at a (Figure 9.2).

Substituting $x = a$ into p_2, we see immediately that $p_2(a) = f(a)$, so the first matching condition is met. Differentiating p_2 once, we have

$$p_2'(x) = f'(a) + 2c_2(x - a).$$

So $p_2'(a) = f'(a)$, and the second matching condition is also met. Because $p_2''(a) = 2c_2$, the third matching condition is

$$p_2''(a) = 2c_2 = f''(a).$$

It follows that $c_2 = \frac{1}{2}f''(a)$; therefore, the quadratic approximating polynomial is

$$p_2(x) = \underbrace{f(a) + f'(a)(x - a)}_{p_1(x)} + \frac{f''(a)}{2}(x - a)^2.$$

EXAMPLE 1 **Linear and quadratic approximations for $\ln x$**

a. Find the linear approximation to $f(x) = \ln x$ at $x = 1$.

b. Find the quadratic approximation to $f(x) = \ln x$ at $x = 1$.

c. Use these approximations to estimate $\ln 1.05$.

SOLUTION

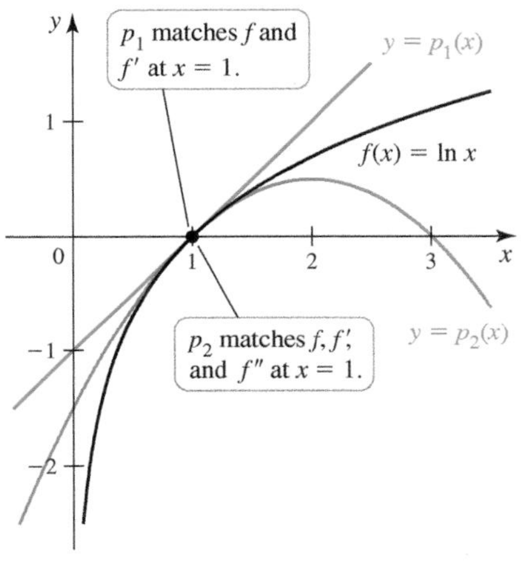

Figure 9.3

a. Note that $f(1) = 0$, $f'(x) = 1/x$, and $f'(1) = 1$. Therefore, the linear approximation to $f(x) = \ln x$ at $x = 1$ is

$$p_1(x) = f(1) + f'(1)(x - 1) = 0 + 1(x - 1) = x - 1.$$

As shown in Figure 9.3, p_1 matches f in value $(p_1(1) = f(1))$ and in slope $(p_1'(1) = f'(1))$ at $x = 1$.

b. We first compute $f''(x) = -1/x^2$ and $f''(1) = -1$. Building on the linear approximation found in part (a), the quadratic approximation is

$$p_2(x) = \underbrace{x - 1}_{p_1(x)} + \underbrace{\frac{1}{2}f''(1)}_{c_2}(x - 1)^2$$

$$= (x - 1) - \frac{1}{2}(x - 1)^2.$$

Because p_2 matches f in value, slope, and concavity at $x = 1$, it provides a better approximation to f near $x = 1$ (Figure 9.3).

c. To approximate $\ln 1.05$, we substitute $x = 1.05$ into each polynomial approximation:

$$p_1(1.05) = 1.05 - 1 = 0.05 \text{ and} \qquad \text{Linear approximation}$$

$$p_2(1.05) = (1.05 - 1) - \frac{1}{2}(1.05 - 1)^2 = 0.04875. \qquad \text{Quadratic approximation}$$

The value of $\ln 1.05$ given by a calculator, rounded to five decimal places, is 0.04879, showing the improvement in quadratic approximation over linear approximation.

Related Exercises 7–14 ◀

We now extend the idea of linear and quadratic approximation to obtain higher-degree polynomials that generally provide better approximations.

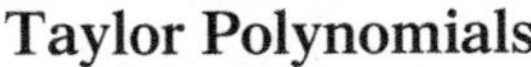

Taylor Polynomials

➤ Building on ideas that were already circulating in the early 18th century, Brook Taylor (1685–1731) published Taylor's Theorem in 1715. He is also credited with discovering integration by parts.

Assume that f and its first n derivatives exist at a; our goal is to find an nth-degree polynomial that approximates the values of f near a. The first step is to use p_2 to obtain a cubic polynomial p_3 of the form

$$p_3(x) = p_2(x) + c_3(x - a)^3$$

that satisfies the four matching conditions

$$p_3(a) = f(a), \quad p_3'(a) = f'(a), \quad p_3''(a) = f''(a), \quad \text{and} \quad p_3'''(a) = f'''(a).$$

Because p_3 is built "on top of" p_2, the first three matching conditions are met. The last condition, $p_3'''(a) = f'''(a)$, is used to determine c_3. A short calculation shows that $p_3'''(x) = 3 \cdot 2c_3 = 3!c_3$, so the last matching condition is $p_3'''(a) = 3!c_3 = f'''(a)$. Solving for c_3, we have $c_3 = \frac{f'''(a)}{3!}$. Therefore, the cubic approximating polynomial is

➤ Recall that $2! = 2 \cdot 1$, $3! = 3 \cdot 2 \cdot 1$, $k! = k \cdot (k-1)!$, and by definition, $0! = 1$.

$$p_3(x) = \underbrace{f(a) + f'(a)(x-a) + \frac{f''(a)}{2!}(x-a)^2}_{p_2(x)} + \frac{f'''(a)}{3!}(x-a)^3.$$

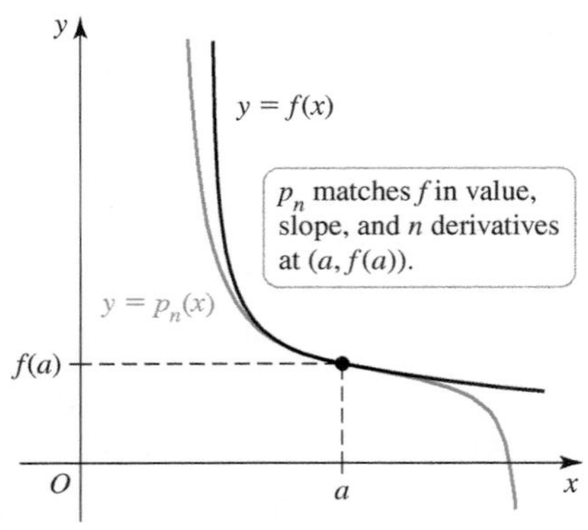

Figure 9.4

QUICK CHECK 1 Verify that p_3 satisfies $p_3^{(k)}(a) = f^{(k)}(a)$, for $k = 0, 1, 2,$ and 3. ◄

Continuing in this fashion (Exercise 74), building each new polynomial on the previous polynomial, the nth approximating polynomial for f at a is

$$p_n(x) = f(a) + f'(a)(x-a) + \frac{f''(a)}{2!}(x-a)^2 + \cdots + \frac{f^{(n)}(a)}{n!}(x-a)^n.$$

It satisfies the $n + 1$ matching conditions

$$p_n(a) = f(a), \quad p_n'(a) = f'(a), \quad p_n''(a) = f''(a), \ldots, p_n^{(n)}(a) = f^{(n)}(a).$$

These conditions ensure that the graph of p_n conforms as closely as possible to the graph of f near a (Figure 9.4).

➤ Recall that $f^{(n)}$ denotes the nth derivative of f. By convention, the zeroth derivative $f^{(0)}$ is f itself.

DEFINITION Taylor Polynomials

Let f be a function with $f', f'', \ldots,$ and $f^{(n)}$ defined at a. The ***n*th-order Taylor polynomial** for f with its **center** at a, denoted p_n, has the property that it matches f in value, slope, and all derivatives up to the nth derivative at a; that is,

$$p_n(a) = f(a), p_n'(a) = f'(a), \ldots, \text{ and } p_n^{(n)}(a) = f^{(n)}(a).$$

The nth-order Taylor polynomial centered at a is

$$p_n(x) = f(a) + f'(a)(x-a) + \frac{f''(a)}{2!}(x-a)^2 + \cdots + \frac{f^{(n)}(a)}{n!}(x-a)^n.$$

More compactly, $p_n(x) = \sum_{k=0}^{n} c_k(x-a)^k$, where the **coefficients** are

$$c_k = \frac{f^{(k)}(a)}{k!}, \qquad \text{for } k = 0, 1, 2, \ldots, n.$$

EXAMPLE 2 Taylor polynomials for $\sin x$ Find the Taylor polynomials $p_1, \ldots, p_7$ centered at $x = 0$ for $f(x) = \sin x$.

SOLUTION We begin by differentiating f repeatedly and evaluating the derivatives at 0; these calculations allow us to compute c_k, for $k = 0, 1, \ldots, 7$. Notice that a pattern emerges:

$$\begin{aligned} f(x) &= \sin x \Rightarrow f(0) = 0 \\ f'(x) &= \cos x \Rightarrow f'(0) = 1 \\ f''(x) &= -\sin x \Rightarrow f''(0) = 0 \\ f'''(x) &= -\cos x \Rightarrow f'''(0) = -1 \\ f^{(4)}(x) &= \sin x \Rightarrow f^{(4)}(0) = 0. \end{aligned}$$

The derivatives of $\sin x$ at 0 cycle through the values $\{0, 1, 0, -1\}$. Therefore, $f^{(5)}(0) = 1$, $f^{(6)}(0) = 0$, and $f^{(7)}(0) = -1$.

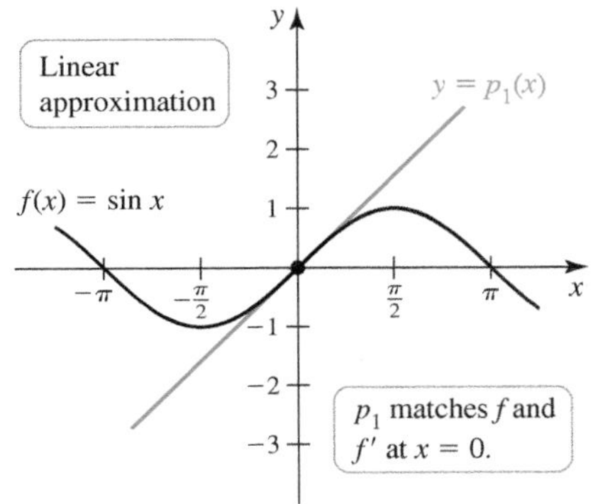

Figure 9.5

We now construct the Taylor polynomials that approximate $f(x) = \sin x$ near 0, beginning with the linear polynomial. The polynomial of order $n = 1$ is

$$p_1(x) = f(0) + f'(0)(x - 0) = x,$$

whose graph is the line through the origin with slope 1 (Figure 9.5). Notice that f and p_1 agree in value $(f(0) = p_1(0) = 0)$ and in slope $(f'(0) = p_1{}'(0) = 1)$ at 0. We see that p_1 provides a good fit to f near 0, but the graphs diverge visibly for $|x| > 0.5$.

The polynomial of order $n = 2$ is

$$p_2(x) = \underbrace{f(0)}_{0} + \underbrace{f'(0)}_{1}x + \underbrace{\frac{f''(0)}{2!}}_{0}x^2 = x,$$

so p_2 is the same as p_1.

The polynomial of order $n = 3$ is

$$p_3(x) = \underbrace{f(0) + f'(0)x + \frac{f''(0)}{2!}x^2}_{p_2(x) = x} + \underbrace{\frac{f'''(0)}{3!}}_{-1/3!}x^3 = x - \frac{x^3}{6}.$$

We have designed p_3 to agree with f in value, slope, concavity, and third derivative at 0 (Figure 9.6). Consequently, p_3 provides a better approximation to f over a larger interval than p_1.

➤ It is worth repeating that the next polynomial in the sequence is obtained by adding one new term to the previous polynomial. For example,

$$p_3(x) = p_2(x) + \frac{f'''(a)}{3!}(x - a)^3.$$

QUICK CHECK 2 Verify the following properties for $f(x) = \sin x$ and $p_3(x) = x - x^3/6$:

$$f(0) = p_3(0),$$
$$f'(0) = p_3{}'(0),$$
$$f''(0) = p_3{}''(0), \text{ and}$$
$$f'''(0) = p_3{}'''(0).$$ ◄

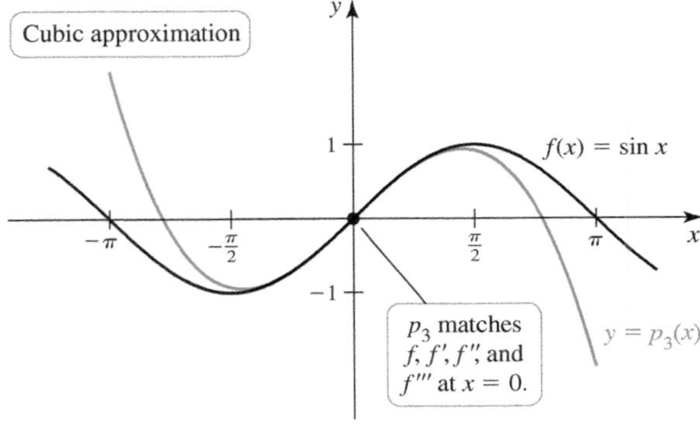

Figure 9.6

The procedure for finding Taylor polynomials may be extended to polynomials of any order. Because the even derivatives of $f(x) = \sin x$ are zero at $x = 0$, $p_4(x) = p_3(x)$. For the same reason, $p_6(x) = p_5(x)$:

$$p_6(x) = p_5(x) = x - \frac{x^3}{3!} + \frac{x^5}{5!}. \qquad c_5 = \frac{f^{(5)}(0)}{5!} = \frac{1}{5!}$$

Finally, the Taylor polynomial of order $n = 7$ is

$$p_7(x) = x - \frac{x^3}{3!} + \frac{x^5}{5!} - \frac{x^7}{7!}. \qquad c_7 = \frac{f^{(7)}(0)}{7!} = -\frac{1}{7!}$$

From Figure 9.7 we see that as the order of the Taylor polynomials increases, more accurate approximations to $f(x) = \sin x$ are obtained over larger intervals centered at 0. For example, p_7 is a good fit to $f(x) = \sin x$ over the interval $[-\pi, \pi]$. Notice that $\sin x$ and its Taylor polynomials (centered at 0) are all odd functions.

Related Exercises 15–22 ◄

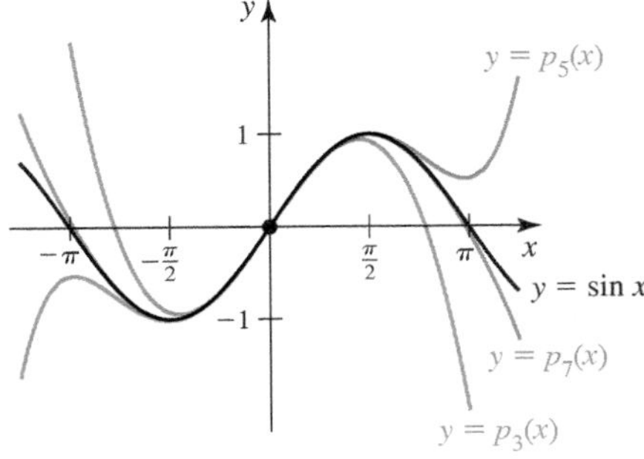

Figure 9.7

QUICK CHECK 3 Why do the Taylor polynomials for $\sin x$ centered at 0 consist only of odd powers of x? ◄

Approximations with Taylor Polynomials

Taylor polynomials find widespread use in approximating functions, as illustrated in the following examples.

EXAMPLE 3 Taylor polynomials for e^x

a. Find the Taylor polynomials of order $n = 0, 1, 2,$ and 3 for $f(x) = e^x$ centered at 0. Graph f and the polynomials.

b. Use the polynomials in part (a) to approximate $e^{0.1}$ and $e^{-0.25}$. Find the absolute errors, $|f(x) - p_n(x)|$, in the approximations. Use calculator values for the exact values of f.

➤ Recall that if c is an approximation to x, the absolute error in c is $|x - c|$ and the relative error in c is $|x - c|/|x|$. We use *error* to refer to *absolute error.*

SOLUTION

a. Recall that the coefficients for the Taylor polynomials centered at 0 are

$$c_k = \frac{f^{(k)}(0)}{k!}, \qquad \text{for } k = 0, 1, 2, \ldots, n.$$

With $f(x) = e^x$, we have $f^{(k)}(x) = e^x$, $f^{(k)}(0) = 1$, and $c_k = 1/k!$, for $k = 0, 1, 2, 3 \ldots$. The first four polynomials are

$$p_0(x) = f(0) = 1,$$

$$p_1(x) = \underbrace{f(0)}_{p_1(x)\,=\,1} + \underbrace{f'(0)}_{1}x = 1 + x,$$

$$p_2(x) = \underbrace{f(0) + f'(0)x}_{p_1(x)\,=\,1\,+\,x} + \underbrace{\frac{f''(0)}{2!}}_{1/2}x^2 = 1 + x + \frac{x^2}{2}, \text{ and}$$

$$p_3(x) = \underbrace{f(0) + f'(0)x + \frac{f''(0)}{2!}x^2}_{p_2(x)\,=\,1\,+\,x\,+\,x^2/2} + \underbrace{\frac{f^{(3)}(0)}{3!}}_{1/6}x^3 = 1 + x + \frac{x^2}{2} + \frac{x^3}{6}.$$

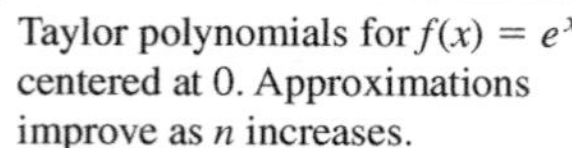

Taylor polynomials for $f(x) = e^x$ centered at 0. Approximations improve as n increases.

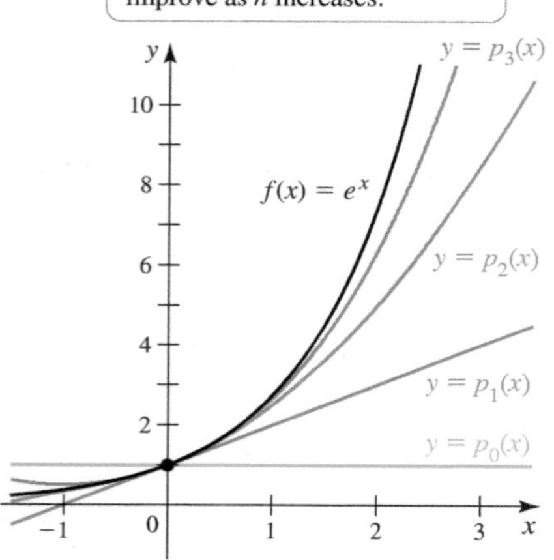

Figure 9.8

Notice that each successive polynomial provides a better fit to $f(x) = e^x$ near 0 (Figure 9.8). Continuing the pattern in these polynomials, the nth-order Taylor polynomial for e^x centered at 0 is

$$p_n(x) = 1 + x + \frac{x^2}{2!} + \frac{x^3}{3!} + \cdots + \frac{x^n}{n!} = \sum_{k=0}^{n} \frac{x^k}{k!}.$$

b. We evaluate $p_n(0.1)$ and $p_n(-0.25)$, for $n = 0, 1, 2,$ and 3, and compare these values to the calculator values of $e^{0.1} \approx 1.1051709$ and $e^{-0.25} \approx 0.77880078$. The results are shown in Table 9.1. Observe that the errors in the approximations decrease as n increases. In addition, the errors in approximating $e^{0.1}$ are smaller in magnitude than the errors in approximating $e^{-0.25}$ because $x = 0.1$ is closer to the center of the polynomials than $x = -0.25$. Reasonable approximations based on these calculations are $e^{0.1} \approx 1.105$ and $e^{-0.25} \approx 0.78$.

➤ A rule of thumb in finding estimates based on several approximations: Keep all the digits that are common to the last two approximations after rounding.

Table 9.1

n	Approximation $p_n(0.1)$	Absolute Error $\lvert e^{0.1} - p_n(0.1)\rvert$	Approximation $p_n(-0.25)$	Absolute Error $\lvert e^{-0.25} - p_n(-0.25)\rvert$
0	1	1.1×10^{-1}	1	2.2×10^{-1}
1	1.1	5.2×10^{-3}	0.75	2.9×10^{-2}
2	1.105	1.7×10^{-4}	0.78125	2.4×10^{-3}
3	1.105167	4.3×10^{-6}	0.778646	1.5×10^{-4}

Related Exercises 23–28 ◄

QUICK CHECK 4 Write out the next two Taylor polynomials p_4 and p_5 for $f(x) = e^x$ in Example 3. ◄

EXAMPLE 4 Approximating a real number using Taylor polynomials Use polynomials of order $n = 0, 1, 2$, and 3 to approximate $\sqrt{18}$.

SOLUTION Letting $f(x) = \sqrt{x}$, we choose the center $a = 16$ because it is near 18, and f and its derivatives are easy to evaluate at 16. The Taylor polynomials have the form

$$p_n(x) = f(16) + f'(16)(x - 16) + \frac{f''(16)}{2!}(x - 16)^2 + \cdots + \frac{f^{(n)}(16)}{n!}(x - 16)^n.$$

We now evaluate the required derivatives:

$$f(x) = \sqrt{x} \Rightarrow f(16) = 4,$$

$$f'(x) = \frac{1}{2}x^{-1/2} \Rightarrow f'(16) = \frac{1}{8},$$

$$f''(x) = -\frac{1}{4}x^{-3/2} \Rightarrow f''(16) = -\frac{1}{256}, \text{ and}$$

$$f'''(x) = \frac{3}{8}x^{-5/2} \Rightarrow f'''(16) = \frac{3}{8192}.$$

Therefore, the polynomial p_3 (which includes p_0, p_1, and p_2) is

$$p_3(x) = \underbrace{\underbrace{\underbrace{4}_{p_0(x)} + \frac{1}{8}(x - 16)}_{p_1(x)} - \frac{1}{512}(x - 16)^2}_{p_2(x)} + \frac{1}{16{,}384}(x - 16)^3.$$

The Taylor polynomials (Figure 9.9) give better approximations to f as the order of the approximation increases.

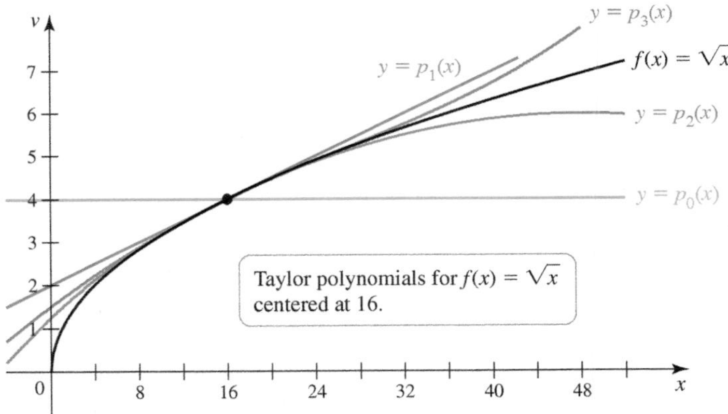

Figure 9.9

Letting $x = 18$, we obtain the approximations to $\sqrt{18}$ and the associated absolute errors shown in Table 9.2. (A calculator is used for the value of $\sqrt{18}$.) As expected, the errors decrease as n increases. Based on these calculations, a reasonable approximation is $\sqrt{18} \approx 4.24$.

QUICK CHECK 5 At what point would you center the Taylor polynomials for $\sqrt{x}$ and $\sqrt[4]{x}$ to approximate $\sqrt{51}$ and $\sqrt[4]{15}$, respectively? ◄

Table 9.2

n	**Approximation $p_n(18)$**	**Absolute Error $\lvert\sqrt{18} - p_n(18)\rvert$**
0	4	2.4×10^{-1}
1	4.25	7.4×10^{-3}
2	4.242188	4.5×10^{-4}
3	4.242676	3.5×10^{-5}

Related Exercises 29–48 ◄

Remainder in a Taylor Polynomial

Taylor polynomials provide good approximations to functions near a specific point. But how accurate are the approximations? To answer this question we define the *remainder* in a Taylor polynomial. If p_n is the Taylor polynomial for f of order n, then the remainder at the point x is

$$R_n(x) = f(x) - p_n(x).$$

The absolute value of the remainder is the error made in approximating $f(x)$ by $p_n(x)$. Equivalently, we have $f(x) = p_n(x) + R_n(x)$, which says that f consists of two components: the polynomial approximation and the associated remainder.

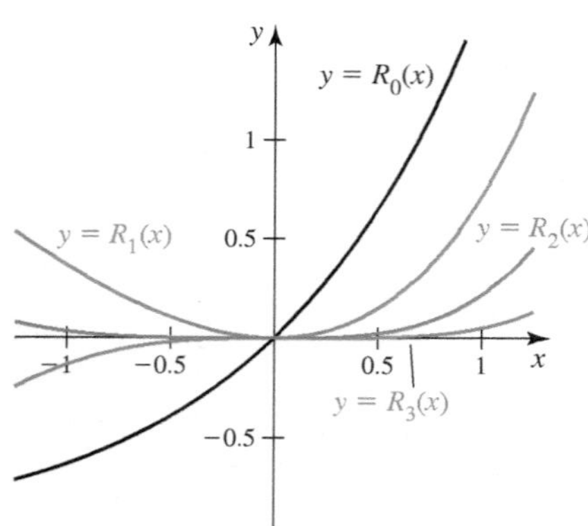

Figure 9.10

> **DEFINITION Remainder in a Taylor Polynomial**
>
> Let p_n be the Taylor polynomial of order n for f. The **remainder** in using p_n to approximate f at the point x is
>
> $$R_n(x) = f(x) - p_n(x).$$

The idea of a remainder is illustrated in Figure 9.10, where we see the remainders associated with various Taylor polynomials for $f(x) = e^x$ centered at 0 (Example 3). For fixed order n, the remainders tend to increase in magnitude as x moves farther from the center of the polynomials (in this case 0). And for fixed x, remainders decrease in magnitude to zero with increasing n.

The remainder for a Taylor polynomial may be written quite concisely, which enables us to estimate remainders. The following result is known as *Taylor's Theorem* (or the *Remainder Theorem*).

➤ The remainder R_n for a Taylor polynomial can be expressed in several different forms. The form stated in Theorem 9.1 is called the *Lagrange form* of the remainder.

> **THEOREM 9.1 Taylor's Theorem (Remainder Theorem)**
>
> Let f have continuous derivatives up to $f^{(n+1)}$ on an open interval I containing a. For all x in I,
>
> $$f(x) = p_n(x) + R_n(x),$$
>
> where p_n is the nth-order Taylor polynomial for f centered at a and the remainder is
>
> $$R_n(x) = \frac{f^{(n+1)}(c)}{(n+1)!}(x-a)^{n+1},$$
>
> for some point c between x and a.

Discussion: We make two observations about Theorem 9.1 and outline a proof in Exercise 92. First, the case $n = 0$ is the Mean Value Theorem (Section 4.6), which states that

$$\frac{f(x) - f(a)}{x - a} = f'(c),$$

where c is a point between x and a. Rearranging this expression, we have

$$\begin{aligned} f(x) &= \underbrace{f(a)}_{p_0(x)} + \underbrace{f'(c)(x-a)}_{R_0(x)} \\ &= p_0(x) + R_0(x), \end{aligned}$$

which is Taylor's Theorem with $n = 0$. Not surprisingly, the term $f^{(n+1)}(c)$ in Taylor's Theorem comes from a Mean Value Theorem argument.

The second observation makes the remainder easier to remember. If you write the $(n+1)$st Taylor polynomial p_{n+1}, the highest-degree term is $\dfrac{f^{(n+1)}(a)}{(n+1)!}(x-a)^{n+1}$. Replacing $f^{(n+1)}(a)$ with $f^{(n+1)}(c)$ results in the remainder for p_n.

Estimating the Remainder

The remainder has both practical and theoretical importance. We deal with practical matters now and theoretical matters in Section 9.3. The remainder is used to estimate errors in approximations and to determine the number of terms of a Taylor polynomial needed to achieve a prescribed accuracy.

Because c is generally unknown, the difficulty in estimating the remainder is finding a bound for $|f^{(n+1)}(c)|$. Assuming this can be done, the following theorem gives a standard estimate for the remainder term.

THEOREM 9.2 Estimate of the Remainder

Let n be a fixed positive integer. Suppose there exists a number M such that $|f^{(n+1)}(c)| \leq M$, for all c between a and x inclusive. The remainder in the nth-order Taylor polynomial for f centered at a satisfies

$$|R_n(x)| = |f(x) - p_n(x)| \leq M\frac{|x - a|^{n+1}}{(n + 1)!}.$$

Proof: The proof requires taking the absolute value of the remainder in Theorem 9.1, replacing $|f^{(n+1)}(c)|$ with a larger quantity M, and forming an inequality. ◀

We now give three examples that demonstrate how the remainder is computed and used in different ways.

EXAMPLE 5 Estimating the remainder for cos *x* Find a bound for the magnitude of the remainder for the Taylor polynomials of $f(x) = \cos x$ centered at 0.

SOLUTION According to Theorem 9.1 with $a = 0$, we have

$$R_n(x) = \frac{f^{(n+1)}(c)}{(n + 1)!}x^{n+1},$$

where c is a point between 0 and x. Notice that $f^{(n+1)}(c) = \pm\sin c$ or $f^{(n+1)}(c) = \pm\cos c$ depending on the value of n. In all cases, $|f^{(n+1)}(c)| \leq 1$. Therefore, we take $M = 1$ in Theorem 9.2, and the absolute value of the remainder can be bounded as

$$|R_n(x)| = \left|\frac{f^{(n+1)}(c)}{(n + 1)!}x^{n+1}\right| \leq \frac{|x|^{n+1}}{(n + 1)!}.$$

For example, if we approximate cos 0.1 using the Taylor polynomial p_{10}, the remainder satisfies

$$|R_{10}(0.1)| \leq \frac{0.1^{11}}{11!} \approx 2.5 \times 10^{-19}.$$

Related Exercises 49–54 ◀

EXAMPLE 6 Estimating a remainder Consider again Example 4 in which we approximated $\sqrt{18}$ using the Taylor polynomial

$$p_3(x) = 4 + \frac{1}{8}(x - 16) - \frac{1}{512}(x - 16)^2 + \frac{1}{16{,}384}(x - 16)^3.$$

In that example, we computed the error in the approximation knowing the exact value of $\sqrt{18}$ (obtained with a calculator). In the more realistic case in which we do not know the exact value, Theorem 9.2 allows us to estimate remainders (or errors). Applying this theorem with $n = 3$, $a = 16$, and $x = 18$, we find that the remainder in approximating $\sqrt{18}$ by $p_3(18)$ satisfies the bound

$$|R_3(18)| \leq M\frac{(18 - 16)^4}{4!} = \frac{2}{3}M,$$

where M is a number that satisfies $|f^{(4)}(c)| \le M$, for all c between 16 and 18 inclusive. In this particular problem, we find that $f^{(4)}(c) = -\frac{15}{16}c^{-7/2}$, so M must be chosen (as small as possible) such that $|f^{(4)}(c)| = \frac{15}{16}c^{-7/2} = \frac{15}{16c^{7/2}} \le M$, for $16 \le c \le 18$. You can verify that $\frac{15}{16c^{7/2}}$ is a decreasing function of c on $[16, 18]$ and has a maximum value of approximately 5.7×10^{-5} at $c = 16$ (Figure 9.11). Therefore, a bound on the remainder is

$$|R_3(18)| \le \frac{2}{3}M \approx \frac{2}{3} \cdot 5.7 \times 10^{-5} \approx 3.8 \times 10^{-5}.$$

Notice that the actual error computed in Example 4 (Table 9.2) is 3.5×10^{-5}, which is less than the bound on the remainder—as it should be.

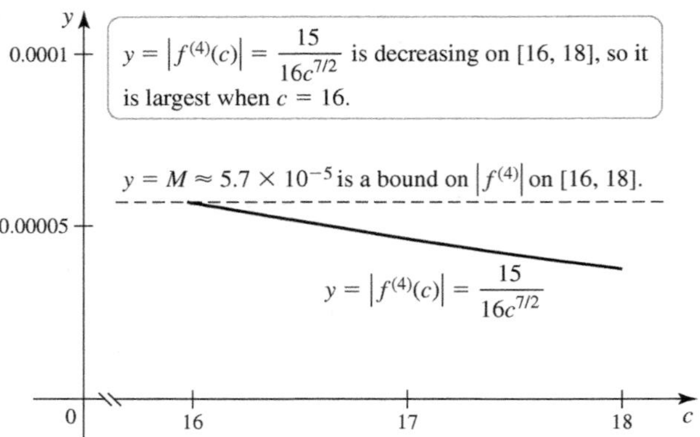

Figure 9.11

Related Exercises 55–60

EXAMPLE 7 Estimating the remainder for e^x Find a bound on the remainder in approximating $e^{0.45}$ using the Taylor polynomial of order $n = 6$ for $f(x) = e^x$ centered at 0.

SOLUTION Using Theorem 9.2, a bound on the remainder is given by

$$|R_n(x)| \le M\frac{|x - a|^{n+1}}{(n + 1)!},$$

where M is chosen such that $|f^{(n+1)}(c)| \le M$, for all c between a and x inclusive. Notice that $f(x) = e^x$ implies that $f^{(k)}(x) = e^x$, for $k = 0, 1, 2, \ldots$. In this particular problem, we have $n = 6$, $a = 0$, and $x = 0.45$, so the bound on the remainder takes the form

$$|R_6(0.45)| \le M\frac{|0.45 - 0|^7}{7!} \approx 7.4 \times 10^{-7} M,$$

where M is chosen such that $|f^{(7)}(c)| = e^c \le M$, for all c in the interval $[0, 0.45]$. Because e^c is an increasing function of c, its maximum value on the interval $[0, 0.45]$ occurs at $c = 0.45$ and is $e^{0.45}$. However, $e^{0.45}$ cannot be evaluated exactly (it is the number we are approximating), so we must find a number M such that $e^{0.45} \le M$. Here is one of many ways to obtain a bound: We observe that $e^{0.45} < e^{1/2} < 4^{1/2} = 2$ and take $M = 2$ (Figure 9.12). Therefore, a bound on the remainder is

$$|R_6(0.45)| \le 7.4 \times 10^{-7} M \approx 1.5 \times 10^{-6}.$$

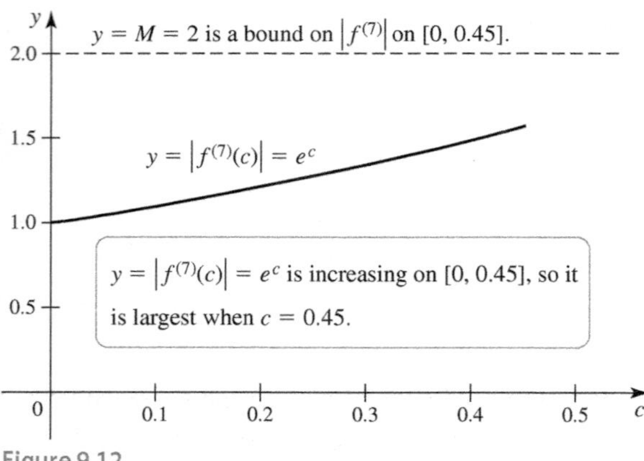

Figure 9.12

➤ Recall that if $f(x) = e^x$, then

$$p_n(x) = \sum_{k=0}^{n} \frac{x^k}{k!}.$$

QUICK CHECK 6 In Example 7, find an approximate upper bound for $R_7(0.45)$. ◄

Using the Taylor polynomial derived in Example 3 with $n = 6$, the resulting approximation to $e^{0.45}$ is

$$p_6(0.45) = \sum_{k=0}^{6} \frac{0.45^k}{k!} \approx 1.5683114;$$

it has an error that does not exceed 1.5×10^{-6}.

Related Exercises 55–60 ◄

EXAMPLE 8 **Working with the remainder** The nth-order Taylor polynomial for $f(x) = \ln(1 - x)$ centered at 0 is

$$p_n(x) = -\sum_{k=1}^{n} \frac{x^k}{k} = -x - \frac{x^2}{2} - \frac{x^3}{3} - \cdots - \frac{x^n}{n}.$$

a. Find a bound on the error in approximating $\ln(1 - x)$ by $p_3(x)$ for values of x in the interval $\left[-\frac{1}{2}, \frac{1}{2}\right]$.

b. How many terms of the Taylor polynomial are needed to approximate values of $f(x) = \ln(1 - x)$ with an error less than 10^{-3} on the interval $\left[-\frac{1}{2}, \frac{1}{2}\right]$?

SOLUTION

a. The remainder for the Taylor polynomial p_3 is $R_3(x) = \dfrac{f^{(4)}(c)}{4!}x^4$, where c is between 0 and x. Computing four derivatives of f, we find that $f^{(4)}(x) = -\dfrac{6}{(1 - x)^4}$. On the interval $\left[-\frac{1}{2}, \frac{1}{2}\right]$, the maximum magnitude of this derivative occurs at $x = \frac{1}{2}$ (because the denominator is smallest at $x = \frac{1}{2}$) and is $6/\left(\frac{1}{2}\right)^4 = 96$. Similarly, the factor x^4 has its maximum magnitude at $x = \pm\frac{1}{2}$ and it is $\left(\frac{1}{2}\right)^4 = \frac{1}{16}$. Therefore, $|R_3(x)| \le \dfrac{96}{4!}\left(\frac{1}{16}\right) = 0.25$ on the interval $\left[-\frac{1}{2}, \frac{1}{2}\right]$. The error in approximating $f(x)$ by $p_3(x)$, for $-\frac{1}{2} \le x \le \frac{1}{2}$, does not exceed 0.25.

b. For any positive integer n, the remainder is $R_n(x) = \dfrac{f^{(n+1)}(c)}{(n + 1)!}x^{n+1}$. Differentiating f several times reveals that

$$f^{(n+1)}(x) = -\frac{n!}{(1 - x)^{n+1}}.$$

On the interval $\left[-\frac{1}{2}, \frac{1}{2}\right]$, the maximum magnitude of this derivative occurs at $x = \frac{1}{2}$ and is $n!/\left(\frac{1}{2}\right)^{n+1}$. Similarly, x^{n+1} has its maximum magnitude at $x = \pm\frac{1}{2}$, and it is $\left(\frac{1}{2}\right)^{n+1}$. Therefore, a bound on the remainder is

$$\begin{aligned} |R_n(x)| &= \frac{1}{(n + 1)!} \cdot \underbrace{|f^{(n+1)}(c)|}_{\le n!2^{n+1}} \cdot \underbrace{|x|^{n+1}}_{\le \left(\frac{1}{2}\right)^{n+1}} \\ &\le \frac{1}{(n + 1)!} \cdot n!2^{n+1} \cdot \frac{1}{2^{n+1}} \\ &= \frac{1}{n + 1}. \end{aligned}$$

$\dfrac{n!}{(n + 1)!} = \dfrac{1}{n + 1}$

To ensure that the error is less than 10^{-3} on the entire interval $\left[-\frac{1}{2}, \frac{1}{2}\right]$, n must satisfy $|R_n| \le \dfrac{1}{n + 1} < 10^{-3}$ or $n > 999$. The error is likely to be significantly less than 10^{-3} if x is near 0.

Related Exercises 61–72 ◄

SECTION 9.1 EXERCISES

Review Questions

1. Suppose you use a second-order Taylor polynomial centered at 0 to approximate a function f. What matching conditions are satisfied by the polynomial?

2. Does the accuracy of an approximation given by a Taylor polynomial generally increase or decrease with the order of the approximation? Explain.

3. The first three Taylor polynomials for $f(x) = \sqrt{1 + x}$ centered at 0 are $p_0(x) = 1$, $p_1(x) = 1 + \frac{x}{2}$, and $p_2(x) = 1 + \frac{x}{2} - \frac{x^2}{8}$. Find three approximations to $\sqrt{1.1}$.

4. In general, how many terms do the Taylor polynomials p_2 and p_3 have in common?

5. How is the remainder $R_n(x)$ in a Taylor polynomial defined?

6. Explain how to estimate the remainder in an approximation given by a Taylor polynomial.

Basic Skills

T 7–14. Linear and quadratic approximation

a. Find the linear approximating polynomial for the following functions centered at the given point a.
b. Find the quadratic approximating polynomial for the following functions centered at the given point a.
c. Use the polynomials obtained in parts (a) and (b) to approximate the given quantity.

7. $f(x) = 8x^{3/2}$, $a = 1$; approximate $8 \cdot 1.1^{3/2}$.

8. $f(x) = \frac{1}{x}$, $a = 1$; approximate $\frac{1}{1.05}$.

9. $f(x) = e^{-x}$, $a = 0$; approximate $e^{-0.2}$.

10. $f(x) = \sqrt{x}$, $a = 4$; approximate $\sqrt{3.9}$.

11. $f(x) = (1 + x)^{-1}$, $a = 0$; approximate $\frac{1}{1.05}$.

12. $f(x) = \cos x$, $a = \pi/4$; approximate $\cos(0.24\pi)$.

13. $f(x) = x^{1/3}$, $a = 8$; approximate $7.5^{1/3}$.

14. $f(x) = \tan^{-1} x$, $a = 0$; approximate $\tan^{-1} 0.1$.

T 15–22. Taylor polynomials

a. Find the nth-order Taylor polynomials of the given function centered at 0, for n = 0, 1, and 2.
b. Graph the Taylor polynomials and the function.

15. $f(x) = \cos x$
16. $f(x) = e^{-x}$
17. $f(x) = \ln(1 - x)$
18. $f(x) = (1 + x)^{-1/2}$
19. $f(x) = \tan x$
20. $f(x) = (1 + x)^{-2}$
21. $f(x) = (1 + x)^{-3}$
22. $f(x) = \sin^{-1} x$

T 23–28. Approximations with Taylor polynomials

a. Use the given Taylor polynomial p_2 to approximate the given quantity.
b. Compute the absolute error in the approximation assuming the exact value is given by a calculator.

23. Approximate $\sqrt{1.05}$ using $f(x) = \sqrt{1 + x}$ and $p_2(x) = 1 + x/2 - x^2/8$.

24. Approximate $\sqrt[3]{1.1}$ using $f(x) = \sqrt[3]{1 + x}$ and $p_2(x) = 1 + x/3 - x^2/9$.

25. Approximate $\frac{1}{\sqrt{1.08}}$ using $f(x) = \frac{1}{\sqrt{1 + x}}$ and $p_2(x) = 1 - x/2 + 3x^2/8$.

26. Approximate $\ln 1.06$ using $f(x) = \ln(1 + x)$ and $p_2(x) = x - x^2/2$.

27. Approximate $e^{-0.15}$ using $f(x) = e^{-x}$ and $p_2(x) = 1 - x + x^2/2$.

28. Approximate $\frac{1}{1.12^3}$ using $f(x) = \frac{1}{(1 + x)^3}$ and $p_2(x) = 1 - 3x + 6x^2$.

T 29–38. Taylor polynomials centered at $a \neq 0$

a. Find the nth-order Taylor polynomials for the following functions centered at the given point a, for n = 0, 1, and 2.
b. Graph the Taylor polynomials and the function.

29. $f(x) = x^3$, $a = 1$
30. $f(x) = 8\sqrt{x}$, $a = 1$
31. $f(x) = \sin x$, $a = \pi/4$
32. $f(x) = \cos x$, $a = \pi/6$
33. $f(x) = \sqrt{x}$, $a = 9$
34. $f(x) = \sqrt[3]{x}$, $a = 8$
35. $f(x) = \ln x$, $a = e$
36. $f(x) = \sqrt[4]{x}$, $a = 16$
37. $f(x) = \tan^{-1} x + x^2 + 1$, $a = 1$
38. $f(x) = e^x$, $a = \ln 2$

T 39–48. Approximations with Taylor polynomials

a. Approximate the given quantities using Taylor polynomials with n = 3.
b. Compute the absolute error in the approximation assuming the exact value is given by a calculator.

39. $e^{0.12}$
40. $\cos(-0.2)$
41. $\tan(-0.1)$
42. $\ln 1.05$
43. $\sqrt{1.06}$
44. $\sqrt[4]{79}$
45. $\sqrt{101}$
46. $\sqrt[3]{126}$
47. $\sinh 0.5$
48. $\tanh 0.5$

49–54. Remainders *Find the remainder R_n for the nth-order Taylor polynomial centered at a for the given functions. Express the result for a general value of n.*

49. $f(x) = \sin x$, $a = 0$
50. $f(x) = \cos 2x$, $a = 0$
51. $f(x) = e^{-x}$, $a = 0$
52. $f(x) = \cos x$, $a = \pi/2$
53. $f(x) = \sin x$, $a = \pi/2$
54. $f(x) = 1/(1 - x)$, $a = 0$

T 55–60. Estimating errors *Use the remainder to find a bound on the error in approximating the following quantities with the nth-order Taylor polynomial centered at 0. Estimates are not unique.*

55. $\sin 0.3$, $n = 4$
56. $\cos 0.45$, $n = 3$
57. $e^{0.25}$, $n = 4$
58. $\tan 0.3$, $n = 2$
59. $e^{-0.5}$, $n = 4$
60. $\ln 1.04$, $n = 3$

T **61–66. Error bounds** *Use the remainder to find a bound on the error in the following approximations on the given interval. Error bounds are not unique.*

61. $\sin x \approx x - x^3/6$ on $[-\pi/4, \pi/4]$

62. $\cos x \approx 1 - x^2/2$ on $[-\pi/4, \pi/4]$

63. $e^x \approx 1 + x + x^2/2$ on $\left[-\frac{1}{2}, \frac{1}{2}\right]$

64. $\tan x \approx x$ on $[-\pi/6, \pi/6]$

65. $\ln(1 + x) \approx x - x^2/2$ on $[-0.2, 0.2]$

66. $\sqrt{1 + x} \approx 1 + x/2$ on $[-0.1, 0.1]$

67–72. Number of terms *What is the minimum order of the Taylor polynomial required to approximate the following quantities with an absolute error no greater than 10^{-3}? (The answer depends on your choice of a center.)*

67. $e^{-0.5}$ **68.** $\sin 0.2$ **69.** $\cos(-0.25)$

70. $\ln 0.85$ **71.** $\sqrt{1.06}$ **72.** $1/\sqrt{0.85}$

Further Explorations

73. Explain why or why not Determine whether the following statements are true and give an explanation or counterexample.

a. Only even powers of x appear in the Taylor polynomials for $f(x) = e^{-2x}$ centered at 0.
b. Let $f(x) = x^5 - 1$. The Taylor polynomial for f of order 10 centered at 0 is f itself.
c. Only even powers of x appear in the nth-order Taylor polynomial for $f(x) = \sqrt{1 + x^2}$ centered at 0.
d. Suppose f'' is continuous on an interval that contains a, where f has an inflection point at a. Then the second-order Taylor polynomial for f at a is linear.

74. Taylor coefficients for $x = a$ Follow the procedure in the text to show that the nth-order Taylor polynomial that matches f and its derivatives up to order n at a has coefficients

$$c_k = \frac{f^{(k)}(a)}{k!}, \text{ for } k = 0, 1, 2, \ldots, n.$$

75. Matching functions with polynomials Match functions a–f with Taylor polynomials A–F (all centered at 0). Give reasons for your choices.

a. $\sqrt{1 + 2x}$ **A.** $p_2(x) = 1 + 2x + 2x^2$

b. $\dfrac{1}{\sqrt{1 + 2x}}$ **B.** $p_2(x) = 1 - 6x + 24x^2$

c. e^{2x} **C.** $p_2(x) = 1 + x - \dfrac{x^2}{2}$

d. $\dfrac{1}{1 + 2x}$ **D.** $p_2(x) = 1 - 2x + 4x^2$

e. $\dfrac{1}{(1 + 2x)^3}$ **E.** $p_2(x) = 1 - x + \dfrac{3}{2}x^2$

f. e^{-2x} **F.** $p_2(x) = 1 - 2x + 2x^2$

T **76. Dependence of errors on x** Consider $f(x) = \ln(1 - x)$ and its Taylor polynomials given in Example 8.

a. Graph $y = |f(x) - p_2(x)|$ and $y = |f(x) - p_3(x)|$ on the interval $\left[-\frac{1}{2}, \frac{1}{2}\right]$ (two curves).
b. At what points of $\left[-\frac{1}{2}, \frac{1}{2}\right]$ is the error largest? Smallest?
c. Are these results consistent with the theoretical error bounds obtained in Example 8?

Applications

T **77–84. Small argument approximations** *Consider the following common approximations when x is near zero.*

a. *Estimate $f(0.1)$ and give a bound on the error in the approximation.*
b. *Estimate $f(0.2)$ and give a bound on the error in the approximation.*

77. $f(x) = \sin x \approx x$ **78.** $f(x) = \tan x \approx x$

79. $f(x) = \cos x \approx 1 - x^2/2$ **80.** $f(x) = \tan^{-1} x \approx x$

81. $f(x) = \sqrt{1 + x} \approx 1 + x/2$

82. $f(x) = \ln(1 + x) \approx x - x^2/2$

83. $f(x) = e^x \approx 1 + x$ **84.** $f(x) = \sin^{-1} x \approx x$

T **85. Errors in approximations** Suppose you approximate $f(x) = \sec x$ at the points $x = -0.2, -0.1, 0.0, 0.1$, and 0.2 using the Taylor polynomials $p_2(x) = 1 + x^2/2$ and $p_4(x) = 1 + x^2/2 + 5x^4/24$. Assume that the exact value of $\sec x$ is given by a calculator.

a. Complete the table showing the absolute errors in the approximations at each point. Show two significant digits.

x	$\lvert \sec x - p_2(x) \rvert$	$\lvert \sec x - p_4(x) \rvert$
-0.2		
-0.1		
0.0		
0.1		
0.2		

b. In each error column, how do the errors vary with x? For what values of x are the errors largest and smallest in magnitude?

T **86–89. Errors in approximations** *Carry out the procedure described in Exercise 85 with the following functions and Taylor polynomials.*

86. $f(x) = \cos x,\ p_2(x) = 1 - \dfrac{x^2}{2},\ p_4(x) = 1 - \dfrac{x^2}{2} + \dfrac{x^4}{24}$

87. $f(x) = e^{-x},\ p_1(x) = 1 - x,\ p_2(x) = 1 - x + \dfrac{x^2}{2}$

88. $f(x) = \ln(1 + x),\ p_1(x) = x,\ p_2(x) = x - \dfrac{x^2}{2}$

89. $f(x) = \tan x,\ p_1(x) = x,\ p_3(x) = x + \dfrac{x^3}{3}$

T **90. Best expansion point** Suppose you wish to approximate $\cos(\pi/12)$ using Taylor polynomials. Is the approximation more accurate if you use Taylor polynomials centered at 0 or $\pi/6$? Use a calculator for numerical experiments and check for consistency with Theorem 9.2. Does the answer depend on the order of the polynomial?

T **91. Best expansion point** Suppose you wish to approximate $e^{0.35}$ using Taylor polynomials. Is the approximation more accurate if you use Taylor polynomials centered at 0 or $\ln 2$? Use a calculator for numerical experiments and check for consistency with Theorem 9.2. Does the answer depend on the order of the polynomial?

Additional Exercises

92. Proof of Taylor's Theorem There are several proofs of Taylor's Theorem, which lead to various forms of the remainder. The following proof is instructive because it leads to two different forms of the remainder and it relies on the Fundamental Theorem of Calculus, integration by parts, and the Mean Value Theorem for Integrals. Assume that f has at least $n + 1$ continuous derivatives on an interval containing a.

a. Show that the Fundamental Theorem of Calculus can be written in the form

$$f(x) = f(a) + \int_a^x f'(t)\, dt.$$

b. Use integration by parts ($u = f'(t)$, $dv = dt$) to show that

$$f(x) = f(a) + (x - a)f'(a) + \int_a^x (x - t)f''(t)\, dt.$$

c. Show that n integrations by parts gives

$$f(x) = f(a) + \frac{f'(a)}{1!}(x - a) + \frac{f''(a)}{2!}(x - a)^2 + \cdots + \frac{f^{(n)}(a)}{n!}(x - a)^n + \underbrace{\int_a^x \frac{f^{(n+1)}(t)}{n!}(x - t)^n\, dt}_{R_n(x)}.$$

d. *Challenge:* The result in part (c) looks like $f(x) = p_n(x) + R_n(x)$, where p_n is the nth-order Taylor polynomial and R_n is a new form of the remainder, known as the integral form of the remainder. Use the Mean Value Theorem for Integrals (Section 5.4) to show that R_n can be expressed in the form

$$R_n(x) = \frac{f^{(n+1)}(c)}{(n + 1)!}(x - a)^{n+1},$$

where c is between a and x.

93. Tangent line is p_1 Let f be differentiable at $x = a$.

a. Find the equation of the line tangent to the curve $y = f(x)$ at $(a, f(a))$.

b. Verify that the Taylor polynomial p_1 centered at a describes the tangent line found in part (a).

94. Local extreme points and inflection points Suppose f has continuous first and second derivatives at a.

a. Show that if f has a local maximum at a, then the Taylor polynomial p_2 centered at a also has a local maximum at a.

b. Show that if f has a local minimum at a, then the Taylor polynomial p_2 centered at a also has a local minimum at a.

c. Is it true that if f has an inflection point at a, then the Taylor polynomial p_2 centered at a also has an inflection point at a?

d. Are the converses in parts (a) and (b) true? If p_2 has a local extreme point at a, does f have the same type of point at a?

T **95. Approximating $\sin x$** Let $f(x) = \sin x$ and let p_n and q_n be nth-order Taylor polynomials for f centered at 0 and π, respectively.

a. Find p_5 and q_5.

b. Graph f, p_5, and q_5 on the interval $[-\pi, 2\pi]$. On what interval is p_5 a better approximation to f than q_5? On what interval is q_5 a better approximation to f than p_5?

c. Complete the following table showing the errors in the approximations given by p_5 and q_5 at selected points.

x	$\lvert \sin x - p_5(x) \rvert$	$\lvert \sin x - q_5(x) \rvert$
$\pi/4$		
$\pi/2$		
$3\pi/4$		
$5\pi/4$		
$7\pi/4$		

d. At which points in the table is p_5 a better approximation to f than q_5? At which points do p_5 and q_5 give comparable approximations to f? Explain your observations.

T **96. Approximating $\ln x$** Let $f(x) = \ln x$ and let p_n and q_n be the nth-order Taylor polynomials for f centered at 1 and e, respectively.

a. Find p_3 and q_3.

b. Graph f, p_3, and q_3 on the interval $(0, 4]$.

c. Complete the following table showing the errors in the approximations given by p_3 and q_3 at selected points.

x	$\lvert \ln x - p_3(x) \rvert$	$\lvert \ln x - q_3(x) \rvert$
0.5		
1.0		
1.5		
2		
2.5		
3		
3.5		

d. At which points in the table is p_3 a better approximation to f than q_3? Explain your observations.

T **97. Approximating square roots** Let p_1 and q_1 be the first-order Taylor polynomials for $f(x) = \sqrt{x}$ centered at 36 and 49, respectively.

a. Find p_1 and q_1.

b. Complete the following table showing the errors when using p_1 and q_1 to approximate $f(x)$ at $x = 37, 39, 41, 43, 45,$ and 47. Use a calculator to obtain an exact value of $f(x)$.

x	$\lvert \sqrt{x} - p_1(x) \rvert$	$\lvert \sqrt{x} - q_1(x) \rvert$
37		
39		
41		
43		
45		
47		

c. At which points in the table is p_1 a better approximation to f than q_1? Explain this result.

T **98. A different kind of approximation** When approximating a function f using a Taylor polynomial, we use information about f and its derivatives at one point. An alternative approach (called *interpolation*) uses information about f at several different points. Suppose we wish to approximate $f(x) = \sin x$ on the interval $[0, \pi]$.

a. Write the (quadratic) Taylor polynomial p_2 for f centered at $\frac{\pi}{2}$.

b. Now consider a quadratic interpolating polynomial $q(x) = ax^2 + bx + c$. The coefficients a, b, and c are chosen such that the following conditions are satisfied:

$$q(0) = f(0), q\left(\frac{\pi}{2}\right) = f\left(\frac{\pi}{2}\right), \text{ and } q(\pi) = f(\pi).$$

Show that $q(x) = -\frac{4}{\pi^2}x^2 + \frac{4}{\pi}x$.

c. Graph f, p_2, and q on $[0, \pi]$.

d. Find the error in approximating $f(x) = \sin x$ at the points $\frac{\pi}{4}, \frac{\pi}{2}, \frac{3\pi}{4}$, and π using p_2 and q.

e. Which function, p_2 or q, is a better approximation to f on $[0, \pi]$? Explain.

QUICK CHECK ANSWERS

3. $f(x) = \sin x$ is an odd function, and its even-ordered derivatives are zero at 0, so its Taylor polynomials are also odd functions. **4.** $p_4(x) = p_3(x) + \frac{x^4}{4!}$; $p_5(x) = p_4(x) + \frac{x^5}{5!}$ **5.** $x = 49$ and $x = 16$ are good choices. **6.** Because $e^{0.45} < 2$, $|R_7(0.45)| < 2\frac{0.45^8}{8!} \approx 8.3 \times 10^{-8}$.◄

9.2 Properties of Power Series

The preceding section demonstrated that Taylor polynomials provide accurate approximations to many functions and that, in general, the approximations improve as the degree of the polynomials increases. In this section, we take the next step and let the degree of the Taylor polynomials increase without bound to produce a *power series.*

Geometric Series as Power Series

A good way to become familiar with power series is to return to *geometric series*, first encountered in Section 8.3. Recall that for a fixed number r,

$$\sum_{k=0}^{\infty} r^k = 1 + r + r^2 + \cdots = \frac{1}{1-r}, \qquad \text{provided } |r| < 1.$$

It's a small change to replace the real number r with the variable x. In doing so, the geometric series becomes a new representation of a familiar function:

$$\sum_{k=0}^{\infty} x^k = 1 + x + x^2 + \cdots = \frac{1}{1-x}, \qquad \text{provided } |x| < 1.$$

This infinite series is a power series and it is a representation of the function $1/(1 - x)$ that is valid on the interval $|x| < 1$.

In general, power series are used to represent familiar functions such as trigonometric, exponential, and logarithmic functions. They are also used to define new functions. For example, consider the function defined by

$$g(x) = \sum_{k=1}^{\infty} \frac{(-1)^k k}{4^k} x^{2k}.$$

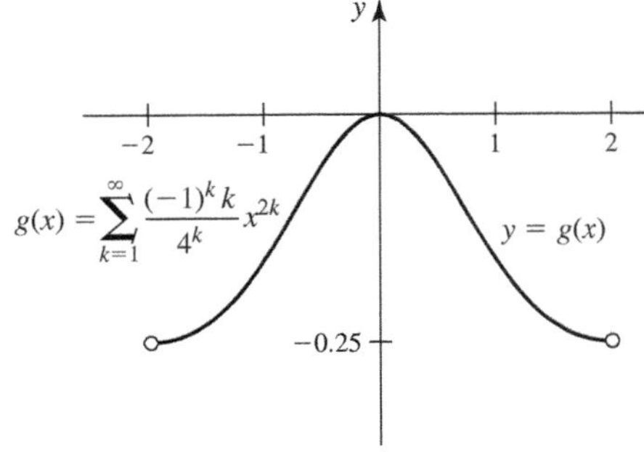

Figure 9.13

➤ Figure 9.13 shows an approximation to the graph of g made by summing the first 500 terms of the power series at selected values of x on the interval $(-2, 2)$.

The term *function* is used advisedly because it's not yet clear whether g really is a function. If so, is it continuous? Does it have a derivative? Judging by its graph (Figure 9.13), g appears to be an ordinary continuous and differentiable function on $(-2, 2)$ (which is identified at the end of the chapter). In fact, power series satisfy the defining property of all functions: For each admissible value of x, a power series has at most one value. For this reason, we refer to a power series as a function, although the domain, properties, and identity of the function may need to be discovered.

QUICK CHECK 1 By substituting $x = 0$ in the power series for g, evaluate $g(0)$ for the function in Figure 9.13.◄

Convergence of Power Series

First let's establish some terminology associated with power series.

> **DEFINITION Power Series**
>
> A **power series** has the general form
>
> $$\sum_{k=0}^{\infty} c_k (x - a)^k,$$
>
> where a and c_k are real numbers, and x is a variable. The c_k's are the **coefficients** of the power series and a is the **center** of the power series. The set of values of x for which the series converges is its **interval of convergence**. The **radius of convergence** of the power series, denoted R, is the distance from the center of the series to the boundary of the interval of convergence (Figure 9.14).

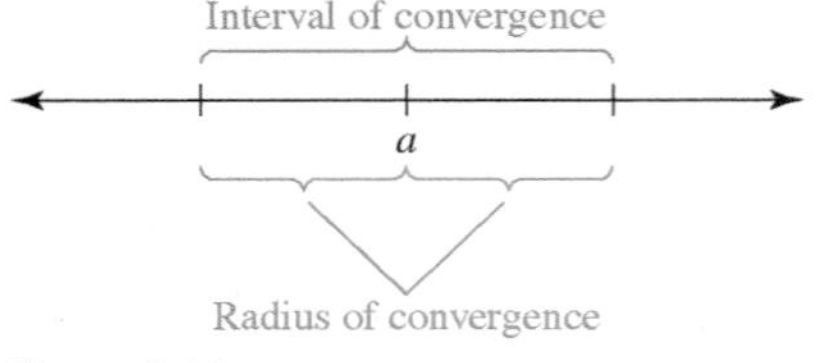

Figure 9.14

How do we determine the interval of convergence for a given power series? The presence of the terms x^k or $(x - a)^k$ in a power series suggests using the Ratio Test or the Root Test. Because these terms could be positive or negative, we test a power series for absolute convergence (remember that the Ratio and Root Tests apply only to series with positive terms). By Theorem 8.21, if we determine the values of x for which the series converges absolutely, we have a set of values for which the series converges.

Before turning to examples, we point out some important facts. Suppose we test the series $\sum a_k$ for absolute convergence using the Ratio Test. If

$$r = \lim_{k \to \infty} \left| \frac{a_{k+1}}{a_k} \right| < 1,$$

it follows that $\sum |a_k|$ converges, which in turn implies that $\sum a_k$ converges (Theorem 8.21). On the other hand, if $r > 1$, then for large k we have $|a_{k+1}| > |a_k|$, which means the terms of the sequence $\{a_k\}$ grow in magnitude as $k \to \infty$. Therefore, $\lim_{k \to \infty} a_k \neq 0$, and we conclude that $\sum a_k$ diverges by the Divergence Test (recall that the Divergence Test applies to *arbitrary* series). If $r = 1$, the Ratio Test is inconclusive, and we use other tests to determine convergence.

A similar argument can be made when using the Root Test to determine the interval of convergence. We first test the series for absolute convergence. When $\rho < 1$, the series converges absolutely (and therefore converges), but when $\rho > 1$, the terms of the series do not tend to 0, so the series diverges by the Divergence Test. If $\rho = 1$, the test is inconclusive, and other tests must be used.

The following examples illustrate how the Ratio and Root Tests are used to determine the interval and radius of convergence.

EXAMPLE 1 Interval and radius of convergence Find the interval and radius of convergence for each power series.

a. $\displaystyle\sum_{k=0}^{\infty} \frac{x^k}{k!}$ **b.** $\displaystyle\sum_{k=0}^{\infty} \frac{(-1)^k (x - 2)^k}{4^k}$ **c.** $\displaystyle\sum_{k=1}^{\infty} k!\, x^k$

SOLUTION

a. The center of the power series is 0 and the terms of the series are $x^k/k!$. Due to the presence of the factor $k!$, we test the series for absolute convergence using the Ratio Test:

$$r = \lim_{k \to \infty} \frac{|x^{k+1}/(k+1)!|}{|x^k/k!|} \quad \text{Ratio Test for absolute convergence}$$

$$= \lim_{k \to \infty} \frac{|x|^{k+1}}{|x|^k} \cdot \frac{k!}{(k+1)!} \quad \text{Invert and multiply.}$$

$$= |x| \lim_{k \to \infty} \frac{1}{k+1} = 0. \quad \text{Simplify and take the limit with } x \text{ fixed.}$$

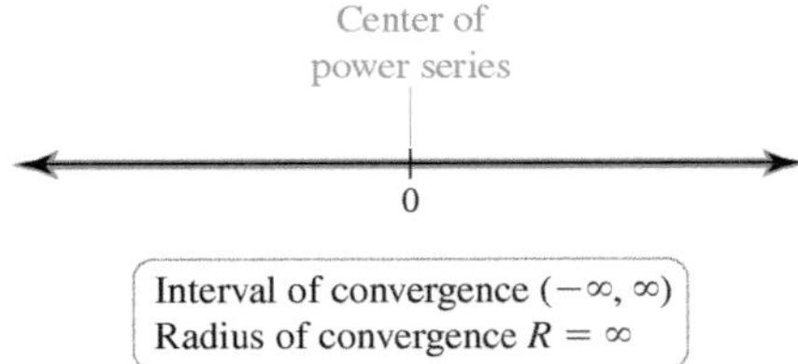

Figure 9.15

Notice that in taking the limit as $k \to \infty$, x is held fixed. Because $r = 0$ for all real numbers x, the series converges absolutely for all x. Using Theorem 8.21, we conclude that the series converges for all x. Therefore, the interval of convergence is $(-\infty, \infty)$ (Figure 9.15) and the radius of convergence is $R = \infty$.

b. We test for absolute convergence using the Root Test:

$$\rho = \lim_{k\to\infty} \sqrt[k]{\left|\frac{(-1)^k(x-2)^k}{4^k}\right|} = \frac{|x-2|}{4}.$$

In this case, ρ depends on the value of x. For absolute convergence, x must satisfy

$$\rho = \frac{|x-2|}{4} < 1,$$

which implies that $|x - 2| < 4$. Using standard techniques for solving inequalities, the solution set is $-4 < x - 2 < 4$, or $-2 < x < 6$. We conclude that the series converges on $(-2, 6)$ (by Theorem 8.21, absolute convergence implies convergence). When $-\infty < x < -2$ or $6 < x < \infty$, we have $\rho > 1$, so the series diverges on these intervals (the terms of the series do not approach 0 as $k \to \infty$ and the Divergence Test applies).

➤ Either the Ratio Test or the Root Test works for the power series in Example 1b.

The Root Test does not give information about convergence at the endpoints $x = -2$ and $x = 6$, because at these points, the Root Test results in $\rho = 1$. To test for convergence at the endpoints, we substitute each endpoint into the series and carry out separate tests. At $x = -2$, the power series becomes

$$\sum_{k=0}^{\infty} \frac{(-1)^k(x-2)^k}{4^k} = \sum_{k=0}^{\infty} \frac{4^k}{4^k} \quad \text{Substitute } x = -2 \text{ and simplify.}$$

$$= \sum_{k=0}^{\infty} 1. \quad \text{Diverges by Divergence Test}$$

➤ The Ratio and Root Tests determine the radius of convergence conclusively. However, the interval of convergence is not determined until the endpoints are tested.

The series clearly diverges at the left endpoint. At $x = 6$, the power series is

$$\sum_{k=0}^{\infty} \frac{(-1)^k(x-2)^k}{4^k} = \sum_{k=0}^{\infty} (-1)^k \frac{4^k}{4^k} \quad \text{Substitute } x = 6 \text{ and simplify.}$$

$$= \sum_{k=0}^{\infty} (-1)^k. \quad \text{Diverges by Divergence Test}$$

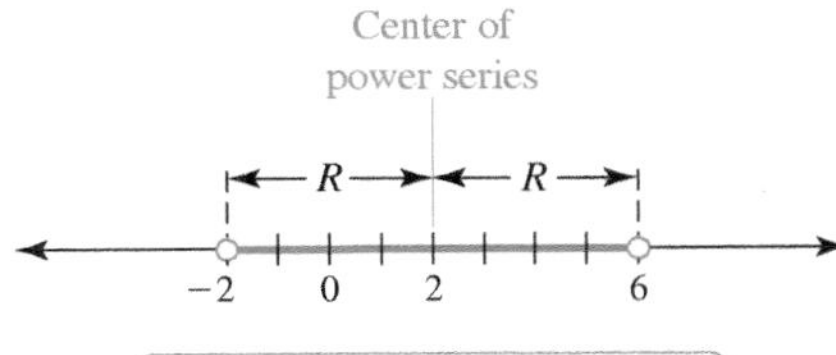

Figure 9.16

This series also diverges at the right endpoint. Therefore, the interval of convergence is $(-2, 6)$, excluding the endpoints (Figure 9.16), and the radius of convergence is $R = 4$.

c. In this case, the Ratio Test is preferable:

$$\begin{aligned} r &= \lim_{k\to\infty} \frac{|(k+1)!\,x^{k+1}|}{|k!\,x^k|} && \text{Ratio Test for absolute convergence} \\ &= |x| \lim_{k\to\infty} \frac{(k+1)!}{k!} && \text{Simplify.} \\ &= |x| \lim_{k\to\infty} (k+1) && \text{Simplify.} \\ &= \infty. && \text{If } x \neq 0 \end{aligned}$$

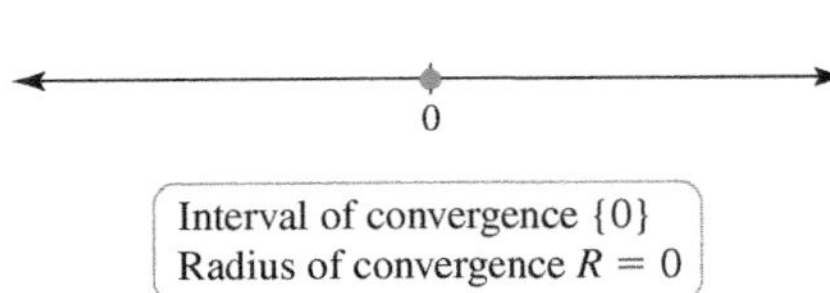

Figure 9.17

We see that $r > 1$ for all $x \neq 0$, so the series diverges on $(-\infty, 0)$ and $(0, \infty)$.

The only way to satisfy $r < 1$ is to take $x = 0$, in which case the power series has a value of 0. The interval of convergence of the power series consists of the single point $x = 0$ (Figure 9.17), and the radius of convergence is $R = 0$.

Related Exercises 9–28 ◀

Example 1 illustrates the three common types of intervals of convergence, which are summarized in the following theorem (see Appendix B for a proof).

➤ Theorem 9.3 implies that the interval of convergence is symmetric about the center of the series; the radius of convergence R is determined by analyzing r from the Ratio Test (or ρ from the Root Test). The theorem says nothing about convergence at the endpoints. For example, the intervals of convergence $(2, 6)$, $(2, 6]$, $[2, 6)$, and $[2, 6]$ all have a radius of convergence of $R = 2$.

> **THEOREM 9.3 Convergence of Power Series**
>
> A power series $\sum_{k=0}^{\infty} c_k(x - a)^k$ centered at a converges in one of three ways:
>
> 1. The series converges for all x, in which case the interval of convergence is $(-\infty, \infty)$ and the radius of convergence is $R = \infty$.
> 2. There is a real number $R > 0$ such that the series converges for $|x - a| < R$ and diverges for $|x - a| > R$, in which case the radius of convergence is R.
> 3. The series converges only at a, in which case the radius of convergence is $R = 0$.

QUICK CHECK 2 What are the interval and radius of convergence of the geometric series $\sum x^k$? ◄

EXAMPLE 2 Interval and radius of convergence Use the Ratio Test to find the radius and interval of convergence of $\sum_{k=1}^{\infty} \frac{(x - 2)^k}{\sqrt{k}}$.

➤ The power series in Example 2 could also be analyzed using the Root Test.

SOLUTION

$$\begin{aligned} r &= \lim_{k\to\infty} \frac{|(x - 2)^{k+1}/\sqrt{k + 1}|}{|(x - 2)^k/\sqrt{k}|} && \text{Ratio Test for absolute convergence} \\ &= |x - 2| \lim_{k\to\infty} \sqrt{\frac{k}{k + 1}} && \text{Simplify.} \\ &= |x - 2| \underbrace{\sqrt{\lim_{k\to\infty} \frac{k}{k + 1}}}_{1} && \text{Limit Law} \\ &= |x - 2| && \text{Limit equals 1.} \end{aligned}$$

The series converges absolutely (and therefore converges) for all x such that $r < 1$, which implies $|x - 2| < 1$, or $1 < x < 3$. On the intervals $-\infty < x < 1$ and $3 < x < \infty$, we have $r > 1$ and the series diverges.

We now test the endpoints. Substituting $x = 1$ gives the series

$$\sum_{k=1}^{\infty} \frac{(x - 2)^k}{\sqrt{k}} = \sum_{k=1}^{\infty} \frac{(-1)^k}{\sqrt{k}}.$$

This series converges by the Alternating Series Test (the terms of the series decrease in magnitude and approach 0 as $k \to \infty$). Substituting $x = 3$ gives the series

$$\sum_{k=1}^{\infty} \frac{(x - 2)^k}{\sqrt{k}} = \sum_{k=1}^{\infty} \frac{1}{\sqrt{k}},$$

which is a divergent p-series. We conclude that the interval of convergence is $1 \le x < 3$ and the radius of convergence is $R = 1$ (Figure 9.18).

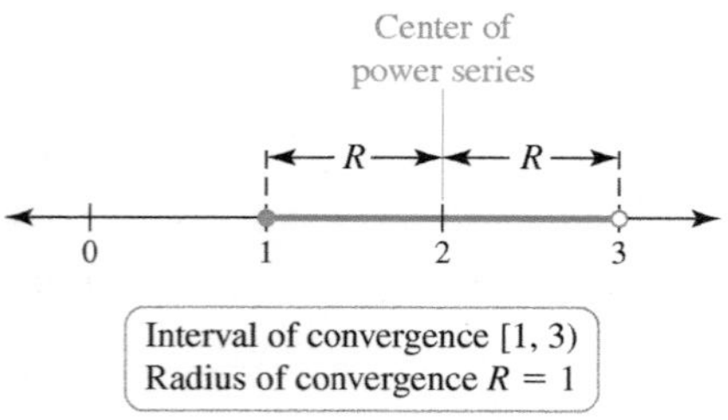

Center of power series

R R

0 1 2 3

Interval of convergence $[1, 3)$
Radius of convergence $R = 1$

Figure 9.18

Related Exercises 9–28 ◄

Combining Power Series

A power series defines a function on its interval of convergence. When power series are combined algebraically, new functions are defined. The following theorem, stated without proof, gives three common ways to combine power series.

➤ New power series can also be defined as the product and quotient of power series. The calculation of the coefficients of such series is more challenging (Exercise 75).

➤ Theorem 9.4 also applies to power series centered at points other than $x = 0$. Property 1 applies directly; Properties 2 and 3 apply with slight modifications.

THEOREM 9.4 Combining Power Series
Suppose the power series $\sum c_k x^k$ and $\sum d_k x^k$ converge to $f(x)$ and $g(x)$, respectively, on an interval I.

1. **Sum and difference:** The power series $\sum (c_k \pm d_k)x^k$ converges to $f(x) \pm g(x)$ on I.
2. **Multiplication by a power:** Suppose m is an integer such that $k + m \geq 0$ for all terms of the power series $x^m \sum c_k x^k = \sum c_k x^{k+m}$. This series converges to $x^m f(x)$ for all $x \neq 0$ in I. When $x = 0$, the series converges to $\lim_{x \to 0} x^m f(x)$.
3. **Composition:** If $h(x) = bx^m$, where m is a positive integer and b is a nonzero real number, the power series $\sum c_k (h(x))^k$ converges to the composite function $f(h(x))$, for all x such that $h(x)$ is in I.

EXAMPLE 3 Combining power series Given the geometric series

$$\frac{1}{1 - x} = \sum_{k=0}^{\infty} x^k = 1 + x + x^2 + x^3 + \cdots, \qquad \text{for } |x| < 1,$$

find the power series and interval of convergence for the following functions.

a. $\dfrac{x^5}{1 - x}$ **b.** $\dfrac{1}{1 - 2x}$ **c.** $\dfrac{1}{1 + x^2}$

SOLUTION

a.
$$\begin{aligned}\frac{x^5}{1 - x} &= x^5 (1 + x + x^2 + \cdots) \qquad \text{Theorem 9.4, Property 2}\\ &= x^5 + x^6 + x^7 + \cdots\\ &= \sum_{k=0}^{\infty} x^{k+5}\end{aligned}$$

This geometric series has a ratio $r = x$ and converges when $|r| = |x| < 1$. The interval of convergence is $|x| < 1$.

b. We substitute $2x$ for x in the power series for $\dfrac{1}{1 - x}$:

$$\begin{aligned}\frac{1}{1 - 2x} &= 1 + (2x) + (2x)^2 + \cdots \qquad \text{Theorem 9.4, Property 3}\\ &= \sum_{k=0}^{\infty} (2x)^k.\end{aligned}$$

This geometric series has a ratio $r = 2x$ and converges provided $|r| = |2x| < 1$ or $|x| < \frac{1}{2}$. The interval of convergence is $|x| < \frac{1}{2}$.

c. We substitute $-x^2$ for x in the power series for $\dfrac{1}{1 - x}$:

$$\begin{aligned}\frac{1}{1 + x^2} &= 1 + (-x^2) + (-x^2)^2 + \cdots \qquad \text{Theorem 9.4, Property 3}\\ &= 1 - x^2 + x^4 - \cdots\\ &= \sum_{k=0}^{\infty} (-1)^k x^{2k}.\end{aligned}$$

This geometric series has a ratio of $r = -x^2$ and converges provided $|r| = |-x^2| = |x^2| < 1$ or $|x| < 1$.

Related Exercises 29–40 ◀

Differentiating and Integrating Power Series

Some properties of polynomials carry over to power series, but others do not. For example, a polynomial is defined for all values of x, whereas a power series is defined only on its interval of convergence. In general, the properties of polynomials carry over to power series when the power series is restricted to its interval of convergence. The following result illustrates this principle.

➤ Theorem 9.5 makes no claim about the convergence of the differentiated or integrated series at the endpoints of the interval of convergence.

THEOREM 9.5 Differentiating and Integrating Power Series
Suppose the power series $\sum c_k(x-a)^k$ converges for $|x-a| < R$ and defines a function f on that interval.

1. Then f is differentiable (which implies continuous) for $|x-a| < R$, and f' is found by differentiating the power series for f term by term; that is,

$$f'(x) = \sum k c_k (x-a)^{k-1},$$

for $|x-a| < R$.

2. The indefinite integral of f is found by integrating the power series for f term by term; that is,

$$\int f(x)dx = \sum c_k \frac{(x-a)^{k+1}}{k+1} + C,$$

for $|x-a| < R$, where C is an arbitrary constant.

The proof of this theorem requires advanced ideas and is omitted. However, some discussion is in order before turning to examples. The statements in Theorem 9.5 about term-by-term differentiation and integration say two things. First, the differentiated and integrated power series converge, provided x belongs to the interior of the interval of convergence. But the theorem claims more than convergence. According to the theorem, the differentiated and integrated power series converge to the derivative and indefinite integral of f, respectively, on the interior of the interval of convergence. Let's use this theorem to develop new power series.

EXAMPLE 4 Differentiating and integrating power series Consider the geometric series

$$f(x) = \frac{1}{1-x} = \sum_{k=0}^{\infty} x^k = 1 + x + x^2 + x^3 + \cdots, \quad \text{for } |x| < 1.$$

a. Differentiate this series term by term to find the power series for f' and identify the function it represents.

b. Integrate this series term by term and identify the function it represents.

SOLUTION

a. We know that $f'(x) = (1-x)^{-2}$. Differentiating the series, we find that

$$\begin{aligned} f'(x) &= \frac{d}{dx}(1 + x + x^2 + x^3 + \cdots) && \text{Differentiate the power series for } f. \\ &= 1 + 2x + 3x^2 + \cdots && \text{Differentiate term by term.} \\ &= \sum_{k=0}^{\infty}(k+1)x^k. && \text{Summation notation} \end{aligned}$$

Therefore, on the interval $|x| < 1$,

$$f'(x) = (1-x)^{-2} = \sum_{k=0}^{\infty}(k+1)x^k.$$

Theorem 9.5 makes no claim about convergence of the differentiated series to f' at the endpoints. In this case, substituting $x = \pm 1$ into the power series for f' reveals that the series diverges at both endpoints.

b. Integrating f and integrating the power series term by term, we have

$$\int \frac{dx}{1 - x} = \int (1 + x + x^2 + x^3 + \cdots)\, dx,$$

which implies that

$$-\ln|1 - x| = x + \frac{x^2}{2} + \frac{x^3}{3} + \frac{x^4}{4} + \cdots + C,$$

where C is an arbitrary constant. Notice that the left side is 0 when $x = 0$. The right side is 0 when $x = 0$ provided we choose $C = 0$. Because $|x| < 1$, the absolute value sign on the left side may be removed. Multiplying both sides by -1, we have a series representation for $\ln(1 - x)$:

$$\ln(1 - x) = -x - \frac{x^2}{2} - \frac{x^3}{3} - \frac{x^4}{4} - \cdots = -\sum_{k=1}^{\infty} \frac{x^k}{k}.$$

It is interesting to test the endpoints of the interval $|x| < 1$. When $x = 1$, the series is (a multiple of) the divergent harmonic series, and when $x = -1$, the series is the convergent alternating harmonic series (Section 8.6). So the interval of convergence is $-1 \leq x < 1$. Although we know the series converges at $x = -1$, Theorem 9.5 guarantees convergence to $\ln(1 - x)$ only at the interior points. We cannot use Theorem 9.5 to claim that the series converges to $\ln 2$ at $x = -1$. In fact, it does, as shown in Section 9.3.

Related Exercises 41–46 ◄

QUICK CHECK 3 Use the result of Example 4 to write a series representation for $\ln \frac{1}{2} = -\ln 2$. ◄

EXAMPLE 5 **Functions to power series** Find power series representations centered at 0 for the following functions and give their intervals of convergence.

a. $\tan^{-1} x$ **b.** $\ln\left(\frac{1 + x}{1 - x}\right)$

SOLUTION In both cases, we work with known power series and use differentiation, integration, and other combinations.

a. The key is to recall that

$$\int \frac{dx}{1 + x^2} = \tan^{-1} x + C$$

and that, by Example 3c,

$$\frac{1}{1 + x^2} = 1 - x^2 + x^4 - \cdots, \qquad \text{provided } |x| < 1.$$

We now integrate both sides of this last expression:

$$\int \frac{dx}{1 + x^2} = \int (1 - x^2 + x^4 - \cdots)\, dx,$$

which implies that

$$\tan^{-1} x = x - \frac{x^3}{3} + \frac{x^5}{5} - \cdots + C.$$

Substituting $x = 0$ and noting that $\tan^{-1} 0 = 0$, the two sides of this equation agree provided we choose $C = 0$. Therefore,

$$\tan^{-1} x = x - \frac{x^3}{3} + \frac{x^5}{5} - \cdots = \sum_{k=0}^{\infty} \frac{(-1)^k x^{2k+1}}{2k + 1}.$$

➤ Again, Theorem 9.5 does not guarantee that the power series in Example 5a converges to $\tan^{-1} x$ at $x = \pm 1$. In fact, it does.

By Theorem 9.5, this power series converges to $\tan^{-1} x$ for $|x| < 1$. Testing the endpoints separately, we find that it also converges at $x = \pm 1$. Therefore, the interval of convergence is $[-1, 1]$.

b. We have already seen (Example 4) that

$$\ln (1 - x) = -x - \frac{x^2}{2} - \frac{x^3}{3} - \cdots.$$

➤ Nicolaus Mercator (1620–1687) and Sir Isaac Newton (1642–1727) independently derived the power series for $\ln (1 + x)$, which is called the *Mercator series*.

Replacing x with $-x$ (Property 3 of Theorem 9.4), we have

$$\ln (1 - (-x)) = \ln (1 + x) = x - \frac{x^2}{2} + \frac{x^3}{3} - \cdots.$$

Subtracting these two power series gives

$$\begin{aligned}
\ln \left(\frac{1 + x}{1 - x} \right) &= \ln (1 + x) - \ln (1 - x) && \text{Properties of logarithms} \\
&= \underbrace{\left(x - \frac{x^2}{2} + \frac{x^3}{3} - \cdots \right)}_{\ln (1 + x)} - \underbrace{\left(-x - \frac{x^2}{2} - \frac{x^3}{3} - \cdots \right)}_{\ln (1 - x)}, && \text{for } |x| < 1 \\
&= 2\left(x + \frac{x^3}{3} + \frac{x^5}{5} + \cdots \right) && \text{Combine; use Property 1 of Theorem 9.4.} \\
&= 2\sum_{k=0}^{\infty} \frac{x^{2k+1}}{2k + 1}. && \text{Summation notation}
\end{aligned}$$

This power series is the difference of two power series, both of which converge on the interval $|x| < 1$. Therefore, by Theorem 9.4, the new series also converges on $|x| < 1$.

Related Exercises 47–52 ◀

QUICK CHECK 4 Verify that the power series in Example 5b does not converge at the endpoints $x = \pm 1$. ◀

If you look carefully, every example in this section is ultimately based on the geometric series. Using this single series, we were able to develop power series for many other functions. Imagine what we could do with a few more basic power series. The following section accomplishes precisely that end. There, we discover power series for many of the standard functions of calculus.

SECTION 9.2 EXERCISES

Review Questions

1. Write the first four terms of a power series with coefficients c_0, c_1, c_2, and c_3 centered at 0.
2. Write the first four terms of a power series with coefficients c_0, c_1, c_2, and c_3 centered at 3.
3. What tests are used to determine the radius of convergence of a power series?
4. Explain why a power series is tested for *absolute* convergence.
5. Do the interval and radius of convergence of a power series change when the series is differentiated or integrated? Explain.
6. What is the radius of convergence of the power series $\sum c_k (x/2)^k$ if the radius of convergence of $\sum c_k x^k$ is R?
7. What is the interval of convergence of the power series $\sum (4x)^k$?
8. How are the radii of convergence of the power series $\sum c_k x^k$ and $\sum (-1)^k c_k x^k$ related?

Basic Skills

9–28. Interval and radius of convergence *Determine the radius of convergence of the following power series. Then test the endpoints to determine the interval of convergence.*

9. $\sum (2x)^k$

10. $\sum \frac{(2x)^k}{k!}$

11. $\sum \frac{(x-1)^k}{k}$

12. $\sum \frac{(x-1)^k}{k!}$

13. $\sum (kx)^k$

14. $\sum k!\,(x-10)^k$

15. $\sum \sin^k\left(\frac{1}{k}\right)x^k$

16. $\sum \frac{2^k(x-3)^k}{k}$

17. $\sum \left(\frac{x}{3}\right)^k$

18. $\sum (-1)^k \frac{x^k}{5^k}$

19. $\sum \frac{x^k}{k^k}$

20. $\sum (-1)^k \frac{k(x-4)^k}{2^k}$

21. $\sum \frac{k^2 x^{2k}}{k!}$

22. $\sum k\,(x-1)^k$

23. $\sum \frac{x^{2k+1}}{3^{k-1}}$

24. $\sum \left(-\frac{x}{10}\right)^{2k}$

25. $\sum \frac{(x-1)^k k^k}{(k+1)^k}$

26. $\sum \frac{(-2)^k (x+3)^k}{3^{k+1}}$

27. $\sum \frac{k^{20} x^k}{(2k+1)!}$

28. $\sum (-1)^k \frac{x^{3k}}{27^k}$

29–34. Combining power series *Use the geometric series*

$$f(x) = \frac{1}{1-x} = \sum_{k=0}^{\infty} x^k, \quad \text{for } |x| < 1,$$

to find the power series representation for the following functions (centered at 0). Give the interval of convergence of the new series.

29. $f(3x) = \frac{1}{1-3x}$

30. $g(x) = \frac{x^3}{1-x}$

31. $h(x) = \frac{2x^3}{1-x}$

32. $f(x^3) = \frac{1}{1-x^3}$

33. $p(x) = \frac{4x^{12}}{1-x}$

34. $f(-4x) = \frac{1}{1+4x}$

35–40. Combining power series *Use the power series representation*

$$f(x) = \ln(1-x) = -\sum_{k=1}^{\infty} \frac{x^k}{k}, \quad \text{for } -1 \le x < 1,$$

to find the power series for the following functions (centered at 0). Give the interval of convergence of the new series.

35. $f(3x) = \ln(1-3x)$

36. $g(x) = x^3 \ln(1-x)$

37. $h(x) = x\ln(1-x)$

38. $f(x^3) = \ln(1-x^3)$

39. $p(x) = 2x^6 \ln(1-x)$

40. $f(-4x) = \ln(1+4x)$

41–46. Differentiating and integrating power series *Find the power series representation for g centered at 0 by differentiating or integrating the power series for f (perhaps more than once). Give the interval of convergence for the resulting series.*

41. $g(x) = \frac{2}{(1-2x)^2}$ using $f(x) = \frac{1}{1-2x}$

42. $g(x) = \frac{1}{(1-x)^3}$ using $f(x) = \frac{1}{1-x}$

43. $g(x) = \frac{1}{(1-x)^4}$ using $f(x) = \frac{1}{1-x}$

44. $g(x) = \frac{x}{(1+x^2)^2}$ using $f(x) = \frac{1}{1+x^2}$

45. $g(x) = \ln(1-3x)$ using $f(x) = \frac{1}{1-3x}$

46. $g(x) = \ln(1+x^2)$ using $f(x) = \frac{x}{1+x^2}$

47–52. Functions to power series *Find power series representations centered at 0 for the following functions using known power series. Give the interval of convergence for the resulting series.*

47. $f(x) = \frac{1}{1+x^2}$

48. $f(x) = \frac{1}{1-x^4}$

49. $f(x) = \frac{3}{3+x}$

50. $f(x) = \ln\sqrt{1-x^2}$

51. $f(x) = \ln\sqrt{4-x^2}$

52. $f(x) = \tan^{-1}(4x^2)$

Further Explorations

53. **Explain why or why not** Determine whether the following statements are true and give an explanation or counterexample.
    a. The interval of convergence of the power series $\sum c_k (x-3)^k$ could be $(-2, 8)$.
    b. The series $\sum (-2x)^k$ converges on the interval $-\frac{1}{2} < x < \frac{1}{2}$.
    c. If $f(x) = \sum c_k x^k$ on the interval $|x| < 1$, then $f(x^2) = \sum c_k x^{2k}$ on the interval $|x| < 1$.
    d. If $f(x) = \sum c_k x^k = 0$, for all x on an interval $(-a, a)$, then $c_k = 0$, for all k.

54. **Radius of convergence** Find the radius of convergence of $\sum \left(1 + \frac{1}{k}\right)^{k^2} x^k$.

55. **Radius of convergence** Find the radius of convergence of $\sum \frac{k!x^k}{k^k}$.

56–59. Summation notation *Write the following power series in summation (sigma) notation.*

56. $1 + \frac{x}{2} + \frac{x^2}{4} + \frac{x^3}{6} + \cdots$

57. $1 - \frac{x}{2} + \frac{x^2}{3} - \frac{x^3}{4} + \cdots$

58. $x - \frac{x^3}{4} + \frac{x^5}{9} - \frac{x^7}{16} + \cdots$

59. $-\frac{x^2}{1!} + \frac{x^4}{2!} - \frac{x^6}{3!} + \frac{x^8}{4!} - \cdots$

60. **Scaling power series** If the power series $f(x) = \sum c_k x^k$ has an interval of convergence of $|x| < R$, what is the interval of convergence of the power series for $f(ax)$, where $a \neq 0$ is a real number?

61. **Shifting power series** If the power series $f(x) = \sum c_k x^k$ has an interval of convergence of $|x| < R$, what is the interval of convergence of the power series for $f(x-a)$, where $a \neq 0$ is a real number?

62–67. Series to functions *Find the function represented by the following series and find the interval of convergence of the series. (Not all these series are power series.)*

62. $\sum_{k=0}^{\infty} (x^2+1)^{2k}$

63. $\sum_{k=0}^{\infty} (\sqrt{x}-2)^k$

64. $\sum_{k=1}^{\infty} \frac{x^{2k}}{4k}$

65. $\sum_{k=0}^{\infty} e^{-kx}$

66. $\sum_{k=1}^{\infty} \frac{(x-2)^k}{3^{2k}}$

67. $\sum_{k=0}^{\infty} \left(\frac{x^2-1}{3}\right)^k$

68. A useful substitution Replace x with $x - 1$ in the series $\ln(1 + x) = \sum_{k=1}^{\infty} \frac{(-1)^{k+1}x^k}{k}$ to obtain a power series for $\ln x$ centered at $x = 1$. What is the interval of convergence for the new power series?

69–72. Exponential function *In Section 9.3, we show that the power series for the exponential function centered at 0 is*

$$e^x = \sum_{k=0}^{\infty} \frac{x^k}{k!}, \quad \text{for } -\infty < x < \infty.$$

Use the methods of this section to find the power series for the following functions. Give the interval of convergence for the resulting series.

69. $f(x) = e^{-x}$

70. $f(x) = e^{2x}$

71. $f(x) = e^{-3x}$

72. $f(x) = x^2e^x$

Additional Exercises

73. Powers of x multiplied by a power series Prove that if $f(x) = \sum_{k=0}^{\infty} c_k x^k$ converges with radius of convergence R, then the power series for $x^m f(x)$ also converges with radius of convergence R, for positive integers m.

T 74. Remainders Let

$$f(x) = \sum_{k=0}^{\infty} x^k = \frac{1}{1 - x} \quad \text{and} \quad S_n(x) = \sum_{k=0}^{n-1} x^k.$$

The remainder in truncating the power series after n terms is $R_n(x) = f(x) - S_n(x)$, which depends on x.

a. Show that $R_n(x) = x^n/(1 - x)$.

b. Graph the remainder function on the interval $|x| < 1$ for $n = 1, 2, 3$. Discuss and interpret the graph. Where on the interval is $|R_n(x)|$ largest? Smallest?

c. For fixed n, minimize $|R_n(x)|$ with respect to x. Does the result agree with the observations in part (b)?

d. Let $N(x)$ be the number of terms required to reduce $|R_n(x)|$ to less than 10^{-6}. Graph the function $N(x)$ on the interval $|x| < 1$. Discuss and interpret the graph.

75. Product of power series Let

$$f(x) = \sum_{k=0}^{\infty} c_k x^k \quad \text{and} \quad g(x) = \sum_{k=0}^{\infty} d_k x^k.$$

a. Multiply the power series together as if they were polynomials, collecting all terms that are multiples of 1, x, and x^2. Write the first three terms of the product $f(x)g(x)$.

b. Find a general expression for the coefficient of x^n in the product series, for $n = 0, 1, 2, \ldots$.

76. Inverse sine Given the power series

$$\frac{1}{\sqrt{1 - x^2}} = 1 + \frac{1}{2}x^2 + \frac{1 \cdot 3}{2 \cdot 4}x^4 + \frac{1 \cdot 3 \cdot 5}{2 \cdot 4 \cdot 6}x^6 + \cdots,$$

for $-1 < x < 1$, find the power series for $f(x) = \sin^{-1} x$ centered at 0.

T 77. Computing with power series Consider the following function and its power series:

$$f(x) = \frac{1}{(1 - x)^2} = \sum_{k=1}^{\infty} kx^{k-1}, \quad \text{for } -1 < x < 1.$$

a. Let $S_n(x)$ be the sum of the first n terms of the series. With $n = 5$ and $n = 10$, graph $f(x)$ and $S_n(x)$ at the sample points $x = -0.9, -0.8, \ldots, -0.1, 0, 0.1, \ldots, 0.8, 0.9$ (two graphs). Where is the difference in the graphs the greatest?

b. What value of n is needed to guarantee that $|f(x) - S_n(x)| < 0.01$ at all of the sample points?

QUICK CHECK ANSWERS

1. $g(0) = 0$ **2.** $|x| < 1, R = 1$ **3.** Substituting $x = 1/2$, $\ln(1/2) = -\ln 2 = -\sum_{k=1}^{\infty} \frac{1}{2^k k}$ ◄

9.3 Taylor Series

In the preceding section, we saw that a power series represents a function on its interval of convergence. This section explores the opposite question: Given a function, what is its power series representation? We have already made significant progress in answering this question because we know how Taylor polynomials are used to approximate functions. We now extend Taylor polynomials to produce power series—called *Taylor series*—that provide series representations for functions.

Taylor Series for a Function

Suppose a function f has derivatives $f^{(k)}(a)$ of *all* orders at the point a. If we write the nth-order Taylor polynomial for f centered at a and allow n to increase indefinitely, a power series is obtained:

$$\underbrace{c_0 + c_1(x - a) + c_2(x - a)^2 + \cdots + c_n(x - a)^n}_{\text{Taylor polynomial of order } n} + \underbrace{\cdots}_{n \to \infty} = \sum_{k=0}^{\infty} c_k(x - a)^k.$$

The coefficients of the Taylor polynomial are given by

$$c_k = \frac{f^{(k)}(a)}{k!}, \quad \text{for } k = 0, 1, 2, \ldots.$$

➤ Maclaurin series are named after the Scottish mathematician Colin Maclaurin (1698–1746), who described them (with credit to Taylor) in a textbook in 1742.

These coefficients are also the coefficients of the power series, which is called the *Taylor series for f centered at a*. It is the natural extension of the set of Taylor polynomials for f at a. The special case of a Taylor series centered at 0 is called a *Maclaurin series*.

DEFINITION Taylor/Maclaurin Series for a Function

Suppose the function f has derivatives of all orders on an interval centered at the point a. The **Taylor series for f centered at a** is

$$f(a) + f'(a)(x-a) + \frac{f''(a)}{2!}(x-a)^2 + \frac{f^{(3)}(a)}{3!}(x-a)^3 + \cdots$$

$$= \sum_{k=0}^{\infty} \frac{f^{(k)}(a)}{k!}(x-a)^k.$$

A Taylor series centered at 0 is called a **Maclaurin series**.

For the Taylor series to be useful, we need to know two things:

➤ There are unusual cases in which the Taylor series for a function converges to a different function (Exercise 90).

- the values of x for which the Taylor series converges, and
- the values of x for which the Taylor series for f *equals* f.

The second question is subtle and is postponed for a few pages. For now, we find the Taylor series for f centered at a point, but we refrain from saying $f(x)$ equals the power series.

QUICK CHECK 1 Verify that if the Taylor series for f centered at a is evaluated at $x = a$, then the Taylor series equals $f(a)$. ◄

EXAMPLE 1 Maclaurin series and convergence Find the Maclaurin series (which is the Taylor series centered at 0) for the following functions. Find the interval of convergence.

a. $f(x) = \cos x$ **b.** $f(x) = \dfrac{1}{1-x}$

SOLUTION The procedure for finding the coefficients of a Taylor series is the same as for Taylor polynomials; most of the work is computing the derivatives of f.

a. The Maclaurin series has the form

$$\sum_{k=0}^{\infty} c_k x^k, \quad \text{where } c_k = \frac{f^{(k)}(0)}{k!}, \quad \text{for } k = 0, 1, 2, \ldots.$$

We evaluate derivatives of $f(x) = \cos x$ at $x = 0$.

$$\begin{aligned}
f(x) &= \cos x \Rightarrow f(0) = 1\\
f'(x) &= -\sin x \Rightarrow f'(0) = 0\\
f''(x) &= -\cos x \Rightarrow f''(0) = -1\\
f'''(x) &= \sin x \Rightarrow f'''(0) = 0\\
f^{(4)}(x) &= \cos x \Rightarrow f^{(4)}(0) = 1\\
&\vdots \qquad\qquad\quad \vdots
\end{aligned}$$

➤ In Example 1a, we note that both $\cos x$ and its Maclaurin series are even functions. Be cautions with this observation. A Taylor series for an even function centered at a point different from 0 may be even, odd, or neither. A similar behavior occurs with odd functions.

Because the odd-order derivatives are zero, $c_k = \frac{f^{(k)}(0)}{k!} = 0$ when k is odd. Using the even-order derivatives, we have

$$c_0 = f(0) = 1, \qquad c_2 = \frac{f^{(2)}(0)}{2!} = -\frac{1}{2!},$$
$$c_4 = \frac{f^{(4)}(0)}{4!} = \frac{1}{4!}, \qquad c_6 = \frac{f^{(6)}(0)}{6!} = -\frac{1}{6!},$$

and in general, $c_{2k} = \frac{(-1)^k}{(2k)!}$. Therefore, the Maclaurin series for f is

$$1 - \frac{x^2}{2!} + \frac{x^4}{4!} - \frac{x^6}{6!} + \cdots = \sum_{k=0}^{\infty} \frac{(-1)^k}{(2k)!} x^{2k}.$$

Notice that this series contains all the Taylor polynomials. In this case, it consists only of even powers of x, reflecting the fact that $\cos x$ is an even function.

For what values of x does the series converge? As discussed in Section 9.2, we apply the Ratio Test to $\sum_{k=0}^{\infty} \left| \frac{(-1)^k}{(2k)!} x^{2k} \right|$ to test for absolute convergence:

$$r = \lim_{k\to\infty} \left| \frac{(-1)^{k+1} x^{2(k+1)}/(2(k+1))!}{(-1)^k x^{2k}/(2k)!} \right| \qquad r = \lim_{k\to\infty} \left| \frac{a_{k+1}}{a_k} \right|$$
$$= \lim_{k\to\infty} \left| \frac{x^2}{(2k+2)(2k+1)} \right| = 0. \qquad \text{Simplify and take the limit with } x \text{ fixed.}$$

➤ Recall that

$$(2k + 2)! = (2k + 2)(2k + 1)(2k)!.$$

Therefore, $\frac{(2k)!}{(2k+2)!} = \frac{1}{(2k+2)(2k+1)}$.

In this case, $r < 1$ for all x, so the Maclaurin series converges absolutely for all x, which implies (by Theorem 8.21) that the series converges for all x. We conclude that the interval of convergence is $-\infty < x < \infty$.

b. We proceed in a similar way with $f(x) = 1/(1 - x)$ by evaluating the derivatives of f at 0:

$$f(x) = \frac{1}{1-x} \Rightarrow f(0) = 1,$$
$$f'(x) = \frac{1}{(1-x)^2} \Rightarrow f'(0) = 1,$$
$$f''(x) = \frac{2}{(1-x)^3} \Rightarrow f''(0) = 2!,$$
$$f'''(x) = \frac{3 \cdot 2}{(1-x)^4} \Rightarrow f'''(0) = 3!,$$
$$f^{(4)}(x) = \frac{4 \cdot 3 \cdot 2}{(1-x)^5} \Rightarrow f^{(4)}(0) = 4!,$$

and in general, $f^{(k)}(0) = k!$. Therefore, the Maclaurin series coefficients are $c_k = \frac{f^{(k)}(0)}{k!} = \frac{k!}{k!} = 1$, for $k = 0, 1, 2, \ldots$. The series for f centered at 0 is

$$1 + x + x^2 + x^3 + \cdots = \sum_{k=0}^{\infty} x^k.$$

This power series is familiar! The Maclaurin series for $f(x) = 1/(1 - x)$ is a geometric series. We could apply the Ratio Test, but we have already demonstrated that this series converges for $|x| < 1$.

Related Exercises 9–20 ◀

QUICK CHECK 2 Based on Example 1b, what is the Taylor series for $f(x) = (1 + x)^{-1}$? ◀

The preceding example has an important lesson. *There is only one power series representation for a given function about a given point; however, there may be several ways to find it.*

EXAMPLE 2 **Center other than 0** Find the first four nonzero terms of the Taylor series for $f(x) = \sqrt[3]{x}$ centered at 8.

SOLUTION Notice that f has derivatives of all orders at $x = 8$. The Taylor series centered at 8 has the form

$$\sum_{k=0}^{\infty} c_k(x - 8)^k, \quad \text{where } c_k = \frac{f^{(k)}(8)}{k!}.$$

Next, we evaluate derivatives:

$$f(x) = x^{1/3} \Rightarrow f(8) = 2,$$

$$f'(x) = \frac{1}{3}x^{-2/3} \Rightarrow f'(8) = \frac{1}{12},$$

$$f''(x) = -\frac{2}{9}x^{-5/3} \Rightarrow f''(8) = -\frac{1}{144}, \text{ and}$$

$$f'''(x) = \frac{10}{27}x^{-8/3} \Rightarrow f'''(8) = \frac{5}{3456}.$$

We now assemble the power series:

$$2 + \frac{1}{12}(x - 8) + \frac{1}{2!}\left(-\frac{1}{144}\right)(x - 8)^2 + \frac{1}{3!}\left(\frac{5}{3456}\right)(x - 8)^3 + \cdots$$

$$= 2 + \frac{1}{12}(x - 8) - \frac{1}{288}(x - 8)^2 + \frac{5}{20{,}736}(x - 8)^3 + \cdots.$$

Related Exercises 21–28 ◄

EXAMPLE 3 **Manipulating Maclaurin series** Let $f(x) = e^x$.

a. Find the Maclaurin series for f.

b. Find its interval of convergence.

c. Use the Maclaurin series for e^x to find the Maclaurin series for the functions $x^4 e^x$, e^{-2x}, and e^{-x^2}.

SOLUTION

a. The coefficients of the Taylor polynomials for $f(x) = e^x$ centered at 0 are $c_k = 1/k!$ (Example 3, Section 9.1). They are also the coefficients of the Maclaurin series. Therefore, the Maclaurin series for e^x is

$$1 + \frac{x}{1!} + \frac{x^2}{2!} + \cdots + \frac{x^n}{n!} + \cdots = \sum_{k=0}^{\infty} \frac{x^k}{k!}.$$

b. By the Ratio Test,

$$r = \lim_{k\to\infty} \left| \frac{x^{k+1}/(k + 1)!}{x^k/k!} \right| \quad \text{Substitute } (k + 1)\text{st and } k\text{th terms.}$$

$$= \lim_{k\to\infty} \left| \frac{x}{k + 1} \right| = 0. \quad \text{Simplify; take the limit with } x \text{ fixed.}$$

Because $r < 1$ for all x, the interval of convergence is $-\infty < x < \infty$.

c. As stated in Theorem 9.4, power series may be added, multiplied by powers of x, or composed with functions on their intervals of convergence. Therefore, the Maclaurin series for $x^4 e^x$ is

$$x^4 \sum_{k=0}^{\infty} \frac{x^k}{k!} = \sum_{k=0}^{\infty} \frac{x^{k+4}}{k!} = x^4 + \frac{x^5}{1!} + \frac{x^6}{2!} + \cdots + \frac{x^{k+4}}{k!} + \cdots.$$

Similarly, e^{-2x} is the composition $f(-2x)$. Replacing x with $-2x$ in the Maclaurin series for f, the series representation for e^{-2x} is

$$\sum_{k=0}^{\infty} \frac{(-2x)^k}{k!} = \sum_{k=0}^{\infty} \frac{(-1)^k (2x)^k}{k!} = 1 - 2x + 2x^2 - \frac{4}{3}x^3 + \cdots.$$

The Maclaurin series for e^{-x^2} is obtained by replacing x with $-x^2$ in the power series for f. The resulting series is

$$\sum_{k=0}^{\infty} \frac{(-x^2)^k}{k!} = \sum_{k=0}^{\infty} \frac{(-1)^k x^{2k}}{k!} = 1 - x^2 + \frac{x^4}{2!} - \frac{x^6}{3!} + \cdots.$$

QUICK CHECK 3 Find the first three terms of the Maclaurin series for $2xe^x$ and e^{-x}. ◄

Because the interval of convergence of $f(x) = e^x$ is $-\infty < x < \infty$, the manipulations used to obtain the series for $x^4 e^x$, e^{-2x}, or e^{-x^2} do not change the interval of convergence. If in doubt about the interval of convergence of a new series, apply the Ratio Test.

Related Exercises 29–38 ◄

The Binomial Series

We know from algebra that if p is a positive integer, then $(1 + x)^p$ is a polynomial of degree p. In fact,

$$(1 + x)^p = \binom{p}{0} + \binom{p}{1}x + \binom{p}{2}x^2 + \cdots + \binom{p}{p}x^p,$$

where the binomial coefficients $\binom{p}{k}$ are defined as follows.

➤ For nonnegative integers p and k with $0 \le k \le p$, the binomial coefficients may also be defined as $\binom{p}{k} = \frac{p!}{k!(p-k)!}$, where $0! = 1$. The coefficients form the rows of Pascal's triangle. The coefficients of $(1 + x)^5$ form the sixth row of the triangle.

1
1 1
1 2 1
1 3 3 1
1 4 6 4 1
1 5 10 10 5 1

DEFINITION Binomial Coefficients

For real numbers p and integers $k \ge 1$,

$$\binom{p}{k} = \frac{p(p-1)(p-2)\cdots(p-k+1)}{k!}, \qquad \binom{p}{0} = 1.$$

For example,

$$(1 + x)^5 = \underbrace{\binom{5}{0}}_{1} + \underbrace{\binom{5}{1}}_{5}x + \underbrace{\binom{5}{2}}_{10}x^2 + \underbrace{\binom{5}{3}}_{10}x^3 + \underbrace{\binom{5}{4}}_{5}x^4 + \underbrace{\binom{5}{5}}_{1}x^5$$
$$= 1 + 5x + 10x^2 + 10x^3 + 5x^4 + x^5.$$

QUICK CHECK 4 Evaluate the binomial coefficients $\binom{-3}{2}$ and $\binom{\frac{1}{2}}{3}$. ◄

Our goal is to extend this idea to the functions $f(x) = (1 + x)^p$, where $p \ne 0$ is a real number. The result is a Taylor series called the *binomial series.*

THEOREM 9.6 Binomial Series

For real numbers $p \neq 0$, the Taylor series for $f(x) = (1 + x)^p$ centered at 0 is the **binomial series**

$$\sum_{k=0}^{\infty} \binom{p}{k} x^k = 1 + \sum_{k=1}^{\infty} \frac{p(p-1)(p-2)\cdots(p-k+1)}{k!} x^k$$
$$= 1 + px + \frac{p(p-1)}{2!}x^2 + \frac{p(p-1)(p-2)}{3!}x^3 + \cdots.$$

The series converges for $|x| < 1$ (and possibly at the endpoints, depending on p). If p is a nonnegative integer, the series terminates and results in a polynomial of degree p.

Proof: We seek a power series centered at 0 of the form

$$\sum_{k=0}^{\infty} c_k x^k, \quad \text{where } c_k = \frac{f^{(k)}(0)}{k!}, \quad \text{for } k = 0, 1, 2, \ldots.$$

➤ To evaluate $\binom{p}{k}$, start with p and successively subtract 1 until k factors are obtained; then take the product of these k factors and divide by $k!$. Recall that $\binom{p}{0} = 1$.

The job is to evaluate the derivatives of f at 0:

$$\begin{aligned}
f(x) &= (1+x)^p \Rightarrow f(0) = 1, \\
f'(x) &= p(1+x)^{p-1} \Rightarrow f'(0) = p, \\
f''(x) &= p(p-1)(1+x)^{p-2} \Rightarrow f''(0) = p(p-1), \text{ and} \\
f'''(x) &= p(p-1)(p-2)(1+x)^{p-3} \Rightarrow f'''(0) = p(p-1)(p-2).
\end{aligned}$$

A pattern emerges: The kth derivative $f^{(k)}(0)$ involves the k factors $p(p-1)(p-2)\cdots(p-k+1)$. In general, we have

$$f^{(k)}(0) = p(p-1)(p-2)\cdots(p-k+1).$$

Therefore,

$$c_k = \frac{f^{(k)}(0)}{k!} = \frac{p(p-1)(p-2)\cdots(p-k+1)}{k!} = \binom{p}{k}, \quad \text{for } k = 0, 1, 2, \ldots.$$

The Taylor series for $f(x) = (1 + x)^p$ centered at 0 is

$$\binom{p}{0} + \binom{p}{1}x + \binom{p}{2}x^2 + \binom{p}{3}x^3 + \cdots = \sum_{k=0}^{\infty} \binom{p}{k} x^k.$$

This series has the same general form for all values of p. When p is a nonnegative integer, the series terminates and it is a polynomial of degree p.

The interval of convergence for the binomial series is determined by the Ratio Test. Holding p and x fixed, the relevant limit is

$$r = \lim_{k\to\infty} \left| \frac{x^{k+1}p(p-1)\cdots(p-k+1)(p-k)/(k+1)!}{x^k p(p-1)\cdots(p-k+1)/k!} \right| \quad \text{Ratio of } (k+1)\text{st to } k\text{th term}$$

$$= |x| \underbrace{\lim_{k\to\infty} \left| \frac{p-k}{k+1} \right|}_{\text{approaches } 1} \quad \text{Cancel factors and simplify.}$$

$$= |x|. \quad \text{With } p \text{ fixed, } \lim_{k\to\infty} \left| \frac{(p-k)}{k+1} \right| = 1.$$

➤ In Theorem 9.6, it can be shown that the interval of convergence for the binomial series is
- $(-1, 1)$ if $p \leq -1$,
- $(-1, 1]$ if $-1 < p < 0$, and
- $[-1, 1]$ if $p > 0$ and not an integer.

Absolute convergence requires that $r = |x| < 1$. Therefore, the series converges for $|x| < 1$. Depending on the value of p, the interval of convergence may include the endpoints; see margin note. ◀

EXAMPLE 4 **Binomial series** Consider the function $f(x) = \sqrt{1 + x}$.

➤ A binomial series is a Taylor series. Because the series in Example 4 is centered at 0, it is also a Maclaurin series.

a. Find the first four terms of the binomial series for f centered at 0.

b. Approximate $\sqrt{1.15}$ to three decimal places. Assume the series for f converges to f on its interval of convergence, which is $[-1, 1]$.

SOLUTION

a. We use the formula for the binomial coefficients with $p = \frac{1}{2}$ to compute the first four coefficients:

$$c_0 = 1, \qquad c_1 = \binom{\frac{1}{2}}{1} = \frac{\left(\frac{1}{2}\right)}{1!} = \frac{1}{2},$$

$$c_2 = \binom{\frac{1}{2}}{2} = \frac{\frac{1}{2}\left(-\frac{1}{2}\right)}{2!} = -\frac{1}{8}, \qquad c_3 = \binom{\frac{1}{2}}{3} = \frac{\frac{1}{2}\left(-\frac{1}{2}\right)\left(-\frac{3}{2}\right)}{3!} = \frac{1}{16}.$$

The leading terms of the binomial series are

$$1 + \frac{1}{2}x - \frac{1}{8}x^2 + \frac{1}{16}x^3 - \cdots.$$

Table 9.3

n	**Approximation $p_n(0.15)$**
0	1.0
1	1.075
2	1.0721875
3	1.072398438

➤ The remainder theorem for alternating series (Section 8.6) could be used in Example 4 to estimate the number of terms of the Maclaurin series needed to achieve a desired accuracy.

b. Truncating the binomial series in part (a) produces Taylor polynomials p_n that may be used to approximate $f(0.15) = \sqrt{1.15}$. With $x = 0.15$, we find the polynomial approximations shown in Table 9.3. Four terms of the power series $(n = 3)$ give $\sqrt{1.15} \approx 1.072$. Because the approximations with $n = 2$ and $n = 3$ agree to three decimal places, when rounded, the approximation 1.072 is accurate to three decimal places.

Related Exercises 39–44 ◀

QUICK CHECK 5 Use two and three terms of the binomial series in Example 4 to approximate $\sqrt{1.1}$. ◀

EXAMPLE 5 **Working with binomial series** Consider the functions

$$f(x) = \sqrt[3]{1 + x} \quad \text{and} \quad g(x) = \sqrt[3]{c + x}, \text{ where } c > 0 \text{ is a constant.}$$

a. Find the first four terms of the binomial series for f centered at 0.

b. Use part (a) to find the first four terms of the binomial series for g centered at 0.

c. Use part (b) to approximate $\sqrt[3]{23}, \sqrt[3]{24}, \ldots, \sqrt[3]{31}$. Assume the series for g converges to g on its interval of convergence.

SOLUTION

a. Because $f(x) = (1 + x)^{1/3}$, we find the binomial coefficients with $p = \frac{1}{3}$.

$$c_0 = \binom{\frac{1}{3}}{0} = 1, \qquad c_1 = \binom{\frac{1}{3}}{1} = \frac{\left(\frac{1}{3}\right)}{1!} = \frac{1}{3},$$

$$c_2 = \binom{\frac{1}{3}}{2} = \frac{\left(\frac{1}{3}\right)\left(\frac{1}{3} - 1\right)}{2!} = -\frac{1}{9}, \qquad c_3 = \binom{\frac{1}{3}}{3} = \frac{\left(\frac{1}{3}\right)\left(\frac{1}{3} - 1\right)\left(\frac{1}{3} - 2\right)}{3!} = \frac{5}{81}\cdots$$

The first four terms of the binomial series are

$$1 + \frac{1}{3}x - \frac{1}{9}x^2 + \frac{5}{81}x^3 - \cdots.$$

b. To avoid deriving a new series for $g(x) = \sqrt[3]{c + x}$, a few steps of algebra allow us to use part (a). Note that

$$g(x) = \sqrt[3]{c + x} = \sqrt[3]{c\left(1 + \frac{x}{c}\right)} = \sqrt[3]{c} \cdot \sqrt[3]{1 + \frac{x}{c}} = \sqrt[3]{c} \cdot f\left(\frac{x}{c}\right).$$

In other words, g can be expressed in terms of f, for which we already have a binomial series. The binomial series for g is obtained by substituting x/c into the binomial series for f and multiplying by $\sqrt[3]{c}$:

$$g(x) = \sqrt[3]{c}\underbrace{\left(1 + \frac{1}{3}\left(\frac{x}{c}\right) - \frac{1}{9}\left(\frac{x}{c}\right)^2 + \frac{5}{81}\left(\frac{x}{c}\right)^3 - \cdots\right)}_{f(x/c)}.$$

It can be shown that the series for f in part (a) converges to $f(x)$ for $|x| \leq 1$. Therefore, the series for $f(x/c)$ converges to $f(x/c)$ provided $|x/c| \leq 1$, or, equivalently, for $|x| \leq c$.

c. The series of part (b) may be truncated after four terms to approximate cube roots. For example, note that $\sqrt[3]{29} = \sqrt[3]{\underbrace{27}_{c} + \underbrace{2}_{x}}$, so we take $c = 27$ and $x = 2$.

The choice $c = 27$ is made because 29 is near 27 and $\sqrt[3]{c} = \sqrt[3]{27} = 3$ is easy to evaluate. Substituting $c = 27$ and $x = 2$, we find that

$$\sqrt[3]{29} \approx \sqrt[3]{27}\left(1 + \frac{1}{3}\left(\frac{2}{27}\right) - \frac{1}{9}\left(\frac{2}{27}\right)^2 + \frac{5}{81}\left(\frac{2}{27}\right)^3\right) \approx 3.0723.$$

The same method is used to approximate the cube roots of 23, 24, . . . , 30, 31 (Table 9.4). The absolute error is the difference between the approximation and the value given by a calculator. Notice that the errors increase as we move away from 27.

Table 9.4

	Approximation	Absolute Error
$\sqrt[3]{23}$	2.8439	6.7×10^{-5}
$\sqrt[3]{24}$	2.8845	2.0×10^{-5}
$\sqrt[3]{25}$	2.9240	3.9×10^{-6}
$\sqrt[3]{26}$	2.9625	2.4×10^{-7}
$\sqrt[3]{27}$	3	0
$\sqrt[3]{28}$	3.0366	2.3×10^{-7}
$\sqrt[3]{29}$	3.0723	3.5×10^{-6}
$\sqrt[3]{30}$	3.1072	1.7×10^{-5}
$\sqrt[3]{31}$	3.1414	5.4×10^{-5}

Related Exercises 45–56 ◀

Convergence of Taylor Series

It may seem that the story of Taylor series is over. But there is a technical point that is easily overlooked. Given a function f, we know how to write its Taylor series centered at a point a, and we know how to find its interval of convergence. We still do not know that the series actually converges to f. The remaining task is to determine when the Taylor series for f actually converges to f on its interval of convergence. Fortunately, the necessary tools have already been presented in Taylor's Theorem (Theorem 9.1), which gives the remainder for Taylor polynomials.

Assume f has derivatives of *all* orders on an open interval containing the point a. Taylor's Theorem tells us that

$$f(x) = p_n(x) + R_n(x),$$

where p_n is the nth-order Taylor polynomial for f centered at a,

$$R_n(x) = \frac{f^{(n+1)}(c)}{(n+1)!}(x - a)^{n+1}$$

is the remainder, and c is a point between x and a. We see that the remainder, $R_n(x) = f(x) - p_n(x)$, measures the difference between f and the approximating polynomial p_n.

When we say the Taylor series converges to f at a point x, we mean the value of the Taylor series at x equals $f(x)$; that is, $\lim_{n\to\infty} p_n(x) = f(x)$. The following theorem makes these ideas precise.

THEOREM 9.7 Convergence of Taylor Series
Let f have derivatives of all orders on an open interval I containing a. The Taylor series for f centered at a converges to f, for all x in I, if and only if $\lim_{n\to\infty} R_n(x) = 0$, for all x in I, where

$$R_n(x) = \frac{f^{(n+1)}(c)}{(n+1)!}(x-a)^{n+1}$$

is the remainder at x (with c between x and a).

Proof: The theorem requires derivatives of *all* orders. Therefore, by Taylor's Theorem (Theorem 9.1), the remainder exists in the given form for all n. Let p_n denote the nth-order Taylor polynomial and note that $\lim_{n\to\infty} p_n(x)$ is the Taylor series for f centered at a, evaluated at a point x in I.

First, assume that $\lim_{n\to\infty} R_n(x) = 0$ on the interval I and recall that $p_n(x) = f(x) - R_n(x)$. Taking limits of both sides, we have

$$\underbrace{\lim_{n\to\infty} p_n(x)}_{\text{Taylor series}} = \lim_{n\to\infty} (f(x) - R_n(x)) = \underbrace{\lim_{n\to\infty} f(x)}_{f(x)} - \underbrace{\lim_{n\to\infty} R_n(x)}_{0} = f(x).$$

We conclude that the Taylor series $\lim_{n\to\infty} p_n(x)$ equals $f(x)$, for all x in I.

Conversely, if the Taylor series converges to f, then $f(x) = \lim_{n\to\infty} p_n(x)$ and

$$0 = f(x) - \lim_{n\to\infty} p_n(x) = \lim_{n\to\infty} \underbrace{(f(x) - p_n(x))}_{R_n(x)} = \lim_{n\to\infty} R_n(x).$$

It follows that $\lim_{n\to\infty} R_n(x) = 0$, for all x in I. ◄

Even with an expression for the remainder, it may be difficult to show that $\lim_{n\to\infty} R_n(x) = 0$. The following examples illustrate cases in which it is possible.

EXAMPLE 6 Remainder in the Maclaurin series for e^x Show that the Maclaurin series for $f(x) = e^x$ converges to $f(x)$, for $-\infty < x < \infty$.

SOLUTION As shown in Example 3, the Maclaurin series for $f(x) = e^x$ is

$$\sum_{k=0}^{\infty} \frac{x^k}{k!} = 1 + x + \frac{x^2}{2!} + \cdots + \frac{x^n}{n!} + \cdots,$$

which converges for $-\infty < x < \infty$. In Example 7 of Section 9.1 it was shown that the remainder is

$$R_n(x) = \frac{e^c}{(n+1)!}x^{n+1},$$

where c is between 0 and x. Notice that the intermediate point c varies with n, but it is always between 0 and x. Therefore, e^c is between $e^0 = 1$ and e^x; in fact, $e^c \le e^{|x|}$, for all n. It follows that

$$|R_n(x)| \le \frac{e^{|x|}}{(n+1)!}|x|^{n+1}.$$

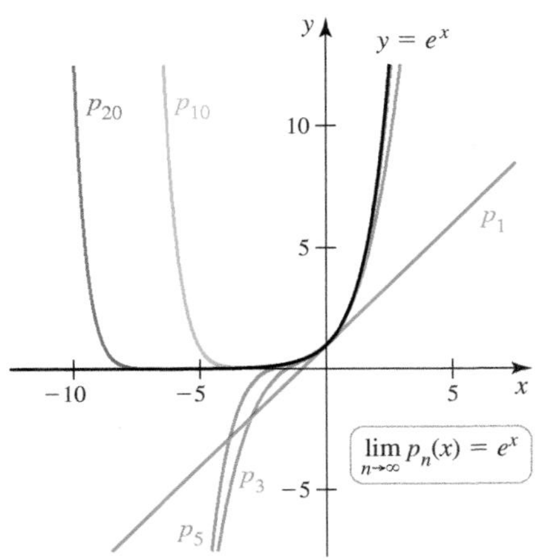

Figure 9.19

Holding x fixed, we have

$$\lim_{n\to\infty} |R_n(x)| = \lim_{n\to\infty} \frac{e^{|x|}}{(n+1)!}|x|^{n+1} = e^{|x|} \lim_{n\to\infty} \frac{|x|^{n+1}}{(n+1)!} = 0,$$

where we used the fact that $\lim_{n\to\infty} x^n/n! = 0$, for $-\infty < x < \infty$ (Section 8.2). Because $\lim_{n\to\infty} |R_n(x)| = 0$, it follows that for all real numbers x, the Taylor series converges to e^x, or

$$e^x = \sum_{k=0}^{\infty} \frac{x^k}{k!} = 1 + x + \frac{x^2}{2!} + \cdots + \frac{x^n}{n!} + \cdots.$$

The convergence of the Taylor series to e^x is illustrated in Figure 9.19, where Taylor polynomials of increasing degree are graphed together with e^x.

Related Exercises 57–60 ◀

EXAMPLE 7 Maclaurin series convergence for cos *x* Show that the Maclaurin series for cos x,

$$1 - \frac{x^2}{2!} + \frac{x^4}{4!} - \frac{x^6}{6!} + \cdots = \sum_{k=0}^{\infty} (-1)^k \frac{x^{2k}}{(2k)!},$$

converges to $f(x) = \cos x$, for $-\infty < x < \infty$.

SOLUTION To show that the power series converges to f, we must show that $\lim_{n\to\infty} |R_n(x)| = 0$, for $-\infty < x < \infty$. According to Taylor's Theorem with $a = 0$,

$$R_n(x) = \frac{f^{(n+1)}(c)}{(n+1)!} x^{n+1},$$

where c is between 0 and x. Notice that $f^{(n+1)}(c) = \pm \sin c$ or $f^{(n+1)}(c) = \pm \cos c$. In all cases, $|f^{(n+1)}(c)| \le 1$. Therefore, the absolute value of the remainder term is bounded as

$$|R_n(x)| = \left| \frac{f^{(n+1)}(c)}{(n+1)!} x^{n+1} \right| \le \frac{|x|^{n+1}}{(n+1)!}.$$

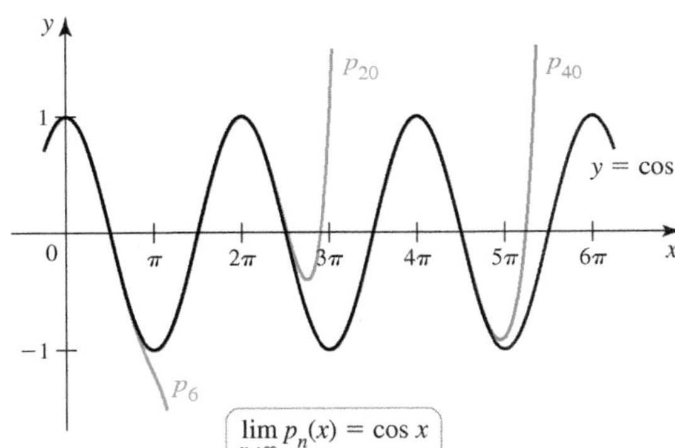

Figure 9.20

Holding x fixed and using $\lim_{n\to\infty} x^n/n! = 0$, we see that $\lim_{n\to\infty} R_n(x) = 0$ for all x. Therefore, the given power series converges to $f(x) = \cos x$, for all x; that is, $\cos x = \sum_{k=0}^{\infty} \frac{(-1)^k x^{2k}}{(2k)!}$. The convergence of the Taylor series to cos x is illustrated in Figure 9.20.

Related Exercises 57–60 ◀

The procedure used in Examples 6 and 7 can be carried out for all the Taylor series we have worked with so far (with varying degrees of difficulty). In each case, the Taylor series converges to the function it represents on the interval of convergence. Table 9.5 summarizes commonly used Taylor series centered at 0 and the functions to which they converge.

➤ Table 9.5 asserts, without proof, that in several cases, the Taylor series for f converges to f at the endpoints of the interval of convergence. Proving convergence at the endpoints generally requires advanced techniques. It may also be done using the following theorem:

Suppose the Taylor series for f centered at 0 converges to f on the interval $(-R, R)$. If the series converges at $x = R$, then it converges to $\lim_{x \to R^-} f(x)$. If the series converges at $x = -R$, then it converges to $\lim_{x \to -R^+} f(x)$.

For example, this theorem would allow us to conclude that the series for $\ln(1 + x)$ converges to $\ln 2$ at $x = 1$.

Table 9.5

$$\frac{1}{1-x} = 1 + x + x^2 + \cdots + x^k + \cdots = \sum_{k=0}^{\infty} x^k, \quad \text{for } |x| < 1$$

$$\frac{1}{1+x} = 1 - x + x^2 - \cdots + (-1)^k x^k + \cdots = \sum_{k=0}^{\infty} (-1)^k x^k, \quad \text{for } |x| < 1$$

$$e^x = 1 + x + \frac{x^2}{2!} + \cdots + \frac{x^k}{k!} + \cdots = \sum_{k=0}^{\infty} \frac{x^k}{k!}, \quad \text{for } |x| < \infty$$

$$\sin x = x - \frac{x^3}{3!} + \frac{x^5}{5!} - \cdots + \frac{(-1)^k x^{2k+1}}{(2k+1)!} + \cdots = \sum_{k=0}^{\infty} \frac{(-1)^k x^{2k+1}}{(2k+1)!}, \quad \text{for } |x| < \infty$$

$$\cos x = 1 - \frac{x^2}{2!} + \frac{x^4}{4!} - \cdots + \frac{(-1)^k x^{2k}}{(2k)!} + \cdots = \sum_{k=0}^{\infty} \frac{(-1)^k x^{2k}}{(2k)!}, \quad \text{for } |x| < \infty$$

$$\ln(1+x) = x - \frac{x^2}{2} + \frac{x^3}{3} - \cdots + \frac{(-1)^{k+1} x^k}{k} + \cdots = \sum_{k=1}^{\infty} \frac{(-1)^{k+1} x^k}{k}, \quad \text{for } -1 < x \le 1$$

$$-\ln(1-x) = x + \frac{x^2}{2} + \frac{x^3}{3} + \cdots + \frac{x^k}{k} + \cdots = \sum_{k=1}^{\infty} \frac{x^k}{k}, \quad \text{for } -1 \le x < 1$$

$$\tan^{-1} x = x - \frac{x^3}{3} + \frac{x^5}{5} - \cdots + \frac{(-1)^k x^{2k+1}}{2k+1} + \cdots = \sum_{k=0}^{\infty} \frac{(-1)^k x^{2k+1}}{2k+1}, \quad \text{for } |x| \le 1$$

$$\sinh x = x + \frac{x^3}{3!} + \frac{x^5}{5!} + \cdots + \frac{x^{2k+1}}{(2k+1)!} + \cdots = \sum_{k=0}^{\infty} \frac{x^{2k+1}}{(2k+1)!}, \quad \text{for } |x| < \infty$$

$$\cosh x = 1 + \frac{x^2}{2!} + \frac{x^4}{4!} + \cdots + \frac{x^{2k}}{(2k)!} + \cdots = \sum_{k=0}^{\infty} \frac{x^{2k}}{(2k)!}, \quad \text{for } |x| < \infty$$

$$(1+x)^p = \sum_{k=0}^{\infty} \binom{p}{k} x^k, \text{ for } |x| < 1 \text{ and } \binom{p}{k} = \frac{p(p-1)(p-2)\cdots(p-k+1)}{k!}, \binom{p}{0} = 1$$

➤ As noted on p. 689, the binomial series may converge to $(1 + x)^p$ at $x = \pm 1$, depending on the value of p.

SECTION 9.3 EXERCISES

Review Questions

1. How are the Taylor polynomials for a function f centered at a related to the Taylor series for the function f centered at a?
2. What conditions must be satisfied by a function f to have a Taylor series centered at a?
3. How do you find the coefficients of the Taylor series for f centered at a?
4. How do you find the interval of convergence of a Taylor series?
5. Suppose you know the Maclaurin series for f and it converges for $|x| < 1$. How do you find the Maclaurin series for $f(x^2)$ and where does it converge?
6. For what values of p does the Taylor series for $f(x) = (1 + x)^p$ centered at 0 terminate?
7. In terms of the remainder, what does it mean for a Taylor series for a function f to converge to f?
8. Write the Maclaurin series for e^{2x}.

Basic Skills

9–20. Maclaurin series

a. Find the first four nonzero terms of the Maclaurin series for the given function.

b. Write the power series using summation notation.

c. Determine the interval of convergence of the series.

9. $f(x) = e^{-x}$
10. $f(x) = \cos 2x$
11. $f(x) = (1 + x^2)^{-1}$
12. $f(x) = \ln(1 + 4x)$
13. $f(x) = e^{2x}$
14. $f(x) = (1 + 2x)^{-1}$
15. $f(x) = \tan^{-1} \frac{x}{2}$
16. $f(x) = \sin 3x$
17. $f(x) = 3^x$
18. $f(x) = \log_3(x + 1)$
19. $f(x) = \cosh 3x$
20. $f(x) = \sinh 2x$

21–28. Taylor series centered at $a \neq 0$

a. *Find the first four nonzero terms of the Taylor series for the given function centered at a.*
b. *Write the power series using summation notation.*

21. $f(x) = \sin x, a = \pi/2$
22. $f(x) = \cos x, a = \pi$
23. $f(x) = 1/x, a = 1$
24. $f(x) = 1/x, a = 2$
25. $f(x) = \ln x, a = 3$
26. $f(x) = e^x, a = \ln 2$
27. $f(x) = 2^x, a = 1$
28. $f(x) = 10^x, a = 2$

29–38. Manipulating Taylor series *Use the Taylor series in Table 9.5 to find the first four nonzero terms of the Taylor series for the following functions centered at 0.*

29. $\ln(1 + x^2)$
30. $\sin x^2$
31. $\dfrac{1}{1 - 2x}$
32. $\ln(1 + 2x)$
33. $\begin{cases} \dfrac{e^x - 1}{x} & \text{if } x \neq 0 \\ 1 & \text{if } x = 0 \end{cases}$
34. $\cos x^3$
35. $(1 + x^4)^{-1}$
36. $x \tan^{-1} x^2$
37. $\sinh x^2$
38. $\cosh 3x$

T 39–44. Binomial series

a. *Find the first four nonzero terms of the binomial series centered at 0 for the given function.*
b. *Use the first four nonzero terms of the series to approximate the given quantity.*

39. $f(x) = (1 + x)^{-2}$; approximate $1/1.21 = 1/1.1^2$.
40. $f(x) = \sqrt{1 + x}$; approximate $\sqrt{1.06}$.
41. $f(x) = \sqrt[4]{1 + x}$; approximate $\sqrt[4]{1.12}$.
42. $f(x) = (1 + x)^{-3}$; approximate $1/1.331 = 1/1.1^3$.
43. $f(x) = (1 + x)^{-2/3}$; approximate $1.18^{-2/3}$.
44. $f(x) = (1 + x)^{2/3}$; approximate $1.02^{2/3}$.

45–50. Working with binomial series *Use properties of power series, substitution, and factoring to find the first four nonzero terms of the Maclaurin series for the following functions. Give the interval of convergence for the new series (Theorem 9.4 is useful). Use the Maclaurin series*

$$\sqrt{1 + x} = 1 + \frac{x}{2} - \frac{x^2}{8} + \frac{x^3}{16} - \cdots, \quad \text{for } -1 \le x \le 1.$$

45. $\sqrt{1 + x^2}$
46. $\sqrt{4 + x}$
47. $\sqrt{9 - 9x}$
48. $\sqrt{1 - 4x}$
49. $\sqrt{a^2 + x^2}, a > 0$
50. $\sqrt{4 - 16x^2}$

51–56. Working with binomial series *Use properties of power series, substitution, and factoring of constants to find the first four nonzero terms of the Maclaurin series for the following functions. Use the Maclaurin series*

$$(1 + x)^{-2} = 1 - 2x + 3x^2 - 4x^3 + \cdots, \quad \text{for } -1 < x < 1.$$

51. $(1 + 4x)^{-2}$
52. $\dfrac{1}{(1 - 4x)^2}$
53. $\dfrac{1}{(4 + x^2)^2}$
54. $(x^2 - 4x + 5)^{-2}$
55. $\dfrac{1}{(3 + 4x)^2}$
56. $\dfrac{1}{(1 + 4x^2)^2}$

57–60. Remainders *Find the remainder in the Taylor series centered at the point a for the following functions. Then show that $\lim_{n\to\infty} R_n(x) = 0$ for all x in the interval of convergence.*

57. $f(x) = \sin x, a = 0$
58. $f(x) = \cos 2x, a = 0$
59. $f(x) = e^{-x}, a = 0$
60. $f(x) = \cos x, a = \pi/2$

Further Explorations

61. **Explain why or why not** Determine whether the following statements are true and give an explanation or counterexample.
    a. The function $f(x) = \sqrt{x}$ has a Taylor series centered at 0.
    b. The function $f(x) = \csc x$ has a Taylor series centered at $\pi/2$.
    c. If f has a Taylor series that converges only on $(-2, 2)$, then $f(x^2)$ has a Taylor series that also converges only on $(-2, 2)$.
    d. If $p(x)$ is the Taylor series for f centered at 0, then $p(x - 1)$ is the Taylor series for f centered at 1.
    e. The Taylor series for an even function about 0 has only even powers of x.

62–69. Any method

a. *Use any analytical method to find the first four nonzero terms of the Taylor series centered at 0 for the following functions. You do not need to use the definition of the Taylor series coefficients.*
b. *Determine the radius of convergence of the series.*

62. $f(x) = \cos 2x + 2 \sin x$
63. $f(x) = \dfrac{e^x + e^{-x}}{2}$
64. $f(x) = \begin{cases} \dfrac{\sin x}{x} & \text{if } x \neq 0 \\ 1 & \text{if } x = 0 \end{cases}$
65. $f(x) = (1 + x^2)^{-2/3}$
66. $f(x) = x^2 \cos x^2$
67. $f(x) = \sqrt{1 - x^2}$
68. $f(x) = b^x$, for $b > 0, b \neq 1$
69. $f(x) = \dfrac{1}{x^4 + 2x^2 + 1}$

T 70–73. Approximating powers *Compute the coefficients for the Taylor series for the following functions about the given point a and then use the first four terms of the series to approximate the given number.*

70. $f(x) = \sqrt{x}$ with $a = 36$; approximate $\sqrt{39}$.
71. $f(x) = \sqrt[3]{x}$ with $a = 64$; approximate $\sqrt[3]{60}$.
72. $f(x) = 1/\sqrt{x}$ with $a = 4$; approximate $1/\sqrt{3}$.
73. $f(x) = \sqrt[4]{x}$ with $a = 16$; approximate $\sqrt[4]{13}$.

74. **Geometric/binomial series** Recall that the Taylor series for $f(x) = 1/(1 - x)$ about 0 is the geometric series $\sum_{k=0}^{\infty} x^k$. Show that this series can also be found as a binomial series.

75. Integer coefficients Show that the first five nonzero coefficients of the Taylor series (binomial series) for $f(x) = \sqrt{1 + 4x}$ about 0 are integers. (In fact, *all* the coefficients are integers.)

76. Choosing a good center Suppose you want to approximate $\sqrt{72}$ using four terms of a Taylor series. Compare the accuracy of the approximations obtained using Taylor series for $\sqrt{x}$ centered at 64 and 81.

77. Alternative means By comparing the first four terms, show that the Maclaurin series for $\sin^2 x$ can be found (a) by squaring the Maclaurin series for $\sin x$, (b) by using the identity $\sin^2 x = (1 - \cos 2x)/2$, or (c) by computing the coefficients using the definition.

78. Alternative means By comparing the first four terms, show that the Maclaurin series for $\cos^2 x$ can be found (a) by squaring the Maclaurin series for $\cos x$, (b) by using the identity $\cos^2 x = (1 + \cos 2x)/2$, or (c) by computing the coefficients using the definition.

79. Designer series Find a power series that has (2, 6) as an interval of convergence.

80–81. Patterns in coefficients *Find the next two terms of the following Taylor series.*

80. $\sqrt{1 + x}$: $1 + \frac{1}{2}x - \frac{1}{2 \cdot 4}x^2 + \frac{1 \cdot 3}{2 \cdot 4 \cdot 6}x^3 - \cdots$.

81. $\frac{1}{\sqrt{1 + x}}$: $1 - \frac{1}{2}x + \frac{1 \cdot 3}{2 \cdot 4}x^2 - \frac{1 \cdot 3 \cdot 5}{2 \cdot 4 \cdot 6}x^3 + \cdots$.

82. Composition of series Use composition of series to find the first three terms of the Maclaurin series for the following functions.

a. $e^{\sin x}$ **b.** $e^{\tan x}$ **c.** $\sqrt{1 + \sin^2 x}$

Applications

T **83–86. Approximations** *Choose a Taylor series and center point to approximate the following quantities with an error of 10^{-4} or less.*

83. $\cos 40°$

84. $\sin(0.98\pi)$

85. $\sqrt[3]{83}$

86. $1/\sqrt[4]{17}$

87. Different approximation strategies Suppose you want to approximate $\sqrt[3]{128}$ to within 10^{-4} of the exact value.

a. Use a Taylor polynomial for $f(x) = (125 + x)^{1/3}$ centered at 0.

b. Use a Taylor polynomial for $f(x) = x^{1/3}$ centered at 125.

c. Compare the two approaches. Are they equivalent?

Additional Exercises

88. Mean Value Theorem Explain why the Mean Value Theorem (Theorem 4.9 of Section 4.6) is a special case of Taylor's Theorem.

89. Version of the Second Derivative Test Assume that f has at least two continuous derivatives on an interval containing a with $f'(a) = 0$. Use Taylor's Theorem to prove the following version of the Second Derivative Test.

a. If $f''(x) > 0$ on some interval containing a, then f has a local minimum at a.

b. If $f''(x) < 0$ on some interval containing a, then f has a local maximum at a.

90. Nonconvergence to *f* Consider the function

$$f(x) = \begin{cases} e^{-1/x^2} & \text{if } x \neq 0 \\ 0 & \text{if } x = 0. \end{cases}$$

a. Use the definition of the derivative to show that $f'(0) = 0$.

b. Assume the fact that $f^{(k)}(0) = 0$, for $k = 1, 2, 3, \ldots$. (You can write a proof using the definition of the derivative.) Write the Taylor series for f centered at 0.

c. Explain why the Taylor series for f does not converge to f for $x \neq 0$.

QUICK CHECK ANSWERS

1. When evaluated at $x = a$, all terms of the series are zero except the first term, which is $f(a)$. Therefore, the series equals $f(a)$ at this point. **2.** $1 - x + x^2 - x^3 + x^4 - \cdots$ **3.** $2x + 2x^2 + x^3$; $1 - x + x^2/2$ **4.** 6, 1/16 **5.** 1.05, 1.04875 ◄

9.4 Working with Taylor Series

We now know the Taylor series for many familiar functions, and we have tools for working with power series. The goal of this final section is to illustrate additional techniques associated with power series. As you will see, power series cover the entire landscape of calculus from limits and derivatives to integrals and approximation. We present five different topics that you can explore selectively.

Limits by Taylor Series

An important use of Taylor series is evaluating limits. Two examples illustrate the essential ideas.

EXAMPLE 1 **A limit by Taylor series** Evaluate $\lim_{x\to 0} \frac{x^2 + 2\cos x - 2}{3x^4}$.

➤ L'Hôpital's Rule may be impractical when it must be used more than once on the same limit or when derivatives are difficult to compute.

SOLUTION Because the limit has the indeterminate form 0/0, l'Hôpital's Rule can be used, which requires four applications of the rule. Alternatively, because the limit involves values of x near 0, we substitute the Maclaurin series for $\cos x$. Recalling that

$$\cos x = 1 - \frac{x^2}{2} + \frac{x^4}{24} - \frac{x^6}{720} + \cdots, \quad \text{Table 9.5, page 694}$$

we have

➤ In using series to evaluate limits, it is often not obvious how many terms of the Taylor series to use. When in doubt, include extra (higher-order) terms. The dots in the calculation stand for powers of x greater than the last power that appears.

$$\lim_{x\to 0} \frac{x^2 + 2\cos x - 2}{3x^4} = \lim_{x\to 0} \frac{x^2 + 2\left(1 - \frac{x^2}{2} + \frac{x^4}{24} - \frac{x^6}{720} + \cdots\right) - 2}{3x^4} \quad \text{Substitute for } \cos x.$$

$$= \lim_{x\to 0} \frac{x^2 + \left(2 - x^2 + \frac{x^4}{12} - \frac{x^6}{360} + \cdots\right) - 2}{3x^4} \quad \text{Simplify.}$$

$$= \lim_{x\to 0} \frac{\frac{x^4}{12} - \frac{x^6}{360} + \cdots}{3x^4} \quad \text{Simplify.}$$

$$= \lim_{x\to 0} \left(\frac{1}{36} - \frac{x^2}{1080} + \cdots\right) = \frac{1}{36}. \quad \text{Use Theorem 9.4, Property 2; evaluate limit.}$$

Related Exercises 7–24 ◀

QUICK CHECK 1 Use the Taylor series $\sin x = x - x^3/6 + \cdots$ to verify that $\lim_{x\to 0} (\sin x)/x = 1$. ◀

EXAMPLE 2 **A limit by Taylor series** Evaluate

$$\lim_{x\to\infty} \left(6x^5 \sin\frac{1}{x} - 6x^4 + x^2\right).$$

SOLUTION A Taylor series may be centered at any finite point in the domain of the function, but we don't have the tools needed to expand a function about $x = \infty$. Using a technique introduced earlier, we replace x with $1/t$ and note that as $x \to \infty$, $t \to 0^+$. The new limit becomes

$$\lim_{x\to\infty} \left(6x^5 \sin\frac{1}{x} - 6x^4 + x^2\right) = \lim_{t\to 0^+} \left(\frac{6\sin t}{t^5} - \frac{6}{t^4} + \frac{1}{t^2}\right) \quad \text{Replace } x \text{ with } 1/t.$$

$$= \lim_{t\to 0^+} \left(\frac{6\sin t - 6t + t^3}{t^5}\right). \quad \text{Common denominator}$$

This limit has the indeterminate form 0/0. We now expand $\sin t$ in a Taylor series centered at $t = 0$. Because

$$\sin t = t - \frac{t^3}{6} + \frac{t^5}{120} - \frac{t^7}{5040} + \cdots, \quad \text{Table 9.5, page 694}$$

the value of the original limit is

$$\lim_{t\to0^+}\left(\frac{6\sin t - 6t + t^3}{t^5}\right)$$

$$= \lim_{t\to0^+}\left(\frac{6\left(t - \frac{t^3}{6} + \frac{t^5}{120} - \frac{t^7}{5040} + \cdots\right) - 6t + t^3}{t^5}\right)$$ Substitute for $\sin t$.

$$= \lim_{t\to0^+}\left(\frac{\frac{t^5}{20} - \frac{t^7}{840} + \cdots}{t^5}\right)$$ Simplify.

$$= \lim_{t\to0^+}\left(\frac{1}{20} - \frac{t^2}{840} + \cdots\right) = \frac{1}{20}.$$ Use Theorem 9.4, Property 2; evaluate limit.

Related Exercises 7–24 ◀

Differentiating Power Series

The following examples illustrate ways in which term-by-term differentiation (Theorem 9.5) may be used.

EXAMPLE 3 **Power series for derivatives** Differentiate the Maclaurin series for $f(x) = \sin x$ to verify that $\frac{d}{dx}(\sin x) = \cos x$.

SOLUTION The Maclaurin series for $f(x) = \sin x$ is

$$\sin x = x - \frac{x^3}{3!} + \frac{x^5}{5!} - \frac{x^7}{7!} + \cdots,$$

and it converges for $-\infty < x < \infty$. By Theorem 9.5, the differentiated series also converges for $-\infty < x < \infty$ and it converges to $f'(x)$. Differentiating, we have

QUICK CHECK 2 Differentiate the power series for $\cos x$ (given in Example 3) and identify the result. ◀

$$\frac{d}{dx}\left(x - \frac{x^3}{3!} + \frac{x^5}{5!} - \frac{x^7}{7!} + \cdots\right) = 1 - \frac{x^2}{2!} + \frac{x^4}{4!} - \frac{x^6}{6!} + \cdots = \cos x.$$

The differentiated series is the Maclaurin series for $\cos x$, confirming that $f'(x) = \cos x$.

Related Exercises 25–32 ◀

EXAMPLE 4 **A differential equation** Find a power series solution of the differential equation $y'(t) = y + 2$, subject to the initial condition $y(0) = 6$. Identify the function represented by the power series.

SOLUTION Because the initial condition is given at $t = 0$, we assume the solution has a Taylor series centered at 0 of the form $y(t) = \sum_{k=0}^{\infty} c_k t^k$, where the coefficients c_k must be determined. Recall that the coefficients of the Taylor series are given by

$$c_k = \frac{y^{(k)}(0)}{k!}, \quad \text{for } k = 0, 1, 2, \ldots.$$

If we can determine $y^{(k)}(0)$, for $k = 0, 1, 2, \ldots$, the coefficients of the series are also determined.

Substituting the initial condition $t = 0$ and $y = 6$ into the power series

$$y(t) = c_0 + c_1 t + c_2 t^2 + \cdots,$$

we find that

$$6 = c_0 + c_1(0) + c_2(0)^2 + \cdots.$$

It follows that $c_0 = 6$. To determine $y'(0)$, we substitute $t = 0$ into the differential equation; the result is $y'(0) = y(0) + 2 = 6 + 2 = 8$. Therefore, $c_1 = y'(0)/1! = 8$.

The remaining derivatives are obtained by successively differentiating the differential equation and substituting $t = 0$. We find that $y''(0) = y'(0) = 8$, $y'''(0) = y''(0) = 8$, and in general, $y^{(k)}(0) = 8$, for $k = 2, 3, 4, \ldots$. Therefore,

$$c_k = \frac{y^{(k)}(0)}{k!} = \frac{8}{k!}, \quad \text{for } k = 1, 2, 3, \ldots,$$

and the Taylor series for the solution is

$$\begin{aligned} y(t) &= c_0 + c_1 t + c_2 t^2 + \cdots \\ &= 6 + \frac{8}{1!}t + \frac{8}{2!}t^2 + \frac{8}{3!}t^3 + \cdots. \end{aligned}$$

To identify the function represented by this series, we write

$$\begin{aligned} y(t) &= \underbrace{-2 + 8}_{6} + \frac{8}{1!}t + \frac{8}{2!}t^2 + \frac{8}{3!}t^3 + \cdots \\ &= -2 + 8\underbrace{\left(1 + t + \frac{t^2}{2!} + \frac{t^3}{3!} + \cdots\right)}_{e^t}. \end{aligned}$$

➤ You should check that $y(t) = -2 + 8e^t$ satisfies $y'(t) = y + 2$ and $y(0) = 6$.

The power series that appears is the Taylor series for e^t. Therefore, the solution is $y = -2 + 8e^t$.

Related Exercises 33–36 ◀

Integrating Power Series

The following example illustrates the use of power series in approximating integrals that cannot be evaluated by analytical methods.

EXAMPLE 5 **Approximating a definite integral** Approximate the value of the integral $\int_0^1 e^{-x^2}\,dx$ with an error no greater than 5×10^{-4}.

SOLUTION The antiderivative of e^{-x^2} cannot be expressed in terms of familiar functions. The strategy is to write the Maclaurin series for e^{-x^2} and integrate it term by term. Recall that integration of a power series is valid within its interval of convergence (Theorem 9.5). Beginning with the Maclaurin series

$$e^x = 1 + x + \frac{x^2}{2!} + \frac{x^3}{3!} + \cdots + \frac{x^n}{n!} + \cdots,$$

which converges for $-\infty < x < \infty$, we replace x with $-x^2$ to obtain

$$e^{-x^2} = 1 - x^2 + \frac{x^4}{2!} - \frac{x^6}{3!} + \cdots + \frac{(-1)^n x^{2n}}{n!} + \cdots,$$

which also converges for $-\infty < x < \infty$. By the Fundamental Theorem of Calculus,

$$\begin{aligned} \int_0^1 e^{-x^2}\,dx &= \left(x - \frac{x^3}{3} + \frac{x^5}{5 \cdot 2!} - \frac{x^7}{7 \cdot 3!} + \cdots + \frac{(-1)^n x^{2n+1}}{(2n+1)n!} + \cdots\right)\Bigg|_0^1 \\ &= 1 - \frac{1}{3} + \frac{1}{5 \cdot 2!} - \frac{1}{7 \cdot 3!} + \cdots + \frac{(-1)^n}{(2n+1)n!} + \cdots. \end{aligned}$$

➤ The integral in Example 5 is important in statistics and probability theory because of its relationship to the *normal distribution*.

Because the definite integral is expressed as an alternating series, the magnitude of the remainder in truncating the series after n terms is less than the magnitude of the first neglected term, which is $\left|\frac{(-1)^{n+1}}{(2n+3)(n+1)!}\right|$. By trial and error, we find that the magnitude of this term is less than 5×10^{-4} if $n \geq 5$ (with $n = 5$, we have $\frac{1}{13 \cdot 6!} \approx 1.07 \times 10^{-4}$). The sum of the terms of the series up to $n = 5$ gives the approximation

$$\int_0^1 e^{-x^2}\,dx \approx 1 - \frac{1}{3} + \frac{1}{5 \cdot 2!} - \frac{1}{7 \cdot 3!} + \frac{1}{9 \cdot 4!} - \frac{1}{11 \cdot 5!} \approx 0.747.$$

Related Exercises 37–44 ◀

Representing Real Numbers

When values of x are substituted into a convergent power series, the result may be a series representation of a familiar real number. The following example illustrates some techniques.

EXAMPLE 6 Evaluating infinite series

a. Use the Maclaurin series for $f(x) = \tan^{-1} x$ to evaluate

$$1 - \frac{1}{3} + \frac{1}{5} - \cdots = \sum_{k=0}^{\infty} \frac{(-1)^k}{2k + 1}.$$

b. Let $f(x) = (e^x - 1)/x$, for $x \neq 0$, and $f(0) = 1$. Use the Maclaurin series for f to evaluate $f'(1)$ and $\sum_{k=1}^{\infty} \frac{k}{(k + 1)!}$.

SOLUTION

➤ The series in Example 6a (known as the *Gregory series*) is one of a multitude of series representations of π. Because this series converges slowly, it does not provide an efficient way to approximate π.

a. From Table 9.5 (page 694), we see that for $|x| \leq 1$,

$$\tan^{-1} x = x - \frac{x^3}{3} + \frac{x^5}{5} - \cdots + \frac{(-1)^k x^{2k+1}}{2k + 1} + \cdots = \sum_{k=0}^{\infty} \frac{(-1)^k x^{2k+1}}{2k + 1}.$$

Substituting $x = 1$, we have

$$\tan^{-1} 1 = 1 - \frac{1^3}{3} + \frac{1^5}{5} - \cdots = \sum_{k=0}^{\infty} \frac{(-1)^k}{2k + 1}.$$

Because $\tan^{-1} 1 = \pi/4$, the value of the series is $\pi/4$.

b. Using the Maclaurin series for e^x, the series for $f(x) = (e^x - 1)/x$ is

$$f(x) = \frac{e^x - 1}{x} = \frac{1}{x}\left(\left(1 + x + \frac{x^2}{2!} + \frac{x^3}{3!} + \cdots\right) - 1\right) \quad \text{Substitute series for } e^x.$$

$$= 1 + \frac{x}{2!} + \frac{x^2}{3!} + \frac{x^3}{4!} + \cdots = \sum_{k=1}^{\infty} \frac{x^{k-1}}{k!}, \quad \text{Theorem 9.4, Property 2}$$

which converges for $-\infty < x < \infty$. By the Quotient Rule,

$$f'(x) = \frac{xe^x - (e^x - 1)}{x^2}.$$

Differentiating the series for f term by term (Theorem 9.5), we find that

$$f'(x) = \frac{d}{dx}\left(1 + \frac{x}{2!} + \frac{x^2}{3!} + \frac{x^3}{4!} + \cdots\right)$$

$$= \frac{1}{2!} + \frac{2x}{3!} + \frac{3x^2}{4!} + \cdots = \sum_{k=1}^{\infty} \frac{kx^{k-1}}{(k + 1)!}.$$

We now have two expressions for f'; they are evaluated at $x = 1$ to show that

$$f'(1) = 1 = \sum_{k=1}^{\infty} \frac{k}{(k + 1)!}.$$

Related Exercises 45–54 ◀

QUICK CHECK 3 What value of x would you substitute into the Maclaurin series for $\tan^{-1} x$ to obtain a series representation for $\pi/6$? ◀

Representing Functions as Power Series

Power series have a fundamental role in mathematics in defining functions and providing alternative representations of familiar functions. As an overall review, we close this chapter with two examples that use many techniques for working with power series.

EXAMPLE 7 **Identify the series** Identify the function represented by the power series $\sum_{k=0}^{\infty} \frac{(1-2x)^k}{k!}$ and give its interval of convergence.

SOLUTION The Maclaurin series for the exponential function,

$$e^x = \sum_{k=0}^{\infty} \frac{x^k}{k!},$$

converges for $-\infty < x < \infty$. Replacing x with $1 - 2x$ produces the given series:

$$\sum_{k=0}^{\infty} \frac{(1-2x)^k}{k!} = e^{1-2x}.$$

This replacement is allowed because $1 - 2x$ is within the interval of convergence of the series for e^x; that is, $-\infty < 1 - 2x < \infty$, for all x. Therefore, the given series represents e^{1-2x}, for $-\infty < x < \infty$. *Related Exercises 55–64* ◀

EXAMPLE 8 **Mystery series** The power series $\sum_{k=1}^{\infty} \frac{(-1)^k k}{4^k} x^{2k}$ appeared in the opening of Section 9.2. Determine the interval of convergence of the power series and find the function it represents on this interval.

SOLUTION Applying the Ratio Test to the series, we determine that it converges when $|x^2/4| < 1$, which implies that $|x| < 2$. A quick check of the endpoints of the original series confirms that it diverges at $x = \pm 2$. Therefore, the interval of convergence is $|x| < 2$.

To find the function represented by the series, we apply several maneuvers until we obtain a geometric series. First note that

$$\sum_{k=1}^{\infty} \frac{(-1)^k k}{4^k} x^{2k} = \sum_{k=1}^{\infty} k\left(-\frac{1}{4}\right)^k x^{2k}.$$

The series on the right is not a geometric series because of the presence of the factor k. The key is to realize that k could appear in this way through differentiation; specifically, something like $\frac{d}{dx}(x^{2k}) = 2kx^{2k-1}$. To achieve terms of this form, we write

$$\underbrace{\sum_{k=1}^{\infty} \frac{(-1)^k k}{4^k} x^{2k}}_{\text{original series}} = \sum_{k=1}^{\infty} k\left(-\frac{1}{4}\right)^k x^{2k}$$

$$= \frac{1}{2}\sum_{k=1}^{\infty} 2k\left(-\frac{1}{4}\right)^k x^{2k} \qquad \text{Multiply and divide by 2.}$$

$$= \frac{x}{2}\sum_{k=1}^{\infty} 2k\left(-\frac{1}{4}\right)^k x^{2k-1}. \qquad \text{Remove } x \text{ from the series.}$$

Now we identify the last series as the derivative of another series:

$$\underbrace{\sum_{k=1}^{\infty} \frac{(-1)^k k}{4^k} x^{2k}}_{\text{original series}} = \frac{x}{2}\sum_{k=1}^{\infty}\left(-\frac{1}{4}\right)^k \underbrace{2kx^{2k-1}}_{\frac{d}{dx}(x^{2k})}$$

$$= \frac{x}{2}\sum_{k=1}^{\infty}\left(-\frac{1}{4}\right)^k \frac{d}{dx}(x^{2k}) \qquad \text{Identify a derivative.}$$

$$= \frac{x}{2}\frac{d}{dx}\left(\sum_{k=1}^{\infty}\left(-\frac{x^2}{4}\right)^k\right). \qquad \text{Combine factors; differentiate term by term.}$$

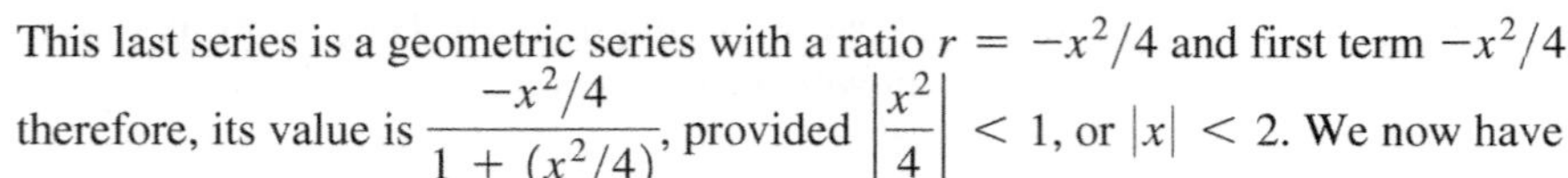

This last series is a geometric series with a ratio $r = -x^2/4$ and first term $-x^2/4$; therefore, its value is $\dfrac{-x^2/4}{1 + (x^2/4)}$, provided $\left|\dfrac{x^2}{4}\right| < 1$, or $|x| < 2$. We now have

$$\underbrace{\sum_{k=1}^{\infty} \frac{(-1)^k k}{4^k} x^{2k}}_{\text{original series}} = \frac{x}{2}\frac{d}{dx}\left(\sum_{k=1}^{\infty}\left(-\frac{x^2}{4}\right)^k\right)$$

$$= \frac{x}{2}\frac{d}{dx}\left(\frac{-x^2/4}{1 + (x^2/4)}\right) \qquad \text{Sum of geometric series}$$

$$= \frac{x}{2}\frac{d}{dx}\left(\frac{-x^2}{4 + x^2}\right) \qquad \text{Simplify.}$$

$$= -\frac{4x^2}{(4 + x^2)^2}. \qquad \text{Differentiate and simplify.}$$

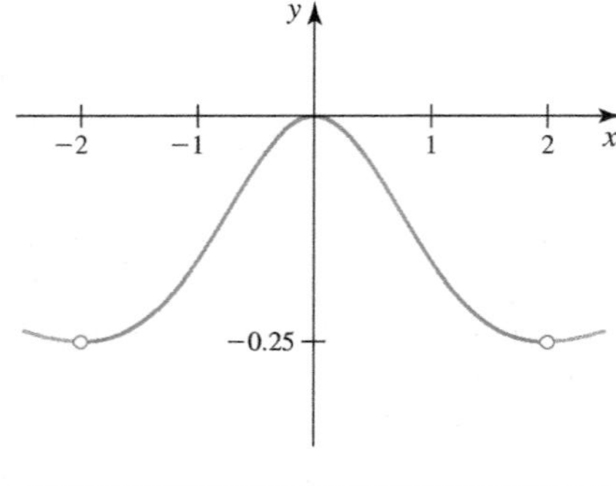

$\displaystyle\sum_{k=1}^{\infty} \frac{(-1)^k k}{4^k} x^{2k} = -\frac{4x^2}{(4 + x^2)^2}$ on $(-2, 2)$

Figure 9.21

Therefore, the function represented by the power series on $(-2, 2)$ has been uncovered; it is

$$f(x) = -\frac{4x^2}{(4 + x^2)^2}.$$

Notice that f is defined for $-\infty < x < \infty$ (Figure 9.21), but its power series centered at 0 converges to f only on $(-2, 2)$.

Related Exercises 55–64 ◄

SECTION 9.4 EXERCISES

Review Questions

1. Explain the strategy presented in this section for evaluating a limit of the form $\lim_{x \to a} f(x)/g(x)$, where f and g have Taylor series centered at a.
2. Explain the method presented in this section for approximating $\int_a^b f(x)\,dx$, where f has a Taylor series with an interval of convergence centered at a that includes b.
3. How would you approximate $e^{-0.6}$ using the Taylor series for e^x?
4. Suggest a Taylor series and a method for approximating π.
5. If $f(x) = \sum_{k=0}^{\infty} c_k x^k$ and the series converges for $|x| < b$, what is the power series for $f'(x)$?
6. What condition must be met by a function f for it to have a Taylor series centered at a?

Basic Skills

7–24. Limits *Evaluate the following limits using Taylor series.*

7. $\displaystyle\lim_{x \to 0} \frac{e^x - 1}{x}$
8. $\displaystyle\lim_{x \to 0} \frac{\tan^{-1} x - x}{x^3}$
9. $\displaystyle\lim_{x \to 0} \frac{-x - \ln(1 - x)}{x^2}$
10. $\displaystyle\lim_{x \to 0} \frac{\sin 2x}{x}$
11. $\displaystyle\lim_{x \to 0} \frac{e^x - e^{-x}}{x}$
12. $\displaystyle\lim_{x \to 0} \frac{1 + x - e^x}{4x^2}$
13. $\displaystyle\lim_{x \to 0} \frac{2\cos 2x - 2 + 4x^2}{2x^4}$
14. $\displaystyle\lim_{x \to \infty} x \sin \frac{1}{x}$
15. $\displaystyle\lim_{x \to 0} \frac{\ln(1 + x) - x + x^2/2}{x^3}$
16. $\displaystyle\lim_{x \to 4} \frac{x^2 - 16}{\ln(x - 3)}$
17. $\displaystyle\lim_{x \to 0} \frac{3\tan^{-1} x - 3x + x^3}{x^5}$
18. $\displaystyle\lim_{x \to 0} \frac{\sqrt{1 + x} - 1 - (x/2)}{4x^2}$
19. $\displaystyle\lim_{x \to 0} \frac{12x - 8x^3 - 6\sin 2x}{x^5}$
20. $\displaystyle\lim_{x \to 1} \frac{x - 1}{\ln x}$
21. $\displaystyle\lim_{x \to 2} \frac{x - 2}{\ln(x - 1)}$
22. $\displaystyle\lim_{x \to \infty} x(e^{1/x} - 1)$
23. $\displaystyle\lim_{x \to 0} \frac{e^{-2x} - 4e^{-x/2} + 3}{2x^2}$
24. $\displaystyle\lim_{x \to 0} \frac{(1 - 2x)^{-1/2} - e^x}{8x^2}$

25–32. Power series for derivatives

a. Differentiate the Taylor series about 0 for the following functions.
b. Identify the function represented by the differentiated series.
c. Give the interval of convergence of the power series for the derivative.

25. $f(x) = e^x$
26. $f(x) = \cos x$
27. $f(x) = \ln(1 + x)$
28. $f(x) = \sin x^2$
29. $f(x) = e^{-2x}$
30. $f(x) = (1 - x)^{-1}$
31. $f(x) = \tan^{-1} x$
32. $f(x) = -\ln(1 - x)$

33–36. Differential equations

a. Find a power series for the solution of the following differential equations, subject to the given initial condition.
b. Identify the function represented by the power series.

33. $y'(t) - y = 0,\ y(0) = 2$
34. $y'(t) + 4y = 8,\ y(0) = 0$
35. $y'(t) - 3y = 10,\ y(0) = 2$
36. $y'(t) = 6y + 9,\ y(0) = 2$

T 37–44. Approximating definite integrals *Use a Taylor series to approximate the following definite integrals. Retain as many terms as needed to ensure the error is less than 10^{-4}.*

37. $\int_0^{0.25} e^{-x^2}\,dx$

38. $\int_0^{0.2} \sin x^2\,dx$

39. $\int_{-0.35}^{0.35} \cos 2x^2\,dx$

40. $\int_0^{0.2} \sqrt{1 + x^4}\,dx$

41. $\int_0^{0.35} \tan^{-1} x\,dx$

42. $\int_0^{0.4} \ln(1 + x^2)\,dx$

43. $\int_0^{0.5} \frac{dx}{\sqrt{1 + x^6}}$

44. $\int_0^{0.2} \frac{\ln(1 + t)}{t}\,dt$

45–50. Approximating real numbers *Use an appropriate Taylor series to find the first four nonzero terms of an infinite series that is equal to the following numbers.*

45. e^2

46. $\sqrt{e}$

47. $\cos 2$

48. $\sin 1$

49. $\ln \frac{3}{2}$

50. $\tan^{-1} \frac{1}{2}$

51. **Evaluating an infinite series** Let $f(x) = (e^x - 1)/x$, for $x \neq 0$, and $f(0) = 1$. Use the Taylor series for f about 0 and evaluate $f(1)$ to find the value of $\sum_{k=0}^{\infty} \frac{1}{(k + 1)!}$.

52. **Evaluating an infinite series** Let $f(x) = (e^x - 1)/x$, for $x \neq 0$, and $f(0) = 1$. Use the Taylor series for f and f' about 0 to evaluate $f'(2)$ to find the value of $\sum_{k=1}^{\infty} \frac{k\,2^{k-1}}{(k + 1)!}$.

53. **Evaluating an infinite series** Write the Taylor series for $f(x) = \ln(1 + x)$ about 0 and find its interval of convergence. Assume the Taylor series converges to f on the interval of convergence. Evaluate $f(1)$ to find the value of $\sum_{k=1}^{\infty} \frac{(-1)^{k+1}}{k}$ (the alternating harmonic series).

54. **Evaluating an infinite series** Write the Maclaurin series for $f(x) = \ln(1 + x)$ and find the interval of convergence. Evaluate $f(-\frac{1}{2})$ to find the value of $\sum_{k=1}^{\infty} \frac{1}{k \cdot 2^k}$.

55–64. Representing functions by power series *Identify the functions represented by the following power series.*

55. $\sum_{k=0}^{\infty} \frac{x^k}{2^k}$

56. $\sum_{k=0}^{\infty} (-1)^k \frac{x^k}{3^k}$

57. $\sum_{k=0}^{\infty} (-1)^k \frac{x^{2k}}{4^k}$

58. $\sum_{k=0}^{\infty} 2^k x^{2k+1}$

59. $\sum_{k=1}^{\infty} \frac{x^k}{k}$

60. $\sum_{k=0}^{\infty} \frac{(-1)^k x^{k+1}}{4^k}$

61. $\sum_{k=1}^{\infty} (-1)^k \frac{kx^{k+1}}{3^k}$

62. $\sum_{k=1}^{\infty} \frac{x^{2k}}{k}$

63. $\sum_{k=2}^{\infty} \frac{k(k - 1)x^k}{3^k}$

64. $\sum_{k=2}^{\infty} \frac{x^k}{k(k - 1)}$

Further Explorations

65. **Explain why or why not** Determine whether the following statements are true and give an explanation or counterexample.

    a. To evaluate $\int_0^2 \frac{dx}{1 - x}$, one could expand the integrand in a Taylor series and integrate term by term.

    b. To approximate $\pi/3$, one could substitute $x = \sqrt{3}$ into the Taylor series for $\tan^{-1} x$.

    c. $\sum_{k=0}^{\infty} \frac{(\ln 2)^k}{k!} = 2$.

66–68. Limits with a parameter *Use Taylor series to evaluate the following limits. Express the result in terms of the parameter(s).*

66. $\lim_{x \to 0} \frac{e^{ax} - 1}{x}$

67. $\lim_{x \to 0} \frac{\sin ax}{\sin bx}$

68. $\lim_{x \to 0} \frac{\sin ax - \tan^{-1} ax}{bx^3}$

69. **A limit by Taylor series** Use Taylor series to evaluate $\lim_{x \to 0} \left(\frac{\sin x}{x} \right)^{1/x^2}$.

70. **Inverse hyperbolic sine** The *inverse hyperbolic sine* is defined in several ways; among them are

$$\sinh^{-1} x = \ln(x + \sqrt{x^2 + 1}) = \int_0^x \frac{dt}{\sqrt{1 + t^2}}.$$

Find the first four terms of the Taylor series for $\sinh^{-1} x$ using these two definitions (and be sure they agree).

71–74. Derivative trick *Here is an alternative way to evaluate higher derivatives of a function f that may save time. Suppose you can find the Taylor series for f centered at the point a without evaluating derivatives (for example, from a known series). Explain why $f^{(k)}(a) = k!$ multiplied by the coefficient of $(x - a)^k$. Use this idea to evaluate $f^{(3)}(0)$ and $f^{(4)}(0)$ for the following functions. Use known series and do not evaluate derivatives.*

71. $f(x) = e^{\cos x}$

72. $f(x) = \frac{x^2 + 1}{\sqrt[3]{1 + x}}$

73. $f(x) = \int_0^x \sin t^2\,dt$

74. $f(x) = \int_0^x \frac{1}{1 + t^4}\,dt$

Applications

75. **Probability: tossing for a head** The expected (average) number of tosses of a fair coin required to obtain the first head is $\sum_{k=1}^{\infty} k(\frac{1}{2})^k$. Evaluate this series and determine the expected number of tosses. (*Hint:* Differentiate a geometric series.)

76. **Probability: sudden death playoff** Teams A and B go into sudden death overtime after playing to a tie. The teams alternate possession of the ball, and the first team to score wins. Each team has a $\frac{1}{6}$ chance of scoring when it has the ball, with Team A having the ball first.

    a. The probability that Team A ultimately wins is $\sum_{k=0}^{\infty} \frac{1}{6}(\frac{5}{6})^{2k}$. Evaluate this series.

    b. The expected number of rounds (possessions by either team) required for the overtime to end is $\frac{1}{6}\sum_{k=1}^{\infty} k(\frac{5}{6})^{k-1}$. Evaluate this series.

T 77. **Elliptic integrals** The period of a pendulum is given by

$$T = 4\sqrt{\frac{\ell}{g}} \int_0^{\pi/2} \frac{d\theta}{\sqrt{1 - k^2 \sin^2 \theta}} = 4\sqrt{\frac{\ell}{g}}\,F(k),$$

where ℓ is the length of the pendulum, $g \approx 9.8\ \text{m/s}^2$ is the acceleration due to gravity, $k = \sin(\theta_0/2)$, and θ_0 is the initial angular displacement of the pendulum (in radians). The integral in this formula $F(k)$ is called an *elliptic integral*, and it cannot be evaluated analytically.

a. Approximate $F(0.1)$ by expanding the integrand in a Taylor (binomial) series and integrating term by term.
b. How many terms of the Taylor series do you suggest using to obtain an approximation to $F(0.1)$ with an error less than 10^{-3}?
c. Would you expect to use fewer or more terms (than in part (b)) to approximate $F(0.2)$ to the same accuracy? Explain.

78. Sine integral function The function $\text{Si}(x) = \int_0^x \frac{\sin t}{t}\, dt$ is called the *sine integral function*.

a. Expand the integrand in a Taylor series about 0.
b. Integrate the series to find a Taylor series for Si.
c. Approximate Si(0.5) and Si(1). Use enough terms of the series so the error in the approximation does not exceed 10^{-3}.

T **79. Fresnel integrals** The theory of optics gives rise to the two *Fresnel integrals*

$$S(x) = \int_0^x \sin t^2\, dt \quad \text{and} \quad C(x) = \int_0^x \cos t^2\, dt.$$

a. Compute $S'(x)$ and $C'(x)$.
b. Expand $\sin t^2$ and $\cos t^2$ in a Maclaurin series and then integrate to find the first four nonzero terms of the Maclaurin series for S and C.
c. Use the polynomials in part (b) to approximate $S(0.05)$ and $C(-0.25)$.
d. How many terms of the Maclaurin series are required to approximate $S(0.05)$ with an error no greater than 10^{-4}?
e. How many terms of the Maclaurin series are required to approximate $C(-0.25)$ with an error no greater than 10^{-6}?

T **80. Error function** An essential function in statistics and the study of the normal distribution is the *error function*

$$\text{erf}\,(x) = \frac{2}{\sqrt{\pi}} \int_0^x e^{-t^2}\, dt.$$

a. Compute the derivative of erf (x).
b. Expand e^{-t^2} in a Maclaurin series; then integrate to find the first four nonzero terms of the Maclaurin series for erf.
c. Use the polynomial in part (b) to approximate erf (0.15) and erf (−0.09).
d. Estimate the error in the approximations of part (c).

T **81. Bessel functions** Bessel functions arise in the study of wave propagation in circular geometries (for example, waves on a circular drum head). They are conveniently defined as power series. One of an infinite family of Bessel functions is

$$J_0(x) = \sum_{k=0}^{\infty} \frac{(-1)^k}{2^{2k}(k!)^2} x^{2k}.$$

a. Write out the first four terms of J_0.
b. Find the radius and interval of convergence of the power series for J_0.
c. Differentiate J_0 twice and show (by keeping terms through x^6) that J_0 satisfies the equation $x^2y''(x) + xy'(x) + x^2y(x) = 0$.

Additional Exercises

82. Power series for sec x Use the identity $\sec x = \frac{1}{\cos x}$ and long division to find the first three terms of the Maclaurin series for sec x.

83. Symmetry

a. Use infinite series to show that $\cos x$ is an even function. That is, show $\cos(-x) = \cos x$.
b. Use infinite series to show that $\sin x$ is an odd function. That is, show $\sin(-x) = -\sin x$.

84. Behavior of csc x We know that $\lim_{x\to 0^+} \csc x = \infty$. Use long division to determine exactly how csc x grows as $x \to 0^+$. Specifically, find a, b, and c (all positive) in the following sentence: As $x \to 0^+$, $\csc x \approx \frac{a}{x^b} + cx$.

85. L'Hôpital's Rule by Taylor series Suppose f and g have Taylor series about the point a.

a. If $f(a) = g(a) = 0$ and $g'(a) \neq 0$, evaluate $\lim_{x\to a} f(x)/g(x)$ by expanding f and g in their Taylor series. Show that the result is consistent with l'Hôpital's Rule.
b. If $f(a) = g(a) = f'(a) = g'(a) = 0$ and $g''(a) \neq 0$, evaluate $\lim_{x\to a} \frac{f(x)}{g(x)}$ by expanding f and g in their Taylor series. Show that the result is consistent with two applications of l'Hôpital's Rule.

T **86. Newton's derivation of the sine and arcsine series** Newton discovered the binomial series and then used it ingeniously to obtain many more results. Here is a case in point.

a. Referring to the figure, show that $x = \sin s$ or $s = \sin^{-1} x$.
b. The area of a circular sector of radius r subtended by an angle θ is $\frac{1}{2}r^2\theta$. Show that the area of the circular sector APE is $s/2$, which implies that

$$s = 2\int_0^x \sqrt{1 - t^2}\, dt - x\sqrt{1 - x^2}.$$

c. Use the binomial series for $f(x) = \sqrt{1 - x^2}$ to obtain the first few terms of the Taylor series for $s = \sin^{-1} x$.
d. Newton next inverted the series in part (c) to obtain the Taylor series for $x = \sin s$. He did this by assuming that $\sin s = \sum a_k s^k$ and solving $x = \sin(\sin^{-1} x)$ for the coefficients a_k. Find the first few terms of the Taylor series for $\sin s$ using this idea (a computer algebra system might be helpful as well).

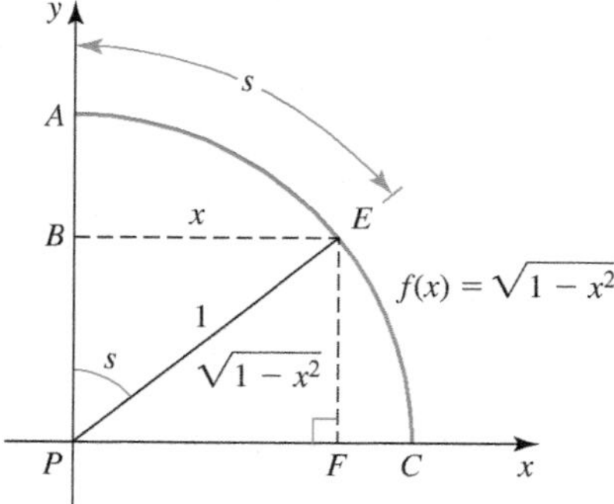

QUICK CHECK ANSWERS

1. $\frac{\sin x}{x} = \frac{x - x^3/3! + \cdots}{x} = 1 - \frac{x^2}{3!} + \cdots \to 1$ as $x \to 0$
2. The result is the power series for $-\sin x$. **3.** $x = 1/\sqrt{3}$ (which lies in the interval of convergence) ◄

CHAPTER 9 REVIEW EXERCISES

1. **Explain why or why not** Determine whether the following statements are true and give an explanation or counterexample.
   a. Let p_n be the nth-order Taylor polynomial for f centered at 2. The approximation $p_3(2.1) \approx f(2.1)$ is likely to be more accurate than the approximation $p_2(2.2) \approx f(2.2)$.
   b. If the Taylor series for f centered at 3 has a radius of convergence of 6, then the interval of convergence is $[-3, 9]$.
   c. The interval of convergence of the power series $\sum c_k x^k$ could be $\left(-\frac{7}{3}, \frac{7}{3}\right)$.
   d. The Maclaurin series for $f(x) = (1 + x)^{12}$ has a finite number of nonzero terms.

2–9. Taylor polynomials *Find the nth-order Taylor polynomial for the following functions centered at the given point a.*

2. $f(x) = \sin 2x, n = 3, a = 0$
3. $f(x) = \cos x^2, n = 2, a = 0$
4. $f(x) = e^{-x}, n = 2, a = 0$
5. $f(x) = \ln(1 + x), n = 3, a = 0$
6. $f(x) = \cos x, n = 2, a = \pi/4$
7. $f(x) = \ln x, n = 2, a = 1$
8. $f(x) = \sinh 2x, n = 4, a = 0$
9. $f(x) = \cosh x, n = 3, a = \ln 2$

T 10–13. Approximations

a. Find the Taylor polynomials of order $n = 0, 1,$ and 2 for the given functions centered at the given point a.
b. Make a table showing the approximations and the absolute error in these approximations using a calculator for the exact function value.

10. $f(x) = \cos x, a = 0$; approximate $\cos(-0.08)$.
11. $f(x) = e^x, a = 0$; approximate $e^{-0.08}$.
12. $f(x) = \sqrt{1 + x}, a = 0$; approximate $\sqrt{1.08}$.
13. $f(x) = \sin x, a = \pi/4$; approximate $\sin(\pi/5)$.

14–16. Estimating remainders *Find the remainder term $R_n(x)$ for the Taylor series centered at 0 for the following functions. Find an upper bound for the magnitude of the remainder on the given interval for the given value of n. (The bound is not unique.)*

14. $f(x) = e^x$; bound $R_3(x)$, for $|x| < 1$.
15. $f(x) = \sin x$; bound $R_3(x)$, for $|x| < \pi$.
16. $f(x) = \ln(1 - x)$; bound $R_3(x)$, for $|x| < 1/2$.

17–24. Radius and interval of convergence *Use the Ratio or Root Test to determine the radius of convergence of the following power series. Test the endpoints to determine the interval of convergence, when appropriate.*

17. $\sum \frac{k^2 x^k}{k!}$
18. $\sum \frac{x^{4k}}{k^2}$
19. $\sum (-1)^k \frac{(x + 1)^{2k}}{k!}$
20. $\sum \frac{(x - 1)^k}{k \cdot 5^k}$
21. $\sum \left(\frac{x}{9}\right)^{3k}$
22. $\sum \frac{(x + 2)^k}{\sqrt{k}}$
23. $\sum \frac{(x + 2)^k}{2^k \ln k}$
24. $x + \frac{x^3}{3} + \frac{x^5}{5} + \frac{x^7}{7} + \cdots$

25–30. Power series from the geometric series *Use the geometric series $\sum_{k=0}^{\infty} x^k = \frac{1}{1 - x}$, for $|x| < 1$, to determine the Maclaurin series and the interval of convergence for the following functions.*

25. $f(x) = \frac{1}{1 - x^2}$
26. $f(x) = \frac{1}{1 + x^3}$
27. $f(x) = \frac{1}{1 + 5x}$
28. $f(x) = \frac{10x}{1 + x}$
29. $f(x) = \frac{1}{(1 - 10x)^2}$
30. $f(x) = \ln(1 - 4x)$

31–38. Taylor series *Write out the first three nonzero terms of the Taylor series for the following functions centered at the given point a. Then write the series using summation notation.*

31. $f(x) = e^{3x}, a = 0$
32. $f(x) = 1/x, a = 1$
33. $f(x) = \cos x, a = \pi/2$
34. $f(x) = \frac{x^2}{1 + x}, a = 0$
35. $f(x) = \tan^{-1} 4x, a = 0$
36. $f(x) = \sin 2x, a = -\pi/2$
37. $f(x) = \cosh 3x, a = 0$
38. $f(x) = \frac{1}{4 + x^2}, a = 0$

39–42. Binomial series *Write out the first three terms of the Maclaurin series for the following functions.*

39. $f(x) = (1 + x)^{1/3}$
40. $f(x) = (1 + x)^{-1/2}$
41. $f(x) = (1 + x/2)^{-3}$
42. $f(x) = (1 + 2x)^{-5}$

43–46. Convergence *Write the remainder term $R_n(x)$ for the Taylor series for the following functions centered at the given point a. Then show that $\lim_{n\to\infty} |R_n(x)| = 0$, for all x in the given interval.*

43. $f(x) = e^{-x}, a = 0, -\infty < x < \infty$
44. $f(x) = \sin x, a = 0, -\infty < x < \infty$
45. $f(x) = \ln(1 + x), a = 0, -\frac{1}{2} \leq x \leq \frac{1}{2}$
46. $f(x) = \sqrt{1 + x}, a = 0, -\frac{1}{2} \leq x \leq \frac{1}{2}$

47–52. Limits by power series *Use Taylor series to evaluate the following limits.*

47. $\lim_{x\to 0} \frac{x^2/2 - 1 + \cos x}{x^4}$
48. $\lim_{x\to 0} \frac{2 \sin x - \tan^{-1} x - x}{2x^5}$
49. $\lim_{x\to 4} \frac{\ln(x - 3)}{x^2 - 16}$

50. $\lim_{x\to 0} \frac{\sqrt{1+2x} - 1 - x}{x^2}$

51. $\lim_{x\to 0} \frac{\sec x - \cos x - x^2}{x^4}$ $\left(\textit{Hint: } \text{The Maclaurin series for } \sec x \text{ is } 1 + \frac{x^2}{2} + \frac{5x^4}{24} + \frac{61x^6}{720} + \cdots.\right)$

52. $\lim_{x\to 0} \frac{(1+x)^{-2} - \sqrt[3]{1-6x}}{2x^2}$

T **53–56. Definite integrals by power series** *Use a Taylor series to approximate the following definite integrals. Retain as many terms as necessary to ensure the error is less than* 10^{-3}.

53. $\int_0^{1/2} e^{-x^2}\, dx$

54. $\int_0^{1/2} \tan^{-1} x\, dx$

55. $\int_0^{1} x \cos x\, dx$

56. $\int_0^{1/2} x^2 \tan^{-1} x\, dx$

T **57–60. Approximating real numbers** *Use an appropriate Taylor series to find the first four nonzero terms of an infinite series that is equal to the following numbers. There is more than one way to choose the center of the series.*

57. $\sqrt{119}$

58. $\sin 20°$

59. $\tan^{-1}(-\frac{1}{3})$

60. $\sinh(-1)$

61. A differential equation Find a power series solution of the differential equation $y'(x) - 4y + 12 = 0$, subject to the condition $y(0) = 4$. Identify the solution in terms of known functions.

T **62. Rejected quarters** The probability that a random quarter is *not* rejected by a vending machine is given by the integral $11.4\int_0^{0.14} e^{-102x^2}\, dx$ (assuming that the weights of quarters are normally distributed with a mean of 5.670 g and a standard deviation of 0.07 g). Expand the integrand in $n = 2$ and $n = 3$ terms of a Taylor series and integrate to find two estimates of the probability. Check for agreement between the two estimates.

T **63. Approximating ln 2** Consider the following three ways to approximate ln 2.

a. Use the Taylor series for $\ln(1 + x)$ centered at 0 and evaluate it at $x = 1$ (convergence was asserted in Table 9.5). Write the resulting infinite series.

b. Use the Taylor series for $\ln(1 - x)$ centered at 0 and the identity $\ln 2 = -\ln \frac{1}{2}$. Write the resulting infinite series.

c. Use the property $\ln(a/b) = \ln a - \ln b$ and the series of parts (a) and (b) to find the Taylor series for $f(x) = \ln\left(\frac{1+x}{1-x}\right)$ centered at 0.

d. At what value of x should the series in part (c) be evaluated to approximate ln 2? Write the resulting infinite series for ln 2.

e. Using four terms of the series, which of the three series derived in parts (a)–(d) gives the best approximation to ln 2? Can you explain why?

T **64. Graphing Taylor polynomials** Consider the function $f(x) = (1 + x)^{-4}$.

a. Find the Taylor polynomials p_0, p_1, p_2, and p_3 centered at 0.

b. Use a graphing utility to plot the Taylor polynomials and f, for $-1 < x < 1$.

c. For each Taylor polynomial, give the interval on which its graph appears indistinguishable from the graph of f.

Chapter 9 Guided Projects

Applications of the material in this chapter and related topics can be found in the following Guided Projects. For additional information, see the Preface.

- Series approximations to π
- Euler's formula (Taylor series with complex numbers)
- Stirling's formula and $n!$
- Three-sigma quality control
- Fourier series

11

Vectors and Vector-Valued Functions

Chapter Preview We now make a significant departure from previous chapters by stepping out of the xy-plane ($\mathbb{R}^2$) into three-dimensional space ($\mathbb{R}^3$). The fundamental concept of a *vector*—a quantity with magnitude and direction—is introduced in two and three dimensions. We then put vectors in motion by introducing *vector-valued functions*, or simply *vector functions*. The calculus of vector functions is a direct extension of everything you already know about limits, derivatives, and integrals. Also, with the calculus of vector functions, we can solve a wealth of practical problems involving the motion of objects in space. The chapter closes with an exploration of arc length, curvature, and tangent and normal vectors, all important features of space curves.

11.1 Vectors in the Plane

Imagine a raft drifting down a river, carried by the current. The speed and direction of the raft at a point may be represented by an arrow (Figure 11.1). The length of the arrow represents the speed of the raft at that point; longer arrows correspond to greater speeds. The orientation of the arrow gives the direction in which the raft is headed at that point. The arrows at points A and C in Figure 11.1 have the same length and direction, indicating that the raft has the same speed and heading at these locations. The arrow at B is shorter and points to the left of the rock, indicating that the raft slows down as it nears the rock.

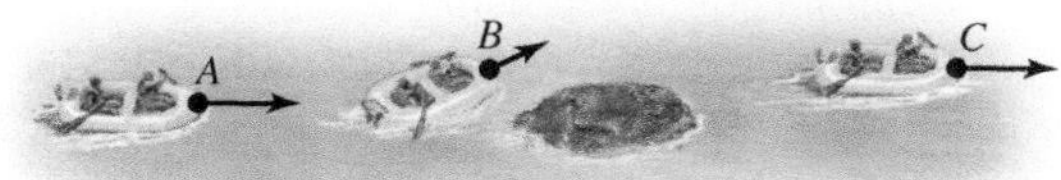

Figure 11.1

Basic Vector Operations

The arrows that describe the raft's motion are examples of *vectors*—quantities that have both *length* (or *magnitude*) and *direction*. Vectors arise naturally in many situations. For example, electric and magnetic fields, the flow of air over an airplane wing, and the velocity and acceleration of elementary particles are described by vectors (Figure 11.2). In this section, we examine vectors in the xy-plane and then extend the concept to three dimensions in Section 11.2.

The vector whose *tail* is at the point P and whose *head* is at the point Q is denoted $\overrightarrow{PQ}$ (Figure 11.3). The vector $\overrightarrow{QP}$ has its tail at Q and its head at P. We also label vectors with single boldfaced characters such as $\mathbf{u}$ and $\mathbf{v}$.

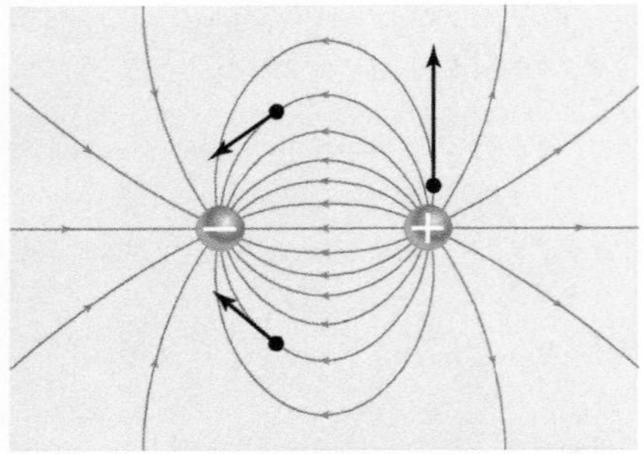

Electric field vectors due to two charges

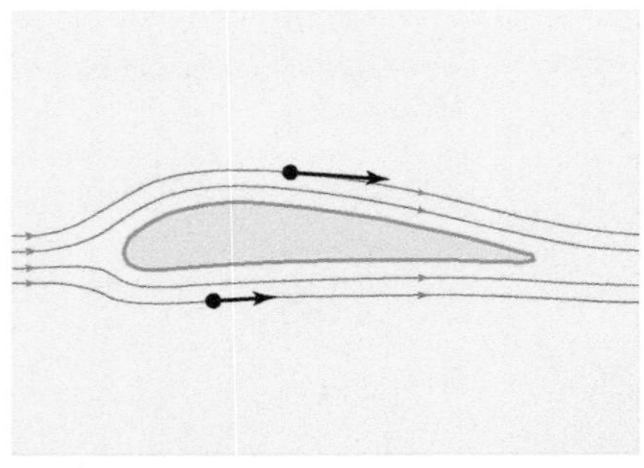

Velocity vectors of air flowing over an airplane wing

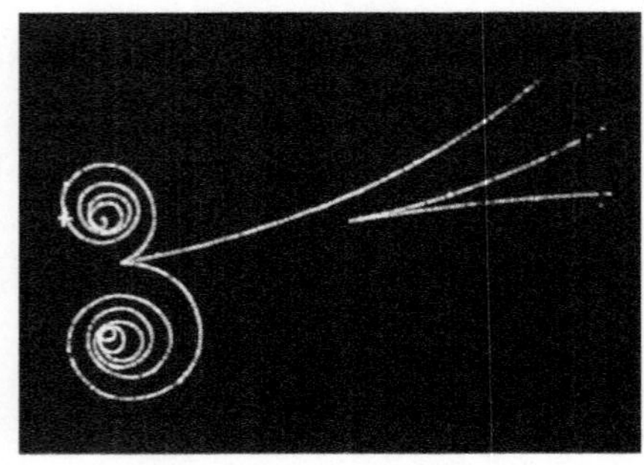

Tracks of elementary particles in a cloud chamber are aligned with the velocity vectors of the particles.

Figure 11.2

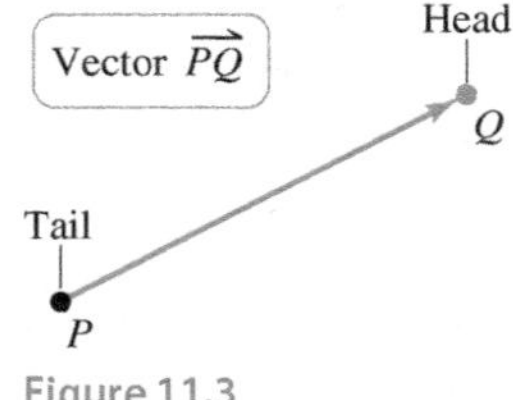

Figure 11.3

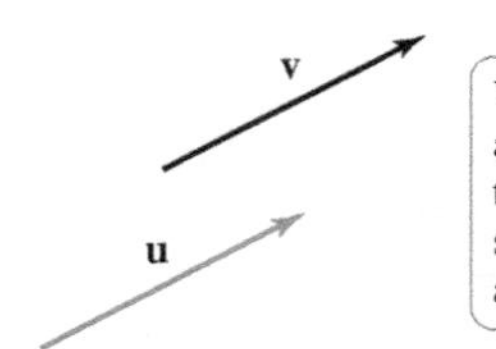

Figure 11.4

Two vectors **u** and **v** are *equal*, written $\mathbf{u} = \mathbf{v}$, if they have equal length and point in the same direction (Figure 11.4). An important fact is that equal vectors do not necessarily have the same location. *Any* two vectors with the same length and direction are equal.

Not all quantities are represented by vectors. For example, mass, temperature, and price have magnitude, but no direction. Such quantities are described by real numbers and are called *scalars*.

➤ In this book, *scalar* is another word for *real number*.

➤ The vector **v** is commonly handwritten as $\vec{v}$. The zero vector is handwritten as $\vec{0}$.

Vectors, Equal Vectors, Scalars, Zero Vector

Vectors are quantities that have both length (or magnitude) and direction. Two vectors are **equal** if they have the same magnitude and direction. Quantities having magnitude but no direction are called **scalars**. One exception is the **zero vector**, denoted **0**: It has length 0 and no direction.

Scalar Multiplication

A scalar c and a vector **v** can be combined using scalar-vector multiplication, or simply *scalar multiplication*. The resulting vector, denoted $c\mathbf{v}$, is called a *scalar multiple* of **v**. The magnitude of $c\mathbf{v}$ is $|c|$ multiplied by the magnitude of **v**. The vector $c\mathbf{v}$ has the same direction as **v** if $c > 0$. If $c < 0$, then $c\mathbf{v}$ and **v** point in opposite directions. If $c = 0$, then the product $0\mathbf{v} = \mathbf{0}$ (the zero vector).

For example, the vector $3\mathbf{v}$ is three times as long as **v** and has the same direction as **v**. The vector $-2\mathbf{v}$ is twice as long as **v**, but it points in the opposite direction. The vector $\frac{1}{2}\mathbf{v}$ points in the same direction as **v** and has half the length of **v** (Figure 11.5). The vectors **v**, $3\mathbf{v}$, $-2\mathbf{v}$, and $\frac{1}{2}\mathbf{v}$ are examples of *parallel vectors*: Each one is a scalar multiple of the others.

Same direction as **v** and half as long as **v**.

$\frac{1}{2}\mathbf{v}$

Twice as long as **v**, pointing in the opposite direction.

$-2\mathbf{v}$

$3\mathbf{v}$

Same direction as **v** and three times as long as **v**.

v

Figure 11.5

DEFINITION Scalar Multiples and Parallel Vectors

Given a scalar c and a vector **v**, the **scalar multiple** $c\mathbf{v}$ is a vector whose magnitude is $|c|$ multiplied by the magnitude of **v**. If $c > 0$, then $c\mathbf{v}$ has the same direction as **v**. If $c < 0$, then $c\mathbf{v}$ and **v** point in opposite directions. Two vectors are **parallel** if they are scalar multiples of each other.

➤ For convenience, we write $-\mathbf{u}$ for $(-1)\mathbf{u}$, $-c\mathbf{u}$ for $(-c)\mathbf{u}$, and $\mathbf{u}/c$ for $\frac{1}{c}\mathbf{u}$.

Notice that $0\mathbf{v} = \mathbf{0}$ for all vectors $\mathbf{v}$. It follows that *the zero vector is parallel to all vectors*. While it may seem counterintuitive, this result turns out to be a useful convention.

QUICK CHECK 1 Describe the magnitude and direction of the vector $-5\mathbf{v}$ relative to $\mathbf{v}$. ◄

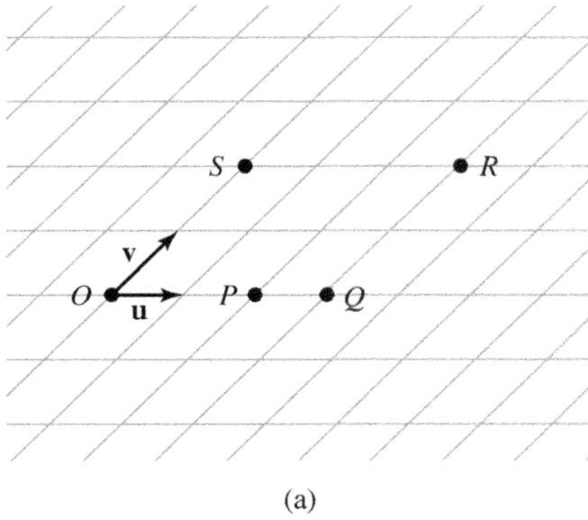

(a)

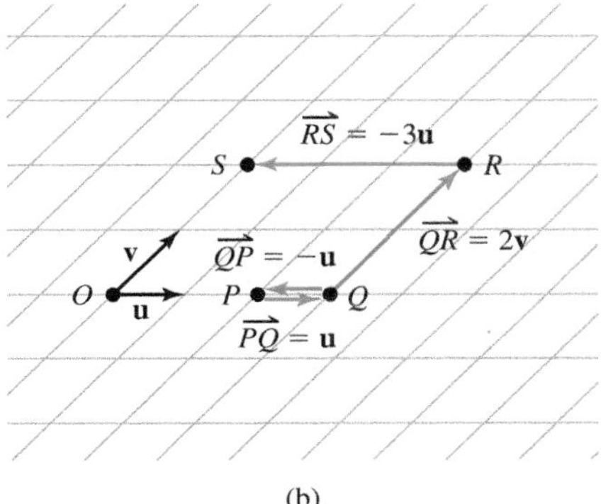

(b)

Figure 11.6

EXAMPLE 1 Parallel vectors Using Figure 11.6a, write the following vectors in terms of $\mathbf{u}$ or $\mathbf{v}$.

a. $\overrightarrow{PQ}$ **b.** $\overrightarrow{QP}$ **c.** $\overrightarrow{QR}$ **d.** $\overrightarrow{RS}$

SOLUTION

a. The vector $\overrightarrow{PQ}$ has the same direction and length as $\mathbf{u}$; therefore, $\overrightarrow{PQ} = \mathbf{u}$. These two vectors are equal even though they have different locations (Figure 11.6b).

b. Because $\overrightarrow{QP}$ and $\mathbf{u}$ have equal length but opposite directions, $\overrightarrow{QP} = (-1)\mathbf{u} = -\mathbf{u}$.

c. $\overrightarrow{QR}$ points in the same direction as $\mathbf{v}$ and is twice as long as $\mathbf{v}$, so $\overrightarrow{QR} = 2\mathbf{v}$.

d. $\overrightarrow{RS}$ points in the direction opposite that of $\mathbf{u}$ with three times the length of $\mathbf{u}$. Consequently, $\overrightarrow{RS} = -3\mathbf{u}$.

Related Exercises 17–20 ◄

Vector Addition and Subtraction

To illustrate the idea of vector addition, consider a plane flying horizontally at a constant speed in a crosswind (Figure 11.7). The length of vector $\mathbf{v}_a$ represents the plane's *airspeed*, which is the speed the plane would have in still air; $\mathbf{v}_a$ points in the direction of the nose of the plane. The wind vector $\mathbf{w}$ points in the direction of the crosswind and has a length equal to the speed of the crosswind. The combined effect of the motion of the plane and the wind is the *vector sum* $\mathbf{v}_g = \mathbf{v}_a + \mathbf{w}$, which is the velocity of the plane relative to the ground.

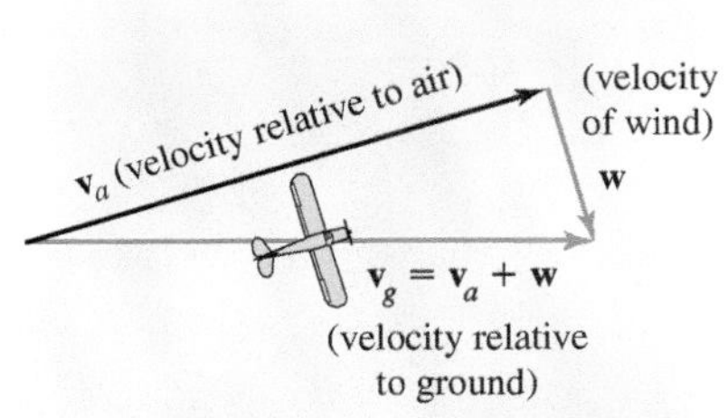

Figure 11.7

QUICK CHECK 2 Sketch the sum $\mathbf{v}_a + \mathbf{w}$ in Figure 11.7 if the direction of $\mathbf{w}$ is reversed. ◄

Figure 11.8 illustrates two ways to form the vector sum of two nonzero vectors $\mathbf{u}$ and $\mathbf{v}$ geometrically. The first method, called the **Triangle Rule**, places the tail of $\mathbf{v}$ at the head of $\mathbf{u}$. The sum $\mathbf{u} + \mathbf{v}$ is the vector that extends from the tail of $\mathbf{u}$ to the head of $\mathbf{v}$ (Figure 11.8b).

When $\mathbf{u}$ and $\mathbf{v}$ are not parallel, another way to form $\mathbf{u} + \mathbf{v}$ is to use the **Parallelogram Rule**. The *tails* of $\mathbf{u}$ and $\mathbf{v}$ are connected to form adjacent sides of a parallelogram; then the remaining two sides of the parallelogram are sketched. The sum $\mathbf{u} + \mathbf{v}$ is the vector that coincides with the diagonal of the parallelogram, beginning at the tails of $\mathbf{u}$ and $\mathbf{v}$ (Figure 11.8c). The Triangle Rule and Parallelogram Rule each produce the same vector sum $\mathbf{u} + \mathbf{v}$.

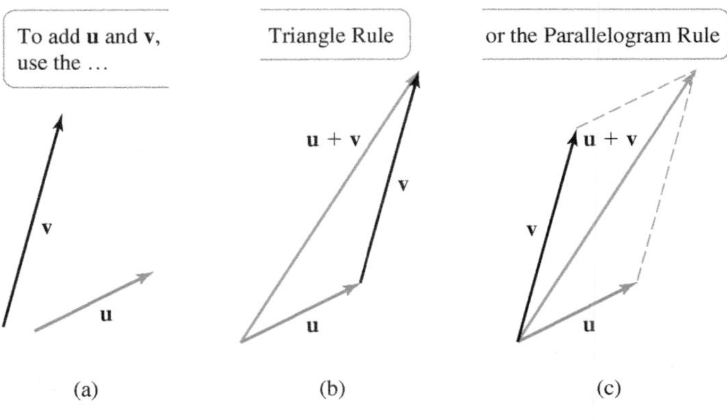

Figure 11.8

QUICK CHECK 3 Use the Triangle Rule to show that the vectors in Figure 11.8 satisfy $\mathbf{u} + \mathbf{v} = \mathbf{v} + \mathbf{u}$. ◄

The difference $\mathbf{u} - \mathbf{v}$ is defined to be the sum $\mathbf{u} + (-\mathbf{v})$. By the Triangle Rule, the tail of $-\mathbf{v}$ is placed at the head of $\mathbf{u}$; then $\mathbf{u} - \mathbf{v}$ extends from the tail of $\mathbf{u}$ to the head of $-\mathbf{v}$ (Figure 11.9a). Equivalently, when the tails of $\mathbf{u}$ and $\mathbf{v}$ coincide, $\mathbf{u} - \mathbf{v}$ has its tail at the head of $\mathbf{v}$ and its head at the head of $\mathbf{u}$ (Figure 11.9b).

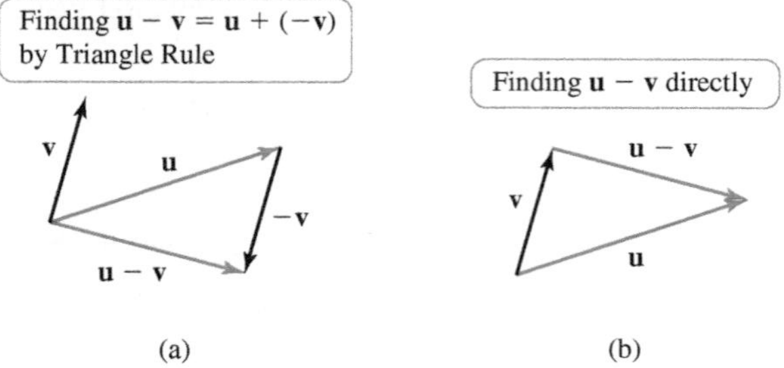

Figure 11.9

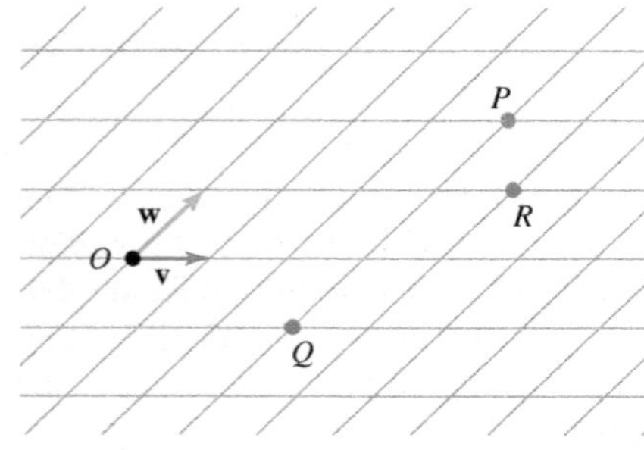

Figure 11.10

EXAMPLE 2 **Vector operations** Use Figure 11.10 to write the following vectors as sums of scalar multiples of $\mathbf{v}$ and $\mathbf{w}$.

a. $\overrightarrow{OP}$ **b.** $\overrightarrow{OQ}$ **c.** $\overrightarrow{QR}$

SOLUTION

a. Using the Triangle Rule, we start at O, move three lengths of $\mathbf{v}$ in the direction of $\mathbf{v}$ and then two lengths of $\mathbf{w}$ in the direction of $\mathbf{w}$ to reach P. Therefore, $\overrightarrow{OP} = 3\mathbf{v} + 2\mathbf{w}$ (Figure 11.11a).

b. The vector $\overrightarrow{OQ}$ coincides with the diagonal of a parallelogram having adjacent sides equal to $3\mathbf{v}$ and $-\mathbf{w}$. By the Parallelogram Rule, $\overrightarrow{OQ} = 3\mathbf{v} - \mathbf{w}$ (Figure 11.11b).

c. The vector $\overrightarrow{QR}$ lies on the diagonal of a parallelogram having adjacent sides equal to $\mathbf{v}$ and $2\mathbf{w}$. Therefore, $\overrightarrow{QR} = \mathbf{v} + 2\mathbf{w}$ (Figure 11.11c).

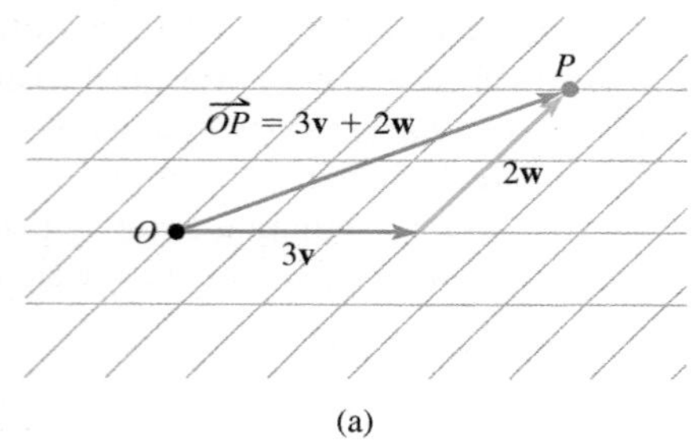

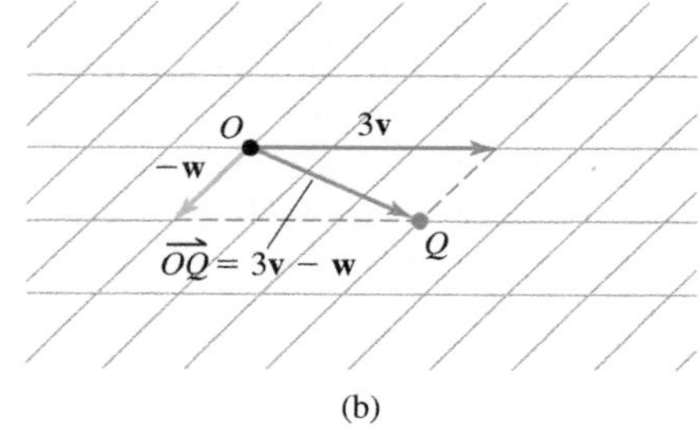

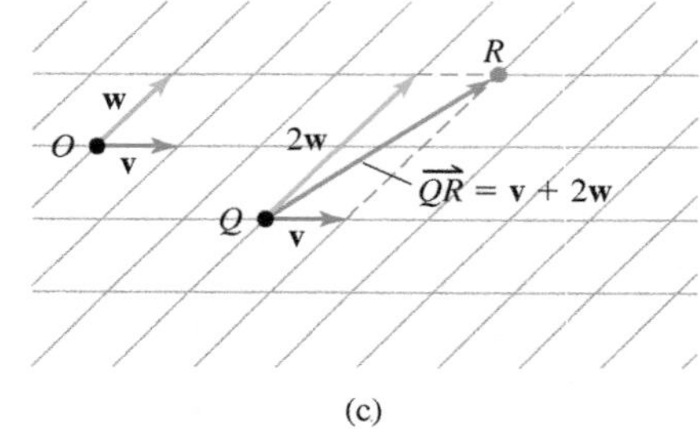

Figure 11.11

Related Exercises 21–22 ◀

Vector Components

So far, vectors have been examined from a geometric point of view. To do calculations with vectors, it is necessary to introduce a coordinate system. We begin by considering a vector $\mathbf{v}$ whose tail is at the origin in the Cartesian plane and whose head is at the point (v_1, v_2) (Figure 11.12a).

➤ Round brackets (a, b) enclose the *coordinates* of a point, while angle brackets $\langle a, b \rangle$ enclose the *components* of a vector. Note that in component form, the zero vector is $\mathbf{0} = \langle 0, 0 \rangle$.

> **DEFINITION** **Position Vectors and Vector Components**
>
> A vector $\mathbf{v}$ with its tail at the origin and head at the point (v_1, v_2) is called a **position vector** (or is said to be in **standard position**) and is written $\langle v_1, v_2 \rangle$. The real numbers v_1 and v_2 are the x- and y-**components** of $\mathbf{v}$, respectively. The position vectors $\mathbf{u} = \langle u_1, u_2 \rangle$ and $\mathbf{v} = \langle v_1, v_2 \rangle$ are **equal** if and only if $u_1 = v_1$ and $u_2 = v_2$.

There are infinitely many vectors equal to the position vector $\mathbf{v}$, all with the same length and direction (Figure 11.12b). It is important to abide by the convention that $\mathbf{v} = \langle v_1, v_2 \rangle$ refers to the position vector $\mathbf{v}$ *or to any other vector equal to* $\mathbf{v}$.

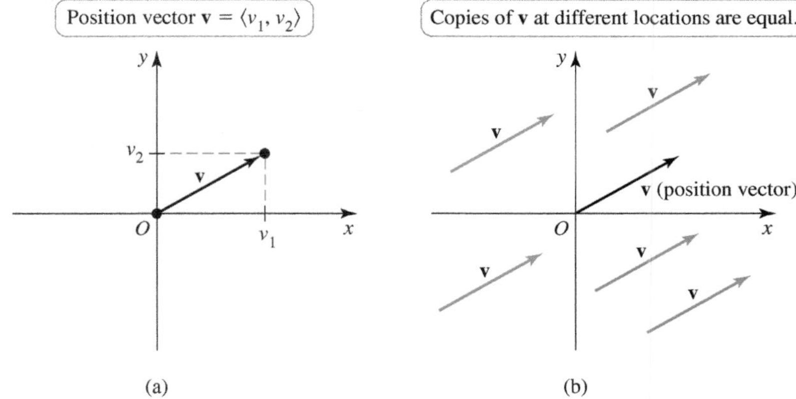

Figure 11.12

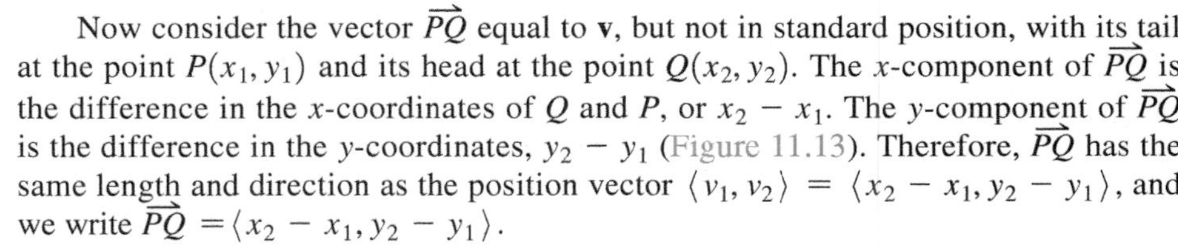
Now consider the vector $\overrightarrow{PQ}$ equal to $\mathbf{v}$, but not in standard position, with its tail at the point $P(x_1, y_1)$ and its head at the point $Q(x_2, y_2)$. The x-component of $\overrightarrow{PQ}$ is the difference in the x-coordinates of Q and P, or $x_2 - x_1$. The y-component of $\overrightarrow{PQ}$ is the difference in the y-coordinates, $y_2 - y_1$ (Figure 11.13). Therefore, $\overrightarrow{PQ}$ has the same length and direction as the position vector $\langle v_1, v_2 \rangle = \langle x_2 - x_1, y_2 - y_1 \rangle$, and we write $\overrightarrow{PQ} = \langle x_2 - x_1, y_2 - y_1 \rangle$.

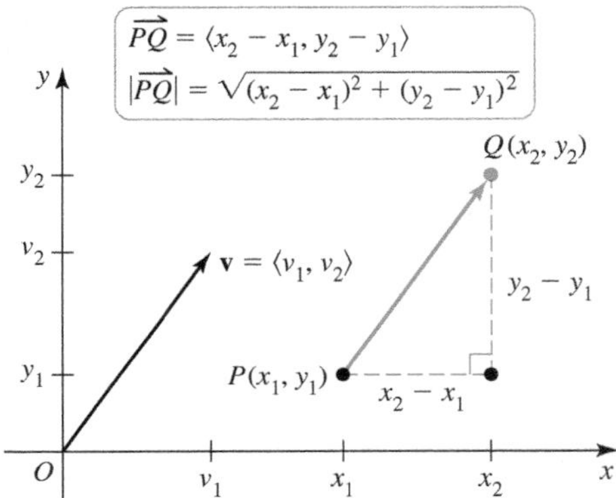

Figure 11.13

QUICK CHECK 4 Given the points $P(2, 3)$ and $Q(-4, 1)$, find the components of $\overrightarrow{PQ}$. ◀

As already noted, there are infinitely many vectors equal to a given position vector. All these vectors have the same length and direction; therefore, they are all equal. In other words, two arbitrary vectors are **equal** if they are equal to the same position vector. For example, the vector $\overrightarrow{PQ}$ from $P(2, 5)$ to $Q(6, 3)$ and the vector $\overrightarrow{AB}$ from $A(7, 12)$ to $B(11, 10)$ are equal because they both equal the position vector $\langle 4, -2 \rangle$.

Magnitude

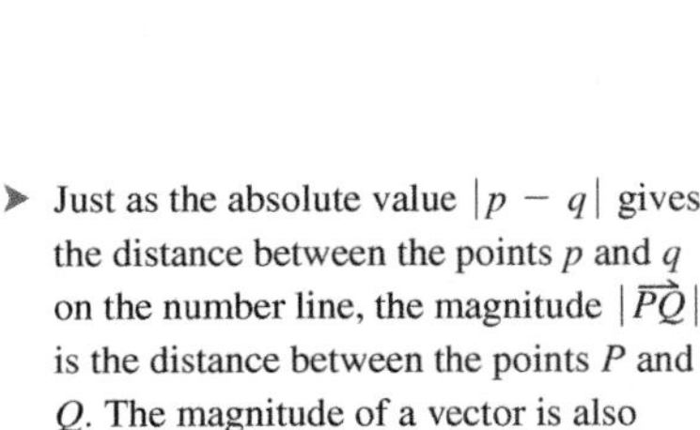
➤ Just as the absolute value $|p - q|$ gives the distance between the points p and q on the number line, the magnitude $|\overrightarrow{PQ}|$ is the distance between the points P and Q. The magnitude of a vector is also called its **norm**.

The magnitude of a vector is simply its length. By the Pythagorean Theorem and Figure 11.13, we have the following definition.

> DEFINITION **Magnitude of a Vector**
>
> Given the points $P(x_1, y_1)$ and $Q(x_2, y_2)$, the **magnitude**, or **length**, of $\overrightarrow{PQ} = \langle x_2 - x_1, y_2 - y_1 \rangle$, denoted $|\overrightarrow{PQ}|$, is the distance between P and Q:
>
> $$|\overrightarrow{PQ}| = \sqrt{(x_2 - x_1)^2 + (y_2 - y_1)^2}.$$
>
> The magnitude of the position vector $\mathbf{v} = \langle v_1, v_2 \rangle$ is $|\mathbf{v}| = \sqrt{v_1^2 + v_2^2}$.

EXAMPLE 3 **Calculating components and magnitude** Given the points $O(0, 0)$, $P(-3, 4)$, and $Q(6, 5)$, find the components and magnitude of the following vectors.

a. $\overrightarrow{OP}$ **b.** $\overrightarrow{PQ}$

SOLUTION

a. The vector $\overrightarrow{OP}$ is the position vector whose head is located at $P(-3, 4)$. Therefore, $\overrightarrow{OP} = \langle -3, 4 \rangle$ and its magnitude is $|\overrightarrow{OP}| = \sqrt{(-3)^2 + 4^2} = 5$.

b. $\overrightarrow{PQ} = \langle 6 - (-3), 5 - 4 \rangle = \langle 9, 1 \rangle$ and $|\overrightarrow{PQ}| = \sqrt{9^2 + 1^2} = \sqrt{82}$.

Related Exercises 23–27 ◀

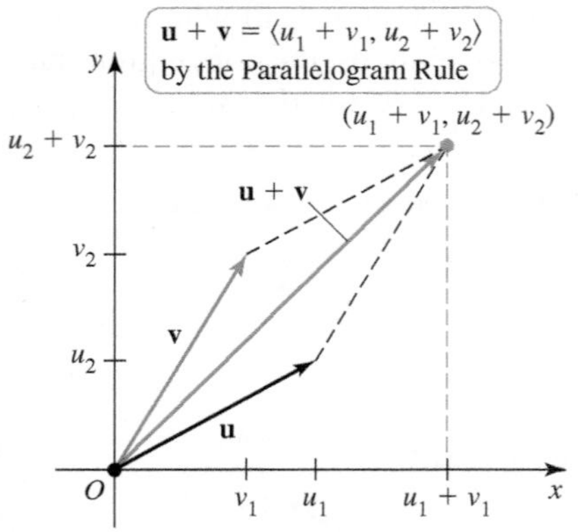

Figure 11.14

Vector Operations in Terms of Components

We now show how vector addition, vector subtraction, and scalar multiplication are performed using components. Suppose $\mathbf{u} = \langle u_1, u_2 \rangle$ and $\mathbf{v} = \langle v_1, v_2 \rangle$. The vector sum of **u** and **v** is $\mathbf{u} + \mathbf{v} = \langle u_1 + v_1, u_2 + v_2 \rangle$. This definition of a vector sum is consistent with the Parallelogram Rule given earlier (Figure 11.14).

For a scalar c and a vector **u**, the scalar multiple $c\mathbf{u}$ is $c\mathbf{u} = \langle cu_1, cu_2 \rangle$; that is, the scalar c multiplies each component of **u**. If $c > 0$, **u** and $c\mathbf{u}$ have the same direction (Figure 11.15a). If $c < 0$, **u** and $c\mathbf{u}$ have opposite directions (Figure 11.15b). In either case, $|c\mathbf{u}| = |c||\mathbf{u}|$ (Exercise 87).

Notice that $\mathbf{u} - \mathbf{v} = \mathbf{u} + (-\mathbf{v})$, where $-\mathbf{v} = \langle -v_1, -v_2 \rangle$. Therefore, the vector difference of **u** and **v** is $\mathbf{u} - \mathbf{v} = \langle u_1 - v_1, u_2 - v_2 \rangle$.

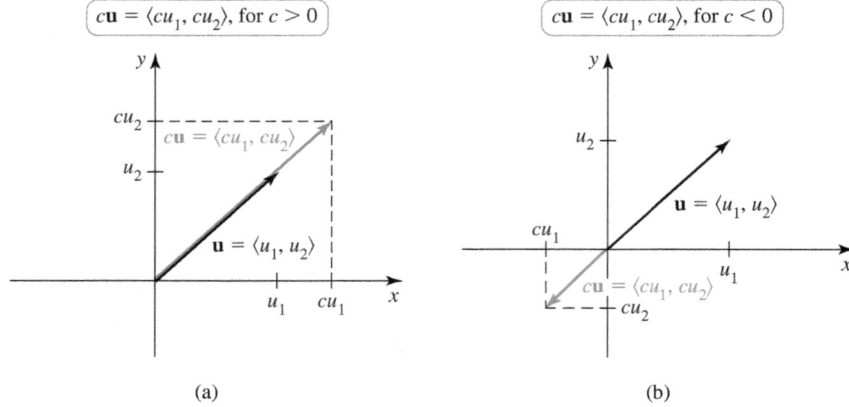

Figure 11.15

> **DEFINITION Vector Operations in $\mathbb{R}^2$**
>
> Suppose c is a scalar, $\mathbf{u} = \langle u_1, u_2 \rangle$, and $\mathbf{v} = \langle v_1, v_2 \rangle$.
>
> $\mathbf{u} + \mathbf{v} = \langle u_1 + v_1, u_2 + v_2 \rangle$ Vector addition
>
> $\mathbf{u} - \mathbf{v} = \langle u_1 - v_1, u_2 - v_2 \rangle$ Vector subtraction
>
> $c\mathbf{u} = \langle cu_1, cu_2 \rangle$ Scalar multiplication

➤ Recall that $\mathbb{R}^2$ (pronounced *R-two*) stands for the *xy*-plane or the set of all ordered pairs of real numbers.

EXAMPLE 4 Vector operations Let $\mathbf{u} = \langle -1, 2 \rangle$ and $\mathbf{v} = \langle 2, 3 \rangle$.

a. Evaluate $|\mathbf{u} + \mathbf{v}|$.

b. Simplify $2\mathbf{u} - 3\mathbf{v}$.

c. Find two vectors half as long as **u** and parallel to **u**.

SOLUTION

a. Because $\mathbf{u} + \mathbf{v} = \langle -1, 2 \rangle + \langle 2, 3 \rangle = \langle 1, 5 \rangle$, we have $|\mathbf{u} + \mathbf{v}| = \sqrt{1^2 + 5^2} = \sqrt{26}$.

b. $2\mathbf{u} - 3\mathbf{v} = 2\langle -1, 2 \rangle - 3\langle 2, 3 \rangle = \langle -2, 4 \rangle - \langle 6, 9 \rangle = \langle -8, -5 \rangle$

c. The vectors $\frac{1}{2}\mathbf{u} = \frac{1}{2}\langle -1, 2 \rangle = \langle -\frac{1}{2}, 1 \rangle$ and $-\frac{1}{2}\mathbf{u} = -\frac{1}{2}\langle -1, 2 \rangle = \langle \frac{1}{2}, -1 \rangle$ have half the length of **u** and are parallel to **u**.

Related Exercises 28–41 ◄

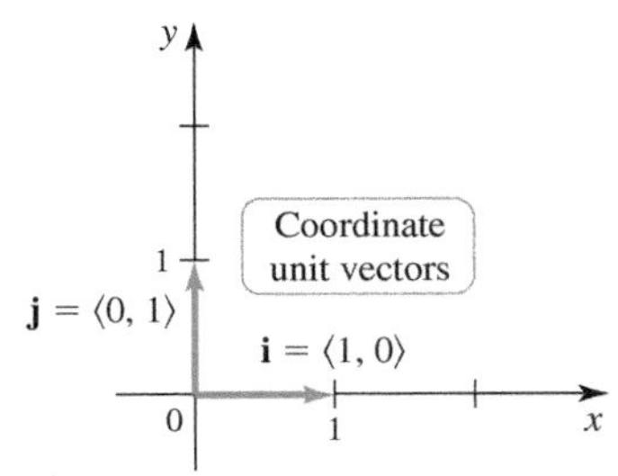

Figure 11.16

Unit Vectors

A **unit vector** is any vector with length 1. Two useful unit vectors are the **coordinate unit vectors** $\mathbf{i} = \langle 1, 0 \rangle$ and $\mathbf{j} = \langle 0, 1 \rangle$ (Figure 11.16). These vectors are directed along the coordinate axes and allow us to express all vectors in an alternative form. For example, by the Triangle Rule (Figure 11.17a),

$$\langle 3, 4 \rangle = 3\langle 1, 0 \rangle + 4\langle 0, 1 \rangle = 3\mathbf{i} + 4\mathbf{j}.$$

In general, the vector $\mathbf{v} = \langle v_1, v_2 \rangle$ (Figure 11.17b) is also written

$$\mathbf{v} = v_1\langle 1, 0 \rangle + v_2\langle 0, 1 \rangle = v_1\mathbf{i} + v_2\mathbf{j}.$$

➤ Coordinate unit vectors are also called **standard basis vectors**.

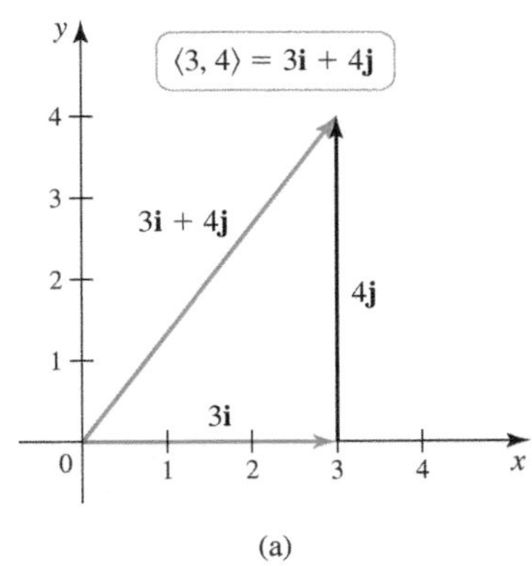

(a)

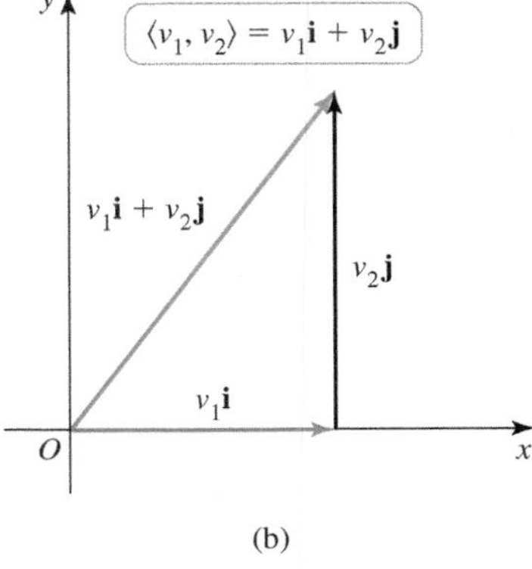

(b)

Figure 11.17

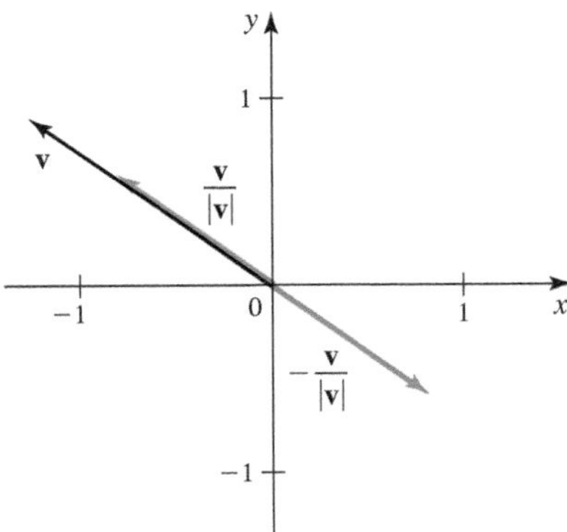

Figure 11.18

Given a nonzero vector $\mathbf{v}$, we sometimes need to construct a new vector parallel to $\mathbf{v}$ of a specified length. Dividing $\mathbf{v}$ by its length, we obtain the vector $\mathbf{u} = \frac{\mathbf{v}}{|\mathbf{v}|}$. Because $\mathbf{u}$ is a positive scalar multiple of $\mathbf{v}$, it follows that $\mathbf{u}$ has the same direction as $\mathbf{v}$. Furthermore, $\mathbf{u}$ is a unit vector because $|\mathbf{u}| = \frac{|\mathbf{v}|}{|\mathbf{v}|} = 1$. The vector $-\mathbf{u} = -\frac{\mathbf{v}}{|\mathbf{v}|}$ is also a unit vector (Figure 11.18). Therefore, $\pm\frac{\mathbf{v}}{|\mathbf{v}|}$ are unit vectors parallel to $\mathbf{v}$ that point in opposite directions.

To construct a vector that points in the direction of $\mathbf{v}$ and has a specified length $c > 0$, we form the vector $\frac{c\mathbf{v}}{|\mathbf{v}|}$. It is a positive scalar multiple of $\mathbf{v}$, so it points in the direction of $\mathbf{v}$, and its length is $\left|\frac{c\mathbf{v}}{|\mathbf{v}|}\right| = |c|\frac{|\mathbf{v}|}{|\mathbf{v}|} = c$. The vector $-\frac{c\mathbf{v}}{|\mathbf{v}|}$ points in the opposite direction and also has length c.

QUICK CHECK 5 Find vectors of length 10 parallel to the unit vector $\mathbf{u} = \left\langle \frac{3}{5}, \frac{4}{5} \right\rangle$. ◄

EXAMPLE 5 **Magnitude and unit vectors** Consider the points $P(1, -2)$ and $Q(6, 10)$.

a. Find $\overrightarrow{PQ}$ and two unit vectors parallel to $\overrightarrow{PQ}$.

b. Find two vectors of length 2 parallel to $\overrightarrow{PQ}$.

SOLUTION

a. $\overrightarrow{PQ} = \langle 6 - 1, 10 - (-2) \rangle = \langle 5, 12 \rangle$, or $5\mathbf{i} + 12\mathbf{j}$. Because $|\overrightarrow{PQ}| = \sqrt{5^2 + 12^2} = \sqrt{169} = 13$, a unit vector parallel to $\overrightarrow{PQ}$ is

$$\frac{\overrightarrow{PQ}}{|\overrightarrow{PQ}|} = \frac{\langle 5, 12 \rangle}{13} = \left\langle \frac{5}{13}, \frac{12}{13} \right\rangle = \frac{5}{13}\mathbf{i} + \frac{12}{13}\mathbf{j}.$$

The unit vector parallel to $\overrightarrow{PQ}$ with the opposite direction is $\left\langle -\frac{5}{13}, -\frac{12}{13} \right\rangle$.

b. To obtain two vectors of length 2 that are parallel to $\overrightarrow{PQ}$, we multiply the unit vector $\frac{5}{13}\mathbf{i} + \frac{12}{13}\mathbf{j}$ by ± 2:

$$2\left(\frac{5}{13}\mathbf{i} + \frac{12}{13}\mathbf{j}\right) = \frac{10}{13}\mathbf{i} + \frac{24}{13}\mathbf{j} \quad \text{and} \quad -2\left(\frac{5}{13}\mathbf{i} + \frac{12}{13}\mathbf{j}\right) = -\frac{10}{13}\mathbf{i} - \frac{24}{13}\mathbf{j}.$$

Related Exercises 42–47 ◄

QUICK CHECK 6 Verify that the vector $\left(\frac{5}{13}, \frac{12}{13}\right)$ has length 1. ◄

Properties of Vector Operations

➤ The Parallelogram Rule illustrates the commutative property $\mathbf{u} + \mathbf{v} = \mathbf{v} + \mathbf{u}$.

When we stand back and look at vector operations, ten general properties emerge. For example, the first property says that vector addition is commutative, which means $\mathbf{u} + \mathbf{v} = \mathbf{v} + \mathbf{u}$. This property is proved by letting $\mathbf{u} = \langle u_1, u_2 \rangle$ and $\mathbf{v} = \langle v_1, v_2 \rangle$. By the commutative property of addition for real numbers,

$$\mathbf{u} + \mathbf{v} = \langle u_1 + v_1, u_2 + v_2 \rangle = \langle v_1 + u_1, v_2 + u_2 \rangle = \mathbf{v} + \mathbf{u}.$$

The proofs of other properties are outlined in Exercises 82–85.

SUMMARY Properties of Vector Operations

Suppose $\mathbf{u}$, $\mathbf{v}$, and $\mathbf{w}$ are vectors and a and c are scalars. Then the following properties hold (for vectors in any number of dimensions).

1. $\mathbf{u} + \mathbf{v} = \mathbf{v} + \mathbf{u}$	Commutative property of addition
2. $(\mathbf{u} + \mathbf{v}) + \mathbf{w} = \mathbf{u} + (\mathbf{v} + \mathbf{w})$	Associative property of addition
3. $\mathbf{v} + \mathbf{0} = \mathbf{v}$	Additive identity
4. $\mathbf{v} + (-\mathbf{v}) = \mathbf{0}$	Additive inverse
5. $c(\mathbf{u} + \mathbf{v}) = c\mathbf{u} + c\mathbf{v}$	Distributive property 1
6. $(a + c)\mathbf{v} = a\mathbf{v} + c\mathbf{v}$	Distributive property 2
7. $0\mathbf{v} = \mathbf{0}$	Multiplication by zero scalar
8. $c\mathbf{0} = \mathbf{0}$	Multiplication by zero vector
9. $1\mathbf{v} = \mathbf{v}$	Multiplicative identity
10. $a(c\mathbf{v}) = (ac)\mathbf{v}$	Associative property of scalar multiplication

These properties allow us to solve vector equations. For example, to solve the equation $\mathbf{u} + \mathbf{v} = \mathbf{w}$ for $\mathbf{u}$, we proceed as follows:

$$\begin{aligned} (\mathbf{u} + \mathbf{v}) + (-\mathbf{v}) &= \mathbf{w} + (-\mathbf{v}) && \text{Add } -\mathbf{v} \text{ to both sides.} \\ \mathbf{u} + \underbrace{(\mathbf{v} + (-\mathbf{v}))}_{\mathbf{0}} &= \mathbf{w} + (-\mathbf{v}) && \text{Property 2} \\ \mathbf{u} + \mathbf{0} &= \mathbf{w} - \mathbf{v} && \text{Property 4} \\ \mathbf{u} &= \mathbf{w} - \mathbf{v}. && \text{Property 3} \end{aligned}$$

QUICK CHECK 7 Solve $3\mathbf{u} + 4\mathbf{v} = 12\mathbf{w}$ for $\mathbf{u}$. ◄

Applications of Vectors

Vectors have countless practical applications, particularly in the physical sciences and engineering. These applications are explored throughout the remainder of the book. For now, we present two common uses of vectors: to describe velocities and forces.

➤ *Velocity of the boat relative to the water* means the velocity (direction and speed) the boat would have in still water (or relative to someone traveling with the current).

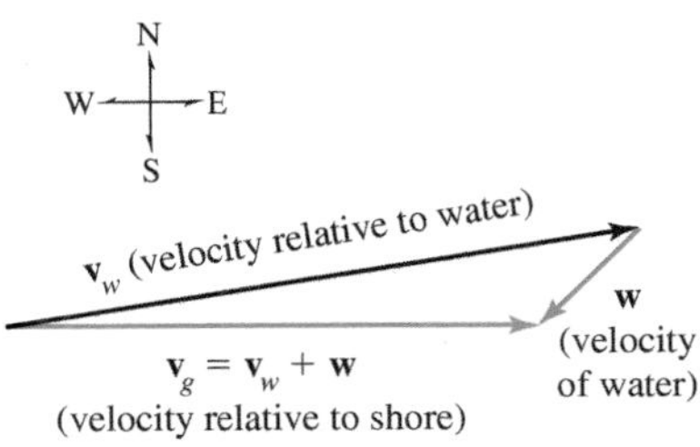

Figure 11.19

Velocity Vectors Consider a motorboat crossing a river whose current is everywhere represented by the constant vector **w** (Figure 11.19); this means that $|\mathbf{w}|$ is the speed of the moving water and **w** points in the direction of the moving water. Assume that the vector $\mathbf{v}_w$ gives the velocity of the boat relative to the water. The combined effect of **w** and $\mathbf{v}_w$ is the sum $\mathbf{v}_g = \mathbf{v}_w + \mathbf{w}$, which is velocity of the boat that would be observed by someone on the shore (or on the ground).

EXAMPLE 6 **Speed of a boat in a current** Suppose the water in a river moves southwest (45° west of south) at 4 mi/hr and a motorboat travels due east at 15 mi/hr relative to the shore. Determine the speed of the boat and its heading relative to the moving water (Figure 11.19).

SOLUTION To solve this problem, the vectors are placed in a coordinate system (Figure 11.20). Because the boat moves east at 15 mi/hr, the velocity relative to the shore is $\mathbf{v}_g = \langle 15, 0 \rangle$. To obtain the components of $\mathbf{w} = \langle w_x, w_y \rangle$, observe that $|\mathbf{w}| = 4$ and the lengths of the sides of the 45–45–90 triangle in Figure 11.20 are

$$|w_x| = |w_y| = |\mathbf{w}| \cos 45° = \frac{4}{\sqrt{2}} = 2\sqrt{2}.$$

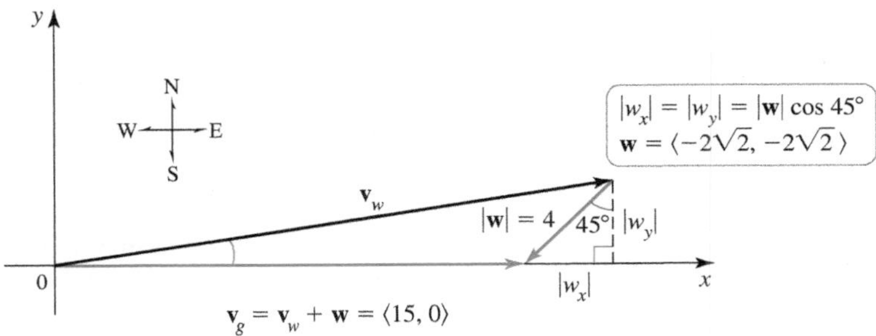

Figure 11.20

Given the orientation of **w** (southwest), $\mathbf{w} = \langle -2\sqrt{2}, -2\sqrt{2} \rangle$. Because $\mathbf{v}_g = \mathbf{v}_w + \mathbf{w}$ (Figure 11.20),

➤ Recall that the lengths of the legs of a 45–45–90 triangle are equal and are $1/\sqrt{2}$ times the length of the hypotenuse.

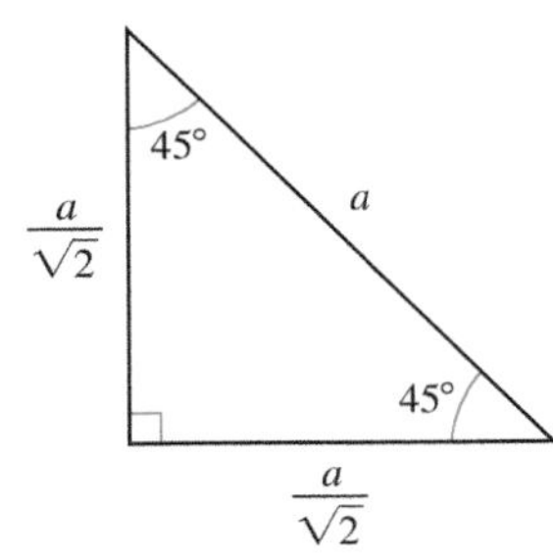

$$\begin{aligned} \mathbf{v}_w = \mathbf{v}_g - \mathbf{w} &= \langle 15, 0 \rangle - \langle -2\sqrt{2}, -2\sqrt{2} \rangle \\ &= \langle 15 + 2\sqrt{2}, 2\sqrt{2} \rangle. \end{aligned}$$

The magnitude of $\mathbf{v}_w$ is

$$|\mathbf{v}_w| = \sqrt{(15 + 2\sqrt{2})^2 + (2\sqrt{2})^2} \approx 18.$$

Therefore, the speed of the boat relative to the water is approximately 18 mi/hr.

The heading of the boat is given by the angle θ between $\mathbf{v}_w$ and the positive x-axis. The x-component of $\mathbf{v}_w$ is $15 + 2\sqrt{2}$ and the y-component is $2\sqrt{2}$. Therefore,

$$\theta = \tan^{-1}\left(\frac{2\sqrt{2}}{15 + 2\sqrt{2}}\right) \approx 9°.$$

The heading of the boat is approximately 9° north of east, and its speed relative to the water is approximately 18 mi/hr.

Related Exercises 48–53 ◄

➤ The magnitude of **F** is typically measured in pounds (lb) or newtons (N), where $1 \text{ N} = 1 \text{ kg-m/s}^2$.

➤ The vector $\langle \cos\theta, \sin\theta \rangle$ is a unit vector. Therefore, any position vector **v** may be written $\mathbf{v} = \langle |\mathbf{v}|\cos\theta, |\mathbf{v}|\sin\theta \rangle$, where θ is the angle that **v** makes with the positive x-axis.

Force Vectors Suppose a child pulls on the handle of a wagon at an angle of θ with the horizontal (Figure 11.21a). The vector **F** represents the force exerted on the wagon; it has a magnitude $|\mathbf{F}|$ and a direction given by θ. We denote the horizontal and vertical components of **F** by F_x and F_y, respectively. From Figure 11.21b, we see that $F_x = |\mathbf{F}|\cos\theta$, $F_y = |\mathbf{F}|\sin\theta$, and the force vector is $\mathbf{F} = \langle |\mathbf{F}|\cos\theta, |\mathbf{F}|\sin\theta \rangle$.

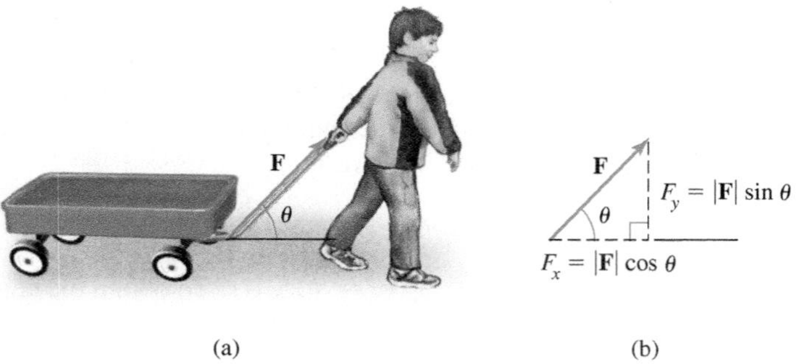

Figure 11.21

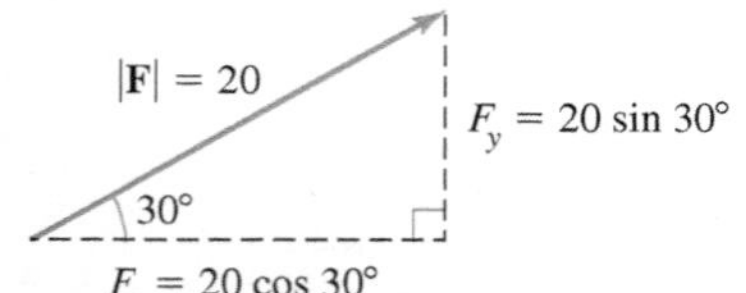

Figure 11.22

EXAMPLE 7 Finding force vectors A child pulls a wagon (Figure 11.21) with a force of $|\mathbf{F}| = 20$ lb at an angle of $\theta = 30°$ to the horizontal. Find the force vector **F**.

SOLUTION The force vector (Figure 11.22) is

$$\mathbf{F} = \langle |\mathbf{F}|\cos\theta, |\mathbf{F}|\sin\theta \rangle = \langle 20\cos 30°, 20\sin 30° \rangle = \langle 10\sqrt{3}, 10 \rangle.$$

Related Exercises 54–58 ◀

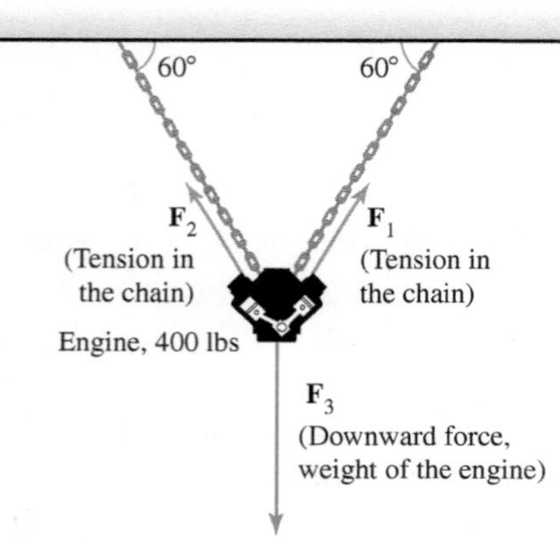

Figure 11.23

EXAMPLE 8 Balancing forces A 400-lb engine is suspended from two chains that form 60° angles with a horizontal ceiling (Figure 11.23). How much weight does each chain support?

SOLUTION Let $\mathbf{F}_1$ and $\mathbf{F}_2$ denote the forces exerted by the chains on the engine and let $\mathbf{F}_3$ be the downward force due to the weight of the engine (Figure 11.23). Placing the vectors in a standard coordinate system (Figure 11.24), we find that $\mathbf{F}_1 = \langle |\mathbf{F}_1|\cos 60°, |\mathbf{F}_1|\sin 60° \rangle$, $\mathbf{F}_2 = \langle -|\mathbf{F}_2|\cos 60°, |\mathbf{F}_2|\sin 60° \rangle$, and $\mathbf{F}_3 = \langle 0, -400 \rangle$.

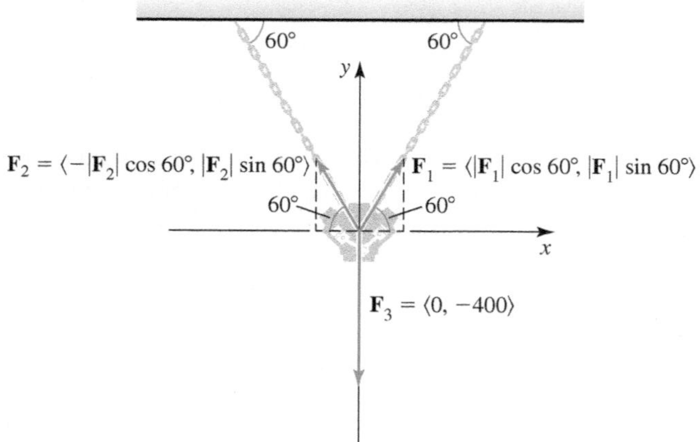

Figure 11.24

➤ The components of $\mathbf{F}_2$ in Example 8 can also be computed using an angle of 120°. That is, $\mathbf{F}_2 = \langle |\mathbf{F}_2|\cos 120°, |\mathbf{F}_2|\sin 120° \rangle$.

If the engine is in equilibrium (so the chains and engine are stationary), the sum of the forces is zero; that is, $\mathbf{F}_1 + \mathbf{F}_2 + \mathbf{F}_3 = \mathbf{0}$ or $\mathbf{F}_1 + \mathbf{F}_2 = -\mathbf{F}_3$. Therefore,

$$\langle |\mathbf{F}_1|\cos 60° - |\mathbf{F}_2|\cos 60°, |\mathbf{F}_1|\sin 60° + |\mathbf{F}_2|\sin 60° \rangle = \langle 0, 400 \rangle.$$

Equating corresponding components, we obtain two equations to be solved for $|\mathbf{F}_1|$ and $|\mathbf{F}_2|$:

$$|\mathbf{F}_1| \cos 60° - |\mathbf{F}_2| \cos 60° = 0 \text{ and}$$
$$|\mathbf{F}_1| \sin 60° + |\mathbf{F}_2| \sin 60° = 400.$$

Factoring the first equation, we find that $(|\mathbf{F}_1| - |\mathbf{F}_2|) \cos 60° = 0$, which implies that $|\mathbf{F}_1| = |\mathbf{F}_2|$. Replacing $|\mathbf{F}_2|$ with $|\mathbf{F}_1|$ in the second equation gives $2|\mathbf{F}_1| \sin 60° = 400$. Noting that $\sin 60° = \sqrt{3}/2$ and solving for $|\mathbf{F}_1|$, we find that $|\mathbf{F}_1| = 400/\sqrt{3} \approx 231$. Each chain must be able to support a weight of approximately 231 lb.

Related Exercises 54–58 ◀

SECTION 11.1 EXERCISES

Review Questions

1. Interpret the following statement: Points have a location, but no size or direction; nonzero vectors have a size and direction, but no location.
2. What is a position vector?
3. Draw x- and y-axes on a page and mark two points P and Q. Then draw $\overrightarrow{PQ}$ and $\overrightarrow{QP}$.
4. On the diagram of Exercise 3, draw the position vector that is equal to $\overrightarrow{PQ}$.
5. Given a position vector $\mathbf{v}$, why are there infinitely many vectors equal to $\mathbf{v}$?
6. Explain how to add two vectors geometrically.
7. Explain how to find a scalar multiple of a vector geometrically.
8. Given two points P and Q, how are the components of $\overrightarrow{PQ}$ determined?
9. If $\mathbf{u} = \langle u_1, u_2 \rangle$ and $\mathbf{v} = \langle v_1, v_2 \rangle$, how do you find $\mathbf{u} + \mathbf{v}$?
10. If $\mathbf{v} = \langle v_1, v_2 \rangle$ and c is a scalar, how do you find $c\mathbf{v}$?
11. How do you compute the magnitude of $\mathbf{v} = \langle v_1, v_2 \rangle$?
12. Express the vector $\mathbf{v} = \langle v_1, v_2 \rangle$ in terms of the unit vectors $\mathbf{i}$ and $\mathbf{j}$.
13. How do you compute $|\overrightarrow{PQ}|$ from the coordinates of the points P and Q?
14. Explain how to find two unit vectors parallel to a vector $\mathbf{v}$.
15. How do you find a vector of length 10 in the direction of $\mathbf{v} = \langle 3, -2 \rangle$?
16. If a force of magnitude 100 is directed 45° south of east, what are its components?

Basic Skills

17–22. Vector operations *Refer to the figure and carry out the following vector operations.*

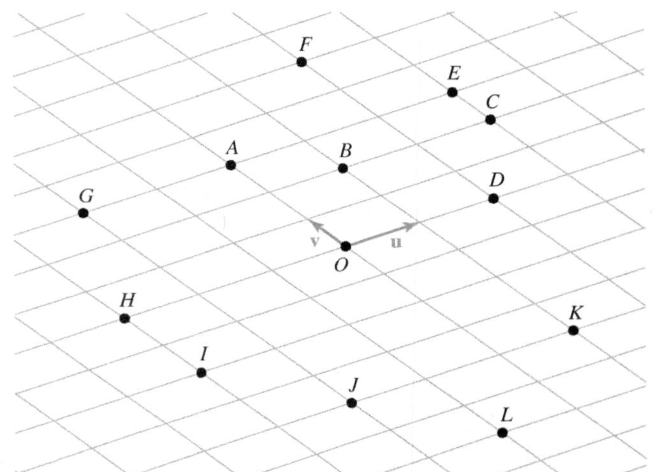

17. **Scalar multiples** Which of the following vectors equals $\overrightarrow{CE}$? (There may be more than one correct answer.)

    a. $\mathbf{v}$ **b.** $\frac{1}{2}\overrightarrow{HI}$ **c.** $\frac{1}{3}\overrightarrow{OA}$ **d.** $\mathbf{u}$ **e.** $\frac{1}{2}\overrightarrow{IH}$

18. **Scalar multiples** Which of the following vectors equals $\overrightarrow{BK}$? (There may be more than one correct answer.)

    a. $6\mathbf{v}$ **b.** $-6\mathbf{v}$ **c.** $3\,\overrightarrow{HI}$ **d.** $3\,\overrightarrow{IH}$ **e.** $2\,\overrightarrow{AO}$

19. **Scalar multiples** Write the following vectors as scalar multiples of $\mathbf{u}$ or $\mathbf{v}$.

    a. $\overrightarrow{OA}$ **b.** $\overrightarrow{OD}$ **c.** $\overrightarrow{OH}$ **d.** $\overrightarrow{AG}$ **e.** $\overrightarrow{CE}$

20. **Scalar multiples** Write the following vectors as scalar multiples of $\mathbf{u}$ or $\mathbf{v}$.

    a. $\overrightarrow{IH}$ **b.** $\overrightarrow{HI}$ **c.** $\overrightarrow{JK}$ **d.** $\overrightarrow{FD}$ **e.** $\overrightarrow{EA}$

21. Vector addition Write the following vectors as sums of scalar multiples of **u** and **v**.

a. $\overrightarrow{OE}$ **b.** $\overrightarrow{OB}$ **c.** $\overrightarrow{OF}$ **d.** $\overrightarrow{OG}$ **e.** $\overrightarrow{OC}$
f. $\overrightarrow{OI}$ **g.** $\overrightarrow{OJ}$ **h.** $\overrightarrow{OK}$ **i.** $\overrightarrow{OL}$

22. Vector addition Write the following vectors as sums of scalar multiples of **u** and **v**.

a. $\overrightarrow{BF}$ **b.** $\overrightarrow{DE}$ **c.** $\overrightarrow{AF}$ **d.** $\overrightarrow{AD}$ **e.** $\overrightarrow{CD}$
f. $\overrightarrow{JD}$ **g.** $\overrightarrow{JI}$ **h.** $\overrightarrow{DB}$ **i.** $\overrightarrow{IL}$

23. Components and magnitudes Define the points $O(0, 0)$, $P(3, 2)$, $Q(4, 2)$, and $R(-6, -1)$. For each vector, do the following.

(i) Sketch the vector in an *xy*-coordinate system.
(ii) Compute the magnitude of the vector.

a. $\overrightarrow{OP}$ **b.** $\overrightarrow{QP}$ **c.** $\overrightarrow{RQ}$

24–27. Components and equality *Define the points* $P(-3, -1)$, $Q(-1, 2)$, $R(1, 2)$, $S(3, 5)$, $T(4, 2)$, *and* $U(6, 4)$.

24. Sketch $\overrightarrow{PU}$, $\overrightarrow{TR}$, and $\overrightarrow{SQ}$ and the corresponding position vectors.

25. Sketch $\overrightarrow{QU}$, $\overrightarrow{PT}$, and $\overrightarrow{RS}$ and the corresponding position vectors.

26. Find the equal vectors among $\overrightarrow{PQ}$, $\overrightarrow{RS}$, and $\overrightarrow{TU}$.

27. Which of the vectors $\overrightarrow{QT}$ or $\overrightarrow{SU}$ is equal to $\langle 5, 0 \rangle$?

28–33. Vector operations *Let* $\mathbf{u} = \langle 4, -2 \rangle$, $\mathbf{v} = \langle -4, 6 \rangle$, *and* $\mathbf{w} = \langle 0, 8 \rangle$. *Express the following vectors in the form* $\langle a, b \rangle$.

28. $\mathbf{u} + \mathbf{v}$ **29.** $\mathbf{w} - \mathbf{u}$ **30.** $2\mathbf{u} + 3\mathbf{v}$
31. $\mathbf{w} - 3\mathbf{v}$ **32.** $10\mathbf{u} - 3\mathbf{v} + \mathbf{w}$ **33.** $8\mathbf{w} + \mathbf{v} - 6\mathbf{u}$

34–41. Vector operations *Let* $\mathbf{u} = \langle 3, -4 \rangle$, $\mathbf{v} = \langle 1, 1 \rangle$, *and* $\mathbf{w} = \langle -1, 0 \rangle$.

34. Find $|\mathbf{u} + \mathbf{v}|$. **35.** Find $|-2\mathbf{v}|$.

36. Find $|\mathbf{u} + \mathbf{v} + \mathbf{w}|$. **37.** Find $|2\mathbf{u} + 3\mathbf{v} - 4\mathbf{w}|$.

38. Find two vectors parallel to **u** with four times the magnitude of **u**.

39. Find two vectors parallel to **v** with three times the magnitude of **v**.

40. Which has the greater magnitude, 2**u** or 7**v**?

41. Which has the greater magnitude, $\mathbf{u} - \mathbf{v}$ or $\mathbf{w} - \mathbf{u}$?

42–47. Unit vectors *Define the points* $P(-4, 1)$, $Q(3, -4)$, *and* $R(2, 6)$.

42. Express $\overrightarrow{PQ}$ in the form $a\mathbf{i} + b\mathbf{j}$.

43. Express $\overrightarrow{QR}$ in the form $a\mathbf{i} + b\mathbf{j}$.

44. Find the unit vector with the same direction as $\overrightarrow{QR}$.

45. Find two unit vectors parallel to $\overrightarrow{PR}$.

46. Find two vectors parallel to $\overrightarrow{RP}$ with length 4.

47. Find two vectors parallel to $\overrightarrow{QP}$ with length 4.

48. A boat in a current The water in a river moves south at 10 mi/hr. A motorboat travels due east at a speed of 20 mi/hr relative to the shore. Determine the speed and direction of the boat relative to the moving water.

49. Another boat in a current The water in a river moves south at 5 km/hr. A motorboat travels due east at a speed of 40 km/hr relative to the water. Determine the speed of the boat relative to the shore.

50. Parachute in the wind In still air, a parachute with a payload falls vertically at a terminal speed of 4 m/s. Find the direction and magnitude of its terminal velocity relative to the ground if it falls in a steady wind blowing horizontally from west to east at 10 m/s.

51. Airplane in a wind An airplane flies horizontally from east to west at 320 mi/hr relative to the air. If it flies in a steady 40 mi/hr wind that blows horizontally toward the southwest (45° south of west), find the speed and direction of the airplane relative to the ground.

52. Canoe in a current A woman in a canoe paddles due west at 4 mi/hr relative to the water in a current that flows northwest at 2 mi/hr. Find the speed and direction of the canoe relative to the shore.

53. Boat in a wind A sailboat floats in a current that flows due east at 1 m/s. Due to a wind, the boat's actual speed relative to the shore is $\sqrt{3}$ m/s in a direction 30° north of east. Find the speed and direction of the wind.

54. Towing a boat A boat is towed with a force of 150 lb with a rope that makes an angle of 30° to the horizontal. Find the horizontal and vertical components of the force.

55. Pulling a suitcase Suppose you pull a suitcase with a strap that makes a 60° angle with the horizontal. The magnitude of the force you exert on the suitcase is 40 lb.

a. Find the horizontal and vertical components of the force.
b. Is the horizontal component of the force greater if the angle of the strap is 45° instead of 60°?
c. Is the vertical component of the force greater if the angle of the strap is 45° instead of 60°?

56. Which is greater? Which has a greater horizontal component, a 100-N force directed at an angle of 60° above the horizontal or a 60-N force directed at an angle of 30° above the horizontal?

57. Suspended load If a 500-lb load is suspended by two chains (see figure), what is the magnitude of the force each chain must be able to support?

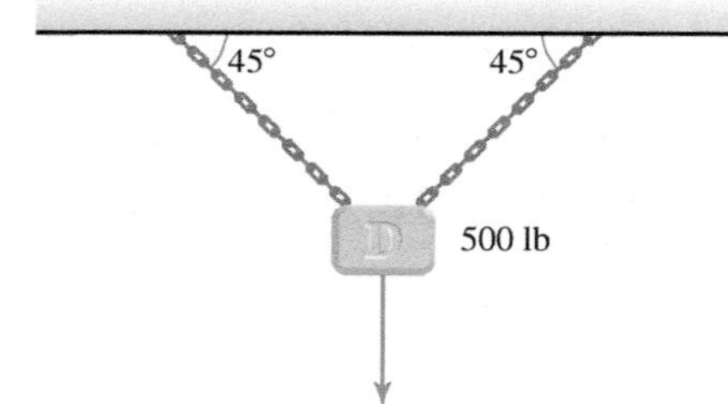

58. Net force Three forces are applied to an object, as shown in the figure. Find the magnitude and direction of the sum of the forces.

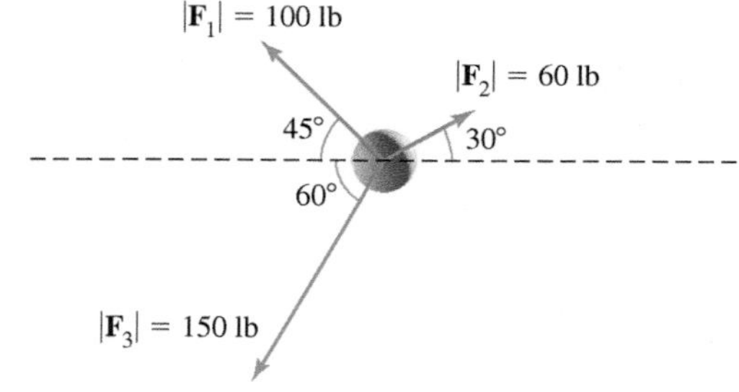

Further Explorations

59. Explain why or why not Determine whether the following statements are true and give an explanation or counterexample.

a. José travels from point A to point B in the plane by following vector $\mathbf{u}$, then vector $\mathbf{v}$, and then vector $\mathbf{w}$. If he starts at A and follows $\mathbf{w}$, then $\mathbf{v}$, and then $\mathbf{u}$, he still arrives at B.
b. Maria travels from A to B in the plane by following the vector $\mathbf{u}$. By following $-\mathbf{u}$, she returns from B to A.
c. $|\mathbf{u} + \mathbf{v}| \geq |\mathbf{u}|$, for all vectors $\mathbf{u}$ and $\mathbf{v}$.
d. $|\mathbf{u} + \mathbf{v}| \geq |\mathbf{u}| + |\mathbf{v}|$, for all vectors $\mathbf{u}$ and $\mathbf{v}$.
e. Parallel vectors have the same length.
f. If $\overrightarrow{AB} = \overrightarrow{CD}$, then $A = C$ and $B = D$.
g. If $\mathbf{u}$ and $\mathbf{v}$ are perpendicular, then $|\mathbf{u} + \mathbf{v}| = |\mathbf{u}| + |\mathbf{v}|$.
h. If $\mathbf{u}$ and $\mathbf{v}$ are parallel and have the same direction, then $|\mathbf{u} + \mathbf{v}| = |\mathbf{u}| + |\mathbf{v}|$.

60. Finding vectors from two points Given the points $A(-2, 0)$, $B(6, 16)$, $C(1, 4)$, $D(5, 4)$, $E(\sqrt{2}, \sqrt{2})$, and $F(3\sqrt{2}, -4\sqrt{2})$, find the position vector equal to the following vectors.

a. $\overrightarrow{AB}$ b. $\overrightarrow{AC}$ c. $\overrightarrow{EF}$ d. $\overrightarrow{CD}$

61. Unit vectors

a. Find two unit vectors parallel to $\mathbf{v} = 6\mathbf{i} - 8\mathbf{j}$.
b. Find b if $\mathbf{v} = \langle \frac{1}{3}, b \rangle$ is a unit vector.
c. Find all values of a such that $\mathbf{w} = a\mathbf{i} - \dfrac{a}{3}\mathbf{j}$ is a unit vector.

62. Equal vectors For the points $A(3, 4)$, $B(6, 10)$, $C(a + 2, b + 5)$, and $D(b + 4, a - 2)$, find the values of a and b such that $\overrightarrow{AB} = \overrightarrow{CD}$.

63–66. Vector equations *Use the properties of vectors to solve the following equations for the unknown vector* $\mathbf{x} = \langle a, b \rangle$. *Let* $\mathbf{u} = \langle 2, -3 \rangle$ *and* $\mathbf{v} = \langle -4, 1 \rangle$.

63. $10\mathbf{x} = \mathbf{u}$

64. $2\mathbf{x} + \mathbf{u} = \mathbf{v}$

65. $3\mathbf{x} - 4\mathbf{u} = \mathbf{v}$

66. $-4\mathbf{x} = \mathbf{u} - 8\mathbf{v}$

67–69. Linear combinations *A sum of scalar multiples of two or more vectors (such as* $c_1\mathbf{u} + c_2\mathbf{v} + c_3\mathbf{w}$, *where* c_i *are scalars) is called a* ***linear combination*** *of the vectors. Let* $\mathbf{i} = \langle 1, 0 \rangle$, $\mathbf{j} = \langle 0, 1 \rangle$, $\mathbf{u} = \langle 1, 1 \rangle$, *and* $\mathbf{v} = \langle -1, 1 \rangle$.

67. Express $\langle 4, -8 \rangle$ as a linear combination of $\mathbf{i}$ and $\mathbf{j}$ (that is, find scalars c_1 and c_2 such that $\langle 4, -8 \rangle = c_1\mathbf{i} + c_2\mathbf{j}$).

68. Express $\langle 4, -8 \rangle$ as a linear combination of $\mathbf{u}$ and $\mathbf{v}$.

69. For arbitrary real numbers a and b, express $\langle a, b \rangle$ as a linear combination of $\mathbf{u}$ and $\mathbf{v}$.

70–71. Solving vector equations *Solve the following pairs of equations for the vectors* $\mathbf{u}$ *and* $\mathbf{v}$. *Assume* $\mathbf{i} = \langle 1, 0 \rangle$ *and* $\mathbf{j} = \langle 0, 1 \rangle$.

70. $2\mathbf{u} = \mathbf{i}, \mathbf{u} - 4\mathbf{v} = \mathbf{j}$

71. $2\mathbf{u} + 3\mathbf{v} = \mathbf{i}, \mathbf{u} - \mathbf{v} = \mathbf{j}$

72–75. Designer vectors *Find the following vectors.*

72. The vector that is 3 times $\langle 3, -5 \rangle$ plus -9 times $\langle 6, 0 \rangle$

73. The vector in the direction of $\langle 5, -12 \rangle$ with length 3

74. The vector in the direction opposite that of $\langle 6, -8 \rangle$ with length 10

75. The position vector for your final location if you start at the origin and walk along $\langle 4, -6 \rangle$ followed by $\langle 5, 9 \rangle$

Applications

76. Ant on a page An ant walks due east at a constant speed of 2 mi/hr on a sheet of paper that rests on a table. Suddenly, the sheet of paper starts moving southeast at $\sqrt{2}$ mi/hr. Describe the motion of the ant relative to the table.

77. Clock vectors Consider the 12 vectors that have their tails at the center of a (circular) clock and their heads at the numbers on the edge of the clock.

a. What is the sum of these 12 vectors?
b. If the 12:00 vector is removed, what is the sum of the remaining 11 vectors?
c. By removing one or more of these 12 clock vectors, explain how to make the sum of the remaining vectors as large as possible in magnitude.
d. Consider the 11 vectors that originate at the number 12 at the top of the clock and point to the other 11 numbers. What is the sum of the vectors?

(*Source: Calculus,* Gilbert Strang, Wellesley-Cambridge Press, 1991)

78. Three-way tug-of-war Three people located at A, B, and C pull on ropes tied to a ring. Find the magnitude and direction of the force with which the person at C must pull so that no one moves (the system is in equilibrium).

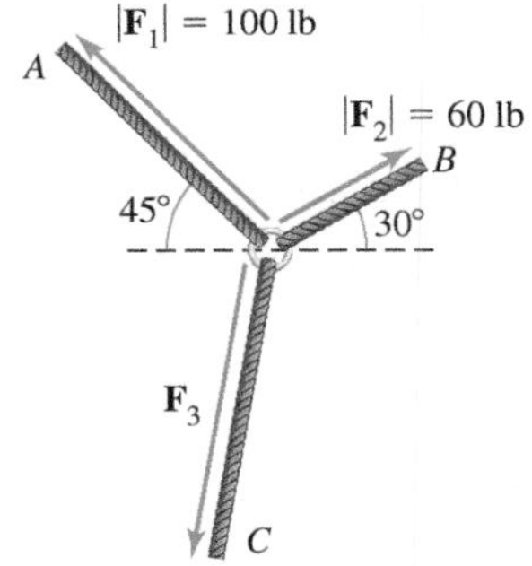

79. Net force Jack pulls east on a rope attached to a camel with a force of 40 lb. Jill pulls north on a rope attached to the same camel with a force of 30 lb. What is the magnitude and direction of the force on the camel? Assume the vectors lie in a horizontal plane.

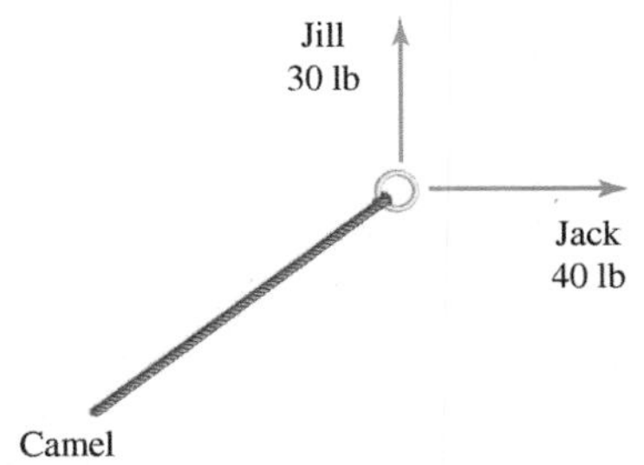

80. Mass on a plane A 100-kg object rests on an inclined plane at an angle of 30° to the floor. Find the components of the force perpendicular to and parallel to the plane. (The vertical component of the force exerted by an object of mass m is its weight, which is mg, where $g = 9.8\ \text{m/s}^2$ is the acceleration due to gravity.)

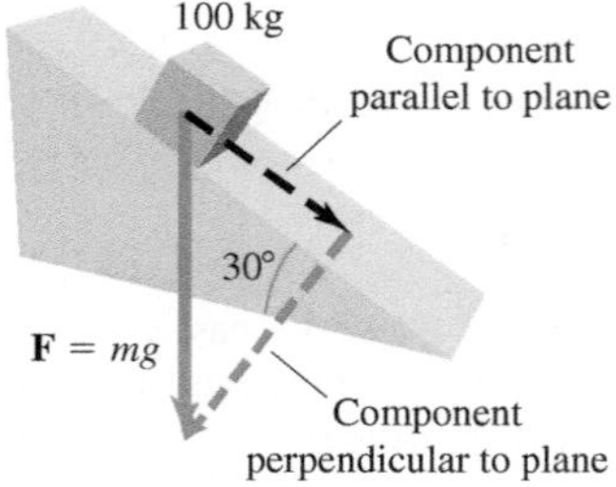

Additional Exercises

81–85. Vector properties *Prove the following vector properties using components. Then make a sketch to illustrate the property geometrically. Suppose* **u**, **v**, *and* **w** *are vectors in the xy-plane and a and c are scalars.*

81. $\mathbf{u} + \mathbf{v} = \mathbf{v} + \mathbf{u}$ — Commutative property

82. $(\mathbf{u} + \mathbf{v}) + \mathbf{w} = \mathbf{u} + (\mathbf{v} + \mathbf{w})$ — Associative property

83. $a(c\mathbf{v}) = (ac)\mathbf{v}$ — Associative property

84. $a(\mathbf{u} + \mathbf{v}) = a\mathbf{u} + a\mathbf{v}$ — Distributive property 1

85. $(a + c)\mathbf{v} = a\mathbf{v} + c\mathbf{v}$ — Distributive property 2

86. Midpoint of a line segment Use vectors to show that the midpoint of the line segment joining $P(x_1, y_1)$ and $Q(x_2, y_2)$ is the point $\left(\frac{x_1 + x_2}{2}, \frac{y_1 + y_2}{2}\right)$ (*Hint:* Let O be the origin and let M be the midpoint of PQ. Draw a picture and show that $\overrightarrow{OM} = \overrightarrow{OP} + \frac{1}{2}\overrightarrow{PQ} = \overrightarrow{OP} + \frac{1}{2}(\overrightarrow{OQ} - \overrightarrow{OP})$.)

87. Magnitude of scalar multiple Prove that $|c\mathbf{v}| = |c||\mathbf{v}|$, where c is a scalar and $\mathbf{v}$ is a vector.

88. Equality of vectors Assume $\overrightarrow{PQ}$ equals $\overrightarrow{RS}$. Does it follow that $\overrightarrow{PR}$ is equal to $\overrightarrow{QS}$? Explain your answer.

89. Linear independence A pair of nonzero vectors in the plane is *linearly dependent* if one vector is a scalar multiple of the other. Otherwise, the pair is *linearly independent*.

a. Which pairs of the following vectors are linearly dependent and which are linearly independent: $\mathbf{u} = \langle 2, -3 \rangle$, $\mathbf{v} = \langle -12, 18 \rangle$, and $\mathbf{w} = \langle 4, 6 \rangle$?

b. Geometrically, what does it mean for a pair of nonzero vectors in the plane to be linearly dependent? Linearly independent?

c. Prove that if a pair of vectors **u** and **v** is linearly independent, then given any vector **w**, there are constants c_1 and c_2 such that $\mathbf{w} = c_1\mathbf{u} + c_2\mathbf{v}$.

90. Perpendicular vectors Show that two nonzero vectors $\mathbf{u} = \langle u_1, u_2 \rangle$ and $\mathbf{v} = \langle v_1, v_2 \rangle$ are perpendicular to each other if $u_1 v_1 + u_2 v_2 = 0$.

91. Parallel and perpendicular vectors Let $\mathbf{u} = \langle a, 5 \rangle$ and $\mathbf{v} = \langle 2, 6 \rangle$.

a. Find the value of a such that **u** is parallel to **v**.

b. Find the value of a such that **u** is perpendicular to **v**.

92. The Triangle Inequality Suppose **u** and **v** are vectors in the plane.

a. Use the Triangle Rule for adding vectors to explain why $|\mathbf{u} + \mathbf{v}| \le |\mathbf{u}| + |\mathbf{v}|$. This result is known as the *Triangle Inequality*.

b. Under what conditions is $|\mathbf{u} + \mathbf{v}| = |\mathbf{u}| + |\mathbf{v}|$?

QUICK CHECK ANSWERS

1. The vector $-5\mathbf{v}$ is five times as long as **v** and points in the opposite direction. **2.** $\mathbf{v}_a + \mathbf{w}$ points in a northeasterly direction. **3.** Constructing $\mathbf{u} + \mathbf{v}$ and $\mathbf{v} + \mathbf{u}$ using the Triangle Rule produces vectors having the same direction and magnitude. **4.** $\overrightarrow{PQ} = \langle -6, -2 \rangle$
5. $10\mathbf{u} = \langle 6, 8 \rangle$ and $-10\mathbf{u} = \langle -6, -8 \rangle$
6. $\left|\left\langle \frac{5}{13}, \frac{12}{13} \right\rangle\right| = \sqrt{\frac{25 + 144}{169}} = \sqrt{\frac{169}{169}} = 1$
7. $\mathbf{u} = -\frac{4}{3}\mathbf{v} + 4\mathbf{w}$ ◄

11.2 Vectors in Three Dimensions

Up to this point, our study of calculus has been limited to functions, curves, and vectors that can be plotted in the two-dimensional xy-plane. However, a two-dimensional coordinate system is insufficient for modeling many physical phenomena. For example, to describe the trajectory of a jet gaining altitude, we need two coordinates, say x and y, to measure east–west and north–south distances. In addition, another coordinate, say z, is needed to measure the altitude of the jet. By adding a third coordinate and creating an ordered triple (x, y, z), the location of the jet can be described. The set of all points described by the triples (x, y, z) is called *three-dimensional space*, xyz-space, or $\mathbb{R}^3$. Many of the properties of xyz-space are extensions of familiar ideas you have seen in the xy-plane.

The *xyz*-Coordinate System

➤ The notation $\mathbb{R}^3$ (pronounced *R-three*) stands for the set of all ordered triples of real numbers.

A three-dimensional coordinate system is created by adding a new axis, called the ***z*-axis**, to the familiar *xy*-coordinate system. The new *z*-axis is inserted through the origin perpendicular to the *x*- and *y*-axes (Figure 11.25). The result is a new coordinate system called the **three-dimensional rectangular coordinate system** or the ***xyz*-coordinate system**.

The coordinate system described here is a conventional **right-handed coordinate system**: If the curled fingers of the right hand are rotated from the positive *x*-axis to the positive *y*-axis, the thumb points in the direction of the positive *z*-axis (Figure 11.25).

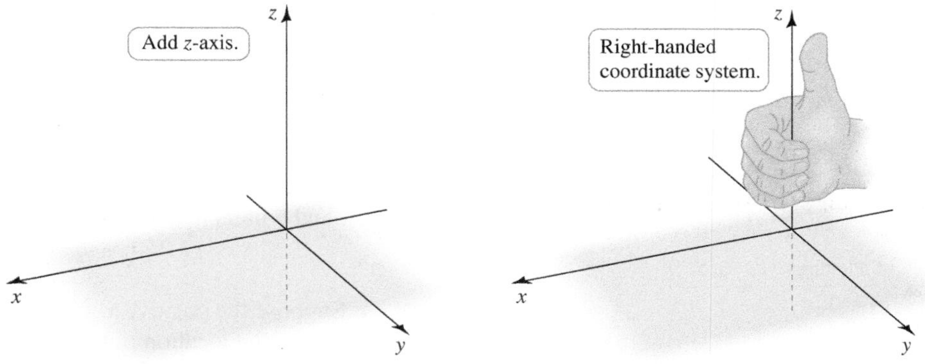

Figure 11.25

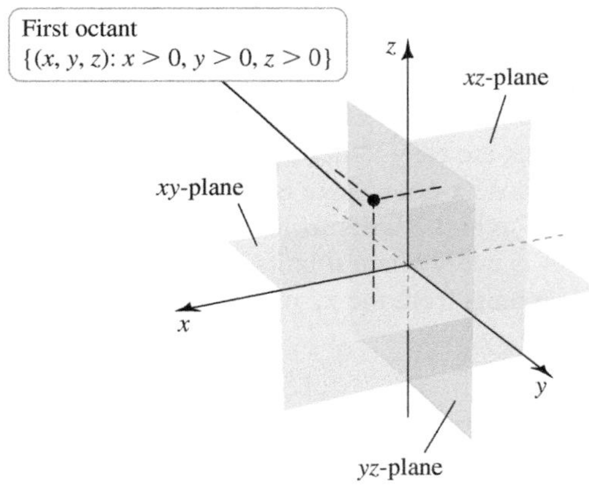

Figure 11.26

The coordinate plane containing the *x*-axis and *y*-axis is still called the *xy*-plane. We now have two new coordinate planes: the ***xz*-plane** containing the *x*-axis and the *z*-axis, and the ***yz*-plane** containing the *y*-axis and the *z*-axis. Taken together, these three coordinate planes divide *xyz*-space into eight regions called **octants** (Figure 11.26).

The point where all three axes intersect is the **origin**, which has coordinates $(0, 0, 0)$. An ordered triple (a, b, c) refers to the point in *xyz*-space that is found by starting at the origin, moving *a* units in the *x*-direction, *b* units in the *y*-direction, and *c* units in the *z*-direction. With a negative coordinate, you move in the negative direction along the corresponding coordinate axis. To visualize this point, it's helpful to construct a rectangular box with one vertex at the origin and the opposite vertex at the point (a, b, c) (Figure 11.27).

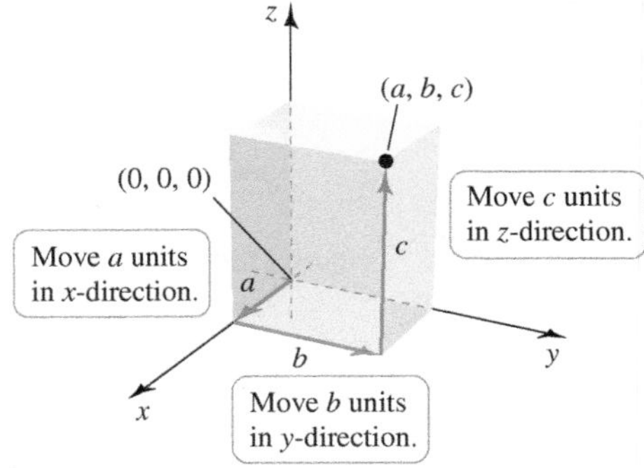

Figure 11.27

EXAMPLE 1 **Plotting points in *xyz*-space** Plot the following points.

a. $(3, 4, 5)$ **b.** $(-2, -3, 5)$

SOLUTION

a. Starting at $(0, 0, 0)$, we move 3 units in the *x*-direction to the point $(3, 0, 0)$, then 4 units in the *y*-direction to the point $(3, 4, 0)$, and finally, 5 units in the *z*-direction to reach the point $(3, 4, 5)$ (Figure 11.28).

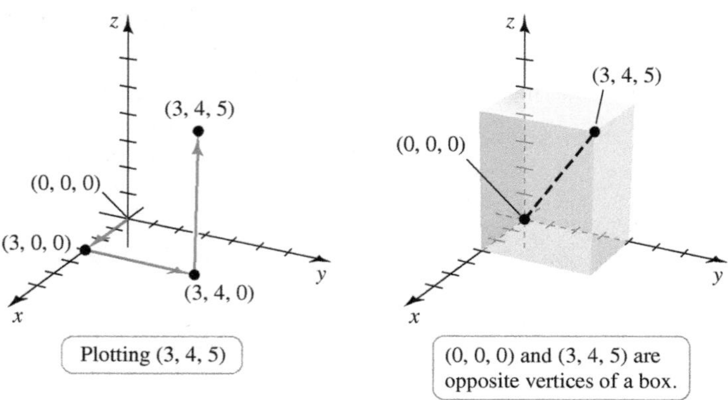

Figure 11.28

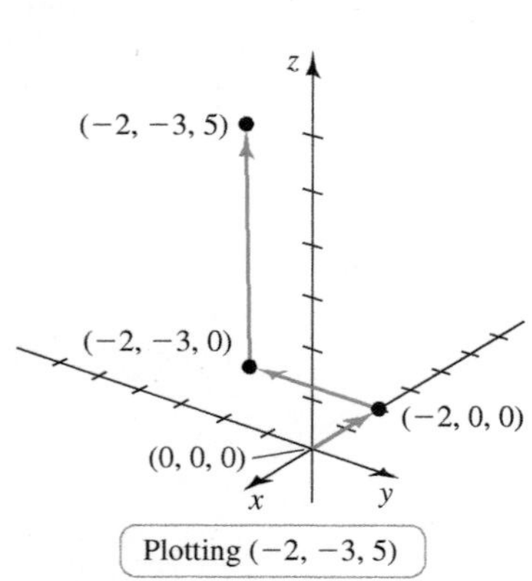

Figure 11.29

b. We move -2 units in the x-direction to $(-2, 0, 0)$, -3 units in the y-direction to $(-2, -3, 0)$, and 5 units in the z-direction to reach $(-2, -3, 5)$ (Figure 11.29).

Related Exercises 9–14 ◄

QUICK CHECK 1 Suppose the positive x-, y-, and z-axes point east, north, and upward, respectively. Describe the location of the points $(-1, -1, 0)$, $(1, 0, 1)$, and $(-1, -1, -1)$ relative to the origin. ◄

Equations of Simple Planes

➤ Planes that are not parallel to the coordinate planes are discussed in Section 12.1.

The xy-plane consists of all points in xyz-space that have a z-coordinate of 0. Therefore, the xy-plane is the set $\{(x, y, z): z = 0\}$; it is represented by the equation $z = 0$. Similarly, the xz-plane has the equation $y = 0$, and the yz-plane has the equation $x = 0$.

Planes parallel to one of the coordinate planes are easy to describe. For example, the equation $x = 2$ describes the set of all points whose x-coordinate is 2 and whose y- and z-coordinates are arbitrary; this plane is parallel to and 2 units from the yz-plane. Similarly, the equation $y = a$ describes a plane that is everywhere a units from the xz-plane, and $z = a$ is the equation of a horizontal plane a units from the xy-plane (Figure 11.30).

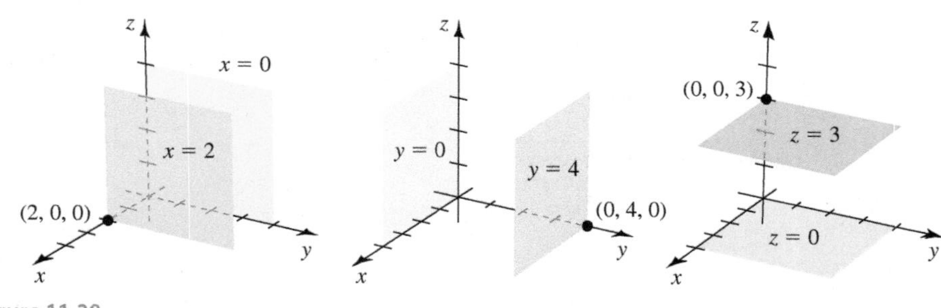

Figure 11.30

QUICK CHECK 2 To which coordinate planes are the planes $x = -2$ and $z = 16$ parallel? ◄

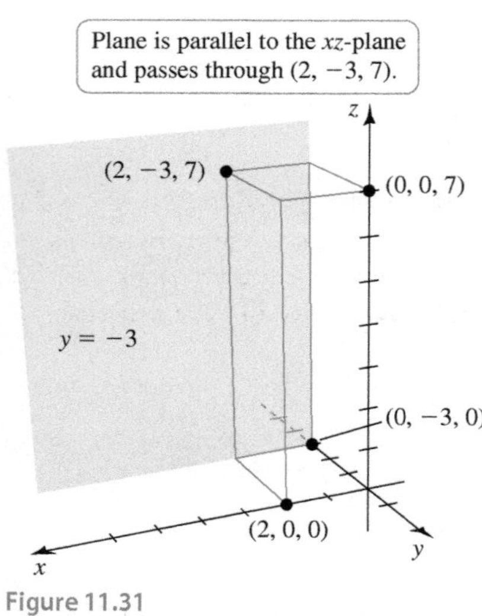

Figure 11.31

EXAMPLE 2 Parallel planes Determine the equation of the plane parallel to the xz-plane passing through the point $(2, -3, 7)$.

SOLUTION Points on a plane parallel to the xz-plane have the same y-coordinate. Therefore, the plane passing through the point $(2, -3, 7)$ with a y-coordinate of -3 has the equation $y = -3$ (Figure 11.31).

Related Exercises 15–22 ◄

Distances in *xyz*-Space

Recall that the distance between two points (x_1, y_1) and (x_2, y_2) in the xy-plane is $\sqrt{(x_2 - x_1)^2 + (y_2 - y_1)^2}$. This distance formula is useful in deriving a similar formula for the distance between two points $P(x_1, y_1, z_1)$ and $Q(x_2, y_2, z_2)$ in xyz-space.

Figure 11.32 shows the points P and Q, together with the auxiliary point $R(x_2, y_2, z_1)$, which has the same z-coordinate as P and the same x- and y-coordinates as Q. The line segment PR has length $|PR| = \sqrt{(x_2 - x_1)^2 + (y_2 - y_1)^2}$ and is one leg of the right triangle $\triangle PRQ$. The length of the hypotenuse of that triangle is the distance between P and Q:

$$\sqrt{|PR|^2 + |RQ|^2} = \sqrt{\underbrace{(x_2 - x_1)^2 + (y_2 - y_1)^2}_{|PR|^2} + \underbrace{(z_2 - z_1)^2}_{|RQ|^2}}.$$

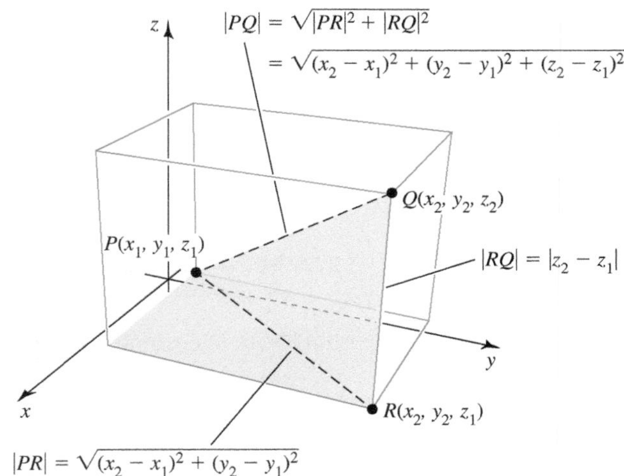

Figure 11.32

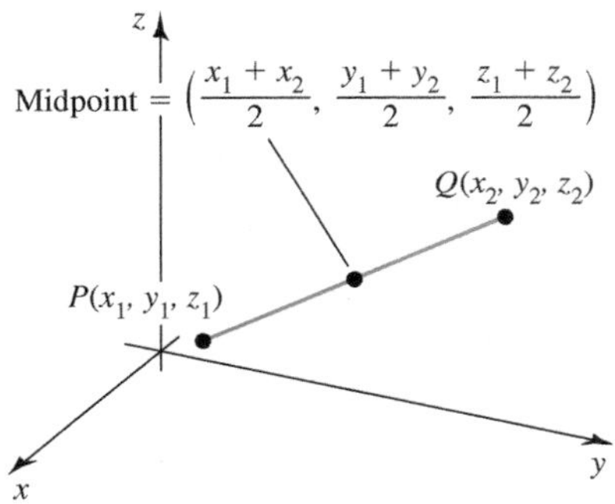

Figure 11.33

Distance Formula in xyz-Space

The distance between the points $P(x_1, y_1, z_1)$ and $Q(x_2, y_2, z_2)$ is

$$\sqrt{(x_2 - x_1)^2 + (y_2 - y_1)^2 + (z_2 - z_1)^2}.$$

By using the distance formula, we can derive the formula (Exercise 79) for the **midpoint** of the line segment joining $P(x_1, y_1, z_1)$ and $Q(x_2, y_2, z_2)$, which is found by averaging the x-, y-, and z-coordinates (Figure 11.33):

$$\text{Midpoint} = \left(\frac{x_1 + x_2}{2}, \frac{y_1 + y_2}{2}, \frac{z_1 + z_2}{2}\right).$$

Equation of a Sphere

A *sphere* is the set of all points that are a constant distance r from a point (a, b, c); r is the *radius* of the sphere and (a, b, c) is the *center* of the sphere. A *ball* centered at (a, b, c) with radius r consists of all the points inside and on the sphere centered at (a, b, c) with radius r (Figure 11.34). We now use the distance formula to translate these statements.

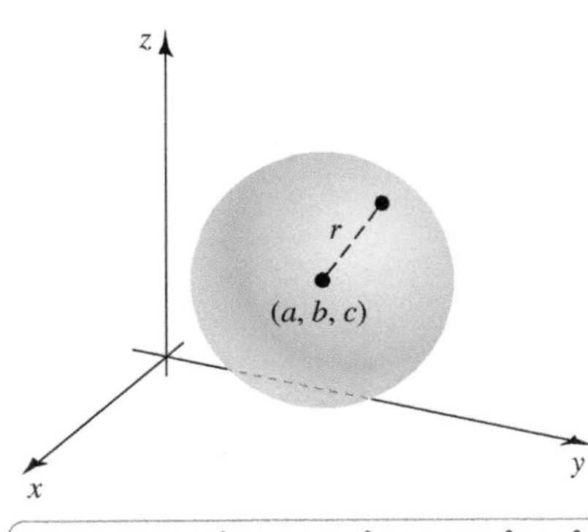

Sphere: $(x - a)^2 + (y - b)^2 + (z - c)^2 = r^2$
Ball: $(x - a)^2 + (y - b)^2 + (z - c)^2 \le r^2$

Figure 11.34

➤ Just as a circle is the boundary of a disk in two dimensions, a *sphere* is the boundary of a *ball* in three dimensions. We have defined a *closed ball*, which includes its boundary. An *open ball* does not contain its boundary.

Spheres and Balls

A **sphere** centered at (a, b, c) with radius r is the set of points satisfying the equation

$$(x - a)^2 + (y - b)^2 + (z - c)^2 = r^2.$$

A **ball** centered at (a, b, c) with radius r is the set of points satisfying the inequality

$$(x - a)^2 + (y - b)^2 + (z - c)^2 \le r^2.$$

EXAMPLE 3 Equation of a sphere Consider the points $P(1, -2, 5)$ and $Q(3, 4, -6)$. Find an equation of the sphere for which the line segment PQ is a diameter.

SOLUTION The center of the sphere is the midpoint of PQ:

$$\left(\frac{1+3}{2}, \frac{-2+4}{2}, \frac{5-6}{2}\right) = \left(2, 1, -\frac{1}{2}\right).$$

The diameter of the sphere is the distance $|PQ|$, which is

$$\sqrt{(3-1)^2 + (4+2)^2 + (-6-5)^2} = \sqrt{161}.$$

Therefore, the sphere's radius is $\frac{1}{2}\sqrt{161}$, its center is $(2, 1, -\frac{1}{2})$, and it is described by the equation

$$(x-2)^2 + (y-1)^2 + \left(z + \frac{1}{2}\right)^2 = \left(\frac{1}{2}\sqrt{161}\right)^2 = \frac{161}{4}.$$

Related Exercises 23–28 ◄

EXAMPLE 4 Identifying equations Describe the set of points that satisfy the equation $x^2 + y^2 + z^2 - 2x + 6y - 8z = -1$.

SOLUTION We simplify the equation by completing the square and factoring:

$$\begin{aligned} (x^2 - 2x) + (y^2 + 6y) + (z^2 - 8z) &= -1 && \text{Group terms.} \\ (x^2 - 2x + 1) + (y^2 + 6y + 9) + (z^2 - 8z + 16) &= 25 && \text{Complete the square.} \\ (x-1)^2 + (y+3)^2 + (z-4)^2 &= 25. && \text{Factor.} \end{aligned}$$

The equation describes a sphere of radius 5 with center $(1, -3, 4)$.

Related Exercises 29–38 ◄

QUICK CHECK 3 Describe the solution set of the equation

$$(x-1)^2 + y^2 + (z+1)^2 + 4 = 0. ◄$$

Vectors in $\mathbb{R}^3$

Vectors in $\mathbb{R}^3$ are straightforward extensions of vectors in the xy-plane; we simply include a third component. The position vector $\mathbf{v} = \langle v_1, v_2, v_3 \rangle$ has its tail at the origin and its head at the point (v_1, v_2, v_3). Vectors having the same magnitude and direction are equal. Therefore, the vector from $P(x_1, y_1, z_1)$ to $Q(x_2, y_2, z_2)$ is denoted $\overrightarrow{PQ}$ and is equal to the position vector $\langle x_2 - x_1, y_2 - y_1, z_2 - z_1 \rangle$. It is also equal to all vectors such as $\overrightarrow{RS}$ (Figure 11.35) that have the same length and direction as $\mathbf{v}$.

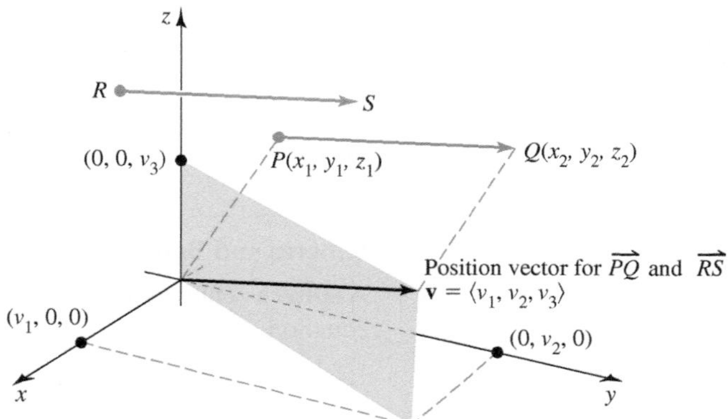

Figure 11.35

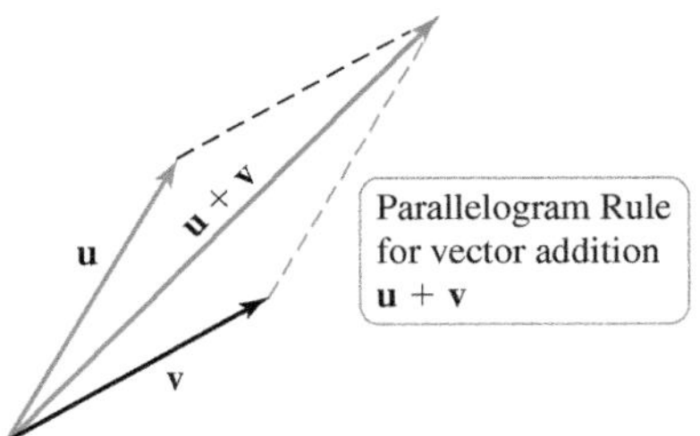

The operations of vector addition and scalar multiplication in $\mathbb{R}^2$ generalize in a natural way to three dimensions. For example, the sum of two vectors is found geometrically using the Triangle Rule or the Parallelogram Rule (Section 11.1). The sum is found analytically by adding the respective components of the two vectors. As with two-dimensional vectors, scalar multiplication corresponds to stretching or compressing a vector, possibly with a reversal of direction. Two nonzero vectors are parallel if one is a scalar multiple of the other (Figure 11.36).

QUICK CHECK 4 Which of the following vectors are parallel to each other?

a. $\mathbf{u} = \langle -2, 4, -6 \rangle$ **b.** $\mathbf{v} = \langle 4, -8, 12 \rangle$ **c.** $\mathbf{w} = \langle -1, 2, 3 \rangle$ ◄

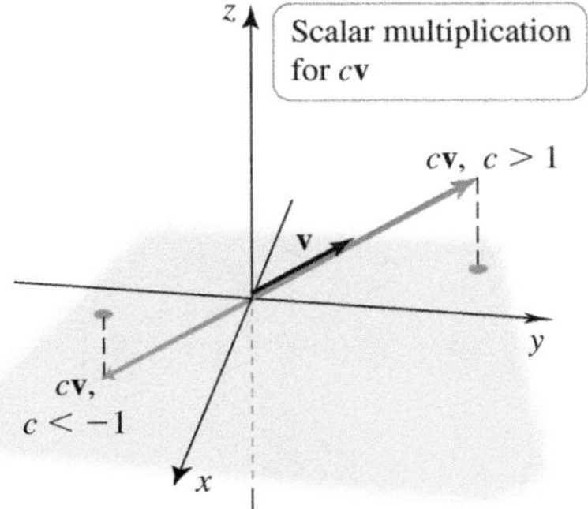

Figure 11.36

> **DEFINITION Vector Operations in $\mathbb{R}^3$**
>
> Let c be a scalar, $\mathbf{u} = \langle u_1, u_2, u_3 \rangle$, and $\mathbf{v} = \langle v_1, v_2, v_3 \rangle$.
>
> $$\mathbf{u} + \mathbf{v} = \langle u_1 + v_1, u_2 + v_2, u_3 + v_3 \rangle \quad \text{Vector addition}$$
> $$\mathbf{u} - \mathbf{v} = \langle u_1 - v_1, u_2 - v_2, u_3 - v_3 \rangle \quad \text{Vector subtraction}$$
> $$c\mathbf{u} = \langle cu_1, cu_2, cu_3 \rangle \quad \text{Scalar multiplication}$$

EXAMPLE 5 Vectors in $\mathbb{R}^3$ Let $\mathbf{u} = \langle 2, -4, 1 \rangle$ and $\mathbf{v} = \langle 3, 0, -1 \rangle$. Find the components of the following vectors and draw them in $\mathbb{R}^3$.

a. $\frac{1}{2}\mathbf{u}$ **b.** $-2\mathbf{v}$ **c.** $\mathbf{u} + 2\mathbf{v}$

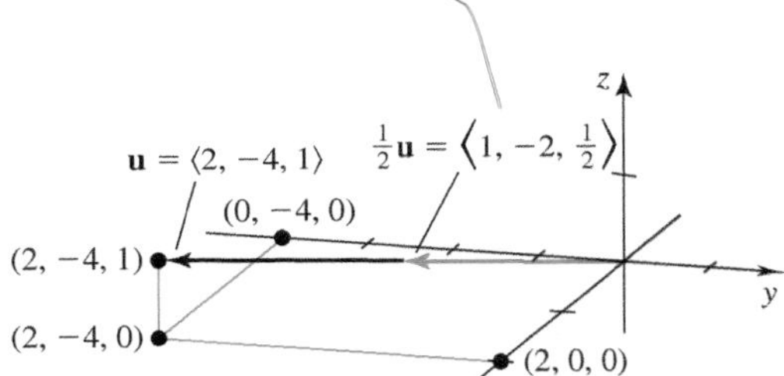

Figure 11.37

Figure 11.38

SOLUTION

a. Using the definition of scalar multiplication, $\frac{1}{2}\mathbf{u} = \frac{1}{2}\langle 2, -4, 1 \rangle = \left\langle 1, -2, \frac{1}{2} \right\rangle$. The vector $\frac{1}{2}\mathbf{u}$ has the same direction as $\mathbf{u}$ with half the magnitude of $\mathbf{u}$ (Figure 11.37).

b. Using scalar multiplication, $-2\mathbf{v} = -2\langle 3, 0, -1 \rangle = \langle -6, 0, 2 \rangle$. The vector $-2\mathbf{v}$ has the opposite direction as $\mathbf{v}$ and twice the magnitude of $\mathbf{v}$ (Figure 11.38).

c. Using vector addition and scalar multiplication,

$$\mathbf{u} + 2\mathbf{v} = \langle 2, -4, 1 \rangle + 2\langle 3, 0, -1 \rangle = \langle 8, -4, -1 \rangle.$$

The vector $\mathbf{u} + 2\mathbf{v}$ is drawn by applying the Parallelogram Rule to $\mathbf{u}$ and $2\mathbf{v}$ (Figure 11.39).

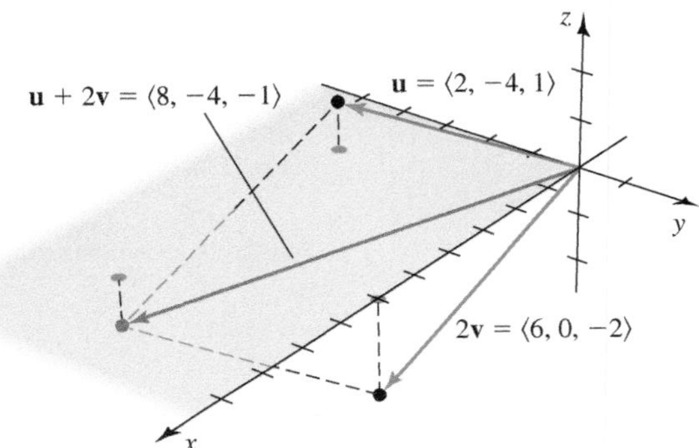

Figure 11.39

Related Exercises 39–44 ◄

Magnitude and Unit Vectors

The magnitude of the vector $\overrightarrow{PQ}$ from $P(x_1, y_1, z_1)$ to $Q(x_2, y_2, z_2)$ is denoted $|\overrightarrow{PQ}|$; it is the distance between P and Q and is given by the distance formula (Figure 11.40).

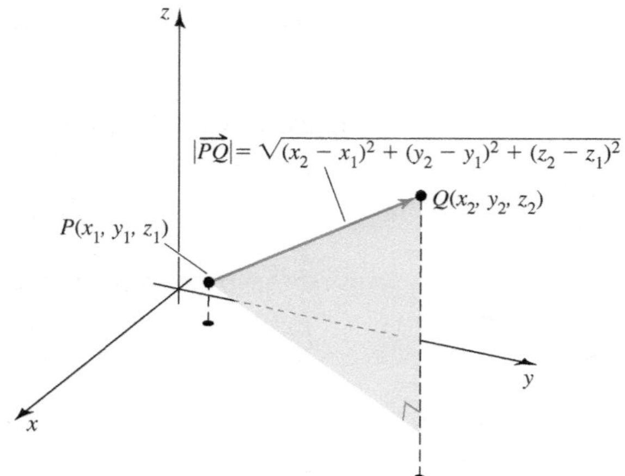

Figure 11.40

> DEFINITION **Magnitude of a Vector**
>
> The **magnitude** (or **length**) of the vector $\overrightarrow{PQ} = \langle x_2 - x_1, y_2 - y_1, z_2 - z_1 \rangle$ is the distance from $P(x_1, y_1, z_1)$ to $Q(x_2, y_2, z_2)$:
>
> $$|\overrightarrow{PQ}| = \sqrt{(x_2 - x_1)^2 + (y_2 - y_1)^2 + (z_2 - z_1)^2}.$$

The coordinate unit vectors introduced in Section 11.1 extend naturally to three dimensions. The three coordinate unit vectors in $\mathbb{R}^3$ (Figure 11.41) are

$$\mathbf{i} = \langle 1, 0, 0 \rangle, \quad \mathbf{j} = \langle 0, 1, 0 \rangle, \quad \text{and} \quad \mathbf{k} = \langle 0, 0, 1 \rangle.$$

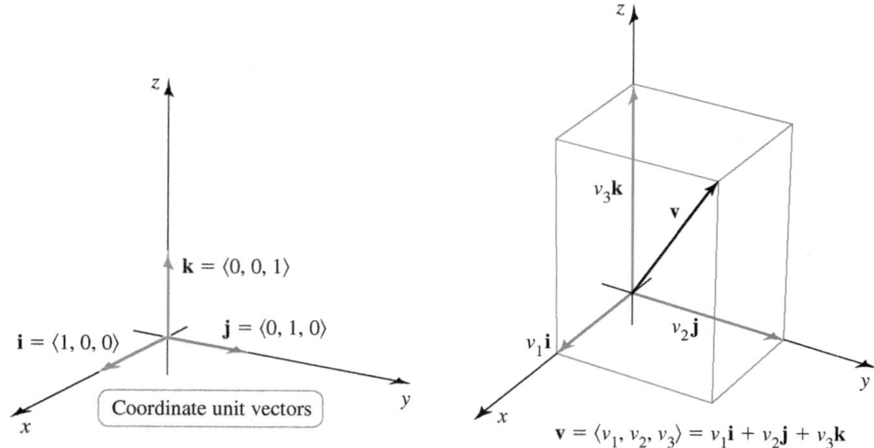

Figure 11.41

These unit vectors give an alternative way of expressing position vectors. If $\mathbf{v} = \langle v_1, v_2, v_3 \rangle$, then we have

$$\mathbf{v} = v_1 \langle 1, 0, 0 \rangle + v_2 \langle 0, 1, 0 \rangle + v_3 \langle 0, 0, 1 \rangle = v_1\mathbf{i} + v_2\mathbf{j} + v_3\mathbf{k}.$$

EXAMPLE 6 **Magnitudes and unit vectors** Consider the points $P(5, 3, 1)$ and $Q(-7, 8, 1)$.

a. Express $\overrightarrow{PQ}$ in terms of the unit vectors **i**, **j**, and **k**.

b. Find the magnitude of $\overrightarrow{PQ}$.

c. Find the position vector of magnitude 10 in the direction of $\overrightarrow{PQ}$.

SOLUTION

a. $\overrightarrow{PQ}$ is equal to the position vector $\langle -7 - 5, 8 - 3, 1 - 1 \rangle = \langle -12, 5, 0 \rangle$. Therefore, $\overrightarrow{PQ} = -12\mathbf{i} + 5\mathbf{j}$.

b. $|\overrightarrow{PQ}| = |-12\mathbf{i} + 5\mathbf{j}| = \sqrt{12^2 + 5^2} = \sqrt{169} = 13$

c. The unit vector in the direction of $\overrightarrow{PQ}$ is $\mathbf{u} = \dfrac{\overrightarrow{PQ}}{|\overrightarrow{PQ}|} = \dfrac{1}{13}\langle -12, 5, 0 \rangle$. Therefore, the vector in the direction of **u** with a magnitude of 10 is $10\mathbf{u} = \dfrac{10}{13}\langle -12, 5, 0 \rangle$.

Related Exercises 45–50 ◀

QUICK CHECK 5 Which vector has the smaller magnitude: $\mathbf{u} = 3\mathbf{i} - \mathbf{j} - \mathbf{k}$ or $\mathbf{v} = 2(\mathbf{i} + \mathbf{j} + \mathbf{k})$? ◀

EXAMPLE 7 **Flight in crosswinds** A plane is flying horizontally due north in calm air at 300 mi/hr when it encounters a horizontal crosswind blowing southeast at 40 mi/hr and a downdraft blowing vertically downward at 30 mi/hr. What are the resulting speed and direction of the plane relative to the ground?

SOLUTION Let the unit vectors **i**, **j**, and **k** point east, north, and upward, respectively (Figure 11.42). The velocity of the plane relative to the air (300 mi/hr due north) is $\mathbf{v}_a = 300\mathbf{j}$. The crosswind blows 45° south of east, so its component to the east is $40 \cos 45° = 20\sqrt{2}$ (in the **i** direction) and its component to the south is $40 \cos 45° = 20\sqrt{2}$ (in the $-\mathbf{j}$ direction). Therefore, the crosswind may be expressed as $\mathbf{w} = 20\sqrt{2}\mathbf{i} - 20\sqrt{2}\mathbf{j}$. Finally, the downdraft in the negative **k** direction is $\mathbf{d} = -30\mathbf{k}$. The velocity of the plane relative to the ground is the sum of $\mathbf{v}_a$, **w**, and **d**:

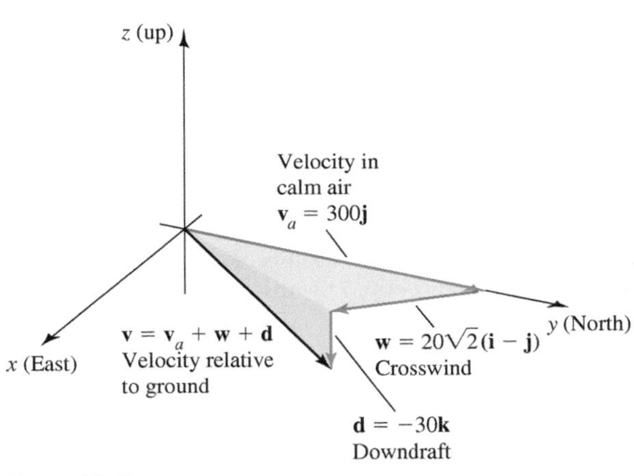

Figure 11.42

$$\begin{aligned} \mathbf{v} &= \mathbf{v}_a + \mathbf{w} + \mathbf{d} \\ &= 300\mathbf{j} + (20\sqrt{2}\mathbf{i} - 20\sqrt{2}\mathbf{j}) - 30\mathbf{k} \\ &= 20\sqrt{2}\mathbf{i} + (300 - 20\sqrt{2})\mathbf{j} - 30\mathbf{k}. \end{aligned}$$

Figure 11.42 shows the velocity vector of the plane. A quick calculation shows that the speed is $|\mathbf{v}| \approx 275$ mi/hr. The direction of the plane is slightly east of north and downward. In the next section, we present methods for precisely determining the direction of a vector.

Related Exercises 51–56 ◀

SECTION 11.2 EXERCISES

Review Questions

1. Explain how to plot the point $(3, -2, 1)$ in $\mathbb{R}^3$.
2. What is the y-coordinate of all points in the xz-plane?
3. Describe the plane $x = 4$.
4. What position vector is equal to the vector from $(3, 5, -2)$ to $(0, -6, 3)$?
5. Let $\mathbf{u} = \langle 3, 5, -7 \rangle$ and $\mathbf{v} = \langle 6, -5, 1 \rangle$. Evaluate $\mathbf{u} + \mathbf{v}$ and $3\mathbf{u} - \mathbf{v}$.
6. What is the magnitude of a vector joining two points $P(x_1, y_1, z_1)$ and $Q(x_2, y_2, z_2)$?
7. Which point is farther from the origin, $(3, -1, 2)$ or $(0, 0, -4)$?
8. Express the vector from $P(-1, -4, 6)$ to $Q(1, 3, -6)$ as a position vector in terms of **i**, **j**, and **k**.

Basic Skills

9–12. Points in $\mathbb{R}^3$ *Find the coordinates of the vertices A, B, and C of the following rectangular boxes.*

9.

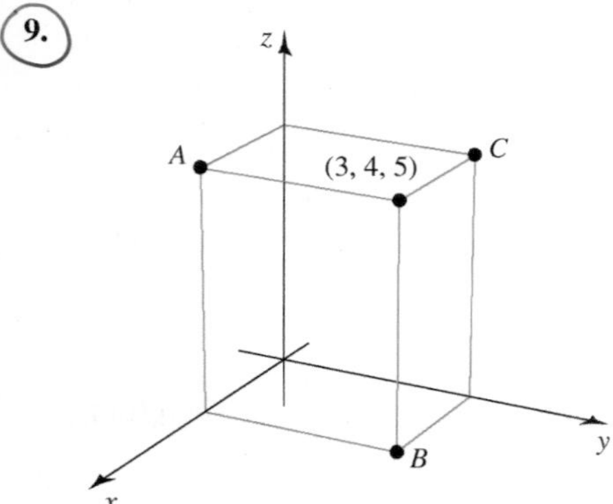

10.

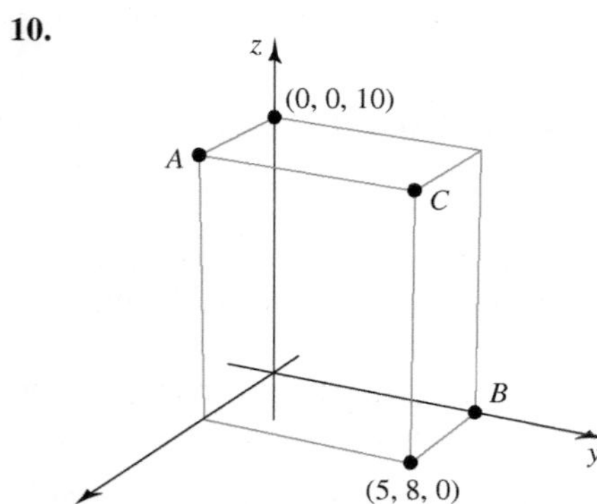

11.

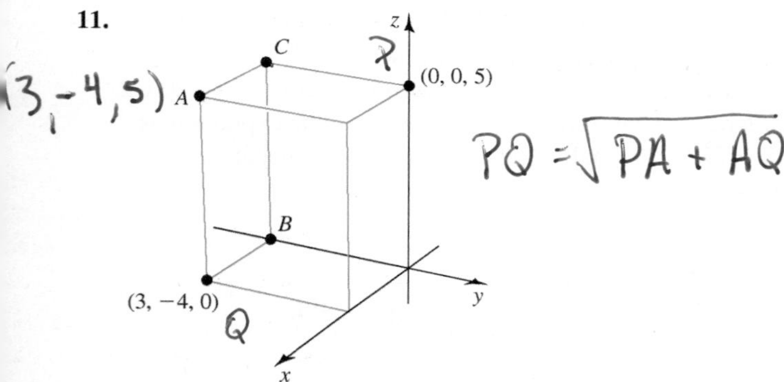

12. Assume all the edges have the same length.

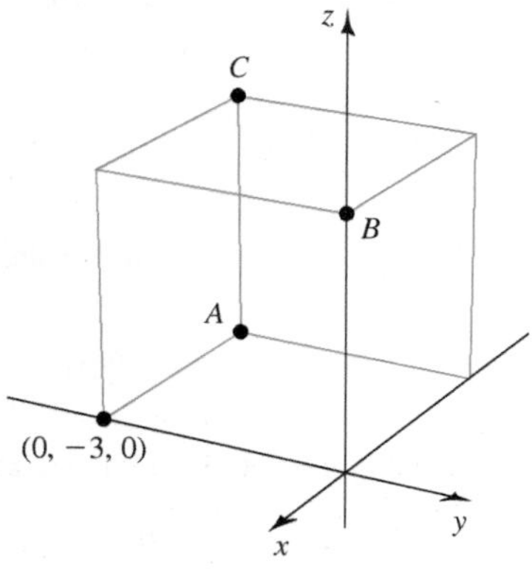

13–14. Plotting points in $\mathbb{R}^3$ *For each point $P(x, y, z)$ given below, let $A(x, y, 0)$, $B(x, 0, z)$, and $C(0, y, z)$ be points in the xy-, xz-, and yz-planes, respectively. Plot and label the points A, B, C, and P in $\mathbb{R}^3$.*

13. **a.** $P(2, 2, 4)$ **b.** $P(1, 2, 5)$ **c.** $P(-2, 0, 5)$

14. **a.** $P(-3, 2, 4)$ **b.** $P(4, -2, -3)$ **c.** $P(-2, -4, -3)$

15–20. Sketching planes *Sketch the following planes in the window $[0, 5] \times [0, 5] \times [0, 5]$.*

15. $x = 2$ **16.** $z = 3$ **17.** $y = 2$ **18.** $z = y$

19. The plane that passes through $(2, 0, 0)$, $(0, 3, 0)$, and $(0, 0, 4)$

20. The plane parallel to the xz-plane containing the point $(1, 2, 3)$

21. Planes Sketch the plane parallel to the xy-plane through $(2, 4, 2)$ and find its equation.

22. Planes Sketch the plane parallel to the yz-plane through $(2, 4, 2)$ and find its equation.

23–26. Spheres and balls *Find an equation or inequality that describes the following objects.*

23. A sphere with center $(1, 2, 3)$ and radius 4

24. A sphere with center $(1, 2, 0)$ passing through the point $(3, 4, 5)$

25. A ball with center $(-2, 0, 4)$ and radius 1

26. A ball with center $(0, -2, 6)$ with the point $(1, 4, 8)$ on its boundary

27. Midpoints and spheres Find an equation of the sphere passing through $P(1, 0, 5)$ and $Q(2, 3, 9)$ with its center at the midpoint of PQ.

28. Midpoints and spheres Find an equation of the sphere passing through $P(-4, 2, 3)$ and $Q(0, 2, 7)$ with its center at the midpoint of PQ.

29–38. Identifying sets *Give a geometric description of the following sets of points.*

29. $(x - 1)^2 + y^2 + z^2 - 9 = 0$

30. $(x + 1)^2 + y^2 + z^2 - 2y - 24 = 0$

31. $x^2 + y^2 + z^2 - 2y - 4z - 4 = 0$

32. $x^2 + y^2 + z^2 - 6x + 6y - 8z - 2 = 0$

33. $x^2 + y^2 - 14y + z^2 \geq -13$

34. $x^2 + y^2 - 14y + z^2 \leq -13$

35. $x^2 + y^2 + z^2 - 8x - 14y - 18z \leq 79$

36. $x^2 + y^2 + z^2 - 8x + 14y - 18z \geq 65$

37. $x^2 - 2x + y^2 + 6y + z^2 + 10 = 0$

38. $x^2 - 4x + y^2 + 6y + z^2 + 14 = 0$

39–44. Vector operations *For the given vectors* **u** *and* **v**, *evaluate the following expressions.*

a. $3\mathbf{u} + 2\mathbf{v}$ **b.** $4\mathbf{u} - \mathbf{v}$ **c.** $|\mathbf{u} + 3\mathbf{v}|$

39. $\mathbf{u} = \langle 4, -3, 0 \rangle$, $\mathbf{v} = \langle 0, 1, 1 \rangle$

40. $\mathbf{u} = \langle -2, -3, 0 \rangle$, $\mathbf{v} = \langle 1, 2, 1 \rangle$

41. $\mathbf{u} = \langle -2, 1, -2 \rangle, \mathbf{v} = \langle 1, 1, 1 \rangle$

42. $\mathbf{u} = \langle -5, 0, 2 \rangle, \mathbf{v} = \langle 3, 1, 1 \rangle$

43. $\mathbf{u} = \langle -7, 11, 8 \rangle, \mathbf{v} = \langle 3, -5, -1 \rangle$

44. $\mathbf{u} = \langle -4, -8\sqrt{3}, 2\sqrt{2} \rangle, \mathbf{v} = \langle 2, 3\sqrt{3}, -\sqrt{2} \rangle$

45–50. Unit vectors and magnitude *Consider the following points P and Q.*

a. Find $\overrightarrow{PQ}$ and state your answer in two forms: $\langle a, b, c \rangle$ and $a\mathbf{i} + b\mathbf{j} + c\mathbf{k}$.
b. Find the magnitude of $\overrightarrow{PQ}$.
c. Find two unit vectors parallel to $\overrightarrow{PQ}$.

45. $P(1, 5, 0), Q(3, 11, 2)$

46. $P(5, 11, 12), Q(1, 14, 13)$

47. $P(-3, 1, 0), Q(-3, -4, 1)$

48. $P(3, 8, 12), Q(3, 9, 11)$

49. $P(0, 0, 2), Q(-2, 4, 0)$

50. $P(a, b, c), Q(1, 1, -1)$ (a, b, and c are real numbers)

51. **Flight in crosswinds** A model airplane is flying horizontally due north at 20 mi/hr when it encounters a horizontal crosswind blowing east at 20 mi/hr and a downdraft blowing vertically downward at 10 mi/hr.
    a. Find the position vector that represents the velocity of the plane relative to the ground.
    b. Find the speed of the plane relative to the ground.

52. **Another crosswind flight** A model airplane is flying horizontally due east at 10 mi/hr when it encounters a horizontal crosswind blowing south at 5 mi/hr and an updraft blowing vertically upward at 5 mi/hr.
    a. Find the position vector that represents the velocity of the plane relative to the ground.
    b. Find the speed of the plane relative to the ground.

53. **Crosswinds** A small plane is flying horizontally due east in calm air at 250 mi/hr when it is hit by a horizontal crosswind blowing southwest at 50 mi/hr and a 30-mi/hr updraft. Find the resulting speed of the plane and describe with a sketch the approximate direction of the velocity relative to the ground.

54. **Combined force** An object at the origin is acted on by the forces $\mathbf{F}_1 = 20\mathbf{i} - 10\mathbf{j}$, $\mathbf{F}_2 = 30\mathbf{j} + 10\mathbf{k}$, and $\mathbf{F}_3 = 40\mathbf{i} + 20\mathbf{k}$. Find the magnitude of the combined force and describe the approximate direction of the force.

55. **Submarine course** A submarine climbs at an angle of 30° above the horizontal with a heading to the northeast. If its speed is 20 knots, find the components of the velocity in the east, north, and vertical directions.

56. **Maintaining equilibrium** An object is acted upon by the forces $\mathbf{F}_1 = \langle 10, 6, 3 \rangle$ and $\mathbf{F}_2 = \langle 0, 4, 9 \rangle$. Find the force $\mathbf{F}_3$ that must act on the object so that the sum of the forces is zero.

Further Explorations

57. **Explain why or why not** Determine whether the following statements are true and give an explanation or counterexample.
    a. Suppose $\mathbf{u}$ and $\mathbf{v}$ both make a 45° angle with $\mathbf{w}$ in $\mathbb{R}^3$. Then $\mathbf{u} + \mathbf{v}$ makes a 45° angle with $\mathbf{w}$.
    b. Suppose $\mathbf{u}$ and $\mathbf{v}$ both make a 90° angle with $\mathbf{w}$ in $\mathbb{R}^3$. Then $\mathbf{u} + \mathbf{v}$ can never make a 90° angle with $\mathbf{w}$.
    c. $\mathbf{i} + \mathbf{j} + \mathbf{k} = \mathbf{0}$.
    d. The intersection of the planes $x = 1$, $y = 1$, and $z = 1$ is a point.

58–60. Sets of points *Describe with a sketch the sets of points (x, y, z) satisfying the following equations.*

58. $(x + 1)(y - 3) = 0$

59. $x^2y^2z^2 > 0$

60. $y - z = 0$

61–64. Sets of points

61. Give a geometric description of the set of points (x, y, z) satisfying the pair of equations $z = 0$ and $x^2 + y^2 = 1$. Sketch a figure of this set of points.

62. Give a geometric description of the set of points (x, y, z) satisfying the pair of equations $z = x^2$ and $y = 0$. Sketch a figure of this set of points.

63. Give a geometric description of the set of points (x, y, z) that lie on the intersection of the sphere $x^2 + y^2 + z^2 = 5$ and the plane $z = 1$.

64. Give a geometric description of the set of points (x, y, z) that lie on the intersection of the sphere $x^2 + y^2 + z^2 = 36$ and the plane $z = 6$.

65. **Describing a circle** Find a pair of equations describing a circle of radius 3 centered at $(2, 4, 1)$ that lies in a plane parallel to the xz-plane.

66. **Describing a line** Find a pair of equations describing a line passing through the point $(-2, -5, 1)$ that is parallel to the x-axis.

67–70. Parallel vectors of varying lengths *Find vectors parallel to* $\mathbf{v}$ *of the given length.*

67. $\mathbf{v} = \langle 6, -8, 0 \rangle$; length $= 20$

68. $\mathbf{v} = \langle 3, -2, 6 \rangle$; length $= 10$

69. $\mathbf{v} = \overrightarrow{PQ}$ with $P(3, 4, 0)$ and $Q(2, 3, 1)$; length $= 3$

70. $\mathbf{v} = \overrightarrow{PQ}$ with $P(1, 0, 1)$ and $Q(2, -1, 1)$; length $= 3$

71. **Collinear points** Determine whether the points P, Q, and R are collinear (lie on a line) by comparing $\overrightarrow{PQ}$ and $\overrightarrow{PR}$. If the points are collinear, determine which point lies between the other two points.
    a. $P(1, 6, -5), Q(2, 5, -3), R(4, 3, 1)$
    b. $P(1, 5, 7), Q(5, 13, -1), R(0, 3, 9)$
    c. $P(1, 2, 3), Q(2, -3, 6), R(3, -1, 9)$
    d. $P(9, 5, 1), Q(11, 18, 4), R(6, 3, 0)$

72. **Collinear points** Determine the values of x and y such that the points $(1, 2, 3)$, $(4, 7, 1)$, and $(x, y, 2)$ are collinear (lie on a line).

73. **Lengths of the diagonals of a box** What is the longest diagonal of a rectangular 2 ft × 3 ft × 4 ft box?

Applications

T 74. **Forces on an inclined plane** An object on an inclined plane does not slide provided the component of the object's weight parallel to the plane $|\mathbf{W}_{\text{par}}|$ is less than or equal to the magnitude of the opposing frictional force $|\mathbf{F}_{\text{f}}|$. The magnitude of the frictional force, in turn, is proportional to the component of the object's weight perpendicular to the plane $|\mathbf{W}_{\text{perp}}|$ (see figure). The constant of proportionality is the coefficient of static friction $\mu > 0$.

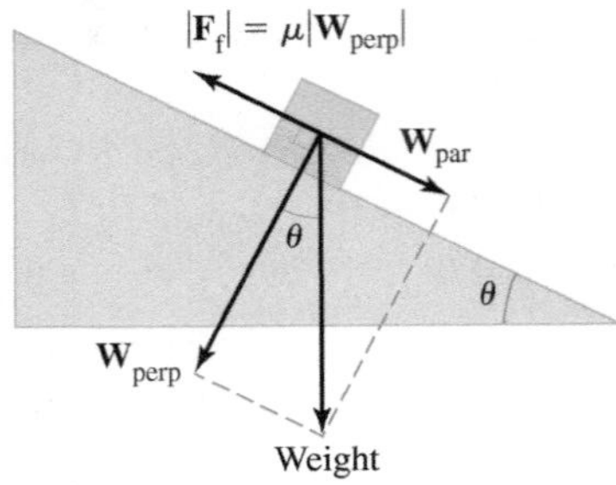

a. Suppose a 100-lb block rests on a plane that is tilted at an angle of $\theta = 20°$ to the horizontal. Find $|\mathbf{W}_{\text{par}}|$ and $|\mathbf{W}_{\text{perp}}|$.
b. The condition for the block not sliding is $|\mathbf{W}_{\text{par}}| \leq \mu|\mathbf{W}_{\text{perp}}|$. If $\mu = 0.65$, does the block slide?
c. What is the critical angle above which the block slides with $\mu = 0.65$?

75. Three-cable load A 500-kg load hangs from three cables of equal length that are anchored at the points $(-2, 0, 0)$, $(1, \sqrt{3}, 0)$, and $(1, -\sqrt{3}, 0)$. The load is located at $(0, 0, -2\sqrt{3})$. Find the vectors describing the forces on the cables due to the load.

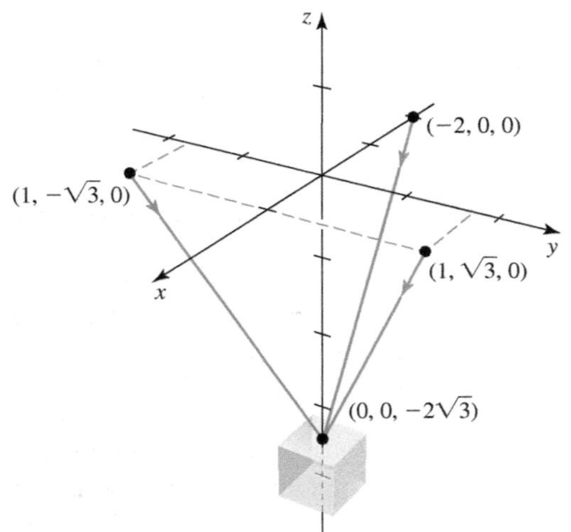

76. Four-cable load A 500-lb load hangs from four cables of equal length that are anchored at the points $(\pm 2, 0, 0)$ and $(0, \pm 2, 0)$. The load is located at $(0, 0, -4)$. Find the vectors describing the forces on the cables due to the load.

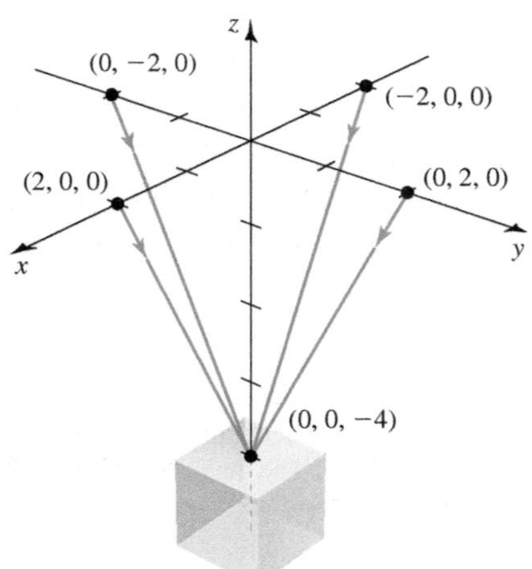

Additional Exercises

77. Possible parallelograms The points $O(0, 0, 0)$, $P(1, 4, 6)$, and $Q(2, 4, 3)$ lie at three vertices of a parallelogram. Find all possible locations of the fourth vertex.

78. Diagonals of parallelograms Two sides of a parallelogram are formed by the vectors $\mathbf{u}$ and $\mathbf{v}$. Prove that the diagonals of the parallelogram are $\mathbf{u} + \mathbf{v}$ and $\mathbf{u} - \mathbf{v}$.

79. Midpoint formula Prove that the midpoint of the line segment joining $P(x_1, y_1, z_1)$ and $Q(x_2, y_2, z_2)$ is

$$\left(\frac{x_1 + x_2}{2}, \frac{y_1 + y_2}{2}, \frac{z_1 + z_2}{2}\right).$$

80. Equation of a sphere For constants a, b, c, and d, show that the equation

$$x^2 + y^2 + z^2 - 2ax - 2by - 2cz = d$$

describes a sphere centered at (a, b, c) with radius r, where $r^2 = d + a^2 + b^2 + c^2$, provided $d + a^2 + b^2 + c^2 > 0$.

81. Medians of a triangle—coordinate free Assume that $\mathbf{u}$, $\mathbf{v}$, and $\mathbf{w}$ are vectors in $\mathbb{R}^3$ that form the sides of a triangle (see figure). Use the following steps to prove that the medians intersect at a point that divides each median in a 2:1 ratio. The proof does not use a coordinate system.

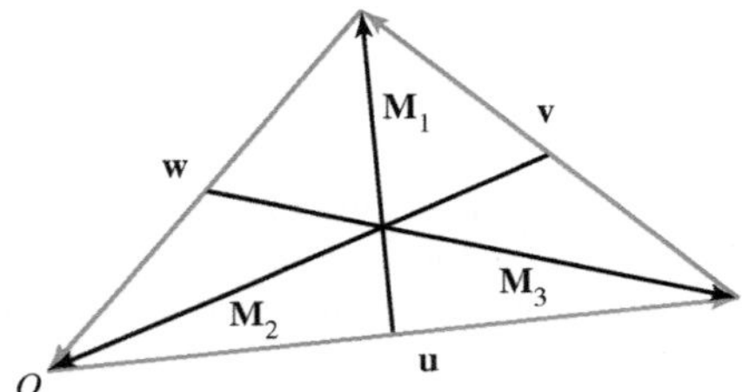

a. Show that $\mathbf{u} + \mathbf{v} + \mathbf{w} = \mathbf{0}$.
b. Let $\mathbf{M}_1$ be the median vector from the midpoint of $\mathbf{u}$ to the opposite vertex. Define $\mathbf{M}_2$ and $\mathbf{M}_3$ similarly. Using the geometry of vector addition show that $\mathbf{M}_1 = \mathbf{u}/2 + \mathbf{v}$. Find analogous expressions for $\mathbf{M}_2$ and $\mathbf{M}_3$.
c. Let $\mathbf{a}$, $\mathbf{b}$, and $\mathbf{c}$ be the vectors from O to the points one-third of the way along $\mathbf{M}_1$, $\mathbf{M}_2$, and $\mathbf{M}_3$, respectively. Show that $\mathbf{a} = \mathbf{b} = \mathbf{c} = (\mathbf{u} - \mathbf{w})/3$.
d. Conclude that the medians intersect at a point that divides each median in a 2:1 ratio.

82. Medians of a triangle—with coordinates In contrast to the proof in Exercise 81, we now use coordinates and position vectors to prove the same result. Without loss of generality, let $P(x_1, y_1, 0)$ and $Q(x_2, y_2, 0)$ be two points in the xy-plane and let $R(x_3, y_3, z_3)$ be a third point, such that P, Q, and R do not lie on a line. Consider $\triangle PQR$.

a. Let M_1 be the midpoint of the side PQ. Find the coordinates of M_1 and the components of the vector $\overrightarrow{RM_1}$.
b. Find the vector $\overrightarrow{OZ_1}$ from the origin to the point Z_1 two-thirds of the way along $\overrightarrow{RM_1}$.
c. Repeat the calculation of part (b) with the midpoint M_2 of RQ and the vector $\overrightarrow{PM_2}$ to obtain the vector $\overrightarrow{OZ_2}$.
d. Repeat the calculation of part (b) with the midpoint M_3 of PR and the vector $\overrightarrow{QM_3}$ to obtain the vector $\overrightarrow{OZ_3}$.
e. Conclude that the medians of $\triangle PQR$ intersect at a point. Give the coordinates of the point.
f. With $P(2, 4, 0)$, $Q(4, 1, 0)$, and $R(6, 3, 4)$, find the point at which the medians of $\triangle PQR$ intersect.

83. The amazing quadrilateral property—coordinate free The points P, Q, R, and S, joined by the vectors $\mathbf{u}$, $\mathbf{v}$, $\mathbf{w}$, and $\mathbf{x}$, are the vertices of a quadrilateral in $\mathbb{R}^3$. *The four points needn't lie in a plane* (see figure). Use the following steps to prove that the line segments joining the midpoints of the sides of the quadrilateral form a parallelogram. The proof does not use a coordinate system.

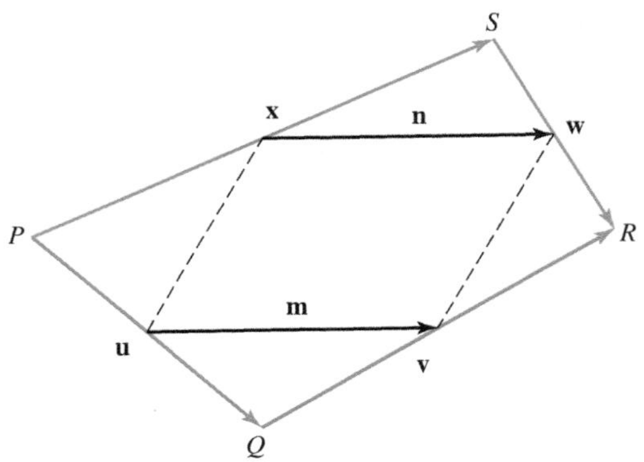

a. Use vector addition to show that $\mathbf{u} + \mathbf{v} = \mathbf{w} + \mathbf{x}$.
b. Let $\mathbf{m}$ be the vector that joins the midpoints of PQ and QR. Show that $\mathbf{m} = (\mathbf{u} + \mathbf{v})/2$.
c. Let $\mathbf{n}$ be the vector that joins the midpoints of PS and SR. Show that $\mathbf{n} = (\mathbf{x} + \mathbf{w})/2$.
d. Combine parts (a), (b), and (c) to conclude that $\mathbf{m} = \mathbf{n}$.
e. Explain why part (d) implies that the line segments joining the midpoints of the sides of the quadrilateral form a parallelogram.

84. The amazing quadrilateral property—with coordinates Prove the quadrilateral property in Exercise 83, assuming the coordinates of P, Q, R, and S are $P(x_1, y_1, 0)$, $Q(x_2, y_2, 0)$, $R(x_3, y_3, 0)$, and $S(x_4, y_4, z_4)$, where we assume that P, Q, and R lie in the xy-plane without loss of generality.

QUICK CHECK ANSWERS

1. Southwest; due east and upward; southwest and downward **2.** yz-plane; xy-plane **3.** No solution **4.** $\mathbf{u}$ and $\mathbf{v}$ are parallel. **5.** $|\mathbf{u}| = \sqrt{11}$ and $|\mathbf{v}| = \sqrt{12} = 2\sqrt{3}$; $\mathbf{u}$ has the smaller magnitude. ◄

11.3 Dot Products

➤ The dot product is also called the *scalar product*, a term we do not use in order to avoid confusion with *scalar multiplication*.

The *dot product* is used to determine the angle between two vectors. It is also a tool for calculating *projections*—the measure of how much of a given vector lies in the direction of another vector.

To see the usefulness of the dot product, consider an example. Recall that the work done by a constant force F in moving an object a distance d is $W = Fd$ (Section 6.7). This rule is valid provided the force acts in the direction of motion (Figure 11.43a). Now assume the force is a vector $\mathbf{F}$ applied at an angle θ to the direction of motion; the resulting displacement of the object is a vector $\mathbf{d}$. In this case, the work done by the force is the component of the force in the direction of motion multiplied by the distance moved by the object, which is $W = (|\mathbf{F}| \cos \theta)|\mathbf{d}|$ (Figure 11.43b). We call this product of the magnitudes of two vectors and the cosine of the angle between them the dot product.

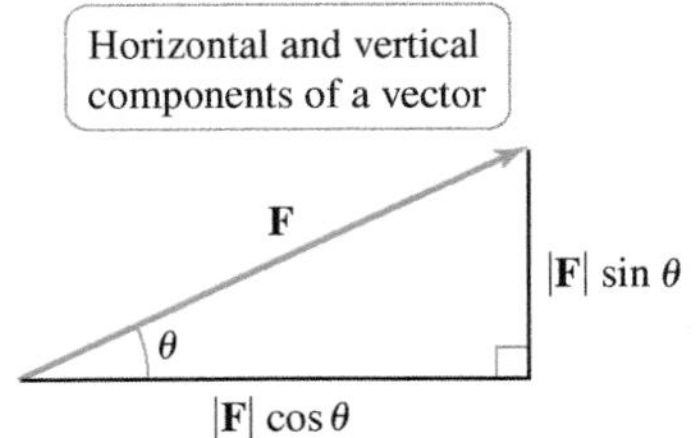

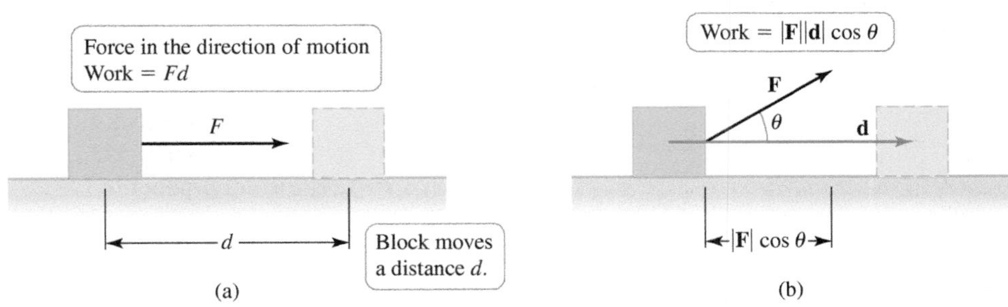

Figure 11.43

Two Forms of the Dot Product

The example of work done by a force leads to our first definition of the dot product. We then give an equivalent formula that is often better suited for computation.

DEFINITION Dot Product

Given two nonzero vectors **u** and **v** in two or three dimensions, their **dot product** is

$$\mathbf{u} \cdot \mathbf{v} = |\mathbf{u}||\mathbf{v}| \cos \theta,$$

where θ is the angle between **u** and **v** with $0 \leq \theta \leq \pi$ (Figure 11.44). If $\mathbf{u} = \mathbf{0}$ or $\mathbf{v} = \mathbf{0}$, then $\mathbf{u} \cdot \mathbf{v} = 0$, and θ is undefined.

The dot product of two vectors is itself a scalar. Two special cases immediately arise:

- **u** and **v** are parallel ($\theta = 0$ or $\theta = \pi$) if and only if $\mathbf{u} \cdot \mathbf{v} = \pm|\mathbf{u}||\mathbf{v}|$.
- **u** and **v** are perpendicular ($\theta = \pi/2$) if and only if $\mathbf{u} \cdot \mathbf{v} = 0$.

The second case gives rise to the important property of *orthogonality*.

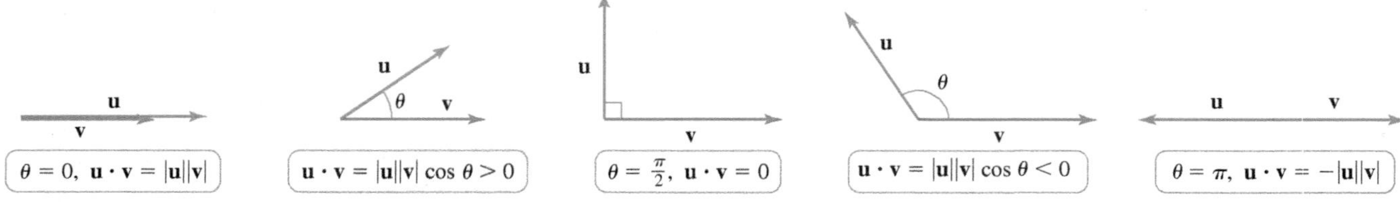

Figure 11.44

➤ In two and three dimensions, *orthogonal* and *perpendicular* are used interchangeably. *Orthogonal* is a more general term that also applies in more than three dimensions.

DEFINITION Orthogonal Vectors

Two vectors **u** and **v** are **orthogonal** if and only if $\mathbf{u} \cdot \mathbf{v} = 0$. The zero vector is orthogonal to all vectors. In two or three dimensions, two nonzero orthogonal vectors are perpendicular to each other.

QUICK CHECK 1 Sketch two nonzero vectors **u** and **v** with $\theta = 0$. Sketch two nonzero vectors **u** and **v** with $\theta = \pi$. ◄

EXAMPLE 1 Dot products Compute the dot products of the following vectors.

a. $\mathbf{u} = 2\mathbf{i} - 6\mathbf{j}$ and $\mathbf{v} = 12\mathbf{k}$

b. $\mathbf{u} = \langle \sqrt{3}, 1 \rangle$ and $\mathbf{v} = \langle 0, 1 \rangle$

SOLUTION

a. The vector **u** lies in the *xy*-plane and the vector **v** is perpendicular to the *xy*-plane. Therefore, $\theta = \dfrac{\pi}{2}$, **u** and **v** are orthogonal, and $\mathbf{u} \cdot \mathbf{v} = 0$ (Figure 11.45a).

b. As shown in Figure 11.45b, **u** and **v** form two sides of a 30–60–90 triangle in the *xy*-plane, with an angle of $\pi/3$ between them. Because $|\mathbf{u}| = 2$, $|\mathbf{v}| = 1$, and $\cos \pi/3 = 1/2$, the dot product is

$$\mathbf{u} \cdot \mathbf{v} = |\mathbf{u}||\mathbf{v}| \cos \theta = 2 \cdot 1 \cdot \frac{1}{2} = 1.$$

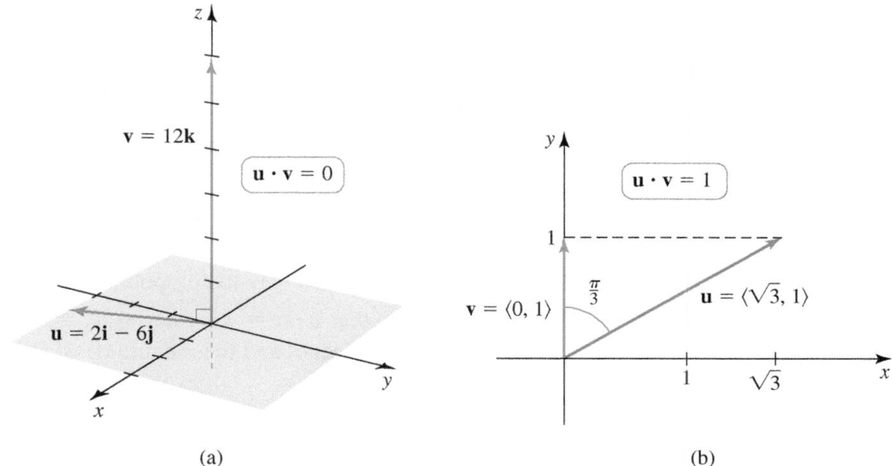

Figure 11.45

Related Exercises 9–14 ◀

The definition of the dot product requires knowing the angle θ between the vectors. Often the angle is not known; in fact, it may be exactly what we seek. For this reason, we present another method for computing the dot product that does not require knowing θ.

➤ In $\mathbb{R}^2$ with $\mathbf{u} = \langle u_1, u_2 \rangle$ and $\mathbf{v} = \langle v_1, v_2 \rangle$, $\mathbf{u} \cdot \mathbf{v} = u_1v_1 + u_2v_2$.

THEOREM 11.1 Dot Product

Given two vectors $\mathbf{u} = \langle u_1, u_2, u_3 \rangle$ and $\mathbf{v} = \langle v_1, v_2, v_3 \rangle$,

$$\mathbf{u} \cdot \mathbf{v} = u_1v_1 + u_2v_2 + u_3v_3.$$

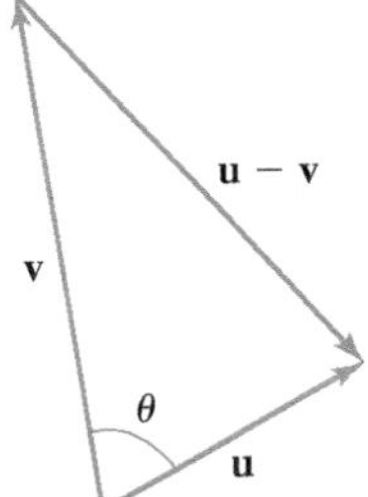

Figure 11.46

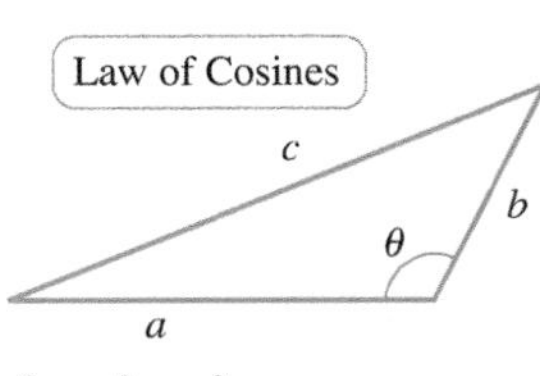

$c^2 = a^2 + b^2 - 2ab\cos\theta$

Proof: Consider two position vectors $\mathbf{u} = \langle u_1, u_2, u_3 \rangle$ and $\mathbf{v} = \langle v_1, v_2, v_3 \rangle$, and suppose θ is the angle between them. The vector $\mathbf{u} - \mathbf{v}$ forms the third side of a triangle (Figure 11.46). By the Law of Cosines,

$$|\mathbf{u} - \mathbf{v}|^2 = |\mathbf{u}|^2 + |\mathbf{v}|^2 - 2\underbrace{|\mathbf{u}||\mathbf{v}|\cos\theta}_{\mathbf{u}\cdot\mathbf{v}}.$$

The definition of the dot product, $\mathbf{u} \cdot \mathbf{v} = |\mathbf{u}||\mathbf{v}|\cos\theta$, allows us to write

$$\mathbf{u} \cdot \mathbf{v} = |\mathbf{u}||\mathbf{v}|\cos\theta = \frac{1}{2}(|\mathbf{u}|^2 + |\mathbf{v}|^2 - |\mathbf{u} - \mathbf{v}|^2). \quad (1)$$

Using the definition of magnitude, we find that

$$|\mathbf{u}|^2 = u_1^2 + u_2^2 + u_3^2, \quad |\mathbf{v}|^2 = v_1^2 + v_2^2 + v_3^2,$$

and

$$|\mathbf{u} - \mathbf{v}|^2 = (u_1 - v_1)^2 + (u_2 - v_2)^2 + (u_3 - v_3)^2.$$

Expanding the terms in $|\mathbf{u} - \mathbf{v}|^2$ and simplifying yields

$$|\mathbf{u}|^2 + |\mathbf{v}|^2 - |\mathbf{u} - \mathbf{v}|^2 = 2(u_1v_1 + u_2v_2 + u_3v_3).$$

Substituting into expression (1) gives a compact expression for the dot product:

$$\mathbf{u} \cdot \mathbf{v} = u_1v_1 + u_2v_2 + u_3v_3.$$ ◀

This new representation of $\mathbf{u} \cdot \mathbf{v}$ has two immediate consequences.

1. Combining it with the definition of dot product gives

$$\mathbf{u} \cdot \mathbf{v} = u_1v_1 + u_2v_2 + u_3v_3 = |\mathbf{u}||\mathbf{v}| \cos \theta.$$

If $\mathbf{u}$ and $\mathbf{v}$ are both nonzero, then

$$\cos \theta = \frac{u_1v_1 + u_2v_2 + u_3v_3}{|\mathbf{u}||\mathbf{v}|} = \frac{\mathbf{u} \cdot \mathbf{v}}{|\mathbf{u}||\mathbf{v}|},$$

and we have a way to compute θ.

2. Notice that $\mathbf{u} \cdot \mathbf{u} = u_1^2 + u_2^2 + u_3^2 = |\mathbf{u}|^2$. Therefore, we have a relationship between the dot product and the magnitude of a vector: $|\mathbf{u}| = \sqrt{\mathbf{u} \cdot \mathbf{u}}$ or $|\mathbf{u}|^2 = \mathbf{u} \cdot \mathbf{u}$.

QUICK CHECK 2 Use Theorem 11.1 to compute the dot products $\mathbf{i} \cdot \mathbf{j}$, $\mathbf{i} \cdot \mathbf{k}$, and $\mathbf{j} \cdot \mathbf{k}$ for the unit coordinate vectors. What do you conclude about the angles between these vectors? ◀

EXAMPLE 2 Dot products and angles Let $\mathbf{u} = \langle \sqrt{3}, 1, 0 \rangle$, $\mathbf{v} = \langle 1, \sqrt{3}, 0 \rangle$, and $\mathbf{w} = \langle 1, \sqrt{3}, 2\sqrt{3} \rangle$.

a. Compute $\mathbf{u} \cdot \mathbf{v}$.

b. Find the angle between $\mathbf{u}$ and $\mathbf{v}$.

c. Find the angle between $\mathbf{u}$ and $\mathbf{w}$.

SOLUTION

a. $\mathbf{u} \cdot \mathbf{v} = \langle \sqrt{3}, 1, 0 \rangle \cdot \langle 1, \sqrt{3}, 0 \rangle = \sqrt{3} + \sqrt{3} + 0 = 2\sqrt{3}$

b. Note that $|\mathbf{u}| = \sqrt{\mathbf{u} \cdot \mathbf{u}} = \sqrt{\langle \sqrt{3}, 1, 0 \rangle \cdot \langle \sqrt{3}, 1, 0 \rangle} = 2$ and similarly $|\mathbf{v}| = 2$. Therefore,

$$\cos \theta = \frac{\mathbf{u} \cdot \mathbf{v}}{|\mathbf{u}||\mathbf{v}|} = \frac{2\sqrt{3}}{2 \cdot 2} = \frac{\sqrt{3}}{2}.$$

Because $0 \le \theta \le \pi$, it follows that $\theta = \cos^{-1} \frac{\sqrt{3}}{2} = \frac{\pi}{6}$.

c. $\cos \theta = \dfrac{\mathbf{u} \cdot \mathbf{w}}{|\mathbf{u}||\mathbf{w}|} = \dfrac{\langle \sqrt{3}, 1, 0 \rangle \cdot \langle 1, \sqrt{3}, 2\sqrt{3} \rangle}{|\langle \sqrt{3}, 1, 0 \rangle||\langle 1, \sqrt{3}, 2\sqrt{3} \rangle|} = \dfrac{2\sqrt{3}}{2 \cdot 4} = \dfrac{\sqrt{3}}{4}$

It follows that

$$\theta = \cos^{-1} \frac{\sqrt{3}}{4} \approx 1.12 \text{ rad} \approx 64.3°.$$

Related Exercises 15–24 ◀

Properties of Dot Products The properties of the dot product in the following theorem are easily proved using vector components (Exercises 76–80).

> Theorem 11.1 extends to vectors with any number of components. If $\mathbf{u} = \langle u_1, \ldots, u_n \rangle$ and $\mathbf{v} = \langle v_1, \ldots, v_n \rangle$, then
>
> $$\mathbf{u} \cdot \mathbf{v} = u_1v_1 + \cdots + u_nv_n.$$
>
> The properties in Theorem 11.2 also apply in two or more dimensions.

THEOREM 11.2 Properties of the Dot Product

Suppose $\mathbf{u}$, $\mathbf{v}$, and $\mathbf{w}$ are vectors and let c be a scalar.

1. $\mathbf{u} \cdot \mathbf{v} = \mathbf{v} \cdot \mathbf{u}$ — Commutative property
2. $c(\mathbf{u} \cdot \mathbf{v}) = (c\mathbf{u}) \cdot \mathbf{v} = \mathbf{u} \cdot (c\mathbf{v})$ — Associative property
3. $\mathbf{u} \cdot (\mathbf{v} + \mathbf{w}) = \mathbf{u} \cdot \mathbf{v} + \mathbf{u} \cdot \mathbf{w}$ — Distributive property

Orthogonal Projections

Given vectors **u** and **v**, how closely aligned are they? That is, how much of **u** points in the direction of **v**? This question is answered using *projections.* As shown in Figure 11.47a, the projection of the vector **u** onto a nonzero vector **v**, denoted $\text{proj}_{\mathbf{v}}\mathbf{u}$, is the "shadow" cast by **u** onto the line through **v**. The projection of **u** onto **v** is itself a vector; it points in the same direction as **v** if the angle between **u** and **v** lies in the interval $0 \le \theta < \pi/2$ (Figure 11.47b); it points in the direction opposite that of **v** if the angle between **u** and **v** lies in the interval $\pi/2 < \theta \le \pi$ (Figure 11.47c). If $\theta = \frac{\pi}{2}$, **u** and **v** are orthogonal, and there is no shadow.

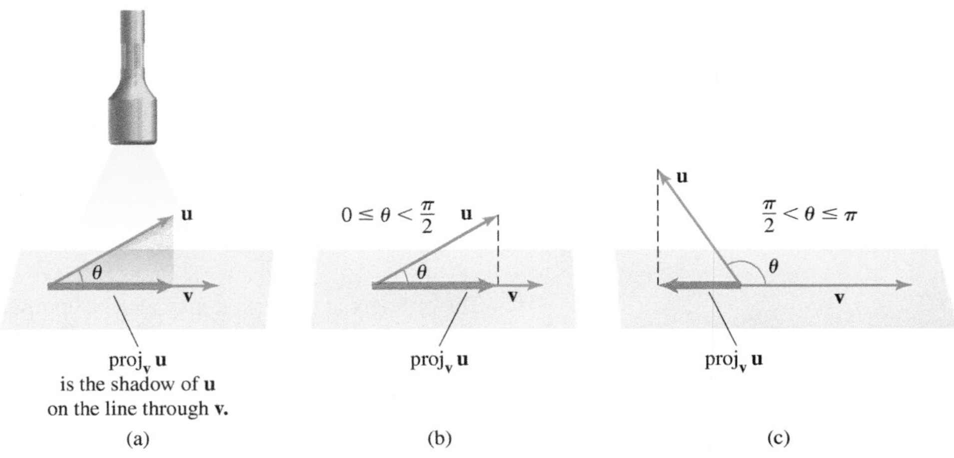

Figure 11.47

To find the projection of **u** onto **v**, we proceed as follows: With the tails of **u** and **v** together, we drop a perpendicular line segment from the head of **u** to the point P on the line through **v** (Figure 11.48). The vector $\overrightarrow{OP}$ is the *orthogonal projection of* **u** *onto* **v**. An expression for $\text{proj}_{\mathbf{v}}\mathbf{u}$ is found using two observations.

- If $0 \le \theta < \pi/2$, then $\text{proj}_{\mathbf{v}}\mathbf{u}$ has length $|\mathbf{u}| \cos \theta$ and points in the direction of the unit vector $\mathbf{v}/|\mathbf{v}|$ (Figure 11.48a). Therefore,

$$\text{proj}_{\mathbf{v}}\mathbf{u} = \underbrace{|\mathbf{u}| \cos \theta}_{\text{length}} \underbrace{\left(\frac{\mathbf{v}}{|\mathbf{v}|}\right)}_{\text{direction}}.$$

We define the *scalar component of* **u** *in the direction of* **v** to be $\text{scal}_{\mathbf{v}}\mathbf{u} = |\mathbf{u}| \cos \theta$. In this case, $\text{scal}_{\mathbf{v}}\mathbf{u}$ is the length of $\text{proj}_{\mathbf{v}}\mathbf{u}$.

- If $\pi/2 < \theta \le \pi$, then $\text{proj}_{\mathbf{v}}\mathbf{u}$ has length $-|\mathbf{u}| \cos \theta$ (which is positive) and points in the direction of $-\mathbf{v}/|\mathbf{v}|$ (Figure 11.48b). Therefore,

$$\text{proj}_{\mathbf{v}}\mathbf{u} = \underbrace{-|\mathbf{u}| \cos \theta}_{\text{length}} \underbrace{\left(-\frac{\mathbf{v}}{|\mathbf{v}|}\right)}_{\text{direction}} = |\mathbf{u}| \cos \theta \left(\frac{\mathbf{v}}{|\mathbf{v}|}\right).$$

In this case, $\text{scal}_{\mathbf{v}}\mathbf{u} = |\mathbf{u}| \cos \theta < 0$.

We see that in both cases, the expression for $\text{proj}_{\mathbf{v}}\mathbf{u}$ is the same:

$$\text{proj}_{\mathbf{v}}\mathbf{u} = \underbrace{|\mathbf{u}| \cos \theta}_{\text{scal}_{\mathbf{v}}\mathbf{u}} \left(\frac{\mathbf{v}}{|\mathbf{v}|}\right) = \text{scal}_{\mathbf{v}}\mathbf{u}\left(\frac{\mathbf{v}}{|\mathbf{v}|}\right).$$

Note that if $\theta = \frac{\pi}{2}$, $\text{proj}_{\mathbf{v}}\mathbf{u} = \mathbf{0}$ and $\text{scal}_{\mathbf{v}}\mathbf{u} = 0$.

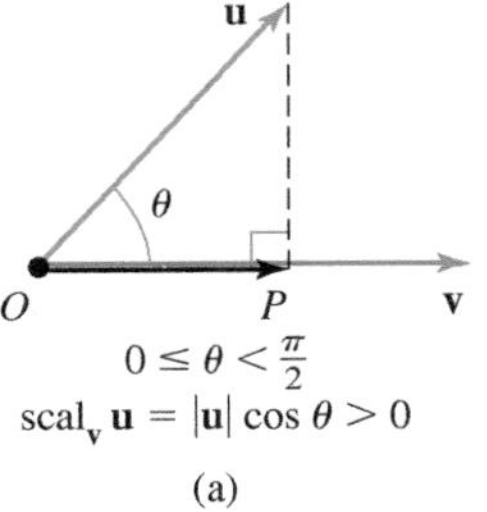

$0 \le \theta < \frac{\pi}{2}$
$\text{scal}_{\mathbf{v}}\,\mathbf{u} = |\mathbf{u}| \cos \theta > 0$
(a)

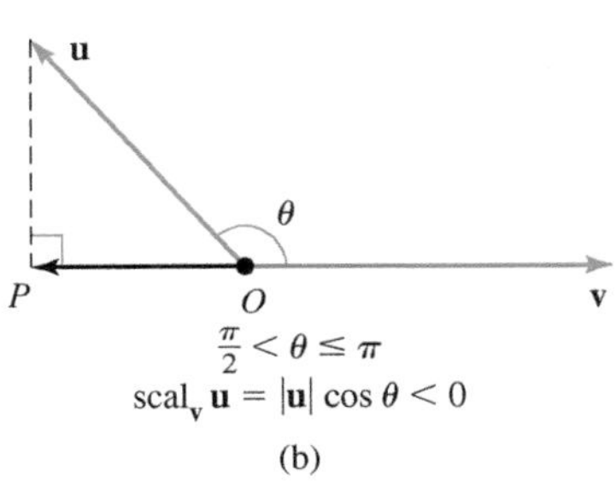

$\frac{\pi}{2} < \theta \le \pi$
$\text{scal}_{\mathbf{v}}\,\mathbf{u} = |\mathbf{u}| \cos \theta < 0$
(b)

Figure 11.48

➤ Notice that $\text{scal}_{\mathbf{v}}\mathbf{u}$ may be positive, negative, or zero. However, $|\text{scal}_{\mathbf{v}}\mathbf{u}|$ is the length of $\text{proj}_{\mathbf{v}}\mathbf{u}$. The projection $\text{proj}_{\mathbf{v}}\mathbf{u}$ is defined for all vectors **u**, but only for nonzero vectors **v**.

Using properties of the dot product, $\text{proj}_{\mathbf{v}}\mathbf{u}$ may be written in different ways:

$$\begin{aligned}\text{proj}_{\mathbf{v}}\mathbf{u} &= |\mathbf{u}|\cos\theta\left(\frac{\mathbf{v}}{|\mathbf{v}|}\right)\\ &= \frac{\mathbf{u}\cdot\mathbf{v}}{|\mathbf{v}|}\left(\frac{\mathbf{v}}{|\mathbf{v}|}\right) && |\mathbf{u}|\cos\theta = \frac{|\mathbf{u}||\mathbf{v}|\cos\theta}{|\mathbf{v}|} = \frac{\mathbf{u}\cdot\mathbf{v}}{|\mathbf{v}|}\\ &= \underbrace{\left(\frac{\mathbf{u}\cdot\mathbf{v}}{\mathbf{v}\cdot\mathbf{v}}\right)}_{\text{scalar}}\mathbf{v}. && \text{Regroup terms; } |\mathbf{v}|^2 = \mathbf{v}\cdot\mathbf{v}\end{aligned}$$

QUICK CHECK 3 Let $\mathbf{u} = 4\mathbf{i} - 3\mathbf{j}$. By inspection (not calculations), find the orthogonal projection of **u** onto **i** and onto **j**. Find the scalar component of **u** in the direction of **i** and in the direction of **j**. ◄

The first two expressions show that $\text{proj}_{\mathbf{v}}\mathbf{u}$ is a scalar multiple of the unit vector $\frac{\mathbf{v}}{|\mathbf{v}|}$, whereas the last expression shows that $\text{proj}_{\mathbf{v}}\mathbf{u}$ is a scalar multiple of **v**.

DEFINITION (Orthogonal) Projection of u onto v

The **orthogonal projection of u onto v**, denoted $\text{proj}_{\mathbf{v}}\mathbf{u}$, where $\mathbf{v} \neq \mathbf{0}$, is

$$\text{proj}_{\mathbf{v}}\mathbf{u} = |\mathbf{u}|\cos\theta\left(\frac{\mathbf{v}}{|\mathbf{v}|}\right).$$

The orthogonal projection may also be computed with the formulas

$$\text{proj}_{\mathbf{v}}\mathbf{u} = \text{scal}_{\mathbf{v}}\mathbf{u}\left(\frac{\mathbf{v}}{|\mathbf{v}|}\right) = \left(\frac{\mathbf{u}\cdot\mathbf{v}}{\mathbf{v}\cdot\mathbf{v}}\right)\mathbf{v},$$

where the **scalar component of u in the direction of v** is

$$\text{scal}_{\mathbf{v}}\mathbf{u} = |\mathbf{u}|\cos\theta = \frac{\mathbf{u}\cdot\mathbf{v}}{|\mathbf{v}|}.$$

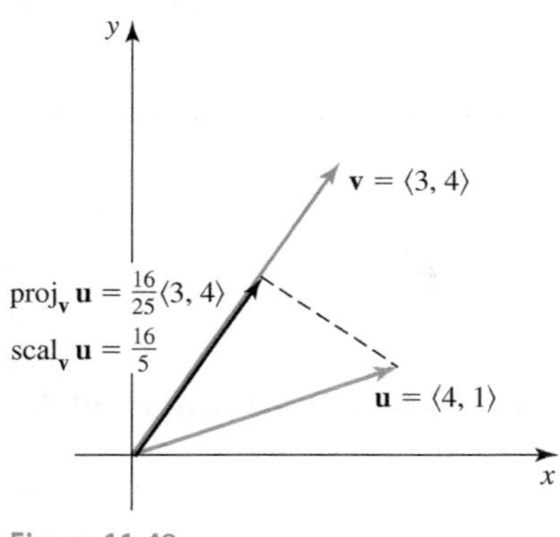

Figure 11.49

EXAMPLE 3 Orthogonal projections Find $\text{proj}_{\mathbf{v}}\mathbf{u}$ and $\text{scal}_{\mathbf{v}}\mathbf{u}$ for the following vectors and illustrate each result.

a. $\mathbf{u} = \langle 4, 1\rangle, \mathbf{v} = \langle 3, 4\rangle$

b. $\mathbf{u} = \langle -4, -3\rangle, \mathbf{v} = \langle 1, -1\rangle$

SOLUTION

a. The scalar component of **u** in the direction of **v** (Figure 11.49) is

$$\text{scal}_{\mathbf{v}}\mathbf{u} = \frac{\mathbf{u}\cdot\mathbf{v}}{|\mathbf{v}|} = \frac{\langle 4, 1\rangle\cdot\langle 3, 4\rangle}{|\langle 3, 4\rangle|} = \frac{16}{5}.$$

Because $\frac{\mathbf{v}}{|\mathbf{v}|} = \left\langle \frac{3}{5}, \frac{4}{5}\right\rangle$, we have

$$\text{proj}_{\mathbf{v}}\mathbf{u} = \text{scal}_{\mathbf{v}}\mathbf{u}\left(\frac{\mathbf{v}}{|\mathbf{v}|}\right) = \frac{16}{5}\left\langle \frac{3}{5}, \frac{4}{5}\right\rangle = \frac{16}{25}\langle 3, 4\rangle.$$

b. Using another formula for $\text{proj}_{\mathbf{v}}\mathbf{u}$, we have

$$\text{proj}_{\mathbf{v}}\mathbf{u} = \left(\frac{\mathbf{u}\cdot\mathbf{v}}{\mathbf{v}\cdot\mathbf{v}}\right)\mathbf{v} = \left(\frac{\langle -4, -3\rangle\cdot\langle 1, -1\rangle}{\langle 1, -1\rangle\cdot\langle 1, -1\rangle}\right)\langle 1, -1\rangle = -\frac{1}{2}\langle 1, -1\rangle.$$

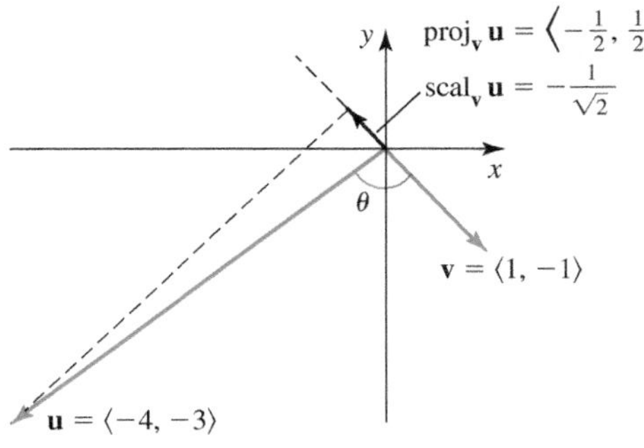

Figure 11.50

The vectors $\mathbf{v}$ and $\text{proj}_{\mathbf{v}}\mathbf{u}$ point in opposite directions because $\pi/2 < \theta \leq \pi$ (Figure 11.50). This fact is reflected in the scalar component of $\mathbf{u}$ in the direction of $\mathbf{v}$, which is negative:

$$\text{scal}_{\mathbf{v}}\mathbf{u} = \frac{\langle -4, -3 \rangle \cdot \langle 1, -1 \rangle}{|\langle 1, -1 \rangle|} = -\frac{1}{\sqrt{2}}.$$

Related Exercises 25–36 ◄

Applications of Dot Products

Work and Force In the opening of this section, we observed that if a constant force $\mathbf{F}$ acts at an angle θ to the direction of motion of an object (Figure 11.51), the work done by the force is

$$W = |\mathbf{F}| \cos\theta\, |\mathbf{d}| = \mathbf{F} \cdot \mathbf{d}.$$

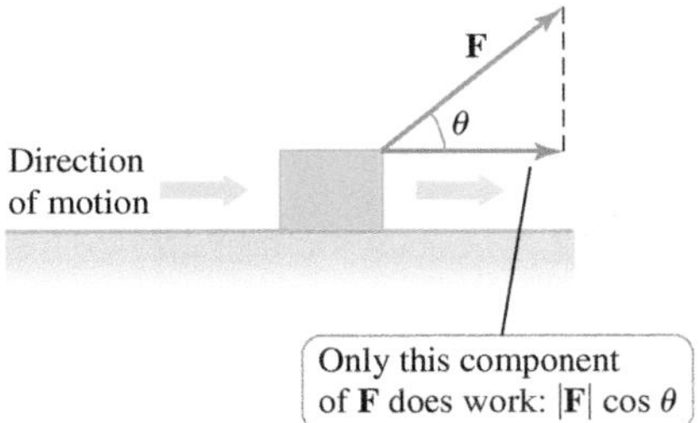

Figure 11.51

Notice that the work is a scalar, and if the force acts in a direction orthogonal to the motion, then $\theta = \pi/2$, $\mathbf{F} \cdot \mathbf{d} = 0$, and no work is done by the force.

DEFINITION Work

Let a constant force $\mathbf{F}$ be applied to an object, producing a displacement $\mathbf{d}$. If the angle between $\mathbf{F}$ and $\mathbf{d}$ is θ, then the **work** done by the force is

$$W = |\mathbf{F}||\mathbf{d}| \cos\theta = \mathbf{F} \cdot \mathbf{d}.$$

➤ If the unit of force is newtons (N) and the distance is measured in meters, then the unit of work is joules (J), where 1 J = 1 N-m. If force is measured in lb and distance is measured in ft, then work has units of ft-lb.

EXAMPLE 4 Calculating work A force $\mathbf{F} = \langle 3, 3, 2 \rangle$ (in newtons) moves an object along a line segment from $P(1, 1, 0)$ to $Q(6, 6, 0)$ (in meters). What is the work done by the force? Interpret the result.

SOLUTION The displacement of the object is $\mathbf{d} = \overrightarrow{PQ} = \langle 6 - 1, 6 - 1, 0 - 0 \rangle = \langle 5, 5, 0 \rangle$. Therefore, the work done by the force is

$$W = \mathbf{F} \cdot \mathbf{d} = \langle 3, 3, 2 \rangle \cdot \langle 5, 5, 0 \rangle = 30 \text{ J}.$$

To interpret this result, notice that the angle between the force and the displacement vector satisfies

$$\cos\theta = \frac{\mathbf{F} \cdot \mathbf{d}}{|\mathbf{F}||\mathbf{d}|} = \frac{\langle 3, 3, 2 \rangle \cdot \langle 5, 5, 0 \rangle}{|\langle 3, 3, 2 \rangle||\langle 5, 5, 0 \rangle|} = \frac{30}{\sqrt{22}\sqrt{50}} \approx 0.905.$$

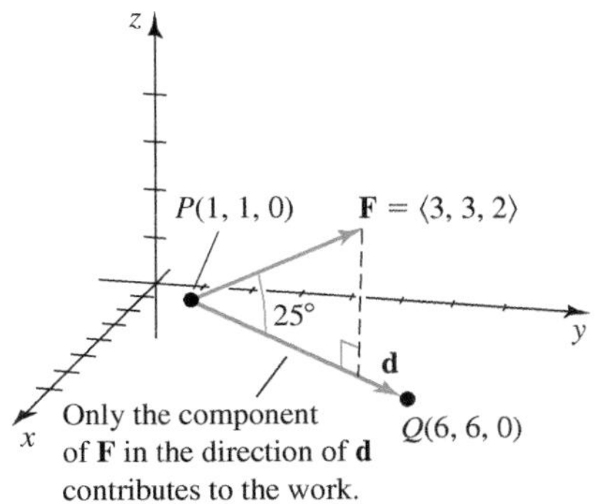

Figure 11.52

Therefore, $\theta \approx 0.44$ rad $\approx 25°$. The magnitude of the force is $|\mathbf{F}| = \sqrt{22} \approx 4.7$ N, but only the component of that force in the direction of motion, $|\mathbf{F}| \cos\theta \approx \sqrt{22} \cos 0.44 \approx 4.2$ N, contributes to the work (Figure 11.52).

Related Exercises 37–42 ◄

Parallel and Normal Forces Projections find frequent use in expressing a force in terms of orthogonal components. A common situation arises when an object rests on an inclined plane (Figure 11.53). The gravitational force on the object equals its weight, which is directed vertically downward. The projections of the gravitational force in the directions **parallel** to and **normal** (or perpendicular) to the plane are of interest. Specifically, the projection of the force parallel to the plane determines the tendency of the object to slide down the plane, while the projection of the force normal to the plane determines its tendency to "stick" to the plane.

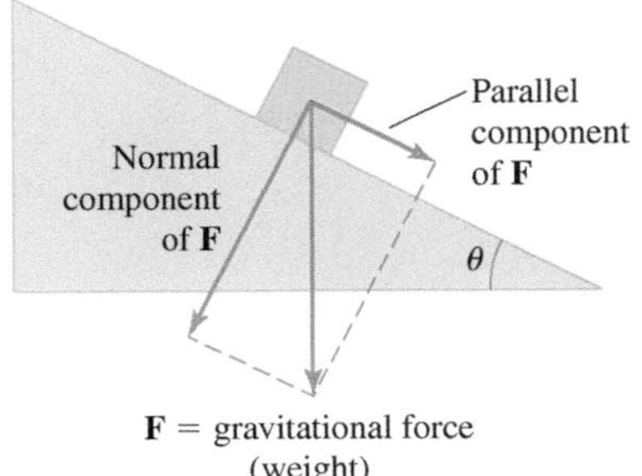

Figure 11.53

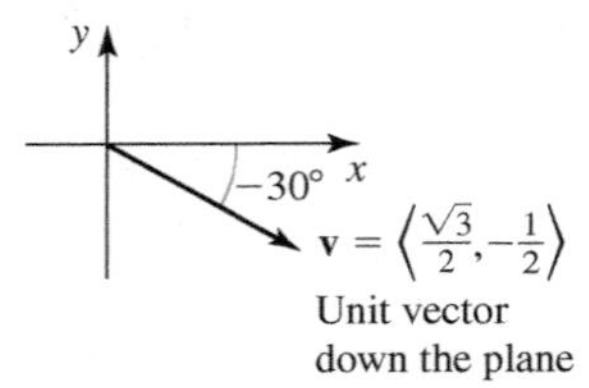

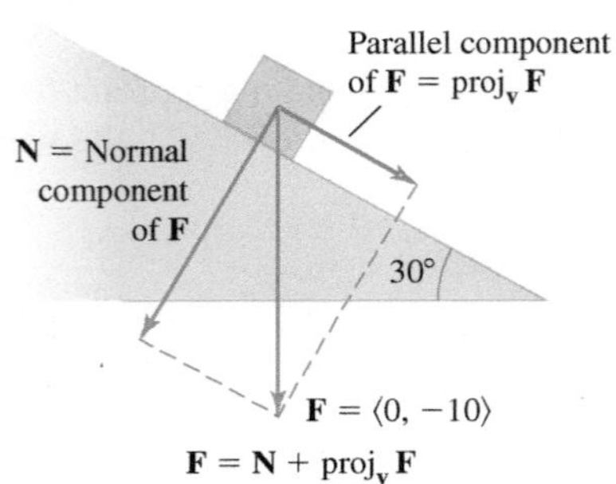

Figure 11.54

EXAMPLE 5 Components of a force A 10-lb block rests on a plane that is inclined at 30° below the horizontal. Find the components of the gravitational force parallel and normal (perpendicular) to the plane.

SOLUTION The gravitational force **F** acting on the block equals the weight of the block (10 lb), which we regard as a point mass. Using the coordinate system shown in Figure 11.54, the force acts in the negative y-direction; therefore, $\mathbf{F} = \langle 0, -10 \rangle$. The direction *down* the plane is given by the unit vector $\mathbf{v} = \langle \cos(-30°), \sin(-30°) \rangle = \left\langle \frac{\sqrt{3}}{2}, -\frac{1}{2} \right\rangle$ (check that $|\mathbf{v}| = 1$). The component of the gravitational force parallel to the plane is

$$\text{proj}_{\mathbf{v}}\mathbf{F} = \underbrace{\left(\frac{\mathbf{F} \cdot \mathbf{v}}{\mathbf{v} \cdot \mathbf{v}}\right)}_{\mathbf{v}\cdot\mathbf{v}=1}\mathbf{v} = \left(\underbrace{\langle 0, -10 \rangle}_{\mathbf{F}} \cdot \underbrace{\left\langle \frac{\sqrt{3}}{2}, -\frac{1}{2} \right\rangle}_{\mathbf{v}}\right) \underbrace{\left\langle \frac{\sqrt{3}}{2}, -\frac{1}{2} \right\rangle}_{\mathbf{v}} = 5\left\langle \frac{\sqrt{3}}{2}, -\frac{1}{2} \right\rangle.$$

Let the component of **F** normal to the plane be **N**. Note that $\mathbf{F} = \text{proj}_{\mathbf{v}}\mathbf{F} + \mathbf{N}$ so that

$$\mathbf{N} = \mathbf{F} - \text{proj}_{\mathbf{v}}\mathbf{F} = \langle 0, -10 \rangle - 5\left\langle \frac{\sqrt{3}}{2}, -\frac{1}{2} \right\rangle = -5\left\langle \frac{\sqrt{3}}{2}, \frac{3}{2} \right\rangle.$$

Figure 11.54 shows how the components of **F** parallel and normal to the plane combine to form the total force **F**.

Related Exercises 43–46 ◄

SECTION 11.3 EXERCISES

Review Questions

1. Express the dot product of **u** and **v** in terms of their magnitudes and the angle between them.
2. Express the dot product of **u** and **v** in terms of the components of the vectors.
3. Compute $\langle 2, 3, -6 \rangle \cdot \langle 1, -8, 3 \rangle$.
4. What is the dot product of two orthogonal vectors?
5. Explain how to find the angle between two nonzero vectors.
6. Use a sketch to illustrate the projection of **u** onto **v**.
7. Use a sketch to illustrate the scalar component of **u** in the direction of **v**.
8. Explain how the work done by a force in moving an object is computed using dot products.

Basic Skills

9–12. Dot product from the definition *Consider the following vectors* **u** *and* **v**. *Sketch the vectors, find the angle between the vectors, and compute the dot product using the definition* $\mathbf{u} \cdot \mathbf{v} = |\mathbf{u}||\mathbf{v}| \cos \theta$.

9. $\mathbf{u} = 4\mathbf{i}$ and $\mathbf{v} = 6\mathbf{j}$
10. $\mathbf{u} = \langle -3, 2, 0 \rangle$ and $\mathbf{v} = \langle 0, 0, 6 \rangle$
11. $\mathbf{u} = \langle 10, 0 \rangle$ and $\mathbf{v} = \langle 10, 10 \rangle$
12. $\mathbf{u} = \langle -\sqrt{3}, 1 \rangle$ and $\mathbf{v} = \langle \sqrt{3}, 1 \rangle$
13. **Dot product from the definition** Compute $\mathbf{u} \cdot \mathbf{v}$ if **u** and **v** are unit vectors and the angle between them is $\pi/3$.
14. **Dot product from the definition** Compute $\mathbf{u} \cdot \mathbf{v}$ if **u** is a unit vector, $|\mathbf{v}| = 2$, and the angle between them is $3\pi/4$.

T **15–24. Dot products and angles** *Compute the dot product of the vectors* **u** *and* **v**, *and find the angle between the vectors.*

15. $\mathbf{u} = \mathbf{i} + \mathbf{j}$ and $\mathbf{v} = \mathbf{i} - \mathbf{j}$
16. $\mathbf{u} = \langle 10, 0 \rangle$ and $\mathbf{v} = \langle -5, 5 \rangle$
17. $\mathbf{u} = \mathbf{i}$ and $\mathbf{v} = \mathbf{i} + \sqrt{3}\,\mathbf{j}$
18. $\mathbf{u} = \sqrt{2}\,\mathbf{i} + \sqrt{2}\,\mathbf{j}$ and $\mathbf{v} = -\sqrt{2}\,\mathbf{i} - \sqrt{2}\,\mathbf{j}$
19. $\mathbf{u} = 4\mathbf{i} + 3\mathbf{j}$ and $\mathbf{v} = 4\mathbf{i} - 6\mathbf{j}$
20. $\mathbf{u} = \langle 3, 4, 0 \rangle$ and $\mathbf{v} = \langle 0, 4, 5 \rangle$
21. $\mathbf{u} = \langle -10, 0, 4 \rangle$ and $\mathbf{v} = \langle 1, 2, 3 \rangle$
22. $\mathbf{u} = \langle 3, -5, 2 \rangle$ and $\mathbf{v} = \langle -9, 5, 1 \rangle$
23. $\mathbf{u} = 2\mathbf{i} - 3\mathbf{k}$ and $\mathbf{v} = \mathbf{i} + 4\mathbf{j} + 2\mathbf{k}$
24. $\mathbf{u} = \mathbf{i} - 4\mathbf{j} - 6\mathbf{k}$ and $\mathbf{v} = 2\mathbf{i} - 4\mathbf{j} + 2\mathbf{k}$

25–28. Sketching orthogonal projections *Find* $\text{proj}_{\mathbf{v}}\mathbf{u}$ *and* $\text{scal}_{\mathbf{v}}\mathbf{u}$ *by inspection without using formulas.*

25.

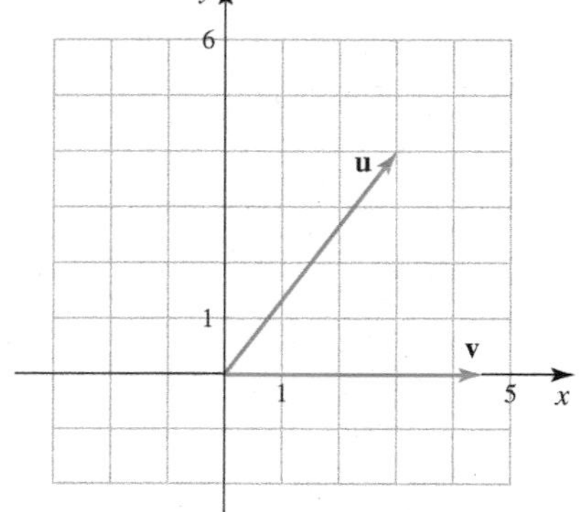

26.

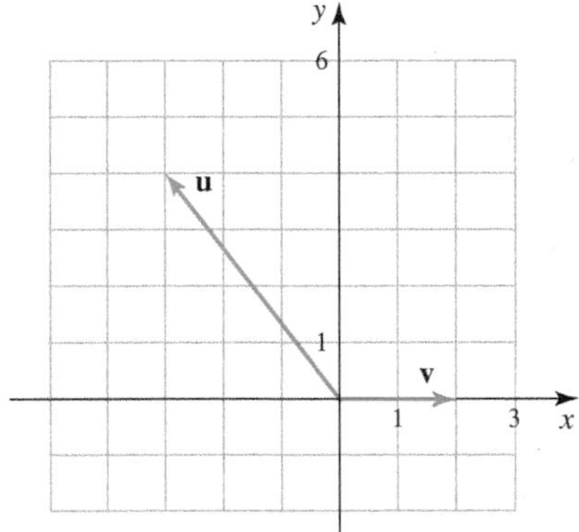

27.

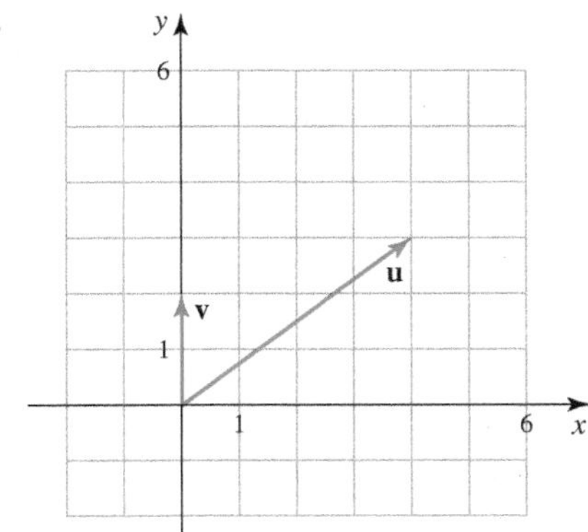

28.

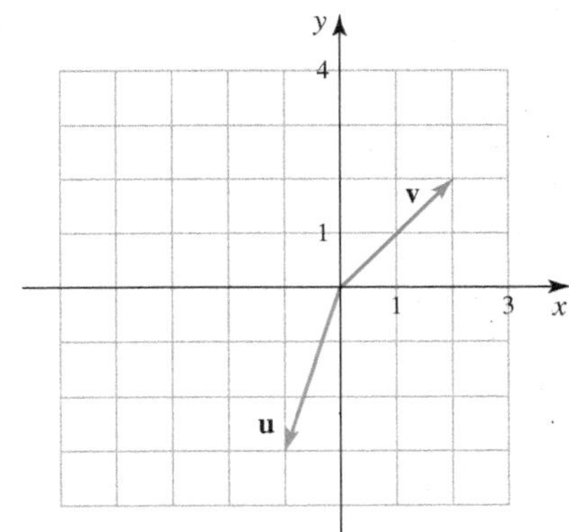

29–36. Calculating orthogonal projections *For the given vectors* **u** *and* **v**, *calculate* $\text{proj}_{\mathbf{v}}\mathbf{u}$ *and* $\text{scal}_{\mathbf{v}}\mathbf{u}$.

29. $\mathbf{u} = \langle -1, 4 \rangle$ and $\mathbf{v} = \langle -4, 2 \rangle$

30. $\mathbf{u} = \langle 10, 5 \rangle$ and $\mathbf{v} = \langle 2, 6 \rangle$

31. $\mathbf{u} = \langle 3, 3, -3 \rangle$ and $\mathbf{v} = \langle 1, -1, 2 \rangle$

32. $\mathbf{u} = \langle 13, 0, 26 \rangle$ and $\mathbf{v} = \langle 4, -1, -3 \rangle$

33. $\mathbf{u} = \langle -8, 0, 2 \rangle$ and $\mathbf{v} = \langle 1, 3, -3 \rangle$

34. $\mathbf{u} = \langle 5, 0, 15 \rangle$ and $\mathbf{v} = \langle 0, 4, -2 \rangle$

35. $\mathbf{u} = 5\,\mathbf{i} + \mathbf{j} - 5\,\mathbf{k}$ and $\mathbf{v} = -\mathbf{i} + \mathbf{j} - 2\,\mathbf{k}$

36. $\mathbf{u} = \mathbf{i} + 4\mathbf{j} + 7\mathbf{k}$ and $\mathbf{v} = 2\mathbf{i} - 4\mathbf{j} + 2\mathbf{k}$

37–42. Computing work *Calculate the work done in the following situations.*

37. A suitcase is pulled 50 ft along a horizontal sidewalk with a constant force of 30 lb at an angle of 30° above the horizontal.

T 38. A stroller is pushed 20 m with a constant force of 10 N at an angle of 15° below the horizontal.

39. A sled is pulled 10 m along horizontal ground with a constant force of 5 N at an angle of 45° above the horizontal.

40. A constant force $\mathbf{F} = \langle 4, 3, 2 \rangle$ (in newtons) moves an object from $(0, 0, 0)$ to $(8, 6, 0)$. (Distance is measured in meters.)

41. A constant force $\mathbf{F} = \langle 40, 30 \rangle$ (in newtons) is used to move a sled horizontally 10 m.

42. A constant force $\mathbf{F} = \langle 2, 4, 1 \rangle$ (in newtons) moves an object from $(0, 0, 0)$ to $(2, 4, 6)$. (Distance is measured in meters.)

43–46. Parallel and normal forces *Find the components of the vertical force* $\mathbf{F} = \langle 0, -10 \rangle$ *in the directions parallel to and normal to the following inclined planes. Show that the total force is the sum of the two component forces.*

43. A plane that makes an angle of $\pi/4$ with the positive x-axis

44. A plane that makes an angle of $\pi/6$ with the positive x-axis

45. A plane that makes an angle of $\pi/3$ with the positive x-axis

46. A plane that makes an angle of $\theta = \tan^{-1}\frac{4}{5}$ with the positive x-axis

Further Explorations

47. **Explain why or why not** Determine whether the following statements are true and give an explanation or counterexample.
   a. $\text{proj}_{\mathbf{v}}\mathbf{u} = \text{proj}_{\mathbf{u}}\mathbf{v}$.
   b. If nonzero vectors **u** and **v** have the same magnitude, they make equal angles with $\mathbf{u} + \mathbf{v}$.
   c. $(\mathbf{u} \cdot \mathbf{i})^2 + (\mathbf{u} \cdot \mathbf{j})^2 + (\mathbf{u} \cdot \mathbf{k})^2 = |\mathbf{u}|^2$.
   d. If **u** is orthogonal to **v** and **v** is orthogonal to **w**, then **u** is orthogonal to **w**.
   e. The vectors orthogonal to $\langle 1, 1, 1 \rangle$ lie on the same line.
   f. If $\text{proj}_{\mathbf{v}}\mathbf{u} = \mathbf{0}$, then vectors **u** and **v** (both nonzero) are orthogonal.

48–52. Orthogonal vectors *Let a and b be real numbers.*

48. Find all unit vectors orthogonal to $\mathbf{v} = \langle 3, 4, 0 \rangle$.

49. Find all vectors $\langle 1, a, b \rangle$ orthogonal to $\langle 4, -8, 2 \rangle$.

50. Describe all unit vectors orthogonal to $\mathbf{v} = \mathbf{i} + \mathbf{j} + \mathbf{k}$.

51. Find three mutually orthogonal unit vectors in $\mathbb{R}^3$ besides $\pm\mathbf{i}$, $\pm\mathbf{j}$, and $\pm\mathbf{k}$.

52. Find two vectors that are orthogonal to $\langle 0, 1, 1 \rangle$ and to each other.

53. **Equal angles** Consider the set of all unit position vectors **u** in $\mathbb{R}^3$ that make a 60° angle with the unit vector **k** in $\mathbb{R}^3$.
   a. Prove that $\text{proj}_{\mathbf{k}}\mathbf{u}$ is the same for all vectors in this set.
   b. Is $\text{scal}_{\mathbf{k}}\mathbf{u}$ the same for all vectors in this set?

54–57. Vectors with equal projections *Given a fixed vector* **v**, *there is an infinite set of vectors* **u** *with the same value of* $\text{proj}_{\mathbf{v}}\mathbf{u}$.

54. Find another vector that has the same projection onto $\mathbf{v} = \langle 1, 1 \rangle$ as $\mathbf{u} = \langle 1, 2 \rangle$. Draw a picture.

55. Let $\mathbf{v} = \langle 1, 1 \rangle$. Give a description of the position vectors **u** such that $\text{proj}_{\mathbf{v}}\mathbf{u} = \text{proj}_{\mathbf{v}}\langle 1, 2 \rangle$.

56. Find another vector that has the same projection onto $\mathbf{v} = \langle 1, 1, 1 \rangle$ as $\mathbf{u} = \langle 1, 2, 3 \rangle$.

57. Let $\mathbf{v} = \langle 0, 0, 1 \rangle$. Give a description of all position vectors $\mathbf{u}$ such that $\text{proj}_{\mathbf{v}}\mathbf{u} = \text{proj}_{\mathbf{v}}\langle 1, 2, 3 \rangle$.

58–61. Decomposing vectors *For the following vectors* $\mathbf{u}$ *and* $\mathbf{v}$, *express* $\mathbf{u}$ *as the sum* $\mathbf{u} = \mathbf{p} + \mathbf{n}$, *where* $\mathbf{p}$ *is parallel to* $\mathbf{v}$ *and* $\mathbf{n}$ *is orthogonal to* $\mathbf{v}$.

58. $\mathbf{u} = \langle 4, 3 \rangle, \mathbf{v} = \langle 1, 1 \rangle$

59. $\mathbf{u} = \langle -2, 2 \rangle, \mathbf{v} = \langle 2, 1 \rangle$

60. $\mathbf{u} = \langle 4, 3, 0 \rangle, \mathbf{v} = \langle 1, 1, 1 \rangle$

61. $\mathbf{u} = \langle -1, 2, 3 \rangle, \mathbf{v} = \langle 2, 1, 1 \rangle$

62–65. Distance between a point and a line *Carry out the following steps to determine the (least) distance between the point* P *and the line* ℓ *through the origin.*

a. Find any vector $\mathbf{v}$ *in the direction of* ℓ.
b. Find the position vector $\mathbf{u}$ *corresponding to* P.
c. Find $\text{proj}_{\mathbf{v}}\mathbf{u}$.
d. Show that $\mathbf{w} = \mathbf{u} - \text{proj}_{\mathbf{v}}\mathbf{u}$ *is a vector orthogonal to* $\mathbf{v}$ *whose length is the distance between* P *and the line* ℓ.
e. Find $\mathbf{w}$ *and* $|\mathbf{w}|$. *Explain why* $|\mathbf{w}|$ *is the least distance between* P *and* ℓ.

62. $P(2, -5)$; $\ell: y = 3x$

63. $P(-12, 4)$; $\ell: y = 2x$

64. $P(0, 2, 6)$; ℓ is parallel to $\langle 3, 0, -4 \rangle$.

65. $P(1, 1, -1)$; ℓ is parallel to $\langle -6, 8, 3 \rangle$.

66–68. Orthogonal unit vectors in $\mathbb{R}^2$ *Consider the vectors* $\mathbf{I} = \langle 1/\sqrt{2}, 1/\sqrt{2} \rangle$ *and* $\mathbf{J} = \langle -1/\sqrt{2}, 1/\sqrt{2} \rangle$.

66. Show that $\mathbf{I}$ and $\mathbf{J}$ are orthogonal unit vectors.

67. Express $\mathbf{I}$ and $\mathbf{J}$ in terms of the usual unit coordinate vectors $\mathbf{i}$ and $\mathbf{j}$. Then write $\mathbf{i}$ and $\mathbf{j}$ in terms of $\mathbf{I}$ and $\mathbf{J}$.

68. Write the vector $\langle 2, -6 \rangle$ in terms of $\mathbf{I}$ and $\mathbf{J}$.

69. Orthogonal unit vectors in $\mathbb{R}^3$ Consider the vectors $\mathbf{I} = \langle 1/2, 1/2, 1/\sqrt{2} \rangle$, $\mathbf{J} = \langle -1/\sqrt{2}, 1/\sqrt{2}, 0 \rangle$, and $\mathbf{K} = \langle 1/2, 1/2, -1/\sqrt{2} \rangle$.

a. Sketch $\mathbf{I}$, $\mathbf{J}$, and $\mathbf{K}$ and show that they are unit vectors.
b. Show that $\mathbf{I}$, $\mathbf{J}$, and $\mathbf{K}$ are pairwise orthogonal.
c. Express the vector $\langle 1, 0, 0 \rangle$ in terms of $\mathbf{I}$, $\mathbf{J}$, and $\mathbf{K}$.

T **70–71. Angles of a triangle** *For the given points* P, Q, *and* R, *find the approximate measurements of the angles of* $\triangle PQR$.

70. $P(1, -4), Q(2, 7), R(-2, 2)$

71. $P(0, -1, 3), Q(2, 2, 1), R(-2, 2, 4)$

Applications

72. Flow through a circle Suppose water flows in a thin sheet over the xy-plane with a uniform velocity given by the vector $\mathbf{v} = \langle 1, 2 \rangle$; this means that at all points of the plane, the velocity of the water has components 1 m/s in the x-direction and 2 m/s in the y-direction (see figure). Let C be an imaginary unit circle (that does not interfere with the flow).

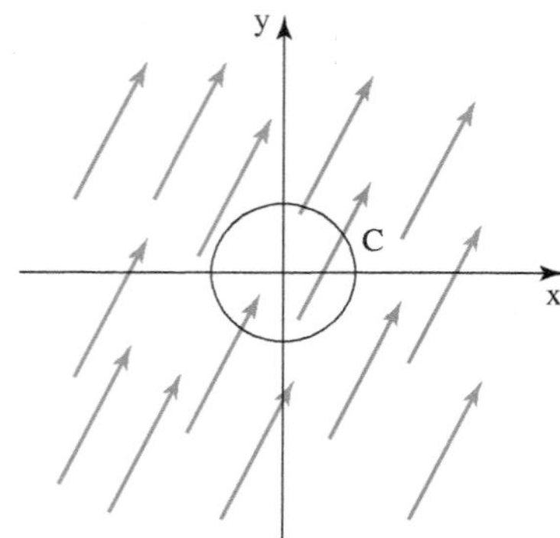

a. Show that at the point (x, y) on the circle C, the outward-pointing unit vector normal to C is $\mathbf{n} = \langle x, y \rangle$.
b. Show that at the point $(\cos\theta, \sin\theta)$ on the circle C, the outward-pointing unit vector normal to C is also $\mathbf{n} = \langle \cos\theta, \sin\theta \rangle$.
c. Find all points on C at which the velocity is normal to C.
d. Find all points on C at which the velocity is tangential to C.
e. At each point on C, find the component of $\mathbf{v}$ normal to C. Express the answer as a function of (x, y) and as a function of θ.
f. What is the net flow through the circle? That is, does water accumulate inside the circle?

73. Heat flux Let D be a solid heat-conducting cube formed by the planes $x = 0$, $x = 1$, $y = 0$, $y = 1$, $z = 0$, and $z = 1$. The heat flow at every point of D is given by the constant vector $\mathbf{Q} = \langle 0, 2, 1 \rangle$.

a. Through which faces of D does $\mathbf{Q}$ point into D?
b. Through which faces of D does $\mathbf{Q}$ point out of D?
c. On which faces of D is $\mathbf{Q}$ tangential to D (pointing neither in nor out of D)?
d. Find the scalar component of $\mathbf{Q}$ normal to the face $x = 0$.
e. Find the scalar component of $\mathbf{Q}$ normal to the face $z = 1$.
f. Find the scalar component of $\mathbf{Q}$ normal to the face $y = 0$.

74. Hexagonal circle packing The German mathematician Gauss proved that the densest way to pack circles with the same radius in the plane is to place the centers of the circles on a hexagonal grid (see figure). Some molecular structures use this packing or its three-dimensional analog. Assume all circles have a radius of 1 and let $\mathbf{r}_{ij}$ be the vector that extends from the center of circle i to the center of circle j, for $i, j = 0, 1, \ldots, 6$.

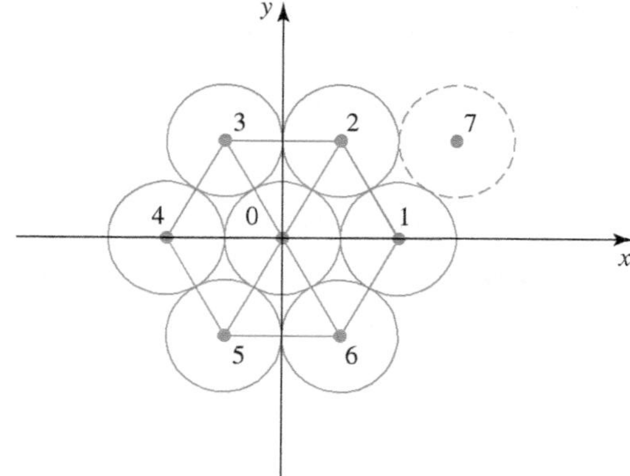

a. Find $\mathbf{r}_{0j}$, for $j = 1, 2, \ldots, 6$.
b. Find $\mathbf{r}_{12}$, $\mathbf{r}_{34}$, and $\mathbf{r}_{61}$.
c. Imagine circle 7 is added to the arrangement as shown in the figure. Find $\mathbf{r}_{07}$, $\mathbf{r}_{17}$, $\mathbf{r}_{47}$, and $\mathbf{r}_{75}$.

75. Hexagonal sphere packing Imagine three unit spheres (radius equal to 1) with centers at $O(0, 0, 0)$, $P(\sqrt{3}, -1, 0)$, and $Q(\sqrt{3}, 1, 0)$. Now place another unit sphere symmetrically on top of these spheres with its center at R (see figure).

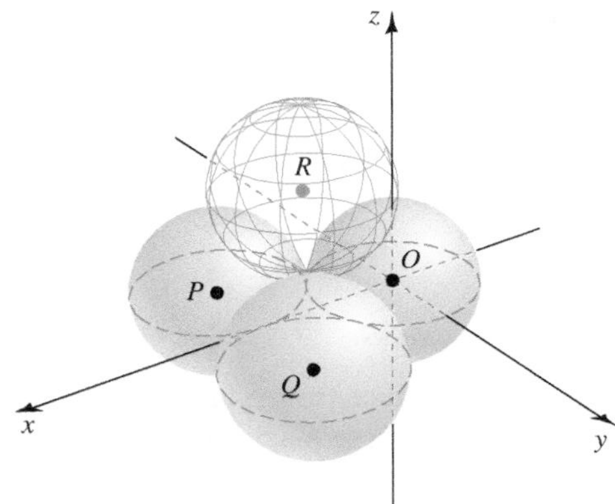

a. Find the coordinates of R. (*Hint:* The distance between the centers of any two spheres is 2.)
b. Let $\mathbf{r}_{IJ}$ be the vector from the center of sphere I to the center of sphere J. Find $\mathbf{r}_{OP}$, $\mathbf{r}_{OQ}$, $\mathbf{r}_{PQ}$, $\mathbf{r}_{OR}$, and $\mathbf{r}_{PR}$.

Additional Exercises

76–80. Properties of dot products *Let* $\mathbf{u} = \langle u_1, u_2, u_3 \rangle$, $\mathbf{v} = \langle v_1, v_2, v_3 \rangle$, *and* $\mathbf{w} = \langle w_1, w_2, w_3 \rangle$. *Prove the following vector properties, where c is a scalar.*

76. $|\mathbf{u} \cdot \mathbf{v}| \le |\mathbf{u}||\mathbf{v}|$

77. $\mathbf{u} \cdot \mathbf{v} = \mathbf{v} \cdot \mathbf{u}$ Commutative property

78. $c(\mathbf{u} \cdot \mathbf{v}) = (c\mathbf{u}) \cdot \mathbf{v} = \mathbf{u} \cdot (c\mathbf{v})$ Associative property

79. $\mathbf{u} \cdot (\mathbf{v} + \mathbf{w}) = \mathbf{u} \cdot \mathbf{v} + \mathbf{u} \cdot \mathbf{w}$ Distributive property

80. Distributive properties

a. Show that $(\mathbf{u} + \mathbf{v}) \cdot (\mathbf{u} + \mathbf{v}) = |\mathbf{u}|^2 + 2\,\mathbf{u} \cdot \mathbf{v} + |\mathbf{v}|^2$.
b. Show that $(\mathbf{u} + \mathbf{v}) \cdot (\mathbf{u} + \mathbf{v}) = |\mathbf{u}|^2 + |\mathbf{v}|^2$ if $\mathbf{u}$ is orthogonal to $\mathbf{v}$.
c. Show that $(\mathbf{u} + \mathbf{v}) \cdot (\mathbf{u} - \mathbf{v}) = |\mathbf{u}|^2 - |\mathbf{v}|^2$.

81. Prove or disprove For fixed values of a, b, c, and d, the value of $\text{proj}_{\langle ka, kb \rangle} \langle c, d \rangle$ is constant for all nonzero values of k, for $\langle a, b \rangle \neq \langle 0, 0 \rangle$.

82. Orthogonal lines Recall that two lines $y = mx + b$ and $y = nx + c$ are orthogonal provided $mn = -1$ (the slopes are negative reciprocals of each other). Prove that the condition $mn = -1$ is equivalent to the orthogonality condition $\mathbf{u} \cdot \mathbf{v} = 0$, where $\mathbf{u}$ points in the direction of one line and $\mathbf{v}$ points in the direction of the other line.

83. Direction angles and cosines Let $\mathbf{v} = \langle a, b, c \rangle$ and let α, β, and γ be the angles between $\mathbf{v}$ and the positive x-axis, the positive y-axis, and the positive z-axis, respectively (see figure).

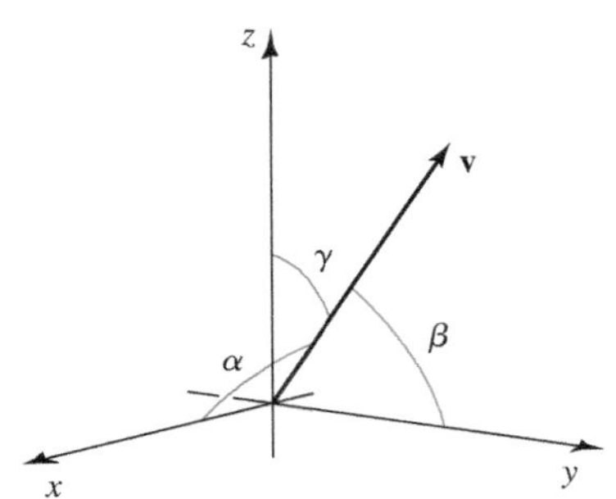

a. Prove that $\cos^2 \alpha + \cos^2 \beta + \cos^2 \gamma = 1$.
b. Find a vector that makes a 45° angle with $\mathbf{i}$ and $\mathbf{j}$. What angle does it make with $\mathbf{k}$?
c. Find a vector that makes a 60° angle with $\mathbf{i}$ and $\mathbf{j}$. What angle does it make with $\mathbf{k}$?
d. Is there a vector that makes a 30° angle with $\mathbf{i}$ and $\mathbf{j}$? Explain.
e. Find a vector $\mathbf{v}$ such that $\alpha = \beta = \gamma$. What is the angle?

84–88. Cauchy–Schwarz Inequality *The definition* $\mathbf{u} \cdot \mathbf{v} = |\mathbf{u}||\mathbf{v}| \cos \theta$ *implies that* $|\mathbf{u} \cdot \mathbf{v}| \le |\mathbf{u}||\mathbf{v}|$ *(because* $|\cos \theta| \le 1$*). This inequality, known as the Cauchy–Schwarz Inequality, holds in any number of dimensions and has many consequences.*

84. What conditions on $\mathbf{u}$ and $\mathbf{v}$ lead to equality in the Cauchy–Schwarz Inequality?

85. Verify that the Cauchy–Schwarz Inequality holds for $\mathbf{u} = \langle 3, -5, 6 \rangle$ and $\mathbf{v} = \langle -8, 3, 1 \rangle$.

86. Geometric-arithmetic mean Use the vectors $\mathbf{u} = \langle \sqrt{a}, \sqrt{b} \rangle$ and $\mathbf{v} = \langle \sqrt{b}, \sqrt{a} \rangle$ to show that $\sqrt{ab} \le (a + b)/2$, where $a \ge 0$ and $b \ge 0$.

87. Triangle Inequality Consider the vectors $\mathbf{u}$, $\mathbf{v}$, and $\mathbf{u} + \mathbf{v}$ (in any number of dimensions). Use the following steps to prove that $|\mathbf{u} + \mathbf{v}| \le |\mathbf{u}| + |\mathbf{v}|$.

a. Show that $|\mathbf{u} + \mathbf{v}|^2 = (\mathbf{u} + \mathbf{v}) \cdot (\mathbf{u} + \mathbf{v}) = |\mathbf{u}|^2 + 2\mathbf{u} \cdot \mathbf{v} + |\mathbf{v}|^2$.
b. Use the Cauchy–Schwarz Inequality to show that $|\mathbf{u} + \mathbf{v}|^2 \le (|\mathbf{u}| + |\mathbf{v}|)^2$.
c. Conclude that $|\mathbf{u} + \mathbf{v}| \le |\mathbf{u}| + |\mathbf{v}|$.
d. Interpret the Triangle Inequality geometrically in $\mathbb{R}^2$ or $\mathbb{R}^3$.

88. Algebra inequality Show that

$$(u_1 + u_2 + u_3)^2 \le 3(u_1^2 + u_2^2 + u_3^2),$$

for any real numbers u_1, u_2, and u_3. (*Hint:* Use the Cauchy-Schwarz Inequality in three dimensions with $\mathbf{u} = \langle u_1, u_2, u_3 \rangle$ and choose $\mathbf{v}$ in the right way.)

89. Diagonals of a parallelogram Consider the parallelogram with adjacent sides $\mathbf{u}$ and $\mathbf{v}$.

a. Show that the diagonals of the parallelogram are $\mathbf{u} + \mathbf{v}$ and $\mathbf{u} - \mathbf{v}$.
b. Prove that the diagonals have the same length if and only if $\mathbf{u} \cdot \mathbf{v} = 0$.
c. Show that the sum of the squares of the lengths of the diagonals equals the sum of the squares of the lengths of the sides.

90. Distance between a point and a line in the plane Use projections to find a general formula for the (least) distance between the point $P(x_0, y_0)$ and the line $ax + by = c$. (See Exercises 62–65.)

QUICK CHECK ANSWERS

1. If $\theta = 0$, $\mathbf{u}$ and $\mathbf{v}$ are parallel and point in the same direction. If $\theta = \pi$, $\mathbf{u}$ and $\mathbf{v}$ are parallel and point in opposite directions. **2.** All these dot products are zero, and the unit vectors are mutually orthogonal. The angle between two different unit vectors is $\pi/2$. **3.** $\text{proj}_{\mathbf{i}}\mathbf{u} = 4\mathbf{i}$, $\text{proj}_{\mathbf{j}}\mathbf{u} = -3\mathbf{j}$, $\text{scal}_{\mathbf{i}}\mathbf{u} = 4$, $\text{scal}_{\mathbf{j}}\mathbf{u} = -3$ ◄

11.4 Cross Products

The dot product combines two vectors to produce a *scalar* result. There is an equally fundamental way to combine two vectors in $\mathbb{R}^3$ and obtain a *vector* result. This operation, known as the *cross product* (or *vector product*), may be motivated by a physical application.

Suppose you want to loosen a bolt with a wrench. As you apply force to the end of the wrench in the plane perpendicular to the bolt, the "twisting power" you generate depends on three variables:

- the magnitude of the force $\mathbf{F}$ applied to the wrench;
- the length $|\mathbf{r}|$ of the wrench;
- the angle at which the force is applied to the wrench.

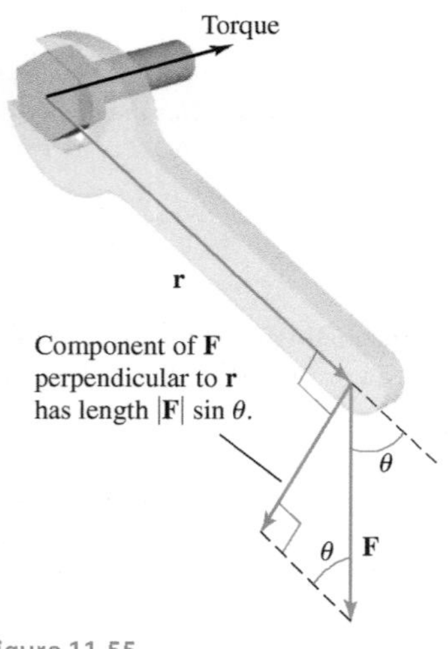

Figure 11.55

The twisting generated by a force acting at a distance from a pivot point is called **torque** (from the Latin *to twist*). The torque is a vector whose magnitude is proportional to $|\mathbf{F}|$, $|\mathbf{r}|$, and $\sin\theta$, where θ is the angle between $\mathbf{F}$ and $\mathbf{r}$ (Figure 11.55). If the force is applied parallel to the wrench—for example, if you pull the wrench ($\theta = 0$) or push the wrench ($\theta = \pi$)—there is no twisting effect; if the force is applied perpendicular to the wrench ($\theta = \pi/2$), the twisting effect is maximized. The direction of the torque vector is defined to be orthogonal to both $\mathbf{F}$ and $\mathbf{r}$. As we will see shortly, the torque is expressed in terms of the cross product of $\mathbf{F}$ and $\mathbf{r}$.

The Cross Product

The preceding physical example leads to the following definition of the cross product.

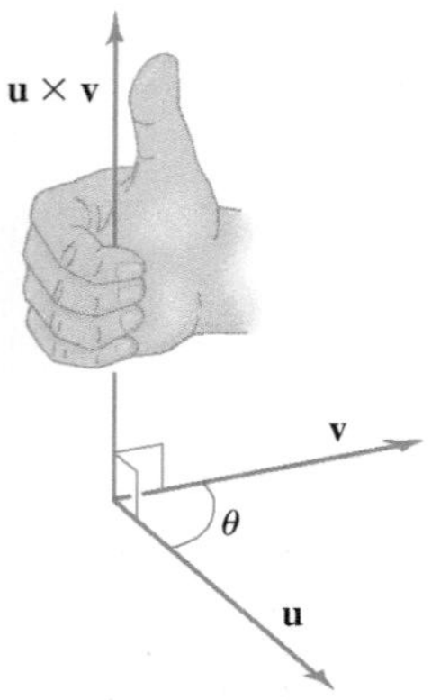

Figure 11.56

> **DEFINITION Cross Product**
>
> Given two nonzero vectors $\mathbf{u}$ and $\mathbf{v}$ in $\mathbb{R}^3$, the **cross product** $\mathbf{u} \times \mathbf{v}$ is a vector with magnitude
>
> $$|\mathbf{u} \times \mathbf{v}| = |\mathbf{u}||\mathbf{v}| \sin\theta,$$
>
> where $0 \le \theta \le \pi$ is the angle between $\mathbf{u}$ and $\mathbf{v}$. The direction of $\mathbf{u} \times \mathbf{v}$ is given by the **right-hand rule**: When you put the vectors tail to tail and let the fingers of your right hand curl from $\mathbf{u}$ to $\mathbf{v}$, the direction of $\mathbf{u} \times \mathbf{v}$ is the direction of your thumb, orthogonal to both $\mathbf{u}$ and $\mathbf{v}$ (Figure 11.56). When $\mathbf{u} \times \mathbf{v} = \mathbf{0}$, the direction of $\mathbf{u} \times \mathbf{v}$ is undefined.

The following theorem is a consequence of the definition of the cross product.

QUICK CHECK 1 Sketch the vectors $\mathbf{u} = \langle 1, 2, 0 \rangle$ and $\mathbf{v} = \langle -1, 2, 0 \rangle$. Which way does $\mathbf{u} \times \mathbf{v}$ point? Which way does $\mathbf{v} \times \mathbf{u}$ point? ◄

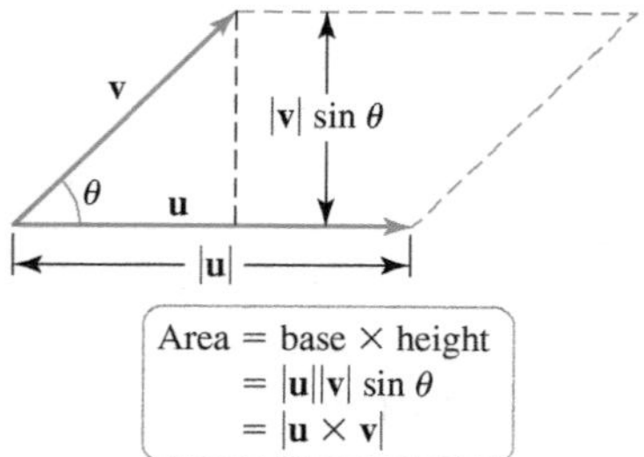

Figure 11.57

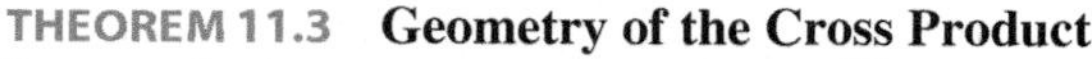

> **THEOREM 11.3 Geometry of the Cross Product**
>
> Let $\mathbf{u}$ and $\mathbf{v}$ be two nonzero vectors in $\mathbb{R}^3$.
>
> 1. The vectors $\mathbf{u}$ and $\mathbf{v}$ are parallel ($\theta = 0$ or $\theta = \pi$) if and only if $\mathbf{u} \times \mathbf{v} = \mathbf{0}$.
> 2. If $\mathbf{u}$ and $\mathbf{v}$ are two sides of a parallelogram (Figure 11.57), then the area of the parallelogram is
>
> $$|\mathbf{u} \times \mathbf{v}| = |\mathbf{u}||\mathbf{v}| \sin\theta.$$

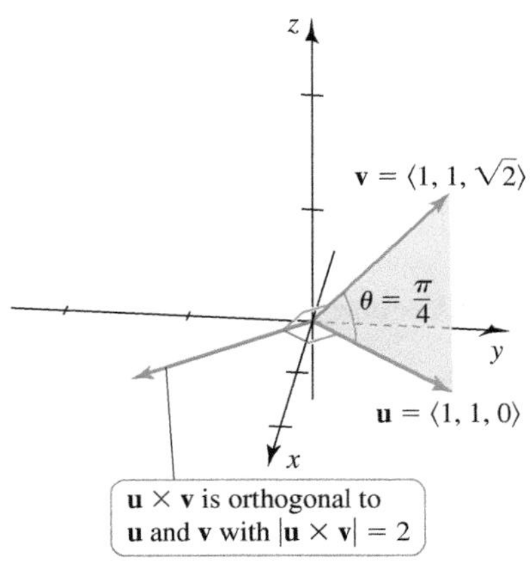

Figure 11.58

EXAMPLE 1 **A cross product** Find the magnitude and direction of $\mathbf{u} \times \mathbf{v}$, where $\mathbf{u} = \langle 1, 1, 0 \rangle$ and $\mathbf{v} = \langle 1, 1, \sqrt{2} \rangle$.

SOLUTION Because $\mathbf{u}$ is one side of a 45–45–90 triangle and $\mathbf{v}$ is the hypotenuse (Figure 11.58), we have $\theta = \pi/4$ and $\sin\theta = \frac{1}{\sqrt{2}}$. Also, $|\mathbf{u}| = \sqrt{2}$ and $|\mathbf{v}| = 2$, so the magnitude of $\mathbf{u} \times \mathbf{v}$ is

$$|\mathbf{u} \times \mathbf{v}| = |\mathbf{u}|\,|\mathbf{v}| \sin\theta = \sqrt{2} \cdot 2 \cdot \frac{1}{\sqrt{2}} = 2.$$

The direction of $\mathbf{u} \times \mathbf{v}$ is given by the right-hand rule: $\mathbf{u} \times \mathbf{v}$ is orthogonal to $\mathbf{u}$ and $\mathbf{v}$ (Figure 11.58).

Related Exercises 7–14 ◀

Properties of the Cross Product

The cross product has several algebraic properties that simplify calculations. For example, scalars factor out of a cross product; that is, if a and b are scalars, then (Exercise 69)

$$(a\mathbf{u}) \times (b\mathbf{v}) = ab(\mathbf{u} \times \mathbf{v}).$$

The order in which the cross product is performed is important. The magnitudes of $\mathbf{u} \times \mathbf{v}$ and $\mathbf{v} \times \mathbf{u}$ are equal. However, applying the right-hand rule shows that $\mathbf{u} \times \mathbf{v}$ and $\mathbf{v} \times \mathbf{u}$ point in opposite directions. Therefore, $\mathbf{u} \times \mathbf{v} = -(\mathbf{v} \times \mathbf{u})$. There are two distributive properties for the cross product, whose proofs are omitted.

QUICK CHECK 2 Explain why the vector $2\mathbf{u} \times 3\mathbf{v}$ points in the same direction as $\mathbf{u} \times \mathbf{v}$. ◀

THEOREM 11.4 **Properties of the Cross Product**
Let $\mathbf{u}$, $\mathbf{v}$, and $\mathbf{w}$ be nonzero vectors in $\mathbb{R}^3$, and let a and b be scalars.

1. $\mathbf{u} \times \mathbf{v} = -(\mathbf{v} \times \mathbf{u})$ — Anticommutative property
2. $(a\mathbf{u}) \times (b\mathbf{v}) = ab(\mathbf{u} \times \mathbf{v})$ — Associative property
3. $\mathbf{u} \times (\mathbf{v} + \mathbf{w}) = (\mathbf{u} \times \mathbf{v}) + (\mathbf{u} \times \mathbf{w})$ — Distributive property
4. $(\mathbf{u} + \mathbf{v}) \times \mathbf{w} = (\mathbf{u} \times \mathbf{w}) + (\mathbf{v} \times \mathbf{w})$ — Distributive property

EXAMPLE 2 **Cross products of unit vectors** Evaluate all the cross products among the coordinate unit vectors $\mathbf{i}$, $\mathbf{j}$, and $\mathbf{k}$.

SOLUTION These vectors are mutually orthogonal, which means the angle between any two distinct vectors is $\theta = \pi/2$ and $\sin\theta = 1$. Furthermore, $|\mathbf{i}| = |\mathbf{j}| = |\mathbf{k}| = 1$. Therefore, the cross product of any two distinct vectors has magnitude 1. By the right-hand rule, when the fingers of the right hand curl from $\mathbf{i}$ to $\mathbf{j}$, the thumb points in the direction of the positive z-axis (Figure 11.59). The unit vector in the positive z-direction is $\mathbf{k}$, so $\mathbf{i} \times \mathbf{j} = \mathbf{k}$. Similar calculations show that $\mathbf{j} \times \mathbf{k} = \mathbf{i}$ and $\mathbf{k} \times \mathbf{i} = \mathbf{j}$.

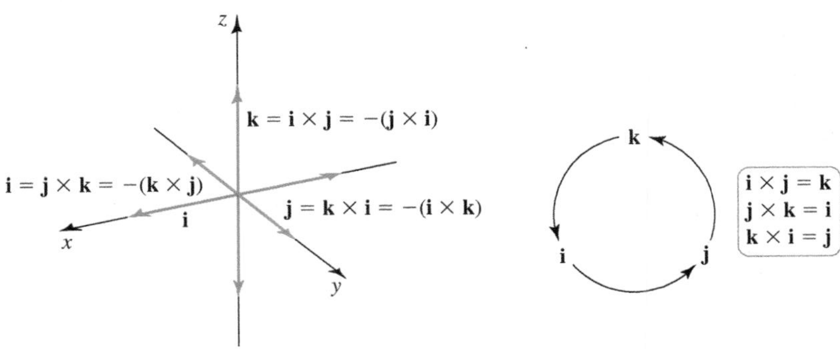

Figure 11.59

By property 1 of Theorem 11.4, $\mathbf{j} \times \mathbf{i} = -(\mathbf{i} \times \mathbf{j}) = -\mathbf{k}$, so $\mathbf{j} \times \mathbf{i}$ and $\mathbf{i} \times \mathbf{j}$ point in opposite directions. Similarly, $\mathbf{k} \times \mathbf{j} = -\mathbf{i}$ and $\mathbf{i} \times \mathbf{k} = -\mathbf{j}$. These relationships are easily remembered with the circle diagram in Figure 11.59. Finally, the angle between any unit vector and itself is $\theta = 0$. Therefore, $\mathbf{i} \times \mathbf{i} = \mathbf{j} \times \mathbf{j} = \mathbf{k} \times \mathbf{k} = \mathbf{0}$.

Related Exercises 15–20 ◄

> **THEOREM 11.5 Cross Products of Coordinate Unit Vectors**
>
> $$\mathbf{i} \times \mathbf{j} = -(\mathbf{j} \times \mathbf{i}) = \mathbf{k} \qquad \mathbf{j} \times \mathbf{k} = -(\mathbf{k} \times \mathbf{j}) = \mathbf{i}$$
> $$\mathbf{k} \times \mathbf{i} = -(\mathbf{i} \times \mathbf{k}) = \mathbf{j} \qquad \mathbf{i} \times \mathbf{i} = \mathbf{j} \times \mathbf{j} = \mathbf{k} \times \mathbf{k} = \mathbf{0}$$

What is missing so far is an efficient method for finding the components of the cross product of two vectors in $\mathbb{R}^3$. Let $\mathbf{u} = u_1\mathbf{i} + u_2\mathbf{j} + u_3\mathbf{k}$ and $\mathbf{v} = v_1\mathbf{i} + v_2\mathbf{j} + v_3\mathbf{k}$. Using the distributive properties of the cross product (Theorem 11.4), we have

$$\begin{aligned}\mathbf{u} \times \mathbf{v} &= (u_1\mathbf{i} + u_2\mathbf{j} + u_3\mathbf{k}) \times (v_1\mathbf{i} + v_2\mathbf{j} + v_3\mathbf{k}) \\ &= u_1v_1 \underbrace{(\mathbf{i} \times \mathbf{i})}_{0} + u_1v_2 \underbrace{(\mathbf{i} \times \mathbf{j})}_{\mathbf{k}} + u_1v_3 \underbrace{(\mathbf{i} \times \mathbf{k})}_{-\mathbf{j}} \\ &\quad + u_2v_1 \underbrace{(\mathbf{j} \times \mathbf{i})}_{-\mathbf{k}} + u_2v_2 \underbrace{(\mathbf{j} \times \mathbf{j})}_{0} + u_2v_3 \underbrace{(\mathbf{j} \times \mathbf{k})}_{\mathbf{i}} \\ &\quad + u_3v_1 \underbrace{(\mathbf{k} \times \mathbf{i})}_{\mathbf{j}} + u_3v_2 \underbrace{(\mathbf{k} \times \mathbf{j})}_{-\mathbf{i}} + u_3v_3 \underbrace{(\mathbf{k} \times \mathbf{k})}_{0}.\end{aligned}$$

➤ The determinant of the matrix A is denoted both $|A|$ and $\det A$. The formula for the determinant of a 3×3 matrix A is

$$\begin{vmatrix} a_1 & a_2 & a_3 \\ b_1 & b_2 & b_3 \\ c_1 & c_2 & c_3 \end{vmatrix} = a_1\begin{vmatrix} b_2 & b_3 \\ c_2 & c_3 \end{vmatrix} - a_2\begin{vmatrix} b_1 & b_3 \\ c_1 & c_3 \end{vmatrix} + a_3\begin{vmatrix} b_1 & b_2 \\ c_1 & c_2 \end{vmatrix},$$

where

$$\begin{vmatrix} a & b \\ c & d \end{vmatrix} = ad - bc.$$

This formula looks impossible to remember until we see that it fits the pattern used to evaluate 3×3 determinants. Specifically, if we compute the determinant of the matrix

$$\begin{array}{rcc} \text{Unit vectors} & \rightarrow \\ \text{Components of } \mathbf{u} & \rightarrow \\ \text{Components of } \mathbf{v} & \rightarrow \end{array} \begin{pmatrix} \mathbf{i} & \mathbf{j} & \mathbf{k} \\ u_1 & u_2 & u_3 \\ v_1 & v_2 & v_3 \end{pmatrix}$$

(expanding about the first row), the following formula for the cross product emerges (see margin note).

> **THEOREM 11.6 Evaluating the Cross Product**
> Let $\mathbf{u} = u_1\mathbf{i} + u_2\mathbf{j} + u_3\mathbf{k}$ and $\mathbf{v} = v_1\mathbf{i} + v_2\mathbf{j} + v_3\mathbf{k}$. Then
>
> $$\mathbf{u} \times \mathbf{v} = \begin{vmatrix} \mathbf{i} & \mathbf{j} & \mathbf{k} \\ u_1 & u_2 & u_3 \\ v_1 & v_2 & v_3 \end{vmatrix} = \begin{vmatrix} u_2 & u_3 \\ v_2 & v_3 \end{vmatrix}\mathbf{i} - \begin{vmatrix} u_1 & u_3 \\ v_1 & v_3 \end{vmatrix}\mathbf{j} + \begin{vmatrix} u_1 & u_2 \\ v_1 & v_2 \end{vmatrix}\mathbf{k}.$$

EXAMPLE 3 Area of a triangle Find the area of the triangle with vertices $O(0, 0, 0)$, $P(2, 3, 4)$, and $Q(3, 2, 0)$ (Figure 11.60).

SOLUTION First consider the parallelogram, two of whose sides are the vectors $\overrightarrow{OP}$ and $\overrightarrow{OQ}$. By Theorem 11.3, the area of this parallelogram is $|\overrightarrow{OP} \times \overrightarrow{OQ}|$. Computing the cross product, we find that

$$\begin{aligned}\overrightarrow{OP} \times \overrightarrow{OQ} &= \begin{vmatrix} \mathbf{i} & \mathbf{j} & \mathbf{k} \\ 2 & 3 & 4 \\ 3 & 2 & 0 \end{vmatrix} = \begin{vmatrix} 3 & 4 \\ 2 & 0 \end{vmatrix}\mathbf{i} - \begin{vmatrix} 2 & 4 \\ 3 & 0 \end{vmatrix}\mathbf{j} + \begin{vmatrix} 2 & 3 \\ 3 & 2 \end{vmatrix}\mathbf{k} \\ &= -8\mathbf{i} + 12\mathbf{j} - 5\mathbf{k}.\end{aligned}$$

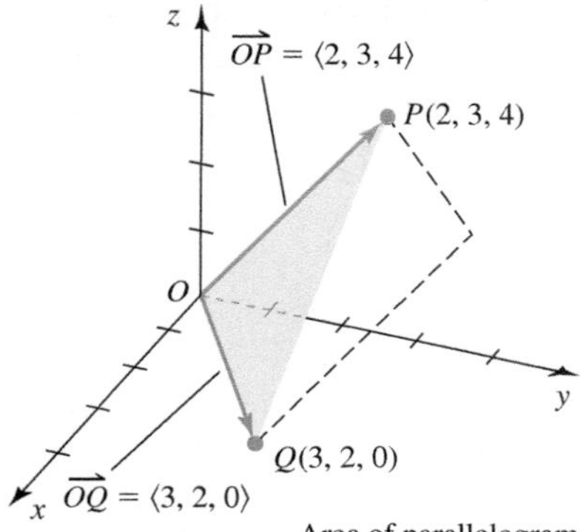

Figure 11.60

Therefore, the area of the parallelogram is

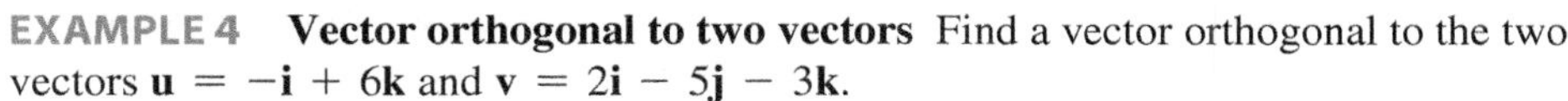

$$|\overrightarrow{OP} \times \overrightarrow{OQ}| = |-8\mathbf{i} + 12\mathbf{j} - 5\mathbf{k}| = \sqrt{233} \approx 15.26.$$

The triangle with vertices O, P, and Q comprises half of the parallelogram, so its area is $\sqrt{233}/2 \approx 7.63$.

Related Exercises 21–34 ◀

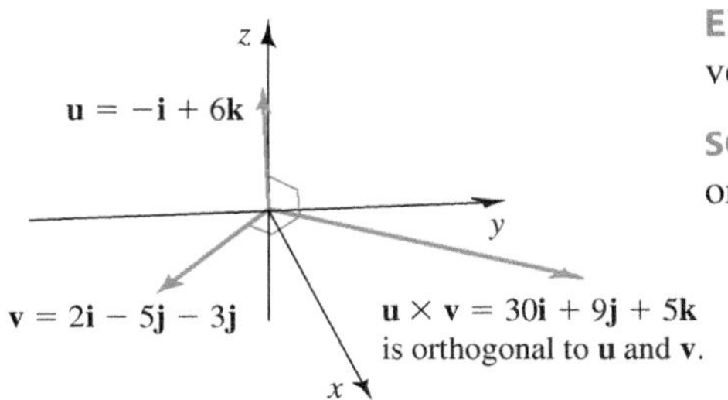

Figure 11.61

EXAMPLE 4 Vector orthogonal to two vectors Find a vector orthogonal to the two vectors $\mathbf{u} = -\mathbf{i} + 6\mathbf{k}$ and $\mathbf{v} = 2\mathbf{i} - 5\mathbf{j} - 3\mathbf{k}$.

SOLUTION A vector orthogonal to $\mathbf{u}$ and $\mathbf{v}$ is parallel to $\mathbf{u} \times \mathbf{v}$ (Figure 11.61). One such orthogonal vector is

$$\begin{aligned}\mathbf{u} \times \mathbf{v} &= \begin{vmatrix} \mathbf{i} & \mathbf{j} & \mathbf{k} \\ -1 & 0 & 6 \\ 2 & -5 & -3 \end{vmatrix} \\ &= (0 + 30)\mathbf{i} - (3 - 12)\mathbf{j} + (5 - 0)\mathbf{k} \\ &= 30\mathbf{i} + 9\mathbf{j} + 5\mathbf{k}.\end{aligned}$$

Any scalar multiple of this vector is also orthogonal to $\mathbf{u}$ and $\mathbf{v}$.

Related Exercises 35–38 ◀

QUICK CHECK 3 A good check on a cross product calculation is to verify that $\mathbf{u}$ and $\mathbf{v}$ are orthogonal to the computed $\mathbf{u} \times \mathbf{v}$. In Example 4, verify that $\mathbf{u} \cdot (\mathbf{u} \times \mathbf{v}) = 0$ and $\mathbf{v} \cdot (\mathbf{u} \times \mathbf{v}) = 0$. ◀

Applications of the Cross Product

We now investigate two physical applications of the cross product.

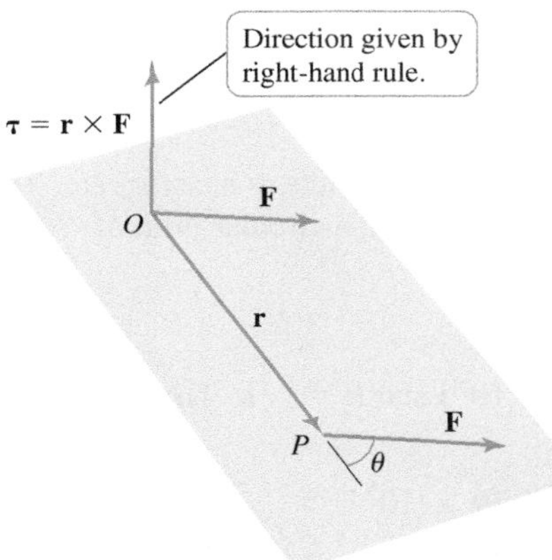

Figure 11.62

Torque Returning to the example of applying a force to a wrench, suppose a force $\mathbf{F}$ is applied to the point P at the head of a vector $\mathbf{r} = \overrightarrow{OP}$ (Figure 11.62). The **torque**, or twisting effect, produced by the force about the point O is given by $\boldsymbol{\tau} = \mathbf{r} \times \mathbf{F}$. The torque vector has a magnitude of

$$|\boldsymbol{\tau}| = |\mathbf{r} \times \mathbf{F}| = |\mathbf{r}||\mathbf{F}| \sin \theta,$$

where θ is the angle between $\mathbf{r}$ and $\mathbf{F}$. The direction of the torque is given by the right-hand rule; it is orthogonal to both $\mathbf{r}$ and $\mathbf{F}$. As noted earlier, if $\mathbf{r}$ and $\mathbf{F}$ are parallel, then $\sin \theta = 0$ and the torque is zero. For a given $\mathbf{r}$ and $\mathbf{F}$, the maximum torque occurs when $\mathbf{F}$ is applied in a direction orthogonal to $\mathbf{r}$ ($\theta = \pi/2$).

EXAMPLE 5 Tightening a bolt A force of 20 N is applied to a wrench attached to a bolt in a direction perpendicular to the bolt (Figure 11.63). Which produces more torque: applying the force at an angle of 60° on a wrench that is 0.15 m long or applying the force at an angle of 135° on a wrench that is 0.25 m long? In each case, what is the direction of the torque?

➤ When standard threads are added to the bolt in Figure 11.63, the forces used in Example 5 cause the bolt to move upward into a nut—in the direction of the torque.

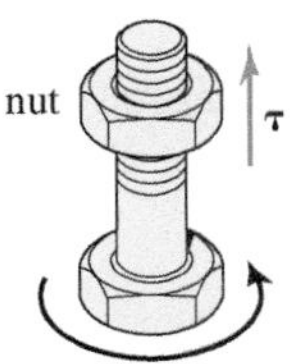

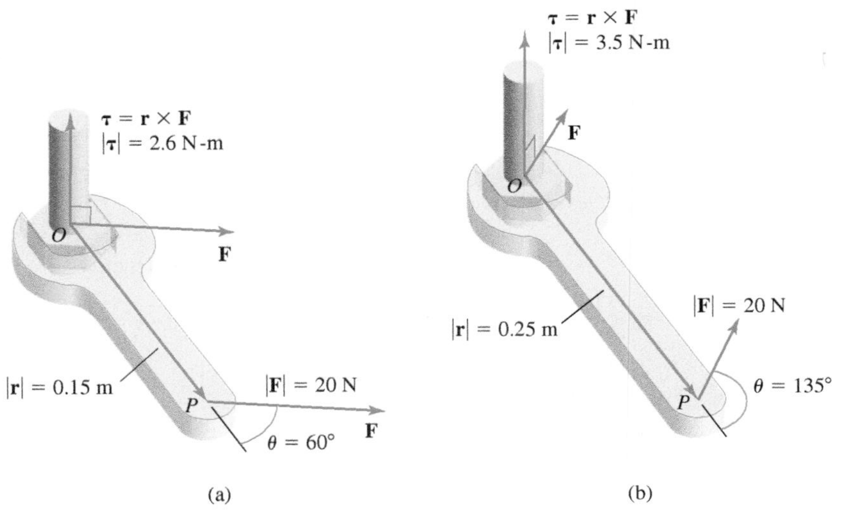

Figure 11.63

SOLUTION The magnitude of the torque in the first case is

$$|\boldsymbol{\tau}| = |\mathbf{r}||\mathbf{F}| \sin\theta = (0.15 \text{ m})(20 \text{ N}) \sin 60^\circ \approx 2.6 \text{ N-m}.$$

In the second case, the magnitude of the torque is

$$|\boldsymbol{\tau}| = |\mathbf{r}||\mathbf{F}| \sin\theta = (0.25 \text{ m})(20 \text{ N}) \sin 135^\circ \approx 3.5 \text{ N-m}.$$

The second instance gives the greater torque. In both cases, the torque is orthogonal to **r** and **F**, parallel to the shaft of the bolt (Figure 11.63).

Related Exercises 39–44 ◄

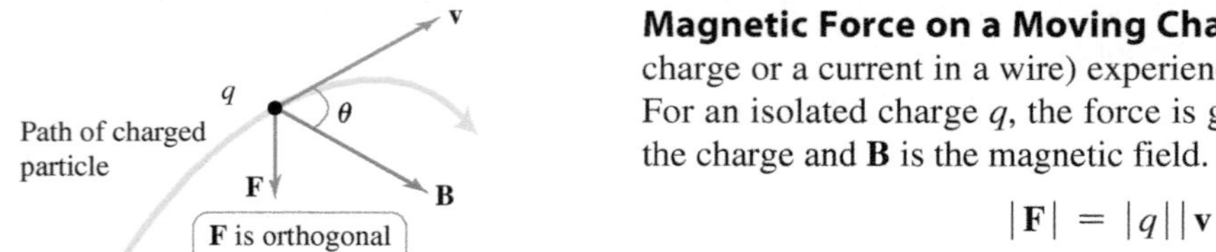

Figure 11.64

Magnetic Force on a Moving Charge Moving electric charges (either an isolated charge or a current in a wire) experience a force when they pass through a magnetic field. For an isolated charge q, the force is given by $\mathbf{F} = q(\mathbf{v} \times \mathbf{B})$, where **v** is the velocity of the charge and **B** is the magnetic field. The magnitude of the force is

$$|\mathbf{F}| = |q||\mathbf{v} \times \mathbf{B}| = |q||\mathbf{v}||\mathbf{B}| \sin\theta,$$

where θ is the angle between **v** and **B** (Figure 11.64). Note that the sign of the charge also determines the direction of the force. If the velocity vector is parallel to the magnetic field, the charge experiences no force. The maximum force occurs when the velocity is orthogonal to the magnetic field.

➤ The standard unit of magnetic field strength is the tesla (T, named after Nicola Tesla). A typical strong bar magnet has a strength of about 1 T. In terms of other units, 1 T = 1 kg/(C-s), where C is the unit of charge called the *coulomb*.

EXAMPLE 6 **Force on a proton** A proton with a mass of 1.7×10^{-27} kg and a charge of $q = +1.6 \times 10^{-19}$ coulombs (C) moves along the x-axis with a speed of $|\mathbf{v}| = 9 \times 10^5$ m/s. When it reaches $(0, 0, 0)$, a uniform magnetic field is turned on. The field has a constant strength of 1 tesla (1 T) and is directed along the negative z-axis (Figure 11.65).

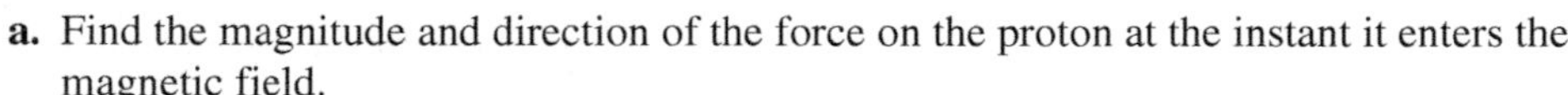

a. Find the magnitude and direction of the force on the proton at the instant it enters the magnetic field.

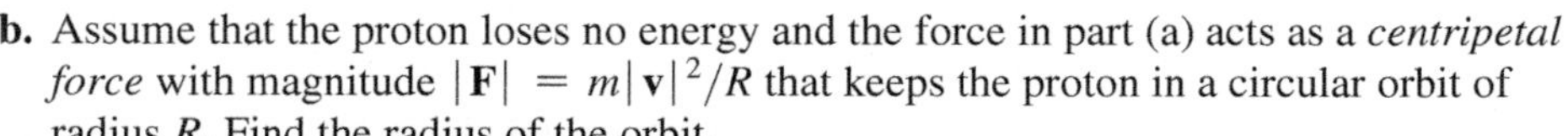

b. Assume that the proton loses no energy and the force in part (a) acts as a *centripetal force* with magnitude $|\mathbf{F}| = m|\mathbf{v}|^2/R$ that keeps the proton in a circular orbit of radius R. Find the radius of the orbit.

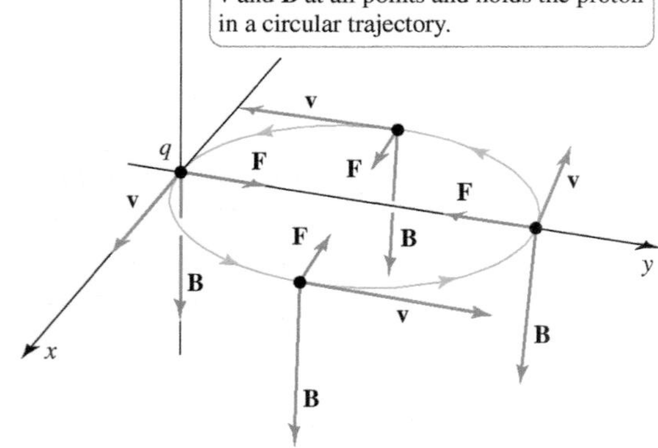

Figure 11.65

SOLUTION

a. Expressed as vectors, we have $\mathbf{v} = 9 \times 10^5\, \mathbf{i}$ and $\mathbf{B} = -\mathbf{k}$. Therefore, the force on the proton in newtons is

$$\begin{aligned}\mathbf{F} = q(\mathbf{v} \times \mathbf{B}) &= 1.6 \times 10^{-19}\big((9 \times 10^5\, \mathbf{i}) \times (-\mathbf{k})\big)\\ &= 1.44 \times 10^{-13}\mathbf{j}.\end{aligned}$$

As shown in Figure 11.65, when the proton enters the magnetic field in the positive x-direction, the force acts in the positive y-direction, which changes the path of the proton.

b. The magnitude of the force acting on the proton remains 1.44×10^{-13} N at all times (from part (a)). Equating this force to the centripetal force $|\mathbf{F}| = m|\mathbf{v}|^2/R$, we find that

$$R = \frac{m|\mathbf{v}|^2}{|\mathbf{F}|} = \frac{(1.7 \times 10^{-27} \text{ kg})\,(9 \times 10^5 \text{ m/s})^2}{1.44 \times 10^{-13} \text{ N}} \approx 0.01 \text{ m}.$$

Assuming no energy loss, the proton moves in a circular orbit of radius 0.01 m.

Related Exercises 45–48 ◄

SECTION 11.4 EXERCISES

Review Questions

1. Explain how to find the magnitude of the cross product $\mathbf{u} \times \mathbf{v}$.
2. Explain how to find the direction of the cross product $\mathbf{u} \times \mathbf{v}$.
3. What is the magnitude of the cross product of two parallel vectors?
4. If $\mathbf{u}$ and $\mathbf{v}$ are orthogonal, what is the magnitude of $\mathbf{u} \times \mathbf{v}$?
5. Explain how to use a determinant to compute $\mathbf{u} \times \mathbf{v}$.
6. Explain how to find the torque produced by a force using cross products.

Basic Skills

7–8. Cross products from the definition *Find the cross product $\mathbf{u} \times \mathbf{v}$ in each figure.*

7.

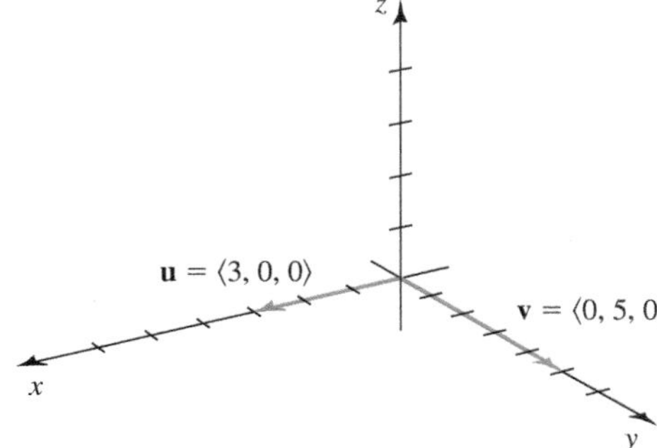

8.

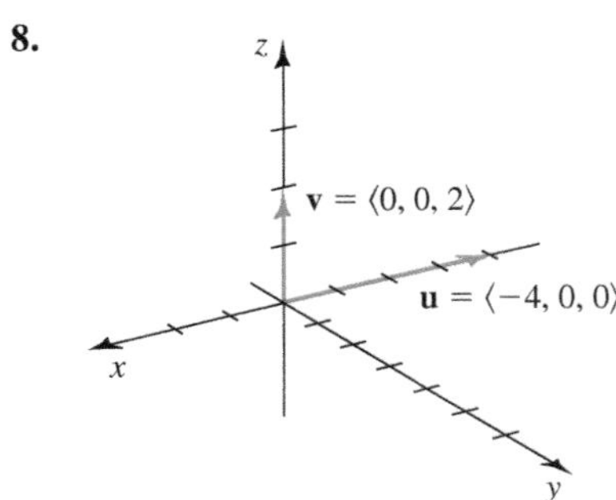

9–12. Cross products from the definition *Sketch the following vectors $\mathbf{u}$ and $\mathbf{v}$. Then compute $|\mathbf{u} \times \mathbf{v}|$ and show the cross product on your sketch.*

9. $\mathbf{u} = \langle 0, -2, 0 \rangle, \mathbf{v} = \langle 0, 1, 0 \rangle$
10. $\mathbf{u} = \langle 0, 4, 0 \rangle, \mathbf{v} = \langle 0, 0, -8 \rangle$
11. $\mathbf{u} = \langle 3, 3, 0 \rangle, \mathbf{v} = \langle 3, 3, 3\sqrt{2} \rangle$
12. $\mathbf{u} = \langle 0, -2, -2 \rangle, \mathbf{v} = \langle 0, 2, -2 \rangle$
13. **Magnitude of a cross product** Compute $|\mathbf{u} \times \mathbf{v}|$ if $\mathbf{u}$ and $\mathbf{v}$ are unit vectors and the angle between $\mathbf{u}$ and $\mathbf{v}$ is $\pi/4$.
14. **Magnitude of a cross product** Compute $|\mathbf{u} \times \mathbf{v}|$ if $|\mathbf{u}| = 3$ and $|\mathbf{v}| = 4$ and the angle between $\mathbf{u}$ and $\mathbf{v}$ is $2\pi/3$.

15–20. Coordinate unit vectors *Compute the following cross products. Then make a sketch showing the two vectors and their cross product.*

15. $\mathbf{j} \times \mathbf{k}$
16. $\mathbf{i} \times \mathbf{k}$
17. $-\mathbf{j} \times \mathbf{k}$
18. $3\mathbf{j} \times \mathbf{i}$
19. $-2\mathbf{i} \times 3\mathbf{k}$
20. $2\mathbf{j} \times (-5)\mathbf{i}$

21–24. Area of a parallelogram *Find the area of the parallelogram that has two adjacent sides $\mathbf{u}$ and $\mathbf{v}$.*

21. $\mathbf{u} = 3\mathbf{i} - \mathbf{j}, \mathbf{v} = 3\mathbf{j} + 2\mathbf{k}$
22. $\mathbf{u} = -3\mathbf{i} + 2\mathbf{k}, \mathbf{v} = \mathbf{i} + \mathbf{j} + \mathbf{k}$
23. $\mathbf{u} = 2\mathbf{i} - \mathbf{j} - 2\mathbf{k}, \mathbf{v} = 3\mathbf{i} + 2\mathbf{j} - \mathbf{k}$
24. $\mathbf{u} = 8\mathbf{i} + 2\mathbf{j} - 3\mathbf{k}, \mathbf{v} = 2\mathbf{i} + 4\mathbf{j} - 4\mathbf{k}$

25–28. Area of a triangle *For the given points A, B, and C, find the area of the triangle with vertices A, B, and C.*

25. $A(0, 0, 0), B(3, 0, 1), C(1, 1, 0)$
26. $A(1, 2, 3), B(5, 1, 5), C(2, 3, 3)$
27. $A(5, 6, 2), B(7, 16, 4), C(6, 7, 3)$
28. $A(-1, -5, -3), B(-3, -2, -1), C(0, -5, -1)$

29–34. Computing cross products *Find the cross products $\mathbf{u} \times \mathbf{v}$ and $\mathbf{v} \times \mathbf{u}$ for the following vectors $\mathbf{u}$ and $\mathbf{v}$.*

29. $\mathbf{u} = \langle 3, 5, 0 \rangle, \mathbf{v} = \langle 0, 3, -6 \rangle$
30. $\mathbf{u} = \langle -4, 1, 1 \rangle, \mathbf{v} = \langle 0, 1, -1 \rangle$
31. $\mathbf{u} = \langle 2, 3, -9 \rangle, \mathbf{v} = \langle -1, 1, -1 \rangle$
32. $\mathbf{u} = \langle 3, -4, 6 \rangle, \mathbf{v} = \langle 1, 2, -1 \rangle$
33. $\mathbf{u} = 3\mathbf{i} - \mathbf{j} - 2\mathbf{k}, \mathbf{v} = \mathbf{i} + 3\mathbf{j} - 2\mathbf{k}$
34. $\mathbf{u} = 2\mathbf{i} - 10\mathbf{j} + 15\mathbf{k}, \mathbf{v} = 0.5\mathbf{i} + \mathbf{j} - 0.6\mathbf{k}$

35–38. Orthogonal vectors *Find a vector orthogonal to the given vectors.*

35. $\langle 0, 1, 2 \rangle$ and $\langle -2, 0, 3 \rangle$
36. $\langle 1, 2, 3 \rangle$ and $\langle -2, 4, -1 \rangle$
37. $\langle 8, 0, 4 \rangle$ and $\langle -8, 2, 1 \rangle$
38. $\langle 6, -2, 4 \rangle$ and $\langle 1, 2, 3 \rangle$
39. **Tightening a bolt** Suppose you apply a force of 20 N to a 0.25-meter-long wrench attached to a bolt in a direction perpendicular to the bolt. Determine the magnitude of the torque when the force is applied at an angle of 45° to the wrench.
40. **Opening a laptop** A force of 1.5 lb is applied in a direction perpendicular to the screen of a laptop at a distance of 10 in from the hinge of the screen. Find the magnitude of the torque (in ft-lb) that is applied.

41–44. Computing torque *Answer the following questions about torque.*

41. Let $\mathbf{r} = \overrightarrow{OP} = \mathbf{i} + \mathbf{j} + \mathbf{k}$. A force $\mathbf{F} = \langle 20, 0, 0 \rangle$ is applied at P. Find the torque about O that is produced.
42. Let $\mathbf{r} = \overrightarrow{OP} = \mathbf{i} - \mathbf{j} + 2\mathbf{k}$. A force $\mathbf{F} = \langle 10, 10, 0 \rangle$ is applied at P. Find the torque about O that is produced.
43. Let $\mathbf{r} = \overrightarrow{OP} = 10\mathbf{i}$. Which is greater (in magnitude): the torque about O when a force $\mathbf{F} = 5\mathbf{i} - 5\mathbf{k}$ is applied at P or the torque about O when a force $\mathbf{F} = 4\mathbf{i} - 3\mathbf{j}$ is applied at P?
44. A pump handle has a pivot at $(0, 0, 0)$ and extends to $P(5, 0, -5)$. A force $\mathbf{F} = \langle 1, 0, -10 \rangle$ is applied at P. Find the magnitude and direction of the torque about the pivot.

45–48. Force on a moving charge *Answer the following questions about force on a moving charge.*

45. A particle with a positive unit charge ($q = 1$) enters a constant magnetic field $\mathbf{B} = \mathbf{i} + \mathbf{j}$ with a velocity $\mathbf{v} = 20\mathbf{k}$. Find the magnitude and direction of the force on the particle. Make a sketch of the magnetic field, the velocity, and the force.

46. A particle with a unit negative charge ($q = -1$) enters a constant magnetic field $\mathbf{B} = 5\mathbf{k}$ with a velocity $\mathbf{v} = \mathbf{i} + 2\mathbf{j}$. Find the magnitude and direction of the force on the particle. Make a sketch of the magnetic field, the velocity, and the force.

47. An electron ($q = -1.6 \times 10^{-19}$ C) enters a constant 2-T magnetic field at an angle of 45° to the field with a speed of 2×10^5 m/s. Find the magnitude of the force on the electron.

48. A proton ($q = 1.6 \times 10^{-19}$ C) with velocity $2 \times 10^6\,\mathbf{j}$ m/s experiences a force in newtons of $\mathbf{F} = 5 \times 10^{-12}\,\mathbf{k}$ as it passes through the origin. Find the magnitude and direction of the magnetic field at that instant.

Further Explorations

49. **Explain why or why not** Determine whether the following statements are true and give an explanation or counterexample.
    a. The cross product of two nonzero vectors is a nonzero vector.
    b. $|\mathbf{u} \times \mathbf{v}|$ is less than both $|\mathbf{u}|$ and $|\mathbf{v}|$.
    c. If $\mathbf{u}$ points east and $\mathbf{v}$ points south, then $\mathbf{u} \times \mathbf{v}$ points west.
    d. If $\mathbf{u} \times \mathbf{v} = \mathbf{0}$ and $\mathbf{u} \cdot \mathbf{v} = 0$, then either $\mathbf{u} = \mathbf{0}$ or $\mathbf{v} = \mathbf{0}$.
    e. Law of Cancellation? If $\mathbf{u} \times \mathbf{v} = \mathbf{u} \times \mathbf{w}$, then $\mathbf{v} = \mathbf{w}$.

50–51. Collinear points *Use cross products to determine whether the points A, B, and C are collinear.*

50. $A(3, 2, 1)$, $B(5, 4, 7)$, and $C(9, 8, 19)$

51. $A(-3, -2, 1)$, $B(1, 4, 7)$, and $C(4, 10, 14)$

52. **Finding an unknown** Find the value of a such that $\langle a, a, 2\rangle \times \langle 1, a, 3\rangle = \langle 2, -4, 2\rangle$.

53. **Parallel vectors** Evaluate $\langle a, b, a\rangle \times \langle b, a, b\rangle$. For what nonzero values of a and b are the vectors $\langle a, b, a\rangle$ and $\langle b, a, b\rangle$ parallel?

54–57. Areas of triangles *Find the area of the following triangles T.*

54. The sides of T are $\mathbf{u} = \langle 0, 6, 0\rangle$, $\mathbf{v} = \langle 4, 4, 4\rangle$, and $\mathbf{u} - \mathbf{v}$.

55. The sides of T are $\mathbf{u} = \langle 3, 3, 3\rangle$, $\mathbf{v} = \langle 6, 0, 6\rangle$, and $\mathbf{u} - \mathbf{v}$.

56. The vertices of T are $O(0, 0, 0)$, $P(2, 4, 6)$, and $Q(3, 5, 7)$.

57. The vertices of T are $O(0, 0, 0)$, $P(1, 2, 3)$, and $Q(6, 5, 4)$.

58. **A unit cross product** Under what conditions is $\mathbf{u} \times \mathbf{v}$ a unit vector?

59. **Vector equation** Find all vectors $\mathbf{u}$ that satisfy the equation
$$\langle 1, 1, 1\rangle \times \mathbf{u} = \langle -1, -1, 2\rangle.$$

60. **Vector equation** Find all vectors $\mathbf{u}$ that satisfy the equation
$$\langle 1, 1, 1\rangle \times \mathbf{u} = \langle 0, 0, 1\rangle.$$

61. **Area of a triangle** Find the area of the triangle with vertices on the coordinate axes at the points $(a, 0, 0)$, $(0, b, 0)$, and $(0, 0, c)$, in terms of a, b, and c.

62–64. Scalar triple product *Another operation with vectors is the scalar triple product, defined to be* $\mathbf{u} \cdot (\mathbf{v} \times \mathbf{w})$, *for vectors* $\mathbf{u}$, $\mathbf{v}$, *and* $\mathbf{w}$ *in* $\mathbb{R}^3$.

62. Express $\mathbf{u}$, $\mathbf{v}$, and $\mathbf{w}$ in terms of their components and show that $\mathbf{u} \cdot (\mathbf{v} \times \mathbf{w})$ equals the determinant
$$\begin{vmatrix} u_1 & u_2 & u_3 \\ v_1 & v_2 & v_3 \\ w_1 & w_2 & w_3 \end{vmatrix}.$$

63. a. Consider the *parallelepiped* (slanted box) determined by the position vectors $\mathbf{u}$, $\mathbf{v}$, and $\mathbf{w}$ (see figure). Show that the volume of the parallelepiped is the absolute value of the scalar triple product $|\mathbf{u} \cdot (\mathbf{v} \times \mathbf{w})|$.
    b. Use the scalar triple product to find the volume of the parallelepiped determined by the vectors $\mathbf{u} = \langle 3, 1, 0\rangle$, $\mathbf{v} = \langle 2, 4, 1\rangle$, and $\mathbf{w} = \langle 1, 1, 5\rangle$.

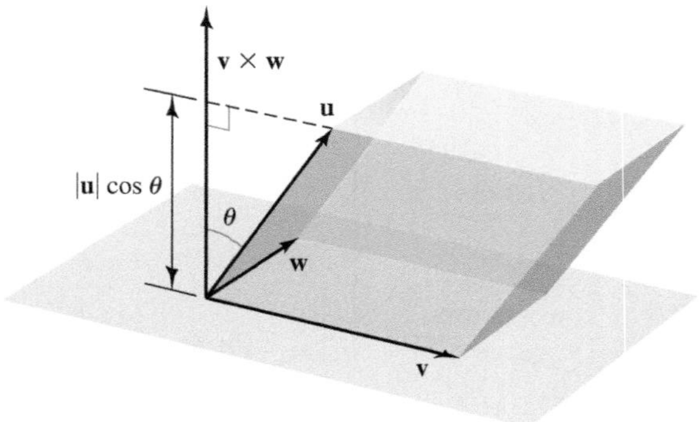

64. Prove that $\mathbf{u} \cdot (\mathbf{v} \times \mathbf{w}) = (\mathbf{u} \times \mathbf{v}) \cdot \mathbf{w}$.

Applications

65. **Bicycle brakes** A set of caliper brakes exerts a force on the rim of a bicycle wheel that creates a frictional force $\mathbf{F}$ of 40 N perpendicular to the radius of the wheel (see figure). Assuming the wheel has a radius of 66 cm, find the magnitude and direction of the torque about the axle of the wheel.

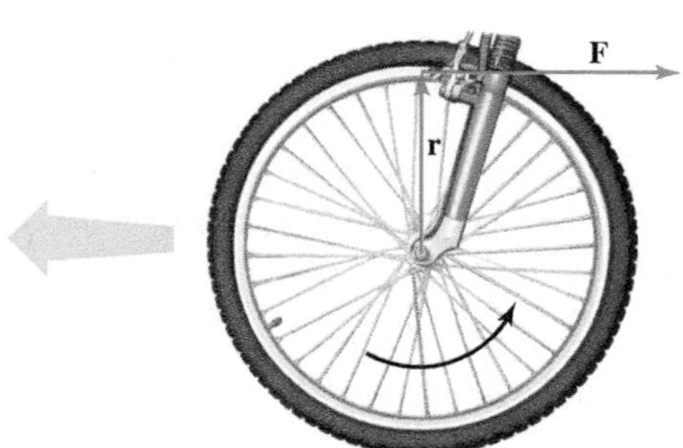

66. **Arm torque** A horizontally outstretched arm supports a weight of 20 lb in a hand (see figure). If the distance from the shoulder to the elbow is 1 ft and the distance from the elbow to the hand is 1 ft, find the magnitude and describe the direction of the torque about (a) the shoulder and (b) the elbow. (The units of torque in this case are ft-lb.)

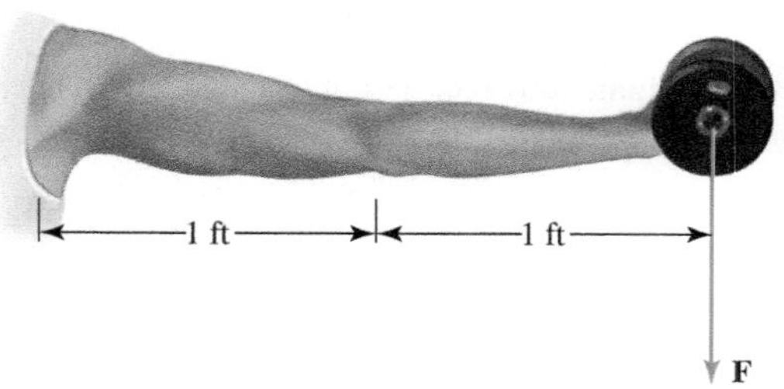

67. Electron speed An electron with a mass of 9.1×10^{-31} kg and a charge of -1.6×10^{-19} C travels in a circular path with no loss of energy in a magnetic field of 0.05 T that is orthogonal to the path of the electron (see figure). If the radius of the path is 0.002 m, what is the speed of the electron?

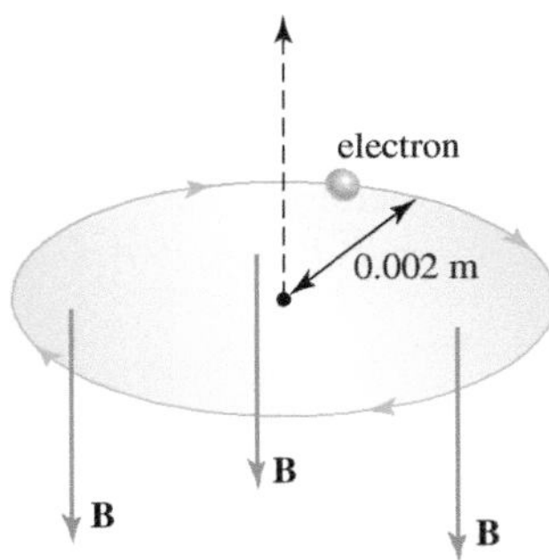

Additional Exercises

68. Three proofs Prove that $\mathbf{u} \times \mathbf{u} = \mathbf{0}$ in three ways.

a. Use the definition of the cross product.
b. Use the determinant formulation of the cross product.
c. Use the property that $\mathbf{u} \times \mathbf{v} = -(\mathbf{v} \times \mathbf{u})$.

69. Associative property Prove in two ways that for scalars a and b, $(a\mathbf{u}) \times (b\mathbf{v}) = ab(\mathbf{u} \times \mathbf{v})$. Use the definition of the cross product and the determinant formula.

70–72. Possible identities *Determine whether the following statements are true using a proof or counterexample. Assume that* **u**, **v**, *and* **w** *are nonzero vectors in* $\mathbb{R}^3$.

70. $\mathbf{u} \times (\mathbf{u} \times \mathbf{v}) = \mathbf{0}$

71. $(\mathbf{u} - \mathbf{v}) \times (\mathbf{u} + \mathbf{v}) = 2\mathbf{u} \times \mathbf{v}$

72. $\mathbf{u} \cdot (\mathbf{v} \times \mathbf{w}) = \mathbf{w} \cdot (\mathbf{u} \times \mathbf{v})$

73–74. Identities *Prove the following identities. Assume that* **u**, **v**, **w**, *and* **x** *are nonzero vectors in* $\mathbb{R}^3$.

73. $\mathbf{u} \times (\mathbf{v} \times \mathbf{w}) = (\mathbf{u} \cdot \mathbf{w})\mathbf{v} - (\mathbf{u} \cdot \mathbf{v})\mathbf{w}$ Vector triple product

74. $(\mathbf{u} \times \mathbf{v}) \cdot (\mathbf{w} \times \mathbf{x}) = (\mathbf{u} \cdot \mathbf{w})(\mathbf{v} \cdot \mathbf{x}) - (\mathbf{u} \cdot \mathbf{x})(\mathbf{v} \cdot \mathbf{w})$

75. Cross product equations Suppose **u** and **v** are known nonzero vectors in $\mathbb{R}^3$.

a. Prove that the equation $\mathbf{u} \times \mathbf{z} = \mathbf{v}$ has a nonzero solution **z** if and only if $\mathbf{u} \cdot \mathbf{v} = 0$. (*Hint:* Take the dot product of both sides with **v**.)
b. Explain this result geometrically.

QUICK CHECK ANSWERS

1. $\mathbf{u} \times \mathbf{v}$ points in the positive z-direction; $\mathbf{v} \times \mathbf{u}$ points in the negative z-direction. **2.** The vector $2\mathbf{u}$ points in the same direction as **u** and the vector $3\mathbf{v}$ points in the same direction as **v**. So the right-hand rule gives the same direction for $2\mathbf{u} \times 3\mathbf{v}$ as it does for $\mathbf{u} \times \mathbf{v}$. **3.** $\mathbf{u} \cdot (\mathbf{u} \times \mathbf{v}) = \langle -1, 0, 6 \rangle \cdot \langle 30, 9, 5 \rangle = -30 + 0 + 30 = 0$. A similar calculation shows that $\mathbf{v} \cdot (\mathbf{u} \times \mathbf{v}) = 0$. ◄

11.5 Lines and Curves in Space

Imagine a projectile moving along a path in three-dimensional space; it could be an electron or a comet, a soccer ball or a rocket. If you take a snapshot of the object, its position is described by a static position vector $\mathbf{r} = \langle x, y, z \rangle$. However, if you want to describe the full trajectory of the object as it unfolds in time, you must represent the object's position with a *vector-valued function* such as $\mathbf{r}(t) = \langle x(t), y(t), z(t) \rangle$ whose components change in time (Figure 11.66). The goal of this section is to describe continuous motion by using vector-valued functions.

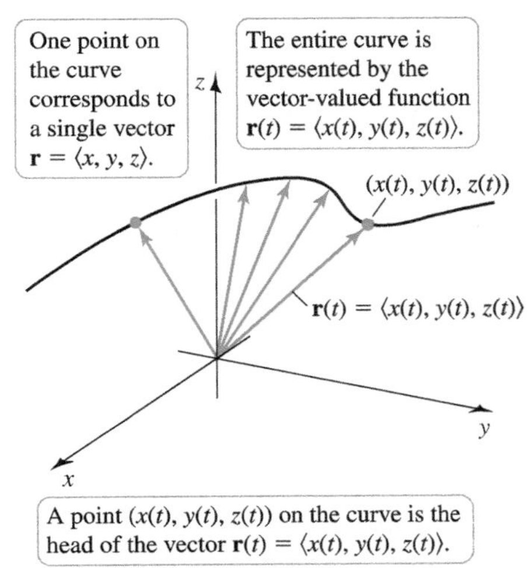

Figure 11.66

Vector-Valued Functions

A function of the form $\mathbf{r}(t) = \langle x(t), y(t), z(t) \rangle$ may be viewed in two ways.

- It is a set of three parametric equations that describe a curve in space.
- It is also a **vector-valued function**, which means that the three dependent variables (x, y, and z) are the components of **r**, and each component varies with respect to a single independent variable t (that often represents time).

Here is the connection between these perspectives: As t varies, a point $(x(t), y(t), z(t))$ on a parametric curve is also the head of the position vector $\mathbf{r}(t) = \langle x(t), y(t), z(t) \rangle$. In other words, a vector-valued function is a set of parametric equations written in vector form. It is useful to keep both of these interpretations in mind as you work with vector-valued functions.

Lines in Space

Two distinct points in $\mathbb{R}^3$ determine a unique line. Alternatively, one point and a direction also determine a unique line. We use both of these properties to derive parametric equations for lines in space. The result is an example of a vector-valued function in $\mathbb{R}^3$.

Let ℓ be the line passing through the point $P_0(x_0, y_0, z_0)$ parallel to the nonzero vector $\mathbf{v} = \langle a, b, c \rangle$, where P_0 and $\mathbf{v}$ are given. The fixed point P_0 is associated with the position vector $\mathbf{r}_0 = \overrightarrow{OP_0} = \langle x_0, y_0, z_0 \rangle$. We let $P(x, y, z)$ be a variable point on ℓ and let $\mathbf{r} = \overrightarrow{OP} = \langle x, y, z \rangle$ be the position vector associated with P (Figure 11.67). Because ℓ is parallel to $\mathbf{v}$, the vector $\overrightarrow{P_0P}$ is also parallel to $\mathbf{v}$; therefore, $\overrightarrow{P_0P} = t\mathbf{v}$, where t is a real number. By vector addition, we see that $\overrightarrow{OP} = \overrightarrow{OP_0} + \overrightarrow{P_0P}$, or $\overrightarrow{OP} = \overrightarrow{OP_0} + t\mathbf{v}$. It follows that

$$\underbrace{\langle x, y, z \rangle}_{\mathbf{r} = \overrightarrow{OP}} = \underbrace{\langle x_0, y_0, z_0 \rangle}_{\mathbf{r}_0 = \overrightarrow{OP_0}} + t\underbrace{\langle a, b, c \rangle}_{\mathbf{v}} \quad \text{or} \quad \mathbf{r} = \mathbf{r}_0 + t\mathbf{v}.$$

Equating components, the line is described by the parametric equations

$$x = x_0 + at, \quad y = y_0 + bt, \quad z = z_0 + ct, \quad \text{for } -\infty < t < \infty.$$

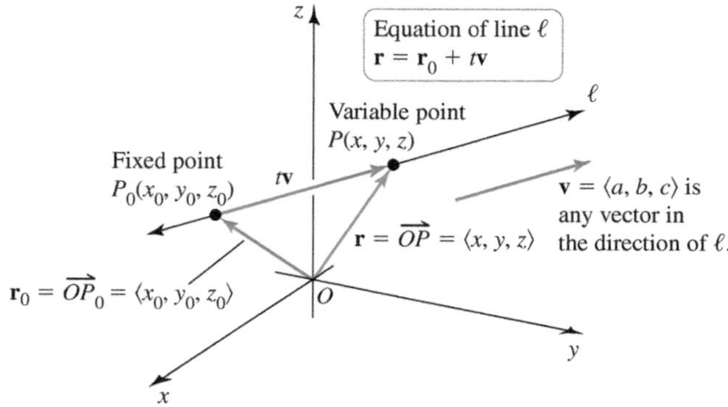

Figure 11.67

QUICK CHECK 1 Describe the line $\mathbf{r}(t) = t\mathbf{k}$, for $-\infty < t < \infty$. Describe the line $\mathbf{r}(t) = t(\mathbf{i} + \mathbf{j} + 0\mathbf{k})$, for $-\infty < t < \infty$. ◄

➤ There are infinitely many equations for the same line. The direction vector is determined only up to a scalar multiple.

The parameter t determines the location of points on the line, where $t = 0$ corresponds to P_0. If t increases from 0, we move along the line in the direction of $\mathbf{v}$, and if t decreases from 0, we move along the line in the direction of $-\mathbf{v}$. As t varies over all real numbers $(-\infty < t < \infty)$, the vector $\mathbf{r}$ sweeps out the entire line ℓ. If, instead of knowing the direction $\mathbf{v}$ of the line, we are given two points $P_0(x_0, y_0, z_0)$ and $P_1(x_1, y_1, z_1)$, then the direction of the line is $\mathbf{v} = \overrightarrow{P_0P_1} = \langle x_1 - x_0, y_1 - y_0, z_1 - z_0 \rangle$.

> **Equation of a Line**
>
> An **equation of the line** passing through the point $P_0(x_0, y_0, z_0)$ in the direction of the vector $\mathbf{v} = \langle a, b, c \rangle$ is $\mathbf{r} = \mathbf{r}_0 + t\mathbf{v}$, or
>
> $$\langle x, y, z \rangle = \langle x_0, y_0, z_0 \rangle + t\langle a, b, c \rangle, \quad \text{for} \quad -\infty < t < \infty.$$
>
> Equivalently, the corresponding parametric equations of the line are
>
> $$x = x_0 + at, \quad y = y_0 + bt, \quad z = z_0 + ct, \quad \text{for} \quad -\infty < t < \infty.$$

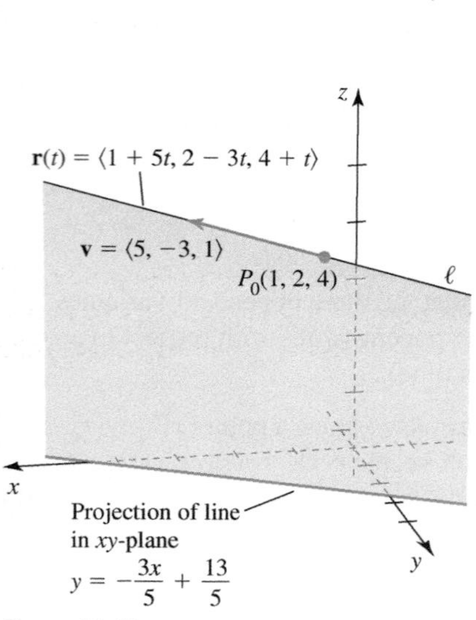

$\mathbf{r}(t) = \langle 1 + 5t, 2 - 3t, 4 + t \rangle$

$\mathbf{v} = \langle 5, -3, 1 \rangle$

$P_0(1, 2, 4)$

Projection of line in xy-plane $y = -\frac{3x}{5} + \frac{13}{5}$

Figure 11.68

EXAMPLE 1 Equations of lines Find an equation of the line ℓ that passes through the point $P_0(1, 2, 4)$ in the direction of $\mathbf{v} = \langle 5, -3, 1 \rangle$.

SOLUTION We are given $\mathbf{r}_0 = \langle 1, 2, 4 \rangle$. Therefore, an equation of the line is

$$\mathbf{r}(t) = \mathbf{r}_0 + t\mathbf{v} = \langle 1, 2, 4 \rangle + t\langle 5, -3, 1 \rangle = \langle 1 + 5t, 2 - 3t, 4 + t \rangle,$$

for $-\infty < t < \infty$ (Figure 11.68). The corresponding parametric equations are

$$x = 1 + 5t, \quad y = 2 - 3t, \quad z = 4 + t, \quad \text{for} \quad -\infty < t < \infty.$$

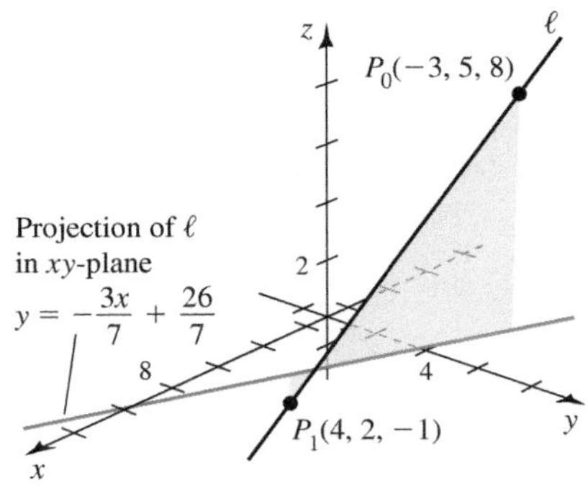

(a)

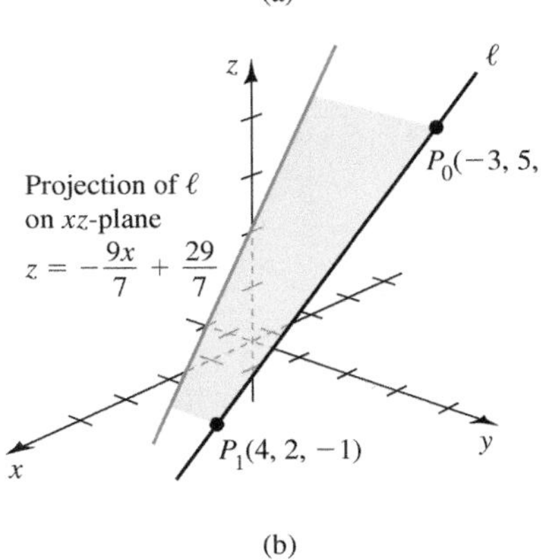

(b)

Figure 11.69

The line is easier to visualize if it is plotted together with its projection in the xy-plane. Setting $z = 0$ (the equation of the xy-plane), parametric equations of the projection line are $x = 1 + 5t$, $y = 2 - 3t$, and $z = 0$. Eliminating t from these equations, an equation of the projection line is $y = -\frac{3}{5}x + \frac{13}{5}$ (Figure 11.68).

Related Exercises 9–24 ◀

EXAMPLE 2 Equations of lines Let ℓ be the line that passes through the points $P_0(-3, 5, 8)$ and $P_1(4, 2, -1)$.

a. Find an equation of ℓ.

b. Find equations of the projections of ℓ on the xy- and xz-planes. Then graph those projection lines.

SOLUTION

a. The direction of the line is

$$\mathbf{v} = \overrightarrow{P_0P_1} = \langle 4 - (-3), 2 - 5, -1 - 8 \rangle = \langle 7, -3, -9 \rangle.$$

Therefore, with $\mathbf{r}_0 = \langle -3, 5, 8 \rangle$, an equation of ℓ is

$$\begin{aligned}\mathbf{r}(t) &= \mathbf{r}_0 + t\mathbf{v}\\ &= \langle -3, 5, 8 \rangle + t\langle 7, -3, -9 \rangle\\ &= \langle -3 + 7t, 5 - 3t, 8 - 9t \rangle.\end{aligned}$$

b. Setting the z-component of the equation of ℓ equal to zero, parametric equations of the projection of ℓ on the xy-plane are $x = -3 + 7t$, $y = 5 - 3t$. Eliminating t from these equations gives the equation $y = -\frac{3}{7}x + \frac{26}{7}$ (Figure 11.69a) in the xy-plane. Parametric equations of the projection of ℓ on the xz-plane (setting $y = 0$) are $x = -3 + 7t$, $z = 8 - 9t$. Eliminating t gives the equation $z = -\frac{9}{7}x + \frac{29}{7}$ (Figure 11.69b) in the xz-plane.

Related Exercises 9–24 ◀

➤ A related problem: To find the point at which the line in Example 2 intersects the xy-plane, we set $z = 0$, solve for t, and find the corresponding x- and y-coordinates: $z = 0$ implies $t = \frac{8}{9}$, which implies $x = \frac{29}{9}$ and $y = \frac{7}{3}$.

QUICK CHECK 2 In the equation of the line

$$\mathbf{r}(t) = \langle x_0, y_0, z_0 \rangle + t\langle x_1 - x_0, y_1 - y_0, z_1 - z_0 \rangle,$$

what value of t corresponds to the point $P_0(x_0, y_0, z_0)$? What value of t corresponds to the point $P_1(x_1, y_1, z_1)$? ◀

EXAMPLE 3 Equation of a line segment Find an equation of the line segment that extends from $P_0(3, -1, 4)$ to $P_1(0, 5, 2)$.

SOLUTION The same ideas used to find an equation of an entire line work here. We just restrict the values of the parameter t, so that only the given line segment is generated. The direction of the line segment is

$$\mathbf{v} = \overrightarrow{P_0P_1} = \langle 0 - 3, 5 - (-1), 2 - 4 \rangle = \langle -3, 6, -2 \rangle.$$

Letting $\mathbf{r}_0 = \langle 3, -1, 4 \rangle$, an equation of the line through P_0 and P_1 is

$$\mathbf{r}(t) = \mathbf{r}_0 + t\mathbf{v} = \langle 3 - 3t, -1 + 6t, 4 - 2t \rangle.$$

Notice that if $t = 0$, then $\mathbf{r}(0) = \langle 3, -1, 4 \rangle$, which is a vector with endpoint P_0. If $t = 1$, then $\mathbf{r}(1) = \langle 0, 5, 2 \rangle$, which is a vector with endpoint P_1. Letting t vary from 0 to 1 generates the line segment from P_0 to P_1 (Figure 11.70). Therefore, an equation of the line segment is

$$\mathbf{r}(t) = \langle 3 - 3t, -1 + 6t, 4 - 2t \rangle, \quad \text{for } 0 \le t \le 1.$$

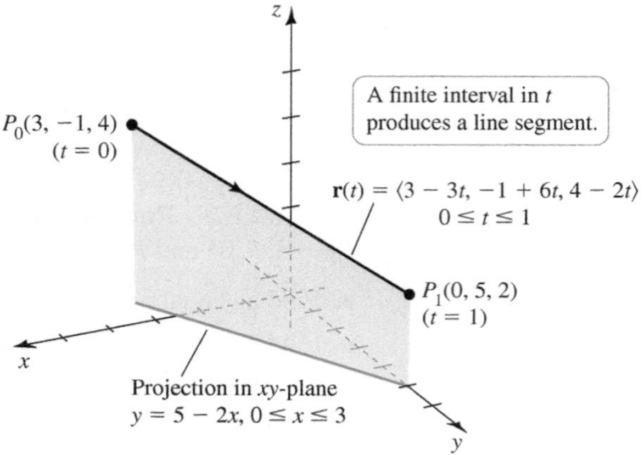

Figure 11.70

Related Exercises 25–28 ◀

Curves in Space

➤ When f, g, and h are linear functions of t, the resulting curve is a line or line segment.

We now explore general vector-valued functions of the form

$$\mathbf{r}(t) = \langle f(t), g(t), h(t) \rangle = f(t)\mathbf{i} + g(t)\mathbf{j} + h(t)\mathbf{k},$$

where f, g, and h are defined on an interval $a \leq t \leq b$. The **domain** of **r** is the largest set of values of t on which all of f, g, and h are defined.

Figure 11.71 illustrates how a parameterized curve is generated by such a function. As the parameter t varies over the interval $a \leq t \leq b$, each value of t produces a position vector that corresponds to a point on the curve, starting at the initial vector $\mathbf{r}(a)$ and ending at the terminal vector $\mathbf{r}(b)$. The resulting parameterized curve can either have finite length or extend indefinitely. The curve may also cross itself or close and retrace itself.

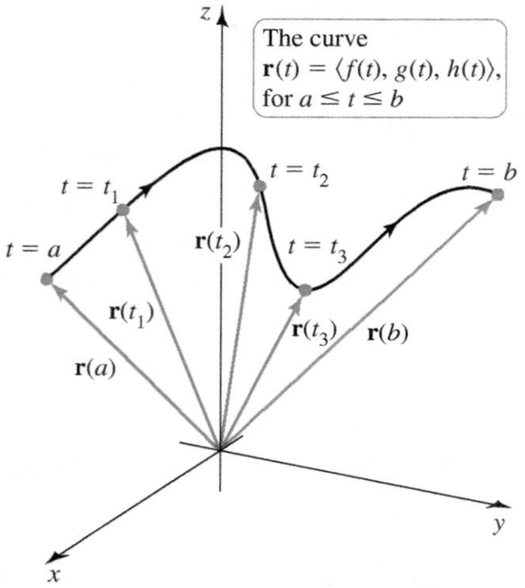

Figure 11.71

Orientation of Curves If a smooth curve C is viewed only as a set of points, then at any point of C, it is possible to draw tangent vectors in two directions (Figure 11.72a). On the other hand, a parameterized curve described by the function $\mathbf{r}(t)$, where $a \leq t \leq b$, has a natural direction, or **orientation**. The *positive* orientation is the direction in which the curve is generated as the parameter increases from a to b. For example, the positive orientation of the circle $\mathbf{r}(t) = \langle \cos t, \sin t \rangle$, for $0 \leq t \leq 2\pi$, is counterclockwise (Figure 11.72b). The orientation of a parameterized curve and its tangent vectors are consistent: The positive orientation of the curve is the direction in which the tangent vectors point along the curve. A precise definition of the tangent vector is given in Section 11.6.

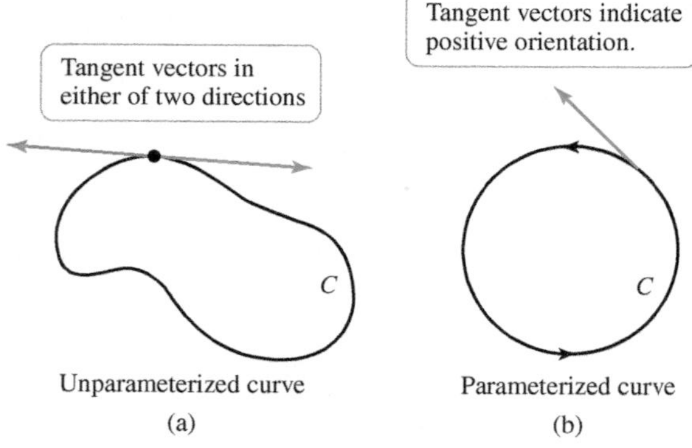

Figure 11.72

EXAMPLE 4 **A helix** Graph the curve described by the equation

$$\mathbf{r}(t) = 4\cos t\,\mathbf{i} + \sin t\,\mathbf{j} + \frac{t}{2\pi}\mathbf{k},$$

where (a) $0 \le t \le 2\pi$ and (b) $-\infty < t < \infty$.

SOLUTION

a. We begin by setting $z = 0$ to determine the projection of the curve in the xy-plane. The resulting function $\mathbf{r}(t) = 4\cos t\,\mathbf{i} + \sin t\,\mathbf{j}$ implies that $x = 4\cos t$ and $y = \sin t$; these equations describe an ellipse in the xy-plane whose positive direction is counterclockwise (Figure 11.73a). Because $z = \frac{t}{2\pi}$, the value of z increases from 0 to 1 as t increases from 0 to 2π. Therefore, the curve rises out of the xy-plane to create a helix (or coil). Over the interval $[0, 2\pi]$, the helix begins at $(4, 0, 0)$, circles the z-axis once, and ends at $(4, 0, 1)$ (Figure 11.73b).

b. Letting the parameter vary over the interval $-\infty < t < \infty$ generates a helix that winds around the z-axis endlessly in both directions (Figure 11.73c). The positive orientation is in the upward direction (increasing z-direction).

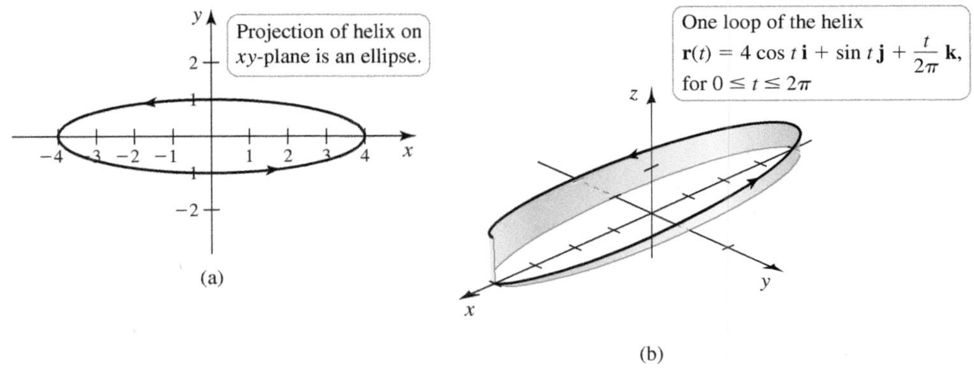

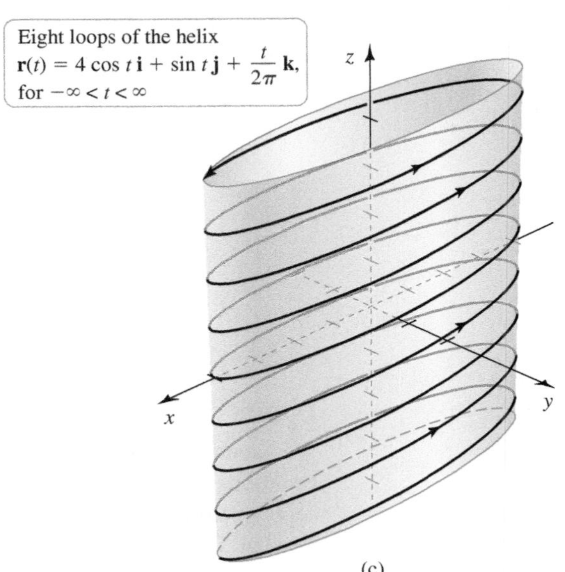

Figure 11.73

➤ Recall that the functions $\sin at$ and $\cos at$ oscillate a times over the interval $[0, 2\pi]$. Therefore, their period is $2\pi/a$.

Related Exercises 29–36 ◀

EXAMPLE 5 **Roller coaster curve** Graph the curve

$$\mathbf{r}(t) = \cos t\,\mathbf{i} + \sin t\,\mathbf{j} + 0.4\sin 2t\,\mathbf{k}, \quad \text{for } 0 \le t \le 2\pi.$$

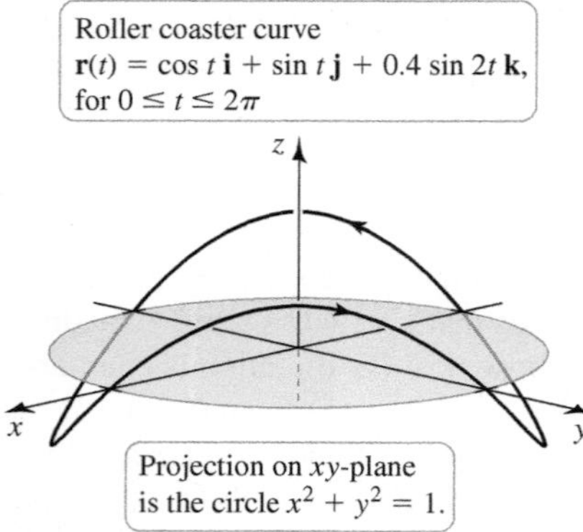

Figure 11.74

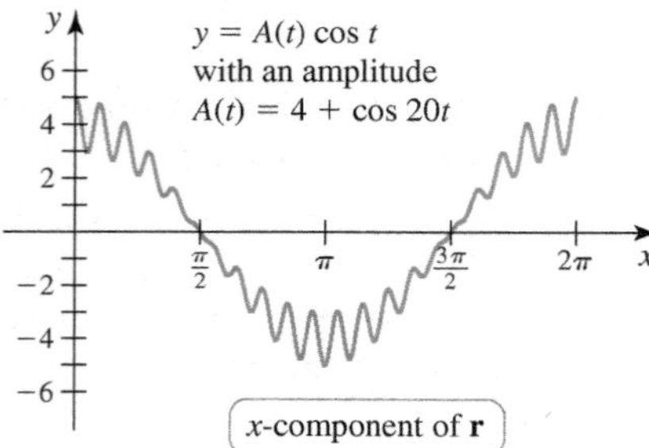

Figure 11.75

SOLUTION Without the z-component, the resulting function $\mathbf{r}(t) = \cos t\,\mathbf{i} + \sin t\,\mathbf{j}$ describes a circle of radius 1 in the xy-plane. The z-component of the function varies between -0.4 and 0.4 with a period of π units. Therefore, on the interval $[0, 2\pi]$, the z-coordinates of points on the curve oscillate twice between -0.4 and 0.4, while the x- and y-coordinates describe a circle. The result is a curve that circles the z-axis once in the counterclockwise direction with two peaks and two valleys (Figure 11.74).

Related Exercises 37–40 ◀

EXAMPLE 6 Slinky curve Graph the curve

$$\mathbf{r}(t) = (4 + \cos 20t)\cos t\,\mathbf{i} + (4 + \cos 20t)\sin t\,\mathbf{j} + 0.4\sin 20t\,\mathbf{k},$$

for $0 \le t \le 2\pi$.

SOLUTION The factor $A(t) = 4 + \cos 20t$ that appears in the x- and y-components is a varying amplitude for $\cos t\,\mathbf{i}$ and $\sin t\,\mathbf{j}$. Its effect is seen in the graph of the x-component $A(t)\cos t$ (Figure 11.75). For $0 \le t \le 2\pi$, the curve consists of one period of $4\cos t$ with 20 small oscillations superimposed on it. As a result, the x-component of $\mathbf{r}$ varies from -5 to 5 with 20 small oscillations along the way. A similar behavior is seen in the y-component of $\mathbf{r}$. Finally, the z-component of $\mathbf{r}$, which is $0.4\sin 20t$, oscillates between -0.4 and 0.4 twenty times over $[0, 2\pi]$. Combining these effects, we discover a coil-shaped curve that circles the z-axis in the counterclockwise direction and closes on itself. Figure 11.76 shows two views, one looking along the xy-plane and the other from overhead on the z-axis.

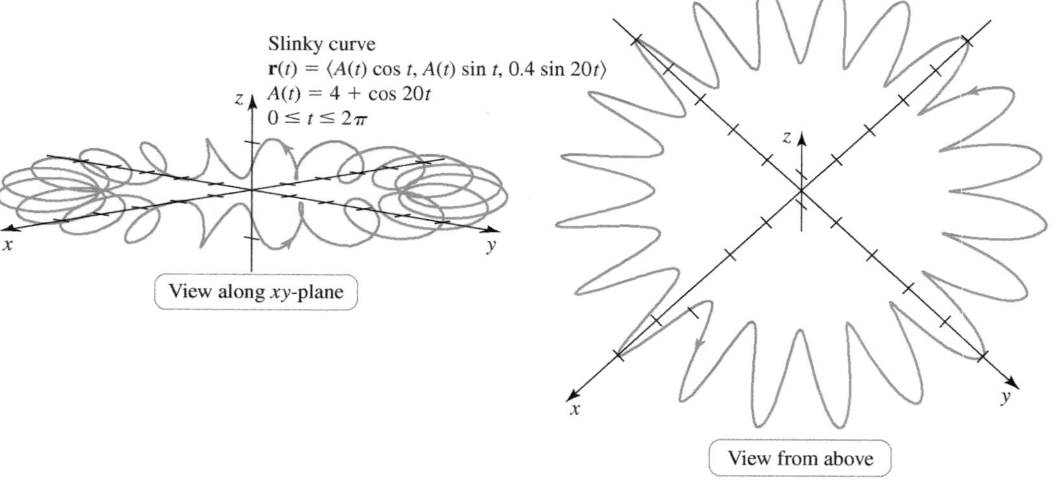

Figure 11.76

Related Exercises 37–40 ◀

Limits and Continuity for Vector-Valued Functions

We have presented vector-valued functions and established their relationship to parametric equations. The next step is to investigate the calculus of vector-valued functions. The concepts of limits, derivatives, and integrals of vector-valued functions are direct extensions of what you have already learned.

The limit of a vector-valued function $\mathbf{r}(t) = f(t)\mathbf{i} + g(t)\mathbf{j} + h(t)\mathbf{k}$ is defined much as it is for scalar-valued functions. If there is a vector $\mathbf{L}$ such that the scalar function $|\mathbf{r}(t) - \mathbf{L}|$ can be made arbitrarily small by taking t sufficiently close to a, then we write $\lim_{t\to a} \mathbf{r}(t) = \mathbf{L}$ and say the limit of $\mathbf{r}$ as t approaches a is $\mathbf{L}$.

> **DEFINITION Limit of a Vector-Valued Function**
>
> A vector-valued function $\mathbf{r}$ approaches the limit $\mathbf{L}$ as t approaches a, written $\lim_{t\to a} \mathbf{r}(t) = \mathbf{L}$, provided $\lim_{t\to a} |\mathbf{r}(t) - \mathbf{L}| = 0$.

Notice that while $\mathbf{r}$ is vector valued, $|\mathbf{r}(t) - \mathbf{L}|$ is a function of the single variable t, to which our familiar limit theorems apply. Therefore, this definition and a short calculation (Exercise 78) lead to a straightforward method for computing limits of the vector-valued function $\mathbf{r} = \langle f, g, h \rangle$. Suppose that

$$\lim_{t\to a} f(t) = L_1, \quad \lim_{t\to a} g(t) = L_2, \quad \text{and} \quad \lim_{t\to a} h(t) = L_3.$$

Then

$$\lim_{t\to a} \mathbf{r}(t) = \left\langle \lim_{t\to a} f(t), \lim_{t\to a} g(t), \lim_{t\to a} h(t) \right\rangle = \langle L_1, L_2, L_3 \rangle.$$

In other words, the limit of $\mathbf{r}$ is determined by computing the limits of its components.

The limits laws in Chapter 2 have analogs for vector-valued functions. For example, if $\lim_{t\to a} \mathbf{r}(t)$ and $\lim_{t\to a} \mathbf{s}(t)$ exist and c is a scalar, then

$$\lim_{t\to a} (\mathbf{r}(t) + \mathbf{s}(t)) = \lim_{t\to a} \mathbf{r}(t) + \lim_{t\to a} \mathbf{s}(t) \quad \text{and} \quad \lim_{t\to a} c\mathbf{r}(t) = c \lim_{t\to a} \mathbf{r}(t).$$

The idea of continuity also extends directly to vector-valued functions. A function $\mathbf{r}(t) = f(t)\mathbf{i} + g(t)\mathbf{j} + h(t)\mathbf{k}$ is continuous at a provided $\lim_{t\to a} \mathbf{r}(t) = \mathbf{r}(a)$. Specifically, if the component functions f, g, and h are continuous at a, then $\mathbf{r}$ is also continuous at a and vice versa. The function $\mathbf{r}$ is continuous on an interval I if it is continuous for all t in I.

➤ Continuity is often taken as part of the definition of a parameterized curve.

Continuity has the same intuitive meaning in this setting as it does for scalar-valued functions. If $\mathbf{r}$ is continuous on an interval, the curve it describes has no breaks or gaps, which is an important property when $\mathbf{r}$ describes the trajectory of an object.

EXAMPLE 7 **Limits and continuity** Consider the function

$$\mathbf{r}(t) = \cos \pi t\, \mathbf{i} + \sin \pi t\, \mathbf{j} + e^{-t}\, \mathbf{k}, \quad \text{for } t \geq 0.$$

a. Evaluate $\lim_{t\to 2} \mathbf{r}(t)$.

b. Evaluate $\lim_{t\to \infty} \mathbf{r}(t)$.

c. At what points is $\mathbf{r}$ continuous?

SOLUTION

a. We evaluate the limit of each component of $\mathbf{r}$:

$$\lim_{t\to 2} \mathbf{r}(t) = \lim_{t\to 2} (\underbrace{\cos \pi t}_{\to 1}\, \mathbf{i} + \underbrace{\sin \pi t}_{\to 0}\, \mathbf{j} + \underbrace{e^{-t}}_{\to e^{-2}}\mathbf{k}) = \mathbf{i} + e^{-2}\mathbf{k}.$$

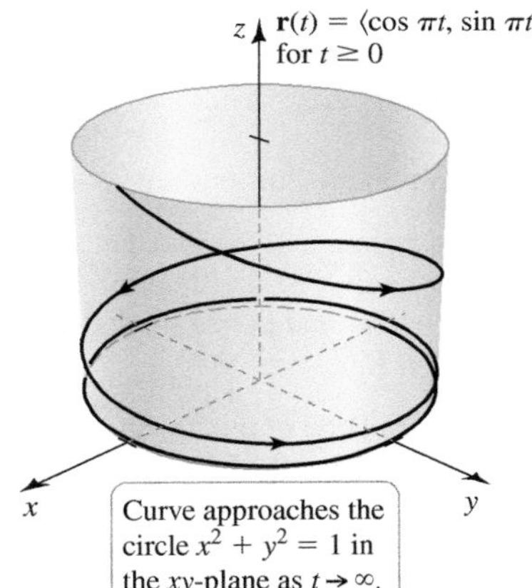

Figure 11.77

b. Note that although $\lim_{t\to\infty} e^{-t} = 0$, $\lim_{t\to\infty} \cos t$ and $\lim_{t\to\infty} \sin t$ do not exist. Therefore, $\lim_{t\to\infty} \mathbf{r}(t)$ does not exist. As shown in Figure 11.77, the curve is a coil that approaches the unit circle in the xy-plane.

c. Because the components of $\mathbf{r}$ are continuous for all t, $\mathbf{r}$ is also continuous for all t.

Related Exercises 41–46 ◄

SECTION 11.5 EXERCISES

Review Questions

1. How many independent variables does the function $\mathbf{r}(t) = \langle f(t), g(t), h(t) \rangle$ have?

2. How many dependent scalar variables does the function $\mathbf{r}(t) = \langle f(t), g(t), h(t) \rangle$ have?

3. Why is $\mathbf{r}(t) = \langle f(t), g(t), h(t) \rangle$ called a vector-valued function?

4. Explain how to find a vector in the direction of the line segment from $P_0(x_0, y_0, z_0)$ to $P_1(x_1, y_1, z_1)$.

5. What is an equation of the line through the points $P_0(x_0, y_0, z_0)$ and $P_1(x_1, y_1, z_1)$?

6. In what plane does the curve $\mathbf{r}(t) = t\,\mathbf{i} + t^2\,\mathbf{k}$ lie?

7. How do you evaluate $\lim_{t\to a} \mathbf{r}(t)$, where $\mathbf{r}(t) = \langle f(t), g(t), h(t) \rangle$?

8. How do you determine whether $\mathbf{r}(t) = f(t)\,\mathbf{i} + g(t)\,\mathbf{j} + h(t)\,\mathbf{k}$ is continuous at $t = a$?

Basic Skills

9–24. Equations of lines *Find equations of the following lines.*

9. The line through $(0, 0, 1)$ in the direction of the vector $\mathbf{v} = \langle 4, 7, 0 \rangle$

10. The line through $(-3, 2, -1)$ in the direction of the vector $\mathbf{v} = \langle 1, -2, 0 \rangle$

11. The line through $(0, 0, 1)$ parallel to the y-axis

12. The line through $(0, 0, 1)$ parallel to the x-axis

13. The line through $(0, 0, 0)$ and $(1, 2, 3)$

14. The line through $(1, 0, 1)$ and $(3, -3, 3)$

15. The line through $(-3, 4, 6)$ and $(5, -1, 0)$

16. The line through $(0, 4, 8)$ and $(10, -5, -4)$

17. The line through $(0, 0, 0)$ that is parallel to the line $\mathbf{r}(t) = \langle 3 - 2t, 5 + 8t, 7 - 4t \rangle$

18. The line through $(1, -3, 4)$ that is parallel to the line $\mathbf{r}(t) = \langle 3 + 4t, 5 - t, 7 \rangle$

19. The line through $(0, 0, 0)$ that is perpendicular to both $\mathbf{u} = \langle 1, 0, 2 \rangle$ and $\mathbf{v} = \langle 0, 1, 1 \rangle$

20. The line through $(-3, 4, 2)$ that is perpendicular to both $\mathbf{u} = \langle 1, 1, -5 \rangle$ and $\mathbf{v} = \langle 0, 4, 0 \rangle$

21. The line through $(-2, 5, 3)$ that is perpendicular to both $\mathbf{u} = \langle 1, 1, 2 \rangle$ and the x-axis

22. The line through $(0, 2, 1)$ that is perpendicular to both $\mathbf{u} = \langle 4, 3, -5 \rangle$ and the z-axis

23. The line through $(1, 2, 3)$ that is perpendicular to the lines $\mathbf{r}_1(t) = \langle 3 - 2t, 5 + 8t, 7 - 4t \rangle$ and $\mathbf{r}_2(t) = \langle -2t, 5 + t, 7 - t \rangle$

24. The line through $(1, 0, -1)$ that is perpendicular to the lines $\mathbf{r}_1(t) = \langle 3 + 2t, 3t, -4t \rangle$ and $\mathbf{r}_2(t) = \langle t, t, -t \rangle$

25–28. Line segments *Find an equation of the line segment joining the first point to the second point.*

25. $(0, 0, 0)$ and $(1, 2, 3)$

26. $(1, 0, 1)$ and $(0, -2, 1)$

27. $(2, 4, 8)$ and $(7, 5, 3)$

28. $(-1, -8, 4)$ and $(-9, 5, -3)$

29–36. Curves in space *Graph the curves described by the following functions, indicating the positive orientation.*

29. $\mathbf{r}(t) = \langle \cos t, 0, \sin t \rangle$ for $0 \le t \le 2\pi$

30. $\mathbf{r}(t) = \langle 0, 4\cos t, 16\sin t \rangle$ for $0 \le t \le 2\pi$

31. $\mathbf{r}(t) = \cos t\,\mathbf{i} + \mathbf{j} + \sin t\,\mathbf{k}$, for $0 \le t \le 2\pi$

32. $\mathbf{r}(t) = 2\cos t\,\mathbf{i} + 2\sin t\,\mathbf{j} + 2\,\mathbf{k}$, for $0 \le t \le 2\pi$

T 33. $\mathbf{r}(t) = t\cos t\,\mathbf{i} + t\sin t\,\mathbf{j} + t\,\mathbf{k}$, for $0 \le t \le 6\pi$

T 34. $\mathbf{r}(t) = 4\sin t\,\mathbf{i} + 4\cos t\,\mathbf{j} + e^{-t/10}\mathbf{k}$, for $0 \le t < \infty$

T 35. $\mathbf{r}(t) = e^{-t/20}\sin t\,\mathbf{i} + e^{-t/20}\cos t\,\mathbf{j} + t\,\mathbf{k}$, for $0 \le t < \infty$

T 36. $\mathbf{r}(t) = e^{-t/10}\mathbf{i} + 3\cos t\,\mathbf{j} + 3\sin t\,\mathbf{k}$, for $0 \le t < \infty$

T **37–40. Exotic curves** *Graph the curves described by the following functions. Use analysis to anticipate the shape of the curve before using a graphing utility.*

37. $\mathbf{r}(t) = 0.5\cos 15t\,\mathbf{i} + (8 + \sin 15t)\cos t\,\mathbf{j} + (8 + \sin 15t)\sin t\,\mathbf{k}$, for $0 \le t \le 2\pi$

38. $\mathbf{r}(t) = 2\cos t\,\mathbf{i} + 4\sin t\,\mathbf{j} + \cos 10t\,\mathbf{k}$, for $0 \le t \le 2\pi$

39. $\mathbf{r}(t) = \sin t\,\mathbf{i} + \sin^2 t\,\mathbf{j} + t/(5\pi)\,\mathbf{k}$, for $0 \le t \le 10\pi$

40. $\mathbf{r}(t) = \cos t \sin 3t\,\mathbf{i} + \sin t \sin 3t\,\mathbf{j} + \sqrt{t}\,\mathbf{k}$, for $0 \le t \le 9$

41–46. Limits *Evaluate the following limits.*

41. $\lim_{t \to \pi/2} \left(\cos 2t\,\mathbf{i} - 4\sin t\,\mathbf{j} + \frac{2t}{\pi}\mathbf{k} \right)$

42. $\lim_{t \to \ln 2} (2e^t\mathbf{i} + 6e^{-t}\mathbf{j} - 4e^{-2t}\mathbf{k})$

43. $\lim_{t \to \infty} \left(e^{-t}\mathbf{i} - \frac{2t}{t + 1}\mathbf{j} + \tan^{-1} t\,\mathbf{k} \right)$

44. $\lim_{t \to 2} \left(\frac{t}{t^2 + 1}\mathbf{i} - 4e^{-t}\sin \pi t\,\mathbf{j} + \frac{1}{\sqrt{4t + 1}}\mathbf{k} \right)$

45. $\lim_{t \to 0} \left(\frac{\sin t}{t}\mathbf{i} - \frac{e^t - t - 1}{t}\mathbf{j} + \frac{\cos t + t^2/2 - 1}{t^2}\mathbf{k} \right)$

46. $\lim_{t \to 0} \left(\frac{\tan t}{t}\mathbf{i} - \frac{3t}{\sin t}\mathbf{j} + \sqrt{t + 1}\,\mathbf{k} \right)$

Further Explorations

47. **Explain why or why not** Determine whether the following statements are true and give an explanation or counterexample.

    a. The line $\mathbf{r}(t) = \langle 3, -1, 4 \rangle + t\langle 6, -2, 8 \rangle$ passes through the origin.
    b. Any two nonparallel lines in $\mathbb{R}^3$ intersect.
    c. The curve $\mathbf{r}(t) = \langle e^{-t}, \sin t, -\cos t \rangle$ approaches a circle as $t \to \infty$.
    d. If $\mathbf{r}(t) = e^{-t^2}\langle 1, 1, 1 \rangle$ then $\lim_{t \to \infty} \mathbf{r}(t) = \lim_{t \to -\infty} \mathbf{r}(t)$.

48. **Point of intersection** Determine an equation of the line that is perpendicular to the lines $\mathbf{r}(t) = \langle -2 + 3t, 2t, 3t \rangle$ and $\mathbf{R}(s) = \langle -6 + s, -8 + 2s, -12 + 3s \rangle$ and passes through the point of intersection of the lines $\mathbf{r}$ and $\mathbf{R}$.

49. **Point of intersection** Determine an equation of the line that is perpendicular to the lines $\mathbf{r}(t) = \langle 4t, 1 + 2t, 3t \rangle$ and $\mathbf{R}(s) = \langle -1 + s, -7 + 2s, -12 + 3s \rangle$ and passes through the point of intersection of the lines $\mathbf{r}$ and $\mathbf{R}$.

50–55. Skew lines *A pair of lines in $\mathbb{R}^3$ are said to be* **skew** *if they are neither parallel nor intersecting. Determine whether the following pairs of lines are parallel, intersecting, or skew. If the lines intersect, determine the point(s) of intersection.*

50. $\mathbf{r}(t) = \langle 3 + 4t, 1 - 6t, 4t \rangle$;
$\mathbf{R}(s) = \langle -2s, 5 + 3s, 4 - 2s \rangle$

51. $\mathbf{r}(t) = \langle 1 + 6t, 3 - 7t, 2 + t \rangle$;
$\mathbf{R}(s) = \langle 10 + 3s, 6 + s, 14 + 4s \rangle$

52. $\mathbf{r}(t) = \langle 4 + 5t, -2t, 1 + 3t \rangle$;
$\mathbf{R}(s) = \langle 10s, 6 + 4s, 4 + 6s \rangle$

53. $\mathbf{r}(t) = \langle 4, 6 - t, 1 + t \rangle$;
$\mathbf{R}(s) = \langle -3 - 7s, 1 + 4s, 4 - s \rangle$

54. $\mathbf{r}(t) = \langle 4 + t, -2t, 1 + 3t \rangle$;
$\mathbf{R}(s) = \langle 1 - 7s, 6 + 14s, 4 - 21s \rangle$

55. $\mathbf{r}(t) = \langle 1 + 2t, 7 - 3t, 6 + t \rangle$;
$\mathbf{R}(s) = \langle -9 + 6s, 22 - 9s, 1 + 3s \rangle$

56–59. Domains *Find the domain of the following vector-valued functions.*

56. $\mathbf{r}(t) = \dfrac{2}{t-1}\mathbf{i} + \dfrac{3}{t+2}\mathbf{j}$

57. $\mathbf{r}(t) = \sqrt{t+2}\,\mathbf{i} + \sqrt{2-t}\,\mathbf{j}$

58. $\mathbf{r}(t) = \cos 2t\,\mathbf{i} + e^{\sqrt{t}}\mathbf{j} + \dfrac{12}{t}\mathbf{k}$

59. $\mathbf{r}(t) = \sqrt{4-t^2}\,\mathbf{i} + \sqrt{t}\,\mathbf{j} - \dfrac{2}{\sqrt{1+t}}\mathbf{k}$

60–63. Line-plane intersections *Find the point (if it exists) at which the following planes and lines intersect.*

60. $x = 3$; $\mathbf{r}(t) = \langle t, t, t \rangle$

61. $z = 4$; $\mathbf{r}(t) = \langle 2t+1, -t+4, t-6 \rangle$

62. $y = -2$; $\mathbf{r}(t) = \langle 2t+1, -t+4, t-6 \rangle$

63. $z = -8$; $\mathbf{r}(t) = \langle 3t-2, t-6, -2t+4 \rangle$

64–66. Curve-plane intersections *Find the points (if they exist) at which the following planes and curves intersect.*

64. $y = 1$; $\mathbf{r}(t) = \langle 10\cos t, 2\sin t, 1 \rangle$, for $0 \le t \le 2\pi$

65. $z = 16$; $\mathbf{r}(t) = \langle t, 2t, 4+3t \rangle$, for $-\infty < t < \infty$

66. $y + x = 0$; $\mathbf{r}(t) = \langle \cos t, \sin t, t \rangle$, for $0 \le t \le 4\pi$

67. Matching functions with graphs Match functions a–f with the appropriate graphs A–F.

a. $\mathbf{r}(t) = \langle t, -t, t \rangle$ **b.** $\mathbf{r}(t) = \langle t^2, t, t \rangle$
c. $\mathbf{r}(t) = \langle 4\cos t, 4\sin t, 2 \rangle$ **d.** $\mathbf{r}(t) = \langle 2t, \sin t, \cos t \rangle$
e. $\mathbf{r}(t) = \langle \sin t, \cos t, \sin 2t \rangle$ **f.** $\mathbf{r}(t) = \langle \sin t, 2t, \cos t \rangle$

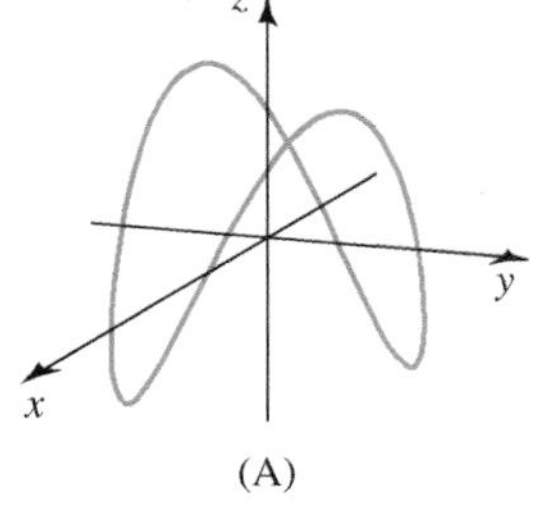

(A)

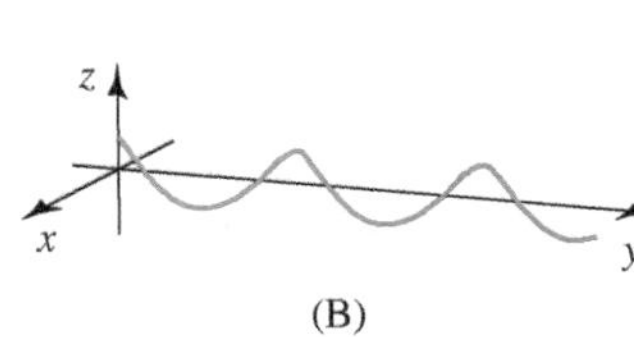

(B)

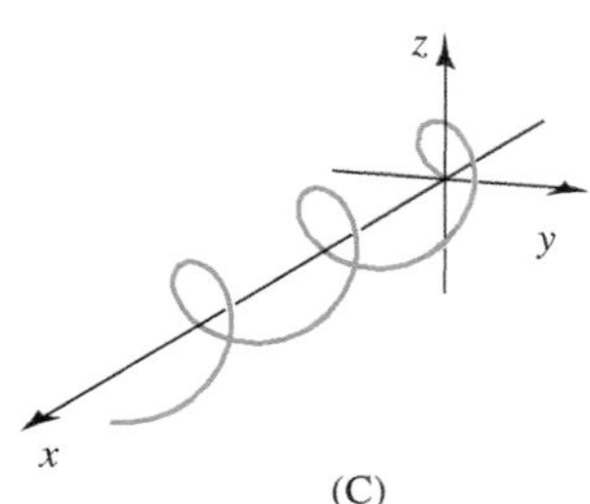

(C)

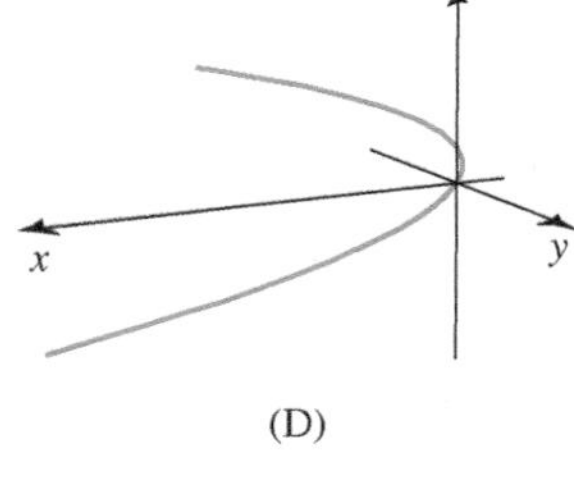

(D)

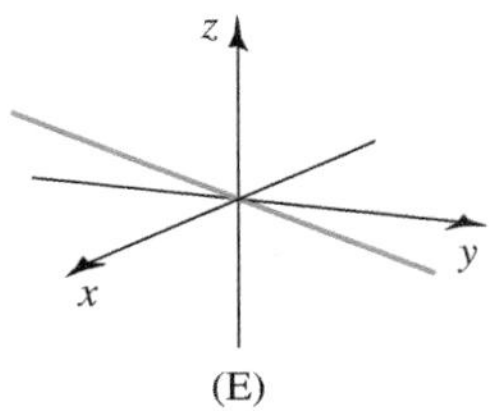

(E)

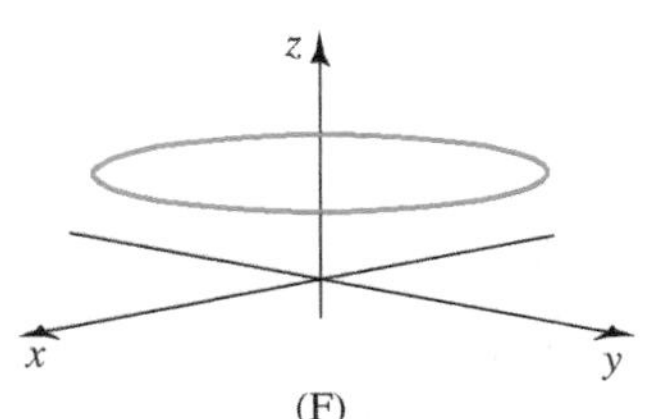

(F)

68. Intersecting lines and colliding particles Consider the lines

$$\mathbf{r}(t) = \langle 2+2t, 8+t, 10+3t \rangle \text{ and}$$
$$\mathbf{R}(s) = \langle 6+s, 10-2s, 16-s \rangle.$$

a. Determine whether the lines intersect (have a common point) and if so, find the coordinates of that point.

b. If **r** and **R** describe the paths of two particles, do the particles collide? Assume that $t \ge 0$ and $s \ge 0$ measure time in seconds, and that motion starts at $s = t = 0$.

69. Upward path Consider the curve described by the vector function $\mathbf{r}(t) = (50e^{-t}\cos t)\mathbf{i} + (50e^{-t}\sin t)\mathbf{j} + (5 - 5e^{-t})\mathbf{k}$, for $t \ge 0$.

a. What is the initial point of the path corresponding to $\mathbf{r}(0)$?

b. What is $\lim_{t\to\infty} \mathbf{r}(t)$?

c. Sketch the curve.

d. Eliminate the parameter t to show that $z = 5 - r/10$, where $r^2 = x^2 + y^2$.

70–73. Closed plane curves *Consider the curve* $\mathbf{r}(t) = (a\cos t + b\sin t)\mathbf{i} + (c\cos t + d\sin t)\mathbf{j} + (e\cos t + f\sin t)\mathbf{k}$, *where a, b, c, d, e, and f are real numbers. It can be shown that this curve lies in a plane.*

70. Assuming the curve lies in a plane, show that it is a circle centered at the origin with radius R provided $a^2 + c^2 + e^2 = b^2 + d^2 + f^2 = R^2$ and $ab + cd + ef = 0$.

T 71. Graph the following curve and describe it.

$$\mathbf{r}(t) = \left(\frac{1}{\sqrt{2}}\cos t + \frac{1}{\sqrt{3}}\sin t\right)\mathbf{i} + \left(-\frac{1}{\sqrt{2}}\cos t + \frac{1}{\sqrt{3}}\sin t\right)\mathbf{j} + \left(\frac{1}{\sqrt{3}}\sin t\right)\mathbf{k}$$

T 72. Graph the following curve and describe it.

$$\mathbf{r}(t) = (2\cos t + 2\sin t)\mathbf{i} + (-\cos t + 2\sin t)\mathbf{j} + (\cos t - 2\sin t)\mathbf{k}$$

73. Find a general expression for a nonzero vector orthogonal to the plane containing the curve.

$$\mathbf{r}(t) = (a\cos t + b\sin t)\mathbf{i} + (c\cos t + d\sin t)\mathbf{j} + (e\cos t + f\sin t)\mathbf{k},$$

where $\langle a, c, e \rangle \times \langle b, d, f \rangle \ne \mathbf{0}$.

Applications

Applications of parametric curves are considered in detail in Section 11.7.

T 74. Golf slice A golfer launches a tee shot down a horizontal fairway; it follows a path given by $\mathbf{r}(t) = \langle at, (75 - 0.1a)t, -5t^2 + 80t \rangle$, where $t \ge 0$ measures time in seconds and **r** has units of feet. The y-axis points straight down the fairway and the z-axis points vertically upward. The parameter a is the slice factor that determines how much the shot deviates from a straight path down the fairway.

a. With no slice ($a = 0$), sketch and describe the shot. How far does the ball travel horizontally (the distance between the point the ball leaves the ground and the point where it first strikes the ground)?

b. With a slice ($a = 0.2$), sketch and describe the shot. How far does the ball travel horizontally?

c. How far does the ball travel horizontally with $a = 2.5$?

Additional Exercises

75–77. Curves on spheres

T **75.** Graph the curve $\mathbf{r}(t) = \langle \frac{1}{2}\sin 2t, \frac{1}{2}(1 - \cos 2t), \cos t \rangle$ and prove that it lies on the surface of a sphere centered at the origin.

76. Prove that for integers m and n, the curve

$$\mathbf{r}(t) = \langle a \sin mt \cos nt, b \sin mt \sin nt, c \cos mt \rangle$$

lies on the surface of a sphere provided $a^2 + b^2 = c^2$.

77. Find the period of the function in Exercise 76; that is, in terms of m and n, find the smallest positive real number T such that $\mathbf{r}(t + T) = \mathbf{r}(t)$ for all t.

78. Limits of vector functions Let $\mathbf{r}(t) = \langle f(t), g(t), h(t) \rangle$.

a. Assume that $\lim_{t \to a} \mathbf{r}(t) = \mathbf{L} = \langle L_1, L_2, L_3 \rangle$, which means that $\lim_{t \to a} |\mathbf{r}(t) - \mathbf{L}| = 0$. Prove that

$$\lim_{t \to a} f(t) = L_1, \quad \lim_{t \to a} g(t) = L_2, \quad \text{and} \quad \lim_{t \to a} h(t) = L_3.$$

b. Assume that $\lim_{t \to a} f(t) = L_1$, $\lim_{t \to a} g(t) = L_2$, and $\lim_{t \to a} h(t) = L_3$. Prove that $\lim_{t \to a} \mathbf{r}(t) = \mathbf{L} = \langle L_1, L_2, L_3 \rangle$, which means that $\lim_{t \to a} |\mathbf{r}(t) - \mathbf{L}| = 0$.

79. Distance between a point and a line Show that the (least) distance d between a point Q and a line $\mathbf{r} = \mathbf{r}_0 + t\mathbf{v}$ (both in $\mathbb{R}^3$) is $d = \dfrac{|\overrightarrow{PQ} \times \mathbf{v}|}{|\mathbf{v}|}$, where P is a point on the line.

80–82. Calculating the distance from a point to a line *Use the formula in Exercise 79 to find the (least) distance between the given point Q and line $\mathbf{r}$.*

80. $Q(5, 6, 1)$; $\mathbf{r}(t) = \langle 1 + 3t, 3 - 4t, t + 1 \rangle$

81. $Q(-5, 2, 9)$; $\mathbf{r}(t) = \langle 5t + 7, 2 - t, 12t + 4 \rangle$

82. $Q(6, 6, 7)$, $\mathbf{r}(t) = \langle 3t, -3t, 4 \rangle$

QUICK CHECK ANSWERS

1. The z-axis; the line $y = x$ in the xy-plane **2.** When $t = 0$, the point on the line is P_0; when $t = 1$, the point on the line is P_1. ◄

11.6 Calculus of Vector-Valued Functions

We now turn to the topic of ultimate interest in this chapter: the calculus of vector-valued functions. Everything you learned about differentiating and integrating functions of the form $y = f(x)$ carries over to vector-valued functions $\mathbf{r}(t)$; you simply apply the rules of differentiation and integration to the individual components of $\mathbf{r}$.

The Derivative and Tangent Vector

Consider the function $\mathbf{r}(t) = f(t)\,\mathbf{i} + g(t)\,\mathbf{j} + h(t)\,\mathbf{k}$, where f, g, and h are differentiable functions on an interval $a < t < b$. The first task is to explain the meaning of the *derivative* of a vector-valued function and to show how to compute it. We begin with the definition of the derivative—now with a vector perspective:

$$\mathbf{r}'(t) = \lim_{\Delta t \to 0} \frac{\Delta \mathbf{r}}{\Delta t} = \lim_{\Delta t \to 0} \frac{\mathbf{r}(t + \Delta t) - \mathbf{r}(t)}{\Delta t}.$$

Before computing this limit, we look at its geometry. The function $\mathbf{r}(t) = f(t)\,\mathbf{i} + g(t)\,\mathbf{j} + h(t)\,\mathbf{k}$ describes a parameterized curve in space. Let P be a point on that curve associated with the position vector $\mathbf{r}(t)$ and let Q be a nearby point associated with the position vector $\mathbf{r}(t + \Delta t)$, where $\Delta t > 0$ is a small increment in t (Figure 11.78a). The difference $\Delta \mathbf{r} = \mathbf{r}(t + \Delta t) - \mathbf{r}(t)$ is the vector $\overrightarrow{PQ}$, where we assume $\Delta \mathbf{r} \neq \mathbf{0}$. Because Δt is a scalar, the direction of $\Delta \mathbf{r}/\Delta t$ is the same as the direction of $\overrightarrow{PQ}$.

As Δt approaches 0, Q approaches P and the vector $\Delta \mathbf{r}/\Delta t$ approaches a limiting vector that we denote $\mathbf{r}'(t)$ (Figure 11.78b). This new vector $\mathbf{r}'(t)$ has two important interpretations.

➤ An analogous argument can be given for $\Delta t < 0$, with the same result. Figure 11.78 illustrates the tangent vector $\mathbf{r}'$ for $\Delta t > 0$.

- The vector $\mathbf{r}'(t)$ points in the direction of the curve at P. For this reason, $\mathbf{r}'(t)$ is a *tangent vector* at P (provided it is not the zero vector).
- The vector $\mathbf{r}'(t)$ is the *derivative* of $\mathbf{r}$ with respect to t; it gives the rate of change of the function $\mathbf{r}(t)$ at the point P. In fact, if $\mathbf{r}(t)$ is the position function of a moving object, then $\mathbf{r}'(t)$ is the velocity vector of the object, which always points in the direction of motion, and $|\mathbf{r}'(t)|$ is the speed of the object.

➤ Section 11.7 is devoted to problems of motion in two and three dimensions.

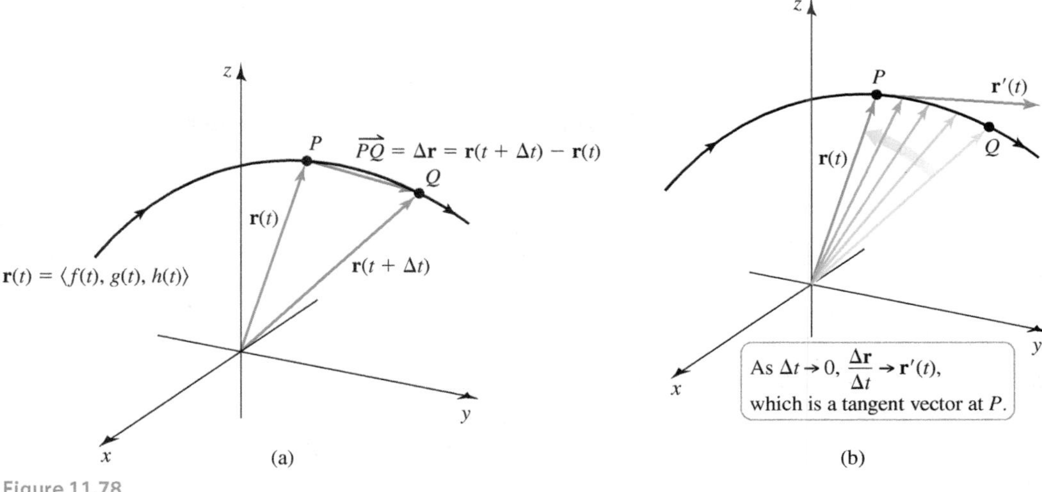

Figure 11.78

We now evaluate the limit that defines $\mathbf{r}'(t)$ by expressing $\mathbf{r}$ in terms of its components and using the properties of limits.

$$
\begin{aligned}
\mathbf{r}'(t) &= \lim_{\Delta t \to 0} \frac{\mathbf{r}(t + \Delta t) - \mathbf{r}(t)}{\Delta t} \\
&= \lim_{\Delta t \to 0} \frac{(f(t + \Delta t)\,\mathbf{i} + g(t + \Delta t)\,\mathbf{j} + h(t + \Delta t)\,\mathbf{k}) - (f(t)\,\mathbf{i} + g(t)\,\mathbf{j} + h(t)\,\mathbf{k})}{\Delta t} && \text{Substitute components of } \mathbf{r}. \\
&= \lim_{\Delta t \to 0} \left(\frac{f(t + \Delta t) - f(t)}{\Delta t}\,\mathbf{i} + \frac{g(t + \Delta t) - g(t)}{\Delta t}\,\mathbf{j} + \frac{h(t + \Delta t) - h(t)}{\Delta t}\,\mathbf{k} \right) && \text{Rearrange terms inside of limit.} \\
&= \underbrace{\lim_{\Delta t \to 0} \frac{f(t + \Delta t) - f(t)}{\Delta t}}_{f'(t)}\,\mathbf{i} + \underbrace{\lim_{\Delta t \to 0} \frac{g(t + \Delta t) - g(t)}{\Delta t}}_{g'(t)}\,\mathbf{j} + \underbrace{\lim_{\Delta t \to 0} \frac{h(t + \Delta t) - h(t)}{\Delta t}}_{h'(t)}\,\mathbf{k} && \text{Limit of sum equals sum of limits.}
\end{aligned}
$$

Because f, g, and h are differentiable scalar-valued functions of the variable t, the three limits in the last step are identified as the derivatives of f, g, and h, respectively. Therefore, there are no surprises:

$$\mathbf{r}'(t) = f'(t)\,\mathbf{i} + g'(t)\,\mathbf{j} + h'(t)\,\mathbf{k}.$$

In other words, to differentiate the vector-valued function $\mathbf{r}(t)$, we simply differentiate each of its components with respect to t.

DEFINITION Derivative and Tangent Vector

Let $\mathbf{r}(t) = f(t)\,\mathbf{i} + g(t)\,\mathbf{j} + h(t)\,\mathbf{k}$, where f, g, and h are differentiable functions on (a, b). Then $\mathbf{r}$ has a **derivative** (or is **differentiable**) on (a, b) and

$$\mathbf{r}'(t) = f'(t)\,\mathbf{i} + g'(t)\,\mathbf{j} + h'(t)\,\mathbf{k}.$$

Provided $\mathbf{r}'(t) \neq \mathbf{0}$, $\mathbf{r}'(t)$ is a **tangent vector** at the point corresponding to $\mathbf{r}(t)$.

EXAMPLE 1 **Derivative of vector functions** Compute the derivative of the following functions.

a. $\mathbf{r}(t) = \langle t^3, 3t^2, t^3/6 \rangle$
b. $\mathbf{r}(t) = e^{-t}\mathbf{i} + 10\sqrt{t}\,\mathbf{j} + 2\cos 3t\,\mathbf{k}$

SOLUTION

a. $\mathbf{r}'(t) = \langle 3t^2, 6t, t^2/2 \rangle$; note that $\mathbf{r}$ is differentiable for all t and $\mathbf{r}'(0) = \mathbf{0}$.

b. $\mathbf{r}'(t) = -e^{-t}\mathbf{i} + \dfrac{5}{\sqrt{t}}\mathbf{j} - 6\sin 3t\,\mathbf{k}$; the function $\mathbf{r}$ is differentiable for $t > 0$.

Related Exercises 7–20 ◄

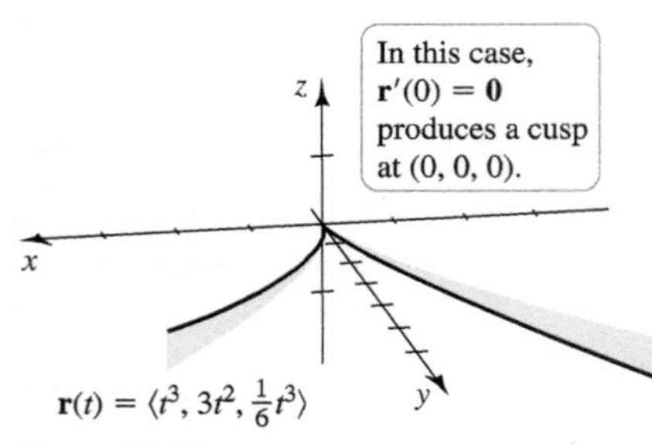

Figure 11.79

➤ If a curve has a cusp at a point, then $\mathbf{r}'(t) = \mathbf{0}$ at that point. However, the converse is not true; it may happen that $\mathbf{r}'(t) = \mathbf{0}$ at a point that is not a cusp (Exercise 89).

QUICK CHECK 1 Let $\mathbf{r}(t) = \langle t, t, t \rangle$. Compute $\mathbf{r}'(t)$ and interpret the result. ◄

The condition that $\mathbf{r}'(t) \neq \mathbf{0}$ in order for the tangent vector to be defined requires explanation. Consider the function $\mathbf{r}(t) = \langle t^3, 3t^2, t^3/6 \rangle$. As shown in Example 1a, $\mathbf{r}'(0) = \mathbf{0}$; that is, all three components of $\mathbf{r}'(t)$ are zero simultaneously when $t = 0$. We see in Figure 11.79 that this otherwise smooth curve has a *cusp*, or a sharp point, at the origin. If $\mathbf{r}$ describes the motion of an object, then $\mathbf{r}'(t) = \mathbf{0}$ means that the velocity (and speed) of the object is zero at a point. At such a stationary point, the object *may* change direction abruptly, creating a cusp in its trajectory. For this reason, we say a function $\mathbf{r}(t) = \langle f(t), g(t), h(t) \rangle$ is **smooth** on an interval if f, g, and h are differentiable *and* $\mathbf{r}'(t) \neq \mathbf{0}$ on that interval. Smooth curves have no cusps or corners.

Unit Tangent Vector In situations in which only the direction (but not the length) of the tangent vector is of interest, we work with the *unit tangent vector*. It is the vector with magnitude 1, formed by dividing $\mathbf{r}'(t)$ by its length.

> **DEFINITION Unit Tangent Vector**
> Let $\mathbf{r}(t) = f(t)\,\mathbf{i} + g(t)\,\mathbf{j} + h(t)\,\mathbf{k}$ be a smooth parameterized curve, for $a \leq t \leq b$. The **unit tangent vector** for a particular value of t is
> $$\mathbf{T}(t) = \frac{\mathbf{r}'(t)}{|\mathbf{r}'(t)|}.$$

QUICK CHECK 2 Suppose $\mathbf{r}'(t)$ has units m/s. Explain why $\mathbf{T}(t) = \mathbf{r}'(t)/|\mathbf{r}'(t)|$ is dimensionless (has no units) and carries information only about direction. ◄

EXAMPLE 2 **Unit tangent vectors** Find the unit tangent vectors for the following parameterized curves.

a. $\mathbf{r}(t) = \langle t^2, 4t, 4\ln t \rangle$, for $t > 0$
b. $\mathbf{r}(t) = \langle 10, 3\cos t, 3\sin t \rangle$, for $0 \leq t \leq 2\pi$

SOLUTION

a. A tangent vector is $\mathbf{r}'(t) = \langle 2t, 4, 4/t \rangle$, which has a magnitude of

$$\begin{aligned} |\mathbf{r}'(t)| &= \sqrt{(2t)^2 + 4^2 + \left(\frac{4}{t}\right)^2} && \text{Definition of magnitude} \\ &= \sqrt{4t^2 + 16 + \frac{16}{t^2}} && \text{Expand.} \\ &= \sqrt{\left(2t + \frac{4}{t}\right)^2} && \text{Factor.} \\ &= 2t + \frac{4}{t}. && \text{Simplify.} \end{aligned}$$

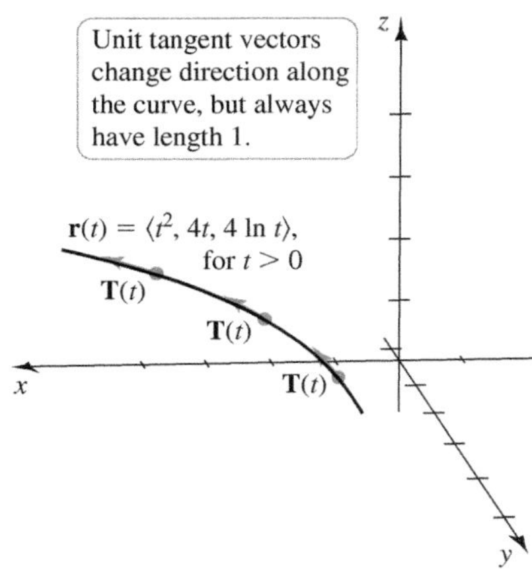

Figure 11.80

Therefore, the unit tangent vector for a particular value of t is

$$\mathbf{T}(t) = \frac{\langle 2t, 4, 4/t \rangle}{2t + 4/t}.$$

As shown in Figure 11.80, the unit tangent vectors change direction along the curve but maintain unit length.

b. In this case, $\mathbf{r}'(t) = \langle 0, -3 \sin t, 3 \cos t \rangle$ and

$$|\mathbf{r}'(t)| = \sqrt{0^2 + (-3 \sin t)^2 + (3 \cos t)^2} = \sqrt{9\underbrace{(\sin^2 t + \cos^2 t)}_{1}} = 3.$$

Therefore, the unit tangent vector for a particular value of t is

$$\mathbf{T}(t) = \frac{1}{3}\langle 0, -3 \sin t, 3 \cos t \rangle = \langle 0, -\sin t, \cos t \rangle.$$

The direction of $\mathbf{T}$ changes along the curve, but its length remains 1.

Related Exercises 21–30 ◀

Derivative Rules The rules for derivatives for single-variable functions either carry over directly to vector-valued functions or have close analogs. These rules are generally proved by working on the individual components of the vector function.

THEOREM 11.7 Derivative Rules

Let $\mathbf{u}$ and $\mathbf{v}$ be differentiable vector-valued functions and let f be a differentiable scalar-valued function, all at a point t. Let $\mathbf{c}$ be a constant vector. The following rules apply.

1. $\frac{d}{dt}(\mathbf{c}) = \mathbf{0}$ Constant Rule
2. $\frac{d}{dt}(\mathbf{u}(t) + \mathbf{v}(t)) = \mathbf{u}'(t) + \mathbf{v}'(t)$ Sum Rule
3. $\frac{d}{dt}(f(t)\mathbf{u}(t)) = f'(t)\mathbf{u}(t) + f(t)\mathbf{u}'(t)$ Product Rule
4. $\frac{d}{dt}(\mathbf{u}(f(t))) = \mathbf{u}'(f(t))f'(t)$ Chain Rule
5. $\frac{d}{dt}(\mathbf{u}(t) \cdot \mathbf{v}(t)) = \mathbf{u}'(t) \cdot \mathbf{v}(t) + \mathbf{u}(t) \cdot \mathbf{v}'(t)$ Dot Product Rule
6. $\frac{d}{dt}(\mathbf{u}(t) \times \mathbf{v}(t)) = \mathbf{u}'(t) \times \mathbf{v}(t) + \mathbf{u}(t) \times \mathbf{v}'(t)$ Cross Product Rule

➤ With the exception of the Cross Product Rule, these rules apply to vector-valued functions with any number of components. Notice that we have three new product rules, all of which mimic the original Product Rule. In Rule 4, $\mathbf{u}$ must be differentiable at $f(t)$.

QUICK CHECK 3 Let $\mathbf{u}(t) = \langle t, t, t \rangle$ and $\mathbf{v}(t) = \langle 1, 1, 1 \rangle$. Compute $\frac{d}{dt}(\mathbf{u}(t) \cdot \mathbf{v}(t))$ using Derivative Rule 5 and show that it agrees with the result obtained by first computing the dot product and differentiating directly. ◀

The proofs of these rules are assigned in Exercises 86–88 with the exception of the following representative proofs.

Proof of the Chain Rule: Let $\mathbf{u}(t) = \langle u_1(t), u_2(t), u_3(t) \rangle$, which implies that

$$\mathbf{u}(f(t)) = u_1(f(t))\,\mathbf{i} + u_2(f(t))\,\mathbf{j} + u_3(f(t))\,\mathbf{k}.$$

We now apply the ordinary Chain Rule componentwise:

$$\begin{aligned}
\frac{d}{dt}\big(\mathbf{u}(f(t))\big) &= \frac{d}{dt}\big(u_1(f(t))\,\mathbf{i} + u_2(f(t))\,\mathbf{j} + u_3(f(t))\,\mathbf{k}\big) && \text{Components of } \mathbf{u}\\
&= \frac{d}{dt}\big(u_1(f(t))\big)\,\mathbf{i} + \frac{d}{dt}\big(u_2(f(t))\big)\,\mathbf{j} + \frac{d}{dt}\big(u_3(f(t))\big)\,\mathbf{k} && \text{Derivative of a sum}\\
&= u_1'(f(t))f'(t)\,\mathbf{i} + u_2'(f(t))f'(t)\,\mathbf{j} + u_3'(f(t))f'(t)\,\mathbf{k} && \text{Chain Rule}\\
&= \big(u_1'(f(t))\,\mathbf{i} + u_2'(f(t))\,\mathbf{j} + u_3'(f(t))\,\mathbf{k}\big)f'(t) && \text{Factor } f'(t).\\
&= \mathbf{u}'(f(t))f'(t). && \text{Definition of } \mathbf{u}'
\end{aligned}$$

➤

Proof of the Dot Product Rule: One proof of the Dot Product Rule uses the standard Product Rule on each component. Let $\mathbf{u}(t) = \langle u_1(t), u_2(t), u_3(t)\rangle$ and $\mathbf{v}(t) = \langle v_1(t), v_2(t), v_3(t)\rangle$. Then

$$\begin{aligned}
\frac{d}{dt}(\mathbf{u}\cdot\mathbf{v}) &= \frac{d}{dt}(u_1 v_1 + u_2 v_2 + u_3 v_3) && \text{Definition of dot product}\\
&= u_1' v_1 + u_1 v_1' + u_2' v_2 + u_2 v_2' + u_3' v_3 + u_3 v_3' && \text{Product Rule}\\
&= \underbrace{u_1' v_1 + u_2' v_2 + u_3' v_3}_{\mathbf{u}'\cdot\mathbf{v}} + \underbrace{u_1 v_1' + u_2 v_2' + u_3 v_3'}_{\mathbf{u}\cdot\mathbf{v}'} && \text{Rearrange.}\\
&= \mathbf{u}'\cdot\mathbf{v} + \mathbf{u}\cdot\mathbf{v}'.
\end{aligned}$$

➤

EXAMPLE 3 **Derivative rules** Compute the following derivatives, where

$$\mathbf{u}(t) = t\,\mathbf{i} + t^2\,\mathbf{j} - t^3\,\mathbf{k} \quad\text{and}\quad \mathbf{v}(t) = \sin t\,\mathbf{i} + 2\cos t\,\mathbf{j} + \cos t\,\mathbf{k}.$$

a. $\frac{d}{dt}(\mathbf{v}(t^2))$ **b.** $\frac{d}{dt}(t^2\,\mathbf{v}(t))$ **c.** $\frac{d}{dt}(\mathbf{u}(t)\cdot\mathbf{v}(t))$

SOLUTION

a. Note that $\mathbf{v}'(t) = \cos t\,\mathbf{i} - 2\sin t\,\mathbf{j} - \sin t\,\mathbf{k}$. Using the Chain Rule, we have

$$\frac{d}{dt}(\mathbf{v}(t^2)) = \mathbf{v}'(t^2)\frac{d}{dt}(t^2) = \underbrace{(\cos t^2\,\mathbf{i} - 2\sin t^2\,\mathbf{j} - \sin t^2\,\mathbf{k})}_{\mathbf{v}'(t^2)}(2t).$$

b.

$$\begin{aligned}
\frac{d}{dt}(t^2\,\mathbf{v}(t)) &= \frac{d}{dt}(t^2)\mathbf{v}(t) + t^2\frac{d}{dt}(\mathbf{v}(t)) && \text{Product Rule}\\
&= 2t\,\mathbf{v}(t) + t^2\,\mathbf{v}'(t)\\
&= 2t\underbrace{(\sin t\,\mathbf{i} + 2\cos t\,\mathbf{j} + \cos t\,\mathbf{k})}_{\mathbf{v}(t)} + t^2\underbrace{(\cos t\,\mathbf{i} - 2\sin t\,\mathbf{j} - \sin t\,\mathbf{k})}_{\mathbf{v}'(t)} && \text{Differentiate.}\\
&= (2t\sin t + t^2\cos t)\,\mathbf{i} + (4t\cos t - 2t^2\sin t)\,\mathbf{j} + (2t\cos t - t^2\sin t)\,\mathbf{k} && \text{Collect terms.}
\end{aligned}$$

c.

$$\begin{aligned}
\frac{d}{dt}(\mathbf{u}(t)\cdot\mathbf{v}(t)) &= \mathbf{u}'(t)\cdot\mathbf{v}(t) + \mathbf{u}(t)\cdot\mathbf{v}'(t) && \text{Dot Product Rule}\\
&= (\mathbf{i} + 2t\,\mathbf{j} - 3t^2\,\mathbf{k})\cdot(\sin t\,\mathbf{i} + 2\cos t\,\mathbf{j} + \cos t\,\mathbf{k})\\
&\quad + (t\,\mathbf{i} + t^2\,\mathbf{j} - t^3\,\mathbf{k})\cdot(\cos t\,\mathbf{i} - 2\sin t\,\mathbf{j} - \sin t\,\mathbf{k}) && \text{Differentiate.}\\
&= (\sin t + 4t\cos t - 3t^2\cos t) + (t\cos t - 2t^2\sin t + t^3\sin t) && \text{Dot products}\\
&= (1 - 2t^2 + t^3)\sin t + (5t - 3t^2)\cos t && \text{Simplify.}
\end{aligned}$$

Note that the result is a scalar. The same result is obtained if you first compute $\mathbf{u}\cdot\mathbf{v}$ and then differentiate.

Related Exercises 31–40 ➤

Higher-Order Derivatives Higher-order derivatives of vector-valued functions are computed in the expected way: We simply differentiate each component multiple times. Second derivatives feature prominently in the next section, playing the role of acceleration.

EXAMPLE 4 Higher-order derivatives Compute the first, second, and third derivative of $\mathbf{r}(t) = \langle t^2, 8 \ln t, 3e^{-2t} \rangle$.

SOLUTION Differentiating once, we have $\mathbf{r}'(t) = \langle 2t, 8/t, -6e^{-2t} \rangle$. Differentiating again produces $\mathbf{r}''(t) = \langle 2, -8/t^2, 12e^{-2t} \rangle$. Differentiating once more, we have $\mathbf{r}'''(t) = \langle 0, 16/t^3, -24e^{-2t} \rangle$.

Related Exercises 41–46 ◄

Integrals of Vector-Valued Functions

An **antiderivative** of the vector function $\mathbf{r}$ is a function $\mathbf{R}$ such that $\mathbf{R}' = \mathbf{r}$. If

$$\mathbf{r}(t) = f(t)\mathbf{i} + g(t)\mathbf{j} + h(t)\mathbf{k},$$

then an antiderivative of $\mathbf{r}$ is

$$\mathbf{R}(t) = F(t)\mathbf{i} + G(t)\mathbf{j} + H(t)\mathbf{k},$$

where F, G, and H are antiderivatives of f, g, and h, respectively. This fact follows by differentiating the components of $\mathbf{R}$ and verifying that $\mathbf{R}' = \mathbf{r}$. The collection of all antiderivatives of $\mathbf{r}$ is the *indefinite integral* of $\mathbf{r}$.

DEFINITION Indefinite Integral of a Vector-Valued Function

Let $\mathbf{r}(t) = f(t)\mathbf{i} + g(t)\mathbf{j} + h(t)\mathbf{k}$ be a vector function and let $\mathbf{R}(t) = F(t)\mathbf{i} + G(t)\mathbf{j} + H(t)\mathbf{k}$, where F, G, and H are antiderivatives of f, g, and h, respectively. The **indefinite integral** of $\mathbf{r}$ is

$$\int \mathbf{r}(t)\,dt = \mathbf{R}(t) + \mathbf{C},$$

where $\mathbf{C}$ is an arbitrary constant vector. Alternatively, in component form,

$$\int \langle f(t), g(t), h(t) \rangle\,dt = \langle F(t), G(t), H(t) \rangle + \langle C_1, C_2, C_3 \rangle.$$

EXAMPLE 5 Indefinite integrals Compute

$$\int \left(\frac{t}{\sqrt{t^2+2}}\mathbf{i} + e^{-3t}\mathbf{j} + (\sin 4t + 1)\mathbf{k} \right) dt.$$

➤ The substitution $u = t^2 + 2$ is used to evaluate the $\mathbf{i}$-component of the integral.

SOLUTION We compute the indefinite integral of each component:

$$\begin{aligned}
&\int \left(\frac{t}{\sqrt{t^2+2}}\mathbf{i} + e^{-3t}\mathbf{j} + (\sin 4t + 1)\mathbf{k} \right) dt \\
&= \left(\sqrt{t^2+2} + C_1\right)\mathbf{i} + \left(-\frac{1}{3}e^{-3t} + C_2\right)\mathbf{j} + \left(-\frac{1}{4}\cos 4t + t + C_3\right)\mathbf{k} \\
&= \sqrt{t^2+2}\,\mathbf{i} - \frac{1}{3}e^{-3t}\mathbf{j} + \left(t - \frac{1}{4}\cos 4t\right)\mathbf{k} + \mathbf{C}. \quad \text{Let } \mathbf{C} = C_1\mathbf{i} + C_2\mathbf{j} + C_3\mathbf{k}.
\end{aligned}$$

The constants C_1, C_2, and C_3 are combined to form one vector constant $\mathbf{C}$ at the end of the calculation.

Related Exercises 47–52 ◄

QUICK CHECK 4 Let $\mathbf{r}(t) = \langle 1, 2t, 3t^2 \rangle$. Compute $\int \mathbf{r}(t)\,dt$. ◄

EXAMPLE 6 Finding one antiderivative Find $\mathbf{r}(t)$ such that $\mathbf{r}'(t) = \langle 10, \sin t, t \rangle$ and $\mathbf{r}(0) = \mathbf{j}$.

SOLUTION The required function $\mathbf{r}$ is an antiderivative of $\langle 10, \sin t, t \rangle$:

$$\mathbf{r}(t) = \int \langle 10, \sin t, t \rangle\, dt = \left\langle 10t, -\cos t, \frac{t^2}{2} \right\rangle + \mathbf{C},$$

where $\mathbf{C}$ is an arbitrary constant vector. The condition $\mathbf{r}(0) = \mathbf{j}$ allows us to determine $\mathbf{C}$; substituting $t = 0$ implies that $\mathbf{r}(0) = \langle 0, -1, 0 \rangle + \mathbf{C} = \mathbf{j}$, where $\mathbf{j} = \langle 0, 1, 0 \rangle$. Solving for $\mathbf{C}$, we have $\mathbf{C} = \langle 0, 1, 0 \rangle - \langle 0, -1, 0 \rangle = \langle 0, 2, 0 \rangle$. Therefore,

$$\mathbf{r}(t) = \left\langle 10t, 2 - \cos t, \frac{t^2}{2} \right\rangle.$$

Related Exercises 53–58 ◄

Definite integrals are evaluated by applying the Fundamental Theorem of Calculus to each component of a vector-valued function.

DEFINITION Definite Integral of a Vector-Valued Function

Let $\mathbf{r}(t) = f(t)\,\mathbf{i} + g(t)\,\mathbf{j} + h(t)\,\mathbf{k}$, where f, g, and h are integrable on the interval $[a, b]$. The **definite integral** of $\mathbf{r}$ on $[a, b]$ is

$$\int_a^b \mathbf{r}(t)\, dt = \left(\int_a^b f(t)\, dt\right)\mathbf{i} + \left(\int_a^b g(t)\, dt\right)\mathbf{j} + \left(\int_a^b h(t)\, dt\right)\mathbf{k}$$

EXAMPLE 7 Definite integrals Evaluate

$$\int_0^{\pi} \left(\mathbf{i} + 3\cos\frac{t}{2}\,\mathbf{j} - 4t\,\mathbf{k}\right) dt.$$

SOLUTION

$$\begin{aligned}\int_0^{\pi} \left(\mathbf{i} + 3\cos\frac{t}{2}\,\mathbf{j} - 4t\,\mathbf{k}\right) dt &= t\,\mathbf{i}\Big|_0^{\pi} + 6\sin\frac{t}{2}\,\mathbf{j}\Big|_0^{\pi} - 2t^2\,\mathbf{k}\Big|_0^{\pi} && \text{Evaluate integrals for each component.}\\ &= \pi\,\mathbf{i} + 6\mathbf{j} - 2\pi^2\,\mathbf{k} && \text{Simplify.}\end{aligned}$$

Related Exercises 59–66 ◄

With the tools of differentiation and integration in hand, we are prepared to tackle some practical problems, notably the motion of objects in space.

SECTION 11.6 EXERCISES

Review Questions

1. What is the derivative of $\mathbf{r}(t) = \langle f(t), g(t), h(t) \rangle$?
2. Explain the geometric meaning of $\mathbf{r}'(t)$.
3. Given a tangent vector on an oriented curve, how do you find the unit tangent vector?
4. Compute $\mathbf{r}''(t)$ when $\mathbf{r}(t) = \langle t^{10}, 8t, \cos t \rangle$.
5. How do you find the indefinite integral of $\mathbf{r}(t) = \langle f(t), g(t), h(t) \rangle$?
6. How do you evaluate $\int_a^b \mathbf{r}(t)\, dt$?

Basic Skills

7–14. Derivatives of vector-valued functions *Differentiate the following functions.*

7. $\mathbf{r}(t) = \langle \cos t, t^2, \sin t \rangle$
8. $\mathbf{r}(t) = 4e^t\,\mathbf{i} + 5\mathbf{j} + \ln t\,\mathbf{k}$
9. $\mathbf{r}(t) = \langle 2t^3, 6\sqrt{t}, 3/t \rangle$
10. $\mathbf{r}(t) = \langle 4, 3\cos 2t, 2\sin 3t \rangle$
11. $\mathbf{r}(t) = e^t\,\mathbf{i} + 2e^{-t}\,\mathbf{j} - 4e^{2t}\,\mathbf{k}$
12. $\mathbf{r}(t) = \tan t\,\mathbf{i} + \sec t\,\mathbf{j} + \cos^2 t\,\mathbf{k}$
13. $\mathbf{r}(t) = \langle te^{-t}, t\ln t, t\cos t \rangle$
14. $\mathbf{r}(t) = \langle (t+1)^{-1}, \tan^{-1} t, \ln(t+1) \rangle$

15–20. Tangent vectors *Find a tangent vector at the given value of t for the following parameterized curves.*

15. $\mathbf{r}(t) = \langle t, 3t^2, t^3 \rangle, t = 1$

16. $\mathbf{r}(t) = \langle e^t, e^{3t}, e^{5t} \rangle, t = 0$

17. $\mathbf{r}(t) = \langle t, \cos 2t, 2 \sin t \rangle, t = \pi/2$

18. $\mathbf{r}(t) = \langle 2 \sin t, 3 \cos t, \sin (t/2) \rangle, t = \pi$

19. $\mathbf{r}(t) = 2t^4 \mathbf{i} + 6t^{3/2} \mathbf{j} + \frac{10}{t} \mathbf{k}, t = 1$

20. $\mathbf{r}(t) = 2e^t \mathbf{i} + e^{-2t} \mathbf{j} + 4e^{2t} \mathbf{k}, t = \ln 3$

21–26. Unit tangent vectors *Find the unit tangent vector for the following parameterized curves.*

21. $\mathbf{r}(t) = \langle 2t, 2t, t \rangle$, for $0 \leq t \leq 1$

22. $\mathbf{r}(t) = \langle \cos t, \sin t, 2 \rangle$, for $0 \leq t \leq 2\pi$

23. $\mathbf{r}(t) = \langle 8, \cos 2t, 2 \sin 2t \rangle$, for $0 \leq t \leq 2\pi$

24. $\mathbf{r}(t) = \langle \sin t, \cos t, \cos t \rangle$, for $0 \leq t \leq 2\pi$

25. $\mathbf{r}(t) = \langle t, 2, 2/t \rangle$, for $t \geq 1$

26. $\mathbf{r}(t) = \langle e^{2t}, 2e^{2t}, 2e^{-3t} \rangle$, for $t \geq 0$

27–30. Unit tangent vectors at a point *Find the unit tangent vector at the given value of t for the following parameterized curves.*

27. $\mathbf{r}(t) = \langle \cos 2t, 4, 3 \sin 2t \rangle$, for $0 \leq t \leq \pi$; $t = \pi/2$

28. $\mathbf{r}(t) = \langle \sin t, \cos t, e^{-t} \rangle$, for $0 \leq t \leq \pi$; $t = 0$

29. $\mathbf{r}(t) = \langle 6t, 6, 3/t \rangle$, for $0 < t < 2$; $t = 1$

30. $\mathbf{r}(t) = \langle \sqrt{7}e^t, 3e^t, 3e^t \rangle$, for $0 \leq t \leq 1$; $t = \ln 2$

31–36. Derivative rules *Let*

$$\mathbf{u}(t) = 2t^3 \mathbf{i} + (t^2 - 1)\mathbf{j} - 8\mathbf{k} \text{ and } \mathbf{v}(t) = e^t \mathbf{i} + 2e^{-t} \mathbf{j} - e^{2t} \mathbf{k}.$$

Compute the derivative of the following functions.

31. $(t^{12} + 3t)\mathbf{u}(t)$

32. $(4t^8 - 6t^3)\mathbf{v}(t)$

33. $\mathbf{u}(t^4 - 2t)$

34. $\mathbf{v}(\sqrt{t})$

35. $\mathbf{u}(t) \cdot \mathbf{v}(t)$

36. $\mathbf{u}(t) \times \mathbf{v}(t)$

37–40. Derivative rules *Compute the following derivatives.*

37. $\frac{d}{dt}(t^2(\mathbf{i} + 2\mathbf{j} - 2t\,\mathbf{k}) \cdot (e^t \mathbf{i} + 2e^t \mathbf{j} - 3e^{-t} \mathbf{k}))$

38. $\frac{d}{dt}((t^3 \mathbf{i} - 2t\,\mathbf{j} - 2\mathbf{k}) \times (t\,\mathbf{i} - t^2 \mathbf{j} - t^3 \mathbf{k}))$

39. $\frac{d}{dt}((3t^2 \mathbf{i} + \sqrt{t}\,\mathbf{j} - 2t^{-1} \mathbf{k}) \cdot (\cos t\,\mathbf{i} + \sin 2t\,\mathbf{j} - 3t\,\mathbf{k}))$

40. $\frac{d}{dt}((t^3 \mathbf{i} + 6\mathbf{j} - 2\sqrt{t}\,\mathbf{k}) \times (3t\,\mathbf{i} - 12t^2 \mathbf{j} - 6t^{-2} \mathbf{k}))$

41–46. Higher-order derivatives *Compute* $\mathbf{r}''(t)$ *and* $\mathbf{r}'''(t)$ *for the following functions.*

41. $\mathbf{r}(t) = \langle t^2 + 1, t + 1, 1 \rangle$

42. $\mathbf{r}(t) = \langle 3t^{12} - t^2, t^8 + t^3, t^{-4} - 2 \rangle$

43. $\mathbf{r}(t) = \langle \cos 3t, \sin 4t, \cos 6t \rangle$

44. $\mathbf{r}(t) = \langle e^{4t}, 2e^{-4t} + 1, 2e^{-t} \rangle$

45. $\mathbf{r}(t) = \sqrt{t + 4}\,\mathbf{i} + \frac{t}{t + 1}\mathbf{j} - e^{-t^2} \mathbf{k}$

46. $\mathbf{r}(t) = \tan t\,\mathbf{i} + \left(t + \frac{1}{t}\right)\mathbf{j} - \ln (t + 1)\,\mathbf{k}$

47–52. Indefinite integrals *Compute the indefinite integral of the following functions.*

47. $\mathbf{r}(t) = \langle t^4 - 3t, 2t - 1, 10 \rangle$

48. $\mathbf{r}(t) = \langle 5t^{-4} - t^2, t^6 - 4t^3, 2/t \rangle$

49. $\mathbf{r}(t) = \langle 2 \cos t, 2 \sin 3t, 4 \cos 8t \rangle$

50. $\mathbf{r}(t) = te^t \mathbf{i} + t \sin t^2 \mathbf{j} - \frac{2t}{\sqrt{t^2 + 4}} \mathbf{k}$

51. $\mathbf{r}(t) = e^{3t} \mathbf{i} + \frac{1}{1 + t^2} \mathbf{j} - \frac{1}{\sqrt{2t}} \mathbf{k}$

52. $\mathbf{r}(t) = 2^t \mathbf{i} + \frac{1}{1 + 2t} \mathbf{j} + \ln t\,\mathbf{k}$

53–58. Finding r from r′ *Find the function* **r** *that satisfies the given conditions.*

53. $\mathbf{r}'(t) = \langle e^t, \sin t, \sec^2 t \rangle$; $\mathbf{r}(0) = \langle 2, 2, 2 \rangle$

54. $\mathbf{r}'(t) = \langle 0, 2, 2t \rangle$; $\mathbf{r}(1) = \langle 4, 3, -5 \rangle$

55. $\mathbf{r}'(t) = \langle 1, 2t, 3t^2 \rangle$; $\mathbf{r}(1) = \langle 4, 3, -5 \rangle$

56. $\mathbf{r}'(t) = \langle \sqrt{t}, \cos \pi t, 4/t \rangle$; $\mathbf{r}(1) = \langle 2, 3, 4 \rangle$

57. $\mathbf{r}'(t) = \langle e^{2t}, 1 - 2e^{-t}, 1 - 2e^t \rangle$; $\mathbf{r}(0) = \langle 1, 1, 1 \rangle$

58. $\mathbf{r}'(t) = \frac{t}{t^2 + 1} \mathbf{i} + te^{-t^2} \mathbf{j} - \frac{2t}{\sqrt{t^2 + 4}} \mathbf{k}$; $\mathbf{r}(0) = \mathbf{i} + \frac{3}{2}\mathbf{j} - 3\mathbf{k}$

59–66. Definite integrals *Evaluate the following definite integrals.*

59. $\int_{-1}^{1} (\mathbf{i} + t\,\mathbf{j} + 3t^2 \mathbf{k})\, dt$

60. $\int_{1}^{4} (6t^2 \mathbf{i} + 8t^3 \mathbf{j} + 9t^2 \mathbf{k})\, dt$

61. $\int_{0}^{\ln 2} (e^t \mathbf{i} + e^t \cos(\pi e^t)\mathbf{j})\, dt$

62. $\int_{1/2}^{1} \left(\frac{3}{1 + 2t}\mathbf{i} - \pi \csc^2\left(\frac{\pi}{2}t\right)\mathbf{k}\right) dt$

63. $\int_{-\pi}^{\pi} (\sin t\,\mathbf{i} + \cos t\,\mathbf{j} + 2t\,\mathbf{k})\, dt$

64. $\int_{0}^{\ln 2} (e^{-t} \mathbf{i} + 2e^{2t} \mathbf{j} - 4e^t \mathbf{k})\, dt$

65. $\int_{0}^{2} te^t(\mathbf{i} + 2\mathbf{j} - \mathbf{k})\, dt$

66. $\int_{0}^{\pi/4} (\sec^2 t\,\mathbf{i} - 2 \cos t\,\mathbf{j} - \mathbf{k})\, dt$

Further Explorations

67. Explain why or why not Determine whether the following statements are true and give an explanation or counterexample.

a. The vectors $\mathbf{r}(t)$ and $\mathbf{r}'(t)$ are parallel for all values of t in the domain.

b. The curve described by the function $\mathbf{r}(t) = \langle t, t^2 - 2t, \cos \pi t \rangle$ is smooth, for $-\infty < t < \infty$.

c. If f, g, and h are odd integrable functions and a is a real number, then

$$\int_{-a}^{a} (f(t)\,\mathbf{i} + g(t)\,\mathbf{j} + h(t)\,\mathbf{k})\,dt = \mathbf{0}.$$

68–71. Tangent lines *Suppose the vector-valued function $\mathbf{r}(t) = \langle f(t), g(t), h(t) \rangle$ is smooth on an interval containing the point t_0. The line tangent to $\mathbf{r}(t)$ at $t = t_0$ is the line parallel to the tangent vector $\mathbf{r}'(t_0)$ that passes through $(f(t_0), g(t_0), h(t_0))$. For each of the following functions, find an equation of the line tangent to the curve at $t = t_0$. Choose an orientation for the line that is the same as the direction of $\mathbf{r}'$.*

68. $\mathbf{r}(t) = \langle e^t, e^{2t}, e^{3t} \rangle$; $t_0 = 0$

69. $\mathbf{r}(t) = \langle 2 + \cos t, 3 + \sin 2t, t \rangle$; $t_0 = \pi/2$

70. $\mathbf{r}(t) = \langle \sqrt{2t+1}, \sin \pi t, 4 \rangle$; $t_0 = 4$

71. $\mathbf{r}(t) = \langle 3t - 1, 7t + 2, t^2 \rangle$; $t_0 = 1$

72–77. Derivative rules *Let $\mathbf{u}(t) = \langle 1, t, t^2 \rangle$, $\mathbf{v}(t) = \langle t^2, -2t, 1 \rangle$, and $g(t) = 2\sqrt{t}$. Compute the derivatives of the following functions.*

72. $\mathbf{u}(t^3)$ **73.** $\mathbf{v}(e^t)$ **74.** $g(t)\mathbf{v}(t)$

75. $\mathbf{v}(g(t))$ **76.** $\mathbf{u}(t) \cdot \mathbf{v}(t)$ **77.** $\mathbf{u}(t) \times \mathbf{v}(t)$

78–83. Relationship between r and r′

78. Consider the circle $\mathbf{r}(t) = \langle a \cos t, a \sin t \rangle$, for $0 \le t \le 2\pi$, where a is a positive real number. Compute $\mathbf{r}'$ and show that it is orthogonal to $\mathbf{r}$ for all t.

79. Consider the parabola $\mathbf{r}(t) = \langle at^2 + 1, t \rangle$, for $-\infty < t < \infty$, where a is a positive real number. Find all points on the parabola at which $\mathbf{r}$ and $\mathbf{r}'$ are orthogonal.

80. Consider the curve $\mathbf{r}(t) = \langle \sqrt{t}, 1, t \rangle$, for $t > 0$. Find all points on the curve at which $\mathbf{r}$ and $\mathbf{r}'$ are orthogonal.

81. Consider the helix $\mathbf{r}(t) = \langle \cos t, \sin t, t \rangle$, for $-\infty < t < \infty$. Find all points on the helix at which $\mathbf{r}$ and $\mathbf{r}'$ are orthogonal.

82. Consider the ellipse $\mathbf{r}(t) = \langle 2 \cos t, 8 \sin t, 0 \rangle$, for $0 \le t \le 2\pi$. Find all points on the ellipse at which $\mathbf{r}$ and $\mathbf{r}'$ are orthogonal.

83. Give two families of curves in $\mathbb{R}^3$ for which $\mathbf{r}$ and $\mathbf{r}'$ are parallel for all t in the domain.

84. Derivative rules Suppose $\mathbf{u}$ and $\mathbf{v}$ are differentiable functions at $t = 0$ with $\mathbf{u}(0) = \langle 0, 1, 1 \rangle$, $\mathbf{u}'(0) = \langle 0, 7, 1 \rangle$, $\mathbf{v}(0) = \langle 0, 1, 1 \rangle$, and $\mathbf{v}'(0) = \langle 1, 1, 2 \rangle$. Evaluate the following expressions.

a. $\left.\dfrac{d}{dt}(\mathbf{u} \cdot \mathbf{v})\right|_{t=0}$ **b.** $\left.\dfrac{d}{dt}(\mathbf{u} \times \mathbf{v})\right|_{t=0}$

c. $\left.\dfrac{d}{dt}(\cos t\,\mathbf{u}(t))\right|_{t=0}$

Additional Exercises

85. Vectors r and r′ for lines

a. If $\mathbf{r}(t) = \langle at, bt, ct \rangle$ with $\langle a, b, c \rangle \ne \langle 0, 0, 0 \rangle$, show that the angle between $\mathbf{r}$ and $\mathbf{r}'$ is constant for all $t > 0$.

b. If $\mathbf{r}(t) = \langle x_0 + at, y_0 + bt, z_0 + ct \rangle$, where x_0, y_0, and z_0 are not all zero, show that the angle between $\mathbf{r}$ and $\mathbf{r}'$ varies with t.

c. Explain the results of parts (a) and (b) geometrically.

86. Proof of Sum Rule By expressing $\mathbf{u}$ and $\mathbf{v}$ in terms of their components, prove that

$$\frac{d}{dt}(\mathbf{u}(t) + \mathbf{v}(t)) = \mathbf{u}'(t) + \mathbf{v}'(t).$$

87. Proof of Product Rule By expressing $\mathbf{u}$ in terms of its components, prove that

$$\frac{d}{dt}(f(t)\mathbf{u}(t)) = f'(t)\mathbf{u}(t) + f(t)\mathbf{u}'(t).$$

88. Proof of Cross Product Rule Prove that

$$\frac{d}{dt}(\mathbf{u}(t) \times \mathbf{v}(t)) = \mathbf{u}'(t) \times \mathbf{v}(t) + \mathbf{u}(t) \times \mathbf{v}'(t).$$

There are two ways to proceed: Either express $\mathbf{u}$ and $\mathbf{v}$ in terms of their three components or use the definition of the derivative.

T **89. Cusps and noncusps**

a. Graph the curve $\mathbf{r}(t) = \langle t^3, t^3 \rangle$. Show that $\mathbf{r}'(0) = \mathbf{0}$ and the curve does not have a cusp at $t = 0$. Explain.

b. Graph the curve $\mathbf{r}(t) = \langle t^3, t^2 \rangle$. Show that $\mathbf{r}'(0) = \mathbf{0}$ and the curve has a cusp at $t = 0$. Explain.

c. The functions $\mathbf{r}(t) = \langle t, t^2 \rangle$ and $\mathbf{p}(t) = \langle t^2, t^4 \rangle$ both satisfy $y = x^2$. Explain how the curves they parameterize are different.

d. Consider the curve $\mathbf{r}(t) = \langle t^m, t^n \rangle$, where $m > 1$ and $n > 1$ are integers with no common factors. Is it true that the curve has a cusp at $t = 0$ if one (not both) of m and n is even? Explain.

90. Motion on a sphere Prove that $\mathbf{r}$ describes a curve that lies on the surface of a sphere centered at the origin ($x^2 + y^2 + z^2 = a^2$ with $a \ge 0$) if and only if $\mathbf{r}$ and $\mathbf{r}'$ are orthogonal at all points of the curve.

QUICK CHECK ANSWERS

1. $\mathbf{r}(t)$ describes a line, so its tangent vector $\mathbf{r}'(t) = \langle 1, 1, 1 \rangle$ has constant direction and magnitude. **2.** Both $\mathbf{r}'$ and $|\mathbf{r}'|$ have units of m/s. In forming $\mathbf{r}'/|\mathbf{r}'|$, the units cancel and $\mathbf{T}(t)$ is without units. **3.** $\dfrac{d}{dt}(\mathbf{u}(t) \cdot \mathbf{v}(t)) = \langle 1, 1, 1 \rangle \cdot \langle 1, 1, 1 \rangle + \langle t, t, t \rangle \cdot \langle 0, 0, 0 \rangle = 3$. $\dfrac{d}{dt}(\langle t, t, t \rangle \cdot \langle 1, 1, 1 \rangle) = \dfrac{d}{dt}(3t) = 3$. **4.** $\langle t, t^2, t^3 \rangle + \mathbf{C}$, where $\mathbf{C} = \langle a, b, c \rangle$, and a, b, and c are real numbers ◄

11.7 Motion in Space

It is a remarkable fact that given the forces acting on an object and its initial position and velocity, the motion of the object in three-dimensional space can be modeled for all future times. To be sure, the accuracy of the results depends on how well the various forces on the object are described. For example, it may be more difficult to predict the trajectory of a spinning soccer ball than the path of a space station orbiting Earth. Nevertheless, as shown in this section, by combining Newton's Second Law of Motion with everything we have learned about vectors, it is possible to solve a variety of moving body problems.

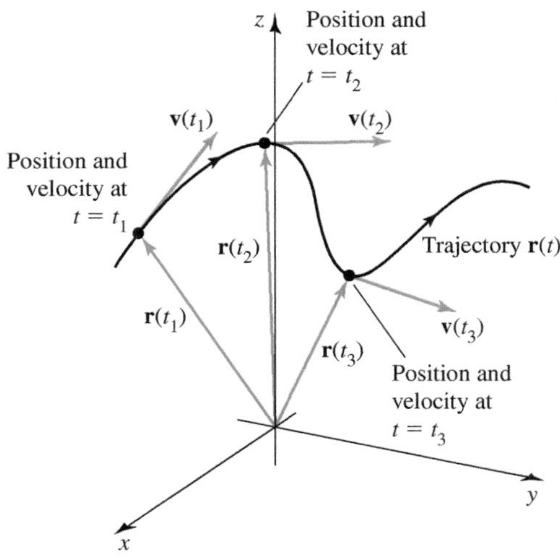

Figure 11.81

Position, Velocity, Speed, Acceleration

Until now, we have studied objects that move in one dimension (along a line). The next step is to consider the motion of objects in two dimensions (in a plane) and three dimensions (in space). We work in a three-dimensional coordinate system and let the vector-valued function $\mathbf{r}(t) = \langle x(t), y(t), z(t) \rangle$ describe the *position* of a moving object at times $t \geq 0$. The curve described by $\mathbf{r}$ is the *path* or *trajectory* of the object (Figure 11.81). Just as with one-dimensional motion, the rate of change of the position function with respect to time is the *instantaneous velocity* of the object—a vector with three components corresponding to the velocity in the x-, y-, and z-directions:

$$\mathbf{v}(t) = \mathbf{r}'(t) = \langle x'(t), y'(t), z'(t) \rangle.$$

This expression should look familiar. The velocity vectors of a moving object are simply tangent vectors; that is, at any point, the velocity vector is tangent to the trajectory (Figure 11.81).

As with one-dimensional motion, the *speed* of an object moving in three dimensions is the magnitude of its velocity vector:

$$|\mathbf{v}(t)| = |\langle x'(t), y'(t), z'(t) \rangle| = \sqrt{x'(t)^2 + y'(t)^2 + z'(t)^2}.$$

The speed is a nonnegative scalar-valued function.

Finally, the *acceleration* of a moving object is the rate of change of the velocity:

$$\mathbf{a}(t) = \mathbf{v}'(t) = \mathbf{r}''(t).$$

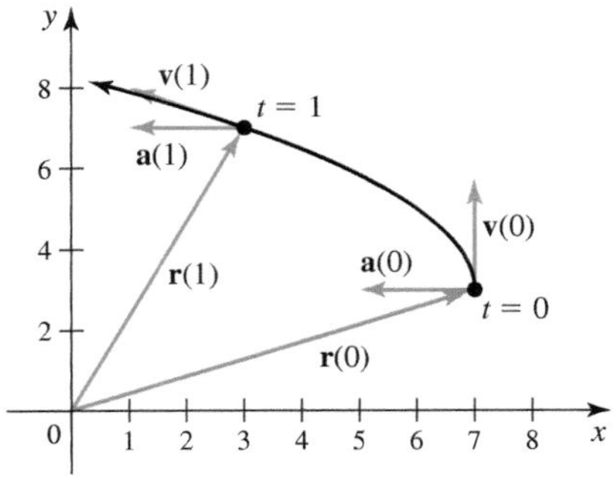

Figure 11.82

While the position vector gives the path of a moving object and the velocity vector is always tangent to the path, the acceleration vector is more difficult to visualize. Figure 11.82 shows one particular instance of two-dimensional motion. The trajectory is a segment of a parabola and is traced out by the position vectors (shown at $t = 0$ and $t = 1$). As expected, the velocity vectors are tangent to the trajectory. In this case, the acceleration is $\mathbf{a} = \langle -2, 0 \rangle$; it is constant in magnitude and direction for all times. The relationships among $\mathbf{r}$, $\mathbf{v}$, and $\mathbf{a}$ are explored in the coming examples.

➤ In the case of two-dimensional motion, $\mathbf{r}(t) = \langle x(t), y(t) \rangle$, $\mathbf{v}(t) = \mathbf{r}'(t)$, and $\mathbf{a}(t) = \mathbf{r}''(t)$.

DEFINITION Position, Velocity, Speed, Acceleration

Let the **position** of an object moving in three-dimensional space be given by $\mathbf{r}(t) = \langle x(t), y(t), z(t) \rangle$, for $t \geq 0$. The **velocity** of the object is

$$\mathbf{v}(t) = \mathbf{r}'(t) = \langle x'(t), y'(t), z'(t) \rangle.$$

The **speed** of the object is the scalar function

$$|\mathbf{v}(t)| = \sqrt{x'(t)^2 + y'(t)^2 + z'(t)^2}.$$

The **acceleration** of the object is $\mathbf{a}(t) = \mathbf{v}'(t) = \mathbf{r}''(t)$.

QUICK CHECK 1 Given $\mathbf{r}(t) = \langle t, t^2, t^3 \rangle$, find $\mathbf{v}(t)$ and $\mathbf{a}(t)$. ◄

EXAMPLE 1 **Velocity and acceleration for circular motion** Consider the two-dimensional motion given by the position vector

$$\mathbf{r}(t) = \langle x(t), y(t) \rangle = \langle 3\cos t, 3\sin t \rangle, \quad \text{for } 0 \le t \le 2\pi.$$

a. Sketch the trajectory of the object.

b. Find the velocity and speed of the object.

c. Find the acceleration of the object.

d. Sketch the position, velocity, and acceleration vectors, for $t = 0, \pi/2, \pi$, and $3\pi/2$.

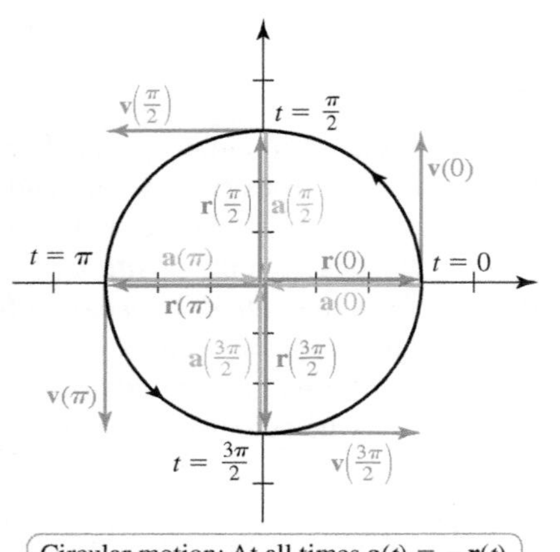

Circular motion: At all times $\mathbf{a}(t) = -\mathbf{r}(t)$ and $\mathbf{v}(t)$ is orthogonal to $\mathbf{r}(t)$ and $\mathbf{a}(t)$.

Figure 11.83

SOLUTION

a. Notice that

$$x(t)^2 + y(t)^2 = 9(\cos^2 t + \sin^2 t) = 9,$$

which is an equation of a circle centered at the origin with radius 3. The object moves on this circle in the counterclockwise direction (Figure 11.83).

b.

$$\begin{aligned} \mathbf{v}(t) &= \langle x'(t), y'(t) \rangle = \langle -3\sin t, 3\cos t \rangle && \text{Velocity vector} \\ |\mathbf{v}(t)| &= \sqrt{x'(t)^2 + y'(t)^2} && \text{Definition of speed} \\ &= \sqrt{(-3\sin t)^2 + (3\cos t)^2} \\ &= \sqrt{9\underbrace{(\sin^2 t + \cos^2 t)}_{1}} = 3 \end{aligned}$$

The velocity vector has a constant magnitude and a continuously changing direction.

c. Differentiating the velocity, we find that $\mathbf{a}(t) = \mathbf{v}'(t) = \langle -3\cos t, -3\sin t \rangle = -\mathbf{r}(t)$. In this case, the acceleration vector is the negative of the position vector at all times.

d. The relationships among $\mathbf{r}$, $\mathbf{v}$, and $\mathbf{a}$ at four points in time are shown in Figure 11.83. The velocity vector is always tangent to the trajectory and has length 3, while the acceleration vector and position vector each have length 3 and point in opposite directions. At all times, $\mathbf{v}$ is orthogonal to $\mathbf{r}$ and $\mathbf{a}$.

Related Exercises 7–18 ◀

EXAMPLE 2 **Comparing trajectories** Consider the trajectories described by the position functions

$$\mathbf{r}(t) = \left\langle t, t^2 - 4, \frac{t^3}{4} - 8 \right\rangle, \quad \text{for } t \ge 0, \text{ and}$$

$$\mathbf{R}(t) = \left\langle t^2, t^4 - 4, \frac{t^6}{4} - 8 \right\rangle, \quad \text{for } t \ge 0,$$

where t is measured in the same time units for both functions.

a. Graph and compare the trajectories using a graphing utility.

b. Find the velocity vectors associated with the position functions.

SOLUTION

a. Plotting the position functions at selected values of t results in the trajectories shown in Figure 11.84. Because $\mathbf{r}(0) = \mathbf{R}(0) = \langle 0, -4, -8 \rangle$, both curves have the same initial point. For $t \ge 0$, the two curves consist of the same points, but they are traced out differently. For example, both curves pass through the point $(4, 12, 8)$, but that point corresponds to $\mathbf{r}(4)$ on the first curve and $\mathbf{R}(2)$ on the second curve. In general, $\mathbf{r}(t^2) = \mathbf{R}(t)$, for $t \ge 0$.

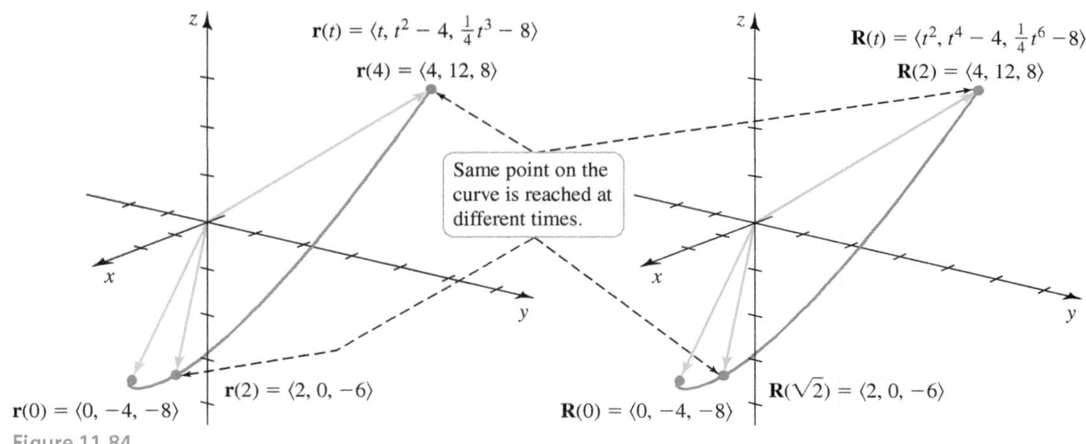

Figure 11.84

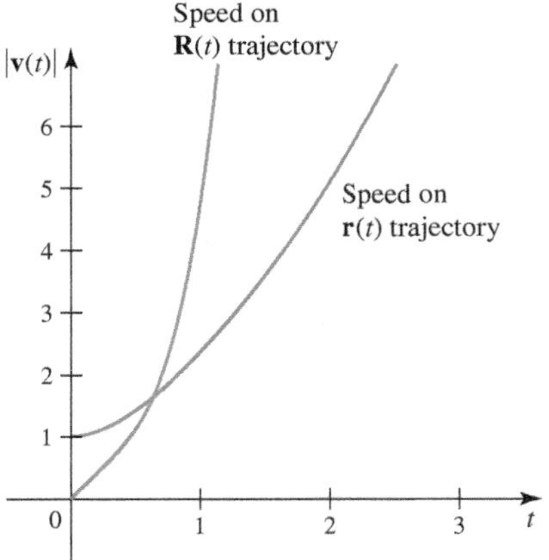

Figure 11.85

b. The velocity vectors are

$$\mathbf{r}'(t) = \left\langle 1, 2t, \frac{3t^2}{4} \right\rangle \quad \text{and} \quad \mathbf{R}'(t) = \left\langle 2t, 4t^3, \frac{3}{2}t^5 \right\rangle.$$

The difference in the motion on the two curves is revealed by the graphs of the speeds associated with the trajectories (Figure 11.85). The object on the first trajectory reaches the point $(4, 12, 8)$ at $t = 4$, where its speed is $|\mathbf{r}'(4)| = |\langle 1, 8, 12 \rangle| \approx 14.5$. The object on the second trajectory reaches the same point $(4, 12, 8)$ at $t = 2$, where its speed is $|\mathbf{R}'(2)| = |\langle 4, 32, 48 \rangle| \approx 57.8$.

Related Exercises 19–24 ◀

QUICK CHECK 2 Find the functions that give the speed of the two objects in Example 2, for $t \geq 0$ (corresponding to the graphs in Figure 11.85). ◀

Straight-Line and Circular Motion

Two types of motion in space arise frequently and deserve to be singled out. First consider a trajectory described by the vector function

$$\mathbf{r}(t) = \langle x_0 + at, y_0 + bt, z_0 + ct \rangle, \quad \text{for } t \geq 0,$$

where $x_0, y_0, z_0, a, b,$ and c are constants. This function describes a straight-line trajectory with an initial point $\langle x_0, y_0, z_0 \rangle$ and a direction given by the vector $\langle a, b, c \rangle$ (Section 11.5). The velocity on this trajectory is the constant $\mathbf{v}(t) = \mathbf{r}'(t) = \langle a, b, c \rangle$ in the direction of the trajectory, and the acceleration is $\mathbf{a} = \langle 0, 0, 0 \rangle$. The motion associated with this function is **uniform** (constant velocity) **straight-line motion**.

➤ See Exercise 61 for a discussion of nonuniform straight-line motion.

A different situation is **circular motion** (Example 1). Consider the two-dimensional circular path

$$\mathbf{r}(t) = \langle A \cos t, A \sin t \rangle, \quad \text{for } 0 \leq t \leq 2\pi,$$

where A is a nonzero constant (Figure 11.86). The velocity and acceleration vectors are

$$\mathbf{v}(t) = \langle -A \sin t, A \cos t \rangle \quad \text{and}$$
$$\mathbf{a}(t) = \langle -A \cos t, -A \sin t \rangle = -\mathbf{r}(t).$$

Notice that $\mathbf{r}$ and $\mathbf{a}$ are parallel, but point in opposite directions. Furthermore, $\mathbf{r} \cdot \mathbf{v} = \mathbf{a} \cdot \mathbf{v} = 0$; therefore, the position and acceleration vectors are both orthogonal to the velocity vectors at any given point (Figure 11.86). Finally, $\mathbf{r}$, $\mathbf{v}$, and $\mathbf{a}$ have constant magnitude A and variable directions. The conclusion that $\mathbf{r} \cdot \mathbf{v} = 0$ applies to any motion for which $|\mathbf{r}|$ is constant; that is, motion on a circle or a sphere (Figure 11.87).

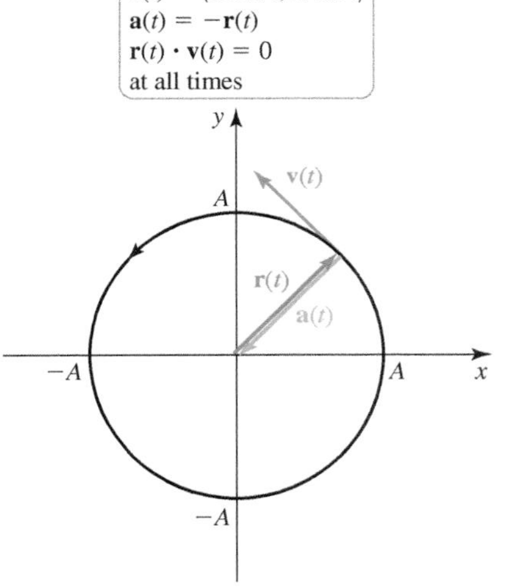

Figure 11.86

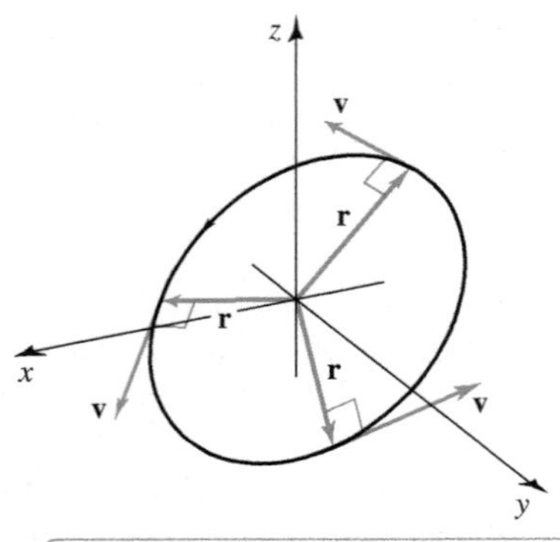

Figure 11.87

> **THEOREM 11.8 Motion with Constant $|\mathbf{r}|$**
> Let $\mathbf{r}$ describe a path on which $|\mathbf{r}|$ is constant (motion on a circle or sphere centered at the origin). Then $\mathbf{r} \cdot \mathbf{v} = 0$, which means the position vector and the velocity vector are orthogonal at all times for which the functions are defined.

Proof: If $\mathbf{r}$ has constant magnitude, then $|\mathbf{r}(t)|^2 = \mathbf{r}(t) \cdot \mathbf{r}(t) = c$ for some constant c. Differentiating the equation $\mathbf{r}(t) \cdot \mathbf{r}(t) = c$, we have

$$
\begin{aligned}
0 &= \frac{d}{dt}(\mathbf{r}(t) \cdot \mathbf{r}(t)) && \text{Differentiate both sides of } |\mathbf{r}(t)|^2 = c \\
&= \mathbf{r}'(t) \cdot \mathbf{r}(t) + \mathbf{r}(t) \cdot \mathbf{r}'(t) && \text{Derivative of dot product (Theorem 11.7)} \\
&= 2\mathbf{r}'(t) \cdot \mathbf{r}(t) && \text{Simplify.} \\
&= 2\mathbf{v}(t) \cdot \mathbf{r}(t). && \mathbf{r}'(t) = \mathbf{v}(t)
\end{aligned}
$$

Because $\mathbf{r}(t) \cdot \mathbf{v}(t) = 0$ for all t, it follows that $\mathbf{r}$ and $\mathbf{v}$ are orthogonal for all t. ◄

EXAMPLE 3 Path on a sphere An object moves on a trajectory described by

$$\mathbf{r}(t) = \langle x(t), y(t), z(t) \rangle = \langle 3 \cos t, 5 \sin t, 4 \cos t \rangle, \quad \text{for } 0 \le t \le 2\pi.$$

a. Show that the object moves on a sphere and find the radius of the sphere.

b. Find the velocity and speed of the object.

➤ For generalizations of this example and explorations of trajectories that lie on spheres and ellipses, see Exercises 79, 82, and 83.

SOLUTION

a.
$$
\begin{aligned}
|\mathbf{r}(t)|^2 &= x(t)^2 + y(t)^2 + z(t)^2 && \text{Square of the distance from the origin} \\
&= (3 \cos t)^2 + (5 \sin t)^2 + (4 \cos t)^2 && \text{Substitute.} \\
&= 25 \cos^2 t + 25 \sin^2 t && \text{Simplify.} \\
&= 25\underbrace{(\cos^2 t + \sin^2 t)}_{1} = 25 && \text{Factor.}
\end{aligned}
$$

Therefore, $|\mathbf{r}(t)| = 5$, for $0 \le t \le 2\pi$, and the trajectory lies on a sphere of radius 5 centered at the origin (Figure 11.88).

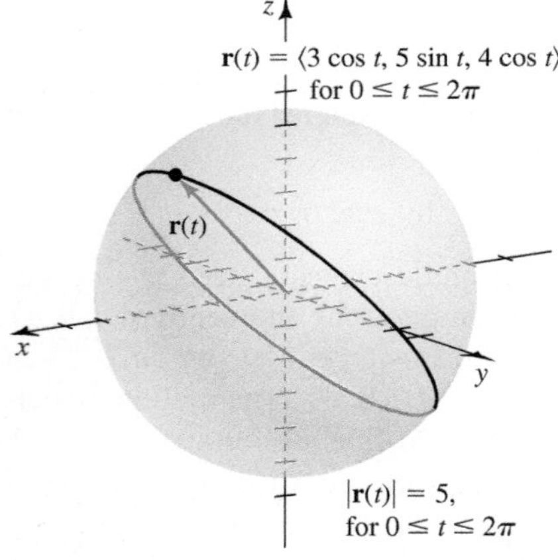

Figure 11.88

b.
$$
\begin{aligned}
\mathbf{v}(t) &= \mathbf{r}'(t) = \langle -3 \sin t, 5 \cos t, -4 \sin t \rangle && \text{Velocity vector} \\
|\mathbf{v}(t)| &= \sqrt{\mathbf{v}(t) \cdot \mathbf{v}(t)} && \text{Speed of the object} \\
&= \sqrt{9 \sin^2 t + 25 \cos^2 t + 16 \sin^2 t} && \text{Evaluate the dot product.} \\
&= \sqrt{25\underbrace{(\sin^2 t + \cos^2 t)}_{1}} && \text{Simplify.} \\
&= 5 && \text{Simplify.}
\end{aligned}
$$

The speed of the object is always 5. You should verify that $\mathbf{r}(t) \cdot \mathbf{v}(t) = 0$, for all t, implying that $\mathbf{r}$ and $\mathbf{v}$ are always orthogonal.

Related Exercises 25–30 ◄

QUICK CHECK 3 Verify that $\mathbf{r}(t) \cdot \mathbf{v}(t) = 0$ in Example 3. ◄

Two-Dimensional Motion in a Gravitational Field

Newton's Second Law of Motion, which is used to model the motion of most objects, states that

$$\underbrace{\text{mass}}_{m} \cdot \underbrace{\text{acceleration}}_{\mathbf{a}(t)\,=\,\mathbf{r}''(t)} = \underbrace{\text{sum of all forces.}}_{\sum \mathbf{F}_k}$$

The governing law says something about the *acceleration* of an object, and in order to describe the motion fully, we must find the velocity and position from the acceleration.

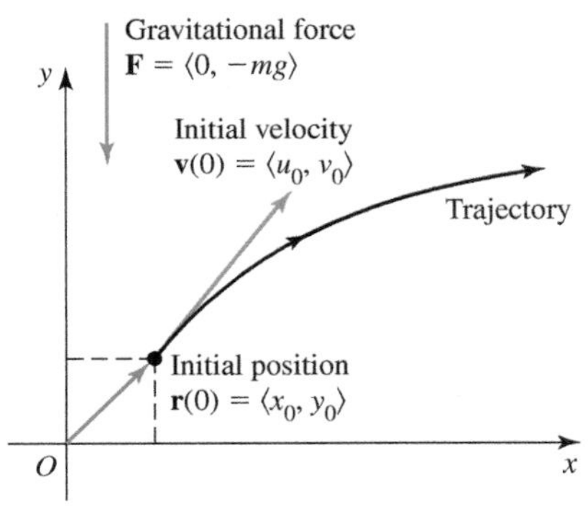

Figure 11.89

Finding Velocity and Position from Acceleration We begin with the case of two-dimensional projectile motion in which the only force acting on the object is the gravitational force; for the moment, air resistance and other possible external forces are neglected.

A convenient coordinate system uses a y-axis that points vertically upward and an x-axis that points in the direction of horizontal motion. The gravitational force is in the negative y-direction and is given by $\mathbf{F} = \langle 0, -mg \rangle$, where m is the mass of the object and $g \approx 9.8 \text{ m/s}^2 \approx 32 \text{ ft/s}^2$ is the acceleration due to gravity (Figure 11.89).

With these observations, Newton's Second Law takes the form

$$m\mathbf{a}(t) = \mathbf{F} = \langle 0, -mg \rangle.$$

Significantly, the mass of the object cancels, leaving the vector equation

$$\mathbf{a}(t) = \langle 0, -g \rangle. \tag{1}$$

In order to find the velocity $\mathbf{v}(t) = \langle x'(t), y'(t) \rangle$ and the position $\mathbf{r}(t) = \langle x(t), y(t) \rangle$ from this equation, we must be given the following **initial conditions**:

$$\text{Initial velocity at } t = 0\text{: } \mathbf{v}(0) = \langle u_0, v_0 \rangle \text{ and}$$
$$\text{Initial position at } t = 0\text{: } \mathbf{r}(0) = \langle x_0, y_0 \rangle.$$

We proceed in two steps.

➤ Recall that an antiderivative of 0 is a constant C and an antiderivative of $-g$ is $-gt + C$.

1. **Solve for the velocity** The velocity is an antiderivative of the acceleration in equation (1). Integrating the acceleration, we have

$$\mathbf{v}(t) = \int \mathbf{a}(t)\, dt = \int \langle 0, -g \rangle\, dt = \langle 0, -gt \rangle + \mathbf{C},$$

➤ You have a choice. You may do these calculations in vector notation as we have done here, or you may work with individual components.

where $\mathbf{C}$ is an arbitrary constant vector. The arbitrary constant is determined by substituting $t = 0$ and using the initial condition $\mathbf{v}(0) = \langle u_0, v_0 \rangle$. We find that $\mathbf{v}(0) = \langle 0, 0 \rangle + \mathbf{C} = \langle u_0, v_0 \rangle$, or $\mathbf{C} = \langle u_0, v_0 \rangle$. Therefore, the velocity is

$$\mathbf{v}(t) = \langle 0, -gt \rangle + \langle u_0, v_0 \rangle = \langle u_0, -gt + v_0 \rangle. \tag{2}$$

Notice that the horizontal component of velocity is simply the initial horizontal velocity u_0 for all time. The vertical component of velocity decreases linearly from its initial value of v_0.

2. **Solve for the position** The position is an antiderivative of the velocity given by equation (2):

$$\mathbf{r}(t) = \int \mathbf{v}(t)\, dt = \int \langle u_0, -gt + v_0 \rangle\, dt = \left\langle u_0 t, -\frac{1}{2}gt^2 + v_0 t \right\rangle + \mathbf{C},$$

where **C** is an arbitrary constant vector. Substituting $t = 0$, we have $\mathbf{r}(0) = \langle 0, 0 \rangle + \mathbf{C} = \langle x_0, y_0 \rangle$, which implies that $\mathbf{C} = \langle x_0, y_0 \rangle$. Therefore, the position of the object, for $t \geq 0$, is

$$\mathbf{r}(t) = \left\langle u_0 t, -\frac{1}{2}gt^2 + v_0 t \right\rangle + \langle x_0, y_0 \rangle = \Big\langle \underbrace{u_0 t + x_0}_{x(t)}, \underbrace{-\frac{1}{2}gt^2 + v_0 t + y_0}_{y(t)} \Big\rangle.$$

SUMMARY Two-Dimensional Motion in a Gravitational Field

Consider an object moving in a plane with a horizontal x-axis and a vertical y-axis, subject only to the force of gravity. Given the initial velocity $\mathbf{v}(0) = \langle u_0, v_0 \rangle$ and the initial position $\mathbf{r}(0) = \langle x_0, y_0 \rangle$, the velocity of the object, for $t \geq 0$, is

$$\mathbf{v}(t) = \langle x'(t), y'(t) \rangle = \langle u_0, -gt + v_0 \rangle$$

and the position is

$$\mathbf{r}(t) = \langle x(t), y(t) \rangle = \left\langle u_0 t + x_0, -\frac{1}{2}gt^2 + v_0 t + y_0 \right\rangle.$$

EXAMPLE 4 Flight of a baseball A baseball is hit from 3 ft above home plate with an initial velocity in ft/s of $\mathbf{v}(0) = \langle u_0, v_0 \rangle = \langle 80, 80 \rangle$. Neglect all forces other than gravity.

a. Find the position and velocity of the ball between the time it is hit and the time it first hits the ground.

b. Show that the trajectory of the ball is a segment of a parabola.

c. Assuming a flat playing field, how far does the ball travel horizontally? Plot the trajectory of the ball.

d. What is the maximum height of the ball?

e. Does the ball clear a 20-ft fence that is 380 ft from home plate (directly under the path of the ball)?

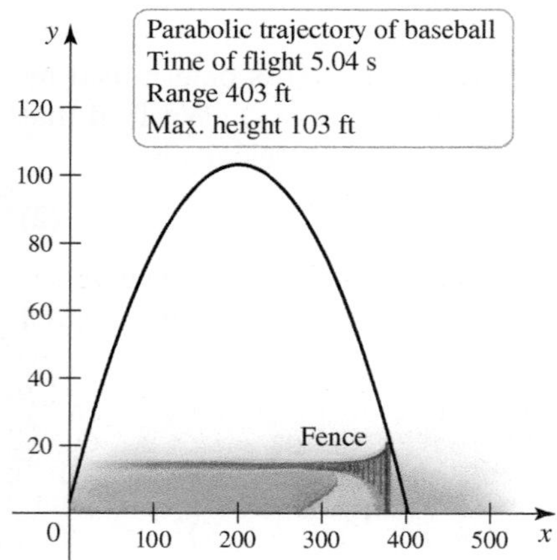

Figure 11.90

➤ The equation in part (c) can be solved using the quadratic formula or a root-finder on a calculator.

SOLUTION Assume the origin is located at home plate. Because distances are measured in feet, we use $g = 32\ \text{ft/s}^2$.

a. Substituting $x_0 = 0$ and $y_0 = 3$ into the equation for **r**, the position of the ball is

$$\mathbf{r}(t) = \langle x(t), y(t) \rangle = \langle 80t, -16t^2 + 80t + 3 \rangle, \quad \text{for } t \geq 0. \tag{3}$$

We then compute $\mathbf{v}(t) = \mathbf{r}'(t) = \langle 80, -32t + 80 \rangle$.

b. Equation (3) says that the horizontal position is $x = 80t$ and the vertical position is $y = -16t^2 + 80t + 3$. Substituting $t = x/80$ into the equation for y gives

$$y = -16\left(\frac{x}{80}\right)^2 + x + 3 = -\frac{x^2}{400} + x + 3,$$

which is an equation of a parabola.

c. The ball lands on the ground at the value of $t > 0$ at which $y = 0$. Solving $y(t) = -16t^2 + 80t + 3 = 0$, we find that $t \approx -0.04$ and $t \approx 5.04$ s. The first root is not relevant for the problem at hand, so we conclude that the ball lands when $t \approx 5.04$ s. The horizontal distance traveled by the ball is $x(5.04) \approx 403$ ft. The path of the ball in the xy-coordinate system on the time interval $[0, 5.04]$ is shown in Figure 11.90.

d. The ball reaches its maximum height at the time its vertical velocity is zero. Solving $y'(t) = -32t + 80 = 0$, we find that $t = 2.5$ s. The height at that time is $y(2.5) = 103$ ft.

e. The ball reaches a horizontal distance of 380 ft (the distance to the fence) when $x(t) = 80t = 380$. Solving for t, we find that $t = 4.75$ s. The height of the ball at that time is $y(4.75) = 22$ ft. So, indeed, the ball clears a 20-ft fence.

Related Exercises 31–36 ◄

QUICK CHECK 4 Write the functions $x(t)$ and $y(t)$ in Example 4 in the case that $x_0 = 0$, $y_0 = 2$, $u_0 = 100$, and $v_0 = 60$. ◄

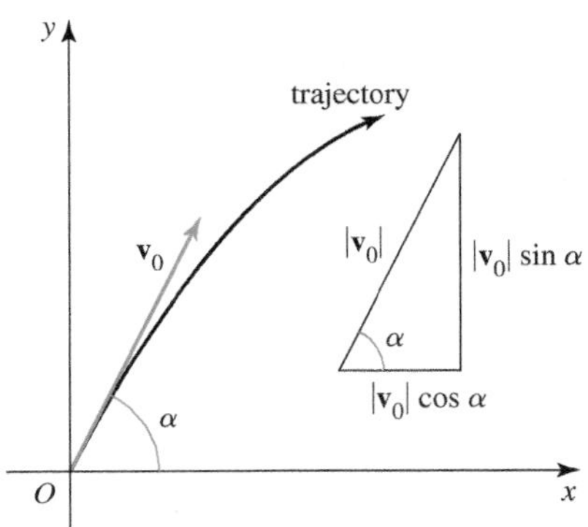

Figure 11.91

Range, Time of Flight, Maximum Height Having solved one specific motion problem, we can make some general observations about two-dimensional projectile motion in a gravitational field. Assume that the motion of an object begins at the origin; that is, $x_0 = y_0 = 0$. Assume also that the object is launched at an angle of α $(0 \le \alpha \le \pi/2)$ above the horizontal with an initial speed $|\mathbf{v}_0|$ (Figure 11.91). This means that the initial velocity is

$$\langle u_0, v_0 \rangle = \langle |\mathbf{v}_0| \cos\alpha, |\mathbf{v}_0| \sin\alpha \rangle.$$

Substituting these values into the general expressions for the velocity and position, we find that the velocity of the object is

$$\mathbf{v}(t) = \langle u_0, -gt + v_0 \rangle = \langle |\mathbf{v}_0| \cos\alpha, -gt + |\mathbf{v}_0| \sin\alpha \rangle.$$

The position of the object (with $x_0 = y_0 = 0$) is

$$\mathbf{r}(t) = \langle x(t), y(t) \rangle = \langle (|\mathbf{v}_0| \cos\alpha)t, -gt^2/2 + (|\mathbf{v}_0| \sin\alpha)t \rangle.$$

Notice that the motion is determined entirely by the parameters $|\mathbf{v}_0|$ and α. Several general conclusions now follow.

➤ The other root of the equation $y(t) = 0$ is $t = 0$, the time the object leaves the ground.

1. Assuming the object is launched from the origin over horizontal ground, it returns to the ground when $y(t) = -gt^2/2 + (|\mathbf{v}_0| \sin\alpha)t = 0$. Solving for t, the **time of flight** is $T = 2|\mathbf{v}_0| \sin\alpha/g$.
2. The **range** of the object, which is the horizontal distance it travels, is the x-coordinate of the trajectory when $t = T$:

$$\begin{aligned} x(T) &= (|\mathbf{v}_0| \cos\alpha)T \\ &= (|\mathbf{v}_0| \cos\alpha)\frac{2|\mathbf{v}_0| \sin\alpha}{g} && \text{Substitute for } T. \\ &= \frac{2|\mathbf{v}_0|^2 \sin\alpha\cos\alpha}{g} && \text{Simplify.} \\ &= \frac{|\mathbf{v}_0|^2 \sin 2\alpha}{g}. && 2\sin\alpha\cos\alpha = \sin 2\alpha \end{aligned}$$

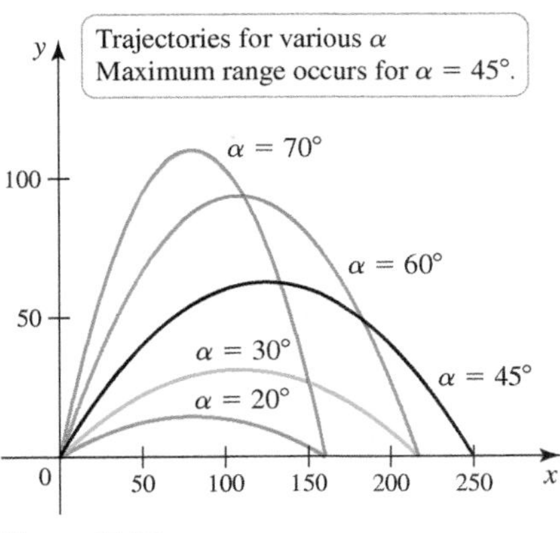

Figure 11.92

Note that on the interval $0 \le \alpha \le \pi/2$, $\sin 2\alpha$ has a maximum value of 1 when $\alpha = \pi/4$, so the maximum range is $|\mathbf{v}_0|^2/g$. In other words, in an ideal world, firing an object from the ground at an angle of $\pi/4$ (45°) maximizes its range. Notice that the ranges obtained with the angles α and $\pi/2 - \alpha$ are equal (Figure 11.92).

QUICK CHECK 5 Show that the range attained with an angle α equals the range attained with the angle $\pi/2 - \alpha$. ◄

3. The maximum height of the object is reached when the vertical velocity is zero, or when $y'(t) = -gt + |\mathbf{v}_0| \sin\alpha = 0$. Solving for t, the maximum height is reached at $t = |\mathbf{v}_0|(\sin\alpha)/g = T/2$, which is half the time of flight. The object spends equal amounts of time ascending and descending. The maximum height is

$$y\left(\frac{T}{2}\right) = \frac{(|\mathbf{v}_0| \sin\alpha)^2}{2g}.$$

4. Finally, by eliminating t from the equations for $x(t)$ and $y(t)$, it can be shown (Exercise 78) that the trajectory of the object is a segment of a parabola.

➤ Use caution with the formulas in the summary box: They are applicable only when the initial position of the object is the origin.

SUMMARY Two-Dimensional Motion

Assume an object traveling over horizontal ground, acted on only by the gravitational force, has an initial position $\langle x_0, y_0 \rangle = \langle 0, 0 \rangle$ and initial velocity $\langle u_0, v_0 \rangle = \langle |\mathbf{v}_0| \cos\alpha, |\mathbf{v}_0| \sin\alpha \rangle$. The trajectory, which is a segment of a parabola, has the following properties.

$$\text{time of flight} = T = \frac{2|\mathbf{v}_0| \sin\alpha}{g}$$

$$\text{range} = \frac{|\mathbf{v}_0|^2 \sin 2\alpha}{g}$$

$$\text{maximum height} = y\left(\frac{T}{2}\right) = \frac{(|\mathbf{v}_0| \sin\alpha)^2}{2g}$$

EXAMPLE 5 Flight of a golf ball A golf ball is driven down a horizontal fairway with an initial speed of 55 m/s at an initial angle of 25° (from a tee with negligible height). Neglect all forces except gravity and assume that the ball's trajectory lies in a plane.

a. How far does the ball travel horizontally and when does it land?

b. What is the maximum height of the ball?

c. At what angles should the ball be hit to reach a green that is 300 m from the tee?

SOLUTION

a. Using the range formula with $\alpha = 25°$ and $|\mathbf{v}_0| = 55$ m/s, the ball travels

$$\frac{|\mathbf{v}_0|^2 \sin 2\alpha}{g} = \frac{(55\text{ m/s})^2 \sin 50°}{9.8\text{ m/s}^2} \approx 236\text{ m}.$$

The time of the flight is

$$T = \frac{2|\mathbf{v}_0| \sin\alpha}{g} = \frac{2(55\text{ m/s}) \sin 25°}{9.8\text{ m/s}^2} \approx 4.7\text{ s}.$$

b. The maximum height of the ball is

$$\frac{(|\mathbf{v}_0| \sin\alpha)^2}{2g} = \frac{((55\text{ m/s})(\sin 25°))^2}{2(9.8\text{ m/s}^2)} \approx 27.6\text{ m}.$$

c. Letting R denote the range and solving the range formula for $\sin 2\alpha$, we find that $\sin 2\alpha = Rg/|\mathbf{v}_0|^2$. For a range of $R = 300$ m and an initial speed of $|\mathbf{v}_0| = 55$ m/s, the required angle satisfies

$$\sin 2\alpha = \frac{Rg}{|\mathbf{v}_0|^2} = \frac{(300\text{ m})(9.8\text{ m/s}^2)}{(55\text{ m/s})^2} \approx 0.972.$$

To travel a horizontal distance of exactly 300 m, the required angles are $\alpha = \frac{1}{2}\sin^{-1} 0.972 \approx 38.2°$ or $51.8°$.

Related Exercises 37–42 ◀

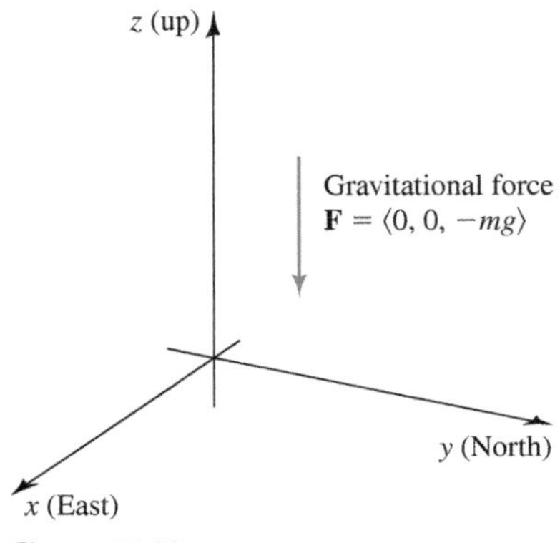

Figure 11.93

Three-Dimensional Motion

To solve three-dimensional motion problems, we adopt a coordinate system in which the x- and y-axes point in two perpendicular horizontal directions (for example, east and north), while the positive z-axis points vertically upward (Figure 11.93). Newton's Second Law now has three components and appears in the form

$$m\mathbf{a}(t) = \langle mx''(t), my''(t), mz''(t) \rangle = \mathbf{F}.$$

If only the gravitational force is present (now in the negative z-direction), then the force vector is $\mathbf{F} = \langle 0, 0, -mg \rangle$; the equation of motion is then $\mathbf{a}(t) = \langle 0, 0, -g \rangle$. Other effects, such as crosswinds, spins, or slices, can be modeled by including other force components.

EXAMPLE 6 **Projectile motion** A small projectile is fired over horizontal ground in an easterly direction with an initial speed of $|\mathbf{v}_0| = 300$ m/s at an angle of $\alpha = 30°$ above the horizontal. A crosswind blows from south to north, producing an acceleration of the projectile of 0.36 m/s^2 to the north.

a. Where does the projectile land? How far does it land from its launch site?

b. In order to correct for the crosswind and make the projectile land due east of the launch site, at what angle from due east must the projectile be fired? Assume the initial speed $|\mathbf{v}_0| = 300$ m/s and the angle of elevation $\alpha = 30°$ are the same as in part (a).

SOLUTION

a. Letting $g = 9.8$ m/s^2, the equations of motion are $\mathbf{a}(t) = \mathbf{v}'(t) = \langle 0, 0.36, -9.8 \rangle$. Proceeding as in the two-dimensional case, the indefinite integral of the acceleration is the velocity function

$$\mathbf{v}(t) = \langle 0, 0.36t, -9.8t \rangle + \mathbf{C},$$

where $\mathbf{C}$ is an arbitrary constant. With an initial speed $|\mathbf{v}_0| = 300$ m/s and an angle of elevation of $\alpha = 30°$ (Figure 11.94a), the initial velocity is

$$\mathbf{v}(0) = \langle 300 \cos 30°, 0, 300 \sin 30° \rangle = \langle 150\sqrt{3}, 0, 150 \rangle.$$

Substituting $t = 0$ and using the initial condition, we find that $\mathbf{C} = \langle 150\sqrt{3}, 0, 150 \rangle$. Therefore, the velocity function is

$$\mathbf{v}(t) = \langle 150\sqrt{3}, 0.36t, -9.8t + 150 \rangle.$$

Integrating the velocity function produces the position function

$$\mathbf{r}(t) = \langle 150\sqrt{3}t, 0.18t^2, -4.9t^2 + 150t \rangle + \mathbf{C}.$$

Using the initial condition $\mathbf{r}(0) = \langle 0, 0, 0 \rangle$, we find that $\mathbf{C} = \langle 0, 0, 0 \rangle$, and the position function is

$$\mathbf{r}(t) = \langle x(t), y(t), z(t) \rangle = \langle 150\sqrt{3}t, 0.18t^2, -4.9t^2 + 150t \rangle.$$

The projectile lands when $z(t) = -4.9t^2 + 150t = 0$. Solving for t, the positive root, which gives the time of flight, is $T = 150/4.9 \approx 30.6$ s. The x- and y-coordinates at that time are

$$x(T) \approx 7953 \text{ m} \quad \text{and} \quad y(T) \approx 169 \text{ m}.$$

Therefore, the projectile lands approximately 7953 m east and 169 m north of the firing site. Because the projectile started at $(0, 0, 0)$, it traveled a horizontal distance of $\sqrt{7953^2 + 169^2} \approx 7955$ m (Figure 11.94a).

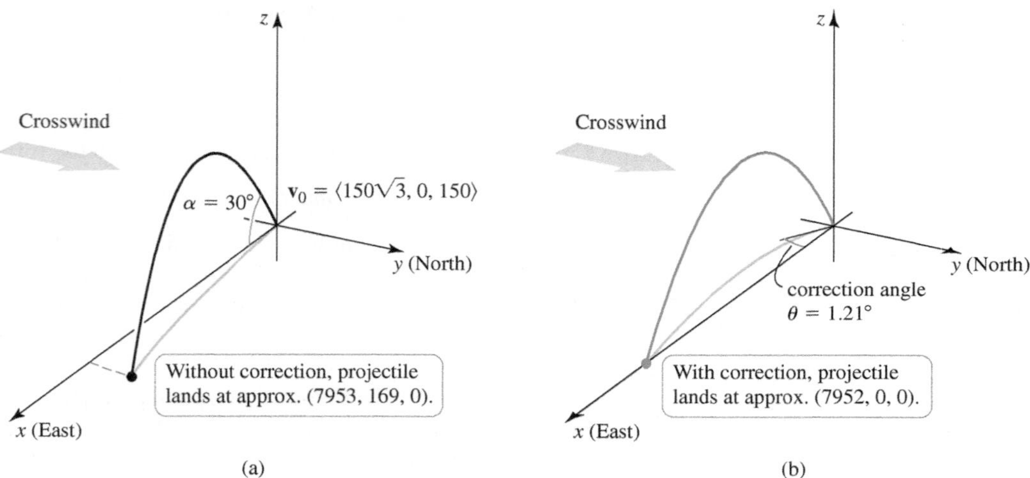

Figure 11.94

b. Keeping the initial speed of the projectile equal to $|\mathbf{v}_0| = 300$ m/s, we decompose the horizontal component of the speed, $150\sqrt{3}$ m/s, into an east component, $u_0 = 150\sqrt{3}\cos\theta$, and a north component, $v_0 = 150\sqrt{3}\sin\theta$, where θ is the angle relative to due east; we must determine the correction angle θ (Figure 11.94b). The x- and y-components of the position are

$$x(t) = (150\sqrt{3}\cos\theta)t \quad \text{and} \quad y(t) = 0.18t^2 + (150\sqrt{3}\sin\theta)t.$$

These changes in the initial velocity affect the x- and y-equations, but not the z-equation. Therefore, the time of flight is still $T = 150/4.9 \approx 30.6$ s. The aim is to choose θ so that the projectile lands on the x-axis (due east from the launch site), which means $y(T) = 0$. Solving

$$y(T) = 0.18T^2 + (150\sqrt{3}\sin\theta)T = 0,$$

with $T = 150/4.9$, we find that $\sin\theta \approx -0.0212$; therefore, $\theta \approx -0.0212$ rad $\approx -1.21°$. In other words, the projectile must be fired at a horizontal angle of 1.21° to the *south* of east to correct for the northerly crosswind (Figure 11.94b). The landing location of the projectile is $x(T) \approx 7952$ m and $y(T) = 0$.

Related Exercises 43–52 ◀

SECTION 11.7 EXERCISES

Review Questions

1. Given the position function $\mathbf{r}$ of a moving object, explain how to find the velocity, speed, and acceleration of the object.
2. What is the relationship between the position and velocity vectors for motion on a circle?
3. Write Newton's Second Law of Motion in vector form.
4. Write Newton's Second Law of Motion for three-dimensional motion with only the gravitational force (acting in the z-direction).
5. Given the acceleration of an object and its initial velocity, how do you find the velocity of the object, for $t \geq 0$?
6. Given the velocity of an object and its initial position, how do you find the position of the object, for $t \geq 0$?

Basic Skills

7–18. Velocity and acceleration from position *Consider the following position functions.*

a. Find the velocity and speed of the object.
b. Find the acceleration of the object.

7. $\mathbf{r}(t) = \langle 3t^2 + 1, 4t^2 + 3 \rangle$, for $t \geq 0$
8. $\mathbf{r}(t) = \left\langle \frac{5}{2}t^2 + 3, 6t^2 + 10 \right\rangle$, for $t \geq 0$
9. $\mathbf{r}(t) = \langle 2 + 2t, 1 - 4t \rangle$, for $t \geq 0$
10. $\mathbf{r}(t) = \langle 1 - t^2, 3 + 2t^3 \rangle$, for $t \geq 0$
11. $\mathbf{r}(t) = \langle 8\sin t, 8\cos t \rangle$, for $0 \leq t \leq 2\pi$
12. $\mathbf{r}(t) = \langle 3\cos t, 4\sin t \rangle$, for $0 \leq t \leq 2\pi$

13. $\mathbf{r}(t) = \left\langle t^2 + 3, t^2 + 10, \frac{1}{2}t^2 \right\rangle$, for $t \geq 0$

14. $\mathbf{r}(t) = \langle 2e^{2t} + 1, e^{2t} - 1, 2e^{2t} - 10 \rangle$, for $t \geq 0$

15. $\mathbf{r}(t) = \langle 3 + t, 2 - 4t, 1 + 6t \rangle$, for $t \geq 0$

16. $\mathbf{r}(t) = \langle 3 \sin t, 5 \cos t, 4 \sin t \rangle$, for $0 \leq t \leq 2\pi$

17. $\mathbf{r}(t) = \langle 1, t^2, e^{-t} \rangle$, for $t \geq 0$

18. $\mathbf{r}(t) = \langle 13 \cos 2t, 12 \sin 2t, 5 \sin 2t \rangle$, for $0 \leq t \leq \pi$

T **19–24. Comparing trajectories** *Consider the following position functions* **r** *and* **R** *for two objects.*

a. Find the interval $[c, d]$ over which the **R** *trajectory is the same as the* **r** *trajectory over $[a, b]$.*
b. Find the velocity for both objects.
c. Graph the speed of the two objects over the intervals $[a, b]$ and $[c, d]$, respectively.

19. $\mathbf{r}(t) = \langle t, t^2 \rangle, [a, b] = [0, 2]$,
$\mathbf{R}(t) = \langle 2t, 4t^2 \rangle$ on $[c, d]$

20. $\mathbf{r}(t) = \langle 1 + 3t, 2 + 4t \rangle, [a, b] = [0, 6]$,
$\mathbf{R}(t) = \langle 1 + 9t, 2 + 12t \rangle$ on $[c, d]$

21. $\mathbf{r}(t) = \langle \cos t, 4 \sin t \rangle, [a, b] = [0, 2\pi]$,
$\mathbf{R}(t) = \langle \cos 3t, 4 \sin 3t \rangle$ on $[c, d]$

22. $\mathbf{r}(t) = \langle 2 - e^t, 4 - e^{-t} \rangle, [a, b] = [0, \ln 10]$,
$\mathbf{R}(t) = \langle 2 - t, 4 - 1/t \rangle$ on $[c, d]$

23. $\mathbf{r}(t) = \langle 4 + t^2, 3 - 2t^4, 1 + 3t^6 \rangle, [a, b] = [0, 6]$,
$\mathbf{R}(t) = \langle 4 + \ln t, 3 - 2 \ln^2 t, 1 + 3 \ln^3 t \rangle$ on $[c, d]$
For graphing, let $c = 1$ and $d = 20$.

24. $\mathbf{r}(t) = \langle 2 \cos 2t, \sqrt{2} \sin 2t, \sqrt{2} \sin 2t \rangle, [a, b] = [0, \pi]$,
$\mathbf{R}(t) = \langle 2 \cos 4t, \sqrt{2} \sin 4t, \sqrt{2} \sin 4t \rangle$ on $[c, d]$

25–30. Trajectories on circles and spheres *Determine whether the following trajectories lie on a circle in $\mathbb{R}^2$ or sphere in $\mathbb{R}^3$ centered at the origin. If so, find the radius of the circle or sphere and show that the position vector and the velocity vector are everywhere orthogonal.*

25. $\mathbf{r}(t) = \langle 8 \cos 2t, 8 \sin 2t \rangle$, for $0 \leq t \leq \pi$

26. $\mathbf{r}(t) = \langle 4 \sin t, 2 \cos t \rangle$, for $0 \leq t \leq 2\pi$

27. $\mathbf{r}(t) = \langle \sin t + \sqrt{3} \cos t, \sqrt{3} \sin t - \cos t \rangle$, for $0 \leq t \leq 2\pi$

28. $\mathbf{r}(t) = \langle 3 \sin t, 5 \cos t, 4 \sin t \rangle$, for $0 \leq t \leq 2\pi$

29. $\mathbf{r}(t) = \langle \sin t, \cos t, \cos t \rangle$, for $0 \leq t \leq 2\pi$

30. $\mathbf{r}(t) = \langle \sqrt{3} \cos t + \sqrt{2} \sin t, -\sqrt{3} \cos t + \sqrt{2} \sin t, \sqrt{2} \sin t \rangle$, for $0 \leq t \leq 2\pi$

31–36. Solving equations of motion *Given an acceleration vector, initial velocity $\langle u_0, v_0 \rangle$, and initial position $\langle x_0, y_0 \rangle$, find the velocity and position vectors, for $t \geq 0$.*

31. $\mathbf{a}(t) = \langle 0, 1 \rangle, \langle u_0, v_0 \rangle = \langle 2, 3 \rangle, \langle x_0, y_0 \rangle = \langle 0, 0 \rangle$

32. $\mathbf{a}(t) = \langle 1, 2 \rangle, \langle u_0, v_0 \rangle = \langle 1, 1 \rangle, \langle x_0, y_0 \rangle = \langle 2, 3 \rangle$

33. $\mathbf{a}(t) = \langle 0, 10 \rangle, \langle u_0, v_0 \rangle = \langle 0, 5 \rangle, \langle x_0, y_0 \rangle = \langle 1, -1 \rangle$

34. $\mathbf{a}(t) = \langle 1, t \rangle, \langle u_0, v_0 \rangle = \langle 2, -1 \rangle, \langle x_0, y_0 \rangle = \langle 0, 8 \rangle$

35. $\mathbf{a}(t) = \langle \cos t, 2 \sin t \rangle, \langle u_0, v_0 \rangle = \langle 0, 1 \rangle, \langle x_0, y_0 \rangle = \langle 1, 0 \rangle$

36. $\mathbf{a}(t) = \langle e^{-t}, 1 \rangle, \langle u_0, v_0 \rangle = \langle 1, 0 \rangle, \langle x_0, y_0 \rangle = \langle 0, 0 \rangle$

T **37–42. Two-dimensional motion** *Consider the motion of the following objects. Assume the x-axis is horizontal, the positive y-axis is vertical, the ground is horizontal, and only the gravitational force acts on the object.*

a. Find the velocity and position vectors, for $t \geq 0$.
b. Graph the trajectory.
c. Determine the time of flight and range of the object.
d. Determine the maximum height of the object.

37. A soccer ball has an initial position $\langle x_0, y_0 \rangle = \langle 0, 0 \rangle$ when it is kicked with an initial velocity of $\langle u_0, v_0 \rangle = \langle 30, 6 \rangle$ m/s.

38. A golf ball has an initial position $\langle x_0, y_0 \rangle = \langle 0, 0 \rangle$ when it is hit at an angle of 30° with an initial speed of 150 ft/s.

39. A baseball has an initial position (in feet) of $\langle x_0, y_0 \rangle = \langle 0, 6 \rangle$ when it is thrown with an initial velocity of $\langle u_0, v_0 \rangle = \langle 80, 10 \rangle$ ft/s.

40. A baseball is thrown horizontally from a height of 10 ft above the ground with a speed of 132 ft/s.

41. A projectile is launched from a platform 20 ft above the ground at an angle of 60° above the horizontal with a speed of 250 ft/s. Assume the origin is at the base of the platform.

42. A rock is thrown from the edge of a vertical cliff 40 m above the ground at an angle of 45° above the horizontal with a speed of $10\sqrt{2}$ m/s. Assume the origin is at the foot of the cliff.

43–46. Solving equations of motion *Given an acceleration vector, initial velocity $\langle u_0, v_0, w_0 \rangle$, and initial position $\langle x_0, y_0, z_0 \rangle$, find the velocity and position vectors, for $t \geq 0$.*

43. $\mathbf{a}(t) = \langle 0, 0, 10 \rangle, \langle u_0, v_0, w_0 \rangle = \langle 1, 5, 0 \rangle$,
$\langle x_0, y_0, z_0 \rangle = \langle 0, 5, 0 \rangle$

44. $\mathbf{a}(t) = \langle 1, t, 4t \rangle, \langle u_0, v_0, w_0 \rangle = \langle 20, 0, 0 \rangle$,
$\langle x_0, y_0, z_0 \rangle = \langle 0, 0, 0 \rangle$

45. $\mathbf{a}(t) = \langle \sin t, \cos t, 1 \rangle, \langle u_0, v_0, w_0 \rangle = \langle 0, 2, 0 \rangle$,
$\langle x_0, y_0, z_0 \rangle = \langle 0, 0, 0 \rangle$

46. $\mathbf{a}(t) = \langle t, e^{-t}, 1 \rangle, \langle u_0, v_0, w_0 \rangle = \langle 0, 0, 1 \rangle$,
$\langle x_0, y_0, z_0 \rangle = \langle 4, 0, 0 \rangle$

T **47–52. Three-dimensional motion** *Consider the motion of the following objects. Assume the x-axis points east, the y-axis points north, the positive z-axis is vertical and opposite g, the ground is horizontal, and only the gravitational force acts on the object unless otherwise stated.*

a. Find the velocity and position vectors, for $t \geq 0$.
b. Make a sketch of the trajectory.
c. Determine the time of flight and range of the object.
d. Determine the maximum height of the object.

47. A bullet is fired from a rifle 1 m above the ground in a northeast direction. The initial velocity of the bullet is $\langle 200, 200, 0 \rangle$ m/s.

48. A golf ball is hit east down a fairway with an initial velocity of $\langle 50, 0, 30 \rangle$ m/s. A crosswind blowing to the south produces an acceleration of the ball of -0.8 m/s^2.

49. A baseball is hit 3 ft above home plate with an initial velocity of $\langle 60, 80, 80 \rangle$ ft/s. The spin on the baseball produces a horizontal acceleration of the ball of 10 ft/s^2 in the eastward direction.

50. A baseball is hit 3 ft above home plate with an initial velocity of $\langle 30, 30, 80 \rangle$ ft/s. The spin on the baseball produces a horizontal acceleration of the ball of 5 ft/s^2 in the northward direction.

51. A small rocket is fired from a launch pad 10 m above the ground with an initial velocity, in m/s, of $\langle 300, 400, 500 \rangle$. A crosswind blowing to the north produces an acceleration of the rocket of $2.5\ \text{m/s}^2$.

52. A soccer ball is kicked from the point $\langle 0, 0, 0 \rangle$ with an initial velocity of $\langle 0, 80, 80 \rangle$ ft/s. The spin on the ball produces an acceleration of $\langle 1.2, 0, 0 \rangle\ \text{ft/s}^2$.

Further Explorations

53. Explain why or why not Determine whether the following statements are true and give an explanation or counterexample.

a. If the speed of an object is constant, then its velocity components are constant.
b. The functions $\mathbf{r}(t) = \langle \cos t, \sin t \rangle$ and $\mathbf{R}(t) = \langle \sin t^2, \cos t^2 \rangle$ generate the same set of points, for $t \geq 0$.
c. A velocity vector of variable magnitude cannot have a constant direction.
d. If the acceleration of an object is $\mathbf{a}(t) = \mathbf{0}$, for all $t \geq 0$, then the velocity of the object is constant.
e. If you double the initial speed of a projectile, its range also doubles (assume no forces other than gravity act on the projectile).
f. If you double the initial speed of a projectile, its time of flight also doubles (assume no forces other than gravity).
g. A trajectory with $\mathbf{v}(t) = \mathbf{a}(t) \neq \mathbf{0}$, for all t, is possible.

T **54–57. Trajectory properties** *Find the time of flight, range, and maximum height of the following two-dimensional trajectories, assuming no forces other than gravity. In each case, the initial position is $\langle 0, 0 \rangle$ and the initial velocity is $\mathbf{v}_0 = \langle u_0, v_0 \rangle$.*

54. $\langle u_0, v_0 \rangle = \langle 10, 20 \rangle$ ft/s

55. Initial speed $|\mathbf{v}_0| = 150$ m/s, launch angle $\alpha = 30°$

56. $\langle u_0, v_0 \rangle = \langle 40, 80 \rangle$ m/s

57. Initial speed $|\mathbf{v}_0| = 400$ ft/s, launch angle $\alpha = 60°$

58. Motion on the moon The acceleration due to gravity on the moon is approximately $g/6$ (one-sixth its value on Earth). Compare the time of flight, range, and maximum height of a projectile on the moon with the corresponding values on Earth.

59. Firing angles A projectile is fired over horizontal ground from the origin with an initial speed of 60 m/s. What firing angles produce a range of 300 m?

T **60. Firing strategies** Suppose you wish to fire a projectile over horizontal ground from the origin and attain a range of 1000 m.

a. Sketch a graph of the initial speed required for all firing angles $0 < \alpha < \pi/2$.
b. What firing angle requires the least initial speed?

61. Nonuniform straight-line motion Consider the motion of an object given by the position function

$$\mathbf{r}(t) = f(t)\langle a, b, c \rangle + \langle x_0, y_0, z_0 \rangle, \quad \text{for } t \geq 0,$$

where $a, b, c, x_0, y_0,$ and z_0 are constants, and f is a differentiable scalar function, for $t \geq 0$.

a. Explain why this function describes motion along a line.
b. Find the velocity function. In general, is the velocity constant in magnitude or direction along the path?

62. A race Two people travel from $P(4, 0)$ to $Q(-4, 0)$ along the paths given by

$$\mathbf{r}(t) = \langle 4\cos(\pi t/8), 4\sin(\pi t/8) \rangle \quad \text{and}$$
$$\mathbf{R}(t) = \langle 4 - t, (4 - t)^2 - 16 \rangle.$$

a. Graph both paths between P and Q.
b. Graph the speeds of both people between P and Q.
c. Who arrives at Q first?

63. Circular motion Consider an object moving along the circular trajectory $\mathbf{r}(t) = \langle A\cos\omega t, A\sin\omega t \rangle$, where A and ω are constants.

a. Over what time interval $[0, T]$ does the object traverse the circle once?
b. Find the velocity and speed of the object. Is the velocity constant in either direction or magnitude? Is the speed constant?
c. Find the acceleration of the object.
d. How are the position and velocity related? How are the position and acceleration related?
e. Sketch the position, velocity, and acceleration vectors at four different points on the trajectory with $A = \omega = 1$.

64. A linear trajectory An object moves along a straight line from the point $P(1, 2, 4)$ to the point $Q(-6, 8, 10)$.

a. Find a position function $\mathbf{r}$ that describes the motion if it occurs with a constant speed over the time interval $[0, 5]$.
b. Find a position function $\mathbf{r}$ that describes the motion if it occurs with speed e^t.

65. A circular trajectory An object moves clockwise around a circle centered at the origin with radius 5 m beginning at the point $(0, 5)$.

a. Find a position function $\mathbf{r}$ that describes the motion if the object moves with a constant speed, completing 1 lap every 12 s.
b. Find a position function $\mathbf{r}$ that describes the motion if it occurs with speed e^{-t}.

66. A helical trajectory An object moves on the helix $\langle \cos t, \sin t, t \rangle$, for $t \geq 0$.

a. Find a position function $\mathbf{r}$ that describes the motion if it occurs with a constant speed of 10.
b. Find a position function $\mathbf{r}$ that describes the motion if it occurs with speed t.

T **67. Speed on an ellipse** An object moves along an ellipse given by the function $\mathbf{r}(t) = \langle a\cos t, b\sin t \rangle$, for $0 \leq t \leq 2\pi$, where $a > 0$ and $b > 0$.

a. Find the velocity and speed of the object in terms of a and b, for $0 \leq t \leq 2\pi$.
b. With $a = 1$ and $b = 6$, graph the speed function, for $0 \leq t \leq 2\pi$. Mark the points on the trajectory at which the speed is a minimum and a maximum.
c. Is it true that the object speeds up along the flattest (straightest) parts of the trajectory and slows down where the curves are sharpest?
d. For general a and b, find the ratio of the maximum speed to the minimum speed on the ellipse (in terms of a and b).

T **68. Travel on a cycloid** Consider an object moving on a cycloid with the position function $\mathbf{r}(t) = \langle t - \sin t, 1 - \cos t \rangle$, for $0 \leq t \leq 4\pi$.

a. Graph the trajectory.
b. Find the velocity and speed of the object. At what point(s) on the trajectory does the object move fastest? Slowest?

c. Find the acceleration of the object and show that $|\mathbf{a}(t)|$ is constant.

d. Explain why the trajectory has a cusp at $t = 2\pi$.

69. Analyzing a trajectory Consider the trajectory given by the position function

$$\mathbf{r}(t) = \langle 50e^{-t}\cos t, 50e^{-t}\sin t, 5(1 - e^{-t})\rangle, \quad \text{for } t \geq 0.$$

a. Find the initial point ($t = 0$) and the "terminal" point ($\lim_{t\to\infty} \mathbf{r}(t)$) of the trajectory.

b. At what point on the trajectory is the speed the greatest?

c. Graph the trajectory.

Applications

T 70. Golf shot A golfer stands 390 ft (130 yd) horizontally from the hole and 40 ft below the hole (see figure). Assuming the ball is hit with an initial speed of 150 ft/s, at what angle(s) should it be hit to land in the hole? Assume that the path of the ball lies in a plane.

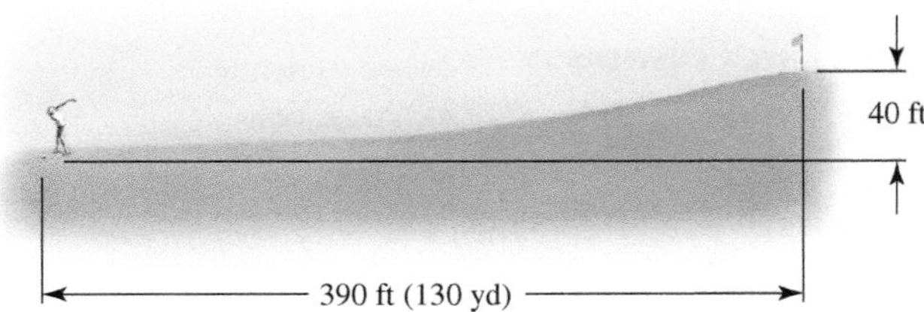

T 71. Another golf shot A golfer stands 420 ft (140 yd) horizontally from the hole and 50 ft above the hole (see figure). Assuming the ball is hit with an initial speed of 120 ft/s, at what angle(s) should it be hit to land in the hole? Assume that the path of the ball lies in a plane.

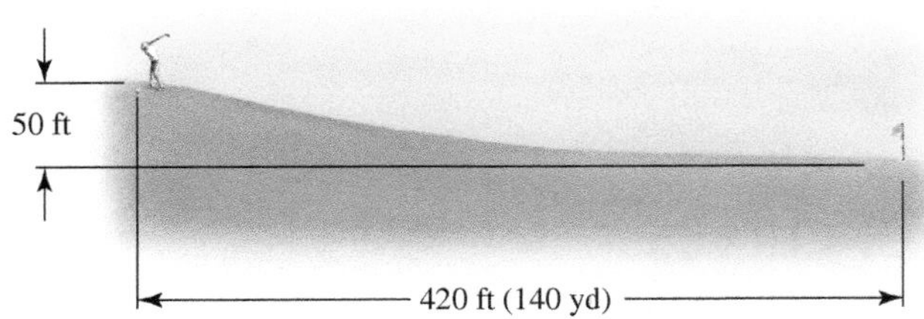

T 72. Initial velocity of a golf shot A golfer stands 390 ft horizontally from the hole and 40 ft below the hole (see figure for Exercise 70). If the ball leaves the ground at an initial angle of 45° with the horizontal, with what initial velocity should it be hit to land in the hole?

T 73. Initial velocity of a golf shot A golfer stands 420 ft horizontally from the hole and 50 ft above the hole (see figure for Exercise 71). If the ball leaves the ground at an initial angle of 30° with the horizontal, with what initial velocity should it be hit to land in the hole?

T 74. Ski jump The lip of a ski jump is 8 m above the outrun that is sloped at an angle of 30° to the horizontal (see figure).

a. If the initial velocity of a ski jumper at the lip of the jump is $\langle 40, 0\rangle$ m/s, what is the length of the jump (distance from the origin to the landing point)? Assume only gravity affects the motion.

b. Assume that air resistance produces a constant horizontal acceleration of 0.15 m/s^2 opposing the motion. What is the length of the jump?

c. Suppose that the takeoff ramp is tilted upward at an angle of θ, so that the skier's initial velocity is $40\langle\cos\theta, \sin\theta\rangle$ m/s. What value of θ maximizes the length of the jump? Express your answer in degrees and neglect air resistance.

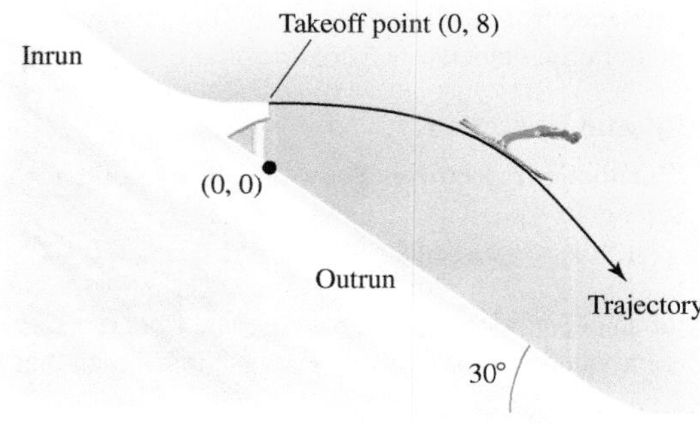

75. Designing a baseball pitch A baseball leaves the hand of a pitcher 6 vertical feet above and 60 horizontal feet from home plate. Assume that the coordinate axes are oriented as shown in the figure.

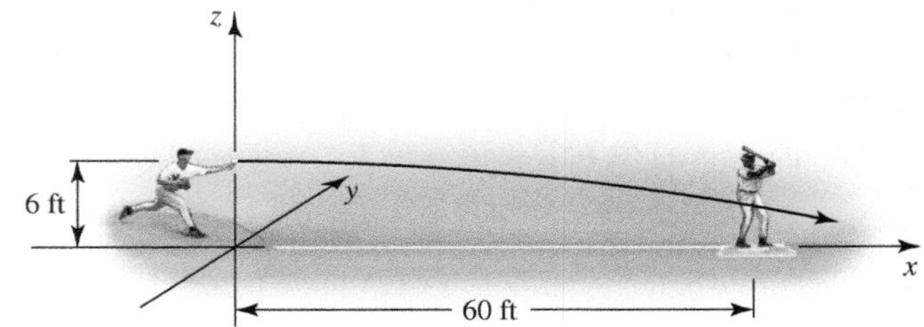

a. In the absence of all forces except gravity, assume that a pitch is thrown with an initial velocity of $\langle 130, 0, -3\rangle$ ft/s (about 90 mi/hr). How far above the ground is the ball when it crosses home plate and how long does it take the pitch to arrive?

b. What vertical velocity component should the pitcher use so that the pitch crosses home plate exactly 3 ft above the ground?

c. A simple model to describe the curve of a baseball assumes that the spin of the ball produces a constant sideways acceleration (in the y-direction) of c ft/s^2. Assume a pitcher throws a curve ball with $c = 8$ ft/s^2 (one-fourth the acceleration of gravity). How far does the ball move in the y-direction by the time it reaches home plate, assuming an initial velocity of $\langle 130, 0, -3\rangle$ ft/s?

d. In part (c), does the ball curve more in the first half of its trip to the plate or in the second half? How does this fact affect the batter?

e. Suppose the pitcher releases the ball from an initial position of $\langle 0, -3, 6\rangle$ with initial velocity $\langle 130, 0, -3\rangle$. What value of the spin parameter c is needed to put the ball over home plate passing through the point $(60, 0, 3)$?

76. Trajectory with a sloped landing Assume an object is launched from the origin with an initial speed $|\mathbf{v}_0|$ at an angle α to the horizontal, where $0 < \alpha < \frac{\pi}{2}$.

a. Find the time of flight, range, and maximum height (relative to the launch point) of the trajectory if the ground slopes *downward* at a constant angle of θ from the launch site, where $0 < \theta < \frac{\pi}{2}$.

b. Find the time of flight, range, and maximum height of the trajectory if the ground slopes *upward* at a constant angle of θ from the launch site. Assume $\tan\theta < \frac{1}{2}\tan\alpha$.

77. Time of flight, range, height Derive the formulas for time of flight, range, and maximum height in the case that an object is launched from the initial position $\langle 0, y_0 \rangle$ above horizontal ground with initial velocity $|\mathbf{v}_0|\langle \cos\alpha, \sin\alpha \rangle$.

Additional Exercises

78. Parabolic trajectories Show that the two-dimensional trajectory

$$x(t) = u_0 t + x_0 \quad\text{and}\quad y(t) = -\frac{gt^2}{2} + v_0 t + y_0, \quad \text{for } 0 \le t \le T,$$

of an object moving in a gravitational field is a segment of a parabola for some value of $T > 0$. Find T such that $y(T) = 0$.

79. Tilted ellipse Consider the curve $\mathbf{r}(t) = \langle \cos t, \sin t, c \sin t \rangle$, for $0 \le t \le 2\pi$, where c is a real number. Assuming the curve lies in a plane, prove that the curve is an ellipse in that plane.

80. Equal area property Consider the ellipse $\mathbf{r}(t) = \langle a\cos t, b \sin t \rangle$, for $0 \le t \le 2\pi$, where a and b are real numbers. Let θ be the angle between the position vector and the x-axis.

a. Show that $\tan\theta = (b/a)\tan t$.

b. Find $\theta'(t)$.

c. Recall that the area bounded by the polar curve $r = f(\theta)$ on the interval $[0, \theta]$ is $A(\theta) = \frac{1}{2}\int_0^\theta (f(u))^2\,du$. Letting $f(\theta(t)) = |\mathbf{r}(\theta(t))|$, show that $A'(t) = \frac{1}{2}ab$.

d. Conclude that as an object moves around the ellipse, it sweeps out equal areas in equal times.

81. Another property of constant $|\mathbf{r}|$ motion Suppose an object moves on the surface of a sphere with $|\mathbf{r}(t)|$ constant for all t. Show that $\mathbf{r}(t)$ and $\mathbf{a}(t) = \mathbf{r}''(t)$ satisfy $\mathbf{r}(t) \cdot \mathbf{a}(t) = -|\mathbf{v}(t)|^2$.

82. Conditions for a circular/elliptical trajectory in the plane An object moves along a path given by

$$\mathbf{r}(t) = \langle a\cos t + b \sin t, c \cos t + d \sin t \rangle, \quad \text{for } 0 \le t \le 2\pi.$$

a. What conditions on a, b, c, and d guarantee that the path is a circle?

b. What conditions on a, b, c, and d guarantee that the path is an ellipse?

83. Conditions for a circular/elliptical trajectory in space An object moves along a path given by

$$\mathbf{r}(t) = \langle a\cos t + b \sin t, c \cos t + d \sin t, e \cos t + f \sin t \rangle,$$
for $0 \le t \le 2\pi$.

a. Show that the curve described by $\mathbf{r}$ lies in a plane.

b. What conditions on a, b, c, d, e, and f guarantee that the curve described by $\mathbf{r}$ is a circle?

QUICK CHECK ANSWERS

1. $\mathbf{v}(t) = \langle 1, 2t, 3t^2 \rangle, \mathbf{a}(t) = \langle 0, 2, 6t \rangle$
2. $|\mathbf{r}'(t)| = \sqrt{1 + 4t^2 + 9t^4/16}$
$|\mathbf{R}'(t)| = \sqrt{4t^2 + 16t^6 + 9t^{10}/4}$
3. $\mathbf{r} \cdot \mathbf{v} = \langle 3\cos t, 5 \sin t, 4 \cos t \rangle \cdot \langle -3 \sin t, 5 \cos t, -4 \sin t \rangle = 0$
4. $x(t) = 100t, y(t) = -16t^2 + 60t + 2$
5. $\sin(2(\pi/2 - \alpha)) = \sin(\pi - 2\alpha) = \sin 2\alpha$ ◄

11.8 Length of Curves

With the methods of Section 11.7, it is possible to model the trajectory of an object moving in three-dimensional space. Although we can predict the position of the object at all times, we still don't have the tools needed to answer a simple question: How far does the object travel along its flight path over a given interval of time? In this section, we answer this question of *arc length*.

Arc Length

➤ Arc length for curves of the form $y = f(x)$ was discussed in Section 6.5. You should look for the parallels between that discussion and the one in this section.

Suppose that a parameterized curve C is given by the vector-valued function $\mathbf{r}(t) = \langle f(t), g(t), h(t) \rangle$, for $a \le t \le b$, where f', g', and h' are continuous on $[a, b]$. We first show how to find the length of the two-dimensional curve $\mathbf{r}(t) = \langle f(t), g(t) \rangle$, for $a \le t \le b$. The modification for three-dimensional curves then follows.

To find the length of the curve between $(f(a), g(a))$ and $(f(b), g(b))$, we first subdivide the interval $[a, b]$ into n subintervals using the grid points

$$a = t_0 < t_1 < t_2 < \cdots < t_n = b.$$

The next step is to connect consecutive points on the curve,

$$(f(t_0), g(t_0)), \ldots, (f(t_k), g(t_k)), \ldots, (f(t_n), g(t_n)),$$

with line segments (Figure 11.95a).

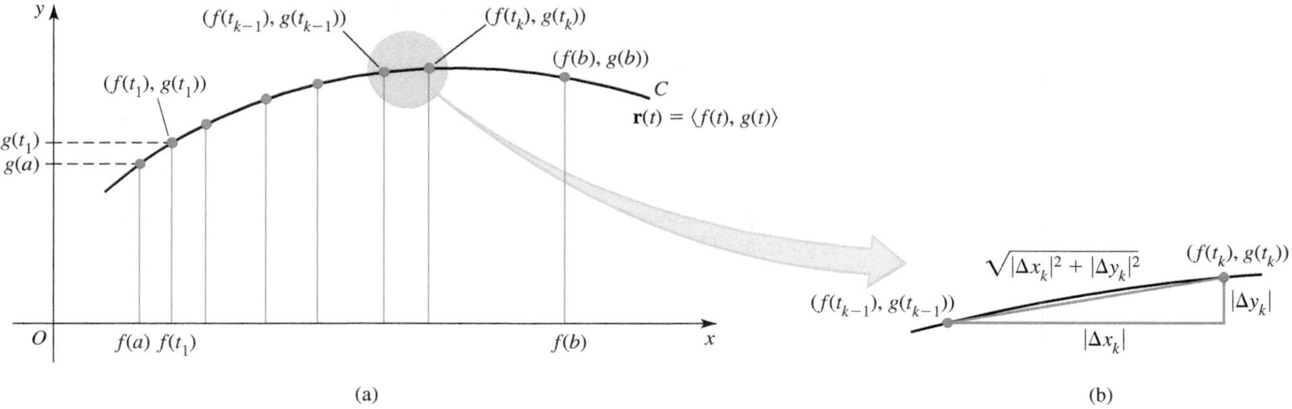

Figure 11.95

The kth line segment is the hypotenuse of a right triangle, whose legs have lengths $|\Delta x_k|$ and $|\Delta y_k|$, where

$$\Delta x_k = f(t_k) - f(t_{k-1}) \quad \text{and} \quad \Delta y_k = g(t_k) - g(t_{k-1}),$$

for $k = 1, 2, \ldots, n$ (Figure 11.95b). Therefore, the length of the kth line segment is

$$\sqrt{|\Delta x_k|^2 + |\Delta y_k|^2}.$$

The length of the entire curve L is approximated by the sum of the lengths of the line segments:

$$L \approx \sum_{k=1}^{n} \sqrt{|\Delta x_k|^2 + |\Delta y_k|^2} = \sum_{k=1}^{n} \sqrt{(\Delta x_k)^2 + (\Delta y_k)^2}. \tag{1}$$

The goal is to express this sum as a Riemann sum.

The change in $x = f(t)$ over the kth subinterval is $\Delta x_k = f(t_k) - f(t_{k-1})$. By the Mean Value Theorem, there is a point t_k^* in (t_{k-1}, t_k) such that

$$\frac{\overbrace{f(t_k) - f(t_{k-1})}^{\Delta x_k}}{\underbrace{t_k - t_{k-1}}_{\Delta t_k}} = f'(t_k^*).$$

So the change in x as t changes by $\Delta t_k = t_k - t_{k-1}$ is

$$\Delta x_k = f(t_k) - f(t_{k-1}) = f'(t_k^*)\Delta t_k.$$

Similarly, the change in y over the kth subinterval is

$$\Delta y_k = g(t_k) - g(t_{k-1}) = g'(\hat{t}_k)\Delta t_k,$$

where $\hat{t}_k$ is also a point in (t_{k-1}, t_k). We substitute these expressions for Δx_k and Δy_k into equation (1):

$$\begin{aligned} L &\approx \sum_{k=1}^{n} \sqrt{(\Delta x_k)^2 + (\Delta y_k)^2} \\ &= \sum_{k=1}^{n} \sqrt{(f'(t_k^*)\Delta t_k)^2 + (g'(\hat{t}_k)\Delta t_k)^2} && \text{Substitute for } \Delta x_k \text{ and } \Delta y_k. \\ &= \sum_{k=1}^{n} \sqrt{f'(t_k^*)^2 + g'(\hat{t}_k)^2}\,\Delta t_k. && \text{Factor } \Delta t_k \text{ out of square root.} \end{aligned}$$

The intermediate points t_k^* and $\hat{t}_k$ both approach t_k as n increases and as Δt_k approaches zero. Therefore, given the conditions on f' and g', the limit of this sum as $n \to \infty$ and $\Delta t_k \to 0$, for all k, exists and equals a definite integral:

$$L = \lim_{n \to \infty} \sum_{k=1}^{n} \sqrt{f'(t_k^*)^2 + g'(\hat{t}_k)^2}\,\Delta t_k = \int_a^b \sqrt{f'(t)^2 + g'(t)^2}\,dt.$$

An analogous arc length formula for three-dimensional curves follows using a similar argument. The length of the curve $\mathbf{r}(t) = \langle f(t), g(t), h(t) \rangle$ on the interval $[a, b]$ is

$$L = \int_a^b \sqrt{f'(t)^2 + g'(t)^2 + h'(t)^2}\,dt.$$

Noting that $\mathbf{r}'(t) = \langle f'(t), g'(t), h'(t) \rangle$, we state the following definition.

➤ Arc length integrals are usually difficult to evaluate exactly. The few easily evaluated integrals appear in the examples and exercises. Often numerical methods must be used to approximate the more challenging integrals (see Example 4).

➤ For curves in the xy-plane, we set $h(t) = 0$ in the definition of arc length.

DEFINITION Arc Length for Vector Functions

Consider the parameterized curve $\mathbf{r}(t) = \langle f(t), g(t), h(t) \rangle$, where f', g', and h' are continuous, and the curve is traversed once for $a \le t \le b$. The **arc length** of the curve between $(f(a), g(a), h(a))$ and $(f(b), g(b), h(b))$ is

$$L = \int_a^b \sqrt{f'(t)^2 + g'(t)^2 + h'(t)^2}\,dt = \int_a^b |\mathbf{r}'(t)|\,dt.$$

QUICK CHECK 1 Use the arc length formula to find the length of the line $\mathbf{r}(t) = \langle t, t \rangle$, for $0 \le t \le 1$. ◀

Let's use the arc length integral to derive the formula for the circumference of a circle.

EXAMPLE 1 Circumference of a circle Prove that the circumference of a circle of radius $a > 0$ is $2\pi a$.

SOLUTION A circle of radius a is described by

$$\mathbf{r}(t) = \langle f(t), g(t) \rangle = \langle a \cos t, a \sin t \rangle, \text{ for } 0 \le t \le 2\pi.$$

➤ An important fact is that the arc length of a smooth parameterized curve is independent of the choice of parameter (Exercise 70).

Note that $f'(t) = -a \sin t$ and $g'(t) = a \cos t$. The circumference is

$$\begin{aligned} L &= \int_0^{2\pi} \sqrt{f'(t)^2 + g'(t)^2}\,dt && \text{Arc length formula} \\ &= \int_0^{2\pi} \sqrt{(-a \sin t)^2 + (a \cos t)^2}\,dt && \text{Substitute for } f' \text{ and } g'. \\ &= a \int_0^{2\pi} \sqrt{\sin^2 t + \cos^2 t}\,dt && \text{Factor } a > 0 \text{ out of square root.} \\ &= a \int_0^{2\pi} 1\,dt && \sin^2 t + \cos^2 t = 1 \\ &= 2\pi a. && \text{Integrate a constant.} \end{aligned}$$

Related Exercises 9–22 ◀

QUICK CHECK 2 What does the arc length formula give for the length of the line $\mathbf{r}(t) = \langle t, t, t \rangle$, for $0 \le t \le 1$? ◀

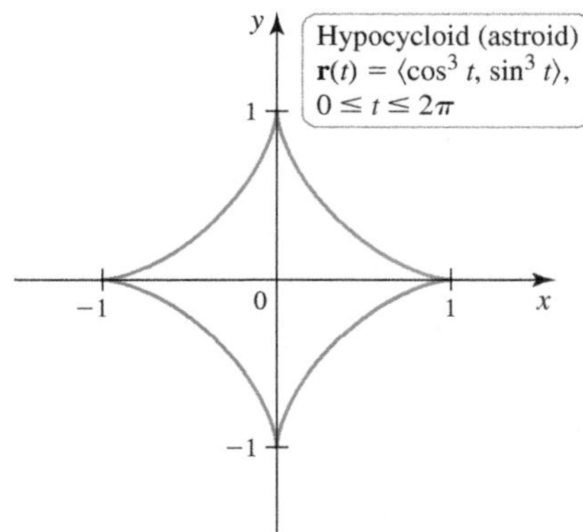

Figure 11.96

EXAMPLE 2 **Length of a hypocycloid (or astroid)** Find the length of the complete hypocycloid given by $\mathbf{r}(t) = \langle \cos^3 t, \sin^3 t \rangle$, where $0 \le t \le 2\pi$ (Figure 11.96).

SOLUTION The length of the entire curve is four times the length of the curve in the first quadrant. You should verify that the curve in the first quadrant is generated as the parameter varies from $t = 0$ (corresponding to $(1, 0)$) to $t = \pi/2$ (corresponding to $(0, 1)$). Letting $f(t) = \cos^3 t$ and $g(t) = \sin^3 t$, we have

$$f'(t) = -3\cos^2 t \sin t \quad \text{and} \quad g'(t) = 3\sin^2 t \cos t.$$

The arc length of the full curve is

$$\begin{aligned}
L &= 4\int_0^{\pi/2} \sqrt{f'(t)^2 + g'(t)^2}\,dt && \text{Factor of 4 by symmetry} \\
&= 4\int_0^{\pi/2} \sqrt{(-3\cos^2 t \sin t)^2 + (3\sin^2 t \cos t)^2}\,dt && \text{Substitute for } f' \text{ and } g'. \\
&= 4\int_0^{\pi/2} \sqrt{9\cos^4 t \sin^2 t + 9\cos^2 t \sin^4 t}\,dt && \text{Simplify terms.} \\
&= 4\int_0^{\pi/2} 3\sqrt{\cos^2 t \sin^2 t \underbrace{(\cos^2 t + \sin^2 t)}_{1}}\,dt && \text{Factor.} \\
&= 12\int_0^{\pi/2} \cos t \sin t\,dt. && \cos t \sin t \ge 0, \text{ for } 0 \le t \le \frac{\pi}{2}
\end{aligned}$$

Letting $u = \sin t$ with $du = \cos t\,dt$, we have

$$L = 12\int_0^{\pi/2} \cos t \sin t\,dt = 12\int_0^1 u\,du = 6.$$

The length of the entire hypocycloid is 6 units.

Related Exercises 9–22 ◀

➤ Recall from Chapter 6 that the distance traveled by an object in one dimension is $\int_a^b |\mathbf{v}(t)|\,dt$. The arc length formula generalizes this formula to three dimensions.

Paths and Trajectories If the function $\mathbf{r}(t) = \langle x(t), y(t), z(t) \rangle$ is the position function for a moving object, then the arc length formula has a natural interpretation. Recall that $\mathbf{v}(t) = \mathbf{r}'(t)$ is the velocity of the object and $|\mathbf{v}(t)| = |\mathbf{r}'(t)|$ is the speed of the object. Therefore, the arc length formula becomes

$$L = \int_a^b |\mathbf{r}'(t)|\,dt = \int_a^b |\mathbf{v}(t)|\,dt.$$

This formula is an analog of the familiar *distance* = *speed* × *elapsed time* formula.

EXAMPLE 3 **Flight of an eagle** An eagle rises at a rate of 100 vertical ft/min on a helical path given by

$$\mathbf{r}(t) = \langle 250\cos t, 250\sin t, 100t \rangle$$

(Figure 11.97), where $\mathbf{r}$ is measured in feet and t is measured in minutes. How far does it travel in 10 min?

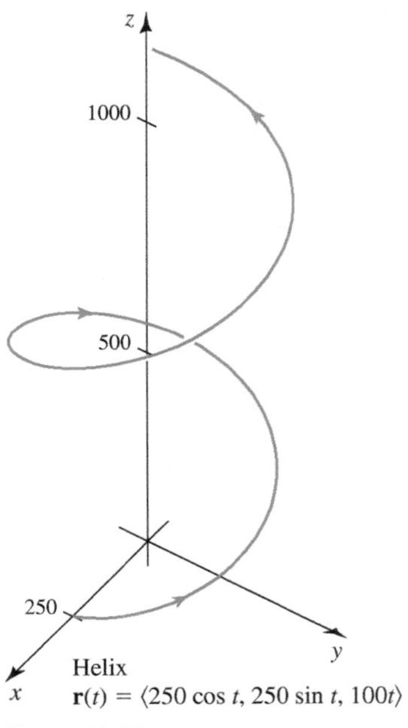

Figure 11.97

SOLUTION The speed of the eagle is

$$\begin{aligned}
|\mathbf{v}(t)| &= \sqrt{x'(t)^2 + y'(t)^2 + z'(t)^2} \\
&= \sqrt{(-250\sin t)^2 + (250\cos t)^2 + 100^2} && \text{Substitute derivatives.} \\
&= \sqrt{250^2(\sin^2 t + \cos^2 t) + 100^2} && \text{Combine terms.} \\
&= \sqrt{250^2 + 100^2} \approx 269. && \sin^2 t + \cos^2 t = 1
\end{aligned}$$

The constant speed makes the arc length integral easy to evaluate:

$$L = \int_0^{10} |\mathbf{v}(t)|\, dt \approx \int_0^{10} 269\, dt = 2690.$$

The eagle travels approximately 2690 ft in 10 min.

Related Exercises 23–26 ◄

QUICK CHECK 3 If the speed of an object is a constant S (as in Example 3), explain why the arc length on the interval $[a, b]$ is $S(b - a)$. ◄

The following application of arc length leads to an integral that is difficult to evaluate exactly.

EXAMPLE 4 Lengths of planetary orbits According to Kepler's first law, the planets revolve about the sun in elliptical orbits. A vector function that describes an ellipse in the xy-plane is

$$\mathbf{r}(t) = \langle a \cos t, b \sin t \rangle, \qquad \text{where } 0 \le t \le 2\pi.$$

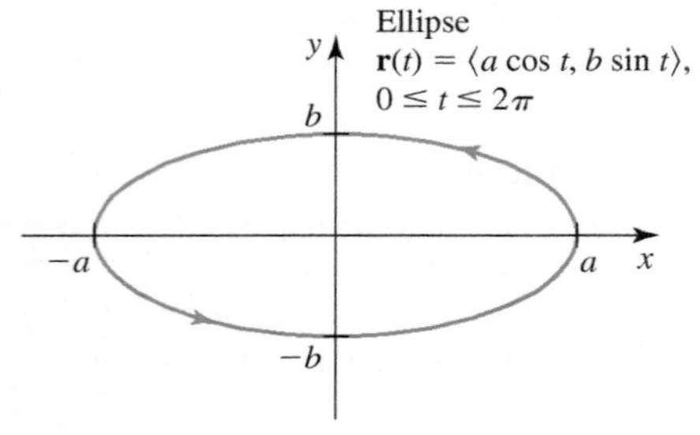

Figure 11.98

If $a > b > 0$, then $2a$ is the length of the major axis and $2b$ is the length of the minor axis (Figure 11.98). Verify the lengths of the planetary orbits given in Table 11.1. Distances are given in terms of the astronomical unit (AU), which is the length of the semimajor axis of Earth's orbit, or about 93 million miles.

➤ The German astronomer and mathematician Johannes Kepler (1571–1630) worked with the meticulously gathered data of Tycho Brahe to formulate three empirical laws obeyed by planets and comets orbiting the sun. The work of Kepler formed the foundation for Newton's laws of gravitation developed 50 years later.

➤ In September 2006, Pluto joined the ranks of Ceres, Haumea, Makemake, and Eris as one of five dwarf planets in our solar system.

Table 11.1

Planet	Semimajor axis, a (AU)	Semiminor axis, b (AU)	$\alpha = b/a$	Orbit length (AU)
Mercury	0.387	0.379	0.979	2.407
Venus	0.723	0.723	1.000	4.543
Earth	1.000	0.999	0.999	6.280
Mars	1.524	1.517	0.995	9.554
Jupiter	5.203	5.179	0.995	32.616
Saturn	9.539	9.524	0.998	59.888
Uranus	19.182	19.161	0.999	120.458
Neptune	30.058	30.057	1.000	188.857

SOLUTION Using the arc length formula, the length of a general elliptical orbit is

$$\begin{aligned} L &= \int_0^{2\pi} \sqrt{x'(t)^2 + y'(t)^2}\, dt \\ &= \int_0^{2\pi} \sqrt{(-a \sin t)^2 + (b \cos t)^2}\, dt \quad \text{Substitute for } x'(t) \text{ and } y'(t). \\ &= \int_0^{2\pi} \sqrt{a^2 \sin^2 t + b^2 \cos^2 t}\, dt. \quad \text{Simplify.} \end{aligned}$$

Factoring a^2 out of the square root and letting $\alpha = b/a$, we have

$$\begin{aligned} L &= \int_0^{2\pi} \sqrt{a^2 (\sin^2 t + (b/a)^2 \cos^2 t)}\, dt \quad \text{Factor out } a^2. \\ &= a \int_0^{2\pi} \sqrt{\sin^2 t + \alpha^2 \cos^2 t}\, dt \quad \text{Let } \alpha = b/a. \\ &= 4a \int_0^{\pi/2} \sqrt{\sin^2 t + \alpha^2 \cos^2 t}\, dt. \quad \text{Use symmetry; quarter orbit on } [0, \pi/2]. \end{aligned}$$

➤ The integral that gives the length of an ellipse is a *complete elliptic integral of the second kind.* Many reference books and software packages provide approximate values of this integral.

Unfortunately, an antiderivative for this integrand cannot be found in terms of elementary functions, so we have two options: This integral is well known and values have been tabulated for various values of α. Alternatively, we may use a calculator to approximate the integral numerically (see Section 7.7). Using numerical integration, the orbit lengths in Table 11.1 are obtained. For example, the length of Mercury's orbit with $a = 0.387$ and $\alpha = 0.979$ is

➤ Though rounded values for α appear in Table 11.1, the calculations in Example 4 were done in full precision and rounded to three decimal places only in the final step.

$$\begin{aligned} L &= 4a\int_0^{\pi/2}\sqrt{\sin^2 t + \alpha^2\cos^2 t}\,dt \\ &= 1.548\int_0^{\pi/2}\sqrt{\sin^2 t + 0.959\cos^2 t}\,dt \quad \text{Simplify.} \\ &\approx 2.407. \quad \text{Approximate using calculator.} \end{aligned}$$

The fact that α is close to 1 for all the planets means that their orbits are nearly circular. For this reason, the lengths of the orbits shown in the table are nearly equal to $2\pi a$, which is the length of a circular orbit with radius a.

Related Exercises 27–30 ◄

Arc Length of a Polar Curve

➤ Recall from Section 10.2 that to convert from polar to Cartesian coordinates we use the relations

$$x = r\cos\theta \quad \text{and} \quad y = r\sin\theta.$$

We now return to polar coordinates and answer the arc length question for polar curves: Given the polar equation $r = f(\theta)$, what is the length of the corresponding curve for $\alpha \le \theta \le \beta$? The key idea is to express the polar equation as a set of parametric equations in Cartesian coordinates and then use the arc length formula derived above. Letting θ play the role of a parameter and using $r = f(\theta)$, parametric equations for the polar curve are

$$x = r\cos\theta = f(\theta)\cos\theta \quad \text{and} \quad y = r\sin\theta = f(\theta)\sin\theta,$$

where $\alpha \le \theta \le \beta$. The arc length formula in terms of the parameter θ is

$$L = \int_\alpha^\beta \sqrt{\left(\frac{dx}{d\theta}\right)^2 + \left(\frac{dy}{d\theta}\right)^2}\,d\theta,$$

where

$$\frac{dx}{d\theta} = f'(\theta)\cos\theta - f(\theta)\sin\theta \quad \text{and} \quad \frac{dy}{d\theta} = f'(\theta)\sin\theta + f(\theta)\cos\theta.$$

When substituted into the arc length formula and simplified, the result is a new arc length integral (Exercise 68).

Arc Length of a Polar Curve

Let f have a continuous derivative on the interval $[\alpha, \beta]$. The **arc length** of the polar curve $r = f(\theta)$ on $[\alpha, \beta]$ is

$$L = \int_\alpha^\beta \sqrt{f(\theta)^2 + f'(\theta)^2}\,d\theta.$$

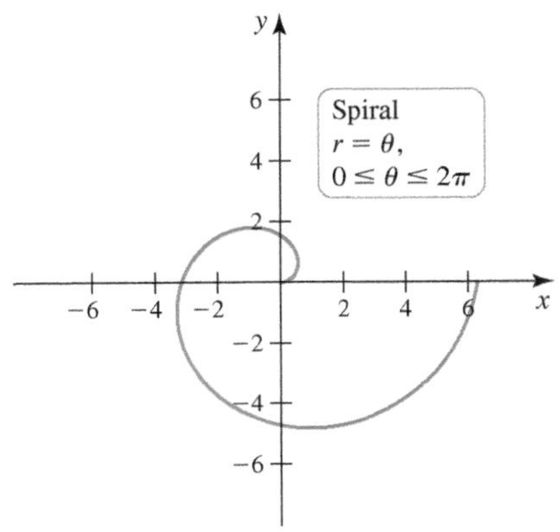

Figure 11.99

QUICK CHECK 4 Use the arc length formula to verify that the circumference of the circle $r = f(\theta) = 1$, for $0 \le \theta \le 2\pi$, is 2π. ◄

EXAMPLE 5 Arc length of polar curves

a. Find the arc length of the spiral $r = f(\theta) = \theta$, for $0 \le \theta \le 2\pi$ (Figure 11.99).

b. Find the arc length of the cardioid $r = 1 + \cos\theta$ (Figure 11.100).

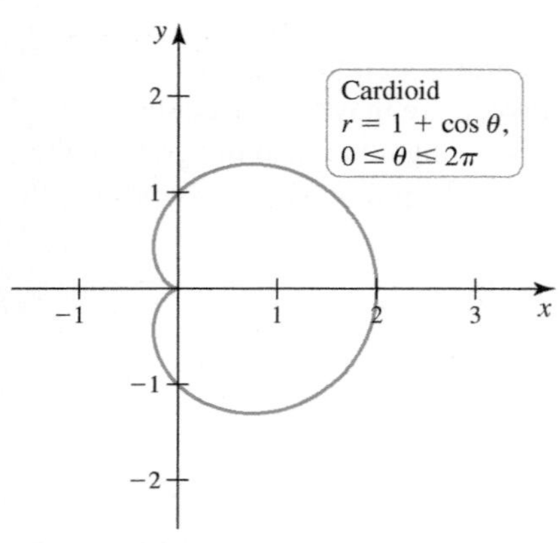

Figure 11.100

SOLUTION

a. $L = \int_0^{2\pi} \sqrt{\theta^2 + 1}\, d\theta$ $\quad$ $f(\theta) = \theta$ and $f'(\theta) = 1$

$= \left(\frac{\theta}{2}\sqrt{\theta^2 + 1} + \frac{1}{2}\ln\left(\theta + \sqrt{\theta^2 + 1}\right)\right)\Big|_0^{2\pi}$ $\quad$ Table of integrals or trigonometric substitution

$= \pi\sqrt{4\pi^2 + 1} + \frac{1}{2}\ln\left(2\pi + \sqrt{4\pi^2 + 1}\right)$ $\quad$ Substitute limits of integration.

≈ 21.26 $\quad$ Evaluate.

b. The cardioid is symmetric about the x-axis and its upper half is generated for $0 \le \theta \le \pi$. The length of the full curve is twice the length of its upper half:

$$L = 2\int_0^{\pi} \sqrt{(1 + \cos\theta)^2 + (-\sin\theta)^2}\, d\theta \qquad f(\theta) = 1 + \cos\theta; f'(\theta) = -\sin\theta$$

$$= 2\int_0^{\pi} \sqrt{2 + 2\cos\theta}\, d\theta \qquad \text{Simplify.}$$

$$= 2\int_0^{\pi} \sqrt{4\cos^2(\theta/2)}\, d\theta \qquad 1 + \cos\theta = 2\cos^2(\theta/2)$$

$$= 4\int_0^{\pi} \cos(\theta/2)\, d\theta \qquad \cos(\theta/2) \ge 0, \text{ for } 0 \le \theta \le \pi$$

$$= 8\sin(\theta/2)\Big|_0^{\pi} = 8. \qquad \text{Integrate and simplify.}$$

Related Exercises 31–40 ◀

Arc Length as a Parameter

Until now, the parameter t used to describe a curve $\mathbf{r}(t) = \langle f(t), g(t), h(t)\rangle$ has been chosen either for convenience or because it represents time in some specified unit. We now introduce the most natural parameter for describing curves; that parameter is *arc length*. Let's see what it means for a curve to be *parameterized by arc length*.

Consider the following two characterizations of the unit circle centered at the origin:

- $\langle \cos t, \sin t\rangle$, for $0 \le t \le 2\pi$
- $\langle \cos 2t, \sin 2t\rangle$, for $0 \le t \le \pi$

In the first description, as the parameter t increases from $t = 0$ to $t = 2\pi$, the full circle is generated and the arc length s of the curve also increases from $s = 0$ to $s = 2\pi$. In other words, as the parameter t increases, it measures the arc length of the curve that is generated (Figure 11.101a).

In the second description, as t varies from $t = 0$ to $t = \pi$, the full circle is generated and the arc length increases from $s = 0$ to $s = 2\pi$. In this case, the length of the interval in t does not equal the length of the curve generated; therefore, the parameter t does not correspond to arc length (Figure 11.101b). In general, there are infinitely many ways to parameterize a given curve; however, for a given initial point and orientation, arc length is the parameter for only one of them.

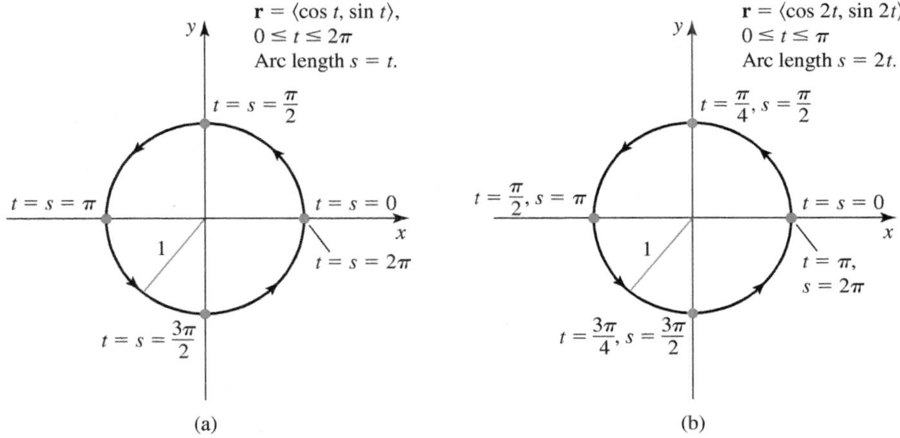

Figure 11.101

QUICK CHECK 5 Consider the portion of a circle $\mathbf{r}(t) = \langle \cos t, \sin t \rangle$, for $a \leq t \leq b$. Show that the arc length of the curve is $b - a$. ◂

The Arc Length Function Suppose that a smooth curve is represented by the function $\mathbf{r}(t) = \langle f(t), g(t), h(t) \rangle$, for $t \geq a$, where t is a parameter. Notice that as t increases, the length of the curve also increases. Using the arc length formula, the length of the curve from $\mathbf{r}(a)$ to $\mathbf{r}(t)$ is

➤ Notice that t is the independent variable of the function $s(t)$, so a different symbol u is used for the variable of integration. It is common to use s as the arc length function.

$$s(t) = \int_a^t \sqrt{f'(u)^2 + g'(u)^2 + h'(u)^2}\, du = \int_a^t |\mathbf{v}(u)|\, du.$$

This equation gives the relationship between the arc length of a curve and any parameter t used to describe the curve.

An important consequence of this relationship arises if we differentiate both sides with respect to t using the Fundamental Theorem of Calculus:

$$\frac{ds}{dt} = \frac{d}{dt}\left(\int_a^t |\mathbf{v}(u)|\, du\right) = |\mathbf{v}(t)|.$$

Specifically, if t represents time and $\mathbf{r}$ is the position of an object moving on the curve, then the rate of change of the arc length with respect to time is the speed of the object. Notice that if $\mathbf{r}(t)$ describes a smooth curve, then $|\mathbf{v}(t)| \neq 0$; hence $ds/dt > 0$, and s is an increasing function of t—as t increases, the arc length also increases. If $\mathbf{r}(t)$ is a curve on which $|\mathbf{v}(t)| = 1$, then

$$s(t) = \int_a^t |\mathbf{v}(u)|\, du = \int_a^t 1\, du = t - a,$$

which means the parameter t corresponds to arc length. These observations are summarized in the following theorem.

THEOREM 11.9 Arc Length as a Function of a Parameter
Let $\mathbf{r}(t)$ describe a smooth curve, for $t \geq a$. The arc length is given by

$$s(t) = \int_a^t |\mathbf{v}(u)|\, du,$$

where $|\mathbf{v}| = |\mathbf{r}'|$. Equivalently, $\frac{ds}{dt} = |\mathbf{v}(t)|$. If $|\mathbf{v}(t)| = 1$, for all $t \geq a$, then the parameter t corresponds to arc length.

EXAMPLE 6 **Arc length parameterization** Consider the helix $\mathbf{r}(t) = \langle 2\cos t, 2\sin t, 4t\rangle$, for $t \ge 0$.

a. Find the arc length function $s(t)$.

b. Find another description of the helix that uses arc length as the parameter.

SOLUTION

a. Note that $\mathbf{r}'(t) = \langle -2\sin t, 2\cos t, 4\rangle$ and

$$\begin{aligned}|\mathbf{v}(t)| = |\mathbf{r}'(t)| &= \sqrt{(-2\sin t)^2 + (2\cos t)^2 + 4^2} \\ &= \sqrt{4(\sin^2 t + \cos^2 t) + 4^2} && \text{Simplify.} \\ &= \sqrt{4 + 4^2} && \sin^2 t + \cos^2 t = 1 \\ &= \sqrt{20} = 2\sqrt{5}. && \text{Simplify.}\end{aligned}$$

Therefore, the relationship between the arc length s and the parameter t is

$$s(t) = \int_a^t |\mathbf{v}(u)|\, du = \int_0^t 2\sqrt{5}\, du = 2\sqrt{5}\, t.$$

An increase of $1/(2\sqrt{5})$ in the parameter t corresponds to an increase of 1 in the arc length. Therefore, the curve is not parameterized by arc length.

b. Substituting $t = s/(2\sqrt{5})$ into the original parametric description of the helix, we find that the description with arc length as a parameter is (using a different function name)

$$\mathbf{r}_1(s) = \left\langle 2\cos\left(\frac{s}{2\sqrt{5}}\right), 2\sin\left(\frac{s}{2\sqrt{5}}\right), \frac{2s}{\sqrt{5}}\right\rangle, \quad \text{for } s \ge 0.$$

This description has the property that an increment of Δs in the parameter corresponds to an increment of exactly Δs in the arc length.

Related Exercises 41–50 ◄

QUICK CHECK 6 Does the line $\mathbf{r}(t) = \langle t, t, t\rangle$ have arc length as a parameter? Explain. ◄

As you will see in Section 11.9, using arc length as a parameter—when it can be done—generally leads to simplified calculations.

SECTION 11.8 EXERCISES

Review Questions

1. Find the length of the line given by $\mathbf{r}(t) = \langle t, 2t\rangle$, for $a \le t \le b$.

2. Explain how to find the length of the curve $\mathbf{r}(t) = \langle f(t), g(t), h(t)\rangle$, for $a \le t \le b$.

3. Express the arc length of a curve in terms of the speed of an object moving along the curve.

4. Suppose an object moves in space with the position function $\mathbf{r}(t) = \langle x(t), y(t), z(t)\rangle$. Write the integral that gives the distance it travels between $t = a$ and $t = b$.

5. An object moves on a trajectory given by $\mathbf{r}(t) = \langle 10\cos 2t, 10\sin 2t\rangle$, for $0 \le t \le \pi$. How far does it travel?

6. How do you find the arc length of the polar curve $r = f(\theta)$, for $\alpha \le \theta \le \beta$, assuming f' is continuous on $[\alpha, \beta]$?

7. Explain what it means for a curve to be parameterized by its arc length.

8. Is the curve $\mathbf{r}(t) = \langle \cos t, \sin t\rangle$ parameterized by its arc length? Explain.

Basic Skills

9–22. Arc length calculations *Find the length of the following two- and three-dimensional curves.*

9. $\mathbf{r}(t) = \langle 3t^2 - 1, 4t^2 + 5\rangle$, for $0 \le t \le 1$

10. $\mathbf{r}(t) = \langle 3t - 1, 4t + 5, t\rangle$, for $0 \le t \le 1$

11. $\mathbf{r}(t) = \langle 3\cos t, 3\sin t\rangle$, for $0 \le t \le \pi$

12. $\mathbf{r}(t) = \langle 4\cos 3t, 4\sin 3t\rangle$, for $0 \le t \le 2\pi/3$

13. $\mathbf{r}(t) = \langle \cos t + t\sin t, \sin t - t\cos t\rangle$, for $0 \le t \le \pi/2$

14. $\mathbf{r}(t) = \langle \cos t + \sin t, \cos t - \sin t\rangle$, for $0 \le t \le 2\pi$

15. $\mathbf{r}(t) = \langle 2 + 3t, 1 - 4t, -4 + 3t\rangle$, for $1 \le t \le 6$

16. $\mathbf{r}(t) = \langle 4\cos t, 4\sin t, 3t\rangle$, for $0 \le t \le 6\pi$

17. $\mathbf{r}(t) = \langle t, 8 \sin t, 8 \cos t \rangle$, for $0 \le t \le 4\pi$

18. $\mathbf{r}(t) = \langle t^2/2, (2t + 1)^{3/2}/3 \rangle$, for $0 \le t \le 2$

19. $\mathbf{r}(t) = \langle e^{2t}, 2e^{2t} + 5, 2e^{2t} - 20 \rangle$, for $0 \le t \le \ln 2$

20. $\mathbf{r}(t) = \langle t^2, t^3 \rangle$, for $0 \le t \le 4$

21. $\mathbf{r}(t) = \langle \cos^3 t, \sin^3 t \rangle$, for $0 \le t \le \pi/2$

22. $\mathbf{r}(t) = \langle 3 \cos t, 4 \cos t, 5 \sin t \rangle$, for $0 \le t \le 2\pi$

23–26. Speed and arc length *For the following trajectories, find the speed associated with the trajectory and then find the length of the trajectory on the given interval.*

23. $\mathbf{r}(t) = \langle 2t^3, -t^3, 5t^3 \rangle$, for $0 \le t \le 4$

24. $\mathbf{r}(t) = \langle 5 \cos t^2, 5 \sin t^2, 12t^2 \rangle$, for $0 \le t \le 2$

25. $\mathbf{r}(t) = \langle 13 \sin 2t, 12 \cos 2t, 5 \cos 2t \rangle$, for $0 \le t \le \pi$

26. $\mathbf{r}(t) = \langle e^t \sin t, e^t \cos t, e^t \rangle$, for $0 \le t \le \ln 2$

T **27–30. Arc length approximations** *Use a calculator to approximate the length of the following curves. In each case, simplify the arc length integral as much as possible before finding an approximation.*

27. $\mathbf{r}(t) = \langle 2 \cos t, 4 \sin t \rangle$, for $0 \le t \le 2\pi$

28. $\mathbf{r}(t) = \langle 2 \cos t, 4 \sin t, 6 \cos t \rangle$, for $0 \le t \le 2\pi$

29. $\mathbf{r}(t) = \langle t, 4t^2, 10 \rangle$, for $-2 \le t \le 2$

30. $\mathbf{r}(t) = \langle e^t, 2e^{-t}, t \rangle$, for $0 \le t \le \ln 3$

31–40. Arc length of polar curves *Find the length of the following polar curves.*

31. The complete circle $r = a \sin \theta$, where $a > 0$

32. The complete cardioid $r = 2 - 2 \sin \theta$

33. The spiral $r = \theta^2$, where $0 \le \theta \le 2\pi$

34. The spiral $r = e^\theta$, where $0 \le \theta \le 2\pi n$, for a positive integer n

35. The complete cardioid $r = 4 + 4 \sin \theta$

36. The spiral $r = 4\theta^2$, for $0 \le \theta \le 6$

37. The spiral $r = 2e^{2\theta}$, for $0 \le \theta \le \ln 8$

38. The curve $r = \sin^2 (\theta/2)$, for $0 \le \theta \le \pi$

39. The curve $r = \sin^3 (\theta/3)$, for $0 \le \theta \le \pi/2$

40. The parabola $r = \sqrt{2}/(1 + \cos \theta)$, for $0 \le \theta \le \pi/2$

41–50. Arc length parameterization *Determine whether the following curves use arc length as a parameter. If not, find a description that uses arc length as a parameter.*

41. $\mathbf{r}(t) = \langle 1, \sin t, \cos t \rangle$, for $t \ge 1$

42. $\mathbf{r}(t) = \left\langle \frac{t}{\sqrt{3}}, \frac{t}{\sqrt{3}}, \frac{t}{\sqrt{3}} \right\rangle$, for $0 \le t \le 10$

43. $\mathbf{r}(t) = \langle t, 2t \rangle$, for $0 \le t \le 3$

44. $\mathbf{r}(t) = \langle t + 1, 2t - 3, 6t \rangle$, for $0 \le t \le 10$

45. $\mathbf{r}(t) = \langle 2 \cos t, 2 \sin t \rangle$, for $0 \le t \le 2\pi$

46. $\mathbf{r}(t) = \langle 5 \cos t, 3 \sin t, 4 \sin t \rangle$, for $0 \le t \le \pi$

47. $\mathbf{r}(t) = \langle \cos t^2, \sin t^2 \rangle$, for $0 \le t \le \sqrt{\pi}$

48. $\mathbf{r}(t) = \langle t^2, 2t^2, 4t^2 \rangle$, for $1 \le t \le 4$

49. $\mathbf{r}(t) = \langle e^t, e^t, e^t \rangle$, for $t \ge 0$

50. $\mathbf{r}(t) = \left\langle \frac{\cos t}{\sqrt{2}}, \frac{\cos t}{\sqrt{2}}, \sin t \right\rangle$, for $0 \le t \le 10$

Further Explorations

51. **Explain why or why not** Determine whether the following statements are true and give an explanation or counterexample.
   a. If an object moves on a trajectory with constant speed S over a time interval $a \le t \le b$, then the length of the trajectory is $S(b - a)$.
   b. The curves defined by $\mathbf{r}(t) = \langle f(t), g(t) \rangle$ and $\mathbf{R}(t) = \langle g(t), f(t) \rangle$ have the same length over the interval $[a, b]$.
   c. The curve $\mathbf{r}(t) = \langle f(t), g(t) \rangle$, for $0 \le a \le t \le b$, and the curve $\mathbf{R}(t) = \langle f(t^2), g(t^2) \rangle$, for $\sqrt{a} \le t \le \sqrt{b}$, have the same length.
   d. The curve $\mathbf{r}(t) = \langle t, t^2, 3t^2 \rangle$, for $1 \le t \le 4$, is parameterized by arc length.

52. **Length of a line segment** Consider the line segment joining the points $P(x_0, y_0, z_0)$ and $Q(x_1, y_1, z_1)$.
   a. Find a parametric description of the line segment PQ.
   b. Use the arc length formula to find the length of PQ.
   c. Use geometry (distance formula) to verify the result of part (b).

53. **Tilted circles** Let the curve C be described by $\mathbf{r}(t) = \langle a \cos t, b \sin t, c \sin t \rangle$, where a, b, and c are real positive numbers.
   a. Assume that C lies in a plane. Show that C is a circle centered at the origin provided $a^2 = b^2 + c^2$.
   b. Find the arc length of the circle.
   c. Assuming that the curve lies in a plane, find the conditions for which $\mathbf{r}(t) = \langle a \cos t + b \sin t, c \cos t + d \sin t, e \cos t + f \sin t \rangle$ describes a circle. Then find its arc length.

54. **A family of arc length integrals** Find the length of the curve $\mathbf{r}(t) = \langle t^m, t^m, t^{3m/2} \rangle$, for $0 \le a \le t \le b$, where m is a real number. Express the result in terms of m, a, and b.

55. **A special case** Suppose a curve is described by $\mathbf{r}(t) = \langle A\, h(t), B\, h(t) \rangle$, for $a \le t \le b$, where A and B are constants and h has a continuous derivative.
   a. Show that the length of the curve is
   $$\sqrt{A^2 + B^2} \int_a^b |h'(t)|\, dt.$$
   b. Use part (a) to find the length of the curve $x = 2t^3$, $y = 5t^3$, for $0 \le t \le 4$.
   c. Use part (a) to find the length of the curve $x = 4/t$, $y = 10/t$, for $1 \le t \le 8$.

56. **Spiral arc length** Consider the spiral $r = 4\theta$, for $\theta \ge 0$.
   a. Use a trigonometric substitution to find the length of the spiral, for $0 \le \theta \le \sqrt{8}$.
   b. Find $L(\theta)$, the length of the spiral on the interval $[0, \theta]$, for any $\theta \ge 0$.
   c. Show that $L'(\theta) > 0$. Is $L''(\theta)$ positive or negative? Interpret your answer.

57. **Spiral arc length** Find the length of the entire spiral $r = e^{-a\theta}$, for $\theta \ge 0$ and $a > 0$.

T **58–61. Arc length using technology** *Use a calculator to find the approximate length of the following curves.*

58. The three-leaf rose $r = 2\cos 3\theta$

59. The lemniscate $r^2 = 6\sin 2\theta$

60. The limaçon $r = 2 - 4\sin\theta$

61. The limaçon $r = 4 - 2\cos\theta$

Applications

62. A cycloid A cycloid is the path traced by a point on a circle rolling on a flat surface (think of a light on the rim of a moving bicycle wheel). The cycloid generated by a circle of radius a is given by the parametric equations

$$x = a(t - \sin t), \quad y = a(1 - \cos t);$$

the parameter range $0 \le t \le 2\pi$ produces one arch of the cycloid (see figure). Show that the length of one arch of a cycloid is $8a$.

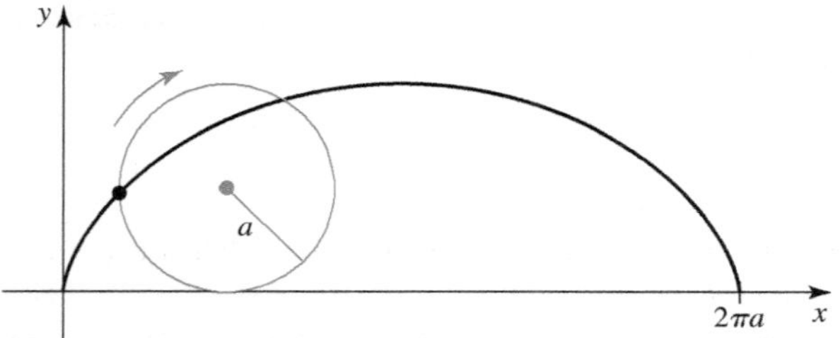

T **63. Projectile trajectories** A projectile (such as a baseball or a cannonball) launched from the origin with an initial horizontal velocity u_0 and an initial vertical velocity v_0 moves in a parabolic trajectory given by

$$x = u_0 t, \; y = -\tfrac{1}{2}gt^2 + v_0 t, \quad \text{for } t \ge 0,$$

where air resistance is neglected and $g \approx 9.8\text{ m/s}^2$ is the acceleration due to gravity (see Section 11.7).

a. Let $u_0 = 20\text{ m/s}$ and $v_0 = 25\text{ m/s}$. Assuming the projectile is launched over horizontal ground, at what time does it return to Earth?

b. Find the integral that gives the length of the trajectory from launch to landing.

c. Evaluate the integral in part (b) by first making the change of variables $u = -gt + v_0$. The resulting integral is evaluated either by making a second change of variables or by using a calculator. What is the length of the trajectory?

d. How far does the projectile land from its launch site?

64. Variable speed on a circle Consider a particle that moves in a plane according to the equations $x = \sin t^2$ and $y = \cos t^2$ with a starting position $(0, 1)$ at $t = 0$.

a. Describe the path of the particle, including the time required to return to the starting position.

b. What is the length of the path in part (a)?

c. Describe how the motion of this particle differs from the motion described by the equations $x = \sin t$ and $y = \cos t$.

d. Consider the motion described by $x = \sin t^n$ and $y = \cos t^n$, where n is a positive integer. Describe the path of the particle, including the time required to return to the starting position.

e. What is the length of the path in part (d) for any positive integer n?

f. If you were watching a race on a circular path between two runners, one moving according to $x = \sin t$ and $y = \cos t$ and one according to $x = \sin t^2$ and $y = \cos t^2$, who would win and when would one runner pass the other?

Additional Exercises

65. Arc length parameterization Prove that the line $\mathbf{r}(t) = \langle x_0 + at, y_0 + bt, z_0 + ct\rangle$ is parameterized by arc length provided $a^2 + b^2 + c^2 = 1$.

66. Arc length parameterization Prove that the curve $\mathbf{r}(t) = \langle a\cos t, b\sin t, c\sin t\rangle$ is parameterized by arc length provided $a^2 = b^2 + c^2 = 1$.

67. Lengths of related curves Suppose a curve is given by $\mathbf{r}(t) = \langle f(t), g(t)\rangle$, where f' and g' are continuous, for $a \le t \le b$. Assume the curve is traversed once, for $a \le t \le b$, and the length of the curve between $(f(a), g(a))$ and $(f(b), g(b))$ is L. Prove that for any nonzero constant c the length of the curve defined by $\mathbf{r}(t) = \langle cf(t), cg(t)\rangle$, for $a \le t \le b$, is $|c|L$.

68. Arc length for polar curves Prove that the length of the curve $r = f(\theta)$, for $\alpha \le \theta \le \beta$, is

$$L = \int_\alpha^\beta \sqrt{f(\theta)^2 + f'(\theta)^2}\, d\theta.$$

69. Arc length for $y = f(x)$ The arc length formula for functions of the form $y = f(x)$ on $[a, b]$ found in Section 6.5 is

$$L = \int_a^b \sqrt{1 + f'(x)^2}\, dx.$$

Derive this formula from the arc length formula for vector curves. (*Hint:* Let $x = t$ be the parameter.)

70. Change of variables Consider the parameterized curves $\mathbf{r}(t) = \langle f(t), g(t), h(t)\rangle$ and $\mathbf{R}(t) = \langle f(u(t)), g(u(t)), h(u(t))\rangle$, where f, g, h, and u are continuously differentiable functions and u has an inverse on $[a, b]$.

a. Show that the curve generated by $\mathbf{r}$ on the interval $a \le t \le b$ is the same as the curve generated by $\mathbf{R}$ on $u^{-1}(a) \le t \le u^{-1}(b)$ (or $u^{-1}(b) \le t \le u^{-1}(a)$).

b. Show that the lengths of the two curves are equal. (*Hint:* Use the Chain Rule and a change of variables in the arc length integral for the curve generated by $\mathbf{R}$.)

QUICK CHECK ANSWERS

1. $\sqrt{2}$ **2.** $\sqrt{3}$

3. $L = \int_a^b |\mathbf{v}(t)|\, dt = \int_a^b S\, dt = S(b - a)$ **4.** 2π

5. For $a \le t \le b$, the curve C generated is $(b - a)/2\pi$ of a full circle. Because the full circle has a length of 2π, the curve C has a length of $b - a$. **6.** No. If t increases by 1 unit, the length of the curve increases by $\sqrt{3}$ units.◄

11.9 Curvature and Normal Vectors

We know how to find tangent vectors and lengths of curves in space, but much more can be said about the shape of such curves. In this section, we introduce several new concepts. *Curvature* measures how *fast* a curve turns at a point, the *normal vector* gives the *direction* in which a curve turns, and the *binormal vector* and the *torsion* describe the twisting of a curve.

Curvature

Imagine driving a car along a winding mountain road. There are two ways to change the velocity of the car (that is, to accelerate). You can change the *speed* of the car or you can change the *direction* of the car. A change of speed is relatively easy to describe, so we postpone that discussion and focus on the change of direction. The rate at which the car changes direction is related to the notion of *curvature*.

Unit Tangent Vector Recall from Section 11.6 that if $\mathbf{r}(t) = \langle x(t), y(t), z(t) \rangle$ is a smooth oriented curve, then the unit tangent vector at a point is the unit vector that points in the direction of the tangent vector $\mathbf{r}'(t)$; that is,

$$\mathbf{T}(t) = \frac{\mathbf{r}'(t)}{|\mathbf{r}'(t)|} = \frac{\mathbf{v}(t)}{|\mathbf{v}(t)|}.$$

Because $\mathbf{T}$ is a unit vector, its length does not change along the curve. The only way $\mathbf{T}$ can change is through a change in direction.

How quickly does $\mathbf{T}$ change (in direction) as we move along the curve? If a small increment in arc length Δs along the curve results in a large change in the direction of $\mathbf{T}$, the curve is turning quickly over that interval and we say it has a large *curvature* (Figure 11.102a). If a small increment Δs in arc length results in a small change in the direction of $\mathbf{T}$, the curve is turning slowly over that interval and it has a small curvature (Figure 11.102b). The magnitude of the rate at which the direction of $\mathbf{T}$ changes with respect to arc length is the curvature of the curve.

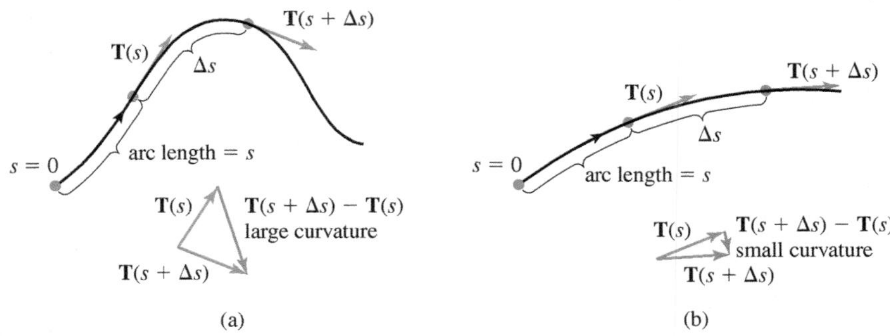

Figure 11.102

> Recall that the unit tangent vector at a point depends on the orientation of the curve. The curvature does not depend on the orientation of the curve, but it does depend on the shape of the curve. The Greek letter κ (kappa) is used to denote curvature.

DEFINITION Curvature

Let $\mathbf{r}$ describe a smooth parameterized curve. If s denotes arc length and $\mathbf{T} = \mathbf{r}'/|\mathbf{r}'|$ is the unit tangent vector, the **curvature** is $\kappa(s) = \left|\frac{d\mathbf{T}}{ds}\right|$.

Note that κ is a nonnegative scalar-valued function. A large value of κ at a point indicates a tight curve that changes direction quickly. If κ is small, then the curve is relatively flat and its direction changes slowly. The minimum curvature (zero) occurs on a straight line where the tangent vector never changes direction along the curve.

In order to evaluate $d\mathbf{T}/ds$, a description of the curve in terms of the arc length appears to be needed, but it may be difficult to obtain. A short calculation leads to the first of two practical curvature formulas.

Letting t be an arbitrary parameter, we begin with the Chain Rule and write $\dfrac{d\mathbf{T}}{dt} = \dfrac{d\mathbf{T}}{ds} \cdot \dfrac{ds}{dt}$. Dividing by $ds/dt = |\mathbf{v}|$ and taking absolute values leads to

$$\kappa = \left|\frac{d\mathbf{T}}{ds}\right| = \frac{|d\mathbf{T}/dt|}{|ds/dt|} = \frac{1}{|\mathbf{v}|}\left|\frac{d\mathbf{T}}{dt}\right|.$$

This derivation is a proof of the following theorem.

THEOREM 11.10 Curvature Formula
Let $\mathbf{r}(t)$ describe a smooth parameterized curve, where t is any parameter. If $\mathbf{v} = \mathbf{r}'$ is the velocity and $\mathbf{T}$ is the unit tangent vector, then the curvature is

$$\kappa(t) = \frac{1}{|\mathbf{v}|}\left|\frac{d\mathbf{T}}{dt}\right| = \frac{|\mathbf{T}'(t)|}{|\mathbf{r}'(t)|}.$$

EXAMPLE 1 Lines have zero curvature Consider the line $\mathbf{r}(t) = \langle x_0 + at, y_0 + bt, z_0 + ct \rangle$, for $-\infty < t < \infty$. Show that $\kappa = 0$ at all points on the line.

SOLUTION Note that $\mathbf{r}'(t) = \langle a, b, c \rangle$ and $|\mathbf{r}'(t)| = |\mathbf{v}(t)| = \sqrt{a^2 + b^2 + c^2}$. Therefore,

$$\mathbf{T}(t) = \frac{\mathbf{r}'(t)}{|\mathbf{r}'(t)|} = \frac{\langle a, b, c \rangle}{\sqrt{a^2 + b^2 + c^2}}.$$

Because $\mathbf{T}$ is a constant, $\dfrac{d\mathbf{T}}{dt} = \mathbf{0}$; therefore, $\kappa = 0$ at all points of the line.

Related Exercises 11–20 ◀

EXAMPLE 2 Circles have constant curvature Consider the circle $\mathbf{r}(t) = \langle R\cos t, R\sin t \rangle$, for $0 \le t \le 2\pi$, where $R > 0$. Show that $\kappa = 1/R$.

SOLUTION We compute $\mathbf{r}'(t) = \langle -R\sin t, R\cos t \rangle$ and

$$\begin{aligned} |\mathbf{v}(t)| = |\mathbf{r}'(t)| &= \sqrt{(-R\sin t)^2 + (R\cos t)^2} \\ &= \sqrt{R^2(\sin^2 t + \cos^2 t)} && \text{Simplify.} \\ &= R. && \sin^2 t + \cos^2 t = 1, R > 0 \end{aligned}$$

Therefore,

$$\mathbf{T}(t) = \frac{\mathbf{r}'(t)}{|\mathbf{r}'(t)|} = \frac{\langle -R\sin t, R\cos t \rangle}{R} = \langle -\sin t, \cos t \rangle, \text{ and}$$

$$\frac{d\mathbf{T}}{dt} = \langle -\cos t, -\sin t \rangle.$$

➤ The curvature of a curve at a point can also be visualized in terms of a **circle of curvature**, which is a circle of radius R that is tangent to the curve at that point. The curvature at the point is $\kappa = 1/R$. See Exercises 70–74.

Combining these observations, the curvature is

$$\kappa = \frac{1}{|\mathbf{v}|}\left|\frac{d\mathbf{T}}{dt}\right| = \frac{1}{R}|\langle -\cos t, -\sin t \rangle| = \frac{1}{R}\underbrace{\sqrt{\cos^2 t + \sin^2 t}}_{1} = \frac{1}{R}.$$

The curvature of a circle is constant; a circle with a small radius has a large curvature and vice versa.

Related Exercises 11–20 ◀

QUICK CHECK 1 What is the curvature of the circle $\mathbf{r}(t) = \langle 3\sin t, 3\cos t \rangle$? ◀

An Alternative Curvature Formula A second curvature formula, which pertains specifically to trajectories of moving objects, is easier to use in some cases. The calculation is instructive because it relies on many properties of vector functions. In the end, a remarkably simple formula emerges.

Again consider a smooth curve $\mathbf{r}(t) = \langle x(t), y(t), z(t) \rangle$, where $\mathbf{v}(t) = \mathbf{r}'(t)$ and $\mathbf{a}(t) = \mathbf{v}'(t)$ are the velocity and acceleration of an object moving along that curve, respectively. We assume that $\mathbf{v}(t) \neq \mathbf{0}$ and $\mathbf{a}(t) \neq \mathbf{0}$. Because $\mathbf{T} = \mathbf{v}/|\mathbf{v}|$, we begin by writing $\mathbf{v} = |\mathbf{v}|\,\mathbf{T}$ and differentiating both sides with respect to t:

$$\mathbf{a} = \frac{d\mathbf{v}}{dt} = \frac{d}{dt}(|\mathbf{v}(t)|\,\mathbf{T}(t)) = \frac{d}{dt}(|\mathbf{v}(t)|)\mathbf{T}(t) + |\mathbf{v}(t)|\frac{d\mathbf{T}}{dt}. \qquad \text{Product Rule (1)}$$

We now form $\mathbf{v} \times \mathbf{a}$:

> Distributive law for cross products:
>
> $\mathbf{w} \times (\mathbf{u} + \mathbf{v}) = (\mathbf{w} \times \mathbf{u}) + (\mathbf{w} \times \mathbf{v})$
>
> $(\mathbf{u} + \mathbf{v}) \times \mathbf{w} = (\mathbf{u} \times \mathbf{w}) + (\mathbf{v} \times \mathbf{w})$

$$\begin{aligned}\mathbf{v} \times \mathbf{a} &= \underbrace{|\mathbf{v}|\mathbf{T}}_{\mathbf{v}} \times \underbrace{\left[\frac{d}{dt}(|\mathbf{v}|)\mathbf{T} + |\mathbf{v}|\frac{d\mathbf{T}}{dt}\right]}_{\mathbf{a}} \\ &= \underbrace{|\mathbf{v}|\mathbf{T} \times \left(\frac{d}{dt}(|\mathbf{v}|)\right)\mathbf{T}}_{\mathbf{0}} + |\mathbf{v}|\mathbf{T} \times |\mathbf{v}|\frac{d\mathbf{T}}{dt} \qquad \text{Distributive law for cross products}\end{aligned}$$

The first term in this expression has the form $a\mathbf{T} \times b\mathbf{T}$, where a and b are scalars. Therefore, $a\mathbf{T}$ and $b\mathbf{T}$ are parallel vectors and $a\mathbf{T} \times b\mathbf{T} = \mathbf{0}$. To simplify the second term, recall that a vector $\mathbf{u}(t)$ of constant length has the property that $\mathbf{u}$ and $d\mathbf{u}/dt$ are orthogonal (Section 11.7). Because $\mathbf{T}$ is a unit vector, it has constant length, and $\mathbf{T}$ and $d\mathbf{T}/dt$ are orthogonal. Furthermore, scalar multiples of $\mathbf{T}$ and $d\mathbf{T}/dt$ are also orthogonal. Therefore, the magnitude of the second term simplifies as follows:

> Recall that the magnitude of the cross product of nonzero vectors is $|\mathbf{u} \times \mathbf{v}| = |\mathbf{u}||\mathbf{v}| \sin\theta$, where θ is the angle between the vectors. If the vectors are orthogonal, $\sin\theta = 1$ and $|\mathbf{u} \times \mathbf{v}| = |\mathbf{u}||\mathbf{v}|$.

$$\begin{aligned}\left||\mathbf{v}|\mathbf{T} \times |\mathbf{v}|\frac{d\mathbf{T}}{dt}\right| &= |\mathbf{v}||\mathbf{T}|\left||\mathbf{v}|\frac{d\mathbf{T}}{dt}\right|\underbrace{\sin\theta}_{1} \qquad |\mathbf{u} \times \mathbf{v}| = |\mathbf{u}||\mathbf{v}|\sin\theta \\ &= |\mathbf{v}|^2\left|\frac{d\mathbf{T}}{dt}\right|\underbrace{|\mathbf{T}|}_{1} \qquad \text{Simplify, } \theta = \pi/2. \\ &= |\mathbf{v}|^2\left|\frac{d\mathbf{T}}{dt}\right|. \qquad |\mathbf{T}| = 1\end{aligned}$$

The final step is to use Theorem 11.10 and substitute $\left|\frac{d\mathbf{T}}{dt}\right| = \kappa|\mathbf{v}|$. Putting these results together, we find that

$$|\mathbf{v} \times \mathbf{a}| = |\mathbf{v}|^2\left|\frac{d\mathbf{T}}{dt}\right| = |\mathbf{v}|^2\kappa|\mathbf{v}| = \kappa|\mathbf{v}|^3.$$

Solving for the curvature gives $\kappa = \dfrac{|\mathbf{v} \times \mathbf{a}|}{|\mathbf{v}|^3}$.

> Note that $\mathbf{a}(t) = \mathbf{0}$ corresponds to straight-line motion and $\kappa = 0$. If $\mathbf{v}(t) = \mathbf{0}$, the object is at rest and κ is undefined.

THEOREM 11.11 Alternative Curvature Formula

Let $\mathbf{r}$ be the position of an object moving on a smooth curve. The **curvature** at a point on the curve is

$$\kappa = \frac{|\mathbf{v} \times \mathbf{a}|}{|\mathbf{v}|^3},$$

where $\mathbf{v} = \mathbf{r}'$ is the velocity and $\mathbf{a} = \mathbf{v}'$ is the acceleration.

QUICK CHECK 2 Use the alternative curvature formula to compute the curvature of the curve $\mathbf{r}(t) = \langle t^2, 10, -10 \rangle$. ◄

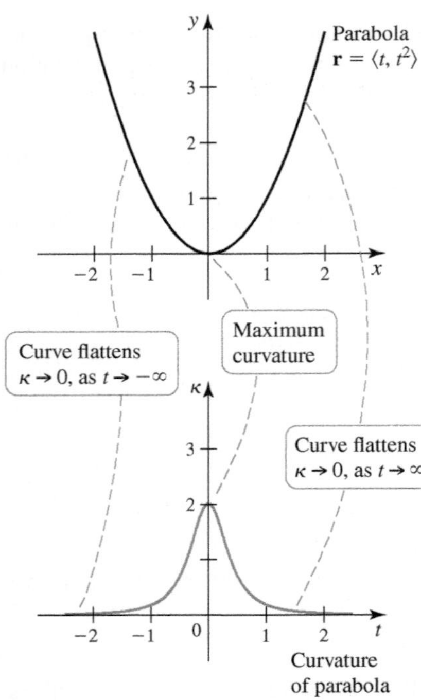

Figure 11.103

EXAMPLE 3 **Curvature of a parabola** Find the curvature of the parabola $\mathbf{r}(t) = \langle t, at^2 \rangle$, for $-\infty < t < \infty$, where $a > 0$ is a real number.

SOLUTION The alternative formula works well in this case. We find that $\mathbf{v}(t) = \mathbf{r}'(t) = \langle 1, 2at \rangle$ and $\mathbf{a}(t) = \mathbf{v}'(t) = \langle 0, 2a \rangle$. To compute the cross product $\mathbf{v} \times \mathbf{a}$, we append a third component of 0 to each vector:

$$\mathbf{v} \times \mathbf{a} = \begin{vmatrix} \mathbf{i} & \mathbf{j} & \mathbf{k} \\ 1 & 2at & 0 \\ 0 & 2a & 0 \end{vmatrix} = 2a\,\mathbf{k}.$$

Therefore, the curvature is

$$\kappa(t) = \frac{|\mathbf{v} \times \mathbf{a}|}{|\mathbf{v}|^3} = \frac{|2a\,\mathbf{k}|}{|\langle 1, 2at \rangle|^3} = \frac{2a}{(1 + 4a^2t^2)^{3/2}}.$$

The curvature is a maximum at the vertex of the parabola where $t = 0$ and $\kappa = 2a$. The curvature decreases as one moves along the curve away from the vertex, as shown in Figure 11.103 with $a = 1$.

Related Exercises 21–26 ◂

EXAMPLE 4 **Curvature of a helix** Find the curvature of the helix $\mathbf{r}(t) = \langle a\cos t, a\sin t, bt \rangle$, for $-\infty < t < \infty$, where $a > 0$ and $b > 0$ are real numbers.

SOLUTION We use the alternative curvature formula, with

$$\mathbf{v}(t) = \mathbf{r}'(t) = \langle -a\sin t, a\cos t, b \rangle \quad \text{and}$$
$$\mathbf{a}(t) = \mathbf{v}'(t) = \langle -a\cos t, -a\sin t, 0 \rangle.$$

The cross product $\mathbf{v} \times \mathbf{a}$ is

$$\mathbf{v} \times \mathbf{a} = \begin{vmatrix} \mathbf{i} & \mathbf{j} & \mathbf{k} \\ -a\sin t & a\cos t & b \\ -a\cos t & -a\sin t & 0 \end{vmatrix} = ab\sin t\,\mathbf{i} - ab\cos t\,\mathbf{j} + a^2\,\mathbf{k}.$$

Therefore,

$$\begin{aligned} |\mathbf{v} \times \mathbf{a}| &= |ab\sin t\,\mathbf{i} - ab\cos t\,\mathbf{j} + a^2\,\mathbf{k}| \\ &= \sqrt{a^2b^2\underbrace{(\sin^2 t + \cos^2 t)}_{1} + a^4} \\ &= a\sqrt{a^2 + b^2}. \end{aligned}$$

By a familiar calculation, $|\mathbf{v}| = |\langle -a\sin t, a\cos t, b \rangle| = \sqrt{a^2 + b^2}$. Therefore,

$$\kappa = \frac{|\mathbf{v} \times \mathbf{a}|}{|\mathbf{v}|^3} = \frac{a\sqrt{a^2 + b^2}}{(\sqrt{a^2 + b^2})^3} = \frac{a}{a^2 + b^2}.$$

A similar calculation shows that all helices of this form have constant curvature.

Related Exercises 21–26 ◂

➤ In the curvature formula for the helix, if $b = 0$, the helix becomes a circle of radius a with $\kappa = \frac{1}{a}$. At the other extreme, holding a fixed and letting $b \to \infty$ stretches and straightens the helix so that $\kappa \to 0$.

Principal Unit Normal Vector

The curvature answers the question of how *fast* a curve turns. The *principal unit normal* vector determines the *direction* in which a curve turns. Specifically, the magnitude of $d\mathbf{T}/ds$ is the curvature: $\kappa = |d\mathbf{T}/ds|$. What about the direction of $d\mathbf{T}/ds$? If only the direction, but not the magnitude, of a vector is of interest, it is convenient to work with a unit vector that has the same direction as the original vector. We apply this idea to $d\mathbf{T}/ds$. The unit vector that points in the direction of $d\mathbf{T}/ds$ is the *principal unit normal vector*.

➤ The principal unit normal vector depends on the shape of the curve but not on the orientation of the curve.

> **DEFINITION Principal Unit Normal Vector**
>
> Let $\mathbf{r}$ describe a smooth curve parameterized by arc length. The **principal unit normal vector** at a point P on the curve at which $\kappa \neq 0$ is
>
> $$\mathbf{N}(s) = \frac{d\mathbf{T}/ds}{|d\mathbf{T}/ds|} = \frac{1}{\kappa}\frac{d\mathbf{T}}{ds}.$$
>
> For other parameters, we use the equivalent formula
>
> $$\mathbf{N}(t) = \frac{d\mathbf{T}/dt}{|d\mathbf{T}/dt|},$$
>
> evaluated at the value of t corresponding to P.

The practical formula $\mathbf{N} = \dfrac{d\mathbf{T}/dt}{|d\mathbf{T}/dt|}$ follows from the definition by using the Chain Rule to write $\dfrac{d\mathbf{T}}{ds} = \dfrac{d\mathbf{T}}{dt} \cdot \dfrac{dt}{ds}$ (Exercise 80). Two important properties of the principal unit normal vector follow from the definition.

> **THEOREM 11.12 Properties of the Principal Unit Normal Vector**
>
> Let $\mathbf{r}$ describe a smooth parameterized curve with unit tangent vector $\mathbf{T}$ and principal unit normal vector $\mathbf{N}$.
>
> 1. $\mathbf{T}$ and $\mathbf{N}$ are orthogonal at all points of the curve; that is, $\mathbf{T} \cdot \mathbf{N} = 0$ at all points where $\mathbf{N}$ is defined.
> 2. The principal unit normal vector points to the inside of the curve—in the direction that the curve is turning.

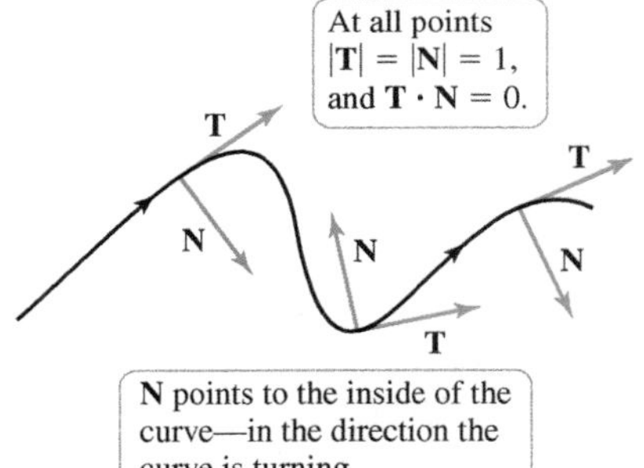

Figure 11.104

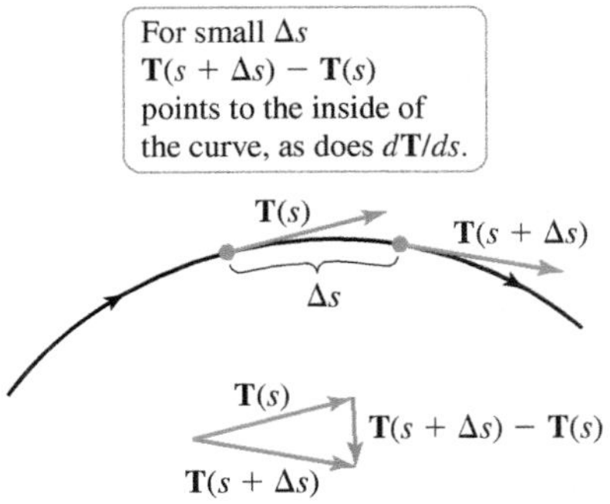

For small Δs $\mathbf{T}(s + \Delta s) - \mathbf{T}(s)$ points to the inside of the curve, as does $d\mathbf{T}/ds$.

Figure 11.105

Proof:

1. As a unit vector, $\mathbf{T}$ has constant length. Therefore, by Theorem 11.8, $\mathbf{T}$ and $d\mathbf{T}/dt$ (or $\mathbf{T}$ and $d\mathbf{T}/ds$) are orthogonal. Because $\mathbf{N}$ is a scalar multiple of $d\mathbf{T}/ds$, $\mathbf{T}$ and $\mathbf{N}$ are orthogonal (Figure 11.104).
2. We motivate—but do not prove—this fact, by recalling that

$$\frac{d\mathbf{T}}{ds} = \lim_{\Delta s \to 0} \frac{\mathbf{T}(s + \Delta s) - \mathbf{T}(s)}{\Delta s}.$$

Therefore, $d\mathbf{T}/ds$ points in the approximate direction of $\mathbf{T}(s + \Delta s) - \mathbf{T}(s)$ when Δs is small. As shown in Figure 11.105, this difference points in the direction in which the curve is turning. Because $\mathbf{N}$ is a positive scalar multiple of $d\mathbf{T}/ds$, it points in the same direction. ◀

QUICK CHECK 3 Consider the parabola $\mathbf{r}(t) = \langle t, -t^2 \rangle$. Does the principal unit normal vector point in the positive y-direction or negative y-direction along the curve? ◀

EXAMPLE 5 Principal unit normal vector for a helix Find the principal unit normal vector for the helix $\mathbf{r}(t) = \langle a \cos t, a \sin t, bt \rangle$, for $-\infty < t < \infty$, where $a > 0$ and $b > 0$ are real numbers.

SOLUTION Several preliminary calculations are needed. First, we have $\mathbf{v}(t) = \mathbf{r}'(t) = \langle -a \sin t, a \cos t, b \rangle$. Therefore,

$$\begin{aligned} |\mathbf{v}(t)| = |\mathbf{r}'(t)| &= \sqrt{(-a \sin t)^2 + (a \cos t)^2 + b^2} \\ &= \sqrt{a^2(\sin^2 t + \cos^2 t) + b^2} && \text{Simplify.} \\ &= \sqrt{a^2 + b^2}. && \sin^2 t + \cos^2 t = 1 \end{aligned}$$

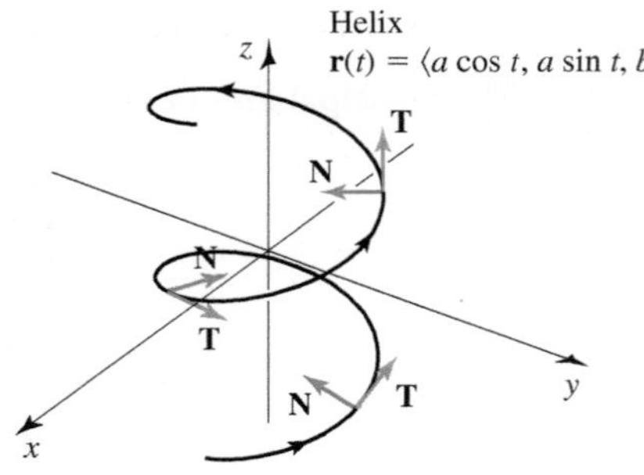

Figure 11.106

The unit tangent vector is

$$\mathbf{T}(t) = \frac{\mathbf{r}'(t)}{|\mathbf{r}'(t)|} = \frac{\langle -a\sin t, a\cos t, b\rangle}{\sqrt{a^2+b^2}}.$$

Notice that **T** points along the curve in an upward direction (at an angle to the horizontal that satisfies the equation $\tan\theta = b/a$) (Figure 11.106). We can now calculate the principal unit normal vector. First, we determine that

$$\frac{d\mathbf{T}}{dt} = \frac{d}{dt}\left(\frac{\langle -a\sin t, a\cos t, b\rangle}{\sqrt{a^2+b^2}}\right) = \frac{\langle -a\cos t, -a\sin t, 0\rangle}{\sqrt{a^2+b^2}}$$

and

$$\left|\frac{d\mathbf{T}}{dt}\right| = \frac{a}{\sqrt{a^2+b^2}}.$$

The principal unit normal vector now follows:

$$\mathbf{N} = \frac{d\mathbf{T}/dt}{|d\mathbf{T}/dt|} = \frac{\dfrac{\langle -a\cos t, -a\sin t, 0\rangle}{\sqrt{a^2+b^2}}}{\dfrac{a}{\sqrt{a^2+b^2}}} = \langle -\cos t, -\sin t, 0\rangle.$$

QUICK CHECK 4 Why is the principal unit normal vector for a straight line undefined? ◂

Several important checks should be made. First note that **N** is a unit vector; that is, $|\mathbf{N}| = 1$. It should also be confirmed that $\mathbf{T}\cdot\mathbf{N} = 0$; that is, the unit tangent vector and the principal unit normal vector are everywhere orthogonal. Finally, **N** is parallel to the xy-plane and points inward toward the z-axis, in the direction the curve turns (Figure 11.106). Notice that in the special case $b = 0$, the trajectory is a circle, but the normal vector is still $\mathbf{N} = \langle -\cos t, -\sin t, 0\rangle$.

Related Exercises 27–34 ◂

Components of the Acceleration

The vectors **T** and **N** may be used to gain insight into how moving objects accelerate. Recall the observation made earlier that the two ways to change the velocity of an object (to accelerate) are to change its *speed* and change its *direction* of motion. We show that changing the speed produces acceleration in the direction of **T** and changing the direction produces acceleration in the direction of **N**.

We begin with the fact that $\mathbf{T} = \frac{\mathbf{v}}{|\mathbf{v}|}$ or $\mathbf{v} = \mathbf{T}|\mathbf{v}| = \mathbf{T}\frac{ds}{dt}$. Differentiating both sides of $\mathbf{v} = \mathbf{T}\frac{ds}{dt}$ with respect to t gives

➤ Recall that the speed is $|\mathbf{v}| = ds/dt$, where s is arc length.

$$\begin{aligned}\mathbf{a} &= \frac{d\mathbf{v}}{dt} = \frac{d}{dt}\left(\mathbf{T}\frac{ds}{dt}\right)\\ &= \frac{d\mathbf{T}}{dt}\frac{ds}{dt} + \mathbf{T}\frac{d^2s}{dt^2} && \text{Product Rule}\\ &= \underbrace{\frac{d\mathbf{T}}{ds}}_{k\mathbf{N}}\underbrace{\frac{ds}{dt}}_{|\mathbf{v}|}\frac{ds}{dt} + \mathbf{T}\frac{d^2s}{dt^2} && \text{Chain Rule: } \frac{d\mathbf{T}}{dt} = \frac{d\mathbf{T}}{ds}\frac{ds}{dt}\\ &= k\mathbf{N}|\mathbf{v}|^2 + \mathbf{T}\frac{d^2s}{dt^2}. && \text{Substitute.}\end{aligned}$$

We now identify the normal and tangential components of the acceleration.

➤ Note that a_N and a_T are defined even at points where $\kappa = 0$ and $\mathbf{N}$ is undefined.

THEOREM 11.13 Tangential and Normal Components of the Acceleration
The acceleration vector of an object moving in space along a smooth curve has the following representation in terms of its **tangential component** a_T (in the direction of $\mathbf{T}$) and its **normal component** a_N (in the direction of $\mathbf{N}$):

$$\mathbf{a} = a_N\mathbf{N} + a_T\mathbf{T},$$

where $a_N = \kappa|\mathbf{v}|^2 = \dfrac{|\mathbf{v} \times \mathbf{a}|}{|\mathbf{v}|}$ and $a_T = \dfrac{d^2s}{dt^2}$.

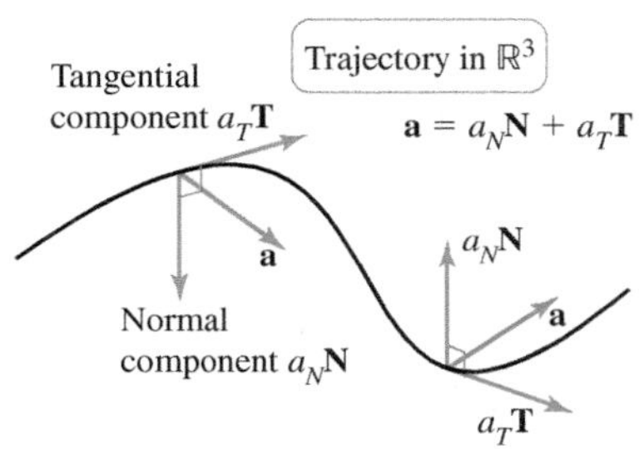

Figure 11.107

The tangential component of the acceleration, in the direction of $\mathbf{T}$, is the usual acceleration $a_T = d^2s/dt^2$ of an object moving along a straight line (Figure 11.107). The normal component, in the direction of $\mathbf{N}$, increases with the speed $|\mathbf{v}|$ and with the curvature. Higher speeds on tighter curves produce greater normal accelerations.

EXAMPLE 6 Acceleration on a circular path Find the components of the acceleration on the circular trajectory

$$\mathbf{r}(t) = \langle R\cos\omega t, R\sin\omega t\rangle,$$

where R and ω are positive real numbers.

SOLUTION We find that $\mathbf{r}'(t) = \langle -R\omega\sin\omega t, R\omega\cos\omega t\rangle$, $|\mathbf{v}(t)| = |\mathbf{r}'(t)| = R\omega$, and, by Example 2, $\kappa = 1/R$. Recall that $ds/dt = |\mathbf{v}(t)|$, which is constant; therefore, $d^2s/dt^2 = 0$ and the tangential component of the acceleration is zero. The acceleration is

$$\mathbf{a} = \kappa|\mathbf{v}|^2\mathbf{N} + \underbrace{\frac{d^2s}{dt^2}}_{0}\mathbf{T} = \frac{1}{R}(R\omega)^2\mathbf{N} = R\omega^2\mathbf{N}.$$

On a circular path (traversed at constant speed), the acceleration is entirely in the normal direction, orthogonal to the tangent vectors. The acceleration increases with the radius of the circle R and with the frequency of the motion ω.

Related Exercises 35–40 ◄

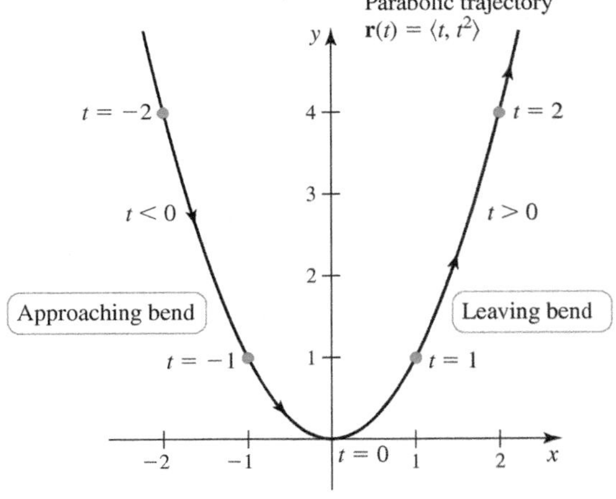

Figure 11.108

EXAMPLE 7 A bend in the road The driver of a car follows the parabolic trajectory $\mathbf{r}(t) = \langle t, t^2\rangle$, for $-2 \le t \le 2$, through a sharp bend (Figure 11.108). Find the tangential and normal components of the acceleration of the car.

SOLUTION The velocity and acceleration vectors are easily computed: $\mathbf{v}(t) = \mathbf{r}'(t) = \langle 1, 2t\rangle$ and $\mathbf{a}(t) = \mathbf{r}''(t) = \langle 0, 2\rangle$. The goal is to express $\mathbf{a} = \langle 0, 2\rangle$ in terms of $\mathbf{T}$ and $\mathbf{N}$. A short calculation reveals that

$$\mathbf{T} = \frac{\mathbf{v}}{|\mathbf{v}|} = \frac{\langle 1, 2t\rangle}{\sqrt{1+4t^2}} \quad\text{and}\quad \mathbf{N} = \frac{d\mathbf{T}/dt}{|d\mathbf{T}/dt|} = \frac{\langle -2t, 1\rangle}{\sqrt{1+4t^2}}.$$

We now have two ways to proceed. One is to compute the normal and tangential components of the acceleration directly using the definitions. More efficient is to note that $\mathbf{T}$ and $\mathbf{N}$ are orthogonal unit vectors, and then to compute the scalar projections of $\mathbf{a} = \langle 0, 2\rangle$ in the directions of $\mathbf{T}$ and $\mathbf{N}$. We find that

$$a_N = \mathbf{a}\cdot\mathbf{N} = \langle 0, 2\rangle \cdot \frac{\langle -2t, 1\rangle}{\sqrt{1+4t^2}} = \frac{2}{\sqrt{1+4t^2}}$$

and

$$a_T = \mathbf{a}\cdot\mathbf{T} = \langle 0, 2\rangle \cdot \frac{\langle 1, 2t\rangle}{\sqrt{1+4t^2}} = \frac{4t}{\sqrt{1+4t^2}}.$$

➤ Using the fact that $|\mathbf{T}| = |\mathbf{N}| = 1$, we have, from Section 11.3,

$$a_N = \text{scal}_{\mathbf{N}}\mathbf{a} = \frac{\mathbf{a}\cdot\mathbf{N}}{|\mathbf{N}|} = \mathbf{a}\cdot\mathbf{N}$$

and

$$a_T = \text{scal}_{\mathbf{T}}\mathbf{a} = \frac{\mathbf{a}\cdot\mathbf{T}}{|\mathbf{T}|} = \mathbf{a}\cdot\mathbf{T} = \frac{\mathbf{v}\cdot\mathbf{a}}{|\mathbf{v}|}.$$

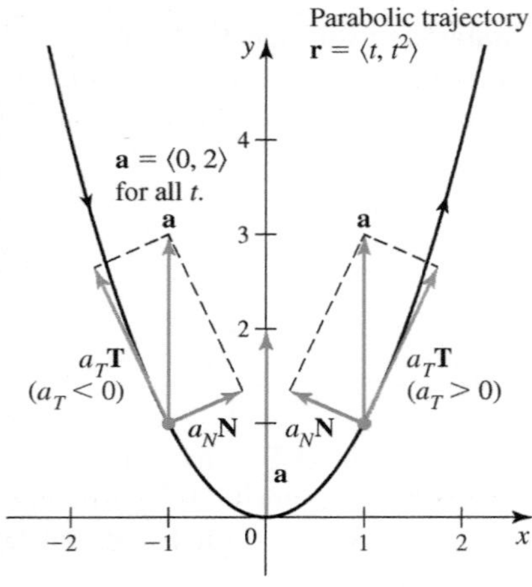

Figure 11.109

You should verify that at all times (Exercise 76),

$$\mathbf{a} = a_N\mathbf{N} + a_T\mathbf{T} = \frac{2}{\sqrt{1 + 4t^2}}(\mathbf{N} + 2t\,\mathbf{T}) = \langle 0, 2 \rangle.$$

Let's interpret these results. First notice that the driver negotiates the curve in a sensible way: The speed $|\mathbf{v}| = \sqrt{1 + 4t^2}$ decreases as the car approaches the origin (the tightest part of the curve) and increases as it moves away from the origin (Figure 11.109). As the car approaches the origin ($t < 0$), $\mathbf{T}$ points in the direction of the trajectory and $\mathbf{N}$ points to the inside of the curve. However, $a_T = \dfrac{d^2s}{dt^2} < 0$ when $t < 0$, so $a_T\mathbf{T}$ points in the direction opposite that of $\mathbf{T}$ (corresponding to a deceleration). As the car leaves the origin ($t > 0$), $a_T > 0$ (corresponding to an acceleration) and $a_T\mathbf{T}$ and $\mathbf{T}$ point in the direction of the trajectory. At all times, $\mathbf{N}$ points to the inside of the curve (Figure 11.109; Exercise 78).

Related Exercises 35–40 ◀

QUICK CHECK 5 Verify that $\mathbf{T}$ and $\mathbf{N}$ given in Example 7 satisfy $|\mathbf{T}| = |\mathbf{N}| = 1$ and that $\mathbf{T} \cdot \mathbf{N} = 0$. ◀

The Binormal Vector and Torsion

We have seen that the curvature function and the principal unit normal vector tell us how quickly and in what direction a curve turns. For curves in two dimensions, these quantities give a fairly complete description of motion along the curve. However, in three dimensions, a curve has more "room" in which to change its course, and another descriptive function is often useful. Figure 11.110 shows a smooth parameterized curve C with its unit tangent vector $\mathbf{T}$ and its principal unit normal vector $\mathbf{N}$ at two different points. These two vectors determine a plane called the *osculating plane* (Figure 11.110b). The question we now ask is, How quickly does the curve C move out of the plane determined by $\mathbf{T}$ and $\mathbf{N}$?

➤ The TNB frame is also called the Frenet-Serret frame, after two 19th-century French mathematicians, Jean Frenet and Joseph Serret.

To answer this question, we begin by defining the *unit binormal vector* $\mathbf{B} = \mathbf{T} \times \mathbf{N}$. By the definition of the cross product, $\mathbf{B}$ is orthogonal to $\mathbf{T}$ and $\mathbf{N}$. Because $\mathbf{T}$ and $\mathbf{N}$ are unit vectors, $\mathbf{B}$ is also a unit vector. Notice that $\mathbf{T}$, $\mathbf{N}$, and $\mathbf{B}$ form a right-handed coordinate system (like the xyz-coordinate system) that changes its orientation as we move along the curve. This coordinate system is often called the **TNB frame** (Figure 11.110).

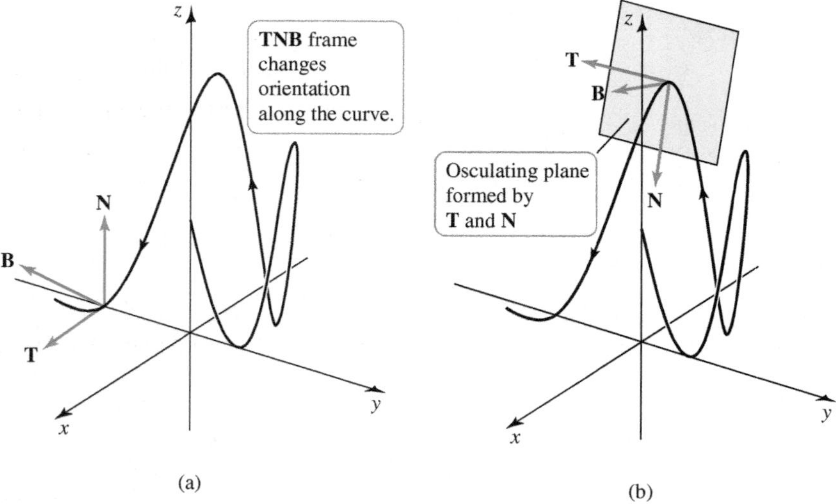

Figure 11.110

QUICK CHECK 6 Explain why $\mathbf{B} = \mathbf{T} \times \mathbf{N}$ is a unit vector. ◀

The rate at which the curve C twists out of the plane determined by $\mathbf{T}$ and $\mathbf{N}$ is the rate at which $\mathbf{B}$ changes as we move along C, which is $\dfrac{d\mathbf{B}}{ds}$. A short calculation leads to a practical formula for the twisting of the curve. Differentiating the cross product $\mathbf{T} \times \mathbf{N}$, we find that

$$\begin{aligned} \frac{d\mathbf{B}}{ds} &= \frac{d}{ds}(\mathbf{T} \times \mathbf{N}) \\ &= \underbrace{\frac{d\mathbf{T}}{ds} \times \mathbf{N}}_{\text{parallel vectors}} + \mathbf{T} \times \frac{d\mathbf{N}}{ds} && \text{Product Rule for cross products} \\ &= \mathbf{T} \times \frac{d\mathbf{N}}{ds}. && \frac{d\mathbf{T}}{ds} \text{ and } \mathbf{N} \text{ are parallel; } \frac{d\mathbf{T}}{ds} \times \mathbf{N} = \mathbf{0}. \end{aligned}$$

Notice that by definition, $\mathbf{N} = \frac{1}{\kappa}\frac{d\mathbf{T}}{ds}$, which implies that $\mathbf{N}$ and $\frac{d\mathbf{T}}{ds}$ are scalar multiples of each other. Therefore, their cross product is the zero vector.

The properties of $\frac{d\mathbf{B}}{ds}$ become clear with the following observations.

- $\frac{d\mathbf{B}}{ds}$ is orthogonal to both $\mathbf{T}$ and $\frac{d\mathbf{N}}{ds}$, because it is the cross product of $\mathbf{T}$ and $\frac{d\mathbf{N}}{ds}$.
- Applying Theorem 11.8 to the unit vector $\mathbf{B}$, it follows that $\frac{d\mathbf{B}}{ds}$ is also orthogonal to $\mathbf{B}$.
- By the previous two observations, $\frac{d\mathbf{B}}{ds}$ is orthogonal to both $\mathbf{B}$ and $\mathbf{T}$, so it must be parallel to $\mathbf{N}$.

➤ Note that $\mathbf{B}$ is a unit vector (of constant length). Therefore, by Theorem 11.8, $\mathbf{B}$ and $\mathbf{B}'(t)$ are orthogonal. Because $\mathbf{B}'(t)$ and $\mathbf{B}'(s)$ are parallel, it follows that $\mathbf{B}$ and $\mathbf{B}'(s)$ are orthogonal.

Because $\frac{d\mathbf{B}}{ds}$ is parallel to (a scalar multiple of) $\mathbf{N}$, we write

$$\frac{d\mathbf{B}}{ds} = -\tau\mathbf{N},$$

where the scalar τ is the *torsion*. Notice that $\left|\frac{d\mathbf{B}}{ds}\right| = |-\tau\mathbf{N}| = |-\tau|$, so the magnitude of the torsion equals the magnitude of $\frac{d\mathbf{B}}{ds}$, which is the rate at which the curve twists out of the $\mathbf{TN}$-plane.

➤ The negative sign in the definition of the torsion is conventional. However, τ may be positive or negative (or zero), and in general, it varies along the curve.

A short calculation gives a method for computing the torsion. We take the dot product of both sides of the equation defining the torsion with $\mathbf{N}$:

$$\begin{aligned} \frac{d\mathbf{B}}{ds} \cdot \mathbf{N} &= -\tau \underbrace{\mathbf{N} \cdot \mathbf{N}}_{1} \\ \frac{d\mathbf{B}}{ds} \cdot \mathbf{N} &= -\tau. && \mathbf{N} \text{ is a unit vector.} \end{aligned}$$

➤ Notice that $\mathbf{B}$ and τ depend on the orientation of the curve.

QUICK CHECK 7 Explain why $\mathbf{N} \cdot \mathbf{N} = 1$. ◄

DEFINITION Unit Binormal Vector and Torsion

Let C be a smooth parameterized curve with unit tangent and principal unit normal vectors $\mathbf{T}$ and $\mathbf{N}$, respectively. Then at each point of the curve at which the curvature is nonzero, the **unit binormal vector** is

$$\mathbf{B} = \mathbf{T} \times \mathbf{N},$$

and the **torsion** is

$$\tau = -\frac{d\mathbf{B}}{ds} \cdot \mathbf{N}.$$

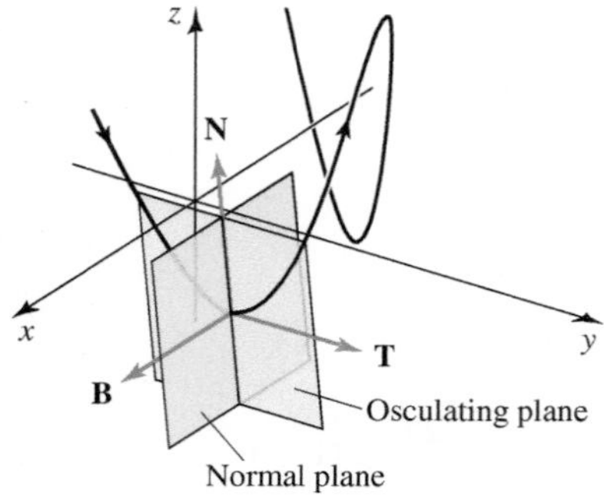

Figure 11.111

➤ The third plane formed by the vectors **T** and **B** is called the *rectifying plane.*

Figure 11.111 provides some interpretation of the curvature and the torsion. First, we see a smooth curve C passing through a point where the mutually orthogonal vectors **T**, **N**, and **B** are defined. The **osculating plane** is defined by the vectors **T** and **N**. The plane orthogonal to the osculating plane containing **N** is called the **normal plane**. Because **N** and $\frac{d\mathbf{B}}{ds}$ are parallel, $\frac{d\mathbf{B}}{ds}$ also lies in the normal plane. The torsion, which is equal in magnitude to $\left|\frac{d\mathbf{B}}{ds}\right|$, gives the rate at which the curve moves *out of* the osculating plane. In a complementary way, the curvature, which is equal to $\left|\frac{d\mathbf{T}}{ds}\right|$, gives the rate at which the curve turns *within* the osculating plane. Two examples will clarify these concepts.

EXAMPLE 8 Unit binormal vector Consider the circle C defined by

$$\mathbf{r}(t) = \langle R\cos t, R\sin t\rangle, \text{ for } 0 \le t \le 2\pi, \text{ with } R > 0.$$

a. Without doing any calculations, find the unit binormal vector **B** and determine the torsion.

b. Use the definition of **B** to calculate **B** and confirm your answer in part (a).

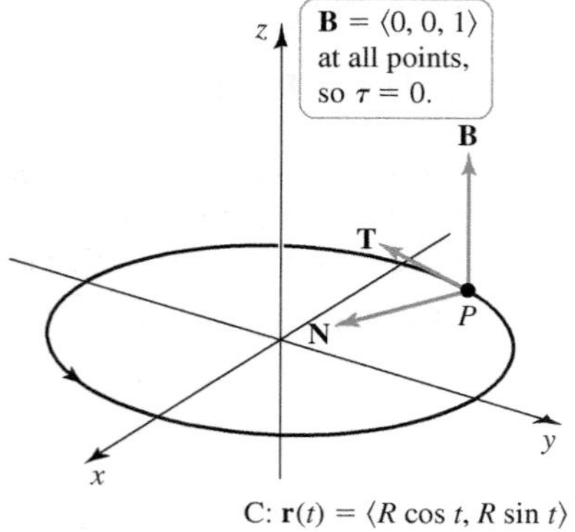

Figure 11.112

SOLUTION

a. The circle C lies in the xy-plane, so at all points on the circle, **T** and **N** are in the xy-plane. Therefore, at all points of the circle, $\mathbf{B} = \mathbf{T} \times \mathbf{N}$ is the unit vector in the positive z-direction (by the right-hand rule); that is, $\mathbf{B} = \mathbf{k}$. Because **B** changes neither in length nor direction, $\frac{d\mathbf{B}}{ds} = \mathbf{0}$ and $\tau = 0$ (Figure 11.112).

b. Building on the calculations of Example 2, we find that

$$\mathbf{T} = \langle -\sin t, \cos t\rangle \quad \text{and} \quad \mathbf{N} = \langle -\cos t, -\sin t\rangle.$$

Therefore, the unit binormal vector is

$$\mathbf{B} = \mathbf{T} \times \mathbf{N} = \begin{vmatrix} \mathbf{i} & \mathbf{j} & \mathbf{k} \\ -\sin t & \cos t & 0 \\ -\cos t & -\sin t & 0 \end{vmatrix} = 0\cdot\mathbf{i} - 0\cdot\mathbf{j} + 1\cdot\mathbf{k} = \mathbf{k}.$$

As in part (a), it follows that the torsion is zero.

Related Exercises 41–48 ◀

Generalizing Example 8, it can be shown that the binormal vector of any curve that lies in the xy-plane is always parallel to the z-axis; therefore, the torsion of the curve is everywhere zero.

EXAMPLE 9 Torsion of a helix Compute the torsion of the helix $\mathbf{r}(t) = \langle a\cos t, a\sin t, bt\rangle$, for $t \ge 0$, $a > 0$, and $b > 0$.

SOLUTION In Example 5, we found that

$$\mathbf{T} = \frac{\langle -a\sin t, a\cos t, b\rangle}{\sqrt{a^2 + b^2}} \quad \text{and} \quad \mathbf{N} = \langle -\cos t, -\sin t, 0\rangle.$$

Therefore,

$$\mathbf{B} = \mathbf{T} \times \mathbf{N} = \frac{1}{\sqrt{a^2 + b^2}} \begin{vmatrix} \mathbf{i} & \mathbf{j} & \mathbf{k} \\ -a\sin t & a\cos t & b \\ -\cos t & -\sin t & 0 \end{vmatrix} = \frac{\langle b\sin t, -b\cos t, a\rangle}{\sqrt{a^2 + b^2}}.$$

The next step is to determine $\frac{d\mathbf{B}}{ds}$, which we do in the same way we computed $\frac{d\mathbf{T}}{ds}$, by writing

$$\frac{d\mathbf{B}}{dt} = \frac{d\mathbf{B}}{ds}\cdot\frac{ds}{dt} \quad \text{or} \quad \frac{d\mathbf{B}}{ds} = \frac{d\mathbf{B}/dt}{ds/dt}.$$

In this case,

$$\frac{ds}{dt} = |\mathbf{r}'(t)| = \sqrt{a^2 \sin^2 t + a^2 \cos^2 t + b^2} = \sqrt{a^2 + b^2}.$$

Computing $\frac{d\mathbf{B}}{dt}$, we have

$$\frac{d\mathbf{B}}{ds} = \frac{d\mathbf{B}/dt}{ds/dt} = \frac{\langle b \cos t, b \sin t, 0 \rangle}{a^2 + b^2}.$$

The final step is to compute the torsion:

$$\tau = -\frac{d\mathbf{B}}{ds} \cdot \mathbf{N} = -\frac{\langle b \cos t, b \sin t, 0 \rangle}{a^2 + b^2} \cdot \langle -\cos t, -\sin t, 0 \rangle = \frac{b}{a^2 + b^2}.$$

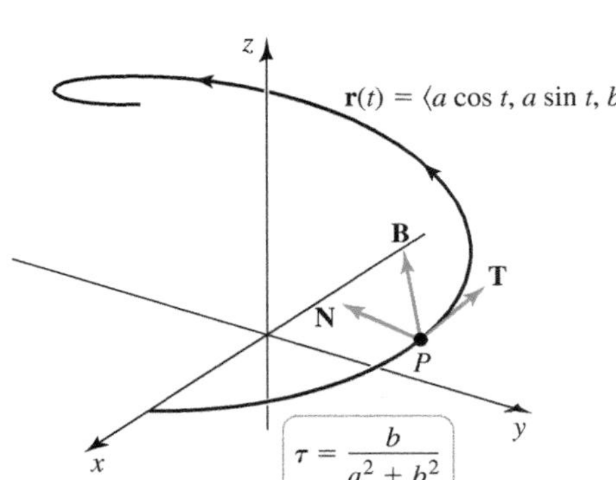

Figure 11.113

We see that the torsion is constant over the helix. In Example 4, we found that the curvature of a helix is also constant. This special property of circular helices means that the curve turns about its axis at a constant rate and rises vertically at a constant rate (Figure 11.113).

Related Exercises 41–48 ◀

Example 9 suggests that the computation of the binormal vector and the torsion can be involved. We close by stating some alternative formulas for **B** and τ that *may* simplify calculations in some cases. Letting $\mathbf{v} = \mathbf{r}'(t)$ and $\mathbf{a} = \mathbf{v}'(t) = \mathbf{r}''(t)$, the binormal vector can be written compactly as (Exercise 83)

$$\mathbf{B} = \mathbf{T} \times \mathbf{N} = \frac{\mathbf{v} \times \mathbf{a}}{|\mathbf{v} \times \mathbf{a}|}.$$

We also state without proof that the torsion may be expressed in either of the forms

$$\tau = \frac{(\mathbf{v} \times \mathbf{a}) \cdot \mathbf{a}'}{|\mathbf{v} \times \mathbf{a}|^2} \quad \text{or} \quad \tau = \frac{(\mathbf{r}' \times \mathbf{r}'') \cdot \mathbf{r}'''}{|\mathbf{r}' \times \mathbf{r}''|^2}.$$

SUMMARY Formulas for Curves in Space

Position function: $\mathbf{r}(t) = \langle x(t), y(t), z(t) \rangle$

Velocity: $\mathbf{v} = \mathbf{r}'$

Acceleration: $\mathbf{a} = \mathbf{v}'$

Unit tangent vector: $\mathbf{T} = \frac{\mathbf{v}}{|\mathbf{v}|}$

Principal unit normal vector: $\mathbf{N} = \frac{d\mathbf{T}/dt}{|d\mathbf{T}/dt|}$ (provided $d\mathbf{T}/dt \neq \mathbf{0}$)

Curvature: $\kappa = \left| \frac{d\mathbf{T}}{ds} \right| = \frac{1}{|\mathbf{v}|} \left| \frac{d\mathbf{T}}{dt} \right| = \frac{|\mathbf{v} \times \mathbf{a}|}{|\mathbf{v}|^3}$

Components of acceleration: $\mathbf{a} = a_N \mathbf{N} + a_T \mathbf{T}$, where $a_N = \kappa |\mathbf{v}|^2 = \frac{|\mathbf{v} \times \mathbf{a}|}{|\mathbf{v}|}$ and $a_T = \frac{d^2 s}{dt^2} = \frac{\mathbf{v} \cdot \mathbf{a}}{|\mathbf{v}|}$

Unit binormal vector: $\mathbf{B} = \mathbf{T} \times \mathbf{N} = \frac{\mathbf{v} \times \mathbf{a}}{|\mathbf{v} \times \mathbf{a}|}$

Torsion: $\tau = -\frac{d\mathbf{B}}{ds} \cdot \mathbf{N} = \frac{(\mathbf{v} \times \mathbf{a}) \cdot \mathbf{a}'}{|\mathbf{v} \times \mathbf{a}|^2} = \frac{(\mathbf{r}' \times \mathbf{r}'') \cdot \mathbf{r}'''}{|\mathbf{r}' \times \mathbf{r}''|^2}$

SECTION 11.9 EXERCISES

Review Questions

1. What is the curvature of a straight line?
2. Explain the meaning of *the curvature of a curve*. Is it a scalar function or a vector function?
3. Give a practical formula for computing the curvature.
4. Interpret *the principal unit normal vector of a curve*. Is it a scalar function or a vector function?
5. Give a practical formula for computing the principal unit normal vector.
6. Explain how to decompose the acceleration vector of a moving object into its tangential and normal components.
7. Explain how the vectors **T**, **N**, and **B** are related geometrically.
8. How do you compute **B**?
9. Give a geometrical interpretation of the torsion.
10. How do you compute the torsion?

Basic Skills

11–20. Curvature *Find the unit tangent vector* **T** *and the curvature* κ *for the following parameterized curves.*

11. $\mathbf{r}(t) = \langle 2t + 1, 4t - 5, 6t + 12 \rangle$
12. $\mathbf{r}(t) = \langle 2\cos t, -2\sin t \rangle$
13. $\mathbf{r}(t) = \langle 2t, 4\sin t, 4\cos t \rangle$
14. $\mathbf{r}(t) = \langle \cos t^2, \sin t^2 \rangle$
15. $\mathbf{r}(t) = \langle \sqrt{3}\sin t, \sin t, 2\cos t \rangle$
16. $\mathbf{r}(t) = \langle t, \ln \cos t \rangle$
17. $\mathbf{r}(t) = \langle t, 2t^2 \rangle$
18. $\mathbf{r}(t) = \langle \cos^3 t, \sin^3 t \rangle$
19. $\mathbf{r}(t) = \left\langle \int_0^t \cos(\pi u^2/2)\,du, \int_0^t \sin(\pi u^2/2)\,du \right\rangle, t > 0$
20. $\mathbf{r}(t) = \left\langle \int_0^t \cos u^2\,du, \int_0^t \sin u^2\,du \right\rangle, t > 0$

21–26. Alternative curvature formula *Use the alternative curvature formula* $\kappa = |\mathbf{v} \times \mathbf{a}|/|\mathbf{v}|^3$ *to find the curvature of the following parameterized curves.*

21. $\mathbf{r}(t) = \langle -3\cos t, 3\sin t, 0 \rangle$
22. $\mathbf{r}(t) = \langle 4t, 3\sin t, 3\cos t \rangle$
23. $\mathbf{r}(t) = \langle 4 + t^2, t, 0 \rangle$
24. $\mathbf{r}(t) = \langle \sqrt{3}\sin t, \sin t, 2\cos t \rangle$
25. $\mathbf{r}(t) = \langle 4\cos t, \sin t, 2\cos t \rangle$
26. $\mathbf{r}(t) = \langle e^t\cos t, e^t\sin t, e^t \rangle$

27–34. Principal unit normal vector *Find the unit tangent vector* **T** *and the principal unit normal vector* **N** *for the following parameterized curves. In each case, verify that* $|\mathbf{T}| = |\mathbf{N}| = 1$ *and* $\mathbf{T} \cdot \mathbf{N} = 0$.

27. $\mathbf{r}(t) = \langle 2\sin t, 2\cos t \rangle$
28. $\mathbf{r}(t) = \langle 4\sin t, 4\cos t, 10t \rangle$
29. $\mathbf{r}(t) = \langle t^2/2, 4 - 3t, 1 \rangle$
30. $\mathbf{r}(t) = \langle t^2/2, t^3/3 \rangle, t > 0$
31. $\mathbf{r}(t) = \langle \cos t^2, \sin t^2 \rangle$
32. $\mathbf{r}(t) = \langle \cos^3 t, \sin^3 t \rangle$
33. $\mathbf{r}(t) = \langle t^2, t \rangle$
34. $r(t) = \langle t, \ln \cos t \rangle$

35–40. Components of the acceleration *Consider the following trajectories of moving objects. Find the tangential and normal components of the acceleration.*

35. $\mathbf{r}(t) = \langle t, 1 + 4t, 2 - 6t \rangle$
36. $\mathbf{r}(t) = \langle 10\cos t, -10\sin t \rangle$
37. $\mathbf{r}(t) = \langle e^t\cos t, e^t\sin t, e^t \rangle$
38. $\mathbf{r}(t) = \langle t, t^2 + 1 \rangle$
39. $\mathbf{r}(t) = \langle t^3, t^2 \rangle$
40. $\mathbf{r}(t) = \langle 20\cos t, 20\sin t, 30t \rangle$

41–44. Computing the binormal vector and torsion *In Exercises 27–30, the unit tangent vector* **T** *and the principal unit normal vector* **N** *were computed for the following parameterized curves. Use the definitions to compute their unit binormal vector and torsion.*

41. $\mathbf{r}(t) = \langle 2\sin t, 2\cos t \rangle$
42. $\mathbf{r}(t) = \langle 4\sin t, 4\cos t, 10t \rangle$
43. $\mathbf{r}(t) = \langle t^2/2, 4 - 3t, 1 \rangle$
44. $\mathbf{r}(t) = \langle t^2/2, t^3/3 \rangle, t > 0$

45–48. Computing the binormal vector and torsion *Use the definitions to compute the unit binormal vector and torsion of the following curves.*

45. $\mathbf{r}(t) = \langle 2\cos t, 2\sin t, -t \rangle$
46. $\mathbf{r}(t) = \langle t, \cosh t, -\sinh t \rangle$
47. $\mathbf{r}(t) = \langle 12t, 5\cos t, 5\sin t \rangle$
48. $\mathbf{r}(t) = \langle \sin t - t\cos t, \cos t + t\sin t, t \rangle$

Further Explorations

49. **Explain why or why not** Determine whether the following statements are true and give an explanation or counterexample.
    a. The position, unit tangent, and principal unit normal vectors (**r**, **T**, and **N**) at a point lie in the same plane.
    b. The vectors **T** and **N** at a point depend on the orientation of a curve.
    c. The curvature at a point depends on the orientation of a curve.
    d. An object with unit speed ($|\mathbf{v}| = 1$) on a circle of radius R has an acceleration of $\mathbf{a} = \mathbf{N}/R$.
    e. If the speedometer of a car reads a constant 60 mi/hr, the car is not accelerating.
    f. A curve in the xy-plane that is concave up at all points has positive torsion.
    g. A curve with large curvature also has large torsion.
50. **Special formula: Curvature for $y = f(x)$** Assume that f is twice differentiable. Prove that the curve $y = f(x)$ has curvature

$$\kappa(x) = \frac{|f''(x)|}{(1 + f'(x)^2)^{3/2}}.$$

(*Hint:* Use the parametric description $x = t, y = f(t)$.)

51–54. Curvature for $y = f(x)$ *Use the result of Exercise 50 to find the curvature function of the following curves.*

51. $f(x) = x^2$

52. $f(x) = \sqrt{a^2 - x^2}$

53. $f(x) = \ln x$

54. $f(x) = \ln \cos x$

55. Special formula: Curvature for plane curves Show that the parametric curve $\mathbf{r}(t) = \langle f(t), g(t) \rangle$, where f and g are twice differentiable, has curvature

$$\kappa(t) = \frac{|f'g'' - f''g'|}{((f')^2 + (g')^2)^{3/2}},$$

where all derivatives are taken with respect to t.

56–59. Curvature for plane curves *Use the result of Exercise 55 to find the curvature function of the following curves.*

56. $\mathbf{r}(t) = \langle a \sin t, a \cos t \rangle$ (circle)

57. $\mathbf{r}(t) = \langle a \sin t, b \cos t \rangle$ (ellipse)

58. $\mathbf{r}(t) = \langle a \cos^3 t, a \sin^3 t \rangle$ (astroid)

59. $\mathbf{r}(t) = \langle t, at^2 \rangle$ (parabola)

When appropriate, consider using the special formulas derived in Exercises 50 and 55 in the remaining exercises.

60–63. Same paths, different velocity *The position functions of objects A and B describe different motion along the same path, for $t \geq 0$.*

a. *Sketch the path followed by both A and B.*
b. *Find the velocity and acceleration of A and B and discuss the differences.*
c. *Express the acceleration of A and B in terms of the tangential and normal components and discuss the differences.*

60. A: $\mathbf{r}(t) = \langle 1 + 2t, 2 - 3t, 4t \rangle$, B: $\mathbf{r}(t) = \langle 1 + 6t, 2 - 9t, 12t \rangle$

61. A: $\mathbf{r}(t) = \langle t, 2t, 3t \rangle$, B: $\mathbf{r}(t) = \langle t^2, 2t^2, 3t^2 \rangle$

62. A: $\mathbf{r}(t) = \langle \cos t, \sin t \rangle$, B: $\mathbf{r}(t) = \langle \cos 3t, \sin 3t \rangle$

63. A: $\mathbf{r}(t) = \langle \cos t, \sin t \rangle$, B: $\mathbf{r}(t) = \langle \cos t^2, \sin t^2 \rangle$

T **64–67. Graphs of the curvature** *Consider the following curves.*

a. *Graph the curve.*
b. *Compute the curvature.*
c. *Graph the curvature as a function of the parameter.*
d. *Identify the points (if any) at which the curve has a maximum or minimum curvature.*
e. *Verify that the graph of the curvature is consistent with the graph of the curve.*

64. $\mathbf{r}(t) = \langle t, t^2 \rangle$, for $-2 \leq t \leq 2$ (parabola)

65. $\mathbf{r}(t) = \langle t - \sin t, 1 - \cos t \rangle$, for $0 \leq t \leq 2\pi$ (cycloid)

66. $\mathbf{r}(t) = \langle t, \sin t \rangle$, for $0 \leq t \leq \pi$ (sine curve)

67. $\mathbf{r}(t) = \langle t^2/2, t^3/3 \rangle$, for $t > 0$

68. Curvature of $\ln x$ Find the curvature of $f(x) = \ln x$, for $x > 0$, and find the point at which it is a maximum. What is the value of the maximum curvature?

69. Curvature of e^x Find the curvature of $f(x) = e^x$ and find the point at which it is a maximum. What is the value of the maximum curvature?

70. Circle and radius of curvature Choose a point P on a smooth curve C in the plane. The **circle of curvature** (or **osculating circle**) at P is the circle that (a) is tangent to C at P, (b) has the same curvature as C at P, and (c) lies on the same side of C as the principal unit normal $\mathbf{N}$ (see figure). The **radius of curvature** is the radius of the circle of curvature. Show that the radius of curvature is $1/\kappa$, where κ is the curvature of C at P.

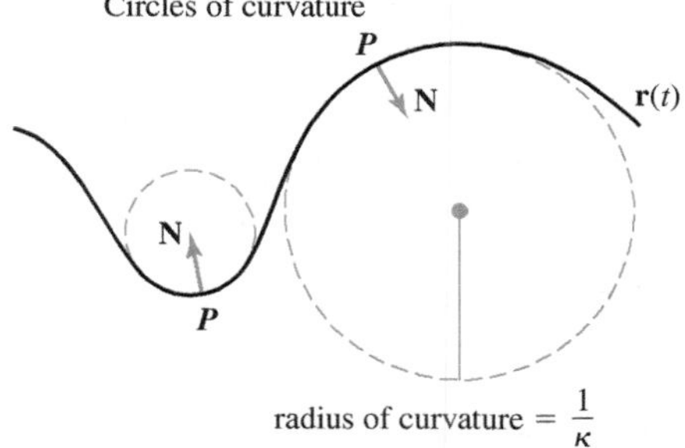

71–74. Finding radii of curvature *Find the radius of curvature (see Exercise 70) of the following curves at the given point. Then write an equation of the circle of curvature at the point.*

71. $\mathbf{r}(t) = \langle t, t^2 \rangle$ (parabola) at $t = 0$

72. $y = \ln x$ at $x = 1$

73. $\mathbf{r}(t) = \langle t - \sin t, 1 - \cos t \rangle$ (cycloid) at $t = \pi$

74. $y = \sin x$ at $x = \pi/2$

75. Curvature of the sine curve The function $f(x) = \sin nx$, where n is a positive real number, has a local maximum at $x = \pi/(2n)$. Compute the curvature κ of f at this point. How does κ vary (if at all) as n varies?

Applications

76. Parabolic trajectory In Example 7 it was shown that for the parabolic trajectory $\mathbf{r}(t) = \langle t, t^2 \rangle$, $\mathbf{a} = \langle 0, 2 \rangle$ and $\mathbf{a} = \frac{2}{\sqrt{1 + 4t^2}}(\mathbf{N} + 2t\,\mathbf{T})$. Show that the second expression for $\mathbf{a}$ reduces to the first expression.

T **77. Parabolic trajectory** Consider the parabolic trajectory

$$x = (V_0 \cos \alpha)\, t, \; y = (V_0 \sin \alpha)\, t - \tfrac{1}{2} g t^2,$$

where V_0 is the initial speed, α is the angle of launch, and g is the acceleration due to gravity. Consider all times $[0, T]$ for which $y \geq 0$.

a. Find and graph the speed, for $0 \leq t \leq T$.
b. Find and graph the curvature, for $0 \leq t \leq T$.
c. At what times (if any) do the speed and curvature have maximum and minimum values?

78. Relationship between T, N, and a Show that if an object accelerates in the sense that $d^2s/dt^2 > 0$ and $\kappa \neq 0$, then the acceleration vector lies between $\mathbf{T}$ and $\mathbf{N}$ in the plane of $\mathbf{T}$ and $\mathbf{N}$. If an object decelerates in the sense that $d^2s/dt^2 < 0$, then the acceleration vector lies in the plane of $\mathbf{T}$ and $\mathbf{N}$, but not between $\mathbf{T}$ and $\mathbf{N}$.

Additional Exercises

79. Zero curvature Prove that the curve

$$\mathbf{r}(t) = \langle a + bt^p, c + dt^p, e + ft^p \rangle,$$

where a, b, c, d, e, and f are real numbers and p is a positive integer, has zero curvature. Give an explanation.

80. Practical formula for N Show that the definition of the principal unit normal vector $\mathbf{N} = \dfrac{d\mathbf{T}/ds}{|d\mathbf{T}/ds|}$ implies the practical formula $\mathbf{N} = \dfrac{d\mathbf{T}/dt}{|d\mathbf{T}/dt|}$. Use the Chain Rule and recall that $|\mathbf{v}| = ds/dt > 0$.

T 81. Maximum curvature Consider the "superparabolas" $f_n(x) = x^{2n}$, where n is a positive integer.

- **a.** Find the curvature function of f_n, for $n = 1, 2$, and 3.
- **b.** Plot f_n and their curvature functions, for $n = 1, 2$, and 3, and check for consistency.
- **c.** At what points does the maximum curvature occur, for $n = 1, 2, 3$?
- **d.** Let the maximum curvature for f_n occur at $x = \pm z_n$. Using either analytical methods or a calculator, determine $\lim_{n\to\infty} z_n$. Interpret your result.

82. Alternative derivation of the curvature Derive the computational formula for curvature using the following steps.

- **a.** Use the tangential and normal components of the acceleration to show that $\mathbf{v} \times \mathbf{a} = \kappa|\mathbf{v}|^3\mathbf{B}$. (Note that $\mathbf{T} \times \mathbf{T} = \mathbf{0}$.)
- **b.** Solve the equation in part (a) for κ and conclude that $\kappa = \dfrac{|\mathbf{v} \times \mathbf{a}|}{|\mathbf{v}^3|}$, as shown in the text.

83. Computational formula for B Use the result of part (a) of Exercise 82 and the formula for κ to show that

$$\mathbf{B} = \frac{\mathbf{v} \times \mathbf{a}}{|\mathbf{v} \times \mathbf{a}|}.$$

84. Torsion formula Show that the formula defining the torsion, $\tau = -\dfrac{d\mathbf{B}}{ds}\cdot\mathbf{N}$, is equivalent to $\tau = -\dfrac{1}{|\mathbf{v}|}\dfrac{d\mathbf{B}}{dt}\cdot\mathbf{N}$. The second formula is generally easier to use.

85. Descartes' four-circle solution Consider the four mutually tangent circles shown in the figure that have radii a, b, c, and d, and curvatures $A = 1/a, B = 1/b, C = 1/c$, and $D = 1/d$. Prove Descartes' result (1643) that

$$(A + B + C + D)^2 = 2(A^2 + B^2 + C^2 + D^2).$$

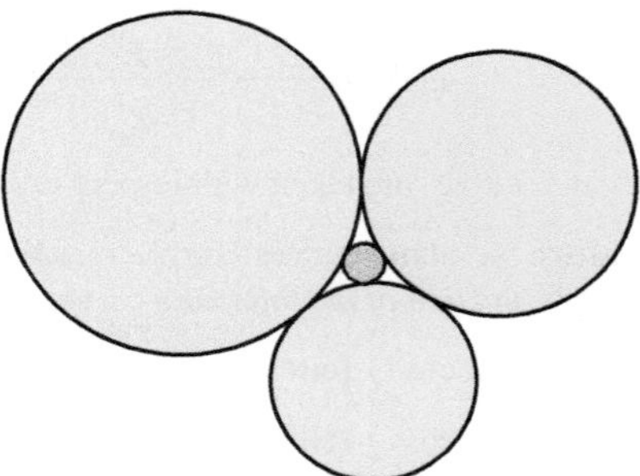

QUICK CHECK ANSWERS

1. $\kappa = \frac{1}{3}$ **2.** $\kappa = 0$ **3.** Negative y-direction **4.** $\kappa = 0$, so $\mathbf{N}$ is undefined. **6.** $|\mathbf{T}| = |\mathbf{N}| = 1$, so $|\mathbf{B}| = 1$ **7.** For any vector, $\mathbf{u}\cdot\mathbf{u} = |\mathbf{u}|^2$. Because $|\mathbf{N}| = 1, \mathbf{N}\cdot\mathbf{N} = 1$. ◄

CHAPTER 11 REVIEW EXERCISES

1. Explain why or why not Determine whether the following statements are true and give an explanation or counterexample.

- **a.** Given two vectors $\mathbf{u}$ and $\mathbf{v}$, it is always true that $2\mathbf{u} + \mathbf{v} = \mathbf{v} + 2\mathbf{u}$.
- **b.** The vector in the direction of $\mathbf{u}$ with the length of $\mathbf{v}$ equals the vector in the direction of $\mathbf{v}$ with the length of $\mathbf{u}$.
- **c.** If $\mathbf{u} \neq \mathbf{0}$ and $\mathbf{u} + \mathbf{v} = \mathbf{0}$, then $\mathbf{u}$ and $\mathbf{v}$ are parallel.
- **d.** If $\mathbf{r}'(t) = \mathbf{0}$, then $\mathbf{r}(t) = \langle a, b, c\rangle$, where a, b, and c are real numbers.
- **e.** The parameterized curve $\mathbf{r}(t) = \langle 5\cos t, 12\cos t, 13\sin t\rangle$ has arc length as a parameter.
- **f.** The position vector and the principal unit normal are always parallel on a smooth curve.

2–5. Drawing vectors *Let* $\mathbf{u} = \langle 3, -4\rangle$ *and* $\mathbf{v} = \langle -1, 2\rangle$. *Use geometry to sketch* **u**, **v**, *and the following vectors.*

2. $\mathbf{u} - \mathbf{v}$

3. $-3\mathbf{v}$

4. $\mathbf{u} + 2\mathbf{v}$

5. $2\mathbf{v} - \mathbf{u}$

6–11. Working with vectors *Let* $\mathbf{u} = \langle 2, 4, -5\rangle$ *and* $\mathbf{v} = \langle -6, 10, 2\rangle$.

6. Compute $\mathbf{u} - 3\mathbf{v}$.

7. Compute $|\mathbf{u} + \mathbf{v}|$.

8. Find the unit vector with the same direction as $\mathbf{u}$.

9. Find a vector parallel to $\mathbf{v}$ with length 20.

10. Compute $\mathbf{u}\cdot\mathbf{v}$ and the angle between $\mathbf{u}$ and $\mathbf{v}$.

11. Compute $\mathbf{u} \times \mathbf{v}$, $\mathbf{v} \times \mathbf{u}$, and the area of the triangle with vertices $(0, 0, 0)$, $(2, 4, -5)$, and $(-6, 10, 2)$.

12. Scalar multiples Find scalars a, b, and c such that

$$\langle 2, 2, 2\rangle = a\langle 1, 1, 0\rangle + b\langle 0, 1, 1\rangle + c\langle 1, 0, 1\rangle.$$

13. Velocity vectors Assume the positive x-axis points east and the positive y-axis points north.

- **a.** An airliner flies northwest at a constant altitude at 550 mi/hr in calm air. Find a and b such that its velocity may be expressed in the form $\mathbf{v} = a\mathbf{i} + b\mathbf{j}$.

b. An airliner flies northwest at a constant altitude at 550 mi/hr relative to the air in a southerly crosswind $\mathbf{w} = \langle 0, 40 \rangle$. Find the velocity of the airliner relative to the ground.

14. Position vectors Let $\overrightarrow{PQ}$ extend from $P(2, 0, 6)$ to $Q(2, -8, 5)$.

a. Find the position vector equal to $\overrightarrow{PQ}$.

b. Find the midpoint M of the line segment PQ. Then find the magnitude of $\overrightarrow{PM}$.

c. Find a vector of length 8 with direction opposite that of $\overrightarrow{PQ}$.

15–17. Spheres and balls *Use set notation to describe the following sets.*

15. The sphere of radius 4 centered at $(1, 0, -1)$

16. The points inside the sphere of radius 10 centered at $(2, 4, -3)$

17. The points outside the sphere of radius 2 centered at $(0, 1, 0)$

18–21. Identifying sets. *Give a geometric description of the following sets of points.*

18. $x^2 - 6x + y^2 + 8y + z^2 - 2z - 23 = 0$

19. $x^2 - x + y^2 + 4y + z^2 - 6z + 11 \le 0$

20. $x^2 + y^2 - 10y + z^2 - 6z = -34$

21. $x^2 - 6x + y^2 + z^2 - 20z + 9 > 0$

22. Combined force An object at the origin is acted on by the forces $\mathbf{F}_1 = -10\,\mathbf{i} + 20\,\mathbf{k}$, $\mathbf{F}_2 = 40\,\mathbf{j} + 10\,\mathbf{k}$, and $\mathbf{F}_3 = -50\mathbf{i} + 20\mathbf{j}$. Find the magnitude of the combined force and use a sketch to illustrate the direction of the combined force.

23. Falling probe A remote sensing probe falls vertically with a terminal velocity of 60 m/s when it encounters a horizontal crosswind blowing north at 4 m/s and an updraft blowing vertically at 10 m/s. Find the magnitude and direction of the resulting velocity relative to the ground.

24. Crosswinds A small plane is flying north in calm air at 250 mi/hr when it is hit by a horizontal crosswind blowing northeast at 40 mi/hr and a 25 mi/hr downdraft. Find the resulting velocity and speed of the plane.

25. Sets of points Describe the set of points satisfying both the equation $x^2 + z^2 = 1$ and $y = 2$.

26–27. Angles and projections

a. Find the angle between **u** *and* **v**.

b. Compute $\text{proj}_{\mathbf{v}}\mathbf{u}$ *and* $\text{scal}_{\mathbf{v}}\mathbf{u}$.

c. Compute $\text{proj}_{\mathbf{u}}\mathbf{v}$ *and* $\text{scal}_{\mathbf{u}}\mathbf{v}$.

26. $\mathbf{u} = -3\mathbf{j} + 4\mathbf{k}$, $\mathbf{v} = -4\mathbf{i} + \mathbf{j} + 5\mathbf{k}$

27. $\mathbf{u} = -\mathbf{i} + 2\mathbf{j} + 2\mathbf{k}$, $\mathbf{v} = 3\mathbf{i} + 6\mathbf{j} + 6\mathbf{k}$

28. Work A 180-lb man stands on a hillside that makes an angle of 30° with the horizontal, producing a force of $\mathbf{W} = \langle 0, -180 \rangle$.

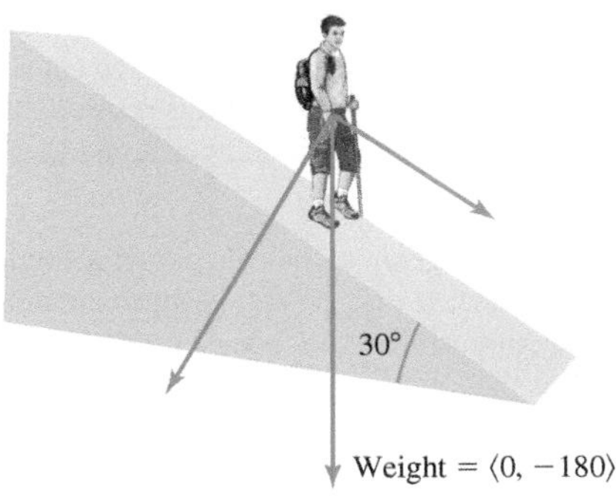

a. Find the component of his weight in the downward direction perpendicular to the hillside and in the downward direction parallel to the hillside.

b. How much work is done when the man moves 10 ft up the hillside?

29. Vectors normal to a plane Find a unit vector normal to the vectors $\langle 2, -6, 9 \rangle$ and $\langle -1, 0, 6 \rangle$.

30. Angle in two ways Find the angle between $\langle 2, 0, -2 \rangle$ and $\langle 2, 2, 0 \rangle$ using (a) the dot product and (b) the cross product.

31. Knee torque Jan does leg lifts with a 10-kg weight attached to her foot, so the resulting force is $mg \approx 98$ N directed vertically downward. If the distance from her knee to the weight is 0.4 m and her lower leg makes an angle of θ to the vertical, find the magnitude of the torque about her knee as her leg is lifted (as a function of θ). What are the minimum and maximum magnitudes of the torque? Does the direction of the torque change as her leg is lifted?

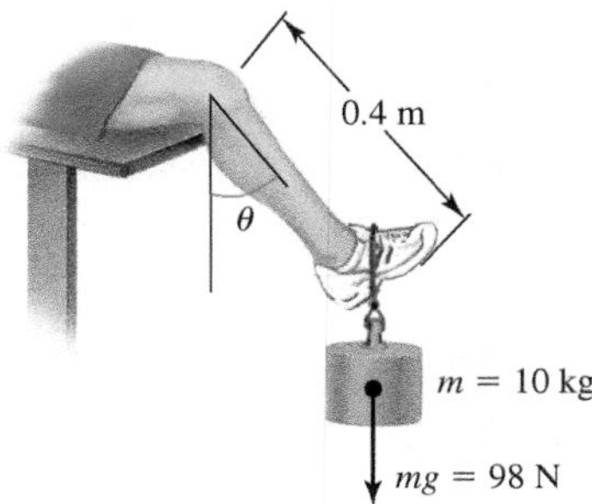

32–36. Lines in space *Find an equation of the following lines or line segments.*

32. The line that passes through the points $(2, 6, -1)$ and $(-6, 4, 0)$

33. The line segment that joins the points $(0, -3, 9)$ and $(2, -8, 1)$

34. The line through the point $(0, 1, 1)$ and parallel to the line $\mathbf{R}(t) = \langle 1 + 2t, 3 - 5t, 7 + 6t \rangle$

35. The line through the point $(0, 1, 1)$ that is orthogonal to both $\langle 0, -1, 3 \rangle$ and $\langle 2, -1, 2 \rangle$

36. The line through the point $(0, 1, 4)$ and orthogonal to the vector $\langle -2, 1, 7 \rangle$ and the y-axis

37. Area of a parallelogram Find the area of the parallelogram with vertices $(1, 2, 3)$, $(1, 0, 6)$, and $(4, 2, 4)$.

38. Area of a triangle Find the area of the triangle with vertices $(1, 0, 3)$, $(5, 0, -1)$, and $(0, 2, -2)$.

T **39–41. Curves in space** *Sketch the curves described by the following functions, indicating the orientation of the curve. Use analysis and describe the shape of the curve before using a graphing utility.*

39. $\mathbf{r}(t) = 4\cos t\,\mathbf{i} + \mathbf{j} + 4\sin t\,\mathbf{k}$, for $0 \le t \le 2\pi$

40. $\mathbf{r}(t) = e^t\,\mathbf{i} + 2e^t\,\mathbf{j} + \mathbf{k}$, for $t \ge 0$

41. $\mathbf{r}(t) = \sin t\,\mathbf{i} + \sqrt{2}\cos t\,\mathbf{j} + \sin t\,\mathbf{k}$, for $0 \le t \le 2\pi$

42–45. Working with vector-valued functions *For each vector-valued function* **r**, *carry out the following steps.*

a. Evaluate $\lim_{t \to 0} \mathbf{r}(t)$ and $\lim_{t \to \infty} \mathbf{r}(t)$, *if each exists.*

b. Find $\mathbf{r}'(t)$ *and evaluate* $\mathbf{r}'(0)$.

c. Find $\mathbf{r}''(t)$.

d. Evaluate $\int \mathbf{r}(t)\,dt$.

42. $\mathbf{r}(t) = \langle t + 1, t^2 - 3 \rangle$

43. $\mathbf{r}(t) = \left\langle \frac{1}{2t + 1}, \frac{t}{t + 1} \right\rangle$

44. $\mathbf{r}(t) = \langle e^{-2t}, te^{-t}, \tan^{-1} t \rangle$

45. $\mathbf{r}(t) = \langle \sin 2t, 3 \cos 4t, t \rangle$

T **46. Orthogonal r and r′** Find all points on the ellipse $\mathbf{r}(t) = \langle 1, 8 \sin t, \cos t \rangle$, for $0 \le t \le 2\pi$, at which $\mathbf{r}(t)$ and $\mathbf{r}'(t)$ are orthogonal. Sketch the curve and the tangent vectors to verify your conclusion.

T **47. Projectile motion** A projectile is launched from the origin, which is a point 50 ft from a 30-ft vertical cliff (see figure). It is launched at a speed of $50\sqrt{2}$ ft/s at an angle of 45° to the horizontal. Assume that the ground is horizontal on top of the cliff and that only the gravitational force affects the motion of the object.

a. Give the coordinates of the landing spot of the projectile on the top of the cliff.
b. What is the maximum height reached by the projectile?
c. What is the time of flight?
d. Write an integral that gives the length of the trajectory.
e. Approximate the length of the trajectory.
f. What is the range of launch angles needed to clear the edge of the cliff?

48. Baseball motion A toddler on level ground throws a baseball into the air at an angle of 30° with the ground from a height of 2 ft. If the ball lands 10 ft from the child, determine the initial speed of the ball.

49. Shooting a basket A basketball player tosses a basketball into the air at an angle of 45° with the ground from a height of 6 ft above the ground. If the ball goes through the basket 15 ft away and 10 ft above the ground, determine the initial velocity of the ball.

50–52. Arc length *Find the arc length of the following curves.*

50. $\mathbf{r}(t) = \langle 2t^{9/2}, t^3 \rangle$, for $0 \le t \le 2$

51. $\mathbf{r}(t) = \left\langle t^2, \frac{4\sqrt{2}}{3} t^{3/2}, 2t \right\rangle$, for $1 \le t \le 3$

52. $\mathbf{r}(t) = \langle t, \ln \sec t, \ln(\sec t + \tan t) \rangle$, for $0 \le t \le \pi/4$

53. Velocity and trajectory length The acceleration of a wayward firework is given by $\mathbf{a}(t) = \sqrt{2}\,\mathbf{j} + 2t\,\mathbf{k}$, for $0 \le t \le 3$. Suppose the initial velocity of the firework is $\mathbf{v}(0) = \mathbf{i}$.

a. Find the velocity of the firework, for $0 \le t \le 3$.
b. Find the length of the trajectory of the firework over the interval $0 \le t \le 3$.

T **54–55. Arc length of polar curves** *Find the approximate length of the following curves.*

54. The limaçon $r = 3 + 2 \cos \theta$

55. The limaçon $r = 3 - 6 \cos \theta$

56–57. Arc length parameterization *Find the description of the following curves that uses arc length as a parameter.*

56. $\mathbf{r}(t) = (1 + 4t)\mathbf{i} - 3t\,\mathbf{j}$, for $t \ge 1$

57. $\mathbf{r}(t) = \left\langle t^2, \frac{4\sqrt{2}}{3} t^{3/2}, 2t \right\rangle$, for $t \ge 0$

58. Tangents and normals for an ellipse Consider the ellipse $\mathbf{r}(t) = \langle 3 \cos t, 4 \sin t \rangle$, for $0 \le t \le 2\pi$.

a. Find the tangent vector $\mathbf{r}'$, the unit tangent vector $\mathbf{T}$, and the principal unit normal vector $\mathbf{N}$ at all points on the curve.
b. At what points does $|\mathbf{r}'|$ have maximum and minimum values?
c. At what points does the curvature have maximum and minimum values? Interpret this result in light of part (b).
d. Find the points (if any) at which $\mathbf{r}$ and $\mathbf{N}$ are parallel.

T **59–62. Properties of space curves** *Do the following calculations.*

a. Find the tangent vector and the unit tangent vector.
b. Find the curvature.
c. Find the principal unit normal vector.
d. Verify that $|\mathbf{N}| = 1$ *and* $\mathbf{T} \cdot \mathbf{N} = 0$.
e. Graph the curve and sketch $\mathbf{T}$ *and* $\mathbf{N}$ *at two points.*

59. $\mathbf{r}(t) = \langle 6 \cos t, 3 \sin t \rangle$, for $0 \le t \le 2\pi$

60. $\mathbf{r}(t) = \cos t\,\mathbf{i} + 2 \sin t\,\mathbf{j} + \mathbf{k}$, for $0 \le t \le 2\pi$

61. $\mathbf{r}(t) = \cos t\,\mathbf{i} + 2 \cos t\,\mathbf{j} + \sqrt{5} \sin t\,\mathbf{k}$, for $0 \le t \le 2\pi$

62. $\mathbf{r}(t) = t\,\mathbf{i} + 2 \cos t\,\mathbf{j} + 2 \sin t\,\mathbf{k}$, for $0 \le t \le 2\pi$

63–66. Analyzing motion *Consider the position vector of the following moving objects.*

a. Find the normal and tangential components of the acceleration.
b. Graph the trajectory and sketch the normal and tangential components of the acceleration at two points on the trajectory. Show that their sum gives the total acceleration.

63. $\mathbf{r}(t) = 2 \cos t\,\mathbf{i} + 2 \sin t\,\mathbf{j}$, for $0 \le t \le 2\pi$

64. $\mathbf{r}(t) = 3t\,\mathbf{i} + (4 - t)\,\mathbf{j} + t\,\mathbf{k}$, for $t \ge 0$

65. $\mathbf{r}(t) = (t^2 + 1)\,\mathbf{i} + 2t\,\mathbf{j}$, for $t \ge 0$

66. $\mathbf{r}(t) = 2 \cos t\,\mathbf{i} + 2 \sin t\,\mathbf{j} + 10t\,\mathbf{k}$, for $0 \le t \le 2\pi$

67. Lines in the plane

a. Use a dot product to find an equation of the line in the xy-plane passing through the point (x_0, y_0) perpendicular to the vector $\langle a, b \rangle$.
b. Given a point $(x_0, y_0, 0)$ and a vector $\mathbf{v} = \langle a, b, 0 \rangle$ in $\mathbb{R}^3$, describe the set of points that satisfy the equation $\langle a, b, 0 \rangle \times \langle x - x_0, y - y_0, 0 \rangle = \mathbf{0}$. Use this result to determine an equation of a line in $\mathbb{R}^2$ passing through (x_0, y_0) parallel to the vector $\langle a, b \rangle$.

68. Length of a DVD groove The capacity of a single-sided, single-layer digital versatile disc (DVD) is approximately 4.7 billion bytes—enough to store a two-hour movie. (Newer double-sided, double-layer DVDs have about four times that capacity, and Blu-ray discs are in the range of 50 gigabytes.) A DVD consists of a single "groove" that spirals outward from the inner edge to the outer edge of the storage region.

a. First consider the spiral given in polar coordinates by $r = t\theta/(2\pi)$, where $0 \le \theta \le 2\pi N$ and successive loops of the spiral are t units apart. Explain why this spiral has N loops and why the entire spiral has a radius of $R = Nt$ units. Sketch three loops of the spiral.

b. Write an integral for the length L of the spiral with N loops.

c. The integral in part (b) can be evaluated exactly, but a good approximation can also be made. Assuming N is large, explain why $\theta^2 + 1 \approx \theta^2$. Use this approximation to simplify the integral in part (b) and show that $L \approx t\pi N^2 = \dfrac{\pi R^2}{t}$.

d. Now consider a DVD with an inner radius of $r = 2.5$ cm and an outer radius of $R = 5.9$ cm. Model the groove by a spiral with a thickness of $t = 1.5$ microns $= 1.5 \times 10^{-6}$ m. Because of the hole in the DVD, the lower limit in the arc length integral is not $\theta = 0$. What are the limits of integration?

e. Use the approximation in part (c) to find the length of the DVD groove. Express your answer in centimeters and miles.

69. Computing the binormal vector and torsion Compute the unit binormal vector **B** and the torsion of the curve $\mathbf{r}(t) = \langle t, t^2, t^3 \rangle$ at $t = 1$.

70–71. Curve analysis *Carry out the following steps for the given curves C.*

a. Find $\mathbf{T}(t)$ *at all points of C.*

b. Find $\mathbf{N}(t)$ *and the curvature at all points of C.*

c. Sketch the curve and show $\mathbf{T}(t)$ *and* $\mathbf{N}(t)$ *at the points of C corresponding to* $t = 0$ *and* $t = \pi/2$.

d. Are the results of parts (a) and (b) consistent with the graph?

e. Find $\mathbf{B}(t)$ *at all points of C.*

f. On the graph of part (c), plot $\mathbf{B}(t)$ *at the points of C corresponding to* $t = 0$ *and* $t = \pi/2$.

g. Describe three calculations that serve to check the accuracy of your results in part (a)–(f).

h. Compute the torsion at all points of C. Interpret this result.

70. C: $\mathbf{r}(t) = \langle 3 \sin t, 4 \sin t, 5 \cos t \rangle$, for $0 \le t \le 2\pi$

71. C: $\mathbf{r}(t) = \langle 3 \sin t, 3 \cos t, 4t \rangle$, for $0 \le t \le 2\pi$

72. Torsion of a plane curve Suppose $\mathbf{r}(t) = \langle f(t), g(t), h(t) \rangle$, where f, g, and h are the quadratic functions $f(t) = a_1t^2 + b_1t + c_1$, $g(t) = a_2t^2 + b_2t + c_2$, and $h(t) = a_3t^2 + b_3t + c_3$, and where at least one of the leading coefficients a_1, a_2, or a_3 is nonzero. Apart from a set of degenerate cases (for example, $\mathbf{r}(t) = \langle t^2, t^2, t^2 \rangle$, whose graph is a line), it can be shown that the graph of $\mathbf{r}(t)$ is a parabola that lies in a plane (Exercise 73).

a. Show by direct computation that $\mathbf{v} \times \mathbf{a}$ is constant. Then explain why the unit binormal vector is constant at all points on the curve. What does this result say about the torsion of the curve?

b. Compute $\mathbf{a}'(t)$ and explain why the torsion is zero at all points on the curve for which the torsion is defined.

73. Families of plane curves Let f and g be continuous on an interval I. Consider the curve

$$C: \mathbf{r}(t) = \langle a_1 f(t) + a_2 g(t) + a_3, b_1 f(t) + b_2 g(t) + b_3, c_1 f(t) + c_2 g(t) + c_3 \rangle,$$

for t in I, and where a_i, b_i, and c_i, for $i = 1, 2$, and 3, are real numbers.

a. Show that, in general, apart from a set of special cases, C lies in a plane.

b. Explain why the torsion is zero at all points of C for which the torsion is defined.

c. Find the plane in which C: $\mathbf{r}(t) = \langle t^2 - 2, -t^2 + t + 2, t - 4 \rangle$ lies.

Chapter 11 Guided Projects

Applications of the material in this chapter and related topics can be found in the following Guided Projects. For additional information, see the Preface.

- Designing a trajectory
- Intercepting a UFO
- CORDIC algorithms: How your calculator works
- Bezier curves for graphic design
- Kepler's laws

12

Functions of Several Variables

Chapter Preview Chapter 11 was devoted to vector-valued functions, which generally have one independent variable and two or more dependent variables. In this chapter, we step into three-dimensional space along a different path by considering functions with several independent variables and one dependent variable. All the familiar properties of single-variable functions—domains, graphs, limits, continuity, and derivatives—have generalizations for multivariable functions, although there are often subtle differences when compared to single-variable functions. With functions of several independent variables, we work with *partial derivatives*, which, in turn, give rise to directional derivatives and the *gradient*, a fundamental concept in calculus. Partial derivatives allow us to find maximum and minimum values of multivariable functions. We define tangent planes, rather than tangent lines, that allow us to make linear approximations. The chapter ends with a survey of optimization problems in several variables.

12.1 Planes and Surfaces

Functions with one independent variable, such as $f(x) = xe^{-x}$, or *equations* in two variables, such as $x^2 + y^2 = 4$, describe curves in $\mathbb{R}^2$. We now add a third variable to the picture and consider functions of two independent variables (for example, $f(x, y) = x^2 + 2y^2$) and equations in three variables (for example, $x^2 + y^2 + 2z^2 = 4$). We see in this chapter that such functions and equations describe *surfaces* that may be displayed in $\mathbb{R}^3$. Just as a line is the simplest curve in $\mathbb{R}^2$, a plane is the simplest surface in $\mathbb{R}^3$.

Equations of Planes

Intuitively, a plane is a flat surface with infinite extent in all directions. Three noncollinear points (not all on the same line) determine a unique plane in $\mathbb{R}^3$. A plane in $\mathbb{R}^3$ is also uniquely determined by one point in the plane and any nonzero vector orthogonal (perpendicular) to the plane. Such a vector, called a *normal vector*, specifies the orientation of the plane.

➤ Just as the slope determines the orientation of a line in $\mathbb{R}^2$, a normal vector determines the orientation of a plane.

DEFINITION **Plane in $\mathbb{R}^3$**

Given a fixed point P_0 and a nonzero **normal vector n**, the set of points P in $\mathbb{R}^3$ for which $\overrightarrow{P_0P}$ is orthogonal to **n** is called a **plane** (Figure 12.1).

QUICK CHECK 1 Describe the plane that is orthogonal to the unit vector $\mathbf{i} = \langle 1, 0, 0 \rangle$ and passes through the point $(1, 2, 3)$. ➤

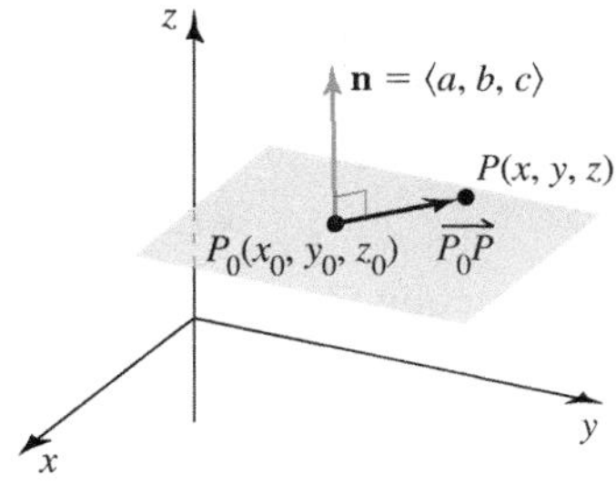

The orientation of a plane is specified by a normal vector **n**. All vectors $\overrightarrow{P_0P}$ in the plane are orthogonal to **n**.

Figure 12.1

We now derive an equation of the plane passing through the point $P_0(x_0, y_0, z_0)$ with nonzero normal vector $\mathbf{n} = \langle a, b, c \rangle$. Notice that for any point $P(x, y, z)$ in the plane, the vector $\overrightarrow{P_0P} = \langle x - x_0, y - y_0, z - z_0 \rangle$ lies in the plane and is orthogonal to **n**. This orthogonality relationship is written and simplified as follows:

$$\begin{aligned} \mathbf{n} \cdot \overrightarrow{P_0P} &= 0 && \text{Dot product of orthogonal vectors} \\ \langle a, b, c \rangle \cdot \langle x - x_0, y - y_0, z - z_0 \rangle &= 0 && \text{Substitute vector components.} \\ a(x - x_0) + b(y - y_0) + c(z - z_0) &= 0 && \text{Expand the dot product.} \\ ax + by + cz &= d. && d = ax_0 + by_0 + cz_0 \end{aligned}$$

This important result states that the most general linear equation in three variables, $ax + by + cz = d$, describes a plane in $\mathbb{R}^3$.

➤ A vector $\mathbf{n} = \langle a, b, c \rangle$ is used to describe a *plane* by specifying a direction *orthogonal* to the plane. By contrast, a vector $\mathbf{v} = \langle a, b, c \rangle$ is used to describe a *line* by specifying a direction *parallel* to the line (Section 11.5).

General Equation of a Plane in $\mathbb{R}^3$

The plane passing through the point $P_0(x_0, y_0, z_0)$ with a nonzero normal vector $\mathbf{n} = \langle a, b, c \rangle$ is described by the equation

$$a(x - x_0) + b(y - y_0) + c(z - z_0) = 0 \quad \text{or} \quad ax + by + cz = d,$$

where $d = ax_0 + by_0 + cz_0$.

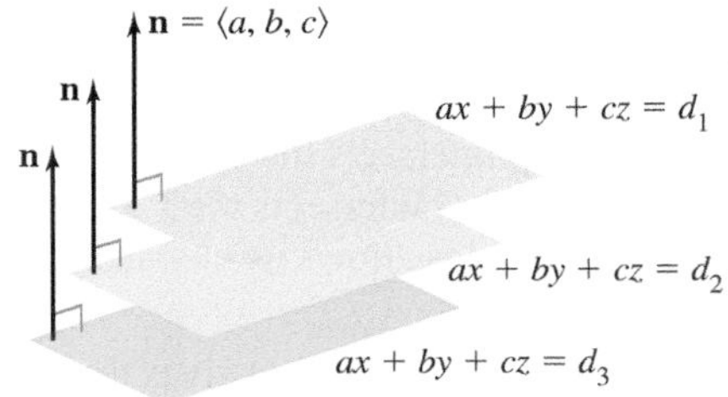

The normal vectors of parallel planes have the same direction.

Figure 12.2

The coefficients a, b, and c in the equation of a plane determine the *orientation* of the plane, while the constant term d determines the *location* of the plane. If a, b, and c are held constant and d is varied, a family of parallel planes is generated, all with the same orientation (Figure 12.2).

QUICK CHECK 2 Consider the equation of a plane in the form $\mathbf{n} \cdot \overrightarrow{P_0P} = 0$. Explain why the equation of the plane depends only on the direction, but not the length, of the normal vector **n**. ◄

EXAMPLE 1 **Equation of a plane** Find an equation of the plane passing through $P_0(2, -3, 4)$ with a normal vector $\mathbf{n} = \langle -1, 2, 3 \rangle$.

SOLUTION Substituting the components of **n** ($a = -1$, $b = 2$, and $c = 3$) and the coordinates of P_0 ($x_0 = 2$, $y_0 = -3$, and $z_0 = 4$) into the equation of a plane, we have

$$\begin{aligned} a(x - x_0) + b(y - y_0) + c(z - z_0) &= 0 && \text{General equation of a plane} \\ (-1)(x - 2) + 2(y - (-3)) + 3(z - 4) &= 0 && \text{Substitute.} \\ -x + 2y + 3z &= 4. && \text{Simplify.} \end{aligned}$$

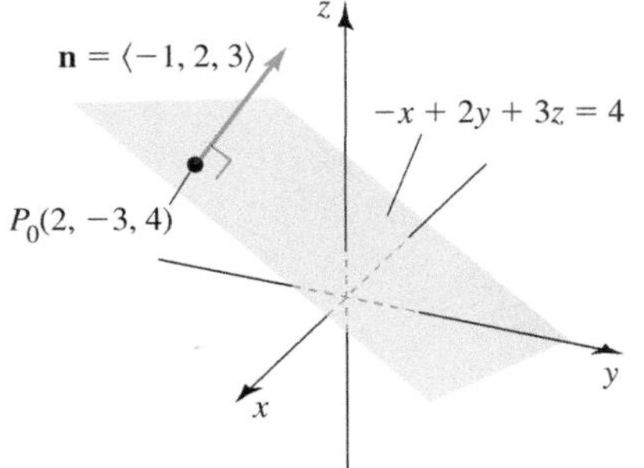

Figure 12.3

The plane is shown in Figure 12.3.

Related Exercises 11–16 ◄

EXAMPLE 2 **A plane through three points** Find an equation of the plane that passes through the (noncollinear) points $P(2, -1, 3)$, $Q(1, 4, 0)$, and $R(0, -1, 5)$.

SOLUTION To write an equation of the plane, we must find a normal vector. Because P, Q, and R lie in the plane, the vectors $\overrightarrow{PQ} = \langle -1, 5, -3 \rangle$ and $\overrightarrow{PR} = \langle -2, 0, 2 \rangle$ also lie in the plane. The cross product $\overrightarrow{PQ} \times \overrightarrow{PR}$ is perpendicular to both $\overrightarrow{PQ}$ and $\overrightarrow{PR}$; therefore, a vector normal to the plane is

➤ Three points P, Q, and R determine a plane provided they are not collinear. If P, Q, and R *are* collinear, then the vectors $\overrightarrow{PQ}$ and $\overrightarrow{PR}$ are parallel, which implies that $\overrightarrow{PQ} \times \overrightarrow{PR} = \mathbf{0}$.

$$\mathbf{n} = \overrightarrow{PQ} \times \overrightarrow{PR} = \begin{vmatrix} \mathbf{i} & \mathbf{j} & \mathbf{k} \\ -1 & 5 & -3 \\ -2 & 0 & 2 \end{vmatrix} = 10\,\mathbf{i} + 8\,\mathbf{j} + 10\,\mathbf{k}.$$

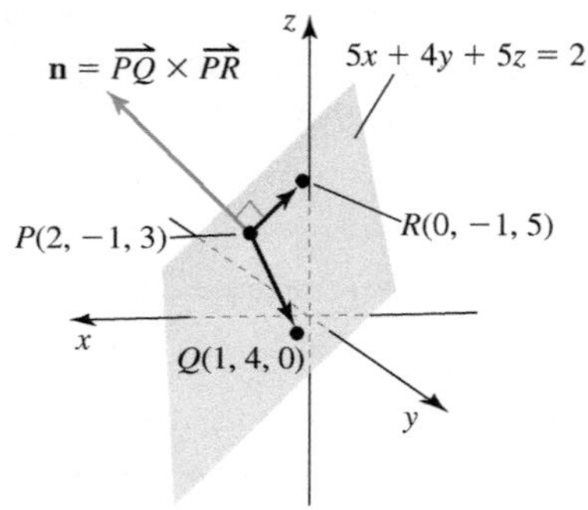

Figure 12.4

Any nonzero scalar multiple of $\mathbf{n}$ may be used as the normal vector. Choosing $\mathbf{n} = \langle 5, 4, 5 \rangle$ and $P_0(2, -1, 3)$ as the fixed point in the plane (Figure 12.4), an equation of the plane is

$$5(x - 2) + 4(y - (-1)) + 5(z - 3) = 0 \quad \text{or} \quad 5x + 4y + 5z = 21.$$

Using either Q or R as the fixed point in the plane leads to an equivalent equation of the plane.

Related Exercises 17–20 ◀

QUICK CHECK 3 Verify in Example 2 that the same equation for the plane results if either Q or R is used as the fixed point in the plane. ◀

EXAMPLE 3 Properties of a plane Let Q be the plane described by the equation $2x - 3y - z = 6$.

a. Find a vector normal to Q.

b. Find the points at which Q intersects the coordinate axes and plot Q.

c. Describe the sets of points at which Q intersects the yz-plane, the xz-plane, and the xy-plane.

SOLUTION

a. The coefficients of x, y, and z in the equation of Q are the components of a vector normal to Q. Therefore, a normal vector is $\mathbf{n} = \langle 2, -3, -1 \rangle$ (or any nonzero multiple of $\mathbf{n}$).

b. The point (x, y, z) at which Q intersects the x-axis must have $y = z = 0$. Substituting $y = z = 0$ into the equation of Q gives $x = 3$, so Q intersects the x-axis at $(3, 0, 0)$. Similarly, Q intersects the y-axis at $(0, -2, 0)$, and Q intersects the z-axis at $(0, 0, -6)$. Connecting the three intercepts with straight lines allows us to visualize the plane (Figure 12.5).

c. All points in the yz-plane have $x = 0$. Setting $x = 0$ in the equation of Q gives the equation $-3y - z = 6$, which, with the condition $x = 0$, describes a line in the yz-plane. If we set $y = 0$, Q intersects the xz-plane in the line $2x - z = 6$, where $y = 0$. If $z = 0$, Q intersects the xy-plane in the line $2x - 3y = 6$, where $z = 0$ (Figure 12.5).

➤ There is a possibility for confusion here. Working in $\mathbb{R}^3$ with no other restrictions, the equation $-3y - z = 6$ describes a plane that is parallel to the x-axis (because x is unspecified). To make it clear that $-3y - z = 6$ is a line in the yz-plane, the condition $x = 0$ is included.

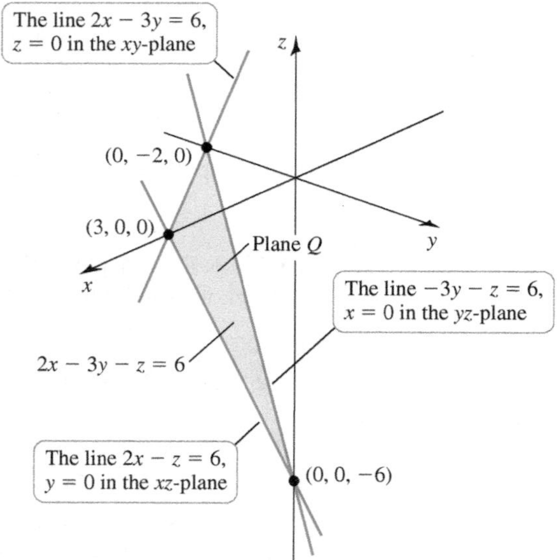

Figure 12.5

Related Exercises 21–24 ◀

Parallel and Orthogonal Planes

The normal vectors of distinct planes tell us about the relative orientation of the planes. Two cases are of particular interest: Two distinct planes may be *parallel* (Figure 12.6a) and two intersecting planes may be *orthogonal* (Figure 12.6b).

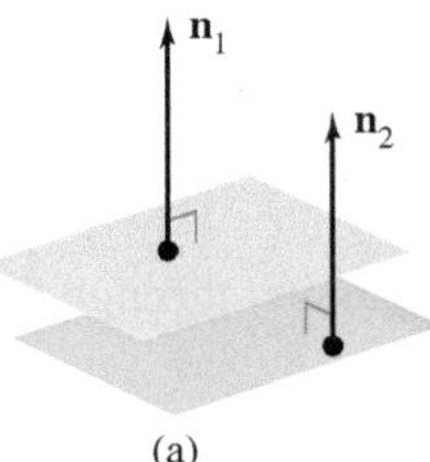

(a)

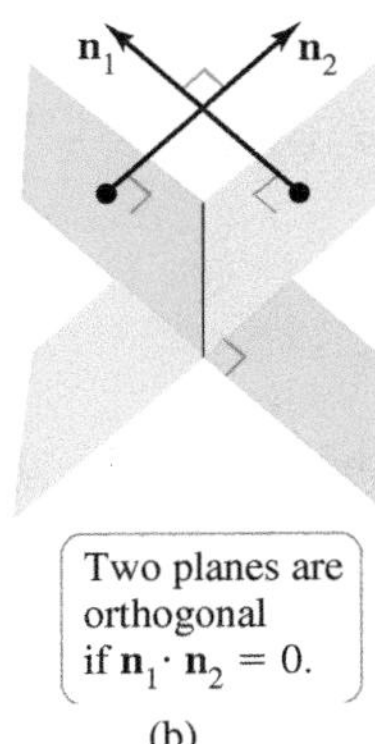

(b)

Figure 12.6

> **DEFINITION Parallel and Orthogonal Planes**
>
> Two distinct planes are **parallel** if their respective normal vectors are parallel (that is, the normal vectors are scalar multiples of each other). Two planes are **orthogonal** if their respective normal vectors are orthogonal (that is, the dot product of the normal vectors is zero).

QUICK CHECK 4 Verify in Example 4 that $\mathbf{n}_R \cdot \mathbf{n}_S = 0$ and $\mathbf{n}_R \cdot \mathbf{n}_T = 0$. ◀

EXAMPLE 4 Parallel and orthogonal planes Which of the following distinct planes are parallel and which are orthogonal?

$$Q:\ 2x - 3y + 6z = 12 \qquad R:\ -x + \tfrac{3}{2}y - 3z = 14$$
$$S:\ 6x + 8y + 2z = 1 \qquad T:\ -9x - 12y - 3z = 7$$

SOLUTION Let $\mathbf{n}_Q$, $\mathbf{n}_R$, $\mathbf{n}_S$, and $\mathbf{n}_T$ be vectors normal to Q, R, S, and T, respectively. Normal vectors may be read from the coefficients of x, y, and z in the equations of the planes.

$$\mathbf{n}_Q = \langle 2, -3, 6 \rangle \qquad \mathbf{n}_R = \left\langle -1, \tfrac{3}{2}, -3 \right\rangle$$
$$\mathbf{n}_S = \langle 6, 8, 2 \rangle \qquad \mathbf{n}_T = \langle -9, -12, -3 \rangle$$

Notice that $\mathbf{n}_Q = -2\mathbf{n}_R$, which implies that Q and R are parallel. Similarly, $\mathbf{n}_T = -\frac{3}{2}\mathbf{n}_S$, so S and T are parallel. Furthermore, $\mathbf{n}_Q \cdot \mathbf{n}_S = 0$ and $\mathbf{n}_Q \cdot \mathbf{n}_T = 0$, which implies that Q is orthogonal to both S and T. Because Q and R are parallel, it follows that R is also orthogonal to both S and T.

Related Exercises 25–30 ◀

EXAMPLE 5 Parallel planes Find an equation of the plane Q that passes through the point $(-2, 4, 1)$ and is parallel to the plane R: $3x - 2y + z = 4$.

SOLUTION The vector $\mathbf{n} = \langle 3, -2, 1 \rangle$ is normal to R. Because Q and R are parallel, $\mathbf{n}$ is also normal to Q. Therefore, an equation of Q, passing through $(-2, 4, 1)$ with normal vector $\langle 3, -2, 1 \rangle$, is

$$3(x + 2) - 2(y - 4) + (z - 1) = 0 \quad \text{or} \quad 3x - 2y + z = -13.$$

Related Exercises 31–34 ◀

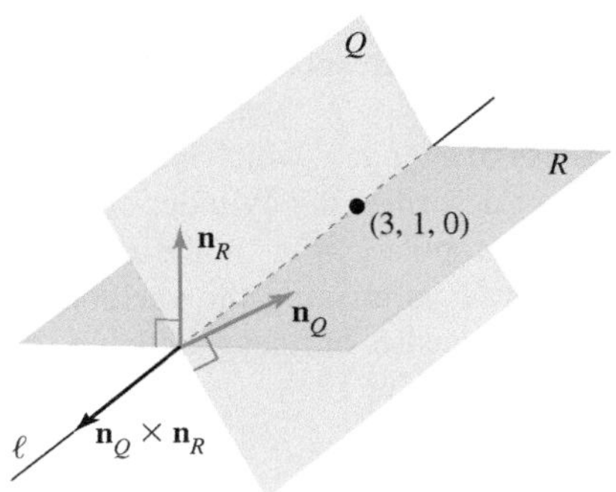

Figure 12.7

EXAMPLE 6 Intersecting planes Find an equation of the line of intersection of the planes Q: $x + 2y + z = 5$ and R: $2x + y - z = 7$.

SOLUTION First note that the vectors normal to the planes, $\mathbf{n}_Q = \langle 1, 2, 1 \rangle$ and $\mathbf{n}_R = \langle 2, 1, -1 \rangle$, are *not* multiples of each other. Therefore, the planes are not parallel and they must intersect in a line; call it ℓ. To find an equation of ℓ, we need two pieces of information: a point on ℓ and a vector pointing in the direction of ℓ. Here is one of several ways to find a point on ℓ. Setting $z = 0$ in the equations of the planes gives equations of the lines in which the planes intersect the xy-plane:

$$x + 2y = 5$$
$$2x + y = 7.$$

➤ By setting $z = 0$ and solving these two equations, we find the point that lies on both planes *and* lies in the xy-plane ($z = 0$).

Solving these equations simultaneously, we find that $x = 3$ and $y = 1$. Combining this result with $z = 0$, we see that $(3, 1, 0)$ is a point on ℓ (Figure 12.7).

We next find a vector parallel to ℓ. Because ℓ lies in Q and R, it is orthogonal to the normal vectors $\mathbf{n}_Q$ and $\mathbf{n}_R$. Therefore, the cross product of $\mathbf{n}_Q$ and $\mathbf{n}_R$ is a vector parallel to ℓ (Figure 12.7). In this case, the cross product is

$$\mathbf{n}_Q \times \mathbf{n}_R = \begin{vmatrix} \mathbf{i} & \mathbf{j} & \mathbf{k} \\ 1 & 2 & 1 \\ 2 & 1 & -1 \end{vmatrix} = -3\,\mathbf{i} + 3\,\mathbf{j} - 3\,\mathbf{k} = \langle -3, 3, -3 \rangle.$$

➤ Another question related to Example 6 concerns the angle between two planes. See Exercise 95 for an example.

An equation of the line ℓ in the direction of the vector $\langle -3, 3, -3 \rangle$ passing through the point $(3, 1, 0)$ is

$$\begin{aligned} \mathbf{r}(t) &= \langle x_0, y_0, z_0 \rangle + t\langle a, b, c \rangle && \text{Equation of a line (Section 11.5)} \\ &= \langle 3, 1, 0 \rangle + t\langle -3, 3, -3 \rangle && \text{Substitute.} \\ &= \langle 3 - 3t, 1 + 3t, -3t \rangle, && \text{Simplify.} \end{aligned}$$

➤ Any nonzero scalar multiple of $\langle -3, 3, -3 \rangle$ can be used for the direction of ℓ. For example, another equation of ℓ is $\mathbf{r}(t) = \langle 3 + t, 1 - t, t \rangle$.

where $-\infty < t < \infty$. You can check that any point (x, y, z) with $x = 3 - 3t$, $y = 1 + 3t$, and $z = -3t$ satisfies the equations of both planes.

Related Exercises 35–38 ◀

Cylinders and Traces

In everyday language, we use the word *cylinder* to describe the surface that forms, say, the wall of a paint can. In the context of three-dimensional surfaces, the term *cylinder* has a more general meaning.

> **DEFINITION Cylinder**
>
> Given a curve C in a plane P and a line ℓ not in P, a **cylinder** is the surface consisting of all lines parallel to ℓ that pass through C (Figure 12.8).

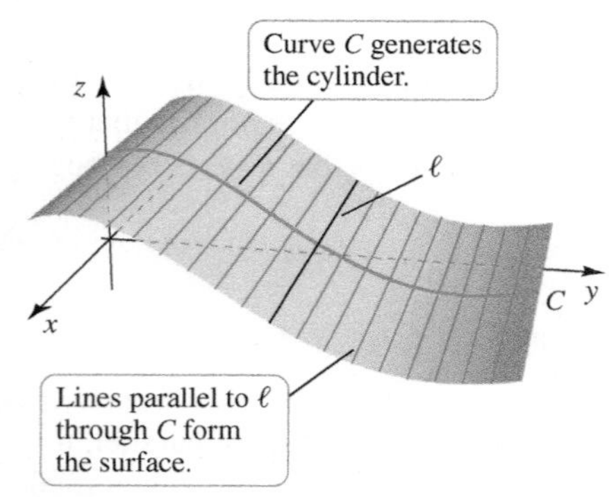

Figure 12.8

A common situation arises when ℓ is one of the coordinate axes or is parallel to a coordinate axis. In these cases, the cylinder is also parallel to one of the coordinate axes. Equations for such cylinders are easy to identify: The variable corresponding to the coordinate axis parallel to ℓ is missing.

For example, working in $\mathbb{R}^3$, the equation $y = x^2$ does not include z, which means that z is arbitrary and can take on all values. Therefore, $y = x^2$ describes the cylinder consisting of all lines parallel to the z-axis that pass through the parabola $y = x^2$ in the xy-plane (Figure 12.9a). In a similar way, the equation $z^2 = y$ in $\mathbb{R}^3$ is missing the variable x, so it describes a cylinder parallel to the x-axis. The cylinder consists of lines parallel to the x-axis that pass through the parabola $z^2 = y$ in the yz-plane (Figure 12.9b).

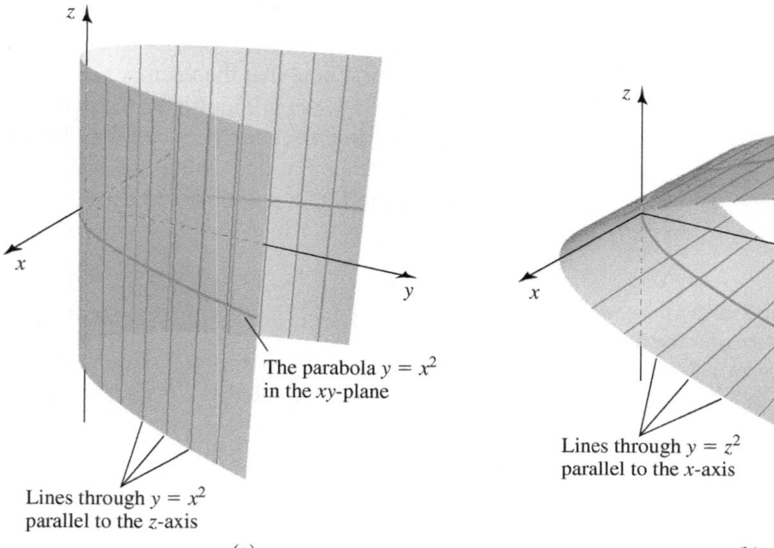

Figure 12.9

QUICK CHECK 5 To which coordinate axis in $\mathbb{R}^3$ is the cylinder $z - 2 \ln x = 0$ parallel? To which coordinate axis in $\mathbb{R}^3$ is the cylinder $y = 4z^2 - 1$ parallel? ◀

Graphing surfaces—and cylinders in particular—is facilitated by identifying the *traces* of the surface.

> **DEFINITION Trace**
>
> A **trace** of a surface is the set of points at which the surface intersects a plane that is parallel to one of the coordinate planes. The traces in the coordinate planes are called the ***xy*-trace**, the ***yz*-trace**, and the ***xz*-trace** (Figure 12.10).

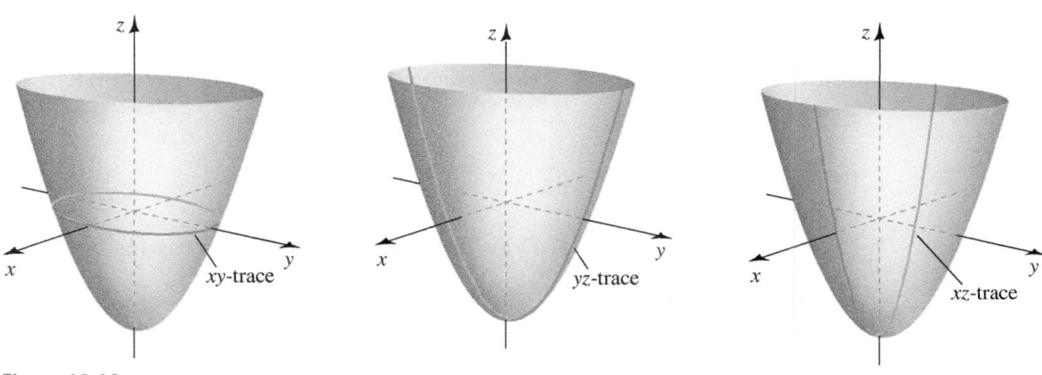

Figure 12.10

EXAMPLE 7 Graphing cylinders Sketch the graphs of the following cylinders in $\mathbb{R}^3$. Identify the axis to which each cylinder is parallel.

a. $x^2 + 4y^2 = 16$ **b.** $x - \sin z = 0$

SOLUTION

a. As an equation in $\mathbb{R}^3$, the variable z is absent. Therefore, z assumes all real values and the graph is a cylinder consisting of lines parallel to the z-axis passing through the curve $x^2 + 4y^2 = 16$ in the xy-plane. You can sketch the cylinder in the following steps.

1. Rewriting the given equation as $\dfrac{x^2}{4^2} + \dfrac{y^2}{2^2} = 1$, we see that the trace of the cylinder in the xy-plane (the xy-trace) is an ellipse. We begin by drawing this ellipse.
2. Next draw a second trace (a copy of the ellipse in Step 1) in a plane parallel to the xy-plane.
3. Now draw lines parallel to the z-axis through the two traces to fill out the cylinder (Figure 12.11a).

The resulting surface, called an *elliptic cylinder*, runs parallel to the z-axis (Figure 12.11b).

b. As an equation in $\mathbb{R}^3$, $x - \sin z = 0$ is missing the variable y. Therefore, y assumes all real values and the graph is a cylinder consisting of lines parallel to the y-axis passing through the curve $x = \sin z$ in the xz-plane. You can sketch the cylinder in the following steps.

1. Graph the curve $x = \sin z$ in the xz-plane, which is the xz-trace of the surface.
2. Draw a second trace (a copy of the curve in Step 1) in a plane parallel to the xz-plane.

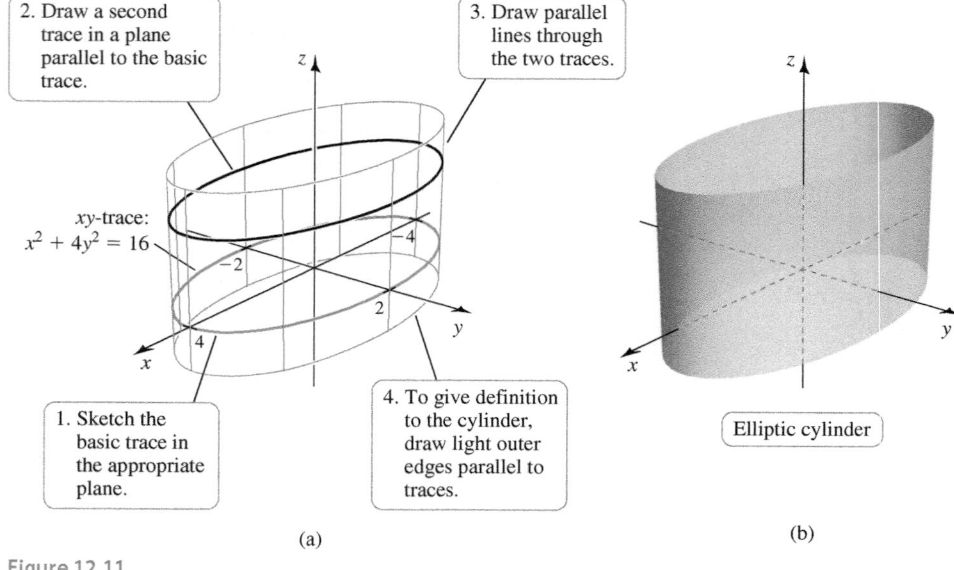

Figure 12.11

3. Draw lines parallel to the y-axis passing through the two traces. (Figure 12.12a).

   The result is a cylinder, running parallel to the y-axis, consisting of copies of the curve $x = \sin z$ (Figure 12.12b).

Related Exercises 39–46 ◄

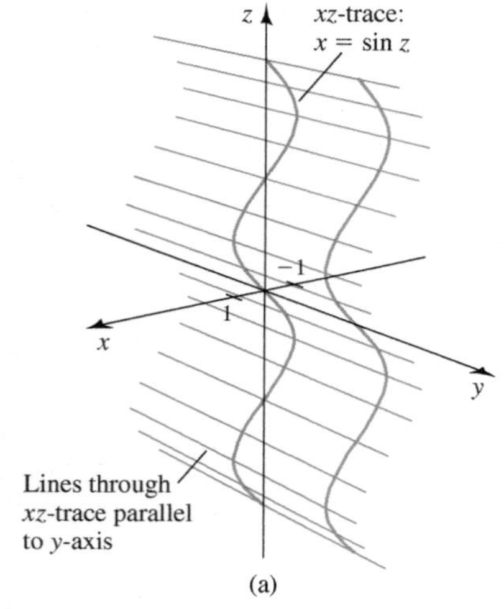

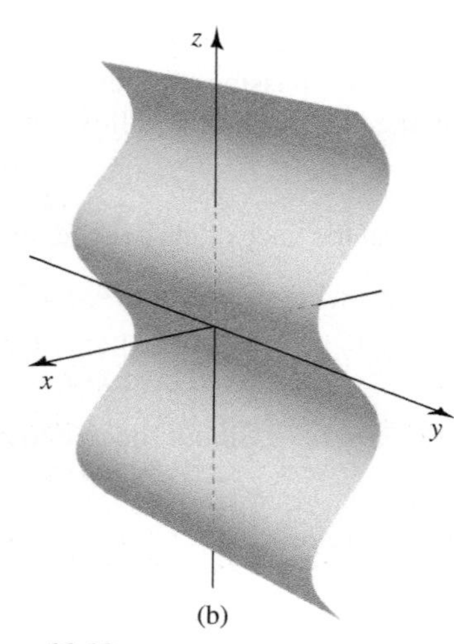

Figure 12.12

➤ Working with quadric surfaces requires familiarity with conic sections (Section 10.4).

Quadric Surfaces

Quadric surfaces are described by the general quadratic (second-degree) equation in three variables,

$$Ax^2 + By^2 + Cz^2 + Dxy + Exz + Fyz + Gx + Hy + Iz + J = 0,$$

where the coefficients $A, \ldots, J$ are constants and not all of A, B, C, D, E, and F are zero. We do not attempt a detailed study of this large family of surfaces. However, a few standard surfaces are worth investigating.

Apart from their mathematical interest, quadric surfaces have a variety of practical uses. Paraboloids (defined in Example 9) share the reflective properties of their two-dimensional counterparts (Section 10.4) and are used to design satellite dishes, headlamps, and mirrors in telescopes. Cooling towers for nuclear power plants have the shape of hyperboloids of one sheet. Ellipsoids appear in the design of water tanks and gears.

Making hand sketches of quadric surfaces can be challenging. Here are a few general ideas to keep in mind as you sketch their graphs.

1. **Intercepts** Determine the points, if any, where the surface intersects the coordinate axes. To find these intercepts, set x, y, and z equal to zero in pairs in the equation of the surface and solve for the third coordinate.
2. **Traces** As illustrated in the following examples, finding traces of the surface helps visualize the surface. For example, setting $z = 0$ or $z = z_0$ (a constant) gives the traces in planes parallel to the xy-plane.
3. Sketch at least two traces in parallel planes (for example, traces with $z = 0$ and $z = \pm 1$). Then draw smooth curves that pass through the traces to fill out the surface.

QUICK CHECK 6 Explain why the elliptic cylinder discussed in Example 7a is a quadric surface. ◄

EXAMPLE 8 **An ellipsoid** The surface defined by the equation $\dfrac{x^2}{a^2} + \dfrac{y^2}{b^2} + \dfrac{z^2}{c^2} = 1$ is an *ellipsoid*. Graph the ellipsoid with $a = 3$, $b = 4$, and $c = 5$.

SOLUTION Setting x, y, and z equal to zero in pairs gives the intercepts $(\pm 3, 0, 0)$, $(0, \pm 4, 0)$, and $(0, 0, \pm 5)$. Note that points in $\mathbb{R}^3$ with $|x| > 3$ or $|y| > 4$ or $|z| > 5$ do not satisfy the equation of the surface (because the left side of the equation is a sum of nonnegative terms that cannot exceed 1). Therefore, the entire surface is contained in the rectangular box defined by $|x| \leq 3$, $|y| \leq 4$, and $|z| \leq 5$.

The trace in the horizontal plane $z = z_0$ is found by substituting $z = z_0$ into the equation of the ellipsoid, which gives

$$\frac{x^2}{9} + \frac{y^2}{16} + \frac{z_0^{\,2}}{25} = 1 \quad \text{or} \quad \frac{x^2}{9} + \frac{y^2}{16} = 1 - \frac{z_0^{\,2}}{25}.$$

➤ The name *ellipsoid* is used in Example 8 because all traces of this surface, when they exist, are ellipses.

If $|z_0| < 5$, then $1 - \dfrac{z_0^{\,2}}{25} > 0$, and the equation describes an ellipse in the horizontal plane $z = z_0$. The largest ellipse parallel to the xy-plane occurs with $z_0 = 0$; it is the xy-trace, which is the ellipse $\dfrac{x^2}{9} + \dfrac{y^2}{16} = 1$ with axes of length 6 and 8 (Figure 12.13a). You can check that the yz-trace, found by setting $x = 0$, is the ellipse $\dfrac{y^2}{16} + \dfrac{z^2}{25} = 1$. The xz-trace (set $y = 0$) is the ellipse $\dfrac{x^2}{9} + \dfrac{z^2}{25} = 1$ (Figure 12.13b). By sketching the xy-, xz-, and yz-traces, an outline of the ellipsoid emerges (Figure 12.13c).

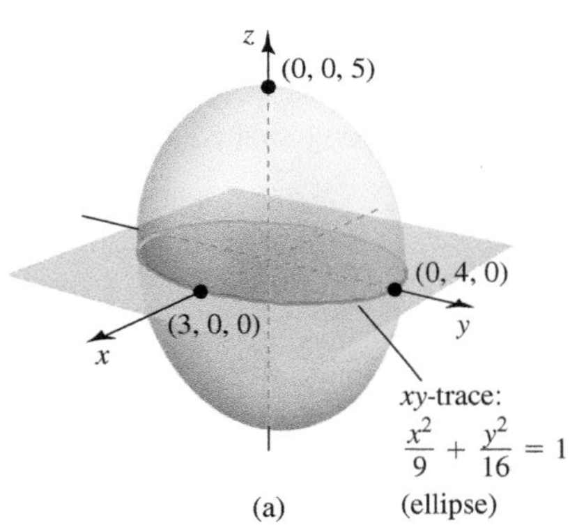

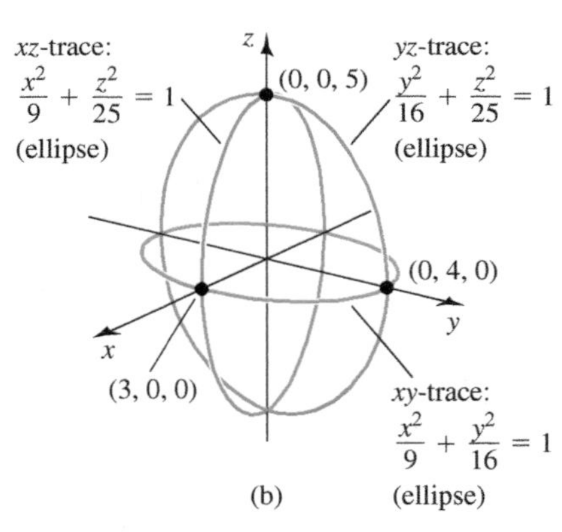

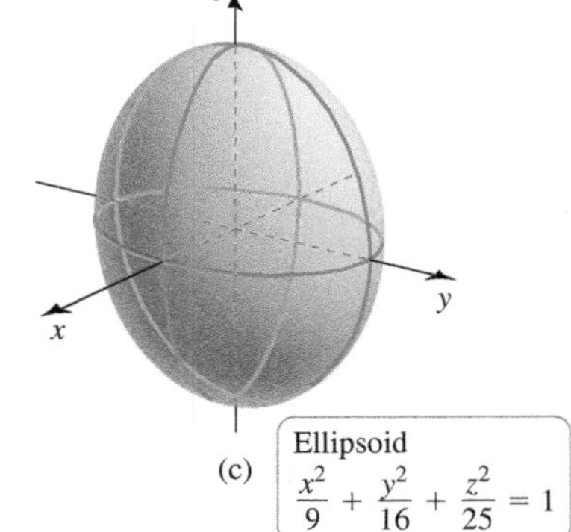

Figure 12.13

Related Exercises 47–50 ◀

QUICK CHECK 7 Assume that $0 < c < b < a$ in the general equation of an ellipsoid. Along which coordinate axis does the ellipsoid have its longest axis? Its shortest axis? ◀

EXAMPLE 9 **An elliptic paraboloid** The surface defined by the equation $z = \dfrac{x^2}{a^2} + \dfrac{y^2}{b^2}$ is an *elliptic paraboloid*. Graph the elliptic paraboloid with $a = 4$ and $b = 2$.

SOLUTION Note that the only intercept of the coordinate axes is $(0, 0, 0)$, which is the *vertex* of the paraboloid. The trace in the horizontal plane $z = z_0$, where $z_0 > 0$, satisfies the equation $\dfrac{x^2}{16} + \dfrac{y^2}{4} = z_0$, which describes an ellipse; there is no horizontal trace when $z_0 < 0$ (Figure 12.14a). The trace in the vertical plane $x = x_0$ is the parabola $z = \dfrac{x_0^2}{16} + \dfrac{y^2}{4}$ (Figure 12.14b); the trace in the vertical plane $y = y_0$ is the parabola $z = \dfrac{x^2}{16} + \dfrac{y_0^2}{4}$ (Figure 12.14c).

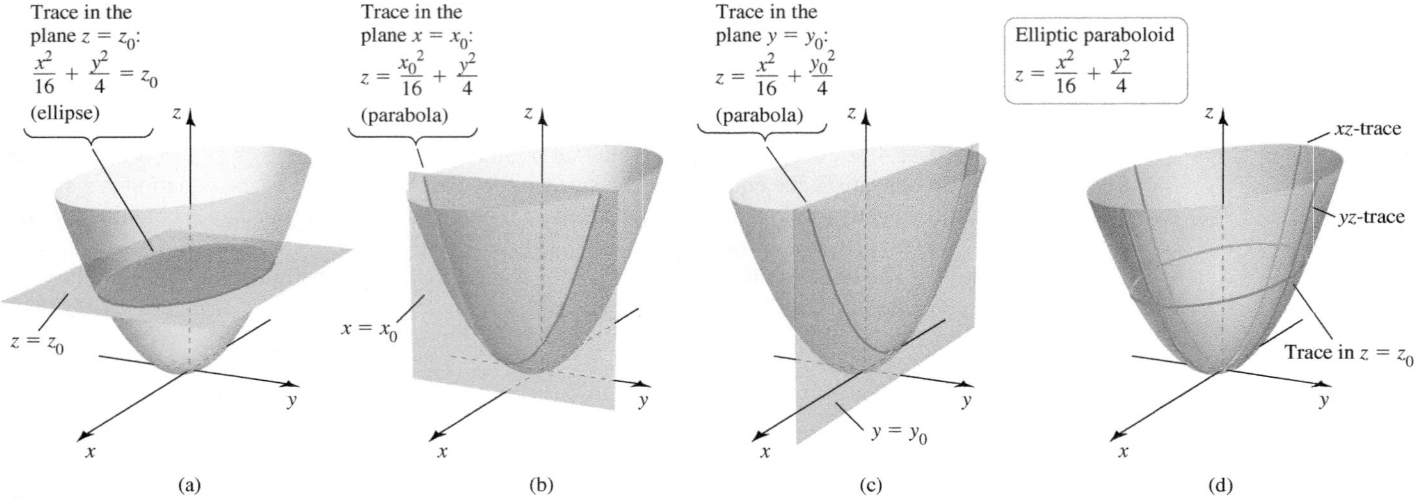

Figure 12.14

➤ The name *elliptic paraboloid* says that the traces of this surface are parabolas and ellipses. Two of the three traces in the coordinate planes are parabolas, so it is called a paraboloid rather than an ellipsoid.

To graph the surface, we sketch the xz-trace $z = \frac{x^2}{16}$ (setting $y = 0$) and the yz-trace $z = \frac{y^2}{4}$ (setting $x = 0$). When these traces are combined with an elliptical trace $\frac{x^2}{16} + \frac{y^2}{4} = z_0$ in a plane $z = z_0$, an outline of the surface appears (Figure 12.14d).

Related Exercises 51–54 ◀

QUICK CHECK 8 The elliptic paraboloid $x = \frac{y^2}{3} + \frac{z^2}{7}$ is a bowl-shaped surface. Along which axis does the bowl open? ◀

EXAMPLE 10 **A hyperboloid of one sheet** Graph the surface defined by the equation $\frac{x^2}{4} + \frac{y^2}{9} - z^2 = 1$.

➤ To be completely accurate, this surface should be called an *elliptic hyperboloid of one sheet* because the traces are ellipses and hyperbolas.

SOLUTION The intercepts of the coordinate axes are $(0, \pm 3, 0)$ and $(\pm 2, 0, 0)$. Setting $z = z_0$, the traces in horizontal planes are ellipses of the form $\frac{x^2}{4} + \frac{y^2}{9} = 1 + z_0^2$. This equation has solutions for all choices of z_0, so the surface has traces in all horizontal planes. These elliptical traces increase in size as $|z_0|$ increases (Figure 12.15a), with the smallest trace being the ellipse $\frac{x^2}{4} + \frac{y^2}{9} = 1$ in the xy-plane. Setting $y = 0$, the xz-trace is the hyperbola $\frac{x^2}{4} - z^2 = 1$; with $x = 0$, the yz-trace is the hyperbola $\frac{y^2}{9} - z^2 = 1$ (Figure 12.15b, c). In fact, the intersection of the surface with any vertical plane is a hyperbola. The resulting surface is a *hyperboloid of one sheet* (Figure 12.15d).

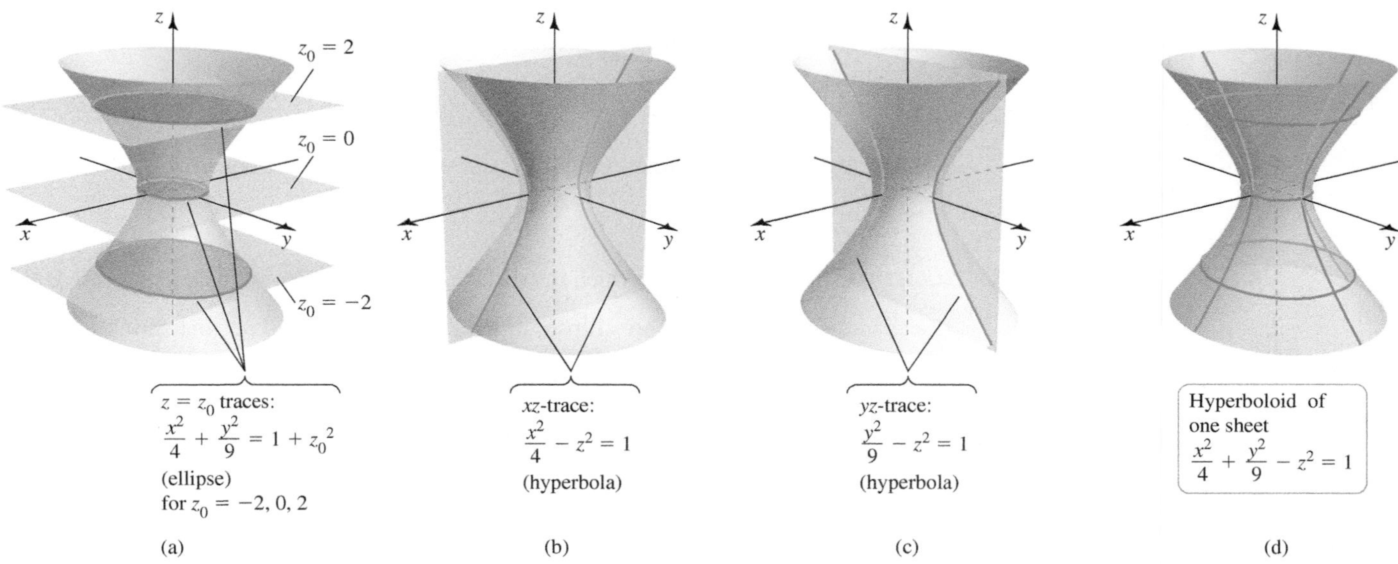

Figure 12.15

Related Exercises 55–58 ◀

QUICK CHECK 9 Which coordinate axis is the axis of the hyperboloid $\frac{y^2}{a^2} + \frac{z^2}{b^2} - \frac{x^2}{c^2} = 1$? ◀

EXAMPLE 11 **A hyperbolic paraboloid** Graph the surface defined by the equation $z = x^2 - \frac{y^2}{4}$.

➤ The name *hyperbolic paraboloid* tells us that the traces are hyperbolas and parabolas. Two of the three traces in the coordinate planes are parabolas, so it is a paraboloid rather than a hyperboloid.

SOLUTION Setting $z = 0$ in the equation of the surface, we see that the xy-trace consists of the two lines $y = \pm 2x$. However, slicing the surface with any other horizontal plane $z = z_0$ produces a hyperbola $x^2 - \frac{y^2}{4} = z_0$. If $z_0 > 0$, then the axis of the hyperbola is parallel to the x-axis. On the other hand, if $z_0 < 0$, then the axis of the hyperbola is parallel to the y-axis (Figure 12.16a). Setting $x = x_0$ produces the trace $z = x_0^2 - \frac{y^2}{4}$, which

➤ The hyperbolic paraboloid has a feature called a *saddle point*. For the surface in Example 11, if you walk from the saddle point at the origin in the direction of the x-axis, you move uphill. If you walk from the saddle point in the direction of the y-axis, you move downhill. Saddle points are examined in detail in Section 12.8.

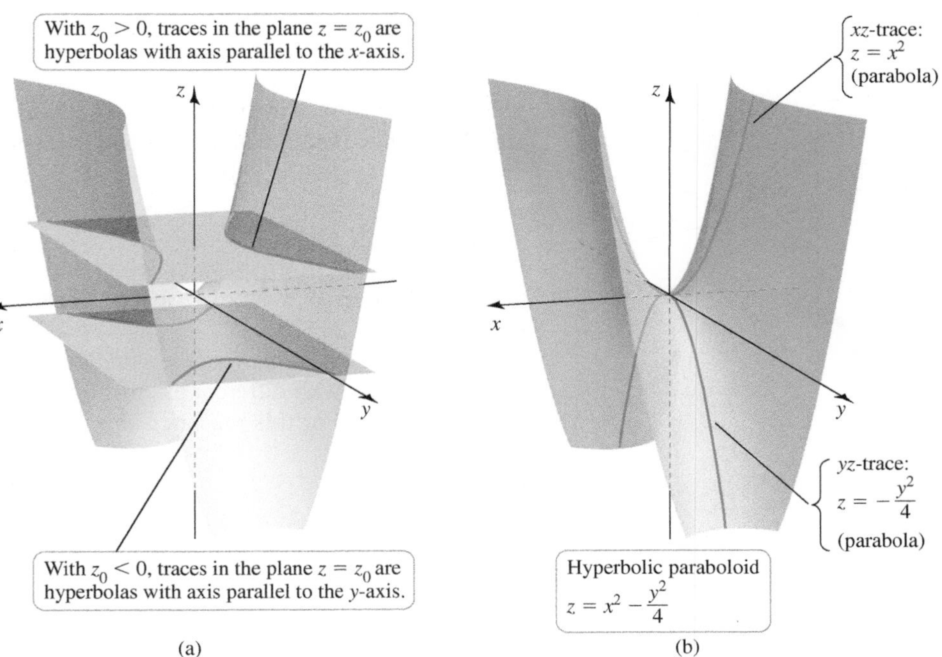

Figure 12.16

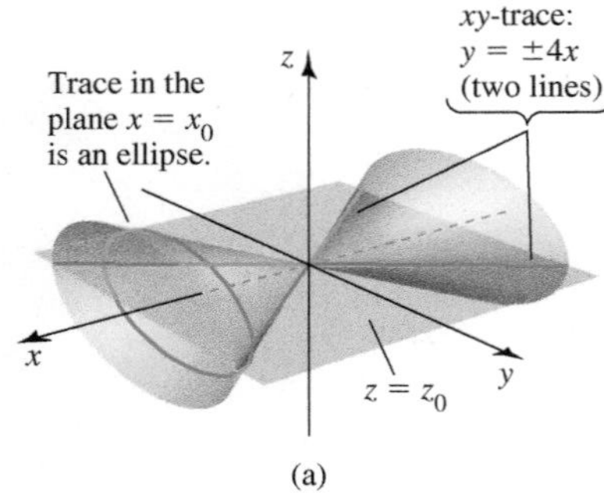

(a)

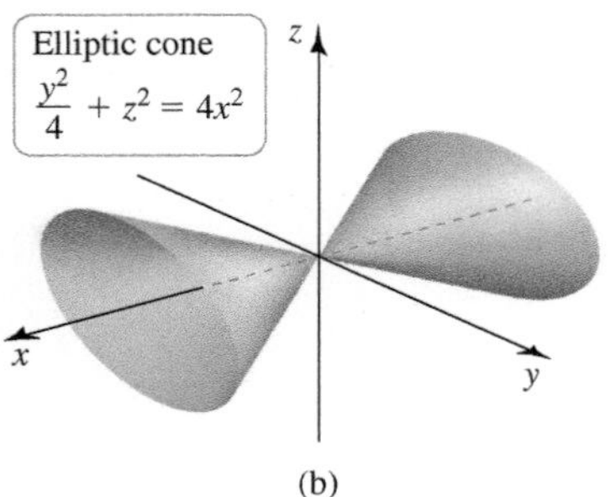

(b)

Figure 12.17

is the equation of a parabola that opens downward in a plane parallel to the yz-plane. You can check that traces in planes parallel to the xz-plane are parabolas that open upward. The resulting surface is a *hyperbolic paraboloid* (Figure 12.16b).

Related Exercises 59–62 ◀

EXAMPLE 12 **Elliptic cones** Graph the surface defined by the equation $\frac{y^2}{4} + z^2 = 4x^2$.

SOLUTION The only point at which the surface intersects the coordinate axes is $(0, 0, 0)$. Traces in the planes $x = x_0$ are ellipses of the form $\frac{y^2}{4} + z^2 = 4x_0^2$ that shrink in size as x_0 approaches 0. Setting $y = 0$, the xz-trace satisfies the equation $z^2 = 4x^2$ or $z = \pm 2x$, which are equations of two lines in the xz-plane that intersect at the origin. Setting $z = 0$, the xy-trace satisfies $y^2 = 16x^2$ or $y = \pm 4x$, which describes two lines in the xy-plane that intersect at the origin (Figure 12.17a). The complete surface consists of two *cones* opening in opposite directions along the x-axis with a common vertex at the origin (Figure 12.17b).

Related Exercises 63–66 ◀

EXAMPLE 13 **A hyperboloid of two sheets** Graph the surface defined by the equation

$$-16x^2 - 4y^2 + z^2 + 64x - 80 = 0.$$

SOLUTION We first regroup terms, giving

$$-16\underbrace{(x^2 - 4x)}_{\text{complete the square}} - 4y^2 + z^2 - 80 = 0,$$

and then complete the square in x:

$$-16(\underbrace{x^2 - 4x + 4}_{(x-2)^2} - 4) - 4y^2 + z^2 - 80 = 0.$$

Collecting terms and dividing by 16 gives the equation

$$-(x - 2)^2 - \frac{y^2}{4} + \frac{z^2}{16} = 1.$$

➤ The equation $-x^2 - \frac{y^2}{4} + \frac{z^2}{16} = 1$ describes a hyperboloid of two sheets with its axis on the z-axis. Therefore, the equation in Example 13 describes the same surface shifted 2 units in the positive x-direction.

Notice that if $z = 0$, the equation has no solution, so the surface does not intersect the xy-plane. The traces in planes parallel to the xz- and yz-planes are hyperbolas. If $|z_0| \geq 4$, the trace in the plane $z = z_0$ is an ellipse. This equation describes a *hyperboloid of two sheets*, with its axis parallel to the z-axis and shifted 2 units in the positive x-direction (Figure 12.18).

Related Exercises 67–70 ◀

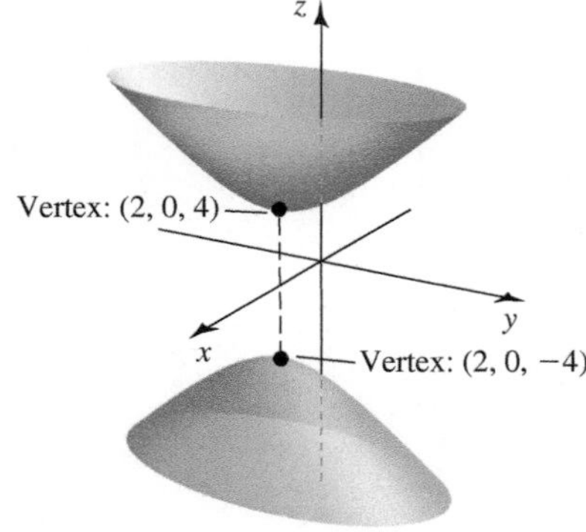

Figure 12.18

QUICK CHECK 10 In which variable(s) should you complete the square to identify the surface $x = y^2 + 2y + z^2 - 4z + 16$? Name and describe the surface. ◀

Table 12.1 summarizes the standard quadric surfaces. It is important to note that the same surfaces with different orientations are obtained when the roles of the variables are interchanged. For this reason, Table 12.1 summarizes many more surfaces than those listed.

Table 12.1

Name	Standard Equation	Features	Graph
Ellipsoid	$\frac{x^2}{a^2} + \frac{y^2}{b^2} + \frac{z^2}{c^2} = 1$	All traces are ellipses.	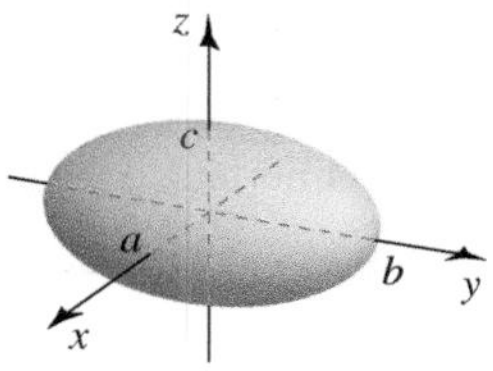
Elliptic paraboloid	$z = \frac{x^2}{a^2} + \frac{y^2}{b^2}$	Traces with $z = z_0 > 0$ are ellipses. Traces with $x = x_0$ or $y = y_0$ are parabolas.	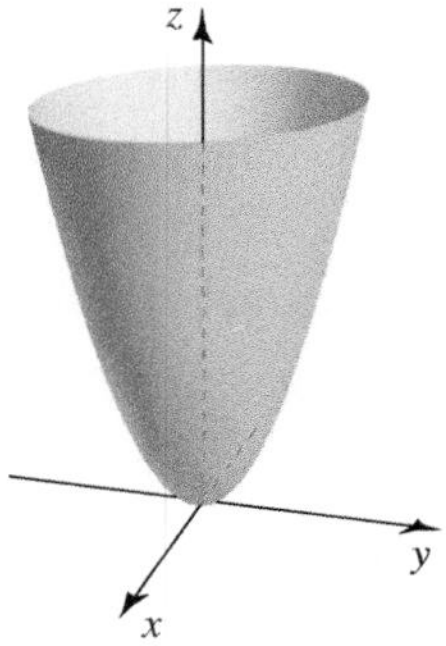
Hyperboloid of one sheet	$\frac{x^2}{a^2} + \frac{y^2}{b^2} - \frac{z^2}{c^2} = 1$	Traces with $z = z_0$ are ellipses for all z_0. Traces with $x = x_0$ or $y = y_0$ are hyperbolas.	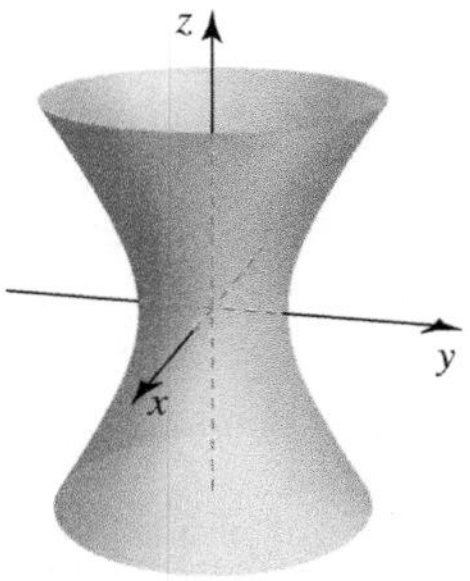
Hyperboloid of two sheets	$-\frac{x^2}{a^2} - \frac{y^2}{b^2} + \frac{z^2}{c^2} = 1$	Traces with $z = z_0$ with $\lvert z_0 \rvert > \lvert c \rvert$ are ellipses. Traces with $x = x_0$ and $y = y_0$ are hyperbolas.	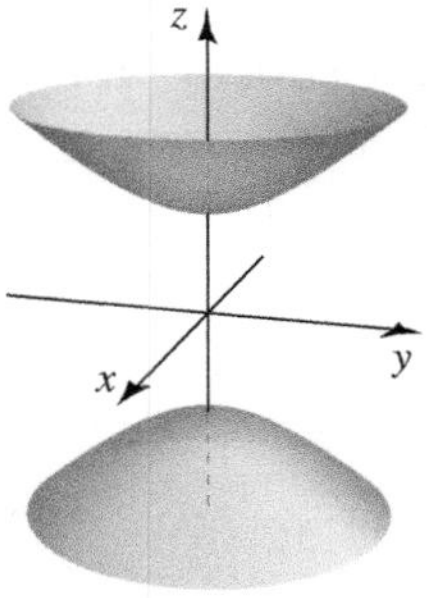
Elliptic cone	$\frac{x^2}{a^2} + \frac{y^2}{b^2} = \frac{z^2}{c^2}$	Traces with $z = z_0 \neq 0$ are ellipses. Traces with $x = x_0$ or $y = y_0$ are hyperbolas or intersecting lines.	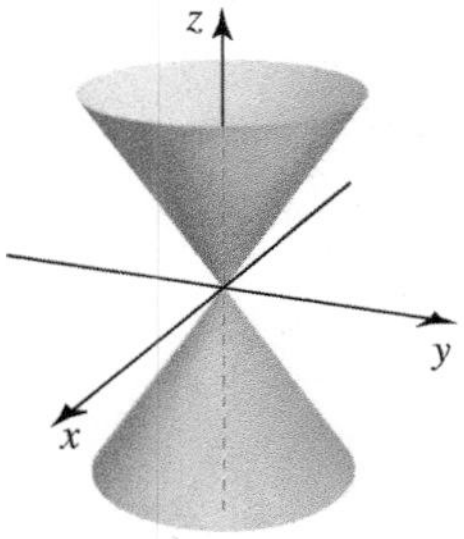
Hyperbolic paraboloid	$z = \frac{x^2}{a^2} - \frac{y^2}{b^2}$	Traces with $z = z_0 \neq 0$ are hyperbolas. Traces with $x = x_0$ or $y = y_0$ are parabolas.	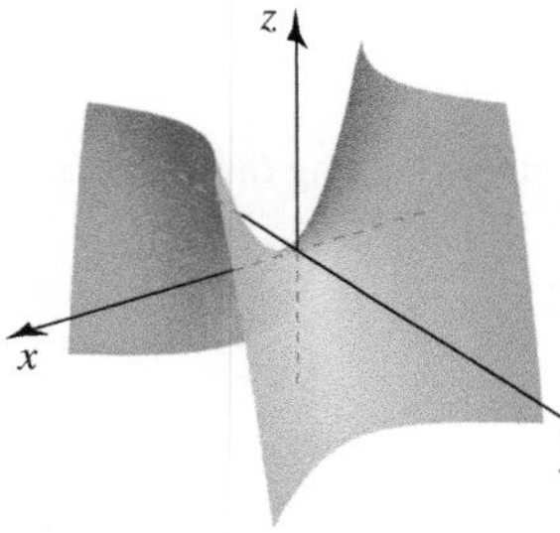

SECTION 12.1 EXERCISES

Review Questions

1. Give two pieces of information which, taken together, uniquely determine a plane.
2. Find a vector normal to the plane $-2x - 3y + 4z = 12$.
3. Where does the plane $-2x - 3y + 4z = 12$ intersect the coordinate axes?
4. Give an equation of the plane with a normal vector $\mathbf{n} = \langle 1, 1, 1 \rangle$ that passes through the point $(1, 0, 0)$.
5. To which coordinate axes are the following cylinders in $\mathbb{R}^3$ parallel: $x^2 + 2y^2 = 8$, $z^2 + 2y^2 = 8$, and $x^2 + 2z^2 = 8$?
6. Describe the graph of $x = z^2$ in $\mathbb{R}^3$.
7. What is a trace of a surface?
8. What is the name of the surface defined by the equation $y = \frac{x^2}{4} + \frac{z^2}{8}$?
9. What is the name of the surface defined by the equation $x^2 + \frac{y^2}{3} + 2z^2 = 1$?
10. What is the name of the surface defined by the equation $-y^2 - \frac{z^2}{2} + x^2 = 1$?

Basic Skills

11–16. Equations of planes *Find an equation of the plane that passes through the point P_0 with a normal vector $\mathbf{n}$.*

11. $P_0(0, 2, -2)$; $\mathbf{n} = \langle 1, 1, -1 \rangle$
12. $P_0(1, 0, -3)$; $\mathbf{n} = \langle 1, -1, 2 \rangle$
13. $P_0(2, 3, 0)$; $\mathbf{n} = \langle -1, 2, -3 \rangle$
14. $P_0(1, 2, -3)$; $\mathbf{n} = \langle -1, 4, -3 \rangle$
15. **Equation of a plane** Find an equation of the plane that is parallel to the vectors $\langle 1, 0, 1 \rangle$ and $\langle 0, 2, 1 \rangle$, passing through the point $(1, 2, 3)$.
16. **Equation of a plane** Find an equation of the plane that is parallel to the vectors $\langle 1, -3, 1 \rangle$ and $\langle 4, 2, 0 \rangle$, passing through the point $(3, 0, -2)$.

17–20. Equations of planes *Find an equation of the following planes.*

17. The plane passing through the points $(1, 0, 3)$, $(0, 4, 2)$, and $(1, 1, 1)$
18. The plane passing through the points $(-1, 1, 1)$, $(0, 0, 2)$, and $(3, -1, -2)$
19. The plane passing through the points $(2, -1, 4)$, $(1, 1, -1)$, and $(-4, 1, 1)$
20. The plane passing through the points $(5, 3, 1)$, $(1, 3, -5)$, and $(-1, 3, 1)$

21–24. Properties of planes *Find the points at which the following planes intersect the coordinate axes and find equations of the lines where the planes intersect the coordinate planes. Sketch a graph of the plane.*

21. $3x - 2y + z = 6$
22. $-4x + 8z = 16$
23. $x + 3y - 5z - 30 = 0$
24. $12x - 9y + 4z + 72 = 0$

25–28. Pairs of planes *Determine whether the following pairs of planes are parallel, orthogonal, or neither.*

25. $x + y + 4z = 10$ and $-x - 3y + z = 10$
26. $2x + 2y - 3z = 10$ and $-10x - 10y + 15z = 10$
27. $3x + 2y - 3z = 10$ and $-6x - 10y + z = 10$
28. $3x + 2y + 2z = 10$ and $-6x - 10y + 19z = 10$

29–30. Equations of planes *For the following sets of planes, determine which pairs of planes in the set are parallel, orthogonal, or identical.*

29. $Q: 3x - 2y + z = 12$; $R: -x + 2y/3 - z/3 = 0$; $S: -x + 2y + 7z = 1$; $T: 3x/2 - y + z/2 = 6$
30. $Q: x + y - z = 0$; $R: y + z = 0$; $S: x - y = 0$; $T: x + y + z = 0$

31–34. Parallel planes *Find an equation of the plane parallel to the plane Q passing through the point P_0.*

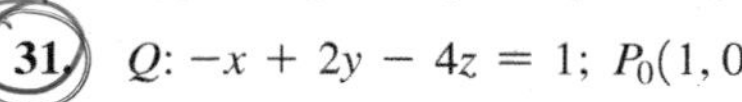

31. $Q: -x + 2y - 4z = 1$; $P_0(1, 0, 4)$
32. $Q: 2x + y - z = 1$; $P_0(0, 2, -2)$
33. $Q: 4x + 3y - 2z = 12$; $P_0(1, -1, 3)$
34. $Q: x - 5y - 2z = 1$; $P_0(1, 2, 0)$

35–38. Intersecting planes *Find an equation of the line of intersection of the planes Q and R.*

35. $Q: -x + 2y + z = 1$; $R: x + y + z = 0$
36. $Q: x + 2y - z = 1$; $R: x + y + z = 1$
37. $Q: 2x - y + 3z - 1 = 0$; $R: -x + 3y + z - 4 = 0$
38. $Q: x - y - 2z = 1$; $R: x + y + z = -1$

39–46. Cylinders in $\mathbb{R}^3$ *Consider the following cylinders in $\mathbb{R}^3$.*

a. Identify the coordinate axis to which the cylinder is parallel.
b. Sketch the cylinder.

39. $z = y^2$
40. $x^2 + 4y^2 = 4$
41. $x^2 + z^2 = 4$
42. $x = z^2 - 4$
43. $y - x^3 = 0$
44. $x - 2z^2 = 0$
45. $z - \ln y = 0$
46. $x - 1/y = 0$

47–70. Quadric surfaces *Consider the following equations of quadric surfaces.*

a. Find the intercepts with the three coordinate axes, when they exist.
b. Find the equations of the xy-, xz-, and yz-traces, when they exist.
c. Sketch a graph of the surface.

Ellipsoids

47. $x^2 + \frac{y^2}{4} + \frac{z^2}{9} = 1$

48. $4x^2 + y^2 + \frac{z^2}{2} = 1$

49. $\frac{x^2}{3} + 3y^2 + \frac{z^2}{12} = 3$

50. $\frac{x^2}{6} + 24y^2 + \frac{z^2}{24} - 6 = 0$

Elliptic paraboloids

51. $x = y^2 + z^2$

52. $z = \frac{x^2}{4} + \frac{y^2}{9}$

53. $9x - 81y^2 - \frac{z^2}{4} = 0$

54. $2y - \frac{x^2}{8} - \frac{z^2}{18} = 0$

Hyperboloids of one sheet

55. $\frac{x^2}{25} + \frac{y^2}{9} - z^2 = 1$

56. $\frac{y^2}{4} + \frac{z^2}{9} - \frac{x^2}{16} = 1$

57. $\frac{y^2}{16} + 36z^2 - \frac{x^2}{4} - 9 = 0$

58. $9z^2 + x^2 - \frac{y^2}{3} - 1 = 0$

Hyperbolic paraboloids

59. $z = \frac{x^2}{9} - y^2$

60. $y = \frac{x^2}{16} - 4z^2$

61. $5x - \frac{y^2}{5} + \frac{z^2}{20} = 0$

62. $6y + \frac{x^2}{6} - \frac{z^2}{24} = 0$

Elliptic cones

63. $x^2 + \frac{y^2}{4} = z^2$

64. $4y^2 + z^2 = x^2$

65. $\frac{z^2}{32} + \frac{y^2}{18} = 2x^2$

66. $\frac{x^2}{3} + \frac{z^2}{12} = 3y^2$

Hyperboloids of two sheets

67. $-x^2 + \frac{y^2}{4} - \frac{z^2}{9} = 1$

68. $1 - 4x^2 + y^2 + \frac{z^2}{2} = 0$

69. $-\frac{x^2}{3} + 3y^2 - \frac{z^2}{12} = 1$

70. $-\frac{x^2}{6} - 24y^2 + \frac{z^2}{24} - 6 = 0$

Further Explorations

71. **Explain why or why not** Determine whether the following statements are true and give an explanation or counterexample.
   a. The plane passing through the point $(1, 1, 1)$ with a normal vector $\mathbf{n} = \langle 1, 2, -3 \rangle$ is the same as the plane passing through the point $(3, 0, 1)$ with a normal vector $\mathbf{n} = \langle -2, -4, 6 \rangle$.
   b. The equations $x + y - z = 1$ and $-x - y + z = 1$ describe the same plane.
   c. Given a plane Q, there is exactly one plane orthogonal to Q.
   d. Given a line ℓ and a point P_0 not on ℓ, there is exactly one plane that contains ℓ and passes through P_0.
   e. Given a plane R and a point P_0, there is exactly one plane that is orthogonal to R and passes through P_0.
   f. Any two distinct lines in $\mathbb{R}^3$ determine a unique plane.
   g. If plane Q is orthogonal to plane R and plane R is orthogonal to plane S, then plane Q is orthogonal to plane S.

72. **Plane containing a line and a point** Find an equation of the plane that passes through the point P_0 and contains the line ℓ.
   a. $P_0(1, -2, 3)$; ℓ: $\mathbf{r} = \langle t, -t, 2t \rangle$
   b. $P_0(-4, 1, 2)$; ℓ: $\mathbf{r} = \langle 2t, -2t, -4t \rangle$

73–74. Lines normal to planes *Find an equation of the line passing through P_0 and normal to the plane P.*

73. $P_0(2, 1, 3)$; P: $2x - 4y + z = 10$

74. $P_0(0, -10, -3)$; P: $x + 4z = 2$

75. **A family of orthogonal planes** Find an equation for a family of planes that are orthogonal to the planes $2x + 3y = 4$ and $-x - y + 2z = 8$.

76. **Orthogonal plane** Find an equation of the plane passing through $(0, -2, 4)$ that is orthogonal to the planes $2x + 5y - 3z = 0$ and $-x + 5y + 2z = 8$.

77. **Three intersecting planes** Describe the set of all points (if any) at which all three planes $x + 3z = 3$, $y + 4z = 6$, and $x + y + 6z = 9$ intersect.

78. **Three intersecting planes** Describe the set of all points (if any) at which all three planes $x + 2y + 2z = 3$, $y + 4z = 6$, and $x + 2y + 8z = 9$ intersect.

79. **Matching graphs with equations** Match equations a–f with surfaces A–F.
   a. $y - z^2 = 0$
   b. $2x + 3y - z = 5$
   c. $4x^2 + \frac{y^2}{9} + z^2 = 1$
   d. $x^2 + \frac{y^2}{9} - z^2 = 1$
   e. $x^2 + \frac{y^2}{9} = z^2$
   f. $y = |x|$

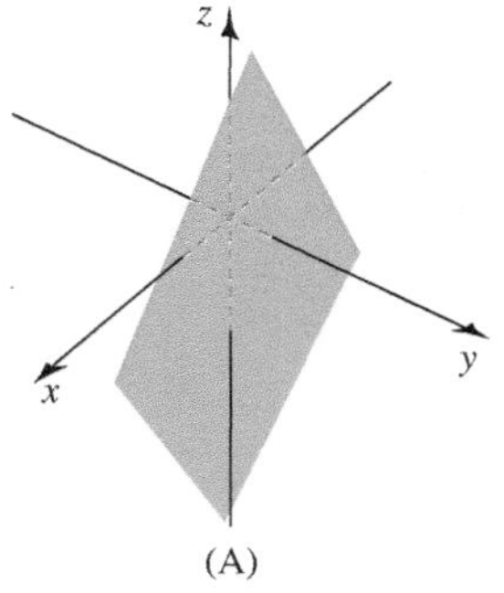

(A)

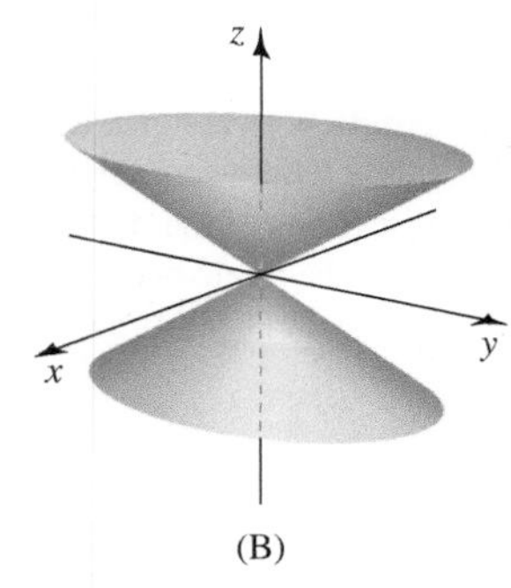

(B)

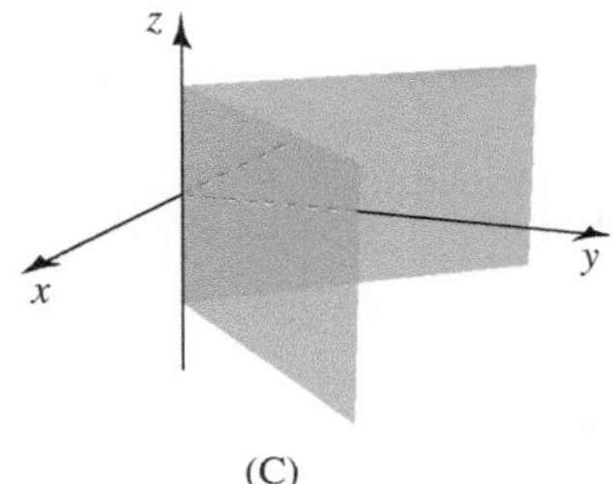

(C)

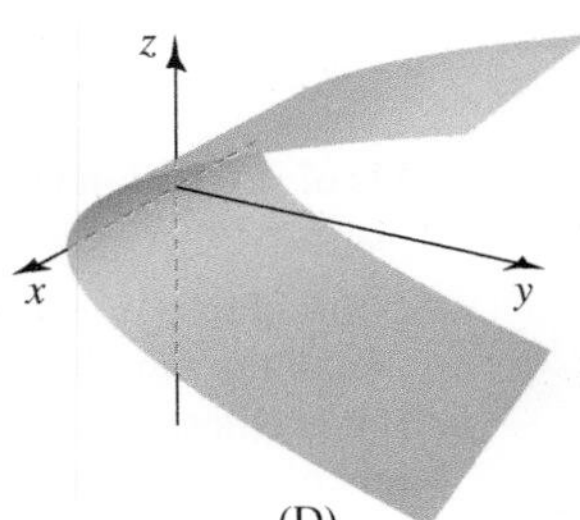

(D)

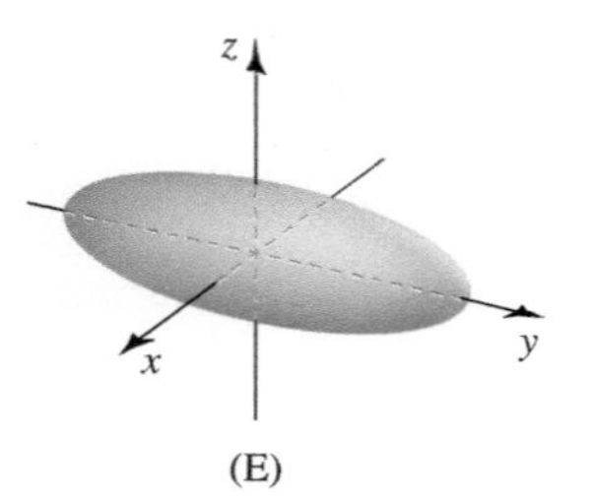

(E)

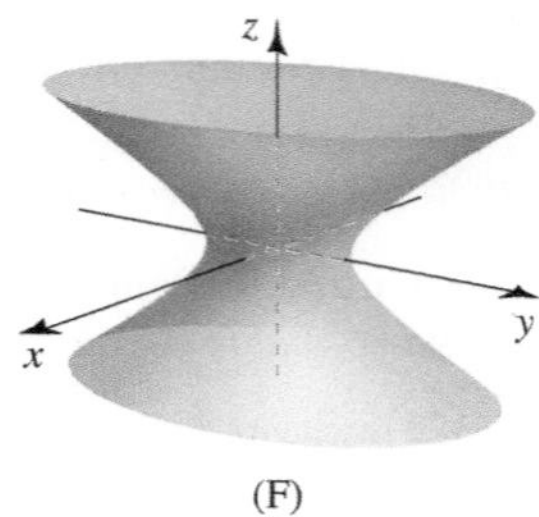

(F)

80–89. Identifying surfaces *Identify and briefly describe the surfaces defined by the following equations.*

80. $z^2 + 4y^2 - x^2 = 1$

81. $y = 4z^2 - x^2$

82. $-y^2 - 9z^2 + x^2/4 = 1$

83. $y = x^2/6 + z^2/16$

84. $x^2 + y^2 + 4z^2 + 2x = 0$

85. $9x^2 + y^2 - 4z^2 + 2y = 0$

86. $x^2 + 4y^2 = 1$

87. $y^2 - z^2 = 2$

88. $-x^2 - y^2 + z^2/9 + 6x - 8y = 26$

89. $x^2/4 + y^2 - 2x - 10y - z^2 + 41 = 0$

90–93. Curve–plane intersections *Find the points (if they exist) at which the following planes and curves intersect.*

90. $y = 2x + 1$; $\mathbf{r}(t) = \langle 10\cos t, 2\sin t, 1\rangle$, for $0 \le t \le 2\pi$

91. $8x + y + z = 60$; $\mathbf{r}(t) = \langle t, t^2, 3t^2\rangle$, for $-\infty < t < \infty$

92. $8x + 15y + 3z = 20$; $\mathbf{r}(t) = \langle 1, \sqrt{t}, -t\rangle$, for $t > 0$

93. $2x + 3y - 12z = 0$; $\mathbf{r}(t) = \langle 4\cos t, 4\sin t, \cos t\rangle$, for $0 \le t \le 2\pi$

94. Intercepts Let a, b, c, and d be constants. Find the points at which the plane $ax + by + cz = d$ intersects the x-, y-, and z-axes.

T **95. Angle between planes** The angle between two planes is the angle θ between the normal vectors of the planes, where the directions of the normal vectors are chosen so that $0 \le \theta < \pi$. Find the angle between the planes $5x + 2y - z = 0$ and $-3x + y + 2z = 0$.

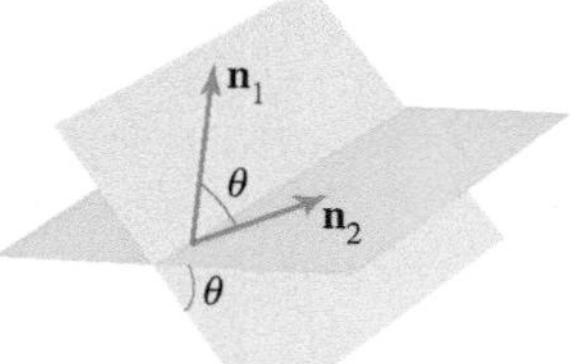

96. Solids of revolution Consider the ellipse $x^2 + 4y^2 = 1$ in the xy-plane.

a. If this ellipse is revolved about the x-axis, what is the equation of the resulting ellipsoid?

b. If this ellipse is revolved about the y-axis, what is the equation of the resulting ellipsoid?

97. Solids of revolution Which of the quadric surfaces in Table 12.1 can be generated by revolving a curve in one of the coordinate planes about a coordinate axis, assuming $a = b = c \neq 0$?

Applications

98. Light cones The idea of a *light cone* appears in the Special Theory of Relativity. The xy-plane (see figure) represents all of three-dimensional space, and the z-axis is the time axis (t-axis). If an event E occurs at the origin, the interior of the future light cone ($t > 0$) represents all events in the future that could be affected by E, assuming that no signal travels faster than the speed of light. The interior of the past light cone ($t < 0$) represents all events in the past that could have affected E, again assuming that no signal travels faster than the speed of light.

a. If time is measured in seconds and distance (x and y) is measured in light-seconds (the distance light travels in 1 s), the light cone makes a 45° angle with the xy-plane. Write the equation of the light cone in this case.

b. Suppose distance is measured in meters and time is measured in seconds. Write the equation of the light cone in this case given that the speed of light is 3×10^8 m/s.

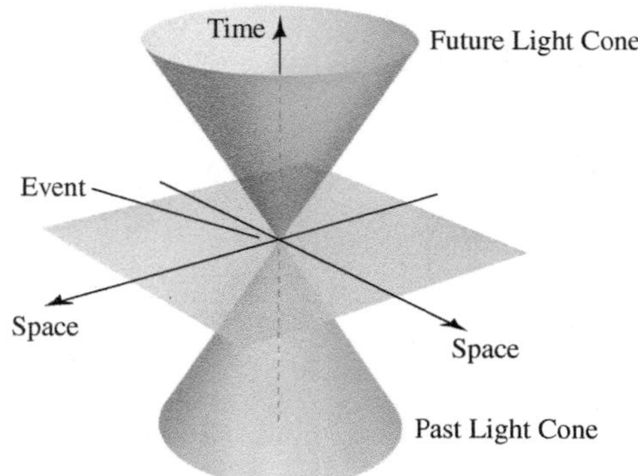

99. T-shirt profits A clothing company makes a profit of \$10 on its long-sleeved T-shirts and \$5 on its short-sleeved T-shirts. Assuming there is a \$200 setup cost, the profit on T-shirt sales is $z = 10x + 5y - 200$, where x is the number of long-sleeved T-shirts sold and y is the number of short-sleeved T-shirts sold. Assume x and y are nonnegative.

a. Graph the plane that gives the profit using the window $[0, 40] \times [0, 40] \times [-400, 400]$.

b. If $x = 20$ and $y = 10$, is the profit positive or negative?

c. Describe the values of x and y for which the company breaks even (for which the profit is zero). Mark this set on your graph.

Additional Exercises

100. Parallel line and plane Show that the plane $ax + by + cz = d$ and the line $\mathbf{r}(t) = \mathbf{r}_0 + \mathbf{v}t$, not in the plane, have no points of intersection if and only if $\mathbf{v} \cdot \langle a, b, c\rangle = 0$. Give a geometric explanation of this result.

101. Tilted ellipse Consider the curve $\mathbf{r}(t) = \langle \cos t, \sin t, c\sin t\rangle$, for $0 \le t \le 2\pi$, where c is a real number.

a. What is the equation of the plane P in which the curve lies?

b. What is the angle between P and the xy-plane?

c. Prove that the curve is an ellipse in P.

102. Distance from a point to a plane

a. Show that the point in the plane $ax + by + cz = d$ nearest the origin is $P(ad/D^2, bd/D^2, cd/D^2)$, where $D^2 = a^2 + b^2 + c^2$. Conclude that the least distance from the plane to the origin is $|d|/D$. (*Hint:* The least distance is along a normal to the plane.)

b. Show that the least distance from the point $P_0(x_0, y_0, z_0)$ to the plane $ax + by + cz = d$ is $|ax_0 + by_0 + cz_0 - d|/D$. (*Hint:* Find the point P on the plane closest to P_0.)

103. Another distance formula. Suppose P is a point in the plane $ax + by + cz = d$. Then the least distance from any point Q to the plane equals the length of the orthogonal projection of $\overrightarrow{PQ}$ onto the normal vector $\mathbf{n} = \langle a, b. c \rangle$.

a. Use this information to show that the least distance from Q to the plane is $\dfrac{|\overrightarrow{PQ} \cdot \mathbf{n}|}{|\mathbf{n}|}$.

b. Find the least distance from the point $(1, 2, -4)$ to the plane $2x - y + 3z = 1$.

104. Ellipsoid–plane intersection Let E be the ellipsoid $x^2/9 + y^2/4 + z^2 = 1$, P be the plane $z = Ax + By$, and C be the intersection of E and P.

a. Is C an ellipse for all values of A and B? Explain.

b. Sketch and interpret the situation in which $A = 0$ and $B \neq 0$.

c. Find an equation of the projection of C on the xy-plane.

d. Assume $A = \frac{1}{6}$ and $B = \frac{1}{2}$. Find a parametric description of C as a curve in $\mathbb{R}^3$. (*Hint:* Assume C is described by $\langle a \cos t + b \sin t, c \cos t + d \sin t, e \cos t + f \sin t \rangle$ and find a, b, c, d, e, and f.)

QUICK CHECK ANSWERS

1. The plane passes through $(1, 2, 3)$ and is parallel to the yz-plane; its equation is $x = 1$. **2.** Because the right side of the equation is 0, the equation can be multiplied by any nonzero constant (changing the length of $\mathbf{n}$) without changing the graph. **5.** y-axis; x-axis **6.** The equation $x^2 + 4y^2 = 16$ is a special case of the general equation for quadric surfaces; all the coefficients except A, B, and J are zero. **7.** x-axis; z-axis **8.** Positive x-axis **9.** x-axis **10.** Complete the square in y and z; elliptic paraboloid with its axis parallel to the x-axis ◀

12.2 Graphs and Level Curves

In Chapter 11, we discussed vector-valued functions with one independent variable and several dependent variables. We now reverse the situation and consider functions with several independent variables and one dependent variable. Such functions are aptly called *functions of several variables* or *multivariable functions*.

To set the stage, consider the following practical questions that illustrate a few of the many applications of functions of several variables.

- What is the probability that one man selected randomly from a large group of men weighs more than 200 pounds and is over 6 feet tall?
- Where on the wing of an airliner flying at a speed of 550 mi/hr is the pressure greatest?
- A physician knows the optimal blood concentration of an antibiotic needed by a patient. What dosage of antibiotic is needed and how often should it be given to reach this optimal level?

Although we don't answer these questions immediately, they provide an idea of the scope and importance of the topic. First, we must introduce the idea of a function of several variables.

Functions of Two Variables

The key concepts related to functions of several variables are most easily presented in the case of two independent variables; the extension to three or more variables is then straightforward. In general, functions of two variables are written *explicitly* in the form

$$z = f(x, y)$$

or *implicitly* in the form

$$F(x, y, z) = 0.$$

Both forms are important, but for now, we consider explicitly defined functions.

The concepts of domain and range carry over directly from functions of a single variable.

> **DEFINITION Function, Domain, and Range with Two Independent Variables**
> A **function** $z = f(x, y)$ assigns to each point (x, y) in a set D in $\mathbb{R}^2$ a unique real number z in a subset of $\mathbb{R}$. The set D is the **domain** of f. The **range** of f is the set of real numbers z that are assumed as the points (x, y) vary over the domain (Figure 12.19).

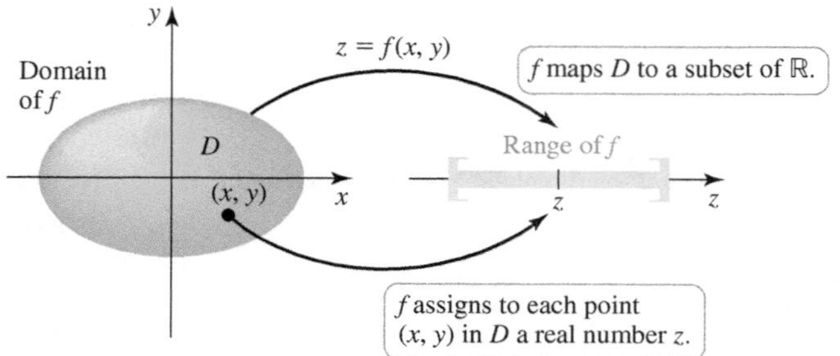

Figure 12.19

As with functions of one variable, a function of several variables may have a domain that is restricted by the context of the problem. For example, if the independent variables correspond to price or length or population, they take only nonnegative values, even though the associated function may be defined for negative values of the variables. If not stated otherwise, D is the set of all points for which the function is defined.

A polynomial in x and y consists of sums and products of polynomials in x and polynomials in y; for example, $f(x, y) = x^2y - 2xy - xy^2$. Such polynomials are defined for all values of x and y, so their domain is $\mathbb{R}^2$. A quotient of two polynomials in x and y, such as $h(x, y) = \dfrac{xy}{x - y}$, is a rational function in x and y. The domain of a rational function excludes points at which the denominator is zero, so the domain of h is $\{(x, y): x \neq y\}$.

EXAMPLE 1 Finding domains Find the domain of the function $g(x, y) = \sqrt{4 - x^2 - y^2}$.

SOLUTION Because g involves a square root, its domain consists of ordered pairs (x, y) for which $4 - x^2 - y^2 \geq 0$ or $x^2 + y^2 \leq 4$. Therefore, the domain of g is $\{(x, y): x^2 + y^2 \leq 4\}$, which is the set of points on or within the circle of radius 2 centered at the origin in the xy-plane (a *disk* of radius 2) (Figure 12.20).

Related Exercises 11–20 ◀

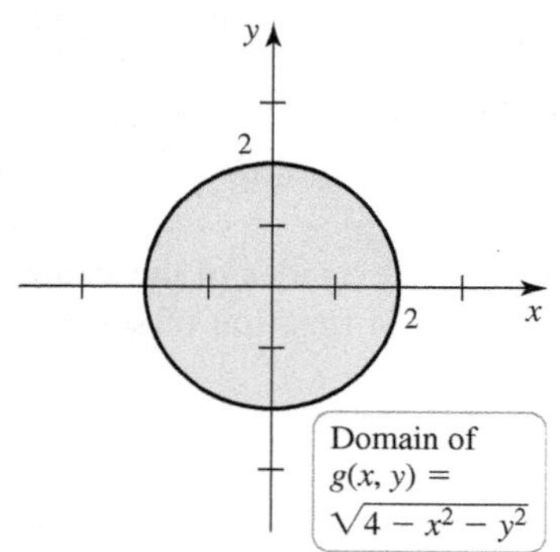

Figure 12.20

QUICK CHECK 1 Find the domains of $f(x, y) = \sin xy$ and $g(x, y) = \sqrt{(x^2 + 1)y}$. ◀

Graphs of Functions of Two Variables

The **graph** of a function f of two variables is the set of points (x, y, z) that satisfy the equation $z = f(x, y)$. More specifically, for each point (x, y) in the domain of f, the point $(x, y, f(x, y))$ lies on the graph of f (Figure 12.21). A similar definition applies to relations of the form $F(x, y, z) = 0$.

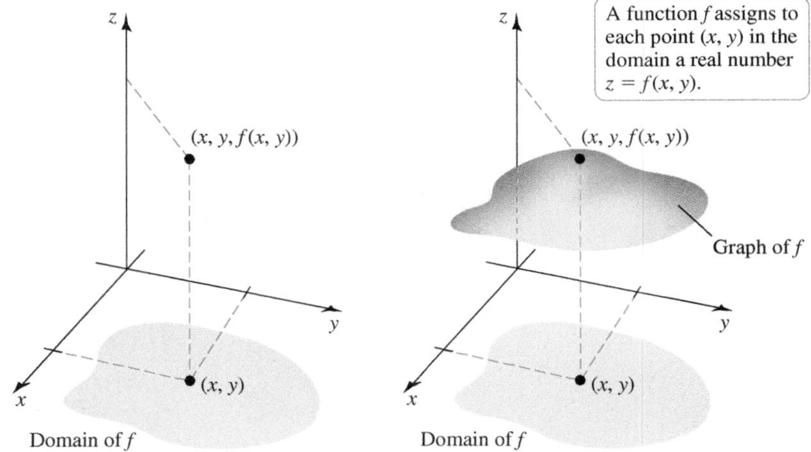

Figure 12.21

An ellipsoid does not pass the vertical line test: not the graph of a function.

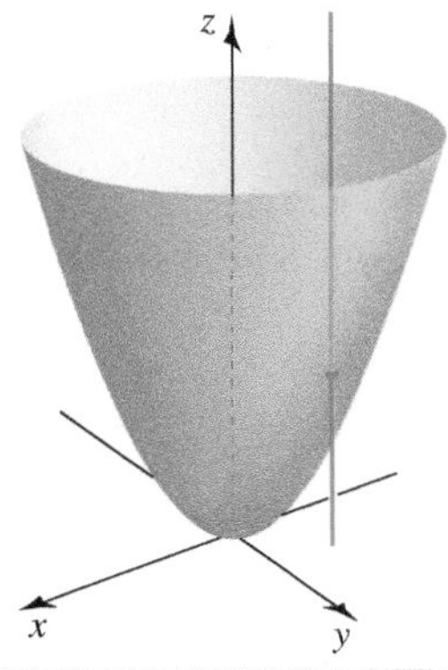

This elliptic paraboloid passes the vertical line test: graph of a function.

Figure 12.22

Like functions of one variable, functions of two variables must pass a **vertical line test**. A relation of the form $F(x, y, z) = 0$ is a function provided every line parallel to the z-axis intersects the graph of the relation at most once. For example, an ellipsoid (discussed in Section 12.1) is not the graph of a function because some vertical lines intersect the surface twice. On the other hand, an elliptic paraboloid of the form $z = ax^2 + by^2$ does represent a function (Figure 12.22).

QUICK CHECK 2 Does the graph of a hyperboloid of one sheet represent a function? Does the graph of a cone with its axis parallel to the x-axis represent a function? ◄

EXAMPLE 2 Graphing two-variable functions Find the domain and range of the following functions. Then sketch a graph.

a. $f(x, y) = 2x + 3y - 12$ **b.** $g(x, y) = x^2 + y^2$

c. $h(x, y) = \sqrt{1 + x^2 + y^2}$

SOLUTION

a. Letting $z = f(x, y)$, we have the equation $z = 2x + 3y - 12$, or $2x + 3y - z = 12$, which describes a plane with a normal vector $\langle 2, 3, -1 \rangle$ (Section 12.1). The domain consists of all points in $\mathbb{R}^2$, and the range is $\mathbb{R}$. We sketch the surface by noting that the x-intercept is $(6, 0, 0)$ (setting $y = z = 0$); the y-intercept is $(0, 4, 0)$ and the z-intercept is $(0, 0, -12)$ (Figure 12.23).

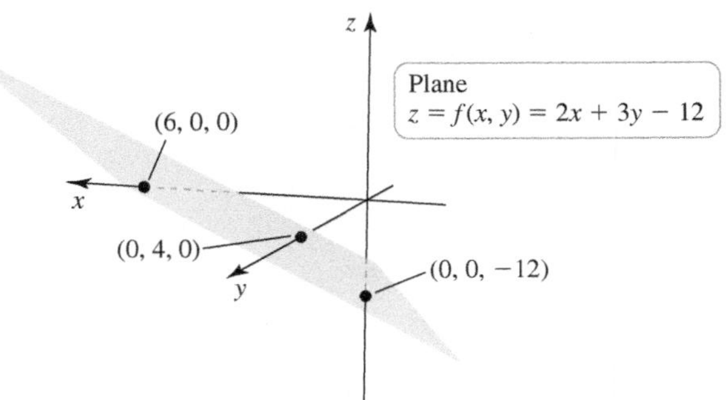

Figure 12.23

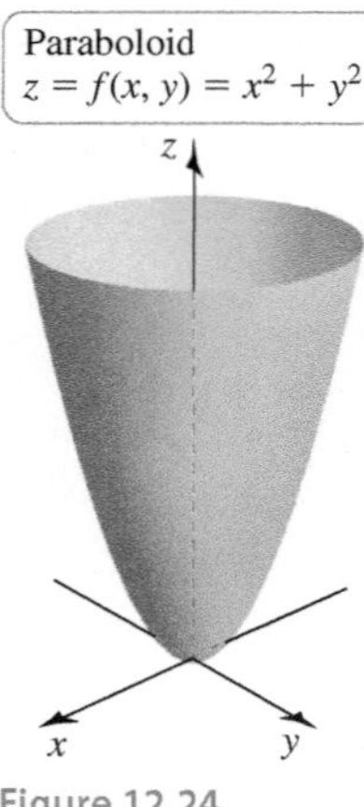

Figure 12.24

b. Letting $z = g(x, y)$, we have the equation $z = x^2 + y^2$, which describes an elliptic paraboloid that opens upward with vertex $(0, 0, 0)$. The domain is $\mathbb{R}^2$ and the range consists of all nonnegative real numbers (Figure 12.24).

c. The domain of the function is $\mathbb{R}^2$ because the quantity under the square root is always positive. Note that $1 + x^2 + y^2 \geq 1$, so the range is $\{z: z \geq 1\}$. Squaring both sides of $z = \sqrt{1 + x^2 + y^2}$, we obtain $z^2 = 1 + x^2 + y^2$, or $-x^2 - y^2 + z^2 = 1$. This is the equation of a hyperboloid of two sheets that opens along the z-axis. Because the range is $\{z: z \geq 1\}$, the given function represents only the upper sheet of the hyperboloid (Figure 12.25; the lower sheet was introduced when we squared the original equation).

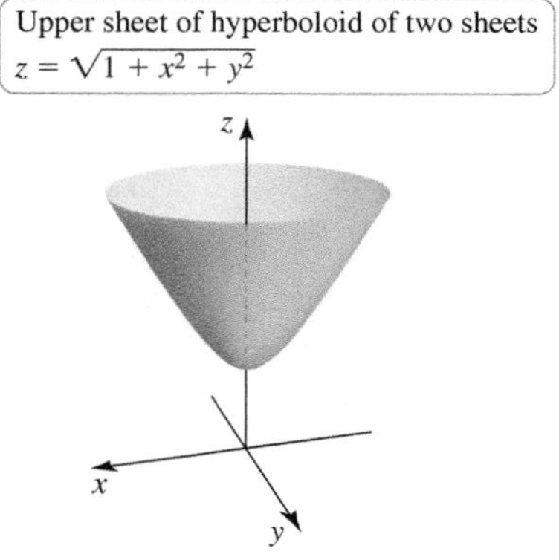

Figure 12.25

Related Exercises 21–29 ◄

QUICK CHECK 3 Find a function whose graph is the lower half of the hyperboloid $-x^2 - y^2 + z^2 = 1$. ◄

➤ To anticipate results that appear later in the chapter, notice how the streams in the topographic map—which flow downhill—cross the level curves roughly at right angles.

Level Curves

Functions of two variables are represented by surfaces in $\mathbb{R}^3$. However, such functions can be represented in another illuminating way, which is used to make topographic maps (Figure 12.26).

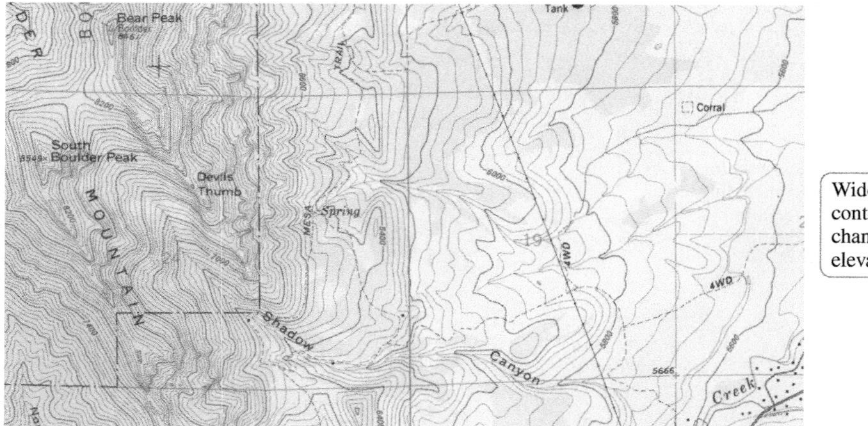

Figure 12.26

➤ A contour curve is a trace in the plane $z = z_0$.

Consider a surface defined by the function $z = f(x, y)$ (Figure 12.27). Now imagine stepping onto the surface and walking along a path on which your elevation has the constant value $z = z_0$. The path you walk on the surface is part of a **contour curve**; the complete contour curve is the intersection of the surface and the horizontal plane $z = z_0$. When the contour curve is projected onto the xy-plane, the result is the curve $f(x, y) = z_0$. This curve in the xy-plane is called a **level curve**.

➤ A level curve may not always be a single curve. It might consist of a point ($x^2 + y^2 = 0$) or it might consist of several lines or curves ($xy = 0$).

Imagine repeating this process with a different constant value of z, say, $z = z_1$. The path you walk this time when projected onto the xy-plane is part of another level curve $f(x, y) = z_1$. A collection of such level curves, corresponding to different values of z, provides a useful two-dimensional representation of the surface (Figure 12.28).

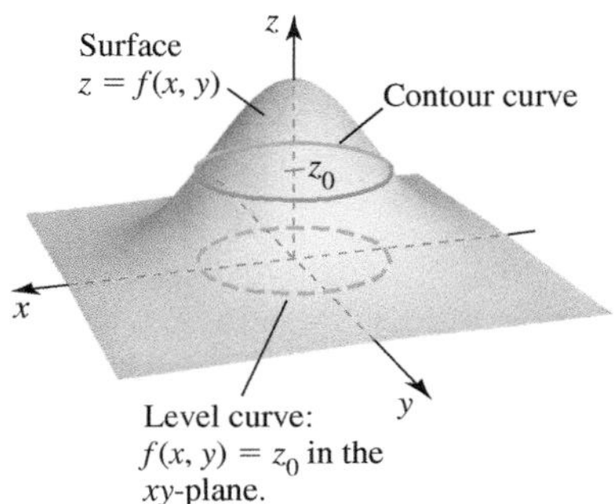

Figure 12.27

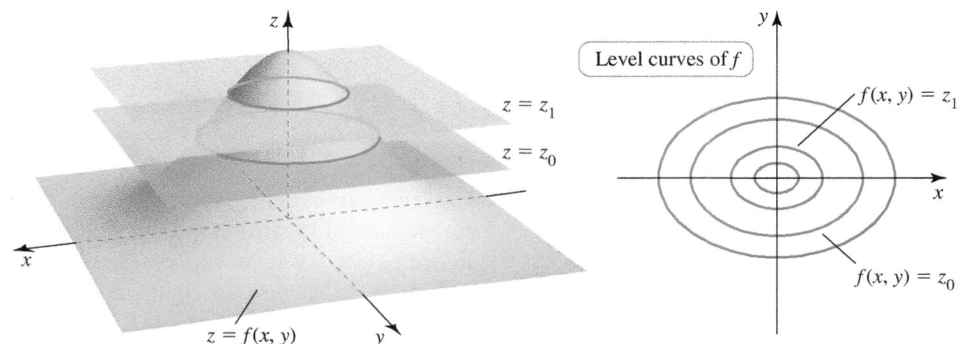

Figure 12.28

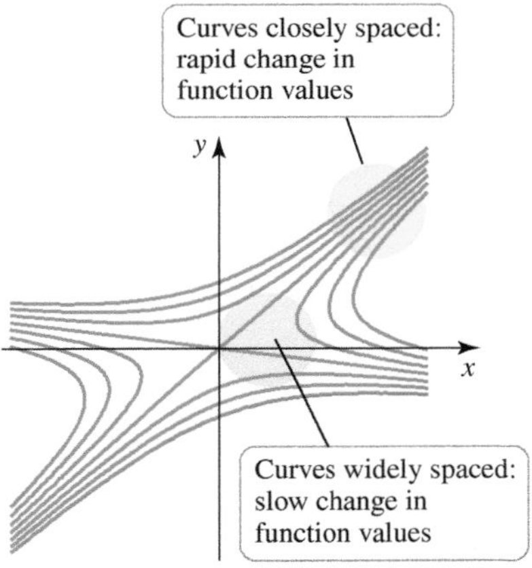

Figure 12.29

QUICK CHECK 4 Can two level curves of a function intersect? Explain. ◄

Assuming that two adjacent level curves always correspond to the same change in z, widely spaced level curves indicate gradual changes in z-values, while closely spaced level curves indicate rapid changes in some directions (Figure 12.29). Concentric closed level curves indicate either a peak or a depression on the surface.

QUICK CHECK 5 Describe in words the level curves of the top half of the sphere $x^2 + y^2 + z^2 = 1$. ◄

EXAMPLE 3 **Level curves** Find and sketch the level curves of the following surfaces.

a. $f(x, y) = y - x^2 - 1$ **b.** $f(x, y) = e^{-x^2-y^2}$

SOLUTION

a. The level curves are described by the equation $y - x^2 - 1 = z_0$, where z_0 is a constant in the range of f. For all values of z_0, these curves are parabolas in the xy-plane, as seen by writing the equation in the form $y = x^2 + z_0 + 1$. For example:

- With $z_0 = 0$, the level curve is the parabola $y = x^2 + 1$; along this curve, the surface has an elevation (z-coordinate) of 0.
- With $z_0 = -1$, the level curve is $y = x^2$; along this curve, the surface has an elevation of -1.
- With $z_0 = 1$, the level curve is $y = x^2 + 2$, along which the surface has an elevation of 1.

As shown in Figure 12.30a, the level curves form a family of shifted parabolas. When these level curves are labeled with their z-coordinates, the graph of the surface $z = f(x, y)$ can be visualized (Figure 12.30b).

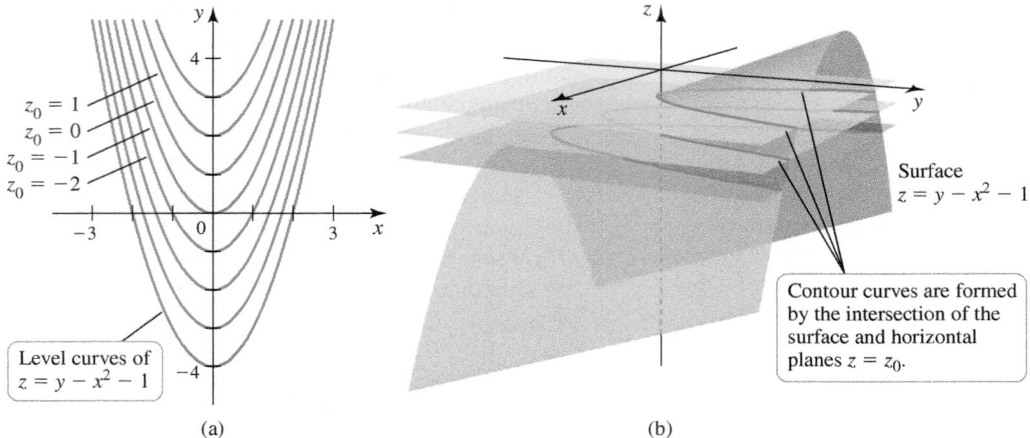

Figure 12.30

b. The level curves satisfy the equation $e^{-x^2-y^2} = z_0$, where z_0 is a positive constant. Taking the natural logarithm of both sides gives the equation $x^2 + y^2 = -\ln z_0$, which describes circular level curves. These curves can be sketched for all values of z_0 with $0 < z_0 \leq 1$ (because the right side of $x^2 + y^2 = -\ln z_0$ must be nonnegative). For example:

- With $z_0 = 1$, the level curve satisfies the equation $x^2 + y^2 = 0$, whose solution is the single point $(0, 0)$; at this point, the surface has an elevation of 1.
- With $z_0 = e^{-1}$, the level curve is $x^2 + y^2 = -\ln e^{-1} = 1$, which is a circle centered at $(0, 0)$ with a radius of 1; along this curve the surface has an elevation of $e^{-1} \approx 0.37$.

In general, the level curves are circles centered at $(0, 0)$; as the radii of the circles increase, the corresponding z-values decrease. Figure 12.31a shows the level curves, with larger z-values corresponding to darker shades. From these labeled level curves, we can reconstruct the graph of the surface (Figure 12.31b).

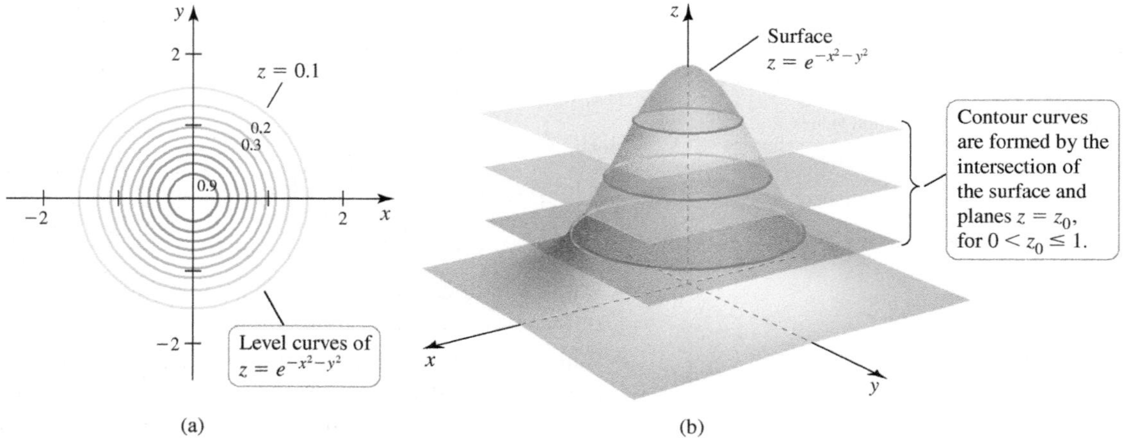

Figure 12.31

Related Exercises 30–38 ◀

QUICK CHECK 6 Does the surface in Example 3b have a level curve for $z_0 = 0$? Explain. ◀

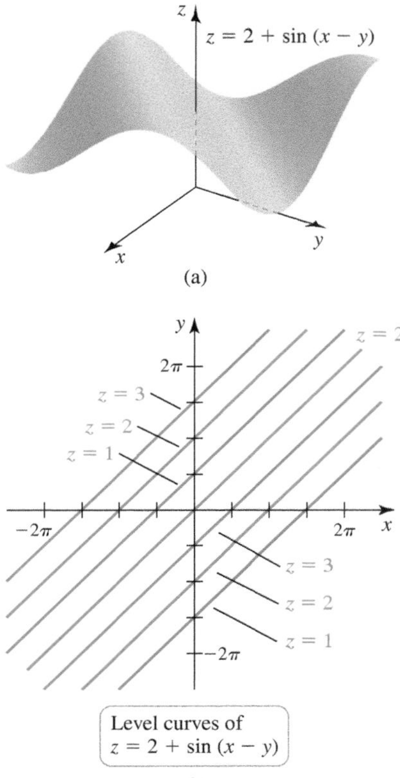

Figure 12.32

EXAMPLE 4 **Level curves** The graph of the function

$$f(x, y) = 2 + \sin(x - y)$$

is shown in Figure 12.32a. Sketch several level curves of the function.

SOLUTION The level curves are $f(x, y) = 2 + \sin(x - y) = z_0$, or $\sin(x - y) = z_0 - 2$. Because $-1 \le \sin(x - y) \le 1$, the admissible values of z_0 satisfy $-1 \le z_0 - 2 \le 1$, or, equivalently, $1 \le z_0 \le 3$. For example, when $z_0 = 2$, the level curves satisfy $\sin(x - y) = 0$. The solutions of this equation are $x - y = k\pi$, or $y = x - k\pi$, where k is an integer. Therefore, the surface has an elevation of 2 on this set of lines. With $z_0 = 1$ (the minimum value of z), the level curves satisfy $\sin(x - y) = -1$. The solutions are $x - y = -\pi/2 + 2k\pi$, where k is an integer; along these lines, the surface has an elevation of 1. Here we have an example in which each level curve is an infinite collection of lines of slope 1 (Figure 12.32b).

Related Exercises 30–38 ◄

Applications of Functions of Two Variables

The following examples offer two of many applications of functions of two variables.

EXAMPLE 5 **A probability function of two variables** Suppose that on a particular day, the fraction of students on campus infected with flu is r, where $0 \le r \le 1$. If you have n random (possibly repeated) encounters with students during the day, the probability of meeting *at least* one infected person is $p(n, r) = 1 - (1 - r)^n$ (Figure 12.33a). Discuss this probability function.

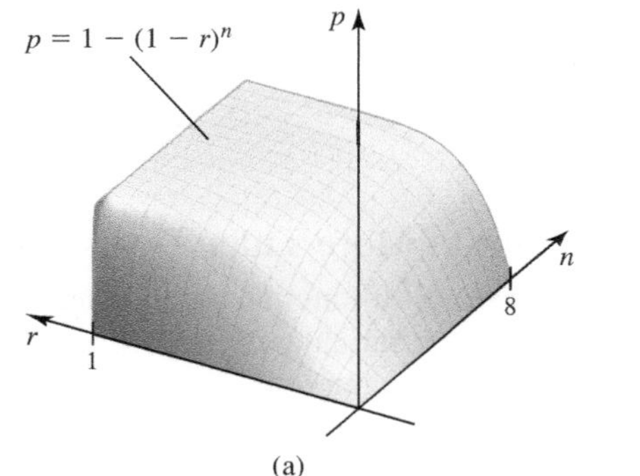

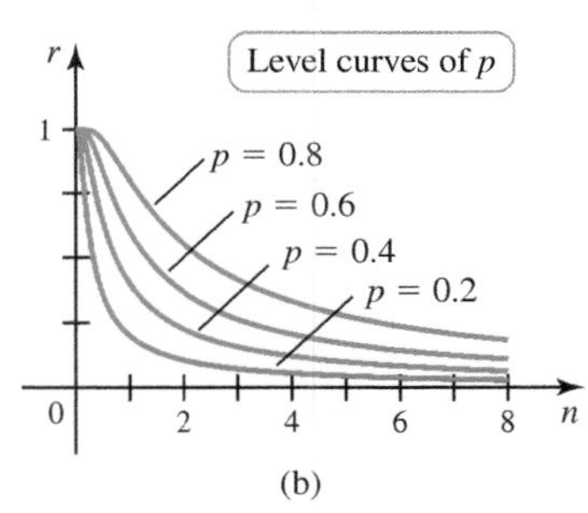

Figure 12.33

Table 12.2

	n: 2	5	10	15	20
r = **0.05**	0.10	0.23	0.40	0.54	0.64
0.1	0.19	0.41	0.65	0.79	0.88
0.3	0.51	0.83	0.97	1	1
0.5	0.75	0.97	1	1	1
0.7	0.91	1	1	1	1

SOLUTION The independent variable r is restricted to the interval $[0, 1]$ because it is a fraction of the population. The other independent variable n is any nonnegative integer; for the purposes of graphing, we treat n as a real number in the interval $[0, 8]$. With $0 \le r \le 1$, note that $0 \le 1 - r \le 1$. If n is nonnegative, then $0 \le (1 - r)^n \le 1$, and it follows that $0 \le p(n, r) \le 1$. Therefore, the range of the function is $[0, 1]$, which is consistent with the fact that p is a probability.

The level curves (Figure 12.33b) show that for a fixed value of n, the probability of at least one encounter increases with r; and for a fixed value of r, the probability increases with n. Therefore, as r increases or as n increases, the probability approaches 1 (at a surprising rate). If 10% of the population is infected ($r = 0.1$) and you have $n = 10$ encounters, then the probability of at least one encounter with an infected person is $p(0.1, 10) \approx 0.651$, which is about 2 in 3.

A numerical view of this function is given in Table 12.2, where we see probabilities tabulated for various values of n and r (rounded to two digits). The numerical values confirm the preceding observations.

Related Exercises 39–45 ◄

QUICK CHECK 7 In Example 5, if 50% of the population is infected, what is the probability of meeting at least one infected person in five encounters? ◄

EXAMPLE 6 Electric potential function in two variables The electric field at points in the xy-plane due to two point charges located at $(0, 0)$ and $(1, 0)$ is related to the electric potential function

$$\varphi(x, y) = \frac{2}{\sqrt{x^2 + y^2}} + \frac{2}{\sqrt{(x - 1)^2 + y^2}}.$$

Discuss the electric potential function.

SOLUTION The domain of the function contains all points of $\mathbb{R}^2$ except $(0, 0)$ and $(1, 0)$ where the charges are located. As these points are approached, the potential function becomes arbitrarily large (Figure 12.34a). The potential approaches zero as x or y increases in magnitude. These observations imply that the range of the potential function is all positive real numbers. The level curves of φ are closed curves, encircling either a single charge (at small distances) or both charges (at larger distances; Figure 12.34b).

➤ The electric potential function, often denoted φ (pronounced *fee* or *fie*), is a scalar-valued function from which the electric field can be computed. Potential functions are discussed in detail in Chapter 14.

➤ A function that grows without bound near a point, as in the case of the electric potential function, is said to have a *singularity* at that point. A singularity is analogous to a vertical asymptote in a function of one variable.

QUICK CHECK 8 In Example 6, what is the electric potential at the point $(\frac{1}{2}, 0)$? ◄

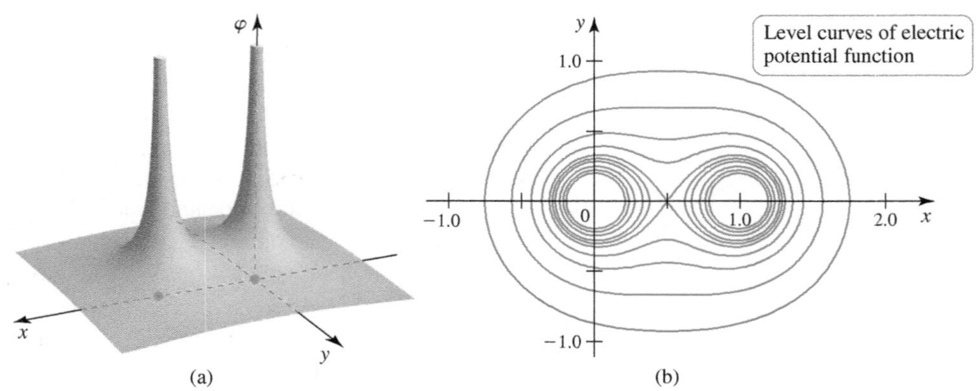

Figure 12.34

Related Exercises 39–45 ◄

Functions of More Than Two Variables

Many properties of functions of two independent variables extend naturally to functions of three or more variables. A function of three variables is defined explicitly in the form $w = f(x, y, z)$ and implicitly in the form $F(x, y, z, w) = 0$. With more than three independent variables, the variables are usually written $x_1, \ldots, x_n$. Table 12.3 shows the progression of functions of several variables.

Table 12.3

Number of Independent Variables	Explicit Form	Implicit Form	Graph Resides In...
1	$y = f(x)$	$F(x, y) = 0$	$\mathbb{R}^2$ (xy-plane)
2	$z = f(x, y)$	$F(x, y, z) = 0$	$\mathbb{R}^3$ (xyz-space)
3	$w = f(x, y, z)$	$F(x, y, z, w) = 0$	$\mathbb{R}^4$
n	$x_{n+1} = f(x_1, x_2, \ldots, x_n)$	$F(x_1, x_2, \ldots, x_n, x_{n+1}) = 0$	$\mathbb{R}^{n+1}$

The concepts of domain and range extend from the one- and two-variable cases in an obvious way.

DEFINITION Function, Domain, and Range with *n* Independent Variables

The **function** $x_{n+1} = f(x_1, x_2, \ldots, x_n)$ assigns a unique real number x_{n+1} to each point $(x_1, x_2, \ldots, x_n)$ in a set D in $\mathbb{R}^n$. The set D is the **domain** of f. The **range** is the set of real numbers x_{n+1} that are assumed as the points $(x_1, x_2, \ldots, x_n)$ vary over the domain.

EXAMPLE 7 **Finding domains** Find the domain of the following functions.

a. $g(x, y, z) = \sqrt{16 - x^2 - y^2 - z^2}$ **b.** $h(x, y, z) = \dfrac{12y^2}{z - y}$

SOLUTION

a. Values of the variables that make the argument of a square root negative must be excluded from the domain. In this case, the quantity under the square root is nonnegative provided

$$16 - x^2 - y^2 - z^2 \geq 0, \quad \text{or} \quad x^2 + y^2 + z^2 \leq 16.$$

Therefore, the domain of g is a closed ball in $\mathbb{R}^3$ of radius 4 centered at the origin.

➤ Recall that a closed ball of radius r is the set of all points on or within a sphere of radius r.

b. Values of the variables that make a denominator zero must be excluded from the domain. In this case, the denominator vanishes for all points in $\mathbb{R}^3$ that satisfy $z - y = 0$, or $y = z$. Therefore, the domain of h is the set $\{(x, y, z): y \neq z\}$. This set is $\mathbb{R}^3$ excluding the points on the plane $y = z$.

Related Exercises 46–52 ◀

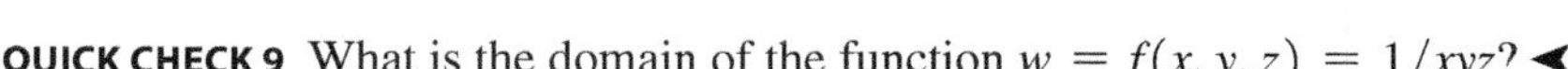

QUICK CHECK 9 What is the domain of the function $w = f(x, y, z) = 1/xyz$? ◀

Graphs of Functions of More Than Two Variables

Graphing functions of *two* independent variables requires a three-dimensional coordinate system, which is the limit of ordinary graphing methods. Clearly, difficulties arise in graphing functions with three or more independent variables. For example, the graph of the function $w = f(x, y, z)$ resides in four dimensions. Here are two approaches to representing functions of three independent variables.

The idea of level curves can be extended. With the function $w = f(x, y, z)$, level curves become **level surfaces**, which are surfaces in $\mathbb{R}^3$ on which w is constant. For example, the level surfaces of the function

$$w = f(x, y, z) = \sqrt{z - x^2 - 2y^2}$$

satisfy $w = \sqrt{z - x^2 - 2y^2} = C$, where C is a nonnegative constant. This equation is satisfied when $z = x^2 + 2y^2 + C^2$. Therefore, the level surfaces are elliptic paraboloids, stacked one inside another (Figure 12.35).

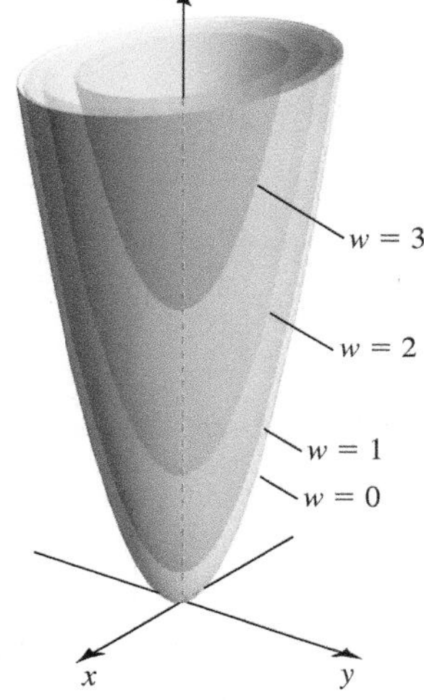

Figure 12.35

Another approach to displaying functions of three variables is to use colors to represent the fourth dimension. Figure 12.36a shows the electrical activity of the heart at one snapshot in time. The three independent variables correspond to locations in the heart. At each point, the value of the electrical activity, which is the dependent variable, is coded by colors.

In Figure 12.36b, the dependent variable is the switching speed in an integrated circuit, again represented by colors, as it varies over points of the domain. Software to produce such images, once expensive and inefficient, has become much more accessible.

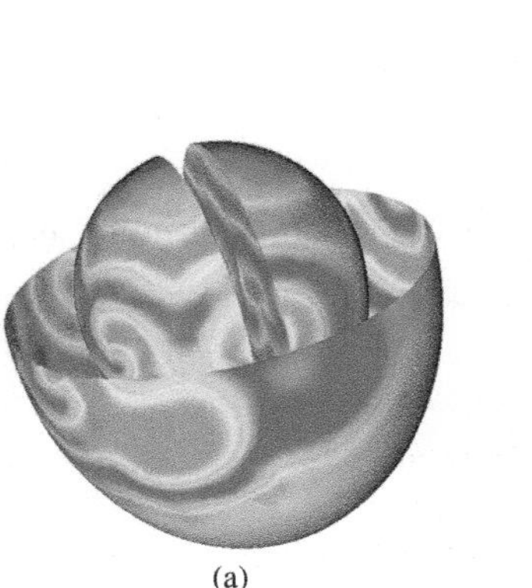

(a)

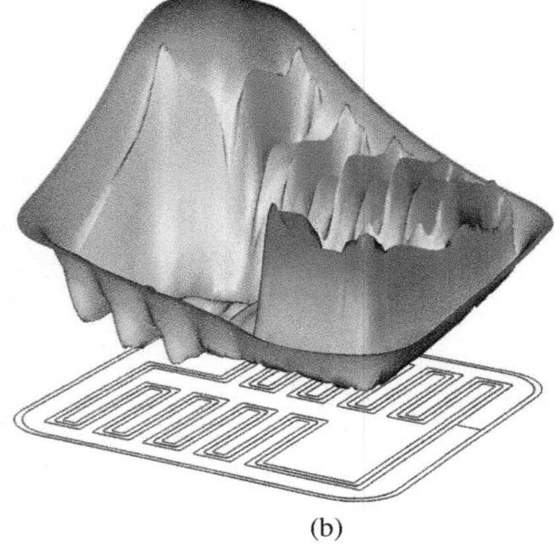

(b)

Figure 12.36

SECTION 12.2 EXERCISES

Review Questions

1. A function is defined by $z = x^2y - xy^2$. Identify the independent and dependent variables.
2. What is the domain of $f(x, y) = x^2y - xy^2$?
3. What is the domain of $g(x, y) = 1/(xy)$?
4. What is the domain of $h(x, y) = \sqrt{x - y}$?
5. How many axes (or how many dimensions) are needed to graph the function $z = f(x, y)$? Explain.
6. Explain how to graph the level curves of a surface $z = f(x, y)$.
7. Describe in words the level curves of the paraboloid $z = x^2 + y^2$.
8. How many axes (or how many dimensions) are needed to graph the level surfaces of $w = f(x, y, z)$? Explain.
9. The domain of $Q = f(u, v, w, x, y, z)$ lies in $\mathbb{R}^n$ for what value of n? Explain.
10. Give two methods for graphically representing a function with three independent variables.

Basic Skills

11–20. Domains *Find the domain of the following functions.*

11. $f(x, y) = 2xy - 3x + 4y$
12. $f(x, y) = \cos(x^2 - y^2)$
13. $f(x, y) = \sqrt{25 - x^2 - y^2}$
14. $f(x, y) = \dfrac{1}{\sqrt{x^2 + y^2 - 25}}$
15. $f(x, y) = \sin\dfrac{x}{y}$
16. $f(x, y) = \dfrac{12}{y^2 - x^2}$
17. $g(x, y) = \ln(x^2 - y)$
18. $f(x, y) = \sin^{-1}(y - x^2)$
19. $g(x, y) = \sqrt{\dfrac{xy}{x^2 + y^2}}$
20. $h(x, y) = \sqrt{x - 2y + 4}$

21–28. Graphs of familiar functions *Use what you learned about surfaces in Section 12.1 to sketch a graph of the following functions. In each case identify the surface and state the domain and range of the function.*

21. $f(x, y) = 3x - 6y + 18$
22. $h(x, y) = 2x^2 + 3y^2$
23. $p(x, y) = x^2 - y^2$
24. $F(x, y) = \sqrt{1 - x^2 - y^2}$
25. $G(x, y) = -\sqrt{1 + x^2 + y^2}$
26. $H(x, y) = \sqrt{x^2 + y^2}$
27. $P(x, y) = \sqrt{x^2 + y^2 - 1}$
28. $g(x, y) = y^3 + 1$

29. **Matching surfaces** Match functions a–d with surfaces A–D in the figure.

    a. $f(x, y) = \cos xy$ **b.** $g(x, y) = \ln(x^2 + y^2)$
    c. $h(x, y) = 1/(x - y)$ **d.** $p(x, y) = 1/(1 + x^2 + y^2)$

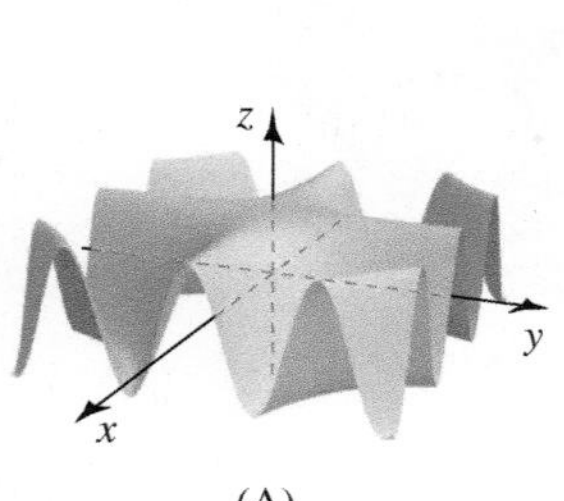

(A)

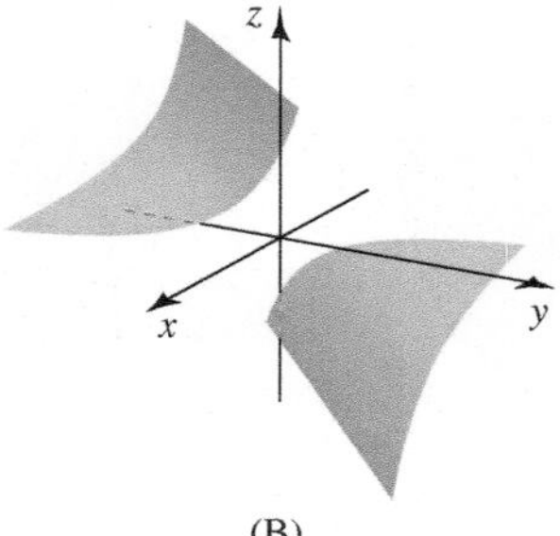

(B)

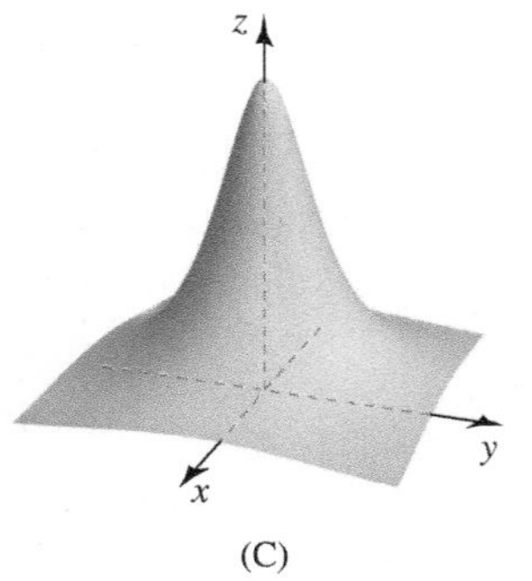

(C)

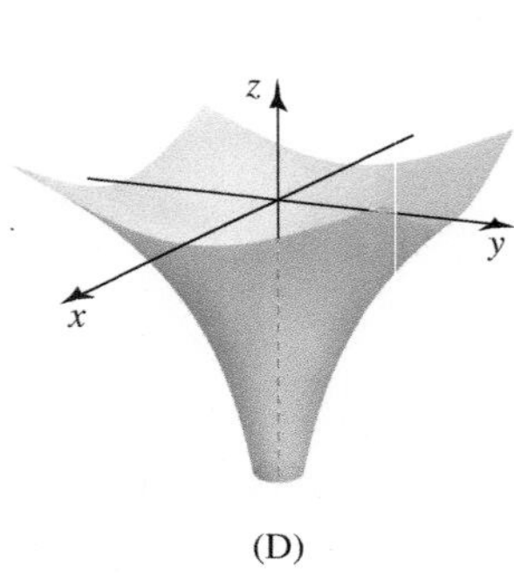

(D)

T 30–37. Level curves *Graph several level curves of the following functions using the given window. Label at least two level curves with their z-values.*

30. $z = x^2 + y^2$; $[-4, 4] \times [-4, 4]$
31. $z = x - y^2$; $[0, 4] \times [-2, 2]$
32. $z = 2x - y$; $[-2, 2] \times [-2, 2]$
33. $z = \sqrt{x^2 + 4y^2}$; $[-8, 8] \times [-8, 8]$
34. $z = e^{-x^2-2y^2}$; $[-2, 2] \times [-2, 2]$
35. $z = \sqrt{25 - x^2 - y^2}$; $[-6, 6] \times [-6, 6]$
36. $z = \sqrt{y - x^2 - 1}$; $[-5, 5] \times [-5, 5]$
37. $z = 3\cos(2x + y)$; $[-2, 2] \times [-2, 2]$
38. **Matching level curves with surfaces** Match surfaces a–f in the figure with level curves A–F.

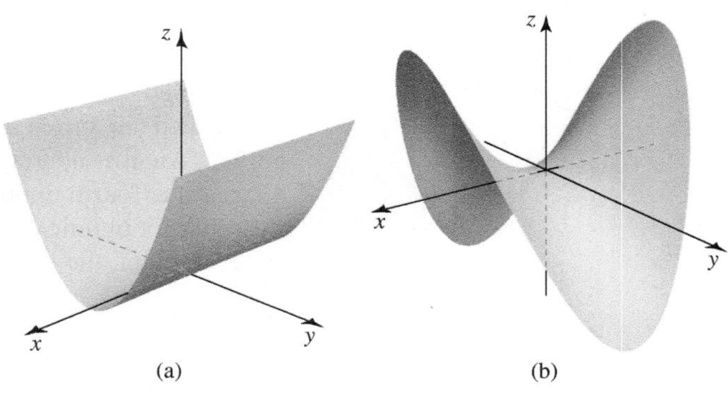

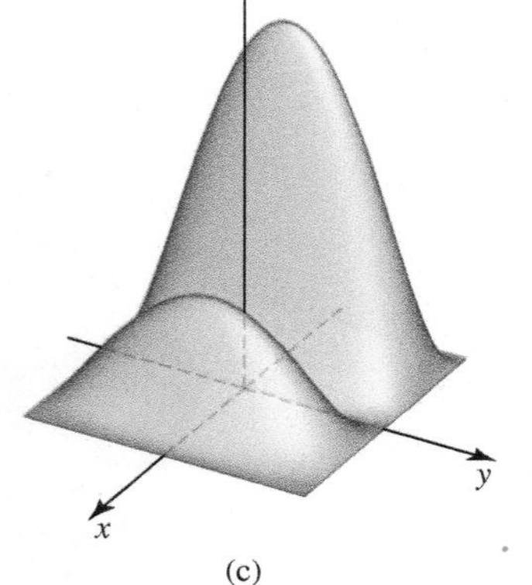

(c)

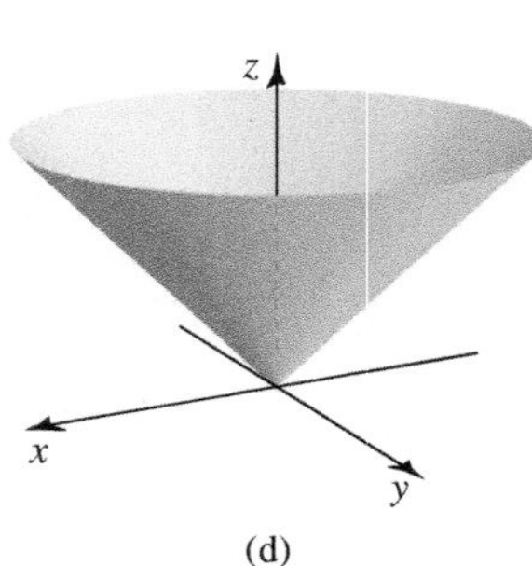

(d)

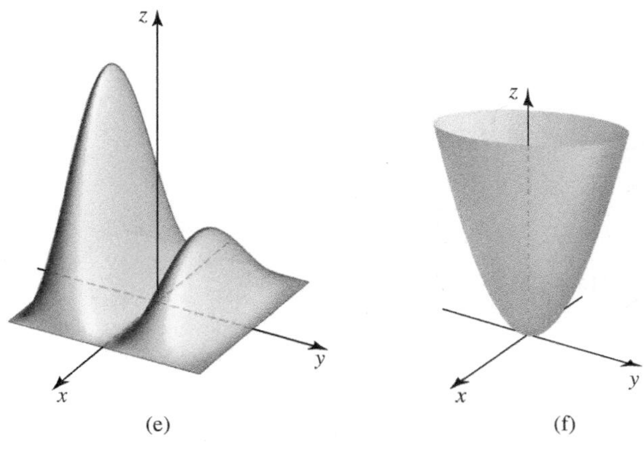

(e) (f)

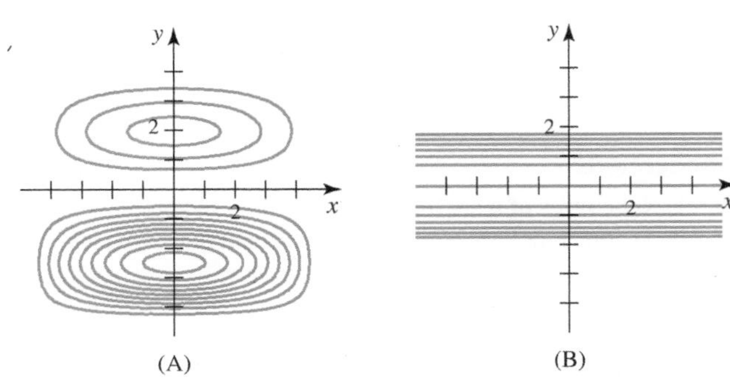
(A) (B)

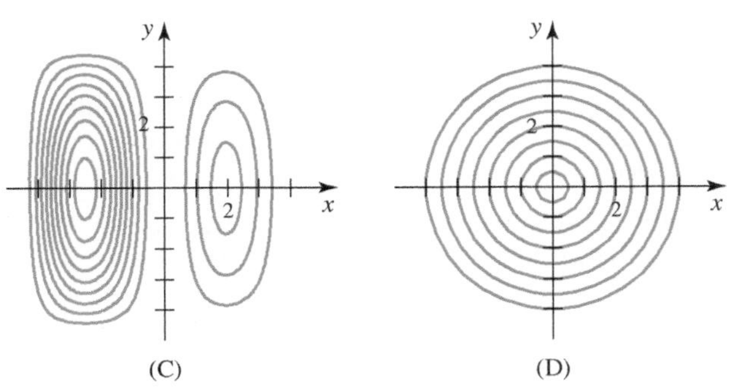
(C) (D)

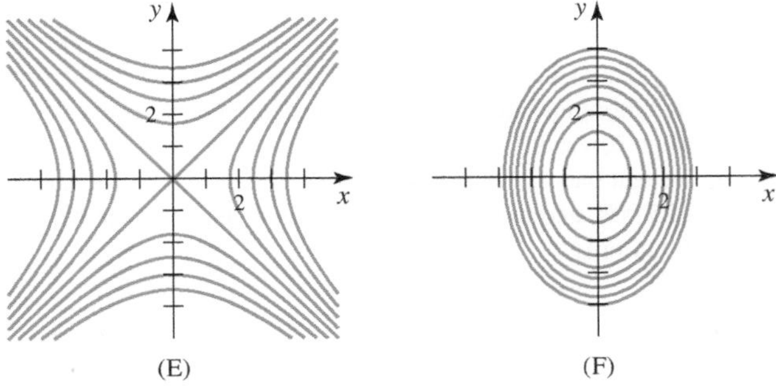
(E) (F)

39. A volume function The volume of a right circular cone of radius r and height h is $V(r, h) = \pi r^2 h/3$.

a. Graph the function in the window $[0, 5] \times [0, 5] \times [0, 150]$.
b. What is the domain of the volume function?
c. What is the relationship between the values of r and h when $V = 100$?

40. Earned run average A baseball pitcher's earned run average (ERA) is $A(e, i) = 9e/i$, where e is the number of earned runs given up by the pitcher and i is the number of innings pitched. Good pitchers have low ERAs. Assume that $e \geq 0$ and $i > 0$ are real numbers.

a. The single-season major league record for the lowest ERA was set by Dutch Leonard of the Detroit Tigers in 1914. During that season, Dutch pitched a total of 224 innings and gave up just 24 earned runs. What was his ERA?
b. Determine the ERA of a relief pitcher who gives up 4 earned runs in one-third of an inning.
c. Graph the level curve $A(e, i) = 3$ and describe the relationship between e and i in this case.

41. Electric potential function The electric potential function for two positive charges, one at $(0, 1)$ with twice the strength as the charge at $(0, -1)$, is given by

$$\varphi(x, y) = \frac{2}{\sqrt{x^2 + (y - 1)^2}} + \frac{1}{\sqrt{x^2 + (y + 1)^2}}.$$

a. Graph the electric potential using the window $[-5, 5] \times [-5, 5] \times [0, 10]$.
b. For what values of x and y is the potential φ defined?
c. Is the electric potential greater at $(3, 2)$ or $(2, 3)$?
d. Describe how the electric potential varies along the line $y = x$.

42. Cobb-Douglas production function The output Q of an economic system subject to two inputs, such as labor L and capital K, is often modeled by the Cobb-Douglas production function $Q(L, K) = cL^a K^b$, where a, b, and c are positive real numbers. When $a + b = 1$, the case is called *constant returns to scale*. Suppose $a = \frac{1}{3}$, $b = \frac{2}{3}$, and $c = 40$.

a. Graph the output function using the window $[0, 20] \times [0, 20] \times [0, 500]$.
b. If L is held constant at $L = 10$, write the function that gives the dependence of Q on K.
c. If K is held constant at $K = 15$, write the function that gives the dependence of Q on L.

43. Resistors in parallel Two resistors wired in parallel in an electrical circuit give an effective resistance of $R(x, y) = \dfrac{xy}{x + y}$, where x and y are the positive resistances of the individual resistors (typically measured in ohms).

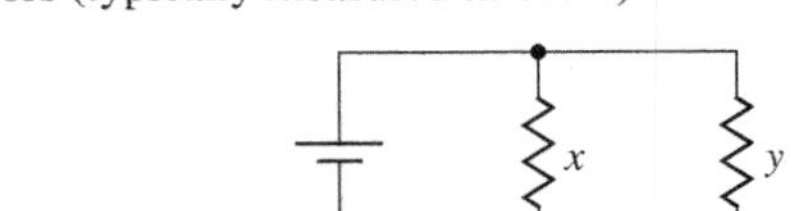

a. Graph the resistance function using the window $[0, 10] \times [0, 10] \times [0, 5]$.
b. Estimate the maximum value of R, for $0 < x \leq 10$ and $0 < y \leq 10$.
c. Explain what it means to say that the resistance function is symmetric in x and y.

44. Water waves A snapshot of a water wave moving toward shore is described by the function $z = 10 \sin (2x - 3y)$, where z is the height of the water surface above (or below) the xy-plane, which is the level of undisturbed water.

a. Graph the height function using the window $[-5, 5] \times [-5, 5] \times [-15, 15]$.
b. For what values of x and y is z defined?

c. What are the maximum and minimum values of the water height?
d. Give a vector in the xy-plane that is orthogonal to the level curves of the crests and troughs of the wave (which is parallel to the direction of wave propagation).

T **45. Approximate mountains** Suppose the elevation of Earth's surface over a 16-mi by 16-mi region is approximated by the function

$$z = 10e^{-(x^2+y^2)} + 5e^{-((x+5)^2+(y-3)^2)/10} + 4e^{-2((x-4)^2+(y+1)^2)}.$$

a. Graph the height function using the window $[-8, 8] \times [-8, 8] \times [0, 15]$.
b. Approximate the points (x, y) where the peaks in the landscape appear.
c. What are the approximate elevations of the peaks?

46–52. Domains of functions of three or more variables *Find the domain of the following functions. If possible, give a description of the domains (for example, all points outside a sphere of radius 1 centered at the origin).*

46. $f(x, y, z) = 2xyz - 3xz + 4yz$

47. $g(x, y, z) = \dfrac{1}{x - z}$

48. $p(x, y, z) = \sqrt{x^2 + y^2 + z^2 - 9}$

49. $f(x, y, z) = \sqrt{y - z}$

50. $Q(x, y, z) = \dfrac{10}{1 + x^2 + y^2 + 4z^2}$

51. $F(x, y, z) = \sqrt{y - x^2}$

52. $f(w, x, y, z) = \sqrt{1 - w^2 - x^2 - y^2 - z^2}$

Further Explorations

53. Explain why or why not Determine whether the following statements are true and give an explanation or counterexample.

a. The domain of the function $f(x, y) = 1 - |x - y|$ is $\{(x, y): x \geq y\}$.
b. The domain of the function $Q = g(w, x, y, z)$ is a region in $\mathbb{R}^3$.
c. All level curves of the plane $z = 2x - 3y$ are lines.

T **54–60. Graphing functions**

a. Determine the domain and range of the following functions.
b. Graph each function using a graphing utility. Be sure to experiment with the graphing window and orientation to give the best perspective of the surface.

54. $g(x, y) = e^{-xy}$

55. $f(x, y) = |xy|$

56. $p(x, y) = 1 - |x - 1| + |y + 1|$

57. $h(x, y) = (x + y)/(x - y)$

58. $G(x, y) = \ln(2 + \sin(x + y))$

59. $F(x, y) = \tan^2(x - y)$

60. $P(x, y) = \cos x \sin 2y$

T **61–64. Peaks and valleys** *The following functions have exactly one isolated peak or one isolated depression (one local maximum or minimum). Use a graphing utility to approximate the coordinates of the peak or depression.*

61. $f(x, y) = x^2y^2 - 8x^2 - y^2 + 6$

62. $g(x, y) = (x^2 - x - 2)(y^2 + 2y)$

63. $h(x, y) = 1 - e^{-(x^2+y^2-2x)}$

64. $p(x, y) = 2 + |x - 1| + |y - 1|$

65. Level curves of planes Prove that the level curves of the plane $ax + by + cz = d$ are parallel lines in the xy-plane, provided $a^2 + b^2 \neq 0$ and $c \neq 0$.

66–69. Level surfaces *Find an equation for the family of level surfaces corresponding to f. Describe the level surfaces.*

66. $f(x, y, z) = \dfrac{1}{x^2 + y^2 + z^2}$

67. $f(x, y, z) = x^2 + y^2 - z$

68. $f(x, y, z) = x^2 - y^2 - z$

69. $f(x, y, z) = \sqrt{x^2 + 2z^2}$

Applications

T **70. Level curves of a savings account** Suppose you make a one-time deposit of P dollars into a savings account that earns interest at an annual rate of $p\%$ compounded continuously. The balance in the account after t years is $B(P, r, t) = Pe^{rt}$, where $r = p/100$ (for example, if the annual interest rate is 4%, then $r = 0.04$). Let the interest rate be fixed at $r = 0.04$.

a. With a target balance of \$2000, find the set of all points (P, t) that satisfy $B = 2000$. This curve gives all deposits P and times t that result in a balance of \$2000.
b. Repeat part (a) with $B = \$500, \$1000, \$1500$, and \$2500, and draw the resulting level curves of the balance function.
c. In general, on one level curve, if t increases, does P increase or decrease?

T **71. Level curves of a savings plan** Suppose you make monthly deposits of P dollars into an account that earns interest at a *monthly* rate of $p\%$. The balance in the account after t years is $B(P, r, t) = P\left(\dfrac{(1 + r)^{12t} - 1}{r}\right)$, where $r = p/100$ (for example, if the annual interest rate is 9%, then $p = \frac{9}{12} = 0.75$ and $r = 0.0075$). Let the time of investment be fixed at $t = 20$ years.

a. With a target balance of \$20,000, find the set of all points (P, r) that satisfy $B = 20{,}000$. This curve gives all deposits P and monthly interest rates r that result in a balance of \$20,000 after 20 years.
b. Repeat part (a) with $B = \$5000, \$10{,}000, \$15{,}000$, and \$25,000, and draw the resulting level curves of the balance function.

72. **Quarterback passer ratings** One measurement of the quality of a quarterback in the National Football League is known as the *quarterback passer rating*. The rating formula is $R(c, t, i, y) = \dfrac{50 + 20c + 80t - 100i + 100y}{24}$, where c is the percentage of passes completed, t is the percentage of passes thrown for touchdowns, i is the percentage of intercepted passes, and y is the yards gained per attempted pass.

  a. In 2012, Green Bay quarterback Aaron Rodgers had the highest passer rating. He completed 67.21% of his passes, 7.07% of his passes were thrown for touchdowns, 1.45% of his passes were intercepted, and he gained an average of 7.78 yards per passing attempt. What was his passer rating in the 2012 season?

  b. If c, t, and y remained fixed, what happens to the quarterback passer rating as i increases? Explain your answer with and without mathematics.

  (*Source: The College Mathematics Journal*, 24, 5, Nov 1993)

T 73. **Ideal Gas Law** Many gases can be modeled by the Ideal Gas Law, $PV = nRT$, which relates the temperature (T, measured in Kelvin (K)), pressure (P, measured in Pascals (Pa)), and volume (V, measured in m^3) of a gas. Assume that the quantity of gas in question is $n = 1$ mole (mol). The gas constant has a value of $R = 8.3\ m^3\text{-Pa/mol-K}$.

  a. Consider T to be the dependent variable and plot several level curves (called *isotherms*) of the temperature surface in the region $0 \le P \le 100{,}000$ and $0 \le V \le 0.5$.

  b. Consider P to be the dependent variable and plot several level curves (called *isobars*) of the pressure surface in the region $0 \le T \le 900$ and $0 < V \le 0.5$.

  c. Consider V to be the dependent variable and plot several level curves of the volume surface in the region $0 \le T \le 900$ and $0 < P \le 100{,}000$.

Additional Exercises

74–77. Challenge domains *Find the domains of the following functions. Specify the domain mathematically and then describe it in words or with a sketch.*

74. $g(x, y, z) = \dfrac{10}{x^2 - (y + z)x + yz}$

75. $f(x, y) = \sin^{-1}(x - y)^2$

76. $f(x, y, z) = \ln(z - x^2 - y^2 + 2x + 3)$

77. $h(x, y, z) = \sqrt[4]{z^2 - xz + yz - xy}$

78. **Other balls** The closed unit ball in $\mathbb{R}^3$ centered at the origin is the set $\{(x, y, z): x^2 + y^2 + z^2 \le 1\}$. Describe the following alternative unit balls.

  a. $\{(x, y, z): |x| + |y| + |z| \le 1\}$

  b. $\{(x, y, z): \max\{|x|, |y|, |z|\} \le 1\}$, where $\max\{a, b, c\}$ is the maximum value of a, b, and c.

QUICK CHECK ANSWERS

1. $\mathbb{R}^2$; $\{(x, y): y \ge 0\}$ **2.** No; no **3.** $z = -\sqrt{1 + x^2 + y^2}$ **4.** No; otherwise the function would have two values at a single point. **5.** Concentric circles **6.** No; $z = 0$ is not in the range of the function. **7.** 0.97 **8.** 8 **9.** $\{(x, y, z): x \ne 0 \text{ and } y \ne 0 \text{ and } z \ne 0\}$ (which is $\mathbb{R}^3$, excluding the coordinate planes) ◄

12.3 Limits and Continuity

You have now seen examples of functions of several variables, but calculus has not yet entered the picture. In this section, we revisit topics encountered in single-variable calculus and see how they apply to functions of several variables. We begin with the fundamental concepts of limits and continuity.

Limit of a Function of Two Variables

A function f of two variables has a limit L as $P(x, y)$ approaches a fixed point $P_0(a, b)$ if $|f(x, y) - L|$ can be made arbitrarily small for all P in the domain that are sufficiently close to P_0. If such a limit exists, we write

$$\lim_{(x,y)\to(a,b)} f(x, y) = \lim_{P\to P_0} f(x, y) = L.$$

To make this definition more precise, *close to* must be defined carefully.

A point x on the number line is close to another point a provided the distance $|x - a|$ is small (Figure 12.37a). In $\mathbb{R}^2$, a point $P(x, y)$ is close to another point $P_0(a, b)$ if the distance between them $|PP_0| = \sqrt{(x - a)^2 + (y - b)^2}$ is small (Figure 12.37b). When we say *for all P close to P_0*, it means that $|PP_0|$ is small for points P *on all sides of P_0*.

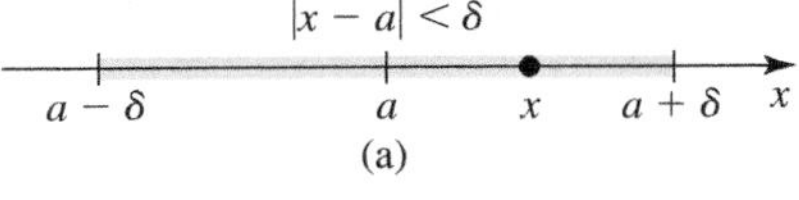

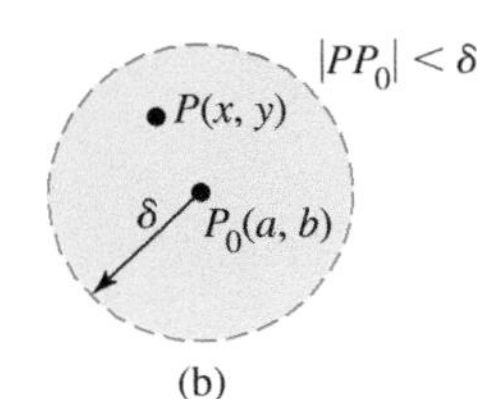

Figure 12.37

➤ The formal definition extends naturally to any number of variables. With n variables, the limit point is $P_0(a_1, \ldots, a_n)$, the variable point is $P(x_1, \ldots, x_n)$, and $|PP_0| = \sqrt{(x_1 - a_1)^2 + \cdots + (x_n - a_n)^2}$.

With this understanding of closeness, we can give a formal definition of a limit with two independent variables. This definition parallels the formal definition of a limit given in Section 2.7 (Figure 12.38).

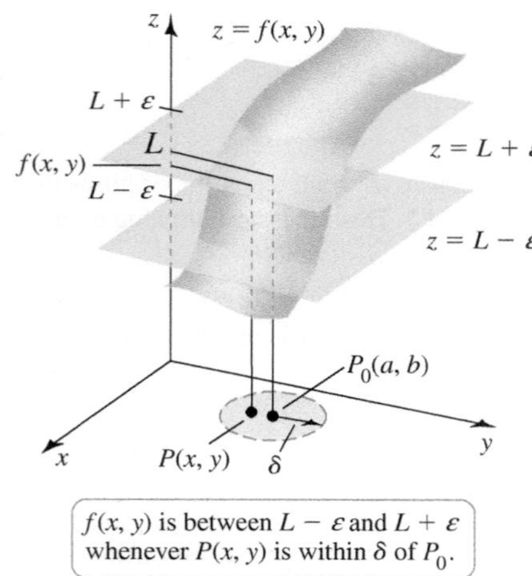

Figure 12.38

DEFINITION Limit of a Function of Two Variables

The function f has the **limit** L as $P(x, y)$ approaches $P_0(a, b)$, written

$$\lim_{(x,y)\to(a,b)} f(x, y) = \lim_{P\to P_0} f(x, y) = L,$$

if, given any $\varepsilon > 0$, there exists a $\delta > 0$ such that

$$|f(x, y) - L| < \varepsilon$$

whenever (x, y) is in the domain of f and

$$0 < |PP_0| = \sqrt{(x - a)^2 + (y - b)^2} < \delta.$$

The condition $|PP_0| < \delta$ means that the distance between $P(x, y)$ and $P_0(a, b)$ is less than δ as P approaches P_0 from all possible directions (Figure 12.39). Therefore, the limit exists only if $f(x, y)$ approaches L as P approaches P_0 *along all possible paths* in the domain of f. As shown in upcoming examples, this interpretation is critical in determining whether a limit exists.

As with functions of one variable, we first establish limits of the simplest functions.

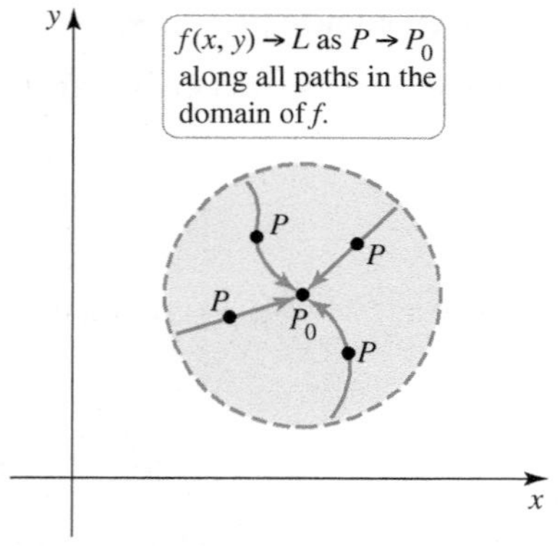

Figure 12.39

THEOREM 12.1 Limits of Constant and Linear Functions

Let a, b, and c be real numbers.

1. Constant function $f(x, y) = c$: $\displaystyle\lim_{(x,y)\to(a,b)} c = c$
2. Linear function $f(x, y) = x$: $\displaystyle\lim_{(x,y)\to(a,b)} x = a$
3. Linear function $f(x, y) = y$: $\displaystyle\lim_{(x,y)\to(a,b)} y = b$

Proof:

1. Consider the constant function $f(x, y) = c$ and assume $\varepsilon > 0$ is given. To prove that the value of the limit is $L = c$, we must produce a $\delta > 0$ such that $|f(x, y) - L| < \varepsilon$ whenever $0 < \sqrt{(x - a)^2 + (y - b)^2} < \delta$. For constant functions, we may use *any* $\delta > 0$. Then for every (x, y) in the domain of f,
$$|f(x, y) - L| = |f(x, y) - c| = |c - c| = 0 < \varepsilon$$
whenever $0 < \sqrt{(x - a)^2 + (y - b)^2} < \delta$.
2. Assume $\varepsilon > 0$ is given and take $\delta = \varepsilon$. The condition $0 < \sqrt{(x - a)^2 + (y - b)^2} < \delta$ implies that
$$0 < \sqrt{(x - a)^2 + (y - b)^2} < \varepsilon \quad \delta = \varepsilon$$
$$\sqrt{(x - a)^2} < \varepsilon \quad (x - a)^2 \le (x - a)^2 + (y - b)^2$$
$$|x - a| < \varepsilon. \quad \sqrt{x^2} = |x| \text{ for real numbers } x$$
Because $f(x, y) = x$ and $L = a$, we have shown that $|f(x, y) - L| < \varepsilon$ whenever $0 < \sqrt{(x - a)^2 + (y - b)^2} < \delta$. Therefore, $\displaystyle\lim_{(x,y)\to(a,b)} f(x, y) = L$, or $\displaystyle\lim_{(x,y)\to(a,b)} x = a$. The proof that $\displaystyle\lim_{(x,y)\to(a,b)} y = b$ is similar (Exercise 82). ◄

Using the three basic limits in Theorem 12.1, we can compute limits of more complicated functions. The only tools needed are limit laws analogous to those given in Theorem 2.3. The proofs of these laws are examined in Exercises 84–85.

THEOREM 12.2 Limit Laws for Functions of Two Variables
Let L and M be real numbers and suppose that $\lim_{(x,y)\to(a,b)} f(x,y) = L$ and $\lim_{(x,y)\to(a,b)} g(x,y) = M$. Assume c is a constant, and m and n are integers.

1. **Sum** $\lim_{(x,y)\to(a,b)} (f(x,y) + g(x,y)) = L + M$
2. **Difference** $\lim_{(x,y)\to(a,b)} (f(x,y) - g(x,y)) = L - M$
3. **Constant multiple** $\lim_{(x,y)\to(a,b)} cf(x,y) = cL$
4. **Product** $\lim_{(x,y)\to(a,b)} f(x,y)g(x,y) = LM$
5. **Quotient** $\lim_{(x,y)\to(a,b)} \frac{f(x,y)}{g(x,y)} = \frac{L}{M}$, provided $M \neq 0$
6. **Power** $\lim_{(x,y)\to(a,b)} (f(x,y))^n = L^n$
7. **Fractional power** If m and n have no common factors and $n \neq 0$, then $\lim_{(x,y)\to(a,b)} (f(x,y))^{m/n} = L^{m/n}$, where we assume $L > 0$ if n is even.

➤ Recall that a polynomial in two variables consists of sums and products of polynomials in x and polynomials in y. A rational function is the quotient of two polynomials.

Combining Theorems 12.1 and 12.2 allows us to find limits of polynomial, rational, and algebraic functions in two variables.

EXAMPLE 1 Limits of two-variable functions Evaluate $\lim_{(x,y)\to(2,8)} (3x^2y + \sqrt{xy})$.

SOLUTION All the operations in this function appear in Theorem 12.2. Therefore, we can apply the limit laws directly.

$$\begin{aligned}
\lim_{(x,y)\to(2,8)} (3x^2y + \sqrt{xy}) &= \lim_{(x,y)\to(2,8)} 3x^2y + \lim_{(x,y)\to(2,8)} \sqrt{xy} && \text{Law 1}\\
&= 3 \lim_{(x,y)\to(2,8)} x^2 \cdot \lim_{(x,y)\to(2,8)} y \\
&\quad + \sqrt{\lim_{(x,y)\to(2,8)} x \cdot \lim_{(x,y)\to(2,8)} y} && \text{Laws 3, 4, 6, 7}\\
&= 3 \cdot 2^2 \cdot 8 + \sqrt{2 \cdot 8} = 100 && \text{Theorem 12.1}
\end{aligned}$$

Related Exercises 11–18 ◄

In Example 1, the value of the limit equals the value of the function at (a,b); in other words, $\lim_{(x,y)\to(a,b)} f(x,y) = f(a,b)$ and the limit can be evaluated by substitution. This is a property of *continuous* functions, discussed later in this section.

QUICK CHECK 1 Which of the following limits exist?

a. $\lim_{(x,y)\to(1,1)} 3x^{12}y^2$ **b.** $\lim_{(x,y)\to(0,0)} 3x^{-2}y^2$ **c.** $\lim_{(x,y)\to(1,2)} \sqrt{x - y^2}$ ◄

Limits at Boundary Points

This is an appropriate place to make some definitions that are used in the remainder of the book.

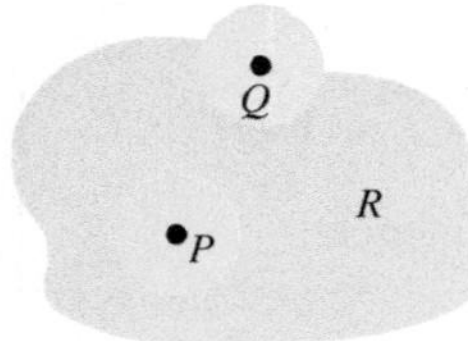

Figure 12.40

DEFINITION Interior and Boundary Points

Let R be a region in $\mathbb{R}^2$. An **interior point** P of R lies entirely within R, which means it is possible to find a disk centered at P that contains only points of R (Figure 12.40).

A **boundary point** Q of R lies on the edge of R in the sense that *every* disk centered at Q contains at least one point in R and at least one point not in R.

For example, let R be the points in $\mathbb{R}^2$ satisfying $x^2 + y^2 < 9$. The boundary points of R lie on the circle $x^2 + y^2 = 9$. The interior points lie inside that circle and satisfy $x^2 + y^2 < 9$. Notice that the boundary points of a set need not lie in the set.

➤ The definitions of interior point and boundary point apply to regions in $\mathbb{R}^3$ if we replace *disk* by *ball*.

➤ Many sets, such as the annulus $\{(x, y): 2 \le x^2 + y^2 < 5\}$, are neither open nor closed.

DEFINITION Open and Closed Sets

A region is **open** if it consists entirely of interior points. A region is **closed** if it contains all its boundary points.

An example of an open region in $\mathbb{R}^2$ is the open disk $\{(x, y): x^2 + y^2 < 9\}$. An example of a closed region in $\mathbb{R}^2$ is the square $\{(x, y): |x| \le 1, |y| \le 1\}$. Later in the book, we encounter interior and boundary points of three-dimensional sets such as balls, boxes, and pyramids.

QUICK CHECK 2 Give an example of a set that contains none of its boundary points. ◄

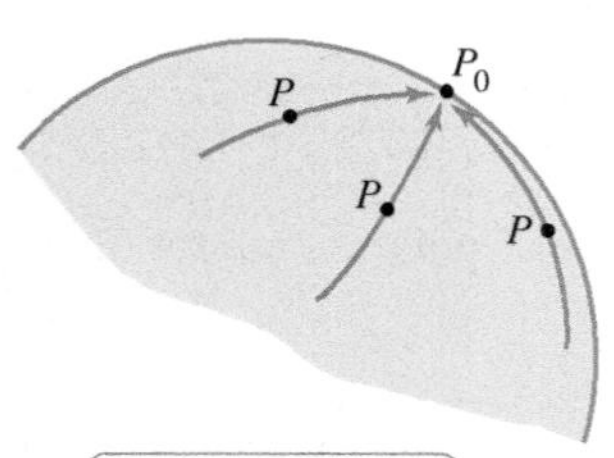

Figure 12.41

Suppose $P_0(a, b)$ is a boundary point of the domain of f. The limit $\lim_{(x,y)\to(a,b)} f(x, y)$ exists, even if P_0 is not in the domain of f, provided $f(x, y)$ approaches the same value as (x, y) approaches (a, b) *along all paths that lie in the domain* (Figure 12.41).

Consider the function $f(x, y) = \dfrac{x^2 - y^2}{x - y}$ whose domain is $\{(x, y): x \ne y\}$. Provided $x \ne y$, we may cancel the factor $(x - y)$ from the numerator and denominator and write

$$f(x, y) = \frac{x^2 - y^2}{x - y} = \frac{(x - y)(x + y)}{x - y} = x + y.$$

➤ Recall that this same method was used with functions of one variable. For example, after the common factor $x - 2$ is canceled, the function

$$g(x) = \frac{x^2 - 4}{x - 2}$$

becomes $g(x) = x + 2$, provided $x \ne 2$. In this case, 2 plays the role of a boundary point.

The graph of f (Figure 12.42) is the plane $z = x + y$, with points corresponding to the line $x = y$ removed.

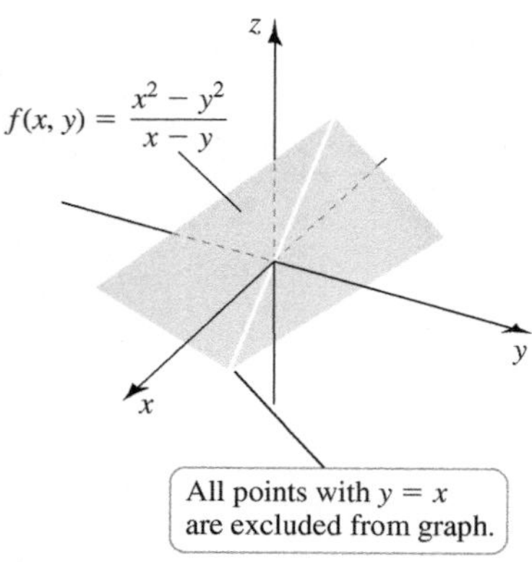

Figure 12.42

Now we examine $\lim_{(x,y)\to(4,4)} \dfrac{x^2 - y^2}{x - y}$, where $(4, 4)$ is a boundary point of the domain of f but does not lie in the domain. For this limit to exist, $f(x, y)$ must approach the same value along all paths to $(4, 4)$ that lie in the domain of f—that is, all paths approaching $(4, 4)$ that do not intersect $x = y$. To evaluate the limit, we proceed as follows:

$$\begin{aligned}\lim_{(x,y)\to(4,4)} \frac{x^2 - y^2}{x - y} &= \lim_{(x,y)\to(4,4)} (x + y) && \text{Assume } x \ne y \text{, cancel } x - y. \\ &= 4 + 4 = 8. && \text{Same limit along all paths in the domain}\end{aligned}$$

To emphasize, we let $(x, y) \to (4, 4)$ along all paths that do not intersect $x = y$, which lies outside the domain of f. Along all admissible paths, the function approaches 8.

QUICK CHECK 3 Can the limit $\lim_{(x,y)\to(0,0)} \dfrac{x^2 - xy}{x}$ be evaluated by direct substitution? ◄

EXAMPLE 2 Limits at boundary points Evaluate $\displaystyle\lim_{(x,y)\to(4,1)} \frac{xy - 4y^2}{\sqrt{x} - 2\sqrt{y}}$.

SOLUTION Points in the domain of this function satisfy $x \geq 0$ and $y \geq 0$ (because of the square roots) and $x \neq 4y$ (to ensure the denominator is nonzero). We see that the point $(4, 1)$ lies on the boundary of the domain. Multiplying the numerator and denominator by the algebraic conjugate of the denominator, the limit is computed as follows:

$$\begin{aligned}
\lim_{(x,y)\to(4,1)} \frac{xy - 4y^2}{\sqrt{x} - 2\sqrt{y}} &= \lim_{(x,y)\to(4,1)} \frac{(xy - 4y^2)(\sqrt{x} + 2\sqrt{y})}{(\sqrt{x} - 2\sqrt{y})(\sqrt{x} + 2\sqrt{y})} && \text{Multiply by conjugate.}\\
&= \lim_{(x,y)\to(4,1)} \frac{y(x - 4y)(\sqrt{x} + 2\sqrt{y})}{x - 4y} && \text{Simplify.}\\
&= \lim_{(x,y)\to(4,1)} y(\sqrt{x} + 2\sqrt{y}) && \text{Cancel } x - 4y, \text{ assumed to be nonzero.}\\
&= 4. && \text{Evaluate limit.}
\end{aligned}$$

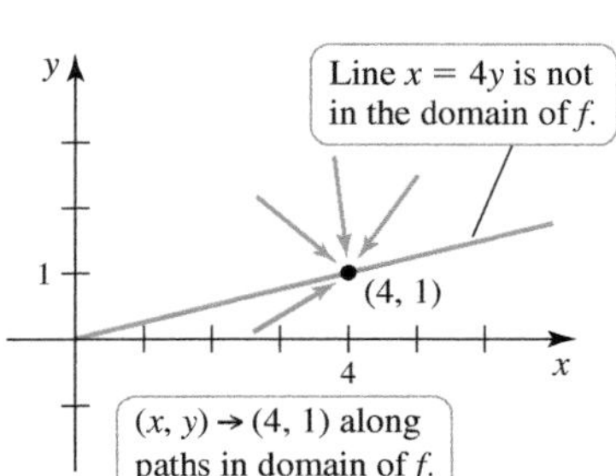

Figure 12.43

Because points on the line $x = 4y$ are outside the domain of the function, we assume that $x - 4y \neq 0$. Along all other paths to $(4, 1)$, the function values approach 4 (Figure 12.43).

Related Exercises 19–26 ◄

EXAMPLE 3 Nonexistence of a limit Investigate the limit $\displaystyle\lim_{(x,y)\to(0,0)} \frac{(x + y)^2}{x^2 + y^2}$.

SOLUTION The domain of the function is $\{(x, y): (x, y) \neq (0, 0)\}$; therefore, the limit is at a boundary point outside the domain. Suppose we let (x, y) approach $(0, 0)$ along the line $y = mx$ for a fixed constant m. Substituting $y = mx$ and noting that $y \to 0$ as $x \to 0$, we have

$$\lim_{\substack{(x,y)\to(0,0)\\ (\text{along } y = mx)}} \frac{(x + y)^2}{x^2 + y^2} = \lim_{x\to 0} \frac{(x + mx)^2}{x^2 + m^2x^2} = \lim_{x\to 0} \frac{x^2(1 + m)^2}{x^2(1 + m^2)} = \frac{(1 + m)^2}{1 + m^2}.$$

➤ Notice that if we choose any path of the form $y = mx$, then $y \to 0$ as $x \to 0$. Therefore, $\displaystyle\lim_{(x,y)\to(0,0)}$ can be replaced by $\displaystyle\lim_{x\to 0}$ along this path. A similar argument applies to paths of the form $y = mx^p$, for $p > 0$.

The constant m determines the direction of approach to $(0, 0)$. Therefore, depending on m, the function approaches different values as (x, y) approaches $(0, 0)$ (Figure 12.44). For example, if $m = 0$, the corresponding limit is 1 and if $m = -1$, the limit is 0. The reason for this behavior is revealed if we plot the surface and look at two level curves. The lines $y = x$ and $y = -x$ (excluding the origin) are level curves of the function for $z = 2$ and $z = 0$, respectively. (Figure 12.45). Therefore, as $(x, y) \to (0, 0)$ along $y = x, f(x, y) \to 2$, and as $(x, y) \to (0, 0)$ along $y = -x, f(x, y) \to 0$. Because the function approaches different values along different paths, we conclude that the *limit does not exist*.

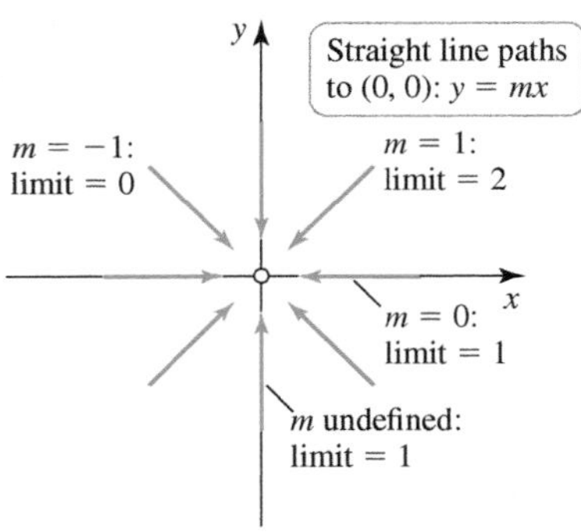

Figure 12.44

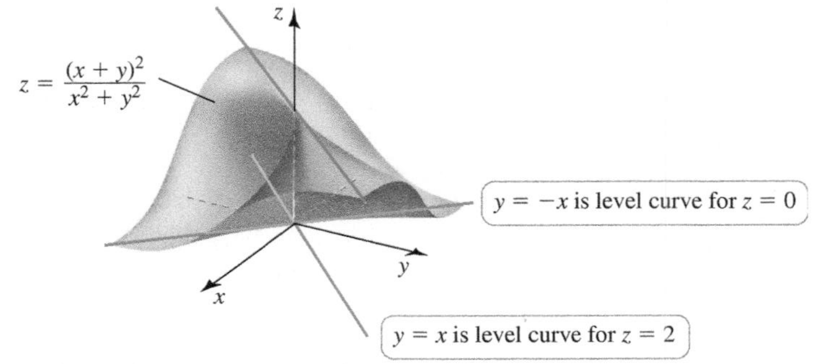

Figure 12.45

Related Exercises 27–32 ◄

The strategy used in Example 3 is an effective way to prove the nonexistence of a limit.

QUICK CHECK 4 What is the analog of the Two-Path Test for functions of a single variable? ◄

PROCEDURE Two-Path Test for Nonexistence of Limits

If $f(x, y)$ approaches two different values as (x, y) approaches (a, b) along two different paths in the domain of f, then $\lim_{(x,y)\to(a,b)} f(x, y)$ does not exist.

Continuity of Functions of Two Variables

The following definition of continuity for functions of two variables is analogous to the continuity definition for functions of one variable.

DEFINITION Continuity

The function f is continuous at the point (a, b) provided

1. f is defined at (a, b).
2. $\lim_{(x,y)\to(a,b)} f(x, y)$ exists.
3. $\lim_{(x,y)\to(a,b)} f(x, y) = f(a, b)$.

A function of two (or more) variables is continuous at a point, provided its limit equals its value at that point (which implies the limit and the value both exist). The definition of continuity applies at boundary points of the domain of f provided the limits in the definition are taken along all paths that lie in the domain. Because limits of polynomials and rational functions can be evaluated by substitution at points of their domains (that is, $\lim_{(x,y)\to(a,b)} f(x, y) = f(a, b)$), it follows that polynomials and rational functions are continuous at all points of their domains.

EXAMPLE 4 Checking continuity Determine the points at which the following function is continuous.

$$f(x, y) = \begin{cases} \dfrac{3xy^2}{x^2 + y^4} & \text{if } (x, y) \neq (0, 0) \\ 0 & \text{if } (x, y) = (0, 0) \end{cases}$$

SOLUTION The function $\dfrac{3xy^2}{x^2 + y^4}$ is a rational function, so it is continuous at all points of its domain, which consists of all points of $\mathbb{R}^2$ except $(0, 0)$. To determine whether f is continuous at $(0, 0)$, we must show that

$$\lim_{(x,y)\to(0,0)} \frac{3xy^2}{x^2 + y^4}$$

exists and equals $f(0, 0) = 0$ along all paths that approach $(0, 0)$.

You can verify that as (x, y) approaches $(0, 0)$ along paths of the form $y = mx$, where m is any constant, the function values approach $f(0, 0) = 0$. However, along parabolic paths of the form $x = my^2$ (where m is a nonzero constant), the limit behaves

➤ The choice of $x = my^2$ for paths to $(0, 0)$ is not obvious. Notice that if x is replaced with my^2 in f, the result involves the same power of y (in this case, y^4) in the numerator and denominator, which may be canceled.

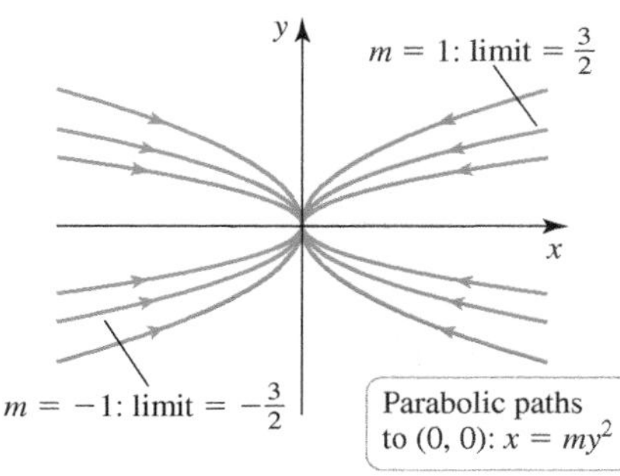

Figure 12.46

differently (Figure 12.46). This time we substitute $x = my^2$ and note that $x \to 0$ as $y \to 0$:

$$\begin{aligned}\lim_{\substack{(x,y)\to(0,0)\\ (\text{along } x = my^2)}} \frac{3xy^2}{x^2 + y^4} &= \lim_{y\to 0} \frac{3(my^2)y^2}{(my^2)^2 + y^4} && \text{Substitute } x = my^2.\\ &= \lim_{y\to 0} \frac{3my^4}{m^2y^4 + y^4} && \text{Simplify.}\\ &= \lim_{y\to 0} \frac{3m}{m^2 + 1} && \text{Cancel } y^4.\\ &= \frac{3m}{m^2 + 1}.\end{aligned}$$

We see that along parabolic paths, the limit depends on the approach path. For example, with $m = 1$, along the path $x = y^2$, the function values approach $\frac{3}{2}$; with $m = -1$, along the path $x = -y^2$, the function values approach $-\frac{3}{2}$ (Figure 12.47). Because $f(x, y)$ approaches two different numbers along two different paths, the limit at $(0, 0)$ does not exist, and f is not continuous at $(0, 0)$.

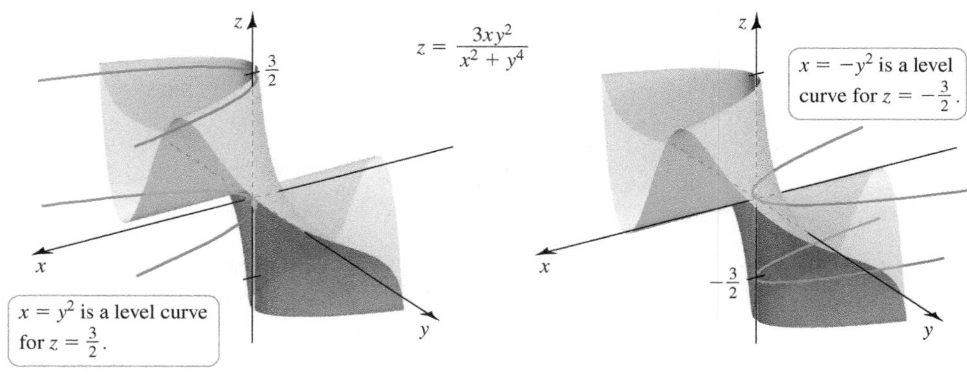

Figure 12.47

Related Exercises 33–40 ◄

QUICK CHECK 5 Which of the following functions are continuous at $(0, 0)$?

a. $f(x, y) = 2x^2y^5$

b. $f(x, y) = \dfrac{2x^2y^5}{x - 1}$

c. $f(x, y) = 2x^{-2}y^5$ ◄

Composite Functions Recall that for functions of a single variable, compositions of continuous functions are also continuous. The following theorem gives the analogous result for functions of two variables; it is proved in Appendix B.

> **THEOREM 12.3 Continuity of Composite Functions**
> If $u = g(x, y)$ is continuous at (a, b) and $z = f(u)$ is continuous at $g(a, b)$, then the composite function $z = f(g(x, y))$ is continuous at (a, b).

With Theorem 12.3, we can easily analyze the continuity of many functions. For example, $\sin x$, $\cos x$, and e^x are continuous functions of a single variable, for all real values of x. Therefore, compositions of these functions with polynomials in x and y (for example, $\sin(x^2y)$ and $e^{x^4-y^2}$) are continuous for all real numbers x and y. Similarly, $\sqrt{x}$ is a continuous function of a single variable, for $x \geq 0$. Therefore, $\sqrt{u(x, y)}$ is continuous at (x, y) provided u is continuous at (x, y) and $u(x, y) \geq 0$. As long as we observe restrictions on domains, then compositions of continuous functions are also continuous.

EXAMPLE 5 Continuity of composite functions. Determine the points at which the following functions are continuous.

a. $h(x, y) = \ln(x^2 + y^2 + 4)$ **b.** $h(x, y) = e^{x/y}$

SOLUTION

a. This function is the composition $f(g(x, y))$, where

$$f(u) = \ln u \quad \text{and} \quad u = g(x, y) = x^2 + y^2 + 4.$$

As a polynomial, g is continuous for all (x, y) in $\mathbb{R}^2$. The function f is continuous for $u > 0$. Because $u = x^2 + y^2 + 4 > 0$ for all (x, y), it follows that h is continuous at all points of $\mathbb{R}^2$.

b. Letting $f(u) = e^u$ and $u = g(x, y) = x/y$, we have $h(x, y) = f(g(x, y))$. Note that f is continuous at all points of $\mathbb{R}$ and g is continuous at all points of $\mathbb{R}^2$ provided $y \neq 0$. Therefore, h is continuous on the set $\{(x, y): y \neq 0\}$.

Related Exercises 41–52 ◀

Functions of Three Variables

The work we have done with limits and continuity of functions of two variables extends to functions of three or more variables. Specifically, the limit laws of Theorem 12.2 apply to functions of the form $w = f(x, y, z)$. Polynomials and rational functions are continuous at all points of their domains, and limits of these functions may be evaluated by direct substitution at all points of their domains. Compositions of continuous functions of the form $f(g(x, y, z))$ are also continuous at points at which $g(x, y, z)$ is in the domain of f.

EXAMPLE 6 Functions of three variables

a. Evaluate $\displaystyle\lim_{(x,y,z)\to(2,\pi/2,0)} \frac{x^2 \sin y}{z^2 + 4}$.

b. Find the points at which $h(x, y, z) = \sqrt{x^2 + y^2 + z^2 - 1}$ is continuous.

SOLUTION

a. This function consists of products and quotients of functions that are continuous at $(2, \pi/2, 0)$. Therefore, the limit is evaluated by direct substitution:

$$\lim_{(x,y,z)\to(2,\pi/2,0)} \frac{x^2 \sin y}{z^2 + 4} = \frac{2^2 \sin(\pi/2)}{0^2 + 4} = 1.$$

b. This function is a composition in which the outer function $f(u) = \sqrt{u}$ is continuous for $u \geq 0$. The inner function

$$g(x, y, z) = x^2 + y^2 + z^2 - 1$$

is nonnegative provided $x^2 + y^2 + z^2 \geq 1$. Therefore, h is continuous at all points on or outside the unit sphere in $\mathbb{R}^3$.

Related Exercises 53–58 ◀

SECTION 12.3 EXERCISES

Review Questions

1. Explain what $\displaystyle\lim_{(x,y)\to(a,b)} f(x, y) = L$ means.

2. Explain why $f(x, y)$ must approach a unique number L as (x, y) approaches (a, b) along *all* paths in the domain in order for $\displaystyle\lim_{(x,y)\to(a,b)} f(x, y)$ to exist.

3. What does it mean to say that limits of polynomials may be evaluated by direct substitution?

4. Suppose (a, b) is on the boundary of the domain of f. Explain how you would determine whether $\displaystyle\lim_{(x,y)\to(a,b)} f(x, y)$ exists.

5. Explain how examining limits along multiple paths may prove the nonexistence of a limit.

6. Explain why evaluating a limit along a finite number of paths does not prove the existence of a limit of a function of several variables.

7. What three conditions must be met for a function f to be continuous at the point (a, b)?

8. Let R be the unit disk $\{(x, y): x^2 + y^2 \leq 1\}$ with $(0, 0)$ removed. Is $(0, 0)$ a boundary point of R? Is R open or closed?

9. At what points of $\mathbb{R}^2$ is a rational function of two variables continuous?

10. Evaluate $\displaystyle\lim_{(x,y,z)\to(1,1,-1)} xy^2z^3$.

Basic Skills

11–18. Limits of functions *Evaluate the following limits.*

11. $\displaystyle\lim_{(x,y)\to(2,9)} 101$

12. $\displaystyle\lim_{(x,y)\to(1,-3)} (3x + 4y - 2)$

13. $\displaystyle\lim_{(x,y)\to(-3,3)} (4x^2 - y^2)$

14. $\displaystyle\lim_{(x,y)\to(2,-1)} (xy^8 - 3x^2y^3)$

15. $\lim_{(x,y)\to(0,\pi)} \frac{\cos xy + \sin xy}{2y}$

16. $\lim_{(x,y)\to(e^2,4)} \ln \sqrt{xy}$

17. $\lim_{(x,y)\to(2,0)} \frac{x^2 - 3xy^2}{x + y}$

18. $\lim_{(u,v)\to(1,-1)} \frac{10uv - 2v^2}{u^2 + v^2}$

19–26. Limits at boundary points *Evaluate the following limits.*

19. $\lim_{(x,y)\to(6,2)} \frac{x^2 - 3xy}{x - 3y}$

20. $\lim_{(x,y)\to(1,-2)} \frac{y^2 + 2xy}{y + 2x}$

21. $\lim_{(x,y)\to(3,1)} \frac{x^2 - 7xy + 12y^2}{x - 3y}$

22. $\lim_{(x,y)\to(-1,1)} \frac{2x^2 - xy - 3y^2}{x + y}$

23. $\lim_{(x,y)\to(2,2)} \frac{y^2 - 4}{xy - 2x}$

24. $\lim_{(x,y)\to(4,5)} \frac{\sqrt{x + y} - 3}{x + y - 9}$

25. $\lim_{(x,y)\to(1,2)} \frac{\sqrt{y} - \sqrt{x + 1}}{y - x - 1}$

26. $\lim_{(u,v)\to(8,8)} \frac{u^{1/3} - v^{1/3}}{u^{2/3} - v^{2/3}}$

27–32. Nonexistence of limits *Use the Two-Path Test to prove that the following limits do not exist.*

27. $\lim_{(x,y)\to(0,0)} \frac{x + 2y}{x - 2y}$

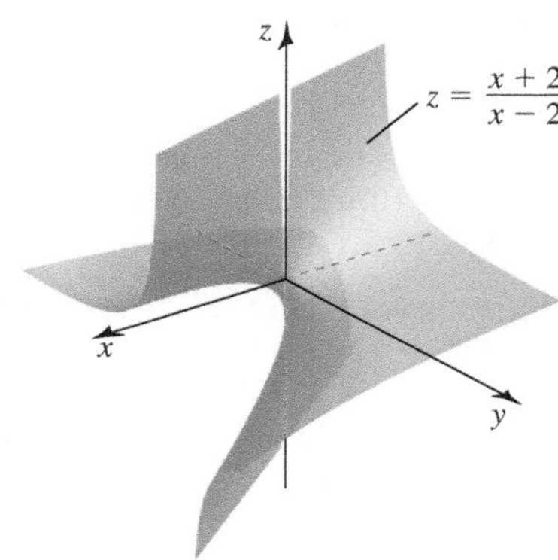

28. $\lim_{(x,y)\to(0,0)} \frac{4xy}{3x^2 + y^2}$

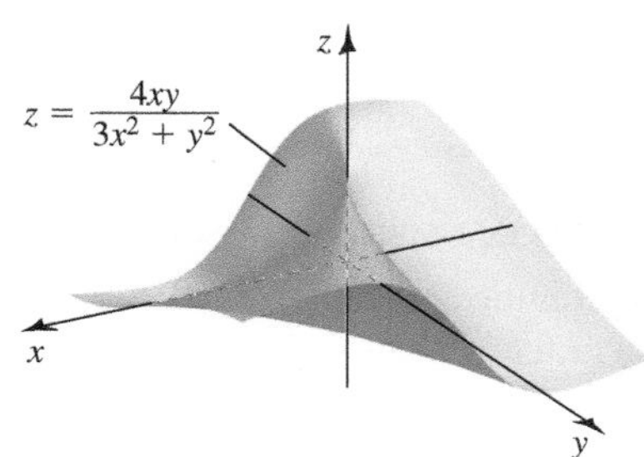

29. $\lim_{(x,y)\to(0,0)} \frac{y^4 - 2x^2}{y^4 + x^2}$

30. $\lim_{(x,y)\to(0,0)} \frac{x^3 - y^2}{x^3 + y^2}$

31. $\lim_{(x,y)\to(0,0)} \frac{y^3 + x^3}{xy^2}$

32. $\lim_{(x,y)\to(0,0)} \frac{y}{\sqrt{x^2 - y^2}}$

33–40. Continuity *At what points of $\mathbb{R}^2$ are the following functions continuous?*

33. $f(x, y) = x^2 + 2xy - y^3$

34. $f(x, y) = \frac{xy}{x^2y^2 + 1}$

35. $p(x, y) = \frac{4x^2y^2}{x^4 + y^2}$

36. $S(x, y) = \frac{2xy}{x^2 - y^2}$

37. $f(x, y) = \frac{2}{x(y^2 + 1)}$

38. $f(x, y) = \frac{x^2 + y^2}{x(y^2 - 1)}$

39. $f(x, y) = \begin{cases} \frac{xy}{x^2 + y^2} & \text{if } (x, y) \neq (0, 0) \\ 0 & \text{if } (x, y) = (0, 0) \end{cases}$

40. $f(x, y) = \begin{cases} \frac{y^4 - 2x^2}{y^4 + x^2} & \text{if } (x, y) \neq (0, 0) \\ 0 & \text{if } (x, y) = (0, 0) \end{cases}$

41–52. Continuity of composite functions *At what points of $\mathbb{R}^2$ are the following functions continuous?*

41. $f(x, y) = \sqrt{x^2 + y^2}$

42. $f(x, y) = e^{x^2+y^2}$

43. $f(x, y) = \sin xy$

44. $g(x, y) = \ln (x - y)$

45. $h(x, y) = \cos (x + y)$

46. $p(x, y) = e^{x-y}$

47. $f(x, y) = \ln (x^2 + y^2)$

48. $f(x, y) = \sqrt{4 - x^2 - y^2}$

49. $g(x, y) = \sqrt[3]{x^2 + y^2 - 9}$

50. $h(x, y) = \frac{\sqrt{x - y}}{4}$

51. $f(x, y) = \begin{cases} \frac{\sin (x^2 + y^2)}{x^2 + y^2} & \text{if } (x, y) \neq (0, 0) \\ 1 & \text{if } (x, y) = (0, 0) \end{cases}$

52. $f(x, y) = \begin{cases} \frac{1 - \cos (x^2 + y^2)}{x^2 + y^2} & \text{if } (x, y) \neq (0, 0) \\ 0 & \text{if } (x, y) = (0, 0) \end{cases}$

53–58. Limits of functions of three variables *Evaluate the following limits.*

53. $\lim_{(x,y,z)\to(1,\ln 2,3)} ze^{xy}$

54. $\lim_{(x,y,z)\to(0,1,0)} (1 + y) \ln e^{xz}$

55. $\lim_{(x,y,z)\to(1,1,1)} \frac{yz - xy - xz - x^2}{yz + xy + xz - y^2}$

56. $\lim_{(x,y,z)\to(1,1,1)} \frac{x - \sqrt{xz} - \sqrt{xy} + \sqrt{yz}}{x - \sqrt{xz} + \sqrt{xy} - \sqrt{yz}}$

57. $\lim_{(x,y,z)\to(1,1,1)} \frac{x^2 + xy - xz - yz}{x - z}$

58. $\lim_{(x,y,z)\to(1,-1,1)} \frac{xz + 5x + yz + 5y}{x + y}$

Further Explorations

59. **Explain why or why not** Determine whether the following statements are true and give an explanation or counterexample.

   a. If the limits $\lim_{(x,0)\to(0,0)} f(x, 0)$ and $\lim_{(0,y)\to(0,0)} f(0, y)$ exist and equal L, then $\lim_{(x,y)\to(0,0)} f(x, y) = L$.

   b. If $\lim_{(x,y)\to(a,b)} f(x, y)$ equals a finite number L, then f is continuous at (a, b).

   c. If f is continuous at (a, b), then $\lim_{(x,y)\to(a,b)} f(x, y)$ exists.

   d. If P is a boundary point of the domain of f, then P is in the domain of f.

60–67. Miscellaneous limits *Use the method of your choice to evaluate the following limits.*

60. $\displaystyle\lim_{(x,y)\to(0,0)} \frac{y^2}{x^8 + y^2}$

61. $\displaystyle\lim_{(x,y)\to(0,1)} \frac{y \sin x}{x(y + 1)}$

62. $\displaystyle\lim_{(x,y)\to(1,1)} \frac{x^2 + xy - 2y^2}{2x^2 - xy - y^2}$

63. $\displaystyle\lim_{(x,y)\to(1,0)} \frac{y \ln y}{x}$

64. $\displaystyle\lim_{(x,y)\to(0,0)} \frac{|xy|}{xy}$

65. $\displaystyle\lim_{(x,y)\to(0,0)} \frac{|x - y|}{|x + y|}$

66. $\displaystyle\lim_{(u,v)\to(-1,0)} \frac{uve^{-v}}{u^2 + v^2}$

67. $\displaystyle\lim_{(x,y)\to(2,0)} \frac{1 - \cos y}{xy^2}$

68–71. Limits using polar coordinates *Limits at* $(0, 0)$ *may be easier to evaluate by converting to polar coordinates. Remember that the same limit must be obtained as* $r \to 0$ *along all paths in the domain to* $(0, 0)$. *Evaluate the following limits or state that they do not exist.*

68. $\displaystyle\lim_{(x,y)\to(0,0)} \frac{x - y}{\sqrt{x^2 + y^2}}$

69. $\displaystyle\lim_{(x,y)\to(0,0)} \frac{x^2y}{x^2 + y^2}$

70. $\displaystyle\lim_{(x,y)\to(0,0)} \tan^{-1}\left(\frac{(2 + (x + y)^2 + (x - y)^2)}{2e^{x^2+y^2}}\right)$

71. $\displaystyle\lim_{(x,y)\to(0,0)} \frac{x^2 + y^2 + x^2y^2}{x^2 + y^2}$

Additional Exercises

72. Sine limits Evaluate the following limits.

a. $\displaystyle\lim_{(x,y)\to(0,0)} \frac{\sin(x + y)}{x + y}$

b. $\displaystyle\lim_{(x,y)\to(0,0)} \frac{\sin x + \sin y}{x + y}$

73. Piecewise function Let

$$f(x, y) = \begin{cases} \dfrac{\sin(x^2 + y^2 - 1)}{x^2 + y^2 - 1} & \text{if } x^2 + y^2 \neq 1 \\ b & \text{if } x^2 + y^2 = 1. \end{cases}$$

Find the value of b for which f is continuous at all points in $\mathbb{R}^2$.

74. Piecewise function Let

$$f(x, y) = \begin{cases} \dfrac{1 + 2xy - \cos xy}{xy} & \text{if } xy \neq 0 \\ a & \text{if } xy = 0. \end{cases}$$

Find the value of a for which f is continuous at all points in $\mathbb{R}^2$.

75. Nonexistence of limits Show that $\displaystyle\lim_{(x,y)\to(0,0)} \frac{ax^my^n}{bx^{m+n} + cy^{m+n}}$ does not exist when a, b, and c are nonzero real numbers and m and n are positive integers.

76. Nonexistence of limits Show that $\displaystyle\lim_{(x,y)\to(0,0)} \frac{ax^{2(p-n)}y^n}{bx^{2p} + cy^p}$ does not exist when a, b, and c are nonzero real numbers and n and p are positive integers with $p \geq n$.

77–80. Limits of composite functions *Evaluate the following limits.*

77. $\displaystyle\lim_{(x,y)\to(1,0)} \frac{\sin xy}{xy}$

78. $\displaystyle\lim_{(x,y)\to(4,0)} x^2y \ln xy$

79. $\displaystyle\lim_{(x,y)\to(0,2)} (2xy)^{xy}$

80. $\displaystyle\lim_{(x,y)\to(0,\pi/2)} \frac{1 - \cos xy}{4x^2y^3}$

81. Filling in a function value The domain of $f(x, y) = e^{-1/(x^2+y^2)}$ excludes $(0, 0)$. How should f be defined at $(0, 0)$ to make it continuous there?

82. Limit proof Use the formal definition of a limit to prove that $\displaystyle\lim_{(x,y)\to(a,b)} y = b$. (*Hint:* Take $\delta = \varepsilon$.)

83. Limit proof Use the formal definition of a limit to prove that $\displaystyle\lim_{(x,y)\to(a,b)} (x + y) = a + b$. (*Hint:* Take $\delta = \varepsilon/2$.)

84. Proof of Limit Law 1 Use the formal definition of a limit to prove that $\displaystyle\lim_{(x,y)\to(a,b)} (f(x, y) + g(x, y)) = \lim_{(x,y)\to(a,b)} f(x, y) + \lim_{(x,y)\to(a,b)} g(x, y)$.

85. Proof of Limit Law 3 Use the formal definition of a limit to prove that $\displaystyle\lim_{(x,y)\to(a,b)} cf(x, y) = c \lim_{(x,y)\to(a,b)} f(x, y)$.

QUICK CHECK ANSWERS

1. The limit exists only for (a). **2.** $\{(x, y): x^2 + y^2 < 2\}$ **3.** If a factor of x is first canceled, then the limit may be evaluated by substitution. **4.** If the left and right limits at a point are not equal, then the two-sided limit does not exist. **5.** (a) and (b) are continuous at $(0, 0)$. ◄

12.4 Partial Derivatives

The derivative of a function of one variable, $y = f(x)$, measures the rate of change of y with respect to x, and it gives slopes of tangent lines. The analogous idea for functions of several variables presents a new twist: Derivatives may be defined with respect to any of the independent variables. For example, we can compute the derivative of $f(x, y)$ with respect to x or y. The resulting derivatives are called *partial derivatives*; they still represent rates of change and they are associated with slopes of tangents. Therefore, much of what you have learned about derivatives applies to functions of several variables. However, much is also different.

Derivatives with Two Variables

Consider a function f defined on a domain D in the xy-plane. Suppose that f represents the elevation of the land (above sea level) over D. Imagine that you are on the surface $z = f(x, y)$ at the point $(a, b, f(a, b))$ and you are asked to determine the slope of the surface where you are standing. Your answer should be, *it depends*!

Figure 12.48a shows a function that resembles the landscape in Figure 12.48b. Suppose you are standing at the point $P(0, 0, f(0, 0))$, which lies on the pass or the saddle. The surface behaves differently depending on the direction in which you walk. If you walk east (positive x-direction), the elevation increases and your path takes you upward on the surface. If you walk north (positive y-direction), the elevation decreases and your path takes you downward on the surface. In fact, in every direction you walk from the point P, the function values change at different rates. So how should the slope or the rate of change at a given point be defined?

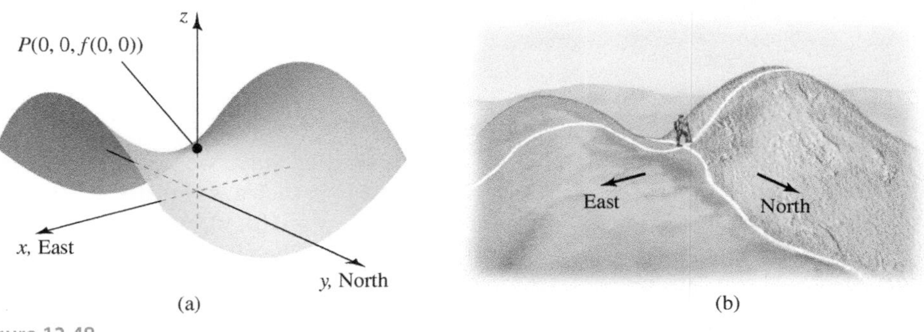

Figure 12.48

The answer to this question involves *partial derivatives*, which arise when we hold all but one independent variable fixed and then compute an ordinary derivative with respect to the remaining variable. Suppose we move along the surface $z = f(x, y)$, starting at the point $(a, b, f(a, b))$ in such a way that $y = b$ is fixed and only x varies. The resulting path is a curve (a trace) on the surface that varies in the x-direction (Figure 12.49). This curve is the intersection of the surface with the vertical plane $y = b$; it is described by $z = f(x, b)$, which is a function of the single variable x. We know how to compute the slope of this curve: It is the ordinary derivative of $f(x, b)$ with respect to x. This derivative is called the *partial derivative of f with respect to x*, denoted $\partial f/\partial x$ or f_x. When evaluated at (a, b), its value is defined by the limit

$$f_x(a, b) = \lim_{h \to 0} \frac{f(a + h, b) - f(a, b)}{h},$$

provided this limit exists. Notice that the y-coordinate is fixed at $y = b$ in this limit. If we replace (a, b) with the variable point (x, y), then f_x becomes a function of x and y.

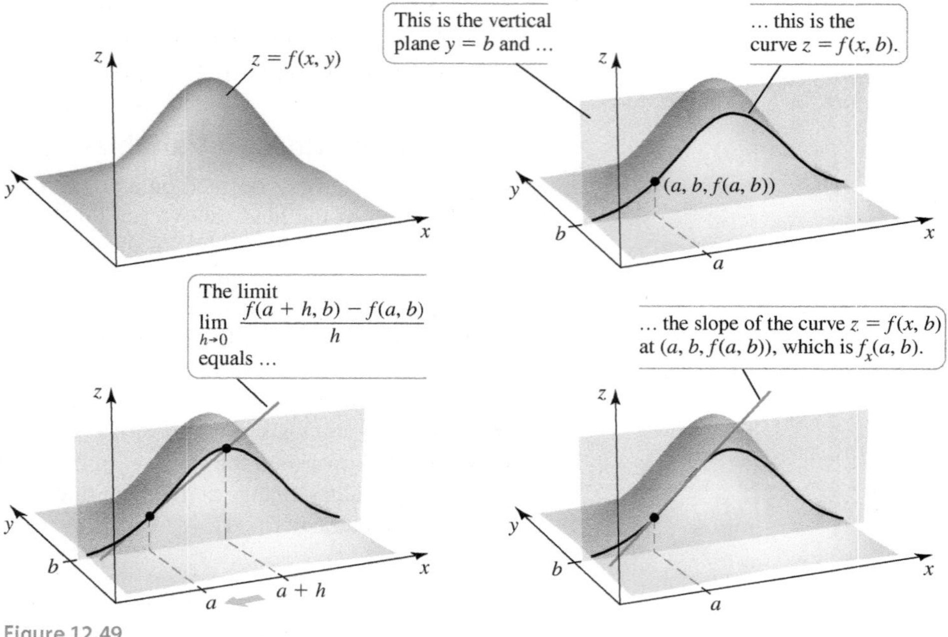

Figure 12.49

In a similar way, we can move along the surface $z = f(x, y)$ from the point $(a, b, f(a, b))$ in such a way that $x = a$ is fixed and only y varies. Now the result is a trace described by $z = f(a, y)$, which is the intersection of the surface and the plane $x = a$ (Figure 12.50). The slope of this curve at (a, b) is given by the ordinary derivative of $f(a, y)$ with respect to y. This derivative is called the *partial derivative of f with respect to y*, denoted $\partial f/\partial y$ or f_y. When evaluated at (a, b), it is defined by the limit

$$f_y(a, b) = \lim_{h \to 0} \frac{f(a, b + h) - f(a, b)}{h},$$

provided this limit exists. If we replace (a, b) with the variable point (x, y), then f_y becomes a function of x and y.

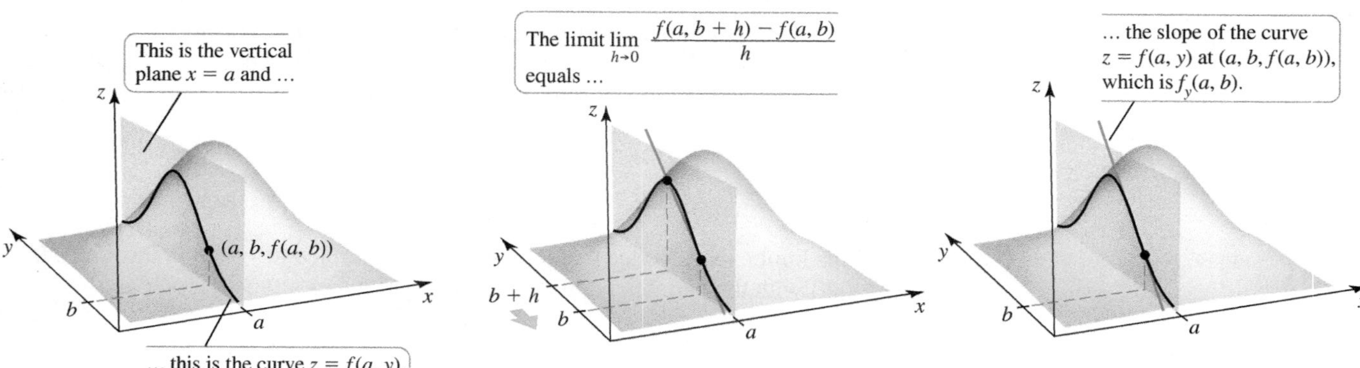

Figure 12.50

> **DEFINITION Partial Derivatives**
>
> The **partial derivative of f with respect to x at the point (a, b)** is
>
> $$f_x(a, b) = \lim_{h \to 0} \frac{f(a + h, b) - f(a, b)}{h}.$$
>
> The **partial derivative of f with respect to y at the point (a, b)** is
>
> $$f_y(a, b) = \lim_{h \to 0} \frac{f(a, b + h) - f(a, b)}{h},$$
>
> provided these limits exist.

➤ Recall that f' is a function, while $f'(a)$ is the value of the derivative at $x = a$. In the same way, f_x and f_y are functions of x and y, while $f_x(a, b)$ and $f_y(a, b)$ are their values at (a, b).

Notation The partial derivatives evaluated at a point (a, b) are denoted in any of the following ways:

$$\frac{\partial f}{\partial x}(a, b) = \left.\frac{\partial f}{\partial x}\right|_{(a,b)} = f_x(a, b) \quad \text{and} \quad \frac{\partial f}{\partial y}(a, b) = \left.\frac{\partial f}{\partial y}\right|_{(a,b)} = f_y(a, b).$$

Notice that the d in the ordinary derivative df/dx has been replaced with ∂ in the partial derivatives $\partial f/\partial x$ and $\partial f/\partial y$. The notation $\partial/\partial x$ is an instruction or operator: It says, "take the partial derivative with respect to x of the function that follows."

Calculating Partial Derivatives We begin by calculating partial derivatives using the limit definition. The procedure in Example 1 should look familiar. It echoes the method used in Chapter 3 when we first introduced ordinary derivatives.

EXAMPLE 1 Partial derivatives from the definition Suppose $f(x, y) = x^2y$. Use the limit definition of partial derivatives to compute $f_x(x, y)$ and $f_y(x, y)$.

SOLUTION We compute the partial derivatives at an arbitrary point (x, y) in the domain. The partial derivative with respect to x is

$$\begin{aligned}
f_x(x, y) &= \lim_{h \to 0} \frac{f(x + h, y) - f(x, y)}{h} && \text{Definition of } f_x \text{ at } (x, y) \\
&= \lim_{h \to 0} \frac{(x + h)^2 y - x^2 y}{h} && \text{Substitute for } f(x + h, y) \text{ and } f(x, y). \\
&= \lim_{h \to 0} \frac{(x^2 + 2xh + h^2 - x^2)y}{h} && \text{Factor and expand.} \\
&= \lim_{h \to 0} (2x + h)y && \text{Simplify and cancel } h. \\
&= 2xy. && \text{Evaluate limit.}
\end{aligned}$$

In a similar way, the partial derivative with respect to y is

$$\begin{aligned}
f_y(x, y) &= \lim_{h \to 0} \frac{f(x, y + h) - f(x, y)}{h} && \text{Definition of } f_y \text{ at } (x, y) \\
&= \lim_{h \to 0} \frac{x^2(y + h) - x^2 y}{h} && \text{Substitute for } f(x, y + h) \text{ and } f(x, y). \\
&= \lim_{h \to 0} \frac{x^2(y + h - y)}{h} && \text{Factor.} \\
&= x^2. && \text{Simplify and evaluate limit.}
\end{aligned}$$

Related Exercises 7–10 ◀

A careful examination of Example 1 reveals a shortcut for evaluating partial derivatives. To compute the partial derivative of f with respect to x, we treat y as a constant and take an ordinary derivative with respect to x:

$$\frac{\partial}{\partial x}(x^2y) = y\underbrace{\frac{\partial}{\partial x}(x^2)}_{2x} = 2xy. \quad \text{Treat } y \text{ as a constant.}$$

Similarly, we treat x (and therefore x^2) as a constant to evaluate the partial derivative of f with respect to y:

$$\frac{\partial}{\partial y}(x^2y) = x^2\underbrace{\frac{\partial}{\partial y}(y)}_{1} = x^2. \quad \text{Treat } x \text{ as a constant.}$$

The next two examples illustrate the process.

EXAMPLE 2 **Partial derivatives** Let $f(x, y) = x^3 - y^2 + 4$.

a. Compute $\dfrac{\partial f}{\partial x}$ and $\dfrac{\partial f}{\partial y}$.

b. Evaluate each derivative at $(2, -4)$.

SOLUTION

a. We compute the partial derivative with respect to x assuming that y is a constant; the Power Rule gives

$$\frac{\partial f}{\partial x} = \frac{\partial}{\partial x}(\underbrace{x^3}_{\text{variable}} - \underbrace{y^2 + 4}_{\substack{\text{constant with}\\ \text{respect to } x}}) = 3x^2 + 0 = 3x^2.$$

The partial derivative with respect to y is computed by treating x as a constant; using the Power Rule gives

$$\frac{\partial f}{\partial y} = \frac{\partial}{\partial y}(\underbrace{x^3}_{\substack{\text{constant}\\ \text{with respect}\\ \text{to } y}} - \underbrace{y^2}_{\text{variable}} + \underbrace{4}_{\text{constant}}) = -2y.$$

QUICK CHECK 1 Compute f_x and f_y for $f(x, y) = 2xy$. ◄

b. It follows that $f_x(2, -4) = (3x^2)|_{(2,-4)} = 12$ and $f_y(2, -4) = (-2y)|_{(2,-4)} = 8$.

Related Exercises 11–28 ◄

EXAMPLE 3 **Partial derivatives** Compute the partial derivatives of the following functions.

a. $f(x, y) = \sin xy$

b. $g(x, y) = x^2e^{xy}$

SOLUTION

a. Treating y as a constant and differentiating with respect to x, we have

$$\frac{\partial f}{\partial x} = \frac{\partial}{\partial x}(\sin xy) = y \cos xy.$$

➤ Recall that

$$\frac{d}{dx}(\sin 2x) = 2 \cos 2x.$$

Replacing 2 with the constant y, we have

$$\frac{\partial}{\partial x}(\sin xy) = y \cos xy.$$

Holding x fixed and differentiating with respect to y, we have

$$\frac{\partial f}{\partial y} = \frac{\partial}{\partial y}(\sin xy) = x \cos xy.$$

b. To compute the partial derivative with respect to x, we call on the Product Rule. Holding y fixed, we have

$$\begin{aligned}\frac{\partial g}{\partial x} &= \frac{\partial}{\partial x}(x^2e^{xy}) \\ &= \frac{\partial}{\partial x}(x^2)e^{xy} + x^2\frac{\partial}{\partial x}(e^{xy}) && \text{Product Rule} \\ &= 2xe^{xy} + x^2ye^{xy} && \text{Evaluate partial derivatives.} \\ &= xe^{xy}(2 + xy). && \text{Simplify.}\end{aligned}$$

➤ Because x and y are *independent* variables,

$$\frac{\partial}{\partial x}(y) = 0 \quad \text{and} \quad \frac{\partial}{\partial y}(x) = 0.$$

Treating x as a constant, the partial derivative with respect to y is

$$\frac{\partial g}{\partial y} = \frac{\partial}{\partial y}(x^2e^{xy}) = x^2\underbrace{\frac{\partial}{\partial y}(e^{xy})}_{xe^{xy}} = x^3e^{xy}.$$

Related Exercises 11–28 ◄

Higher-Order Partial Derivatives

Just as we have higher-order derivatives of functions of one variable, we also have higher-order partial derivatives. For example, given a function f and its partial derivative f_x, we can take the derivative of f_x with respect to x or with respect to y, which accounts for two of the four possible *second-order partial derivatives*. Table 12.4 summarizes the notation for second partial derivatives.

Table 12.4

Notation 1	Notation 2	What we say ...
$\frac{\partial}{\partial x}\left(\frac{\partial f}{\partial x}\right) = \frac{\partial^2 f}{\partial x^2}$	$(f_x)_x = f_{xx}$	*d squared f dx squared* or *f-x-x*
$\frac{\partial}{\partial y}\left(\frac{\partial f}{\partial y}\right) = \frac{\partial^2 f}{\partial y^2}$	$(f_y)_y = f_{yy}$	*d squared f dy squared* or *f-y-y*
$\frac{\partial}{\partial x}\left(\frac{\partial f}{\partial y}\right) = \frac{\partial^2 f}{\partial x \partial y}$	$(f_y)_x = f_{yx}$	*f-y-x*
$\frac{\partial}{\partial y}\left(\frac{\partial f}{\partial x}\right) = \frac{\partial^2 f}{\partial y \partial x}$	$(f_x)_y = f_{xy}$	*f-x-y*

The order of differentiation can make a difference in the **mixed partial derivatives** f_{xy} and f_{yx}. So it is important to use the correct notation to reflect the order in which derivatives are taken. For example, the notations $\frac{\partial^2 f}{\partial x \partial y}$ and f_{yx} both mean $\frac{\partial}{\partial x}\left(\frac{\partial f}{\partial y}\right)$; that is, differentiate first with respect to y, then with respect to x.

QUICK CHECK 2 Which of the following expressions are equivalent to each other: (a) f_{xy}, (b) f_{yx}, or (c) $\frac{\partial^2 f}{\partial y \partial x}$? Write $\frac{\partial^2 f}{\partial p \partial q}$ in subscript notation. ◄

EXAMPLE 4 **Second partial derivatives** Find the four second partial derivatives of $f(x, y) = 3x^4y - 2xy + 5xy^3$.

SOLUTION First, we compute

$$\frac{\partial f}{\partial x} = \frac{\partial}{\partial x}(3x^4y - 2xy + 5xy^3) = 12x^3y - 2y + 5y^3$$

and

$$\frac{\partial f}{\partial y} = \frac{\partial}{\partial y}(3x^4y - 2xy + 5xy^3) = 3x^4 - 2x + 15xy^2.$$

For the second partial derivatives, we have

$$\frac{\partial^2 f}{\partial x^2} = \frac{\partial}{\partial x}\left(\frac{\partial f}{\partial x}\right) = \frac{\partial}{\partial x}(12x^3y - 2y + 5y^3) = 36x^2y,$$

$$\frac{\partial^2 f}{\partial y^2} = \frac{\partial}{\partial y}\left(\frac{\partial f}{\partial y}\right) = \frac{\partial}{\partial y}(3x^4 - 2x + 15xy^2) = 30xy,$$

$$\frac{\partial^2 f}{\partial x \partial y} = \frac{\partial}{\partial x}\left(\frac{\partial f}{\partial y}\right) = \frac{\partial}{\partial x}(3x^4 - 2x + 15xy^2) = 12x^3 - 2 + 15y^2, \text{ and}$$

$$\frac{\partial^2 f}{\partial y \partial x} = \frac{\partial}{\partial y}\left(\frac{\partial f}{\partial x}\right) = \frac{\partial}{\partial y}(12x^3y - 2y + 5y^3) = 12x^3 - 2 + 15y^2.$$

Related Exercises 29–44 ◄

QUICK CHECK 3 Compute f_{xxx} and f_{xxy} for $f(x, y) = x^3y$. ◄

Equality of Mixed Partial Derivatives Notice that the two mixed partial derivatives in Example 4 are equal; that is, $f_{xy} = f_{yx}$. It turns out that most of the functions we encounter in this book have this property. Sufficient conditions for equality of mixed partial derivatives are given in a theorem attributed to the French mathematician Alexis Clairaut (1713–1765). The proof is found in advanced texts.

> **THEOREM 12.4 (Clairaut) Equality of Mixed Partial Derivatives**
> Assume that f is defined on an open set D of $\mathbb{R}^2$, and that f_{xy} and f_{yx} are continuous throughout D. Then $f_{xy} = f_{yx}$ at all points of D.

Assuming sufficient continuity, Theorem 12.4 can be extended to higher derivatives of f. For example, $f_{xyx} = f_{xxy} = f_{yxx}$.

Functions of Three Variables

Everything we learned about partial derivatives of functions with two variables carries over to functions of three or more variables, as illustrated in Example 5.

EXAMPLE 5 Partial derivatives with more than two variables Find f_x, f_y, and f_z when $f(x, y, z) = e^{-xy}\cos z$.

SOLUTION To find f_x, we treat y and z as constants and differentiate with respect to x:

$$\frac{\partial f}{\partial x} = \frac{\partial}{\partial x}(\underbrace{e^{-xy}}_{y \text{ is constant}} \underbrace{\cos z}_{\text{constant}}) = -ye^{-xy}\cos z.$$

Holding x and z constant and differentiating with respect to y, we have

$$\frac{\partial f}{\partial y} = \frac{\partial}{\partial y}(\underbrace{e^{-xy}}_{x \text{ is constant}} \underbrace{\cos z}_{\text{constant}}) = -xe^{-xy}\cos z.$$

To find f_z, we hold x and y constant and differentiate with respect to z:

$$\frac{\partial f}{\partial z} = \frac{\partial}{\partial z}(\underbrace{e^{-xy}}_{\text{constant}} \cos z) = -e^{-xy}\sin z.$$

Related Exercises 45–54 ◄

QUICK CHECK 4 Compute f_{xz} and f_{zz} for $f(x, y, z) = xyz - x^2z + yz^2$. ◄

Applications of Partial Derivatives When functions are used in realistic applications (for example, to describe velocity, pressure, investment fund balance, or population), they often involve more than one independent variable. For this reason, partial derivatives appear frequently in mathematical modeling.

EXAMPLE 6 **Ideal Gas Law** The pressure P, volume V, and temperature T of an ideal gas are related by the equation $PV = kT$, where $k > 0$ is a constant depending on the amount of gas.

a. Determine the rate of change of the pressure with respect to the volume at constant temperature. Interpret the result.

b. Determine the rate of change of the pressure with respect to the temperature at constant volume. Interpret the result.

c. Explain these results using level curves.

➤ Implicit differentiation can also be used with partial derivatives. Instead of solving for P, we could differentiate both sides of $PV = kT$ with respect to V holding T fixed. Using the Product Rule, $P + VP_V = 0$, which implies that $P_V = -P/V$. Substituting $P = kT/V$, we have $P_V = -kT/V^2$.

SOLUTION Expressing the pressure as a function of volume and temperature, we have $P = k\frac{T}{V}$.

a. We find the partial derivative $\partial P/\partial V$ by holding T constant and differentiating P with respect to V:

$$\frac{\partial P}{\partial V} = \frac{\partial}{\partial V}\left(k\frac{T}{V}\right) = kT\frac{\partial}{\partial V}(V^{-1}) = -\frac{kT}{V^2}.$$

➤ In the Ideal Gas Law, temperature is a positive variable because it is measured in degrees Kelvin.

Recognizing that P, V, and T are always positive, we see that $\frac{\partial P}{\partial V} < 0$, which means that the pressure is a decreasing function of volume at a constant temperature.

b. The partial derivative $\partial P/\partial T$ is found by holding V constant and differentiating P with respect to T:

$$\frac{\partial P}{\partial T} = \frac{\partial}{\partial T}\left(k\frac{T}{V}\right) = \frac{k}{V}.$$

In this case, $\partial P/\partial T > 0$, which says that the pressure is an increasing function of temperature at constant volume.

c. The level curves (Section 12.2) of the pressure function are curves in the VT-plane that satisfy $k\frac{T}{V} = P_0$, where P_0 is a constant. Solving for T, the level curves are given by $T = \frac{1}{k}P_0V$. Because $\frac{P_0}{k}$ is a positive constant, the level curves are lines in the first quadrant (Figure 12.51) with slope P_0/k. The fact that $\frac{\partial P}{\partial V} < 0$ (from part (a)) means that if we hold $T > 0$ fixed and move in the direction of increasing V on a *horizontal* line, we cross level curves corresponding to decreasing pressures. Similarly, $\frac{\partial P}{\partial T} > 0$ (from part (b)) means that if we hold $V > 0$ fixed and move in the direction of increasing T on a *vertical* line, we cross level curves corresponding to increasing pressures.

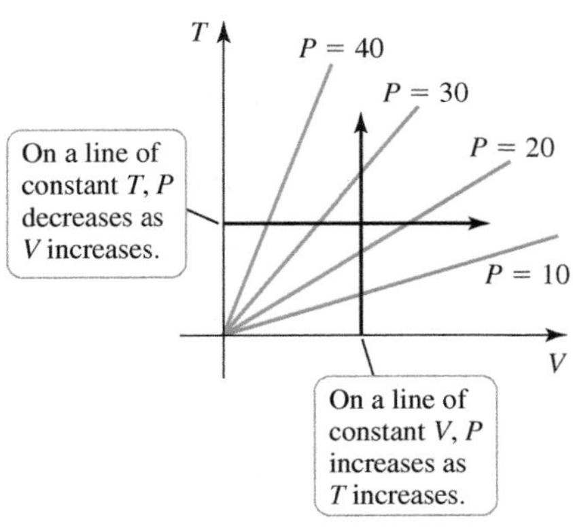

Figure 12.51

Related Exercises 51–52 ◄

QUICK CHECK 5 Explain why, in Figure 12.51, the slopes of the level curves increase as the pressure increases. ◄

Differentiability

We close this section with a technical matter that bears on the remainder of the chapter. Although we know how to compute partial derivatives of a function of several variables, we have not said what it means for such a function to be *differentiable* at a point. It is tempting to conclude that if the partial derivatives f_x and f_y exist at a point, then f is differentiable there. However, it is not so simple.

Recall that a function f of one variable is differentiable at $x = a$ provided the limit

$$f'(a) = \lim_{\Delta x \to 0} \frac{f(a + \Delta x) - f(a)}{\Delta x}$$

exists. If f is differentiable at a, it means that the curve is smooth at the point $(a, f(a))$ (no jumps, corners, or cusps); furthermore, the curve has a unique tangent line at that point with slope $f'(a)$. Differentiability for a function of several variables should carry the same properties: The surface should be smooth at the point in question and something analogous to a unique tangent line should exist at the point.

Staying with the one-variable case, we define the quantity

$$\varepsilon = \underbrace{\frac{f(a + \Delta x) - f(a)}{\Delta x}}_{\text{slope of secant line}} - \underbrace{f'(a)}_{\text{slope of tangent line}},$$

where ε is viewed as a function of Δx. Notice that ε is the difference between the slopes of secant lines and the slope of the tangent line at the point $(a, f(a))$. If f is differentiable at a, then this difference approaches zero as $\Delta x \to 0$; therefore, $\lim_{\Delta x \to 0} \varepsilon = 0$. Multiplying both sides of the definition of ε by Δx gives

$$\varepsilon \Delta x = f(a + \Delta x) - f(a) - f'(a)\,\Delta x.$$

Rearranging, we have the change in the function $y = f(x)$:

$$\Delta y = f(a + \Delta x) - f(a) = f'(a)\,\Delta x + \underbrace{\varepsilon}_{\varepsilon \to 0 \text{ as } \Delta x \to 0}\,\Delta x.$$

➤ Notice that $f'(a)\,\Delta x$ is the approximate change in the function given by a linear approximation.

This expression says that in the one-variable case, if f is differentiable at a, then the change in f between a and a nearby point $a + \Delta x$ is represented by $f'(a)\,\Delta x$ plus a quantity $\varepsilon\,\Delta x$, where $\lim_{\Delta x \to 0} \varepsilon = 0$.

The analogous requirement with several variables is the definition of differentiability for functions or two (or more) variables.

DEFINITION Differentiability

The function $z = f(x, y)$ is **differentiable at (a, b)** provided $f_x(a, b)$ and $f_y(a, b)$ exist and the change $\Delta z = f(a + \Delta x, b + \Delta y) - f(a, b)$ equals

$$\Delta z = f_x(a, b)\,\Delta x + f_y(a, b)\,\Delta y + \varepsilon_1 \Delta x + \varepsilon_2 \Delta y,$$

where for fixed a and b, ε_1 and ε_2 are functions that depend only on Δx and Δy, with $(\varepsilon_1, \varepsilon_2) \to (0, 0)$ as $(\Delta x, \Delta y) \to (0, 0)$. A function is **differentiable** on an open set R if it is differentiable at every point of R.

Several observations are needed here. First, the definition extends to functions of more than two variables. Second, we show how differentiability is related to linear approximation and the existence of a *tangent plane* in Section 12.7. Finally, the conditions of the definition are generally difficult to verify. The following theorem may be useful in checking differentiability.

> **THEOREM 12.5 Conditions for Differentiability**
> Suppose the function f has partial derivatives f_x and f_y defined on an open set containing (a, b), with f_x and f_y continuous at (a, b). Then f is differentiable at (a, b).

As shown in Example 7, the existence of f_x and f_y at (a, b) is not enough to ensure differentiability of f at (a, b). However, by Theorem 12.5, if f_x and f_y are continuous at (a, b) (and defined in an open set containing (a, b)), then we can conclude f is differentiable there. Polynomials and rational functions are differentiable at all points of their domains, as are compositions of exponential, logarithmic, and trigonometric functions with other differentiable functions. The proof of this theorem is given in Appendix B.

We close with the analog of Theorem 3.1, which states that differentiability implies continuity.

> **THEOREM 12.6 Differentiable Implies Continuous**
> If a function f is differentiable at (a, b), then it is continuous at (a, b).

Proof: By the definition of differentiability,

$$\Delta z = f_x(a, b)\,\Delta x + f_y(a, b)\,\Delta y + \varepsilon_1 \Delta x + \varepsilon_2 \Delta y,$$

where $(\varepsilon_1, \varepsilon_2) \to (0, 0)$ as $(\Delta x, \Delta y) \to (0, 0)$. Because f is assumed to be differentiable, as Δx and Δy approach 0, we see that

$$\lim_{(\Delta x, \Delta y) \to (0,0)} \Delta z = 0.$$

➤ Recall that continuity requires that $\lim_{(x,y) \to (a,b)} f(x, y) = f(a, b)$, which is equivalent to $\lim_{(\Delta x, \Delta y) \to (0,0)} f(a + \Delta x, b + \Delta y) = f(a, b)$.

Also, because $\Delta z = f(a + \Delta x, b + \Delta y) - f(a, b)$, it follows that

$$\lim_{(\Delta x, \Delta y) \to (0,0)} f(a + \Delta x, b + \Delta y) = f(a, b),$$

which implies continuity of f at (a, b). ◄

EXAMPLE 7 A nondifferentiable function Discuss the differentiability and continuity of the function

$$f(x, y) = \begin{cases} \dfrac{3xy}{x^2 + y^2} & \text{if } (x, y) \neq (0, 0) \\ 0 & \text{if } (x, y) = (0, 0). \end{cases}$$

SOLUTION As a rational function, f is continuous and differentiable at all points $(x, y) \neq (0, 0)$. The interesting behavior occurs at the origin. Using calculations similar to those in Example 4 in Section 12.3, it can be shown that if the origin is approached along the line $y = mx$, then

$$\lim_{\substack{(x,y) \to (0,0) \\ (\text{along } y = mx)}} \frac{3xy}{x^2 + y^2} = \frac{3m}{m^2 + 1}.$$

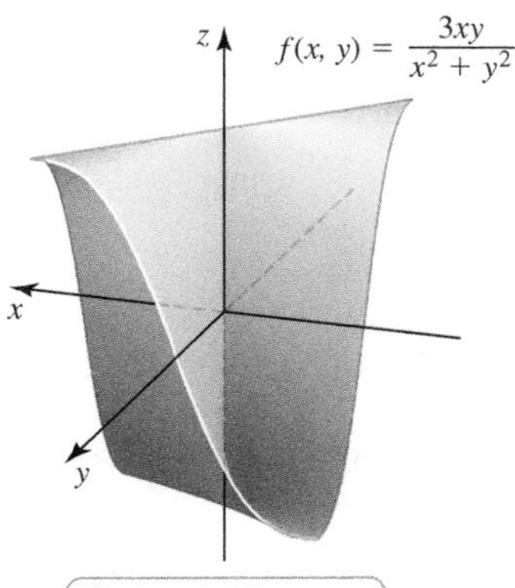

f is not continuous at (0, 0), even though $f_x(0, 0) = f_y(0, 0) = 0$.

Figure 12.52

Therefore, the value of the limit depends on the direction of approach, which implies that the limit does not exist, and f is not continuous at $(0, 0)$. By Theorem 12.6, it follows that f is not differentiable at $(0, 0)$. Figure 12.52 shows the discontinuity of f at the origin.

Let's look at the first partial derivatives of f at $(0, 0)$. A short calculation shows that

$$f_x(0, 0) = \lim_{h \to 0} \frac{f(0 + h, 0) - f(0, 0)}{h} = \lim_{h \to 0} \frac{0 - 0}{h} = 0,$$

$$f_y(0, 0) = \lim_{h \to 0} \frac{f(0, 0 + h) - f(0, 0)}{h} = \lim_{h \to 0} \frac{0 - 0}{h} = 0.$$

➤ The relationships between the existence and continuity of partial derivatives and whether a function is differentiable are further explored in Exercises 90–91.

Despite the fact that its first partial derivatives exist at $(0, 0)$, f is not differentiable at $(0, 0)$. As noted earlier, the existence of first partial derivatives at a point is not enough to ensure differentiability at that point.

Related Exercises 57–58 ◀

SECTION 12.4 EXERCISES

Review Questions

1. Suppose you are standing on the surface $z = f(x, y)$ at the point $(a, b, f(a, b))$. Interpret the meaning of $f_x(a, b)$ and $f_y(a, b)$ in terms of slopes or rates of change.
2. Find f_x and f_y when $f(x, y) = 3x^2y + xy^3$.
3. Find f_x and f_y when $f(x, y) = x \cos xy$.
4. Find the four second partial derivatives of $f(x, y) = 3x^2y + xy^3$.
5. Explain how you would evaluate f_z for the differentiable function $w = f(x, y, z)$.
6. The volume of a right circular cylinder with radius r and height h is $V = \pi r^2 h$. Is the volume an increasing or decreasing function of the radius at a fixed height (assume $r > 0$ and $h > 0$)?

Basic Skills

7–10. Evaluating partial derivatives using limits *Use the limit definition of partial derivatives to evaluate $f_x(x, y)$ and $f_y(x, y)$ for each of the following functions.*

7. $f(x, y) = 5xy$
8. $f(x, y) = x + y^2 + 4$
9. $f(x, y) = \dfrac{x}{y}$
10. $f(x, y) = \sqrt{xy}$

11–28. Partial derivatives *Find the first partial derivatives of the following functions.*

11. $f(x, y) = 3x^2 + 4y^3$
12. $f(x, y) = x^2y$
13. $f(x, y) = 3x^2y + 2$
14. $f(x, y) = y^8 + 2x^6 + 2xy$
15. $f(x, y) = xe^y$
16. $f(x, y) = \ln (x/y)$
17. $g(x, y) = \cos 2xy$
18. $h(x, y) = (y^2 + 1)\, e^x$
19. $f(x, y) = e^{x^2y}$
20. $f(s, t) = \dfrac{s - t}{s + t}$
21. $f(w, z) = \dfrac{w}{w^2 + z^2}$
22. $g(x, z) = x \ln (z^2 + x^2)$
23. $s(y, z) = z^2 \tan yz$
24. $F(p, q) = \sqrt{p^2 + pq + q^2}$
25. $G(s, t) = \dfrac{\sqrt{st}}{s + t}$
26. $h(u, v) = \sqrt{\dfrac{uv}{u - v}}$
27. $f(x, y) = x^{2y}$
28. $f(x, y) = \sqrt{x^2y^3}$

29–38. Second partial derivatives *Find the four second partial derivatives of the following functions.*

29. $h(x, y) = x^3 + xy^2 + 1$
30. $f(x, y) = 2x^5y^2 + x^2y$
31. $f(x, y) = x^2y^3$
32. $f(x, y) = (x + 3y)^2$
33. $f(x, y) = y^3 \sin 4x$
34. $f(x, y) = \cos xy$
35. $p(u, v) = \ln (u^2 + v^2 + 4)$
36. $Q(r, s) = r/s$
37. $F(r, s) = re^s$
38. $H(x, y) = \sqrt{4 + x^2 + y^2}$

39–44. Equality of mixed partial derivatives *Verify that $f_{xy} = f_{yx}$ for the following functions.*

39. $f(x, y) = 2x^3 + 3y^2 + 1$
40. $f(x, y) = xe^y$
41. $f(x, y) = \cos xy$
42. $f(x, y) = 3x^2y^{-1} - 2x^{-1}y^2$
43. $f(x, y) = e^{x+y}$
44. $f(x, y) = \sqrt{xy}$

45–54. Partial derivatives with more than two variables *Find the first partial derivatives of the following functions.*

45. $f(x, y, z) = xy + xz + yz$
46. $g(x, y, z) = 2x^2y - 3xz^4 + 10y^2z^2$
47. $h(x, y, z) = \cos (x + y + z)$
48. $Q(x, y, z) = \tan xyz$
49. $F(u, v, w) = \dfrac{u}{v + w}$
50. $G(r, s, t) = \sqrt{rs + rt + st}$
51. $f(w, x, y, z) = w^2xy^2 + xy^3z^2$
52. $g(w, x, y, z) = \cos (w + x) \sin (y - z)$
53. $h(w, x, y, z) = \dfrac{wz}{xy}$
54. $F(w, x, y, z) = w\sqrt{x + 2y + 3z}$

55. **Gas law calculations** Consider the Ideal Gas Law $PV = kT$, where $k > 0$ is a constant. Solve this equation for V in terms of P and T.
    a. Determine the rate of change of the volume with respect to the pressure at constant temperature. Interpret the result.
    b. Determine the rate of change of the volume with respect to the temperature at constant pressure. Interpret the result.
    c. Assuming $k = 1$, draw several level curves of the volume function and interpret the results as in Example 5.

56. **Volume of a box** A box with a square base of length x and height h has a volume $V = x^2h$.
    a. Compute the partial derivatives V_x and V_h.
    b. For a box with $h = 1.5$ m, use linear approximation to estimate the change in volume if x increases from $x = 0.5$ m to $x = 0.51$ m.
    c. For a box with $x = 0.5$ m, use linear approximation to estimate the change in volume if h decreases from $h = 1.5$ m to $h = 1.49$ m.
    d. For a fixed height, does a 10% change in x always produce (approximately) a 10% change in V? Explain.
    e. For a fixed base length, does a 10% change in h always produce (approximately) a 10% change in V? Explain.

57–58. Nondifferentiability? *Consider the following functions f.*

a. Is f continuous at (0, 0)?
b. Is f differentiable at (0, 0)?
c. If possible, evaluate $f_x(0,0)$ and $f_y(0,0)$.
d. Determine whether f_x and f_y are continuous at (0, 0).
e. Explain why Theorems 12.5 and 12.6 are consistent with the results in parts (a)–(d).

57. $f(x,y) = \begin{cases} -\dfrac{xy}{x^2+y^2} & \text{if } (x,y) \neq (0,0) \\ 0 & \text{if } (x,y) = (0,0) \end{cases}$

58. $f(x,y) = \begin{cases} \dfrac{2xy^2}{x^2+y^4} & \text{if } (x,y) \neq (0,0) \\ 0 & \text{if } (x,y) = (0,0) \end{cases}$

Further Explorations

59. Explain why or why not Determine whether the following statements are true and give an explanation or counterexample.

a. $\dfrac{\partial}{\partial x}(y^{10}) = 10y^9$. **b.** $\dfrac{\partial^2}{\partial x \partial y}(\sqrt{xy}) = \dfrac{1}{\sqrt{xy}}$.

c. If f has continuous partial derivatives of all orders, then $f_{xxy} = f_{yxx}$.

60–63. Estimating partial derivatives *The following table shows values of a function f(x, y) for values of x from 2 to 2.5 and values of y from 3 to 3.5. Use this table to estimate the values of the following partial derivates.*

y \ x	2	2.1	2.2	2.3	2.4	2.5
3	4.243	4.347	4.450	4.550	4.648	4.743
3.1	4.384	4.492	4.598	4.701	4.802	4.902
3.2	4.525	4.637	4.746	4.853	4.957	5.060
3.3	4.667	4.782	4.895	5.005	5.112	5.218
3.4	4.808	4.930	5.043	5.156	5.267	5.376
3.5	4.950	5.072	5.191	5.308	5.422	5.534

60. $f_x(2,3)$

61. $f_y(2,3)$

62. $f_x(2.2,3.4)$

63. $f_y(2.4,3.3)$

64–68. Miscellaneous partial derivatives *Compute the first partial derivatives of the following functions.*

64. $f(x,y) = \ln(1 + e^{-xy})$

65. $f(x,y) = 1 - \tan^{-1}(x^2 + y^2)$

66. $f(x,y) = 1 - \cos(2(x+y)) + \cos^2(x+y)$

67. $h(x,y,z) = (1 + x + 2y)^z$

68. $g(x,y,z) = \dfrac{4x - 2y - 2z}{3y - 6x - 3z}$

69. Partial derivatives and level curves Consider the function $z = x/y^2$.

a. Compute z_x and z_y.
b. Sketch the level curves for $z = 1, 2, 3$, and 4.
c. Move along the horizontal line $y = 1$ in the xy-plane and describe how the corresponding z-values change. Explain how this observation is consistent with z_x as computed in part (a).
d. Move along the vertical line $x = 1$ in the xy-plane and describe how the corresponding z-values change. Explain how this observation is consistent with z_y as computed in part (a).

70. Spherical caps The volume of the cap of a sphere of radius r and thickness h is $V = \dfrac{\pi}{3}h^2(3r - h)$, for $0 \le h \le 2r$.

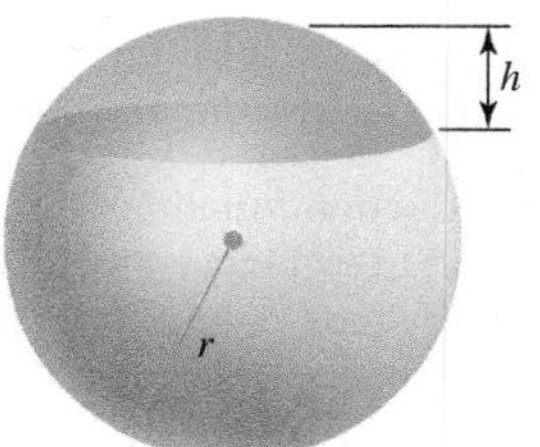

$V = \frac{\pi}{3}h^2(3r - h)$

a. Compute the partial derivatives V_h and V_r.
b. For a sphere of any radius, is the rate of change of volume with respect to r greater when $h = 0.2r$ or when $h = 0.8r$?
c. For a sphere of any radius, for what value of h is the rate of change of volume with respect to r equal to 1?
d. For a fixed radius r, for what value of h $(0 \le h \le 2r)$ is the rate of change of volume with respect to h the greatest?

71. Law of Cosines All triangles satisfy the Law of Cosines $c^2 = a^2 + b^2 - 2ab\cos\theta$ (see figure). Notice that when $\theta = \pi/2$, the Law of Cosines becomes the Pythagorean Theorem. Consider all triangles with a fixed angle $\theta = \pi/3$, in which case c is a function of a and b, where $a > 0$ and $b > 0$.

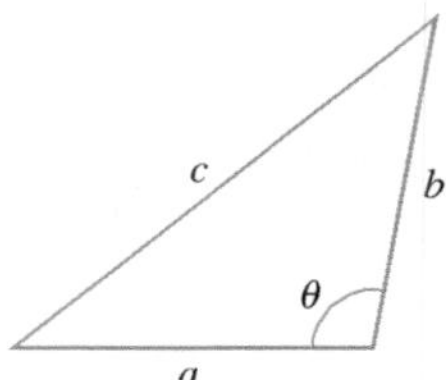

a. Compute $\dfrac{\partial c}{\partial a}$ and $\dfrac{\partial c}{\partial b}$ by solving for c and differentiating.
b. Compute $\dfrac{\partial c}{\partial a}$ and $\dfrac{\partial c}{\partial b}$ by implicit differentiation. Check for agreement with part (a).
c. What relationship between a and b makes c an increasing function of a (for constant b)?

Applications

72. Body mass index The body mass index (BMI) for an adult human is given by the function $B = w/h^2$, where w is the weight measured in kilograms and h is the height measured in meters. (The BMI for units of pounds and inches is $B = 703\,w/h^2$.)

a. Find the rate of change of the BMI with respect to weight at a constant height.
b. For fixed h, is the BMI an increasing or decreasing function of w? Explain.
c. Find the rate of change of the BMI with respect to height at a constant weight.
d. For fixed w, is the BMI an increasing or decreasing function of h? Explain.

73. Electric potential function The electric potential in the xy-plane associated with two positive charges, one at $(0, 1)$ with twice the magnitude as the charge at $(0, -1)$, is

$$\varphi(x, y) = \frac{2}{\sqrt{x^2 + (y - 1)^2}} + \frac{1}{\sqrt{x^2 + (y + 1)^2}}.$$

a. Compute φ_x and φ_y.
b. Describe how φ_x and φ_y behave as $x, y \to \pm\infty$.
c. Evaluate $\varphi_x(0, y)$, for all $y \neq \pm 1$. Interpret this result.
d. Evaluate $\varphi_y(x, 0)$, for all x. Interpret this result.

T **74. Cobb-Douglas production function** The output Q of an economic system subject to two inputs, such as labor L and capital K, is often modeled by the Cobb-Douglas production function $Q(L, K) = cL^aK^b$. Suppose $a = \frac{1}{3}$, $b = \frac{2}{3}$, and $c = 1$.

a. Evaluate the partial derivatives Q_L and Q_K.
b. Suppose $L = 10$ is fixed and K increases from $K = 20$ to $K = 20.5$. Use linear approximation to estimate the change in Q.
c. Suppose $K = 20$ is fixed and L decreases from $L = 10$ to $L = 9.5$. Use linear approximation to estimate the change in Q.
d. Graph the level curves of the production function in the first quadrant of the LK-plane for $Q = 1, 2$, and 3.
e. Use the graph of part (d). If you move along the vertical line $L = 2$ in the positive K-direction, how does Q change? Is this consistent with Q_K computed in part (a)?
f. Use the graph of part (d). If you move along the horizontal line $K = 2$ in the positive L-direction, how does Q change? Is this consistent with Q_L computed in part (a)?

75. Resistors in parallel Two resistors in an electrical circuit with resistance R_1 and R_2 wired in parallel with a constant voltage give an effective resistance of R, where $\frac{1}{R} = \frac{1}{R_1} + \frac{1}{R_2}$.

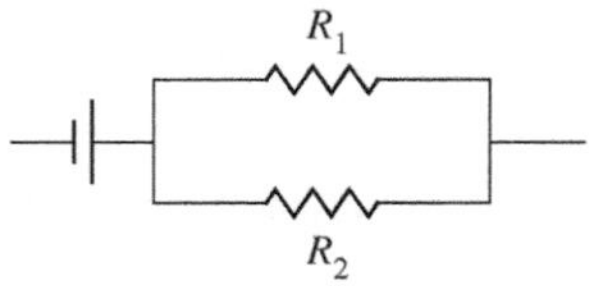

a. Find $\frac{\partial R}{\partial R_1}$ and $\frac{\partial R}{\partial R_2}$ by solving for R and differentiating.
b. Find $\frac{\partial R}{\partial R_1}$ and $\frac{\partial R}{\partial R_2}$ by differentiating implicitly.
c. Describe how an increase in R_1 with R_2 constant affects R.
d. Describe how a decrease in R_2 with R_1 constant affects R.

76. Wave on a string Imagine a string that is fixed at both ends (for example, a guitar string). When plucked, the string forms a standing wave. The displacement u of the string varies with position x and with time t. Suppose it is given by $u = f(x, t) = 2 \sin(\pi x) \sin(\pi t/2)$, for $0 \leq x \leq 1$ and $t \geq 0$ (see figure). At a fixed point in time, the string forms a wave on $[0, 1]$. Alternatively, if you focus on a point on the string (fix a value of x), that point oscillates up and down in time.

a. What is the period of the motion in time?
b. Find the rate of change of the displacement with respect to time at a constant position (which is the vertical velocity of a point on the string).
c. At a fixed time, what point on the string is moving fastest?
d. At a fixed position on the string, when is the string moving fastest?
e. Find the rate of change of the displacement with respect to position at a constant time (which is the slope of the string).
f. At a fixed time, where is the slope of the string greatest?

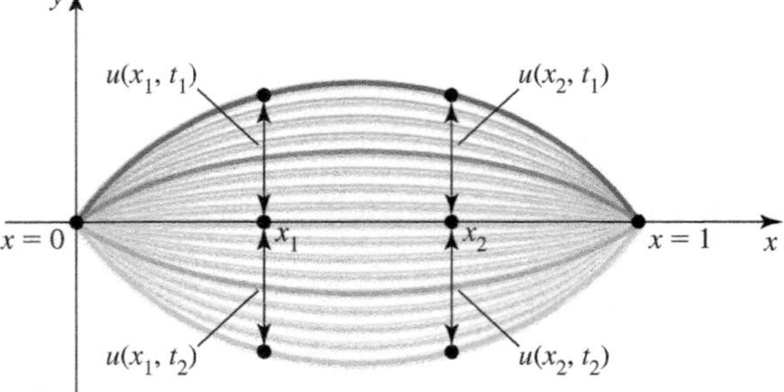

77–79. Wave equation *Traveling waves (for example, water waves or electromagnetic waves) exhibit periodic motion in both time and position. In one dimension, some types of wave motion are governed by the one-dimensional wave equation*

$$\frac{\partial^2 u}{\partial t^2} = c^2 \frac{\partial^2 u}{\partial x^2},$$

where $u(x, t)$ is the height or displacement of the wave surface at position x and time t, and c is the constant speed of the wave. Show that the following functions are solutions of the wave equation.

77. $u(x, t) = \cos(2(x + ct))$

78. $u(x, t) = 5 \cos(2(x + ct)) + 3 \sin(x - ct)$

79. $u(x, t) = A f(x + ct) + B g(x - ct)$, where A and B are constants and f and g are twice differentiable functions of one variable

80–83. Laplace's equation *A classical equation of mathematics is Laplace's equation, which arises in both theory and applications. It governs ideal fluid flow, electrostatic potentials, and the steady-state distribution of heat in a conducting medium. In two dimensions, Laplace's equation is*

$$\frac{\partial^2 u}{\partial x^2} + \frac{\partial^2 u}{\partial y^2} = 0.$$

Show that the following functions are ***harmonic****; that is, they satisfy Laplace's equation.*

80. $u(x, y) = e^{-x} \sin y$

81. $u(x, y) = x(x^2 - 3y^2)$

82. $u(x, y) = e^{ax} \cos ay$, for any real number a

83. $u(x, y) = \tan^{-1}\left(\frac{y}{x - 1}\right) - \tan^{-1}\left(\frac{y}{x + 1}\right)$

84–87. Heat equation *The flow of heat along a thin conducting bar is governed by the one-dimensional heat equation (with analogs for thin plates in two dimensions and for solids in three dimensions)*

$$\frac{\partial u}{\partial t} = k\frac{\partial^2 u}{\partial x^2},$$

where u is a measure of the temperature at a location x on the bar at time t and the positive constant k is related to the conductivity of the material. Show that the following functions satisfy the heat equation with k = 1.

84. $u(x, t) = 10e^{-t}\sin x$

85. $u(x, t) = 4e^{-4t}\cos 2x$

86. $u(x, t) = e^{-t}(2\sin x + 3\cos x)$

87. $u(x, t) = Ae^{-a^2t}\cos ax$, for any real numbers a and A

Additional Exercises

88–89. Differentiability *Use the definition of differentiability to prove that the following functions are differentiable at* $(0, 0)$. *You must produce functions* ε_1 *and* ε_2 *with the required properties.*

88. $f(x, y) = x + y$

89. $f(x, y) = xy$

90–91. Nondifferentiability? *Consider the following functions f.*

a. *Is f continuous at* $(0, 0)$*?*
b. *Is f differentiable at* $(0, 0)$*?*
c. *If possible, evaluate* $f_x(0, 0)$ *and* $f_y(0, 0)$.
d. *Determine whether* f_x *and* f_y *are continuous at* $(0, 0)$.
e. *Explain why Theorems 12.5 and 12.6 are consistent with the results in parts (a)–(d).*

90. $f(x, y) = 1 - |xy|$

91. $f(x, y) = \sqrt{|xy|}$

92. Mixed partial derivatives

a. Consider the function $w = f(x, y, z)$. List all possible second partial derivatives that could be computed.
b. Let $f(x, y, z) = x^2y + 2xz^2 - 3y^2z$ and determine which second partial derivatives are equal.
c. How many second partial derivatives does $p = g(w, x, y, z)$ have?

93. Derivatives of an integral Let h be continuous for all real numbers.

a. Find f_x and f_y when $f(x, y) = \int_x^y h(s)\,ds$.
b. Find f_x and f_y when $f(x, y) = \int_1^{xy} h(s)\,ds$.

94. An identity Show that if $f(x, y) = \frac{ax + by}{cx + dy}$, where a, b, c, and d are real numbers with $ad - bc = 0$, then $f_x = f_y = 0$, for all x and y in the domain of f. Give an explanation.

95. Cauchy-Riemann equations In the advanced subject of complex variables, a function typically has the form $f(x, y) = u(x, y) + iv(x, y)$, where u and v are real-valued functions and $i = \sqrt{-1}$ is the imaginary unit. A function $f = u + iv$ is said to be *analytic* (analogous to differentiable) if it satisfies the Cauchy-Riemann equations: $u_x = v_y$ and $u_y = -v_x$.

a. Show that $f(x, y) = (x^2 - y^2) + i(2xy)$ is analytic.
b. Show that $f(x, y) = x(x^2 - 3y^2) + iy(3x^2 - y^2)$ is analytic.
c. Show that if $f = u + iv$ is analytic, then $u_{xx} + u_{yy} = 0$ and $v_{xx} + v_{yy} = 0$. Assume u and v satisfy the conditions in Theorem 12.4.

QUICK CHECK ANSWERS

1. $f_x = 2y; f_y = 2x$ **2.** (a) and (c) are the same; f_{qp} **3.** $f_{xxx} = 6y; f_{xxy} = 6x$ **4.** $f_{xz} = y - 2x; f_{zz} = 2y$ **5.** The equations of the level curves are $T = \frac{1}{k}P_0V$. As the pressure P_0 increases, the slopes of these lines increase. ◀

12.5 The Chain Rule

In this section, we combine ideas based on the Chain Rule (Section 3.6) with what we know about partial derivatives (Section 12.4) to develop new methods for finding derivatives of functions of several variables. To illustrate the importance of these methods, consider the following situation.

Economists modeling manufacturing systems often work with *production functions* that relate the productivity (output) of the system to all the variables on which it depends (input). A simplified production function might take the form $P = F(L, K, R)$, where L, K, and R represent the availability of labor, capital, and natural resources, respectively. However, the variables L, K, and R may be intermediate variables that depend on other variables. For example, it might be that L is a function of the unemployment rate u, K is a function of the prime interest rate i, and R is a function of time t (seasonal availability of resources). Even in this simplified model, we see that productivity, which is the dependent variable, is ultimately related to many other variables

(Figure 12.53). Of critical interest to an economist is how changes in one variable determine changes in other variables. For instance, if the unemployment rate increases by 0.1% and the interest rate decreases by 0.2%, what is the effect on productivity? In this section, we develop the tools needed to answer such questions.

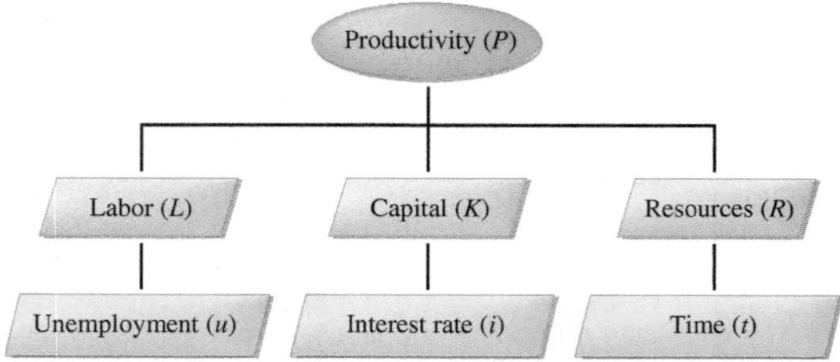

Figure 12.53

The Chain Rule with One Independent Variable

Recall the basic Chain Rule: If y is a function of u and u is a function of t, then $\frac{dy}{dt} = \frac{dy}{du}\frac{du}{dt}$. We first extend the Chain Rule to composite functions of the form $z = f(x, y)$, where x and y are functions of t. What is $\frac{dz}{dt}$?

We illustrate the relationships among the variables t, x, y, and z using a *tree diagram* (Figure 12.54). To find dz/dt, first notice that z depends on x, which in turn depends on t. The change in z with respect to x is the partial derivative $\partial z/\partial x$, while the change in x with respect to t is the ordinary derivative dx/dt. These derivatives appear on the corresponding branches of the tree diagram. Using the Chain Rule idea, the product of these derivatives gives the change in z with respect to t through x.

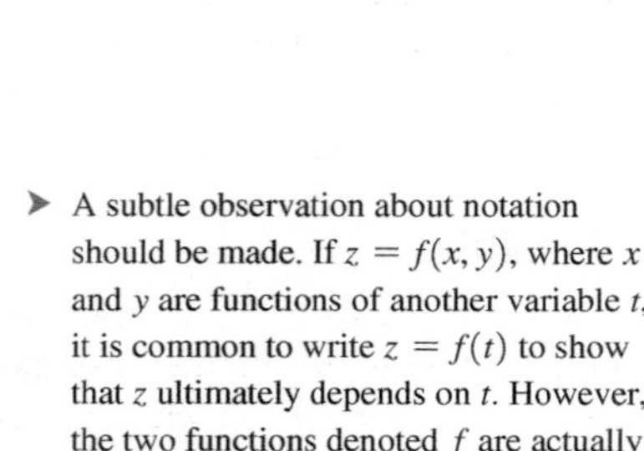

Figure 12.54

Similarly, z also depends on y. The change in z with respect to y is $\partial z/\partial y$, while the change in y with respect to t is dy/dt. The product of these derivatives, which appear on the corresponding branches of the tree, gives the change in z with respect to t through y. Summing the contributions to dz/dt along each branch of the tree leads to the following theorem, whose proof is found in Appendix B.

➤ A subtle observation about notation should be made. If $z = f(x, y)$, where x and y are functions of another variable t, it is common to write $z = f(t)$ to show that z ultimately depends on t. However, the two functions denoted f are actually different. We *should* write (or at least remember) that in fact $z = F(t)$, where F is a function other than f. This distinction is often overlooked for the sake of convenience.

THEOREM 12.7 Chain Rule (One Independent Variable)
Let z be a differentiable function of x and y on its domain, where x and y are differentiable functions of t on an interval I. Then

$$\frac{dz}{dt} = \frac{\partial z}{\partial x}\frac{dx}{dt} + \frac{\partial z}{\partial y}\frac{dy}{dt}.$$

QUICK CHECK 1 Explain why Theorem 12.7 reduces to the Chain Rule for a function of one variable in the case that $z = f(x)$ and $x = g(t)$. ◀

Before presenting examples, several comments are in order.

- With $z = f(x(t), y(t))$, the dependent variable is z and the sole independent variable is t. The variables x and y are **intermediate variables**.
- The choice of notation for partial and ordinary derivatives in the Chain Rule is important. We write the ordinary derivatives dx/dt and dy/dt because x and y depend only on t. We write the partial derivatives $\partial z/\partial x$ and $\partial z/\partial y$ because z is a function of both x and y. Finally, we write dz/dt as an ordinary derivative because z ultimately depends only on t.
- Theorem 12.7 generalizes directly to functions of more than two intermediate variables (Figure 12.55). For example, if $w = f(x, y, z)$, where x, y, and z are functions of the single independent variable t, then

$$\frac{dw}{dt} = \frac{\partial w}{\partial x}\frac{dx}{dt} + \frac{\partial w}{\partial y}\frac{dy}{dt} + \frac{\partial w}{\partial z}\frac{dz}{dt}.$$

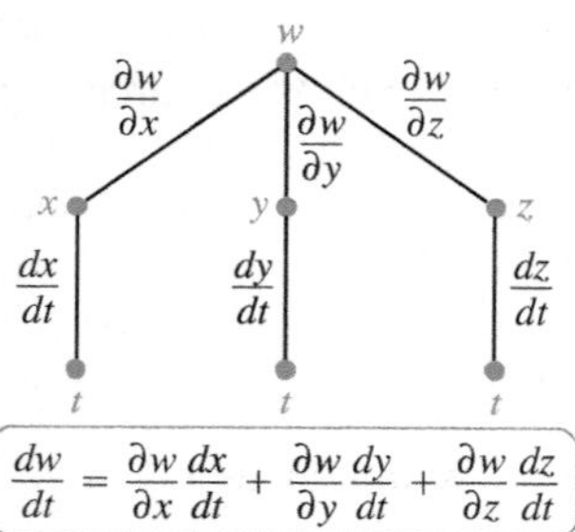

Figure 12.55

➤ If f, x, and y are simple, as in Example 1, it is possible to substitute $x(t)$ and $y(t)$ into f, producing a function of t only, and then differentiate with respect to t. But this approach quickly becomes impractical with more complicated functions, and the Chain Rule offers a great advantage.

EXAMPLE 1 Chain Rule with one independent variable Let $z = x^2 - 3y^2 + 20$, where $x = 2\cos t$ and $y = 2\sin t$.

a. Find $\frac{dz}{dt}$ and evaluate it at $t = \pi/4$.

b. Interpret the result geometrically.

SOLUTION

a. Computing the intermediate derivatives and applying the Chain Rule (Theorem 12.7), we find that

$$\begin{aligned} \frac{dz}{dt} &= \frac{\partial z}{\partial x}\frac{dx}{dt} + \frac{\partial z}{\partial y}\frac{dy}{dt} \\ &= \underbrace{(2x)}_{\frac{\partial z}{\partial x}}\underbrace{(-2\sin t)}_{\frac{dx}{dt}} + \underbrace{(-6y)}_{\frac{\partial z}{\partial y}}\underbrace{(2\cos t)}_{\frac{dy}{dt}} && \text{Evaluate derivatives.} \\ &= -4x\sin t - 12y\cos t && \text{Simplify.} \\ &= -8\cos t\sin t - 24\sin t\cos t && \text{Substitute } x = 2\cos t,\ y = 2\sin t. \\ &= -16\sin 2t. && \text{Simplify; } \sin 2t = 2\sin t\cos t. \end{aligned}$$

Substituting $t = \pi/4$ gives $\left.\frac{dz}{dt}\right|_{t=\pi/4} = -16.$

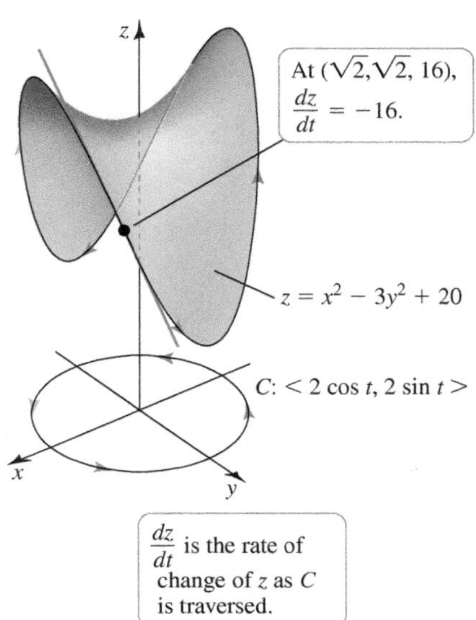

Figure 12.56

b. The parametric equations $x = 2\cos t$, $y = 2\sin t$, for $0 \le t \le 2\pi$, describe a circle C of radius 2 in the xy-plane. Imagine walking on the surface $z = x^2 - 3y^2 + 20$ directly above the circle C consistent with positive (counterclockwise) orientation of C. Your path rises and falls as you walk (Figure 12.56); the rate of change of your elevation z with respect to t is given by dz/dt. For example, when $t = \pi/4$, the corresponding point on the surface is $(\sqrt{2}, \sqrt{2}, 16)$. At that point, z decreases at a rate of -16 (by part (a)) as you walk on the surface above C.

Related Exercises 7–18 ◀

The Chain Rule with Several Independent Variables

The ideas behind the Chain Rule of Theorem 12.7 can be modified to cover a variety of situations in which functions of several variables are composed with one another. For example, suppose z depends on two intermediate variables x and y, each of which depends on the independent variables s and t. Once again, a tree diagram (Figure 12.57) helps organize the relationships among variables. The dependent variable z now ultimately depends on the two independent variables s and t, so it makes sense to ask about the rates of change of z with respect to either s or t, which are $\partial z/\partial s$ and $\partial z/\partial t$, respectively.

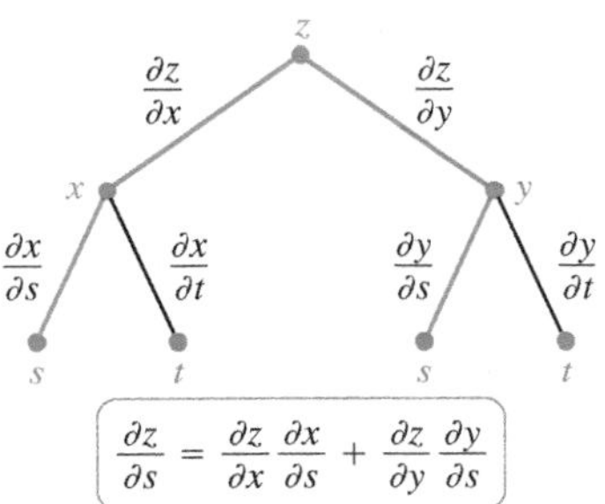

Figure 12.57

To compute $\partial z/\partial s$, we note that there are two paths in the tree (in red in Figure 12.57) that connect z to s and contribute to $\partial z/\partial s$. Along one path, z changes with respect to x (with rate of change $\partial z/\partial x$) and x changes with respect to s (with rate of change $\partial x/\partial s$). Along the other path, z changes with respect to y (with rate of change $\partial z/\partial y$) and y changes with respect to s (with rate of change $\partial y/\partial s$). We use a Chain Rule calculation along each path and combine the results. A similar argument leads to $\partial z/\partial t$ (Figure 12.58).

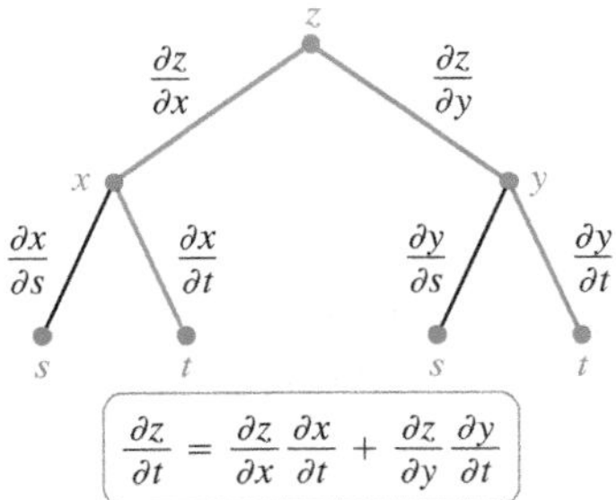

Figure 12.58

THEOREM 12.8 Chain Rule (Two Independent Variables)
Let z be a differentiable function of x and y, where x and y are differentiable functions of s and t. Then

$$\frac{\partial z}{\partial s} = \frac{\partial z}{\partial x}\frac{\partial x}{\partial s} + \frac{\partial z}{\partial y}\frac{\partial y}{\partial s} \quad \text{and} \quad \frac{\partial z}{\partial t} = \frac{\partial z}{\partial x}\frac{\partial x}{\partial t} + \frac{\partial z}{\partial y}\frac{\partial y}{\partial t}.$$

QUICK CHECK 2 Suppose that $w = f(x, y, z)$, where $x = g(s, t)$, $y = h(s, t)$, and $z = p(s, t)$. Extend Theorem 12.8 to write a formula for $\partial w/\partial t$. ◀

EXAMPLE 2 Chain Rule with two independent variables Let $z = \sin 2x \cos 3y$, where $x = s + t$ and $y = s - t$. Evaluate $\partial z/\partial s$ and $\partial z/\partial t$.

SOLUTION The tree diagram in Figure 12.57 gives the Chain Rule formula for $\partial z/\partial s$: We form products of the derivatives along the red branches connecting z to s and add the results. The partial derivative is

$$\begin{aligned}\frac{\partial z}{\partial s} &= \frac{\partial z}{\partial x}\frac{\partial x}{\partial s} + \frac{\partial z}{\partial y}\frac{\partial y}{\partial s}\\ &= \underbrace{2\cos 2x \cos 3y}_{\frac{\partial z}{\partial x}}\cdot\underbrace{1}_{\frac{\partial x}{\partial s}} + \underbrace{(-3\sin 2x \sin 3y)}_{\frac{\partial z}{\partial y}}\cdot\underbrace{1}_{\frac{\partial y}{\partial s}}\\ &= 2\cos(\underbrace{2(s+t)}_{x})\cos(\underbrace{3(s-t)}_{y}) - 3\sin(\underbrace{2(s+t)}_{x})\sin(\underbrace{3(s-t)}_{y}).\end{aligned}$$

Following the branches of Figure 12.58 connecting z to t, we have

$$\begin{aligned}\frac{\partial z}{\partial t} &= \frac{\partial z}{\partial x}\frac{\partial x}{\partial t} + \frac{\partial z}{\partial y}\frac{\partial y}{\partial t}\\ &= \underbrace{2\cos 2x \cos 3y}_{\frac{\partial z}{\partial x}}\cdot\underbrace{1}_{\frac{\partial x}{\partial t}} + \underbrace{(-3\sin 2x \sin 3y)}_{\frac{\partial z}{\partial y}}\cdot\underbrace{-1}_{\frac{\partial y}{\partial t}}\\ &= 2\cos(\underbrace{2(s+t)}_{x})\cos(\underbrace{3(s-t)}_{y}) + 3\sin(\underbrace{2(s+t)}_{x})\sin(\underbrace{3(s-t)}_{y}).\end{aligned}$$

Related Exercises 19–26 ◄

EXAMPLE 3 More variables Let w be a function of x, y, and z, each of which is a function of s and t.

a. Draw a labeled tree diagram showing the relationships among the variables.

b. Write the Chain Rule formula for $\dfrac{\partial w}{\partial s}$.

SOLUTION

a. Because w is a function of x, y, and z, the upper branches of the tree (Figure 12.59) are labeled with the partial derivatives w_x, w_y, and w_z. Each of x, y, and z is a function of two variables, so the lower branches of the tree also require partial derivative labels.

b. Extending Theorem 12.8, we take the three paths through the tree that connect w to s (red branches in Figure 12.59). Multiplying the derivatives that appear on each path and adding gives the result

$$\frac{\partial w}{\partial s} = \frac{\partial w}{\partial x}\frac{\partial x}{\partial s} + \frac{\partial w}{\partial y}\frac{\partial y}{\partial s} + \frac{\partial w}{\partial z}\frac{\partial z}{\partial s}.$$

Related Exercises 19–26 ◄

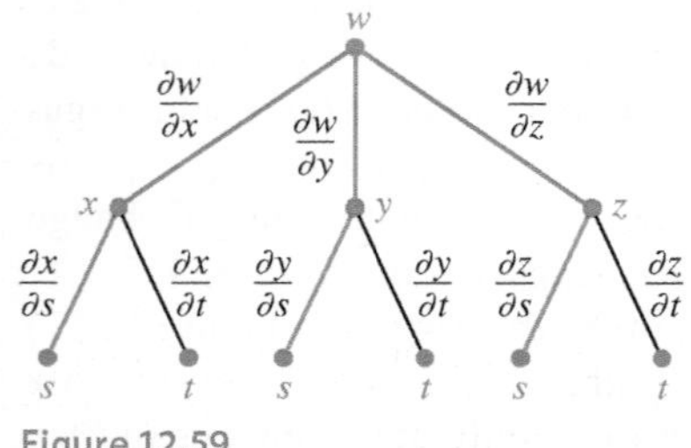

Figure 12.59

QUICK CHECK 3 If Q is a function of w, x, y, and z, each of which is a function of r, s, and t, how many dependent variables, intermediate variables, and independent variables are there? ◄

It is probably clear by now that we can create a Chain Rule for any set of relationships among variables. The key is to draw an accurate tree diagram and label the branches of the tree with the appropriate derivatives.

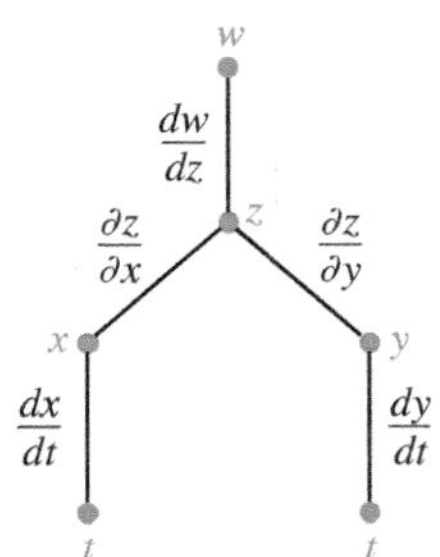

Figure 12.60

EXAMPLE 4 A different kind of tree Let w be a function of z, where z is a function of x and y, and each of x and y is a function of t. Draw a labeled tree diagram and write the Chain Rule formula for dw/dt.

SOLUTION The dependent variable w is related to the independent variable t through two paths in the tree: $w \to z \to x \to t$ and $w \to z \to y \to t$ (Figure 12.60). At the top of the tree, w is a function of the single variable z, so the rate of change is the ordinary derivative dw/dz. The tree below z looks like Figure 12.54. Multiplying the derivatives on each of the two branches connecting w to t and adding the results, we have

$$\frac{dw}{dt} = \frac{dw}{dz}\frac{\partial z}{\partial x}\frac{dx}{dt} + \frac{dw}{dz}\frac{\partial z}{\partial y}\frac{dy}{dt} = \frac{dw}{dz}\left(\frac{\partial z}{\partial x}\frac{dx}{dt} + \frac{\partial z}{\partial y}\frac{dy}{dt}\right).$$

Related Exercises 27–30 ◀

Implicit Differentiation

Using the Chain Rule for partial derivatives, the technique of implicit differentiation can be put in a larger perspective. Recall that if x and y are related through an implicit relationship, such as $\sin xy + \pi y^2 = x$, then dy/dx is computed using implicit differentiation (Section 3.8). Another way to compute dy/dx is to define the function $F(x, y) = \sin xy + \pi y^2 - x$. Notice that the original relationship $\sin xy + \pi y^2 = x$ is $F(x, y) = 0$.

To find dy/dx, we treat x as the independent variable and differentiate both sides of $F(x, y(x)) = 0$ with respect to x. The derivative of the right side is 0. On the left side, we use the Chain Rule of Theorem 12.7:

$$\frac{\partial F}{\partial x}\underbrace{\frac{dx}{dx}}_{1} + \frac{\partial F}{\partial y}\frac{dy}{dx} = 0.$$

Noting that $dx/dx = 1$ and solving for dy/dx, we obtain the following theorem.

➤ The question of whether a relationship of the form $F(x, y) = 0$ or $F(x, y, z) = 0$ determines one or more functions is addressed by a theorem of advanced calculus called the Implicit Function Theorem.

THEOREM 12.9 Implicit Differentiation
Let F be differentiable on its domain and suppose that $F(x, y) = 0$ defines y as a differentiable function of x. Provided $F_y \neq 0$,

$$\frac{dy}{dx} = -\frac{F_x}{F_y}.$$

EXAMPLE 5 Implicit differentiation Find dy/dx when $F(x, y) = \sin xy + \pi y^2 - x = 0$.

SOLUTION Computing the partial derivatives of F with respect to x and y, we find that

$$F_x = y \cos xy - 1 \quad \text{and} \quad F_y = x \cos xy + 2\pi y.$$

➤ The method of Theorem 12.9 generalizes to computing $\frac{\partial z}{\partial x}$ and $\frac{\partial z}{\partial y}$ with functions of the form $F(x, y, z) = 0$ (Exercise 48).

Therefore,

$$\frac{dy}{dx} = -\frac{F_x}{F_y} = -\frac{y \cos xy - 1}{x \cos xy + 2\pi y}.$$

As with many implicit differentiation calculations, the result is left in terms of both x and y. The same result is obtained using the methods of Section 3.8.

Related Exercises 31–36 ◀

QUICK CHECK 4 Use the method of Example 5 to find dy/dx when $F(x, y) = x^2 + xy - y^3 - 7 = 0$. Compare your solution to Example 3 in Section 3.8. Which method is easier? ◀

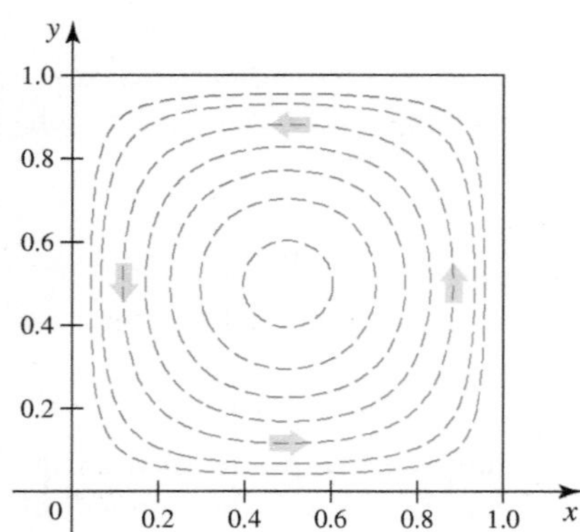

Figure 12.61

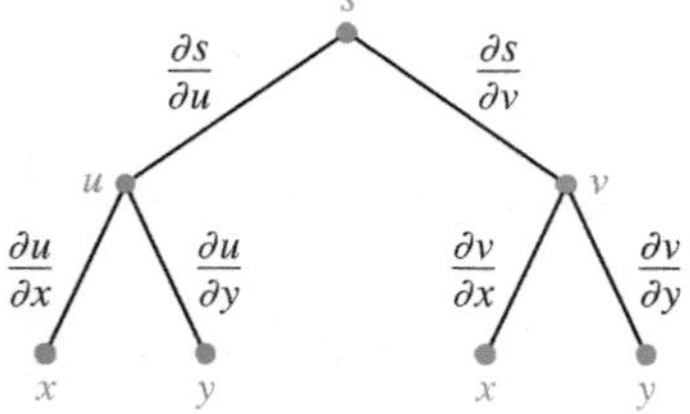

Figure 12.62

EXAMPLE 6 **Fluid flow** A basin of circulating water is represented by the square region $\{(x, y): 0 \le x \le 1, 0 \le y \le 1\}$, where x is positive in the eastward direction and y is positive in the northward direction. The velocity components of the water are

$$\text{the east-west velocity } u(x, y) = 2 \sin \pi x \cos \pi y \text{ and}$$
$$\text{the north-south velocity } v(x, y) = -2 \cos \pi x \sin \pi y;$$

these velocity components produce the flow pattern shown in Figure 12.61. The *streamlines* shown in the figure are the paths followed by small parcels of water. The speed of the water at a point (x, y) is given by the function $s(x, y) = \sqrt{u(x, y)^2 + v(x, y)^2}$. Find $\partial s/\partial x$ and $\partial s/\partial y$, the rates of change of the water speed in the x- and y-directions, respectively.

SOLUTION The dependent variable s depends on the independent variables x and y through the intermediate variables u and v (Figure 12.62). Theorem 12.8 applies here in the form

$$\frac{\partial s}{\partial x} = \frac{\partial s}{\partial u}\frac{\partial u}{\partial x} + \frac{\partial s}{\partial v}\frac{\partial v}{\partial x} \quad \text{and} \quad \frac{\partial s}{\partial y} = \frac{\partial s}{\partial u}\frac{\partial u}{\partial y} + \frac{\partial s}{\partial v}\frac{\partial v}{\partial y}.$$

The derivatives $\partial s/\partial u$ and $\partial s/\partial v$ are easier to find if we square the speed function to obtain $s^2 = u^2 + v^2$ and then use implicit differentiation. To compute $\partial s/\partial u$, we differentiate both sides of $s^2 = u^2 + v^2$ with respect to u:

$$2s\frac{\partial s}{\partial u} = 2u, \quad \text{which implies that} \quad \frac{\partial s}{\partial u} = \frac{u}{s}.$$

Similarly, differentiating $s^2 = u^2 + v^2$ with respect to v gives

$$2s\frac{\partial s}{\partial v} = 2v, \quad \text{which implies that} \quad \frac{\partial s}{\partial v} = \frac{v}{s}.$$

Now the Chain Rule leads to $\dfrac{\partial s}{\partial x}$:

$$\begin{aligned}\frac{\partial s}{\partial x} &= \frac{\partial s}{\partial u}\frac{\partial u}{\partial x} + \frac{\partial s}{\partial v}\frac{\partial v}{\partial x}\\ &= \underbrace{\frac{u}{s}}_{\frac{\partial s}{\partial u}}\underbrace{(2\pi \cos \pi x \cos \pi y)}_{\frac{\partial u}{\partial x}} + \underbrace{\frac{v}{s}}_{\frac{\partial s}{\partial v}}\underbrace{(2\pi \sin \pi x \sin \pi y)}_{\frac{\partial v}{\partial x}}\\ &= \frac{2\pi}{s}(u \cos \pi x \cos \pi y + v \sin \pi x \sin \pi y).\end{aligned}$$

A similar calculation shows that

$$\frac{\partial s}{\partial y} = -\frac{2\pi}{s}(u \sin \pi x \sin \pi y + v \cos \pi x \cos \pi y).$$

As a final step, you could replace s, u, and v with their definitions in terms of x and y.

Related Exercises 37–38 ◀

SECTION 12.5 EXERCISES

Review Questions

1. Suppose $z = f(x, y)$, where x and y are functions of t. How many dependent, intermediate, and independent variables are there?

2. Let z be a function of x and y, while x and y are functions of t. Explain how to find $\dfrac{dz}{dt}$.

3. Suppose w is a function of x, y, and z, which are each functions of t. Explain how to find $\dfrac{dw}{dt}$.

4. Let $z = f(x, y)$, $x = g(s, t)$, and $y = h(s, t)$. Explain how to find $\partial z/\partial t$.

5. Given that $w = F(x, y, z)$, and x, y, and z are functions of r and s, sketch a Chain Rule tree diagram with branches labeled with the appropriate derivatives.

6. Suppose $F(x, y) = 0$ and y is a differentiable function of x. Explain how to find dy/dx.

Basic Skills

7–16. Chain Rule with one independent variable *Use Theorem 12.7 to find the following derivatives. When feasible, express your answer in terms of the independent variable.*

7. dz/dt, where $z = x^2 + y^3$, $x = t^2$, and $y = t$

8. dz/dt, where $z = xy^2$, $x = t^2$, and $y = t$

9. dz/dt, where $z = x \sin y$, $x = t^2$, and $y = 4t^3$

10. dz/dt, where $z = x^2y - xy^3$, $x = t^2$, and $y = t^{-2}$

11. dw/dt, where $w = \cos 2x \sin 3y$, $x = t/2$, and $y = t^4$

12. dz/dt, where $z = \sqrt{r^2 + s^2}$, $r = \cos 2t$, and $s = \sin 2t$

13. dw/dt, where $w = xy \sin z$, $x = t^2$, $y = 4t^3$, and $z = t + 1$

14. dQ/dt, where $Q = \sqrt{x^2 + y^2 + z^2}$, $x = \sin t$, $y = \cos t$, and $z = \cos t$

15. dU/dt, where $U = \ln(x + y + z)$, $x = t$, $y = t^2$, and $z = t^3$

16. dV/dt, where $V = \dfrac{x - y}{y + z}$, $x = t$, $y = 2t$, and $z = 3t$

17. **Changing cylinder** The volume of a right circular cylinder with radius r and height h is $V = \pi r^2 h$.
    a. Assume that r and h are functions of t. Find $V'(t)$.
    b. Suppose that $r = e^t$ and $h = e^{-2t}$, for $t \geq 0$. Use part (a) to find $V'(t)$.
    c. Does the volume of the cylinder in part (b) increase or decrease as t increases?

18. **Changing pyramid** The volume of a pyramid with a square base x units on a side and a height of h is $V = \frac{1}{3}x^2 h$.
    a. Assume that x and h are functions of t. Find $V'(t)$.
    b. Suppose that $x = t/(t + 1)$ and $h = 1/(t + 1)$, for $t \geq 0$. Use part (a) to find $V'(t)$.
    c. Does the volume of the pyramid in part (b) increase or decrease as t increases?

19–26. Chain Rule with several independent variables *Find the following derivatives.*

19. z_s and z_t, where $z = x^2 \sin y$, $x = s - t$, and $y = t^2$

20. z_s and z_t, where $z = \sin(2x + y)$, $x = s^2 - t^2$, and $y = s^2 + t^2$

21. z_s and z_t, where $z = xy - x^2y$, $x = s + t$, and $y = s - t$

22. z_s and z_t, where $z = \sin x \cos 2y$, $x = s + t$, and $y = s - t$

23. z_s and z_t, where $z = e^{x+y}$, $x = st$, and $y = s + t$

24. z_s and z_t, where $z = xy - 2x + 3y$, $x = \cos s$, and $y = \sin t$

25. w_s and w_t, where $w = \dfrac{x - z}{y + z}$, $x = s + t$, $y = st$, and $z = s - t$

26. w_r, w_s, and w_t, where $w = \sqrt{x^2 + y^2 + z^2}$, $x = st$, $y = rs$, and $z = rt$

27–30. Making trees *Use a tree diagram to write the required Chain Rule formula.*

27. w is a function of z, where z is a function of x and y, each of which is a function of t. Find dw/dt.

28. $w = f(x, y, z)$, where $x = g(t)$, $y = h(s, t)$, and $z = p(r, s, t)$. Find $\partial w/\partial t$.

29. $u = f(v)$, where $v = g(w, x, y)$, $w = h(z)$, $x = p(t, z)$, and $y = q(t, z)$. Find $\partial u/\partial z$.

30. $u = f(v, w, x)$, where $v = g(r, s, t)$, $w = h(r, s, t)$, $x = p(r, s, t)$, and $r = F(z)$. Find $\partial u/\partial z$.

31–36. Implicit differentiation *Given the following equations, evaluate dy/dx. Assume that each equation implicitly defines y as a differentiable function of x.*

31. $x^2 - 2y^2 - 1 = 0$

32. $x^3 + 3xy^2 - y^5 = 0$

33. $2 \sin xy = 1$

34. $ye^{xy} - 2 = 0$

35. $\sqrt{x^2 + 2xy + y^4} = 3$

36. $y \ln(x^2 + y^2 + 4) = 3$

37–38. Fluid flow *The x- and y-components of a fluid moving in two dimensions are given by the following functions u and v. The speed of the fluid at (x, y) is $s(x, y) = \sqrt{u(x, y)^2 + v(x, y)^2}$. Use the Chain Rule to find $\partial s/\partial x$ and $\partial s/\partial y$.*

37. $u(x, y) = 2y$ and $v(x, y) = -2x$; $x \geq 0$ and $y \geq 0$

38. $u(x, y) = x(1 - x)(1 - 2y)$ and $v(x, y) = y(y - 1)(1 - 2x)$; $0 \leq x \leq 1, 0 \leq y \leq 1$

Further Explorations

39. **Explain why or why not** Determine whether the following statements are true and give an explanation or counterexample. Assume all partial derivatives exist.
    a. If $z = (x + y) \sin xy$, where x and y are functions of s, then $\dfrac{\partial z}{\partial s} = \dfrac{dz}{dx}\dfrac{dx}{ds}$.
    b. Given that $w = f(x(s, t), y(s, t), z(s, t))$, the rate of change of w with respect to t is dw/dt.

40–41. Derivative practice two ways *Find the indicated derivative in two ways:*

a. Replace x and y to write z as a function of t and differentiate.
b. Use the Chain Rule.

40. $z'(t)$, where $z = \ln(x + y)$, $x = te^t$, and $y = e^t$

41. $z'(t)$, where $z = \frac{1}{x} + \frac{1}{y}$, $x = t^2 + 2t$, and $y = t^3 - 2$

42–46. Derivative practice *Find the indicated derivative for the following functions.*

42. $\partial z/\partial p$, where $z = x/y$, $x = p + q$, and $y = p - q$

43. dw/dt, where $w = xyz$, $x = 2t^4$, $y = 3t^{-1}$, and $z = 4t^{-3}$

44. $\partial w/\partial x$, where $w = \cos z - \cos x \cos y + \sin x \sin y$ and $z = x + y$

45. $\frac{\partial z}{\partial x}$, where $\frac{1}{x} + \frac{1}{y} + \frac{1}{z} = 1$

46. $\partial z/\partial x$, where $xy - z = 1$

47. Change on a line Suppose $w = f(x, y, z)$ and ℓ is the line $\mathbf{r}(t) = \langle at, bt, ct \rangle$, for $-\infty < t < \infty$.

a. Find $w'(t)$ on ℓ (in terms of a, b, c, w_x, w_y, and w_z).
b. Apply part (a) to find $w'(t)$ when $f(x, y, z) = xyz$.
c. Apply part (a) to find $w'(t)$ when $f(x, y, z) = \sqrt{x^2 + y^2 + z^2}$.
d. For a general function $w = f(x, y, z)$, find $w''(t)$.

48. Implicit differentiation rule with three variables Assume that $F(x, y, z(x, y)) = 0$ implicitly defines z as a differentiable function of x and y. Extend Theorem 12.9 to show that

$$\frac{\partial z}{\partial x} = -\frac{F_x}{F_z} \text{ and } \frac{\partial z}{\partial y} = -\frac{F_y}{F_z}.$$

49–51. Implicit differentiation with three variables *Use the result of Exercise 48 to evaluate* $\frac{\partial z}{\partial x}$ *and* $\frac{\partial z}{\partial y}$ *for the following relations.*

49. $xy + xz + yz = 3$

50. $x^2 + 2y^2 - 3z^2 = 1$

51. $xyz + x + y - z = 0$

52. More than one way Let $e^{xyz} = 2$. Find z_x and z_y in three ways (and check for agreement).

a. Use the result of Exercise 48.
b. Take logarithms of both sides and differentiate $xyz = \ln 2$.
c. Solve for z and differentiate $z = \ln 2/(xy)$.

53–56. Walking on a surface *Consider the following surfaces specified in the form $z = f(x, y)$ and the oriented curve C in the xy-plane.*

a. In each case, find $z'(t)$.
b. Imagine that you are walking on the surface directly above the curve C in the direction of positive orientation. Find the values of t for which you are walking uphill (that is, z is increasing).

53. $z = x^2 + 4y^2 + 1$, $C: x = \cos t, y = \sin t;\ 0 \le t \le 2\pi$

54. $z = 4x^2 - y^2 + 1$, $C: x = \cos t, y = \sin t;\ 0 \le t \le 2\pi$

55. $z = \sqrt{1 - x^2 - y^2}$, $C: x = e^{-t}, y = e^{-t};\ t \ge \frac{1}{2}\ln 2$

56. $z = 2x^2 + y^2 + 1$, $C: x = 1 + \cos t, y = \sin t;\ 0 \le t \le 2\pi$

Applications

57. Conservation of energy A projectile with mass m is launched into the air on a parabolic trajectory. For $t \ge 0$, its horizontal and vertical coordinates are $x(t) = u_0 t$ and $y(t) = -\frac{1}{2}gt^2 + v_0 t$, respectively, where u_0 is the initial horizontal velocity, v_0 is the initial vertical velocity, and g is the acceleration due to gravity. Recalling that $u(t) = x'(t)$ and $v(t) = y'(t)$ are the components of the velocity, the energy of the projectile (kinetic plus potential) is

$$E(t) = \frac{1}{2}m(u^2 + v^2) + mgy.$$

Use the Chain Rule to compute $E'(t)$ and show that $E'(t) = 0$, for all $t \ge 0$. Interpret the result.

58. Utility functions in economics Economists use *utility functions* to describe consumers' relative preference for two or more commodities (for example, vanilla vs. chocolate ice cream or leisure time vs. material goods). The Cobb-Douglas family of utility functions has the form $U(x, y) = x^a y^{1-a}$, where x and y are the amounts of two commodities and $0 < a < 1$ is a parameter. Level curves on which the utility function is constant are called *indifference curves*; the utility is the same for all combinations of x and y along an indifference curve (see figure).

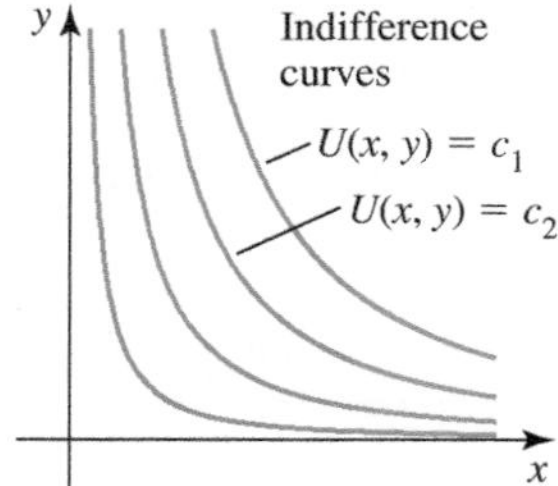

a. The marginal utilities of the commodities x and y are defined to be $\partial U/\partial x$ and $\partial U/\partial y$, respectively. Compute the marginal utilities for the utility function $U(x, y) = x^a y^{1-a}$.
b. The marginal rate of substitution (MRS) is the slope of the indifference curve at the point (x, y). Use the Chain Rule to show that for $U(x, y) = x^a y^{1-a}$, the MRS is $-\frac{a}{1-a}\frac{y}{x}$.
c. Find the MRS for the utility function $U(x, y) = x^{0.4}y^{0.6}$ at $(x, y) = (8, 12)$.

59. Constant volume tori The volume of a solid torus is given by $V = (\pi^2/4)(R + r)(R - r)^2$, where r and R are the inner and outer radii and $R > r$ (see figure).

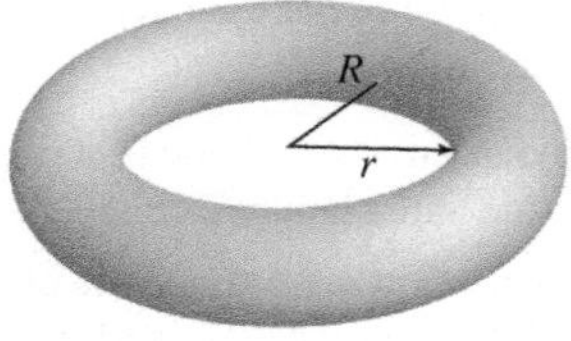

a. If R and r increase at the same rate, does the volume of the torus increase, decrease, or remain constant?
b. If R and r decrease at the same rate, does the volume of the torus increase, decrease, or remain constant?

60. Body surface area One of several empirical formulas that relates the surface area S of a human body to the height h and weight w of the body is the Mosteller formula $S(h, w) = \frac{1}{60}\sqrt{hw}$, where h is measured in centimeters, w is measured in kilograms, and S is measured in square meters. Suppose that h and w are functions of t.

a. Find $S'(t)$.

b. Show that the condition that the surface area remains constant as h and w change is $wh'(t) + hw'(t) = 0$.

c. Show that part (b) implies that for constant surface area, h and w must be inversely related; that is, $h = C/w$, where C is a constant.

61. The Ideal Gas Law The pressure, temperature, and volume of an ideal gas are related by $PV = kT$, where $k > 0$ is a constant. Any two of the variables may be considered independent, which determines the third variable.

a. Use implicit differentiation to compute the partial derivatives $\frac{\partial P}{\partial V}, \frac{\partial T}{\partial P}$, and $\frac{\partial V}{\partial T}$.

b. Show that $\frac{\partial P}{\partial V}\frac{\partial T}{\partial P}\frac{\partial V}{\partial T} = -1$. (See Exercise 67 for a generalization.)

62. Variable density The density of a thin circular plate of radius 2 is given by $\rho(x, y) = 4 + xy$. The edge of the plate is described by the parametric equations $x = 2\cos t$, $y = 2\sin t$, for $0 \le t \le 2\pi$.

a. Find the rate of change of the density with respect to t on the edge of the plate.

b. At what point(s) on the edge of the plate is the density a maximum?

T **63. Spiral through a domain** Suppose you follow the spiral path $C: x = \cos t, y = \sin t, z = t$, for $t \ge 0$, through the domain of the function $w = f(x, y, z) = xyz/(z^2 + 1)$.

a. Find $w'(t)$ along C.

b. Estimate the point (x, y, z) on C at which w has its maximum value.

Additional Exercises

64. Change of coordinates Recall that Cartesian and polar coordinates are related through the transformation equations

$$\begin{cases} x = r\cos\theta \\ y = r\sin\theta \end{cases} \quad \text{or} \quad \begin{cases} r^2 = x^2 + y^2 \\ \tan\theta = y/x. \end{cases}$$

a. Evaluate the partial derivatives x_r, y_r, x_θ, and y_θ.

b. Evaluate the partial derivatives r_x, r_y, θ_x, and θ_y.

c. For a function $z = f(x, y)$, find z_r and z_θ, where x and y are expressed in terms of r and θ.

d. For a function $z = g(r, \theta)$, find z_x and z_y, where r and θ are expressed in terms of x and y.

e. Show that $\left(\frac{\partial z}{\partial x}\right)^2 + \left(\frac{\partial z}{\partial y}\right)^2 = \left(\frac{\partial z}{\partial r}\right)^2 + \frac{1}{r^2}\left(\frac{\partial z}{\partial \theta}\right)^2$.

65. Change of coordinates continued An important derivative operation in many applications is called the Laplacian; in Cartesian coordinates, for $z = f(x, y)$, the Laplacian is $z_{xx} + z_{yy}$. Determine the Laplacian in polar coordinates using the following steps.

a. Begin with $z = g(r, \theta)$ and write z_x and z_y in terms of polar coordinates (see Exercise 64).

b. Use the Chain Rule to find $z_{xx} = \frac{\partial}{\partial x}(z_x)$. There should be two major terms, which, when expanded and simplified, result in five terms.

c. Use the Chain Rule to find $z_{yy} = \frac{\partial}{\partial y}(z_y)$. There should be two major terms, which, when expanded and simplified, result in five terms.

d. Combine parts (b) and (c) to show that

$$z_{xx} + z_{yy} = z_{rr} + \frac{1}{r}z_r + \frac{1}{r^2}z_{\theta\theta}.$$

66. Geometry of implicit differentiation Suppose x and y are related by the equation $F(x, y) = 0$. Interpret the solution of this equation as the set of points (x, y) that lie on the intersection of the surface $z = F(x, y)$ with the xy-plane $(z = 0)$.

a. Make a sketch of a surface and its intersection with the xy-plane. Give a geometric interpretation of the result that $\frac{dy}{dx} = -\frac{F_x}{F_y}$.

b. Explain geometrically what happens at points where $F_y = 0$.

67. General three-variable relationship In the implicit relationship $F(x, y, z) = 0$, any two of the variables may be considered independent, which then determines the third variable. To avoid confusion, we use a subscript to indicate which variable is held fixed in a derivative calculation; for example, $\left(\frac{\partial z}{\partial x}\right)_y$ means that y is held fixed in taking the partial derivative of z with respect to x. (In this context, the subscript does *not* mean a derivative.)

a. Differentiate $F(x, y, z) = 0$ with respect to x holding y fixed to show that $\left(\frac{\partial z}{\partial x}\right)_y = -\frac{F_x}{F_z}$.

b. As in part (a), find $\left(\frac{\partial y}{\partial z}\right)_x$ and $\left(\frac{\partial x}{\partial y}\right)_z$.

c. Show that $\left(\frac{\partial z}{\partial x}\right)_y\left(\frac{\partial y}{\partial z}\right)_x\left(\frac{\partial x}{\partial y}\right)_z = -1$.

d. Find the relationship analogous to part (c) for the case $F(w, x, y, z) = 0$.

68. Second derivative Let $f(x, y) = 0$ define y as a twice differentiable function of x.

a. Show that $y''(x) = -\frac{f_{xx}f_y^2 - 2f_xf_yf_{xy} + f_{yy}f_x^2}{f_y^3}$.

b. Verify part (a) using the function $f(x, y) = xy - 1$.

69. Subtleties of the Chain Rule Let $w = f(x, y, z) = 2x + 3y + 4z$, which is defined for all (x, y, z) in $\mathbb{R}^3$. Suppose that we are interested in the partial derivative w_x on a subset of $\mathbb{R}^3$, such as the plane P given by $z = 4x - 2y$. The point to be made is that the result is not unique unless we specify which variables are considered independent.

a. We could proceed as follows. On the plane P, consider x and y as the independent variables, which means z depends on x and y, so we write $w = f(x, y, z(x, y))$. Differentiate with respect to x holding y fixed to show that $\left(\frac{\partial w}{\partial x}\right)_y = 18$, where the subscript y indicates that y is held fixed.

b. Alternatively, on the plane P, we could consider x and z as the independent variables, which means y depends on x and z, so we write $w = f(x, y(x, z), z)$ and differentiate with respect to x holding z fixed. Show that $\left(\frac{\partial w}{\partial x}\right)_z = 8$, where the subscript z indicates that z is held fixed.

c. Make a sketch of the plane $z = 4x - 2y$ and interpret the results of parts (a) and (b) geometrically.

d. Repeat the arguments of parts (a) and (b) to find $\left(\frac{\partial w}{\partial y}\right)_x$, $\left(\frac{\partial w}{\partial y}\right)_z$, $\left(\frac{\partial w}{\partial z}\right)_x$, and $\left(\frac{\partial w}{\partial z}\right)_y$.

QUICK CHECK ANSWERS

1. If $z = f(x(t))$, then $\frac{\partial z}{\partial y} = 0$, and the original Chain Rule results. **2.** $\frac{\partial w}{\partial t} = \frac{\partial w}{\partial x}\frac{\partial x}{\partial t} + \frac{\partial w}{\partial y}\frac{\partial y}{\partial t} + \frac{\partial w}{\partial z}\frac{\partial z}{\partial t}$ **3.** One dependent variable, four intermediate variables, and three independent variables **4.** $\frac{dy}{dx} = \frac{2x + y}{3y^2 - x}$; in this case, using $\frac{dy}{dx} = -\frac{F_x}{F_y}$ is more efficient. ◄

12.6 Directional Derivatives and the Gradient

Partial derivatives tell us a lot about the rate of change of a function on its domain. However, they do not *directly* answer some important questions. For example, suppose you are standing at a point $(a, b, f(a, b))$ on the surface $z = f(x, y)$. The partial derivatives f_x and f_y tell you the rate of change (or slope) of the surface at that point in the directions parallel to the x-axis and y-axis, respectively. But you could walk in an infinite number of directions from that point and find a different rate of change in every direction. With this observation in mind, we pose several questions.

- Suppose you are standing on a surface and you walk in a direction *other* than a coordinate direction—say, northwest or south-southeast. What is the rate of change of the function in such a direction?
- Suppose you are standing on a surface and you release a ball at your feet and let it roll. In which direction will it roll?
- If you are hiking up a mountain, in what direction should you walk after each step if you want to follow the steepest path?

These questions are answered in this section by introducing the *directional derivative*, followed by one of the central concepts of calculus—the *gradient*.

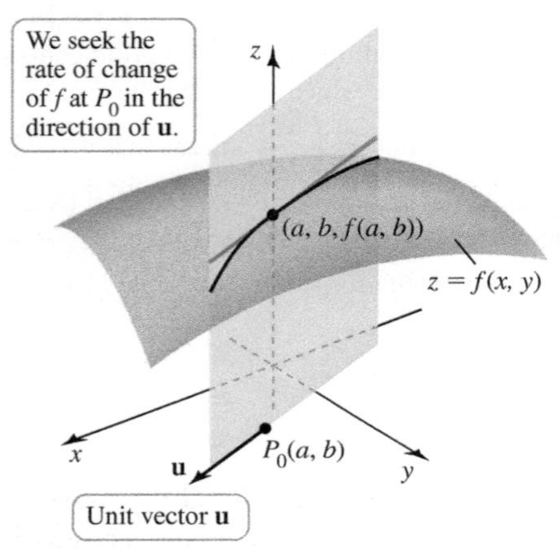

Figure 12.63

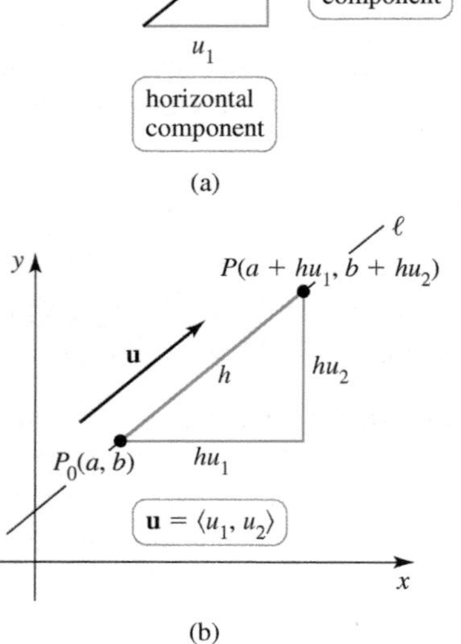

Figure 12.64

Directional Derivatives

Let $(a, b, f(a, b))$ be a point on the surface $z = f(x, y)$ and let **u** be a unit vector in the xy-plane (Figure 12.63). Our aim is to find the rate of change of f in the direction **u** at $P_0(a, b)$. In general, this rate of change is neither $f_x(a, b)$ nor $f_y(a, b)$ (unless $\mathbf{u} = \langle 1, 0 \rangle$ or $\mathbf{u} = \langle 0, 1 \rangle$), but it turns out to be a combination of $f_x(a, b)$ and $f_y(a, b)$.

Figure 12.64a shows the unit vector $\mathbf{u} = \langle u_1, u_2 \rangle$; its horizontal and vertical components are u_1 and u_2, respectively. The derivative we seek must be computed along the line ℓ in the xy-plane through P_0 in the direction of **u**. A neighboring point P, which is h units from P_0 along ℓ, has coordinates $P(a + hu_1, b + hu_2)$ (Figure 12.64b).

Now imagine the plane Q perpendicular to the xy-plane, containing ℓ. This plane cuts the surface $z = f(x, y)$ in a curve C. Consider two points on C corresponding to P_0 and P; they have z-coordinates $f(a, b)$ and $f(a + hu_1, b + hu_2)$ (Figure 12.65). The slope of the secant line between these points is

$$\frac{f(a + hu_1, b + hu_2) - f(a, b)}{h}.$$

The derivative of f in the direction of **u** is obtained by letting $h \to 0$; when the limit exists, it is called the *directional derivative of f at (a, b) in the direction of* **u**. It gives the slope of the line tangent to the curve C in the plane Q.

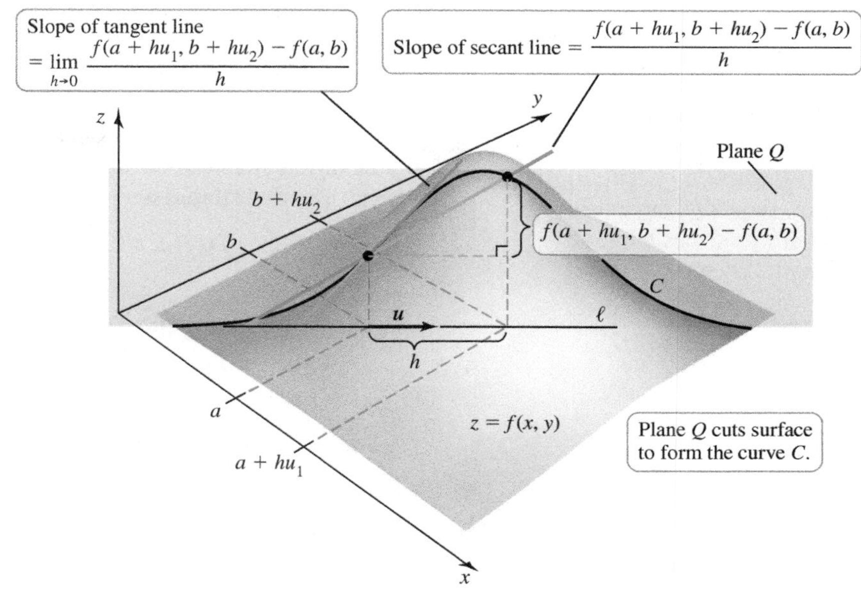

Figure 12.65

➤ The definition of the directional derivative looks like the definition of the ordinary derivative if we write it as

$$\lim_{P\to P_0} \frac{f(P) - f(P_0)}{|P - P_0|},$$

where P approaches P_0 along the line ℓ.

DEFINITION Directional Derivative

Let f be differentiable at (a, b) and let $\mathbf{u} = \langle u_1, u_2 \rangle$ be a unit vector in the xy-plane. The **directional derivative of f at (a, b) in the direction of u** is

$$D_{\mathbf{u}}f(a, b) = \lim_{h\to 0} \frac{f(a + hu_1, b + hu_2) - f(a, b)}{h},$$

provided the limit exists.

QUICK CHECK 1 Explain why, when $\mathbf{u} = \langle 1, 0 \rangle$ in the definition of the directional derivative, the result is $f_x(a, b)$ and when $\mathbf{u} = \langle 0, 1 \rangle$, the result is $f_y(a, b)$. ◄

As with ordinary derivatives, we would prefer to evaluate directional derivatives without taking limits. Fortunately, there is an easy way to express a directional derivative in terms of partial derivatives.

The key is to define a function that is equal to f along the line ℓ through (a, b) in the direction of the unit vector $\mathbf{u} = \langle u_1, u_2 \rangle$. The points on ℓ satisfy the parametric equations

$$x = a + su_1 \quad \text{and} \quad y = b + su_2,$$

where $-\infty < s < \infty$. Because $\mathbf{u}$ is a unit vector, the parameter s corresponds to arc length. As s increases, the points (x, y) move along ℓ in the direction of $\mathbf{u}$ with $s = 0$ corresponding to (a, b). Now we define the function

$$g(s) = f(\underbrace{a + su_1}_{x}, \underbrace{b + su_2}_{y}),$$

➤ To see that s is an arc length parameter, note that the line ℓ may be written in the form

$$\mathbf{r}(s) = \langle a + su_1, b + su_2 \rangle.$$

Therefore, $\mathbf{r}'(s) = \langle u_1, u_2 \rangle$ and $|\mathbf{r}'(s)| = 1$. It follows by the discussion in Section 11.8 that s is an arc length parameter. Because the directional derivative is a derivative with respect to length along ℓ, it is essential that s be an arc length parameter, which occurs only if $\mathbf{u}$ is a unit vector.

which gives the values of f along ℓ. The derivative of f along ℓ is $g'(s)$, and when evaluated at $s = 0$, it is the directional derivative of f at (a, b); that is, $g'(0) = D_{\mathbf{u}}f(a, b)$.

Noting that $\frac{dx}{ds} = u_1$ and $\frac{dy}{ds} = u_2$, we apply the Chain Rule to find that

$$D_{\mathbf{u}}f(a, b) = g'(0) = \left(\frac{\partial f}{\partial x}\underbrace{\frac{dx}{ds}}_{u_1} + \frac{\partial f}{\partial y}\underbrace{\frac{dy}{ds}}_{u_2}\right)\Bigg|_{s=0} \quad \text{Chain Rule}$$

$$= f_x(a, b)u_1 + f_y(a, b)u_2. \quad s = 0 \text{ corresponds to } (a, b).$$

We see that the directional derivative is a weighted average of the partial derivatives $f_x(a, b)$ and $f_y(a, b)$, with the components of $\mathbf{u}$ serving as the weights. In other words, knowing the slope of the surface in the x- and y-directions allows us to find the slope in any direction. Notice that the directional derivative can be written as a dot product, which provides a practical formula for computing directional derivatives.

QUICK CHECK 2 In the parametric description $x = a + su_1$ and $y = b + su_2$, where $\mathbf{u} = \langle u_1, u_2 \rangle$ is a unit vector, show that any positive change Δs in s produces a line segment of length Δs. ◄

THEOREM 12.10 Directional Derivative
Let f be differentiable at (a, b) and let $\mathbf{u} = \langle u_1, u_2 \rangle$ be a unit vector in the xy-plane. The **directional derivative of f at (a, b) in the direction of u** is

$$D_{\mathbf{u}}f(a, b) = \langle f_x(a, b), f_y(a, b) \rangle \cdot \langle u_1, u_2 \rangle.$$

EXAMPLE 1 Computing directional derivatives Consider the paraboloid $z = f(x, y) = \frac{1}{4}(x^2 + 2y^2) + 2$. Let P_0 be the point $(3, 2)$ and consider the unit vectors

$$\mathbf{u} = \left\langle \frac{1}{\sqrt{2}}, \frac{1}{\sqrt{2}} \right\rangle \quad \text{and} \quad \mathbf{v} = \left\langle \frac{1}{2}, -\frac{\sqrt{3}}{2} \right\rangle.$$

a. Find the directional derivative of f at P_0 in the directions of **u** and **v**.

b. Graph the surface and interpret the directional derivatives.

SOLUTION

a. We see that $f_x = x/2$ and $f_y = y$; evaluated at $(3, 2)$, we have $f_x(3, 2) = 3/2$ and $f_y(3, 2) = 2$. The directional derivatives in the directions **u** and **v** are

$$\begin{aligned} D_{\mathbf{u}}f(3, 2) &= \langle f_x(3, 2), f_y(3, 2) \rangle \cdot \langle u_1, u_2 \rangle \\ &= \frac{3}{2} \cdot \frac{1}{\sqrt{2}} + 2 \cdot \frac{1}{\sqrt{2}} = \frac{7}{2\sqrt{2}} \approx 2.47 \text{ and} \\ D_{\mathbf{v}}f(3, 2) &= \langle f_x(3, 2), f_y(3, 2) \rangle \cdot \langle v_1, v_2 \rangle \\ &= \frac{3}{2} \cdot \frac{1}{2} + 2\left(-\frac{\sqrt{3}}{2}\right) = \frac{3}{4} - \sqrt{3} \approx -0.98. \end{aligned}$$

➤ It is understood that the line tangent to C in the direction of **u** lies in the vertical plane Q containing **u**.

b. In the direction of **u**, the directional derivative is approximately 2.47. Because it is positive, the function is increasing at $(3, 2)$ in this direction. Equivalently, if Q is the vertical plane containing **u** and C is the curve along which the surface intersects Q, then the slope of the line tangent to C is approximately 2.47 (Figure 12.66a). In the direction of **v**, the directional derivative is approximately -0.98. Because it is negative, the function is decreasing in this direction. In this case, the vertical plane Q contains **v** and again C is the curve along which the surface intersects Q; the slope of the line tangent to C is approximately -0.98 (Figure 12.66b).

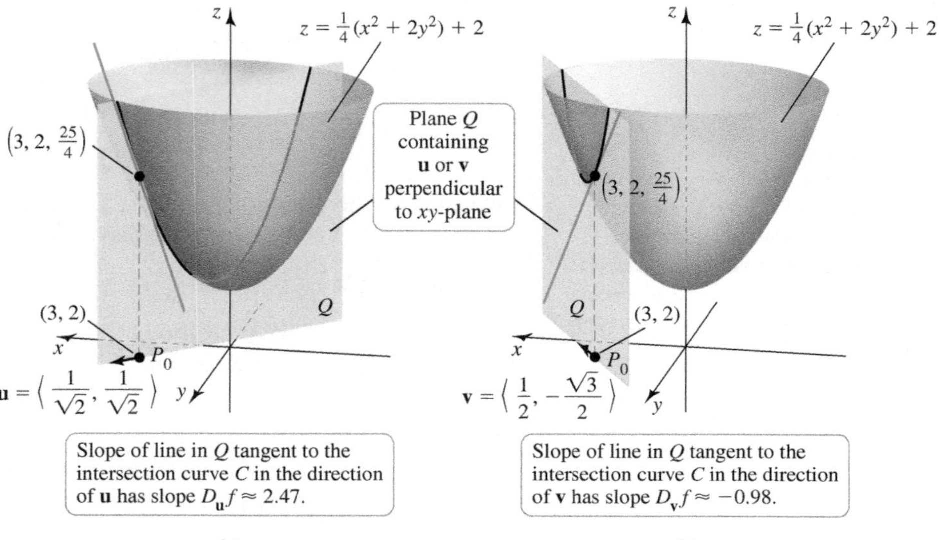

Figure 12.66

QUICK CHECK 3 In Example 1, evaluate $D_{-\mathbf{u}}f(3, 2)$ and $D_{-\mathbf{v}}f(3, 2)$. ◄

Related Exercises 7–8 ◄

The Gradient Vector

We have seen that the directional derivative can be written as a dot product: $D_{\mathbf{u}}f(a, b) = \langle f_x(a, b), f_y(a, b) \rangle \cdot \langle u_1, u_2 \rangle$. The vector $\langle f_x(a, b), f_y(a, b) \rangle$ that appears in the dot product is important in its own right and is called the *gradient* of f.

➤ Recall that the unit coordinate vectors in $\mathbb{R}^2$ are $\mathbf{i} = \langle 1, 0 \rangle$ and $\mathbf{j} = \langle 0, 1 \rangle$. The gradient of f is also written grad f, read *grad f*.

DEFINITION Gradient (Two Dimensions)

Let f be differentiable at the point (x, y). The **gradient** of f at (x, y) is the vector-valued function

$$\nabla f(x, y) = \langle f_x(x, y), f_y(x, y) \rangle = f_x(x, y)\,\mathbf{i} + f_y(x, y)\,\mathbf{j}.$$

With the definition of the gradient, the directional derivative of f at (a, b) in the direction of the unit vector $\mathbf{u}$ can be written

$$D_{\mathbf{u}}f(a, b) = \nabla f(a, b) \cdot \mathbf{u}.$$

The gradient satisfies sum, product, and quotient rules analogous to those for ordinary derivatives (Exercise 81).

EXAMPLE 2 Computing gradients Find $\nabla f(3, 2)$ for $f(x, y) = x^2 + 2xy - y^3$.

SOLUTION Computing $f_x = 2x + 2y$ and $f_y = 2x - 3y^2$, we have

$$\nabla f(x, y) = \langle 2(x + y), 2x - 3y^2 \rangle = 2(x + y)\,\mathbf{i} + (2x - 3y^2)\,\mathbf{j}.$$

Substituting $x = 3$ and $y = 2$ gives

$$\nabla f(3, 2) = \langle 10, -6 \rangle = 10\,\mathbf{i} - 6\,\mathbf{j}.$$

Related Exercises 9–16 ◄

EXAMPLE 3 Computing directional derivatives with gradients Let $f(x, y) = 3 - \frac{x^2}{10} + \frac{xy^2}{10}$.

a. Compute $\nabla f(3, -1)$.

b. Compute $D_{\mathbf{u}}f(3, -1)$, where $\mathbf{u} = \left\langle \frac{1}{\sqrt{2}}, -\frac{1}{\sqrt{2}} \right\rangle$.

c. Compute the directional derivative of f at $(3, -1)$ in the direction of the vector $\langle 3, 4 \rangle$.

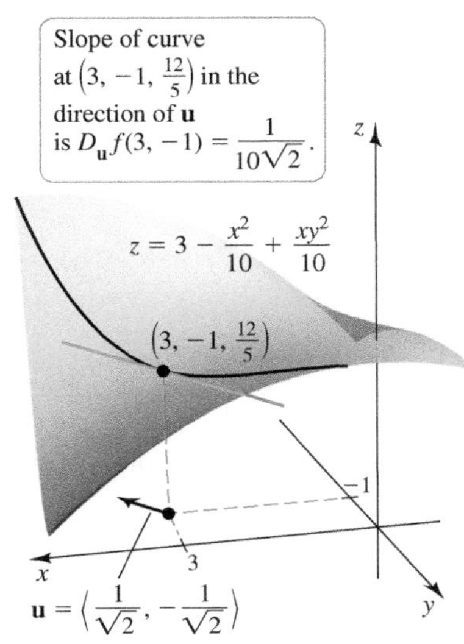

Figure 12.67

SOLUTION

a. Note that $f_x = -x/5 + y^2/10$ and $f_y = xy/5$. Therefore,

$$\nabla f(3, -1) = \left\langle -\frac{x}{5} + \frac{y^2}{10}, \frac{xy}{5} \right\rangle \Big|_{(3,-1)} = \left\langle -\frac{1}{2}, -\frac{3}{5} \right\rangle.$$

b. Before computing the directional derivative, it is important to verify that $\mathbf{u}$ is a unit vector (in this case, it is). The required directional derivative is

$$D_{\mathbf{u}}f(3, -1) = \nabla f(3, -1) \cdot \mathbf{u} = \left\langle -\frac{1}{2}, -\frac{3}{5} \right\rangle \cdot \left\langle \frac{1}{\sqrt{2}}, -\frac{1}{\sqrt{2}} \right\rangle = \frac{1}{10\sqrt{2}}.$$

Figure 12.67 shows the line tangent to the intersection curve in the plane corresponding to $\mathbf{u}$; its slope is $D_{\mathbf{u}}f(3, -1)$.

c. In this case, the direction is given in terms of a nonunit vector. The vector $\langle 3, 4 \rangle$ has length 5, so the unit vector in the direction of $\langle 3, 4 \rangle$ is $\mathbf{u} = \langle \frac{3}{5}, \frac{4}{5} \rangle$. The directional derivative at $(3, -1)$ in the direction of $\mathbf{u}$ is

$$D_{\mathbf{u}}f(3, -1) = \nabla f(3, -1) \cdot \mathbf{u} = \left\langle -\frac{1}{2}, -\frac{3}{5} \right\rangle \cdot \left\langle \frac{3}{5}, \frac{4}{5} \right\rangle = -\frac{39}{50},$$

which gives the slope of the surface in the direction of $\mathbf{u}$ at $(3, -1)$.

Related Exercises 17–26 ◄

Interpretations of the Gradient

The gradient is important not only in calculating directional derivatives; it plays many other roles in multivariable calculus. Our present goal is to develop some intuition about the meaning of the gradient.

➤ Recall that $\mathbf{u} \cdot \mathbf{v} = |\mathbf{u}||\mathbf{v}| \cos \theta$, where θ is the angle between $\mathbf{u}$ and $\mathbf{v}$.

We have seen that the directional derivative of f at (a, b) in the direction of the unit vector $\mathbf{u}$ is $D_{\mathbf{u}}f(a, b) = \nabla f(a, b) \cdot \mathbf{u}$. Using properties of the dot product, we have

$$\begin{aligned} D_{\mathbf{u}}f(a, b) &= \nabla f(a, b) \cdot \mathbf{u} \\ &= |\nabla f(a, b)||\mathbf{u}|\cos \theta \\ &= |\nabla f(a, b)| \cos \theta, \qquad |\mathbf{u}| = 1 \end{aligned}$$

➤ It is important to remember and easy to forget that $\nabla f(a, b)$ lies in the same plane as the domain of f.

where θ is the angle between $\nabla f(a, b)$ and $\mathbf{u}$. It follows that $D_{\mathbf{u}}f(a, b)$ has its maximum value when $\cos \theta = 1$, which corresponds to $\theta = 0$. Therefore, $D_{\mathbf{u}}f(a, b)$ has its maximum value and f has its greatest rate of *increase* when $\nabla f(a, b)$ and $\mathbf{u}$ point in the same direction. Notice that when $\cos \theta = 1$, the actual rate of increase is $D_{\mathbf{u}}f(a, b) = |\nabla f(a, b)|$ (Figure 12.68).

Similarly, when $\theta = \pi$, we have $\cos \theta = -1$, and f has its greatest rate of *decrease* when $\nabla f(a, b)$ and $\mathbf{u}$ point in opposite directions. The actual rate of decrease is $D_{\mathbf{u}}f(a, b) = -|\nabla f(a, b)|$. These observations are summarized as follows: The gradient $\nabla f(a, b)$ points in the *direction of steepest ascent* at (a, b), while $-\nabla f(a, b)$ points in the *direction of steepest descent.*

Notice that $D_{\mathbf{u}}f(a, b) = 0$ when the angle between $\nabla f(a, b)$ and $\mathbf{u}$ is $\pi/2$, which means $\nabla f(a, b)$ and $\mathbf{u}$ are orthogonal (Figure 12.68). These observations justify the following theorem.

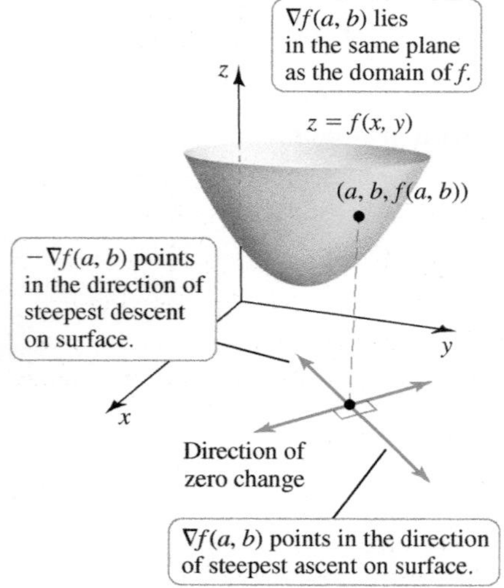

Figure 12.68

> **THEOREM 12.11 Directions of Change**
> Let f be differentiable at (a, b) with $\nabla f(a, b) \neq \mathbf{0}$.
>
> 1. f has its maximum rate of increase at (a, b) in the direction of the gradient $\nabla f(a, b)$. The rate of change in this direction is $|\nabla f(a, b)|$.
> 2. f has its maximum rate of decrease at (a, b) in the direction of $-\nabla f(a, b)$. The rate of change in this direction is $-|\nabla f(a, b)|$.
> 3. The directional derivative is zero in any direction orthogonal to $\nabla f(a, b)$.

EXAMPLE 4 Steepest ascent and descent Consider the bowl-shaped paraboloid $z = f(x, y) = 4 + x^2 + 3y^2$.

a. If you are located on the paraboloid at the point $\left(2, -\frac{1}{2}, \frac{35}{4}\right)$, in which direction should you move in order to *ascend* on the surface at the maximum rate? What is the rate of change?

b. If you are located at the point $\left(2, -\frac{1}{2}, \frac{35}{4}\right)$, in which direction should you move in order to *descend* on the surface at the maximum rate? What is the rate of change?

c. At the point $(3, 1, 16)$, in what direction(s) is there no change in the function values?

SOLUTION

a. At the point $\left(2, -\frac{1}{2}\right)$, the value of the gradient is

$$\nabla f\left(2, -\tfrac{1}{2}\right) = \langle 2x, 6y \rangle \big|_{(2,-1/2)} = \langle 4, -3 \rangle.$$

Therefore, the direction of steepest ascent in the xy-plane is in the direction of the gradient vector $\langle 4, -3 \rangle$ (or $\mathbf{u} = \frac{1}{5}\langle 4, -3 \rangle$, as a unit vector). The rate of change is $\left|\nabla f\left(2, -\frac{1}{2}\right)\right| = |\langle 4, -3 \rangle| = 5$ (Figure 12.69a).

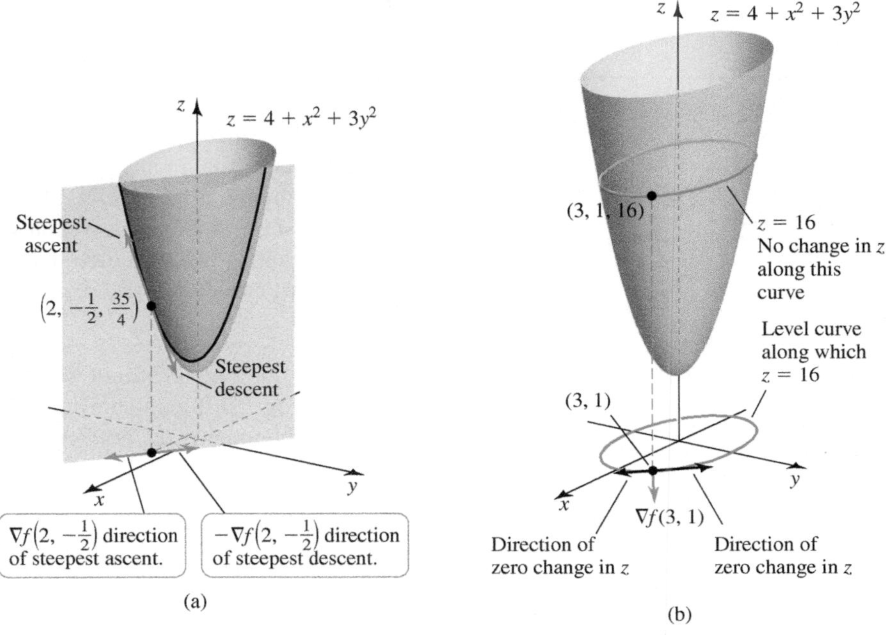

Figure 12.69

b. The direction of steepest *descent* is the direction of $-\nabla f\left(2, -\frac{1}{2}\right) = \langle -4, 3 \rangle$ (or $\mathbf{u} = \frac{1}{5}\langle -4, 3 \rangle$, as a unit vector). The rate of change is $-\left|\nabla f\left(2, -\frac{1}{2}\right)\right| = -5$.

c. At the point $(3, 1)$, the value of the gradient is $\nabla f(3, 1) = \langle 6, 6 \rangle$. The function has zero change if we move in either of the two directions orthogonal to $\langle 6, 6 \rangle$; these two directions are parallel to $\langle 6, -6 \rangle$. In terms of unit vectors, the directions of no change are $\mathbf{u} = \frac{1}{\sqrt{2}}\langle -1, 1 \rangle$ and $\mathbf{u} = \frac{1}{\sqrt{2}}\langle 1, -1 \rangle$ (Figure 12.69b).

➤ Note that $\langle 6, 6 \rangle$ and $\langle 6, -6 \rangle$ are orthogonal because $\langle 6, 6 \rangle \cdot \langle 6, -6 \rangle = 0$.

Related Exercises 27–32 ◄

EXAMPLE 5 **Interpreting directional derivatives** Consider the function $f(x, y) = 3x^2 - 2y^2$.

a. Compute $\nabla f(x, y)$ and $\nabla f(2, 3)$.

b. Let $\mathbf{u} = \langle \cos\theta, \sin\theta \rangle$ be a unit vector. At $(2, 3)$, for what values of θ (measured relative to the positive x-axis), with $0 \le \theta < 2\pi$, does the directional derivative have its maximum and minimum values and what are those values?

SOLUTION

a. The gradient is $\nabla f(x, y) = \langle f_x, f_y \rangle = \langle 6x, -4y \rangle$, and at $(2, 3)$, we have $\nabla f(2, 3) = \langle 12, -12 \rangle$.

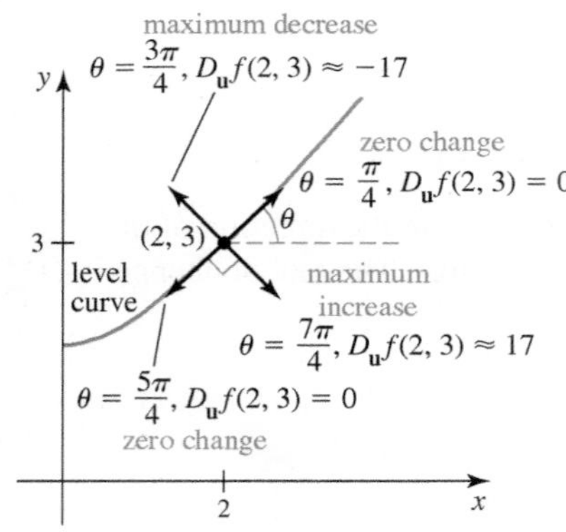

Figure 12.70

b. The gradient $\nabla f(2, 3) = \langle 12, -12 \rangle$ makes an angle of $7\pi/4$ with the positive x-axis. So the maximum rate of change of f occurs in this direction, and that rate of change is $|\nabla f(2, 3)| = |\langle 12, -12 \rangle| = 12\sqrt{2} \approx 17$. The direction of maximum decrease is opposite the direction of the gradient, which corresponds to $\theta = 3\pi/4$. The maximum rate of decrease is the negative of the maximum rate of increase, or $-12\sqrt{2} \approx -17$. The function has zero change in the directions orthogonal to the gradient, which correspond to $\theta = \pi/4$ and $\theta = 5\pi/4$.

Figure 12.70 summarizes these conclusions. Notice that the gradient at $(2, 3)$ appears to be orthogonal to the level curve of f passing through $(2, 3)$. We next see that this is always the case.

Related Exercises 33–42 ◄

The Gradient and Level Curves

Theorem 12.11 states that in any direction orthogonal to the gradient $\nabla f(a, b)$, the function f does not change at (a, b). Recall from Section 12.2 that the curve $f(x, y) = z_0$, where z_0 is a constant, is a *level curve*, on which function values are constant. Combining these two observations, we conclude that the gradient $\nabla f(a, b)$ is orthogonal to the line tangent to the level curve through (a, b).

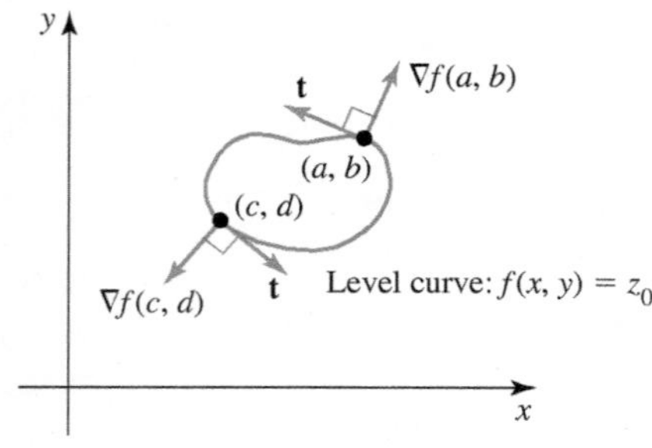

Figure 12.71

> **THEOREM 12.12 The Gradient and Level Curves**
> Given a function f differentiable at (a, b), the line tangent to the level curve of f at (a, b) is orthogonal to the gradient $\nabla f(a, b)$, provided $\nabla f(a, b) \neq \mathbf{0}$.

Proof: A level curve of the function $z = f(x, y)$ is a curve in the xy-plane of the form $f(x, y) = z_0$, where z_0 is a constant. By Theorem 12.9, the slope of the line tangent to the level curve is $y'(x) = -f_x/f_y$.

➤ We have used the fact that the vector $\langle a, b \rangle$ has slope b/a.

It follows that any vector pointing in the direction of the tangent line at the point (a, b) is a scalar multiple of the vector $\mathbf{t} = \langle -f_y(a, b), f_x(a, b) \rangle$ (Figure 12.71). At that same point, the gradient points in the direction $\nabla f(a, b) = \langle f_x(a, b), f_y(a, b) \rangle$. The dot product of $\mathbf{t}$ and $\nabla f(a, b)$ is

$$\begin{aligned} \mathbf{t} \cdot \nabla f(a, b) &= \langle -f_y(a, b), f_x(a, b) \rangle \cdot \langle f_x(a, b), f_y(a, b) \rangle \\ &= -f_x(a, b)\, f_y(a, b) + f_x(a, b) f_y(a, b) \\ &= 0 \end{aligned}$$

which implies that $\mathbf{t}$ and $\nabla f(a, b)$ are orthogonal. ◄

An immediate consequence of Theorem 12.12 is an alternative equation of the tangent line. The curve described by $f(x, y) = z_0$ can be viewed as a level curve in the xy-plane for a surface. By Theorem 12.12, the line tangent to the curve at (a, b) is orthogonal to $\nabla f(a, b)$. Therefore, if (x, y) is a point on the tangent line, then $\nabla f(a, b) \cdot \langle x - a, y - b \rangle = 0$, which, when simplified, gives an equation of the line tangent to the curve $f(x, y) = z_0$:

$$f_x(a, b)(x - a) + f_y(a, b)(y - b) = 0.$$

QUICK CHECK 4 Draw a circle in the xy-plane centered at the origin and regard it is as a level curve of the surface $z = x^2 + y^2$. At the point (a, a) of the level curve in the xy-plane, the slope of the tangent line is -1. Show that the gradient at (a, a) is orthogonal to the tangent line. ◄

EXAMPLE 6 Gradients and level curves Consider the upper sheet $z = f(x, y) = \sqrt{1 + 2x^2 + y^2}$ of a hyperboloid of two sheets.

a. Verify that the gradient at $(1, 1)$ is orthogonal to the corresponding level curve at that point.

b. Find an equation of the line tangent to the level curve at $(1, 1)$.

➤ The fact that $y' = -2x/y$ may also be obtained using Theorem 12.9: If $F(x, y) = 0$, then $y'(x) = -F_x/F_y$.

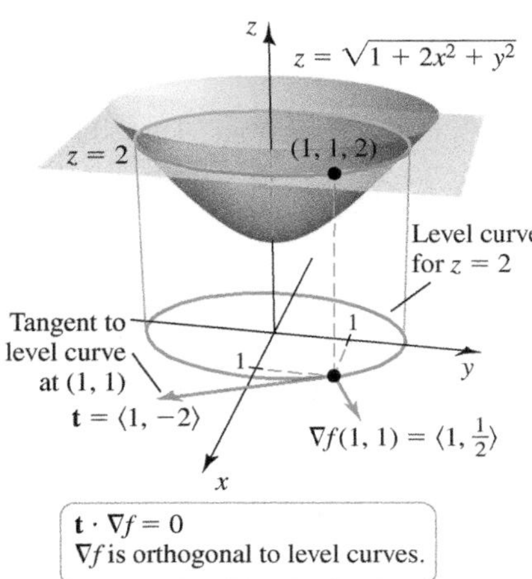

Figure 12.72

SOLUTION

a. You can verify that $(1, 1, 2)$ is on the surface; therefore, $(1, 1)$ is on the level curve corresponding to $z = 2$. Setting $z = 2$ in the equation of the surface and squaring both sides, the equation of the level curve is $4 = 1 + 2x^2 + y^2$, or $2x^2 + y^2 = 3$, which is the equation of an ellipse (Figure 12.72). Differentiating $2x^2 + y^2 = 3$ with respect to x gives $4x + 2yy'(x) = 0$, which implies that the slope of the level curve is $y'(x) = -\frac{2x}{y}$. Therefore, at the point $(1, 1)$, the slope of the tangent line is -2. Any vector proportional to $\mathbf{t} = \langle 1, -2 \rangle$ has slope -2 and points in the direction of the tangent line.

We now compute the gradient:

$$\nabla f(x, y) = \langle f_x, f_y \rangle = \left\langle \frac{2x}{\sqrt{1 + 2x^2 + y^2}}, \frac{y}{\sqrt{1 + 2x^2 + y^2}} \right\rangle.$$

It follows that $\nabla f(1, 1) = \langle 1, \frac{1}{2} \rangle$ (Figure 12.72). The tangent vector $\mathbf{t}$ and the gradient are orthogonal because

$$\mathbf{t} \cdot \nabla f(1, 1) = \langle 1, -2 \rangle \cdot \langle 1, \tfrac{1}{2} \rangle = 0.$$

b. An equation of the line tangent to the level curve at $(1, 1)$ is

$$\underbrace{f_x(1, 1)}_{1}(x - 1) + \underbrace{f_y(1, 1)}_{\frac{1}{2}}(y - 1) = 0,$$

or $y = -2x + 3$.

Related Exercises 43–50 ◄

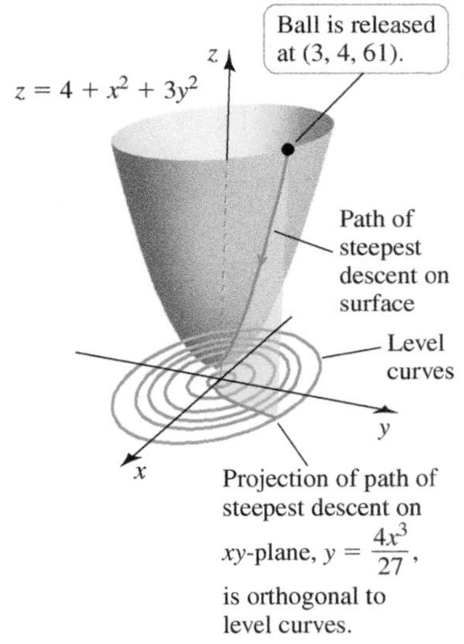

Figure 12.73

EXAMPLE 7 Path of steepest descent Consider the paraboloid $z = f(x, y) = 4 + x^2 + 3y^2$ (Figure 12.73). Beginning at the point $(3, 4, 61)$ on the surface, find the projection in the xy-plane of the path of steepest descent on the surface.

SOLUTION Imagine releasing a ball at $(3, 4, 61)$ and assume that it rolls in the direction of steepest descent at all points. The projection of this path in the xy-plane points in the direction of $-\nabla f(x, y) = \langle -2x, -6y \rangle$, which means that at the point (x, y), the line tangent to the path has slope $y'(x) = (-6y)/(-2x) = 3y/x$. Therefore, the path in the xy-plane satisfies $y'(x) = 3y/x$ and passes through the initial point $(3, 4)$. You can verify that the solution to this differential equation is $y = 4x^3/27$. Therefore, the projection of the path of steepest descent in the xy-plane is the curve $y = 4x^3/27$. The descent ends at $(0, 0)$, which corresponds to the vertex of the paraboloid (Figure 12.73). At all points of the descent, the curve in the xy-plane is orthogonal to the level curves of the surface.

Related Exercises 51–54 ◄

QUICK CHECK 5 Verify that $y = 4x^3/27$ satisfies the equation $y'(x) = 3y/x$, with $y(3) = 4$. ◄

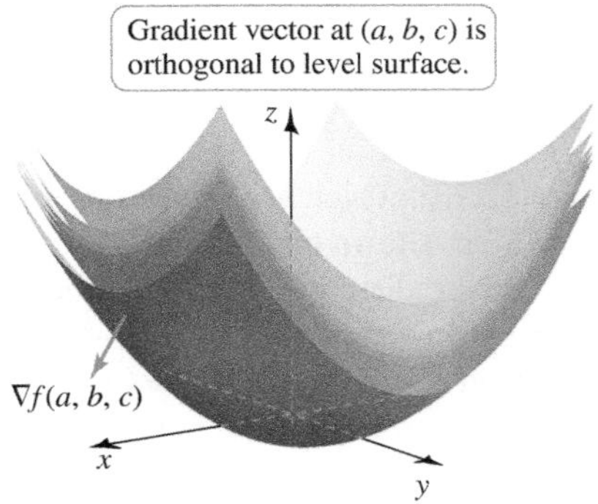

Figure 12.74

The Gradient in Three Dimensions

The directional derivative, the gradient, and the idea of a level curve extend immediately to functions of three variables of the form $w = f(x, y, z)$. The main differences are that the gradient is a vector in $\mathbb{R}^3$ and level curves become *level surfaces* (Section 12.2). Here is how the gradient looks when we step up one dimension.

The easiest way to visualize the surface $w = f(x, y, z)$ is to picture its level surfaces—the surfaces in $\mathbb{R}^3$ on which f has a constant value. The level surfaces are given by the equation $f(x, y, z) = C$, where C is a constant (Figure 12.74). The level surfaces *can* be graphed, and they may be viewed as layers of the full four-dimensional surface (like layers of an onion). With this image in mind, we now extend the concept of a gradient.

Given the function $w = f(x, y, z)$, we argue just as we did in the two-variable case and define the directional derivative. Given a unit vector $\mathbf{u} = \langle u_1, u_2, u_3 \rangle$, the directional derivative of f in the direction of $\mathbf{u}$ at the point (a, b, c) is

$$D_{\mathbf{u}}f(a, b, c) = f_x(a, b, c)\, u_1 + f_y(a, b, c)\, u_2 + f_z(a, b, c)\, u_3.$$

As before, we recognize this expression as a dot product of the vector $\mathbf{u}$ and the vector $\nabla f(x, y, z) = \left\langle \frac{\partial f}{\partial x}, \frac{\partial f}{\partial y}, \frac{\partial f}{\partial z} \right\rangle$, which is the *gradient* in three dimensions. Therefore, the directional derivative in the direction of $\mathbf{u}$ at the point (a, b, c) is

$$D_{\mathbf{u}}f(a, b, c) = \nabla f(a, b, c) \cdot \mathbf{u}.$$

➤ When we introduce the tangent plane in Section 12.7, we can also claim that $\nabla f(a, b, c)$ is orthogonal to the level surface that passes through (a, b, c).

Following the line of reasoning in the two-variable case, f has its maximum rate of *increase* in the direction of $\nabla f(a, b, c)$. The actual rate of increase is $|\nabla f(a, b, c)|$. Similarly, f has its maximum rate of *decrease* in the direction of $-\nabla f(a, b, c)$. Also, in all directions orthogonal to $\nabla f(a, b, c)$, the directional derivative at (a, b, c) is zero.

QUICK CHECK 6 Compute $\nabla f(-1, 2, 1)$, where $f(x, y, z) = xy/z$. ◀

DEFINITION Gradient and Directional Derivative in Three Dimensions

Let f be differentiable at the point (x, y, z). The **gradient** of f at (x, y, z) is the vector-valued function

$$\begin{aligned}\nabla f(x, y, z) &= \langle f_x(x, y, z), f_y(x, y, z), f_z(x, y, z) \rangle \\ &= f_x(x, y, z)\,\mathbf{i} + f_y(x, y, z)\,\mathbf{j} + f_z(x, y, z)\,\mathbf{k}.\end{aligned}$$

The **directional derivative** of f in the direction of the unit vector $\mathbf{u} = \langle u_1, u_2, u_3 \rangle$ at the point (a, b, c) is $D_{\mathbf{u}}f(a, b, c) = \nabla f(a, b, c) \cdot \mathbf{u}$.

EXAMPLE 8 Gradients in three dimensions Consider the function $f(x, y, z) = x^2 + 2y^2 + 4z^2 - 1$ and its level surface $f(x, y, z) = 3$.

a. Find and interpret the gradient at the points $P(2, 0, 0)$, $Q(0, \sqrt{2}, 0)$, $R(0, 0, 1)$, and $S\left(1, 1, \frac{1}{2}\right)$ on the level surface.

b. What are the actual rates of change of f in the directions of the gradients in part (a)?

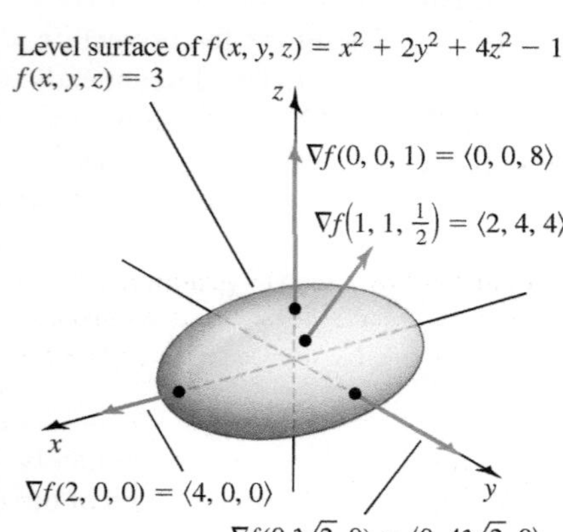

Figure 12.75

SOLUTION

a. The gradient is

$$\nabla f = \langle f_x, f_y, f_z \rangle = \langle 2x, 4y, 8z \rangle.$$

Evaluating the gradient at the four points we find that

$$\begin{aligned}\nabla f(2, 0, 0) &= \langle 4, 0, 0 \rangle, & \nabla f(0, \sqrt{2}, 0) &= \langle 0, 4\sqrt{2}, 0 \rangle, \\ \nabla f(0, 0, 1) &= \langle 0, 0, 8 \rangle, & \nabla f\left(1, 1, \tfrac{1}{2}\right) &= \langle 2, 4, 4 \rangle.\end{aligned}$$

The level surface $f(x, y, z) = 3$ is an ellipsoid (Figure 12.75), which is one layer of a four-dimensional surface. The four points P, Q, R, and S are shown on the level surface with the respective gradient vectors. In each case, the gradient points in the direction that f has its maximum rate of increase. Of particular importance is the fact—to be made clear in the next section—that at each point, the gradient is orthogonal to the level surface.

b. The actual rate of increase of f at (a, b, c) in the direction of the gradient is $|\nabla f(a, b, c)|$. At P, the rate of increase of f in the direction of the gradient is $|\langle 4, 0, 0 \rangle| = 4$; at Q, the rate of increase is $|\langle 0, 4\sqrt{2}, 0 \rangle| = 4\sqrt{2}$; at R, the rate of increase is $|\langle 0, 0, 8 \rangle| = 8$; and at S, the rate of increase is $|\langle 2, 4, 4 \rangle| = 6$.

Related Exercises 55–62 ◀

SECTION 12.6 EXERCISES

Review Questions

1. Explain how a directional derivative is formed from the two partial derivatives f_x and f_y.

2. How do you compute the gradient of the functions $f(x, y)$ and $f(x, y, z)$?

3. Interpret the direction of the gradient vector at a point.

4. Interpret the magnitude of the gradient vector at a point.

5. Given a function f, explain the relationship between the gradient and the level curves of f.

6. The level curves of the surface $z = x^2 + y^2$ are circles in the xy-plane centered at the origin. Without computing the gradient, what is the direction of the gradient at $(1, 1)$ and $(-1, -1)$ (determined up to a scalar multiple)?

Basic Skills

7. **Directional derivatives** Consider the function $f(x, y) = 8 - x^2/2 - y^2$, whose graph is a paraboloid (see figure).

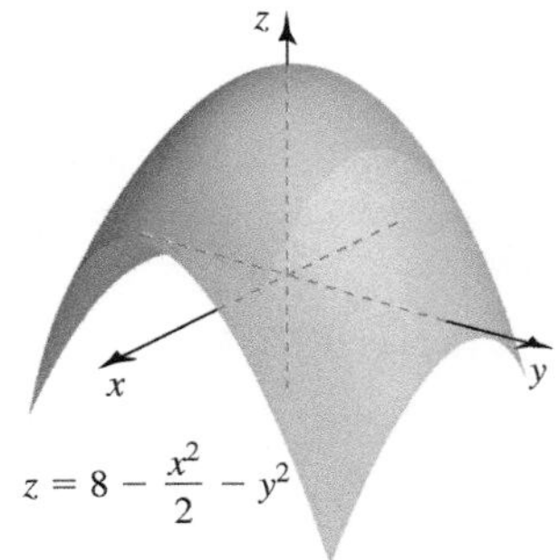

   a. Fill in the table with the values of the directional derivative at the points (a, b) in the directions given by the unit vectors **u**, **v**, and **w**.

	$(a,b) = (2,0)$	$(a,b) = (0,2)$	$(a,b) = (1,1)$
$\mathbf{u} = \langle \frac{\sqrt{2}}{2}, \frac{\sqrt{2}}{2} \rangle$			
$\mathbf{v} = \langle -\frac{\sqrt{2}}{2}, \frac{\sqrt{2}}{2} \rangle$			
$\mathbf{w} = \langle -\frac{\sqrt{2}}{2}, -\frac{\sqrt{2}}{2} \rangle$			

   b. Interpret each of the directional derivatives computed in part (a) at the point (2, 0).

8. **Directional derivatives** Consider the function $f(x, y) = 2x^2 + y^2$, whose graph is a paraboloid (see figure).

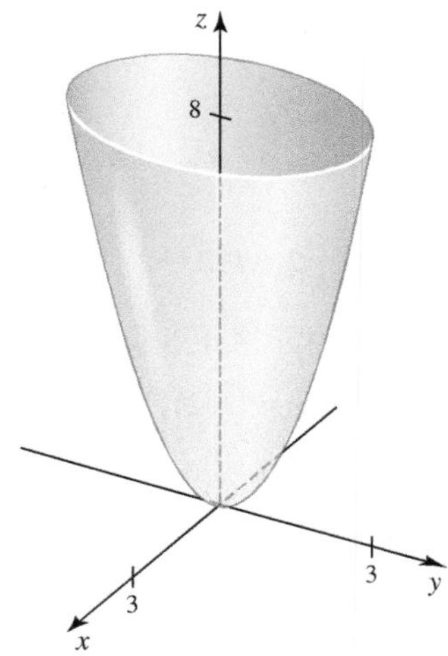

   a. Fill in the table with the values of the directional derivative at the points (a, b) in the directions given by the unit vectors **u**, **v**, and **w**.

	$(a,b) = (1,0)$	$(a,b) = (1,1)$	$(a,b) = (1,2)$
$\mathbf{u} = \langle 1, 0 \rangle$			
$\mathbf{v} = \langle \frac{\sqrt{2}}{2}, \frac{\sqrt{2}}{2} \rangle$			
$\mathbf{w} = \langle 0, 1 \rangle$			

   b. Interpret each of the directional derivatives computed in part (a) at the point (1, 0).

9–16. Computing gradients *Compute the gradient of the following functions and evaluate it at the given point P.*

9. $f(x, y) = 2 + 3x^2 - 5y^2;\ P(2, -1)$

10. $f(x, y) = 4x^2 - 2xy + y^2;\ P(-1, -5)$

11. $g(x, y) = x^2 - 4x^2y - 8xy^2;\ P(-1, 2)$

12. $p(x, y) = \sqrt{12 - 4x^2 - y^2};\ P(-1, -1)$

13. $f(x, y) = xe^{2xy};\ P(1, 0)$

14. $f(x, y) = \sin(3x + 2y);\ P(\pi, 3\pi/2)$

15. $F(x, y) = e^{-x^2-2y^2};\ P(-1, 2)$

16. $h(x, y) = \ln(1 + x^2 + 2y^2);\ P(2, -3)$

17–26. Computing directional derivatives with the gradient *Compute the directional derivative of the following functions at the given point P in the direction of the given vector. Be sure to use a unit vector for the direction vector.*

17. $f(x, y) = x^2 - y^2;\ P(-1, -3);\ \left\langle \frac{3}{5}, -\frac{4}{5} \right\rangle$

18. $f(x, y) = 3x^2 + y^3;\ P(3, 2);\ \left\langle \frac{5}{13}, \frac{12}{13} \right\rangle$

19. $f(x, y) = 10 - 3x^2 + \frac{y^4}{4}$; $P(2, -3)$; $\left\langle \frac{\sqrt{3}}{2}, -\frac{1}{2} \right\rangle$

20. $g(x, y) = \sin \pi(2x - y)$; $P(-1, -1)$; $\left\langle \frac{5}{13}, -\frac{12}{13} \right\rangle$

21. $f(x, y) = \sqrt{4 - x^2 - 2y}$; $P(2, -2)$; $\left\langle \frac{1}{\sqrt{5}}, \frac{2}{\sqrt{5}} \right\rangle$

22. $f(x, y) = 13e^{xy}$; $P(1, 0)$; $\langle 5, 12 \rangle$

23. $f(x, y) = 3x^2 + 2y + 5$; $P(1, 2)$; $\langle -3, 4 \rangle$

24. $h(x, y) = e^{-x-y}$; $P(\ln 2, \ln 3)$; $\langle 1, 1 \rangle$

25. $g(x, y) = \ln(4 + x^2 + y^2)$; $P(-1, 2)$; $\langle 2, 1 \rangle$

26. $f(x, y) = x/(x - y)$; $P(4, 1)$; $\langle -1, 2 \rangle$

27–32. Direction of steepest ascent and descent *Consider the following functions and points P.*

a. *Find the unit vectors that give the direction of steepest ascent and steepest descent at P.*
b. *Find a vector that points in a direction of no change in the function at P.*

27. $f(x, y) = x^2 - 4y^2 - 9$; $P(1, -2)$

28. $f(x, y) = x^2 + 4xy - y^2$; $P(2, 1)$

29. $f(x, y) = x^4 - x^2y + y^2 + 6$; $P(-1, 1)$

30. $p(x, y) = \sqrt{20 + x^2 + 2xy - y^2}$; $P(1, 2)$

31. $F(x, y) = e^{-x^2/2 - y^2/2}$; $P(-1, 1)$

32. $f(x, y) = 2\sin(2x - 3y)$; $P(0, \pi)$

33–38. Interpreting directional derivatives *A function f and a point P are given. Let θ correspond to the direction of the directional derivative.*

a. *Find the gradient and evaluate it at P.*
b. *Find the angles θ (with respect to the positive x-axis) associated with the directions of maximum increase, maximum decrease, and zero change.*
c. *Write the directional derivative at P as a function of θ; call this function g.*
d. *Find the value of θ that maximizes g(θ) and find the maximum value.*
e. *Verify that the value of θ that maximizes g corresponds to the direction of the gradient. Verify that the maximum value of g equals the magnitude of the gradient.*

33. $f(x, y) = 10 - 2x^2 - 3y^2$; $P(3, 2)$

34. $f(x, y) = 8 + x^2 + 3y^2$; $P(-3, -1)$

35. $f(x, y) = \sqrt{2 + x^2 + y^2}$; $P(\sqrt{3}, 1)$

36. $f(x, y) = \sqrt{12 - x^2 - y^2}$; $P(-1, -1/\sqrt{3})$

37. $f(x, y) = e^{-x^2 - 2y^2}$; $P(-1, 0)$

T 38. $f(x, y) = \ln(1 + 2x^2 + 3y^2)$; $P(\frac{3}{4}, -\sqrt{3})$

39–42. Directions of change *Consider the following functions f and points P. Sketch the xy-plane showing P and the level curve through P. Indicate (as in Figure 12.70) the directions of maximum increase, maximum decrease, and no change for f.*

39. $f(x, y) = 8 + 4x^2 + 2y^2$; $P(2, -4)$

40. $f(x, y) = -4 + 6x^2 + 3y^2$; $P(-1, -2)$

T 41. $f(x, y) = x^2 + xy + y^2 + 7$; $P(-3, 3)$

T 42. $f(x, y) = \tan(2x + 2y)$; $P(\pi/16, \pi/16)$

43–46. Level curves *Consider the paraboloid* $f(x, y) = 16 - x^2/4 - y^2/16$ *and the point P on the given level curve of f. Compute the slope of the line tangent to the level curve at P and verify that the tangent line is orthogonal to the gradient at that point.*

43. $f(x, y) = 0$; $P(0, 16)$

44. $f(x, y) = 0$; $P(8, 0)$

45. $f(x, y) = 12$; $P(4, 0)$

46. $f(x, y) = 12$; $P(2\sqrt{3}, 4)$

47–50. Level curves *Consider the upper half of the ellipsoid* $f(x, y) = \sqrt{1 - \frac{x^2}{4} - \frac{y^2}{16}}$ *and the point P on the given level curve of f. Compute the slope of the line tangent to the level curve at P and verify that the tangent line is orthogonal to the gradient at that point.*

47. $f(x, y) = \sqrt{3}/2$; $P(1/2, \sqrt{3})$

48. $f(x, y) = 1/\sqrt{2}$; $P(0, \sqrt{8})$

49. $f(x, y) = 1/\sqrt{2}$; $P(\sqrt{2}, 0)$

50. $f(x, y) = 1/\sqrt{2}$; $P(1, 2)$

51–54. Path of steepest descent *Consider each of the following surfaces and the point P on the surface.*

a. *Find the gradient of f.*
b. *Let C′ be the path of steepest descent on the surface beginning at P and let C be the projection of C′ on the xy-plane. Find an equation of C in the xy-plane.*

51. $f(x, y) = 4 + x$ (a plane); $P(4, 4, 8)$

52. $f(x, y) = y + x$ (a plane); $P(2, 2, 4)$

53. $f(x, y) = 4 - x^2 - 2y^2$ (a paraboloid); $P(1, 1, 1)$

54. $f(x, y) = y + x^{-1}$; $P(1, 2, 3)$

55–62. Gradients in three dimensions *Consider the following functions f, points P, and unit vectors* **u**.

a. *Compute the gradient of f and evaluate it at P.*
b. *Find the unit vector in the direction of maximum increase of f at P.*
c. *Find the rate of change of the function in the direction of maximum increase at P.*
d. *Find the directional derivative at P in the direction of the given vector.*

55. $f(x, y, z) = x^2 + 2y^2 + 4z^2 + 10$; $P(1, 0, 4)$; $\left\langle \frac{1}{\sqrt{2}}, 0, \frac{1}{\sqrt{2}} \right\rangle$

56. $f(x, y, z) = 4 - x^2 + 3y^2 + \frac{z^2}{2}$; $P(0, 2, -1)$; $\left\langle 0, \frac{1}{\sqrt{2}}, -\frac{1}{\sqrt{2}} \right\rangle$

57. $f(x, y, z) = 1 + 4xyz$; $P(1, -1, -1)$; $\left\langle \frac{1}{\sqrt{3}}, \frac{1}{\sqrt{3}}, -\frac{1}{\sqrt{3}} \right\rangle$

58. $f(x, y, z) = xy + yz + xz + 4$; $P(2, -2, 1)$; $\left\langle 0, -\frac{1}{\sqrt{2}}, -\frac{1}{\sqrt{2}} \right\rangle$

59. $f(x, y, z) = 1 + \sin(x + 2y - z)$; $P\left(\frac{\pi}{6}, \frac{\pi}{6}, -\frac{\pi}{6}\right)$; $\left\langle \frac{1}{3}, \frac{2}{3}, \frac{2}{3} \right\rangle$

60. $f(x, y, z) = e^{xyz - 1}$; $P(0, 1, -1)$; $\left\langle -\frac{2}{3}, \frac{2}{3}, -\frac{1}{3} \right\rangle$

61. $f(x, y, z) = \ln(1 + x^2 + y^2 + z^2)$; $P(1, 1, -1)$; $\left\langle \frac{2}{3}, \frac{2}{3}, -\frac{1}{3} \right\rangle$

62. $f(x, y, z) = \frac{x - z}{y - z}$; $P(3, 2, -1)$; $\left\langle \frac{1}{3}, \frac{2}{3}, -\frac{1}{3} \right\rangle$

Further Explorations

63. **Explain why or why not** Determine whether the following statements are true and give an explanation or counterexample.
   a. If $f(x, y) = x^2 + y^2 - 10$, then $\nabla f(x, y) = 2x + 2y$.
   b. Because the gradient gives the direction of maximum increase of a function, the gradient is always positive.
   c. The gradient of $f(x, y, z) = 1 + xyz$ has four components.
   d. If $f(x, y, z) = 4$, then $\nabla f = \mathbf{0}$.

64. **Gradient of a composite function** Consider the function $F(x, y, z) = e^{xyz}$.
   a. Write F as a composite function $f \circ g$, where f is a function of one variable and g is a function of three variables.
   b. Relate ∇F to ∇g.

65–68. Directions of zero change *Find the directions in the xy-plane in which the following functions have zero change at the given point. Express the directions in terms of unit vectors.*

65. $f(x, y) = 12 - 4x^2 - y^2$; $P(1, 2, 4)$

66. $f(x, y) = x^2 - 4y^2 - 8$; $P(4, 1, 4)$

67. $f(x, y) = \sqrt{3 + 2x^2 + y^2}$; $P(1, -2, 3)$

68. $f(x, y) = e^{1-xy}$; $P(1, 0, e)$

69. **Steepest ascent on a plane** Suppose a long sloping hillside is described by the plane $z = ax + by + c$, where a, b, and c are constants. Find the path in the xy-plane, beginning at (x_0, y_0), that corresponds to the path of steepest ascent on the hillside.

70. **Gradient of a distance function** Let (a, b) be a given point in $\mathbb{R}^2$ and let $d = f(x, y)$ be the distance between (a, b) and the variable point (x, y).
   a. Show that the graph of f is a cone.
   b. Show that the gradient of f at any point other than (a, b) is a unit vector.
   c. Interpret the direction and magnitude of ∇f.

71–74. Looking ahead—tangent planes *Consider the following surfaces $f(x, y, z) = 0$, which may be regarded as a level surface of the function $w = f(x, y, z)$. A point $P(a, b, c)$ on the surface is also given.*

a. Find the (three-dimensional) gradient of f and evaluate it at P.
b. The set of all vectors orthogonal to the gradient with their tails at P form a plane. Find an equation of that plane (soon to be called the tangent plane).

71. $f(x, y, z) = x^2 + y^2 + z^2 - 3 = 0$; $P(1, 1, 1)$

72. $f(x, y, z) = 8 - xyz = 0$; $P(2, 2, 2)$

73. $f(x, y, z) = e^{x+y-z} - 1 = 0$; $P(1, 1, 2)$

74. $f(x, y, z) = xy + xz - yz - 1$; $P(1, 1, 1)$

Applications

T 75. **A traveling wave** A snapshot (frozen in time) of a water wave is described by the function $z = 1 + \sin(x - y)$, where z gives the height of the wave and (x, y) are coordinates in the horizontal plane $z = 0$.
   a. Use a graphing utility to graph $z = 1 + \sin(x - y)$.
   b. The crests and the troughs of the waves are aligned in the direction in which the height function has zero change. Find the direction in which the crests and troughs are aligned.
   c. If you were surfing on this wave and wanted the steepest descent from a crest to a trough, in which direction would you point your surfboard (given in terms of a unit vector in the xy-plane)?
   d. Check that your answers to parts (b) and (c) are consistent with the graph of part (a).

76. **Traveling waves in general** Generalize Exercise 75 by considering a wave described by the function $z = A + \sin(ax - by)$, where a, b, and A are real numbers.
   a. Find the direction in which the crests and troughs of the wave are aligned. Express your answer as a unit vector in terms of a and b.
   b. Find the surfer's direction—that is, the direction of steepest descent from a crest to a trough. Express your answer as a unit vector in terms of a and b.

77–79. Potential functions *Potential functions arise frequently in physics and engineering. A potential function has the property that a field of interest (for example, an electric field, a gravitational field, or a velocity field) is the gradient of the potential (or sometimes the negative of the gradient of the potential). (Potential functions are considered in depth in Chapter 14.)*

77. **Electric potential due to a point charge** The electric field due to a point charge of strength Q at the origin has a potential function $\varphi = kQ/r$, where $r^2 = x^2 + y^2 + z^2$ is the square of the distance between a variable point $P(x, y, z)$ and the charge, and $k > 0$ is a physical constant. The electric field is given by $\mathbf{E} = -\nabla\varphi$, where $\nabla\varphi$ is the gradient in three dimensions.
   a. Show that the three-dimensional electric field due to a point charge is given by
   $$\mathbf{E}(x, y, z) = kQ\left\langle \frac{x}{r^3}, \frac{y}{r^3}, \frac{z}{r^3} \right\rangle.$$
   b. Show that the electric field at a point has a magnitude $|\mathbf{E}| = kQ/r^2$. Explain why this relationship is called an inverse square law.

78. **Gravitational potential** The gravitational potential associated with two objects of mass M and m is $\varphi = -GMm/r$, where G is the gravitational constant. If one of the objects is at the origin and the other object is at $P(x, y, z)$, then $r^2 = x^2 + y^2 + z^2$ is the square of the distance between the objects. The gravitational field at P is given by $\mathbf{F} = -\nabla\varphi$, where $\nabla\varphi$ is the gradient in three dimensions. Show that the force has a magnitude $|\mathbf{F}| = GMm/r^2$. Explain why this relationship is called an inverse square law.

79. **Velocity potential** In two dimensions, the motion of an ideal fluid (an incompressible and irrotational fluid) is governed by a velocity potential φ. The velocity components of the fluid, u in the x-direction and v in the y-direction, are given by

$\langle u, v \rangle = \nabla\varphi$. Find the velocity components associated with the velocity potential $\varphi(x, y) = \sin \pi x \sin 2\pi y$.

Additional Exercises

80. Gradients for planes Prove that for the plane described by $f(x, y) = Ax + By$, where A and B are nonzero constants, the gradient is constant (independent of (x, y)). Interpret this result.

81. Rules for gradients Use the definition of the gradient (in two or three dimensions), assume that f and g are differentiable functions on $\mathbb{R}^2$ or $\mathbb{R}^3$, and let c be a constant. Prove the following gradient rules.

a. Constants Rule: $\nabla(cf) = c\nabla f$
b. Sum Rule: $\nabla(f + g) = \nabla f + \nabla g$
c. Product Rule: $\nabla(fg) = (\nabla f)g + f\nabla g$
d. Quotient Rule: $\nabla\left(\dfrac{f}{g}\right) = \dfrac{g\nabla f - f\nabla g}{g^2}$
e. Chain Rule: $\nabla(f \circ g) = f'(g)\nabla g$, where f is a function of one variable

82–87. Using gradient rules *Use the gradient rules of Exercise 81 to find the gradient of the following functions.*

82. $f(x, y) = xy \cos xy$

83. $f(x, y) = \dfrac{x + y}{x^2 + y^2}$

84. $f(x, y) = \ln(1 + x^2 + y^2)$

85. $f(x, y, z) = \sqrt{25 - x^2 - y^2 - z^2}$

86. $f(x, y, z) = (x + y + z)\, e^{xyz}$

87. $f(x, y, z) = \dfrac{x + yz}{y + xz}$

QUICK CHECK ANSWERS

1. If $\mathbf{u} = \langle u_1, u_2 \rangle = \langle 1, 0 \rangle$ then

$$D_{\mathbf{u}}f(a, b) = \lim_{h\to 0} \frac{f(a + hu_1, b + hu_2) - f(a, b)}{h} = \lim_{h\to 0} \frac{f(a + h, b) - f(a, b)}{h} = f_x(a, b).$$

Similarly, when $\mathbf{u} = \langle 0, 1 \rangle$, the partial derivative $f_y(a, b)$ results. **2.** The vector from (a, b) to $(a + \Delta s u_1, b + \Delta s u_2)$ is $\langle \Delta s u_1, \Delta s u_2 \rangle = \Delta s \langle u_1, u_2 \rangle = \Delta s\mathbf{u}$. Its length is $|\Delta s \mathbf{u}| = \Delta s|\mathbf{u}| = \Delta s$. Therefore, s measures arc length. **3.** Reversing (negating) the direction vector negates the directional derivative. So the respective values are approximately -2.47 and 0.98. **4.** The gradient is $\langle 2x, 2y \rangle$, which, evaluated at (a, a), is $\langle 2a, 2a \rangle$. Taking the dot product of the gradient and the vector $\langle -1, 1 \rangle$ (a vector parallel to a line of slope -1), we see that $\langle 2a, 2a \rangle \cdot \langle -1, 1 \rangle = 0$. **6.** $\langle 2, -1, 2 \rangle$ ◄

12.7 Tangent Planes and Linear Approximation

In Section 4.5, we saw that if we zoom in on a point on a smooth curve (one described by a differentiable function), the curve looks more and more like the tangent line at that point. Once we have the tangent line at a point, it can be used to approximate function values and to estimate changes in the dependent variable. In this section, the analogous story is developed in three dimensions. Now we see that differentiability at a point (as discussed in Section 12.4) implies the existence of a tangent *plane* at that point (Figure 12.76).

Consider a smooth surface described by a differentiable function f and focus on a single point on the surface. As we zoom in on that point (Figure 12.77), the surface appears more and more like a plane. The first step is to define this plane carefully; it is called the *tangent plane*. Once we have the tangent plane, we can use it to approximate function values and to estimate changes in the dependent variable.

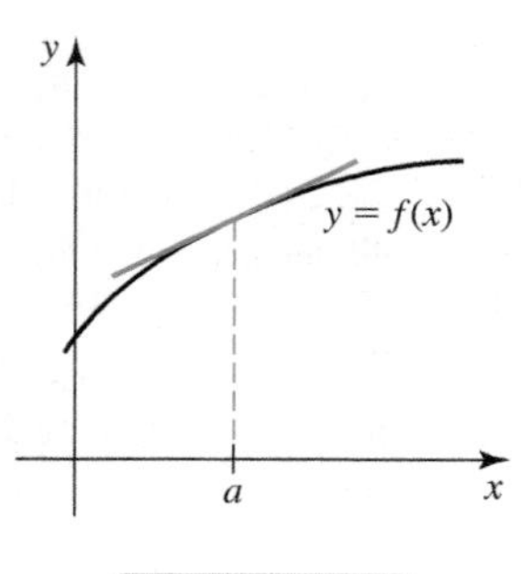

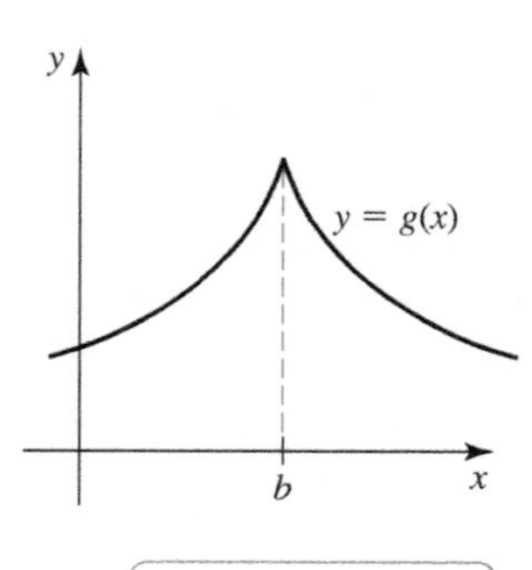

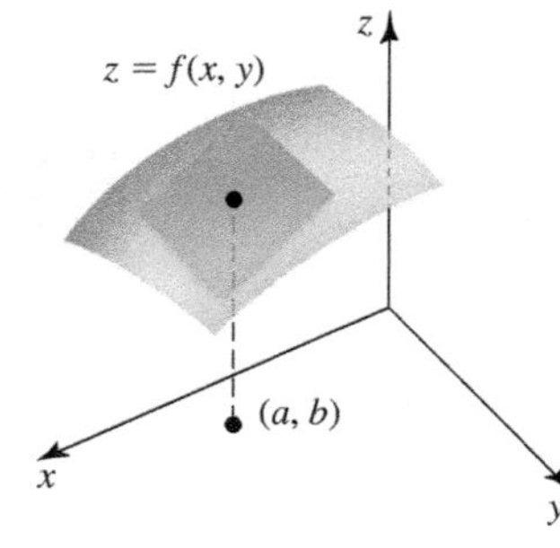

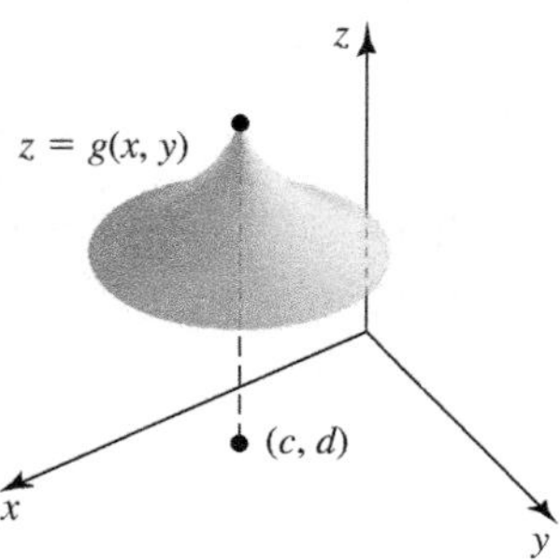

Figure 12.76

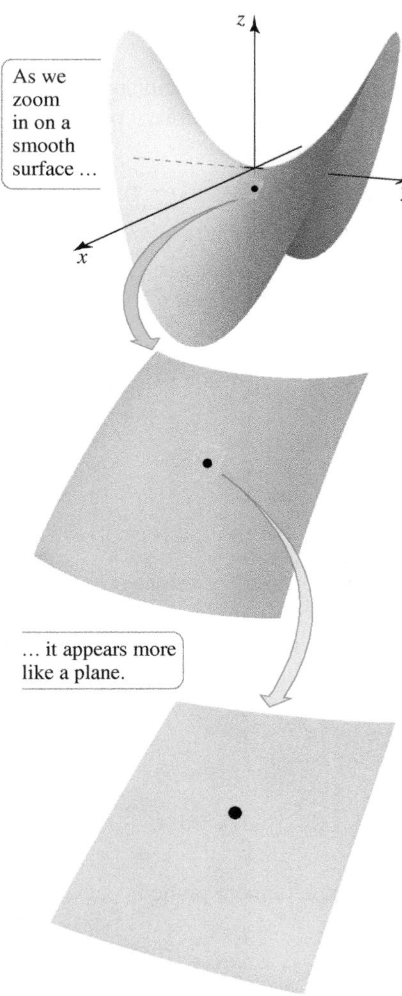

Figure 12.77

Tangent Planes

Recall that a surface in $\mathbb{R}^3$ may be defined in at least two different ways:

- **Explicitly** in the form $z = f(x, y)$ or
- **Implicitly** in the form $F(x, y, z) = 0$.

It is easiest to begin by considering a surface defined implicitly by $F(x, y, z) = 0$, where F is differentiable at a particular point. Such a surface may be viewed as a level surface of a function $w = F(x, y, z)$; it is the level surface for $w = 0$.

QUICK CHECK 1 Write the function $z = xy + x - y$ in the form $F(x, y, z) = 0$. ◄

Tangent Planes for $F(x, y, z) = 0$ To find an equation of the tangent plane, consider a smooth curve C: $\mathbf{r} = \langle x(t), y(t), z(t) \rangle$ that lies on the surface $F(x, y, z) = 0$ (Figure 12.78a). Because the points of C lie on the surface, we have $F(x(t), y(t), z(t)) = 0$. Differentiating both sides of this equation with respect to t, a useful relationship emerges. The derivative of the right side is 0. The Chain Rule applied to the left side yields

$$\begin{aligned} \frac{d}{dt}\big(F(x(t), y(t), z(t))\big) &= \frac{\partial F}{\partial x}\frac{dx}{dt} + \frac{\partial F}{\partial y}\frac{dy}{dt} + \frac{\partial F}{\partial z}\frac{dz}{dt} \\ &= \underbrace{\left\langle \frac{\partial F}{\partial x}, \frac{\partial F}{\partial y}, \frac{\partial F}{\partial z} \right\rangle}_{\nabla F(x, y, z)} \cdot \underbrace{\left\langle \frac{dx}{dt}, \frac{dy}{dt}, \frac{dz}{dt} \right\rangle}_{\mathbf{r}'(t)} \\ &= \nabla F(x, y, z) \cdot \mathbf{r}'(t). \end{aligned}$$

Therefore, $\nabla F(x, y, z) \cdot \mathbf{r}'(t) = 0$ and at any point on the curve, the tangent vector $\mathbf{r}'(t)$ is orthogonal to the gradient.

Now fix a point $P_0(a, b, c)$ on the surface, assume that $\nabla F(a, b, c) \neq \mathbf{0}$, and let C be any smooth curve on the surface passing through P_0. We have shown that any vector tangent to C is orthogonal to $\nabla F(a, b, c)$ at P_0. Because this argument applies to *all* smooth curves on the surface passing through P_0, the tangent vectors for all these curves (with their tails at P_0) are orthogonal to $\nabla F(a, b, c)$; therefore, they all lie in the same plane (Figure 12.78b). This plane is called the *tangent plane* at P_0. We can easily find an equation of the tangent plane because we know both a point on the plane $P_0(a, b, c)$ and a normal vector $\nabla F(a, b, c)$; an equation is

$$\nabla F(a, b, c) \cdot \langle x - a, y - b, z - c \rangle = 0.$$

➤ Recall that an equation of the plane passing though (a, b, c) with a normal vector $\mathbf{n} = \langle n_1, n_2, n_3 \rangle$ is $n_1(x - a) + n_2(y - b) + n_3(z - c) = 0$.

➤ If $\mathbf{r}$ is a position vector corresponding to an arbitrary point on the tangent plane and $\mathbf{r}_0$ is a position vector corresponding to a fixed point (a, b, c) on the plane, then an equation of the tangent plane may be written concisely as

$$\nabla F(a, b, c) \cdot (\mathbf{r} - \mathbf{r}_0) = 0.$$

Notice the analogy with tangent lines and level curves (Section 12.6). An equation of the line tangent to $f(x, y) = 0$ at (a, b) is

$$\nabla f(a, b) \cdot \langle x - a, y - b \rangle = 0.$$

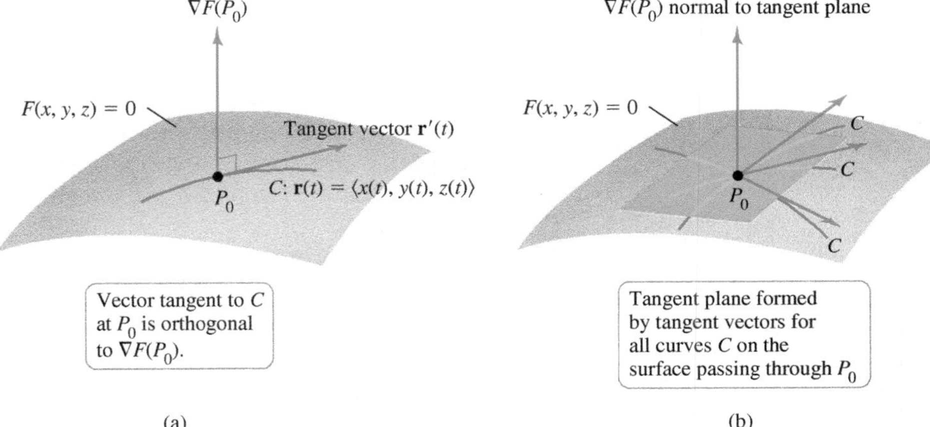

Figure 12.78

> **DEFINITION Equation of the Tangent Plane for $F(x, y, z) = 0$**
>
> Let F be differentiable at the point $P_0(a, b, c)$ with $\nabla F(a, b, c) \neq \mathbf{0}$. The plane tangent to the surface $F(x, y, z) = 0$ at P_0, called the **tangent plane**, is the plane passing through P_0 orthogonal to $\nabla F(a, b, c)$. An equation of the tangent plane is
>
> $$F_x(a, b, c)(x - a) + F_y(a, b, c)(y - b) + F_z(a, b, c)(z - c) = 0.$$

EXAMPLE 1 Equation of a tangent plane Consider the ellipsoid

$$F(x, y, z) = \frac{x^2}{9} + \frac{y^2}{25} + z^2 - 1 = 0.$$

a. Find the equation of the plane tangent to the ellipsoid at $\left(0, 4, \frac{3}{5}\right)$.

b. At what points on the ellipsoid is the tangent plane horizontal?

SOLUTION

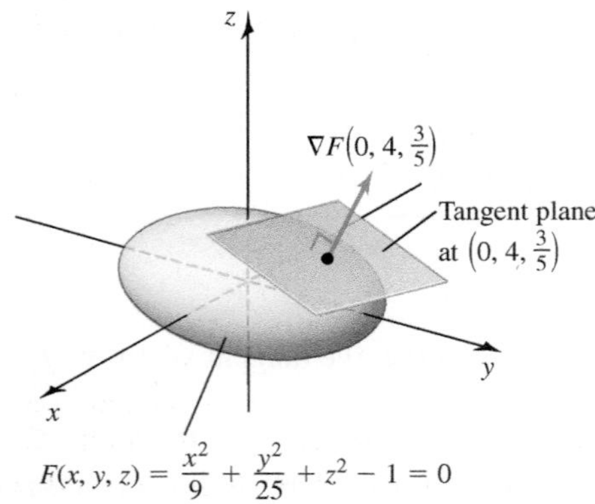

Figure 12.79

a. Notice that we have written the equation of the ellipsoid in the implicit form $F(x, y, z) = 0$. The gradient of F is $\nabla F(x, y, z) = \left\langle \frac{2x}{9}, \frac{2y}{25}, 2z \right\rangle$. Evaluated at $\left(0, 4, \frac{3}{5}\right)$, we have

$$\nabla F\left(0, 4, \frac{3}{5}\right) = \left\langle 0, \frac{8}{25}, \frac{6}{5} \right\rangle.$$

An equation of the tangent plane at this point is

$$0 \cdot (x - 0) + \frac{8}{25}(y - 4) + \frac{6}{5}\left(z - \frac{3}{5}\right) = 0,$$

or $4y + 15z = 25$. The equation does not involve x, so the tangent plane is parallel to (does not intersect) the x-axis (Figure 12.79).

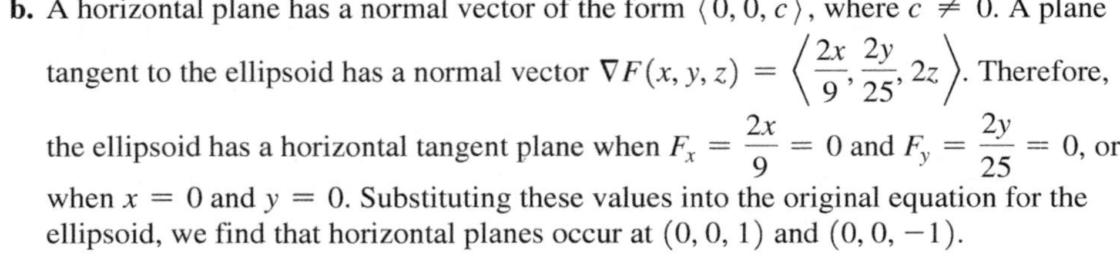

b. A horizontal plane has a normal vector of the form $\langle 0, 0, c \rangle$, where $c \neq 0$. A plane tangent to the ellipsoid has a normal vector $\nabla F(x, y, z) = \left\langle \frac{2x}{9}, \frac{2y}{25}, 2z \right\rangle$. Therefore, the ellipsoid has a horizontal tangent plane when $F_x = \frac{2x}{9} = 0$ and $F_y = \frac{2y}{25} = 0$, or when $x = 0$ and $y = 0$. Substituting these values into the original equation for the ellipsoid, we find that horizontal planes occur at $(0, 0, 1)$ and $(0, 0, -1)$.

Related Exercises 9–16 ◀

➤ This result extends Theorem 12.12, which states that for functions $f(x, y) = 0$, the gradient at a point is orthogonal to the level curve that passes through that point.

The preceding discussion allows us to confirm a claim made in Section 12.6. The surface $F(x, y, z) = 0$ is a level surface of the function $w = F(x, y, z)$ (corresponding to $w = 0$). At any point on that surface, the tangent plane has a normal vector $\nabla F(x, y, z)$. Therefore, the gradient $\nabla F(x, y, z)$ is orthogonal to the level surface $F(x, y, z) = 0$ at all points of the domain at which F is differentiable.

➤ To be clear, when $F(x, y, z) = z - f(x, y)$, we have $F_x = -f_x$, $F_y = -f_y$, and $F_z = 1$.

Tangent Planes for $z = f(x, y)$ Surfaces in $\mathbb{R}^3$ are often defined explicitly in the form $z = f(x, y)$. In this situation, the equation of the tangent plane is a special case of the general equation just derived. The equation $z = f(x, y)$ is written as $F(x, y, z) = z - f(x, y) = 0$, and the gradient of F at the point $(a, b, f(a, b))$ is

$$\begin{aligned}\nabla F(a, b, f(a, b)) &= \langle F_x(a, b, f(a, b)), F_y(a, b, f(a, b)), F_z(a, b, f(a, b)) \rangle \\ &= \langle -f_x(a, b), -f_y(a, b), 1 \rangle.\end{aligned}$$

Using the tangent plane definition, an equation of the plane tangent to the surface $z = f(x, y)$ at the point $(a, b, f(a, b))$ is

$$-f_x(a, b)(x - a) - f_y(a, b)(y - b) + 1(z - f(a, b)) = 0.$$

After some rearranging, we obtain an equation of the tangent plane.

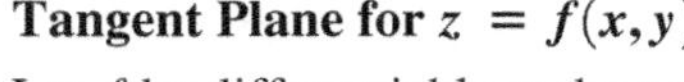

Tangent Plane for $z = f(x, y)$

Let f be differentiable at the point (a, b). An equation of the plane tangent to the surface $z = f(x, y)$ at the point $(a, b, f(a, b))$ is

$$z = f_x(a, b)(x - a) + f_y(a, b)(y - b) + f(a, b).$$

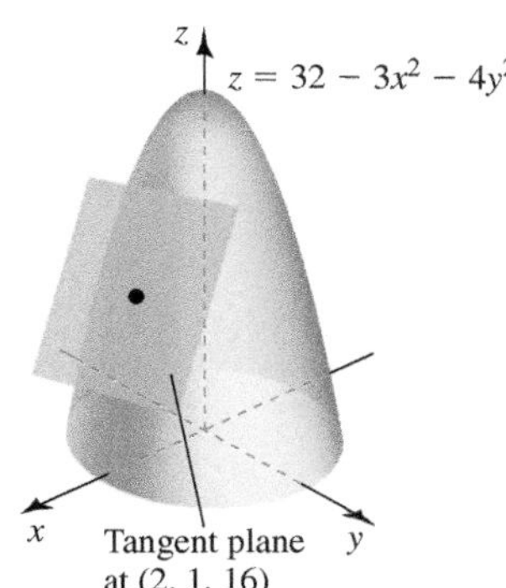

Figure 12.80

EXAMPLE 2 **Tangent plane for $z = f(x, y)$** Find an equation of the plane tangent to the paraboloid $z = f(x, y) = 32 - 3x^2 - 4y^2$ at $(2, 1, 16)$.

SOLUTION The partial derivatives are $f_x = -6x$ and $f_y = -8y$. Evaluating the partial derivatives at $(2, 1)$, we have $f_x(2, 1) = -12$ and $f_y(2, 1) = -8$. Therefore, an equation of the tangent plane (Figure 12.80) is

$$\begin{aligned} z &= f_x(a, b)(x - a) + f_y(a, b)(y - b) + f(a, b) \\ &= -12(x - 2) - 8(y - 1) + 16 \\ &= -12x - 8y + 48. \end{aligned}$$

Related Exercises 17–24 ◀

➤ The term *linear approximation* applies in both $\mathbb{R}^2$ and $\mathbb{R}^3$ because lines in $\mathbb{R}^2$ and planes in $\mathbb{R}^3$ are described by linear functions of the independent variables. In both cases, we call the linear approximation L.

Linear Approximation

With a function of the form $y = f(x)$, the tangent line at a point often gives good approximations to the function near that point. A straightforward extension of this idea applies to approximating functions of two variables with tangent planes. As before, the method is called *linear approximation.*

Figure 12.81 shows the details of linear approximation in the one- and two-variable cases. In the one-variable case (Section 4.5), if f is differentiable at a, the equation of the line tangent to the curve $y = f(x)$ at the point $(a, f(a))$ is

$$L(x) = f(a) + f'(a)(x - a).$$

The tangent line gives an approximation to the function. At points near a, we have $f(x) \approx L(x)$.

The two-variable case is analogous. If f is differentiable at (a, b), an equation of the plane tangent to the surface $z = f(x, y)$ at the point $(a, b, f(a, b))$ is

$$L(x, y) = f_x(a, b)(x - a) + f_y(a, b)(y - b) + f(a, b).$$

This tangent plane is the linear approximation to f at (a, b). At points near (a, b), we have $f(x, y) \approx L(x, y)$.

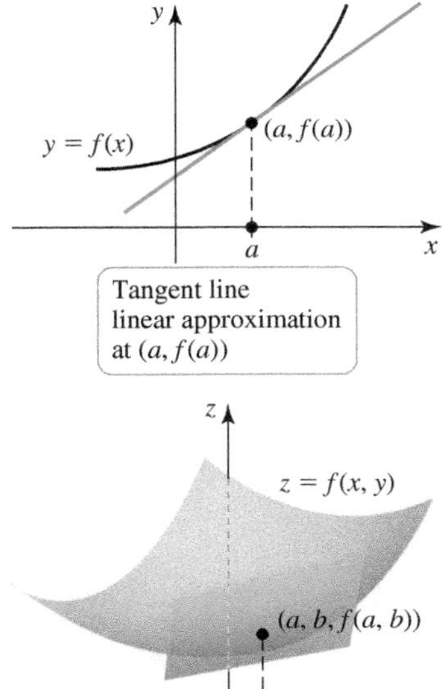

Figure 12.81

DEFINITION **Linear Approximation**

Let f be differentiable at (a, b). The linear approximation to the surface $z = f(x, y)$ at the point $(a, b, f(a, b))$ is the tangent plane at that point, given by the equation

$$L(x, y) = f_x(a, b)(x - a) + f_y(a, b)(y - b) + f(a, b).$$

EXAMPLE 3 **Linear approximation** Let $f(x, y) = \dfrac{5}{x^2 + y^2}$.

a. Find the linear approximation to the function at the point $(-1, 2, 1)$.

b. Use the linear approximation to estimate the value of $f(-1.05, 2.1)$.

SOLUTION

a. The partial derivatives of f are

$$f_x = -\frac{10x}{(x^2 + y^2)^2} \quad \text{and} \quad f_y = -\frac{10y}{(x^2 + y^2)^2}.$$

Evaluated at $(-1, 2)$, we have $f_x(-1, 2) = \frac{2}{5} = 0.4$ and $f_y(-1, 2) = -\frac{4}{5} = -0.8$. Therefore, the linear approximation to the function at $(-1, 2, 1)$ is

$$\begin{aligned} L(x, y) &= f_x(-1, 2)(x - (-1)) + f_y(-1, 2)(y - 2) + f(-1, 2) \\ &= 0.4(x + 1) - 0.8(y - 2) + 1 \\ &= 0.4x - 0.8y + 3. \end{aligned}$$

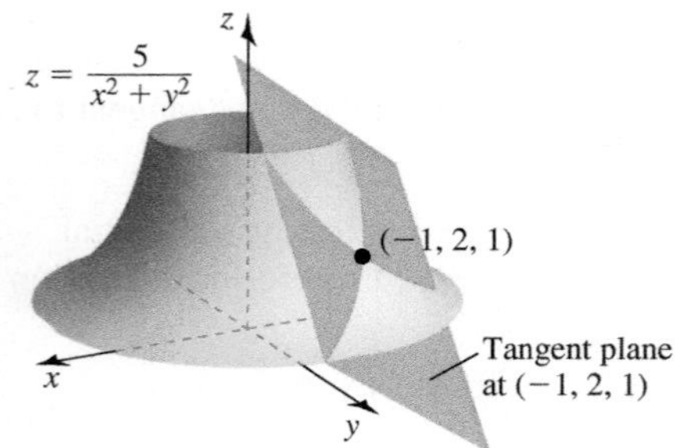

Figure 12.82

The surface and the tangent plane are shown in Figure 12.82.

b. The value of the function at the point $(-1.05, 2.1)$ is approximated by the value of the linear approximation at that point, which is

$$L(-1.05, 2.1) = 0.4(-1.05) - 0.8(2.1) + 3 = 0.90.$$

➤ Relative error $= \dfrac{|\text{approximation} - \text{exact value}|}{|\text{exact value}|}$

In this case, we can easily evaluate $f(-1.05, 2.1) \approx 0.907$ and compare the linear approximation with the exact value; the approximation has a relative error of about 0.8%.

Related Exercises 25–30 ◀

QUICK CHECK 2 Look at the graph of the surface in Example 3 (Figure 12.82) and explain why $f_x(-1, 2) > 0$ and $f_y(-1, 2) < 0$. ◀

Differentials and Change

Recall that for a function of the form $y = f(x)$, if the independent variable changes from x to $x + dx$, the corresponding change Δy in the dependent variable is approximated by the differential $dy = f'(x)\, dx$, which is the change in the linear approximation. Therefore, $\Delta y \approx dy$, with the approximation improving as dx approaches 0.

For functions of the form $z = f(x, y)$, we start with the linear approximation to the surface

$$f(x, y) \approx L(x, y) = f_x(a, b)(x - a) + f_y(a, b)(y - b) + f(a, b).$$

The exact change in the function between the points (a, b) and (x, y) is

$$\Delta z = f(x, y) - f(a, b).$$

Replacing $f(x, y)$ with its linear approximation, the change Δz is approximated by

$$\Delta z \approx \underbrace{L(x, y) - f(a, b)}_{dz} = f_x(a, b)\underbrace{(x - a)}_{dx} + f_y(a, b)\underbrace{(y - b)}_{dy}.$$

➤ Alternative notation for the differential at (a, b) is $dz|_{(a,b)}$ or $df|_{(a,b)}$.

The change in the x-coordinate is $dx = x - a$ and the change in the y-coordinate is $dy = y - b$ (Figure 12.83). As before, we let the differential dz denote the change in the linear approximation. Therefore, the approximate change in the z-coordinate is

$$\Delta z \approx dz = \underbrace{f_x(a, b)\, dx}_{\substack{\text{change in } z \text{ due} \\ \text{to change in } x}} + \underbrace{f_y(a, b)\, dy}_{\substack{\text{change in } z \text{ due} \\ \text{to change in } y}}.$$

This expression says that if we move the independent variables from (a, b) to $(x, y) = (a + dx, b + dy)$, the corresponding change in the dependent variable Δz has two contributions—one due to the change in x and one due to the change in y. If dx and dy are small in magnitude, then so is Δz. The approximation $\Delta z \approx dz$ improves as dx and dy approach 0. The relationships among the differentials are illustrated in Figure 12.83.

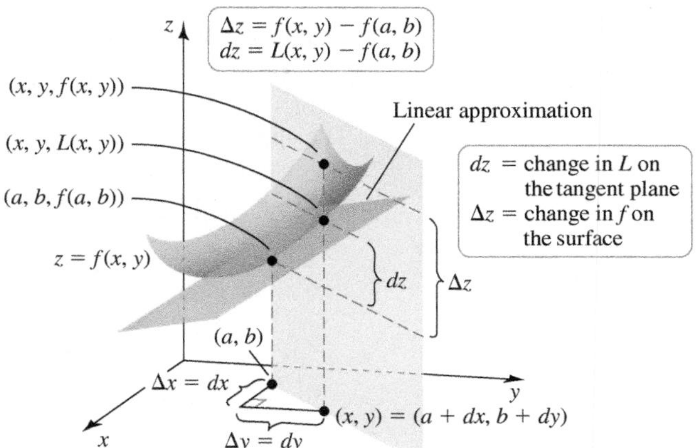

Figure 12.83

QUICK CHECK 3 Explain why, if $dx = 0$ or $dy = 0$ in the change formula for Δz, the result is the change formula for one variable. ◄

> **DEFINITION The differential dz**
>
> Let f be differentiable at the point (a, b). The change in $z = f(x, y)$ as the independent variables change from (a, b) to $(a + dx, b + dy)$ is denoted Δz and is approximated by the differential dz:
>
> $$\Delta z \approx dz = f_x(a, b)\, dx + f_y(a, b)\, dy.$$

EXAMPLE 4 Approximating function change Let $z = f(x, y) = \dfrac{5}{x^2 + y^2}$. Approximate the change in z when the independent variables change from $(-1, 2)$ to $(-0.93, 1.94)$.

SOLUTION If the independent variables change from $(-1, 2)$ to $(-0.93, 1.94)$, then $dx = 0.07$ (an increase) and $dy = -0.06$ (a decrease). Using the values of the partial derivatives evaluated in Example 3, the corresponding change in z is approximately

$$\begin{aligned} dz &= f_x(-1, 2)\, dx + f_y(-1, 2)\, dy \\ &= 0.4(0.07) + (-0.8)(-0.06) \\ &= 0.076. \end{aligned}$$

Again, we can check the accuracy of the approximation. The actual change is $f(-0.93, 1.94) - f(-1, 2) \approx 0.080$, so the approximation has a 5% error.

Related Exercises 31–34 ◄

EXAMPLE 5 **Body mass index** The body mass index (BMI) for an adult human is given by the function $B(w, h) = w/h^2$, where w is weight measured in kilograms and h is height measured in meters.

a. Use differentials to approximate the change in the BMI when weight increases from 55 to 56.5 kg and height increases from 1.65 to 1.66 m.

b. Which produces a greater *percentage* change in the BMI, a 1% change in the weight (at a constant height) or a 1% change in the height (at a constant weight)?

SOLUTION

a. The approximate change in the BMI is $dB = B_w\,dw + B_h\,dh$, where the derivatives are evaluated at $w = 55$ and $h = 1.65$, and the changes in the independent variables are $dw = 1.5$ and $dh = 0.01$. Evaluating the partial derivatives, we find that

$$B_w(w, h) = \frac{1}{h^2}, \qquad B_w(55, 1.65) \approx 0.37,$$

$$B_h(w, h) = -\frac{2w}{h^3}, \qquad B_h(55, 1.65) \approx -24.49.$$

Therefore, the approximate change in the BMI is

$$\begin{aligned} dB &= B_w(55, 1.65)\,dw + B_h(55, 1.65)\,dh \\ &\approx (0.37)(1.5) + (-24.49)(0.01) \\ &\approx 0.56 - 0.25 \\ &= 0.31. \end{aligned}$$

As expected, an increase in weight *increases* the BMI, while an increase in height *decreases* the BMI. In this case, the two contributions combine for a net increase in the BMI.

b. The changes dw, dh, and dB that appear in the differential change formula in part (a) are *absolute changes*. The corresponding *relative*, or *percentage*, changes are $\frac{dw}{w}$, $\frac{dh}{h}$, and $\frac{dB}{B}$. To introduce relative changes into the change formula, we divide both sides of $dB = B_w\,dw + B_h\,dh$ by $B = w/h^2 = wh^{-2}$. The result is

$$\begin{aligned} \frac{dB}{B} &= B_w \frac{dw}{wh^{-2}} + B_h \frac{dh}{wh^{-2}} \\ &= \frac{1}{h^2}\frac{dw}{wh^{-2}} - \frac{2w}{h^3}\frac{dh}{wh^{-2}} \qquad \text{Substitute for } B_w \text{ and } B_h. \\ &= \underbrace{\frac{dw}{w}}_{\substack{\text{relative}\\ \text{change}\\ \text{in } w}} - 2\underbrace{\frac{dh}{h}}_{\substack{\text{relative}\\ \text{change}\\ \text{in } h}}. \qquad \text{Simplify.} \end{aligned}$$

➤ See Exercises 64–65 for general results about relative or percentage changes in functions.

This expression relates the relative changes in w, h, and B. With h constant ($dh = 0$), a 1% change in w ($dw/w = 0.01$) produces approximately a 1% change of the same sign in B. With w constant ($dw = 0$), a 1% change in h ($dh/h = 0.01$) produces approximately a 2% change in B of the opposite sign. We see that the BMI formula is more sensitive to small changes in h than in w.

Related Exercises 35–38 ◄

QUICK CHECK 4 In Example 5, interpret the facts that $B_w > 0$ and $B_h < 0$, for $w, h > 0$. ◄

The differential for functions of two variables extends naturally to more variables. For example, if f is differentiable at (a, b, c) with $w = f(x, y, z)$, then

$$dw = f_x(a, b, c)\,dx + f_y(a, b, c)\,dy + f_z(a, b, c)\,dz.$$

The differential dw (or df) gives the approximate change in f at the point (a, b, c) due to changes of dx, dy, and dz in the independent variables.

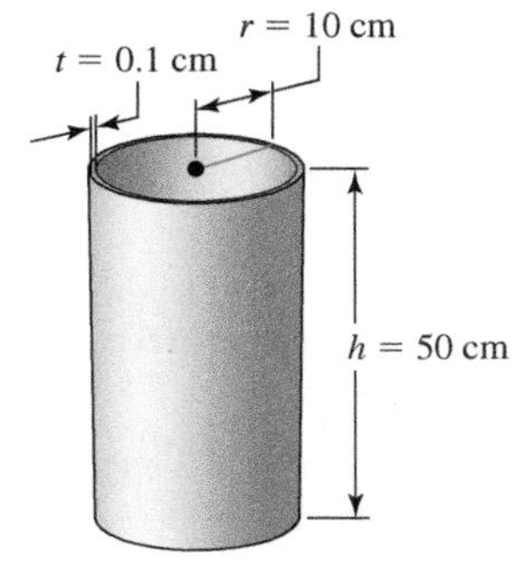

Figure 12.84

EXAMPLE 6 Manufacturing errors A company manufactures cylindrical aluminum tubes to rigid specifications. The tubes are designed to have an outside radius of $r = 10$ cm, a height of $h = 50$ cm, and a thickness of $t = 0.1$ cm (Figure 12.84). The manufacturing process produces tubes with a maximum error of ± 0.05 cm in the radius and height and a maximum error of ± 0.0005 cm in the thickness. The volume of the material used to construct a cylindrical tube is $V(r, h, t) = \pi h t(2r - t)$. Use differentials to estimate the maximum error in the volume of a tube.

SOLUTION The approximate change in the volume of a tube due to changes dr, dh, and dt in the radius, height, and thickness, respectively, is

$$dV = V_r\, dr + V_h\, dh + V_t\, dt.$$

The partial derivatives evaluated at $r = 10$, $h = 50$, and $t = 0.1$ are

$$\begin{aligned} V_r(r, h, t) &= 2\pi h t, & V_r(10, 50, 0.1) &= 10\pi, \\ V_h(r, h, t) &= \pi t(2r - t), & V_h(10, 50, 0.1) &= 1.99\pi, \\ V_t(r, h, t) &= 2\pi h(r - t), & V_t(10, 50, 0.1) &= 990\pi. \end{aligned}$$

We let $dr = dh = 0.05$ and $dt = 0.0005$ be the maximum errors in the radius, height, and thickness, respectively. The maximum error in the volume is approximately

$$\begin{aligned} dV &= V_r(10, 50, 0.1)\, dr + V_h(10, 50, 0.1)\, dh + V_t(10, 50, 0.1)\, dt \\ &= 10\pi(0.05) + 1.99\pi(0.05) + 990\pi(0.0005) \\ &\approx 1.57 + 0.31 + 1.56 \\ &= 3.44. \end{aligned}$$

The maximum error in the volume is approximately 3.44 cm^3. Notice that the "magnification factor" for the thickness (990π) is roughly 100 and 500 times greater than the magnification factors for the radius and height, respectively. This means that for the same errors in r, h, and t, the volume is far more sensitive to errors in the thickness. The partial derivatives allow us to do a sensitivity analysis to determine which independent (input) variables are most critical in producing change in the dependent (output) variable.

Related Exercises 39–44 ◄

SECTION 12.7 EXERCISES

Review Questions

1. Suppose **n** is a vector normal to the tangent plane of the surface $F(x, y, z) = 0$ at a point. How is **n** related to the gradient of F at that point?

2. Write the explicit function $z = xy^2 + x^2y - 10$ in the implicit form $F(x, y, z) = 0$.

3. Write an equation for the plane tangent to the surface $F(x, y, z) = 0$ at the point (a, b, c).

4. Write an equation for the plane tangent to the surface $z = f(x, y)$ at the point $(a, b, f(a, b))$.

5. Explain how to approximate a function f at a point near (a, b) where the values of f, f_x, and f_y are known at (a, b).

6. Explain how to approximate the change in a function f when the independent variables change from (a, b) to $(a + \Delta x, b + \Delta y)$.

7. Write the approximate change formula for a function $z = f(x, y)$ at the point (a, b) in terms of differentials.

8. Write the differential dw for the function $w = f(x, y, z)$.

Basic Skills

9–16. Tangent planes for $F(x, y, z) = 0$ *Find an equation of the plane tangent to the following surfaces at the given points (two planes and two equations).*

9. $x^2 + y + z = 3$; $(1, 1, 1)$ and $(2, 0, -1)$

10. $x^2 + y^3 + z^4 = 2$; $(1, 0, 1)$ and $(-1, 0, 1)$

11. $xy + xz + yz - 12 = 0$; $(2, 2, 2)$ and $(2, 0, 6)$

12. $x^2 + y^2 - z^2 = 0$; $(3, 4, 5)$ and $(-4, -3, 5)$

13. $xy \sin z = 1$; $(1, 2, \pi/6)$ and $(-2, -1, 5\pi/6)$

14. $yze^{xz} - 8 = 0$; $(0, 2, 4)$ and $(0, -8, -1)$

15. $z^2 - x^2/16 - y^2/9 - 1 = 0$; $(4, 3, -\sqrt{3})$ and $(-8, 9, \sqrt{14})$

16. $2x + y^2 - z^2 = 0$; $(0, 1, 1)$ and $(4, 1, -3)$

17–24. Tangent planes for $z = f(x, y)$ *Find an equation of the plane tangent to the following surfaces at the given points (two planes and two equations).*

17. $z = 4 - 2x^2 - y^2$; $(2, 2, -8)$ and $(-1, -1, 1)$

18. $z = 2 + 2x^2 + \frac{y^2}{2}$; $\left(-\frac{1}{2}, 1, 3\right)$ and $(3, -2, 22)$

19. $z = e^{xy}$; $(1, 0, 1)$ and $(0, 1, 1)$

20. $z = \sin xy + 2$; $(1, 0, 2)$ and $(0, 5, 2)$

21. $z = x^2e^{x-y}$; $(2, 2, 4)$ and $(-1, -1, 1)$

22. $z = \ln(1 + xy)$; $(1, 2, \ln 3)$ and $(-2, -1, \ln 3)$

23. $z = (x - y)/(x^2 + y^2)$; $\left(1, 2, -\frac{1}{5}\right)$ and $\left(2, -1, \frac{3}{5}\right)$

24. $z = 2\cos(x - y) + 2$; $(\pi/6, -\pi/6, 3)$ and $(\pi/3, \pi/3, 4)$

25–30. Linear approximation

a. Find the linear approximation to the function f at the given point.
b. Use part (a) to estimate the given function value.

25. $f(x, y) = xy + x - y$; $(2, 3)$; estimate $f(2.1, 2.99)$.

26. $f(x, y) = 12 - 4x^2 - 8y^2$; $(-1, 4)$; estimate $f(-1.05, 3.95)$.

27. $f(x, y) = -x^2 + 2y^2$; $(3, -1)$; estimate $f(3.1, -1.04)$.

28. $f(x, y) = \sqrt{x^2 + y^2}$; $(3, -4)$; estimate $f(3.06, -3.92)$.

29. $f(x, y) = \ln(1 + x + y)$; $(0, 0)$; estimate $f(0.1, -0.2)$.

30. $f(x, y) = (x + y)/(x - y)$; $(3, 2)$; estimate $f(2.95, 2.05)$.

31–34. Approximate function change *Use differentials to approximate the change in z for the given changes in the independent variables.*

31. $z = 2x - 3y - 2xy$ when (x, y) changes from $(1, 4)$ to $(1.1, 3.9)$

32. $z = -x^2 + 3y^2 + 2$ when (x, y) changes from $(-1, 2)$ to $(-1.05, 1.9)$

33. $z = e^{x+y}$ when (x, y) changes from $(0, 0)$ to $(0.1, -0.05)$

34. $z = \ln(1 + x + y)$ when (x, y) changes from $(0, 0)$ to $(-0.1, 0.03)$

35. Changes in torus surface area The surface area of a torus with an inner radius r and an outer radius $R > r$ is $S = 4\pi^2(R^2 - r^2)$.

a. If r increases and R decreases, does S increase or decrease, or is it impossible to say?
b. If r increases and R increases, does S increase or decrease, or is it impossible to say?
c. Estimate the change in the surface area of the torus when r changes from $r = 3.00$ to $r = 3.05$ and R changes from $R = 5.50$ to $R = 5.65$.
d. Estimate the change in the surface area of the torus when r changes from $r = 3.00$ to $r = 2.95$ and R changes from $R = 7.00$ to $R = 7.04$.
e. Find the relationship between the changes in r and R that leaves the surface area (approximately) unchanged.

36. Changes in cone volume The volume of a right circular cone with radius r and height h is $V = \pi r^2h/3$.

a. Approximate the change in the volume of the cone when the radius changes from $r = 6.5$ to $r = 6.6$ and the height changes from $h = 4.20$ to $h = 4.15$.
b. Approximate the change in the volume of the cone when the radius changes from $r = 5.40$ to $r = 5.37$ and the height changes from $h = 12.0$ to $h = 11.96$.

37. Area of an ellipse The area of an ellipse with axes of length $2a$ and $2b$ is $A = \pi ab$. Approximate the percent change in the area when a increases by 2% and b increases by 1.5%.

38. Volume of a paraboloid The volume of a segment of a circular paraboloid (see figure) with radius r and height h is $V = \pi r^2h/2$. Approximate the percent change in the volume when the radius decreases by 1.5% and the height increases by 2.2%.

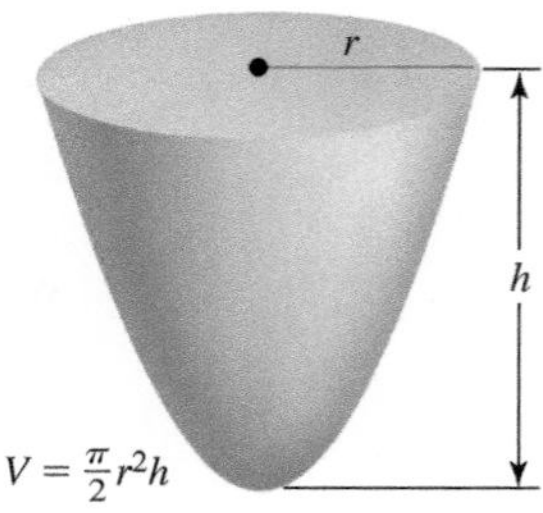

39–42. Differentials with more than two variables *Write the differential dw in terms of the differentials of the independent variables.*

39. $w = f(x, y, z) = xy^2 + x^2z + yz^2$

40. $w = f(x, y, z) = \sin(x + y - z)$

41. $w = f(u, x, y, z) = (u + x)/(y + z)$

42. $w = f(p, q, r, s) = pq/(rs)$

T 43. Law of Cosines The side lengths of any triangle are related by the Law of Cosines,

$$c^2 = a^2 + b^2 - 2ab\cos\theta.$$

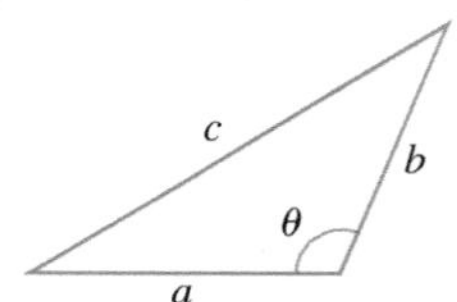

a. Estimate the change in the side length c when a changes from $a = 2$ to $a = 2.03$, b changes from $b = 4.00$ to $b = 3.96$, and θ changes from $\theta = \pi/3$ to $\theta = \pi/3 + \pi/90$.
b. If a changes from $a = 2$ to $a = 2.03$ and b changes from $b = 4.00$ to $b = 3.96$, is the resulting change in c greater in magnitude when $\theta = \pi/20$ (small angle) or when $\theta = 9\pi/20$ (close to a right angle)?

44. Travel cost The cost of a trip that is L miles long, driving a car that gets m miles per gallon, with gas costs of $\$p$/gal is $C = Lp/m$ dollars. Suppose you plan a trip of $L = 1500$ mi in a car that gets $m = 32$ mi/gal, with gas costs of $p = \$3.80$/gal.

a. Explain how the cost function is derived.
b. Compute the partial derivatives C_L, C_m, and C_p. Explain the meaning of the signs of the derivatives in the context of this problem.

c. Estimate the change in the total cost of the trip if L changes from $L = 1500$ to $L = 1520$, m changes from $m = 32$ to 31, and p changes from \$3.80 to \$3.85.

d. Is the total cost of the trip (with $L = 1500$ mi, $m = 32$ mi/gal, and $p = \$3.80$) more sensitive to a 1% change in L, m, or p (assuming the other two variables are fixed)? Explain.

Further Explorations

45. Explain why or why not Determine whether the following statements are true and give an explanation or counterexample.

a. The planes tangent to the cylinder $x^2 + z^2 = 1$ in $\mathbb{R}^3$ all have the form $ax + bz + c = 0$.

b. Suppose $w = xy/z$, for $x > 0$, $y > 0$, and $z > 0$. A decrease in z with x and y fixed results in an increase in w.

c. The gradient $\nabla F(a, b, c)$ lies in the plane tangent to the surface $F(x, y, z) = 0$ at (a, b, c).

46–49. Tangent planes *Find an equation of the plane tangent to the following surfaces at the given point.*

46. $z = \tan^{-1}(x + y)$; $(0, 0, 0)$

47. $z = \tan^{-1} xy$; $(1, 1, \pi/4)$

48. $(x + z)/(y - z) = 2$; $(4, 2, 0)$

49. $\sin xyz = \frac{1}{2}$; $\left(\pi, 1, \frac{1}{6}\right)$

50–53. Horizontal tangent planes *Find the points at which the following surfaces have horizontal tangent planes.*

50. $z = \sin(x - y)$ in the region $-2\pi \le x \le 2\pi$, $-2\pi \le y \le 2\pi$

51. $x^2 + y^2 - z^2 - 2x + 2y + 3 = 0$

52. $x^2 + 2y^2 + z^2 - 2x - 2z - 2 = 0$

53. $z = \cos 2x \sin y$ in the region $-\pi \le x \le \pi$, $-\pi \le y \le \pi$

54. Heron's formula The area of a triangle with sides of length a, b, and c is given by a formula from antiquity called Heron's formula:

$$A = \sqrt{s(s - a)(s - b)(s - c)},$$

where $s = (a + b + c)/2$ is the *semiperimeter* of the triangle.

a. Find the partial derivatives A_a, A_b, and A_c.

b. A triangle has sides of length $a = 2$, $b = 4$, and $c = 5$. Estimate the change in the area when a increases by 0.03, b decreases by 0.08, and c increases by 0.6.

c. For an equilateral triangle with $a = b = c$, estimate the percent change in the area when all sides increase in length by $p\%$.

55. Surface area of a cone A cone with height h and radius r has a lateral surface area (the curved surface only, excluding the base) of $S = \pi r\sqrt{r^2 + h^2}$.

a. Estimate the change in the surface area when r increases from $r = 2.50$ to $r = 2.55$ and h decreases from $h = 0.60$ to $h = 0.58$.

b. When $r = 100$ and $h = 200$, is the surface area more sensitive to a small change in r or a small change in h? Explain.

56. Line tangent to an intersection curve Consider the paraboloid $z = x^2 + 3y^2$ and the plane $z = x + y + 4$, which intersects the paraboloid in a curve C at $(2, 1, 7)$ (see figure). Find the equation of the line tangent to C at the point $(2, 1, 7)$. Proceed as follows.

a. Find a vector normal to the plane at $(2, 1, 7)$.

b. Find a vector normal to the plane tangent to the paraboloid at $(2, 1, 7)$.

c. Argue that the line tangent to C at $(2, 1, 7)$ is orthogonal to both normal vectors found in parts (a) and (b). Use this fact to find a direction vector for the tangent line.

d. Knowing a point on the tangent line and the direction of the tangent line, write an equation of the tangent line in parametric form.

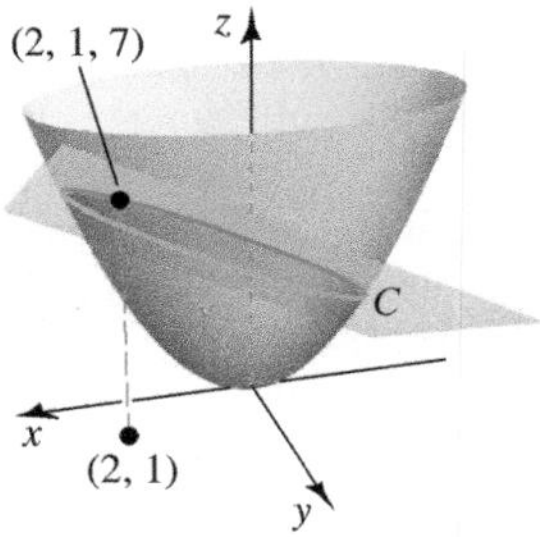

Applications

57. Batting averages Batting averages in baseball are defined by $A = x/y$, where $x \ge 0$ is the total number of hits and $y > 0$ is the total number of at bats. Treat x and y as positive real numbers and note that $0 \le A \le 1$.

a. Use differentials to estimate the change in the batting average if the number of hits increases from 60 to 62 and the number of at bats increases from 175 to 180.

b. If a batter currently has a batting average of $A = 0.350$, does the average decrease if the batter fails to get a hit more than it increases if the batter gets a hit?

c. Does the answer to part (b) depend on the current batting average? Explain.

58. Water-level changes A conical tank with radius 0.50 m and height 2.00 m is filled with water (see figure). Water is released from the tank, and the water level drops by 0.05 m (from 2.00 m to 1.95 m). Approximate the change in the volume of water in the tank. (*Hint:* When the water level drops, both the radius and height of the cone of water change.)

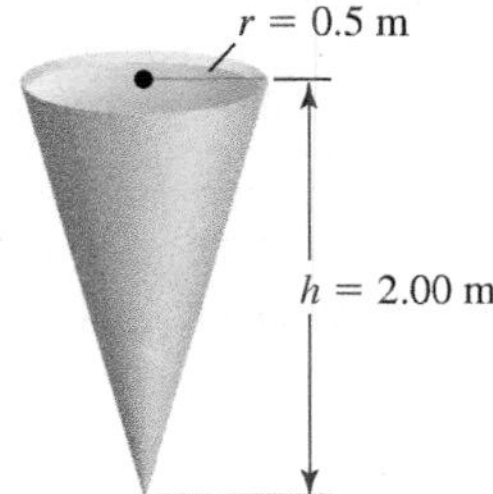

59. Flow in a cylinder Poiseuille's Law is a fundamental law of fluid dynamics that describes the flow velocity of a viscous incompressible fluid in a cylinder (it is used to model blood flow through veins and arteries). It says that in a cylinder of radius R and length L, the velocity of the fluid $r \le R$ units from the center-line of the cylinder is $V = \frac{P}{4L\nu}(R^2 - r^2)$, where P is the difference in the pressure between the ends of the cylinder and ν is the viscosity of the fluid (see figure). Assuming that P and ν are constant, the velocity V along the centerline of the cylinder $(r = 0)$ is $V = kR^2/L$, where k is a constant that we will take to be $k = 1$.

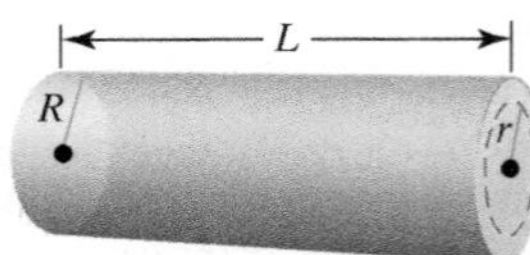

a. Estimate the change in the centerline velocity ($r = 0$) if the radius of the flow cylinder increases from $R = 3$ cm to $R = 3.05$ cm and the length increases from $L = 50$ cm to $L = 50.5$ cm.
b. Estimate the percent change in the centerline velocity if the radius of the flow cylinder R decreases by 1% and the length L increases by 2%.
c. Complete the following sentence: If the radius of the cylinder increases by p%, then the length of the cylinder must increase by approximately ________ % in order for the velocity to remain constant.

60. Floating-point operations In general, real numbers (with infinite decimal expansions) cannot be represented exactly in a computer by floating-point numbers (with finite decimal expansions). Suppose that floating-point numbers on a particular computer carry an error of at most 10^{-16}. Estimate the maximum error that is committed in doing the following arithmetic operations. Express the error in absolute and relative (percent) terms.

a. $f(x, y) = xy$
b. $f(x, y) = x/y$
c. $F(x, y, z) = xyz$
d. $F(x, y, z) = (x/y)/z$

61. Probability of at least one encounter Suppose that in a large group of people, a fraction $0 \le r \le 1$ of the people have flu. The probability that in n random encounters you will meet at least one person with flu is $P = f(n, r) = 1 - (1 - r)^n$. Although n is a positive integer, regard it as a positive real number.

a. Compute f_r and f_n.
b. How sensitive is the probability P to the flu rate r? Suppose you meet $n = 20$ people. Approximately how much does the probability P increase if the flu rate increases from $r = 0.1$ to $r = 0.11$ (with n fixed)?
c. Approximately how much does the probability P increase if the flu rate increases from $r = 0.9$ to $r = 0.91$ with $n = 20$?
d. Interpret the results of parts (b) and (c).

62. Two electrical resistors When two electrical resistors with resistance $R_1 > 0$ and $R_2 > 0$ are wired in parallel in a circuit (see figure), the combined resistance R, measured in ohms (Ω), is given by $\frac{1}{R} = \frac{1}{R_1} + \frac{1}{R_2}$.

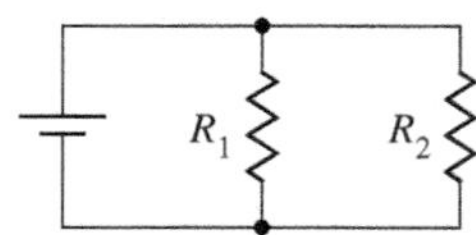

a. Estimate the change in R if R_1 increases from 2 Ω to 2.05 Ω and R_2 decreases from 3 Ω to 2.95 Ω.
b. Is it true that if $R_1 = R_2$ and R_1 increases by the same small amount as R_2 decreases, then R is approximately unchanged? Explain.
c. Is it true that if R_1 and R_2 increase, then R increases? Explain.
d. Suppose $R_1 > R_2$ and R_1 increases by the same small amount as R_2 decreases. Does R increase or decrease?

63. Three electrical resistors Extending Exercise 62, when three electrical resistors with resistance $R_1 > 0$, $R_2 > 0$, and $R_3 > 0$ are wired in parallel in a circuit (see figure), the combined resistance R, measured in ohms (Ω), is given by $\frac{1}{R} = \frac{1}{R_1} + \frac{1}{R_2} + \frac{1}{R_3}$. Estimate the change in R if R_1 increases from 2 Ω to 2.05 Ω, R_2 decreases from 3 Ω to 2.95 Ω, and R_3 increases from 1.5 Ω to 1.55 Ω.

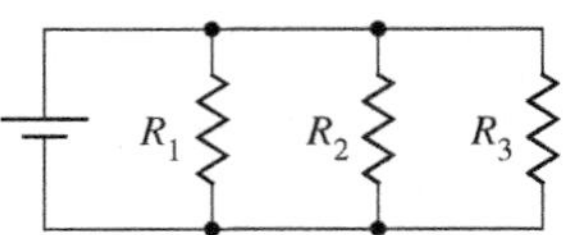

Additional Exercises

64. Power functions and percent change Suppose that $z = f(x, y) = x^a y^b$, where a and b are real numbers. Let dx/x, dy/y, and dz/z be the approximate relative (percent) changes in x, y, and z, respectively. Show that $dz/z = a(dx)/x + b(dy)/y$; that is, the relative changes are additive when weighted by the exponents a and b.

65. Logarithmic differentials Let f be a differentiable function of one or more variables that is positive on its domain.

a. Show that $d(\ln f) = \frac{df}{f}$.
b. Use part (a) to explain the statement that the absolute change in $\ln f$ is approximately equal to the relative change in f.
c. Let $f(x, y) = xy$, note that $\ln f = \ln x + \ln y$, and show that relative changes add; that is, $df/f = dx/x + dy/y$.
d. Let $f(x, y) = x/y$, note that $\ln f = \ln x - \ln y$, and show that relative changes subtract; that is $df/f = dx/x - dy/y$.
e. Show that in a product of n numbers, $f = x_1 x_2 \cdots x_n$, the relative change in f is approximately equal to the sum of the relative changes in the variables.

66. Distance from a plane to an ellipsoid (Adapted from 1938 Putnam Exam) Consider the ellipsoid $x^2/a^2 + y^2/b^2 + z^2/c^2 = 1$ and the plane P given by $Ax + By + Cz + 1 = 0$. Let $h = (A^2 + B^2 + C^2)^{-1/2}$ and $m = (a^2A^2 + b^2B^2 + c^2C^2)^{1/2}$.

a. Find the equation of the plane tangent to the ellipsoid at the point (p, q, r).
b. Find the two points on the ellipsoid at which the tangent plane is parallel to P and find equations of the tangent planes.
c. Show that the distance between the origin and the plane P is h.
d. Show that the distance between the origin and the tangent planes is hm.
e. Find a condition that guarantees that the plane P does not intersect the ellipsoid.

QUICK CHECK ANSWERS

1. $F(x, y, z) = z - xy - x + y = 0$ **2.** If you walk in the positive x-direction from $(-1, 2, 1)$, then you walk uphill. If you walk in the positive y-direction from $(-1, 2, 1)$, then you walk downhill. **3.** If $\Delta x = 0$, then the change formula becomes $\Delta z \approx f_y(a, b)\,\Delta y$, which is the change formula for the single variable y. If $\Delta y = 0$, then the change formula becomes $\Delta z \approx f_x(a, b)\,\Delta x$, which is the change formula for the single variable x. **4.** The BMI increases with weight w and decreases with height h. ◄

12.8 Maximum/Minimum Problems

In Chapter 4, we showed how to use derivatives to find maximum and minimum values of functions of a single variable. When those techniques are extended to functions of two variables, we discover both similarities and differences. The landscape of a surface is far more complicated than the profile of a curve in the plane, so we see more interesting features when working with several variables. In addition to peaks (maximum values) and hollows (minimum values), we encounter winding ridges, long valleys, and mountain passes. Yet despite these complications, many of the ideas used for single-variable functions reappear in higher dimensions. For example, the Second Derivative Test, suitably adapted for two variables, plays a central role. As with single-variable functions, the techniques developed here are useful for solving practical optimization problems.

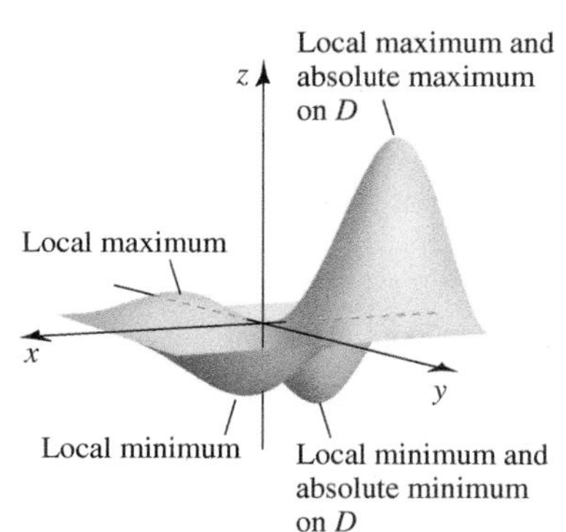

Figure 12.85

Local Maximum/Minimum Values

The concepts of local maximum and minimum values encountered in Chapter 4 extend readily to functions of two variables of the form $z = f(x, y)$. Figure 12.85 shows a general surface defined on a domain D, which is a subset of $\mathbb{R}^2$. The surface has peaks (local high points) and hollows (local low points) at points in the interior of D. The goal is to locate and classify these extreme points.

➤ We maintain the convention adopted in Chapter 4 that local maxima or minima occur at interior points of the domain. Recall that an open disk centered at (a, b) is the set of points within a circle centered at (a, b).

DEFINITION Local Maximum/Minimum Values

A function f has a **local maximum value** at (a, b) if $f(x, y) \le f(a, b)$ for all (x, y) in the domain of f in some open disk centered at (a, b). A function f has a **local minimum value** at (a, b) if $f(x, y) \ge f(a, b)$ for all (x, y) in the domain of f in some open disk centered at (a, b). Local maximum and local minimum values are also called **local extreme values** or **local extrema**.

In familiar terms, a local maximum is a point on a surface from which you cannot walk uphill. A local minimum is a point from which you cannot walk downhill. The following theorem is the analog of Theorem 4.2.

THEOREM 12.13 Derivatives and Local Maximum/Minimum Values

If f has a local maximum or minimum value at (a, b) and the partial derivatives f_x and f_y exist at (a, b), then $f_x(a, b) = f_y(a, b) = 0$.

Proof: Suppose f has a local maximum value at (a, b). The function of one variable $g(x) = f(x, b)$, obtained by holding $y = b$ fixed, also has a local maximum at (a, b). By Theorem 4.2, $g'(a) = 0$. However, $g'(a) = f_x(a, b)$; therefore, $f_x(a, b) = 0$. Similarly, the function $h(y) = f(a, y)$, obtained by holding $x = a$ fixed, has a local maximum at (a, b), which implies that $f_y(a, b) = h'(b) = 0$. An analogous argument is used for the local minimum case. ◄

Suppose f is differentiable at (a, b) (ensuring the existence of a tangent plane) and f has a local extremum at (a, b). Then $f_x(a, b) = f_y(a, b) = 0$, which, when substituted into the equation of the tangent plane, gives the equation $z = f(a, b)$ (a constant). Therefore, if the tangent plane exists at a local extremum, then it is horizontal there.

QUICK CHECK 1 The paraboloid $z = x^2 + y^2 - 4x + 2y + 5$ has a local minimum at $(2, -1)$. Verify the conclusion of Theorem 12.13 for this function. ◄

Recall that for a function of one variable, the condition $f'(a) = 0$ does not guarantee a local extremum at a. A similar precaution must be taken with Theorem 12.13. The conditions $f_x(a, b) = f_y(a, b) = 0$ do not imply that f has a local extremum at (a, b), as we show momentarily. Theorem 12.13 provides *candidates* for local extrema. We call these candidates *critical points*, as we did for functions of one variable. Therefore, the procedure for locating local maximum and minimum values is to find the critical points and then determine whether these candidates correspond to genuine local maximum and minimum values.

DEFINITION Critical Point

An interior point (a, b) in the domain of f is a **critical point** of f if either

1. $f_x(a, b) = f_y(a, b) = 0$, or
2. at least one of the partial derivatives f_x and f_y does not exist at (a, b).

EXAMPLE 1 Finding critical points Find the critical points of $f(x, y) = xy(x - 2)(y + 3)$.

SOLUTION This function is differentiable at all points of $\mathbb{R}^2$, so the critical points occur only at points where $f_x(x, y) = f_y(x, y) = 0$. Computing and simplifying the partial derivatives, these conditions become

$$f_x(x, y) = 2y(x - 1)(y + 3) = 0$$
$$f_y(x, y) = x(x - 2)(2y + 3) = 0.$$

We must now identify all (x, y) pairs that satisfy both equations. The first equation is satisfied if and only if $y = 0, x = 1$, or $y = -3$. We consider each of these cases.

- Substituting $y = 0$, the second equation is $3x(x - 2) = 0$, which has solutions $x = 0$ and $x = 2$. So $(0, 0)$ and $(2, 0)$ are critical points.
- Substituting $x = 1$, the second equation is $-(2y + 3) = 0$, which has the solution $y = -\frac{3}{2}$. So $\left(1, -\frac{3}{2}\right)$ is a critical point.
- Substituting $y = -3$, the second equation is $-3x(x - 2) = 0$, which has roots $x = 0$ and $x = 2$. So $(0, -3)$ and $(2, -3)$ are critical points.

We find that there are five critical points: $(0, 0)$, $(2, 0)$, $\left(1, -\frac{3}{2}\right)$, $(0, -3)$, and $(2, -3)$. Some of these critical points may correspond to local maximum or minimum values. We return to this example and a complete analysis shortly.

Related Exercises 9–18 ◀

Second Derivative Test

Critical points are candidates for local extreme values. With functions of one variable, the Second Derivative Test is used to determine whether critical points correspond to local maxima or minima (the test can also be inconclusive). The analogous test for functions of two variables not only detects local maxima and minima, but also identifies another type of point known as a *saddle point*.

➤ The usual image of a saddle point is that of a mountain pass (or a horse saddle), where you can walk upward in some directions and downward in other directions. The definition of a saddle point given here includes other less common situations. For example, with this definition, the cylinder $z = x^3$ has a line of saddle points along the y-axis.

DEFINITION Saddle Point

A function f has a **saddle point** at a critical point (a, b) if, in every open disk centered at (a, b), there are points (x, y) for which $f(x, y) > f(a, b)$ and points for which $f(x, y) < f(a, b)$.

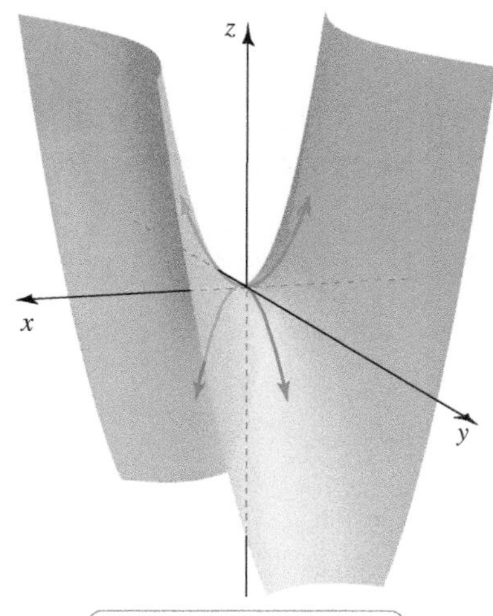

The hyperbolic paraboloid $z = x^2 - y^2$ has a saddle point at (0, 0).

Figure 12.86

If (a, b) is a critical point of f and f has a saddle point at (a, b), then from the point $(a, b, f(a, b))$, it is possible to walk uphill in some directions and downhill in other directions. The function $f(x, y) = x^2 - y^2$ (a hyperbolic paraboloid) is a good example to remember. The surface *rises* from the critical point $(0, 0)$ along the x-axis and *falls* from $(0, 0)$ along the y-axis (Figure 12.86). We can easily check that $f_x(0, 0) = f_y(0, 0) = 0$, demonstrating that critical points do not necessarily correspond to local maxima or minima.

QUICK CHECK 2 Consider the plane tangent to a surface at a saddle point. In what direction does the normal to the plane point? ◀

> **THEOREM 12.14 Second Derivative Test**
> Suppose that the second partial derivatives of f are continuous throughout an open disk centered at the point (a, b), where $f_x(a, b) = f_y(a, b) = 0$. Let $D(x, y) = f_{xx}(x, y)\, f_{yy}(x, y) - (f_{xy}(x, y))^2$.
>
> 1. If $D(a, b) > 0$ and $f_{xx}(a, b) < 0$, then f has a local maximum value at (a, b).
> 2. If $D(a, b) > 0$ and $f_{xx}(a, b) > 0$, then f has a local minimum value at (a, b).
> 3. If $D(a, b) < 0$, then f has a saddle point at (a, b).
> 4. If $D(a, b) = 0$, then the test is inconclusive.

➤ The Second Derivative Test for functions of a single variable states that if a is a critical point with $f'(a) = 0$, then $f''(a) > 0$ implies that f has a local minimum at a, $f''(a) < 0$ implies that f has a local maximum at a, and if $f''(a) = 0$, the test is inconclusive. Theorem 12.14 is easier to remember if you notice the parallels between the two second derivative tests.

The proof of this theorem is given in Appendix B, but a few comments are in order. The test relies on the quantity $D(x, y) = f_{xx}f_{yy} - (f_{xy})^2$, which is called the **discriminant** of f. It can be remembered as the 2×2 determinant of the **Hessian** matrix $\begin{pmatrix} f_{xx} & f_{xy} \\ f_{yx} & f_{yy} \end{pmatrix}$, where $f_{xy} = f_{yx}$, provided these derivatives are continuous (Theorem 12.4). The condition $D(x, y) > 0$ means that the surface has the same general behavior in all directions near (a, b); either the surface rises in all directions or it falls in all directions. In the case that $D(a, b) = 0$, the test is inconclusive: (a, b) could correspond to a local maximum, a local minimum, or a saddle point.

Finally, another useful characterization of a saddle point can be derived from Theorem 12.14: The tangent plane at a saddle point lies both above and below the surface.

QUICK CHECK 3 Compute the discriminant $D(x, y)$ of $f(x, y) = x^2y^2$. ◀

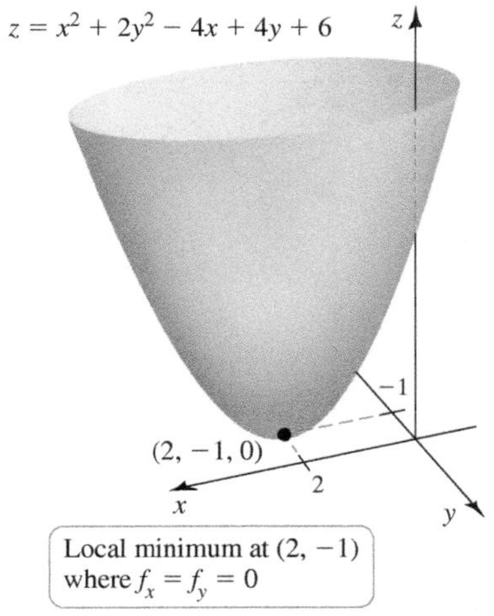

Local minimum at (2, −1) where $f_x = f_y = 0$

Figure 12.87

EXAMPLE 2 Analyzing critical points Use the Second Derivative Test to classify the critical points of $f(x, y) = x^2 + 2y^2 - 4x + 4y + 6$.

SOLUTION We begin with the following derivative calculations:

$$f_x = 2x - 4 \qquad f_y = 4y + 4$$
$$f_{xx} = 2 \qquad f_{xy} = f_{yx} = 0 \qquad f_{yy} = 4.$$

Setting both f_x and f_y equal to zero yields the single critical point $(2, -1)$. The value of the discriminant at the critical point is $D(2, -1) = f_{xx}f_{yy} - (f_{xy})^2 = 8 > 0$. Furthermore, $f_{xx}(2, -1) = 2 > 0$. By the Second Derivative Test, f has a local minimum at $(2, -1)$; the value of the function at that point is $f(2, -1) = 0$ (Figure 12.87).

Related Exercises 19–34 ◀

EXAMPLE 3 Analyzing critical points Use the Second Derivative Test to classify the critical points of $f(x, y) = xy(x - 2)(y + 3)$.

SOLUTION In Example 1, we determined that the critical points of f are $(0, 0)$, $(2, 0)$, $\left(1, -\frac{3}{2}\right)$, $(0, -3)$, and $(2, -3)$. The derivatives needed to evaluate the discriminant are

$$f_x = 2y(x - 1)(y + 3), \qquad f_y = x(x - 2)(2y + 3),$$
$$f_{xx} = 2y(y + 3), \qquad f_{xy} = 2(2y + 3)(x - 1), \qquad f_{yy} = 2x(x - 2).$$

The values of the discriminant at the critical points and the conclusions of the Second Derivative Test are shown in Table 12.5.

Table 12.5

(x, y)	$D(x, y)$	f_{xx}	Conclusion
$(0, 0)$	-36	0	Saddle point
$(2, 0)$	-36	0	Saddle point
$\left(1, -\frac{3}{2}\right)$	9	$-\frac{9}{2}$	Local maximum
$(0, -3)$	-36	0	Saddle point
$(2, -3)$	-36	0	Saddle point

The surface described by f has one local maximum at $\left(1, -\frac{3}{2}\right)$, surrounded by four saddle points (Figure 12.88a). The structure of the surface may also be visualized by plotting the level curves of f (Figure 12.88b).

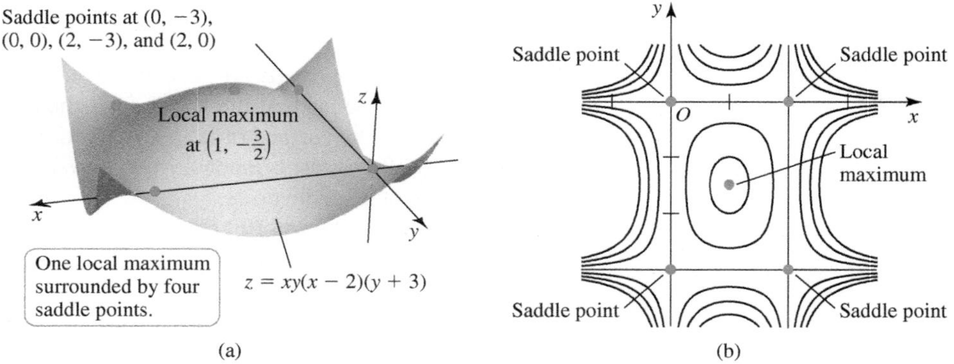

Figure 12.88

Related Exercises 19–34 ◀

➤ Example 4 is a *constrained optimization problem,* in which the goal is to maximize the volume subject to an additional condition called a *constraint.* We return to such problems in the next section and present another method of solution.

EXAMPLE 4 Shipping regulations A shipping company handles rectangular boxes provided the sum of the length, width, and height of the box does not exceed 96 in. Find the dimensions of the box that meets this condition and has the largest volume.

SOLUTION Let x, y, and z be the dimensions of the box; its volume is $V = xyz$. The box with the maximum volume satisfies the condition $x + y + z = 96$, which is used to eliminate any one of the variables from the volume function. Noting that $z = 96 - x - y$, the volume function becomes

$$V(x, y) = xy(96 - x - y).$$

Notice that because x, y, and $96 - x - y$ are dimensions of the box, they must be nonnegative. The condition $96 - x - y \geq 0$ implies that $x + y \leq 96$. Therefore, among points in the xy-plane, the constraint is met only if (x, y) lies in the triangle bounded by the lines $x = 0$, $y = 0$, and $x + y = 96$ (Figure 12.89). This triangle is the domain of the problem, and on its boundary, $V = 0$.

The goal is to find the maximum value of V. The critical points of V satisfy

$$V_x = 96y - 2xy - y^2 = y(96 - 2x - y) = 0$$
$$V_y = 96x - 2xy - x^2 = x(96 - 2y - x) = 0.$$

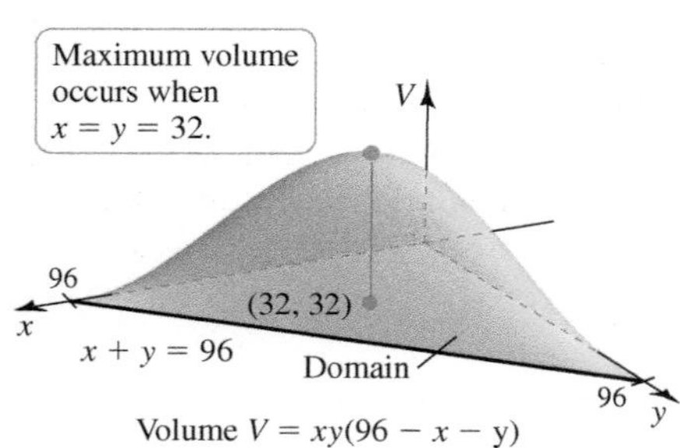

Figure 12.89

You can check that these two equations have four solutions: $(0, 0)$, $(96, 0)$, $(0, 96)$, and $(32, 32)$. The first three solutions lie on the boundary of the domain, where $V = 0$. Therefore, the remaining critical point is $(32, 32)$. The required second derivatives are

$$V_{xx} = -2y, \qquad V_{xy} = 96 - 2x - 2y, \qquad V_{yy} = -2x.$$

The discriminant is

$$D(x, y) = V_{xx}V_{yy} - (V_{xy})^2 = 4xy - (96 - 2x - 2y)^2,$$

which, when evaluated at $(32, 32)$, has the value $D(32, 32) = 3072 > 0$. Therefore, the critical point corresponds to a local maximum or minimum. Noting that $V_{xx}(32, 32) = -64 < 0$, we conclude that the critical point corresponds to a local maximum. The dimensions of the box with maximum volume are $x = 32$, $y = 32$, and $z = 96 - x - y = 32$ (it is a cube). Its volume is 32,768 in^3, which is the maximum volume on the domain.

Related Exercises 35–38 ◀

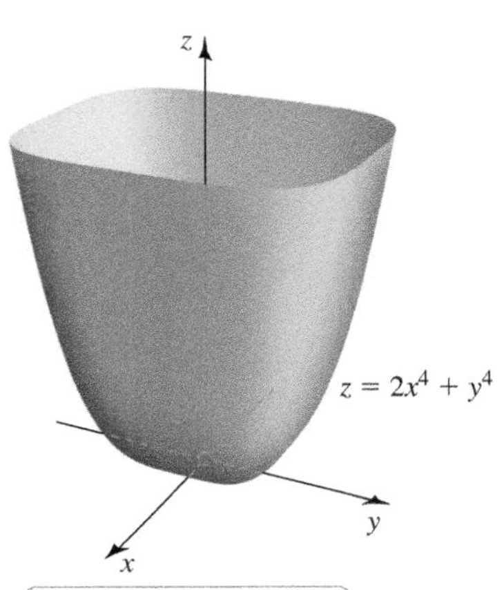

Local minimum at $(0, 0)$, but the Second Derivative Test is inconclusive.

Figure 12.90

➤ The same "flat" behavior occurs with functions of one variable, such as $f(x) = x^4$. Although f has a local minimum at $x = 0$, the Second Derivative Test is inconclusive.

➤ It is not surprising that the Second Derivative Test is inconclusive in Example 5b. The function has a line of local maxima at $(a, 0)$ for $a > 0$, a line of local minima at $(a, 0)$ for $a < 0$, and a saddle point at $(0, 0)$.

EXAMPLE 5 **Inconclusive tests** Apply the Second Derivative Test to the following functions and interpret the results.

a. $f(x, y) = 2x^4 + y^4$ **b.** $f(x, y) = 2 - xy^2$

SOLUTION

a. The critical points of f satisfy the conditions

$$f_x = 8x^3 = 0 \quad \text{and} \quad f_y = 4y^3 = 0,$$

so the sole critical point is $(0, 0)$. The second partial derivatives evaluated at $(0, 0)$ are

$$f_{xx}(0, 0) = f_{xy}(0, 0) = f_{yy}(0, 0) = 0.$$

We see that $D(0, 0) = 0$, and the Second Derivative Test is inconclusive. While the bowl-shaped surface (Figure 12.90) described by f has a local minimum at $(0, 0)$, the surface also has a broad flat bottom, which makes the local minimum "invisible" to the Second Derivative Test.

b. The critical points of this function satisfy

$$f_x(x, y) = -y^2 = 0 \quad \text{and} \quad f_y(x, y) = -2xy = 0.$$

The solutions of these equations have the form $(a, 0)$, where a is a real number. It is easy to check that the second partial derivatives evaluated at $(a, 0)$ are

$$f_{xx}(a, 0) = f_{xy}(a, 0) = 0 \quad \text{and} \quad f_{yy}(a, 0) = -2a.$$

Therefore, the discriminant is $D(a, 0) = 0$, and the Second Derivative Test is inconclusive. Figure 12.91 shows that f has a flat ridge above the x-axis that the Second Derivative Test is unable to classify.

Related Exercises 39–42 ◀

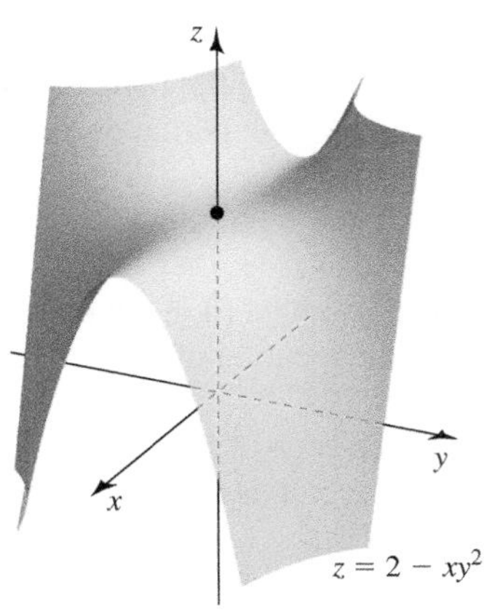

Second derivative test fails to detect saddle point at $(0, 0)$.

Figure 12.91

Absolute Maximum and Minimum Values

As in the one-variable case, we are often interested in knowing where a function of two or more variables attains its extreme values over its domain (or a subset of its domain).

> **DEFINITION** **Absolute Maximum/Minimum Values**
>
> Let f be defined on a set R in $\mathbb{R}^2$ containing the point (a, b). If $f(a, b) \geq f(x, y)$ for every (x, y) in R, then $f(a, b)$ is an **absolute maximum value** of f on R. If $f(a, b) \leq f(x, y)$ for every (x, y) in R, then $f(a, b)$ is an **absolute minimum value** of f on R.

It should be noted that the Extreme Value Theorem of Chapter 4 has an analog in $\mathbb{R}^2$ (or in higher dimensions): A function that is continuous on a closed bounded set in $\mathbb{R}^2$ attains its absolute maximum and absolute minimum values on that set. Absolute maximum and minimum values on a closed bounded set R occur in two ways.

➤ Recall that a *closed set* in $\mathbb{R}^2$ is a set that includes its boundary. A *bounded set* in $\mathbb{R}^2$ is a set that may be enclosed by a circle of finite radius.

- They may be local maximum or minimum values at interior points of R, where they are associated with critical points.
- They may occur on the boundary of R.

Therefore, the search for absolute maximum and minimum values on a closed bounded set is accomplished in the following three steps.

PROCEDURE Finding Absolute Maximum / Minimum Values on Closed Bounded Sets

Let f be continuous on a closed bounded set R in $\mathbb{R}^2$. To find the absolute maximum and minimum values of f on R:

1. Determine the values of f at all critical points in R.
2. Find the maximum and minimum values of f on the boundary of R.
3. The greatest function value found in Steps 1 and 2 is the absolute maximum value of f on R, and the least function value found in Steps 1 and 2 is the absolute minimum value of f on R.

The techniques for carrying out Step 1 of this process have been presented. The challenge often lies in locating extreme values on the boundary. Examples 6 and 7 illustrate two approaches to handling the boundary of R. The first expresses the boundary using functions of a single variable, and the second describes the boundary parametrically. In both cases, finding extreme values on the boundary becomes a one-variable problem. In the next section, we discuss an alternative method for finding extreme values on boundaries.

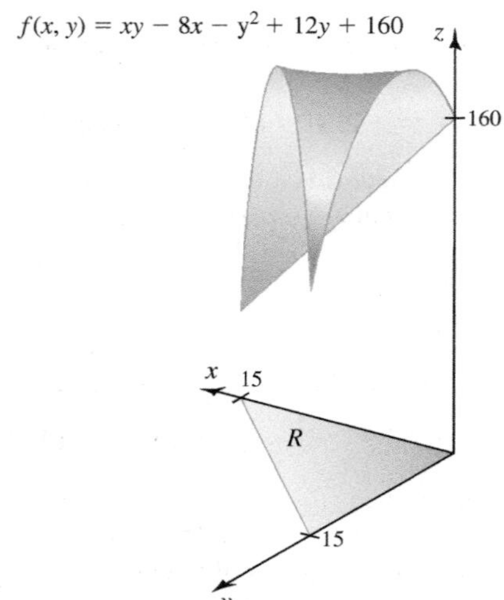

Figure 12.92

EXAMPLE 6 Extreme values over a region Find the absolute maximum and minimum values of $f(x, y) = xy - 8x - y^2 + 12y + 160$ over the triangular region $R = \{(x, y): 0 \le x \le 15, 0 \le y \le 15 - x\}$.

SOLUTION Figure 12.92 shows the graph of f over the region R. The goal is to determine the absolute maximum and minimum values of f over R—including the boundary of R. We begin by finding the critical points of f on the interior of R. The partial derivatives of f are

$$f_x(x, y) = y - 8 \quad \text{and} \quad f_y(x, y) = x - 2y + 12.$$

The conditions $f_x(x, y) = f_y(x, y) = 0$ are satisfied only when $(x, y) = (4, 8)$, which is a point in the interior of R. This critical point is a candidate for the location of an extreme value of f, and the value of the function at this point is $f(4, 8) = 192$.

To search for extrema on the boundary of R, we consider each edge of R separately. Let C_1 be the line segment $\{(x, y): y = 0, \text{for } 0 \le x \le 15\}$ on the x-axis and define the single-variable function g_1 to equal f at all points along C_1 (Figure 12.93). We substitute $y = 0$ and find that g_1 has the form

$$g_1(x) = f(x, 0) = 160 - 8x.$$

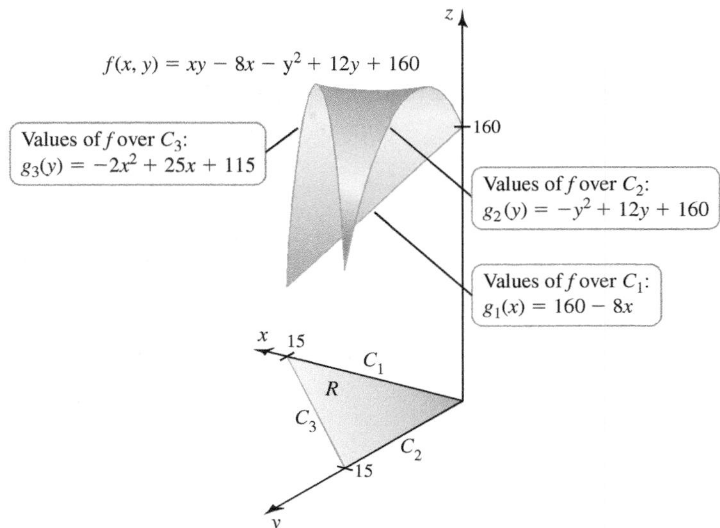

Figure 12.93

Using what we learned in Chapter 4, the candidates for absolute extreme values of g_1 on $0 \le x \le 15$ occur at critical points and endpoints. Specifically, the critical points of g_1 correspond to values where its derivative is zero, but in this case $g_1'(x) = -8$. So there is no critical point, which implies that the extreme values of g_1 occur at the endpoints of the interval $[0, 15]$. At the endpoints, we find that

$$g_1(0) = f(0, 0) = 160 \quad \text{and} \quad g_1(15) = f(15, 0) = 40.$$

Let's set aside this information while we do a similar analysis on the other two edges of the boundary of R.

Let C_2 be the line segment $\{(x, y): x = 0, \text{for } 0 \le y \le 15\}$ and define g_2 to equal f on C_2 (Figure 12.93). Substituting $x = 0$, we see that

$$g_2(y) = f(0, y) = -y^2 + 12y + 160.$$

The critical points of g_2 satisfy

$$g_2'(y) = -2y + 12 = 0,$$

which has the single root $y = 6$. Evaluating g_2 at this point and the endpoints, we have

$$g_2(6) = f(0, 6) = 196, \quad g_2(0) = f(0, 0) = 160, \quad \text{and} \quad g_2(15) = f(0, 15) = 115.$$

Observe that $g_1(0) = g_2(0)$ because C_1 and C_2 intersect at the origin.

Finally, we let C_3 be the line segment $\{(x, y): y = 15 - x, 0 \le x \le 15\}$ and define g_3 to equal f on C_3 (Figure 12.93). Substituting $y = 15 - x$ and simplifying, we find that

$$g_3(x) = f(x, 15 - x) = -2x^2 + 25x + 115.$$

The critical points of g_3 satisfy

$$g_3'(x) = -4x + 25,$$

whose only root on the interval $0 \le x \le 15$ is $x = 6.25$. Evaluating g_3 at this critical point and the endpoints, we have

$$g_3(6.25) = f(6.25, 8.75) = 193.125, \quad g_3(15) = f(15, 0) = 40, \quad \text{and}$$
$$g_3(0) = f(0, 15) = 115.$$

Observe that $g_3(15) = g_1(15)$ and $g_3(0) = g_2(15)$, so only one new candidate for the location of an extreme value is the point $(6.25, 8.75)$.

Collecting and summarizing our work, we have 6 candidates for absolute extreme values:

$$f(4,8) = 192, \quad f(0,0) = 160, \quad f(15,0) = 40, \quad f(0,6) = 196,$$
$$f(0,15) = 115, \quad \text{and} \quad f(6.25, 8.75) = 193.125.$$

We see that f has an absolute minimum value of 40 at $(15, 0)$ and an absolute maximum value of 196 at $(0, 6)$. These findings are illustrated in Figure 12.94.

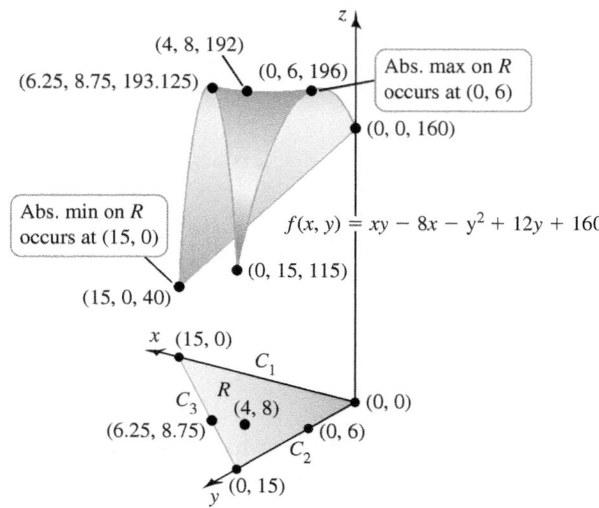

Figure 12.94

Related Exercises 43–52 ◀

EXAMPLE 7 **Absolute maximum and minimum values** Find the absolute maximum and minimum values of $f(x, y) = x^2 + y^2 - 2x + 2y + 5$ on the region $R = \{(x, y): x^2 + y^2 \le 4\}$ (the closed disk centered at $(0, 0)$ with radius 2).

SOLUTION We begin by locating the critical points and the local maxima and minima. The critical points satisfy the equations

$$f_x(x, y) = 2x - 2 = 0 \quad \text{and} \quad f_y(x, y) = 2y + 2 = 0,$$

which have the solution $x = 1$ and $y = -1$. The value of the function at this point is $f(1, -1) = 3$.

➤ Recall that a parametric description of a circle of radius a centered at the origin is $x = a\cos\theta$, $y = a\sin\theta$, for $0 \le \theta \le 2\pi$.

We now determine the maximum and minimum values of f on the boundary of R, which is a circle of radius 2 described by the parametric equations

$$x = 2\cos\theta, \qquad y = 2\sin\theta, \quad \text{for} \quad 0 \le \theta \le 2\pi.$$

Substituting x and y in terms of θ into the function f, we obtain a new function $g(\theta)$ that gives the values of f on the boundary of R:

$$\begin{aligned} g(\theta) &= (2\cos\theta)^2 + (2\sin\theta)^2 - 2(2\cos\theta) + 2(2\sin\theta) + 5 \\ &= 4(\cos^2\theta + \sin^2\theta) - 4\cos\theta + 4\sin\theta + 5 \\ &= -4\cos\theta + 4\sin\theta + 9. \end{aligned}$$

Finding the maximum and minimum boundary values is now a one-variable problem. The critical points of g satisfy

$$g'(\theta) = 4\sin\theta + 4\cos\theta = 0,$$

or $\tan \theta = -1$. Therefore, on the interval $[0, 2\pi]$, g has critical points $\theta = 3\pi/4$ and $\theta = 7\pi/4$, which correspond to the points $(-\sqrt{2}, \sqrt{2})$ and $(\sqrt{2}, -\sqrt{2})$, respectively. Notice that the endpoints of the interval ($\theta = 0$ and $\theta = 2\pi$) correspond to the same point on the boundary of R, namely $(2, 0)$.

Having completed the first two steps of this procedure, we have four function values to consider:

- $f(1, -1) = 3$ (critical point),
- $f(\sqrt{2}, -\sqrt{2}) = 9 - 4\sqrt{2} \approx 3.3$ (boundary point),
- $f(-\sqrt{2}, \sqrt{2}) = 9 + 4\sqrt{2} \approx 14.7$ (boundary point), and
- $f(2, 0) = 5$ (boundary point).

The greatest value of f on R, $f(-\sqrt{2}, \sqrt{2}) = 9 + 4\sqrt{2}$, is the absolute maximum value, and it occurs at a boundary point. The least value, $f(1, -1) = 3$, is the absolute minimum value, and it occurs at an interior point (Figure 12.95a). Also revealing is the plot of the level curves of the surface with the boundary of R superimposed (Figure 12.95b). As the boundary of R is traversed, the values of f vary, reaching a maximum value at $\theta = 3\pi/4$, or $(-\sqrt{2}, \sqrt{2})$, and a minimum value at $\theta = 7\pi/4$, or $(\sqrt{2}, -\sqrt{2})$.

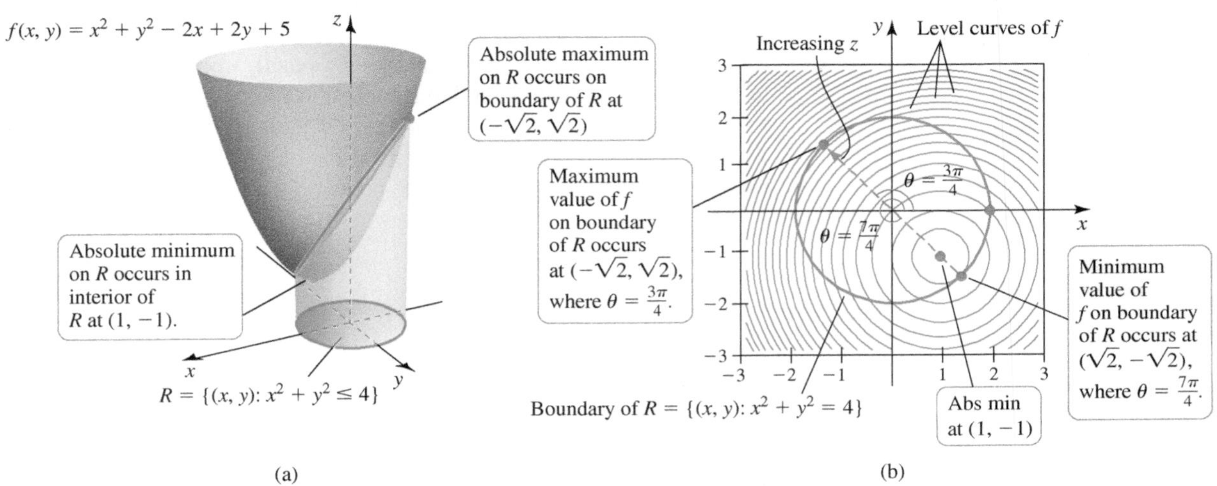

Figure 12.95

Related Exercises 43–52 ◄

Open and / or Unbounded Regions Finding absolute maximum and minimum values of a function on an open region (for example, $R = \{(x, y) = x^2 + y^2 < 9\}$) or an unbounded domain (for example, $R = \{(x, y): x > 0, y > 0\}$) presents additional challenges. Because there is no systematic procedure for dealing with such problems, some ingenuity is generally needed. Notice that absolute extrema may not exist on such regions.

EXAMPLE 8 **Absolute extreme values on an open region** Find the absolute maximum and minimum values of $f(x, y) = 4 - x^2 - y^2$ on the open disk $R = \{(x, y): x^2 + y^2 < 1\}$ (if they exist).

SOLUTION You should verify that f has a critical point at $(0, 0)$ and it corresponds to a local maximum (on an inverted paraboloid). Moving away from $(0, 0)$ in all directions, the function values decrease, so f also has an absolute maximum value of 4 at $(0, 0)$. The boundary of R is the unit circle $\{(x, y): x^2 + y^2 = 1\}$, which is not contained in R. As (x, y) approaches any point on the unit circle along any path in R, the function values $f(x, y) = 4 - (x^2 + y^2)$ decrease and approach 3 but never reach 3. Therefore, f does not have an absolute minimum on R.

Related Exercises 53–60 ◄

QUICK CHECK 4 Does the linear function $f(x, y) = 2x + 3y$ have an absolute maximum or minimum value on the open unit square $\{(x, y): 0 < x < 1, 0 < y < 1\}$? ◄

EXAMPLE 9 **Absolute extreme values on an open region** Find the point(s) on the plane $x + 2y + z = 2$ closest to the point $P(2, 0, 4)$.

SOLUTION Suppose that (x, y, z) is a point on the plane, which means that $z = 2 - x - 2y$. The distance between $P(2, 0, 4)$ and (x, y, z) that we seek to minimize is

$$d(x, y, z) = \sqrt{(x-2)^2 + y^2 + (z-4)^2}.$$

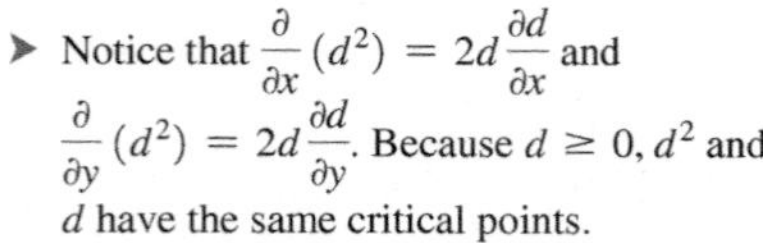

➤ Notice that $\frac{\partial}{\partial x}(d^2) = 2d\frac{\partial d}{\partial x}$ and $\frac{\partial}{\partial y}(d^2) = 2d\frac{\partial d}{\partial y}$. Because $d \geq 0$, d^2 and d have the same critical points.

It is easier to minimize d^2, which has the same critical points as d. Squaring d and eliminating z using $z = 2 - x - 2y$, we have

$$f(x, y) = (d(x, y, z))^2 = (x-2)^2 + y^2 + \underbrace{(-x - 2y - 2)^2}_{z-4}$$

$$= 2x^2 + 5y^2 + 4xy + 8y + 8.$$

The critical points of f satisfy the equations

$$f_x = 4x + 4y = 0 \quad \text{and} \quad f_y = 4x + 10y + 8 = 0,$$

whose only solution is $x = \frac{4}{3}, y = -\frac{4}{3}$. The Second Derivative Test confirms that this point corresponds to a local minimum of f. We now ask: Does $\left(\frac{4}{3}, -\frac{4}{3}\right)$ correspond to the *absolute* minimum value of f over the entire domain of the problem, which is $\mathbb{R}^2$? Because the domain has no boundary, we cannot check values of f on the boundary. Instead, we argue geometrically that there is exactly one point on the plane that is closest to P. We have found a point that is closest to P among nearby points on the plane. As we move away from this point, the values of f increase without bound. Therefore, $\left(\frac{4}{3}, -\frac{4}{3}\right)$ corresponds to the absolute minimum value of f. A graph of f (Figure 12.96) confirms this reasoning, and we conclude that the point $\left(\frac{4}{3}, -\frac{4}{3}, \frac{10}{3}\right)$ is the point on the plane nearest P.

Related Exercises 53–60 ◄

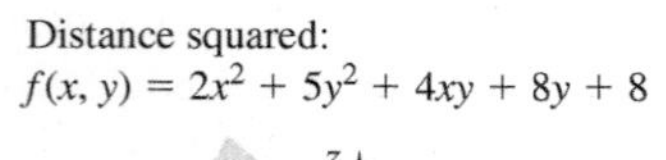

Distance squared:
$f(x, y) = 2x^2 + 5y^2 + 4xy + 8y + 8$

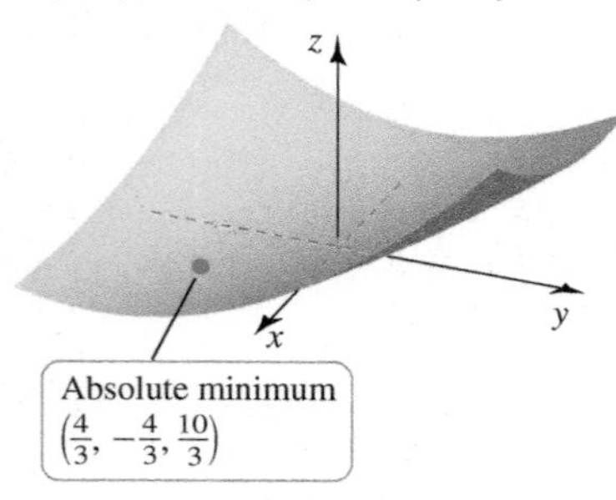

Figure 12.96

SECTION 12.8 EXERCISES

Review Questions

1. Describe the appearance of a smooth surface with a local maximum at a point.
2. Describe the usual appearance of a smooth surface at a saddle point.
3. What are the conditions for a critical point of a function f?
4. If $f_x(a, b) = f_y(a, b) = 0$, does it follow that f has a local maximum or local minimum at (a, b)? Explain.
5. Consider the function $z = f(x, y)$. What is the discriminant of f, and how do you compute it?
6. Explain how the Second Derivative Test is used.
7. What is an absolute minimum value of a function f on a set R in $\mathbb{R}^2$?
8. What is the procedure for locating absolute maximum and minimum values on a closed bounded domain?

Basic Skills

9–18. Critical points *Find all critical points of the following functions.*

9. $f(x, y) = 1 + x^2 + y^2$
10. $f(x, y) = x^2 - 6x + y^2 + 8y$
11. $f(x, y) = (3x - 2)^2 + (y - 4)^2$
12. $f(x, y) = 3x^2 - 4y^2$
13. $f(x, y) = x^4 + y^4 - 16xy$
14. $f(x, y) = x^3/3 - y^3/3 + 3xy$
15. $f(x, y) = x^4 - 2x^2 + y^2 - 4y + 5$
16. $f(x, y) = x^2 + xy - 2x - y + 1$
17. $f(x, y) = x^2 + 6x + y^2 + 8$
18. $f(x, y) = e^{x^2y^2 - 2xy^2 + y^2}$

19–34. Analyzing critical points *Find the critical points of the following functions. Use the Second Derivative Test to determine (if possible) whether each critical point corresponds to a local maximum, local minimum, or saddle point. Confirm your results using a graphing utility.*

19. $f(x, y) = 4 + 2x^2 + 3y^2$
20. $f(x, y) = (4x - 1)^2 + (2y + 4)^2 + 1$
21. $f(x, y) = -4x^2 + 8y^2 - 3$
22. $f(x, y) = x^4 + y^4 - 4x - 32y + 10$
23. $f(x, y) = x^4 + 2y^2 - 4xy$
24. $f(x, y) = xye^{-x-y}$
25. $f(x, y) = \sqrt{x^2 + y^2 - 4x + 5}$
26. $f(x, y) = \tan^{-1} xy$
27. $f(x, y) = 2xye^{-x^2-y^2}$
28. $f(x, y) = x^2 + xy^2 - 2x + 1$

29. $f(x, y) = \dfrac{x}{1 + x^2 + y^2}$

30. $f(x, y) = \dfrac{x - 1}{x^2 + y^2}$

31. $f(x, y) = x^4 + 4x^2(y - 2) + 8(y - 1)^2$

32. $f(x, y) = xe^{-x-y} \sin y$, for $|x| \leq 2, 0 \leq y \leq \pi$

33. $f(x, y) = ye^x - e^y$

34. $f(x, y) = \sin(2\pi x)\cos(\pi y)$, for $|x| \leq \frac{1}{2}$ and $|y| \leq \frac{1}{2}$.

35. Shipping regulations A shipping company handles rectangular boxes provided the sum of the height and the girth of the box does not exceed 96 in. (The girth is the perimeter of the smallest side of the box.) Find the dimensions of the box that meets this condition and has the largest volume.

36. Cardboard boxes A lidless box is to be made using 2 m^2 of cardboard. Find the dimensions of the box with the largest possible volume.

37. Cardboard boxes A lidless cardboard box is to be made with a volume of 4 m^3. Find the dimensions of the box that requires the least amount of cardboard.

38. Optimal box Find the dimensions of the largest rectangular box in the first octant of the xyz-coordinate system that has one vertex at the origin and the opposite vertex on the plane $x + 2y + 3z = 6$.

39–42. Inconclusive tests *Show that the Second Derivative Test is inconclusive when applied to the following functions at* $(0, 0)$. *Describe the behavior of the function at the critical point.*

39. $f(x, y) = 4 + x^4 + 3y^4$

40. $f(x, y) = x^2y - 3$

41. $f(x, y) = x^4y^2$

42. $f(x, y) = \sin(x^2y^2)$

43–52. Absolute maxima and minima *Find the absolute maximum and minimum values of the following functions on the given region R.*

43. $f(x, y) = x^2 + y^2 - 2y + 1$; $R = \{(x, y): x^2 + y^2 \leq 4\}$

44. $f(x, y) = 2x^2 + y^2$; $R = \{(x, y): x^2 + y^2 \leq 16\}$

45. $f(x, y) = 4 + 2x^2 + y^2$;
$R = \{(x, y): -1 \leq x \leq 1, -1 \leq y \leq 1\}$

46. $f(x, y) = 6 - x^2 - 4y^2$;
$R = \{(x, y): -2 \leq x \leq 2, -1 \leq y \leq 1\}$

47. $f(x, y) = 2x^2 - 4x + 3y^2 + 2$;
$R = \{(x, y): (x - 1)^2 + y^2 \leq 1\}$

48. $f(x, y) = x^2 + y^2 - 2x - 2y$; R is the closed region bounded by the triangle with vertices $(0, 0)$, $(2, 0)$, and $(0, 2)$.

49. $f(x, y) = -2x^2 + 4x - 3y^2 - 6y - 1$;
$R = \{(x, y): (x - 1)^2 + (y + 1)^2 \leq 1\}$

50. $f(x, y) = \sqrt{x^2 + y^2 - 2x + 2}$; $R = \{(x, y): x^2 + y^2 \leq 4, y \geq 0\}$

51. $f(x, y) = \dfrac{2y^2 - x^2}{2 + 2x^2y^2}$; R is the closed region bounded by the lines $y = x$, $y = 2x$, and $y = 2$.

52. $f(x, y) = \sqrt{x^2 + y^2}$; R is the closed region bounded by the ellipse $\dfrac{x^2}{4} + y^2 = 1$.

53–56. Absolute extrema on open and/or unbounded regions *If possible, find the absolute maximum and minimum values of the following functions on the region R.*

53. $f(x, y) = x^2 + y^2 - 4$; $R = \{(x, y): x^2 + y^2 < 4\}$

54. $f(x, y) = x + 3y$; $R = \{(x, y): |x| < 1, |y| < 2\}$

55. $f(x, y) = 2e^{-x-y}$; $R = \{(x, y): x \geq 0, y \geq 0\}$

56. $f(x, y) = x^2 - y^2$; $R = \{(x, y);\ |x| < 1, |y| < 1\}$

57–60. Absolute extrema on open and/or unbounded regions

57. Find the point on the plane $x + y + z = 4$ nearest the point $P(0, 3, 6)$.

58. Find the point(s) on the cone $z^2 = x^2 + y^2$ nearest the point $P(1, 4, 0)$.

59. Find the point on the curve $y = x^2$ nearest the line $y = x - 1$. Identify the point on the line.

60. Rectangular boxes with a volume of 10 m^3 are made of two materials. The material for the top and bottom of the box costs $\$10/m^2$ and the material for the sides of the box costs $\$1/m^2$. What are the dimensions of the box that minimize the cost of the box?

Further Explorations

61. Explain why or why not Determine whether the following statements are true and give an explanation or counterexample. Assume that f is differentiable at the points in question.

a. The fact that $f_x(2, 2) = f_y(2, 2) = 0$ implies that f has a local maximum, local minimum, or saddle point at $(2, 2)$.

b. The function f could have a local maximum at (a, b) where $f_y(a, b) \neq 0$.

c. The function f could have both an absolute maximum and an absolute minimum at two different points that are not critical points.

d. The tangent plane is horizontal at a point on a smooth surface corresponding to a critical point.

62–63. Extreme points from contour plots *Based on the level curves that are visible in the following graphs, identify the approximate locations of the local maxima, local minima, and saddle points.*

62.

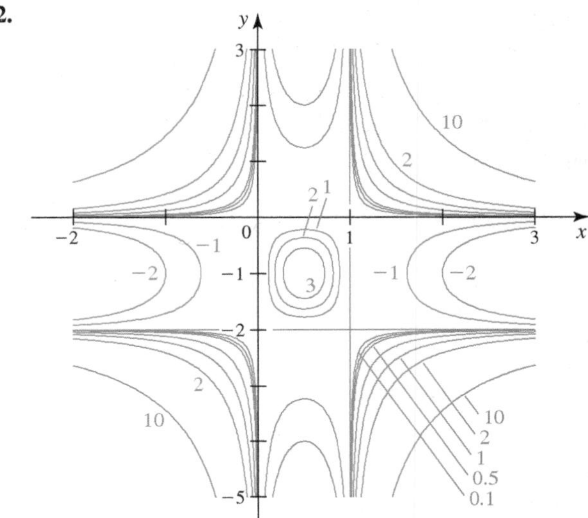

63.

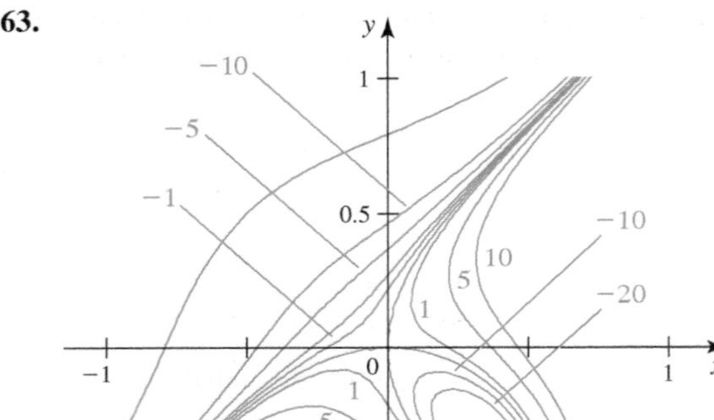

64. Optimal box Find the dimensions of the rectangular box with maximum volume in the first octant with one vertex at the origin and the opposite vertex on the ellipsoid $36x^2 + 4y^2 + 9z^2 = 36$.

65. Least distance What point on the plane $x - y + z = 2$ is closest to the point $(1, 1, 1)$?

66. Maximum/minimum of linear functions Let R be a closed bounded region in $\mathbb{R}^2$ and let $f(x, y) = ax + by + c$, where a, b, and c are real numbers, with a and b not both zero. Give a geometrical argument explaining why the absolute maximum and minimum values of f over R occur on the boundaries of R.

67. Magic triples Let x, y, and z be nonnegative numbers with $x + y + z = 200$.

a. Find the values of x, y, and z that minimize $x^2 + y^2 + z^2$.
b. Find the values of x, y, and z that minimize $\sqrt{x^2 + y^2 + z^2}$.
c. Find the values of x, y, and z that maximize xyz.
d. Find the values of x, y, and z that maximize $x^2y^2z^2$.

68. Powers and roots Assume that $x + y + z = 1$ with $x \geq 0$, $y \geq 0$, and $z \geq 0$.

a. Find the maximum and minimum values of $(1 + x^2)(1 + y^2)(1 + z^2)$.
b. Find the maximum and minimum values of $(1 + \sqrt{x})(1 + \sqrt{y})(1 + \sqrt{z})$.
(*Source: Math Horizons*, Apr 2004)

Applications

T **69. Optimal locations** Suppose n houses are located at the distinct points $(x_1, y_1), (x_2, y_2), \ldots, (x_n, y_n)$. A power substation must be located at a point such that the *sum of the squares* of the distances between the houses and the substation is minimized.

a. Find the optimal location of the substation in the case that $n = 3$ and the houses are located at $(0, 0)$, $(2, 0)$, and $(1, 1)$.
b. Find the optimal location of the substation in the case that $n = 3$ and the houses are located at distinct points (x_1, y_1), (x_2, y_2), and (x_3, y_3).
c. Find the optimal location of the substation in the general case of n houses located at distinct points $(x_1, y_1), (x_2, y_2), \ldots, (x_n, y_n)$.
d. You might argue that the locations found in parts (a), (b), and (c) are not optimal because they result from minimizing the sum of the *squares* of the distances, not the sum of the distances themselves. Use the locations in part (a) and write the function that gives the sum of the distances. Note that minimizing this function is much more difficult than in part (a). Then use a graphing utility to determine whether the optimal location is the same in the two cases. (Also see Exercise 77 about Steiner's problem.)

70–71. Least squares approximation *In its many guises, the least squares approximation arises in numerous areas of mathematics and statistics. Suppose you collect data for two variables (for example, height and shoe size) in the form of pairs* $(x_1, y_1), (x_2, y_2), \ldots, (x_n, y_n)$. *The data may be plotted as a scatterplot in the xy-plane, as shown in the figure. The technique known as* linear regression *asks the question: What is the equation of the line that "best fits" the data? The least squares criterion for best fit requires that the sum of the squares of the vertical distances between the line and the data points is a minimum.*

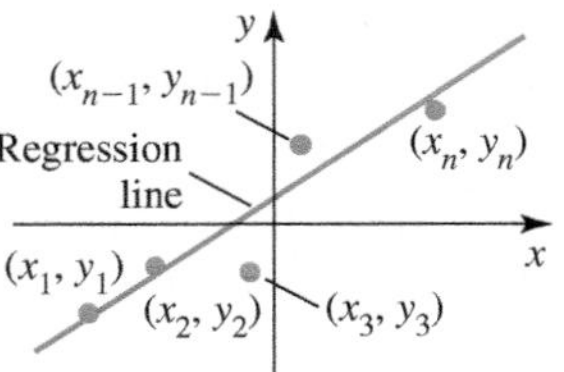

70. Let the equation of the best-fit line be $y = mx + b$, where the slope m and the y-intercept b must be determined using the least squares condition. First assume that there are three data points $(1, 2)$, $(3, 5)$, and $(4, 6)$. Show that the function of m and b that gives the sum of the squares of the vertical distances between the line and the three data points is

$$E(m, b) = ((m + b) - 2)^2 + ((3m + b) - 5)^2 + ((4m + b) - 6)^2.$$

Find the critical points of E and find the values of m and b that minimize E. Graph the three data points and the best-fit line.

T **71.** Generalize the procedure in Exercise 70 by assuming that n data points $(x_1, y_1), (x_2, y_2), \ldots, (x_n, y_n)$ are given. Write the function $E(m, b)$ (summation notation allows for a more compact calculation). Show that the coefficients of the best-fit line are

$$m = \frac{\left(\sum x_k\right)\left(\sum y_k\right) - n\sum x_k y_k}{\left(\sum x_k\right)^2 - n\sum x_k{}^2} \text{ and}$$

$$b = \frac{1}{n}\left(\sum y_k - m\sum x_k\right),$$

where all sums run from $k = 1$ to $k = n$.

T **72–73. Least squares practice** *Use the results of Exercise 71 to find the best-fit line for the following data sets. Plot the points and the best-fit line.*

72. $(0, 0), (2, 3), (4, 5)$

73. $(-1, 0), (0, 6), (3, 8)$

Additional Exercises

74. Second Derivative Test Use the Second Derivative Test to prove that if (a, b) is a critical point of f at which $f_x(a, b) = f_y(a, b) = 0$ and $f_{xx}(a, b) < 0 < f_{yy}(a, b)$ or $f_{yy}(a, b) < 0 < f_{xx}(a, b)$, then f has a saddle point at (a, b).

75. Maximum area triangle Among all triangles with a perimeter of 9 units, find the dimensions of the triangle with the maximum area. It may be easiest to use Heron's formula, which states that the area of a triangle with side length a, b, and c is $A = \sqrt{s(s - a)(s - b)(s - c)}$, where $2s$ is the perimeter of the triangle.

76. Ellipsoid inside a tetrahedron (1946 Putnam Exam) Let P be a plane tangent to the ellipsoid $x^2/a^2 + y^2/b^2 + z^2/c^2 = 1$ at a point in the first octant. Let T be the tetrahedron in the first octant bounded by P and the coordinate planes $x = 0$, $y = 0$, and $z = 0$. Find the minimum volume of T. (The volume of a tetrahedron is one-third the area of the base times the height.)

T 77. Steiner's problem for three points Given three distinct noncollinear points A, B, and C in the plane, find the point P in the plane such that the sum of the distances $|AP| + |BP| + |CP|$ is a minimum. Here is how to proceed with three points, assuming that the triangle formed by the three points has no angle greater than $2\pi/3$ (120°).

a. Assume the coordinates of the three given points are $A(x_1, y_1)$, $B(x_2, y_2)$, and $C(x_3, y_3)$. Let $d_1(x, y)$ be the distance between $A(x_1, y_1)$ and a variable point $P(x, y)$. Compute the gradient of d_1 and show that it is a unit vector pointing along the line between the two points.

b. Define d_2 and d_3 in a similar way and show that ∇d_2 and ∇d_3 are also unit vectors in the direction of the line between the two points.

c. The goal is to minimize $f(x, y) = d_1 + d_2 + d_3$. Show that the condition $f_x = f_y = 0$ implies that $\nabla d_1 + \nabla d_2 + \nabla d_3 = 0$.

d. Explain why part (c) implies that the optimal point P has the property that the three line segments AP, BP, and CP all intersect symmetrically in angles of $2\pi/3$.

e. What is the optimal solution if one of the angles in the triangle is greater than $2\pi/3$ (just draw a picture)?

f. Estimate the Steiner point for the three points $(0, 0)$, $(0, 1)$, and $(2, 0)$.

78. Slicing plane Find an equation of the plane passing through the point $(3, 2, 1)$ that slices off the solid in the first octant with the least volume.

T 79. Two mountains without a saddle Show that the following two functions have two local maxima but no other extreme points (therefore, there is no saddle or basin between the mountains).

a. $f(x, y) = -(x^2 - 1)^2 - (x^2 - e^y)^2$

b. $f(x, y) = 4x^2e^y - 2x^4 - e^{4y}$

(*Source:* Ira Rosenholtz, *Mathematics Magazine*, Feb 1987)

T 80. Solitary critical points A function of *one* variable has the property that a local maximum (or minimum) occurring at the only critical point is also the absolute maximum (or minimum) (for example, $f(x) = x^2$). Does the same result hold for a function of *two* variables? Show that the following functions have the property that they have a single local maximum (or minimum), occurring at the only critical point, but that the local maximum (or minimum) is not an absolute maximum (or minimum) on $\mathbb{R}^2$.

a. $f(x, y) = 3xe^y - x^3 - e^{3y}$

b. $f(x, y) = (2y^2 - y^4)\left(e^x + \frac{1}{1 + x^2}\right) - \frac{1}{1 + x^2}$

This property has the following interpretation. Suppose that a surface has a single local minimum that is not the absolute minimum. Then water can be poured into the basin around the local minimum and the surface never overflows, even though there are points on the surface below the local minimum.

(*Source: Mathematics Magazine*, May 1985, and *Calculus and Analytical Geometry*, 2nd ed., Philip Gillett, 1984)

QUICK CHECK ANSWERS

1. $f_x(2, -1) = f_y(2, -1) = 0$ **2.** Vertically, in the directions $\langle 0, 0, \pm 1 \rangle$ **3.** $D(x, y) = -12x^2y^2$ **4.** It has neither an absolute maximum nor absolute minimum value on this set. ◄

12.9 Lagrange Multipliers

One of many challenges in economics and marketing is predicting the behavior of consumers. Basic models of consumer behavior often involve a *utility function* that expresses consumers' combined preference for several different amenities. For example, a simple utility function might have the form $U = f(\ell, g)$, where ℓ represents the amount of leisure time and g represents the number of consumable goods. The model assumes that consumers try to maximize their utility function, but they do so under certain constraints on the variables of the problem. For example, increasing leisure time may increase utility, but leisure time produces no income for consumable goods. Similarly, consumable goods may also increase utility, but they require income, which reduces leisure time. We first develop a general method for solving such constrained optimization problems and then return to economics problems later in the section.

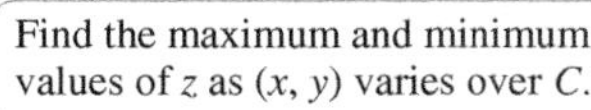

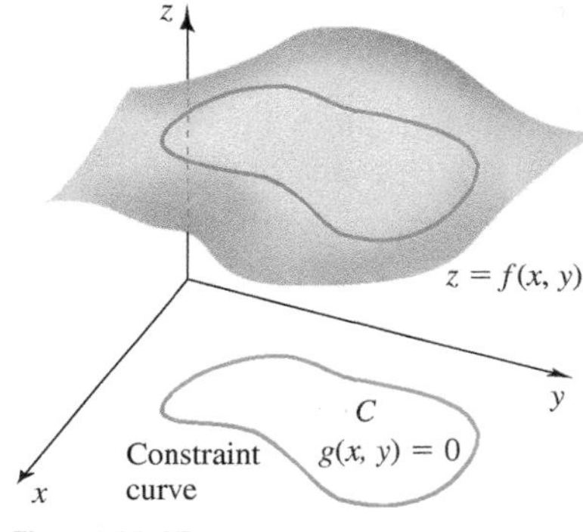

Figure 12.97

The Basic Idea

We start with a typical constrained optimization problem with two independent variables and give its method of solution; a generalization to more variables then follows. We seek maximum and/or minimum values of a differentiable **objective function** f with the restriction that x and y must lie on a **constraint** curve C in the xy-plane given by $g(x, y) = 0$ (Figure 12.97).

The problem and a method of solution are easy to visualize if we return to Example 7 of Section 12.8. Part of that problem was to find the maximum value of $f(x, y) = x^2 + y^2 - 2x + 2y + 5$ on the circle C: $\{(x, y): x^2 + y^2 = 4\}$ (Figure 12.98a). In

Figure 12.98b, we see the level curves of f and the point $P(-\sqrt{2}, \sqrt{2})$ on C at which f has a maximum value. Imagine moving along C toward P; as we approach P, the values of f increase and reach a maximum value at P. Moving past P, the values of f decrease.

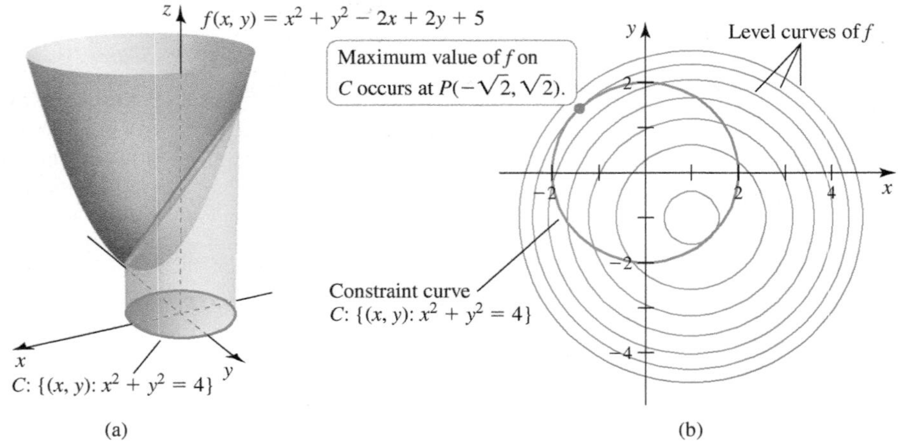

Figure 12.98

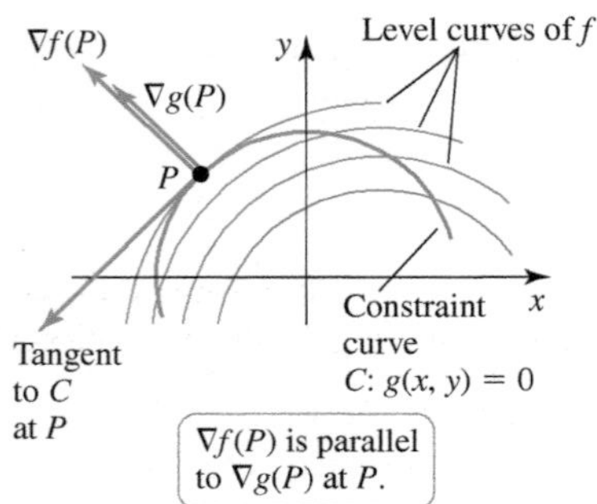

Figure 12.99

Figure 12.99 shows what is special about the point P. We already know that the line tangent to the level curve of f at P is orthogonal to the gradient $\nabla f(P)$ (Theorem 12.12). We also see that the line tangent to the level curve at P is tangent to the constraint curve C at P. We prove this fact shortly.

Furthermore, if we think of the constraint curve C as just one level curve of the function $z = g(x, y)$, then it follows that the gradient $\nabla g(P)$ is also orthogonal to C at P, where we assume that $\nabla g(P) \neq \mathbf{0}$ (Theorem 12.12). Therefore, the gradients $\nabla f(P)$ and $\nabla g(P)$ are parallel. These properties characterize the point P at which f has an extreme value on the constraint curve. They are the basis for the method of *Lagrange multipliers* that we now formalize.

Lagrange Multipliers with Two Independent Variables

The major step in establishing the method of Lagrange multipliers is to prove that Figure 12.99 is drawn correctly; that is, at the point on the constraint curve C where f has an extreme value, the line tangent to C is orthogonal to $\nabla f(a, b)$ and $\nabla g(a, b)$.

➤ The Greek lowercase ℓ is λ; it is read *lambda*.

THEOREM 12.15 Parallel Gradients (Ball Park Theorem)
Let f be a differentiable function in a region of $\mathbb{R}^2$ that contains the smooth curve C given by $g(x, y) = 0$. Assume that f has a local extreme value on C at a point $P(a, b)$. Then $\nabla f(a, b)$ is orthogonal to the line tangent to C at P. Assuming $\nabla g(a, b) \neq \mathbf{0}$, it follows that there is a real number λ (called a **Lagrange multiplier**) such that $\nabla f(a, b) = \lambda \nabla g(a, b)$.

Proof: Because C is smooth, it can be expressed parametrically in the form $C\colon \mathbf{r}(t) = \langle x(t), y(t) \rangle$, where x and y are differentiable functions on an interval in t that contains t_0 with $P(a, b) = (x(t_0), y(t_0))$. As we vary t and follow C, the rate of change of f is given by the Chain Rule:

$$\frac{df}{dt} = \frac{\partial f}{\partial x}\frac{dx}{dt} + \frac{\partial f}{\partial y}\frac{dy}{dt} = \nabla f \cdot \mathbf{r}'(t).$$

At the point $(x(t_0), y(t_0)) = (a, b)$ at which f has a local maximum or minimum value, we have $\left.\frac{df}{dt}\right|_{t=t_0} = 0$, which implies that $\nabla f(a, b) \cdot \mathbf{r}'(t_0) = 0$. Because $\mathbf{r}'(t)$ is tangent to C, the gradient $\nabla f(a, b)$ is orthogonal to the line tangent to C at P.

To prove the second assertion, note that the constraint curve C given by $g(x, y) = 0$ is also a level curve of the surface $z = g(x, y)$. Recall that gradients are orthogonal to

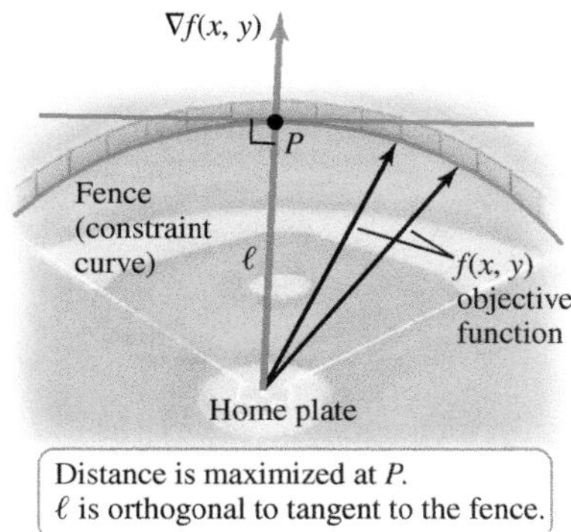

Figure 12.100

level curves. Therefore, at the point $P(a, b)$, $\nabla g(a, b)$ is orthogonal to C at (a, b). Because both $\nabla f(a, b)$ and $\nabla g(a, b)$ are orthogonal to C, the two gradients are parallel, so there is a real number λ such that $\nabla f(a, b) = \lambda \nabla g(a, b)$. ◄

Theorem 12.15 has a nice geometric interpretation that makes it easy to remember. Suppose you walk along the outfield fence at a ballpark, which represents the constraint curve C, and record the distance $f(x, y)$ between you and home plate (which is the objective function). At some instant, you reach a point P that maximizes the distance; it is the point on the fence farthest from home plate. The point P has the property that the line ℓ from home plate to P, which points in the direction of maximum increase of f, is orthogonal to the (line tangent to the) fence at P (Figure 12.100).

QUICK CHECK 1 Explain in terms of functions and gradients why the ballpark analogy for Theorem 12.15 is true. ◄

PROCEDURE Method of Lagrange Multipliers in Two Variables

Let the objective function f and the constraint function g be differentiable on a region of $\mathbb{R}^2$ with $\nabla g(x, y) \neq \mathbf{0}$ on the curve $g(x, y) = 0$. To locate the maximum and minimum values of f subject to the constraint $g(x, y) = 0$, carry out the following steps.

1. Find the values of x, y, and λ (if they exist) that satisfy the equations
$$\nabla f(x, y) = \lambda \nabla g(x, y) \quad \text{and} \quad g(x, y) = 0.$$
2. Among the values (x, y) found in Step 1, select the largest and smallest corresponding function values. These values are the maximum and minimum values of f subject to the constraint.

➤ *In principle*, it is possible to solve a constrained optimization problem by solving the constraint equation for one of the variables and eliminating that variable in the objective function. In practice, this method is often prohibitive, particularly with three or more variables or two or more constraints.

Notice that $\nabla f = \lambda \nabla g$ is a vector equation: $\langle f_x, f_y \rangle = \lambda \langle g_x, g_y \rangle$. It is satisfied provided $f_x = \lambda g_x$ and $f_y = \lambda g_y$. Therefore, the crux of the method is solving the three equations
$$f_x = \lambda g_x, \qquad f_y = \lambda g_y, \qquad \text{and} \qquad g(x, y) = 0$$
for the three variables x, y, and λ.

EXAMPLE 1 Lagrange multipliers with two variables Find the maximum and minimum values of the objective function $f(x, y) = 2x^2 + y^2 + 2$, where x and y lie on the ellipse C given by $g(x, y) = x^2 + 4y^2 - 4 = 0$.

SOLUTION Figure 12.101a shows the elliptic paraboloid $z = f(x, y)$ above the ellipse C in the xy-plane. As the ellipse is traversed, the corresponding function values on the surface vary. The goal is to find the minimum and maximum of these function values. An alternative view is given in Figure 12.101b, where we see the level curves of f and the constraint curve C. As the ellipse is traversed, the values of f vary, reaching maximum and minimum values along the way.

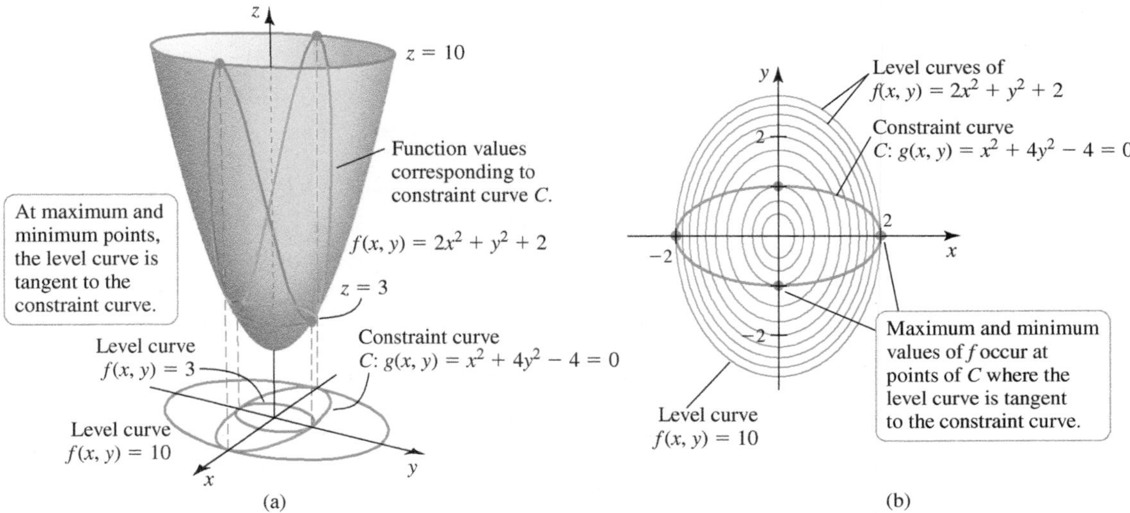

Figure 12.101

Noting that $\nabla f(x, y) = \langle 4x, 2y \rangle$ and $\nabla g(x, y) = \langle 2x, 8y \rangle$, the equations that result from $\nabla f = \lambda \nabla g$ and the constraint are

$$\underbrace{4x = \lambda(2x)}_{f_x = \lambda g_x}, \quad \underbrace{2y = \lambda(8y)}_{f_y = \lambda g_y}, \quad \text{and} \quad \underbrace{x^2 + 4y^2 - 4 = 0}_{g(x, y) = 0},$$

which reduce to the system of equations

$$x(2 - \lambda) = 0, \ (1) \qquad y(1 - 4\lambda) = 0, \ \text{and} \ (2) \qquad x^2 + 4y^2 - 4 = 0. \ (3)$$

The solutions of equation (1) are $x = 0$ or $\lambda = 2$. If $x = 0$, then equation (3) implies that $y = \pm 1$ and (2) implies that $\lambda = \frac{1}{4}$. On the other hand, if $\lambda = 2$ in equation (1), then equation (2) implies that $y = 0$; from (3), we get $x = \pm 2$. Therefore, the candidates for locations of extreme values are $(0, \pm 1)$, with $f(0, \pm 1) = 3$, and $(\pm 2, 0)$, with $f(\pm 2, 0) = 10$. We see that the maximum value of f on C is 10, which occurs at $(2, 0)$ and $(-2, 0)$; the minimum value of f on C is 3, which occurs at $(0, 1)$ and $(0, -1)$. Notice that the value of λ is not used in the final result.

Related Exercises 5–14 ◀

QUICK CHECK 2 Choose any point on the constraint curve in Figure 12.101b other than a solution point. Draw ∇f and ∇g at that point and show that they are not parallel. ◀

Lagrange Multipliers with Three Independent Variables

The technique just outlined extends to three or more independent variables. With three variables, suppose an objective function $w = f(x, y, z)$ is given; its level surfaces are surfaces in $\mathbb{R}^3$ (Figure 12.102a). The constraint equation takes the form $g(x, y, z) = 0$, which is another surface S in $\mathbb{R}^3$ (Figure 12.102b). To find the maximum and minimum values of f on S (assuming they exist), we must find the points (a, b, c) on S at which $\nabla f(a, b, c)$ is parallel to $\nabla g(a, b, c)$, assuming $\nabla g(a, b, c) \neq \mathbf{0}$ (Figure 12.102c, d). The procedure for finding the maximum and minimum values of $f(x, y, z)$, where the point (x, y, z) is constrained to lie on S, is similar to the procedure for two variables.

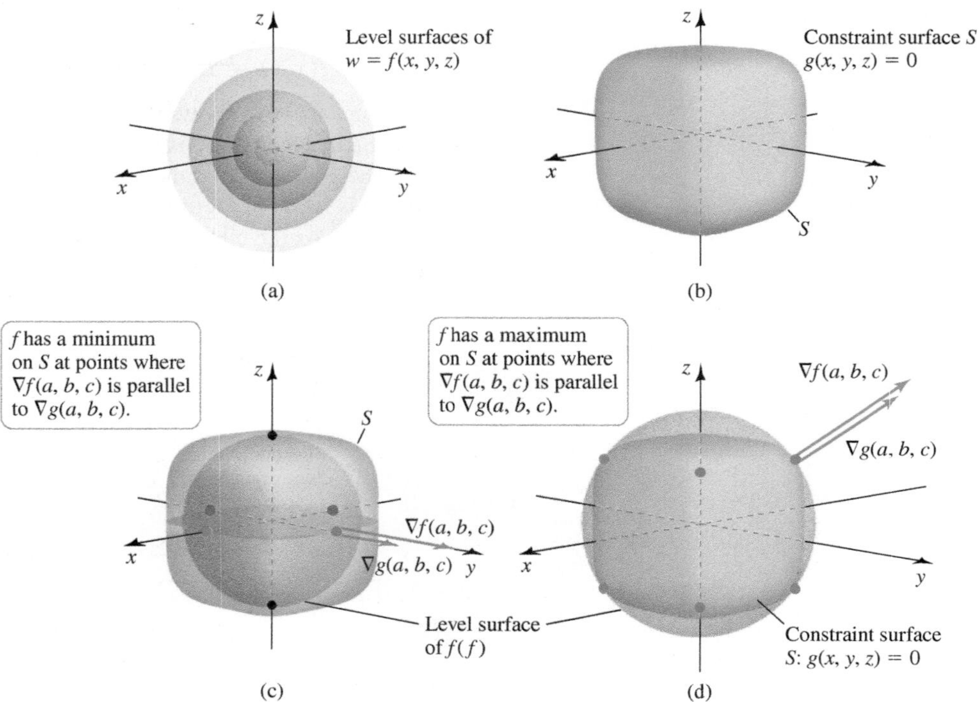

Figure 12.102

> Some books formulate the Lagrange multiplier method by defining $L = f - \lambda g$. The conditions of the method then become $\nabla L = \mathbf{0}$, where $\nabla L = \langle L_x, L_y, L_z, L_\lambda \rangle$.

PROCEDURE Method of Lagrange Multipliers in Three Variables

Let f and g be differentiable on a region of $\mathbb{R}^3$ with $\nabla g(x, y, z) \neq \mathbf{0}$ on the surface $g(x, y, z) = 0$. To locate the maximum and minimum values of f subject to the constraint $g(x, y, z) = 0$, carry out the following steps.

1. Find the values of x, y, z, and λ that satisfy the equations

$$\nabla f(x, y, z) = \lambda \nabla g(x, y, z) \quad \text{and} \quad g(x, y, z) = 0.$$

2. Among the points (x, y, z) found in Step 1, select the largest and smallest corresponding function values. These values are the maximum and minimum values of f subject to the constraint.

Now there are four equations to be solved for x, y, z, and λ:

$$f_x(x, y, z) = \lambda g_x(x, y, z), \qquad f_y(x, y, z) = \lambda g_y(x, y, z),$$
$$f_z(x, y, z) = \lambda g_z(x, y, z), \quad \text{and} \quad g(x, y, z) = 0.$$

> Problems similar to Example 2 were solved in Section 12.8 using ordinary optimization techniques. These methods may or may not be easier to apply than Lagrange multipliers.

EXAMPLE 2 A geometry problem Find the least distance between the point $P(3, 4, 0)$ and the surface of the cone $z^2 = x^2 + y^2$.

SOLUTION Figure 12.103 shows both sheets of the cone and the point $P(3, 4, 0)$. Because P is in the xy-plane, we anticipate two solutions, one for each sheet of the cone. The distance between P and any point $Q(x, y, z)$ on the cone is

$$d(x, y, z) = \sqrt{(x - 3)^2 + (y - 4)^2 + z^2}.$$

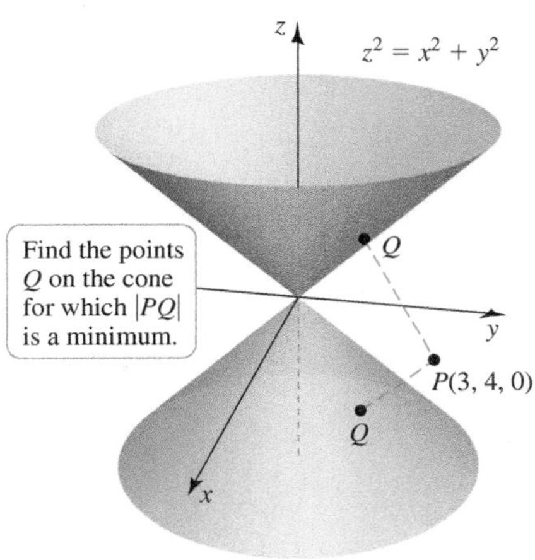

Figure 12.103

In many distance problems, it is easier to work with the *square* of the distance to avoid dealing with square roots. This maneuver is allowable because if a point minimizes $(d(x, y, z))^2$, it also minimizes $d(x, y, z)$. Therefore, we define

$$f(x, y, z) = (d(x, y, z))^2 = (x - 3)^2 + (y - 4)^2 + z^2.$$

The constraint is the condition that the point (x, y, z) must lie on the cone, which implies $z^2 = x^2 + y^2$, or $g(x, y, z) = z^2 - x^2 - y^2 = 0$.

Now we proceed with Lagrange multipliers; the conditions are

$$f_x(x, y, z) = \lambda g_x(x, y, z), \text{ or } 2(x - 3) = \lambda(-2x), \text{ or } x(1 + \lambda) = 3, \quad (4)$$
$$f_y(x, y, z) = \lambda g_y(x, y, z), \text{ or } 2(y - 4) = \lambda(-2y), \text{ or } y(1 + \lambda) = 4, \quad (5)$$
$$f_z(x, y, z) = \lambda g_z(x, y, z), \text{ or } 2z = \lambda(2z), \text{ or } z = \lambda z, \text{ and} \quad (6)$$
$$g(x, y, z) = z^2 - x^2 - y^2 = 0. \quad (7)$$

The solutions of equation (6) (the simplest of the four equations) are either $z = 0$, or $\lambda = 1$ and $z \neq 0$. In the first case, if $z = 0$, then by equation (7), $x = y = 0$; however, $x = 0$ and $y = 0$ do not satisfy (4) and (5). So no solution results from this case.

> With three independent variables, it is possible to impose two constraints. These problems are explored in Exercises 61–65.

On the other hand, if $\lambda = 1$ in equation (6), then by (4) and (5), we find that $x = \frac{3}{2}$ and $y = 2$. Using (7), the corresponding values of z are $\pm\frac{5}{2}$. Therefore, the two solutions and the values of f are

$$x = \tfrac{3}{2}, \quad y = 2, \quad z = \tfrac{5}{2} \quad \text{with } f\left(\tfrac{3}{2}, 2, \tfrac{5}{2}\right) = \tfrac{25}{2}, \text{ and}$$
$$x = \tfrac{3}{2}, \quad y = 2, \quad z = -\tfrac{5}{2} \quad \text{with } f\left(\tfrac{3}{2}, 2, -\tfrac{5}{2}\right) = \tfrac{25}{2}.$$

You can check that moving away from $\left(\frac{3}{2}, 2, \pm\frac{5}{2}\right)$ in any direction on the cone has the effect of increasing the values of f. Therefore, the points correspond to *local* minima of f. Do these points also correspond to *absolute* minima? The domain of this problem is unbounded; however, one can argue geometrically that f increases without bound moving away from $\left(\frac{3}{2}, 2, \pm\frac{5}{2}\right)$ on the cone with $|x| \to \infty$ and $|y| \to \infty$. Therefore, these points correspond to absolute minimum values and the points on the cone nearest to $(3, 4, 0)$ are $\left(\frac{3}{2}, 2, \pm\frac{5}{2}\right)$, at a distance of $\sqrt{\frac{25}{2}} = \frac{5}{\sqrt{2}}$. (Recall that $f = d^2$.)

Related Exercises 15–34 ◀

QUICK CHECK 3 In Example 2, is there a point that *maximizes* the distance between $(3, 4, 0)$ and the cone? If the point $(3, 4, 0)$ were replaced by $(3, 4, 1)$, how many minimizing solutions would there be? ◀

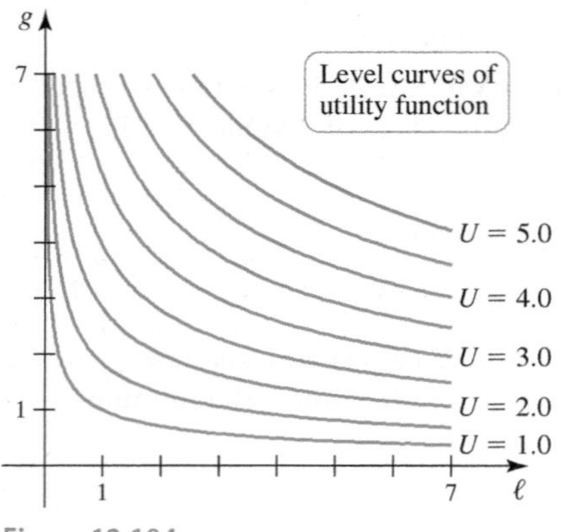

Figure 12.104

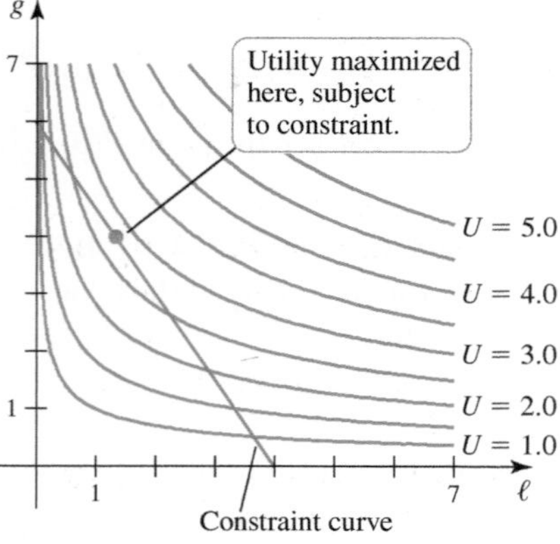

Figure 12.105

Economic Models In the opening of this section, we briefly described how utility functions are used to model consumer behavior. We now look in more detail at some specific—admittedly simple—utility functions and the constraints that are imposed upon them.

As described earlier, a prototype model for consumer behavior uses two independent variables: leisure time ℓ and consumable goods g. A utility function $U = f(\ell, g)$ measures consumer preferences for various combinations of leisure time and consumable goods. The following assumptions about utility functions are commonly made.

1. Utility increases if any variable increases (essentially, *more is better*).
2. Various combinations of leisure time and consumable goods have the same utility; that is, giving up some leisure time for additional consumable goods results in the same utility.

The level curves of a typical utility function are shown in Figure 12.104. Assumption 1 is reflected by the fact that the utility values on the level curves increase as either ℓ or g increases. Consistent with Assumption 2, a single level curve shows the combinations of ℓ and g that have the same utility; for this reason, economists call the level curves *indifference curves*. Notice that if ℓ increases, then g must decrease on a level curve to maintain the same utility, and vice versa.

Economic models assert that consumers maximize utility subject to constraints on leisure time and consumable goods. One assumption that leads to a reasonable constraint is that an increase in leisure time implies a linear decrease in consumable goods. Therefore, the constraint curve is a line with negative slope (Figure 12.105). When such a constraint is superimposed on the level curves of the utility function, the optimization problem becomes evident. Among all points on the constraint line, which one maximizes utility? A solution is marked in the figure; at this point, the utility has a maximum value (between 2.5 and 3.0).

EXAMPLE 3 Constrained optimization of utility Find the maximum value of the utility function $U = f(\ell, g) = \ell^{1/3}g^{2/3}$, subject to the constraint $G(\ell, g) = 3\ell + 2g - 12 = 0$, where $\ell \geq 0$ and $g \geq 0$.

SOLUTION The level curves of the utility function and the linear constraint are shown in Figure 12.105. The solution follows the Lagrange multiplier method with two variables. The gradient of the utility function is

$$\nabla f(\ell, g) = \left\langle \frac{\ell^{-2/3}g^{2/3}}{3}, \frac{2\ell^{1/3}g^{-1/3}}{3} \right\rangle = \frac{1}{3}\left\langle \left(\frac{g}{\ell}\right)^{2/3}, 2\left(\frac{\ell}{g}\right)^{1/3} \right\rangle.$$

The gradient of the constraint function is $\nabla G(\ell, g) = \langle 3, 2 \rangle$. Therefore, the equations that must be solved are

$$\frac{1}{3}\left(\frac{g}{\ell}\right)^{2/3} = 3\lambda, \quad \frac{2}{3}\left(\frac{\ell}{g}\right)^{1/3} = 2\lambda, \quad \text{and} \quad G(\ell, g) = 3\ell + 2g - 12 = 0.$$

Eliminating λ from the first two equations leads to the condition $g = 3\ell$, which, when substituted into the constraint equation, gives the solution $\ell = \frac{4}{3}$ and $g = 4$. The actual value of the utility function at this point is $U = f\left(\frac{4}{3}, 4\right) = 4/\sqrt[3]{3} \approx 2.8$. This solution is consistent with Figure 12.105.

Related Exercises 35–38 ◄

QUICK CHECK 4 In Figure 12.105, explain why, if you move away from the optimal point along the constraint line, the utility decreases. ◄

SECTION 12.9 EXERCISES

Review Questions

1. Explain why, at a point that maximizes or minimizes f subject to a constraint $g(x, y) = 0$, the gradient of f is parallel to the gradient of g. Use a diagram.

2. If $f(x, y) = x^2 + y^2$ and $g(x, y) = 2x + 3y - 4 = 0$, write the Lagrange multiplier conditions that must be satisfied by a point that maximizes or minimizes f subject to $g(x, y) = 0$.

3. If $f(x, y, z) = x^2 + y^2 + z^2$ and $g(x, y, z) = 2x + 3y - 5z + 4 = 0$, write the Lagrange multiplier conditions that must be satisfied by a point that maximizes or minimizes f subject to $g(x, y, z) = 0$.

4. Sketch several level curves of $f(x, y) = x^2 + y^2$ and sketch the constraint line $g(x, y) = 2x + 3y - 4 = 0$. Describe the extrema (if any) that f attains on the constraint line.

Basic Skills

5–14. Lagrange multipliers in two variables *Use Lagrange multipliers to find the maximum and minimum values of f (when they exist) subject to the given constraint.*

5. $f(x, y) = x + 2y$ subject to $x^2 + y^2 = 4$

6. $f(x, y) = xy^2$ subject to $x^2 + y^2 = 1$

7. $f(x, y) = x + y$ subject to $x^2 - xy + y^2 = 1$

8. $f(x, y) = x^2 + y^2$ subject to $2x^2 + 3xy + 2y^2 = 7$

9. $f(x, y) = xy$ subject to $x^2 + y^2 - xy = 9$

10. $f(x, y) = x - y$ subject to $x^2 + y^2 - 3xy = 20$

11. $f(x, y) = e^{2xy}$ subject to $x^2 + y^2 = 16$

12. $f(x, y) = x^2 + y^2$ subject to $x^6 + y^6 = 1$

13. $f(x, y) = y^2 - 4x^2$ subject to $x^2 + 2y^2 = 4$

14. $f(x, y) = xy + x + y$ subject to $x^2y^2 = 4$

15–24. Lagrange multipliers in three variables *Use Lagrange multipliers to find the maximum and minimum values of f (when they exist) subject to the given constraint.*

15. $f(x, y, z) = x + 3y - z$ subject to $x^2 + y^2 + z^2 = 4$

16. $f(x, y, z) = xyz$ subject to $x^2 + 2y^2 + 4z^2 = 9$

17. $f(x, y, z) = x$ subject to $x^2 + y^2 + z^2 - z = 1$

18. $f(x, y, z) = x - z$ subject to $x^2 + y^2 + z^2 - y = 2$

19. $f(x, y, z) = x^2 + y^2 + z^2$ subject to $x^2 + y^2 + z^2 - 4xy = 1$

20. $f(x, y, z) = x + y + z$ subject to $x^2 + y^2 + z^2 - 2x - 2y = 1$

21. $f(x, y, z) = 2x + z^2$ subject to $x^2 + y^2 + 2z^2 = 25$

22. $f(x, y, z) = x^2 + y^2 - z$ subject to $z = 2x^2y^2 + 1$

23. $f(x, y, z) = x^2 + y^2 + z^2$ subject to $xyz = 4$

24. $f(x, y, z) = (xyz)^{1/2}$ subject to $x + y + z = 1$ with $x \geq 0$, $y \geq 0, z \geq 0$

25–34. Applications of Lagrange multipliers *Use Lagrange multipliers in the following problems. When the domain of the objective function is unbounded or open, explain why you have found an absolute maximum or minimum value.*

25. **Shipping regulations** A shipping company requires that the sum of length plus girth of rectangular boxes must not exceed 108 in. Find the dimensions of the box with maximum volume that meets this condition. (The girth is the perimeter of the smallest side of the box.)

26. **Box with minimum surface area** Find the rectangular box with a volume of 16 ft^3 that has minimum surface area.

27. **Extreme distances to an ellipse** Find the minimum and maximum distances between the ellipse $x^2 + xy + 2y^2 = 1$ and the origin.

28. **Maximum area rectangle in an ellipse** Find the dimensions of the rectangle of maximum area with sides parallel to the coordinate axes that can be inscribed in the ellipse $4x^2 + 16y^2 = 16$.

29. **Maximum perimeter rectangle in an ellipse** Find the dimensions of the rectangle of maximum perimeter with sides parallel to the coordinate axes that can be inscribed in the ellipse $2x^2 + 4y^2 = 3$.

30. **Minimum distance to a plane** Find the point on the plane $2x + 3y + 6z - 10 = 0$ closest to the point $(-2, 5, 1)$.

31. **Minimum distance to a surface** Find the point on the surface $4x + y - 1 = 0$ closest to the point $(1, 2, -3)$.

32. **Minimum distance to a cone** Find the points on the cone $z^2 = x^2 + y^2$ closest to the point $(1, 2, 0)$.

33. **Extreme distances to a sphere** Find the minimum and maximum distances between the sphere $x^2 + y^2 + z^2 = 9$ and the point $(2, 3, 4)$.

34. **Maximum volume cylinder in a sphere** Find the dimensions of a right circular cylinder of maximum volume that can be inscribed in a sphere of radius 16.

35–38. Maximizing utility functions *Find the values of ℓ and g with $\ell \geq 0$ and $g \geq 0$ that maximize the following utility functions subject to the given constraints. Give the value of the utility function at the optimal point.*

35. $U = f(\ell, g) = 10\ell^{1/2}g^{1/2}$ subject to $3\ell + 6g = 18$

36. $U = f(\ell, g) = 32\ell^{2/3}g^{1/3}$ subject to $4\ell + 2g = 12$

37. $U = f(\ell, g) = 8\ell^{4/5}g^{1/5}$ subject to $10\ell + 8g = 40$

38. $U = f(\ell, g) = \ell^{1/6}g^{5/6}$ subject to $4\ell + 5g = 20$

Further Explorations

39. **Explain why or why not** Determine whether the following statements are true and give an explanation or counterexample.
    a. Suppose you are standing at the center of a sphere looking at a point P on the surface of the sphere. Your line of sight to P is orthogonal to the plane tangent to the sphere at P.
    b. At a point that maximizes f on the curve $g(x, y) = 0$, the dot product $\nabla f \cdot \nabla g$ is zero.

40–45. Alternative method *Solve the following problems from Section 12.8 using Lagrange multipliers.*

40. Exercise 35 **41.** Exercise 36 **42.** Exercise 37

43. Exercise 38 **44.** Exercise 64 **45.** Exercise 65

 **46–49. Absolute maximum and minimum values** *Find the absolute maximum and minimum values of the following functions over the given regions R. Use Lagrange multipliers to check for extreme points on the boundary.*

46. $f(x, y) = x^2 + 4y^2 + 1$; $R = \{(x, y): x^2 + 4y^2 \le 1\}$

47. $f(x, y) = x^2 - 4y^2 + xy$; $R = \{(x, y): 4x^2 + 9y^2 \le 36\}$

48. $f(x, y) = 2x^2 + y^2 + 2x - 3y$; $R = \{(x, y): x^2 + y^2 \le 1\}$

49. $f(x, y) = (x - 1)^2 + (y + 1)^2$; $R = \{(x, y): x^2 + y^2 \le 4\}$

50–51. Graphical Lagrange multipliers *The following figures show the level curves of f and the constraint curve $g(x, y) = 0$. Estimate the maximum and minimum values of f subject to the constraint. At each point where an extreme value occurs, indicate the direction of ∇f and the direction of ∇g.*

50.

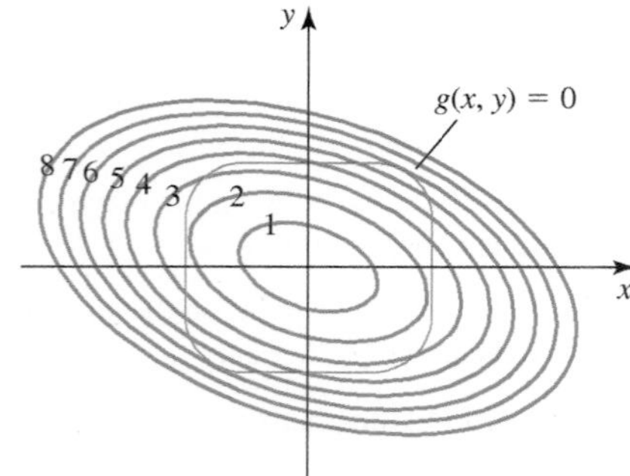

51.

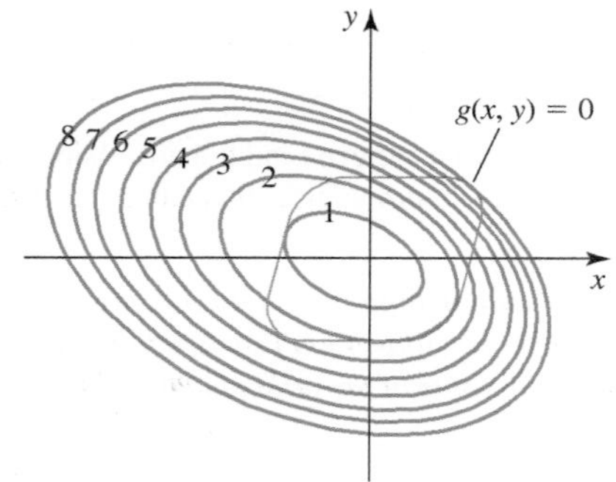

52. Extreme points on flattened spheres The equation $x^{2n} + y^{2n} + z^{2n} = 1$, where n is a positive integer, describes a flattened sphere. Define the extreme points to be the points on the flattened sphere with a maximum distance from the origin.

a. Find all the extreme points on the flattened sphere with $n = 2$. What is the distance between the extreme points and the origin?

b. Find all the extreme points on the flattened sphere for integers $n > 2$. What is the distance between the extreme points and the origin?

c. Give the location of the extreme points in the limit as $n \to \infty$. What is the limiting distance between the extreme points and the origin as $n \to \infty$?

Applications

53–55. Production functions *Economists model the output of manufacturing systems using production functions that have many of the same properties as utility functions. The family of Cobb-Douglas production functions has the form $P = f(K, L) = CK^aL^{1-a}$, where K represents capital, L represents labor, and C and a are positive real numbers with $0 < a < 1$. If the cost of capital is p dollars per unit, the cost of labor is q dollars per unit, and the total available budget is B, then the constraint takes the form $pK + qL = B$. Find the values of K and L that maximize the following production functions subject to the given constraint, assuming $K \ge 0$ and $L \ge 0$.*

53. $P = f(K, L) = K^{1/2}L^{1/2}$ for $20K + 30L = 300$

54. $P = f(K, L) = 10K^{1/3}L^{2/3}$ for $30K + 60L = 360$

55. Given the production function $P = f(K, L) = K^aL^{1-a}$ and the budget constraint $pK + qL = B$, where a, p, q, and B are given, show that P is maximized when $K = aB/p$ and $L = (1 - a)B/q$.

56. Temperature of an elliptical plate The temperature of points on an elliptical plate $x^2 + y^2 + xy \le 1$ is given by $T(x, y) = 25(x^2 + y^2)$. Find the hottest and coldest temperatures on the edge of the elliptical plate.

Additional Exercises

57–59. Maximizing a sum

57. Find the maximum value of $x_1 + x_2 + x_3 + x_4$ subject to the condition that $x_1^2 + x_2^2 + x_3^2 + x_4^2 = 16$.

58. Generalize Exercise 57 and find the maximum value of $x_1 + x_2 + \cdots + x_n$ subject to the condition that $x_1^2 + x_2^2 + \cdots + x_n^2 = c^2$, for a real number c and a positive integer n.

59. Generalize Exercise 57 and find the maximum value of $a_1x_1 + a_2x_2 + \cdots + a_nx_n$ subject to the condition that $x_1^2 + x_2^2 + \cdots + x_n^2 = 1$, for given positive real numbers $a_1, \ldots, a_n$ and a positive integer n.

60. Geometric and arithmetic means Given positive numbers $x_1, \ldots, x_n$, prove that the geometric mean $(x_1x_2\cdots x_n)^{1/n}$ is no greater than the arithmetic mean $(x_1 + \cdots + x_n)/n$ in the following cases.

a. Find the maximum value of xyz, subject to $x + y + z = k$, where k is a real number and $x > 0$, $y > 0$, and $z > 0$. Use the result to prove that

$$(xyz)^{1/3} \le \frac{x + y + z}{3}.$$

b. Generalize part (a) and show that

$$(x_1x_2\cdots x_n)^{1/n} \le \frac{x_1 + \cdots + x_n}{n}.$$

61. **Problems with two constraints** Given a differentiable function $w = f(x, y, z)$, the goal is to find its maximum and minimum values subject to the constraints $g(x, y, z) = 0$ and $h(x, y, z) = 0$, where g and h are also differentiable.

 a. Imagine a level surface of the function f and the constraint surfaces $g(x, y, z) = 0$ and $h(x, y, z) = 0$. Note that g and h intersect (in general) in a curve C on which maximum and minimum values of f must be found. Explain why ∇g and ∇h are orthogonal to their respective surfaces.
 b. Explain why ∇f lies in the plane formed by ∇g and ∇h at a point of C where f has a maximum or minimum value.
 c. Explain why part (b) implies that $\nabla f = \lambda \nabla g + \mu \nabla h$ at a point of C where f has a maximum or minimum value, where λ and μ (the Lagrange multipliers) are real numbers.
 d. Conclude from part (c) that the equations that must be solved for maximum or minimum values of f subject to two constraints are $\nabla f = \lambda \nabla g + \mu \nabla h$, $g(x, y, z) = 0$ and $h(x, y, z) = 0$.

62–65. Two-constraint problems *Use the result of Exercise 61 to solve the following problems.*

62. The planes $x + 2z = 12$ and $x + y = 6$ intersect in a line L. Find the point on L nearest the origin.

63. Find the maximum and minimum values of $f(x, y, z) = xyz$ subject to the conditions that $x^2 + y^2 = 4$ and $x + y + z = 1$.

64. The paraboloid $z = x^2 + 2y^2 + 1$ and the plane $x - y + 2z = 4$ intersect in a curve C. Find the points on C that have maximum and minimum distance from the origin.

65. Find the maximum and minimum values of $f(x, y, z) = x^2 + y^2 + z^2$ on the curve on which the cone $z^2 = 4x^2 + 4y^2$ and the plane $2x + 4z = 5$ intersect.

QUICK CHECK ANSWERS

1. Let $f(x, y)$ be the distance between any point $P(x, y)$ on the fence and home plate O. The key fact is that ∇f always points along the line OP. As P moves along the fence (the constraint curve), $f(x, y)$ increases until a point is reached at which ∇f is orthogonal to the fence. At such a point, f has a maximum value. **3.** The distance between $(3, 4, 0)$ and the cone can be arbitrarily large, so there is no maximizing solution. If the point of interest is not in the xy-plane, there is one minimizing solution. **4.** If you move along the constraint line away from the optimal solution in either direction, you cross level curves of the utility function with decreasing values.◄

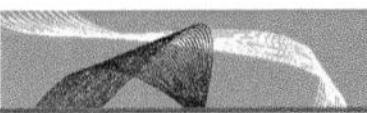

CHAPTER 12 REVIEW EXERCISES

1. **Explain why or why not** Determine whether the following statements are true and give an explanation or counterexample.

 a. The equation $4x - 3y = 12$ describes a line in $\mathbb{R}^3$.
 b. The equation $z^2 = 2x^2 - 6y^2$ determines z as a single function of x and y.
 c. If f has continuous partial derivatives of all orders, then $f_{xxy} = f_{yyx}$.
 d. Given the surface $z = f(x, y)$, the gradient $\nabla f(a, b)$ lies in the plane tangent to the surface at $(a, b, f(a, b))$.
 e. There is always a plane orthogonal to both of two distinct intersecting planes.

2. **Equations of planes** Consider the plane that passes through the point $(6, 0, 1)$ with a normal vector $\mathbf{n} = \langle 3, 4, -6 \rangle$.

 a. Find an equation of the plane.
 b. Find the intercepts of the plane with the three coordinate axes.
 c. Make a sketch of the plane.

3. **Equations of planes** Consider the plane passing through the points $(0, 0, 3)$, $(1, 0, -6)$, and $(1, 2, 3)$.

 a. Find an equation of the plane.
 b. Find the intercepts of the plane with the three coordinate axes.
 c. Make a sketch of the plane.

4–5. Intersecting planes *Find an equation of the line of intersection of the planes Q and R.*

4. $Q: 2x + y - z = 0$, $R: -x + y + z = 1$

5. $Q: -3x + y + 2z = 0$, $R: 3x + 3y + 4z - 12 = 0$

6–7. Equations of planes *Find an equation of the following planes.*

6. The plane passing through $(2, -3, 1)$ normal to the line $\langle x, y, z \rangle = \langle 2 + t, 3t, 2 - 3t \rangle$

7. The plane passing through $(-2, 3, 1)$, $(1, 1, 0)$, and $(-1, 0, 1)$

8–22. Identifying surfaces *Consider the surfaces defined by the following equations.*

a. Identify and briefly describe the surface.
b. Find the xy-, xz-, and yz-traces, when they exist.
c. Find the intercepts with the three coordinate axes, when they exist.
d. Make a sketch of the surface.

8. $z - \sqrt{x} = 0$

9. $3z = \frac{x^2}{12} - \frac{y^2}{48}$

10. $\frac{x^2}{100} + 4y^2 + \frac{z^2}{16} = 1$

11. $y^2 = 4x^2 + z^2/25$

12. $\frac{4x^2}{9} + \frac{9z^2}{4} = y^2$

13. $4z = \frac{x^2}{4} + \frac{y^2}{9}$

14. $\frac{x^2}{16} + \frac{z^2}{36} - \frac{y^2}{100} = 1$

15. $y^2 + 4z^2 - 2x^2 = 1$

16. $-\frac{x^2}{16} + \frac{z^2}{36} - \frac{y^2}{25} = 4$

17. $\frac{x^2}{4} + \frac{y^2}{16} - z^2 = 4$

18. $x = \frac{y^2}{64} - \frac{z^2}{9}$

19. $\frac{x^2}{4} + \frac{y^2}{16} + z^2 = 4$

20. $y - e^{-x} = 0$

21. $\dfrac{y^2}{49} + \dfrac{x^2}{9} = \dfrac{z^2}{64}$

22. $y = 4x^2 + \dfrac{z^2}{9}$

23–26. Domains *Find the domain of the following functions. Make a sketch of the domain in the xy-plane.*

23. $f(x, y) = \dfrac{1}{x^2 + y^2}$

24. $f(x, y) = \ln xy$

25. $f(x, y) = \sqrt{x - y^2}$

26. $f(x, y) = \tan(x + y)$

27. Matching surfaces Match functions a–d with surfaces A–D.

a. $z = \sqrt{2x^2 + 3y^2 + 1} - 1$
b. $z = -3y^2$
c. $z = 2x^2 - 3y^2 + 1$
d. $z = \sqrt{2x^2 + 3y^2 - 1}$

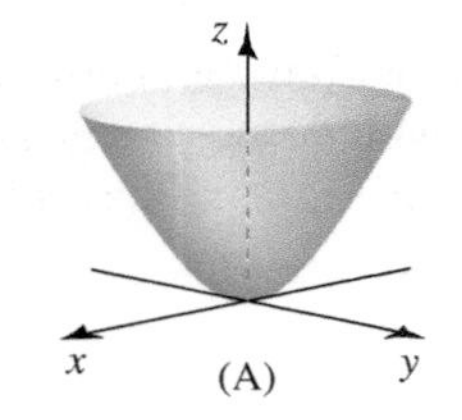

(A)

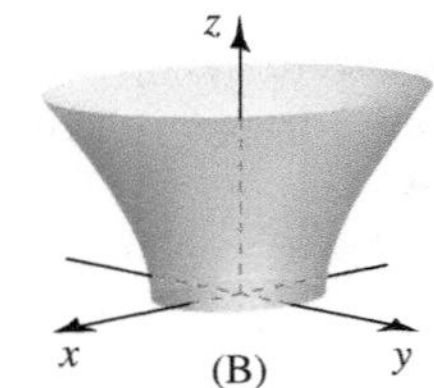

(B)

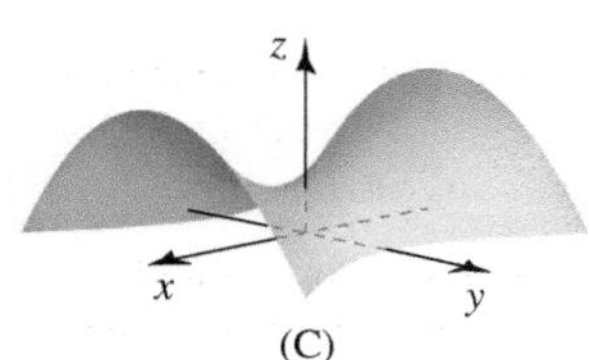

(C)

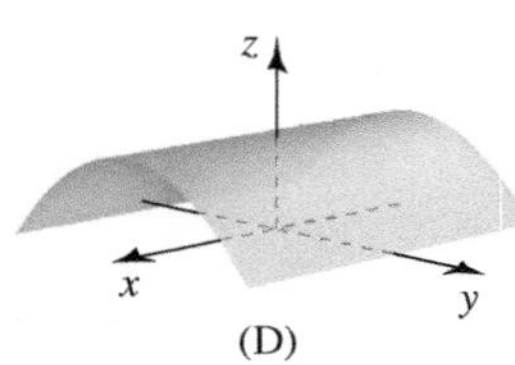

(D)

28–29. Level curves *Make a sketch of several level curves of the following functions. Label at least two level curves with their z-values.*

28. $f(x, y) = x^2 - y$

29. $f(x, y) = 2x^2 + 4y^2$

30. Matching level curves with surfaces Match level curve plots a–d with surfaces A–D.

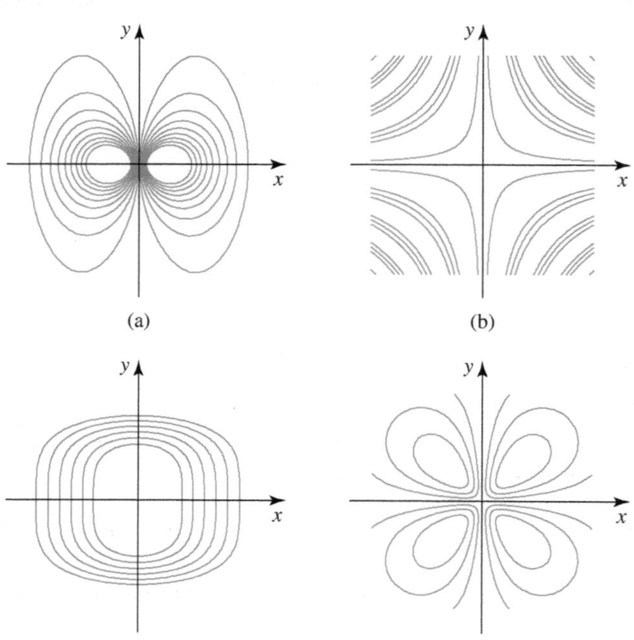

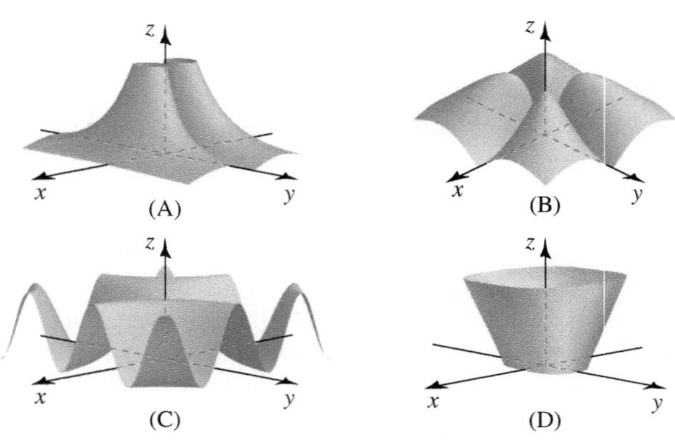

31–38. Limits *Evaluate the following limits or determine that they do not exist.*

31. $\displaystyle\lim_{(x,y)\to(4,-2)} (10x - 5y + 6xy)$

32. $\displaystyle\lim_{(x,y)\to(1,1)} \frac{xy}{x + y}$

33. $\displaystyle\lim_{(x,y)\to(0,0)} \frac{x + y}{xy}$

34. $\displaystyle\lim_{(x,y)\to(0,0)} \frac{\sin xy}{x^2 + y^2}$

35. $\displaystyle\lim_{(x,y)\to(-1,1)} \frac{x^2 - y^2}{x^2 - xy - 2y^2}$

36. $\displaystyle\lim_{(x,y)\to(1,2)} \frac{x^2y}{x^4 + 2y^2}$

37. $\displaystyle\lim_{(x,y,z)\to(\frac{\pi}{2},0,\frac{\pi}{2})} 4\cos y \sin\sqrt{xz}$

38. $\displaystyle\lim_{(x,y,z)\to(5,2,-3)} \tan^{-1}\left(\frac{x + y^2}{z^2}\right)$

39–46. Partial derivatives *Find the first partial derivatives of the following functions.*

39. $f(x, y) = 3x^2y^5$

40. $g(x, y, z) = 4xyz^2 - \dfrac{3x}{y}$

41. $f(x, y) = \dfrac{x^2}{x^2 + y^2}$

42. $g(x, y, z) = \dfrac{xyz}{x + y}$

43. $f(x, y) = xye^{xy}$

44. $g(u, v) = u\cos v - v\sin u$

45. $f(x, y, z) = e^{x+2y+3z}$

46. $H(p, q, r) = p^2\sqrt{q + r}$

47–48. Laplace's equation *Verify that the following functions satisfy Laplace's equation* $\dfrac{\partial^2 u}{\partial x^2} + \dfrac{\partial^2 u}{\partial y^2} = 0.$

47. $u(x, y) = y(3x^2 - y^2)$

48. $u(x, y) = \ln(x^2 + y^2)$

49. Region between spheres Two spheres have the same center and radii r and R, where $0 < r < R$. The volume of the region between the spheres is $V(r, R) = \dfrac{4\pi}{3}(R^3 - r^3)$.

a. First use your intuition. If r is held fixed, how does V change as R increases? What is the sign of V_R? If R is held fixed, how does V change as r increases (up to the value of R)? What is the sign of V_r?
b. Compute V_r and V_R. Are the results consistent with part (a)?
c. Consider spheres with $R = 3$ and $r = 1$. Does the volume change more if R is increased by $\Delta R = 0.1$ (with r fixed) or if r is decreased by $\Delta r = 0.1$ (with R fixed)?

50–53. Chain Rule *Use the Chain Rule to evaluate the following derivatives.*

50. $w'(t)$, where $w = xy \sin z$, $x = t^2$, $y = 4t^3$, and $z = t + 1$

51. $w'(t)$, where $w = \sqrt{x^2 + y^2 + z^2}$, $x = \sin t$, $y = \cos t$, and $z = \cos t$

52. w_s and w_t, where $w = xyz$, $x = 2st$, $y = st^2$, and $z = s^2t$

53. w_r, w_s, and w_t, where $w = \ln (xy^2)$, $x = rst$, and $y = r + s$

54–55. Implicit differentiation *Find dy/dx for the following implicit relations.*

54. $2x^2 + 3xy - 3y^4 = 2$

55. $y \ln (x^2 + y^2) = 4$

56–57. Walking on a surface *Consider the following surfaces and parameterized curves C in the xy-plane.*

a. *In each case, find $z'(t)$ on C.*

b. *Imagine that you are walking on the surface directly above C consistent with the positive orientation of C. Find the values of t for which you are walking uphill.*

56. $z = 4x^2 + y^2 - 2$; $C: x = \cos t, y = \sin t$, for $0 \leq t \leq 2\pi$

57. $z = x^2 - 2y^2 + 4$; $C: x = 2 \cos t, y = 2 \sin t$, for $0 \leq t \leq 2\pi$

58. Constant volume cones Suppose the radius of a right circular cone increases as $r(t) = t^a$ and the height decreases as $h(t) = t^{-b}$, for $t \geq 1$, where a and b are positive constants. What is the relationship between a and b such that the volume of the cone remains constant (that is, $V'(t) = 0$, where $V = (\pi/3)r^2h$)?

59. Directional derivatives Consider the function $f(x, y) = 2x^2 - 4y^2 + 10$, whose graph is shown in the figure.

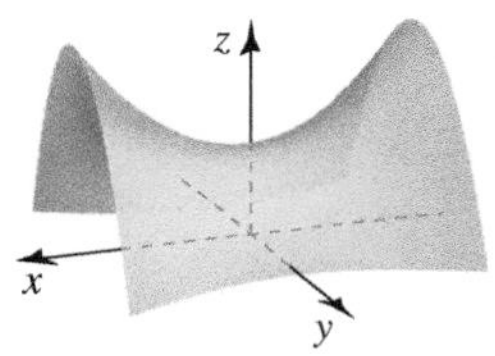

a. Fill in the table showing the value of the directional derivative at points (a, b) in the direction given by the unit vectors **u**, **v**, and **w**.

	$(a,b) = (0,0)$	$(a,b) = (2,0)$	$(a,b) = (1,1)$
$\mathbf{u} = \langle \frac{\sqrt{2}}{2}, \frac{\sqrt{2}}{2} \rangle$			
$\mathbf{v} = \langle -\frac{\sqrt{2}}{2}, \frac{\sqrt{2}}{2} \rangle$			
$\mathbf{w} = \langle -\frac{\sqrt{2}}{2}, -\frac{\sqrt{2}}{2} \rangle$			

b. Interpret each of the directional derivatives computed in part (a) at the point $(2, 0)$.

60–65. Computing gradients *Compute the gradient of the following functions, evaluate it at the given point P, and evaluate the directional derivative at that point in the given direction.*

60. $f(x, y) = x^2$; $P(1, 2)$; $\mathbf{u} = \left\langle \frac{1}{\sqrt{2}}, -\frac{1}{\sqrt{2}} \right\rangle$

61. $g(x, y) = x^2y^3$; $P(-1, 1)$; $\mathbf{u} = \left\langle \frac{5}{13}, \frac{12}{13} \right\rangle$

62. $f(x, y) = \frac{x}{y^2}$; $P(0, 3)$; $\mathbf{u} = \left\langle \frac{\sqrt{3}}{2}, \frac{1}{2} \right\rangle$

63. $h(x, y) = \sqrt{2 + x^2 + 2y^2}$; $P(2, 1)$; $\mathbf{u} = \left\langle \frac{3}{5}, \frac{4}{5} \right\rangle$

64. $f(x, y, z) = xy + yz + xz + 4$; $P(2, -2, 1)$; $\mathbf{u} = \left\langle 0, -\frac{1}{\sqrt{2}}, -\frac{1}{\sqrt{2}} \right\rangle$

65. $f(x, y, z) = 1 + \sin (x + 2y - z)$; $P\left(\frac{\pi}{6}, \frac{\pi}{6}, -\frac{\pi}{6}\right)$; $\mathbf{u} = \left\langle \frac{1}{3}, \frac{2}{3}, \frac{2}{3} \right\rangle$

66–67. Direction of steepest ascent and descent

a. *Find the unit vectors that give the direction of steepest ascent and steepest descent at P.*

b. *Find a unit vector that points in a direction of no change.*

66. $f(x, y) = \ln (1 + xy)$; $P(2, 3)$

67. $f(x, y) = \sqrt{4 - x^2 - y^2}$; $P(-1, 1)$

68–69. Level curves *Let $f(x, y) = 8 - 2x^2 - y^2$. For the following level curves $f(x, y) = C$ and points (a, b), compute the slope of the line tangent to the level curve at (a, b) and verify that the tangent line is orthogonal to the gradient at that point.*

68. $f(x, y) = 5$; $(a, b) = (1, 1)$

69. $f(x, y) = 0$; $(a, b) = (2, 0)$

70. Directions of zero change Find the directions in which the function $f(x, y) = 4x^2 - y^2$ has zero change at the point $(1, 1, 3)$. Express the directions in terms of unit vectors.

71. Electric potential due to a charged cylinder. An infinitely long charged cylinder of radius R with its axis along the z-axis has an electric potential $V = k \ln (R/r)$, where r is the distance between a variable point $P(x, y)$ and the axis of the cylinder $(r^2 = x^2 + y^2)$ and k is a physical constant. The electric field at a point (x, y) in the xy-plane is given by $\mathbf{E} = -\nabla V$, where ∇V is the two-dimensional gradient. Compute the electric field at a point (x, y) with $r > R$.

72–77. Tangent planes *Find an equation of the plane tangent to the following surfaces at the given points.*

72. $z = 2x^2 + y^2$; $(1, 1, 3)$ and $(0, 2, 4)$

73. $x^2 + \frac{y^2}{4} - \frac{z^2}{9} = 1$; $(0, 2, 0)$ and $\left(1, 1, \frac{3}{2}\right)$

74. $xy \sin z - 1 = 0$; $\left(1, 2, \frac{\pi}{6}\right)$ and $\left(-2, -1, \frac{5\pi}{6}\right)$

75. $yze^{xz} - 8 = 0$; $(0, 2, 4)$ and $(0, -8, -1)$

76. $z = x^2e^{x-y}$; $(2, 2, 4)$ and $(-1, -1, 1)$

77. $z = \ln (1 + xy)$; $(1, 2, \ln 3)$ and $(-2, -1, \ln 3)$

T 78–79. Linear approximation

a. *Find the linear approximation to the function f at the point (a, b).*

b. *Use part (a) to estimate the given function value.*

78. $f(x, y) = 4 \cos (2x - y)$; $(a, b) = \left(\frac{\pi}{4}, \frac{\pi}{4}\right)$; estimate $f(0.8, 0.8)$.

79. $f(x, y) = (x + y)e^{xy}$; $(a, b) = (2, 0)$; estimate $f(1.95, 0.05)$.

80. Changes in a function Estimate the change in the function $f(x, y) = -2y^2 + 3x^2 + xy$ when (x, y) changes from $(1, -2)$ to $(1.05, -1.9)$.

81. Volume of a cylinder The volume of a cylinder with radius r and height h is $V = \pi r^2 h$. Find the approximate percentage change in the volume when the radius decreases by 3% and the height increases by 2%.

82. Volume of an ellipsoid The volume of an ellipsoid with axes of length $2a$, $2b$, and $2c$ is $V = \pi abc$. Find the percentage change in the volume when a increases by 2%, b increases by 1.5%, and c decreases by 2.5%.

83. Water-level changes A hemispherical tank with a radius of 1.50 m is filled with water to a depth of 1.00 m. Water is released from the tank and the water level drops by 0.05 m (from 1.00 m to 0.95 m).

a. Approximate the change in the volume of water in the tank. The volume of a spherical cap is $V = \pi h^2(3r - h)/3$, where r is the radius of the sphere and h is the thickness of the cap (in this case, the depth of the water).

b. Approximate the change in the surface area of the water in the tank.

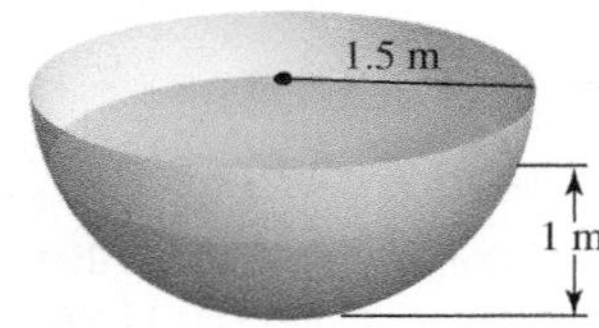

84–87. Analyzing critical points *Identify the critical points of the following functions. Then determine whether each critical point corresponds to a local maximum, local minimum, or saddle point. State when your analysis is inconclusive. Confirm your results using a graphing utility.*

84. $f(x, y) = x^4 + y^4 - 16xy$

85. $f(x, y) = x^3/3 - y^3/3 + 2xy$

86. $f(x, y) = xy(2 + x)(y - 3)$

87. $f(x, y) = 10 - x^3 - y^3 - 3x^2 + 3y^2$

88–91. Absolute maxima and minima *Find the absolute maximum and minimum values of the following functions on the specified region R.*

88. $f(x, y) = x^3/3 - y^3/3 + 2xy$ on the rectangle $R = \{(x, y): 0 \le x \le 3, -1 \le y \le 1\}$

89. $f(x, y) = x^4 + y^4 - 4xy + 1$ on the square $R = \{(x, y): -2 \le x \le 2, -2 \le y \le 2\}$

90. $f(x, y) = x^2y - y^3$ on the triangle $R = \{(x, y): 0 \le x \le 2, 0 \le y \le 2 - x\}$

91. $f(x, y) = xy$ on the semicircular disk $R = \{(x, y): -1 \le x \le 1, 0 \le y \le \sqrt{1 - x^2}\}$

92. Least distance What point on the plane $x + y + 4z = 8$ is closest to the origin? Give an argument showing you have found an absolute minimum of the distance function.

93–96. Lagrange multipliers *Use Lagrange multipliers to find the maximum and minimum values of f (when they exist) subject to the given constraint.*

93. $f(x, y) = 2x + y + 10$ subject to $2(x - 1)^2 + 4(y - 1)^2 = 1$

94. $f(x, y) = x^2y^2$ subject to $2x^2 + y^2 = 1$

95. $f(x, y, z) = x + 2y - z$ subject to $x^2 + y^2 + z^2 = 1$

96. $f(x, y, z) = x^2y^2z$ subject to $2x^2 + y^2 + z^2 = 25$

97. Maximum perimeter rectangle Use Lagrange multipliers to find the dimensions of the rectangle with the maximum perimeter that can be inscribed with sides parallel to the coordinate axes in the ellipse $x^2/a^2 + y^2/b^2 = 1$.

98. Minimum surface area cylinder Use Lagrange multipliers to find the dimensions of the right circular cylinder of minimum surface area (including the circular ends) with a volume of 32π in^3.

99. Minimum distance to a cone Find the point(s) on the cone $z^2 - x^2 - y^2 = 0$ that are closest to the point $(1, 3, 1)$. Give an argument showing you have found an absolute minimum of the distance function.

100. Gradient of a distance function Let $P_0(a, b, c)$ be a fixed point in $\mathbb{R}^3$ and let $d(x, y, z)$ be the distance between P_0 and a variable point $P(x, y, z)$.

a. Compute $\nabla d(x, y, z)$.

b. Show that $\nabla d(x, y, z)$ points in the direction from P_0 to P and has magnitude 1 for all (x, y, z).

c. Describe the level surfaces of d and give the direction of $\nabla d(x, y, z)$ relative to the level surfaces of d.

d. Discuss $\lim_{P \to P_0} \nabla d(x, y, z)$.

Chapter 12 Guided Projects

Applications of the material in this chapter and related topics can be found in the following Guided Projects. For additional information, see the Preface.

- Traveling waves
- Ecological diversity
- Economic production functions

Appendix

The goal of this appendix is to establish the essential notation, terminology, and algebraic skills that are used throughout the book.

Algebra

EXAMPLE 1 Algebra review

a. Evaluate $(-32)^{2/5}$.

b. Simplify $\frac{1}{x-2} - \frac{1}{x+2}$.

c. Solve the equation $\frac{x^4 - 5x^2 + 4}{x - 1} = 0$.

SOLUTION

a. Recall that $(-32)^{2/5} = ((-32)^{1/5})^2$. Because $(-32)^{1/5} = \sqrt[5]{-32} = -2$, we have $(-32)^{2/5} = (-2)^2 = 4$.

Another option is to write $(-32)^{2/5} = ((-32)^2)^{1/5} = 1024^{1/5} = 4$.

b. Finding a common denominator and simplifying leads to

$$\frac{1}{x-2} - \frac{1}{x+2} = \frac{(x+2)-(x-2)}{(x-2)(x+2)} = \frac{4}{x^2-4}.$$

c. Notice that $x = 1$ cannot be a solution of the equation because the left side of the equation is undefined at $x = 1$. Because $x - 1 \neq 0$, both sides of the equation can be multiplied by $x - 1$ to produce $x^4 - 5x^2 + 4 = 0$. After factoring, this equation becomes $(x^2 - 4)(x^2 - 1) = 0$, which implies $x^2 - 4 = (x-2)(x+2) = 0$ or $x^2 - 1 = (x-1)(x+1) = 0$. The roots of $x^2 - 4 = 0$ are $x = \pm 2$, and the roots of $x^2 - 1 = 0$ are $x = \pm 1$. Excluding $x = 1$, the roots of the original equation are $x = -1$ and $x = \pm 2$.

Related Exercises 15–26 ◄

Sets of Real Numbers

Figure A.1 shows the notation for **open intervals**, **closed intervals**, and various **bounded** and **unbounded intervals**. Notice that either interval notation or set notation may be used.

$[a, b] = \{x: a \le x \le b\}$	Closed, bounded interval
$(a, b] = \{x: a < x \le b\}$	Bounded interval
$[a, b) = \{x: a \le x < b\}$	Bounded interval
$(a, b) = \{x: a < x < b\}$	Open, bounded interval
$[a, \infty) = \{x: x \ge a\}$	Unbounded interval
$(a, \infty) = \{x: x > a\}$	Unbounded interval
$(-\infty, b] = \{x: x \le b\}$	Unbounded interval
$(-\infty, b) = \{x: x < b\}$	Unbounded interval
$(-\infty, \infty) = \{x: -\infty < x < \infty\}$	Unbounded interval

Figure A.1

EXAMPLE 2 **Solving inequalities** Solve the following inequalities.

a. $-x^2 + 5x - 6 < 0$ **b.** $\dfrac{x^2 - x - 2}{x - 3} \le 0$

SOLUTION

a. We multiply by -1, reverse the inequality, and then factor:

$$x^2 - 5x + 6 > 0 \quad \text{Multiply by } -1.$$
$$(x - 2)(x - 3) > 0. \quad \text{Factor.}$$

The roots of the corresponding equation $(x - 2)(x - 3) = 0$ are $x = 2$ and $x = 3$. These roots partition the number line (Figure A.2) into three intervals: $(-\infty, 2)$, $(2, 3)$, and $(3, \infty)$. On each interval, the product $(x - 2)(x - 3)$ does not change sign. To determine the sign of the product on a given interval, a **test value** x is selected and the sign of $(x - 2)(x - 3)$ is determined at x.

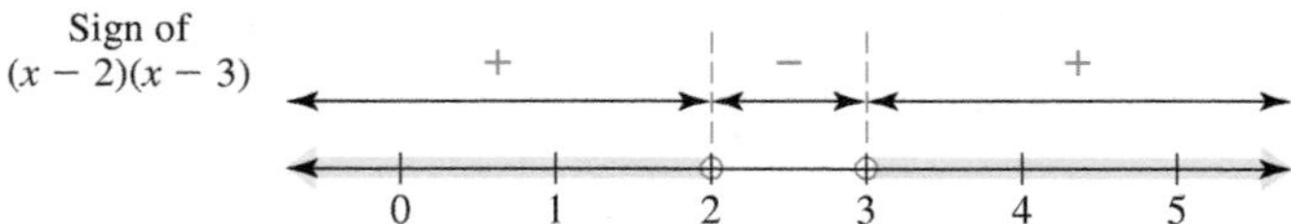

Figure A.2

A convenient choice for x in $(-\infty, 2)$ is $x = 0$. At this test value,

$$(x - 2)(x - 3) = (-2)(-3) > 0.$$

Using a test value of $x = 2.5$ in the interval $(2, 3)$, we have

$$(x - 2)(x - 3) = (0.5)(-0.5) < 0.$$

A test value of $x = 4$ in $(3, \infty)$ gives

$$(x - 2)(x - 3) = (2)(1) > 0.$$

Therefore, $(x - 2)(x - 3) > 0$ on $(-\infty, 2)$ and $(3, \infty)$. We conclude that the inequality $-x^2 + 5x - 6 < 0$ is satisfied for all x in either $(-\infty, 2)$ or $(3, \infty)$ (Figure A.2).

➤ The set of numbers $\{x: x \text{ is in } (-\infty, 2) \text{ or } (3, \infty)\}$ may also be expressed using the union symbol:

$$(-\infty, 2) \cup (3, \infty).$$

b. The expression $\dfrac{x^2 - x - 2}{x - 3}$ can change sign only at points where the numerator or denominator of $\dfrac{x^2 - x - 2}{x - 3}$ equals 0. Because

$$\frac{x^2 - x - 2}{x - 3} = \frac{(x + 1)(x - 2)}{x - 3},$$

the numerator is 0 when $x = -1$ or $x = 2$, and the denominator is 0 at $x = 3$. Therefore, we examine the sign of $\dfrac{(x + 1)(x - 2)}{x - 3}$ on the intervals $(-\infty, -1)$, $(-1, 2)$, $(2, 3)$, and $(3, \infty)$.

Test Value	$x + 1$	$x - 2$	$x - 3$	Result
-2	$-$	$-$	$-$	$-$
0	$+$	$-$	$-$	$+$
2.5	$+$	$+$	$-$	$-$
4	$+$	$+$	$+$	$+$

Using test values on these intervals, we see that $\dfrac{(x + 1)(x - 2)}{x - 3} < 0$ on $(-\infty, -1)$ and $(2, 3)$. Furthermore, the expression is 0 when $x = -1$ and $x = 2$. Therefore, $\dfrac{x^2 - x - 2}{x - 3} \leq 0$ for all values of x in either $(-\infty, -1]$ or $[2, 3)$ (Figure A.3).

Sign of $\dfrac{(x + 1)(x - 2)}{x - 3}$

Figure A.3

Related Exercises 27–30 ◄

Absolute Value

The **absolute value** of a real number x, denoted $|x|$, is the distance between x and the origin on the number line (Figure A.4). More generally, $|x - y|$ is the distance between the points x and y on the number line. The absolute value has the following definition and properties.

➤ The absolute value is useful in simplifying square roots. Because $\sqrt{a}$ is nonnegative, we have $\sqrt{a^2} = |a|$. For example, $\sqrt{3^2} = 3$ and $\sqrt{(-3)^2} = \sqrt{9} = 3$. Note that the solutions of $x^2 = 9$ are $|x| = 3$ or $x = \pm 3$.

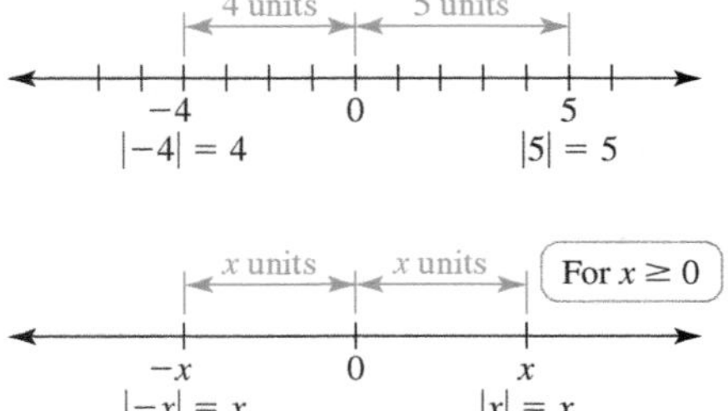

Figure A.4

Definition and Properties of the Absolute Value

The absolute value of a real number x is defined as

$$|x| = \begin{cases} x & \text{if } x \geq 0 \\ -x & \text{if } x < 0. \end{cases}$$

Let a be a positive real number.

1. $|x| = a \Leftrightarrow x = \pm a$
2. $|x| < a \Leftrightarrow -a < x < a$
3. $|x| > a \Leftrightarrow x > a$ or $x < -a$
4. $|x| \leq a \Leftrightarrow -a \leq x \leq a$
5. $|x| \geq a \Leftrightarrow x \geq a$ or $x \leq -a$
6. $|x + y| \leq |x| + |y|$

➤ Property 6 is called the **triangle inequality**.

EXAMPLE 3 **Inequalities with absolute values** Solve the following inequalities. Then sketch the solution on the number line and express it in interval notation.

a. $|x - 2| < 3$ **b.** $|2x - 6| \geq 10$

SOLUTION

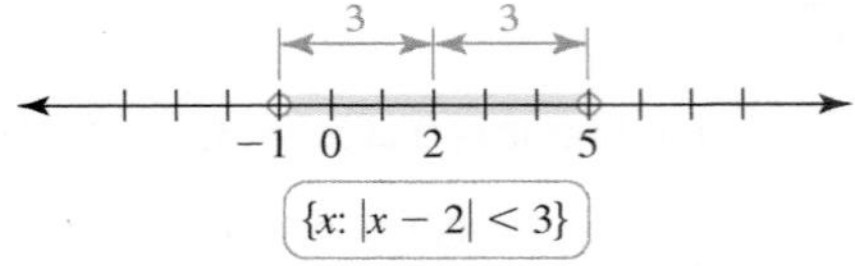

Figure A.5

a. Using property 2 of the absolute value, $|x - 2| < 3$ is written as

$$-3 < x - 2 < 3.$$

Adding 2 to each term of these inequalities results in $-1 < x < 5$ (Figure A.5). This set of numbers is written as $(-1, 5)$ in interval notation.

b. Using property 5, the inequality $|2x - 6| \geq 10$ implies that

$$2x - 6 \geq 10 \quad \text{or} \quad 2x - 6 \leq -10.$$

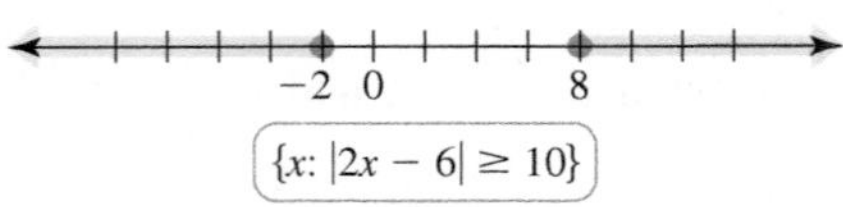

Figure A.6

We add 6 to both sides of the first inequality to obtain $2x \geq 16$, which implies $x \geq 8$. Similarly, the second inequality yields $x \leq -2$ (Figure A.6). In interval notation, the solution is $(-\infty, -2]$ or $[8, \infty)$.

Related Exercises 31–34 ◀

Cartesian Coordinate System

The conventions of the **Cartesian coordinate system** or ***xy*-coordinate system** are illustrated in Figure A.7. The set of real numbers is often denoted $\mathbb{R}$. The set of all ordered pairs of real numbers, which comprise the xy-plane, is often denoted $\mathbb{R}^2$.

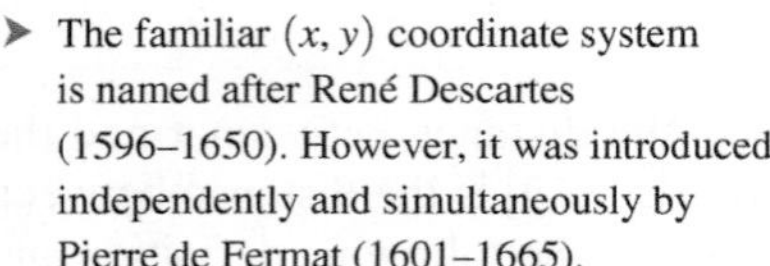

➤ The familiar (x, y) coordinate system is named after René Descartes (1596–1650). However, it was introduced independently and simultaneously by Pierre de Fermat (1601–1665).

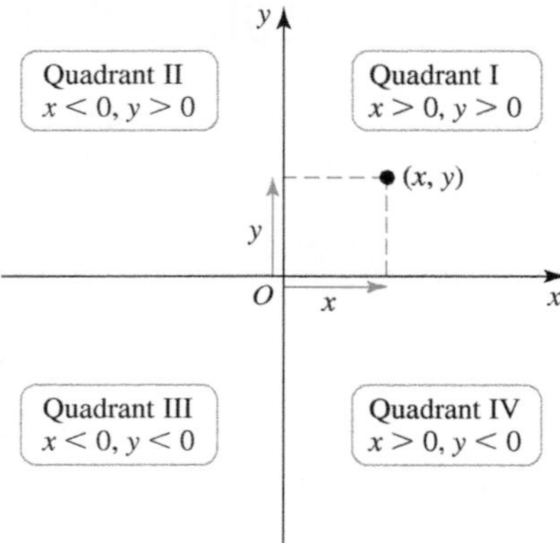

Figure A.7

For any right triangle, $a^2 + b^2 = c^2$.

c b a

$P_2(x_2, y_2)$ $\sqrt{(x_2 - x_1)^2 + (y_2 - y_1)^2}$ $|y_2 - y_1|$ $P_1(x_1, y_1)$ (x_2, y_1) $|x_2 - x_1|$

Figure A.8

Distance Formula and Circles

By the Pythagorean theorem (Figure A.8), we have the following formula for the distance between two points $P_1(x_1, y_1)$ and $P_2(x_2, y_2)$.

> **Distance Formula**
>
> The distance between the points $P_1(x_1, y_1)$ and $P_2(x_2, y_2)$ is
>
> $$|P_1P_2| = \sqrt{(x_2 - x_1)^2 + (y_2 - y_1)^2}.$$

A **circle** is the set of points in the plane whose distance from a fixed point (the **center**) is constant (the **radius**). This definition leads to the following equations that describe a circle.

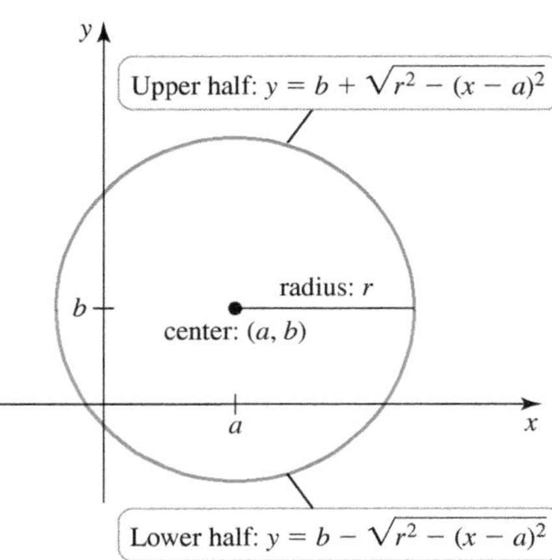

Figure A.9

Equation of a Circle

The equation of a circle centered at (a, b) with radius r is

$$(x - a)^2 + (y - b)^2 = r^2.$$

Solving for y, the equations of the upper and lower halves of the circle (Figure A.9) are

$$y = b + \sqrt{r^2 - (x - a)^2} \quad \text{Upper half of the circle}$$

$$y = b - \sqrt{r^2 - (x - a)^2}. \quad \text{Lower half of the circle}$$

EXAMPLE 4 Sets involving circles

a. Find the equation of the circle with center $(2, 4)$ passing through $(-2, 1)$.

b. Describe the set of points satisfying $x^2 + y^2 - 4x - 6y < 12$.

SOLUTION

a. The radius of the circle equals the length of the line segment between the center $(2, 4)$ and the point on the circle $(-2, 1)$, which is

$$\sqrt{(2 - (-2))^2 + (4 - 1)^2} = 5.$$

Therefore, the equation of the circle is

$$(x - 2)^2 + (y - 4)^2 = 25.$$

b. To put this inequality in a recognizable form, we complete the square on the left side of the inequality:

➤ Recall that the procedure shown here for completing the square works when the coefficient on the quadratic term is 1. When the coefficient is not 1, it must be factored out before completing the square.

$$\begin{aligned} x^2 + y^2 - 4x - 6y &= x^2 - 4x \underbrace{+ 4 - 4}_{\substack{\text{Add and subtract the square} \\ \text{of half the coefficient of } x}} + y^2 - 6y \underbrace{+ 9 - 9}_{\substack{\text{Add and subtract the square} \\ \text{of half the coefficient of } y}} \\ &= \underbrace{x^2 - 4x + 4}_{(x-2)^2} + \underbrace{y^2 - 6y + 9}_{(y-3)^2} - 4 - 9 \\ &= (x - 2)^2 + (y - 3)^2 - 13. \end{aligned}$$

Therefore, the original inequality becomes

$$(x - 2)^2 + (y - 3)^2 - 13 < 12, \quad \text{or} \quad (x - 2)^2 + (y - 3)^2 < 25.$$

➤ A **circle** is the set of all points whose distance from a fixed point is a constant. A **disk** is the set of all points within and possibly on a circle.

This inequality describes those points that lie within the circle centered at $(2, 3)$ with radius 5 (Figure A.10). Note that a dashed curve is used to indicate that the circle itself is not part of the solution.

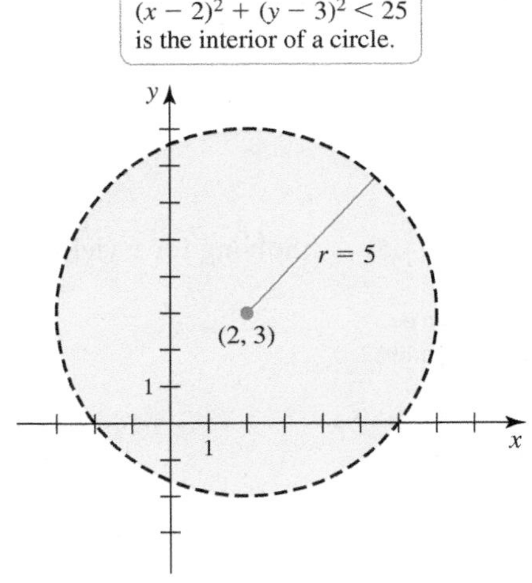

Figure A.10

Related Exercises 35–36 ◀

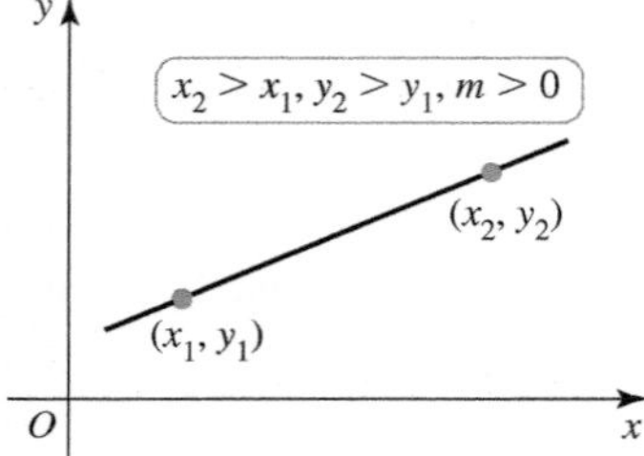

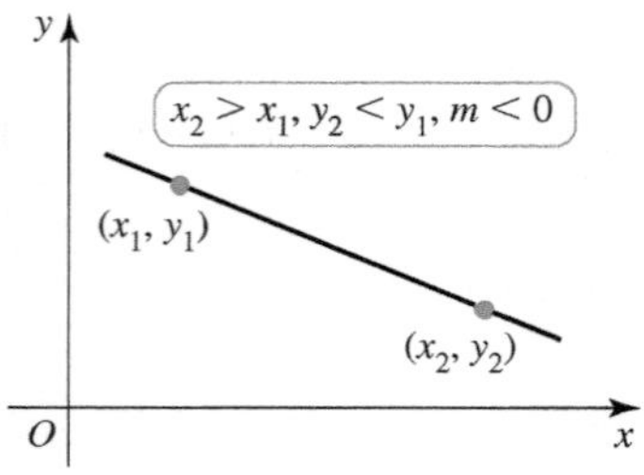

Figure A.11

Equations of Lines

The **slope** m of the line passing through the points $P_1(x_1, y_1)$ and $P_2(x_2, y_2)$ is the *rise over run* (Figure A.11), computed as

$$m = \frac{\text{change in vertical coordinate}}{\text{change in horizontal coordinate}} = \frac{y_2 - y_1}{x_2 - x_1}.$$

Equations of a Line

Point-slope form The equation of the line with slope m passing through the point (x_1, y_1) is $y - y_1 = m(x - x_1)$.

Slope-intercept form The equation of the line with slope m and y-intercept $(0, b)$ is $y = mx + b$ (Figure A.12a).

General linear equation The equation $Ax + By + C = 0$ describes a line in the plane, provided A and B are not both zero.

Vertical and horizontal lines The vertical line that passes through $(a, 0)$ has an equation $x = a$; its slope is undefined. The horizontal line through $(0, b)$ has an equation $y = b$, with slope equal to 0 (Figure A.12b).

➤ Given a particular line, we often talk about *the* equation of a line. But the equation of a specific line is not unique. Having found one equation, we can multiply it by any nonzero constant to produce another equation of the same line.

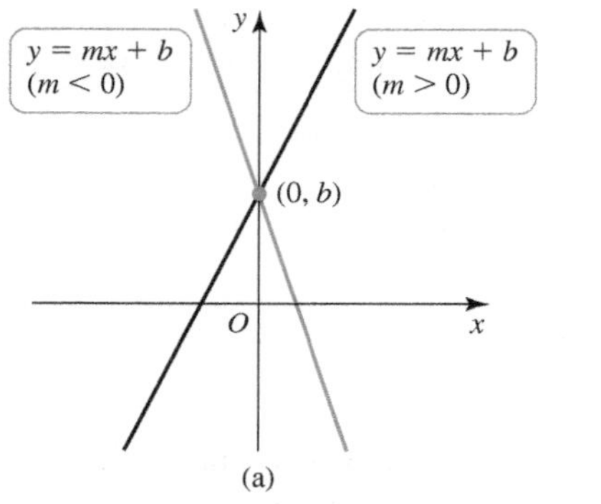

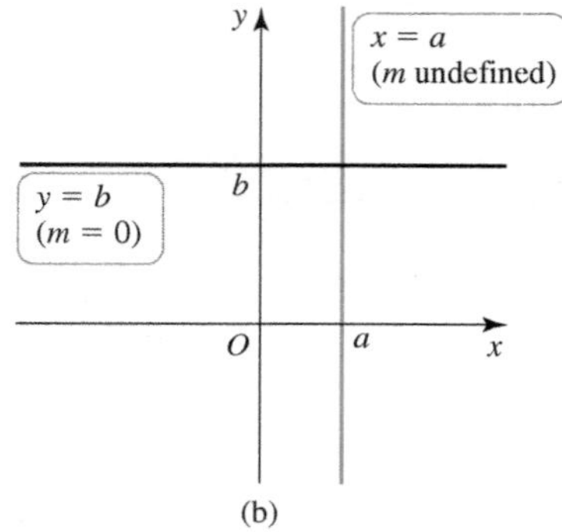

Figure A.12

EXAMPLE 5 Working with linear equations Find an equation of the line passing through the points $(1, -2)$ and $(-4, 5)$.

SOLUTION The slope of the line through the points $(1, -2)$ and $(-4, 5)$ is

$$m = \frac{5 - (-2)}{-4 - 1} = \frac{7}{-5} = -\frac{7}{5}.$$

Using the point $(1, -2)$, the point-slope form of the equation is

$$y - (-2) = -\frac{7}{5}(x - 1).$$

➤ Because both points $(1, -2)$ and $(-4, 5)$ lie on the line and must satisfy the equation of the line, either point can be used to determine an equation of the line.

Solving for y yields the slope-intercept form of the equation:

$$y = -\frac{7}{5}x - \frac{3}{5}.$$

Related Exercises 37–40 ◄

Parallel and Perpendicular Lines

Two lines in the plane may have either of two special relationships to each other: They may be parallel or perpendicular.

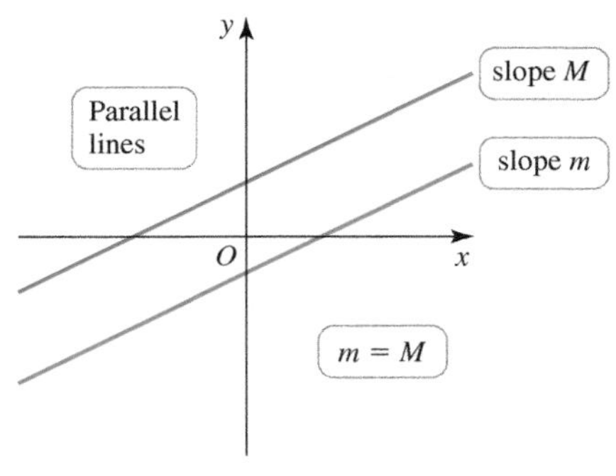

Parallel Lines

Two distinct nonvertical lines are **parallel** if they have the same slope; that is, the lines with equations $y = mx + b$ and $y = Mx + B$ are parallel if and only if $m = M$. Two distinct vertical lines are parallel.

EXAMPLE 6 **Parallel lines** Find an equation of the line parallel to $3x - 6y + 12 = 0$ that intersects the x-axis at $(4, 0)$.

SOLUTION Solving the equation $3x - 6y + 12 = 0$ for y, we have

$$y = \frac{1}{2}x + 2.$$

This line has a slope of $\frac{1}{2}$ and any line parallel to it has a slope of $\frac{1}{2}$. Therefore, the line that passes through $(4, 0)$ with slope $\frac{1}{2}$ has the point-slope equation $y - 0 = \frac{1}{2}(x - 4)$. After simplifying, an equation of the line is

$$y = \frac{1}{2}x - 2.$$

Notice that the slopes of the two lines are the same; only the y-intercepts differ.

Related Exercises 41–42 ◄

➤ The slopes of perpendicular lines are *negative reciprocals* of each other.

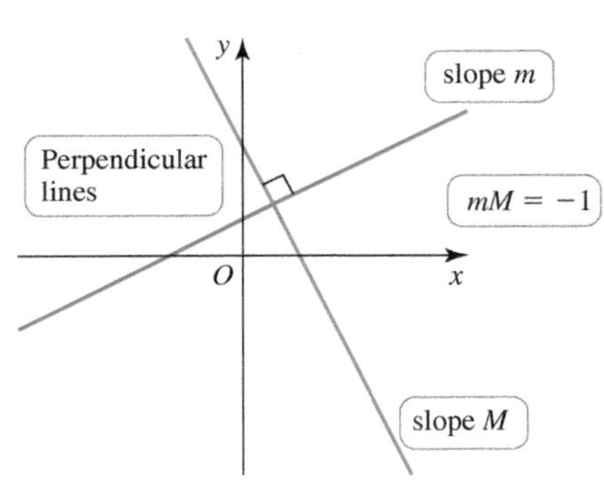

Perpendicular Lines

Two lines with slopes $m \neq 0$ and $M \neq 0$ are **perpendicular** if and only if $mM = -1$, or equivalently, $m = -1/M$.

EXAMPLE 7 **Perpendicular lines** Find an equation of the line passing through the point $(-2, 5)$ perpendicular to the line ℓ: $4x - 2y + 7 = 0$.

SOLUTION The equation of ℓ can be written $y = 2x + \frac{7}{2}$, which reveals that its slope is 2. Therefore, the slope of any line perpendicular to ℓ is $-\frac{1}{2}$. The line with slope $-\frac{1}{2}$ passing through the point $(-2, 5)$ is

$$y - 5 = -\frac{1}{2}(x + 2), \quad \text{or} \quad y = -\frac{x}{2} + 4.$$

Related Exercises 43–44 ◄

APPENDIX A EXERCISES

Review Questions

1. State the meaning of $\{x: -4 < x \leq 10\}$. Express the set $\{x: -4 < x \leq 10\}$ using interval notation and draw it on a number line.
2. Write the interval $(-\infty, 2)$ in set notation and draw it on a number line.
3. Give the definition of $|x|$.
4. Write the inequality $|x - 2| \leq 3$ without absolute value symbols.
5. Write the inequality $|2x - 4| \geq 3$ without absolute value symbols.
6. Write an equation of the set of all points that are a distance 5 units from the point $(2, 3)$.
7. Explain how to find the distance between two points whose coordinates are known.
8. Sketch the set of points $\{(x, y): x^2 + (y - 2)^2 > 16\}$.
9. Give an equation of the upper half of the circle centered at the origin with radius 6.
10. What are the possible solution sets of the equation $x^2 + y^2 + Cx + Dy + E = 0$?
11. Give an equation of the line with slope m that passes through the point $(4, -2)$.

12. Give an equation of the line with slope m and y-intercept $(0, 6)$.

13. What is the relationship between the slopes of two parallel lines?

14. What is the relationship between the slopes of two perpendicular lines?

Basic Skills

15–20. Algebra review *Simplify or evaluate the following expressions without a calculator.*

15. $(1/8)^{-2/3}$

16. $\sqrt[3]{-125} + \sqrt{1/25}$

17. $(u + v)^2 - (u - v)^2$

18. $\dfrac{(a + h)^2 - a^2}{h}$

19. $\dfrac{1}{x + h} - \dfrac{1}{x}$

20. $\dfrac{2}{x + 3} - \dfrac{2}{x - 3}$

21–26. Algebra review

21. Factor $y^2 - y^{-2}$.

22. Solve $x^3 - 9x = 0$.

23. Solve $u^4 - 11u^2 + 18 = 0$.

24. Solve $4^x - 6(2^x) = -8$.

25. Simplify $\dfrac{(x + h)^3 - x^3}{h}$, for $h \neq 0$.

26. Rewrite $\dfrac{\sqrt{x + h} - \sqrt{x}}{h}$, where $h \neq 0$, without square roots in the numerator.

27–30. Solving inequalities *Solve the following inequalities and draw the solution on a number line.*

27. $x^2 - 6x + 5 < 0$

28. $\dfrac{x + 1}{x + 2} < 6$

29. $\dfrac{x^2 - 9x + 20}{x - 6} \leq 0$

30. $x\sqrt{x - 1} > 0$

31–34. Inequalities with absolute values *Solve the following inequalities. Then draw the solution on a number line and express it using interval notation.*

31. $|3x - 4| > 8$

32. $1 \leq |x| \leq 10$

33. $3 < |2x - 1| < 5$

34. $2 < |\frac{x}{2} - 5| < 6$

35–36. Circle calculations *Solve the following problems.*

35. Find the equation of the lower half of the circle with center $(-1, 2)$ and radius 3.

36. Describe the set of points that satisfy $x^2 + y^2 + 6x + 8y \geq 25$.

37–40. Working with linear equations *Find an equation of the line ℓ that satisfies the given condition. Then draw the graph of ℓ.*

37. ℓ has slope $5/3$ and y-intercept $(0, 4)$.

38. ℓ has undefined slope and passes through $(0, 5)$.

39. ℓ has y-intercept $(0, -4)$ and x-intercept $(5, 0)$.

40. ℓ is parallel to the x-axis and passes through the point $(2, 3)$.

41–42. Parallel lines *Find an equation of the following lines and draw their graphs.*

41. The line with y-intercept $(0, 12)$ parallel to the line $x + 2y = 8$

42. The line with x-intercept $(-6, 0)$ parallel to the line $2x - 5 = 0$

43–44. Perpendicular lines *Find an equation of the following lines.*

43. The line passing through $(3, -6)$ perpendicular to the line $y = -3x + 2$

44. The perpendicular bisector of the line joining the points $(-9, 2)$ and $(3, -5)$

Further Explorations

45. **Explain why or why not** State whether the following statements are true and give an explanation or counterexample.

    a. $\sqrt{16} = \pm 4$.

    b. $\sqrt{4^2} = \sqrt{(-4)^2}$.

    c. There are two real numbers that satisfy the condition $|x| = -2$.

    d. $|\pi^2 - 9| < 0$.

    e. The point $(1, 1)$ is inside the circle of radius 1 centered at the origin.

    f. $\sqrt{x^4} = x^2$ for all real numbers x.

    g. $\sqrt{a^2} < \sqrt{b^2}$ implies $a < b$ for all real numbers a and b.

46–48. Intervals to sets *Express the following intervals in set notation. Use absolute value notation when possible.*

46. $(-\infty, 12)$

47. $(-\infty, -2]$ or $[4, \infty)$

48. $(2, 3]$ or $[4, 5)$

49–50. Sets in the plane *Graph each set in the xy-plane.*

49. $\{(x, y): |x - y| = 0\}$

50. $\{(x, y): |x| = |y|\}$

Answers

CHAPTER 5

Section 5.1 Exercises, pp. 343–347

1. Displacement = 105 m

3. Subdivide the interval $[0, \pi/2]$ into several subintervals, which will be the bases of rectangles that fit under the curve. The heights of the rectangles are computed by taking the value of $\cos x$ at the right-hand endpoint of each base. We calculate the area of each rectangle and add them to get a lower bound on the area.
5. 0.5; 1, 1.5, 2, 2.5, 3; 1, 1.5, 2, 2.5; 1.5, 2, 2.5, 3; 1.25, 1.75, 2.25, 2.75
7. Underestimate; the rectangles all fit under the curve.
9. a. 67 ft **b.** 67.75 ft **11.** 40 m **13.** 2.78 m
15. 148.96 mi **17.** 20; 25

19. a. c.

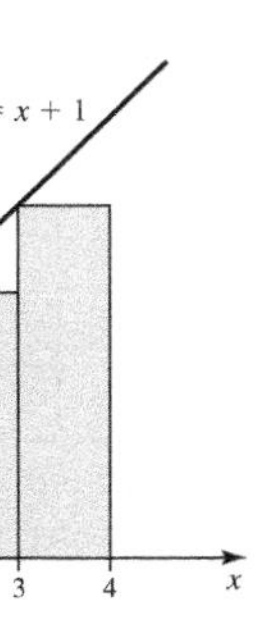

Left Riemann sum underestimates area.

Right Riemann sum overestimates area.

b. $\Delta x = 1; x_0 = 0, x_1 = 1, x_2 = 2, x_3 = 3, x_4 = 4$ **d.** 10, 14

21. a. c.

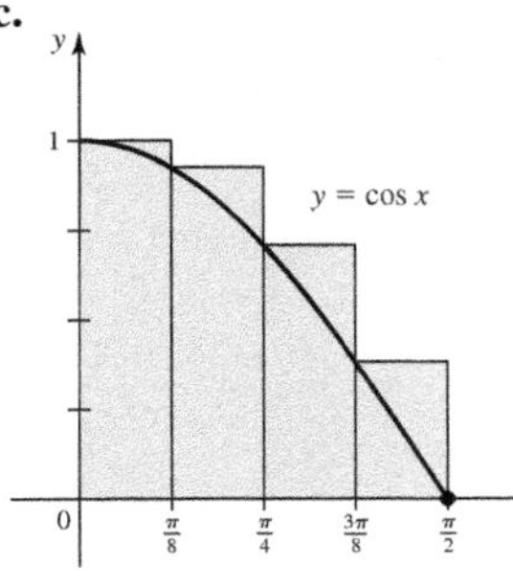

Left Riemann sum overestimates area.

Right Riemann sum underestimates area.

b. $\Delta x = \pi/8; 0, \pi/8, \pi/4, 3\pi/8, \pi/2$ **d.** 1.18; 0.79

23. a. c.

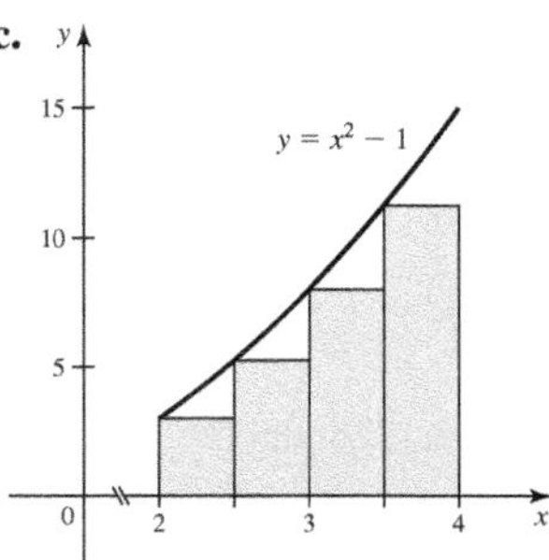

Left Riemann sum underestimates area.

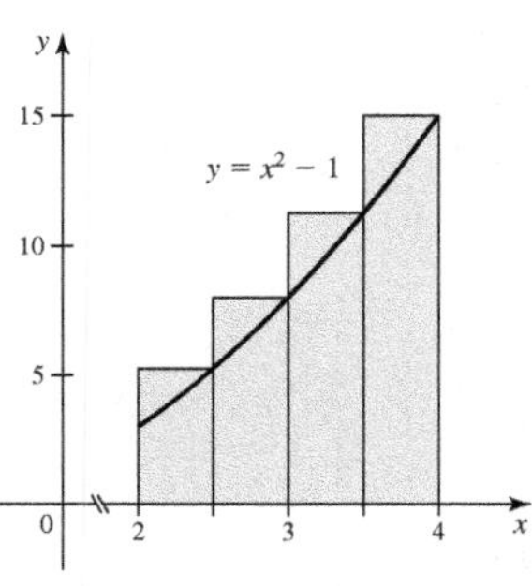

Right Riemann sum overestimates area.

b. $\Delta x = 0.5$; 2, 2.5, 3, 3.5, 4 **d.** 13.75; 19.75

25. a. c.

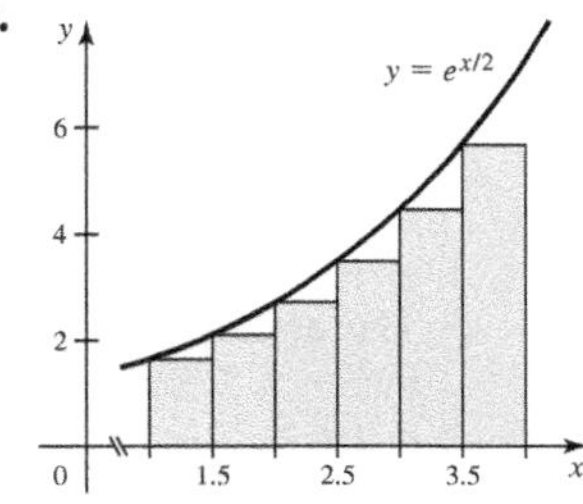

Left Riemann sum underestimates area.

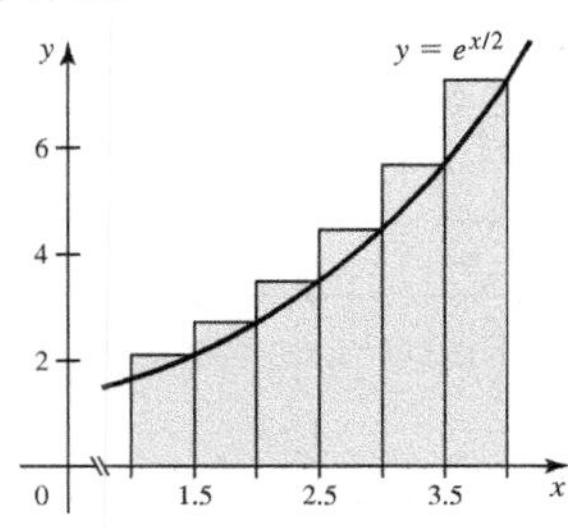

Right Riemann sum overestimates area.

b. $\Delta x = 0.5; x_0 = 1, x_1 = 1.5, x_2 = 2, x_3 = 2.5, x_4 = 3, x_5 = 3.5, x_6 = 4$ **d.** 10.11, 12.98 **27.** 670

29. a. c.

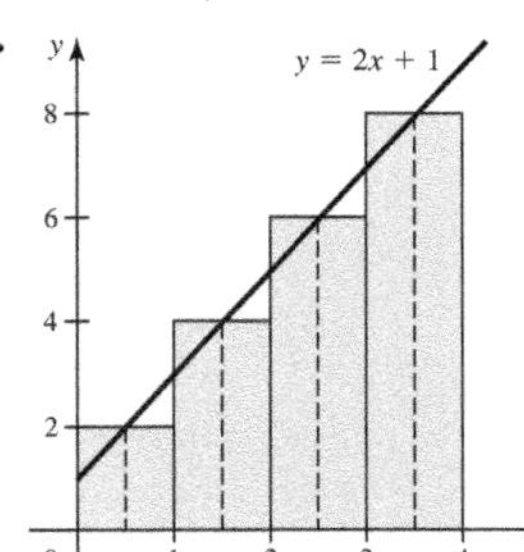

b. $\Delta x = 1$; 0, 1, 2, 3, 4
d. 20

31. a. c.

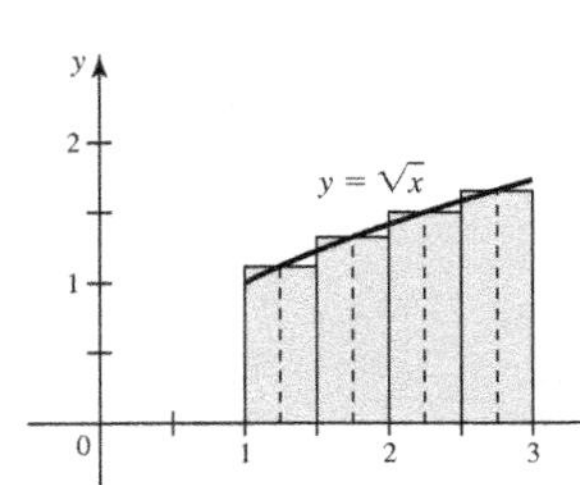

b. $\Delta x = \frac{1}{2}; 1, \frac{3}{2}, 2, \frac{5}{2}, 3$
d. 2.80

33. a. c.

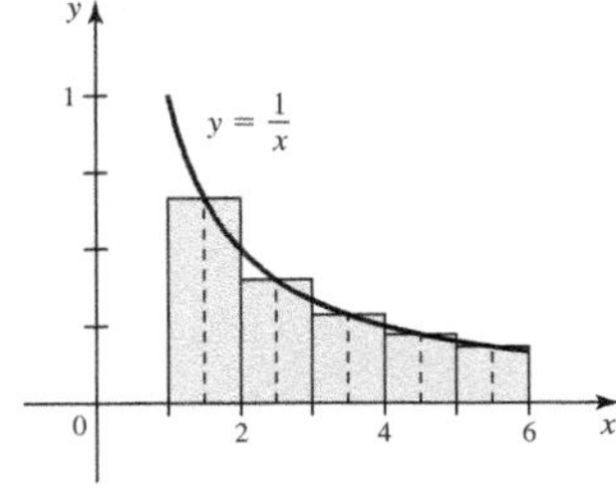

b. $\Delta x = 1$; 1, 2, 3, 4, 5, 6
d. 1.76

35. 5.5, 3.5 **37. b.** 110, 117.5 **39. a.** $\sum_{k=1}^{5} k$ **b.** $\sum_{k=1}^{6}(k+3)$ **c.** $\sum_{k=1}^{4} k^2$ **d.** $\sum_{k=1}^{4}\frac{1}{k}$ **41. a.** 55 **b.** 48 **c.** 30 **d.** 60 **e.** 6 **f.** 6 **g.** 85 **h.** 0 **43. a.** Left: $\frac{1}{10}\sum_{k=1}^{40}\sqrt{\frac{k-1}{10}} \approx 5.23$; right: $\frac{1}{10}\sum_{k=1}^{40}\sqrt{\frac{k}{10}} \approx 5.43$; midpoint: $\frac{1}{10}\sum_{k=1}^{40}\sqrt{\frac{2k-1}{20}} \approx 5.34$ **b.** $\frac{16}{3}$ **45. a.** Left: $\frac{1}{15}\sum_{k=1}^{75}\left(\left(\frac{k+29}{15}\right)^2 - 1\right) \approx 105.17$; right: $\frac{1}{15}\sum_{k=1}^{75}\left(\left(\frac{k+30}{15}\right)^2 - 1\right) \approx 108.17$; midpoint: $\frac{1}{15}\sum_{k=1}^{75}\left(\left(\frac{2k+59}{30}\right)^2 - 1\right) \approx 106.66$ **b.** 106.7

47.

n	Right Riemann sum
10	10.56
30	10.65
60	10.664
80	10.665

The sums approach $\frac{32}{3}$.

49.

n	Right Riemann sum
10	5.655
30	6.074
60	6.178
80	6.205

The sums approach approximately 6.2. The actual limit is 2π.

51.

n	Right Riemann sum
10	1.0844
30	1.0285
60	1.0143
80	1.0107

The sums approach 1.

53. a. True **b.** False **c.** True

55. $\sum_{k=1}^{50}\left(\frac{4k}{50}+1\right)\cdot\frac{4}{50} = 12.16$

57. $\sum_{k=1}^{32}\left(3+\frac{2k-1}{8}\right)^3\cdot\frac{1}{4} \approx 3639.1$

59. Right; $[1, 5]$; 4
61. Midpoint; $[2, 6]$; 4

63. a.

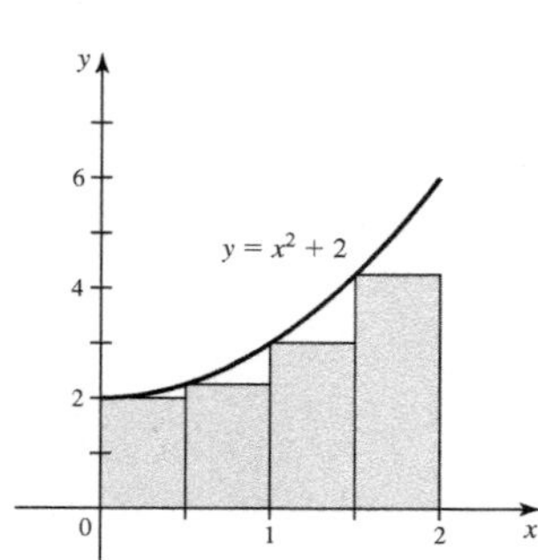

Left Riemann sum is $\frac{23}{4} = 5.75$.

b.

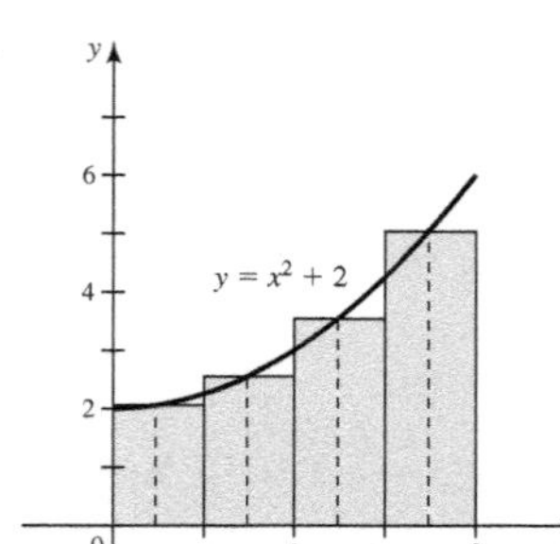

Midpoint Riemann sum is $\frac{53}{8} = 6.625$.

c.

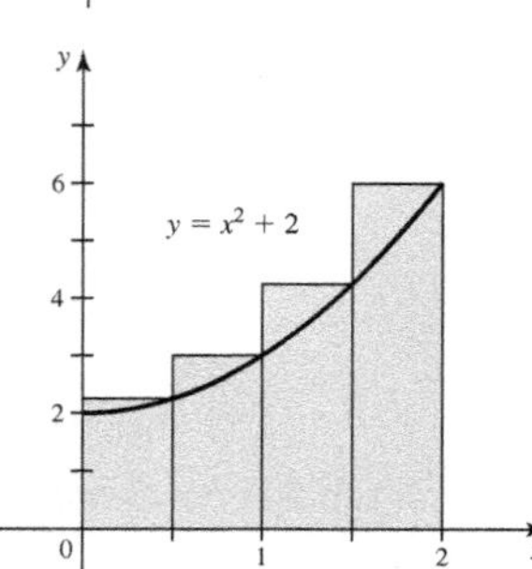

Right Riemann sum is $\frac{31}{4} = 7.75$.

65. Left sum: 34; right sum: 24 **67. a.** The object is speeding up on the interval $(0, 1)$, moving at a constant rate on $(1, 3)$, slowing down on $(3, 5)$, and moving at a constant rate on $(5, 6)$. **b.** 30 m **c.** 50 m **d.** $s(t) = 30 + 10t$ **69. a.** 14.5 g **b.** 29.5 g **c.** 44 g **d.** $x = \frac{19}{3}$ cm **71.** $s(t) = \begin{cases} 30t & \text{if } 0 \le t \le 2 \\ 50t - 40 & \text{if } 2 < t \le 2.5 \\ 44t - 25 & \text{if } 2.5 < t \le 3 \end{cases}$

73.

n	Midpoint Riemann sum
16	0.503906
32	0.500977
64	0.500244

The sums approach 0.5.

75.

n	Midpoint Riemann sum
16	4.7257
32	4.7437
64	4.7485

The sums approach 4.75.

79. Underestimates for decreasing functions, independent of concavity; overestimates for increasing functions, independent of concavity.

Section 5.2 Exercises, pp. 358–361

1. The difference between the area bounded by the curve above the x-axis and the area bounded by the curve below the x-axis **3.** When the function is nonnegative on the entire interval; when the function has negative values on the interval **5.** Both integrals equal 0. **7.** The length of the interval $[a, a]$ is $a - a = 0$, so the net area is 0. **9.** $\frac{a^2}{2}$

11. a.

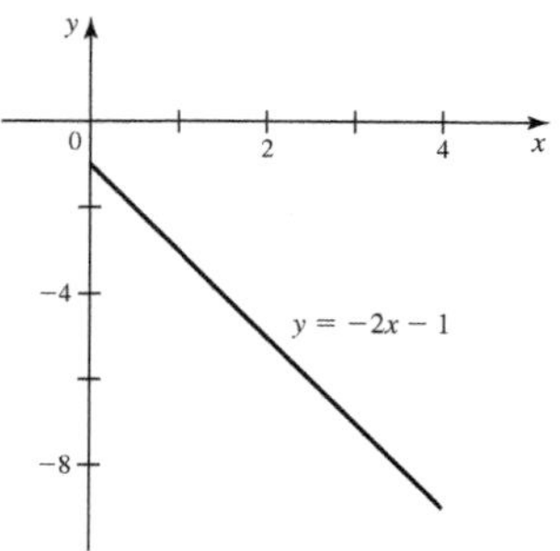

b. −16, −24, −20

13. a.

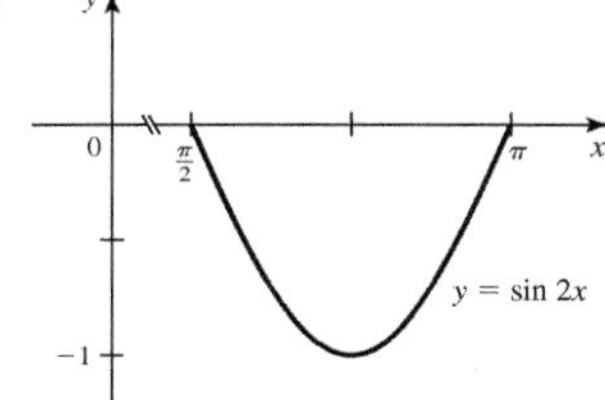

b. −0.948, −0.948, −1.026

15. a.

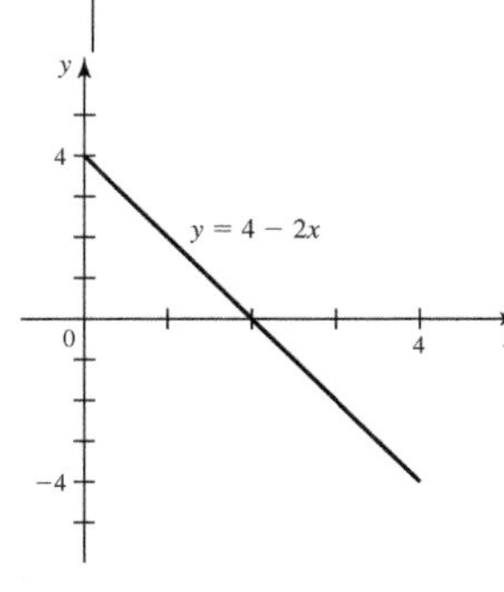

b. 4, −4, 0 **c.** Positive contribution on $[0, 2)$; negative contribution on $(2, 4]$

17. a.

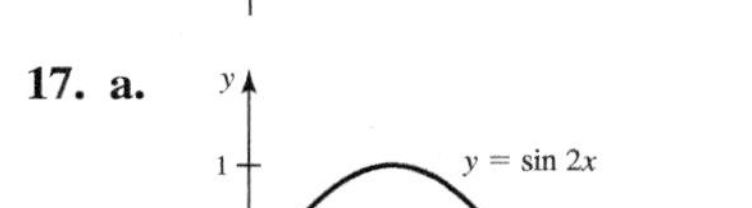

b. 0.735, 0.146, 0.530 **c.** Positive contribution on $(0, \pi/2)$; negative contribution on $(\pi/2, 3\pi/4]$.

19. a.

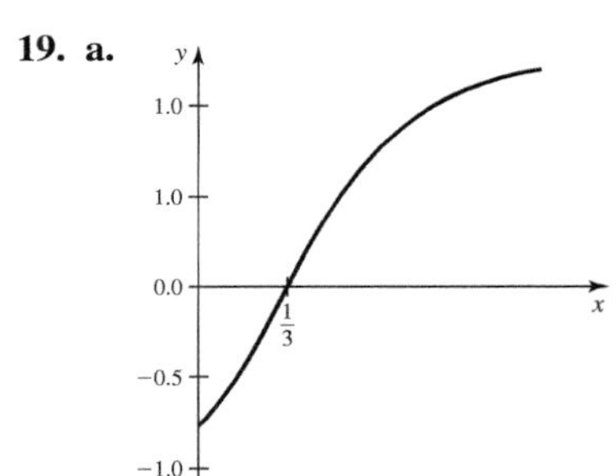

b. 0.082; 0.555; 0.326

c. Positive contribution on $(\frac{1}{3}, 1]$; negative contribution on $[0, \frac{1}{3})$

21. $\int_0^2 (x^2 + 1)\,dx$ **23.** $\int_1^2 x \ln x\,dx$

25. 16

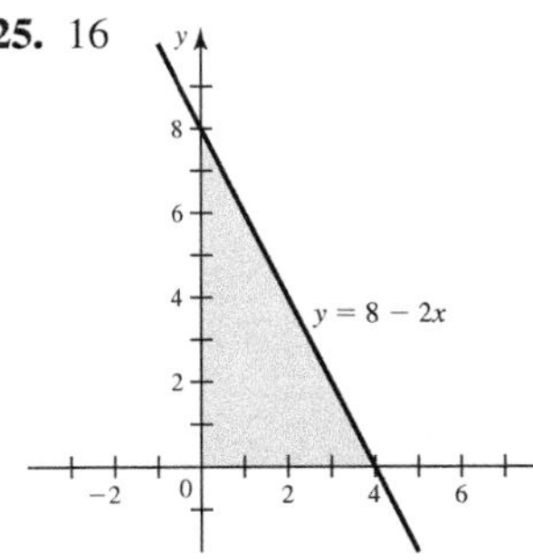

27. $-\frac{5}{2}$

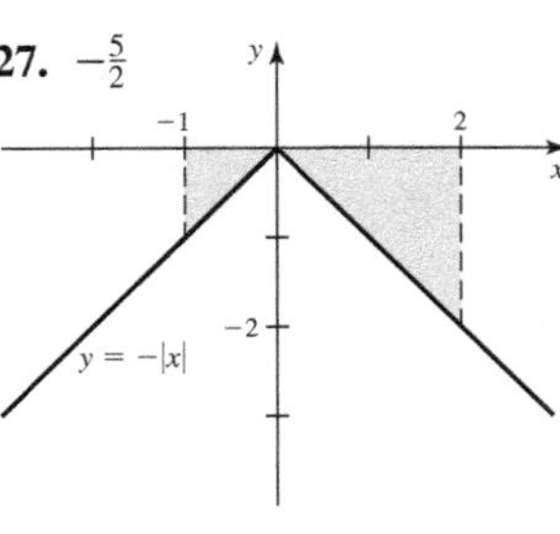

29. 4π

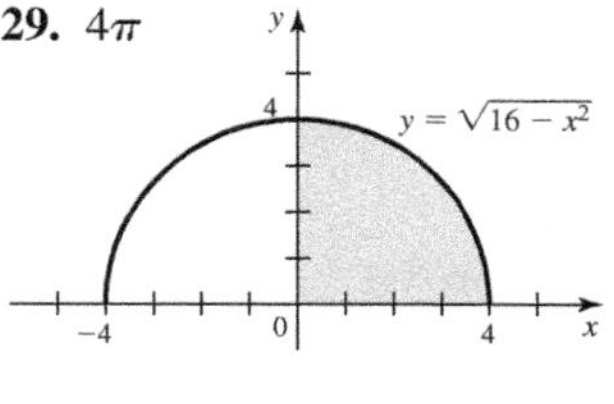

31. 26

33. 16 **35.** 6 **37.** π **39.** -2π **41. a.** −32 **b.** $-\frac{32}{3}$ **c.** −64 **d.** Not possible **43. a.** 10 **b.** −3 **c.** −16 **d.** 3 **45. a.** $\frac{3}{2}$ **b.** $-\frac{3}{4}$ **47.** 6 **49.** 104 **51.** 18 **53. a.** True **b.** True **c.** True **d.** False **e.** False

55. a.

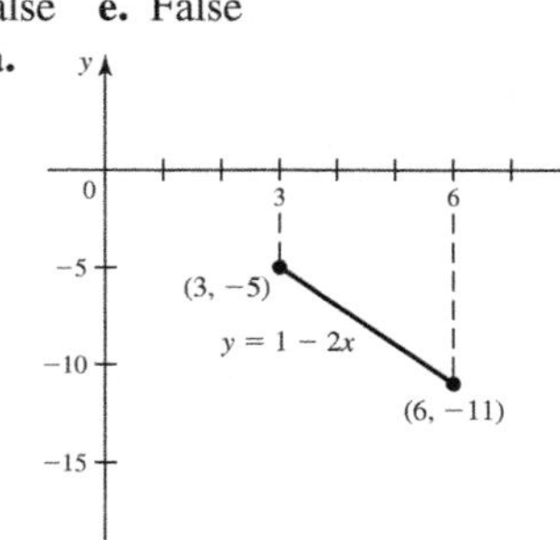

b. $\Delta x = \frac{1}{2}$; 3, 3.5, 4, 4.5, 5, 5.5, 6 **c.** −22.5; −25.5 **d.** The left Riemann sum overestimates the integral; the right Riemann sum underestimates the integral.

57. a.

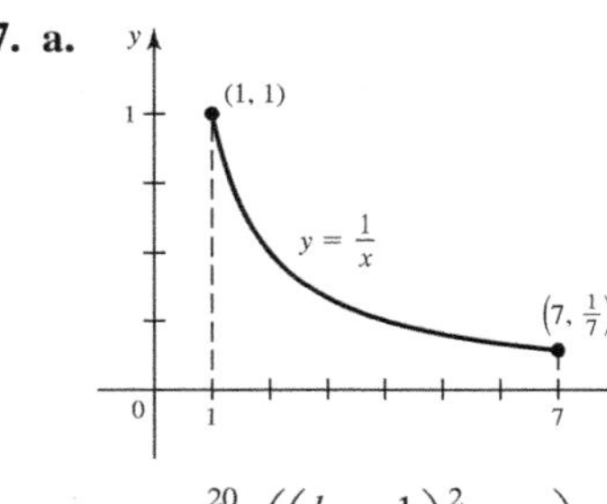

b. $\Delta x = 1$; 1, 2, 3, 4, 5, 6, 7 **c.** $\frac{49}{20}$, $\frac{223}{140}$ **d.** The left Riemann sum overestimates the integral; the right Riemann sum underestimates the integral.

59. a. Left: $\sum_{k=1}^{20}\left(\left(\frac{k-1}{20}\right)^2 + 1\right)\cdot\frac{1}{20} = 1.30875$;

right: $\sum_{k=1}^{20}\left(\left(\frac{k}{20}\right)^2 + 1\right)\cdot\frac{1}{20} = 1.35875$;

left: $\sum_{k=1}^{50}\left(\left(\frac{k-1}{50}\right)^2 + 1\right)\cdot\frac{1}{50} = 1.3234$;

right: $\sum_{k=1}^{50}\left(\left(\frac{k}{50}\right)^2 + 1\right)\cdot\frac{1}{50} = 1.3434$;

left: $\sum_{k=1}^{100}\left(\left(\frac{k-1}{100}\right)^2 + 1\right)\cdot\frac{1}{100} = 1.32835$;

right: $\sum_{k=1}^{100}\left(\left(\frac{k}{100}\right)^2 + 1\right)\cdot\frac{1}{100} = 1.33835$ **b.** $\frac{4}{3}$

61. a. Left: $\sum_{k=1}^{20}\cos^{-1}\left(\frac{k-1}{20}\right)\frac{1}{20} = 1.03619$;

right: $\sum_{k=1}^{20}\cos^{-1}\left(\frac{k}{20}\right)\frac{1}{20} = 0.95765$;

left: $\sum_{k=1}^{50}\cos^{-1}\left(\frac{k-1}{50}\right)\frac{1}{50} = 1.01491$;

right: $\sum_{k=1}^{50}\cos^{-1}\left(\frac{k}{50}\right)\frac{1}{50} = 0.983494$;

left: $\sum_{k=1}^{100} \cos^{-1}\left(\frac{k-1}{100}\right)\frac{1}{100} = 1.00757$;

right: $\sum_{k=1}^{100} \cos^{-1}\left(\frac{k}{100}\right)\frac{1}{100} = 0.99186$ **b.** 1.

63. a. $\frac{3}{n}\sum_{k=1}^{n} \sqrt{2\left(1+\left(k-\frac{1}{2}\right)\frac{3}{n}\right)}$

b.

n	Midpoint Riemann sum
20	9.33380
50	9.33341
100	9.33335

Estimate: $\frac{28}{3}$

65. a. $\frac{4}{n}\sum_{k=1}^{n}\left(4\left(k-\frac{1}{2}\right)\frac{4}{n} - \left(\left(k-\frac{1}{2}\right)\frac{4}{n}\right)^2\right)$

b.

n	Midpoint Riemann sum
20	10.6800
50	10.6688
100	10.6672

Estimate: $\frac{32}{3}$

67. a. 15 **b.** 5 **c.** 3 **d.** -2 **e.** 24 **f.** -10

69. The area is 12; the net area is 0.

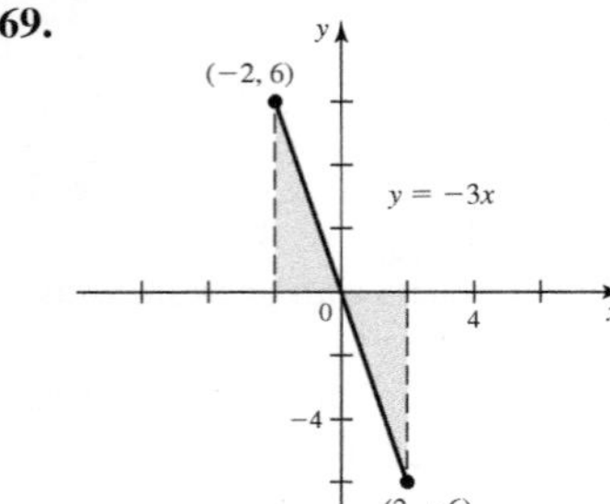
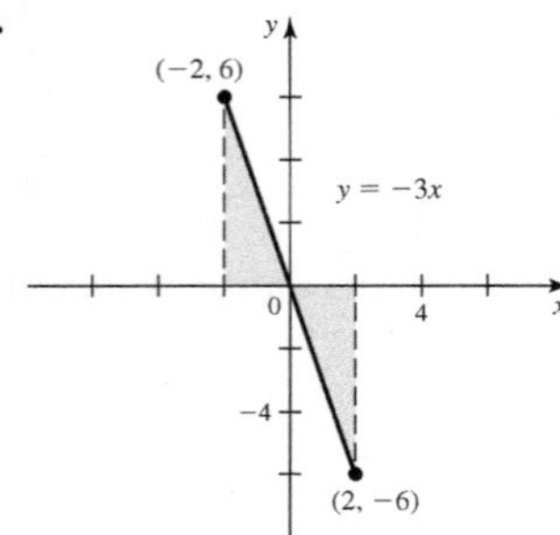

71. The area is 2; the net area is 0.

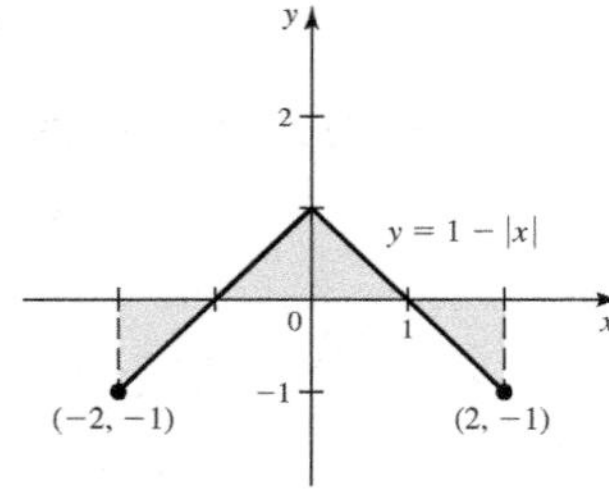

73. 17 **75.** $25\pi/2$ **77.** 25 **79.** 35 **83.** For any such partition on $[0, 1]$, the grid points are $x_k = k/n$, for $k = 0, 1, \ldots, n$. That is, x_k is rational for each k so that $f(x_k) = 1$, for $k = 0, 1, \ldots, n$. Therefore, the left, right, and midpoint Riemann sums are $\sum_{k=1}^{n} 1 \cdot (1/n) = 1$.

Section 5.3 Exercises, pp. 373–376

1. A is an antiderivative of f; $A'(x) = f(x)$

3. Let f be continuous on $[a, b]$. Then $\int_a^b f(x)\,dx = F(b) - F(a)$, where F is any antiderivative of f. **5.** Increasing **7.** The derivative of the integral of f is f, or $\frac{d}{dx}\left(\int_a^x f(t)\,dt\right) = f(x)$. **9.** $f(x), 0$

11. a. 0 **b.** -9 **c.** 25 **d.** 0 **e.** 16

13. a. $A(x) = 5x$ **b.** $A'(x) = 5$

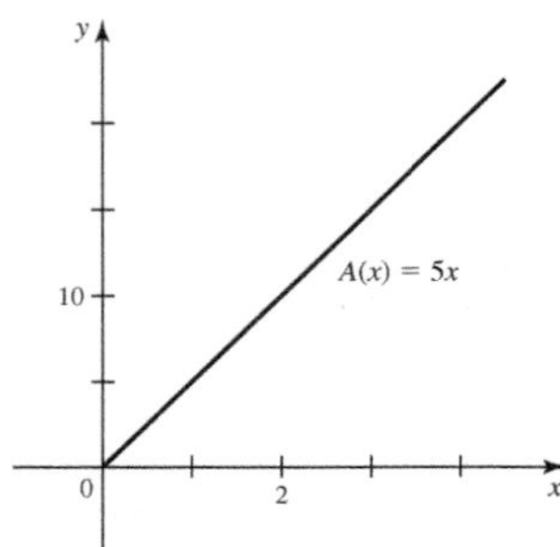

15. a. $A(x) = 5x + 25$ **b.** $A'(x) = 5$

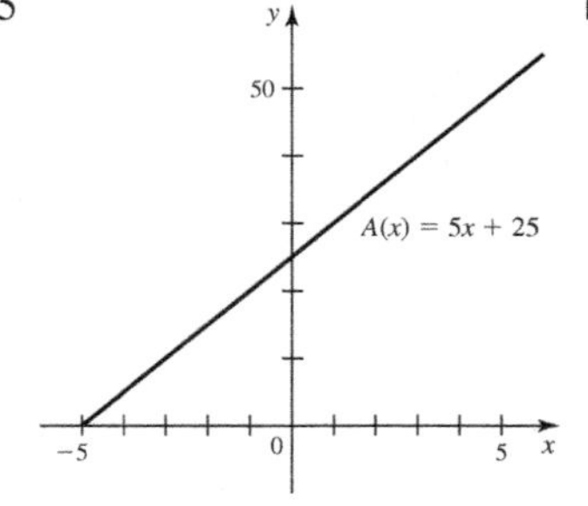

17. a. $A(2) = 2, A(4) = 8; A(x) = \frac{1}{2}x^2$ **b.** $F(4) = 6, F(6) = 16$; $F(x) = \frac{1}{2}x^2 - 2$ **c.** $A(x) - F(x) = \frac{1}{2}x^2 - \left(\frac{1}{2}x^2 - 2\right) = 2$

19. a.

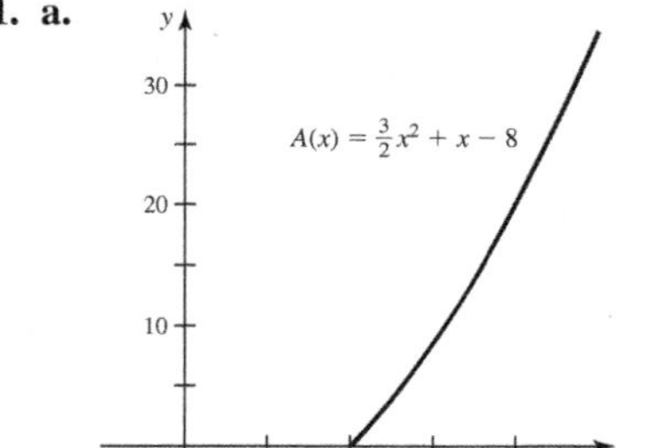

b. $A'(x) = \left(\frac{1}{2}(x+5)^2\right)' = x + 5 = f(x)$

21. a.

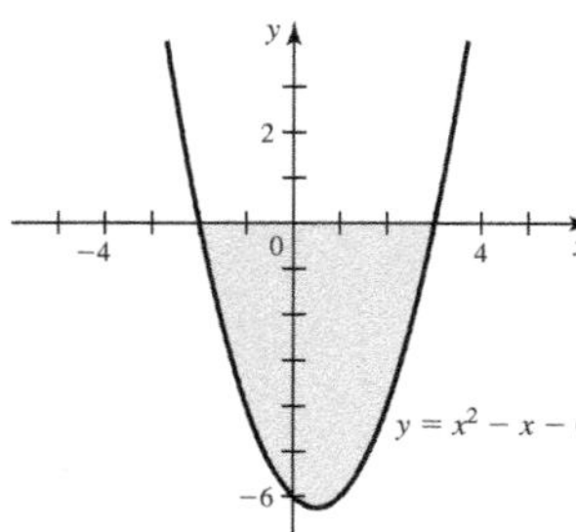

b. $A'(x) = \left(\frac{3}{2}x^2 + x - 8\right)' = 3x + 1 = f(x)$ **23.** $\frac{7}{3}$

25. $-\frac{125}{6}$ **27.** $-\frac{10}{3}$

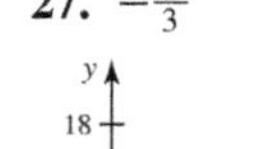

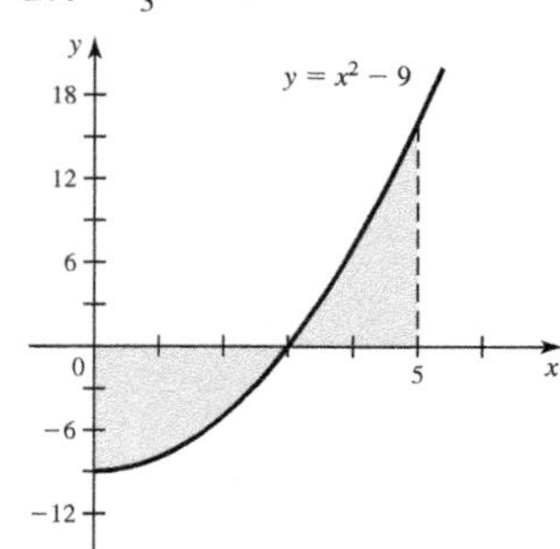

29. 16 **31.** $\frac{7}{6}$ **33.** 8 **35.** $-\frac{32}{3}$ **37.** $-\frac{5}{2}$ **39.** 1 **41.** $-\frac{3}{8}$
43. $\frac{9}{2}$ **45.** $3 \ln 2$ **47.** $\sqrt{2}/4$ **49.** $\pi/12$
51. **(i)** $\frac{14}{3}$ **(ii)** $\frac{14}{3}$ **53.** **(i)** -51.2 **(ii)** 51.2

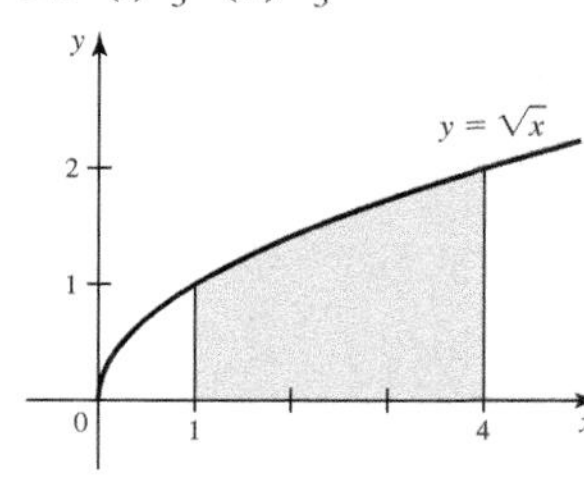

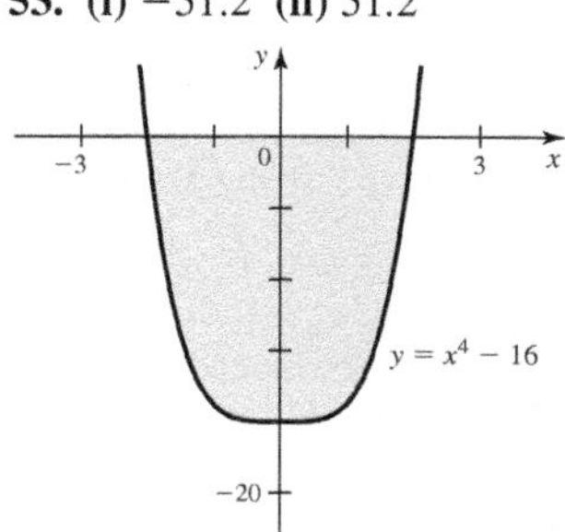

55. $\frac{94}{3}$ **57.** $\ln 2$ **59.** 2 **61.** $x^2 + x + 1$
63. $3/x^4$ **65.** $-\sqrt{x^4 + 1}$ **67.** $2\sqrt{1 + x^2}$ **69.** a–C, b–B, c–D, d–A
71. **a.** $x = 0, x \approx 3$ **b.** Local min at $x \approx 1.5$; local max at $x \approx 8.5$
c.

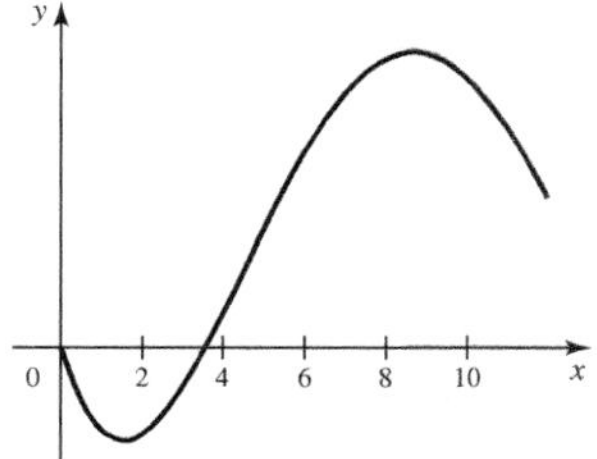

73. **a.** $x = 0, 10$ **b.** Local max at $x = 5$
c.

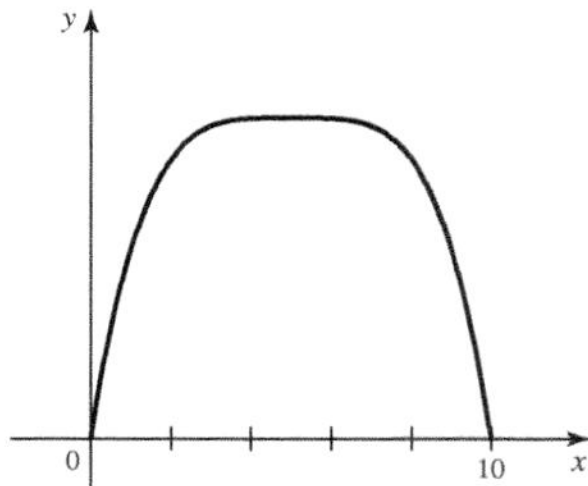

75. $-\pi, -\pi + \frac{9}{2}, -\pi + 9, 5 - \pi$ **77.** **a.** $A(x) = e^x - 1$
b.

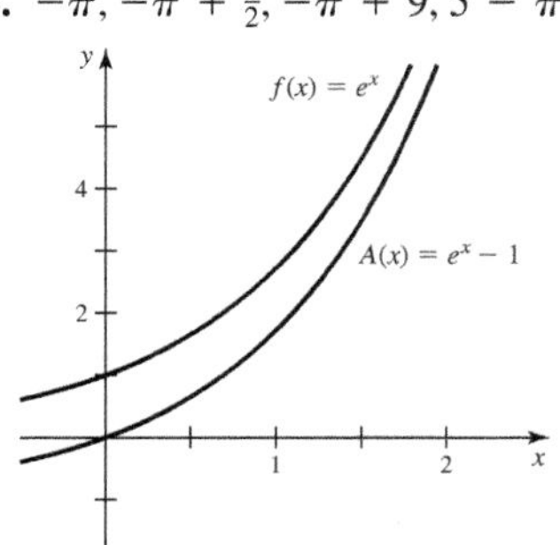

c. $A(\ln 2) = 1$; $A(\ln 4) = 3$

79. **a.** $A(x) = \dfrac{1}{\pi} \sin \pi x$

b.

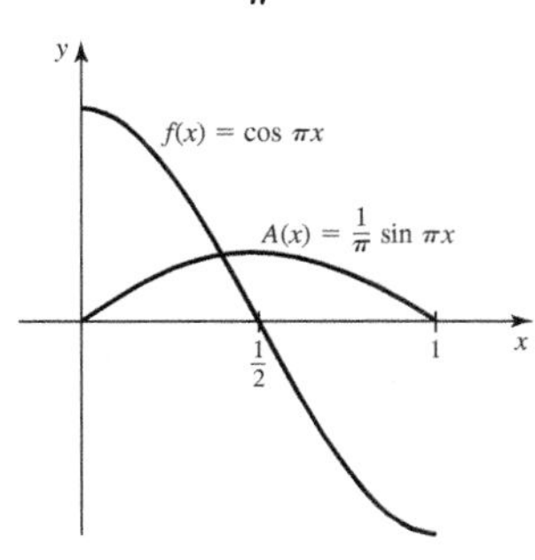

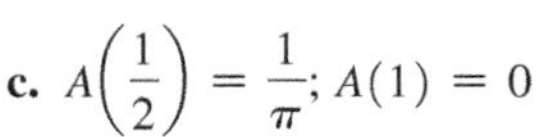

c. $A\left(\dfrac{1}{2}\right) = \dfrac{1}{\pi}$; $A(1) = 0$

81. **a.**

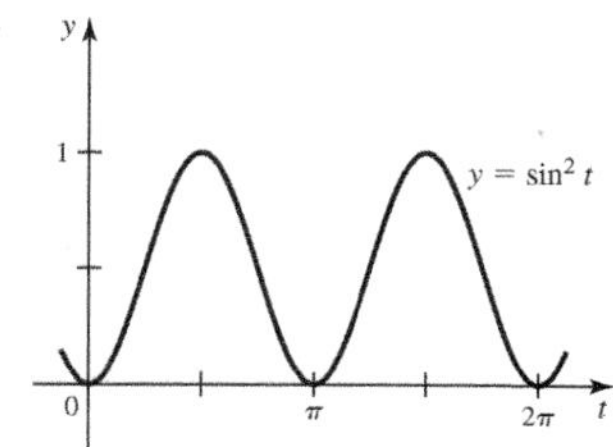

b. $g'(x) = \sin^2 x$

c.

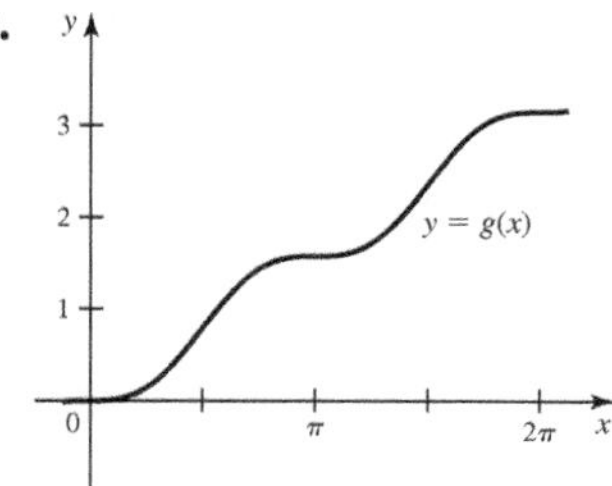

83. **a.**

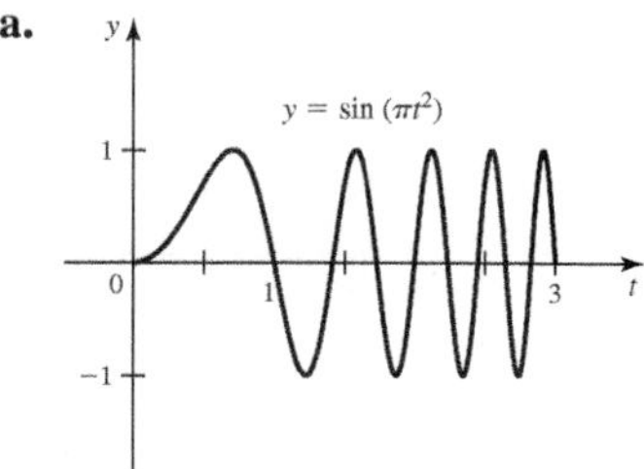

b. $g'(x) = \sin(\pi x^2)$

c.

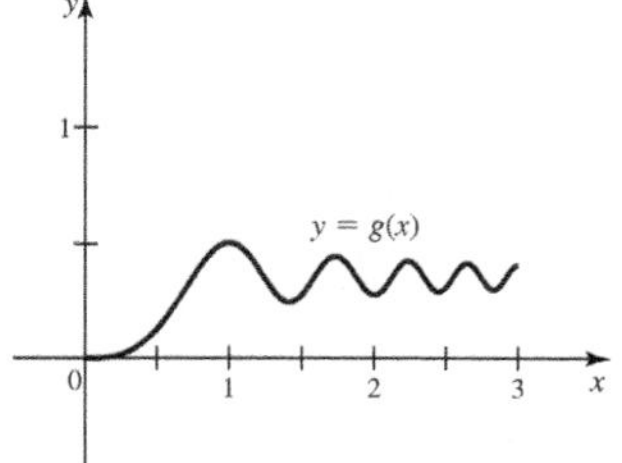

85. **a.** True **b.** True **c.** False **d.** True **e.** True **87.** $\frac{2}{3}$ **89.** 1
91. $\frac{45}{4}$ **93.** $\frac{3}{2} + 4 \ln 2$
95.

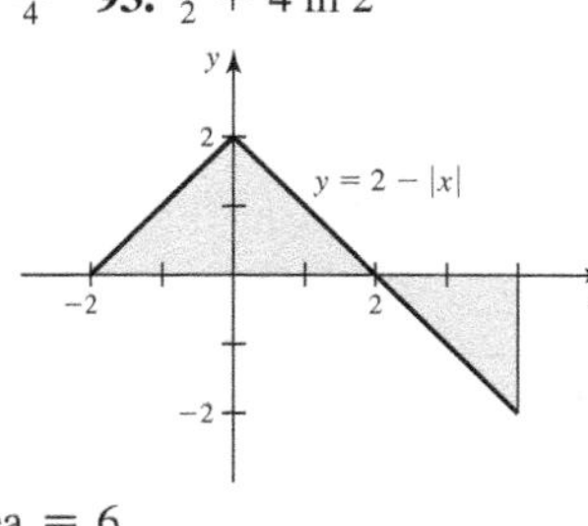

Area = 6

97.

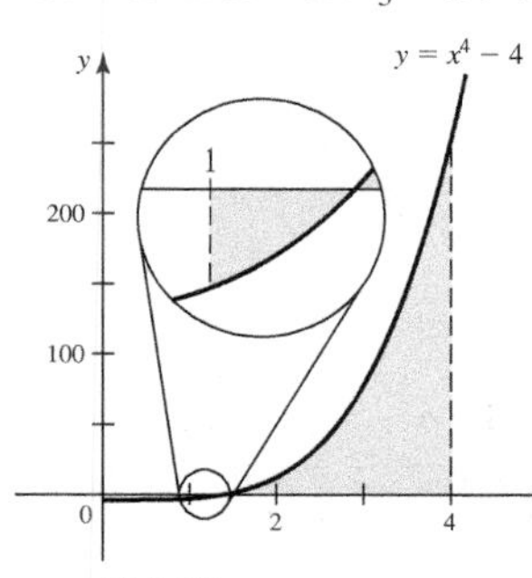

Area ≈ 194.05

99. $f(8) - f(3)$ **101.** $-(\cos^4 x + 6) \sin x$ **103.** $\dfrac{9}{t}$

105. **a.**

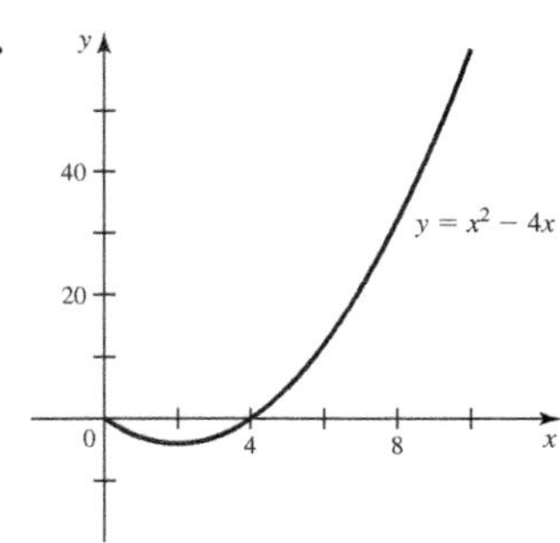

b. $b = 6$ **c.** $b = \dfrac{3a}{2}$

107. 3 **109.** $f(x) = -2\sin x + 3$ **111.** $\pi/2 \approx 1.57$

113. $$(S'(x))^2 + \left(\frac{S''(x)}{2x}\right)^2 = (\sin x^2)^2 + \left(\frac{2x\cos x^2}{2x}\right)^2 = \sin^2 x^2 + \cos^2 x^2 = 1$$

115. c. The summation relationship is a discrete analog of the Fundamental Theorem. Summing the difference quotient and integrating the derivative over the relevant interval give the difference of the function values at the endpoints.

Section 5.4 Exercises, pp. 381–384

1. If f is odd, the regions between f and the positive x-axis and between f and the negative x-axis are reflections of each other through the origin. Therefore, on $[-a, a]$, the areas cancel each other. **3.** Even; even **5.** If f is continuous on $[a, b]$, then there is a c in (a, b) such that $f(c) = \frac{1}{b-a}\int_a^b f(x)\,dx$. **7.** 0 **9.** $\frac{1000}{3}$ **11.** $-\frac{88}{3}$ **13.** 0 **15.** 0

17. 0

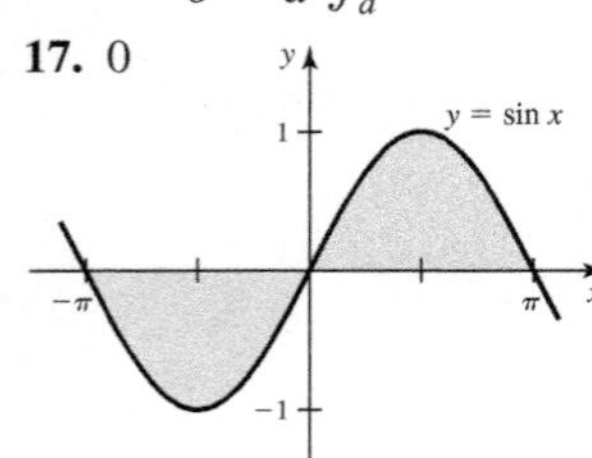

19. 0

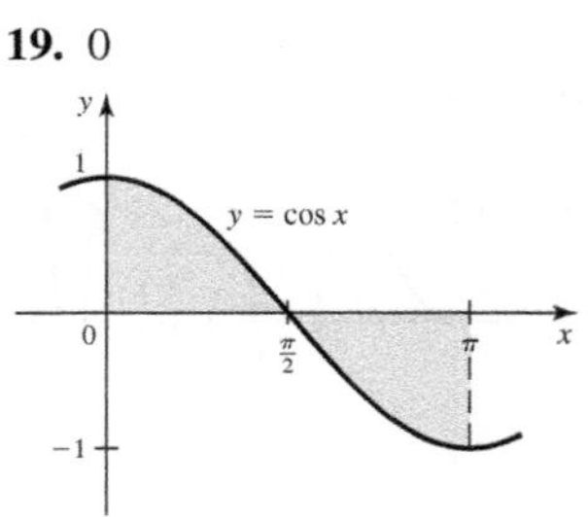

21. 0

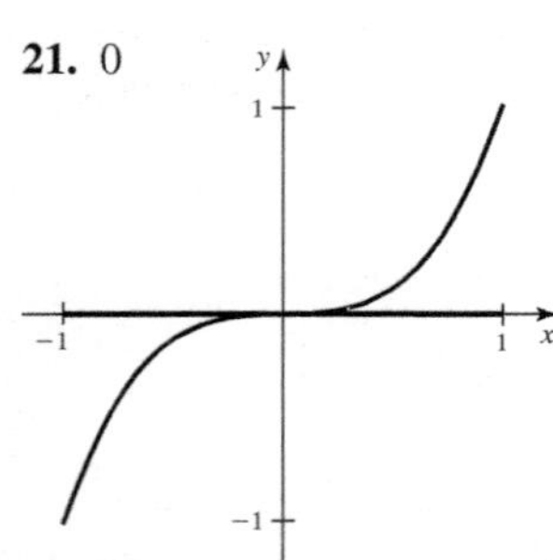

23. $\frac{\pi}{4}$

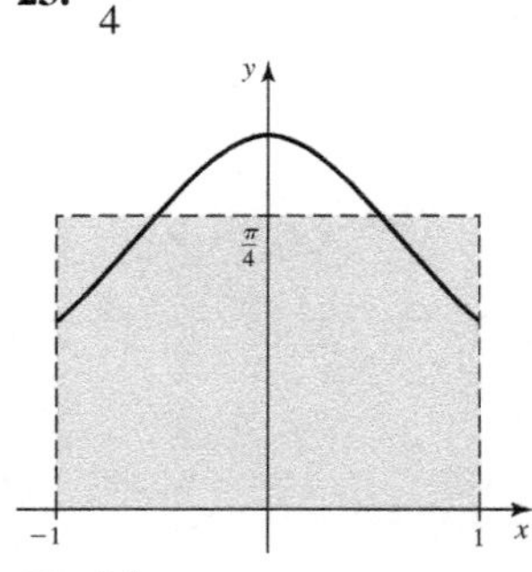

25. $1/(e-1)$

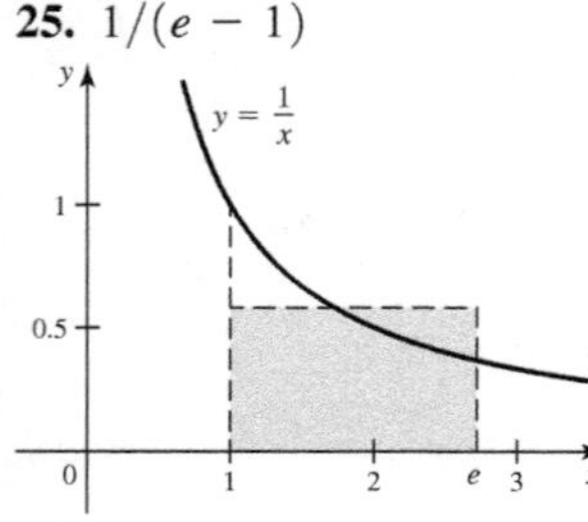

27. $2/\pi$

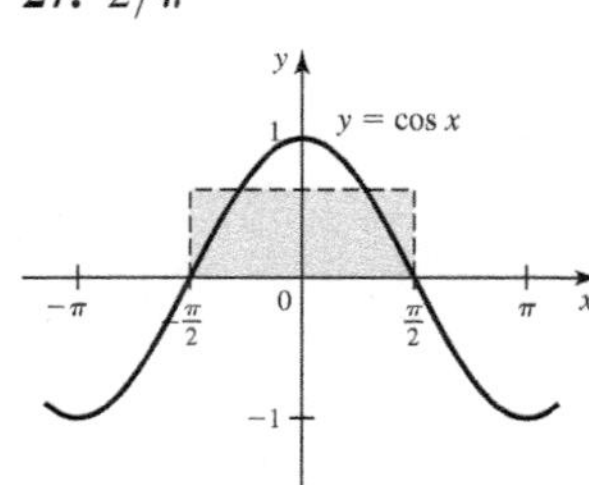

29. $1/(n+1)$

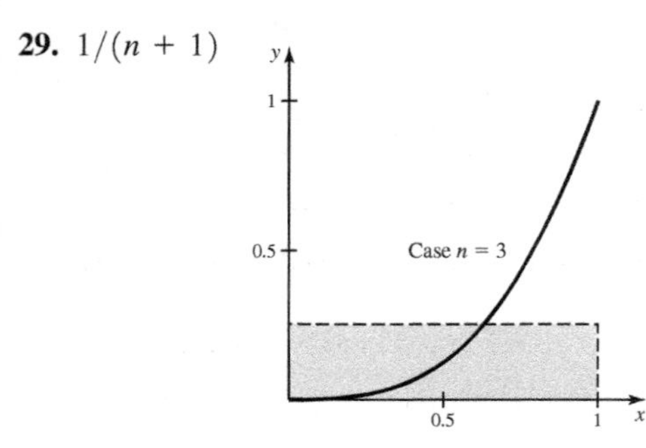

31. 2000 **33.** $20/\pi$ **35.** 2 **37.** $a/\sqrt{3}$ **39.** $c = \pm\frac{1}{2}$ **41. a.** True **b.** True **c.** True **d.** False **43.** 2 **45.** 0 **47.** 420 ft **51. a.** 9 **b.** 0 **53.** $f(g(-x)) = f(g(x)) \Rightarrow$ the integrand is even; $\int_{-a}^{a} f(g(x))\,dx = 2\int_0^a f(g(x))\,dx$ **55.** $p(g(-x)) = p(g(x)) \Rightarrow$ the integrand is even; $\int_{-a}^{a} p(g(x))\,dx = 2\int_0^a p(g(x))\,dx$ **57. a.** $a/6$ **b.** $(3 \pm \sqrt{3})/6$, independent of a **61.** $c = \sqrt[4]{12}$

65.

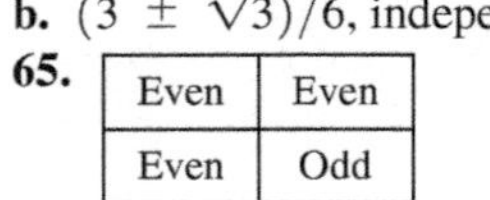

Even	Even
Even	Odd

Section 5.5 Exercises, pp. 390–393

1. The Chain Rule **3.** $u = g(x)$ **5.** We let a become $g(a)$ and b become $g(b)$. **7.** $\frac{x}{2} + \frac{\sin 2x}{4} + C$ **9.** $\frac{(x+1)^{13}}{13} + C$ **11.** $\frac{(2x+1)^{3/2}}{3} + C$ **13.** $\frac{(x^2+1)^5}{5} + C$ **15.** $\frac{1}{4}\sin^4 x + C$ **17.** $\frac{(x^2-1)^{100}}{100} + C$ **19.** $-\frac{(1-4x^3)^{1/2}}{3} + C$ **21.** $\frac{(x^2+x)^{11}}{11} + C$ **23.** $\frac{(x^4+16)^7}{28} + C$ **25.** $\frac{\sin^{-1} 3x}{3} + C$ **27.** $\frac{(x^6-3x^2)^5}{30} + C$ **29.** $\frac{1}{2}\tan^{-1} 2x + C$ **31.** $2\sec^{-1} 2x + C$ **33.** $\frac{2}{3}(x-4)^{1/2}(x+8) + C$ **35.** $\frac{3}{5}(x+4)^{2/3}(x-6) + C$ **37.** $\frac{3}{112}(2x+1)^{4/3}(8x-3) + C$ **39.** $\frac{7}{2}$ **41.** $\frac{1}{3}$ **43.** $(e^9-1)/3$ **45.** $\sqrt{2}-1$ **47.** $\frac{\pi}{6}$ **49.** $\frac{1}{2}\ln 17$ **51.** $\frac{\pi}{9}$ **53.** π **55.** $\frac{\theta}{2} - \frac{1}{4}\sin\left(\frac{6\theta+\pi}{3}\right) + C$ **57.** $\frac{\pi}{4}$ **59.** $\ln\frac{9}{8}$ **61. a.** True **b.** True **c.** False **d.** False **e.** False **63.** $\frac{1}{10}\tan 10x + C$ **65.** $\frac{1}{2}\tan^2 x + C$ **67.** $\frac{1}{7}\sec^7 x + C$ **69.** $\frac{1}{3}$ **71.** $\frac{3}{4}(4 - 3^{2/3})$ **73.** $\frac{32}{3}$ **75.** $-\ln 3$ **77.** $\frac{1}{7}$ **79.** 1 **81.** $\frac{64}{5}$ **83.** $\frac{2}{3}$; constant **85. a.** π/p **b.** 0 **87. a.** 160 **b.** $\frac{4800}{49} \approx 98$ **c.** $\Delta p = \int_0^T \frac{200}{(t+1)^r}\,dt$; decreases as r increases **d.** $r \approx 1.28$ **e.** As $t \to \infty$, the population approaches 100. **89.** $2/\pi$ **93.** One area is $\int_4^9 \frac{(\sqrt{x}-1)^2}{2\sqrt{x}}\,dx$. Changing variables by letting $u = \sqrt{x} - 1$ yields $\int_1^2 u^2\,du$, which is the other area. **95.** $7297/12$ **97.** $\frac{(f^{(p)}(x))^{n+1}}{n+1} + C$ **99.** $\frac{2}{15}(3-2a)(1+a)^{3/2} + \frac{4}{15}a^{5/2}$ **101.** $\frac{1}{3}\sec^3\theta + C$ **103. a.** $I = \frac{1}{8}x - \frac{1}{32}\sin 4x + C$ **b.** $I = \frac{1}{8}x - \frac{1}{32}\sin 4x + C$ **107.** $\frac{4}{3}(-2 + \sqrt{1+x})\sqrt{1+\sqrt{1+x}} + C$ **109.** $\frac{32}{105}$ **111.** $-4 + \sqrt{17}$

Chapter 5 Review Exercises, pp. 394–397

1. a. True **b.** False **c.** True **d.** True **e.** False **f.** True **g.** True **3. a.** 8.5 **b.** −4.5 **c.** 0 **d.** 11.5 **5.** 4π
7. a. $1((3\cdot2-2)+(3\cdot3-2)+(3\cdot4-2))=21$
b. $\sum_{k=1}^{n}\frac{3}{n}\left(3\left(1+\frac{3k}{n}\right)-2\right)$ **c.** $\frac{33}{2}$ **9.** $-\frac{16}{3}$ **11.** 56
13. $\int_0^4 (1+x^5)\,dx=\frac{2060}{3}$ **15.** $\frac{212}{5}$ **17.** 20 **19.** x^9-x^7+C
21. $\frac{7}{6}$ **23.** $\frac{\pi}{6}$ **25.** 1 **27.** $\frac{\pi}{2}$ **29.** $\frac{1}{3}\ln\frac{9}{2}$ **31.** $\frac{256}{3}$ **33.** 8
35. $-\frac{4}{15};\frac{4}{15}$ **37. a.** 20 **b.** 0 **c.** 80 **d.** 10 **e.** 0 **39.** 18
41. 10 **43.** Not enough information
45. Displacement $=0$; distance $=20/\pi$
47. a. $5/2, c=3.5$ **b.** $3, c=3$ and $c=5$ **49.** 24
51. $f(1)=0$; $f'(x)>0$ on $[1,\infty)$; $f''(x)<0$ on $[1,\infty)$

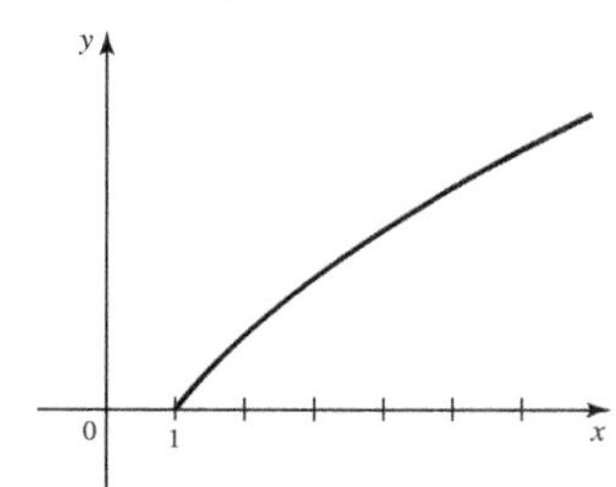

53. a.

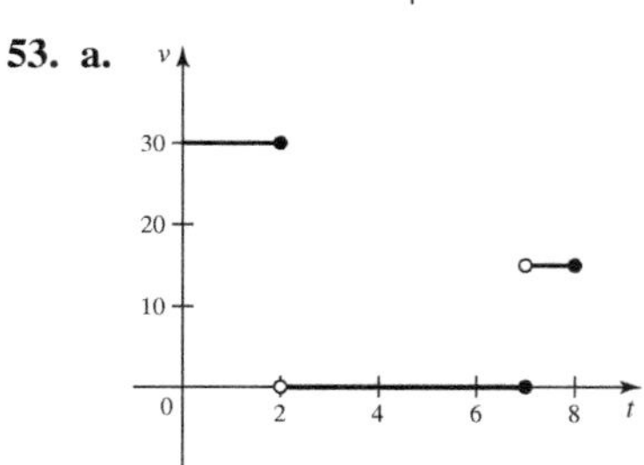

b. 75 **c.** The area is the distance the diver ascends.

55. a. $\frac{3}{2},\frac{5}{6}$ **b.** x **c.** $\frac{1}{2}x^2$ **d.** $-1,\frac{1}{2}$ **e.** 1, 1 **f.** $\frac{3}{2}$ **57.** e^4
63. $\cos\frac{1}{x}+C$ **65.** $\ln|\tan^{-1}x|+C$ **67.** $\ln(e^x+e^{-x})+C$
69. Differentiating the first equation gives the second equation; no.
71. a. Increasing on $(-\infty,1)$ and $(2,\infty)$; decreasing on $(1,2)$
b. Concave up on $(\frac{13}{8},\infty)$; concave down on $(-\infty,\frac{13}{8})$ **c.** Local max at $x=1$; local min at $x=2$ **d.** Inflection point at $x=\frac{13}{8}$

CHAPTER 7

Section 7.1 Exercises, pp. 514–516

1. $u=4-7x$ **3.** $\sin^2 x=\frac{1-\cos 2x}{2}$
5. Complete the square in x^2-4x+5.
7. $\frac{1}{15(3-5x)^3}+C$ **9.** $\frac{\sqrt{2}}{4}$
11. $\frac{1}{2}\ln^2 2x+C$ **13.** $\ln(e^x+1)+C$ **15.** $\frac{1}{2}\ln|e^{2x}-2|+C$
17. $\frac{32}{3}$ **19.** $-\frac{1}{5}\cot^5 x+C$ **21.** $x-\ln|x+1|+C$
23. $\frac{1}{2}\ln(x^2+4)+\tan^{-1}\frac{x}{2}+C$
25. $\frac{\sec^2 t}{2}+\sec t+C$ or $\frac{\tan^2 t}{2}+\sec t+C$
27. $3\sqrt{1-x^2}+2\sin^{-1}x+C$ **29.** $x-2\ln|x+4|+C$
31. $\frac{t^3}{3}-\frac{t^2}{2}+t-3\ln|t+1|+C$ **33.** $\frac{1}{3}\tan^{-1}\left(\frac{x-1}{3}\right)+C$
35. $\sin^{-1}\left(\frac{\theta+3}{6}\right)+C$ **37.** $\tan\theta-\sec\theta+C$
39. $-x-\cot x-\csc x+C$ **41. a.** False **b.** False **c.** False
d. False **43.** $\frac{\ln 4-\pi}{4}$ **45.** $\frac{2\sin^3 x}{3}+C$ **47.** $2\tan^{-1}\sqrt{x}+C$
49. $\frac{1}{2}\ln(x^2+6x+13)-\frac{5}{2}\tan^{-1}\left(\frac{x+3}{2}\right)+C$
51. $-\frac{1}{e^x+1}+C$ **53.** $\frac{1}{2}$ **55. a.** $\frac{\tan^2 x}{2}+C$ **b.** $\frac{\sec^2 x}{2}+C$
c. The antiderivatives differ by a constant.
57. a. $\frac{1}{2}(x+1)^2-2(x+1)+\ln|x+1|+C$
b. $\frac{x^2}{2}-x+\ln|x+1|+C$ **c.** The antiderivatives differ by a constant. **59.** $\frac{\ln 26}{3}$ **61. a.** $\frac{14\pi}{3}$ **b.** $\frac{2}{3}(5\sqrt{5}-1)\pi$
63. $\frac{2048+1763\sqrt{41}}{9375}$ **65.** $\pi\left(\frac{9}{2}-\frac{5\sqrt{5}}{6}\right)$

Section 7.2 Exercises, pp. 520–523

1. Product Rule **3.** $u=x^n$ **5.** Products for which the choice for dv is easily integrated and when the resulting new integral is no more difficult than the original
7. $x\sin x+\cos x+C$ **9.** te^t-e^t+C
11. $\frac{2}{3}(x-2)\sqrt{x+1}+C$ **13.** $\frac{x^3}{3}(\ln x^3-1)+C$
15. $\frac{x^3}{9}(3\ln x-1)+C$ **17.** $-\frac{1}{9x^9}\left(\ln x+\frac{1}{9}\right)+C$
19. $x\tan^{-1}x-\frac{1}{2}\ln(x^2+1)+C$ **21.** $\frac{1}{8}\sin 2x-\frac{x}{4}\cos 2x+C$
23. $-e^{-t}(t^2+2t+2)+C$ **25.** $-\frac{e^{-x}}{17}(\sin 4x+4\cos 4x)+C$
27. $\frac{e^x}{2}(\sin x+\cos x)+C$ **29.** $\frac{1}{4}(1-2x^2)\cos 2x+\frac{1}{2}x\sin 2x+C$
31. π **33.** $-\frac{1}{2}$ **35.** $\frac{1}{9}(5e^6+1)$
37. $\left(\frac{2\sqrt{3}-1}{12}\right)\pi+\frac{1-\sqrt{3}}{2}$ **39.** $\pi(1-\ln 2)$ **41.** $\frac{2\pi}{27}(13e^6-1)$
43. a. False **b.** True **c.** True **45.** Let $u=x^n$ and $dv=\cos ax\,dx$. **47.** Let $u=\ln^n x$ and $dv=dx$.
49. $\frac{x^2\sin 5x}{5}+\frac{2x\cos 5x}{25}-\frac{2\sin 5x}{125}+C$
51. $x\ln^4 x-4x\ln^3 x+12x\ln^2 x-24x\ln x+24x+C$
53. $(\tan x+2)\ln(\tan x+2)-\tan x+C$
55. $\int\log_b x\,dx=\int\frac{\ln x}{\ln b}dx=\frac{1}{\ln b}(x\ln x-x)+C$
57. $2\sqrt{x}\sin\sqrt{x}+2\cos\sqrt{x}+C$ **59.** $2e^3$ **61.** $\pi(\pi-2)$
63. x-axis: $\frac{\pi^2}{2}$; y-axis: $2\pi^2$ **65. a.** Let $u=x$ and $dv=f'(x)\,dx$.
b. $\frac{e^{3x}}{9}(3x-1)+C$ **67.** Use $u=\sec x$ and $dv=\sec^2 x\,dx$.

69. a. $t = k\pi$, for $k = 0, 1, 2, \ldots$

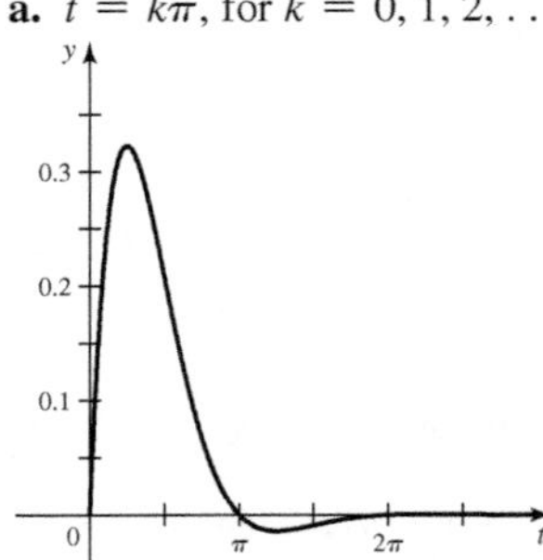

b. $\dfrac{e^{-\pi} + 1}{2\pi}$ **c.** $(-1)^n\left(\dfrac{e^{\pi} + 1}{2\pi e^{(n+1)\pi}}\right)$ **d.** $a_n = a_{n-1} \cdot \dfrac{1}{e^{\pi}}$

71. c. $\int f(x)g(x)dx = f(x)G_1(x) - f'(x)G_2(x) + f''(x)G_3(x) - \int f'''(x)G_3(x)dx$

f and its derivatives		g and its integrals
$f(x)$	+	$g(x)$
$f'(x)$	−	$G_1(x)$
$f''(x)$	+	$G_2(x)$
$f'''(x)$	−	$G_3(x)$

d. $\int x^2e^{0.5x}dx = 2x^2e^{0.5x} - 8xe^{0.5x} + 16e^{0.5x} + C$

f and its derivatives		g and its integrals
x^2	+	$e^{0.5x}$
$2x$	−	$2e^{0.5x}$
2	+	$4e^{0.5x}$
0	−	$8e^{0.5x}$

$\dfrac{d^{(n)}}{dx}(x^2) = 0$, for $n \geq 3$, so all entries in the left column of the table beyond row three are 0, which results in no additional contribution to the antiderivative.

e. $x^3 \sin x + 3x^2 \cos x - 6x \sin x - 6 \cos x + C$; five rows are needed because $\dfrac{d^{(n)}}{dx}(x^3) = 0$, for $n \geq 4$.

f. $\dfrac{d^{(k)}}{dx}(p_n(x)) = 0$, for $k \geq n + 1$

73. a. $\int e^x \cos x\,dx = e^x \sin x + e^x \cos x - \int e^x \cos x\,dx$ **b.** $\frac{1}{2}(e^x \sin x + e^x \cos x) + C$ **c.** $-\frac{3}{13}e^{-2x} \cos 3x - \frac{2}{13}e^{-2x} \sin 3x + C$

75. Let $u = x$ and $dv = f''(x)\,dx$ **77. a.** $I_1 = -\frac{1}{2}e^{-x^2} + C$ **b.** $I_3 = -\frac{1}{2}e^{-x^2}(x^2 + 1) + C$ **c.** $I_5 = -\frac{1}{2}e^{-x^2}(x^4 + 2x^2 + 2) + C$

Section 7.3 Exercises, pp. 529–531

1. $\sin^2 x = \frac{1}{2}(1 - \cos 2x)$; $\cos^2 x = \frac{1}{2}(1 + \cos 2x)$

3. Rewrite $\sin^3 x$ as $(1 - \cos^2 x) \sin x$.

5. A reduction formula expresses an integral with a power in the integrand in terms of another integral with a smaller power in the integrand. **7.** Let $u = \tan x$. **9.** $\frac{x}{2} - \frac{1}{4}\sin 2x + C$

11. $\sin x - \frac{\sin^3 x}{3} + C$ **13.** $-\cos x + \frac{2}{3}\cos^3 x - \frac{\cos^5 x}{5} + C$

15. $\frac{1}{8}x - \frac{1}{32}\sin 4x + C$ **17.** $\frac{\cos^5 x}{5} - \frac{\cos^3 x}{3} + C$

19. $\frac{2}{3}\sin^{3/2} x - \frac{2}{7}\sin^{7/2} x + C$ **21.** $\sec x + 2\cos x - \frac{\cos^3 x}{3} + C$

23. $\frac{\sin^3 2x}{48} + \frac{1}{16}x - \frac{1}{64}\sin 4x + C$ **25.** $\tan x - x + C$

27. $-\frac{\cot^3 x}{3} + \cot x + x + C$

29. $4\tan^5 x - \frac{20}{3}\tan^3 x + 20\tan x - 20x + C$ **31.** $\tan^{10} x + C$

33. $\frac{\sec^3 x}{3} + C$ **35.** $\frac{1}{8}\tan^2 4x + \frac{1}{4}\ln|\cos 4x| + C$

37. $\frac{2}{3}\tan^{3/2} x + C$ **39.** $\tan x - \cot x + C$ **41.** $\frac{4}{3}$ **43.** $\frac{4}{3} - \ln\sqrt{3}$

45. a. True **b.** False **49.** $\frac{1}{2}\ln(\sqrt{2} + \frac{3}{2})$

51. $\frac{1}{3}\tan^3(\ln\theta) + \tan(\ln\theta) + C$ **53.** $\ln 4$ **55.** $8\sqrt{2}/3$

57. $\ln|\sec(e^x + 1) + \tan(e^x + 1)| + C$

59. $\sqrt{2}$ **61.** $2\sqrt{2}/3$ **63.** $\ln(\sqrt{2} + 1)$ **65.** $\frac{1}{2} - \ln\sqrt{2}$

67. $\frac{\cos 4x}{8} - \frac{\cos 10x}{20} + C$ **69.** $\frac{\sin x}{2} - \frac{\sin 5x}{10} + C$

73. a. $\dfrac{\pi}{2}; \dfrac{\pi}{2}$ **b.** $\dfrac{\pi}{2}$ for all n **d.** Yes **e.** $\dfrac{3\pi}{8}$ for all n

Section 7.4 Exercises, pp. 537–540

1. $x = 3\sec\theta$ **3.** $x = 10\sin\theta$ **5.** $\sqrt{4 - x^2}/x$ **7.** $\pi/6$

9. $25\left(\dfrac{2\pi}{3} - \dfrac{\sqrt{3}}{2}\right)$ **11.** $\dfrac{\pi}{12} - \dfrac{\sqrt{3}}{8}$ **13.** $\sin^{-1}\dfrac{x}{4} + C$

15. $-3\ln\left|\dfrac{\sqrt{9 - x^2} + 3}{x}\right| + \sqrt{9 - x^2} + C$

17. $\dfrac{x}{2}\sqrt{64 - x^2} + 32\sin^{-1}\dfrac{x}{8} + C$ **19.** $\dfrac{x}{\sqrt{1 - x^2}} + C$

21. $\dfrac{-\sqrt{x^2 + 9}}{9x} + C$ **23.** $\sin^{-1}\dfrac{x}{6} + C$

25. $\ln(\sqrt{x^2 - 81} + x) + C$ **27.** $x/\sqrt{1 + 4x^2} + C$

29. $8\sin^{-1}(x/4) - x\sqrt{16 - x^2}/2 + C$

31. $\sqrt{x^2 - 9} - 3\sec^{-1}(x/3) + C$

33. $\dfrac{x}{2}\sqrt{4 + x^2} - 2\ln(x + \sqrt{4 + x^2}) + C$

35. $\sin^{-1}\left(\dfrac{x + 1}{2}\right) + C$ **37.** $\dfrac{9}{10}\cos^{-1}\dfrac{5}{3x} - \dfrac{\sqrt{9x^2 - 25}}{2x^2} + C$

39. $\dfrac{1}{10}\left(\tan^{-1}\dfrac{x}{5} - \dfrac{5x}{25 + x^2}\right) + C$

41. $x/\sqrt{100 - x^2} - \sin^{-1}(x/10) + C$

43. $81/(2(81 - x^2)) + \ln\sqrt{81 - x^2} + C$

45. $-1/\sqrt{x^2 - 1} - \sec^{-1} x + C$ **47.** $\ln\left(\dfrac{1 + \sqrt{17}}{4}\right)$

49. $2 - \sqrt{2}$ **51.** $\dfrac{1}{3} + \dfrac{\ln 3}{4}$ **53.** $\sqrt{2}/6$

55. $\frac{1}{16}[1 - \sqrt{3} - \ln(21 - 12\sqrt{3})]$ **57. a.** False **b.** True **c.** False **d.** False **59.** $\dfrac{1}{3}\tan^{-1}\left(\dfrac{x + 3}{3}\right) + C$

61. $\left(\dfrac{x - 1}{2}\right)\sqrt{x^2 - 2x + 10} - \dfrac{9}{2}\ln(x - 1 + \sqrt{x^2 - 2x + 10}) + C$

63. $\dfrac{x - 4}{\sqrt{9 + 8x - x^2}} - \sin^{-1}\left(\dfrac{x - 4}{5}\right) + C$ **65.** $\dfrac{\pi\sqrt{2}}{48}$

67. a. $\dfrac{r^2}{2}(\theta - \sin\theta)$ **69. a.** $\ln 3$ **b.** $\dfrac{\pi}{3}\tan^{-1}\dfrac{4}{3}$ **c.** 4π

71. $\dfrac{1}{4a}(20a\sqrt{1 + 400a^2} + \ln(20a + \sqrt{1 + 400a^2}))$

73. $\frac{1}{81} + \frac{\ln 3}{108}$

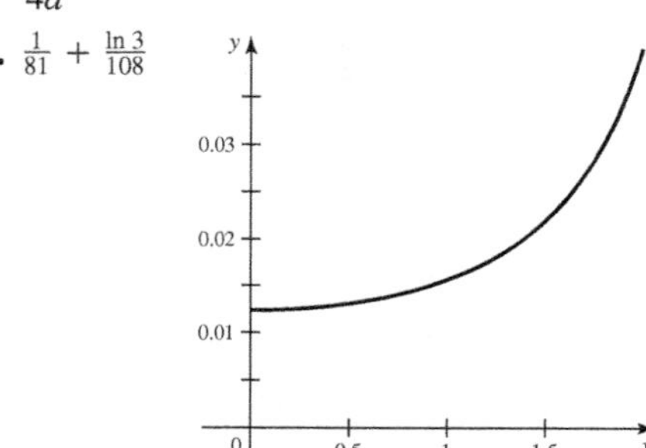

75. $25\left(\sqrt{3} - \ln\sqrt{2 + \sqrt{3}}\right)$

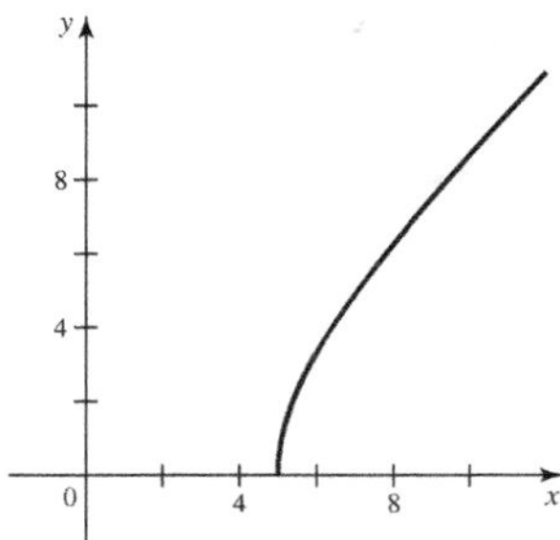

77. $\ln((2 + \sqrt{3})(\sqrt{2} - 1))$ 79. $192\pi^2$

81. b. $\lim_{L\to\infty} \frac{kQ}{a\sqrt{a^2 + L^2}} = \lim_{L\to\infty} 2\rho k \frac{1}{a\sqrt{\left(\frac{a}{L}\right)^2 + 1}} = \frac{2\rho k}{a}$

83. a. $\frac{1}{\sqrt{g}}\left(\frac{\pi}{2} - \sin^{-1}\left(\frac{2\cos b - \cos a + 1}{\cos a + 1}\right)\right)$

b. For $b = \pi$, the descent time is $\frac{\pi}{\sqrt{g}}$, a constant.

87. $\pi - 3\sqrt{3}$

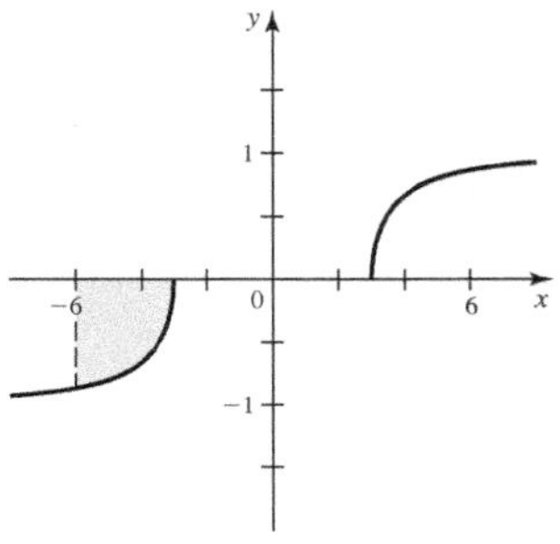

Section 7.5 Exercises, pp. 549–551

1. Rational functions 3. a. $\frac{A}{x - 3}$ b. $\frac{A_1}{x - 4}, \frac{A_2}{(x - 4)^2}, \frac{A_3}{(x - 4)^3}$ c. $\frac{Ax + B}{x^2 + 2x + 6}$ 5. $\frac{1/3}{x - 4} - \frac{1/3}{x + 2}$ 7. $\frac{2}{x - 1} + \frac{3}{x - 2}$ 9. $\frac{1/2}{x - 4} + \frac{1/2}{x + 4}$ 11. $-\frac{3}{x - 1} + \frac{1}{x} + \frac{2}{x - 2}$ 13. $\ln\left|\frac{x - 1}{x + 2}\right| + C$ 15. $3\ln\left|\frac{x - 1}{x + 1}\right| + C$ 17. $-\ln 4$ 19. $\ln|(x - 6)^6(x + 4)^4| + C$ 21. $\ln\left|\frac{(x - 2)^2(x + 1)}{(x + 2)^2(x - 1)}\right| + C$ 23. $\ln\left|\frac{x(x - 2)^3}{(x + 2)^3}\right| + C$ 25. $\ln\left|\frac{(x - 3)^{1/3}(x + 1)}{(x + 3)^{1/3}(x - 1)}\right|^{1/16} + C$ 27. $\frac{9}{x} + \ln\left|\frac{x - 9}{x}\right| + C$ 29. $\ln 2 - \frac{3}{4}$ 31. $-\frac{2}{x} + \ln\left|\frac{x + 1}{x}\right|^2 + C$ 33. $\frac{5}{x} + \ln\left|\frac{x}{x + 1}\right|^6 + C$ 35. $-\frac{6}{x - 3} + \ln\left|\frac{(x - 2)^2}{x - 3}\right| + C$ 37. $\frac{3}{x - 1} + \ln\left|\frac{(x - 1)^5}{x^4}\right| + C$ 39. $\frac{A}{x - 1} + \frac{B}{(x - 1)^2} + \frac{Cx + D}{x^2 + 1}$ 41. $\frac{A}{x - 4} + \frac{B}{(x - 4)^2} + \frac{Cx + D}{x^2 + 3x + 4}$ 43. $\ln|x + 1| + \tan^{-1}x + C$ 45. $\ln(x + 1)^2 + \tan^{-1}(x + 1) + C$ 47. $\ln\left|\frac{(x - 1)^2}{x^2 + 4x + 5}\right| + 14\tan^{-1}(x + 2) + C$ 49. $\ln|(x - 1)^{1/5}(x^2 + 4)^{2/5}| + \frac{2}{5}\tan^{-1}\frac{x}{2} + C$ 51. a. False b. False c. False d. True 53. $\ln 6$ 55. $4\sqrt{2} + \frac{1}{3}\ln\left(\frac{3 - 2\sqrt{2}}{3 + 2\sqrt{2}}\right)$ 57. $\left(\frac{24}{5} - 2\ln 5\right)\pi$ 59. $\frac{2}{3}\pi\ln 2$ 61. $2\pi\left(3 + \ln\frac{2}{5}\right)$ 63. $x - \ln(1 + e^x) + C$ 65. $3x + \ln\frac{(x - 2)^{14}}{|x - 1|} + C$ 67. $\frac{1}{2}(t - \ln(2 + e^t))$ 69. $\frac{1}{4}\ln\left(\frac{1 + \sin t}{1 - \sin t} - \frac{2}{1 + \sin t}\right) + C$ 71. $\ln\left|\frac{e^x - 1}{e^x + 2}\right|^{1/3} + C$ 73. $-\frac{1}{2(e^{2x} + 1)} + C$ 77. $\frac{4}{3}(x + 2)^{3/4} - 2(x + 2)^{1/2} + 4(x + 2)^{1/4} - \ln((x + 2)^{1/4} + 1)^4 + C$ 79. $2\sqrt{x} - 3\sqrt[3]{x} + 6\sqrt[6]{x} - \ln(\sqrt[6]{x} + 1)^6 + C$ 81. $\frac{4}{3}\sqrt{1 + \sqrt{x}}(\sqrt{x} - 2) + C$ 83. $\ln\left(\frac{x^2}{x^2 + 1}\right) + \frac{1}{x^2 + 1} + C$ 85. $\frac{1}{50}\left(\frac{5(3x + 4)}{x^2 + 2x + 2} + 11\tan^{-1}(1 + x) + \ln\left|\frac{(x - 1)^2}{x^2 + 2x + 2}\right|\right) + C$ 87. $\ln\sqrt{\left|\frac{x - 1}{x + 1}\right|} + C$ 89. $\tan x - \sec x + C = -\frac{2}{\tan(x/2) + 1}$ 91. $-\cot x - \csc x + C = -\cot(x/2) + C$ 93. $\frac{1}{\sqrt{2}}\ln\frac{\sqrt{2} + 1}{\sqrt{2} - 1}$ 95. a. Car A b. Car C c. $S_A(t) = 88t - 88\ln|t + 1|$; $S_B(t) = 88\left(t - \ln(t + 1)^2 - \frac{1}{t + 1} + 1\right)$; $S_C(t) = 88(t - \tan^{-1}t)$ d. Car C 97. Because $\frac{x^4(1 - x)^4}{1 + x^2} > 0$ on $(0, 1)$, $\int_0^1 \frac{x^4(1 - x^4)}{1 + x^2}\,dx > 0$; thus, $\frac{22}{7} > \pi$.

Section 7.6 Exercises, pp. 555–557

1. Substitutions, integration by parts, partial fractions 3. The CAS may not include the constant of integration, and it may use a trigonometric identity or other algebraic simplification. 5. $x\cos^{-1}x - \sqrt{1 - x^2} + C$ 7. $\ln(x + \sqrt{16 + x^2}) + C$ 9. $\frac{3}{4}(2u - 7\ln|7 + 2u|) + C$ 11. $-\frac{1}{4}\cot 2x + C$ 13. $\frac{1}{12}(2x - 1)\sqrt{4x + 1} + C$ 15. $\frac{1}{3}\ln\left|x + \sqrt{x^2 - \left(\frac{10}{3}\right)^2}\right| + C$ 17. $\frac{x}{16\sqrt{16 + 9x^2}} + C$ 19. $-\frac{1}{12}\ln\left|\frac{12 + \sqrt{144 - x^2}}{x}\right| + C$ 21. $2x + x\ln^2 x - 2x\ln x + C$ 23. $\frac{x + 5}{2}\sqrt{x^2 + 10x} - \frac{25}{2}\ln|x + 5 + \sqrt{x^2 + 10x}| + C$ 25. $\frac{1}{3}\tan^{-1}\left(\frac{x + 1}{3}\right) + C$ 27. $\ln x - \frac{1}{10}\ln(x^{10} + 1) + C$ 29. $2\ln(\sqrt{x - 6} + \sqrt{x}) + C$ 31. $\ln(e^x + \sqrt{4 + e^{2x}}) + C$ 33. $-\frac{1}{2}\ln\left|\frac{2 + \sin x}{\sin x}\right| + C$ 35. $-\frac{\tan^{-1}x^3}{3x^3} + \ln\left|\frac{x}{(x^6 + 1)^{1/6}}\right| + C$

37. $\frac{2\ln^2 x - 1}{4}\sin^{-1}(\ln x) + \frac{\ln x\sqrt{1 - \ln^2 x}}{4} + C$

39. $4\sqrt{17} + \ln(4 + \sqrt{17})$ **41.** $\sqrt{5} - \sqrt{2} + \ln\left(\frac{2 + 2\sqrt{2}}{1 + \sqrt{5}}\right)$

43. $\frac{128\pi}{3}$ **45.** $\frac{\pi^2}{4}$ **47.** $\frac{(x - 3)\sqrt{3 + 2x}}{3} + C$

49. $\frac{1}{3}\tan 3x - x + C$

51. $\frac{(x^2 - a^2)^{3/2}}{3} - a^2\sqrt{x^2 - a^2} + a^3\cos^{-1}\frac{a}{x} + C$

53. $-\frac{x}{8}(2x^2 - 5a^2)\sqrt{a^2 - x^2} + \frac{3a^4}{8}\sin^{-1}\frac{x}{a} + C$ **55.** $\frac{(\frac{4}{5})^9 - (\frac{2}{3})^9}{9}$

57. $\frac{1540 + 243\ln 3}{8}$ **59.** $\frac{\pi}{4}$ **61.** $2 - \frac{\pi^2}{12} - \ln 4$ **63. a.** True **b.** True **67.** $\frac{1}{8}e^{2x}(4x^3 - 6x^2 + 6x - 3) + C$

69. $\frac{\tan^3 3y}{9} - \frac{\tan 3y}{3} + y + C$

71. $\frac{1}{16}\left((8x^2 - 1)\sin^{-1} 2x + 2x\sqrt{1 - 4x^2}\right) + C$

73. $-\frac{\tan^{-1} x}{x} + \ln\left(\frac{|x|}{\sqrt{x^2 + 1}}\right) + C$ **75. b.** $\frac{\pi}{8}\ln 2$

77. a.

θ_0	T
0.10	6.27927
0.20	6.26762
0.30	6.24854
0.40	6.22253
0.50	6.19021
0.60	6.15236
0.70	6.10979
0.80	6.06338
0.90	6.01399
1.00	5.96247

b. All are within 10%.

79. $\frac{1}{a^2}(ax - b\ln|b + ax|) + C$

81. $\frac{1}{a^2}\left(\frac{(ax + b)^{n+2}}{n + 2} - \frac{b(ax + b)^{n+1}}{n + 1}\right) + C$

83. b. $\frac{63\pi}{512}$ **c.** Decrease

Section 7.7 Exercises, pp. 566–569

1. $\frac{1}{2}$ **3.** The Trapezoid Rule approximates areas under curves using trapezoids. **5.** $-1, 1, 3, 5, 7, 9$ **7.** 1.59×10^{-3}; 5.04×10^{-4} **9.** 1.72×10^{-3}; 6.32×10^{-4} **11.** 576; 640; 656 **13.** 0.643950551 **15.** 704; 672; 664 **17.** 0.622 **19.** $M(25) = 0.63703884$, $T(25) = 0.63578179$; 6.58×10^{-4}, 1.32×10^{-3}

21.

n	$M(n)$	$T(n)$	Error in $M(n)$	Error in $T(n)$
4	99	102	1.00	2.00
8	99.75	100.5	0.250	0.500
16	99.9375	100.125	6.3×10^{-2}	0.125
32	99.984375	100.03125	1.6×10^{-2}	3.1×10^{-2}

23.

n	$M(n)$	$T(n)$	Error in $M(n)$	Error in $T(n)$
4	1.50968181	1.48067370	9.7×10^{-3}	1.9×10^{-2}
8	1.50241228	1.49517776	2.4×10^{-3}	4.8×10^{-3}
16	1.50060256	1.49879502	6.0×10^{-4}	1.2×10^{-3}
32	1.50015061	1.49969879	1.5×10^{-4}	3.0×10^{-4}

25.

n	$M(n)$	$T(n)$	Error in $M(n)$	Error in $T(n)$
4	-1.96×10^{-16}	0	2.0×10^{-16}	0
8	7.63×10^{-17}	-1.41×10^{-16}	7.6×10^{-17}	1.4×10^{-16}
16	1.61×10^{-16}	1.09×10^{-17}	1.6×10^{-16}	1.1×10^{-17}
32	6.27×10^{-17}	-4.77×10^{-17}	6.3×10^{-17}	4.8×10^{-17}

27. 54.5, Trapezoid Rule **29.** 35.0, Trapezoid Rule
31. a. Left sum: 204.917; right sum: 261.375; Trapezoid Rule: 233.146; the approximations measure the average temperature of the curling iron on $[0, 120]$. **b.** Left sum: underestimate; right sum: overestimate; Trapezoid Rule: underestimate **c.** 305°F is the change in temperature over $[0, 120]$. **33. a.** 5907.5 **b.** 5965 **c.** 5917

35. a. $T(25) = 3.19623162$
$T(50) = 3.19495398$
b. $S(50) = 3.19452809$
c. $e_T(50) = 4.3 \times 10^{-4}$
$e_S(50) = 4.5 \times 10^{-8}$

37. a. $T(50) = 1.00008509$
$T(100) = 1.00002127$
b. $S(100) = 1.00000000$
c. $e_T(100) = 2.1 \times 10^{-5}$
$e_S(100) = 4.6 \times 10^{-9}$

39.

n	$T(n)$	$S(n)$	Error in $T(n)$	Error in $S(n)$
4	1820.0000	—	284	—
8	1607.7500	1537.0000	71.8	1
16	1553.9844	1536.0625	18.0	6.3×10^{-2}
32	1540.4990	1536.0039	4.50	3.9×10^{-3}

41.

n	$T(n)$	$S(n)$	Error in $T(n)$	Error in $S(n)$
4	0.46911538	—	5.3×10^{-2}	—
8	0.50826998	0.52132152	1.3×10^{-2}	2.9×10^{-4}
16	0.51825968	0.52158957	3.4×10^{-3}	1.7×10^{-5}
32	0.52076933	0.52160588	8.4×10^{-4}	1.1×10^{-6}

43. a. True **b.** False **c.** True

45.

n	$M(n)$	$T(n)$	Error in $M(n)$	Error in $T(n)$
4	0.40635058	0.40634782	1.4×10^{-6}	1.4×10^{-6}
8	0.40634920	0.40634920	7.6×10^{-10}	7.6×10^{-10}
16	0.40634920	0.40634920	6.6×10^{-13}	6.6×10^{-13}
32	0.40634920	0.40634920	8.9×10^{-16}	7.8×10^{-16}

47.

n	$M(n)$	$T(n)$	Error in $M(n)$	Error in $T(n)$
4	4.72531819	4.72507878	1.2×10^{-4}	1.2×10^{-4}
8	4.72519850	4.72519849	9.1×10^{-9}	9.1×10^{-9}
16	4.72519850	4.72519850	0.	8.9×10^{-16}
32	4.72519850	4.72519850	0.	8.9×10^{-16}

53. Approximations will vary; exact value is 38.753792 ….
55. Approximations will vary; exact value is 68.26894921 ….
57. a. Approximately 1.6×10^{11} barrels
b. Approximately 6.8×10^{10} barrels
59. a. $T(40) = 0.874799972\ldots$
b. $f''(x) = e^x \cos e^x - e^{2x} \sin e^x \quad E_T \leq \dfrac{1}{3200}$
63. Overestimate

Section 7.8 Exercises, pp. 578–581

1. The interval of integration is infinite or the integrand is unbounded on the interval of integration.
3. $\displaystyle\int_0^1 \frac{1}{\sqrt{x}}\,dx = \lim_{b\to 0^+} \int_b^1 \frac{1}{\sqrt{x}}\,dx$ **5.** 1 **7.** 1 **9.** Diverges **11.** $\frac{1}{2}$
13. $\dfrac{1}{a}$ **15.** $\dfrac{1}{(p-1)\,2^{p-1}}$ **17.** 0 **19.** $\dfrac{1}{\pi}$ **21.** $\dfrac{\pi}{4}$ **23.** $\ln 2$
25. Diverges **27.** $\dfrac{1}{4}$ **29.** $\dfrac{\pi}{3}$ **31.** $3\pi/2$ **33.** $\pi/\ln 2$ **35.** 6
37. 2 **39.** Diverges **41.** $2(e-1)$ **43.** Diverges **45.** $4 \cdot 10^{3/4}/3$
47. -4 **49.** π **51.** 2π **53.** $\dfrac{72 \cdot 2^{1/3}\,\pi}{5}$ **55.** Does not exist
57. 0.76 **59.** 10 mi **61. a.** True **b.** False **c.** False **d.** True **e.** True **63. a.** 2 **b.** 0 **65.** 0.886227 **67.** $-\frac{1}{4}$
69. $\frac{1}{2}$; $\sqrt{\pi}/4 \approx 0.443$ **71.** $1/b - 1/a$
73. a. $A(a,b) = \dfrac{e^{-ab}}{a}$, for $a > 0$ **b.** $b = g(a) = -\dfrac{1}{a}\ln 2a$
c. $b^* = -2/e$ **75. a.** $p < \frac{1}{2}$ **b.** $p < 2$ **81.** \$41,666.67
85. 20,000 hr **87. a.** $6.28 \times 10^7 m$ J **b.** 11.2 km/s **c.** ≤ 9 mm
89. a.

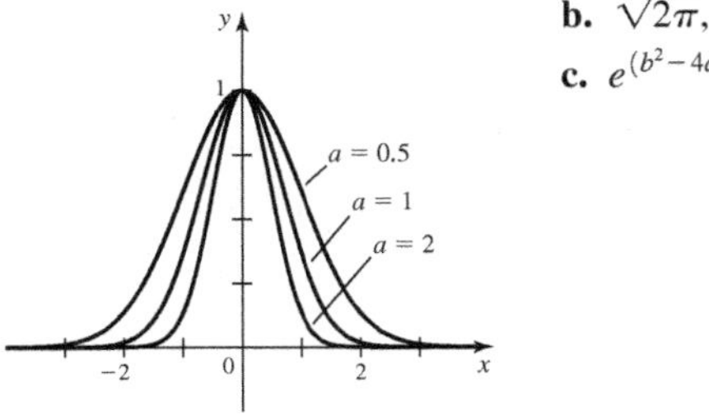

b. $\sqrt{2\pi}, \sqrt{\pi}, \sqrt{\pi/2}$
c. $e^{(b^2-4ac)/(4a)}\sqrt{\pi/a}$

95. a. π **b.** $\pi/(4e^2)$ **97.** $p > 1$ **101.** $a^a - 1$

Section 7.9 Exercises, pp. 589–592

1. Second order **3.** Two
5. Can be written in the form $g(y)y'(t) = h(t)$
7. Integrate both sides with respect to t and convert integral on left side to an integral with respect to y.
17. $y = t^3 - 2t^2 + 10t + 20$ **19.** $y = t^2 + 4\ln t + 1$
21. $y = Ce^{3t} + \frac{4}{3}$ **23.** $y = Ce^{-2x} - 2$ **25.** $y = 7e^{3t} + 2$
27. $y = 2e^{-2t} - 2$ **29. a.** $y = 150(1 - e^{-0.02t})$ **b.** 150 mg
c. $t = \dfrac{\ln 10}{0.02}$ hr ≈ 115 hr

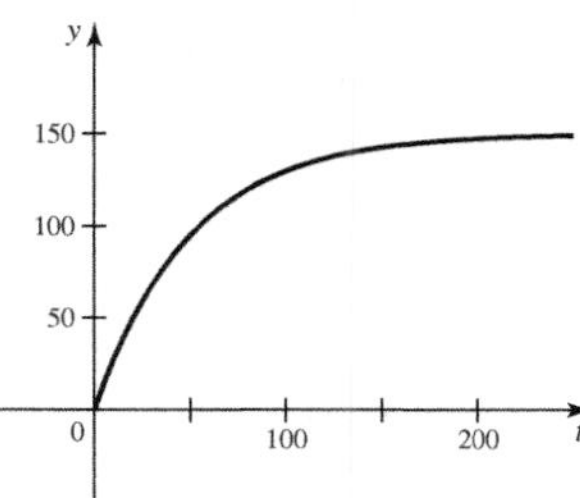

31. $y = \pm\sqrt{2t^3 + C}$ **33.** $y = -2\ln\left(\frac{1}{2}\cos t + C\right)$
35. Not separable **37.** $y = \sqrt{e^t - 1}$ **39.** $y = \ln(e^x + 2)$
41. a. $P = \dfrac{200}{3e^{-0.08t} + 1}$

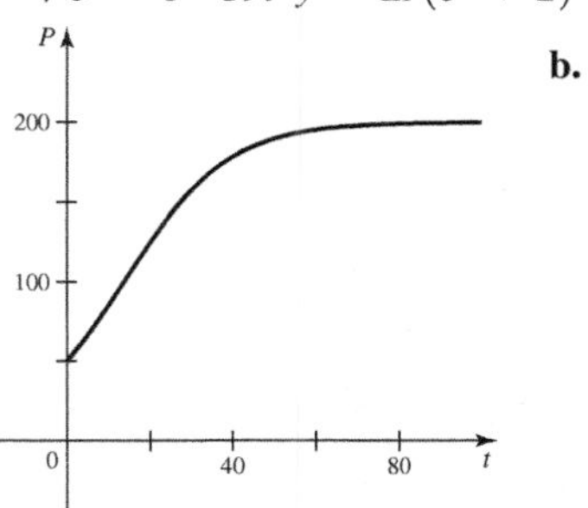

b. 200

43.

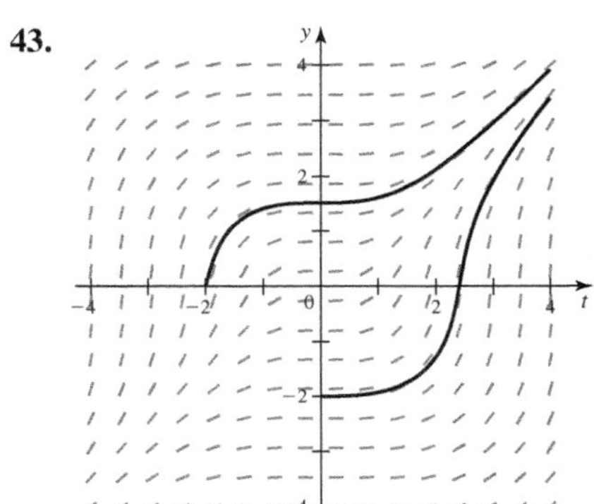

45. A–c, B–b, C–d, D–a **47.**

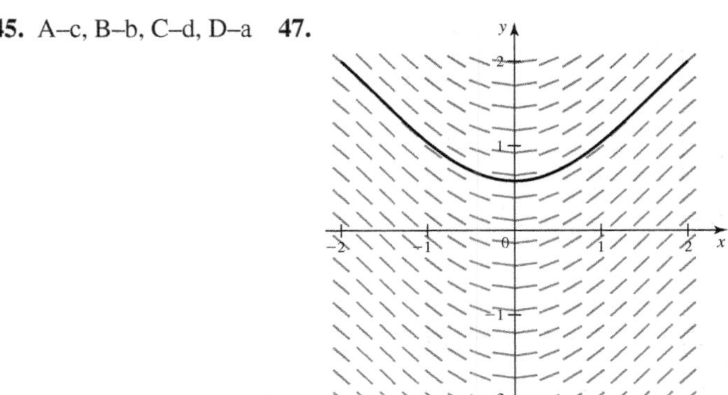

49. a. False **b.** False **c.** False **d.** True

51. a. $y = 0$ **b, c.**

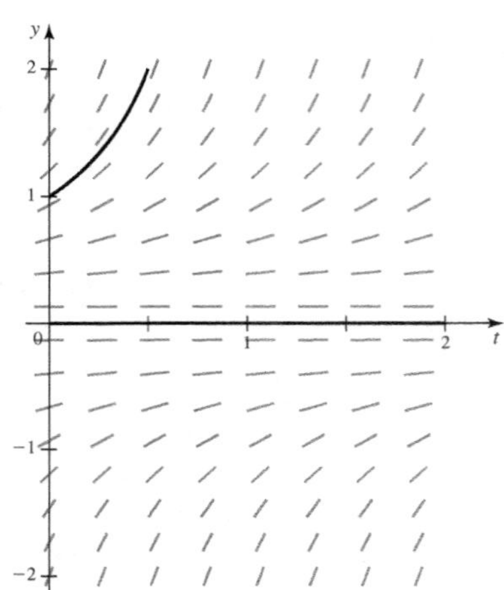

53. a. Equilibrium solutions $y = 0$ and $y = 3$

b.

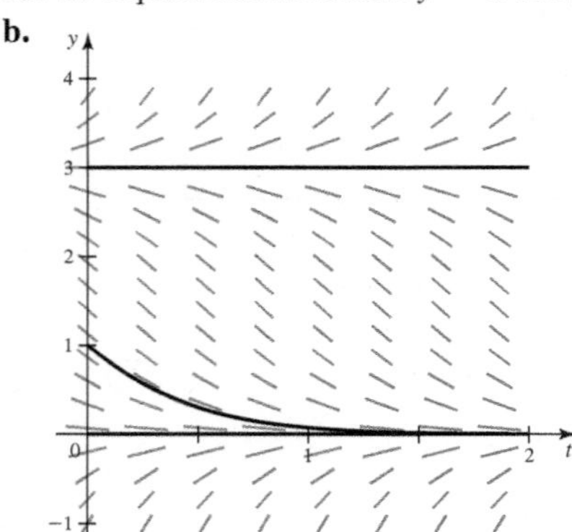

55. a. Equilibrium solutions $y = 0$, $y = 3$, and $y = -2$

b.

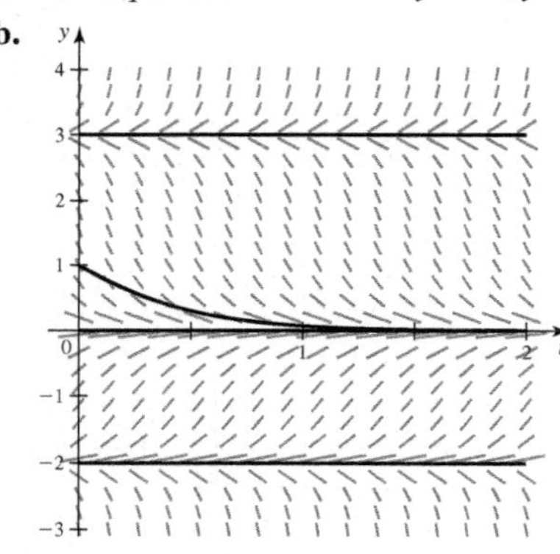

57. $p = 4e^{1-1/t} - 1$ **59.** $w = \tan^{-1}(t^2 + 1)$

61. a. $y = \dfrac{y_0}{(1 - y_0)e^{-kt} + y_0}$ **b.**

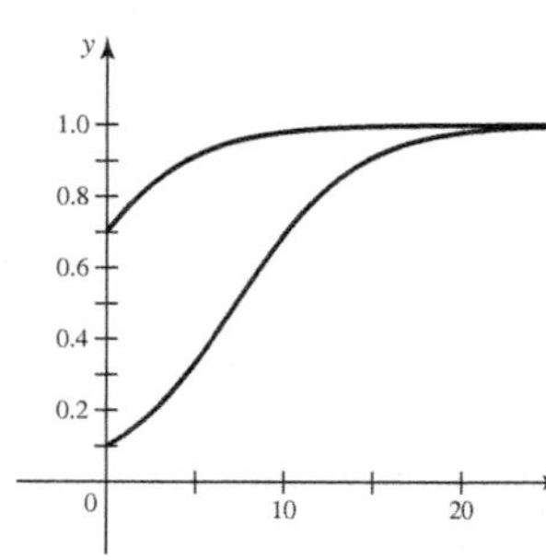

c. For any $0 < y_0 < 1$, $\lim_{t\to\infty} y(t) = 1$. Eventually, everyone knows the rumor.

63. b. $v = \dfrac{mg}{R}$ **c.** $v = \dfrac{g}{b}(1 - e^{-bt})$

d.

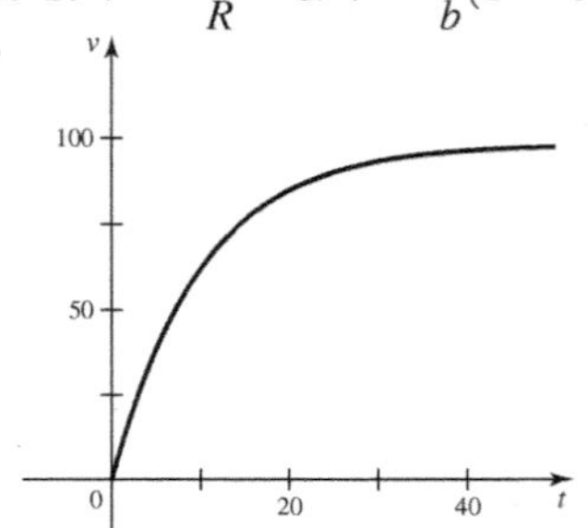

65. a. General solution $y = Ce^{-kt}$ **b.** $y = \dfrac{1}{kt + 1/y_0}$

c.

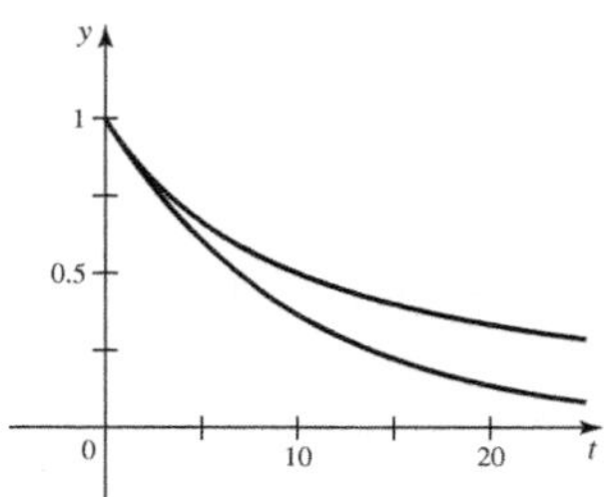

67. a. $B = 20{,}000 - 5000e^{0.05t}$; balance decreases
b. $m = \$2500$; constant balance $= \$50{,}000$

Chapter 7 Review Exercises, pp. 593–595

1. a. True **b.** False **c.** False **d.** True **e.** False
3. $2(x - 8)\sqrt{x + 4} + C$ **5.** $\pi/4$
7. $\sqrt{t - 1} - \tan^{-1}\sqrt{t - 1} + C$ **9.** $\frac{1}{3}\sqrt{x + 2}(x - 4) + C$
11. $x \cosh x - \sinh x + C$ **13.** $\frac{4}{105}$ **15.** $\frac{1}{5}\tan^5 t + C$
17. $\frac{1}{5}\sec^5\theta - \frac{1}{3}\sec^3\theta + C$ **19.** $\sqrt{3} - 1 - \pi/12$
21. $\frac{1}{3}(x^2 - 8)\sqrt{x^2 + 4} + C$ **23.** $2\ln|x| + 3\tan^{-1}(x + 1) + C$
25. $\frac{1}{x + 1} + \ln|(x + 1)(x^2 + 4)| + C$
27. $\frac{\sqrt{6}}{3}\tan^{-1}\sqrt{\frac{2x - 3}{3}} + C$
29. $\frac{1}{4}\sec^3 x \tan x + \frac{3}{8}\sec x \tan x + \frac{3}{8}\ln|\sec x + \tan x| + C$
31. 1.196288 **33. a.** $T(6) = 9.125, M(6) = 8.9375$
b. $T(12) = 9.03125, M(12) = 8.984375$ **35.** 1 **37.** $\pi/2$
39. $-\cot\theta + \csc\theta + C$ **41.** $\frac{e^x}{2}(\sin x - \cos x) + C$
43. $\frac{\theta}{2} + \frac{1}{16}\sin 8\theta + C$ **45.** $(\sec^5 z)/5 + C$
47. $(256 - 147\sqrt{3})/480$ **49.** $\sin^{-1}(x/2) + C$
51. $-\frac{1}{9y}\sqrt{9 - y^2} + C$ **53.** $\pi/9$ **55.** $-\operatorname{sech} x + C$ **57.** $\pi/3$
59. $\frac{1}{8}\ln\left|\frac{x - 5}{x + 3}\right| + C$ **61.** $\frac{\ln 2}{4} + \frac{\pi}{8}$ **63.** 3
65. $\frac{1}{3}\ln\left|\frac{x - 2}{x + 1}\right| + C$ **67.** $2(x - 2\ln|x + 2|) + C$
69. $e^{2t}/2\sqrt{1 + e^{4t}} + C$ **71.** $\pi(e - 2)$ **73.** $\frac{\pi}{2}(e^2 - 3)$
75. y-axis **77. a.** 1.603 **b.** 1.870 **c.** $b\ln b - b = a\ln a - a$
d. Decreasing **79.** $20/(3\pi)$ **81.** 1901 cars

83. a. $I(p) = \frac{1}{(p-1)^2}(1 - pe^{1-p})$ if $p \neq 1$, $I(1) = \frac{1}{2}$

b. $0, \infty$ **c.** $I(0) = 1$ **85.** 0.4054651 **87.** $n = 2$

89. a. $V_1(a) = \pi(a \ln^2 a - 2a \ln a + 2(a - 1))$

b. $V_2(a) = \frac{\pi}{2}(2a^2 \ln a - a^2 + 1)$

c. $V_2(a) > V_1(a)$ for all $a > 1$

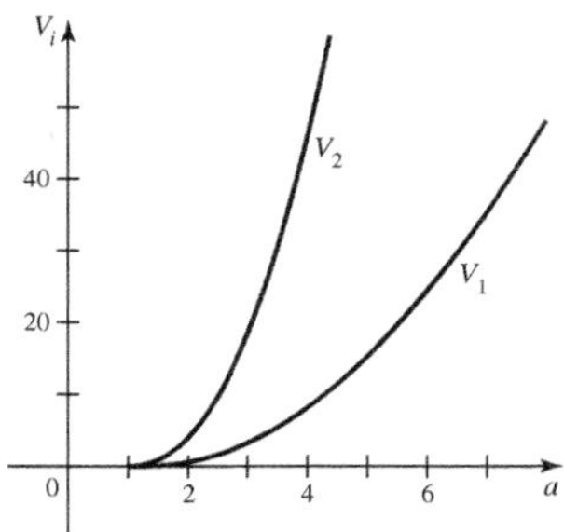

91. $a = \ln 2/(2b)$ **93.** $y = 10e^{2t} - 2$ **95.** $y = \sqrt{t + \ln t + 15}$

97. $\pi/2$

99.

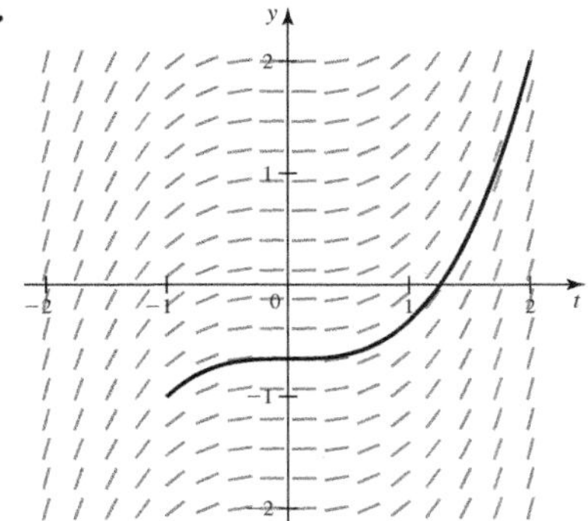

101. $t = \frac{-s - 5 \ln s + 50 + 5 \ln 50}{10}$, where $C \approx 70$

$\lim_{t \to \infty} s(t) = 0$

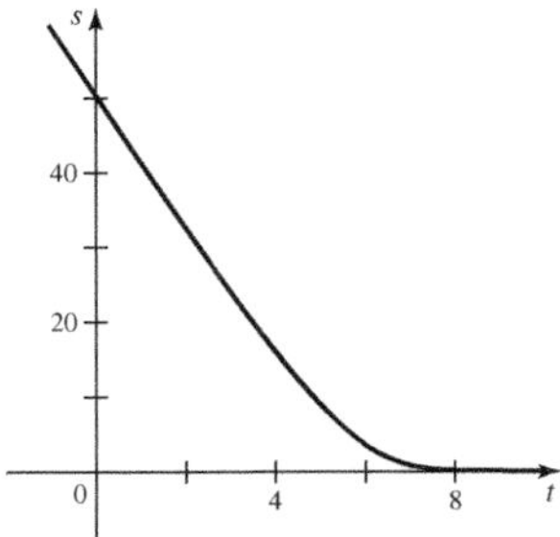

CHAPTER 8

Section 8.1 Exercises, pp. 604–606

1. A sequence is an ordered list of numbers. Example: $1, \frac{1}{3}, \frac{1}{9}, \frac{1}{27}, \ldots$ **3.** 1, 1, 2, 6, 24 **5.** Given a sequence $\{a_1, a_2, \ldots\}$, an infinite series is the sum $a_1 + a_2 + a_3 + \ldots$. Example: $\sum_{k=1}^{\infty} \frac{1}{k^2}$ **7.** 1, 5, 14, 30 **9.** $\frac{1}{10}, \frac{1}{100}, \frac{1}{1000}, \frac{1}{10{,}000}$ **11.** $-\frac{1}{2}, \frac{1}{4}, -\frac{1}{8}, \frac{1}{16}$ **13.** $\frac{4}{3}, \frac{8}{5}, \frac{16}{9}, \frac{32}{17}$ **15.** 2, 1, 0, 1 **17.** 2, 4, 8, 16 **19.** 10, 18, 42, 114 **21.** 0, 2, 15, 679

23. a. $\frac{1}{32}, \frac{1}{64}$ **b.** $a_1 = 1$, $a_{n+1} = \frac{1}{2}a_n$, for $n \geq 1$ **c.** $a_n = \frac{1}{2^{n-1}}$, for $n \geq 1$ **25. a.** $-5, 5$ **b.** $a_1 = -5$, $a_{n+1} = -a_n$ for $n \geq 1$ **c.** $a_n = (-1)^n \cdot 5$, for $n \geq 1$ **27. a.** 32, 64 **b.** $a_1 = 1, a_{n+1} = 2a_n$, for $n \geq 1$ **c.** $a_n = 2^{n-1}$, for $n \geq 1$ **29. a.** 243, 729 **b.** $a_1 = 1, a_{n+1} = 3a_n$, for $n \geq 1$ **c.** $a_n = 3^{n-1}$, for $n \geq 1$ **31.** 9, 99, 999, 9999; diverges **33.** $\frac{1}{10}, \frac{1}{100}, \frac{1}{1000}, \frac{1}{10{,}000}$; converges to 0 **35.** $-\frac{1}{2}, \frac{1}{4}, -\frac{1}{8}, \frac{1}{16}$; converges to 0 **37.** 2, 2, 2, 2; converges to 2 **39.** 54.545, 54.959, 54.996, 55.000; converges to 55 **41.** 0 **43.** Diverges **45.** 1 **47. a.** $\frac{5}{2}, \frac{9}{4}, \frac{17}{8}, \frac{33}{16}$ **b.** 2 **49.** 4 **51.** Diverges **53.** 4 **55. a.** $20, 10, 5, \frac{5}{2}$ **b.** $h_n = 20\left(\frac{1}{2}\right)^n$, for $n \geq 0$ **57. a.** $30, \frac{15}{2}, \frac{15}{8}, \frac{15}{32}$ **b.** $h_n = 30\left(\frac{1}{4}\right)^n$, for $n \geq 0$ **59.** $S_1 = 0.3$, $S_2 = 0.33$, $S_3 = 0.333$, $S_4 = 0.3333$; $\frac{1}{3}$ **61.** $S_1 = 4$, $S_2 = 4.9$, $S_3 = 4.99$, $S_4 = 4.999$; 5 **63. a.** $\frac{2}{3}, \frac{4}{5}, \frac{6}{7}, \frac{8}{9}$ **b.** $S_n = \frac{2n}{2n+1}$ **c.** $\lim_{n \to \infty} S_n = 1$ **65. a.** $\frac{1}{3}, \frac{2}{5}, \frac{3}{7}, \frac{4}{9}$ **b.** $S_n = \frac{n}{2n+1}$ **c.** $\lim_{n \to \infty} S_n = \frac{1}{2}$ **67. a.** True **b.** False **c.** True **69. a.** 40, 70, 92.5, 109.375 **b.** 160 **71. a.** 0.9, 0.99, 0.999, 0.9999 **b.** 1 **73. a.** $\frac{1}{3}, \frac{4}{9}, \frac{13}{27}, \frac{40}{81}$ **b.** $\frac{1}{2}$ **75. a.** $-1, 0, -1, 0$ **b.** Does not exist **77. a.** 0.3, 0.33, 0.333, 0.3333 **b.** $\frac{1}{3}$ **79. a.** $20, 10, 5, \frac{5}{2}, \frac{5}{4}$ **b.** $M_n = 20\left(\frac{1}{2}\right)^n$, for $n \geq 0$ **c.** $M_0 = 20$, $M_{n+1} = \frac{1}{2}M_n$, for $n \geq 0$ **d.** $\lim_{n \to \infty} a_n = 0$ **81. a.** 200, 190, 180.5, 171.475, 162.90125 **b.** $d_n = 200(0.95)^n$, for $n \geq 0$ **c.** $d_0 = 200$, $d_{n+1} = (0.95)d_n$, for $n \geq 0$ **d.** $\lim_{n \to \infty} d_n = 0$.

Section 8.2 Exercises, pp. 616–619

1. $a_n = \frac{1}{n}$, $n \geq 1$ **3.** $a_n = \frac{n}{n+1}$, $n \geq 1$ **5.** Converges for $-1 < r \leq 1$, diverges otherwise **7.** $\{e^{n/100}\}$ grows faster than $\{n^{100}\}$. **9.** 0 **11.** 3/2 **13.** 3 **15.** $\pi/2$ **17.** 0 **19.** e^2 **21.** $e^{1/4}$ **23.** 0 **25.** 1 **27.** 0 **29.** 0 **31.** 6 **33.** Does not exist **35.** Does not exist **37.** 0 **39.** 2 **41.** 0 **43.** Does not exist **45.** Converges monotonically; 0 **47.** Converges, oscillates; 0 **49.** Diverges monotonically **51.** Diverges, oscillates **53.** 0 **55.** 0 **57.** 0 **59. a.** $d_{n+1} = \frac{1}{2}d_n + 80$, $n \geq 1$ **b.** 160 mg **61. a.** \$0, \$100, \$200.75, \$302.26, \$404.53 **b.** $B_{n+1} = 1.0075B_n + 100$, for $n \geq 0$ **c.** During the 43rd month **63.** 0 **65.** Diverges **67.** 0 **69.** Given a tolerance $\varepsilon > 0$, look beyond a_N where $N > 1/\varepsilon$. **71.** Given a tolerance $\varepsilon > 0$, look beyond a_N where $N > \frac{1}{4}\sqrt{3/\varepsilon}$, provided $\varepsilon < \frac{3}{4}$ **73.** Given a tolerance $\varepsilon > 0$, look beyond a_N where $N > c/(\varepsilon b^2)$. **75. a.** True **b.** False **c.** True **d.** True **e.** False **f.** True **77.** $\{n^2 + 2n - 17\}_{n=3}^{\infty}$ **79.** 0 **81.** 1 **83.** 1 **85.** Diverges **87.** 1/2 **89.** 0 **91.** $n = 4$, $n = 6$, $n = 25$ **93. a.** $h_n = (200 + 5n)(0.65 - 0.01n) - 0.45n$, for $n \geq 0$ **b.** The profit is maximized after 8 days. **95.** 0.607 **97. b.** 1, 1.4142, 1.5538, 1.5981, 1.6119 **c.** Approx. 1.618 **e.** $\frac{1 + \sqrt{1 + 4p}}{2}$ **99. b.** 1, 2, 1.5, 1.6667, 1.6 **c.** Approx. 1.618 **e.** $\frac{a + \sqrt{a^2 + 4b}}{2}$ **101. a.** 1, 1, 2, 3, 5, 8, 13, 21, 34, 55 **b.** No **105. d.** 3 **107.** $\{a_n\}$; $n = 36$ **109.** $\{a_n\}$; $n = 19$ **111.** $a < 1$

Section 8.3 Exercises, pp. 623–626

1. The next term in the series is generated by multiplying the previous term by the constant r (the ratio of the series). Example: $2 + 1 + \frac{1}{2} + \frac{1}{4} + \cdots$ **3.** The constant r in the series $\sum_{k=0}^{\infty} ar^k$

5. No **7.** 9841 **9.** Approx. 1.1905 **11.** Approx. 0.5392

13. $\frac{1-\pi^7}{1-\pi}$ **15.** 1 **17.** $\frac{1093}{2916}$ **19.** $\frac{4}{3}$ **21.** 10 **23.** Diverges

25. $\frac{1}{e^2-1}$ **27.** $\frac{1}{7}$ **29.** $\frac{1}{500}$ **31.** $\frac{\pi}{\pi - e}$ **33.** $\frac{2500}{19}$ **35.** $\frac{10}{19}$

37. $\frac{3\pi}{\pi+1}$ **39.** $\frac{9}{460}$ **41.** $0.\overline{3} = \sum_{k=1}^{\infty} 3(0.1)^k = \frac{1}{3}$

43. $0.\overline{1} = \sum_{k=1}^{\infty} (0.1)^k = \frac{1}{9}$ **45.** $0.\overline{09} = \sum_{k=1}^{\infty} 9(0.01)^k = \frac{1}{11}$

47. $0.\overline{037} = \sum_{k=1}^{\infty} 37(0.001)^k = \frac{1}{27}$ **49.** $0.\overline{12} = \sum_{k=0}^{\infty} 0.12(0.01)^k = \frac{4}{33}$

51. $0.\overline{456} = \sum_{k=0}^{\infty} 0.456(0.001)^k = \frac{152}{333}$

53. $0.00\overline{952} = \sum_{k=0}^{\infty} 0.00952(0.001)^k = \frac{238}{24{,}975}$

55. $S_n = \frac{n}{2n+4}; \frac{1}{2}$ **57.** $S_n = \frac{1}{7} - \frac{1}{n+7}; \frac{1}{7}$

59. $S_n = \frac{1}{9} - \frac{1}{4n+1}; \frac{1}{9}$ **61.** $S_n = \ln(n+1)$; diverges

63. $S_n = \frac{1}{p+1} - \frac{1}{n+p+1}; \frac{1}{p+1}$

65. $S_n = \left(\frac{1}{\sqrt{2}} + \frac{1}{\sqrt{3}}\right) - \left(\frac{1}{\sqrt{n+2}} + \frac{1}{\sqrt{n+3}}\right); \frac{1}{\sqrt{2}} + \frac{1}{\sqrt{3}}$

67. $S_n = -\frac{n+1}{4n+3}; -\frac{1}{4}$ **69. a.** True **b.** True **c.** False **d.** True **e.** True **71.** $-\frac{2}{15}$ **73.** $\frac{1}{\ln 2}$ **75. a, b.** $\frac{4}{3}$

77. $\sum_{k=0}^{\infty} \left(\frac{1}{4}\right)^k A_1 = \frac{A_1}{1 - 1/4} = \frac{4}{3}A_1$ **79.** 462 months

81. 0 **83.** There will be twice as many children.

85. $\sqrt{\frac{20}{g}}\left(\frac{1+\sqrt{p}}{1-\sqrt{p}}\right)$ s **87. a.** $L_n = 3\left(\frac{4}{3}\right)^n$, so $\lim_{n\to\infty} L_n = \infty$ **b.** $\lim_{n\to\infty} A_n = \frac{2\sqrt{3}}{5}$

89. $R_n = S - S_n = \frac{1}{1-r} - \left(\frac{1-r^n}{1-r}\right) = \frac{r^n}{1-r}$

91. a. 60 **b.** 9 **93. a.** 13 **b.** 15 **95. a.** $1, \frac{5}{6}, \frac{2}{3}$, undefined, undefined **b.** $(-1, 1)$ **97.** Converges for x in $(-\infty, -2)$ or $(0, \infty)$; $x = \frac{1}{2}$

99. a.

r	−0.9	−0.7	−0.5	−0.2	0	0.2	0.5	0.7	0.9
$f(r)$	0.526	0.588	0.667	0.833	1	1.250	2	3.333	10

b.

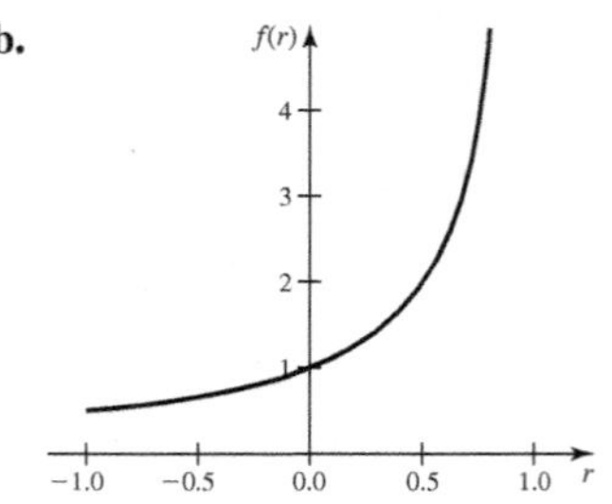

c. $\lim_{r\to 1^-} f(r) = \lim_{r\to 1^-} \frac{1}{1-r} = \infty$; $\lim_{r\to -1^+} f(r) = \lim_{r\to -1^+} \frac{1}{1-r} = \frac{1}{2}$

Section 8.4 Exercises, pp. 638–640

1. The series diverges. **3.** Yes, if the terms are positive and decreasing. **5.** Converges for $p > 1$ and diverges for $p \le 1$ **7.** $R_n = S - S_n$ **9.** Diverges **11.** Diverges **13.** Inconclusive **15.** Diverges **17.** Diverges **19.** Converges **21.** Converges **23.** Diverges **25.** Converges **27.** Test does not apply **29.** Converges **31.** Converges **33.** Diverges

35. a. $\frac{1}{5n^5}$ **b.** 3 **c.** $L_n = S_n + \frac{1}{5(n+1)^5}$; $U_n = S_n + \frac{1}{5n^5}$ **d.** $(1.017342754, 1.017343512)$ **37. a.** $\frac{3^{-n}}{\ln 3}$ **b.** 7 **c.** $L_n = S_n + \frac{3^{-n-1}}{\ln 3}$; $U_n = S_n + \frac{3^{-n}}{\ln 3}$ **d.** $(0.499996671, 0.500006947)$

39. a. $\frac{2}{\sqrt{n}}$ **b.** $4 \times 10^6 + 1$ **c.** $L_n = S_n + \frac{2}{\sqrt{n+1}}$; $U_n = S_n + \frac{2}{\sqrt{n}}$ **d.** $(2.598359182, 2.627792025)$

41. a. $\frac{1}{2n^2}$ **b.** 23 **c.** $L_n = S_n + \frac{1}{2(n+1)^2}$; $U_n = S_n + \frac{1}{2n^2}$ **d.** $(1.201664217, 1.202531986)$ **43.** $\frac{4}{11}$ **45.** -2 **47.** $\frac{113}{30}$ **49.** $\frac{17}{10}$ **51. a.** True **b.** True **c.** False **d.** False **e.** False **f.** False **53.** Converges **55.** Diverges **57.** Converges

59. a. $p > 1$ **b.** $\sum_{k=2}^{\infty} \frac{1}{k(\ln k)^2}$ converges faster.

65. $\zeta(3) \approx 1.202$, $\zeta(5) \approx 1.037$ **67.** $\frac{\pi^2}{8}$ **69. a.** $\frac{1}{2}, \frac{7}{12}, \frac{37}{60}$

71. a. $\sum_{k=2}^{n} \frac{1}{k}$ **b.** The distance can be made arbitrarily large.

Section 8.5 Exercises, pp. 647–649

1. Take the limit of the ratio of consecutive terms of the series as $n \to \infty$. The value of the limit determines whether the series converges. **3.** Find an appropriate comparison series. Then take the limit of the ratio of the terms of the given series and the comparison series as $n \to \infty$. The value of the limit determines whether the series converges. **5.** Ratio Test **7.** $S_{n+1} - S_n = a_{n+1} > 0$; therefore, $S_{n+1} > S_n$. **9.** Converges **11.** Converges **13.** Converges **15.** Diverges

17. Converges **19.** Diverges **21.** Converges **23.** Converges **25.** Converges **27.** Converges **29.** Diverges **31.** Converges **33.** Converges **35.** Diverges **37.** Diverges **39. a.** False **b.** True **c.** True **d.** True **41.** Diverges **43.** Converges **45.** Converges **47.** Diverges **49.** Diverges **51.** Converges **53.** Diverges **55.** Converges **57.** Converges **59.** Converges **61.** Diverges **63.** Converges **65.** Diverges **67.** Converges **69.** Converges **71.** $p > 1$ **73.** $p > 1$ **75.** $p < 1$ **77.** Diverges for all p **79.** Diverges if $|r| \geq 1$ **83.** $0 \leq x < 1$ **85.** $0 \leq x \leq 1$ **87.** $0 \leq x < 2$ **89. a.** e^2 **b.** 0

Section 8.6 Exercises, pp. 656–658

1. Because $S_{n+1} - S_n = (-1)^n a_{n+1}$ alternates sign **3.** Because the remainder $R_n = S - S_n$ alternates sign **5.** $|R_n| = |S - S_n| \leq |S_{n+1} - S_n| = a_{n+1}$ **7.** No; if a series of positive terms converges, if does so absolutely and not conditionally. **9.** Yes, $\sum_{k=1}^{\infty} \frac{(-1)^k}{k^2}$ has this property. **11.** Converges **13.** Diverges **15.** Converges **17.** Converges **19.** Diverges **21.** Diverges **23.** Converges **25.** Diverges **27.** Converges **29.** 10,000 **31.** 5000 **33.** 10 **35.** 3334 **37.** 6 **39.** -0.973 **41.** -0.269 **43.** -0.783 **45.** Converges conditionally **47.** Converges absolutely **49.** Converges absolutely **51.** Diverges **53.** Diverges **55.** Converges absolutely **57. a.** False **b.** True **c.** True **d.** True **e.** False **f.** True **g.** True **61.** The conditions of the Alternating Series Test are met; therefore, $\sum_{k=1}^{\infty} r^k$ converges for $-1 < r < 0$. **65.** x and y are divergent series.

Chapter 8 Review Exercises, pp. 658–660

1. a. False **b.** False **c.** True **d.** False **e.** True **f.** False **g.** False **h.** True **3.** 0 **5.** 1 **7.** $1/e$ **9.** Diverges **11. a.** $\frac{1}{3}, \frac{11}{24}, \frac{21}{40}, \frac{17}{30}$ **b.** $S_1 = \frac{1}{3}, S_n = \frac{1}{2}\left(\frac{3}{2} - \frac{1}{n+1} - \frac{1}{n+2}\right), n \geq 1$ **c.** $3/4$ **13.** Diverges **15.** 1 **17.** 3 **19.** $2/9$ **21. a.** Yes; 1.5 **b.** Convergence uncertain **c.** Appears to diverge **23.** Diverges **25.** Converges **27.** Converges **29.** Converges **31.** Converges **33.** Converges **35.** Converges **37.** Converges **39.** Diverges **41.** Diverges **43.** Converges absolutely **45.** Converges absolutely **47.** Converges absolutely **49.** Diverges **51. a.** 0 **b.** $\frac{5}{9}$ **53.** $a_k = \frac{1}{k}$ **55. a.** Yes; $\lim_{k\to\infty} a_k = 1$ **b.** No; $\lim_{k\to\infty} a_k \neq 0$ **57.** $\lim_{k\to\infty} a_k = 0$, $\lim_{n\to\infty} S_n = 8$ **59.** $0 < p \leq 1$ **61.** 0.25; 6.5×10^{-15} **63.** 100 **65. a.** 803 m, 1283 m, $2000(1 - 0.95^N)$ m **b.** 2000 m **67. a.** $\frac{\pi}{2^{n-1}}$ **b.** 2π **69. a.** $B_{n+1} = 1.0025B_n + 100, B_0 = 100$ **b.** $B_n = 40{,}000(1.0025^{n+1} - 1)$ **71. a.** $T_1 = \frac{\sqrt{3}}{16}, T_2 = \frac{7\sqrt{3}}{64}$ **b.** $T_n = \frac{\sqrt{3}}{4}\left(1 - \left(\frac{3}{4}\right)^n\right)$ **c.** $\lim_{n\to\infty} T_n = \frac{\sqrt{3}}{4}$ **d.** 0

CHAPTER 9

Section 9.1 Exercises, pp. 672–675

1. $f(0) = p_2(0), f'(0) = p_2'(0)$, and $f''(0) = p_2''(0)$ **3.** 1, 1.05, 1.04875 **5.** $R_n(x) = f(x) - p_n(x)$ **7. a.** $p_1(x) = 8 + 12(x - 1)$ **b.** $p_2(x) = 8 + 12(x - 1) + 3(x - 1)^2$ **c.** 9.2; 9.23 **9. a.** $p_1(x) = 1 - x$ **b.** $p_2(x) = 1 - x + \frac{x^2}{2}$ **c.** 0.8, 0.82 **11. a.** $p_1(x) = 1 - x$ **b.** $p_2(x) = 1 - x + x^2$ **c.** 0.95, 0.9525 **13. a.** $p_1(x) = 2 + \frac{1}{12}(x - 8)$ **b.** $p_2(x) = 2 + \frac{1}{12}(x - 8) - \frac{1}{288}(x - 8)^2$ **c.** $1.958\overline{3}$, 1.95747 **15. a.** $p_0(x) = 1, p_1(x) = 1, p_2(x) = 1 - \frac{x^2}{2}$
b.

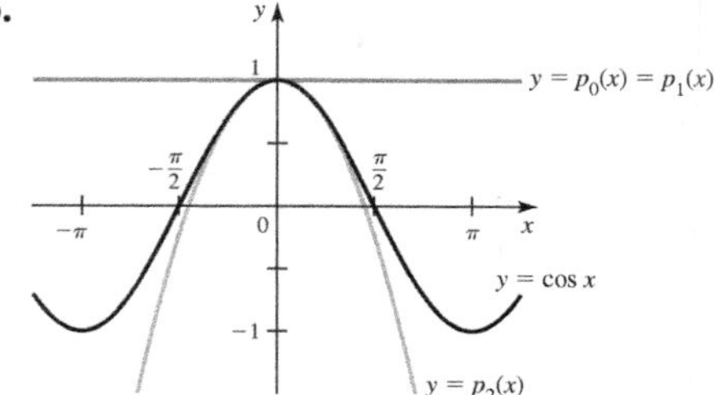

17. a. $p_0(x) = 0, p_1(x) = -x, p_2(x) = -x - \frac{x^2}{2}$
b.

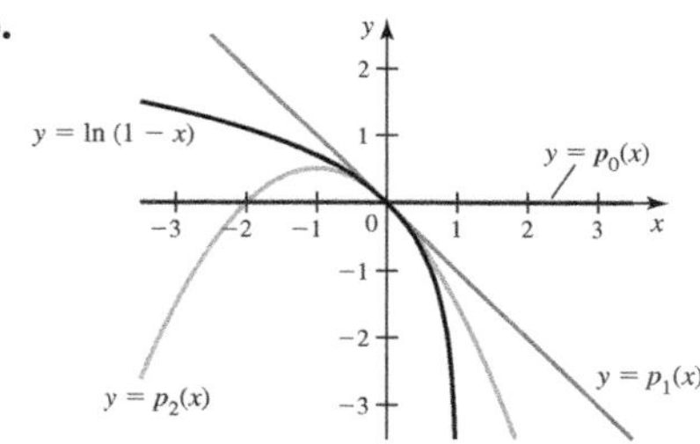

19. a. $p_0(x) = 0, p_1(x) = x, p_2(x) = x$
b.

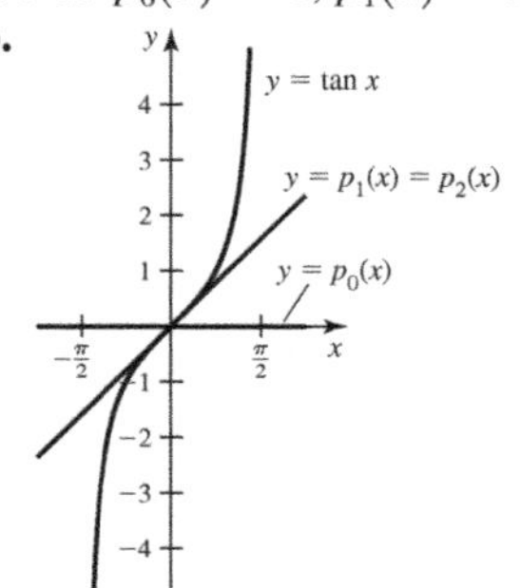

21. a. $p_0(x) = 1, p_1(x) = 1 - 3x, p_2(x) = 1 - 3x + 6x^2$
b.

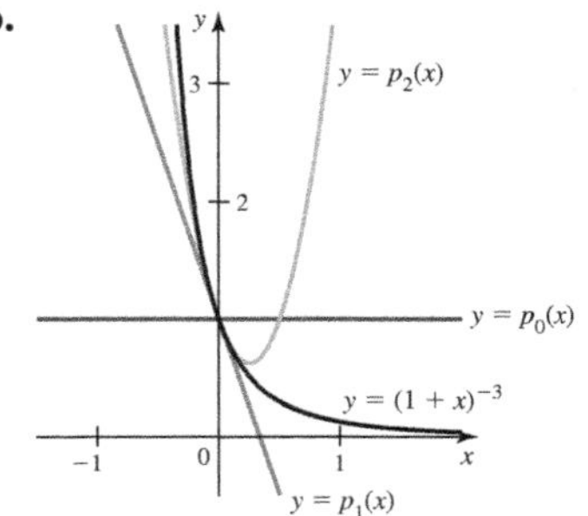

23. a. 1.0247 **b.** 7.6×10^{-6} **25. a.** 0.9624 **b.** 1.5×10^{-4}
27. a. 0.8613 **b.** 5.4×10^{-4}
29. a. $p_0(x) = 1, p_1(x) = 1 + 3(x - 1)$,
$p_2(x) = 1 + 3(x - 1) + 3(x - 1)^2$
b.

31. a. $p_0(x) = \frac{\sqrt{2}}{2}, p_1(x) = \frac{\sqrt{2}}{2} + \frac{\sqrt{2}}{2}\left(x - \frac{\pi}{4}\right)$,

$p_2(x) = \frac{\sqrt{2}}{2} + \frac{\sqrt{2}}{2}\left(x - \frac{\pi}{4}\right) - \frac{\sqrt{2}}{4}\left(x - \frac{\pi}{4}\right)^2$

b.

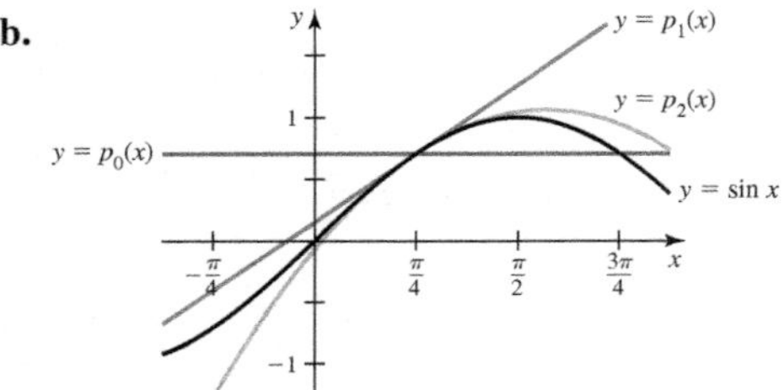

33. a. $p_0(x) = 3, p_1(x) = 3 + \frac{(x - 9)}{6}$,

$p_2(x) = 3 + \frac{(x - 9)}{6} - \frac{(x - 9)^2}{216}$

b.

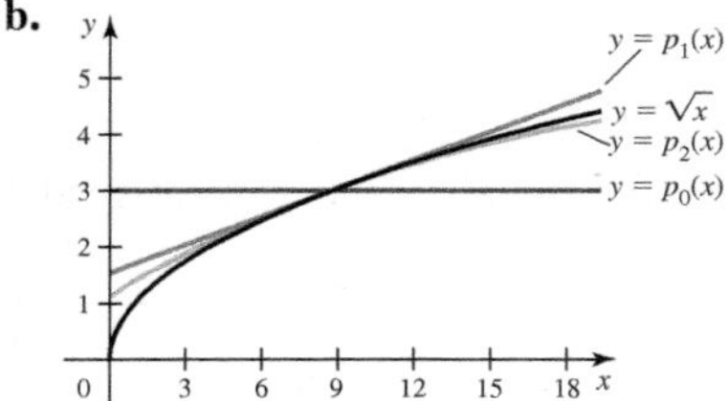

35. a. $p_0(x) = 1, p_1(x) = 1 + \frac{x - e}{e}$,

$p_2(x) = 1 + \frac{x - e}{e} - \frac{(x - e)^2}{2e^2}$

b.

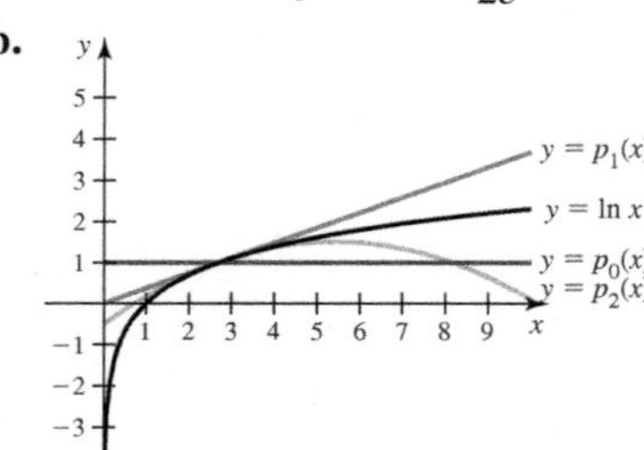

37. a. $p_0(x) = 2 + \frac{\pi}{4}, p_1(x) = 2 + \frac{\pi}{4} + \frac{5}{2}(x - 1)$,

$p_2(x) = 2 + \frac{\pi}{4} + \frac{5}{2}(x - 1) + \frac{3}{4}(x - 1)^2$

b.

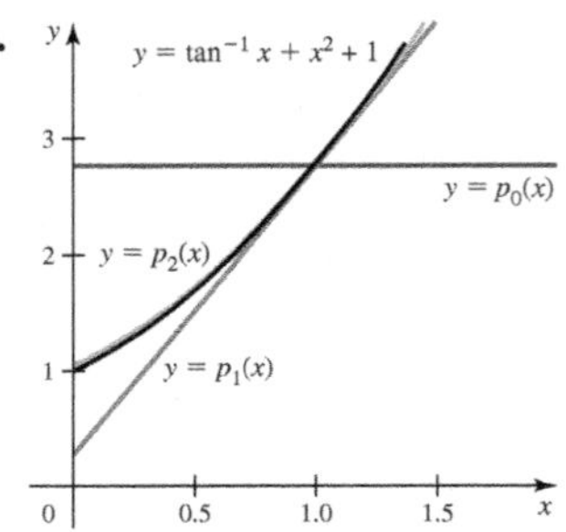

39. a. 1.12749 **b.** 8.9×10^{-6} **41. a.** -0.100333 **b.** 1.3×10^{-6}
43. a. 1.029564 **b.** 4.9×10^{-7} **45. a.** 10.04987563
b. 3.9×10^{-9} **47. a.** 0.520833 **b.** 2.6×10^{-4}

49. $R_n(x) = \frac{\sin^{(n+1)}(c)}{(n + 1)!}x^{n+1}$, for c between x and 0.

51. $R_n(x) = \frac{(-1)^{n+1}e^{-c}}{(n + 1)!}x^{n+1}$, for c between x and 0.

53. $R_n(x) = \frac{\sin^{(n+1)}(c)}{(n + 1)!}\left(x - \frac{\pi}{2}\right)^{n+1}$, for c between x and $\frac{\pi}{2}$.

55. 2.0×10^{-5} **57.** 1.6×10^{-5} $(e^{0.25} < 2)$ **59.** 2.6×10^{-4}
61. With $n = 4$, $|\text{error}| \le 2.5 \times 10^{-3}$
63. With $n = 2$, $|\text{error}| \le 4.2 \times 10^{-2}$ $(e^{0.5} < 2)$
65. With $n = 2$, $|\text{error}| \le 5.4 \times 10^{-3}$
67. 4 **69.** 3 **71.** 1 **73. a.** False **b.** True **c.** True
d. True **75. a.** C **b.** E **c.** A **d.** D **e.** B **f.** F
77. a. 0.1; 1.7×10^{-4} **b.** 0.2; 1.3×10^{-3}
79. a. 0.995; 4.2×10^{-6} **b.** 0.98; 6.7×10^{-5}
81. a. 1.05; 1.3×10^{-3} **b.** 1.1; 5×10^{-3}
83. a. 1.1; 10^{-2} **b.** 1.2; 4×10^{-2}
85. a.

x	$\lvert\sec x - p_2(x)\rvert$	$\lvert\sec x - p_4(x)\rvert$
-0.2	3.4×10^{-4}	5.5×10^{-6}
-0.1	2.1×10^{-5}	8.5×10^{-8}
0.0	0	0
0.1	2.1×10^{-5}	8.5×10^{-8}
0.2	3.4×10^{-4}	5.5×10^{-6}

b. The error increases as $|x|$ increases.

87. a.

x	$\lvert e^{-x} - p_1(x)\rvert$	$\lvert e^{-x} - p_2(x)\rvert$
-0.2	2.1×10^{-2}	1.4×10^{-3}
-0.1	5.2×10^{-3}	1.7×10^{-4}
0.0	0	0
0.1	4.8×10^{-3}	1.6×10^{-4}
0.2	1.9×10^{-2}	1.3×10^{-3}

b. The error increases as $|x|$ increases.

89. a.

x	$\lvert\tan x - p_1(x)\rvert$	$\lvert\tan x - p_3(x)\rvert$
-0.2	2.7×10^{-3}	4.3×10^{-5}
-0.1	3.3×10^{-4}	1.3×10^{-6}
0.0	0	0
0.1	3.3×10^{-4}	1.3×10^{-6}
0.2	2.7×10^{-3}	4.3×10^{-5}

b. The error increases as $|x|$ increases. **91.** Centered at $x = 0$ for all n **93. a.** $y = f(a) + f'(a)(x - a)$

95. a. $p_5(x) = x - \frac{x^3}{6} + \frac{x^5}{120}$;

$q_5(x) = -(x - \pi) + \frac{1}{6}(x - \pi)^3 - \frac{1}{120}(x - \pi)^5$

b.

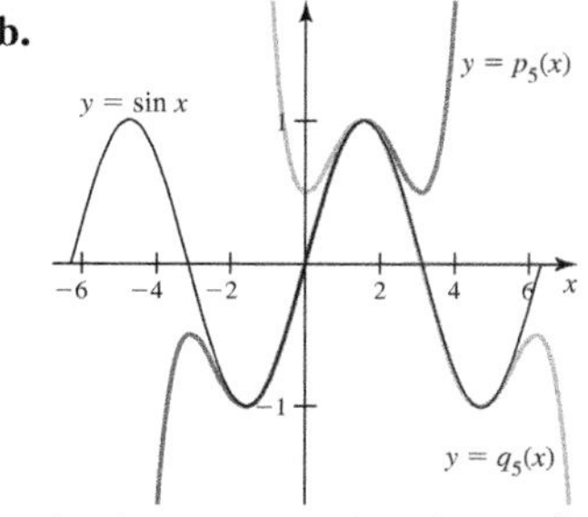

p_5 is a better approximation on $[-\pi, \pi/2)$; q_5 is a better approximation on $(\pi/2, 2\pi]$.

c.

x	$\lvert\sin x - p_5(x)\rvert$	$\lvert\sin x - q_5(x)\rvert$
$\pi/4$	3.6×10^{-5}	7.4×10^{-2}
$\pi/2$	4.5×10^{-3}	4.5×10^{-3}
$3\pi/4$	7.4×10^{-2}	3.6×10^{-5}
$5\pi/4$	2.3	3.6×10^{-5}
$7\pi/4$	20	7.4×10^{-2}

d. p_5 is a better approximation at $x = \pi/4$; at $x = \pi/2$ the errors are equal.

97. a. $p_1(x) = 6 + \frac{1}{12}(x - 36)$; $q_1(x) = 7 + \frac{1}{14}(x - 49)$

b.

x	$\lvert\sqrt{x} - p_1(x)\rvert$	$\lvert\sqrt{x} - q_1(x)\rvert$
37	5.7×10^{-4}	6.0×10^{-2}
39	5.0×10^{-3}	4.1×10^{-2}
41	1.4×10^{-2}	2.5×10^{-2}
43	2.6×10^{-2}	1.4×10^{-2}
45	4.2×10^{-2}	6.1×10^{-3}
47	6.1×10^{-2}	1.5×10^{-3}

c. p_1 is a better approximation at $x = 37, 39, 41$.

Section 9.2 Exercises, pp. 682–684

1. $c_0 + c_1x + c_2x^2 + c_3x^3$ **3.** Ratio and Root Tests **5.** The radius of convergence does not change. The interval of convergence may change. **7.** $|x| < \frac{1}{4}$ **9.** $R = \frac{1}{2}; (-\frac{1}{2}, \frac{1}{2})$ **11.** $R = 1; [0, 2)$ **13.** $R = 0; \{x: x = 0\}$ **15.** $R = \infty; (-\infty, \infty)$ **17.** $R = 3; (-3, 3)$ **19.** $R = \infty; (-\infty, \infty)$ **21.** $R = \infty; (-\infty, \infty)$

23. $R = \sqrt{3}; (-\sqrt{3}, \sqrt{3})$ **25.** $R = 1; (0, 2)$ **27.** $R = \infty; (-\infty, \infty)$ **29.** $\sum_{k=0}^{\infty}(3x)^k; (-\frac{1}{3}, \frac{1}{3})$

31. $2\sum_{k=0}^{\infty}x^{k+3}; (-1, 1)$ **33.** $4\sum_{k=0}^{\infty}x^{k+12}; (-1, 1)$

35. $-\sum_{k=1}^{\infty}\frac{(3x)^k}{k}; [-\frac{1}{3}, \frac{1}{3})$ **37.** $-\sum_{k=1}^{\infty}\frac{x^{k+1}}{k}; [-1, 1)$

39. $-2\sum_{k=1}^{\infty}\frac{x^{k+6}}{k}; [-1, 1)$ **41.** $g(x) = 2\sum_{k=1}^{\infty}k(2x)^{k-1}; (-\frac{1}{2}, \frac{1}{2})$

43. $g(x) = \sum_{k=3}^{\infty}\frac{k(k-1)(k-2)}{6}x^{k-3}; (-1, 1)$

45. $g(x) = -\sum_{k=1}^{\infty}\frac{3^kx^k}{k}; [-\frac{1}{3}, \frac{1}{3})$ **47.** $\sum_{k=0}^{\infty}(-x^2)^k; (-1, 1)$

49. $\sum_{k=0}^{\infty}\left(-\frac{x}{3}\right)^k; (-3, 3)$ **51.** $\ln 2 - \frac{1}{2}\sum_{k=1}^{\infty}\frac{x^{2k}}{k4^k}; (-2, 2)$

53. a. True **b.** True **c.** True **d.** True **55.** e

57. $\sum_{k=0}^{\infty}\frac{(-1)^kx^k}{k+1}$ **59.** $\sum_{k=1}^{\infty}\frac{(-x^2)^k}{k!}$ **61.** $|x - a| < R$

63. $f(x) = \frac{1}{3 - \sqrt{x}}; 1 < x < 9$ **65.** $f(x) = \frac{e^x}{e^x - 1}; 0 < x < \infty$

67. $f(x) = \frac{3}{4 - x^2}; -2 < x < 2$ **69.** $\sum_{k=0}^{\infty}\frac{(-x)^k}{k!}; -\infty < x < \infty$

71. $\sum_{k=0}^{\infty}\frac{(-3x)^k}{k!}; -\infty < x < \infty$

73. $\lim_{k\to\infty}\left|\frac{c_{k+1}x^{k+1}}{c_kx^k}\right| = \lim_{k\to\infty}\left|\frac{c_{k+1}x^{k+m+1}}{c_kx^{k+m}}\right|$, so by the Ratio Test, the two series have the same radius of convergence.

75. a. $f(x)\cdot g(x) = c_0d_0 + (c_0d_1 + c_1d_0)x + (c_0d_2 + c_1d_1 + c_2d_0)x^2 + \cdots$. **b.** $\sum_{k=0}^{n}c_kd_{n-k}$ **77. b.** $n = 112$

Section 9.3 Exercises, pp. 694–696

1. The nth Taylor polynomial is the nth partial sum of the corresponding Taylor series. **3.** Calculate $c_k = \frac{f^{(k)}(a)}{k!}$ for $k = 0, 1, 2, \ldots$.

5. Replace x with x^2 in the Taylor series for $f(x)$; $|x| < 1$.

7. The Taylor series for a function f converges to f on an interval if, for all x in the interval, $\lim_{n\to\infty}R_n(x) = 0$, where $R_n(x)$ is the remainder at x. **9. a.** $1 - x + \frac{x^2}{2!} - \frac{x^3}{3!}$ **b.** $\sum_{k=0}^{\infty}\frac{(-1)^kx^k}{k!}$ **c.** $(-\infty, \infty)$

11. a. $1 - x^2 + x^4 - x^6$ **b.** $\sum_{k=0}^{n}(-1)^kx^{2k}$ **c.** $(-1, 1)$

13. a. $1 + 2x + \frac{(2x)^2}{2!} + \frac{(2x)^3}{3!}$ **b.** $\sum_{k=0}^{\infty}\frac{(2x)^k}{k!}$ **c.** $(-\infty, \infty)$

15. a. $\frac{x}{2} - \frac{x^3}{3\cdot 2^3} + \frac{x^5}{5\cdot 2^5} - \frac{x^7}{7\cdot 2^7}$ **b.** $\sum_{k=0}^{\infty}\frac{(-1)^kx^{2k+1}}{(2k+1)2^{2k+1}}$ **c.** $[-2, 2]$

17. a. $1 + (\ln 3)x + \frac{\ln^2 3}{2}x^2 + \frac{\ln^3 3}{6}x^3$ **b.** $\sum_{k=0}^{\infty}\frac{\ln^k 3}{k!}x^k$ **c.** $(-\infty, \infty)$

19. a. $1 + \frac{(3x)^2}{2} + \frac{(3x)^4}{24} + \frac{(3x)^6}{720}$ **b.** $\sum_{k=0}^{\infty}\frac{(3x)^{2k}}{(2k)!}$ **c.** $(-\infty, \infty)$

21. a. $1 - \frac{(x - \pi/2)^2}{2!} + \frac{(x - \pi/2)^4}{4!} - \frac{(x - \pi/2)^6}{6!}$

b. $\sum_{k=0}^{\infty} \frac{(-1)^k}{(2k)!}(x - \pi/2)^{2k}$

23. a. $1 - (x-1) + (x-1)^2 - (x-1)^3$
b. $\sum_{k=0}^{\infty} (-1)^k (x-1)^k$

25. a. $\ln 3 + \frac{(x-3)}{3} - \frac{(x-3)^2}{3^2 \cdot 2} + \frac{(x-3)^3}{3^3 \cdot 3}$
b. $\ln 3 + \sum_{k=1}^{\infty} \frac{(-1)^{k+1}(x-3)^k}{k3^k}$

27. a. $2 + 2(\ln 2)(x-1) + (\ln^2 2)(x-1)^2 + \frac{\ln^3 2}{3}(x-1)^3$
b. $\sum_{k=0}^{\infty} \frac{2(x-1)^k \ln^k 2}{k!}$ **29.** $x^2 - \frac{x^4}{2} + \frac{x^6}{3} - \frac{x^8}{4}$

31. $1 + 2x + 4x^2 + 8x^3$ **33.** $1 + \frac{x}{2} + \frac{x^2}{6} + \frac{x^3}{24}$

35. $1 - x^4 + x^8 - x^{12}$ **37.** $x^2 + \frac{x^6}{6} + \frac{x^{10}}{120} + \frac{x^{14}}{5040}$

39. a. $1 - 2x + 3x^2 - 4x^3$ **b.** 0.826
41. a. $1 + \frac{1}{4}x - \frac{3}{32}x^2 + \frac{7}{128}x^3$ **b.** 1.029
43. a. $1 - \frac{2}{3}x + \frac{5}{9}x^2 - \frac{40}{81}x^3$ **b.** 0.895

45. $1 + \frac{x^2}{2} - \frac{x^4}{8} + \frac{x^6}{16}; [-1, 1]$ **47.** $3 - \frac{3x}{2} - \frac{3x^2}{8} - \frac{3x^3}{16}; [-1, 1]$

49. $a + \frac{x^2}{2a} - \frac{x^4}{8a^3} + \frac{x^6}{16a^5}; |x| \le a$

51. $1 - 8x + 48x^2 - 256x^3$ **53.** $\frac{1}{16} - \frac{x^2}{32} + \frac{3x^4}{256} - \frac{x^6}{256}$

55. $\frac{1}{9} - \frac{2}{9}\left(\frac{4x}{3}\right) + \frac{3}{9}\left(\frac{4x}{3}\right)^2 - \frac{4}{9}\left(\frac{4x}{3}\right)^3$

57. $R_n(x) = \frac{f^{(n+1)}(c)}{(n+1)!}x^{n+1}$, where c is between 0 and x and $f^{(n+1)}(c) = \pm \sin c$ or $\pm \cos c$. Therefore, $|R_n(x)| \le \frac{|x|^{n+1}}{(n+1)!} \to 0$ as $n \to \infty$, for $-\infty < x < \infty$. **59.** $R_n(x) = \frac{f^{(n+1)}(c)}{(n+1)!}x^{n+1}$, where c is between 0 and x and $f^{(n+1)}(c) = (-1)^n e^{-c}$. Therefore, $|R_n(x)| \le \frac{|x|^{n+1}}{e^c(n+1)!} \to 0$, as $n \to \infty$, for $-\infty < x < \infty$.

61. a. False **b.** True **c.** False **d.** False **e.** True
63. a. $1 + \frac{x^2}{2!} + \frac{x^4}{4!} + \frac{x^6}{6!}$ **b.** $R = \infty$
65. a. $1 - \frac{2}{3}x^2 + \frac{5}{9}x^4 - \frac{40}{81}x^6$ **b.** $R = 1$
67. a. $1 - \frac{1}{2}x^2 - \frac{1}{8}x^4 - \frac{1}{16}x^6$ **b.** $R = 1$
69. a. $1 - 2x^2 + 3x^4 - 4x^6$ **b.** $R = 1$

71. 3.9149 **73.** 1.8989 **79.** $\sum_{k=0}^{\infty}\left(\frac{x-4}{2}\right)^k$

81. $\frac{1 \cdot 3 \cdot 5 \cdot 7}{2 \cdot 4 \cdot 6 \cdot 8}x^4, \frac{-1 \cdot 3 \cdot 5 \cdot 7 \cdot 9}{2 \cdot 4 \cdot 6 \cdot 8 \cdot 10}x^5$ **83.** Use three terms of the Taylor series for $\cos x$ centered at $a = \pi/4$; 0.766
85. Use six terms of the Taylor series for $\sqrt[3]{x}$ centered at $a = 64$; 4.362 **87. a.** Use three terms of the Taylor series for $\sqrt[3]{125 + x}$ centered at $a = 0$; 5.03968 **b.** Use three terms of the Taylor series for $\sqrt[3]{x}$ centered at $a = 125$; 5.03968 **c.** Yes

Section 9.4 Exercises, pp. 702–704

1. Replace f and g with their Taylor series centered at a and evaluate the limit. **3.** Substitute $x = -0.6$ into the Taylor series for e^x centered at 0. Because the resulting series is an alternating series, the error can be estimated. **5.** $f'(x) = \sum_{k=1}^{\infty} kc_k x^{k-1}$ **7.** 1 **9.** $\frac{1}{2}$

11. 2 **13.** $\frac{2}{3}$ **15.** $\frac{1}{3}$ **17.** $\frac{3}{5}$ **19.** $-\frac{8}{5}$ **21.** 1 **23.** $\frac{3}{4}$

25. a. $1 + x + \frac{x^2}{2!} + \cdots + \frac{x^n}{n!} + \cdots$ **b.** e^x **c.** $-\infty < x < \infty$

27. a. $1 - x + x^2 - \cdots (-1)^{n-1}x^{n-1} + \cdots$ **b.** $\frac{1}{1+x}$ **c.** $|x| < 1$

29. a. $-2 + 4x - 8 \cdot \frac{x^2}{2!} + \cdots + (-2)^n \frac{x^{n-1}}{(n-1)!} + \cdots$
b. $-2e^{-2x}$ **c.** $-\infty < x < \infty$ **31. a.** $1 - x^2 + x^4 - \cdots$
b. $\frac{1}{1+x^2}$ **c.** $-1 < x < 1$

33. a. $2 + 2t + \frac{2t^2}{2!} + \cdots + \frac{2t^n}{n!} + \cdots$ **b.** $y(t) = 2e^t$

35. a. $2 + 16t + 24t^2 + 24t^3 + \cdots + \frac{3^{n-1} \cdot 16}{n!}t^n + \cdots$
b. $y(t) = \frac{16}{3}e^{3t} - \frac{10}{3}$ **37.** 0.2448 **39.** 0.6958

41. $\frac{0.35^2}{2} - \frac{0.35^4}{12} \approx 0.0600$ **43.** 0.4994

45. $1 + 2 + \frac{2^2}{2!} + \frac{2^3}{3!}$ **47.** $1 - 2 + \frac{2}{3} - \frac{4}{45}$ **49.** $\frac{1}{2} - \frac{1}{8} + \frac{1}{24} - \frac{1}{64}$

51. $e - 1$ **53.** $\sum_{k=1}^{\infty} \frac{(-1)^{k+1}x^k}{k}$ for $-1 < x \le 1$; ln 2

55. $\frac{2}{2-x}$ **57.** $\frac{4}{4+x^2}$ **59.** $-\ln(1-x)$ **61.** $-\frac{3x^2}{(3+x)^2}$

63. $\frac{6x^2}{(3-x)^3}$ **65. a.** False **b.** False **c.** True **67.** $\frac{a}{b}$ **69.** $e^{-1/6}$

71. $f^{(3)}(0) = 0$; $f^{(4)}(0) = 4e$ **73.** $f^{(3)}(0) = 2$; $f^{(4)}(0) = 0$
75. 2 **77. a.** 1.575 using four terms
b. At least three **c.** More terms would be needed.
79. a. $S'(x) = \sin x^2$; $C'(x) = \cos x^2$
b. $\frac{x^3}{3} - \frac{x^7}{7 \cdot 3!} + \frac{x^{11}}{11 \cdot 5!} - \frac{x^{15}}{15 \cdot 7!}; x - \frac{x^5}{5 \cdot 2!} + \frac{x^9}{9 \cdot 4!} - \frac{x^{13}}{13 \cdot 6!}$
c. $S(0.05) \approx 0.00004166664807$; $C(-0.25) \approx -0.2499023614$
d. 1 **e.** 2 **81. a.** $1 - \frac{x^2}{4} + \frac{x^4}{64} - \frac{x^6}{2304}$ **b.** $-\infty < x < \infty, R = \infty$

83. a. The Maclaurin series for $\cos x$ consists of even powers of x, which are even functions. **b.** The Maclaurin series for $\sin x$ consists of odd powers of x, which are odd functions.

Chapter 9 Review Exercises, pp. 705–706

1. a. True **b.** False **c.** True **d.** True **3.** $p_2(x) = 1$

5. $p_3(x) = x - \frac{x^2}{2} + \frac{x^3}{3}$ **7.** $p_2(x) = (x-1) - \frac{(x-1)^2}{2}$

9. $p_3(x) = \frac{5}{4} + \frac{3}{4}(x - \ln 2) + \frac{5}{8}(x - \ln 2)^2 + \frac{1}{8}(x - \ln 2)^3$

11. a. $p_2(x) = 1 + x + \frac{x^2}{2}$

b.

n	$p_n(x)$	Error
0	1	7.7×10^{-2}
1	0.92	3.1×10^{-3}
2	0.9232	8.4×10^{-5}

13. a. $p_2(x) = \frac{\sqrt{2}}{2} + \frac{\sqrt{2}}{2}\left(x - \frac{\pi}{4}\right) - \frac{\sqrt{2}}{4}\left(x - \frac{\pi}{4}\right)^2$

b.

n	$p_n(x)$	Error
0	0.7071	1.2×10^{-1}
1	0.5960	8.2×10^{-3}
2	0.5873	4.7×10^{-4}

15. $|R_3| < \frac{\pi^4}{4!}$ **17.** $(-\infty, \infty), R = \infty$ **19.** $(-\infty, \infty), R = \infty$
21. $(-9, 9), R = 9$ **23.** $[-4, 0), R = 2$ **25.** $\sum_{k=0}^{\infty} x^{2k}; (-1, 1)$
27. $\sum_{k=0}^{\infty}(-5x)^k; \left(-\frac{1}{5}, \frac{1}{5}\right)$ **29.** $\sum_{k=1}^{\infty} k(10x)^{k-1}; \left(-\frac{1}{10}, \frac{1}{10}\right)$
31. $1 + 3x + \frac{9x^2}{2!}; \sum_{k=0}^{\infty} \frac{(3x)^k}{k!}$
33. $-(x - \pi/2) + \frac{(x - \pi/2)^3}{3!} - \frac{(x - \pi/2)^5}{5!}$; $\sum_{k=0}^{\infty}(-1)^{k+1}\frac{(x - \pi/2)^{2k+1}}{(2k + 1)!}$
35. $4x - \frac{(4x)^3}{3} + \frac{(4x)^5}{5}; \sum_{k=0}^{\infty} \frac{(-1)^k(4x)^{2k+1}}{2k + 1}$
37. $1 + \frac{9x^2}{2!} + \frac{81x^4}{4!}; \sum_{k=0}^{\infty} \frac{(3x)^{2k}}{(2k)!}$ **39.** $1 + \frac{x}{3} - \frac{x^2}{9} + \cdots$
41. $1 - \frac{3}{2}x + \frac{3}{2}x^2 - \cdots$ **43.** $R_n(x) = \frac{(-1)^{n+1}e^{-c}}{(n + 1)!}x^{n+1}$, where c is between 0 and x. $\lim_{n\to\infty} |R_n(x)| = \lim_{n\to\infty} \frac{|x^{n+1}|}{e^{|x|}} \cdot \frac{1}{(n + 1)!} = 0$ for $-\infty < x < \infty$. **45.** $R_n(x) = \frac{(-1)^n(1 + c)^{-(n+1)}}{n + 1}x^{n+1}$ where c is between 0 and x. $\lim_{n\to\infty} |R_n(x)| = \lim_{n\to\infty}\left(\left(\frac{|x|}{1 + c}\right)^{n+1} \cdot \frac{1}{n + 1}\right) < \lim_{n\to\infty}\left(1^{n+1} \cdot \frac{1}{n + 1}\right) = 0$, for $|x| \le \frac{1}{2}$. **47.** $\frac{1}{24}$ **49.** $\frac{1}{8}$ **51.** $\frac{1}{6}$ **53.** 0.4615 **55.** 0.3819
57. $11 - \frac{1}{11} - \frac{1}{2 \cdot 11^3} - \frac{1}{2 \cdot 11^5}$ **59.** $-\frac{1}{3} + \frac{1}{3 \cdot 3^3} - \frac{1}{5 \cdot 3^5} + \frac{1}{7 \cdot 3^7}$
61. $y = 4 + 4x + \frac{4^2}{2!}x^2 + \frac{4^3}{3!}x^3 + \cdots + \frac{4^n}{n!}x^n + \cdots = 3 + e^{4x}$
63. a. $\sum_{k=1}^{\infty} \frac{(-1)^{k+1}}{k}$ **b.** $\sum_{k=1}^{\infty} \frac{1}{k2^k}$ **c.** $2\sum_{k=0}^{\infty} \frac{x^{2k+1}}{2k + 1}$
d. $x = \frac{1}{3}; 2\sum_{k=0}^{\infty} \frac{1}{3^{2k+1}(2k + 1)}$ **e.** Series in part (d)

CHAPTER 11

Section 11.1 Exercises, pp. 767–770

3.

5. There are infinitely many vectors with the same direction and length as **v**. **7.** If the scalar c is positive, scale the given vector by a scaling factor c in the same direction. If $c < 0$, reverse the direction of the vector and scale it by a factor $|c|$.
9. $\mathbf{u} + \mathbf{v} = \langle u_1 + v_1, u_2 + v_2 \rangle$ **11.** $|\langle v_1, v_2 \rangle| = \sqrt{v_1^2 + v_2^2}$
13. If P has coordinates (p_1, p_2) and Q has coordinates (q_1, q_2) then the magnitude of $\overrightarrow{PQ}$ is given by $\sqrt{(q_1 - p_1)^2 + (q_2 - p_2)^2}$.
15. Divide **v** by its length and multiply the result by 10. **17.** a, c, e
19. a. 3**v** **b.** 2**u** **c.** -3**u** **d.** -2**u** **e.** **v** **21. a.** 3**u** + 3**v**
b. **u** + 2**v** **c.** 2**u** + 5**v** **d.** -2**u** + 3**v** **e.** 3**u** + 2**v**
f. -3**u** $-$ 2**v** **g.** -2**u** $-$ 4**v** **h.** **u** $-$ 4**v** **i.** $-$**u** $-$ 6**v**
23. a. $\overrightarrow{OP} = \langle 3, 2 \rangle = 3\mathbf{i} + 2\mathbf{j}$
$|\overrightarrow{OP}| = \sqrt{13}$

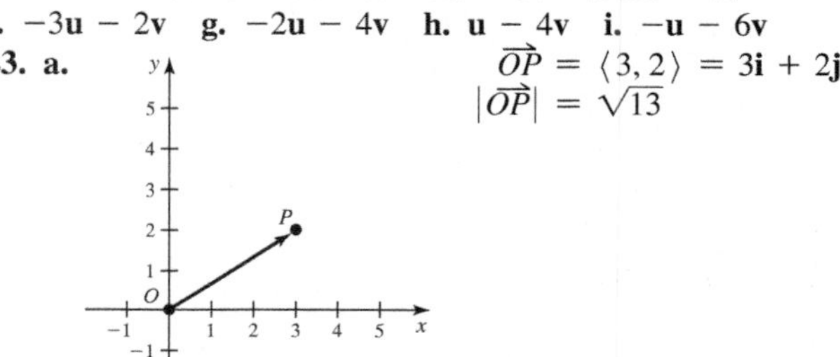

b. $\overrightarrow{QP} = \langle -1, 0 \rangle = -\mathbf{i}$
$|\overrightarrow{QP}| = 1$

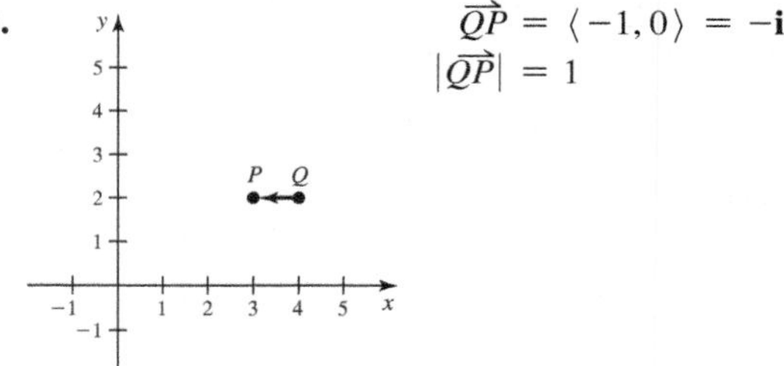

c. $\overrightarrow{RQ} = \langle 10, 3 \rangle = 10\mathbf{i} + 3\mathbf{j}$
$|\overrightarrow{RQ}| = \sqrt{109}$

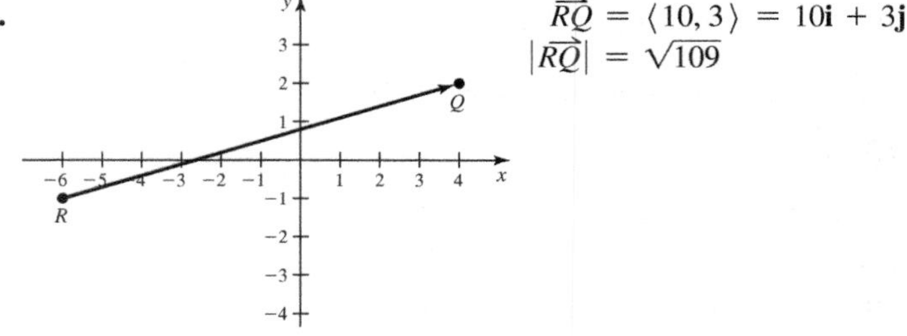

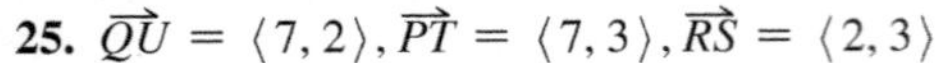

25. $\overrightarrow{QU} = \langle 7, 2\rangle, \overrightarrow{PT} = \langle 7, 3\rangle, \overrightarrow{RS} = \langle 2, 3\rangle$

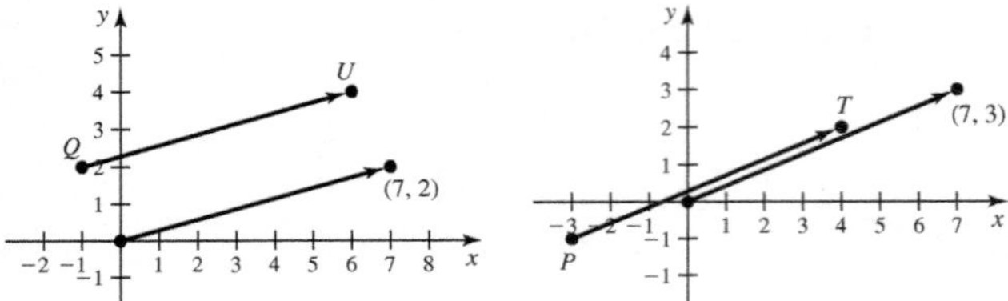

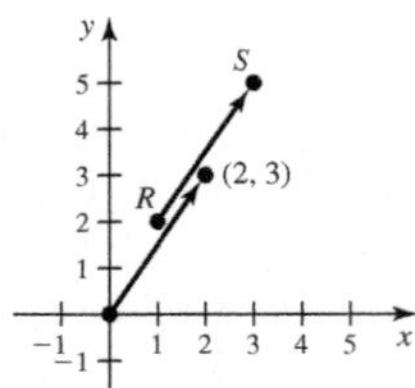

27. $\overrightarrow{QT}$ **29.** $\langle -4, 10\rangle$ **31.** $\langle 12, -10\rangle$ **33.** $\langle -28, 82\rangle$ **35.** $2\sqrt{2}$ **37.** $\sqrt{194}$ **39.** $\langle 3, 3\rangle, \langle -3, -3\rangle$ **41.** $\mathbf{w} - \mathbf{u}$ **43.** $-\mathbf{i} + 10\mathbf{j}$ **45.** $\pm\frac{1}{\sqrt{61}}\langle 6, 5\rangle$ **47.** $\left\langle -\frac{28}{\sqrt{74}}, \frac{20}{\sqrt{74}}\right\rangle, \left\langle \frac{28}{\sqrt{74}}, -\frac{20}{\sqrt{74}}\right\rangle$ **49.** $5\sqrt{65}$ km/hr $\approx$ 40.3 km/hr **51.** 349.43 mi/hr in the direction 4.64° south of west **53.** 1 m/s in the direction 30° east of north **55. a.** $\langle 20, 20\sqrt{3}\rangle$ **b.** Yes **c.** No **57.** $250\sqrt{2}$ lb **59. a.** True **b.** True **c.** False **d.** False **e.** False **f.** False **g.** False **h.** True **61. a.** $\left\langle \frac{3}{5}, -\frac{4}{5}\right\rangle$ and $\left\langle -\frac{3}{5}, \frac{4}{5}\right\rangle$ **b.** $b = \pm\frac{2\sqrt{2}}{3}$ **c.** $a = \pm\frac{3}{\sqrt{10}}$ **63.** $\mathbf{x} = \left\langle \frac{1}{5}, -\frac{3}{10}\right\rangle$ **65.** $\mathbf{x} = \left\langle \frac{4}{3}, -\frac{11}{3}\right\rangle$ **67.** $4\mathbf{i} - 8\mathbf{j}$ **69.** $\langle a, b\rangle = \left(\frac{a+b}{2}\right)\mathbf{u} + \left(\frac{b-a}{2}\right)\mathbf{v}$ **71.** $\mathbf{u} = \frac{1}{5}\mathbf{i} + \frac{3}{5}\mathbf{j}, \mathbf{v} = \frac{1}{5}\mathbf{i} - \frac{2}{5}\mathbf{j}$ **73.** $\left\langle \frac{15}{13}, -\frac{36}{13}\right\rangle$ **75.** $\langle 9, 3\rangle$ **77. a.** 0 **b.** The 6:00 vector **c.** Sum any six consecutive vectors. **d.** A vector pointing from 12:00 to 6:00 with a length 12 times the radius of the clock **79.** 50 lb in the direction 36.87° north of east

81.
$$\begin{aligned}\mathbf{u} + \mathbf{v} &= \langle u_1, u_2\rangle + \langle v_1, v_2\rangle = \langle u_1 + v_1, u_2 + v_2\rangle \\ &= \langle v_1 + u_1, v_2 + u_2\rangle = \langle v_1, v_2\rangle + \langle u_1, u_2\rangle \\ &= \mathbf{v} + \mathbf{u}\end{aligned}$$

83.
$$\begin{aligned}a(c\mathbf{v}) &= a(c\langle v_1, v_2\rangle) = a\langle cv_1, cv_2\rangle \\ &= \langle acv_1, acv_2\rangle = \langle (ac)v_1, (ac)v_2\rangle \\ &= ac\langle v_1, v_2\rangle = (ac)\mathbf{v}\end{aligned}$$

85.
$$\begin{aligned}(a + c)\mathbf{v} &= (a + c)\langle v_1, v_2\rangle \\ &= \langle (a + c)v_1, (a + c)v_2\rangle \\ &= \langle av_1 + cv_1, av_2 + cv_2\rangle \\ &= \langle av_1, av_2\rangle + \langle cv_1, cv_2\rangle \\ &= a\langle v_1, v_2\rangle + c\langle v_1, v_2\rangle \\ &= a\mathbf{v} + c\mathbf{v}\end{aligned}$$

89. a. $\{\mathbf{u}, \mathbf{v}\}$ are linearly dependent. $\{\mathbf{u}, \mathbf{w}\}$ and $\{\mathbf{v}, \mathbf{w}\}$ are linearly independent. **b.** Two linearly dependent vectors are parallel. Two linearly independent vectors are not parallel. **91. a.** $\frac{5}{3}$ **b.** -15

Section 11.2 Exercises, pp. 777–781

1. Move 3 units from the origin in the direction of the positive x-axis, then 2 units in the direction of the negative y-axis, and then 1 unit in the direction of the positive z-axis. **3.** It is parallel to the yz-plane and contains the point $(4, 0, 0)$. **5.** $\mathbf{u} + \mathbf{v} = \langle 9, 0, -6\rangle$; $3\mathbf{u} - \mathbf{v} = \langle 3, 20, -22\rangle$ **7.** $(0, 0, -4)$ **9.** $A(3, 0, 5), B(3, 4, 0), C(0, 4, 5)$ **11.** $A(3, -4, 5), B(0, -4, 0), C(0, -4, 5)$

13. a.

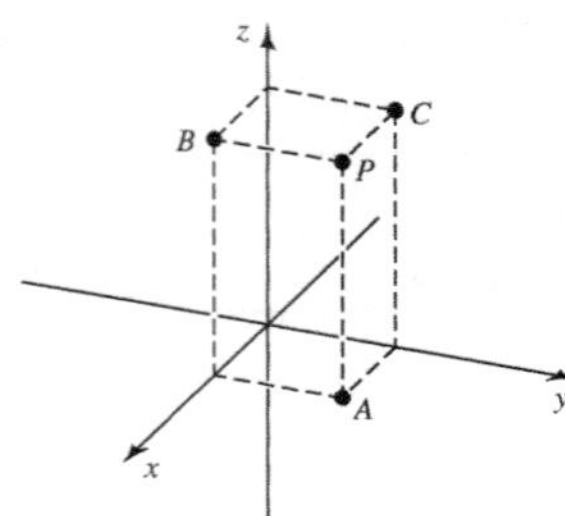

b.

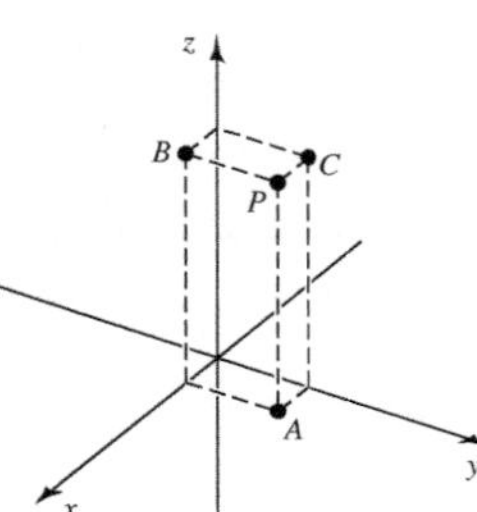

c.

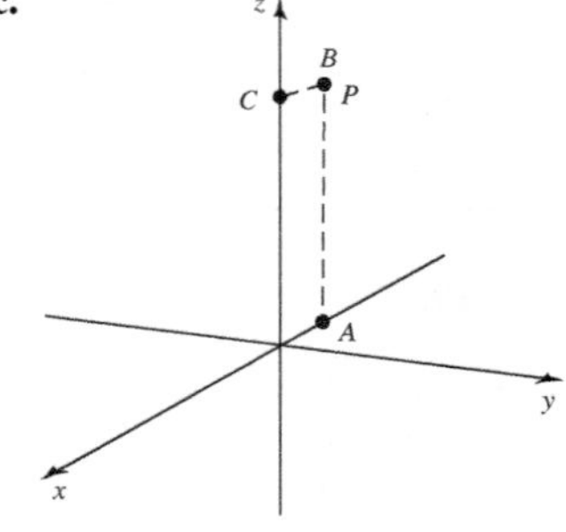

15.

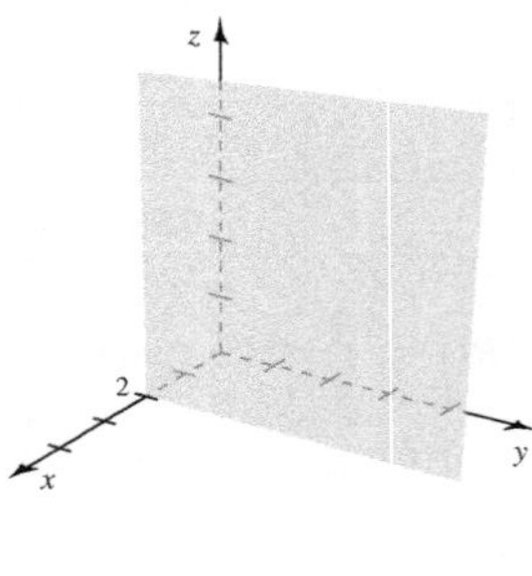

17.

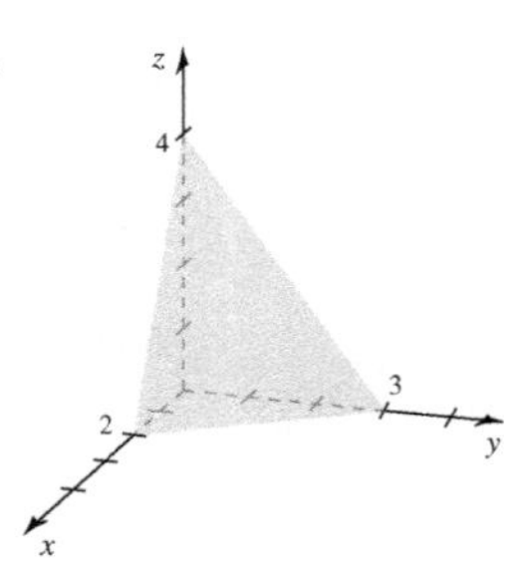

19.

21.

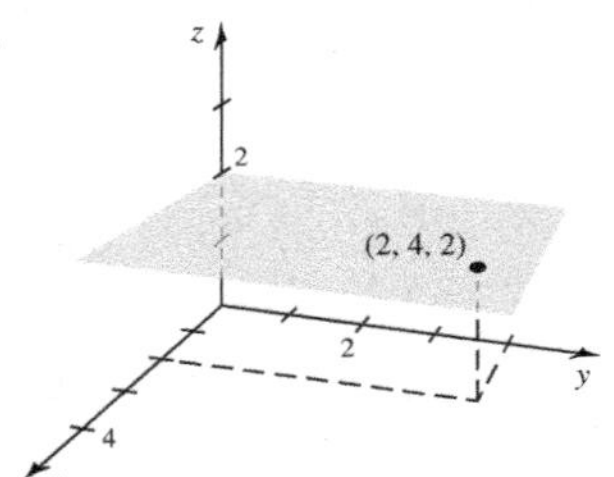

23. $(x - 1)^2 + (y - 2)^2 + (z - 3)^2 = 16$ **25.** $(x + 2)^2 + y^2 + (z - 4)^2 \le 1$ **27.** $\left(x - \frac{3}{2}\right)^2 + \left(y - \frac{3}{2}\right)^2 + (z - 7)^2 = \frac{13}{2}$ **29.** A sphere centered at $(1, 0, 0)$ with radius 3 **31.** A sphere centered at $(0, 1, 2)$ with radius 3 **33.** All points on or outside the sphere with center $(0, 7, 0)$ and radius 6 **35.** The ball centered at $(4, 7, 9)$ with radius 15 **37.** The single point $(1, -3, 0)$ **39.** $\langle 12, -7, 2\rangle$; $\langle 16, -13, -1\rangle$; 5 **41. a.** $\langle -4, 5, -4\rangle$ **b.** $\langle -9, 3, -9\rangle$ **c.** $3\sqrt{2}$ **43. a.** $\langle -15, 23, 22\rangle$ **b.** $\langle -31, 49, 33\rangle$ **c.** $3\sqrt{5}$ **45. a.** $\overrightarrow{PQ} = \langle 2, 6, 2\rangle = 2\mathbf{i} + 6\mathbf{j} + 2\mathbf{k}$ **b.** $|\overrightarrow{PQ}| = 2\sqrt{11}$ **c.** $\left\langle \frac{1}{\sqrt{11}}, \frac{3}{\sqrt{11}}, \frac{1}{\sqrt{11}}\right\rangle$ and $\left\langle -\frac{1}{\sqrt{11}}, -\frac{3}{\sqrt{11}}, -\frac{1}{\sqrt{11}}\right\rangle$ **47. a.** $\overrightarrow{PQ} = \langle 0, -5, 1\rangle = -5\mathbf{j} + \mathbf{k}$ **b.** $|\overrightarrow{PQ}| = \sqrt{26}$ **c.** $\left\langle 0, -\frac{5}{\sqrt{26}}, \frac{1}{\sqrt{26}}\right\rangle$ and $\left\langle 0, \frac{5}{\sqrt{26}}, -\frac{1}{\sqrt{26}}\right\rangle$ **49. a.** $\overrightarrow{PQ} = \langle -2, 4, -2\rangle = -2\mathbf{i} + 4\mathbf{j} - 2\mathbf{k}$ **b.** $|\overrightarrow{PQ}| = 2\sqrt{6}$ **c.** $\left\langle -\frac{1}{\sqrt{6}}, \frac{2}{\sqrt{6}}, -\frac{1}{\sqrt{6}}\right\rangle$ and $\left\langle \frac{1}{\sqrt{6}}, -\frac{2}{\sqrt{6}}, \frac{1}{\sqrt{6}}\right\rangle$ **51. a.** $20\mathbf{i} + 20\mathbf{j} - 10\mathbf{k}$; **b.** 30 mi/hr

53. The speed of the plane is approximately 220 mi/hr; the direction is slightly south of east and upward.

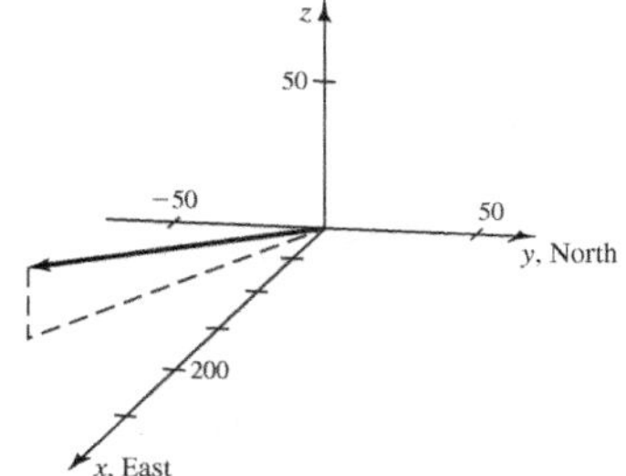

55. $5\sqrt{6}$ knots to the east, $5\sqrt{6}$ knots to the north, 10 knots upward **57. a.** False **b.** False **c.** False **d.** True **59.** All points in $\mathbb{R}^3$ except those on the coordinate axes **61.** A circle of radius 1 centered at (0, 0, 0) in the xy-plane

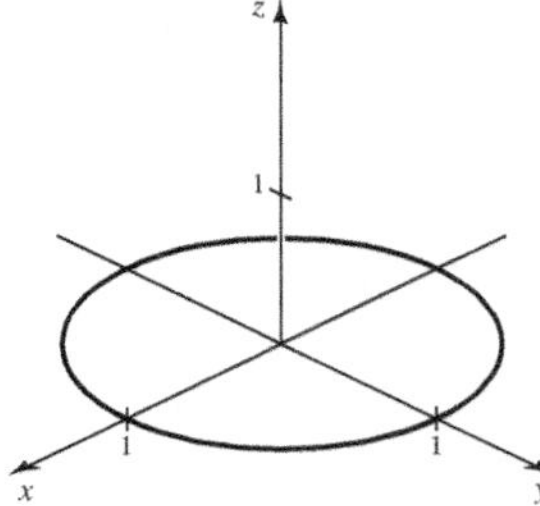

63. A circle of radius 2 centered at (0, 0, 1) in the horizontal plane $z = 1$ **65.** $(x-2)^2 + (z-1)^2 = 9, y = 4$ **67.** $\langle 12, -16, 0\rangle$, $\langle -12, 16, 0\rangle$ **69.** $\langle -\sqrt{3}, -\sqrt{3}, \sqrt{3}\rangle, \langle \sqrt{3}, \sqrt{3}, -\sqrt{3}\rangle$
71. a. Collinear; Q is between P and R. **b.** Collinear; P is between Q and R. **c.** Noncollinear **d.** Noncollinear **73.** $\sqrt{29}$ ft
75. $\frac{250}{3}\left\langle -\frac{1}{\sqrt{3}}, 1, 2\right\rangle, \frac{250}{3}\left\langle -\frac{1}{\sqrt{3}}, -1, -2\right\rangle, \frac{500}{3}\left\langle \frac{1}{\sqrt{3}}, 0, -1\right\rangle$
77. (3, 8, 9), (−1, 0, 3), or (1, 0, −3)

Section 11.3 Exercises, pp. 788–791

1. $\mathbf{u}\cdot\mathbf{v} = |\mathbf{u}||\mathbf{v}|\cos\theta$ **3.** −40
5. $\cos\theta = \frac{\mathbf{u}\cdot\mathbf{v}}{|\mathbf{u}||\mathbf{v}|}$, so $\theta = \cos^{-1}\left(\frac{\mathbf{u}\cdot\mathbf{v}}{|\mathbf{u}||\mathbf{v}|}\right)$
7. $\text{scal}_{\mathbf{v}}\,\mathbf{u}$ is the signed length of the $\text{proj}_{\mathbf{v}}\,\mathbf{u}$.
9. $\frac{\pi}{2}$; 0 **11.** 100; $\frac{\pi}{4}$ **13.** $\frac{1}{2}$ **15.** 0; $\frac{\pi}{2}$
17. 1; $\pi/3$ **19.** −2; 93.2° **21.** 2; 87.2° **23.** −4; 104° **25.** $\langle 3, 0\rangle$; 3
27. $\langle 0, 3\rangle$; 3 **29.** $\frac{6}{5}\langle -2, 1\rangle$; $\frac{6}{\sqrt{5}}$ **31.** $\langle -1, 1, -2\rangle$; $-\sqrt{6}$
33. $\frac{14}{19}\langle -1, -3, 3\rangle$; $-\frac{14}{\sqrt{19}}$ **35.** $-\mathbf{i} + \mathbf{j} - 2\mathbf{k}$; $\sqrt{6}$
37. $750\sqrt{3}$ ft-lb **39.** $25\sqrt{2}$ J **41.** 400 J **43.** $\langle 5, -5\rangle, \langle -5, -5\rangle$
45. $\frac{1}{2}\langle 5\sqrt{3}, -15\rangle, \frac{1}{2}\langle -5\sqrt{3}, -5\rangle$ **47. a.** False **b.** True **c.** True **d.** False **e.** False **f.** True **49.** $\{\langle 1, a, 4a-2\rangle : a \in \mathbb{R}\}$
51. $\left\langle \frac{1}{\sqrt{2}}, \frac{1}{\sqrt{2}}, 0\right\rangle, \left\langle -\frac{1}{\sqrt{2}}, \frac{1}{\sqrt{2}}, 0\right\rangle, \langle 0, 0, 1\rangle$ (one possibility)
53. a. $\text{proj}_{\mathbf{k}}\mathbf{u} = |\mathbf{u}|\cos 60°\left(\frac{\mathbf{k}}{|\mathbf{k}|}\right) = \frac{1}{2}\mathbf{k}$ for all such $\mathbf{u}$ **b.** Yes
55. The heads of the vectors lie on the line $y = 3 - x$.
57. The heads of the vectors lie on the plane $z = 3$.
59. $\mathbf{u} = \left\langle -\frac{4}{5}, -\frac{2}{5}\right\rangle + \left\langle -\frac{6}{5}, \frac{12}{5}\right\rangle$
61. $\mathbf{u} = \left\langle 1, \frac{1}{2}, \frac{1}{2}\right\rangle + \left\langle -2, \frac{3}{2}, \frac{5}{2}\right\rangle$ **63. e.** $|\mathbf{w}| = \frac{28\sqrt{5}}{5}$
65. e. $|\mathbf{w}| = \sqrt{\frac{326}{109}}$

67. $\mathbf{I} = \frac{1}{\sqrt{2}}\mathbf{i} + \frac{1}{\sqrt{2}}\mathbf{j}, \mathbf{J} = -\frac{1}{\sqrt{2}}\mathbf{i} + \frac{1}{\sqrt{2}}\mathbf{j}$;
$\mathbf{i} = \frac{1}{\sqrt{2}}(\mathbf{I} - \mathbf{J}), \mathbf{j} = \frac{1}{\sqrt{2}}(\mathbf{I} + \mathbf{J})$
69. a. $|\mathbf{I}| = |\mathbf{J}| = |\mathbf{K}| = 1$ **b.** $\mathbf{I}\cdot\mathbf{J} = 0, \mathbf{I}\cdot\mathbf{K} = 0, \mathbf{J}\cdot\mathbf{K} = 0$
c. $\langle 1, 0, 0\rangle = \frac{1}{2}\mathbf{I} - \frac{1}{\sqrt{2}}\mathbf{J} + \frac{1}{2}\mathbf{K}$ **71.** $\angle P = 78.8°$, $\angle Q = 47.2°, \angle R = 54.0°$ **73. a.** The faces on $y = 0$ and $z = 0$
b. The faces on $y = 1$ and $z = 1$ **c.** The faces on $x = 0$ and $x = 1$
d. 0 **e.** 1 **f.** 2 **75. a.** $\left(\frac{2}{\sqrt{3}}, 0, \frac{2\sqrt{2}}{\sqrt{3}}\right)$ **b.** $\mathbf{r}_{OP} = \langle \sqrt{3}, -1, 0\rangle$, $\mathbf{r}_{OQ} = \langle \sqrt{3}, 1, 0\rangle, \mathbf{r}_{PQ} = \langle 0, 2, 0\rangle, \mathbf{r}_{OR} = \left\langle \frac{2}{\sqrt{3}}, 0, \frac{2\sqrt{2}}{\sqrt{3}}\right\rangle$,
$\mathbf{r}_{PR} = \left\langle -\frac{\sqrt{3}}{3}, 1, \frac{2\sqrt{2}}{\sqrt{3}}\right\rangle$
83. a. $\cos^2\alpha + \cos^2\beta + \cos^2\gamma$
$$= \left(\frac{\mathbf{v}\cdot\mathbf{i}}{|\mathbf{v}||\mathbf{i}|}\right)^2 + \left(\frac{\mathbf{v}\cdot\mathbf{j}}{|\mathbf{v}||\mathbf{j}|}\right)^2 + \left(\frac{\mathbf{v}\cdot\mathbf{k}}{|\mathbf{v}||\mathbf{k}|}\right)^2$$
$$= \frac{a^2}{a^2+b^2+c^2} + \frac{b^2}{a^2+b^2+c^2} + \frac{c^2}{a^2+b^2+c^2} = 1$$
b. $\langle 1, 1, 0\rangle$, 90° **c.** $\left\langle \frac{1}{\sqrt{2}}, \frac{1}{\sqrt{2}}, 1\right\rangle$, 45° **d.** No. If so, $\left(\frac{\sqrt{3}}{2}\right)^2 + \left(\frac{\sqrt{3}}{2}\right)^2 + \cos^2\gamma = 1$, which has no solution. **e.** 54.7°
85. $|\mathbf{u}\cdot\mathbf{v}| = 33 = \sqrt{33}\cdot\sqrt{33} < \sqrt{70}\cdot\sqrt{74} = |\mathbf{u}||\mathbf{v}|$

Section 11.4 Exercises, pp. 797–799

1. $|\mathbf{u}\times\mathbf{v}| = |\mathbf{u}||\mathbf{v}|\sin\theta$, where $0 \le \theta \le \pi$ is the angle between $\mathbf{u}$ and $\mathbf{v}$ **3.** 0 **5.** $\mathbf{u}\times\mathbf{v} = \begin{vmatrix} \mathbf{i} & \mathbf{j} & \mathbf{k} \\ u_1 & u_2 & u_3 \\ v_1 & v_2 & v_3 \end{vmatrix}$ **7.** $15\mathbf{k}$

9. 0

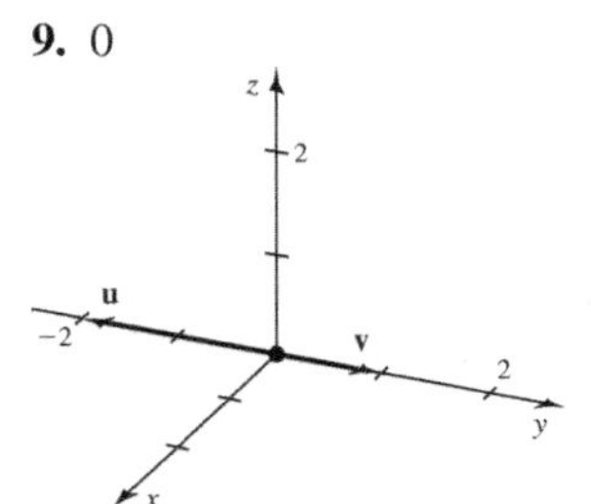

11. 18

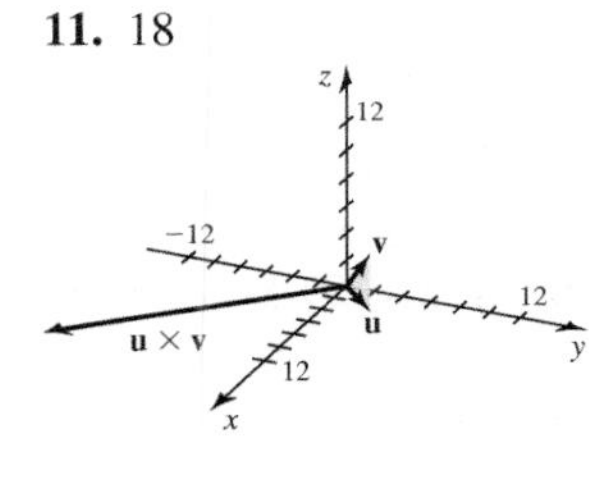

13. $\sqrt{2}/2$ **15.** $\mathbf{i}$

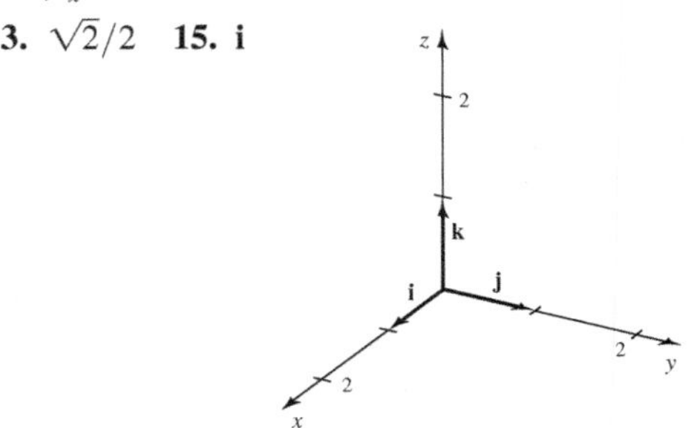

17. $-\mathbf{i}$ **19.** $6\mathbf{j}$

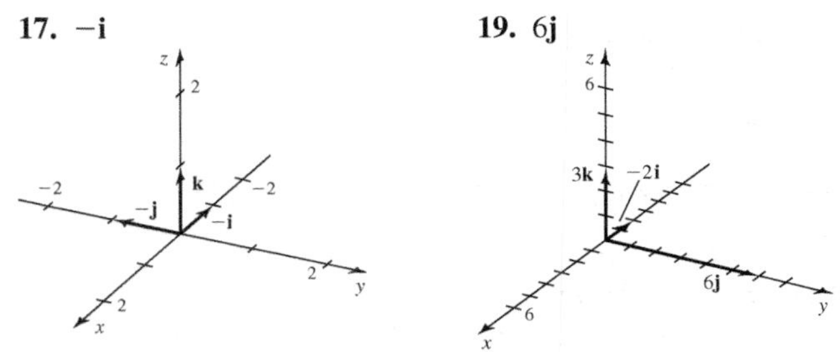

21. 11 **23.** $3\sqrt{10}$ **25.** $\sqrt{11}/2$ **27.** $4\sqrt{2}$
29. $\mathbf{u}\times\mathbf{v} = \langle -30, 18, 9\rangle, \mathbf{v}\times\mathbf{u} = \langle 30, -18, -9\rangle$

31. $\mathbf{u} \times \mathbf{v} = \langle 6, 11, 5 \rangle, \mathbf{v} \times \mathbf{u} = \langle -6, -11, -5 \rangle$
33. $\mathbf{u} \times \mathbf{v} = \langle 8, 4, 10 \rangle, \mathbf{v} \times \mathbf{u} = \langle -8, -4, -10 \rangle$ **35.** $\langle 3, -4, 2 \rangle$
37. $\langle -8, -40, 16 \rangle$ **39.** $5/\sqrt{2}$ N-m **41.** $\langle 0, 20, -20 \rangle$
43. The force $\mathbf{F} = 5\mathbf{i} - 5\mathbf{k}$ produces the greater torque.
45. The magnitude is $20\sqrt{2}$ at a 135° angle with the positive x-axis in the xy-plane.

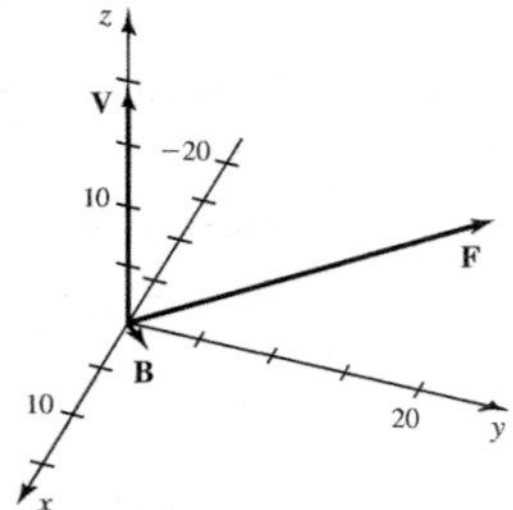

47. 4.53×10^{-14} kg-m/s^2 **49. a.** False **b.** False **c.** False **d.** True **e.** False **51.** Not collinear **53.** $\langle b^2 - a^2, 0, a^2 - b^2 \rangle$. The vectors are parallel when $a = \pm b \neq 0$. **55.** $9\sqrt{2}$ **57.** $\frac{7\sqrt{6}}{2}$
59. $\{\langle u_1, u_1 + 2, u_1 + 1 \rangle : u_1 \in \mathbb{R}\}$ **61.** $\frac{\sqrt{(ab)^2 + (ac)^2 + (bc)^2}}{2}$
63. a. $|\mathbf{u} \cdot (\mathbf{v} \times \mathbf{w})| = |\mathbf{u}||\mathbf{v} \times \mathbf{w}||\cos\theta|$, where $|\mathbf{v} \times \mathbf{w}|$ is the area of the base of the parallelepiped and $|\mathbf{u}||\cos\theta|$ is its height. **b.** 46
65. $|\tau| = 26.4$ N-m; direction: into the page **67.** 1.76×10^7 m/s

Section 11.5 Exercises, pp. 805–808

1. One **3.** Its output is a vector.
5. $\langle x, y, z \rangle = \langle x_0, y_0, z_0 \rangle + t\langle x_1 - x_0, y_1 - y_0, z_1 - z_0 \rangle$
7. $\lim_{t \to a} \mathbf{r}(t) = \langle \lim_{t \to a} f(t), \lim_{t \to a} g(t), \lim_{t \to a} h(t) \rangle$
9. $\mathbf{r}(t) = \langle 0, 0, 1 \rangle + t\langle 4, 7, 0 \rangle$
11. $\langle x, y, z \rangle = \langle 0, 0, 1 \rangle + t\langle 0, 1, 0 \rangle$ **13.** $\langle x, y, z \rangle = t\langle 1, 2, 3 \rangle$
15. $\langle x, y, z \rangle = \langle -3, 4, 6 \rangle + t\langle 8, -5, -6 \rangle$
17. $\mathbf{r}(t) = t\langle -2, 8, -4 \rangle$ **19.** $\mathbf{r}(t) = t\langle -2, -1, 1 \rangle$
21. $\mathbf{r}(t) = \langle -2, 5, 3 \rangle + t\langle 0, 2, -1 \rangle$
23. $\mathbf{r}(t) = \langle 1, 2, 3 \rangle + t\langle -4, 6, 14 \rangle$ **25.** $\langle x, y, z \rangle = t\langle 1, 2, 3 \rangle$, $0 \leq t \leq 1$ **27.** $\langle x, y, z \rangle = \langle 2, 4, 8 \rangle + t\langle 5, 1, -5 \rangle, 0 \leq t \leq 1$

29.

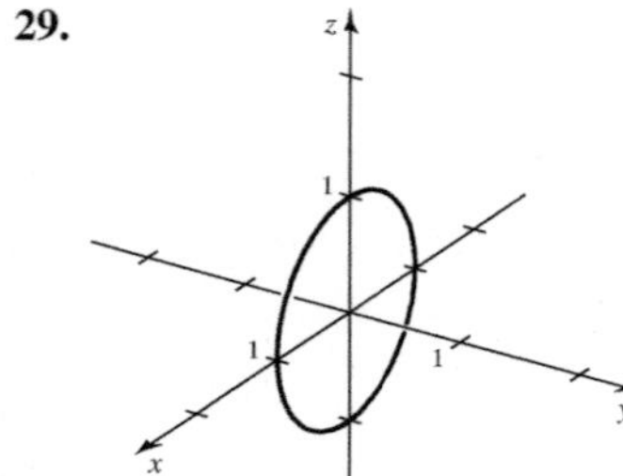

31.

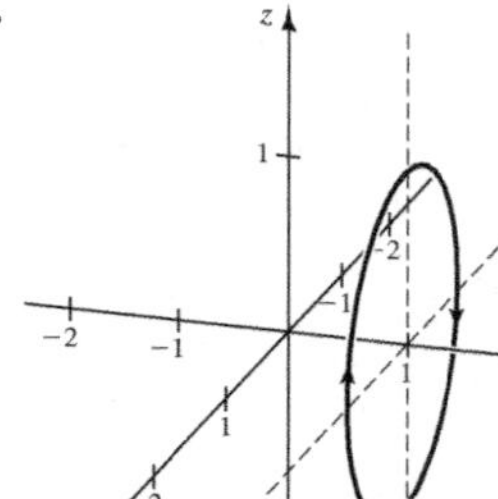

33.

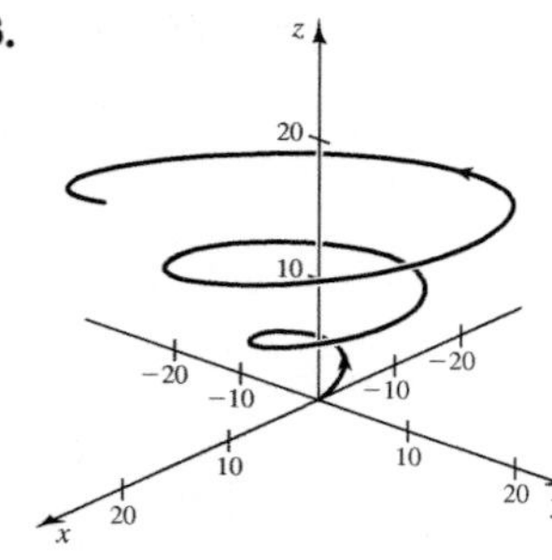

35.

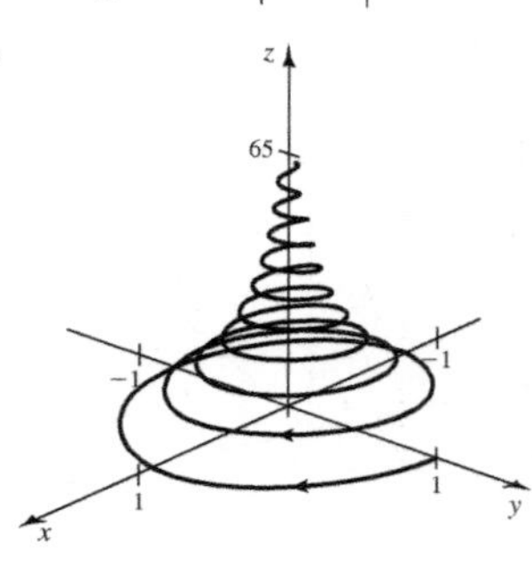

37.

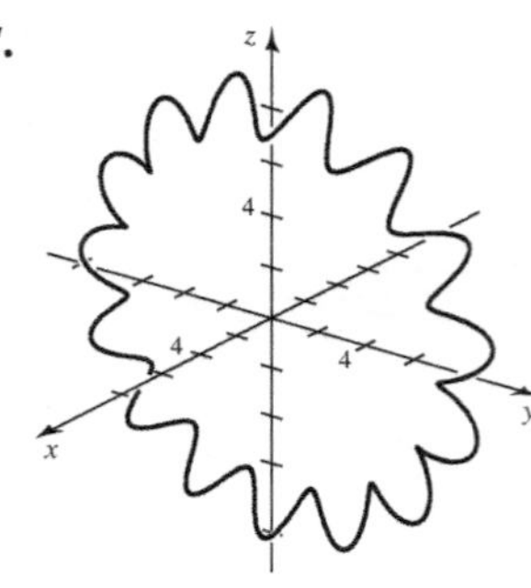

39. When viewed from above, the curve is a portion of the parabola $y = x^2$.

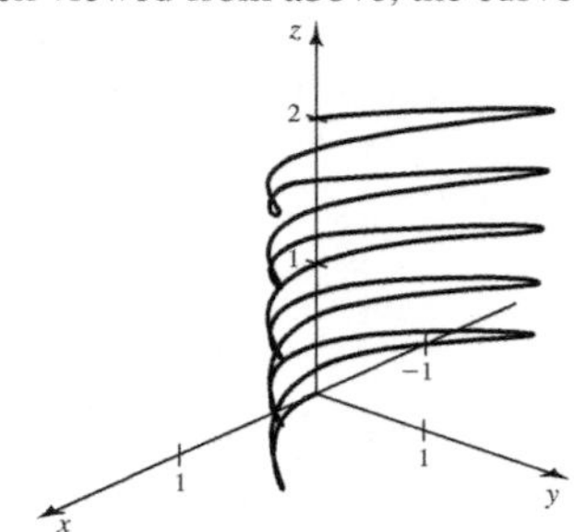

41. $-\mathbf{i} - 4\mathbf{j} + \mathbf{k}$ **43.** $-2\mathbf{j} + \frac{\pi}{2}\mathbf{k}$ **45.** $\mathbf{i}$ **47. a.** True **b.** False **c.** True **d.** True **49.** $\mathbf{r}(t) = \langle 4, 3, 3 \rangle + t\langle 0, -9, 6 \rangle$
51. The lines intersect at $(1, 3, 2)$. **53.** Skew
55. These equations describe the same line. **57.** $\{t : |t| \leq 2\}$
59. $\{t : 0 \leq t \leq 2\}$ **61.** $(21, -6, 4)$ **63.** $(16, 0, -8)$
65. $(4, 8, 16)$ **67. a.** E **b.** D **c.** F **d.** C **e.** A **f.** B
69. a. $(50, 0, 0)$ **b.** $5\mathbf{k}$ **c.**

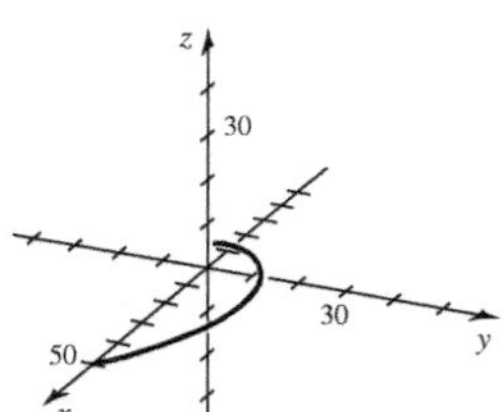

d. $x^2 + y^2 = (50e^{-t})^2$ so $r = 50e^{-t}$. Therefore, $z = 5 - 5e^{-t} = 5 - \frac{r}{10}$.

71. a.

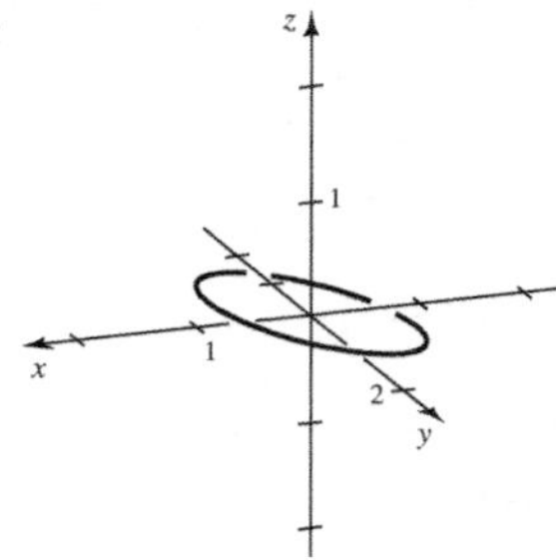

b. Curve is a tilted circle of radius 1 centered at the origin.
73. $\langle cf - ed, be - af, ad - bc \rangle$ or any scalar multiple
75. The curve lies on the sphere $x^2 + y^2 + z^2 = 1$.

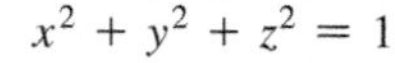

77. $\dfrac{2\pi}{(m, n)}$, where (m, n) = greatest common factor of m and n
81. 13

Section 11.6 Exercises, pp. 814–816

1. $\mathbf{r}'(t) = \langle f'(t), g'(t), h'(t) \rangle$ **3.** $\mathbf{T}(t) = \dfrac{r'(t)}{|r'(t)|}$

5. $\int \mathbf{r}(t)\,dt = \left(\int f(t)\,dt\right)\mathbf{i} + \left(\int g(t)\,dt\right)\mathbf{j} + \left(\int h(t)\,dt\right)\mathbf{k}$

7. $\langle -\sin t, 2t, \cos t \rangle$ **9.** $\left\langle 6t^2, \dfrac{3}{\sqrt{t}}, -\dfrac{3}{t^2} \right\rangle$ **11.** $e^t\mathbf{i} - 2e^{-t}\mathbf{j} - 8e^{2t}\mathbf{k}$

13. $\langle e^{-t}(1 - t), 1 + \ln t, \cos t - t\sin t \rangle$ **15.** $\langle 1, 6, 3 \rangle$
17. $\langle 1, 0, 0 \rangle$ **19.** $8\mathbf{i} + 9\mathbf{j} - 10\mathbf{k}$ **21.** $\langle 2/3, 2/3, 1/3 \rangle$

23. $\dfrac{\langle 0, -\sin 2t, 2\cos 2t \rangle}{\sqrt{1 + 3\cos^2 2t}}$ **25.** $\dfrac{t^2}{\sqrt{t^4 + 4}}\left\langle 1, 0, -\dfrac{2}{t^2} \right\rangle$

27. $\langle 0, 0, -1 \rangle$ **29.** $\left\langle \dfrac{2}{\sqrt{5}}, 0, -\dfrac{1}{\sqrt{5}} \right\rangle$

31. $\langle 30t^{14} + 24t^3, 14t^{13} - 12t^{11} + 9t^2 - 3, -96t^{11} - 24 \rangle$
33. $4t(2t^3 - 1)(t^3 - 2)\langle 3t(t^3 - 2), 1, 0 \rangle$
35. $e^t(2t^3 + 6t^2) - 2e^{-t}(t^2 - 2t - 1) - 16e^{-2t}$
37. $5te^t(t + 2) - 6t^2e^{-t}(t - 3)$

39. $-3t^2\sin t + 6t\cos t + 2\sqrt{t}\cos 2t + \dfrac{1}{2\sqrt{t}}\sin 2t$

41. $\langle 2, 0, 0 \rangle, \langle 0, 0, 0 \rangle$ **43.** $\langle -9\cos 3t, -16\sin 4t, -36\cos 6t \rangle$, $\langle 27\sin 3t, -64\cos 4t, 216\sin 6t \rangle$

45. $\left\langle -\dfrac{1}{4}(t + 4)^{-3/2}, -2(t + 1)^{-3}, 2e^{-t^2}(1 - 2t^2) \right\rangle$, $\left\langle \dfrac{3}{8}(t + 4)^{-5/2}, 6(t + 1)^{-4}, -4te^{-t^2}(3 - 2t^2) \right\rangle$

47. $\left\langle \dfrac{t^5}{5} - \dfrac{3t^2}{2}, t^2 - t, 10t \right\rangle + \mathbf{C}$

49. $\left\langle 2\sin t, -\dfrac{2}{3}\cos 3t, \dfrac{1}{2}\sin 8t \right\rangle + \mathbf{C}$

51. $\frac{1}{3}e^{3t}\mathbf{i} + \tan^{-1}t\,\mathbf{j} - \sqrt{2t}\,\mathbf{k} + \mathbf{C}$
53. $\mathbf{r}(t) = \langle e^t + 1, 3 - \cos t, \tan t + 2 \rangle$
55. $\mathbf{r}(t) = \langle t + 3, t^2 + 2, t^3 - 6 \rangle$
57. $\mathbf{r}(t) = \langle \frac{1}{2}e^{2t} + \frac{1}{2}, 2e^{-t} + t - 1, t - 2e^t + 3 \rangle$
59. $\langle 2, 0, 2 \rangle$ **61.** $\mathbf{i}$ **63.** $\langle 0, 0, 0 \rangle$ **65.** $(e^2 + 1)\langle 1, 2, -1 \rangle$
67. a. False **b.** True **c.** True **69.** $\langle 2 - t, 3 - 2t, \pi/2 + t \rangle$
71. $\langle 2 + 3t, 9 + 7t, 1 + 2t \rangle$ **73.** $\langle 2e^{2t}, -2e^t, 0 \rangle$

75. $\left\langle 4, -\dfrac{2}{\sqrt{t}}, 0 \right\rangle$ **77.** $\langle 1 + 6t^2, 4t^3, -2 - 3t^2 \rangle$ **79.** $(1, 0)$

81. $(1, 0, 0)$ **83.** $\mathbf{r}(t) = \langle a_1t, a_2t, a_3t \rangle$ or $\mathbf{r}(t) = \langle a_1e^{kt}, a_2e^{kt}, a_3e^{kt} \rangle$, where a_i and k are real numbers

Section 11.7 Exercises, pp. 826–830

1. $\mathbf{v}(t) = \mathbf{r}'(t)$, speed $= |\mathbf{r}'(t)|$, $\mathbf{a}(t) = \mathbf{r}''(t)$ **3.** $m\mathbf{a}(t) = \mathbf{F}$

5. $\mathbf{v}(t) = \int \mathbf{a}(t)\,dt = \langle v_1(t), v_2(t) \rangle + \mathbf{C}$. Use initial conditions to find $\mathbf{C}$. **7. a.** $\langle 6t, 8t \rangle, 10t$ **b.** $\langle 6, 8 \rangle$ **9. a.** $\mathbf{v}(t) = \langle 2, -4 \rangle$, $|\mathbf{v}(t)| = 2\sqrt{5}$ **b.** $\mathbf{a}(t) = \langle 0, 0 \rangle$ **11. a.** $\mathbf{v}(t) = \langle 8\cos t, -8\sin t \rangle$, $|\mathbf{v}(t)| = 8$ **b.** $\mathbf{a}(t) = \langle -8\sin t, -8\cos t \rangle$ **13. a.** $\langle 2t, 2t, t \rangle, 3t$ **b.** $\langle 2, 2, 1 \rangle$ **15. a.** $\mathbf{v}(t) = \langle 1, -4, 6 \rangle$, $|\mathbf{v}(t)| = \sqrt{53}$ **b.** $\mathbf{a}(t) = \langle 0, 0, 0 \rangle$ **17. a.** $\mathbf{v}(t) = \langle 0, 2t, -e^{-t} \rangle$, $|\mathbf{v}(t)| = \sqrt{4t^2 + e^{-2t}}$ **b.** $\mathbf{a}(t) = \langle 0, 2, e^{-t} \rangle$ **19. a.** $[c, d] = [0, 1]$

b. $\langle 1, 2t \rangle, \langle 2, 8t \rangle$
c.

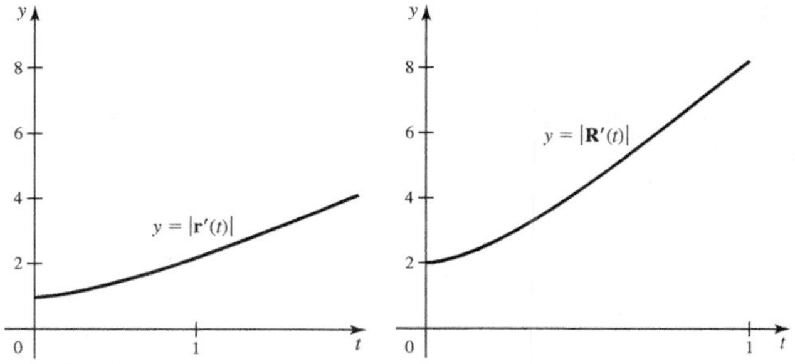

21. a. $\left[0, \frac{2\pi}{3}\right]$ **b.** $\mathbf{V}_\mathbf{r}(t) = \langle -\sin t, 4\cos t \rangle$, $\mathbf{V}_\mathbf{R}(t) = \langle -3\sin 3t, 12\cos 3t \rangle$
c.

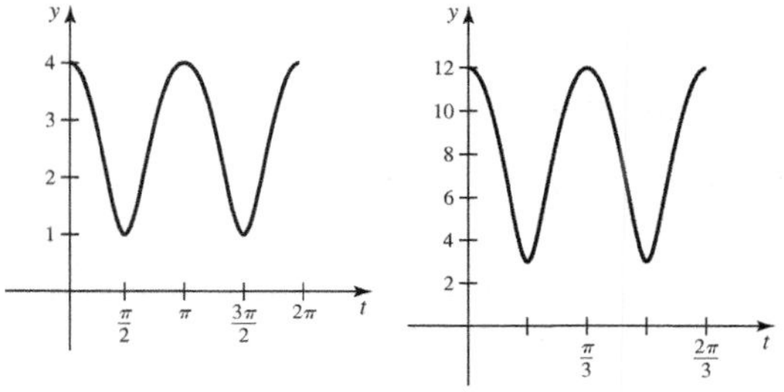

23. a. $[1, e^{36}]$

b. $\mathbf{V}_\mathbf{r}(t) = \langle 2t, -8t^3, 18t^5 \rangle$, $\mathbf{V}_\mathbf{R}(t) = \left\langle \dfrac{1}{t}, -\dfrac{4}{t}\ln t, \dfrac{9}{t}\ln^2 t \right\rangle$

c.

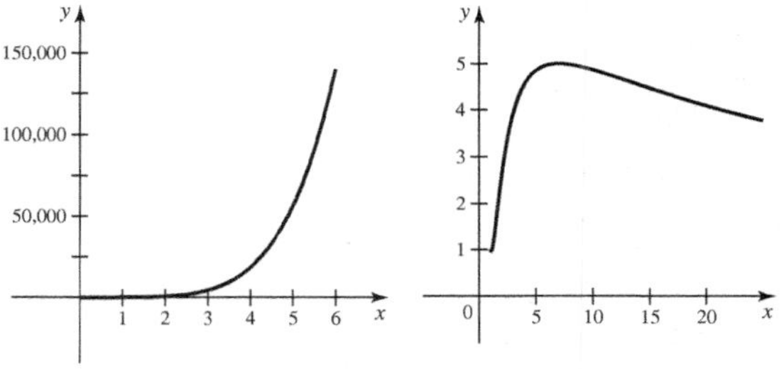

25. $\mathbf{r}(t)$ lies on a circle of radius 8; $\langle -16\sin 2t, 16\cos 2t \rangle \cdot \langle 8\cos 2t, 8\sin 2t \rangle = 0$.
27. $\mathbf{r}(t)$ lies on a sphere of radius 2; $\langle \cos t - \sqrt{3}\sin t, \sqrt{3}\cos t + \sin t \rangle \cdot \langle \sin t + \sqrt{3}\cos t, \sqrt{3}\sin t - \cos t \rangle = 0$.
29. $\mathbf{r}(t)$ does not lie on a sphere.

31. $\mathbf{v}(t) = \langle 2, t + 3 \rangle$, $\mathbf{r}(t) = \left\langle 2t, \dfrac{t^2}{2} + 3t \right\rangle$

33. $\mathbf{v}(t) = \langle 0, 10t + 5 \rangle$, $\mathbf{r}(t) = \langle 1, 5t^2 + 5t - 1 \rangle$
35. $\mathbf{v}(t) = \langle \sin t, -2\cos t + 3 \rangle$, $\mathbf{r}(t) = \langle -\cos t + 2, -2\sin t + 3t \rangle$
37. a. $\mathbf{v}(t) = \langle 30, -9.8t + 6 \rangle$, $\mathbf{r}(t) = \langle 30t, -4.9t^2 + 6t \rangle$
b.

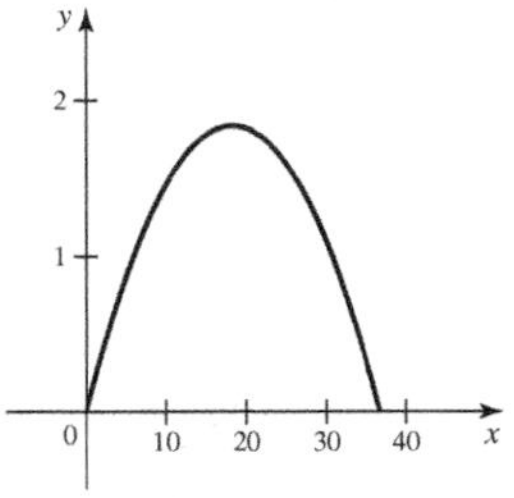

c. $T \approx 1.22$ s, range ≈ 36.7 m
d. 1.84 m

39. a. $\mathbf{v}(t) = \langle 80, 10 - 32t \rangle, \mathbf{r}(t) = \langle 80t, -16t^2 + 10t + 6 \rangle$
b.

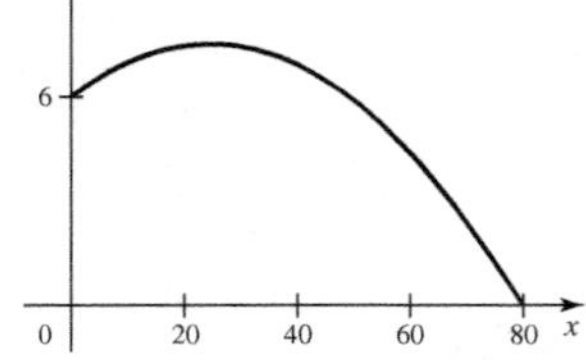

c. 1 s, 80 ft
d. max height $\approx$ 7.56 ft

41. a. $\mathbf{v}(t) = \langle 125, -32t + 125\sqrt{3} \rangle$, $\mathbf{r}(t) = \langle 125t, -16t^2 + 125\sqrt{3}t + 20 \rangle$
b.

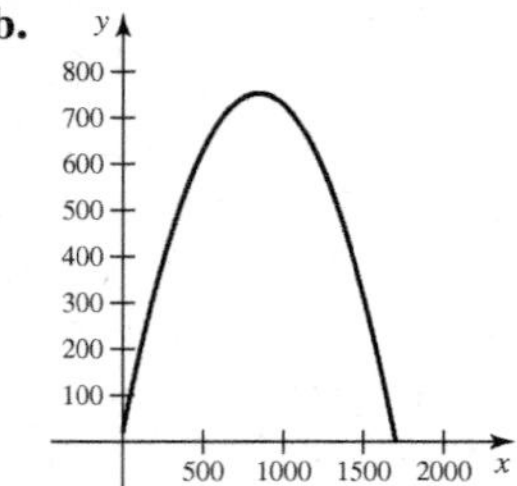

c. 13.6 s, 1702.5 ft **d.** 752.4 ft

43. $\mathbf{v}(t) = \langle 1, 5, 10t \rangle, \mathbf{r}(t) = \langle t, 5t + 5, 5t^2 \rangle$
45. $\mathbf{v}(t) = \langle -\cos t + 1, \sin t + 2, t \rangle$,

$$\mathbf{r}(t) = \left\langle -\sin t + t, -\cos t + 2t + 1, \frac{t^2}{2} \right\rangle$$

47. a. $\mathbf{v}(t) = \langle 200, 200, -9.8t \rangle, \mathbf{r}(t) = \langle 200t, 200t, -4.9t^2 + 1 \rangle$
b.

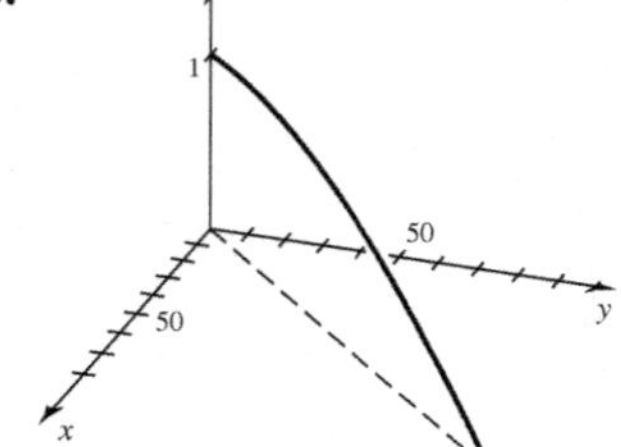

c. 0.452 s, 127.8 m **d.** 1 m

49. a. $\mathbf{v}(t) = \langle 60 + 10t, 80, 80 - 32t \rangle$, $\mathbf{r}(t) = \langle 60t + 5t^2, 80t, 80t - 16t^2 + 3 \rangle$
b.

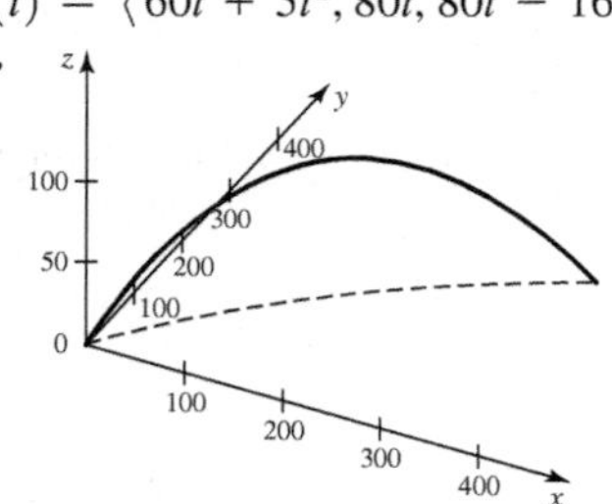

c. 5.04 s, 589 ft
d. 103 ft

51. a. $\mathbf{v}(t) = \langle 300, 2.5t + 400, -9.8t + 500 \rangle$, $\mathbf{r}(t) = \langle 300t, 1.25t^2 + 400t, -4.9t^2 + 500t + 10 \rangle$
b.
c. 102.1 s, 61,941.5 m
d. 12,765.1 m

53. a. False **b.** True **c.** False **d.** True **e.** False **f.** True **g.** True **55.** 15.3 s, 1988.3 m, 287.0 m **57.** 21.7 s, 4330.1 ft, 1875 ft **59.** Approximately 27.4° and 62.6° **61. a.** The direction of $\mathbf{r}$ does not change. **b.** Constant in direction, not in magnitude

63. a. $\left[0, \frac{2\pi}{\omega}\right]$ **b.** $\mathbf{v}(t) = \langle -A\omega \sin \omega t, A\omega \cos \omega t \rangle$ is not constant; $|\mathbf{v}(t)| = |A\omega|$ is constant. **c.** $\mathbf{a}(t) = \langle -A\omega^2 \cos \omega t, -A\omega^2 \sin \omega t \rangle$ **d.** $\mathbf{r}$ and $\mathbf{v}$ are orthogonal; $\mathbf{r}$ and $\mathbf{a}$ are in opposite directions.
e.

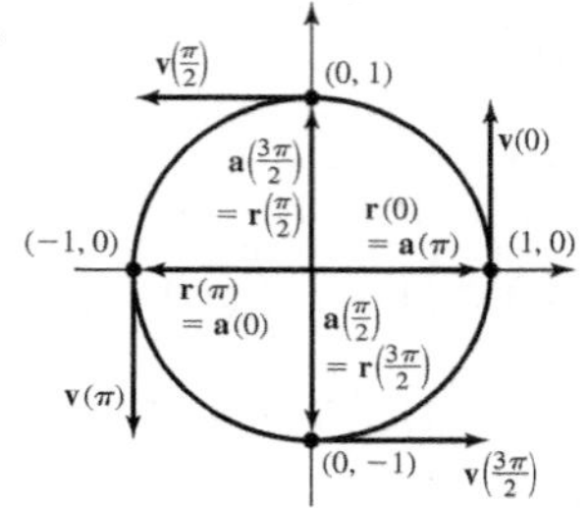

65. a. $\mathbf{r}(t) = \langle 5 \sin (\pi t/6), 5 \cos (\pi t/6) \rangle$
b. $\mathbf{r}(t) = \left\langle 5 \sin\left(\frac{1 - e^{-t}}{5}\right), 5 \cos\left(\frac{1 - e^{-t}}{5}\right)\right\rangle$
67. a. $\mathbf{v}(t) = \langle -a \sin t, b \cos t \rangle$; $|\mathbf{v}(t)| = \sqrt{a^2 \sin^2 t + b^2 \cos^2 t}$
b.

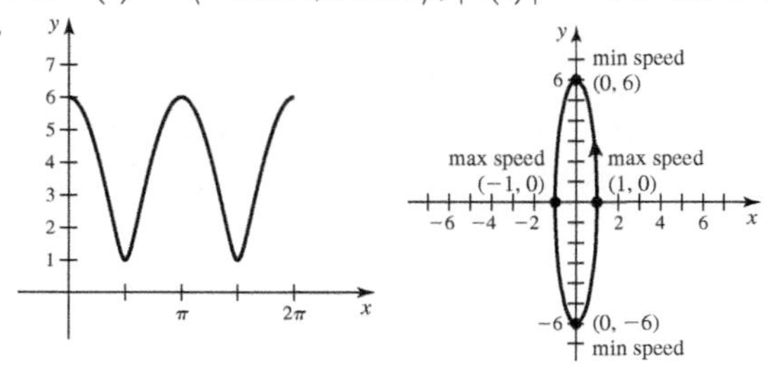

c. Yes **d.** max $\left\{\frac{a}{b}, \frac{b}{a}\right\}$
69. a. $\mathbf{r}(0) = \langle 50, 0, 0 \rangle$, $\lim_{t \to \infty} \mathbf{r}(t) = \langle 0, 0, 5 \rangle$ **b.** At $t = 0$
c.

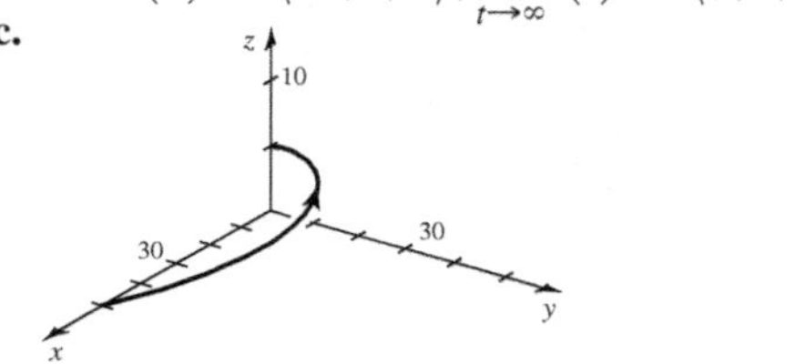

71. Approximately 23.5° or 59.6° **73.** 113.4 ft/s **75. a.** 1.2 ft, 0.46 s **b.** 0.88 ft/s **c.** 0.85 ft **d.** More curve in the second half **e.** $c = 28.17$ ft/s^2 **77.** $T = \dfrac{|\mathbf{v}_0| \sin \alpha + \sqrt{|\mathbf{v}_0|^2 \sin^2 \alpha + 2gy_0}}{g}$, range $= |\mathbf{v}_0| (\cos \alpha) T$, max height $= y_0 + \dfrac{|\mathbf{v}_0|^2 \sin^2 \alpha}{2g}$
79. $\{(\cos t, \sin t, c \sin t) : t \in \mathbb{R}\}$ satisfies the equations $x^2 + y^2 = 1$ and $z - cy = 0$ so that $\langle \cos t, \sin t, c \sin t \rangle$ lies on the intersection of a right circular cylinder and a plane, which is an ellipse.
83. b. $a^2 + c^2 + e^2 = b^2 + d^2 + f^2$ and $ab + cd + ef = 0$

Section 11.8 Exercises, pp. 838–840

1. $\sqrt{5}(b - a)$ **3.** $\int_a^b |\mathbf{v}(t)|\, dt$ **5.** 20π **7.** If the parameter t used to describe a trajectory also measures the arc length s of the curve that is generated, we say the curve has been parameterized by its arc length.
9. 5 **11.** 3π **13.** $\frac{\pi^2}{8}$ **15.** $5\sqrt{34}$ **17.** $4\pi\sqrt{65}$ **19.** 9
21. $\frac{3}{2}$ **23.** $3t^2\sqrt{30}$; $64\sqrt{30}$ **25.** 26; 26π **27.** 19.38 **29.** 32.50
31. πa **33.** $\frac{8}{3}\left((1 + \pi^2)^{3/2} - 1\right)$ **35.** 32 **37.** $63\sqrt{5}$

39. $\dfrac{2\pi - 3\sqrt{3}}{8}$ **41.** Yes

43. No; $\mathbf{r}(s) = \left\langle \dfrac{s}{\sqrt{5}}, \dfrac{2s}{\sqrt{5}} \right\rangle, 0 \le s \le 3\sqrt{5}$

45. No; $\mathbf{r}(s) = \left\langle 2\cos\dfrac{s}{2}, 2\sin\dfrac{s}{2} \right\rangle, 0 \le s \le 4\pi$

47. No; $\mathbf{r}(s) = \langle \cos s, \sin s \rangle, 0 \le s \le \pi$

49. No; $\mathbf{r}(s) = \left\langle \dfrac{s}{\sqrt{3}} + 1, \dfrac{s}{\sqrt{3}} + 1, \dfrac{s}{\sqrt{3}} + 1 \right\rangle, s \ge 0$

51. a. True **b.** True **c.** True **d.** False **53. a.** If $a^2 = b^2 + c^2$, then $|\mathbf{r}(t)|^2 = (a\cos t)^2 + (b\sin t)^2 + (c\sin t)^2 = a^2$ so that $\mathbf{r}(t)$ is a circle centered at the origin of radius $|a|$. **b.** $2\pi a$ **c.** If $a^2 + c^2 + e^2 = b^2 + d^2 + f^2$ and $ab + cd + ef = 0$, then $\mathbf{r}(t)$ is a circle of radius $\sqrt{a^2 + c^2 + e^2}$ and its arc length is $2\pi\sqrt{a^2 + c^2 + e^2}$. **55. a.** $\displaystyle\int_a^b \sqrt{(Ah'(t))^2 + (Bh'(t))^2}\, dt$

$= \displaystyle\int_a^b \sqrt{(A^2 + B^2)(h'(t))^2}\, dt = \sqrt{A^2 + B^2}\int_a^b |h'(t)|\, dt$

b. $64\sqrt{29}$ **c.** $\dfrac{7\sqrt{29}}{4}$ **57.** $\dfrac{\sqrt{1 + a^2}}{a}$ (where $a > 0$) **59.** 12.85

61. 26.73 **63. a.** 5.102 s **b.** $\displaystyle\int_0^{5.102} \sqrt{400 + (25 - 9.8t)^2}\, dt$

c. 124.43 m **d.** 102.04 m **65.** $|\mathbf{v}(t)| = \sqrt{a^2 + b^2 + c^2} = 1$, if $a^2 + b^2 + c^2 = 1$.

67. $\displaystyle\int_a^b |\mathbf{r}'(t)|\, dt = \int_a^b \sqrt{(cf'(t))^2 + (cg'(t))^2}\, dt$

$= |c|\displaystyle\int_a^b \sqrt{(f'(t))^2 + (g'(t))^2}\, dt = |c|L$

69. If $\mathbf{r}(t) = \langle t, f(t) \rangle$, then by definition, the arc length is $\displaystyle\int_a^b \sqrt{(t')^2 + f'(t)^2}\, dt = \int_a^b \sqrt{1 + f'(t)^2}\, dt$

$= \displaystyle\int_a^b \sqrt{1 + f'(x)^2}\, dx.$

Section 11.9 Exercises, pp. 852–854

1. 0 **3.** $\kappa = \dfrac{1}{|\mathbf{v}|}\left|\dfrac{d\mathbf{T}}{dt}\right|$ or $\kappa = \dfrac{|\mathbf{v} \times \mathbf{a}|}{|\mathbf{v}|^3}$ **5.** $\mathbf{N} = \dfrac{d\mathbf{T}/dt}{|d\mathbf{T}/dt|}$

7. These three unit vectors are mutually orthogonal at all points of the curve. **9.** The torsion measures the rate at which the curve rises or twists out of the **TN**-plane at a point. **11.** $\mathbf{T} = \dfrac{\langle 1, 2, 3 \rangle}{\sqrt{14}}, \kappa = 0$

13. $\mathbf{T} = \dfrac{\langle 1, 2\cos t, -2\sin t \rangle}{\sqrt{5}}, \kappa = \dfrac{1}{5}$

15. $\mathbf{T} = \dfrac{\langle \sqrt{3}\cos t, \cos t, -2\sin t \rangle}{2}, \kappa = \dfrac{1}{2}$

17. $\mathbf{T} = \dfrac{\langle 1, 4t \rangle}{\sqrt{1 + 16t^2}}, \kappa = \dfrac{4}{(1 + 16t^2)^{3/2}}$

19. $\mathbf{T} = \left\langle \cos\left(\dfrac{\pi t^2}{2}\right), \sin\left(\dfrac{\pi t^2}{2}\right) \right\rangle, \kappa = \pi t$

21. $\dfrac{1}{3}$ **23.** $\dfrac{2}{(4t^2 + 1)^{3/2}}$ **25.** $\dfrac{2\sqrt{5}}{(20\sin^2 t + \cos^2 t)^{3/2}}$

27. $\mathbf{T} = \langle \cos t, -\sin t \rangle, \mathbf{N} = \langle -\sin t, -\cos t \rangle$

29. $\mathbf{T} = \dfrac{\langle t, -3, 0 \rangle}{\sqrt{t^2 + 9}}, \mathbf{N} = \dfrac{\langle 3, t, 0 \rangle}{\sqrt{t^2 + 9}}$

31. $\mathbf{T} = \langle -\sin t^2, \cos t^2 \rangle, \mathbf{N} = \langle -\cos t^2, -\sin t^2 \rangle$

33. $\mathbf{T} = \dfrac{\langle 2t, 1 \rangle}{\sqrt{4t^2 + 1}}, \mathbf{N} = \dfrac{\langle 1, -2t \rangle}{\sqrt{4t^2 + 1}}$ **35.** $a_N = a_T = 0$

37. $a_T = \sqrt{3}\, e^t; a_N = \sqrt{2}e^t$ **39.** $\mathbf{a} = \dfrac{6t}{\sqrt{9t^2 + 4}}\mathbf{N} + \dfrac{18t^2 + 4}{\sqrt{9t^2 + 4}}\mathbf{T}$

41. $\mathbf{B}(t) = \langle 0, 0, -1 \rangle, \tau = 0$ **43.** $\mathbf{B}(t) = \langle 0, 0, 1 \rangle, \tau = 0$

45. $\mathbf{B}(t) = \dfrac{\langle -\sin t, \cos t, 2 \rangle}{\sqrt{5}}, \tau = -\dfrac{1}{5}$

47. $\mathbf{B}(t) = \dfrac{\langle 5, 12\sin t, -12\cos t \rangle}{13}, \tau = \dfrac{12}{169}$ **49. a.** False **b.** False **c.** False **d.** True **e.** False **f.** False **g.** False

51. $\kappa = \dfrac{2}{(1 + 4x^2)^{3/2}}$ **53.** $\kappa = \dfrac{x}{(x^2 + 1)^{3/2}}$

57. $\kappa = \dfrac{|ab|}{(a^2\cos^2 t + b^2\sin^2 t)^{3/2}}$ **59.** $\kappa = \dfrac{2|a|}{(1 + 4a^2t^2)^{3/2}}$

61. b. $\mathbf{v}_A(t) = \langle 1, 2, 3 \rangle, \mathbf{a}_A(t) = \langle 0, 0, 0 \rangle$ and $\mathbf{v}_B(t) = \langle 2t, 4t, 6t \rangle$, $\mathbf{a}_B(t) = \langle 2, 4, 6 \rangle$; A has constant velocity and zero acceleration while B has increasing speed and constant acceleration. **c.** $\mathbf{a}_A(t) = 0\mathbf{N} + 0\mathbf{T}, \mathbf{a}_B(t) = 0\mathbf{N} + 2\sqrt{14}\,\mathbf{T}$; both normal components are zero since the path is a straight line ($\kappa = 0$).

63. b. $\mathbf{v}_A(t) = \langle -\sin t, \cos t \rangle, \mathbf{a}_A(t) = \langle -\cos t, -\sin t \rangle$
$\mathbf{v}_B(t) = \langle -2t\sin t^2, 2t\cos t^2 \rangle$
$\mathbf{a}_B(t) = \langle -4t^2\cos t^2 - 2\sin t^2, -4t^2\sin t^2 + 2\cos t^2 \rangle$
c. $\mathbf{a}_A(t) = \mathbf{N} + 0\mathbf{T}, \mathbf{a}_B(t) = 4t^2\mathbf{N} + 2\mathbf{T}$; for A, the acceleration is always normal to the curve, but this is not true for B.

65. b. $\kappa = \dfrac{1}{2\sqrt{2(1 - \cos t)}}$ **c.**

d. Minimum curvature at $t = \pi$ **67. b.** $\kappa = \dfrac{1}{t(1 + t^2)^{3/2}}$

c.

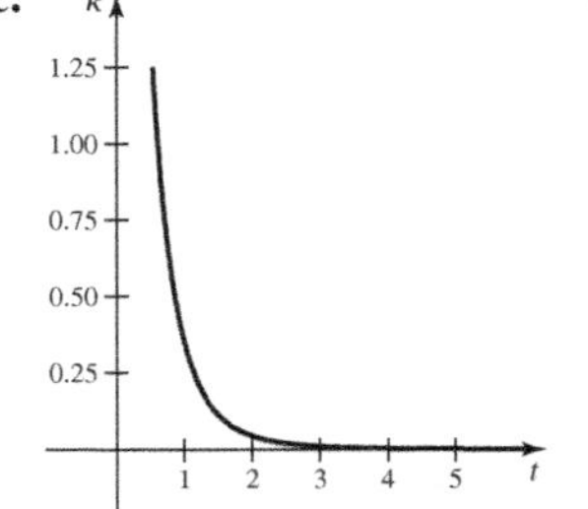

d. No maximum or minimum curvature

69. $\kappa = \dfrac{e^x}{(1 + e^{2x})^{3/2}}, \left(-\dfrac{\ln 2}{2}, \dfrac{1}{\sqrt{2}}\right), \dfrac{2\sqrt{3}}{9}$

71. $\dfrac{1}{\kappa} = \dfrac{1}{2}; x^2 + \left(y - \dfrac{1}{2}\right)^2 = \dfrac{1}{4}$

73. $\dfrac{1}{\kappa} = 4; (x - \pi)^2 + (y + 2)^2 = 16$

75. $\kappa\left(\dfrac{\pi}{2n}\right) = n^2$; κ increases as n increases.

77. a. Speed $= \sqrt{V_0^2 - 2V_0\, gt \sin\alpha + g^2t^2}$
b. $\kappa(t) = \dfrac{gV_0 \cos\alpha}{(V_0^2 - 2V_0\, gt\sin\alpha + g^2t^2)^{3/2}}$
c. Speed has a minimum at $t = \dfrac{V_0 \sin\alpha}{g}$ and $\kappa(t)$ has a maximum at $t = \dfrac{V_0\sin\alpha}{g}$. **79.** $\kappa = \dfrac{1}{|\mathbf{v}|}\cdot\left|\dfrac{d\mathbf{T}}{dt}\right|$, where $\mathbf{T} = \dfrac{\langle b, d, f\rangle}{\sqrt{b^2 + d^2 + f^2}}$ and b, d, f are constant. Therefore, $\dfrac{d\mathbf{T}}{dt} = \mathbf{0}$ so $\kappa = 0$.

81. a. $\kappa_1(x) = \dfrac{2}{(1 + 4x^2)^{3/2}}$

$\kappa_2(x) = \dfrac{12x^2}{(1 + 16x^6)^{3/2}}$

$\kappa_3(x) = \dfrac{30x^4}{(1 + 36x^{10})^{3/2}}$

b.

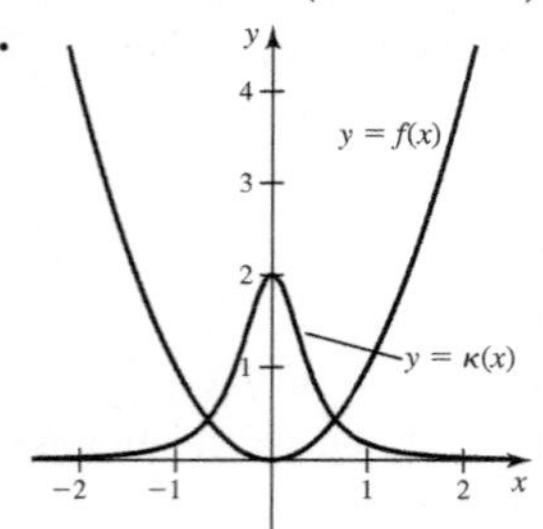

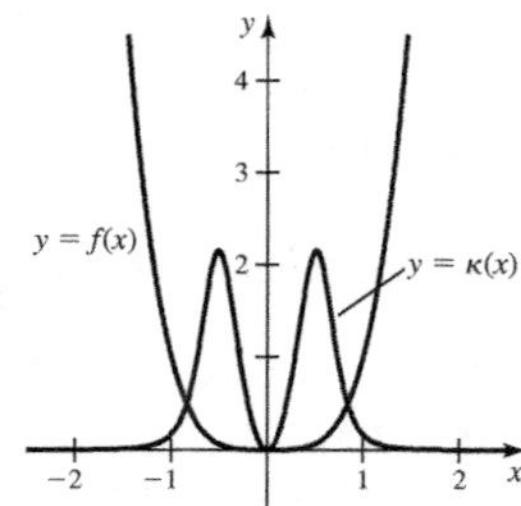

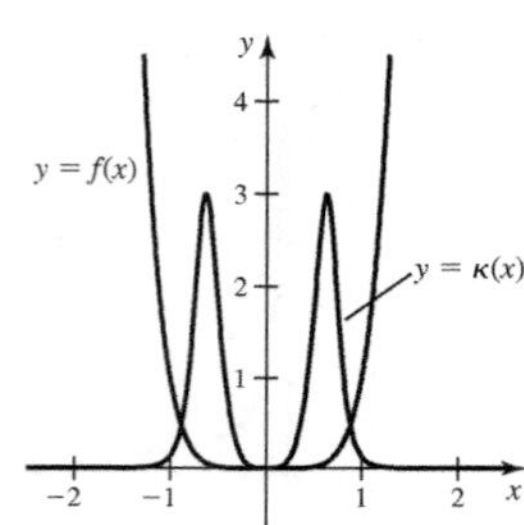

c. κ_1 has its maximum at $x = 0$, κ_2 has its maxima at $x = \pm\sqrt[6]{\frac{1}{56}}$, κ_3 has its maxima at $x = \pm\sqrt[10]{\frac{1}{99}}$. **d.** $\lim_{n\to\infty} z_n = 1$; the graphs of $y = f_n(x)$ show that as $n \to \infty$, the point corresponding to maximum curvature gets arbitrarily close to the point $(1, 0)$

Chapter 11 Review Exercises, pp. 854–857

1. a. True **b.** False **c.** True **d.** True **e.** False **f.** False
3. **5.**

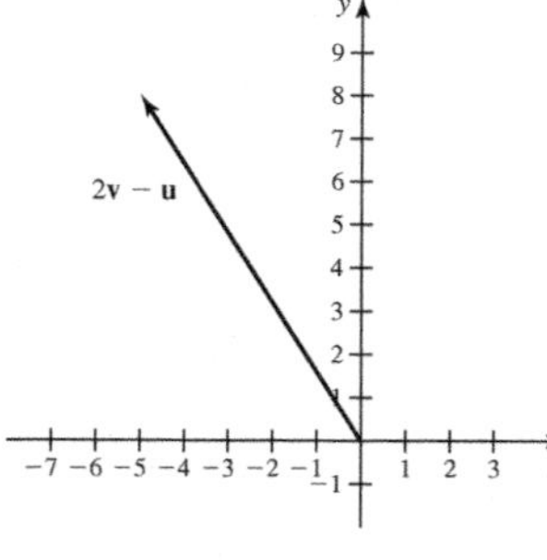

7. $\sqrt{221}$ **9.** $\pm\left\langle -\dfrac{60}{\sqrt{35}}, \dfrac{100}{\sqrt{35}}, \dfrac{20}{\sqrt{35}}\right\rangle$
11. $2\langle 29, 13, 22\rangle, -2\langle 29, 13, 22\rangle, 3\sqrt{166}$
13. a. $\mathbf{v} = -275\sqrt{2}\mathbf{i} + 275\sqrt{2}\mathbf{j}$ **b.** $-275\sqrt{2}\mathbf{i} + (275\sqrt{2} + 40)\mathbf{j}$
15. $\{(x, y, z): (x - 1)^2 + y^2 + (z + 1)^2 = 16\}$

17. $\{(x, y, z): x^2 + (y - 1)^2 + z^2 > 4\}$ **19.** A ball centered at $\left(\frac{1}{2}, -2, 3\right)$ of radius $\frac{3}{2}$ **21.** All points outside a sphere of radius 10 centered at $(3, 0, 10)$ **23.** 50.15 m/s; 85.4° below the horizontal in the northerly horizontal direction **25.** A circle of radius 1 centered at $(0, 2, 0)$ in the vertical plane $y = 2$ **27. a.** 0.68 radian **b.** $\frac{7}{9}\langle 1, 2, 2\rangle; \frac{7}{3}$ **c.** $\frac{7}{3}\langle -1, 2, 2\rangle; 7$ **29.** $\pm\left\langle \dfrac{12}{\sqrt{197}}, \dfrac{7}{\sqrt{197}}, \dfrac{2}{\sqrt{197}}\right\rangle$
31. $T(\theta) = 39.2 \sin\theta$ has a maximum value of 39.2 N-m (when $\theta = \pi/2$) and a minimum value of 0 N-m when $\theta = 0$. Direction does *not* change. **33.** $\langle x, y, z\rangle = \langle 0, -3, 9\rangle + t\langle 2, -5, -8\rangle$, $0 \le t \le 1$ **35.** $\langle t, 1 + 6t, 1 + 2t\rangle$ **37.** 11
39. **41.**

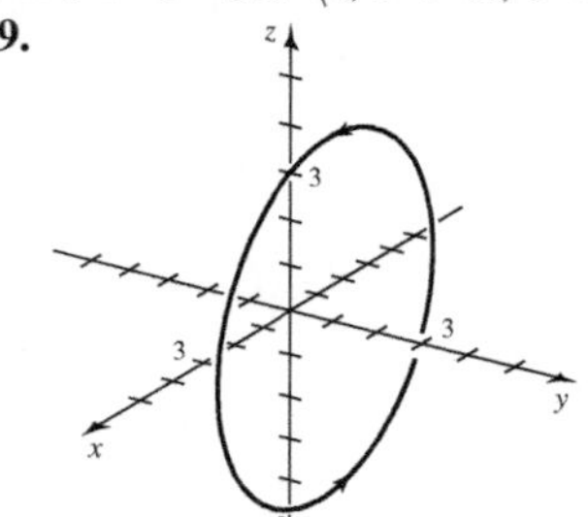

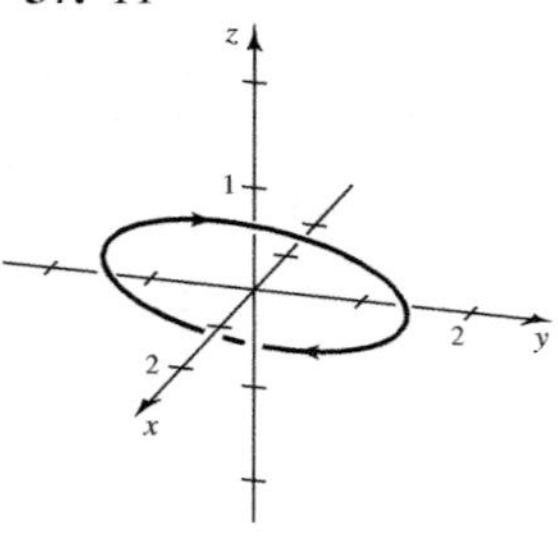

43. a. $\langle 1, 0\rangle; \langle 0, 1\rangle$ **b.** $\left\langle -\dfrac{2}{(2t + 1)^2}, \dfrac{1}{(t + 1)^2}\right\rangle; \langle -2, 1\rangle$
c. $\left\langle \dfrac{8}{(2t + 1)^3}, -\dfrac{2}{(t + 1)^3}\right\rangle$ **d.** $\left\langle \dfrac{1}{2}\ln|2t + 1|, t - \ln|t + 1|\right\rangle + \mathbf{C}$.
45. a. $\langle 0, 3, 0\rangle$; does not exist
b. $\langle 2\cos 2t, -12\sin 4t, 1\rangle; \langle 2, 0, 1\rangle$ **c.** $\langle -4\sin 2t, -48\cos 4t, 0\rangle$
d. $\left\langle -\dfrac{1}{2}\cos 2t, \dfrac{3}{4}\sin 4t, \dfrac{1}{2}t^2\right\rangle + \mathbf{C}$ **47. a.** (116, 30) **b.** 39.1 ft
c. 2.315 s **d.** $\displaystyle\int_0^{2.315} \sqrt{50^2 + (-32t + 50)^2}\, dt$ **e.** 129 ft
f. 41.4° to 79.4° **49.** 25.6 ft/s **51.** 12
53. a. $\mathbf{v}(t) = \mathbf{i} + t\sqrt{2}\mathbf{j} + t^2\mathbf{k}$ **b.** 12 **55.** 40.09
57. $\mathbf{r}(s) = \left\langle (\sqrt{1+s} - 1)^2, \dfrac{4\sqrt{2}}{3}(\sqrt{1+s} - 1)^{3/2}, 2(\sqrt{1+s} - 1)\right\rangle$, for $s \ge 0$ **59. a.** $\mathbf{v} = \langle -6\sin t, 3\cos t\rangle$, $\mathbf{T} = \dfrac{\langle -2\sin t, \cos t\rangle}{\sqrt{1 + 3\sin^2 t}}$
b. $\kappa(t) = \dfrac{2}{3(1 + 3\sin^2 t)^{3/2}}$
c. $\mathbf{N} = \left\langle -\dfrac{\cos t}{\sqrt{1 + 3\sin^2 t}}, -\dfrac{2\sin t}{\sqrt{1 + 3\sin^2 t}}\right\rangle$
d. $|\mathbf{N}| = \sqrt{\dfrac{\cos^2 t + 4\sin^2 t}{1 + 3\sin^2 t}} = \sqrt{\dfrac{(\cos^2 t + \sin^2 t) + 3\sin^2 t}{1 + 3\sin^2 t}} = 1$;
$\mathbf{T}\cdot\mathbf{N} = \dfrac{2\sin t\cos t - 2\sin t\cos t}{1 + 3\sin^2 t} = 0$
e.

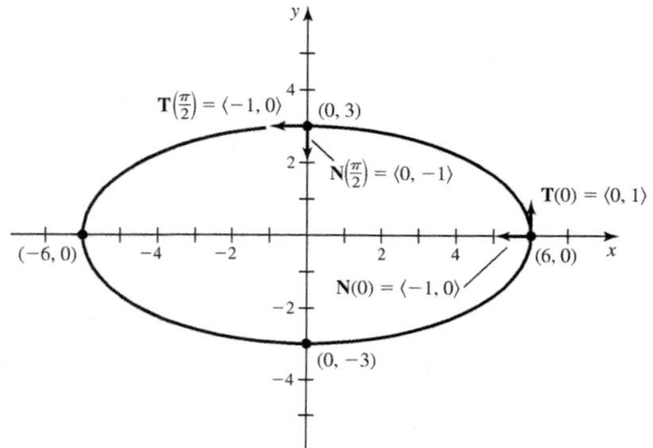

61. a. $\mathbf{v}(t) = \langle -\sin t, -2\sin t, \sqrt{5}\cos t \rangle$, $\mathbf{T}(t) = \left\langle -\frac{1}{\sqrt{5}}\sin t, -\frac{2}{\sqrt{5}}\sin t, \cos t \right\rangle$ **b.** $\kappa(t) = \frac{1}{\sqrt{5}}$

c. $\mathbf{N}(t) = \left\langle -\frac{1}{\sqrt{5}}\cos t, -\frac{2}{\sqrt{5}}\cos t, -\sin t \right\rangle$

d. $|\mathbf{N}(t)| = \sqrt{\frac{1}{5}\cos^2 t + \frac{4}{5}\cos^2 t + \sin^2 t} = 1$;

$\mathbf{T}\cdot\mathbf{N} = \left(\frac{1}{5}\cos t \sin t + \frac{4}{5}\cos t \sin t\right) - \sin t \cos t = 0$

e.

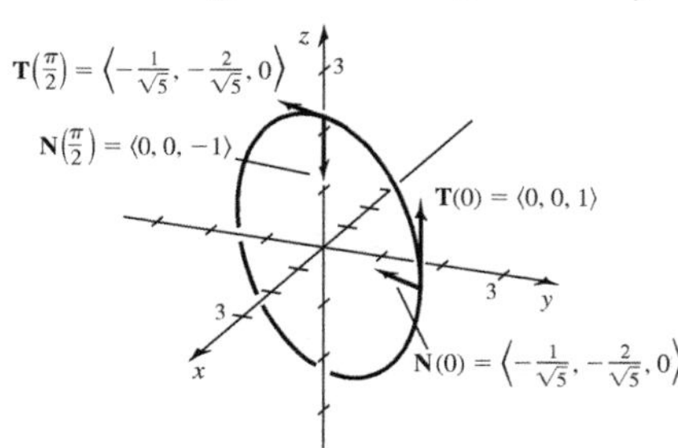

63. a. $\mathbf{a}(t) = 2\mathbf{N} + 0\mathbf{T} = 2\langle -\cos t, -\sin t \rangle$

b.

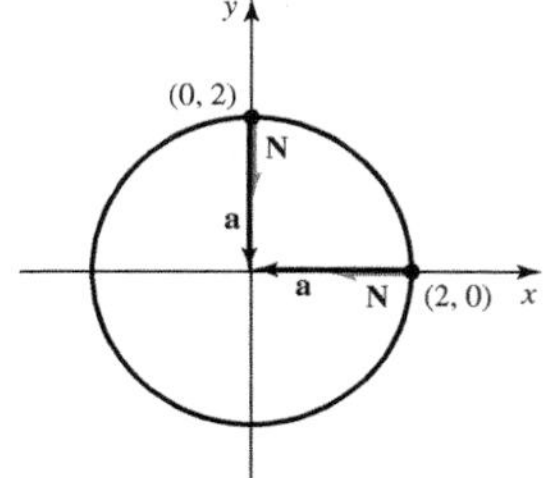

65. a. $a_T = \frac{2t}{\sqrt{t^2+1}}$ and $a_N = \frac{2}{\sqrt{t^2+1}}$

b.

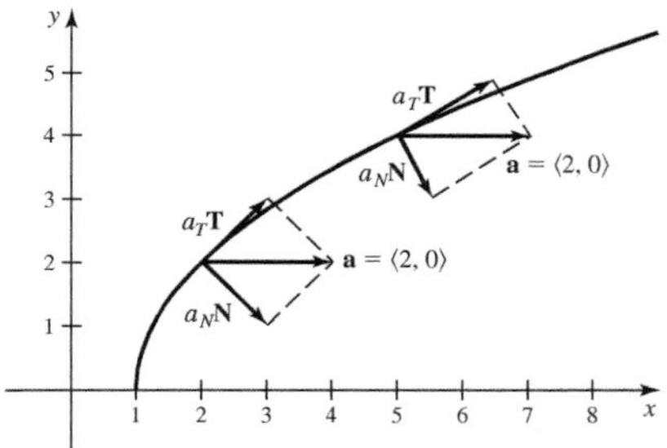

67. a. $a(x - x_0) + b(y - y_0) = 0$ **b.** $a(y - y_0) - b(x - x_0) = 0$

69. $\mathbf{B}(1) = \frac{\langle 3, -3, 1 \rangle}{\sqrt{19}}$; $\tau = \frac{3}{19}$

71. a. $\mathbf{T}(t) = \frac{1}{5}\langle 3\cos t, -3\sin t, 4 \rangle$ **b.** $\mathbf{N}(t) = \langle -\sin t, -\cos t, 0 \rangle$; $\kappa = \frac{3}{25}$ **c.**

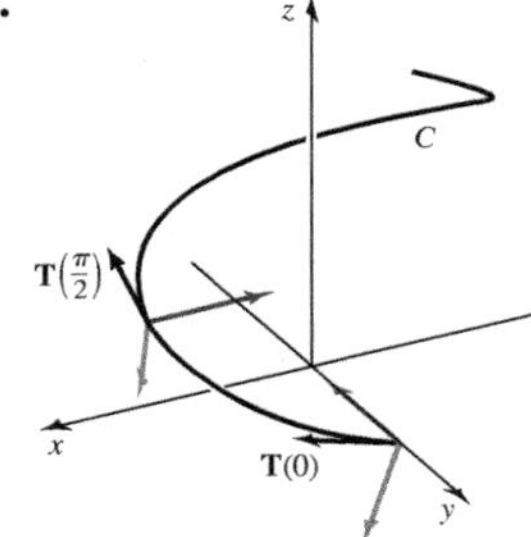

d. Yes **e.** $\mathbf{B}(t) = \frac{1}{5}\langle 4\cos t, -4\sin t, -3 \rangle$ **f.** See graph in part (c).
g. Check that **T**, **N**, and **B** have unit length and are mutually orthogonal. **h.** $\tau = -\frac{4}{25}$ **73. a.** Let $\mathbf{r}(t) = \langle x(t), y(t), z(t) \rangle$ and show there are constants a, b, and c such that $ax + by + cz = 1$, for all t in the interval. **b.** **B** is always normal to the plane and has length 1. Therefore, $\frac{d\mathbf{B}}{ds} = \mathbf{0}$ and $\tau = 0$. **c.** $x + y - z = 4$

CHAPTER 12

Section 12.1 Exercises, pp. 870–873

1. A point and a normal vector **3.** $x = -6, y = -4, z = 3$
5. z-axis; x-axis; y-axis **7.** Intersection of the surface with a plane parallel to one of the coordinate planes **9.** Ellipsoid
11. $x + y - z = 4$ **13.** $-x + 2y - 3z = 4$
15. $2x + y - 2z = -2$ **17.** $7x + 2y + z = 10$
19. $4x + 27y + 10z = 21$ **21.** Intercepts $x = 2, y = -3, z = 6$; $3x - 2y = 6, z = 0$; $-2y + z = 6, x = 0$; and $3x + z = 6, y = 0$

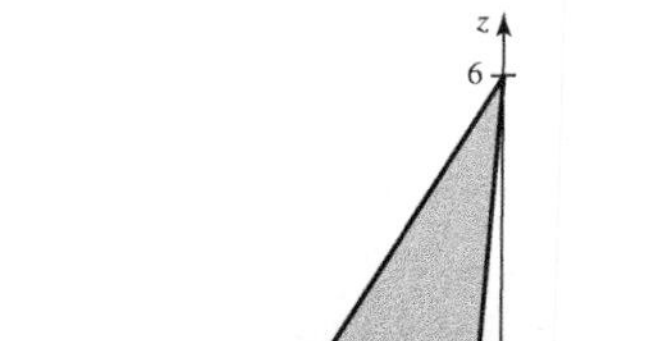

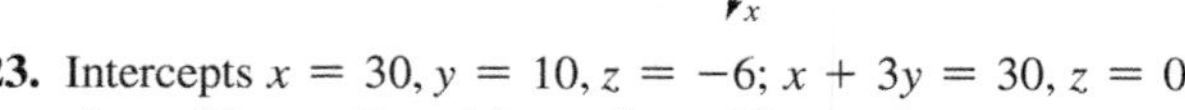

23. Intercepts $x = 30, y = 10, z = -6$; $x + 3y = 30, z = 0$; $x - 5z = 30, y = 0$; and $3y - 5z = 30, x = 0$

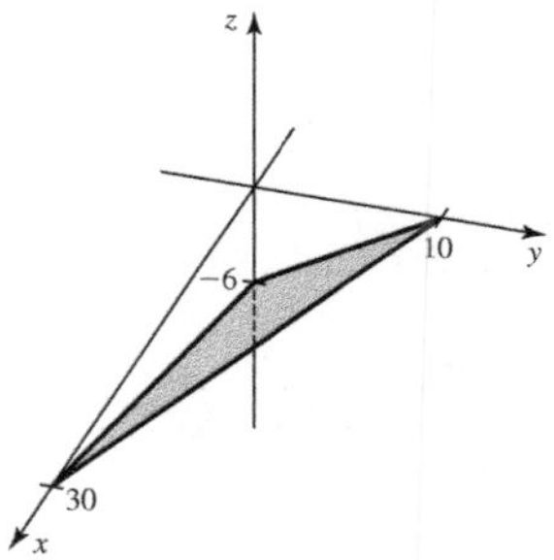

25. Orthogonal **27.** Neither **29.** Q and T are identical; Q, R, and T are parallel; S is orthogonal to Q, R, and T.
31. $-x + 2y - 4z = -17$ **33.** $4x + 3y - 2z = -5$
35. $x = t, y = 1 + 2t, z = -1 - 3t$
37. $x = \frac{7}{5} + 2t, y = \frac{9}{5} + t, z = -t$

39. a. x-axis
b.

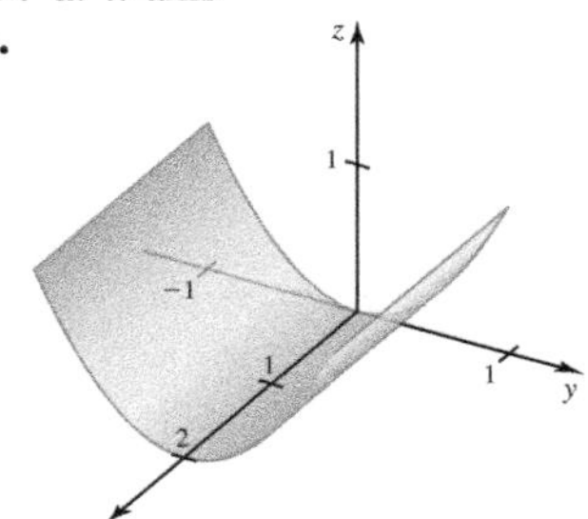

41. a. y-axis
b.

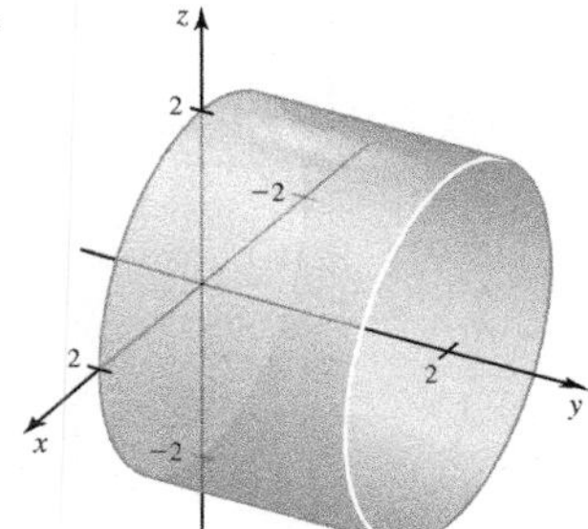

43. **a.** z-axis **b.**

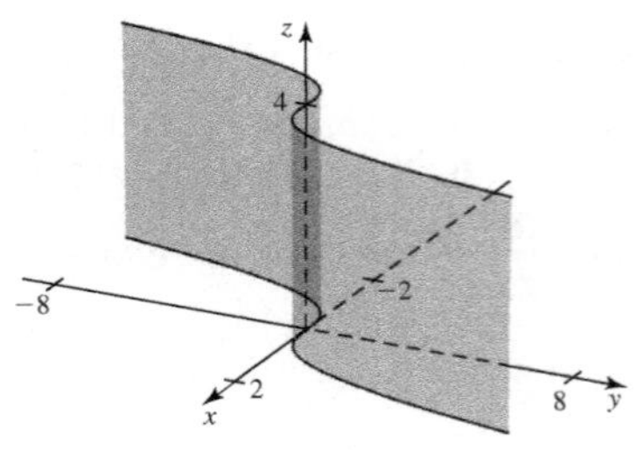

45. **a.** x-axis **b.**

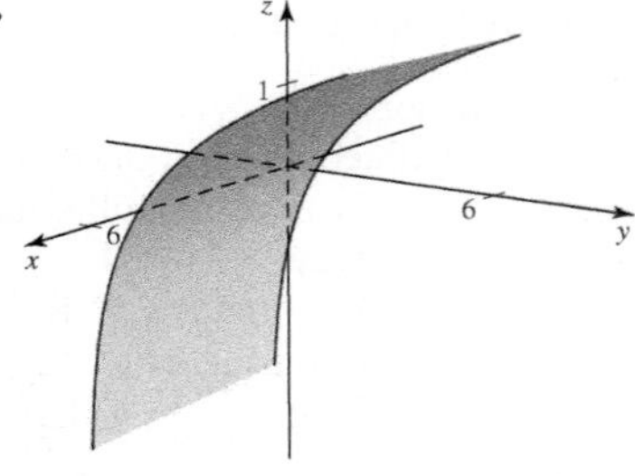

47. **a.** $x = \pm 1, y = \pm 2, z = \pm 3$ **b.** $x^2 + \frac{y^2}{4} = 1, x^2 + \frac{z^2}{9} = 1, \frac{y^2}{4} + \frac{z^2}{9} = 1$ **c.**

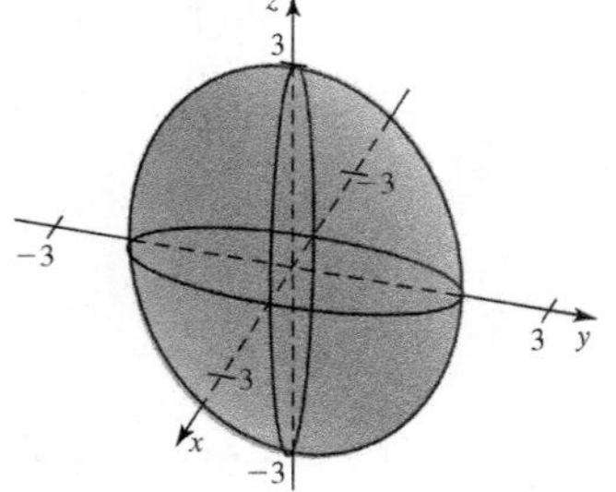

49. **a.** $x = \pm 3, y = \pm 1, z = \pm 6$ **b.** $\frac{x^2}{3} + 3y^2 = 3, \frac{x^2}{3} + \frac{z^2}{12} = 3, 3y^2 + \frac{z^2}{12} = 3$ **c.**

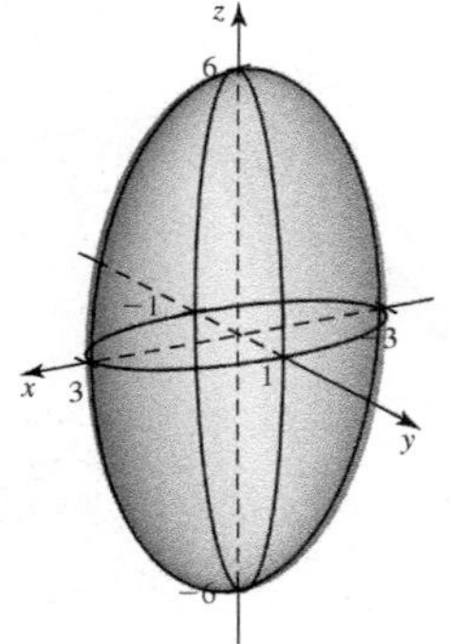

51. **a.** $x = y = z = 0$ **b.** $x = y^2, x = z^2$, origin
c.

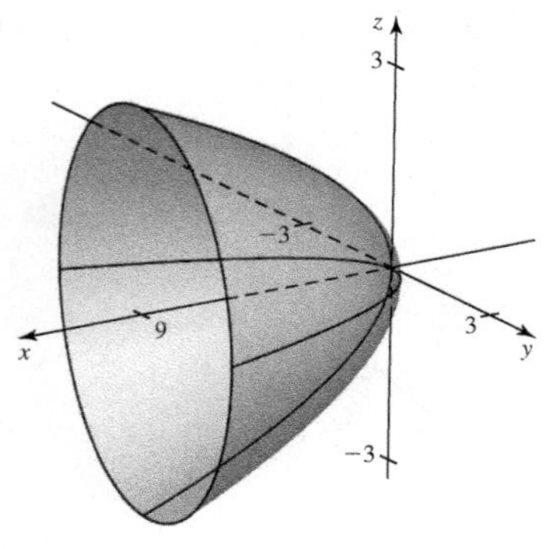

53. **a.** $x = y = z = 0$ **b.** Origin, $x - 9y^2 = 0, 9x - \frac{z^2}{4} = 0$
c.

55. **a.** $x = \pm 5, y = \pm 3$, no z-intercept
b. $\frac{x^2}{25} + \frac{y^2}{9} = 1, \frac{x^2}{25} - z^2 = 1, \frac{y^2}{9} - z^2 = 1$
c.

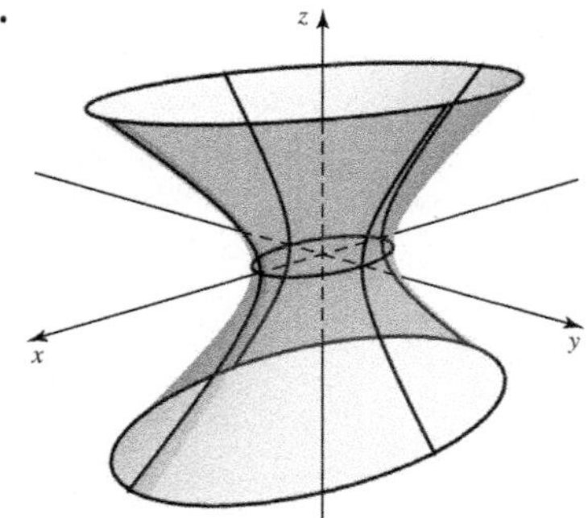

57. **a.** No x-intercept, $y = \pm 12, z = \pm \frac{1}{2}$ **b.** $-\frac{x^2}{4} + \frac{y^2}{16} = 9, -\frac{x^2}{4} + 36z^2 = 9, \frac{y^2}{16} + 36z^2 = 9$
c.

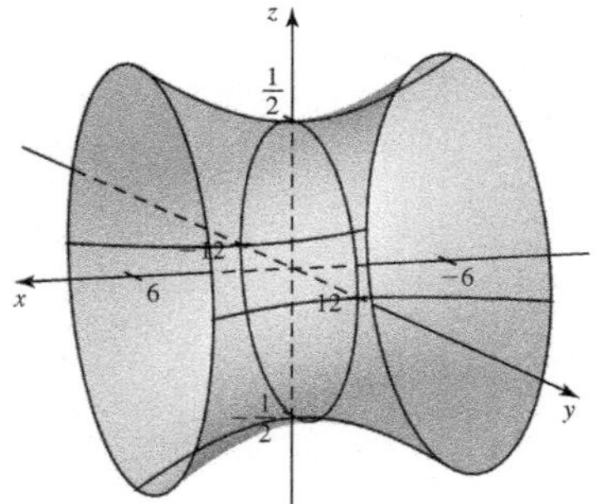

59. **a.** $x = y = z = 0$ **b.** $\frac{x^2}{9} - y^2 = 0, z = \frac{x^2}{9}, z = -y^2$
c.

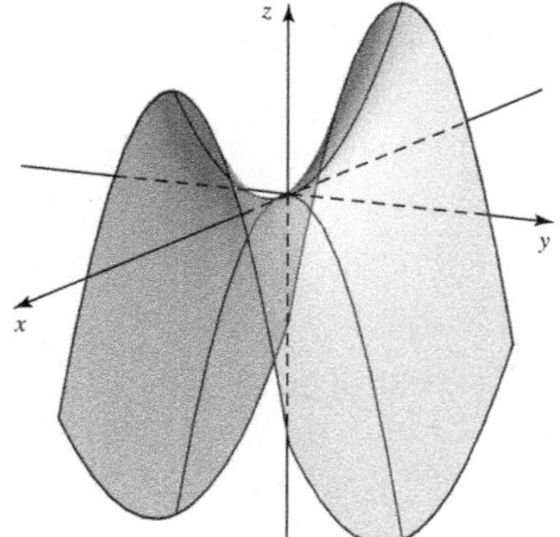

61. a. $x = y = z = 0$
b. $5x - \frac{y^2}{5} = 0, 5x + \frac{z^2}{20} = 0, -\frac{y^2}{5} + \frac{z^2}{20} = 0$
c.

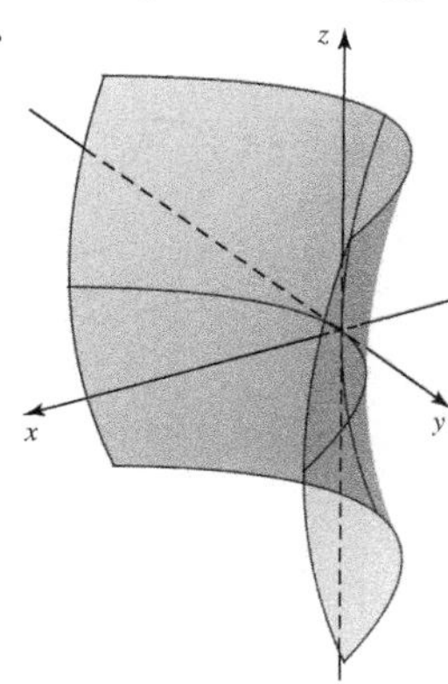

63. a. $x = y = z = 0$ **b.** Origin, $\frac{y^2}{4} = z^2, x^2 = z^2$
c.

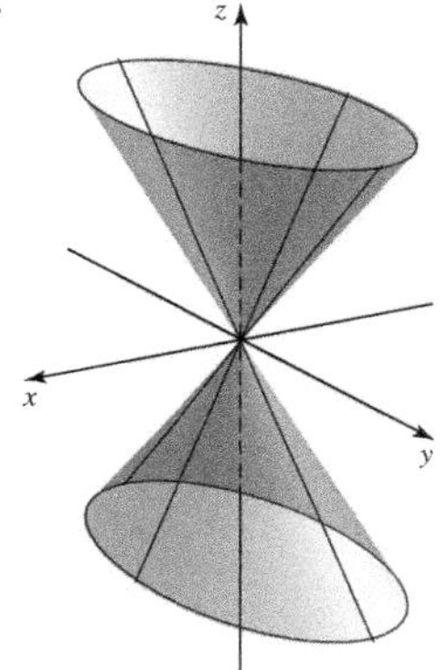

65. a. $x = y = z = 0$ **b.** $\frac{y^2}{18} = 2x^2, \frac{z^2}{32} = 2x^2$, origin
c.

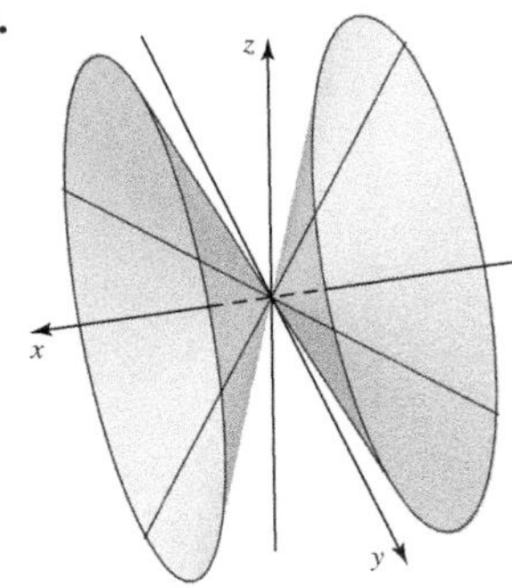

67. a. No x-intercept, $y = \pm 2$, no z-intercept **b.** $-x^2 + \frac{y^2}{4} = 1$, no xz-trace, $\frac{y^2}{4} - \frac{z^2}{9} = 1$
c.

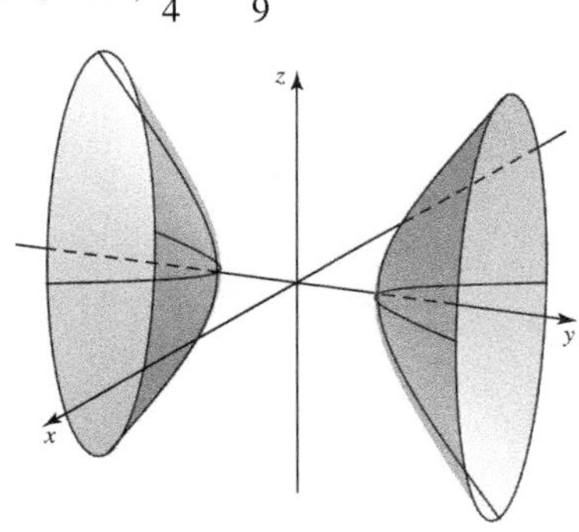

69. a. No x-intercept, $y = \pm\frac{\sqrt{3}}{3}$, no z-intercept
b. $-\frac{x^2}{3} + 3y^2 = 1$, no xz-trace, $3y^2 - \frac{z^2}{12} = 1$
c.

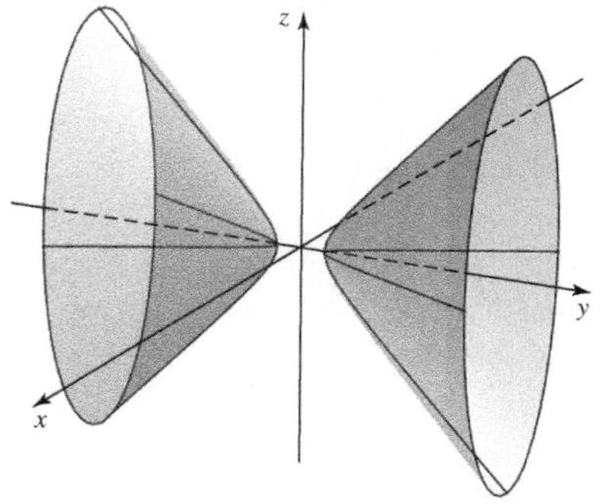

71. a. True **b.** False **c.** False **d.** True **e.** False **f.** False **g.** False **73.** $\mathbf{r}(t) = \langle 2 + 2t, 1 - 4t, 3 + t\rangle$ **75.** $6x - 4y + z = d$ **77.** The planes intersect in the point $(3, 6, 0)$. **79. a.** D **b.** A **c.** E **d.** F **e.** B **f.** C **81.** Hyperbolic paraboloid **83.** Elliptic paraboloid **85.** Hyperboloid of one sheet **87.** Hyperbolic cylinder **89.** Hyperboloid of two sheets **91.** $(3, 9, 27)$ and $(-5, 25, 75)$
93. $\left(\frac{6\sqrt{10}}{5}, \frac{2\sqrt{10}}{5}, \frac{3\sqrt{10}}{10}\right)$ and $\left(-\frac{6\sqrt{10}}{5}, -\frac{2\sqrt{10}}{5}, -\frac{3\sqrt{10}}{10}\right)$
95. $\theta = \cos^{-1}\left(-\frac{\sqrt{105}}{14}\right) \approx 2.392$ rad; $137°$ **97.** All except the hyperbolic paraboloid **99. a.**

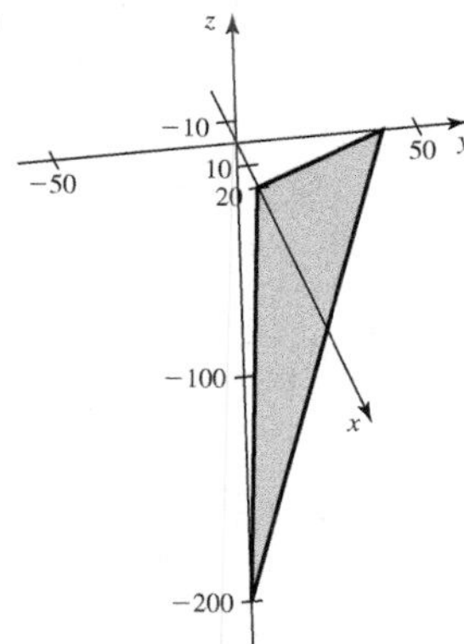

b. Positive **c.** $2x + y = 40$, line in the xy-plane **101. a.** $z = cy$ **b.** $\theta = \tan^{-1} c$ **103. a.** The length of the orthogonal projection of $\overrightarrow{PQ}$ onto the normal vector $\mathbf{n}$ is the magnitude of the scalar component of $\overrightarrow{PQ}$ in the direction of $\mathbf{n}$, which is $\frac{|\overrightarrow{PQ} \cdot \mathbf{n}|}{|\mathbf{n}|}$. **b.** $\frac{13}{\sqrt{14}}$

Section 12.2 Exercises, pp. 882–885

1. Independent: x and y; dependent: z
3. $D = \{(x, y): x \neq 0 \text{ and } y \neq 0\}$ **5.** Three **7.** Circles **9.** $n = 6$
11. $\mathbb{R}^2$ **13.** $\{(x, y): x^2 + y^2 \leq 25\}$ **15.** $D = \{(x, y): y \neq 0\}$
17. $D = \{(x, y): y < x^2\}$
19. $D = \{(x, y): xy \geq 0, (x, y) \neq (0, 0)\}$

21. Plane; domain $= \mathbb{R}^2$, range $= \mathbb{R}$

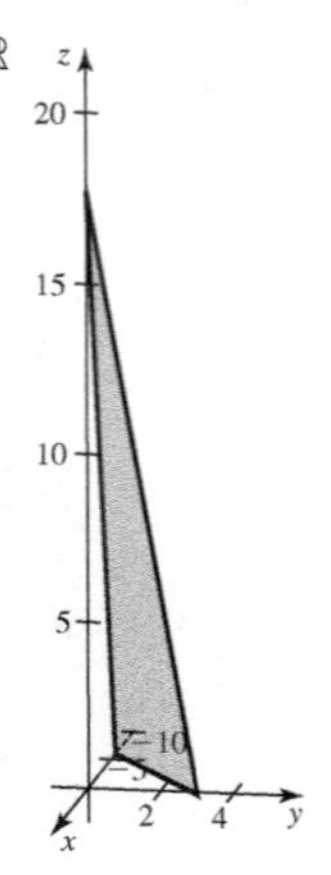

23. Hyperbolic paraboloid; domain $= \mathbb{R}^2$, range $= \mathbb{R}$

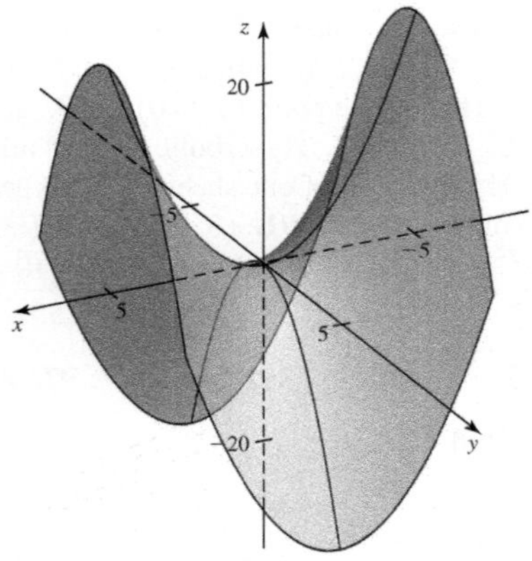

25. Lower part of a hyperboloid of two sheets; domain $= \mathbb{R}^2$, range $= (-\infty, -1]$

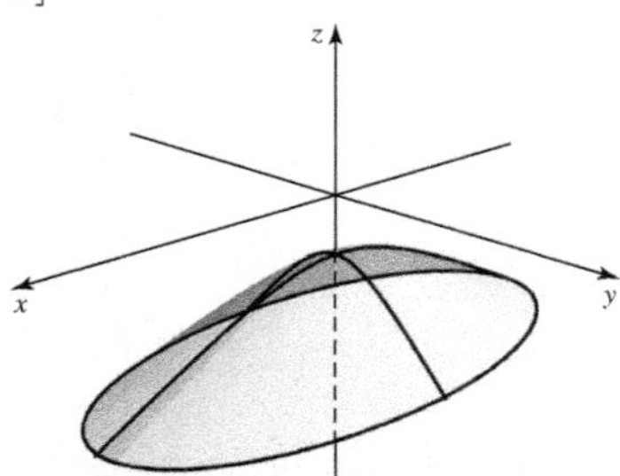

27. Upper half of a hyperboloid of one sheet; domain $= \{(x, y): x^2 + y^2 \geq 1\}$, range $= [0, \infty)$

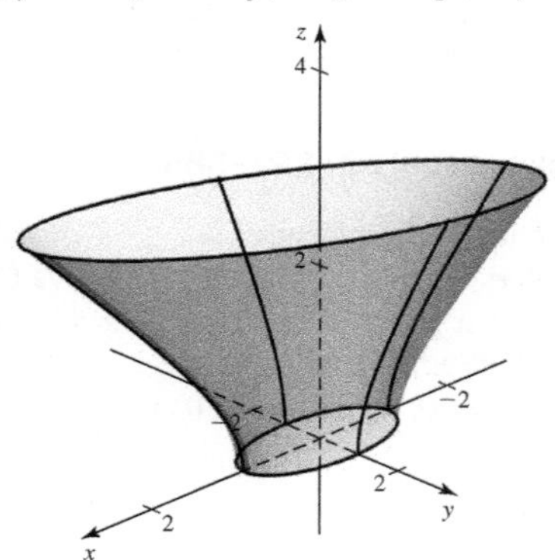

29. a. A **b.** D **c.** B **d.** C **31.**

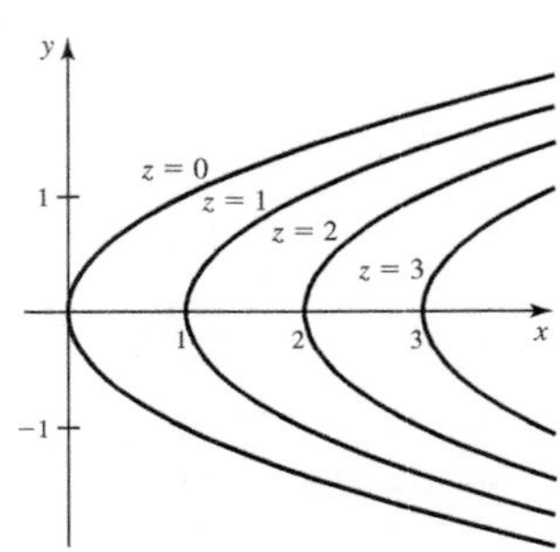

33.

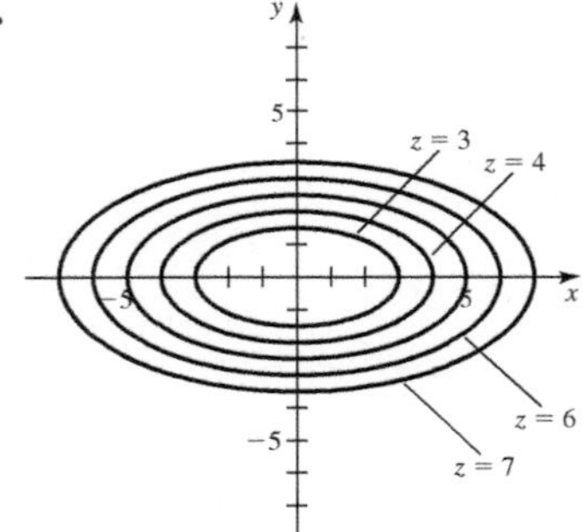

35.

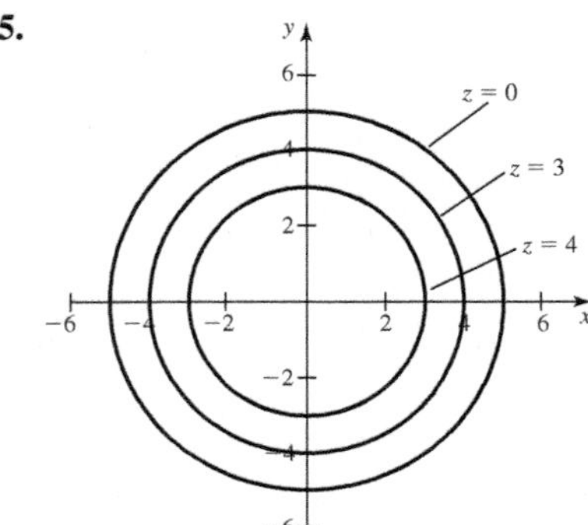

37.

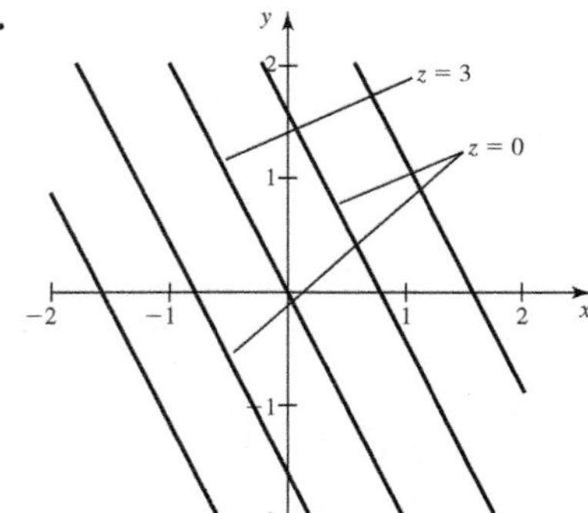

39. a.

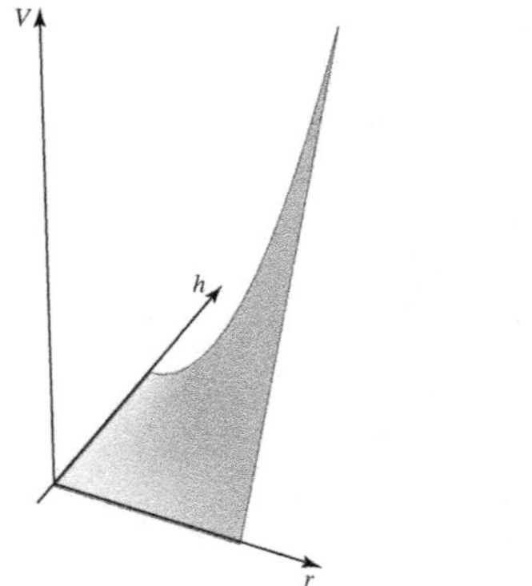

b. $D = \{(r, h): r > 0, h > 0\}$ **c.** $h = 300/(\pi r^2)$

41. a.

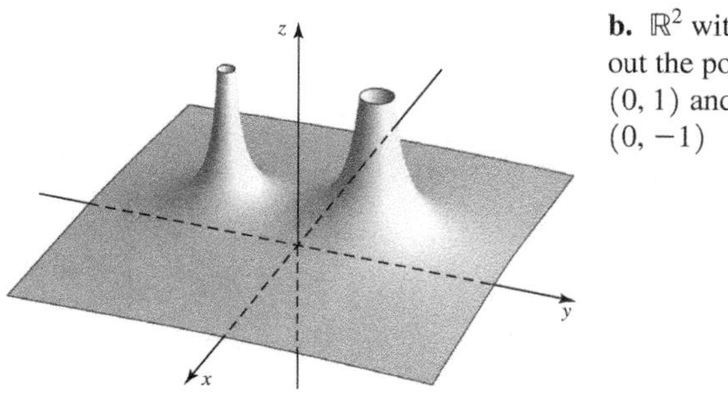

b. $\mathbb{R}^2$ without the points $(0, 1)$ and $(0, -1)$

c. $\varphi(2, 3)$ is greater. **d.**

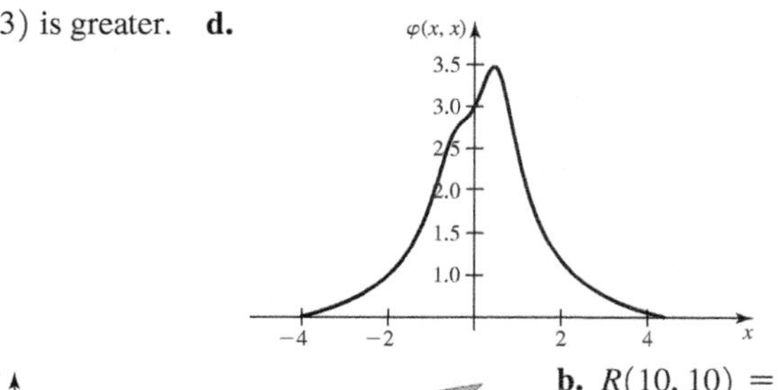

43. a.

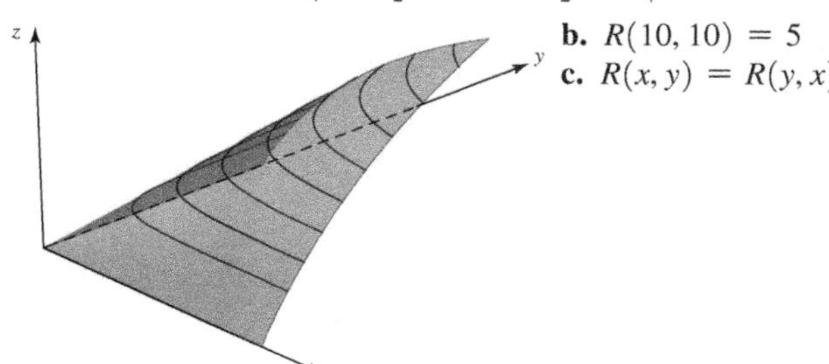

b. $R(10, 10) = 5$
c. $R(x, y) = R(y, x)$

45. a.

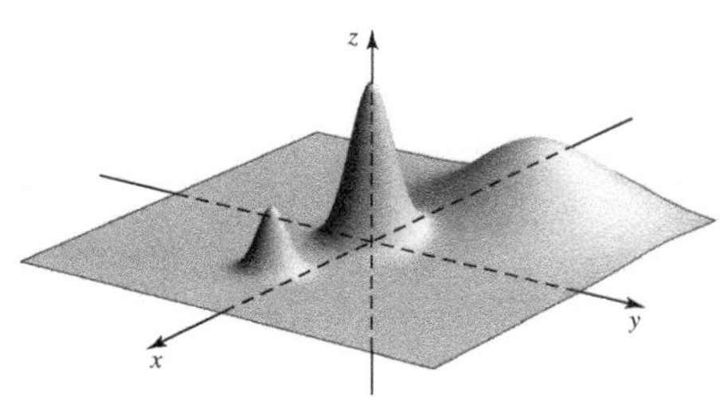

b. $(0, 0), (-5, 3), (4, -1)$
c. $f(0, 0) = 10.17$, $f(-5, 3) = 5.00$, $f(4, -1) = 4.00$
47. $D = \{(x, y, z): x \neq z\}$; all points not on the plane $x = z$
49. $D = \{(x, y, z): y \geq z\}$; all points on or below the plane $y = z$
51. $D = \{(x, y, z): x^2 \leq y\}$; all points on the side of the vertical cylinder $y = x^2$ that contains the positive y-axis **53. a.** False **b.** False **c.** True **55. a.** $D = \mathbb{R}^2$, range $= [0, \infty)$
b.

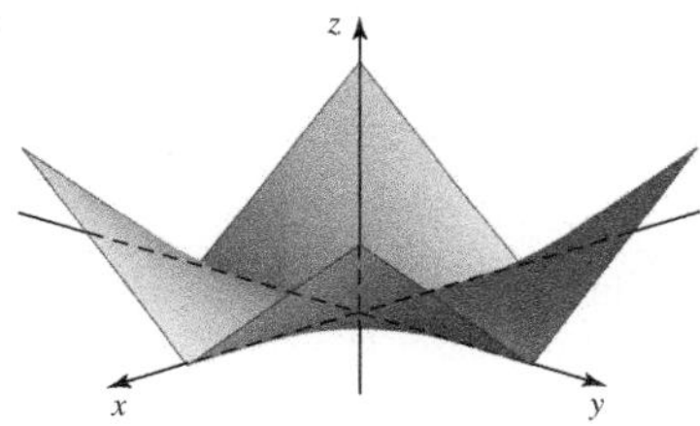

57. a. $D = \{(x, y): x \neq y\}$, range $= \mathbb{R}$
b.

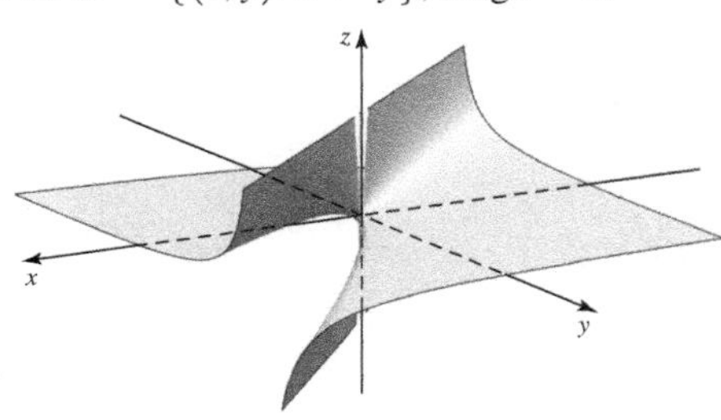

59. a. $D = \{(x, y): y \neq x + \pi/2 + n\pi \text{ for any integer } n\}$, range $= [0, \infty)$ **b.**

61. Peak at the origin **63.** Depression at $(1, 0)$ **65.** The level curves are $ax + by = d - cz_0$, where z_0 is a constant, which are lines with slope $-a/b$ if $b \neq 0$ or vertical lines if $b = 0$.
67. $z = x^2 + y^2 - C$; paraboloids with vertices at $(0, 0, -C)$
69. $x^2 + 2z^2 = C$; elliptic cylinders parallel to the y-axis
71. a. $P = \dfrac{20{,}000r}{(1 + r)^{240} - 1}$ **b.** $P = \dfrac{Br}{(1 + r)^{240} - 1}$, with $B = 5000, 10{,}000, 15{,}000, 25{,}000$

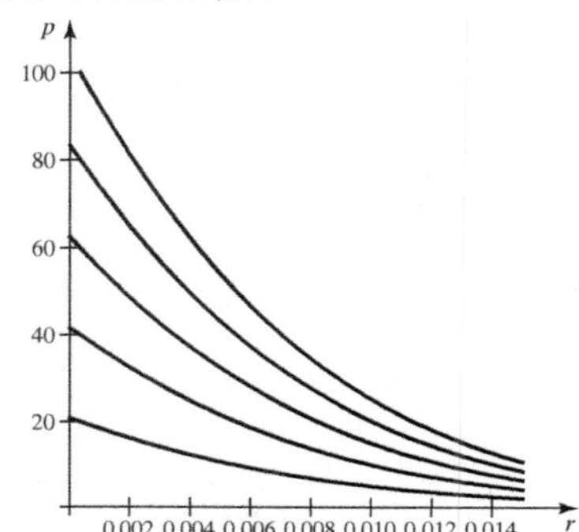

73. a.

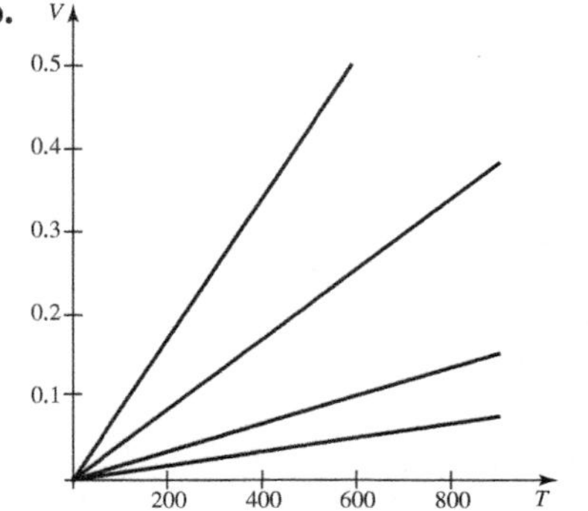

b.

c.

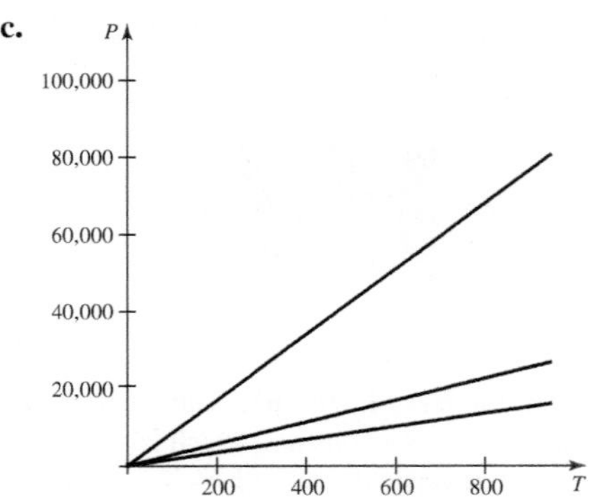

75. $D = \{(x, y): x - 1 \le y \le x + 1\}$
77. $D = \{(x, y, z): (x \le z \text{ and } y \ge -z) \text{ or } (x \ge z \text{ and } y \le -z)\}$

Section 12.3 Exercises, pp. 892–894

1. The values of $f(x, y)$ are arbitrarily close to L for all (x, y) sufficiently close to (a, b). **3.** Because polynomials of n variables are continuous on all of $\mathbb{R}^n$, limits of polynomials can be evaluated with direct substitution. **5.** If the function approaches different values along different paths, the limit does not exist. **7.** f must be defined, the limit must exist, and the limit must equal the function value. **9.** At any point where the denominator is nonzero **11.** 101 **13.** 27 **15.** $1/(2\pi)$ **17.** 2 **19.** 6 **21.** -1 **23.** 2 **25.** $1/(2\sqrt{2}) = \sqrt{2}/4$ **27.** $L = 1$ along $y = 0$, and $L = -1$ along $x = 0$ **29.** $L = 1$ along $x = 0$, and $L = -2$ along $y = 0$ **31.** $L = 2$ along $y = x$, and $L = 0$ along $y = -x$ **33.** $\mathbb{R}^2$ **35.** All points except $(0, 0)$ **37.** $\{(x, y): x \ne 0\}$ **39.** All points except $(0, 0)$ **41.** $\mathbb{R}^2$ **43.** $\mathbb{R}^2$ **45.** $\mathbb{R}^2$ **47.** All points except $(0, 0)$ **49.** $\mathbb{R}^2$ **51.** $\mathbb{R}^2$ **53.** 6 **55.** -1 **57.** 2 **59. a.** False **b.** False **c.** True **d.** False **61.** $\frac{1}{2}$ **63.** 0 **65.** Does not exist **67.** $\frac{1}{4}$ **69.** 0 **71.** 1 **73.** $b = 1$ **77.** 1 **79.** 1 **81.** 0

Section 12.4 Exercises, pp. 904–907

1. $f_x(a, b)$ is the slope of the surface in the direction parallel to the positive x-axis, $f_y(a, b)$ is the slope of the surface in the direction parallel to the positive y-axis, both taken at (a, b).
3. $f_x(x, y) = \cos xy - xy \sin xy$; $f_y(x, y) = -x^2 \sin xy$
5. Think of x and y as being fixed, and take the derivative with respect to the variable z. **7.** $f_x(x, y) = 5y$; $f_y(x, y) = 5x$
9. $f_x(x, y) = \dfrac{1}{y}$; $f_y(x, y) = -\dfrac{x}{y^2}$ **11.** $f_x(x, y) = 6x$; $f_y(x, y) = 12y^2$
13. $f_x(x, y) = 6xy$; $f_y(x, y) = 3x^2$ **15.** $f_x(x, y) = e^y$; $f_y(x, y) = xe^y$
17. $g_x(x, y) = -2y \sin 2xy$; $g_y(x, y) = -2x \sin 2xy$
19. $f_x(x, y) = 2xye^{x^2y}$; $f_y(x, y) = x^2e^{x^2y}$ **21.** $f_w(w, z) = \dfrac{z^2 - w^2}{(w^2 + z^2)^2}$; $f_z(w, z) = -\dfrac{2wz}{(w^2 + z^2)^2}$ **23.** $s_y(y, z) = z^3 \sec^2 yz$; $s_z(y, z) = 2z \tan yz + yz^2 \sec^2 yz$ **25.** $G_s(s, t) = \dfrac{\sqrt{st}(t - s)}{2s(s + t)^2}$; $G_t(s, t) = \dfrac{\sqrt{st}(s - t)}{2t(s + t)^2}$ **27.** $f_x(x, y) = 2yx^{2y-1}$; $f_y(x, y) = 2x^{2y} \ln x$
29. $h_{xx}(x, y) = 6x$; $h_{xy}(x, y) = 2y$; $h_{yx}(x, y) = 2y$; $h_{yy}(x, y) = 2x$
31. $f_{xx}(x, y) = 2y^3$; $f_{xy}(x, y) = f_{yx}(x, y) = 6xy^2$; $f_{yy}(x, y) = 6x^2y$
33. $f_{xx}(x, y) = -16y^3 \sin 4x$; $f_{xy}(x, y) = 12y^2 \cos 4x$; $f_{yx}(x, y) = 12y^2 \cos 4x$; $f_{yy}(x, y) = 6y \sin 4x$
35. $p_{uu}(u, v) = \dfrac{-2u^2 + 2v^2 + 8}{(u^2 + v^2 + 4)^2}$; $p_{uv}(u, v) = -\dfrac{4uv}{(u^2 + v^2 + 4)^2}$; $p_{vu}(u, v) = -\dfrac{4uv}{(u^2 + v^2 + 4)^2}$; $p_{vv}(u, v) = \dfrac{2u^2 - 2v^2 + 8}{(u^2 + v^2 + 4)^2}$

37. $F_{rr}(r, s) = 0$; $F_{rs}(r, s) = e^s$; $F_{sr}(r, s) = e^s$; $F_{ss}(r, s) = re^s$
39. $f_{xy} = 0 = f_{yx}$ **41.** $f_{xy} = -(xy \cos xy + \sin xy) = f_{yx}$
43. $f_{xy} = e^{x+y} = f_{yx}$ **45.** $f_x(x, y, z) = y + z$; $f_y(x, y, z) = x + z$; $f_z(x, y, z) = x + y$ **47.** $h_x(x, y, z) = h_y(x, y, z) = h_z(x, y, z) = -\sin(x + y + z)$
49. $F_u(u, v, w) = \dfrac{1}{v + w}$; $F_v(u, v, w) = F_w(u, v, w) = -\dfrac{u}{(v + w)^2}$
51. $f_w(w, x, y, z) = 2wxy^2$; $f_x(w, x, y, z) = w^2y^2 + y^3z^2$; $f_y(w, x, y, z) = 2w^2xy + 3xy^2z^2$; $f_z(w, x, y, z) = 2xy^3z$
53. $h_w(w, x, y, z) = \dfrac{z}{xy}$; $h_x(w, x, y, z) = -\dfrac{wz}{x^2y}$; $h_y(w, x, y, z) = -\dfrac{wz}{xy^2}$; $h_z(w, x, y, z) = \dfrac{w}{xy}$ **55. a.** $\dfrac{\partial V}{\partial P} = -\dfrac{kT}{P^2}$; volume decreases with pressure at fixed temperature **b.** $\dfrac{\partial V}{\partial T} = \dfrac{k}{P}$; volume increases with temperature at fixed pressure
c.

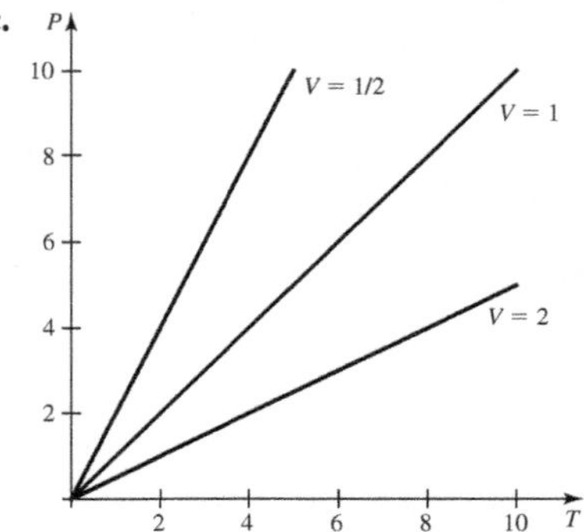

57. a. No **b.** No. **c.** $f_x(0, 0) = f_y(0, 0) = 0$ **d.** f_x and f_y are not continuous at $(0, 0)$. **59. a.** False **b.** False **c.** True
61. 1.41 **63.** 1.55 (answer will vary)
65. $f_x(x, y) = -\dfrac{2x}{1 + (x^2 + y^2)^2}$; $f_y(x, y) = -\dfrac{2y}{1 + (x^2 + y^2)^2}$
67. $h_x(x, y, z) = z(1 + x + 2y)^{z-1}$; $h_y(x, y, z) = 2z(1 + x + 2y)^{z-1}$; $h_z(x, y, z) = (1 + x + 2y)^z \ln(1 + x + 2y)$
69. a. $z_x(x, y) = \dfrac{1}{y^2}$; $z_y(x, y) = -\dfrac{2x}{y^3}$

b.

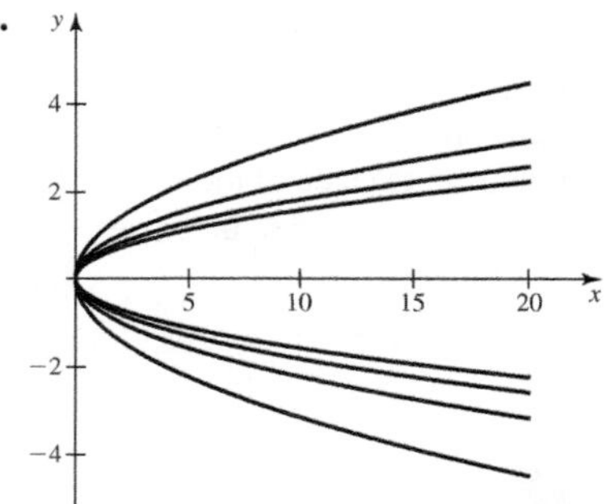

c. z increases as x increases. **d.** z increases as y increases when $y < 0$, z is undefined for $y = 0$, and z decreases as y increases for $y > 0$. **71. a.** $\dfrac{\partial c}{\partial a} = \dfrac{2a - b}{2\sqrt{a^2 + b^2 - ab}}$; $\dfrac{\partial c}{\partial b} = \dfrac{2b - a}{2\sqrt{a^2 + b^2 - ab}}$
b. $\dfrac{\partial c}{\partial a} = \dfrac{2a - b}{2c}$; $\dfrac{\partial c}{\partial b} = \dfrac{2b - a}{2c}$ **c.** $a > \frac{1}{2}b$
73. a. $\varphi_x(x, y) = -\dfrac{2x}{(x^2 + (y - 1)^2)^{3/2}} - \dfrac{x}{(x^2 + (y + 1)^2)^{3/2}}$; $\varphi_y(x, y) = -\dfrac{2(y - 1)}{(x^2 + (y - 1)^2)^{3/2}} - \dfrac{y + 1}{(x^2 + (y + 1)^2)^{3/2}}$

b. They both approach zero. **c.** $\varphi_x(0, y) = 0$

d. $\varphi_y(x, 0) = \dfrac{1}{(x^2 + 1)^{3/2}}$

75. a. $\dfrac{\partial R}{\partial R_1} = \dfrac{R_2^2}{(R_1 + R_2)^2}; \dfrac{\partial R}{\partial R_2} = \dfrac{R_1^2}{(R_1 + R_2)^2}$

b. $\dfrac{\partial R}{\partial R_1} = \dfrac{R^2}{R_1^2}; \dfrac{\partial R}{\partial R_2} = \dfrac{R^2}{R_2^2}$ **c.** Increase **d.** Decrease

77. $\dfrac{\partial^2 u}{\partial t^2} = -4c^2 \cos(2(x + ct)) = c^2 \dfrac{\partial^2 u}{\partial x^2}$

79. $\dfrac{\partial^2 u}{\partial t^2} = c^2 Af''(x + ct) + c^2 Bg''(x - ct) = c^2 \dfrac{\partial^2 u}{\partial x^2}$

81. $u_{xx} = 6x \quad u_{yy} = -6x$

83. $u_{xx} = \dfrac{2(x - 1)y}{((x - 1)^2 + y^2)^2} - \dfrac{2(x + 1)y}{((x + 1)^2 + y^2)^2}$;

$u_{yy} = -\dfrac{2(x - 1)y}{((x - 1)^2 + y^2)^2} + \dfrac{2(x + 1)y}{((x + 1)^2 + y^2)^2}$

85. $u_t = -16e^{-4t} \cos 2x = u_{xx}$ **87.** $u_t = -a^2 A e^{-a^2 t} \cos ax = u_{xx}$ **89.** $\varepsilon_1 = \Delta y, \varepsilon_2 = 0$ or $\varepsilon_1 = 0, \varepsilon_2 = \Delta x$ **91. a.** f is continuous at $(0, 0)$. **b.** f is not differentiable at $(0, 0)$. **c.** $f_x(0, 0) = f_y(0, 0) = 0$ **d.** f_x and f_y are not continuous at $(0, 0)$. **e.** Theorem 12.5 does not apply because f_x and f_y are not continuous at $(0, 0)$; Theorem 12.6 does not apply because f is not differentiable at $(0, 0)$. **93. a.** $f_x(x, y) = -h(x); f_y(x, y) = h(y)$ **b.** $f_x(x, y) = yh(xy); f_y(x, y) = xh(xy)$

Section 12.5 Exercises, pp. 913–916

1. One dependent, two intermediate, and one independent variable **3.** Multiply each of the partial derivatives of w by the t-derivative of the corresponding function and add all these expressions.

5.

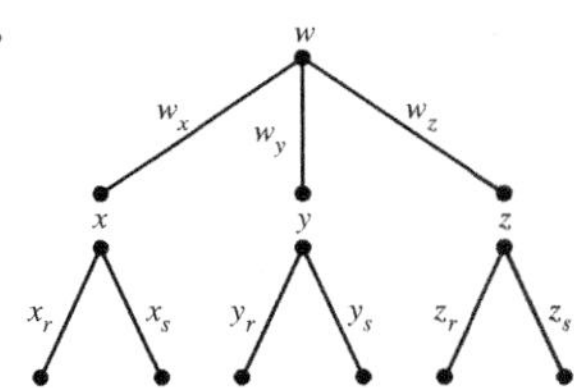

7. $4t^3 + 3t^2$ **9.** $z'(t) = 2t \sin 4t^3 + 12t^4 \cos 4t^3$ **11.** $w'(t) = -\sin t \sin 3t^4 + 12t^3 \cos t \cos 3t^4$ **13.** $w'(t) = 20t^4 \sin(t + 1) + 4t^5 \cos(t + 1)$

15. $U'(t) = \dfrac{1 + 2t + 3t^2}{t + t^2 + t^3}$

17. a. $V'(t) = 2\pi r(t)h(t)r'(t) + \pi r(t)^2 h'(t)$ **b.** $V'(t) = 0$ **c.** The volume remains constant. **19.** $z_s = 2(s - t) \sin t^2$; $z_t = 2(s - t)(t(s - t) \cos t^2 - \sin t^2)$ **21.** $z_s = 2s - 3s^2 - 2st + t^2; z_t = -s^2 - 2t + 2st + 3t^2$ **23.** $z_s = (t + 1)e^{st+s+t}; z_t = (s + 1)e^{st+s+t}$

25. $w_s = -\dfrac{2t(t + 1)}{(st + s - t)^2}; w_t = \dfrac{2s}{(st + s - t)^2}$

27.

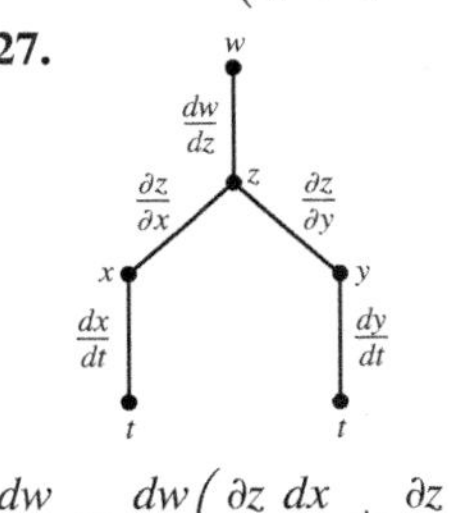

$$\frac{dw}{dt} = \frac{dw}{dz}\left(\frac{\partial z}{\partial x}\frac{dx}{dt} + \frac{\partial z}{\partial y}\frac{dy}{dt}\right)$$

29. $\dfrac{\partial u}{\partial z} = \dfrac{du}{dv}\left(\dfrac{\partial v}{\partial w}\dfrac{dw}{dz} + \dfrac{\partial v}{\partial x}\dfrac{\partial x}{\partial z} + \dfrac{\partial v}{\partial y}\dfrac{\partial y}{\partial z}\right)$

31. $\dfrac{dy}{dx} = \dfrac{x}{2y}$ **33.** $\dfrac{dy}{dx} = -\dfrac{y}{x}$ **35.** $\dfrac{dy}{dx} = -\dfrac{x + y}{2y^3 + x}$

37. $\dfrac{\partial s}{\partial x} = \dfrac{2x}{\sqrt{x^2 + y^2}}; \dfrac{\partial s}{\partial y} = \dfrac{2y}{\sqrt{x^2 + y^2}}$ **39. a.** False **b.** False

41. $z'(t) = -\dfrac{2t + 2}{(t + 2t)} - \dfrac{3t^2}{(t^3 - 2)}$ **43.** $w'(t) = 0$

45. $\dfrac{\partial z}{\partial x} = -\dfrac{z^2}{x^2}$ **47. a.** $w'(t) = af_x + bf_y + cf_z$ **b.** $w'(t) = ayz + bxz + cxy = 3abct^2$

c. $w'(t) = \sqrt{a^2 + b^2 + c^2}\dfrac{t}{|t|}$

d. $w''(t) = a^2 f_{xx} + b^2 f_{yy} + c^2 f_{zz} + 2abf_{xy} + 2acf_{xz} + 2bcf_{yz}$

49. $\dfrac{\partial z}{\partial x} = -\dfrac{y + z}{x + y}; \dfrac{\partial z}{\partial y} = -\dfrac{x + z}{x + y}$ **51.** $\dfrac{\partial z}{\partial x} = -\dfrac{yz + 1}{xy - 1}; \dfrac{\partial z}{\partial y} = -\dfrac{xz + 1}{xy - 1}$

53. a. $z'(t) = -2x \sin t + 8y \cos t = 3 \sin 2t$ **b.** $0 < t < \pi/2$ and $\pi < t < 3\pi/2$ **55. a.** $z'(t) = \dfrac{(x + y)e^{-t}}{\sqrt{1 - x^2 - y^2}} = \dfrac{2e^{-2t}}{\sqrt{1 - 2e^{-2t}}}$

b. All $t \geq \frac{1}{2} \ln 2$ **57.** $E'(t) = mx'x'' + my'y'' + mgy' = 0$ **59. a.** The volume increases. **b.** The volume decreases.

61. a. $\dfrac{\partial P}{\partial V} = -\dfrac{P}{V}; \dfrac{\partial T}{\partial P} = \dfrac{V}{k}; \dfrac{\partial V}{\partial T} = \dfrac{k}{P}$ **b.** Follows directly from part (a)

63. a. $w'(t) = \dfrac{2t(t^2 + 1) \cos 2t - (t^2 - 1) \sin 2t}{2(t^2 + 1)^2}$

b. Max value of $t \approx 0.838$, $(x, y, z) \approx (0.669, 0.743, 0.838)$

65. a. $z_x = \dfrac{x}{r} z_r - \dfrac{y}{r^2} z_\theta; z_y = \dfrac{y}{r} z_r + \dfrac{x}{r^2} z_\theta$

b. $z_{xx} = \dfrac{x^2}{r^2} z_{rr} + \dfrac{y^2}{r^4} z_{\theta\theta} - \dfrac{2xy}{r^3} z_{r\theta} + \dfrac{y^2}{r^3} z_r + \dfrac{2xy}{r^4} z_\theta$

c. $z_{yy} = \dfrac{y^2}{r^2} z_{rr} + \dfrac{x^2}{r^4} z_{\theta\theta} + \dfrac{2xy}{r^3} z_{r\theta} + \dfrac{x^2}{r^3} z_r - \dfrac{2xy}{r^4} z_\theta$

d. Add the results from (b) and (c). **67. a.** $\left(\dfrac{\partial z}{\partial x}\right)_y = -\dfrac{F_x}{F_z}$

b. $\left(\dfrac{\partial y}{\partial z}\right)_x = -\dfrac{F_z}{F_y}; \left(\dfrac{\partial x}{\partial y}\right)_z = -\dfrac{F_y}{F_x}$ **c.** Follows from (a) and (b) by multiplication **d.** $\left(\dfrac{\partial w}{\partial x}\right)_{y,z}\left(\dfrac{\partial z}{\partial w}\right)_{x,y}\left(\dfrac{\partial y}{\partial z}\right)_{x,w}\left(\dfrac{\partial x}{\partial y}\right)_{z,w} = 1$

69. a. $\left(\dfrac{\partial w}{\partial x}\right)_y = f_x + f_z \dfrac{dz}{dx} = 18$ **b.** $\left(\dfrac{\partial w}{\partial x}\right)_z = f_x + f_y \dfrac{dy}{dx} = 8$

d. $\left(\dfrac{\partial w}{\partial y}\right)_x = -5; \left(\dfrac{\partial w}{\partial y}\right)_z = 4; \left(\dfrac{\partial w}{\partial z}\right)_x = \dfrac{5}{2}; \left(\dfrac{\partial w}{\partial z}\right)_y = \dfrac{9}{2}$

Section 12.6 Exercises, pp. 925–928

1. Form the dot product between the unit direction vector **u** and the gradient of the function. **3.** Direction of steepest ascent **5.** The gradient is orthogonal to the level curves of f.

7. a.

	$(a,b) = (2,0)$	$(a,b) = (0,2)$	$(a,b) = (1,1)$
$\mathbf{u} = \langle \frac{\sqrt{2}}{2}, \frac{\sqrt{2}}{2} \rangle$	$-\sqrt{2}$	$-2\sqrt{2}$	$-3\sqrt{2}/2$
$\mathbf{v} = \langle -\frac{\sqrt{2}}{2}, \frac{\sqrt{2}}{2} \rangle$	$\sqrt{2}$	$-2\sqrt{2}$	$-\sqrt{2}/2$
$\mathbf{w} = \langle -\frac{\sqrt{2}}{2}, -\frac{\sqrt{2}}{2} \rangle$	$\sqrt{2}$	$2\sqrt{2}$	$3\sqrt{2}/2$

b. The function is decreasing at $(2, 0)$ in the direction of $\mathbf{u}$ and increasing at $(2, 0)$ in the directions of $\mathbf{v}$ and $\mathbf{w}$.
9. $\nabla f(x, y) = \langle 6x, -10y \rangle$, $\nabla f(2, -1) = \langle 12, 10 \rangle$
11. $\nabla g(x, y) = \langle 2(x - 4xy - 4y^2), -4x(x + 4y) \rangle$, $\nabla g(-1, 2) = \langle -18, 28 \rangle$ **13.** $\nabla f(x, y) = e^{2xy} \langle 1 + 2xy, 2x^2 \rangle$, $\nabla f(1, 0) = \langle 1, 2 \rangle$ **15.** $\nabla F(x, y) = -2e^{-x^2-2y^2} \langle x, 2y \rangle$, $\nabla F(-1, 2) = 2e^{-9} \langle 1, -4 \rangle$ **17.** -6 **19.** $\frac{27}{2} - 6\sqrt{3}$

21. $-\frac{2}{\sqrt{5}}$ **23.** -2 **25.** 0 **27. a.** Direction of steepest ascent: $\frac{1}{\sqrt{65}}\langle 1, 8 \rangle$; direction of steepest descent: $-\frac{1}{\sqrt{65}}\langle 1, 8 \rangle$

b. $\langle -8, 1 \rangle$ **29. a.** Direction of steepest ascent: $\frac{1}{\sqrt{5}}\langle -2, 1 \rangle$; direction of steepest descent: $\frac{1}{\sqrt{5}}\langle 2, -1 \rangle$ **b.** $\langle 1, 2 \rangle$

31. a. Direction of steepest ascent: $\frac{1}{\sqrt{2}}\langle 1, -1 \rangle$; direction of steepest descent: $\frac{1}{\sqrt{2}}\langle -1, 1 \rangle$ **b.** $\langle 1, 1 \rangle$

33. a. $\nabla f(3, 2) = -12\mathbf{i} - 12\mathbf{j}$ **b.** Direction of max increase, $\theta = \frac{5\pi}{4}$; direction of max decrease, $\theta = \frac{\pi}{4}$; directions of no change, $\theta = \frac{3\pi}{4}, \frac{7\pi}{4}$ **c.** $g(\theta) = -12\cos\theta - 12\sin\theta$ **d.** $\theta = \frac{5\pi}{4}$, $g\left(\frac{5\pi}{4}\right) = 12\sqrt{2}$ **e.** $\nabla f(3, 2) = 12\sqrt{2}\left\langle \cos\frac{5\pi}{4}, \sin\frac{5\pi}{4} \right\rangle$, $|\nabla f(3, 2)| = 12\sqrt{2}$ **35. a.** $\nabla f(\sqrt{3}, 1) = \frac{\sqrt{6}}{6}\langle \sqrt{3}, 1 \rangle$
b. Direction of max increase, $\theta = \frac{\pi}{6}$; direction of max decrease, $\theta = \frac{7\pi}{6}$; directions of no change, $\theta = \frac{2\pi}{3}, \frac{5\pi}{3}$

c. $g(\theta) = \frac{\sqrt{2}}{2}\cos\theta + \frac{\sqrt{6}}{6}\sin\theta$ **d.** $\theta = \frac{\pi}{6}$, $g\left(\frac{\pi}{6}\right) = \frac{\sqrt{6}}{3}$
e. $\nabla f(\sqrt{3}, 1) = \frac{\sqrt{6}}{3}\langle \cos\frac{\pi}{6}, \sin\frac{\pi}{6} \rangle$, $|\nabla f(\sqrt{3}, 1)| = \frac{\sqrt{6}}{3}$
37. a. $\nabla F(-1, 0) = \frac{2}{e}\mathbf{i}$ **b.** Direction of max increase, $\theta = 0$; direction of max decrease, $\theta = \pi$; directions of no change, $\theta = \pm\frac{\pi}{2}$ **c.** $g(\theta) = \frac{2}{e}\cos\theta$ **d.** $\theta = 0$, $g(0) = \frac{2}{e}$
e. $\nabla F(-1, 0) = \frac{2}{e}\langle \cos 0, \sin 0 \rangle$, $|\nabla F(-1, 0)| = \frac{2}{e}$
39.

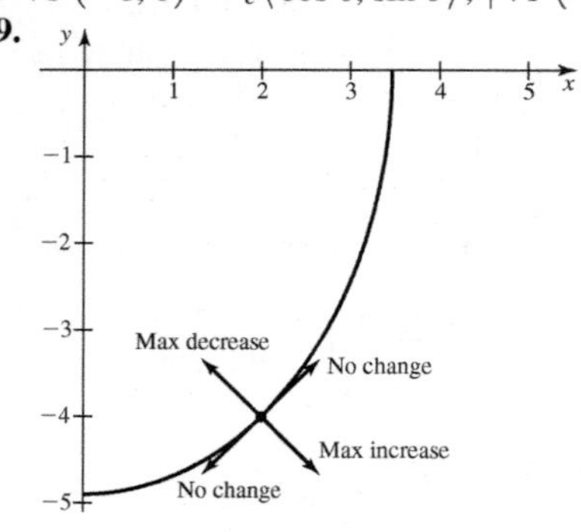

41.

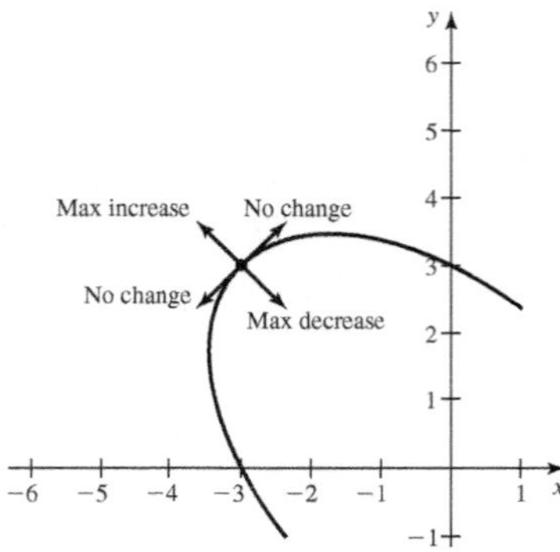

43. $y' = 0$ **45.** Vertical tangent **47.** $y' = -2/\sqrt{3}$ **49.** Vertical tangent **51. a.** $\nabla f = \langle 1, 0 \rangle$ **b.** $x = 4 - t, y = 4, t \geq 0$
53. a. $\nabla f = \langle -2x, -4y \rangle$ **b.** $y = x^2, x \geq 1$
55. a. $\nabla f(x, y, z) = 2x\mathbf{i} + 4y\mathbf{j} + 8z\mathbf{k}$, $\nabla f(1, 0, 4) = 2\mathbf{i} + 32\mathbf{k}$
b. $\frac{1}{\sqrt{257}}(\mathbf{i} + 16\mathbf{k})$ **c.** $2\sqrt{257}$ **d.** $17\sqrt{2}$ **57. a.** $\nabla f(x, y, z) = 4yz\mathbf{i} + 4xz\mathbf{j} + 4xy\mathbf{k}$, $\nabla f(1, -1, -1) = 4\mathbf{i} - 4\mathbf{j} - 4\mathbf{k}$
b. $\frac{1}{\sqrt{3}}(\mathbf{i} - \mathbf{j} - \mathbf{k})$ **c.** $4\sqrt{3}$ **d.** $\frac{4}{\sqrt{3}}$
59. a. $\nabla f(x, y, z) = \cos(x + 2y - z)(\mathbf{i} + 2\mathbf{j} - \mathbf{k})$, $\nabla f\left(\frac{\pi}{6}, \frac{\pi}{6}, -\frac{\pi}{6}\right) = -\frac{1}{2}\mathbf{i} - \mathbf{j} + \frac{1}{2}\mathbf{k}$ **b.** $\frac{1}{\sqrt{6}}(-\mathbf{i} - 2\mathbf{j} + \mathbf{k})$
c. $\sqrt{6}/2$ **d.** $-\frac{1}{2}$

61. a. $\nabla f(x, y, z) = \frac{2}{1 + x^2 + y^2 + z^2}(x\mathbf{i} + y\mathbf{j} + z\mathbf{k})$, $\nabla f(1, 1, -1) = \frac{1}{2}\mathbf{i} + \frac{1}{2}\mathbf{j} - \frac{1}{2}\mathbf{k}$ **b.** $\frac{1}{\sqrt{3}}(\mathbf{i} + \mathbf{j} - \mathbf{k})$ **c.** $\frac{\sqrt{3}}{2}$
d. $\frac{5}{6}$ **63. a.** False **b.** False **c.** False **d.** True **65.** $\pm\frac{1}{\sqrt{5}}(\mathbf{i} - 2\mathbf{j})$

67. $\pm\frac{1}{\sqrt{2}}(\mathbf{i} + \mathbf{j})$ **69.** $x = x_0 + at, y = y_0 + bt$
71. a. $\nabla f(x, y, z) = \langle 2x, 2y, 2z \rangle$, $\nabla f(1, 1, 1) = \langle 2, 2, 2 \rangle$
b. $x + y + z = 3$ **73. a.** $\nabla f(x, y, z) = e^{x+y-z}\langle 1, 1, -1 \rangle$, $\nabla f(1, 1, 2) = \langle 1, 1, -1 \rangle$ **b.** $x + y - z = 0$
75. a.

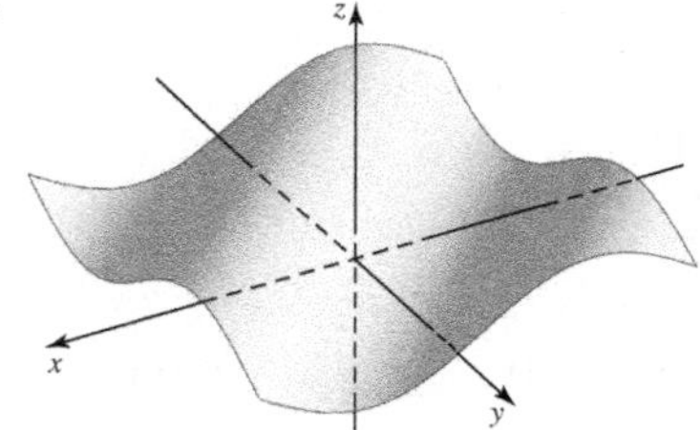

b. $\mathbf{v} = \pm\langle 1, 1 \rangle$ **c.** $\mathbf{v} = \pm\langle 1, -1 \rangle$
79. $\langle u, v \rangle = \langle \pi\cos\pi x\sin 2\pi y, 2\pi\sin\pi x\cos 2\pi y \rangle$
83. $\nabla f(x, y) = \frac{1}{(x^2 + y^2)^2}\langle y^2 - x^2 - 2xy, x^2 - y^2 - 2xy \rangle$
85. $\nabla f(x, y, z) = -\frac{1}{\sqrt{25 - x^2 - y^2 - z^2}}\langle x, y, z \rangle$
87.
$$\nabla f(x, y, z) = \frac{(y + xz)\langle 1, z, y \rangle - (x + yz)\langle z, 1, x \rangle}{(y + xz)^2} = \frac{1}{(y + xz)^2}\langle y(1 - z^2), x(z^2 - 1), y^2 - x^2 \rangle$$

Section 12.7 Exercises, pp. 935–938

1. The gradient of f is a multiple of **n**.
3. $F_x(a,b,c)(x-a) + F_y(a,b,c)(y-b) + F_z(a,b,c)(z-c) = 0$
5. Multiply the change in x by $f_x(a,b)$ and the change in y by $f_y(a,b)$, and add both terms to f. **7.** $dz = f_x(a,b)\,dx + f_y(a,b)\,dy$
9. $2x + y + z = 4;\ 4x + y + z = 7$
11. $x + y + z = 6;\ 3x + 4y + z = 12$
13. $x + \frac{1}{2}y + \sqrt{3}z = 2 + \frac{\sqrt{3}\pi}{6}$ and $\frac{1}{2}x + y + \sqrt{3}z = \frac{5\sqrt{3}\pi}{6} - 2$
15. $\frac{1}{2}x + \frac{2}{3}y + 2\sqrt{3}z = -2$ and $x - 2y + 2\sqrt{14}z = 2$
17. $z = -8x - 4y + 16$ and $z = 4x + 2y + 7$
19. $z = y + 1$ and $z = x + 1$ **21.** $z = 8x - 4y - 4$ and $z = -x - y - 1$ **23.** $z = \frac{7}{25}x - \frac{1}{25}y - \frac{2}{5}$ and $z = -\frac{7}{25}x + \frac{1}{25}y + \frac{6}{5}$
25. a. $L(x,y) = 4x + y - 6$ **b.** $L(2.1, 2.99) = 5.39$
27. a. $L(x,y) = -6x - 4y + 7$ **b.** $L(3.1, -1.04) = -7.44$
29. a. $L(x,y) = x + y$ **b.** $L(0.1, -0.2) = -0.1$
31. $dz = -6dx - 5dy = -0.1$ **33.** $dz = dx + dy = 0.05$
35. a. The surface area decreases. **b.** Impossible to say **c.** $dS \approx 53.3$ **d.** $dS = 33.95$ **e.** $RdR = rdr$ **37.** $\frac{dA}{A} = 3.5\%$
39. $dw = (y^2 + 2xz)\,dx + (2xy + z^2)\,dy + (x^2 + 2yz)\,dz$
41. $dw = \frac{dx}{y+z} - \frac{u+x}{(y+z)^2}dy - \frac{u+x}{(y+z)^2}dz + \frac{du}{y+z}$
43. a. $dc = 0.035$ **b.** When $\theta = \frac{\pi}{20}$ **45. a.** True **b.** True **c.** False **47.** $z = \frac{1}{2}x + \frac{1}{2}y + \frac{\pi}{4} - 1$
49. $\frac{1}{6}(x - \pi) + \frac{\pi}{6}(y - 1) + \pi\left(z - \frac{1}{6}\right) = 0$ **51.** $(1, -1, 1)$ and $(1, -1, -1)$ **53.** Points with $x = 0, \pm\frac{\pi}{2}, \pm\pi$ and $y = \pm\frac{\pi}{2}$, or points with $x = \pm\frac{\pi}{4}, \pm\frac{3\pi}{4}$ and $y = 0, \pm\pi$ **55. a.** $dS = 0.749$ **b.** More sensitive to changes in r **57. a.** $dA = \frac{2}{1225} = 0.00163$ **b.** No. The batting average increases more if he gets a hit than it would decrease if he fails to get a hit. **c.** Yes. The answer depends on whether A is less than 0.500 or greater than 0.500.
59. a. $dV = \frac{21}{5000} = 0.0042$ **b.** $\frac{dV}{V} = -4\%$ **c.** $2p\%$
61. a. $f_r = n(1-r)^{n-1}, f_n = -(1-r)^n \ln(1-r)$ **b.** $\Delta P \approx 0.027$ **c.** $\Delta P \approx 2 \times 10^{-20}$ **63.** $dR = 7/540 \approx 0.013\Omega$
65. a. Apply the Chain Rule. **b.** Follows directly from (a) **c.** $d(\ln(xy)) = \frac{dx}{x} + \frac{dy}{y}$ **d.** $d(\ln(x/y)) = \frac{dx}{x} - \frac{dy}{y}$ **e.** $\frac{df}{f} = \frac{dx_1}{x_1} + \frac{dx_2}{x_2} + \cdots + \frac{dx_n}{x_n}$

Section 12.8 Exercises, pp. 948–951

1. It is locally the highest point on the surface; you cannot get to a higher point in any direction. **3.** The partial derivatives are both zero or do not exist. **5.** The discriminant is a determinant; it is defined as $D(a,b) = f_{xx}(a,b)f_{yy}(a,b) - f_{xy}^2(a,b)$. **7.** f has an absolute minimum value on R at (a,b) if $f(a,b) \le f(x,y)$ for all (x,y) in R
9. $(0,0)$ **11.** $(\frac{2}{3}, 4)$ **13.** $(0,0), (2,2)$, and $(-2,-2)$
15. $(0,2), (\pm 1, 2)$ **17.** $(-3, 0)$ **19.** Local min at $(0,0)$
21. Saddle point at $(0,0)$ **23.** Saddle point at $(0,0)$; local min at $(1,1)$ and at $(-1,-1)$ **25.** Local min at $(2,0)$ **27.** Saddle point at $(0,0)$; local max at $\left(\frac{1}{\sqrt{2}}, \frac{1}{\sqrt{2}}\right)$ and $\left(-\frac{1}{\sqrt{2}}, -\frac{1}{\sqrt{2}}\right)$; local min at $\left(\frac{1}{\sqrt{2}}, -\frac{1}{\sqrt{2}}\right)$ and $\left(-\frac{1}{\sqrt{2}}, \frac{1}{\sqrt{2}}\right)$ **29.** Local min: $(-1,0)$; local max: $(1,0)$ **31.** Saddle point: $(0,1)$; local min: $(\pm 2, 0)$ **33.** Saddle point at $(0,0)$ **35.** Height $= 32$ in, base is 16 in $\times$ 16 in; volume is 8192 in^3 **37.** 2 m $\times$ 2 m $\times$ 1 m **39.** Critical point at $(0,0)$, $D(0,0) = 0$, absolute min **41.** Critical points along the x- and y-axes, all absolute min **43.** Absolute min: $0 = f(0,1)$; absolute max: $9 = f(0,-2)$ **45.** Absolute min: $4 = f(0,0)$; absolute max: $7 = f(\pm 1, \pm 1)$ **47.** Absolute min: $0 = f(1,0)$; absolute max: $3 = f(1,1) = f(1,-1)$ **49.** Absolute min: $1 = f(1,-2) = f(1,0)$; absolute max: $4 = f(1,-1)$ **51.** Absolute min: $0 = f(0,0)$; absolute max: $\frac{7}{8} = f\left(\frac{1}{\sqrt{2}}, \sqrt{2}\right)$ **53.** Absolute min: $-4 = f(0,0)$; no absolute max on R **55.** Absolute max: $2 = f(0,0)$; no absolute min on R
57. $P\left(-\frac{5}{3}, \frac{4}{3}, \frac{13}{3}\right)$ **59.** $\left(\frac{1}{2}, \frac{1}{4}\right); \left(\frac{7}{8}, -\frac{1}{8}\right)$ **61. a.** True **b.** False **c.** True **d.** True **63.** Local min at $(0.3, -0.3)$; saddle point at $(0,0)$ **65.** $P(\frac{4}{3}, \frac{2}{3}, \frac{4}{3})$ **67. a.–d.** $x = y = z = \frac{200}{3}$
69. a. $P(1, \frac{1}{3})$ **b.** $P(\frac{1}{3}(x_1 + x_2 + x_3), \frac{1}{3}(y_1 + y_2 + y_3))$ **c.** $P(\bar{x}, \bar{y})$, where $\bar{x} = \frac{1}{n}\sum_{k=1}^{n} x_k$ and $\bar{y} = \frac{1}{n}\sum_{k=1}^{n} y_k$
d. $d(x,y) = \sqrt{x^2 + y^2} + \sqrt{(x-2)^2 + y^2} + \sqrt{(x-1)^2 + (y-1)^2}$. The absolute min of this function is $1 + \sqrt{3} = f\left(1, \frac{1}{\sqrt{3}}\right)$. **73.** $y = \frac{22}{13}x + \frac{46}{13}$ **75.** $a = b = c = 3$
77. a. $\nabla d_1(x,y) = \frac{x - x_1}{d_1(x,y)}\mathbf{i} + \frac{y - y_1}{d_1(x,y)}\mathbf{j}$
b. $\nabla d_2(x,y) = \frac{x - x_2}{d_2(x,y)}\mathbf{i} + \frac{y - y_2}{d_2(x,y)}\mathbf{j}$; $\nabla d_3(x,y) = \frac{x - x_3}{d_3(x,y)}\mathbf{i} + \frac{y - y_3}{d_3(x,y)}\mathbf{j}$
c. Follows from $\nabla f = \nabla d_1 + \nabla d_2 + \nabla d_3$ **d.** Three unit vectors add to zero. **e.** P is the vertex at the large angle. **f.** $P(0.255457, 0.304504)$
79. a. Local max at $(1,0), (-1,0)$ **b.** $(1,0)$ and $(-1,0)$

Section 12.9 Exercises, pp. 957–959

1. The level curve of f must be tangent to the curve $g = 0$ at the optimal point; therefore, the gradients are parallel. **3.** $2x = 2\lambda$, $2y = 3\lambda$, $2z = -5\lambda$, $2x + 3y - 5z + 4 = 0$ **5.** Min: $-2\sqrt{5}$ at $\left(-\frac{2}{\sqrt{5}}, -\frac{4}{\sqrt{5}}\right)$; max: $2\sqrt{5}$ at $\left(\frac{2}{\sqrt{5}}, \frac{4}{\sqrt{5}}\right)$ **7.** Min: -2 at $(-1,-1)$; max: 2 at $(1,1)$ **9.** Min: -3 at $(-\sqrt{3}, \sqrt{3})$ and $(\sqrt{3}, -\sqrt{3})$; max: 9 at $(3,3)$ and $(-3,-3)$ **11.** Min: e^{-16} at $(2\sqrt{2}, -2\sqrt{2})$ and $(-2\sqrt{2}, 2\sqrt{2})$; max: e^{16} at $(-2\sqrt{2}, -2\sqrt{2})$ and $(2\sqrt{2}, 2\sqrt{2})$ **13.** Min: -16 at $(\pm 2, 0)$; max: 2 at $(0, \pm\sqrt{2})$ **15.** Min: $-2\sqrt{11}$ at $\left(-\frac{2}{\sqrt{11}}, -\frac{6}{\sqrt{11}}, \frac{2}{\sqrt{11}}\right)$; max: $2\sqrt{11}$ at $\left(\frac{2}{\sqrt{11}}, \frac{6}{\sqrt{11}}, -\frac{2}{\sqrt{11}}\right)$ **17.** Min: $-\frac{\sqrt{5}}{2}$ at $\left(-\frac{\sqrt{5}}{2}, 0, \frac{1}{2}\right)$; max: $\frac{\sqrt{5}}{2}$ at $\left(\frac{\sqrt{5}}{2}, 0, \frac{1}{2}\right)$ **19.** Min: $\frac{1}{3}$ at $\left(-\frac{1}{\sqrt{6}}, \frac{1}{\sqrt{6}}, 0\right)$ and $\left(\frac{1}{\sqrt{6}}, -\frac{1}{\sqrt{6}}, 0\right)$; max: 1 at $(0, 0, \pm 1)$
21. Min: -10 at $(-5, 0, 0)$; max: $\frac{29}{2}$ at $\left(2, 0, \pm\sqrt{\frac{21}{2}}\right)$
23. Min: $6\sqrt[3]{2} = f(\pm\sqrt[3]{4}, \pm\sqrt[3]{4}, \pm\sqrt[3]{4})$; no max
25. 18 in $\times$ 18 in $\times$ 36 in **27.** Min: 0.6731; max: 1.1230

29. 2×1 **31.** $\left(-\frac{3}{17}, \frac{29}{17}, -3\right)$ **33.** Min: $\sqrt{38 - 6\sqrt{29}}$ (or $\sqrt{29} - 3$); max: $\sqrt{38 + 6\sqrt{29}}$ (or $\sqrt{29} + 3$) **35.** $\ell = 3$ and $g = \frac{3}{2}$; $U = 15\sqrt{2}$ **37.** $\ell = \frac{16}{5}$ and $g = 1$; $U = 20.287$
39. a. True **b.** False **41.** $\frac{\sqrt{6}}{3}\text{ m} \times \frac{\sqrt{6}}{3}\text{ m} \times \frac{\sqrt{6}}{6}\text{ m}$
43. $2 \times 1 \times \frac{2}{3}$ **45.** $P\left(\frac{4}{3}, \frac{2}{3}, \frac{4}{3}\right)$ **47.** Min: $-\frac{7 + \sqrt{661}}{2}$; max: $\frac{\sqrt{661} - 7}{2}$ **49.** Min: 0; max: $6 + 4\sqrt{2}$ **51.** Min: 1; max: 8
53. $K = 7.5$ and $L = 5$ **55.** $K = aB/p$ and $L = (1 - a)B/q$
57. Max: 8 **59.** Max: $\sqrt{a_1{}^2 + a_2{}^2 + a_3{}^2 + \cdots + a_n{}^2}$
61. a. Gradients are perpendicular to level surfaces. **b.** If the gradient was not in the plane spanned by ∇g and ∇h, f could be increased (decreased) by moving the point slightly. **c.** ∇f is a linear combination of ∇g and ∇h, since it belongs to the plane spanned by these two vectors. **d.** The gradient condition from part (c), as well as the constraints, must be satisfied. **63.** Min: $2 - 4\sqrt{2}$; max: $2 + 4\sqrt{2}$
65. Min: $\frac{5}{4} = f\left(\frac{1}{2}, 0, 1\right)$; max: $\frac{125}{36} = f\left(-\frac{5}{6}, 0, \frac{5}{3}\right)$

Chapter 12 Review Exercises, pp. 959–962

1. a. False **b.** False **c.** False **d.** False **e.** True
3. a. $18x - 9y + 2z = 6$ **b.** $x = \frac{1}{3}, y = -\frac{2}{3}, z = 3$
c.

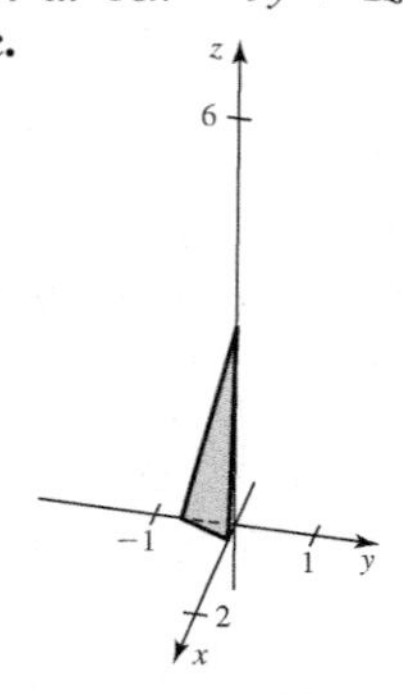

5. $x = t, y = 12 - 9t, z = -6 + 6t$ **7.** $3x + y + 7z = 4$
9. a. Hyperbolic paraboloid **b.** $y^2 = 4x^2, z = \frac{x^2}{36}, z = -\frac{y^2}{144}$
c. $x = y = z = 0$
d.

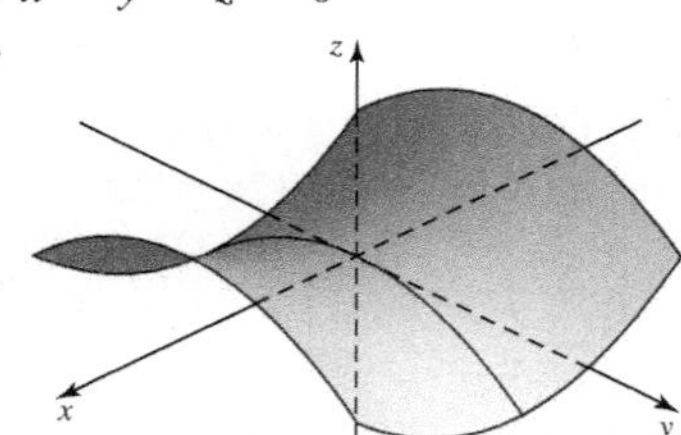

11. a. Elliptic cone **b.** $y^2 = 4x^2$, origin, $y^2 = \frac{z^2}{25}$ **c.** Origin
d.

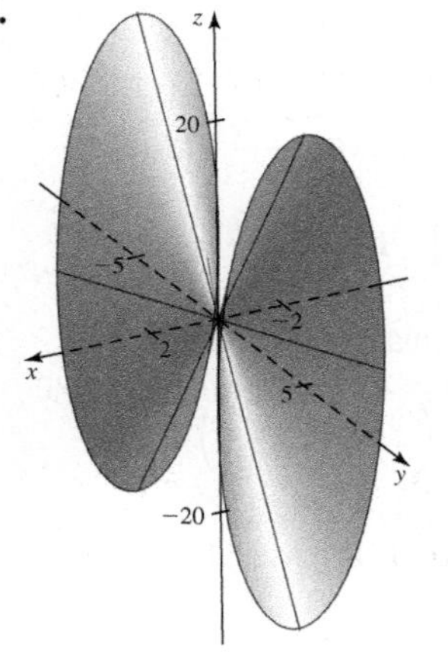

13. a. Elliptic paraboloid **b.** Origin, $z = \frac{x^2}{16}, z = \frac{y^2}{36}$ **c.** Origin
d.

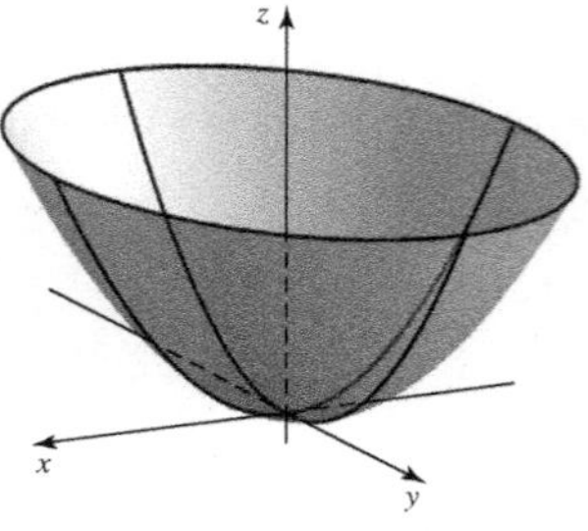

15. a. Hyperboloid of one sheet **b.** $y^2 - 2x^2 = 1, 4z^2 - 2x^2 = 1, y^2 + 4z^2 = 1$ **c.** No x-intercept, $y = \pm 1, z = \pm\frac{1}{2}$
d.

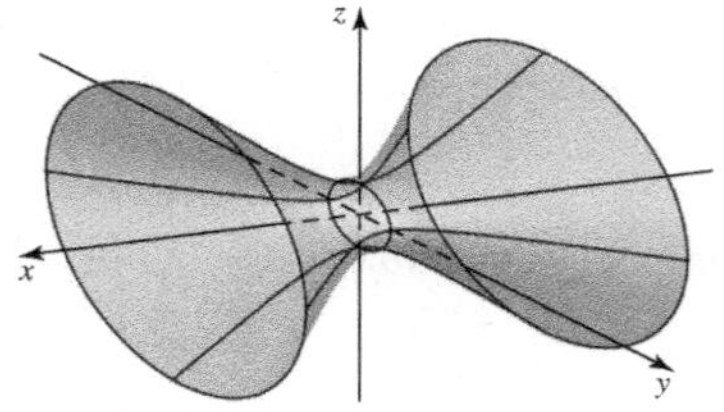

17. a. Hyperboloid of one sheet
b. $\frac{x^2}{4} + \frac{y^2}{16} = 4, \frac{x^2}{4} - z^2 = 4, \frac{y^2}{16} - z^2 = 4$
c. $x = \pm 4, y = \pm 8$, no z-intercept
d.

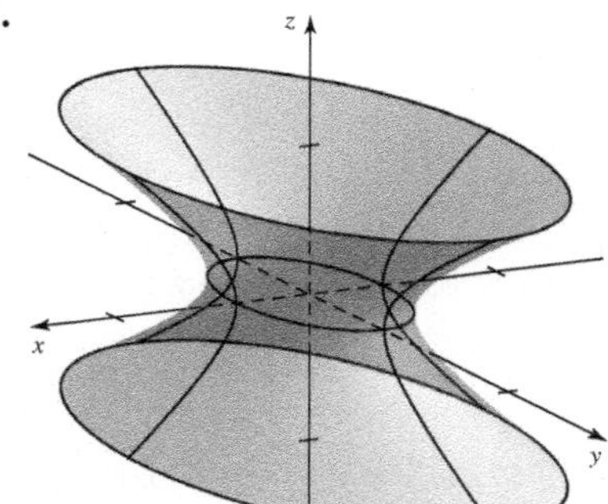

19. a. Ellipsoid **b.** $\frac{x^2}{4} + \frac{y^2}{16} = 4, \frac{x^2}{4} + z^2 = 4, \frac{y^2}{16} + z^2 = 4$
c. $x = \pm 4, y = \pm 8, z = \pm 2$
d.

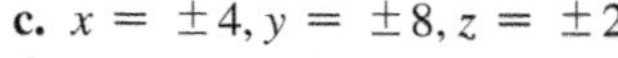

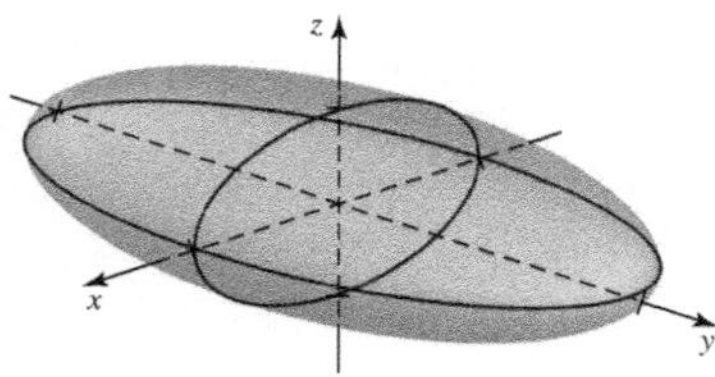

21. a. Elliptic cone **b.** Origin, $\frac{x^2}{9} = \frac{z^2}{64}, \frac{y^2}{49} = \frac{z^2}{64}$. **c.** Origin
d.

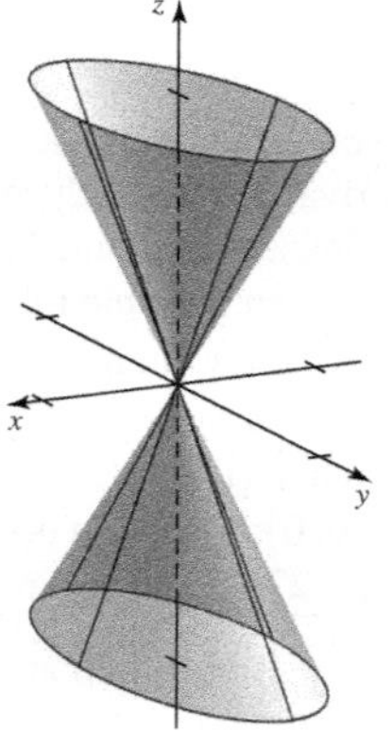

23. $D = \{(x, y): (x, y) \neq (0, 0)\}$

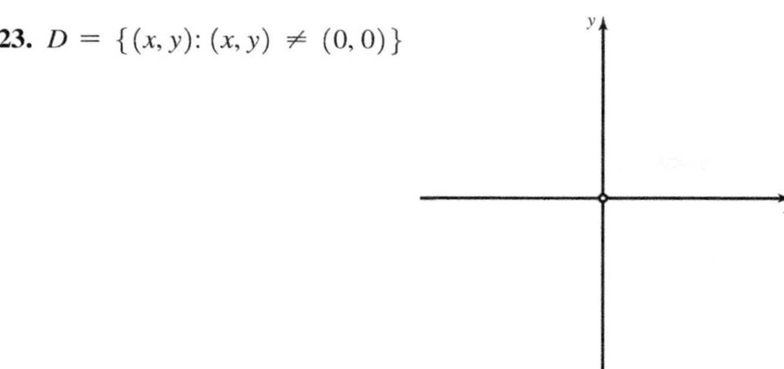

25. $D = \{(x, y): x \geq y^2\}$

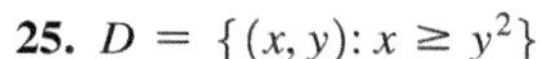

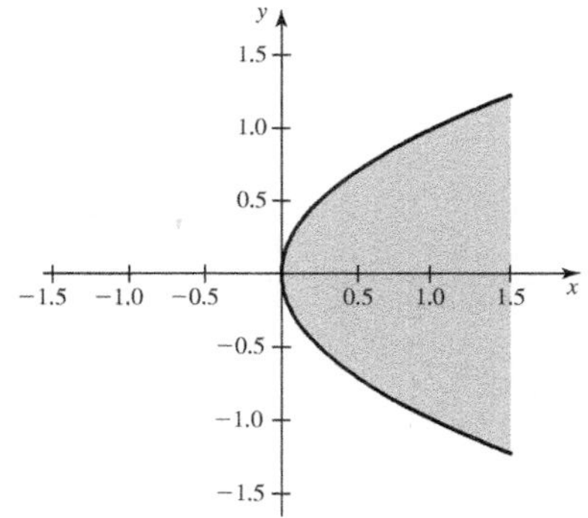

27. a. A **b.** D **c.** C **d.** B **29.**

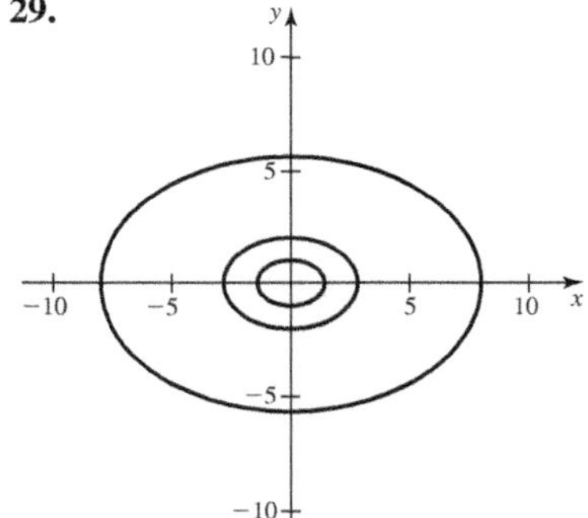

31. 2 **33.** Does not exist **35.** $\frac{2}{3}$ **37.** 4

39. $f_x = 6xy^5; f_y = 15x^2y^4$ **41.** $f_x = \frac{2xy^2}{(x^2 + y^2)^2}; f_y = -\frac{2x^2y}{(x^2 + y^2)^2}$

43. $f_x = y(1 + xy)e^{xy}$; $f_y = x(1 + xy)e^{xy}$ **45.** $f_x = e^{x+2y+3z}$; $f_y = 2e^{x+2y+3z}$; $f_z = 3e^{x+2y+3z}$ **47.** $\frac{\partial^2 u}{\partial x^2} = 6y = -\frac{\partial^2 u}{\partial y^2}$ **49. a.** V increases with R if r is fixed, $V_R > 0$; V decreases if r increases and R is fixed, $V_r < 0$. **b.** $V_r = -4\pi r^2$; $V_R = 4\pi R^2$ **c.** The volume increases more if R is increased. **51.** $w'(t) = -\frac{\cos t \sin t}{\sqrt{1 + \cos^2 t}}$

53. $w_r = \frac{3r + s}{r(r + s)}; w_s = \frac{r + 3s}{s(r + s)}; w_t = \frac{1}{t}$

55. $\frac{dy}{dx} = -\frac{2xy}{2y^2 + (x^2 + y^2)\ln(x^2 + y^2)}$

57. a. $z'(t) = -24 \sin t \cos t = -12 \sin 2t$

b. $z'(t) > 0$ for $\frac{\pi}{2} < t < \pi$ and $\frac{3\pi}{2} < t < 2\pi$

59. a.

	$(a,b) = (0,0)$	$(a,b) = (2,0)$	$(a,b) = (1,1)$
$\mathbf{u} = \langle \frac{\sqrt{2}}{2}, \frac{\sqrt{2}}{2} \rangle$	0	$4\sqrt{2}$	$-2\sqrt{2}$
$\mathbf{v} = \langle -\frac{\sqrt{2}}{2}, \frac{\sqrt{2}}{2} \rangle$	0	$-4\sqrt{2}$	$-6\sqrt{2}$
$\mathbf{w} = \langle -\frac{\sqrt{2}}{2}, -\frac{\sqrt{2}}{2} \rangle$	0	$-4\sqrt{2}$	$2\sqrt{2}$

b. The function is increasing at $(2, 0)$ in the direction of $\mathbf{u}$ and decreasing at $(2, 0)$in the directions of $\mathbf{v}$ and $\mathbf{w}$.

61. $\nabla g = \langle 2xy^3, 3x^2y^2 \rangle$; $\nabla g(-1, 1) = \langle -2, 3 \rangle$; $D_{\mathbf{u}}\, g(-1, 1) = 2$

63. $\nabla h = \left\langle \frac{x}{\sqrt{2 + x^2 + 2y^2}}, \frac{2y}{\sqrt{2 + x^2 + 2y^2}} \right\rangle$; $\nabla h(2, 1) = \left\langle \frac{\sqrt{2}}{2}, \frac{\sqrt{2}}{2} \right\rangle$; $D_{\mathbf{u}}\, h(2, 1) = \frac{7\sqrt{2}}{10}$

65. $\nabla f = \langle \cos(x + 2y - z), 2\cos(x + 2y - z), -\cos(x + 2y - z) \rangle$; $\nabla f\left(\frac{\pi}{6}, \frac{\pi}{6}, -\frac{\pi}{6}\right) = \left\langle -\frac{1}{2}, -1, \frac{1}{2} \right\rangle$; $D_{\mathbf{u}} f\left(\frac{\pi}{6}, \frac{\pi}{6}, -\frac{\pi}{6}\right) = -\frac{1}{2}$

67. a. Direction of steepest ascent: $\mathbf{u} = \frac{\sqrt{2}}{2}\mathbf{i} - \frac{\sqrt{2}}{2}\mathbf{j}$; direction of steepest descent: $\mathbf{u} = -\frac{\sqrt{2}}{2}\mathbf{i} + \frac{\sqrt{2}}{2}\mathbf{j}$

b. No change: $\mathbf{u} = \pm\left(\frac{\sqrt{2}}{2}\mathbf{i} + \frac{\sqrt{2}}{2}\mathbf{j}\right)$

69. Tangent line is vertical; $\nabla f(2, 0) = -8\mathbf{i}$

71. $E = \frac{kx}{x^2 + y^2}\mathbf{i} + \frac{ky}{x^2 + y^2}\mathbf{j}$

73. $y = 2$ and $12x + 3y - 2z = 12$

75. $16x + 2y + z - 8 = 0$ and $8x + y + 8z + 16 = 0$

77. $z = \ln 3 + \frac{2}{3}(x - 1) + \frac{1}{3}(y - 2)$; $z = \ln 3 - \frac{1}{3}(x + 2) - \frac{2}{3}(y + 1)$ **79. a.** $L(x, y) = x + 5y$ **b.** $L(1.95, 0.05) = 2.2$ **81.** -4% **83. a.** $dV = -0.1\pi$ m^3 **b.** $dS = -0.05\pi$ m^2 **85.** Saddle point at $(0, 0)$; local min at $(2, -2)$ **87.** Saddle points at $(0, 0)$ and $(-2, 2)$; local max at $(0, 2)$; local min at $(-2, 0)$ **89.** Absolute min: $-1 = f(1, 1) = f(-1, -1)$; absolute max: $49 = f(2, -2) = f(-2, 2)$ **91.** Absolute min: $-\frac{1}{2} = f\left(-\frac{1}{\sqrt{2}}, \frac{1}{\sqrt{2}}\right)$; absolute max: $\frac{1}{2} = f\left(\frac{1}{\sqrt{2}}, \frac{1}{\sqrt{2}}\right)$

93. Max: $\frac{29}{2} = f\left(\frac{5}{3}, \frac{7}{6}\right)$; min: $\frac{23}{2} = f\left(\frac{1}{3}, \frac{5}{6}\right)$

95. Max: $f\left(\frac{\sqrt{6}}{6}, \frac{\sqrt{6}}{3}, -\frac{\sqrt{6}}{6}\right) = \sqrt{6}$; min: $f\left(-\frac{\sqrt{6}}{6}, -\frac{\sqrt{6}}{3}, \frac{\sqrt{6}}{6}\right) = -\sqrt{6}$

97. $\frac{2a^2}{\sqrt{a^2 + b^2}}$ by $\frac{2b^2}{\sqrt{a^2 + b^2}}$

99. $x = \frac{1}{2} + \frac{\sqrt{10}}{20}, y = \frac{3}{2} + \frac{3\sqrt{10}}{20} = 3x, z = \frac{1}{2} + \frac{\sqrt{10}}{2} = \sqrt{10}x$

APPENDIX A

Exercises, pp. 1157–1158

1. The set of real numbers greater than -4 and less than or equal to 10; $(-4, 10]$;

3. $|x| = \begin{cases} x & \text{if } x \geq 0 \\ -x & \text{if } x < 0 \end{cases}$ **5.** $2x - 4 \geq 3$ or $2x - 4 \leq -3$

7. Take the square root of the sum of the squares of the differences of the x- and y-coordinates. **9.** $y = \sqrt{36 - x^2}$

11. $m = \frac{y + 2}{x - 4}$ or $y = m(x - 4) - 2$ **13.** They are equal.

15. 4 **17.** $4uv$ **19.** $-\frac{h}{x(x + h)}$ **21.** $(y - y^{-1})(y + y^{-1})$

23. $u = \pm\sqrt{2}, \pm 3$ **25.** $3x^2 + 3xh + h^2$

27. $(1, 5)$

29. $(-\infty, 4] \cup [5, 6)$

31. $\{x: x < -4/3 \quad \text{or} \quad x > 4\}$; $\left(-\infty, -\frac{4}{3}\right) \cup (4, \infty)$

33. $\{x: -2 < x < -1 \quad \text{or} \quad 2 < x < 3\}$; $(-2, -1) \cup (2, 3)$

35. $y = 2 - \sqrt{9 - (x + 1)^2}$

37. $y = \dfrac{5}{3}x + 4$

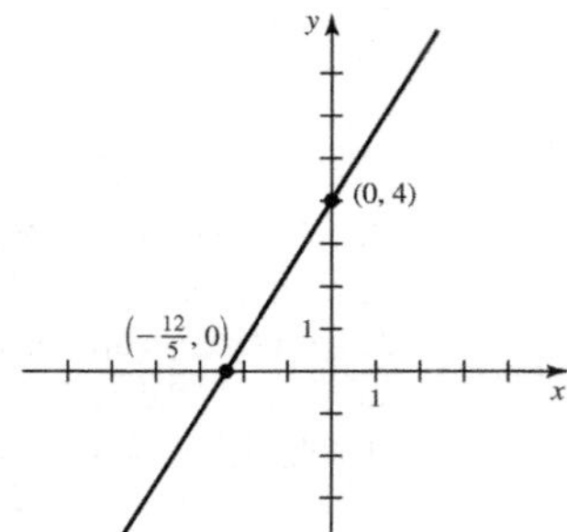

39. $y = \dfrac{4}{5}x - 4$

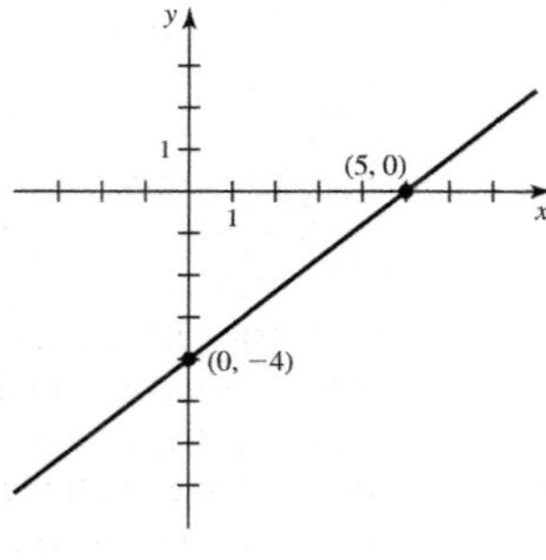

41. $x + 2y = 24$

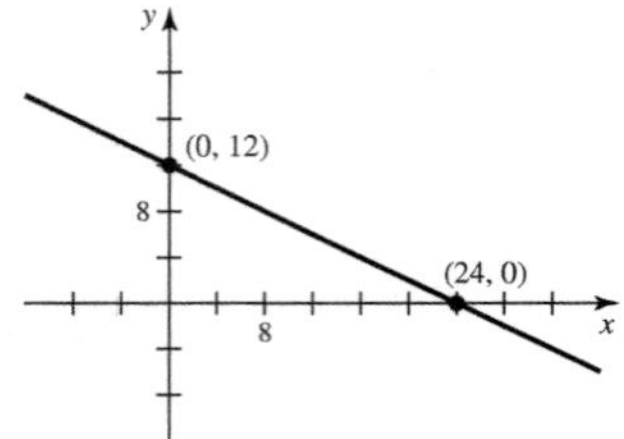

43. $y = \dfrac{1}{3}x - 7$ **45. a.** False **b.** True **c.** False **d.** False **e.** False **f.** True **g.** False **47.** $\{x: |x - 1| \geq 3\}$

49.

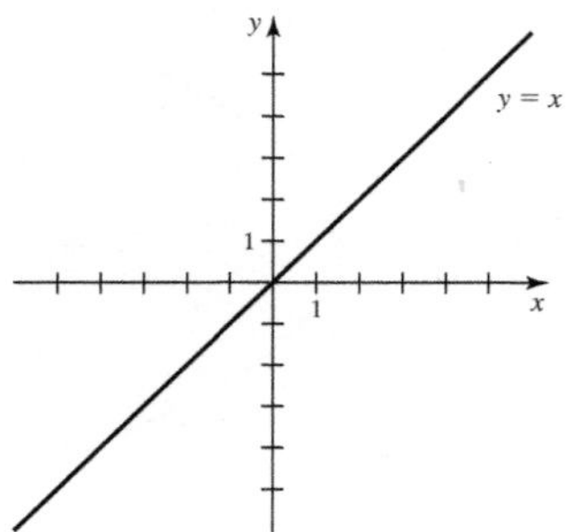

Index

Note: Page numbers in *italics* indicate figures, "t" indicated a table, "e" indicates an exercise, and GP indicates Guided Projects.

A

B

E

F

G

H

I

J

K

L

Q

R

U

W

X

Y

Z

Student's Solutions Manual

Chapters 5, 7-9 taken from *Student's Solutions Manual*, Single Variable by Mark Woodward
for *Calculus: Early Transcendentals*, Second Edition by William Briggs, Lyle Cochran, and Bernard Gillett

Chapters 11-12 taken from *Student Solutions Manual, Multivariable* by Mark Woodward
for *Calculus*, Second Edition and *Calculus: Early Transcendentals*, Second Edition
by William L. Briggs and Lyle Cochran, and Bernard Gillett

Chapter 5

Integration

5.1 Approximating Areas under Curves

5.1.1

In the first 2 seconds, the object moves $15 \cdot 2 = 30$ meters. In the next three seconds, the object moves $25 \cdot 3 = 75$ meters, so the total displacement is $75 + 30 = 105$ meters.

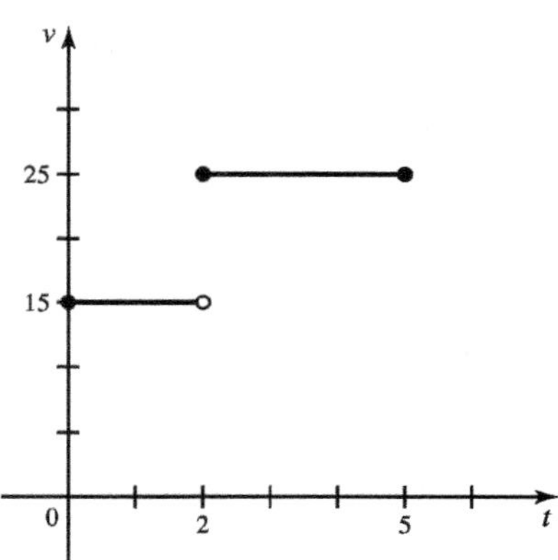

5.1.3 Subdivide the interval from 0 to $\pi/2$ into subintervals. On each subinterval, pick a sample point (like the left endpoint, or the right endpoint, or the midpoint, for example) and call the first sample point x_1 and the second sample point x_2 and so on. For each sample point x_i, calculate the area of the rectangle which lies over the subinterval and has height $f(x_i) = \cos x_i$. Do this for each subinterval, and add the areas of the corresponding rectangles together. This will give an approximation to the area under the curve, with generally a better approximation occurring as n increases – where n is the number of subintervals used.

5.1.5 Because the interval $[1, 3]$ has length 2, if we subdivide it into 4 subintervals, each will have length $\Delta x = \frac{2}{4} = \frac{1}{2}$. The grid points will be $x_0 = 1$, $x_1 = 1 + \Delta x = 1.5$, $x_2 = 1 + 2\Delta x = 2$, $x_3 = 1 + 3\Delta x = 2.5$, and $x_4 = 1 + 4\Delta x = 3$.

If we use the left-hand side of each subinterval, we will use 1, 1.5, 2, and 2.5.

If we use the right-hand side of each subinterval, we will use 1.5, 2, 2.5, and 3.

If we use the midpoint of each subinerval, we will use 1.25, 1.75, 2.25, and 2.75.

5.1.7 It is an underestimate. If we use the right-hand side of each subinterval to determine the height of the rectangles, the height of each rectangle will be the minimum of f over the subinterval, so the sum of the areas of the rectangles will be less than the corresponding area under the curve.

5.1.9

a. On the first subinterval, the midpoint is .5, and $v(.5) = 1.75$. On the 2nd subinterval, the midpoint is 1.5 and $v(1.5) = 7.75$. Continuing in this manner, we obtain the estimate to the displacement of

$$v(.5) \cdot 1 + v(1.5) \cdot 1 + v(2.5) \cdot 1 + v(3.5) \cdot 1 = 1.75 + 7.75 + 19.75 + 37.75 = 67.$$

b. This time the midpoints are at .25, .75, 1.25 .... Each subinterval has length $\frac{1}{2}$. Thus, the estimate is given by

$$\begin{aligned}&v(.25)\cdot .5+v(.75)\cdot .5+v(1.25)\cdot .5+v(1.75)\cdot .5+v(2.25)\cdot .5+v(2.75)\cdot .5+v(3.25)\cdot .5+v(3.75)\cdot .5\\&=.5(1.1875+2.6875+5.6875+10.1875+16.1875+23.6875+32.6875+43.1875)\\&=.5(135.5)=67.75.\end{aligned}$$

5.1.11

The left-hand grid points are 0 and 4. The length of each subinterval is $8/2=4$. So the left Riemann sum is given by $v(0)\cdot 4+v(4)\cdot 4=4\cdot(1+9)=40$.

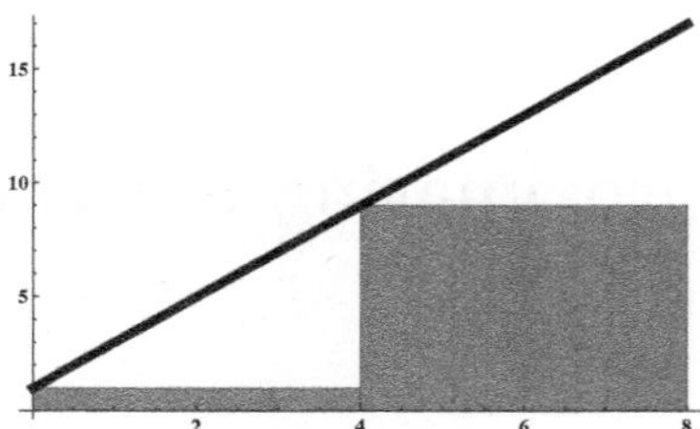

5.1.13

The left-hand grid points are 0, 2, 4, and 6. The length of each subinterval is 2. So the left Riemann sum is given by $v(0)\cdot 2+v(2)\cdot 2+v(4)\cdot 2+v(6)\cdot 2=2\cdot\left(\frac{1}{1}+\frac{1}{5}+\frac{1}{9}+\frac{1}{13}\right)\approx 2.776$.

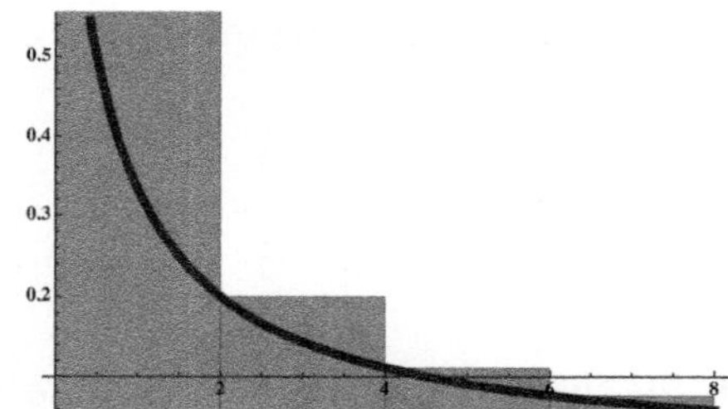

5.1.15

The left-hand grid points are 0, 3, 6, 9, and 12. The length of each subinterval is 3. So the left Riemann sum is given by $\sum_{k=1}^{5} v(3(k-1))\cdot 3 = 12+24+12\sqrt{7}+12\sqrt{10}+12\sqrt{13}\approx 148.963$.

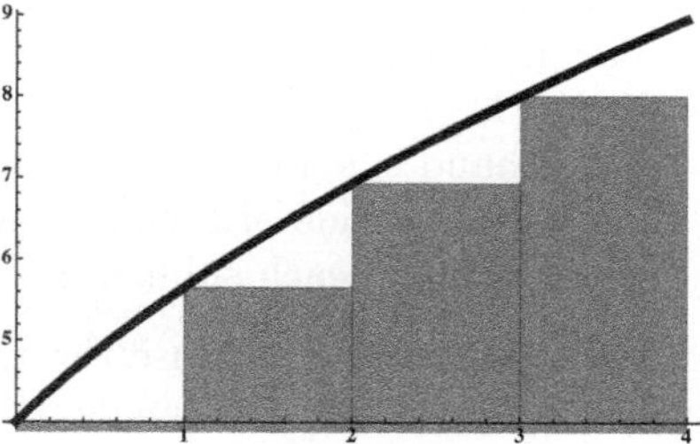

5.1.17 The left Riemann sum is given by $f(1)+f(2)+f(3)+f(4)+f(5)=2+3+4+5+6=20$.

The right Riemann sum is given by $f(2)+f(3)+f(4)+f(5)+f(6)=3+4+5+6+7=25$.

5.1.19

a.

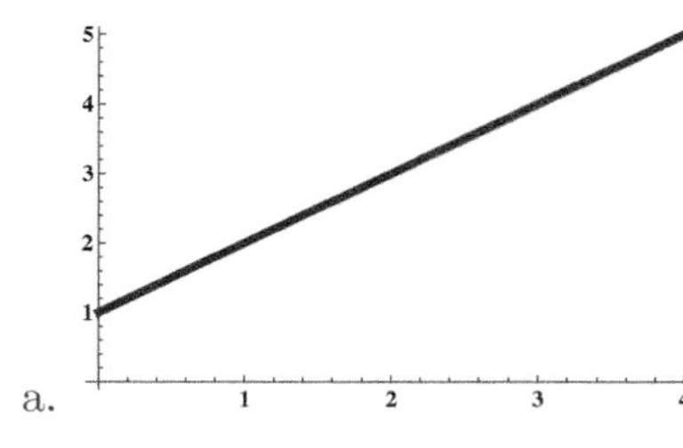

b. We have $\Delta x = \frac{4-0}{4} = 1$. The grid points are $x_0 = 0$, $x_1 = 1$, $x_2 = 2$, $x_3 = 3$, and $x_4 = 4$.

c.

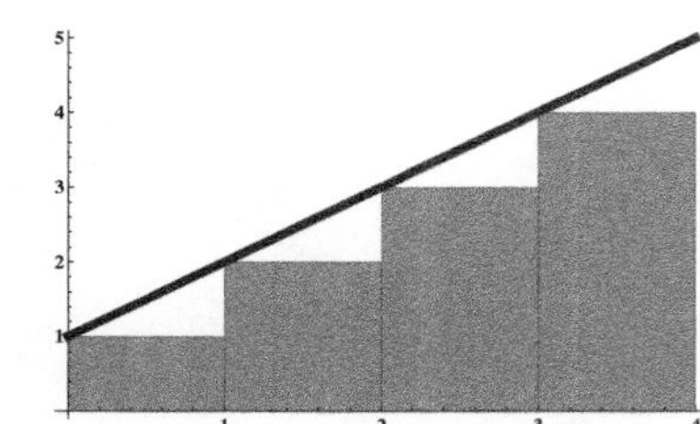

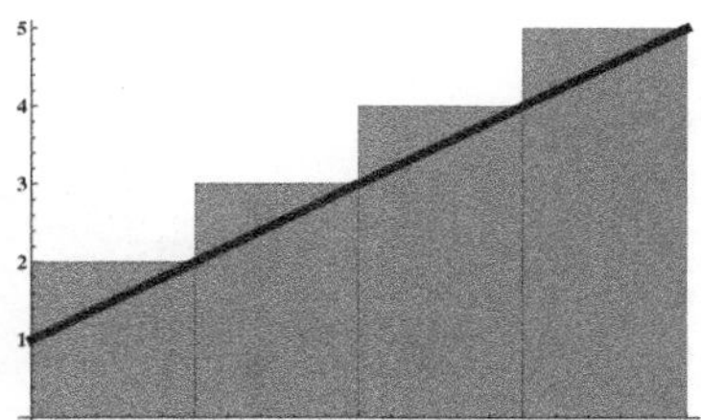

d. The left Riemann sum is $1 \cdot 1 + 2 \cdot 1 + 3 \cdot 1 + 4 \cdot 1 = 10$, which is an underestimate of the area under the curve. The right Riemann sum is $2 \cdot 1 + 3 \cdot 1 + 4 \cdot 1 + 5 \cdot 1 = 14$ which is an overestimate of the area under the curve.

5.1.21

a.

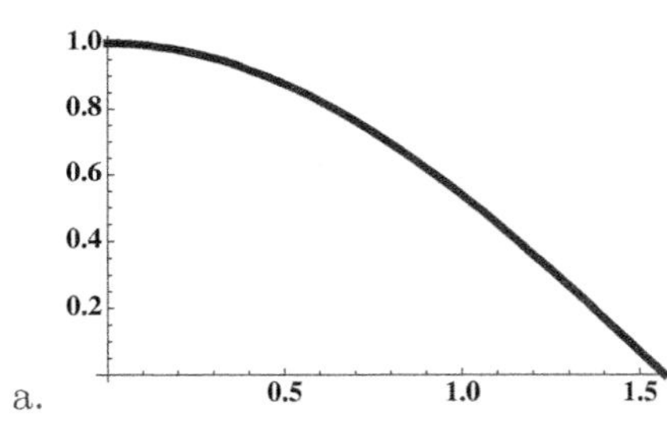

b. We have $\Delta x = \frac{\pi/2-0}{4} = \frac{\pi}{8}$. The grid points are $x_0 = 0$, $x_1 = \frac{\pi}{8}$, $x_2 = \frac{\pi}{4}$, $x_3 = \frac{3\pi}{8}$, and $x_4 = \frac{\pi}{2}$.

c.

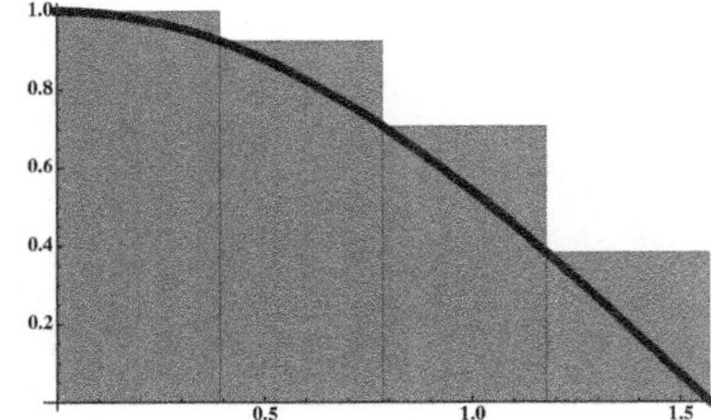

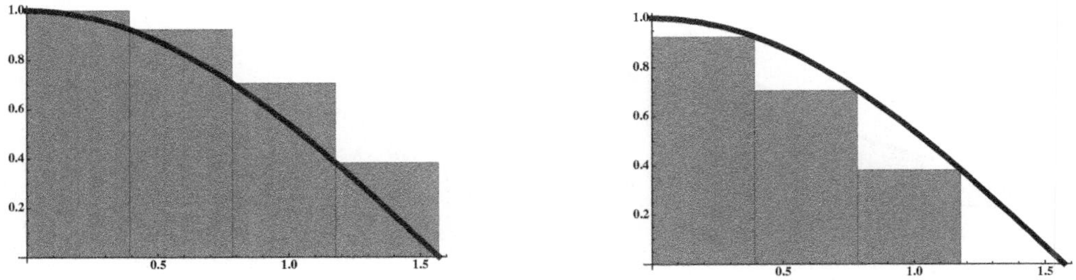

d. The left Riemann sum is $1 \cdot \frac{\pi}{8} + \cos(\pi/8) \cdot \frac{\pi}{8} + \cos(\pi/4) \cdot \frac{\pi}{8} + \cos(3\pi/8) \cdot \frac{\pi}{8} \approx 1.185$, which is an overestimate of the area under the curve. The right Riemann sum is $\cos(\pi/8) \cdot \frac{\pi}{8} + \cos(\pi/4) \cdot \frac{\pi}{8} + \cos(3\pi/8) \cdot \frac{\pi}{8} + 0 \cdot \frac{\pi}{8} \approx 0.791$ which is an underestimate of the area under the curve.

5.1.23

a. 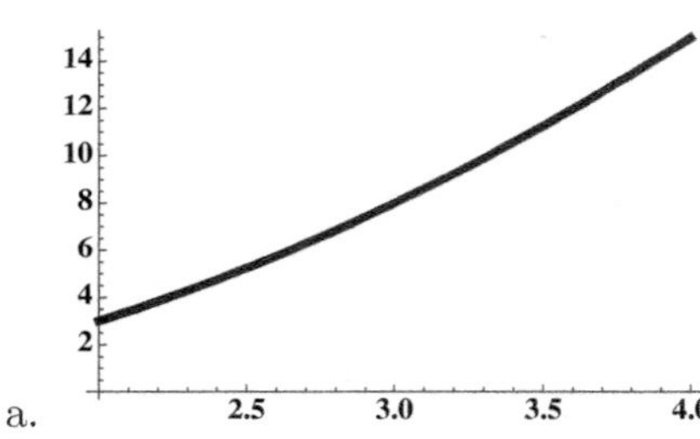

b. We have $\Delta x = \frac{4-2}{4} = \frac{1}{2}$. The grid points are $x_0 = 2$, $x_1 = 2.5$, $x_2 = 3$, $x_3 = 3.5$, and $x_4 = 4$.

c. 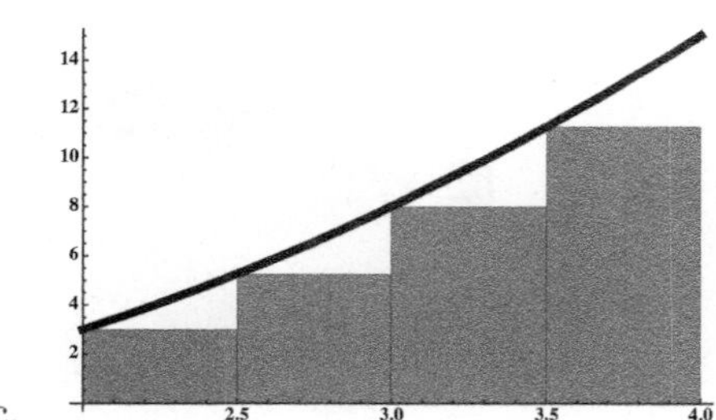

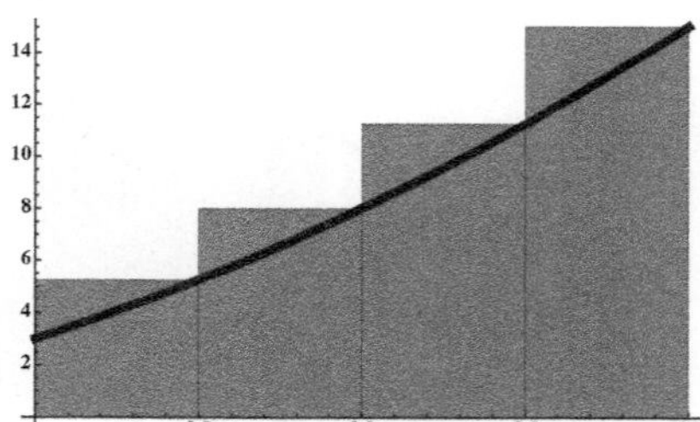

d. The left Riemann sum is $(3+5.25+8+11.25)\cdot 0.5 = 13.75$, which is an underestimate of the area under the curve. The right Riemann sum is $(5.25 + 8 + 11.25 + 15) \cdot 0.5 = 19.75$ which is an overestimate of the area under the curve.

5.1.25

a. 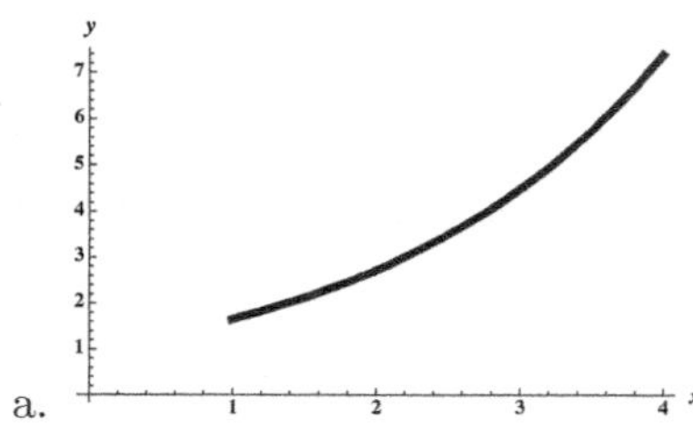

b. We have $\Delta x = \frac{4-1}{6} = \frac{1}{2}$. The grid points are $x_0 = 1$, $x_1 = 1.5$, $x_2 = 2$, $x_3 = 2.5$, $x_4 = 3$, $x_5 = 3.5$, and $x_6 = 4$.

c. 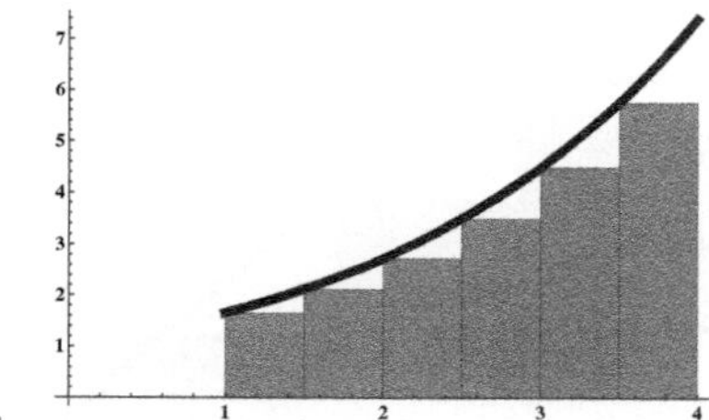

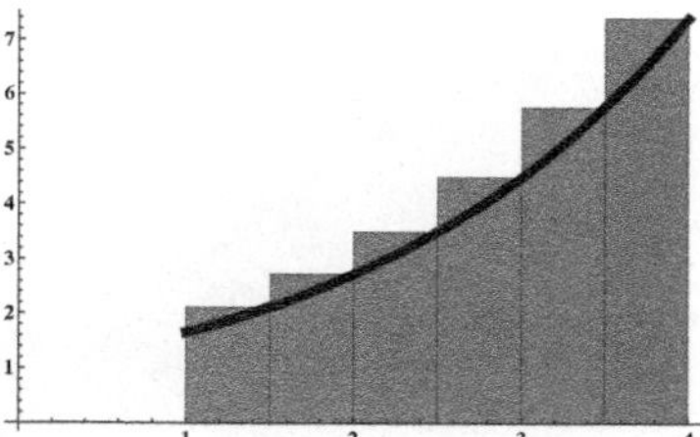

d. The left Riemann sum is $\frac{1}{2}\left(e^{1/2} + e^{3/4} + e + e^{5/4} + e^{3/2} + e^{7/4}\right) \approx 10.105$, which is an underestimate of the area under the curve. The right Riemann sum is $\frac{1}{2}\left(e^{3/4} + e + e^{5/4} + e^{3/2} + e^{7/4} + e^2\right) \approx 12.975$ which is an overestimate of the area under the curve.

5.1.27 We have $\Delta x = 2$, so the midpoints are 1, 3, 5, 7, and 9. So the midpoint Riemann sum is $2(f(1) + f(3) + f(5) + f(7) + f(9)) = 670$.

5.1.29

a. 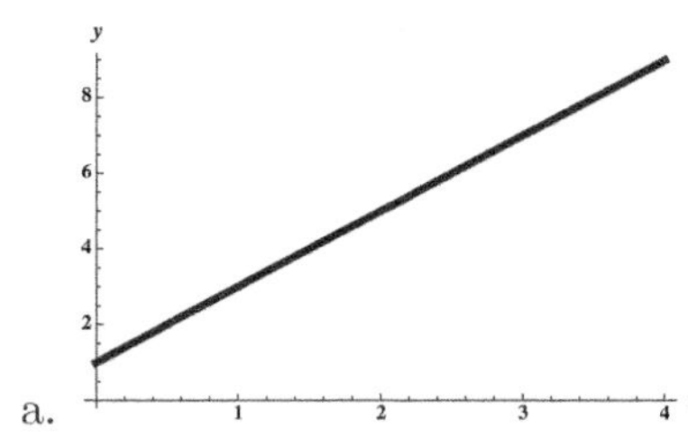

b. We have $\Delta x = \frac{4-0}{4} = 1$. The gridpoints are $x_0 = 0$, $x_1 = 1$, $x_2 = 2$, $x_3 = 3$, and $x_4 = 4$, so the midpoints are .5, 1.5, 2.5, and 3.5.

c. 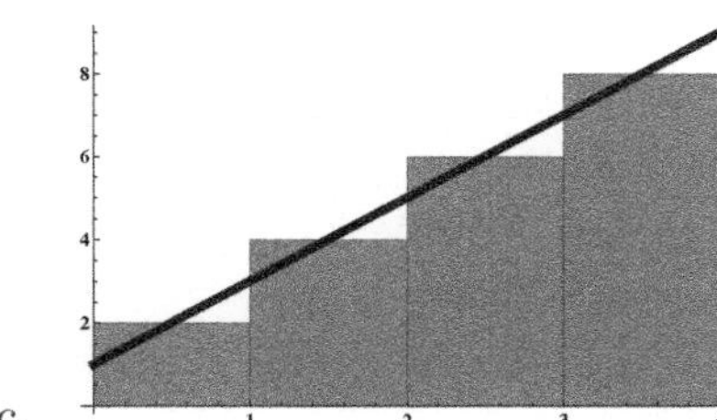

d. The midpoint Riemann sum is $1(2+4+6+8) = 20$.

5.1.31

a. 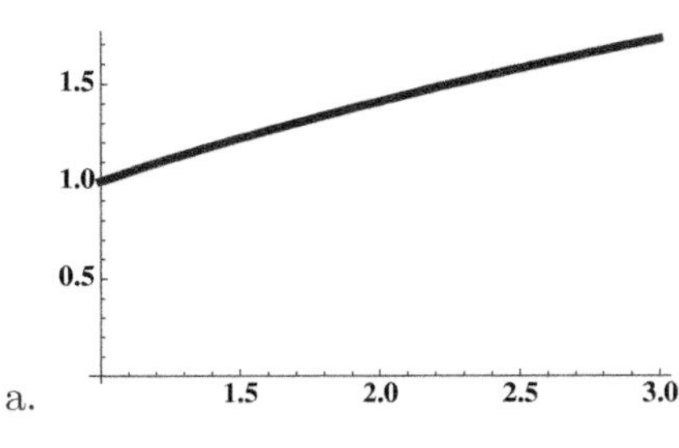

b. We have $\Delta x = \frac{3-1}{4} = \frac{1}{2}$. So the midpoints are 1.25, 1.75, 2.25, and 2.75.

c. 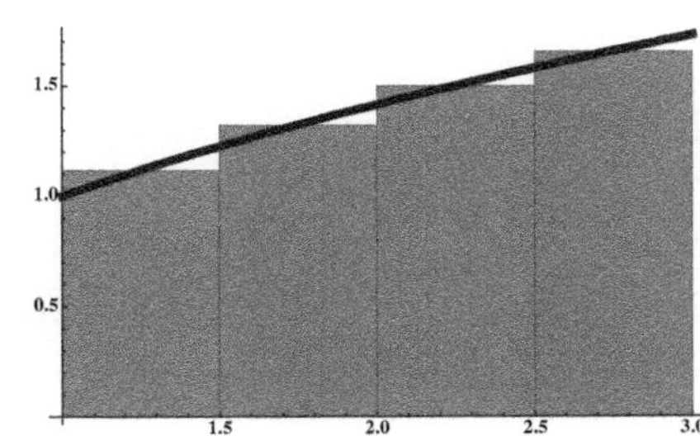

d. The midpoint Riemann sum is $.5(\sqrt{1.25}+\sqrt{1.75}+\sqrt{2.25}+\sqrt{2.75}) \approx 2.800$.

5.1.33

a. 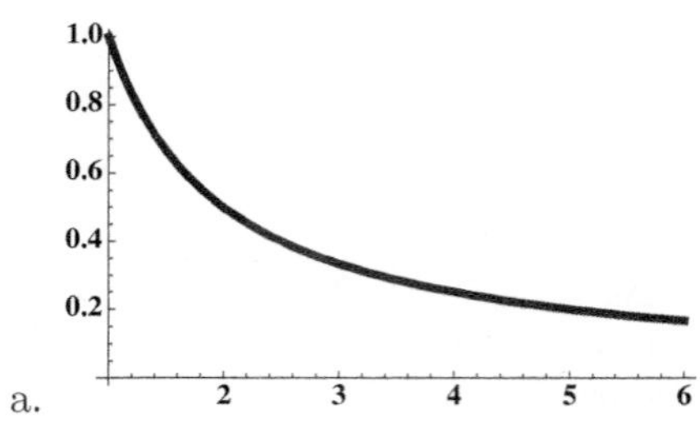

b. We have $\Delta x = \frac{6-1}{5} = 1$. So the midpoints are 1.5, 2.5, 3.5, 4.5, and 5.5.

c. 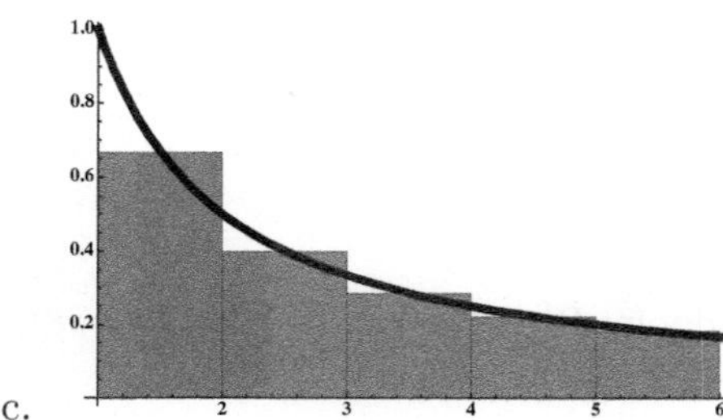

d. The midpoint Riemann sum is $2/3 + 2/5 + 2/7 + 2/9 + 2/11 \approx 1.756$.

5.1.35 Note that $\Delta x = \frac{2-0}{4} = .5$. So the left Riemann sum is given by $.5(5+3+2+1) = 5.5$ and the right Riemann sum is given by $.5(3+2+1+1) = 3.5$.

5.1.37

a. 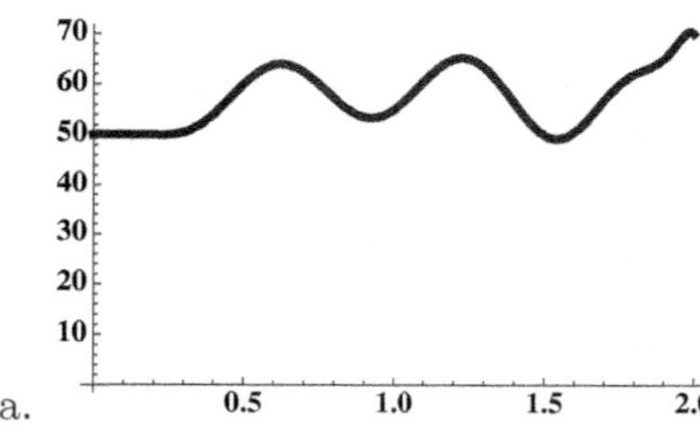

b. With $n = 2$, we have $\Delta x = \frac{2-0}{2} = 1$, so the midpoints are .5 and 1.5. So the midpoint Riemann sum is $60 + 50 = 110$. For $n = 4$, we have $\Delta x = \frac{2-0}{4} = \frac{1}{2}$, so the midpoints are .25, .75, 1.25, and 1.75. The midpoint Riemann sum in this case is $0.5(50 + 60 + 65 + 60) = \frac{235}{2} = 117.5$.

5.1.39

a. $\displaystyle\sum_{k=1}^{5} k.$

b. $\displaystyle\sum_{k=1}^{6} (k+3).$

c. $\displaystyle\sum_{k=1}^{4} k^2.$

d. $\displaystyle\sum_{k=1}^{4} \frac{1}{k}.$

5.1.41

a. $\displaystyle\sum_{k=1}^{10} k = 1 + 2 + 3 + \ldots + 10 = 55.$

b. $\displaystyle\sum_{k=1}^{6} (2k+1) = 3 + 5 + 7 + 9 + 11 + 13 = 48.$

c. $\displaystyle\sum_{k=1}^{4} k^2 = 1 + 4 + 9 + 16 = 30.$

d. $\displaystyle\sum_{n=1}^{5} (1+n^2) = 2 + 5 + 10 + 17 + 26 = 60.$

e. $\displaystyle\sum_{m=1}^{3} \frac{2m+2}{3} = \frac{4}{3} + \frac{6}{3} + \frac{8}{3} = 6.$

f. $\displaystyle\sum_{j=1}^{3} (3j-4) = -1 + 2 + 5 = 6.$

g. $\displaystyle\sum_{p=1}^{5} (2p+p^2) = 3 + 8 + 15 + 24 + 35 = 85.$

h. $\displaystyle\sum_{n=0}^{4} \sin\frac{n\pi}{2} = 0 + 1 + 0 + (-1) + 0 = 0.$

5.1.43 Note that $\Delta x = \frac{1}{10}$, and $x_k = a + k\Delta x = \frac{k}{10}$.

a. The left Riemann sum is given by $\sum_{k=0}^{39} \sqrt{k/10} \cdot (1/10) \approx 5.227$.

The right Riemann sum is given by $\sum_{k=1}^{40} \sqrt{k/10} \cdot (1/10) \approx 5.427$.

The midpoint Riemann sum is given by $\sum_{k=0}^{39} \sqrt{(1/20) + (k/10)} \cdot (1/10) \approx 5.335$.

b. It appears that the actual area is about $5 + 1/3$.

5.1.45 Note that $\Delta x = \frac{1}{15}$, and $x_k = 2 + k\Delta x = 2 + (k/15)$. So $f(x_k) = (2 + (k/15))^2 - 1$.

a. The left Riemann sum is given by $\sum_{k=0}^{74} [(2 + (k/15))^2 - 1] \cdot (1/15) \approx 105.170$.

The right Riemann sum is given by $\sum_{k=1}^{75} [(2 + (k/15))^2 - 1] \cdot (1/15) \approx 108.170$.

The midpoint Riemann sum is given by $\sum_{k=0}^{74} [((61/30) + (k/15))^2 - 1] \cdot (1/15) \approx 106.665$.

b. It appears that the actual area is about $106 + 2/3$.

5.1.47 The right Riemann sum is given by $A_n = \sum_{k=1}^{n} f(x_k)\Delta x = \sum_{k=1}^{n} \left(4 - \left(-2 + \frac{4k}{n}\right)^2\right) \cdot \frac{4}{n}$.

n	A_n
10	10.560
30	10.655
60	10.664
80	10.665

It appears that A_n is approaching $10\frac{2}{3}$.

5.1.49 The right Riemann sum is given by $A_n = \sum_{k=1}^{n} f(x_k)\Delta x = \sum_{k=1}^{n} \left(2 - 2\sin\left(\frac{-\pi}{2} + \frac{\pi k}{n}\right)\right) \cdot \frac{\pi}{n}$.

n	A_n
10	5.6549
30	6.0737
60	6.1785
80	6.2046

It appears that A_n is approaching 2π.

5.1.51 The right Riemann sum is given by $A_n = \sum_{k=1}^{n} f(x_k)\Delta x = \sum_{k=1}^{n} \ln\left(1 + \frac{k(e-1)}{n}\right) \cdot \frac{e-1}{n}$.

n	A_n
10	1.08436
30	1.02847
60	1.01428
80	1.01071

It appears that A_n is approaching 1.

5.1.53

a. True. Because the curve is a straight line, the region under the curve and over each subinterval is a trapezoid. The formula for the area of such a trapezoid over $[x_i, x_{i+1}]$ is $\frac{f(x_i)+f(x_{i+1})}{2} \cdot \Delta x = \frac{2x_i+5+2x_{i+1}+5}{2} \cdot \Delta x = (x_i + x_{i+1} + 5)\Delta x$ and the area given by using the midpoint formula is $f\left(\frac{x_i+x_{i+1}}{2}\right)\Delta x = (x_i + x_{i+1} + 5)\Delta x$. So the area under the curve is exactly given by the midpoint Riemann sum. Note that this holds for any straight line.

b. False. The left Riemann sum will underestimate the area under an increasing function.

c. True. The value of f at the midpoint will always be between the value of f at the endpoints, if f is monotonic increasing or monotonic decreasing.

5.1.55 $\sum_{k=1}^{50}\left(\frac{2k}{25}+1\right)\cdot\frac{2}{25} = 12.16.$

5.1.57 $\sum_{k=0}^{31}\left(3+\frac{1}{8}+\frac{k}{4}\right)^3\cdot\frac{1}{4} \approx 3639.125.$

5.1.59 This is the right Riemann sum for f on the interval $[1, 5]$ for $n = 4$.

5.1.61 This is the midpoint Riemann sum for f on the interval $[2, 6]$ for $n = 4$.

5.1.63 For all of the calculations below, we have $\Delta x = \frac{1}{2}$, and grid points $x_0 = 0$, $x_1 = .5$, $x_2 = 1$, $x_3 = 2.5$, and $x_4 = 2$.

a.

The left Riemann sum is given by $\frac{1}{2}(f(0) + f(.5) + f(1) + f(1.5))$ which is equal to $\frac{1}{2}(2 + 2.25 + 3 + 4.25) = 5.75$.

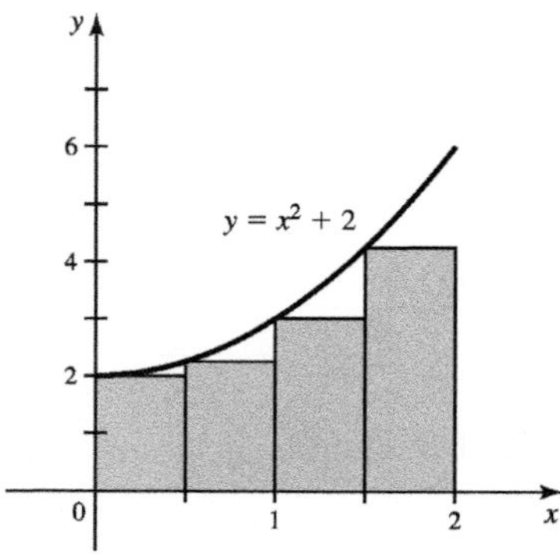

b.

The midpoint Riemann sum is given by $\frac{1}{2}(f(.25) + f(.75) + f(1.25) + f(1.75))$ which is equal to $\frac{1}{2}(2.0625 + 2.5625 + 3.5625 + 5.0625) = 6.625$.

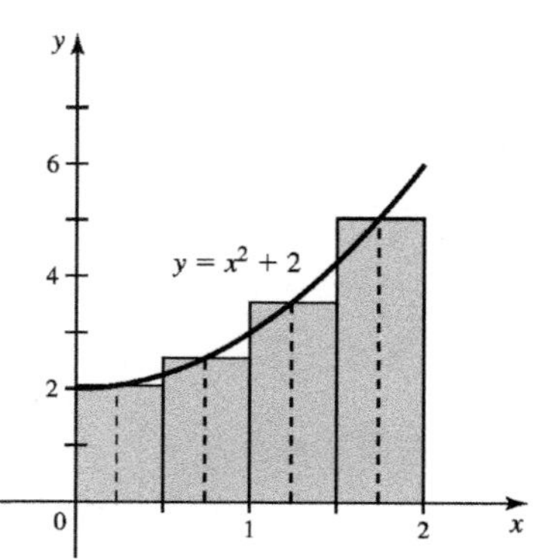

c.

The right Riemann sum is given by $\frac{1}{2}(f(.5)+f(1)+f(1.5)+f(2))$ which is equal to $\frac{1}{2}(2.25+3+4.25+6)=7.75$.

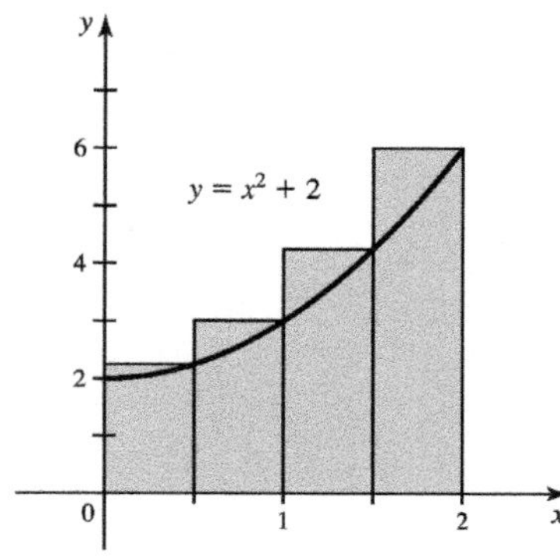

5.1.65 We have $\Delta x = \frac{7-1}{6} = 1$. The left Riemann sum is given by $1(10+9+7+5+2+1)=34$ and the right Riemann sum is given by $1(9+7+5+2+1+0)=24$.

5.1.67

a. During the first second, the velocity steadily increases from 0 to 20, then it remains constant until $t=3$. From $t=3$ until $t=5$ it steadily decreases, and then remains constant until $t=6$.

b. Between $t=0$ and $t=2$ the area under the curve is $\frac{1}{2}\cdot 1\cdot 20+1\cdot 20=30$.

c. Between $t=2$ and $t=5$ the displacement is the sum of the area of a rectangle with area 20 and a trapezoid with area 30, so the displacement is 50 meters.

d. Between $t=0$ and $t=5$ the displacement is 80. Between $t=5$ and any time $t\ge 5$ the displacement is $10(t-5)$ so the displacement between $t=0$ and $t\ge 5$ is $80+10(t-5)$.

5.1.69

a. Between 0 and 5, the area under the curve is given by the area of a square of area 4 and the area of a trapezoid of area 10.5, so the total area is 14.5.

b. Between 5 and 10, the area under the curve is given by the area of a trapezoid of area 5.5 and the area of a rectangle of area $4\cdot 6=24$, so the total area is 29.5.

c. The mass of the entire rod would be the total area under the curve from 0 to 10, which would be $14.5+29.5=44$ grams.

d. At $x=\frac{19}{3}$ there is a mass of 22 on each side. Note that from 0 to 6 the mass is 20 grams, so the center of mass is a little greater than 6.

5.1.71 If $0\le t\le 2$, the displacement is $30t$. If $2\le t\le 2.5$, the displacement is $60+50(t-2)$. If $2.5\le t\le 3$, the displacement is $85+44(t-2.5)$.

$$\text{Thus, } d(t)=\begin{cases}30t & \text{if } 0\le t\le 2,\\ 50t-40 & \text{if } 2\le t\le 2.5\\ 44t-25 & \text{if } 2.5\le t\le 3.\end{cases}$$

5.1.73 Using the left Riemann sum

$$\sum_{k=0}^{n-1}\left|\left(-1+\frac{2k}{n}\right)\left(\left(-1+\frac{2k}{n}\right)^2-1\right)\right|\cdot\frac{2}{n},$$

we have

n	16	32	64
A_n	.492188	.498047	.499512

It appears that the areas are approaching .5.

5.1.75 Using the left Riemann sum

$$\sum_{k=0}^{n-1} \left| 1 - \left(-1 + \frac{3k}{n} \right)^3 \right| \cdot \frac{3}{n},$$

we have

n	16	32	64
A_n	4.33054	4.52814	4.63592

It appears that the areas are approaching 4.75.

5.1.77 The midpoint Riemann sum gives

$$\sum_{k=0}^{n-1} f\left(a + \frac{b-a}{2n} + \frac{k(b-a)}{n}\right) \cdot \frac{b-a}{n} = \sum_{k=0}^{n-1} \left(m\left(a + \frac{b-a}{2n} + \frac{k(b-a)}{n}\right) + c\right) \cdot \frac{b-a}{n} =$$

$$m \cdot a \cdot n \cdot \frac{b-a}{n} + \frac{m(b-a)^2 n}{2n^2} + \frac{(n-1)n}{2} \cdot \frac{m(b-a)^2}{n^2} + \frac{cn(b-a)}{n} =$$

$$m \cdot a \cdot (b-a) + \frac{m(b-a)^2}{2n} + \frac{m(b-a)^2}{2} - \frac{m(b-a)^2}{2n} + c(b-a) =$$

$$m \cdot a \cdot (b-a) + \frac{m(b-a)^2}{2} + c(b-a) = (b-a) \cdot \left(\frac{m(a+b)}{2} + c\right).$$

This proves that the midpoint Riemann sum is independent of n. Because the region in question is a trapezoid, we know that the exact area is given by the width of the subinterval times the average value at the endpoints, which is $(b-a)\left(\frac{f(a)+f(b)}{2}\right) = (b-a)\left(\frac{ma+c+mb+c}{2}\right) = (b-a)\left(\frac{m(a+b)}{2} + c\right)$.

5.1.79 For a function that is concave up and increasing, each rectangle of the right Riemann sum will have its top edge above the curve, since the value of the function at the right edge of the rectangle will be larger than at any other point in the rectangle. Thus this will be an overestimate. For a function that is concave up and decreasing, however, each rectangle will lie wholly below the curve, since the value of the function at the right edge will be smaller than at any other point in the rectangle. Thus this will be an underestimate. For a function that is concave down and increasing, each rectangle of the right Riemann sum will have its top edge above the curve, since the value of the function at the right edge of the rectangle will be larger than at any other point in the rectangle. Thus this will be an overestimate. Finally, for a function that is concave down and decreasing, however, each rectangle will lie wholly below the curve, since the value of the function at the right edge will be smaller than at any other point in the rectangle. Thus this will be an underestimate. Graphs of each of the four situations are below:

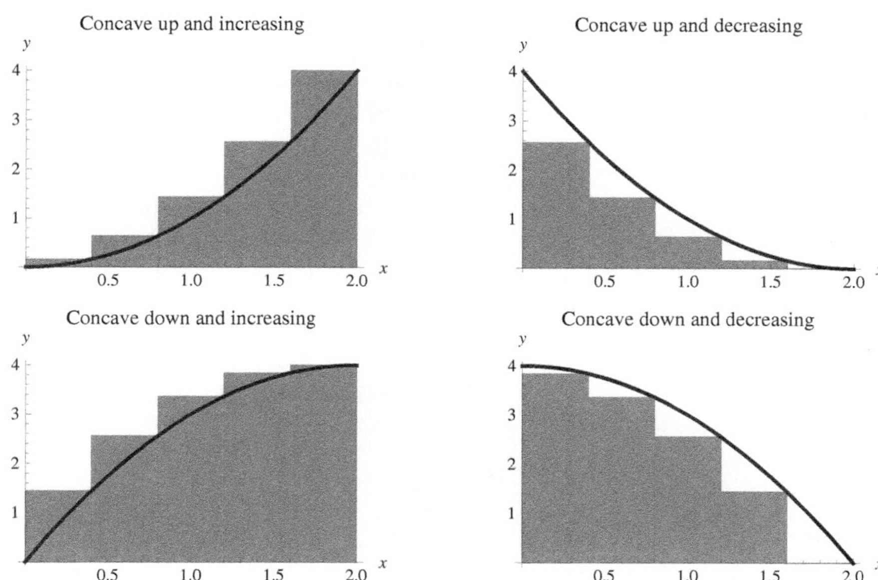

So the answer is

	Increasing on $[a,b]$	Decreasing on $[a,b]$
Concave up on $[a,b]$	Overestimate	Underestimate
Concave down on $[a,b]$	Overestimate	Underestimate

5.2 Definite Integrals

5.2.1 The net area is the difference between the area above the x-axis and below the curve, and below the x-axis and above the curve.

5.2.3 When the function is strictly above the x-axis, the net area is equal to the area. The net area differs from the area when the function dips below the x-axis so that the area below the x-axis and above the curve is nonzero.

5.2.5 Because each of the functions $\sin x$ and $\cos x$ have the same amount of area above the x-axis as below between 0 and 2π, these both have value 0.

5.2.7 Because a region "from $x = a$ to $x = a$" has no width, its area is zero. This is akin to asking for the area of a one-dimensional object.

5.2.9 This integral represents the area under $y = x$ between $x = 0$ and $x = a$, which is a right triangle. The length of the base of the triangle is a and the height is a, so the area is $\frac{1}{2} \cdot a^2$, so $\displaystyle\int_0^a x\,dx = \frac{a^2}{2}$.

5.2.11

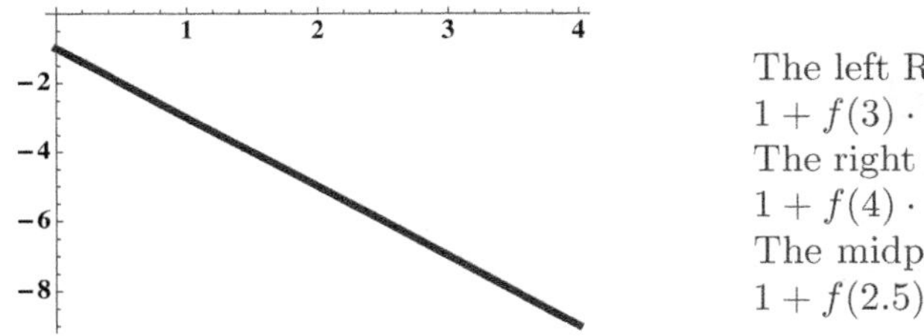

The left Riemann sum is $f(0)\cdot 1 + f(1)\cdot 1 + f(2)\cdot 1 + f(3)\cdot 1 = -1 - 3 - 5 - 7 = -16$.
The right Riemann sum is $f(1)\cdot 1 + f(2)\cdot 1 + f(3)\cdot 1 + f(4)\cdot 1 = -3 - 5 - 7 - 9 = -24$.
The midpoint Riemann sum is $f(.5)\cdot 1 + f(1.5)\cdot 1 + f(2.5)\cdot 1 + f(3.5)\cdot 1 = -2 - 4 - 6 - 8 = -20$.

5.2.13

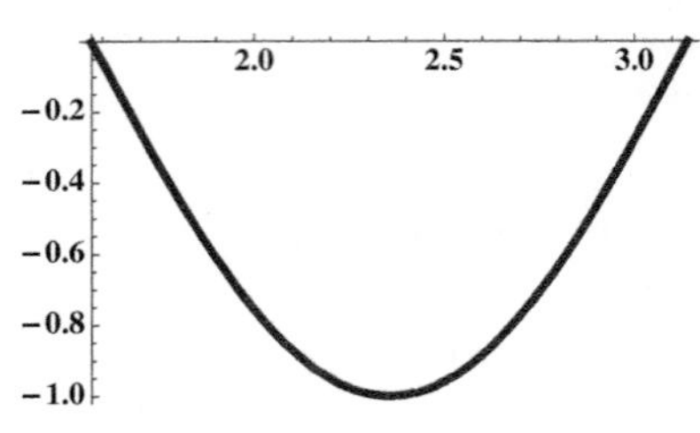

We have $\Delta x = \frac{\pi/2}{4} = \frac{\pi}{8}$. The left Riemann sum is $f(\pi/2)\cdot\frac{\pi}{8} + f(5\pi/8)\cdot\frac{\pi}{8} + f(6\pi/8)\cdot\frac{\pi}{8} + f(7\pi/8)\cdot\frac{\pi}{8} = \left(0 - \sqrt{2}/2 - 1 - \sqrt{2}/2\right)\cdot\frac{\pi}{8} = \frac{\pi}{8}\cdot(-1-\sqrt{2}) \approx -.948$.
The right Riemann sum is $f(5\pi/8)\cdot\frac{\pi}{8} + f(6\pi/8)\cdot\frac{\pi}{8} + f(7\pi/8)\cdot\frac{\pi}{8} + f(\pi)\cdot\frac{\pi}{8} = \left(-\sqrt{2}/2 - 1 - \sqrt{2}/2 - 0\right)\cdot\frac{\pi}{8} = \frac{\pi}{8}\cdot(-1-\sqrt{2}) \approx -.948$.
The midpoint Riemann sum is $f(9\pi/16)\cdot\frac{\pi}{8} + f(11\pi/16)\cdot\frac{\pi}{8} + f(13\pi/16)\cdot\frac{\pi}{8} + f(15\pi/16)\cdot\frac{\pi}{8} \approx \frac{\pi}{8}\cdot(-0.382683 - .92388 - .92388 - 0.382683) \approx -1.026$.

5.2.15

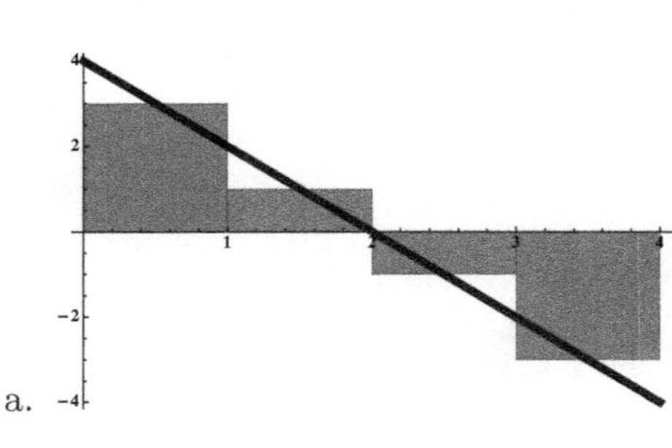

a.

b. The left Riemann sum $\sum_{k=0}^{3} f(x_k)\cdot 1 = 4$.

The right Riemann sum $\sum_{k=1}^{4} f(x_k)\cdot 1 = -4$.

The midpoint Riemann sum $\sum_{k=1}^{4} f(x_k^*)\cdot 1 = 0$.

c. The rectangles whose height is $f(x_k)$ contribute positively when $x_k < 2$ and negatively when $x_k > 2$.

5.2.17

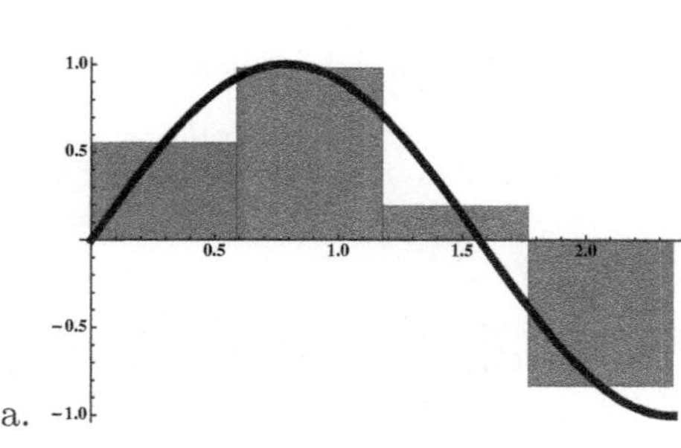

a.

b. The left Riemann sum $\sum_{k=0}^{3} f(x_k)\cdot\frac{3\pi}{16} \approx .7353$.

The right Riemann sum $\sum_{k=1}^{4} f(x_k)\cdot\frac{3\pi}{16} \approx 0.146$.

The midpoint Riemann sum $\sum_{k=1}^{4} f\left(x_k^*\right)\cdot\frac{3\pi}{16} \approx 0.530$.

c. The rectangles whose height is $f(x_k)$ contribute positively when $x_k < \frac{\pi}{2}$ and negatively when $x_k > \frac{\pi}{2}$.

5.2.19

a. 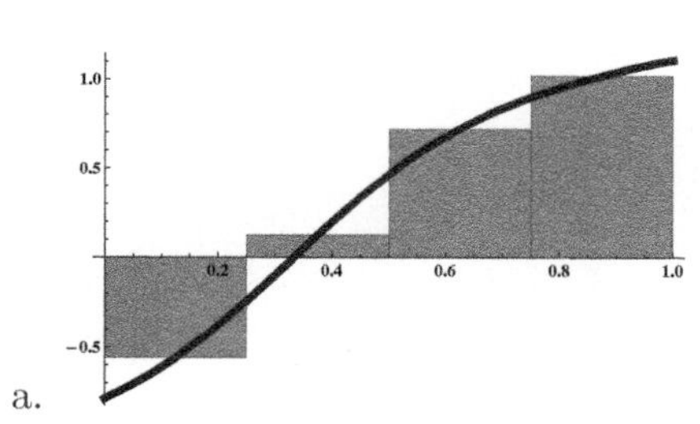

b. The left Riemann sum $\sum_{k=0}^{3} f(x_k) \cdot \frac{1}{4} \approx 0.082$.

The right Riemann sum $\sum_{k=1}^{4} f(x_k) \cdot \frac{1}{4} \approx 0.555$.

The midpoint Riemann sum $\sum_{k=1}^{4} f\left(x_k^*\right) \cdot \frac{1}{4} \approx 0.326$.

c. The rectangles whose height is $f(x_k)$ contribute positively when $x_k > 1/3$ and negatively when $x_k < 1/3$.

5.2.21 This is $\int_0^2 (x^2 + 1)\, dx$.

5.2.23 This is $\int_1^2 x \ln(x)\, dx$.

5.2.25

The region in question is a triangle with base 4 and height 8, so the area is $\frac{1}{2} \cdot 8 \cdot 4 = 16$, and this is therefore the value of the definite integral as well.

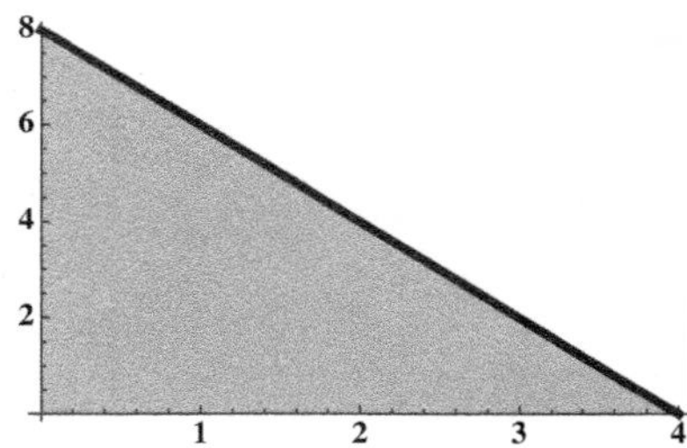

5.2.27

The region consists of two triangles, both below the axis. One has base 1 and height 1, the other has base 2 and height 2, so the net area is $-\frac{1}{2} \cdot 1 \cdot 1 - \frac{1}{2} \cdot 2 \cdot 2 = -2.5$.

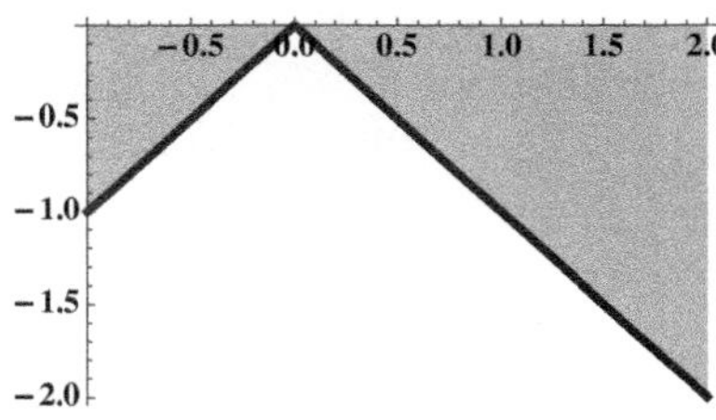

5.2.29

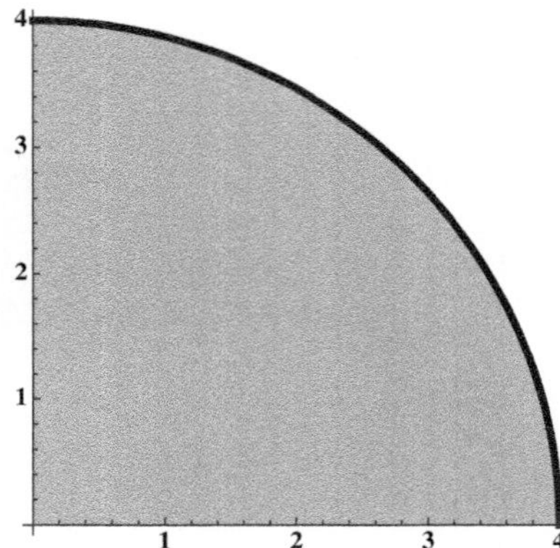

The region consists of a quarter circle of radius 4, situated above the axis. So the net area is $\frac{\pi \cdot 4^2}{4} = 4\pi$.

5.2.31

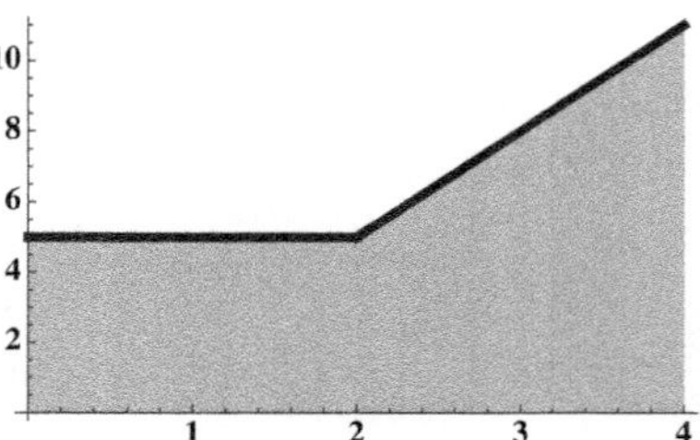

The region consists of a rectangle of area 10 above the axis, and a trapezoid of area 16 above the axis, so the net area is $10 + 16 = 26$.

5.2.33 $\int_0^a f(x)\,dx = 16.$

5.2.35 $\int_a^c f(x)\,dx = 11 - 5 = 6.$

5.2.37 $\int_0^\pi x \sin x\,dx = A(R_1) + A(R_2) = 1 + \pi - 1 = \pi.$

5.2.39 $\int_0^{2\pi} x \sin x\,dx = A(R_1) + A(R_2) - A(R_3) - A(R_4) = 1 + \pi - 1 - \pi - 1 - 2\pi + 1 = -2\pi.$

5.2.41

a. $\int_4^0 3x(4-x)\,dx = -\int_0^4 3x(4-x)\,dx = -32.$

b. $\int_0^4 x(x-4)\,dx = \frac{-1}{3}\int_0^4 3x(4-x)\,dx = \frac{-1}{3} \cdot 32 = \frac{-32}{3}.$

c. $\int_4^0 6x(4-x)\,dx = -2 \cdot \int_0^4 3x(4-x)\,dx = -2 \cdot 32 = -64.$

d. $\int_0^8 3x(4-x)\,dx = \int_0^4 3x(4-x)\,dx + \int_4^8 3x(4-x)\,dx = 32 + \int_4^8 3x(4-x)\,dx$. It is not possible to evaluate the given integral from the information given.

5.2.43

a. $\int_0^3 5f(x)\,dx = 5\int_0^3 f(x)\,dx = 5\cdot 2 = 10.$

b. $\int_3^6 (-3g(x))\,dx = -3\int_3^6 g(x)\,dx = -3\cdot 1 = -3.$

c. $\int_3^6 (3f(x) - g(x))\,dx = 3\int_3^6 f(x)\,dx - \int_3^6 g(x)\,dx = 3(-5) - 1 = -16.$

d. $\int_6^3 [f(x) + 2g(x)]\,dx = -\left[\int_3^6 f(x)\,dx + 2\int_3^6 g(x)\,dx\right] = -[-5 + 2\cdot 1] = 3.$

5.2.45

a. $\int_0^1 (4x - 2x^3)\,dx = -2\int_0^1 (x^3 - 2x)\,dx = -2\cdot\frac{-3}{4} = \frac{3}{2}.$

b. $\int_1^0 (2x - x^3)\,dx = \int_0^1 (x^3 - 2x)\,dx = \frac{-3}{4}.$

5.2.47

$$\begin{aligned}\int_0^2 (2x+1)\,dx &= \lim_{n\to\infty}\sum_{k=1}^n f(x_k)\Delta x = \lim_{n\to\infty}\sum_{k=1}^n \left[2\left(\frac{2k}{n}\right)+1\right]\frac{2}{n}\\ &= \lim_{n\to\infty}\left[\frac{8}{n^2}\sum_{k=1}^n k + \frac{2}{n}\sum_{k=1}^n 1\right]\\ &= \lim_{n\to\infty}\left[\frac{8}{n^2}\cdot\frac{n(n+1)}{2} + \frac{2}{n}\cdot n\right]\\ &= \lim_{n\to\infty}\left[\frac{4(n+1)}{n} + 2\right] = 4 + 2 = 6.\end{aligned}$$

5.2.49

$$\begin{aligned}\int_3^7 (4x+6)\,dx &= \lim_{n\to\infty}\sum_{k=1}^n f(x_k)\Delta x = \lim_{n\to\infty}\sum_{k=1}^n \left[4\left(3+\frac{4k}{n}\right)+6\right]\frac{4}{n}\\ &= \lim_{n\to\infty}\left[\frac{64}{n^2}\sum_{k=1}^n k + \frac{72}{n}\sum_{k=1}^n 1\right]\\ &= \lim_{n\to\infty}\left[\frac{64}{n^2}\cdot\frac{n(n+1)}{2} + \frac{72}{n}\cdot n\right]\\ &= \lim_{n\to\infty}\left[\frac{32(n+1)}{n} + 72\right] = 104.\end{aligned}$$

5.2.51

$$\begin{aligned}\int_1^4 (x^2-1)\,dx &= \lim_{n\to\infty}\sum_{k=1}^n f(x_k)\Delta x = \lim_{n\to\infty}\sum_{k=1}^n \left[\left(1+\frac{3k}{n}\right)^2-1\right]\frac{3}{n}\\ &= \lim_{n\to\infty}\left[\frac{18}{n^2}\sum_{k=1}^n k + \frac{27}{n^3}\sum_{k=1}^n k^2\right]\\ &= \lim_{n\to\infty}\left[\frac{18}{n^2}\cdot\frac{n(n+1)}{2} + \frac{27}{n^3}\cdot\frac{n(n+1)(2n+1)}{6}\right]\\ &= \lim_{n\to\infty}\left[\frac{9(n+1)}{n} + \frac{18n^2+27n+9}{2n^2}\right] = 9 + 9 = 18.\end{aligned}$$

5.2.53

a. True. See problem 76 in the previous section for a proof.

b. True. See problem 77 in the previous section for a proof.

c. True. Because both of those function are periodic with period $\frac{2\pi}{a}$, and both have the same amount of area above the axis as below for one period, the net area of each between 0 and $\frac{2\pi}{a}$ is zero.

d. False. For example $\int_0^{2\pi} \sin x\, dx = 0 = \int_{2\pi}^{0} \sin x\, dx$, but $\sin x$ is not a constant function.

e. False. Because x is not a constant, it can not be factored outside of the integral. For example $\int_0^1 x \cdot 1\, dx \neq x \int_0^1 1\, dx$.

5.2.55

a. 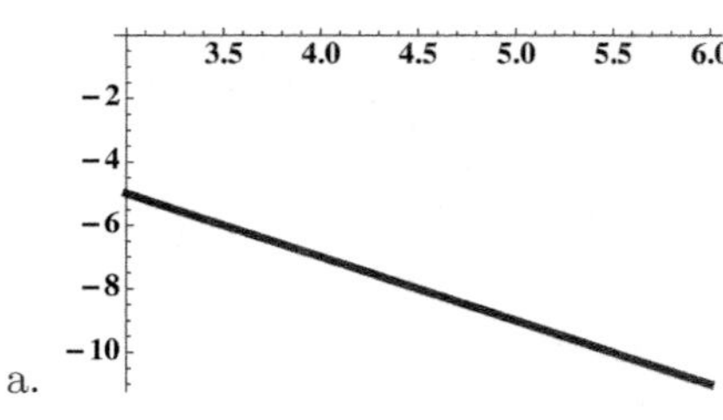

b. $\Delta x = \frac{1}{2}$, so the grid points are at 3, 3.5, 4, 4.5, 5, 5.5, and 6.

c. The left Riemann sum is $.5(-5-6-7-8-9-10) = -22.5$. The right Riemann sum is $.5(-6-7-8-9-10-11) = -25.5$.

d. The left Riemann sum overestimates the true value, while the right Riemann sum underestimates it.

5.2.57

a. 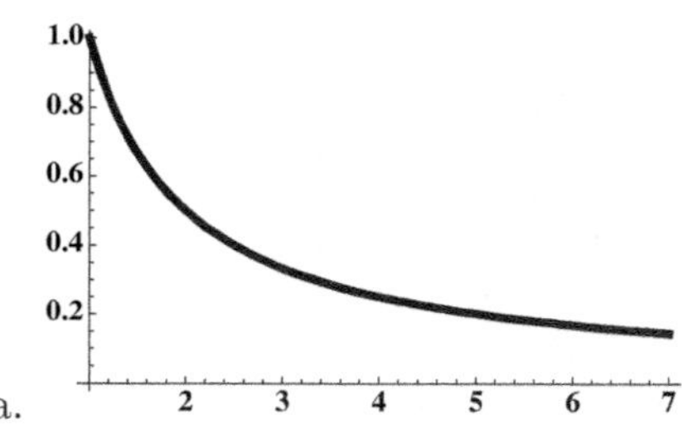

b. $\Delta x = 1$, so the grid points are at 1, 2, 3, 4, 5, 6, and 7.

c. The left Riemann sum is approximately $1 + 0.5 + 0.333333 + 0.25 + -.2 + 0.166666 = 2.45$. The right Riemann sum is approximately $.5 + 0.333333 + 0.25 + 0.2 + 0.166666 + 0.142857 \approx 1.593$.

d. The left Riemann sum overestimates the true value, while the right Riemann sum underestimates it.

5.2.59

a. $\sum_{k=1}^{20} \left(\left(\frac{k-1}{20}\right)^2 + 1\right) \cdot \frac{1}{20} \approx 1.309.$ $\sum_{k=1}^{20} \left(\left(\frac{k}{20}\right)^2 + 1\right) \cdot \frac{1}{20} \approx 1.359.$

$\sum_{k=1}^{50} \left(\left(\frac{k-1}{50}\right)^2 + 1\right) \cdot \frac{1}{50} \approx 1.323.$ $\sum_{k=1}^{50} \left(\left(\frac{k}{50}\right)^2 + 1\right) \cdot \frac{1}{50} \approx 1.343.$

$\sum_{k=1}^{100} \left(\left(\frac{k-1}{100}\right)^2 + 1\right) \cdot \frac{1}{100} \approx 1.328.$ $\sum_{k=1}^{100} \left(\left(\frac{k}{100}\right)^2 + 1\right) \cdot \frac{1}{100} \approx 1.338.$

b. It appears that the integral's value is about $\frac{4}{3}$.

5.2.61

a. $\displaystyle\sum_{k=1}^{20} \cos^{-1}((k-1)/20) \cdot \frac{1}{20} \approx 1.036.$ $\displaystyle\sum_{k=1}^{20} \cos^{-1}(k/20) \cdot \frac{1}{20} \approx 0.958.$

$\displaystyle\sum_{k=1}^{50} \cos^{-1}((k-1)/50) \cdot \frac{1}{50} \approx 1.015.$ $\displaystyle\sum_{k=1}^{50} \cos^{-1}(k/50) \cdot \frac{1}{50} \approx 0.983.$

$\displaystyle\sum_{k=1}^{100} \cos^{-1}((k-1)/100) \cdot \frac{1}{100} \approx 1.008.$ $\displaystyle\sum_{k=1}^{100} \cos^{-1}(k/100) \cdot \frac{1}{100} \approx 0.992.$

b. It appears that the integral's value is 1.

5.2.63

a. $\displaystyle\sum_{k=1}^{n} 2\sqrt{1+\frac{3}{2n}+\frac{3(k-1)}{n}} \cdot \frac{3}{n}.$

b.

n	20	50	100
Midpoint Sum	9.3338	9.33341	9.33335

It appears that the integral's value is about $\frac{28}{3}$.

5.2.65

a. $\displaystyle\sum_{k=1}^{n} \left(4\left(\frac{2}{n}+\frac{4(k-1)}{n}\right)-\left(\frac{2}{n}+\frac{4(k-1)}{n}\right)^2\right) \cdot \frac{4}{n}.$

b.

n	20	50	100
Midpoint Sum	10.68	10.6688	10.6672

It appears that the integral's value is about $\frac{32}{3}$.

5.2.67

a. $\displaystyle\int_1^4 3f(x)\,dx = 3\int_1^4 f(x)\,dx = 3\cdot\left(\int_1^6 f(x)\,dx - \int_4^6 f(x)\,dx\right) = 3\cdot(10-5) = 15.$

b. $\displaystyle\int_1^6 (f(x)-g(x))\,dx = \int_1^6 f(x)\,dx - \int_1^6 g(x)\,dx = 10-5 = 5.$

c. $\displaystyle\int_1^4 (f(x)-g(x))\,dx = \int_1^4 f(x)\,dx - \int_1^4 g(x)\,dx = \left(\int_1^6 f(x)\,dx - \int_4^6 f(x)\,dx\right) - 2 = (10-5)-2 = 3.$

d. $\displaystyle\int_4^6 (g(x)-f(x)\,dx = \int_4^6 g(x)\,dx - \int_4^6 f(x)\,dx = \left(\int_1^6 g(x)\,dx - \int_1^4 g(x)\,dx\right) - 5 = (5-2)-5 = -2.$

e. $\displaystyle\int_4^6 8g(x)\,dx = 8\left(\int_1^6 g(x)\,dx - \int_1^4 g(x)\,dx\right) = 8(5-2) = 24.$

f. $\displaystyle\int_4^1 2f(x)\,dx = -2\int_1^4 f(x)\,dx = -2\cdot\left(\int_1^6 f(x)\,dx - \int_4^6 f(x)\,dx\right) = -2(10-5) = -10.$

5.2.69

The region above the axis is a triangle with base 2 and height $f(-2) = 6$, and the region below the axis is a triangle with base 2 and height $-f(2) = 6$, so the net area is 0, and the area is 12.

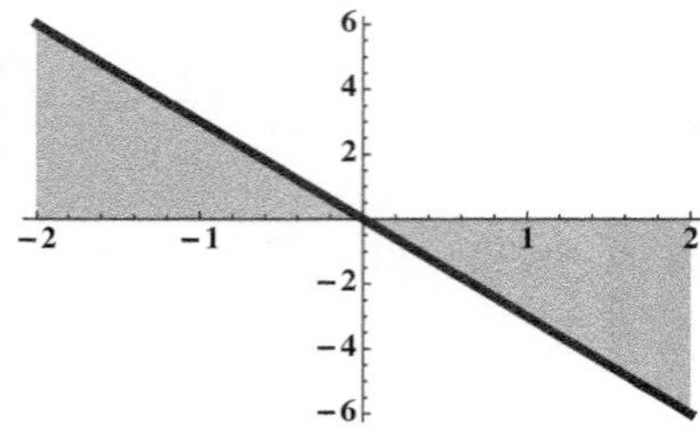

5.2.71

The region above the axis is a triangle with base 2 and height $f(0) = 1$, while the region below the axis consists of two triangles each with base 1 and height 1, so the net area is 0, and the area is 2.

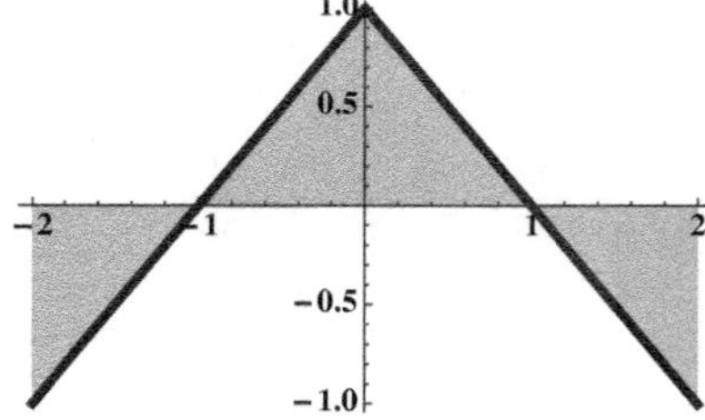

5.2.73

The region in question consists of two triangles above the axis, one with base 1 and height 2, and one with base 4 and height 8, so the net area is $\frac{1}{2} \cdot 1 \cdot 2 + \frac{1}{2} \cdot 4 \cdot 8 = 17$.

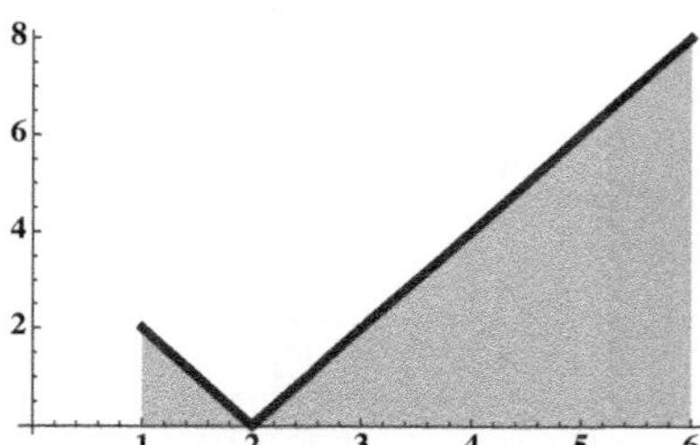

5.2.75

The region in question is a semicircle above the axis with radius 5, so the area is $\frac{1}{2}\pi \cdot 5^2 = \frac{25\pi}{2}$.

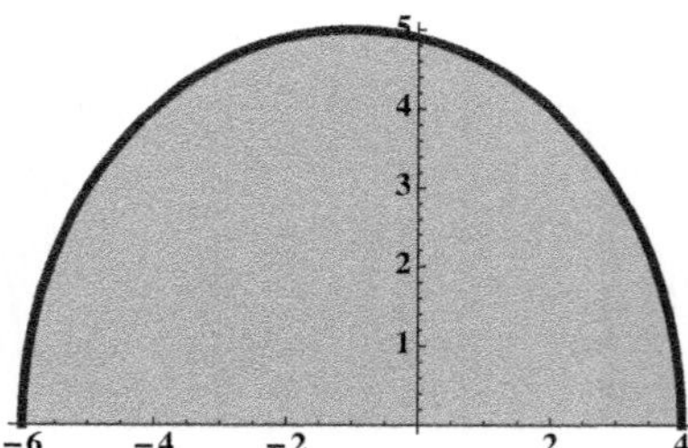

5.2.77 $\int_0^{10} f(x)\,dx = \int_0^5 2\,dx + \int_5^{10} 3\,dx = 10 + 15 = 25.$

5.2.79 $\int_1^5 x\lfloor x \rfloor\,dx = \int_1^2 x\lfloor x \rfloor\,dx + \int_2^3 x\lfloor x \rfloor\,dx + \int_3^4 x\lfloor x \rfloor\,dx + \int_4^5 x\lfloor x \rfloor\,dx = \int_1^2 x\,dx + \int_2^3 2x\,dx + \int_3^4 3x\,dx +$ $\int_4^5 4x\,dx$. Each of these integrals represents the area of a trapezoid with base 1. The value of the integral is $\frac{1+2}{2} + \frac{4+6}{2} + \frac{9+12}{2} + \frac{16+20}{2} = 35$.

5.2.81

$$\begin{aligned}\int_a^b cf(x)\,dx &= \lim_{\Delta\to 0}\sum_{k=1}^n cf(x_k^*)\Delta x_k \\ &= \lim_{\Delta\to 0} c\sum_{k=1}^n f(x_k^*)\Delta x_k \\ &= c\lim_{\Delta\to 0}\sum_{k=1}^n f(x_k^*)\Delta x_k = c\int_a^b f(x)\,dx.\end{aligned}$$

5.2.83 Let n be a positive integer. Let $\Delta x = \frac{1}{n}$. Note that each grid point $\frac{k}{n}$ for $0 \le k \le n$ where i is an integer is a rational number. So $f(x_k) = 1$ for each grid point. So the right Riemann sum is $\sum_{k=1}^n f(x_k)\frac{1}{n} = \frac{1}{n}\sum_{k=1}^n 1 = \frac{1}{n}\cdot n = 1$. The left Riemann sum calculation is similar, as is the midpoint Riemann sum calculation (because the grid midpoints are also rational numbers – they are the average of two rational numbers and hence are rational as well).

5.2.85

a. Note that for all values of $k = 1, 2, \ldots, n$, we have $x_{k-1}x_{k-1} \le x_{k-1}x_k$, so $\sqrt{x_{k-1}x_{k-1}} \le \sqrt{x_{k-1}x_k}$, and thus $x_{k-1} \le \sqrt{x_{k-1}x_k}$. Similarly, $x_{k-1}x_k \le x_kx_k$, so $\sqrt{x_{k-1}x_k} \le \sqrt{x_kx_k} = x_k$, so $\sqrt{x_{k-1}x_k} \le x_k$. Thus $x_{k-1} \le \sqrt{x_{k-1}x_k} \le x_k$ for all $k = 1, 2, \ldots, n$.

b. $\frac{1}{x_{k-1}} - \frac{1}{x_k} = \frac{x_k}{x_{k-1}x_k} - \frac{x_{k-1}}{x_{k-1}x_k} = \frac{x_k - x_{k-1}}{x_{k-1}x_k} = \frac{\Delta x_k}{x_{k-1}x_k}$, for all $k = 1, 2, \ldots, n$.

c. The Riemann sum is $\sum_{k=1}^n \frac{\Delta x_k}{\overline{x_k}^2}$. Using $\overline{x_k} = \sqrt{x_{k-1}x_k}$, we have

$$\sum_{k=1}^n \frac{\Delta x_k}{x_{k-1}x_k} = \sum_{k=1}^n \left(\frac{1}{x_{k-1}} - \frac{1}{x_k}\right),$$

where the last equality follows from part (b). Now note that the sum telescopes (that is, has many canceling terms).

$$\begin{aligned}\sum_{k=1}^n \left(\frac{1}{x_{k-1}} - \frac{1}{x_k}\right) &= \left(\frac{1}{x_0} - \frac{1}{x_1}\right) + \left(\frac{1}{x_1} - \frac{1}{x_2}\right) + \cdots + \left(\frac{1}{x_{n-2}} - \frac{1}{x_{n-1}}\right) + \left(\frac{1}{x_{n-1}} - \frac{1}{x_n}\right) \\ &= \frac{1}{x_0} + \left(-\frac{1}{x_1} + \frac{1}{x_1}\right) + \left(-\frac{1}{x_2} + \frac{1}{x_2}\right) + \cdots + \left(-\frac{1}{x_{n-1}} + \frac{1}{x_{n-1}}\right) - \frac{1}{x_n} \\ &= \frac{1}{x_0} - \frac{1}{x_n} \\ &= \frac{1}{a} - \frac{1}{b}.\end{aligned}$$

d. The integral is the limit of the Riemann sum as $n \to \infty$. Thus we have

$$\int_a^b \frac{dx}{x^2} = \lim_{n\to\infty}\sum_{k=1}^n \frac{\Delta x_k}{\overline{x_k}^2} = \lim_{n\to\infty}\left(\frac{1}{a} - \frac{1}{b}\right) = \frac{1}{a} - \frac{1}{b}.$$

5.3 Fundamental Theorem of Calculus

5.3.1 A is also an antiderivative of f.

5.3.3 The fundamental theorem says that $\int_a^b f(x)\,dx = F(b) - F(a)$ where F is any antiderivative of f. So to evaluate $\int_a^b f(x)\,dx$, one could find an antiderivative $F(x)$, and then evaluate this at a and b and then subtract, obtaining $F(b) - F(a)$.

5.3.5

$A(x) = \int_0^x (3-t)\,dt$ represents the area between 0 and x and below this curve. As x increases (but remains less than 3), the trapezoidal region's area increases, so the area function increases until x is 3.

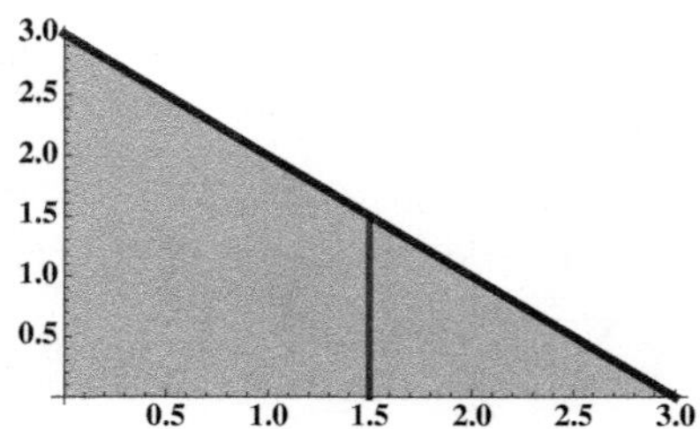

5.3.7 $\frac{d}{dx}\int_a^x f(t)\,dt = f(x)$, and $\int f'(x)\,dx = f(x) + C$.

5.3.9 $\frac{d}{dx}\int_a^x f(t)\,dt = f(x)$, and $\frac{d}{dx}\int_a^b f(t)\,dt = 0$. The latter is the derivative of a constant, the former follows from the Fundamental Theorem.

5.3.11

a. $A(-2) = \int_{-2}^{-2} f(t)\,dt = 0$.

b. $F(8) = \int_4^8 f(t)\,dt = -9$.

c. $A(4) = \int_{-2}^{4} f(t)\,dt = 8 + 17 = 25$.

d. $F(4) = \int_4^4 f(t)\,dt = 0$.

e. $A(8) = \int_{-2}^{8} f(t)\,dt = 25 - 9 = 16$.

5.3.13

a. $A(x) = \int_0^x f(t)\,dt = \int_0^x 5\,dt = 5x$.

b. $A'(x) = 5 = f(x)$.

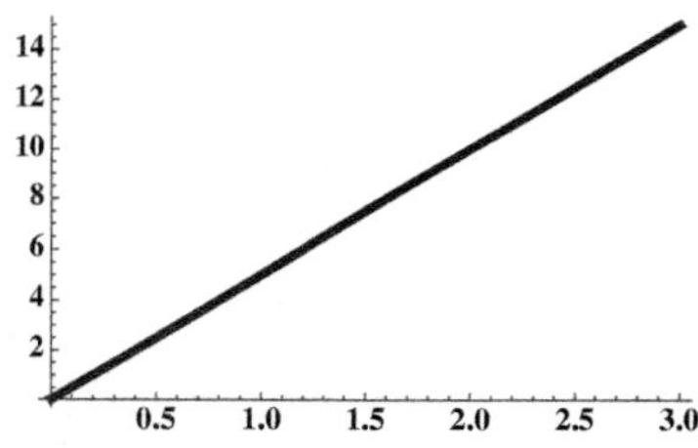

5.3.15

a. $A(x) = \int_{-5}^x f(t)\,dt = \int_{-5}^x 5\,dt = 5(x+5)$.

b. $A'(x) = 5 = f(x)$.

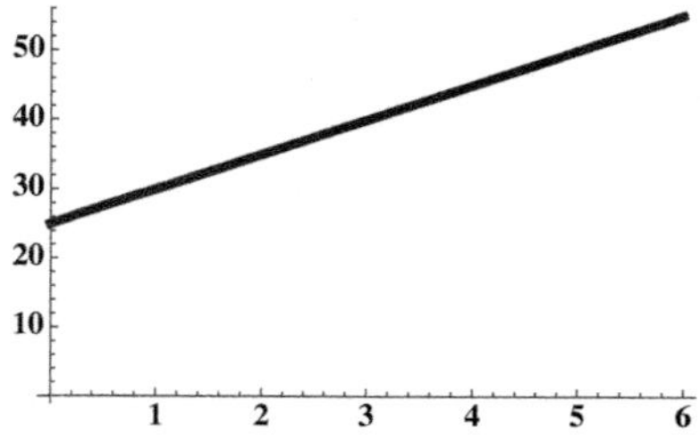

5.3.17

a. $A(2) = \int_0^2 t\,dt = 2$. $A(4) = \int_0^4 t\,dt = 8$. Because the region whose area is $A(x) = \int_0^x t\,dt$ is a triangle with base x and height x, its value is $\frac{1}{2}x^2$.

b. $F(4) = \int_2^4 t\,dt = 6$. $F(6) = \int_2^6 t\,dt = 16$. Because the region whose area is $A(x) = \int_2^x t\,dt$ is a trapezoid with base $x-2$ and $h_1 = 2$ and $h_2 = x$, its value is $(x-2)\frac{2+x}{2} = \frac{x^2-4}{2} = \frac{x^2}{2} - 2$.

c. We have $A(x) - F(x) = \frac{x^2}{2} - (\frac{x^2}{2} - 2) = 2$, a constant.

5.3.19

a. The region is a triangle with base $x+5$ and height $x+5$, so its area is $A(x) = \frac{1}{2}(x+5)^2$.

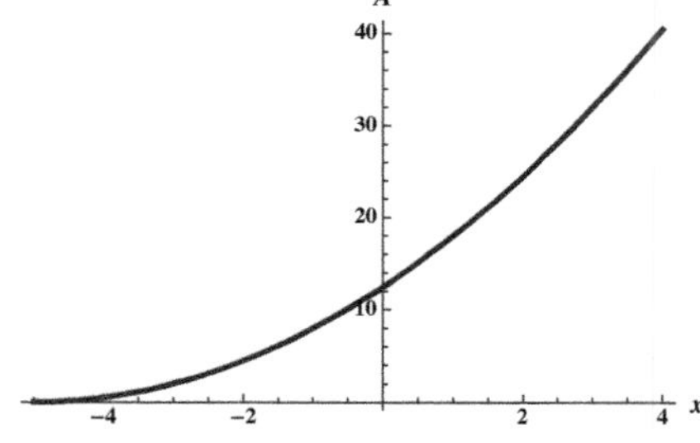

b. $A'(x) = x + 5 = f(x)$.

5.3.21

a. The region is a trapezoid with base $x-2$ and heights $h_1 = f(2) = 7$ and $h_2 = f(x) = 3x+1$, so its area is $A(x) = (x-2)\cdot\frac{7+3x+1}{2} = (x-2)\cdot(\frac{3}{2}x+4) = \frac{3}{2}x^2 + x - 8$.

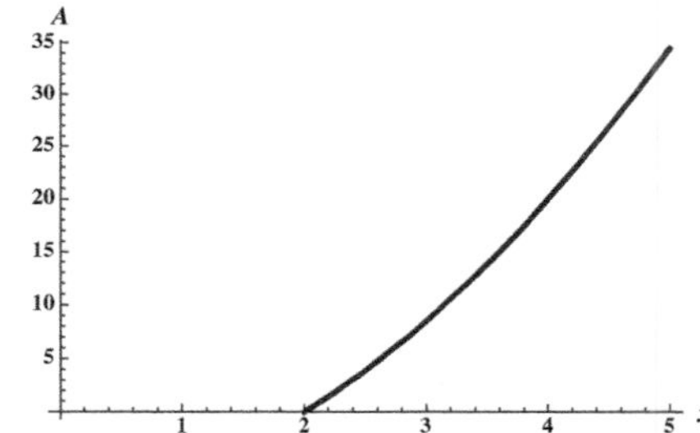

b. $A'(x) = 3x + 1 = f(x)$.

5.3.23 $\displaystyle\int_0^1 (x^2 - 2x + 3)\,dx = \left(\frac{x^3}{3} - x^2 + 3x\right)\Big|_0^1 = \frac{1}{3} - 1 + 3 - (0 - 0 + 0) = \frac{7}{3}$. It does appear that the area is between 2 and 3.

5.3.25

$$\int_{-2}^{3}(x^2 - x - 6)\,dx = \left(\frac{x^3}{3} - \frac{x^2}{2} - 6x\right)\Big|_{-2}^{3} = \frac{-125}{6}.$$

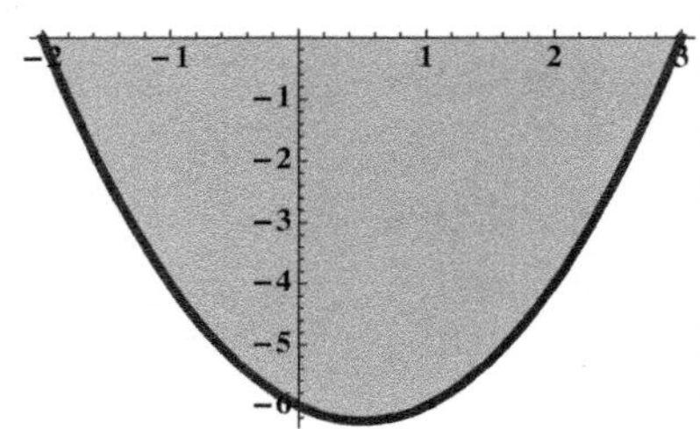

5.3.27

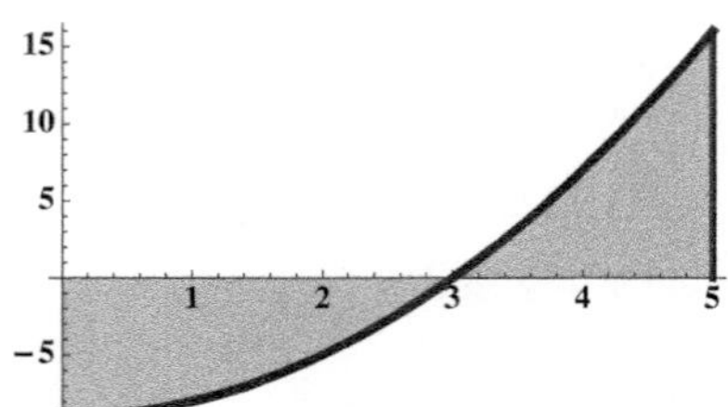

$\int_0^5 (x^2-9)\,dx = \left(\frac{x^3}{3}-9x\right)\Big|_0^5 = \frac{125}{3} - 45 - (0-0) = \frac{-10}{3}.$

5.3.29 $\int_0^2 4x^3\,dx = x^4\Big|_0^2 = 16-0=16.$

5.3.31 $\int_0^1 (x+\sqrt{x})\,dx = \left(\frac{x^2}{2}+\frac{2x^{3/2}}{3}\right)\Big|_0^1 = \frac{1}{2}+\frac{2}{3}-(0+0)=\frac{7}{6}.$

5.3.33 $\int_1^9 \frac{2}{\sqrt{x}}\,dx = \int_1^9 2x^{-1/2}\,dx = 4x^{1/2}\Big|_1^9 = 12-4=8.$

5.3.35 $\int_{-2}^2 (x^2-4)\,dx = \left(\frac{x^3}{3}-4x\right)\Big|_{-2}^2 = \frac{8}{3}-8-\left(\frac{-8}{3}+8\right) = \frac{16}{3}-16=-\frac{32}{3}.$

5.3.37 $\int_{1/2}^1 (x^{-3}-8)\,dx = \left(\frac{x^{-2}}{-2}-8x\right)\Big|_{1/2}^1 = \frac{-1}{2}-8-(-2-4) = -\frac{5}{2}.$

5.3.39 $\int_0^{\pi/4} \sec^2\theta\,d\theta = \tan\theta\Big|_0^{\pi/4} = 1-0=1.$

5.3.41 $\int_{-2}^{-1} x^{-3}\,dx = \frac{x^{-2}}{-2}\Big|_{-2}^{-1} = \frac{-1}{2x^2}\Big|_{-2}^{-1} = \frac{-1}{2}-\left(-\frac{1}{8}\right) = -\frac{3}{8}.$

5.3.43 $\int_1^4 (1-x)(x-4)\,dx = \int_1^4 (-x^2+5x-4)\,dx = \left(\frac{-x^3}{3}+\frac{5x^2}{2}-4x\right)\Big|_1^4 = \frac{9}{2}.$

5.3.45 $\int_1^2 \frac{3}{t}\,dt = 3\ln|t|\Big|_1^2 = 3\ln 2 - 3\ln 1 = \ln 8.$

5.3.47 $\int_0^{\pi/8} \cos 2x\,dx = \left(\frac{\sin 2x}{2}\right)\Big|_0^{\pi/8} = \frac{\sqrt{2}/2-0}{2} = \frac{\sqrt{2}}{4}.$

5.3.49 $\int_1^{\sqrt{3}} \frac{1}{1+x^2}\,dx = \tan^{-1}x\Big|_1^{\sqrt{3}} = \tan^{-1}\sqrt{3} - \tan^{-1}1 = \pi/3-\pi/4=\pi/12.$

5.3.51

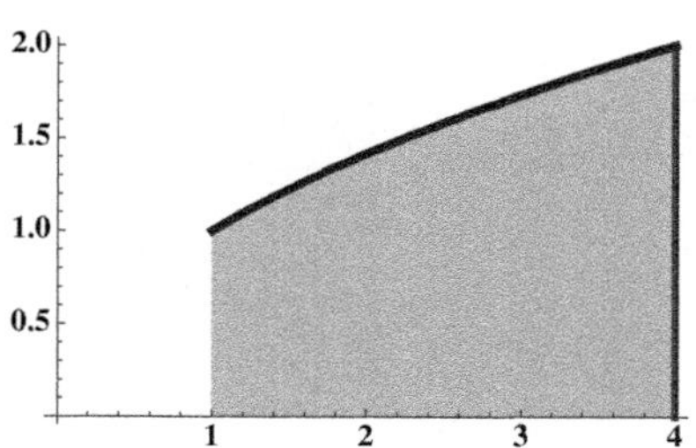

The area (and net area) of this region is given by $\int_1^4 \sqrt{x}\,dx = \frac{2}{3}x^{3/2}\Big|_1^4 = \frac{16}{3}-\frac{2}{3}=\frac{14}{3}.$

5.3.53

The net area of this region is given by $\int_{-2}^{2}(x^4 - 16)\,dx = \left(\frac{x^5}{5} - 16x\right)\Big|_{-2}^{2} = \frac{32}{5} - 32 - \left(\frac{-32}{5} + 32\right) = \frac{64}{5} - 64 = \frac{-256}{5}$. Thus the area is $\frac{256}{5}$.

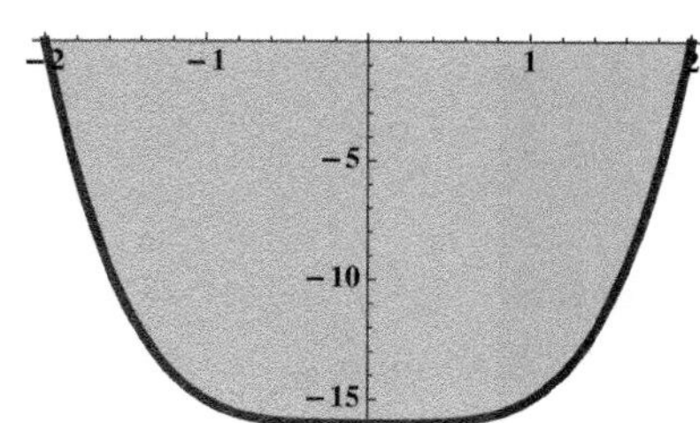

5.3.55 Because this region is below the axis, the area of it is given by $-\int_2^4(x^2-25)\,dx = -\left(\frac{x^3}{3} - 25x\right)\Big|_2^4 = -\left(\frac{64}{3} - 100 - \left(\frac{8}{3} - 50\right)\right) = 50 - \frac{56}{3} = \frac{94}{3}$.

5.3.57 Because this region is below the axis, the area of it is given by $-\int_{-2}^{-1}\frac{1}{x}\,dx = -\left(\ln|x|\Big|_{-2}^{-1}\right) = \ln 2 - \ln 1 = \ln 2$.

5.3.59 The area is given by

$$-\int_{-\pi/4}^{0}\sin x\,dx + \int_0^{3\pi/4}\sin x\,dx = \left(\cos x\Big|_{-\pi/4}^{0}\right) + \left(-\cos x\Big|_0^{3\pi/4}\right) = \left(1 - \frac{\sqrt{2}}{2}\right) + \left(1 + \frac{\sqrt{2}}{2}\right) = 2.$$

5.3.61 By a direct application of the Fundamental Theorem, this is $x^2 + x + 1$.

5.3.63 By the Fundamental Theorem and the chain rule, this is $\frac{1}{x^6}\cdot 3x^2 = \frac{3}{x^4}$.

5.3.65 This is $-\frac{d}{dx}\int_1^x \sqrt{t^4+1}\,dt = -\sqrt{x^4+1}$.

5.3.67 This can be written as

$$\frac{d}{dx}\left(\int_{-x}^{0}\sqrt{1+t^2}\,dt + \int_0^x\sqrt{1+t^2}\,dt\right) = \frac{d}{dx}\left(-\int_0^{-x}\sqrt{1+t^2}\,dt + \int_0^x\sqrt{1+t^2}\,dt\right)$$
$$= -\sqrt{1+(-x)^2}(-1) + \sqrt{1+x^2} = 2\sqrt{1+x^2}.$$

5.3.69

(a) matches with (C) – its area function is increasing linearly.
(b) matches with (B) – its area function increases then decreases.
(c) matches with (D) – its area function is always increasing on $[0, b]$, although not linearly.
(d) matches with (A) – its area function decreases at first and then eventually increases.

5.3.71

a. It appears that $A(x) = 0$ for $x = 0$ and at about $x = 3$.

b. A has a local minimum at about $x = 1.5$ where the area function changes from decreasing to increasing, and a local max at around $x = 8.5$ where the area function changes from increasing to decreasing.

c.

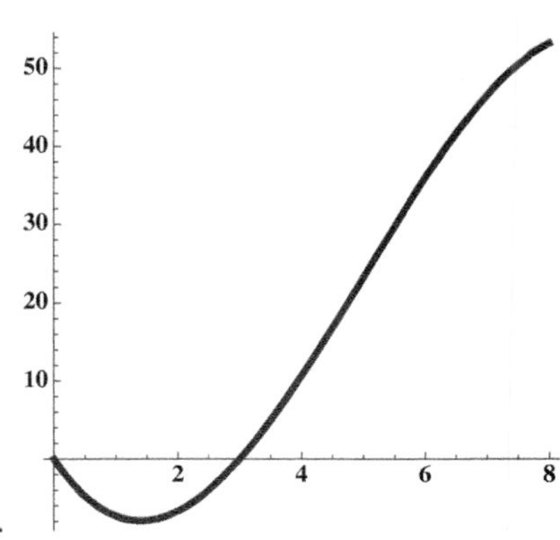

5.3.73

a. It appears that $A(x) = 0$ for $x = 0$ and $x = 10$.

b. A has a local maximum at $x = 5$ where the area function changes from increasing to decreasing.

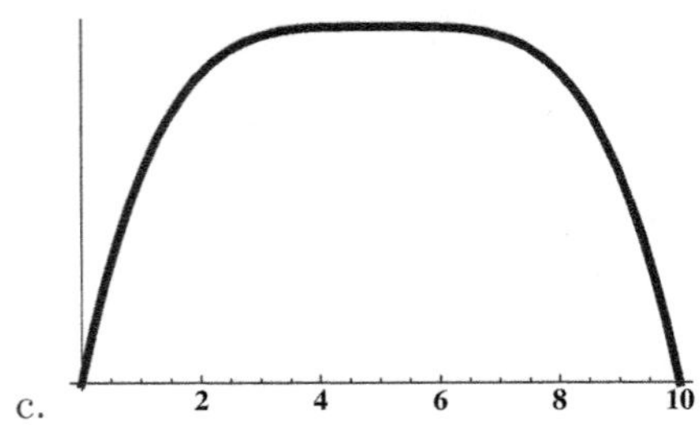

5.3.75 $A(2) = -\frac{1}{4}\pi \cdot 2^2 = -\pi$. $A(5) = -\pi + \frac{1}{2} \cdot 3 \cdot 3 = \frac{9}{2} - \pi$. $A(8) = \frac{9}{2} - \pi + \frac{1}{2} \cdot 3 \cdot 3 = 9 - \pi$. $A(12) = 9 - \pi - \frac{1}{2} \cdot 4 \cdot 2 = 5 - \pi$.

5.3.77

a. $A(x) = \int_0^x e^t \, dt = e^t \Big|_0^x = e^x - (1)$.

c. $A(\ln 2) = e^{\ln 2} - 1 = 2 - 1 = 1$. $A(\ln 4) = e^{\ln 4} - 1 = 4 - 1 = 3$. There is twice as much area under the curve between $\ln 2$ and $\ln 4$ as there is between 0 and $\ln 2$.

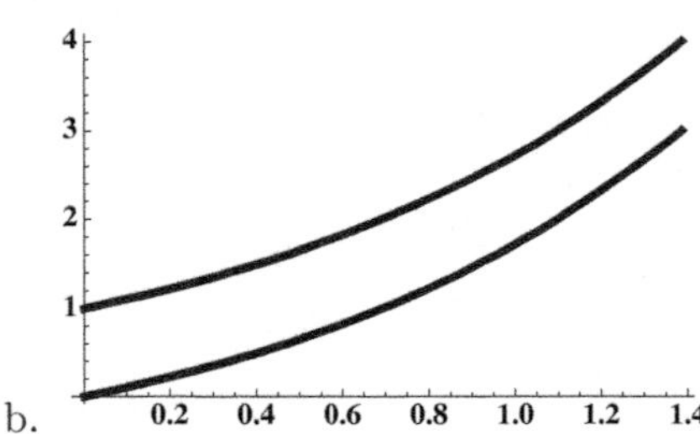

5.3.79

a. $A(x) = \int_0^x \cos \pi t \, dt = \frac{1}{\pi} \sin \pi t \Big|_0^x = \frac{\sin \pi x}{\pi}$.

c. $A(1/2) = \frac{1}{\pi}$. $A(1) = \frac{\sin \pi}{\pi} = 0$. The area bounded between the x-axis and the curve on $[0, 1/2]$ is equal to the area bounded between the x-axis and the curve on $[1/2, 1]$.

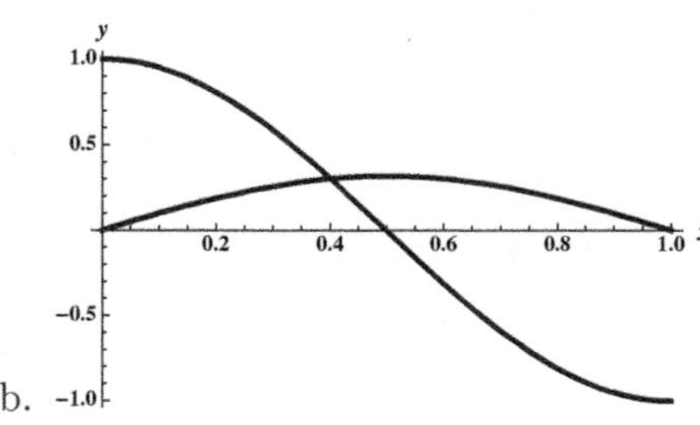

5.3.81

a. 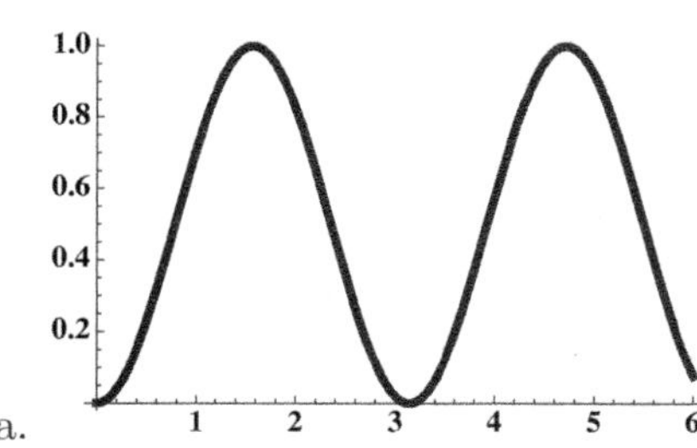

b. $g'(x) = \sin^2 x$.

c. 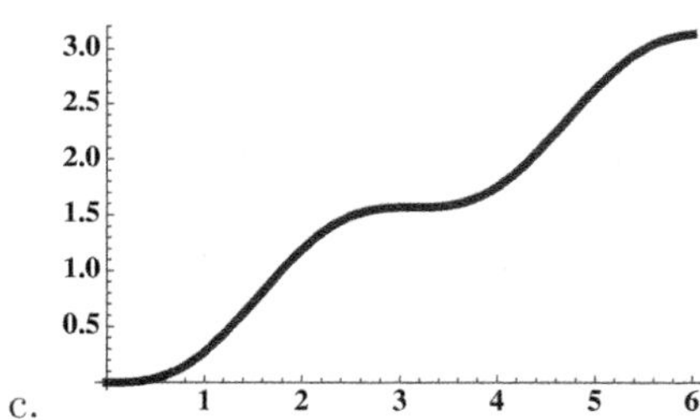

Note that g' is always positive, so g is always increasing. There are inflection points where g' changes from increasing to decreasing, and vice versa.

5.3.83

a. 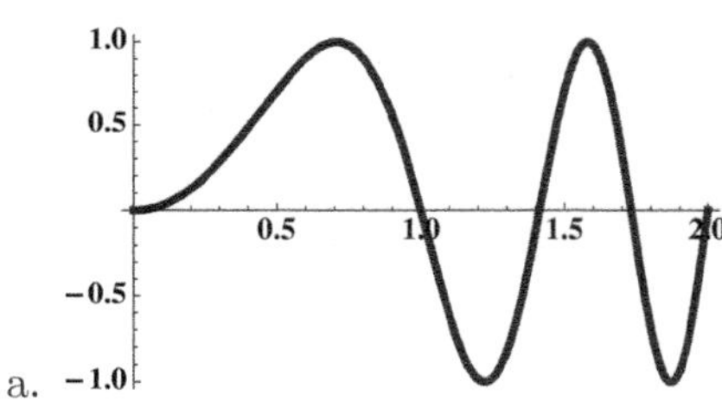

b. $g'(x) = \sin(\pi x^2)$.

c. 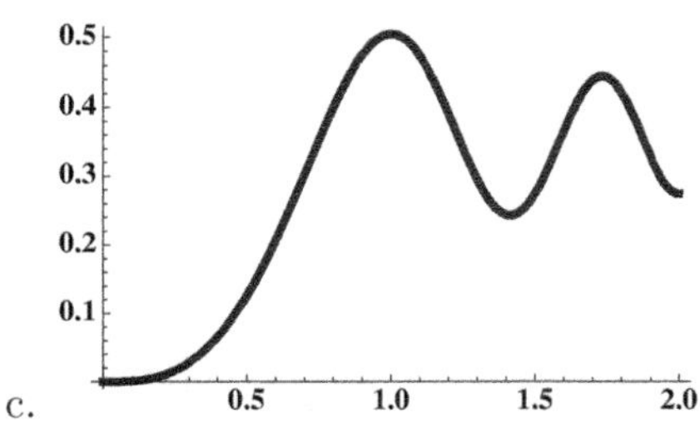

Note that g is increasing where $g' > 0$ and g is decreasing when $g' < 0$. Also, where g' is increasing, g is concave up and where g' is decreasing, g is concave down.

5.3.85

a. True. The net area under the curve increases as x increases, as long as f is above the axis.

b. True. The net area decreases as x increases, as long as f is below the axis.

c. False. These do not have the same derivative, so they are not antiderivatives of the same function.

d. True, because the two functions differ by a constant, and thus have the same derivative.

e. True, because the derivative of a constant is zero.

5.3.87

$$\int_1^4 \frac{x-2}{\sqrt{x}}\,dx = \int_1^4 \left(\frac{x}{\sqrt{x}} - \frac{2}{\sqrt{x}}\right)dx = \int_1^4 \left(x^{1/2} - 2x^{-1/2}\right)dx$$
$$= \left(\frac{2}{3}x^{3/2} - 4x^{1/2}\right)\Big|_1^4 = \frac{16}{3} - 8 - \left(\frac{2}{3} - 4\right) = \frac{14}{3} - \frac{12}{3} = \frac{2}{3}.$$

5.3.89 $\displaystyle\int_0^{\pi/3} \sec x \tan x\,dx = \sec x\Big|_0^{\pi/3} = 2 - 1 = 1.$

5.3.91 $\displaystyle\int_1^8 \sqrt[3]{y}\,dy = \frac{3}{4}y^{4/3}\Big|_1^8 = 12 - \frac{3}{4} = \frac{45}{4}.$

5.3.93 $\displaystyle\int_1^2 \frac{z^2+4}{z}\,dz = \int_1^2 \left(z + \frac{4}{z}\right)dz = \left(\frac{z^2}{2} + 4\ln z\right)\Big|_1^2 = 2 + 4\ln 2 - \left(\frac{1}{2} + 0\right) = \ln 16 + \frac{3}{2}.$

5.3.95

We can use geometry – there is a triangle with base 4 and height 2 and a triangle with base 2 and height 2, so the total area is $\frac{1}{2}\cdot 4\cdot 2 + \frac{1}{2}\cdot 2\cdot 2 = 6$.

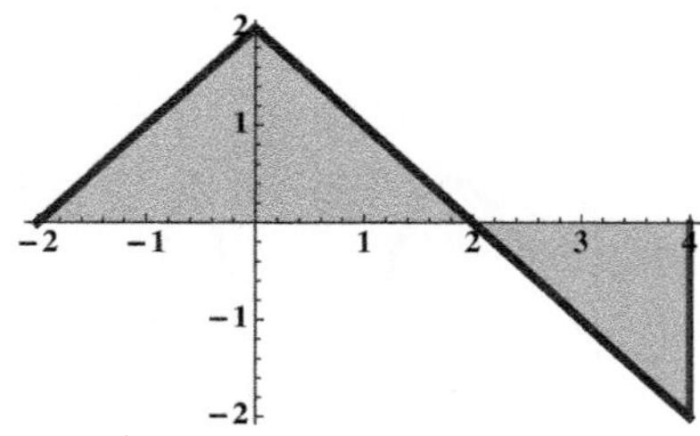

5.3.97

Because the region is below the axis on $[1, \sqrt{2}]$ and above on $[\sqrt{2}, 4]$ we need to compute $\displaystyle\int_{\sqrt{2}}^4 (x^4 - 4)\,dx - \int_1^{\sqrt{2}} (x^4 - 4)\,dx = \left(\frac{x^5}{5} - 4x\right)\Big|_{\sqrt{2}}^4 - \left(\frac{x^5}{5} - 4x\right)\Big|_1^{\sqrt{2}} = \frac{1024}{5} - 16 - (4\sqrt{2}/5 - 4\sqrt{2}) - (4\sqrt{2}/5 - 4\sqrt{2}) + \frac{1}{5} - 4 = 185 + \frac{32\sqrt{2}}{5}$

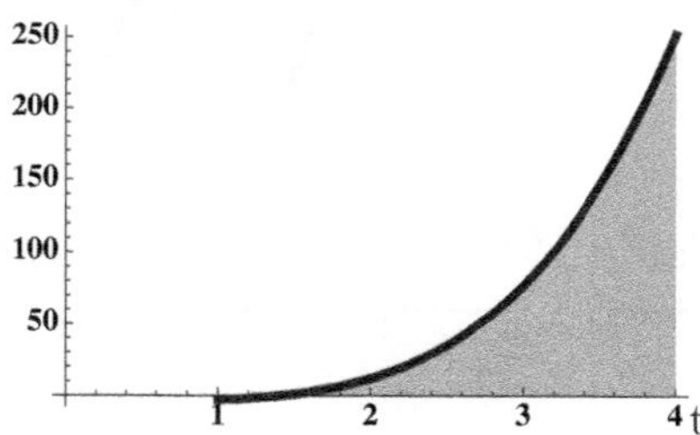

5.3.99 $\displaystyle\int_3^8 f'(t)\,dt = f(8) - f(3).$

5.3.101 $\displaystyle\frac{d}{dx}\int_0^{\cos x} (t^4 + 6)\,dt = -(\cos^4 x + 6)\sin x.$

5.3.103 $\displaystyle\frac{d}{dt}\left(\int_1^t \frac{3}{x}\,dx - \int_{t^2}^1 \frac{3}{x}\,dx\right) = \frac{d}{dt}\int_1^t \frac{3}{x}\,dx + \frac{d}{dt}\int_1^{t^2} \frac{3}{x}\,dx = \frac{3}{t} + \frac{6t}{t^2} = \frac{9}{t}.$

5.3.105

a. 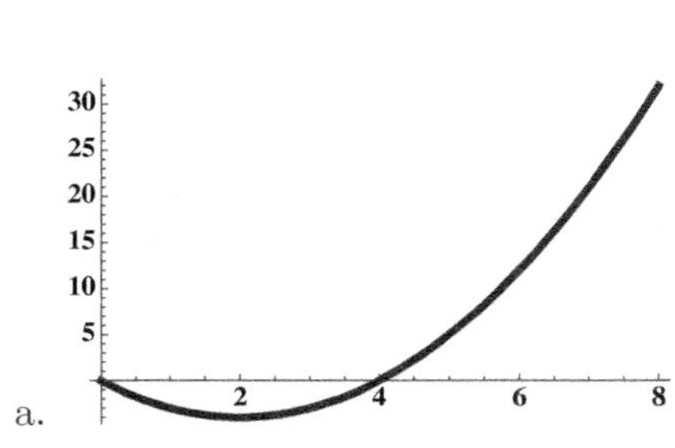

b. We seek b so that $\int_0^b (x^2 - 4x) = 0$ for $b > 0$. We have $\left(\frac{x^3}{3} - 2x^2\right)\Big|_0^b = \frac{b^3}{3} - 2b^2 = 0$, which occurs for $\frac{b}{3} = 2$, or $b = 6$.

c. We seek b so that $\int_0^b (x^2 - ax) = 0$ for $b > 0$. We have $\left(\frac{x^3}{3} - \frac{ax^2}{2}\right)\Big|_0^b = \frac{b^3}{3} - \frac{ab^2}{2} = 0$, which occurs for $\frac{b}{3} = \frac{a}{2}$, or $b = \frac{3a}{2}$.

5.3.107 Because $\frac{d}{db}\int_{-1}^b x^2(3-x)\,dx = b^2(3-b)$ we see that this function of b has critical points at $b = 0$ and $b = 3$. Note also that the integrand is positive on $[0, 3]$, but is negative on $[3, \infty)$. So the maximum for this area function occurs at $b = 3$.

5.3.109 Differentiating both sides of the given equation yields $f(x) = -2\sin x + 3$.

5.3.111 Using a computer or calculator, we obtain:

x	500	1000	1500	2000
$S(x)$	1.5726	1.57023	1.57087	1.57098

This appears to be approaching $\frac{\pi}{2}$.
Note that between 0 and π, the area is approximately half the area of a rectangle with height 1 and base π, and then from π on there is approximately as much area above the axis as below.

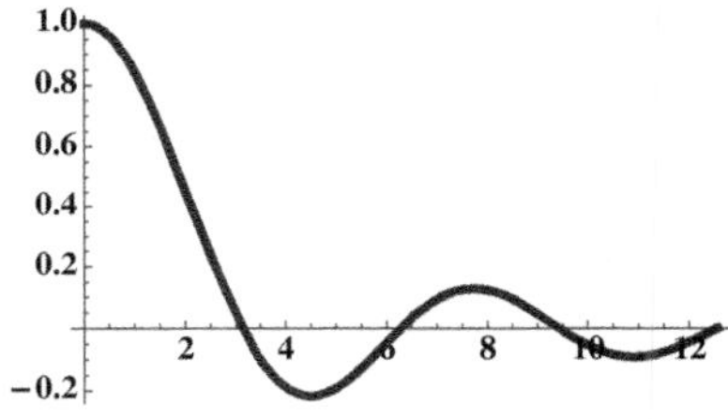

5.3.113 By the Fundamental Theorem, $S'(x) = \sin x^2$, so $S''(x) = 2x\cos x^2$, so

$$S'(x)^2 + \left(\frac{S''(x)}{2x}\right)^2 = \sin^2 x^2 + \cos^2 x^2 = 1.$$

5.3.115

a. By definition of Reimann sums, $\int_a^b f'(x)\,dx$ is approximated by $\sum_{k=1}^n f'(x_{k-1})\Delta x$. But $f'(x_{k-1}) = \lim_{h\to 0}\frac{f(x_{k-1}+h) - f(x_{k-1})}{h}$. If $h = \Delta x$, then we have $f'(x_{k-1}) \approx \frac{f(x_{k-1}+\Delta x) - f(x_{k-1})}{\Delta x} = \frac{f(x_k) - f(x_{k-1})}{\Delta x}$, so that

$$\int_a^b f'(x)\,dx \approx \sum_{k=1}^n \frac{f(x_k) - f(x_{k-1})}{\Delta x}\cdot\Delta x.$$

b. Canceling the Δx factors we obtain

$$\begin{aligned}\int_a^b f'(x)\,dx &\approx \sum_{k=1}^n \frac{f(x_k) - f(x_{k-1})}{\Delta x}\cdot\Delta x\\ &= \sum_{k=1}^n (f(x_k) - f(x_{k-1}))\\ &= (f(x_1) - f(x_0)) + (f(x_2) - f(x_1)) + \cdots + (f(x_{n-1}) - f(x_{n-2})) + (f(x_n) - f(x_{n-1}))\\ &= f(x_n) - f(x_0) = f(b) - f(a).\end{aligned}$$

c. The analogy between the two situations is that both (a) the sum of difference quotients and (b) integral of a derivative are equal to the difference in function values at the endpoints.

5.4 Working with Integrals

5.4.1 If f is odd, it is symmetric about the origin, which guarantees that between $-a$ and a, there is as much area above the axis and under f as there is below the axis and above f, so the net area must be 0.

5.4.3 $f(x) = x^{12}$ is an even function, because $f(-x) = (-x)^{12} = x^{12} = f(x)$. $g(x) = \sin x^2$ is also even, because $g(-x) = \sin((-x)^2) = \sin x^2 = g(x)$.

5.4.5 The average value of a continuous function on a closed interval $[a, b]$ will always be between the maximum and the minimum value of f on that interval. Because the function is continuous, the Intermediate Value Theorem assures us that the function will take on each value between the maximum and the minimum somewhere on the interval.

5.4.7 Because x^9 is an odd function, $\int_{-2}^{2} x^9\,dx = 0$.

5.4.9 $\int_{-2}^{2} (3x^8 - 2)\,dx = 2\int_{0}^{2} (3x^8 - 2)\,dx = 2\left(\frac{x^9}{3} - 2x\right)\Big|_0^2 = \left(\frac{1024}{3}\right) - 8 = \frac{1000}{3}$.

5.4.11 Note that the first two terms of the integrand form an odd function, and the last two terms form an even function. $\int_{-2}^{2} (x^9 - 3x^5 + 2x^2 - 10)\,dx = 2\int_{0}^{2} (2x^2 - 10)\,dx = 2\left(\frac{2x^3}{3} - 10x\right)\Big|_0^2 = \frac{32}{3} - 40 = -\frac{88}{3}$.

5.4.13 $\int_{-10}^{10} \frac{x}{\sqrt{200 - x^2}}\,dx = 0$ because the integrand is an odd function.

5.4.15 Because the integrand is an odd function and the interval is symmetric about 0, this integral's value is 0.

5.4.17

Because the integrand is an odd function and the interval is symmetric about 0, this integral's value is 0.

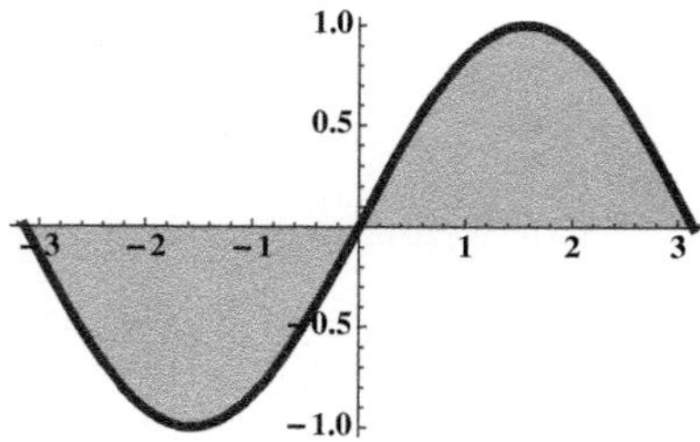

5.4.19

Because of the symmetry of the cosine function, the net area is zero between 0 and π.

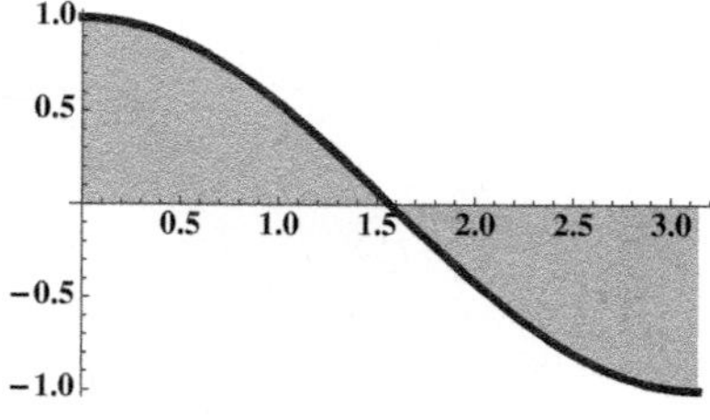

5.4.21

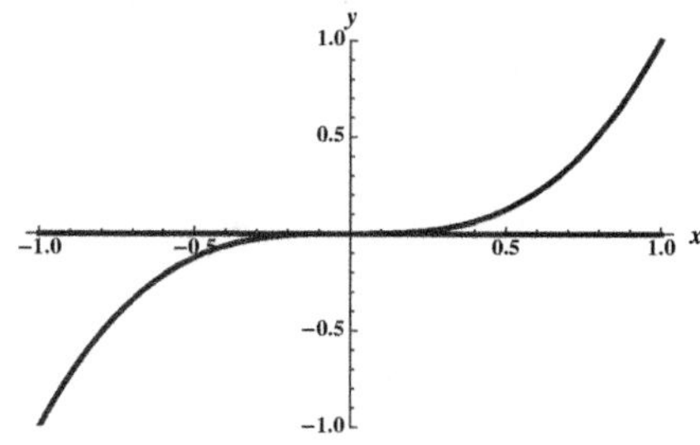

The average value is $\frac{1}{1-(-1)}\int_{-1}^{1} x^3\,dx = \frac{1}{2}\left(x^4/4\right)\Big|_{-1}^{1} = 0.$

5.4.23

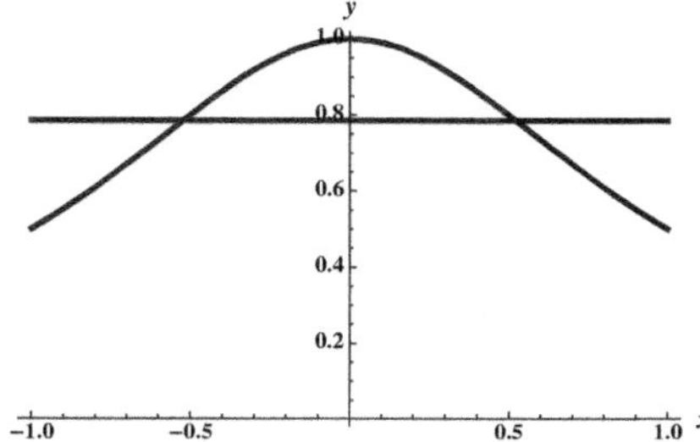

The average value is $\frac{1}{1-(-1)}\int_{-1}^{1} \frac{1}{x^2+1}\,dx = \frac{1}{2}\tan^{-1}x\Big|_{-1}^{1} = \frac{\pi/4-(-\pi/4)}{2} = \frac{\pi}{4}.$

5.4.25

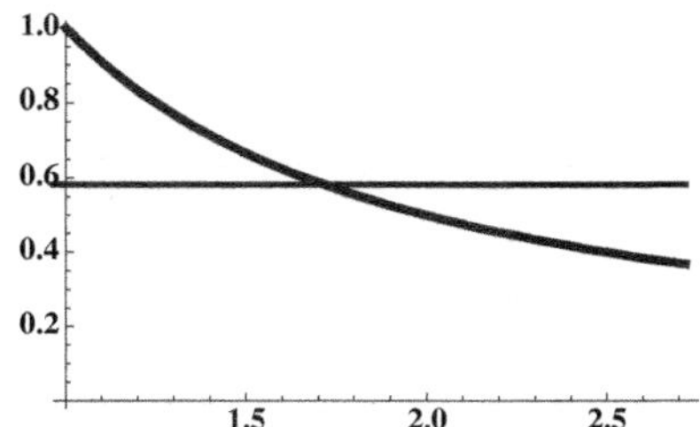

The average value is $\frac{1}{e-1}\int_{1}^{e} \frac{1}{x}\,dx = \frac{1}{e-1}\left(\ln|x|\right)\Big|_{1}^{e} = \frac{1}{e-1} \approx .582.$

5.4.27

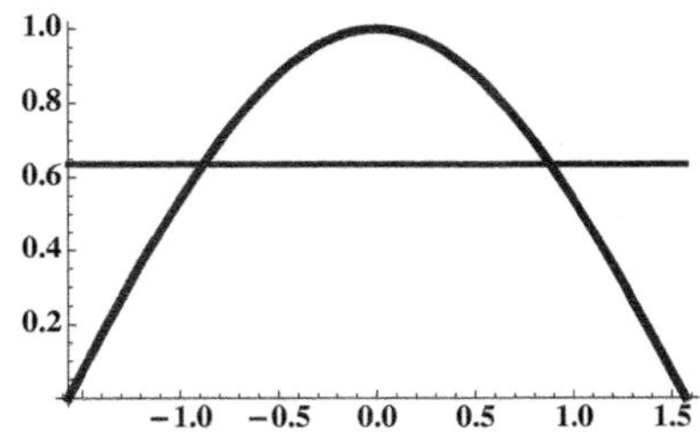

The average value is $\frac{1}{\pi}\int_{-\pi/2}^{\pi/2} \cos x\,dx = \frac{1}{\pi}\left(\sin x\right)\Big|_{-\pi/2}^{\pi/2} = \frac{1}{\pi}\cdot(1--1) = \frac{2}{\pi} \approx .6366.$

5.4.29

The average value is $\frac{1}{1}\int_0^1 x^n\,dx = \left(\frac{x^{n+1}}{n+1}\right)\Big|_0^1 = \frac{1}{n+1}$. The picture shown is for the case $n = 3$.

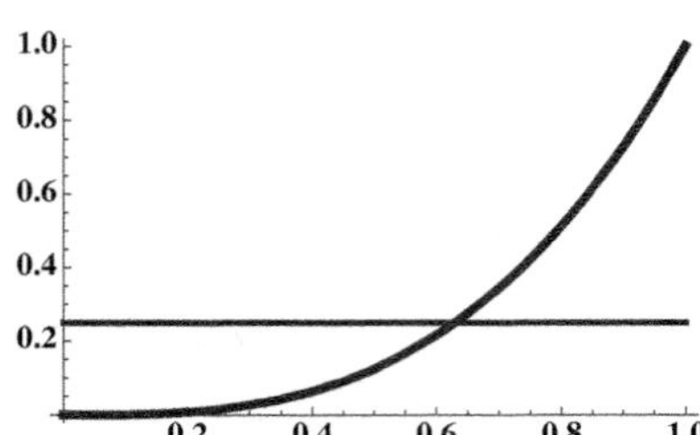

5.4.31 The average distance to the axis is given by $\frac{1}{20}\int_0^{20} 30x(20-x)\,dx$. This is equal to $\frac{1}{20}\int_0^{20}(600x - 30x^2)\,dx = \frac{1}{20}\left(300x^2 - 10x^3\right)\Big|_0^{20} = 2000$.

5.4.33 The average height is $\frac{1}{\pi}\int_0^{\pi} 10\sin x\,dx = \frac{1}{\pi}\left(-10\cos x\right)\Big|_0^{\pi} = \frac{1}{\pi}\left(10 - -10\right) = \frac{20}{\pi}$.

5.4.35 The average value is $\frac{1}{4}\int_0^4 (8-2x)\,dx = \frac{1}{4}\left(8x - x^2\right)\Big|_0^4 = 4$. The function has a value of 4 when $8 - 2x = 4$, which occurs when $x = 2$.

5.4.37 The average value is $\frac{1}{a}\int_0^a \left(1 - \frac{x^2}{a^2}\right)dx = \frac{1}{a}\left(x - \frac{x^3}{3a^2}\right)\Big|_0^a = \frac{2}{3}$. The function attains this value when $\frac{2}{3} = 1 - \frac{x^2}{a^2}$, which is when $x^2 = \frac{a^2}{3}$, which on the given interval occurs for $x = \sqrt{3}a/3$.

5.4.39 The average value is $\frac{1}{2}\int_{-1}^1 (1-|x|)\,dx = \frac{1}{2}\int_{-1}^0 (1+x)\,dx + \frac{1}{2}\int_0^1 (1-x)\,dx = \frac{1}{2}\left(x + \frac{x^2}{2}\right)\Big|_{-1}^0 + \frac{1}{2}\left(x - \frac{x^2}{2}\right)\Big|_0^1 = \frac{1}{4} + \frac{1}{4} = \frac{1}{2}$. The function attains this value twice, once on $[-1, 0]$ when $1 + x = \frac{1}{2}$ which occurs when $x = -\frac{1}{2}$, and once on $[0, 1]$ when $1 - x = \frac{1}{2}$ which occurs when $x = \frac{1}{2}$.

5.4.41

a. True. Because of the symmetry, the net area between 0 and 4 will be twice the net area between 0 and 2.

b. True. This follows because the symmetry implies that the net area from a to $a + 2$ is the opposite of the net area from $a - 2$ to a.

c. True. If $f(x) = cx + d$ on $[a, b]$ the value at the midpoint is $c \cdot \frac{a+b}{2} + d$, and the average value is $\frac{1}{b-a}\int_a^b (cx+d)\,dx = \frac{1}{b-a}\left(\frac{cx^2}{2} + dx\right)\Big|_a^b = \frac{1}{b-a}\left(\frac{cb^2}{2} + db - \left(\frac{ca^2}{2} + da\right)\right) = \frac{c}{2}\cdot(a+b) + d$.

d. False, for example, when $a = 1$, we have that the maximum value of $x - x^2$ on $[0, 1]$ occurs at $\frac{1}{2}$ and is equal to $\frac{1}{4}$, but the average value is $\int_0^1 (x - x^2)\,dx = \left(\frac{x^2}{2} - \frac{x^2}{3}\right)\Big|_0^1 = \frac{1}{2} - \frac{1}{3} = \frac{1}{6}$.

5.4.43 $\sec^2 x$ is even, so the value of this integral is $2\int_0^{\pi/4} \sec^2 x\,dx = 2\left(\tan x\right)\Big|_0^{\pi/4} = 2\cdot(1-0) = 2$.

5.4.45 The integrand is an odd function, so the value of this integral is zero.

5.4.47 The average height of the arch is given by

$$\frac{1}{630}\int_{-315}^{315}\left(630-\frac{630}{315^2}x^2\right)dx = \frac{630}{630}\left(x-\frac{x^3}{3\cdot 315^2}\right)\bigg|_{-315}^{315} = (315-105-(-315+105)) = 420 \text{ ft}.$$

5.4.49

a. $d^2 = x^2+y^2 = x^2+b^2(1-(x^2/a^2))$. The average value of d^2 is $\frac{1}{2a}\int_{-a}^{a}\left(b^2+\left(1-\frac{b^2}{a^2}\right)x^2\right)dx =$ $\frac{1}{2a}\left(b^2x+\frac{(1-(b^2/a^2))\,x^3}{3}\right)\bigg|_{-a}^{a} = \frac{1}{2a}\left(b^2a+\frac{a^3}{3}-\frac{b^2a}{3}-\left(-b^2a-\frac{a^3}{3}+\frac{b^2a}{3}\right)\right) = \frac{2b^2}{3}+\frac{a^2}{3}.$

b. If $a=b=R$, the above becomes $\frac{2R^2}{3}+\frac{R^2}{3}=R^2$.

c. $D^2 = (x-\sqrt{a^2-b^2})^2+y^2 = x^2-2x\sqrt{a^2-b^2}+y^2+a^2-b^2 = \left(1-\frac{b^2}{a^2}\right)x^2-2\sqrt{a^2-b^2}x+a^2$. So the average value of D^2 is $\frac{1}{2a}\int_{-a}^{a}D^2\,dx = \frac{1}{2a}\int_{-a}^{a}\left[\left(1-\frac{b^2}{a^2}\right)x^2+a^2\right]dx-\frac{1}{a}\int_{-a}^{a}x\sqrt{a^2-b^2}\,dx =$ $\frac{1}{a}\int_0^a\left[\left(1-\frac{b^2}{a^2}\right)x^2+a^2\right]dx+0 = \frac{1}{3}(a^2-b^2)+a^2 = \frac{4a^2-b^2}{3}.$

5.4.51

a. Because $\int_{-8}^{8}f(x)\,dx = 18 = 2\int_0^8 f(x)\,dx$, we have $\int_0^8 f(x)\,dx = \frac{18}{2} = 9$.

b. Because $xf(x)$ is an odd function when $f(x)$ is even, we have $\int_{-8}^{8}xf(x)\,dx = 0$.

5.4.53 $f(g(-x)) = f(g(x))$, so $f(g(x))$ is an even function, and $\int_{-a}^{a}f(g(x))\,dx = 2\int_0^a f(g(x))\,dx$.

5.4.55 $p(g(-x)) = p(g(x))$, so $p(g(x))$ is an even function, and $\int_{-a}^{a}p(g(x))\,dx = 2\int_0^a p(g(x))\,dx$.

5.4.57

a. The average value is $\int_0^1(ax-ax^2)\,dx = \left(\frac{ax^2}{2}-\frac{ax^3}{3}\right)\bigg|_0^1 = \frac{a}{2}-\frac{a}{3} = \frac{a}{6}$.

b. The function is equal to its average value when $\frac{a}{6} = ax-ax^2$ which occurs when $6x-6x^2=1$, so when $6x^2-6x+1=0$. On the given interval, this occurs for $x = \frac{6\pm\sqrt{12}}{12} = \frac{3\pm\sqrt{3}}{6}$.

5.4.59

a. The area of the triangle is $\frac{1}{2}\cdot 2a\cdot a^2 = a^3$. The area under the parabola is $\int_{-a}^{a}(a^2-x^2)\,dx =$

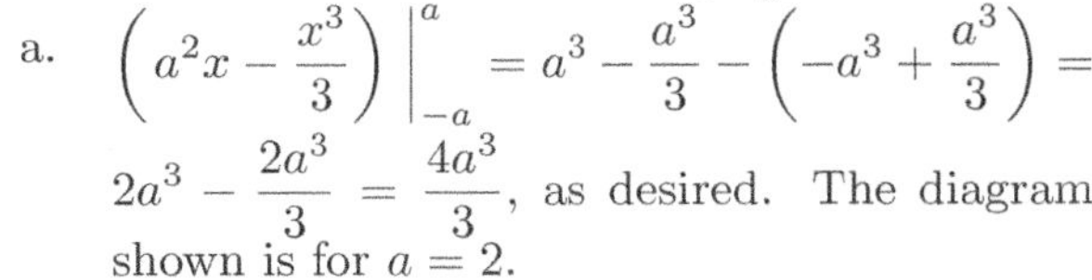

$\left(a^2x-\frac{x^3}{3}\right)\bigg|_{-a}^{a} = a^3-\frac{a^3}{3}-\left(-a^3+\frac{a^3}{3}\right) =$ $2a^3-\frac{2a^3}{3} = \frac{4a^3}{3}$, as desired. The diagram shown is for $a=2$.

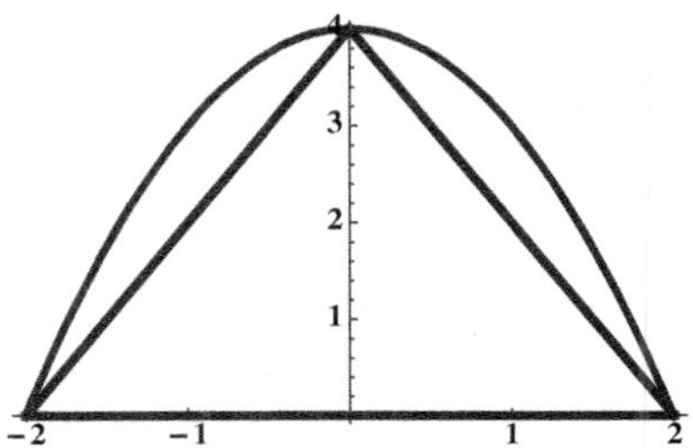

b. The area of the rectangle described is $2a\cdot a^2 = 2a^3$, and $\frac{2}{3}$ of this is $\frac{4a^3}{3}$, which is the area under the parabola derived above.

5.4.61 $\int_0^c x(x-c)^2\,dx = \int_0^c (x^3 - 2cx^2 + c^2x)\,dx = \left(\frac{x^4}{4} - 2c\frac{x^3}{3} + \frac{c^2x^2}{2}\right)\Big|_0^c = \frac{c^4}{4} - \frac{2c^4}{3} + \frac{c^4}{2} = \frac{c^4}{12}$. This is one when $c = \sqrt[4]{12}$.

5.4.63

a. The left Riemann sum is given by $\frac{\pi}{2n}\sum_{k=0}^{n-1} \sin((k\pi)/(2n))$.

b.

$$\begin{aligned}\lim_{\theta\to 0} \theta\left(\frac{\cos\theta + \sin\theta - 1}{2(1-\cos\theta)}\right)\left(\frac{1+\cos\theta}{1+\cos\theta}\right) &= \lim_{\theta\to 0}\frac{\theta}{2}\left(\frac{(1+\cos\theta)(\cos\theta+\sin\theta-1)}{\sin^2\theta}\right)\\ &= \left(\frac{1}{2}\lim_{\theta\to 0}\frac{\theta}{\sin\theta}\cdot\frac{1+\cos\theta}{1}\right)\left(\lim_{\theta\to 0}\frac{\cos\theta-1}{\sin\theta} + \lim_{\theta\to 0}\frac{\sin\theta}{\sin\theta}\right)\\ &= \frac{1}{2}\cdot 1\cdot 2\left(\lim_{\theta\to 0}\frac{\frac{\cos -1}{\theta}}{\frac{\sin\theta}{\theta}} + 1\right) = 1(0+1) = 1.\end{aligned}$$

c. Using the previous result, the left Riemann sum is given by $\frac{\pi}{2n}\left(\frac{\cos(\pi/(2n))+\sin(\pi/(2n))-1}{2(1-\cos(\pi/(2n)))}\right)$. Let $\theta = \frac{\pi}{2n}$. Then as $n\to\infty$, $\theta\to 0$, and the limit of the left Riemann sum as $n\to\infty$ is 1.

5.4.65 Suppose f is even, so that $f(-x) = f(x)$. Then $f^n(x) = f^n(-x)$, so that f^n is an even function, no matter what the parity of n is.

Suppose g is an odd function, so that $g(-x) = -g(x)$. Then $g^n(-x) = (-1)^n g^n(x)$, so g^n is even when n is even, and is odd when n is odd.

Summarizing, we have:

	f is even	f is odd
n is even	f^n is even	f^n is even
n is odd	f^n is even	f^n is odd

5.4.67

a. Because of the symmetry, $\int_{c-a}^{c} (f(x)-d)\,dx = \int_c^{c+a} (d - f(x))\,dx$. Thus, $\int_{c-a}^{c+a} f(x)\,dx = \int_{c-a}^{c} (f(x) - d + d)\,dx + \int_c^{c+a} f(x)\,dx = \int_{c-a}^{c} d\,dx + \int_{c-a}^{c}(f(x)-d)\,dx + \int_c^{c+a} f(x)\,dx = ad + \int_c^{c+a}(d - f(x))\,dx + \int_c^{c+a} f(x)\,dx = ad + ad + 0 = 2ad$.

b. The curve is symmetric about $(\pi/4, 1/2)$. To see this, we will show that if $\sin^2(\pi/4 - x) = (1/2) - r$, then $\sin^2(\pi/4 + x) = (1/2) + r$. Using a double angle identity, we have $\sin^2(\pi/4 - x) = \frac{1}{2} - \frac{1}{2}\cos\left(\frac{\pi}{2} - 2x\right) = \frac{1}{2} - \frac{1}{2}\sin 2x$. On the other hand, $\sin^2(\pi/4 + x) = \frac{1}{2} - \frac{1}{2}\cos\left(\frac{\pi}{2} + 2x\right) = \frac{1}{2} + \frac{1}{2}\sin(2x)$.

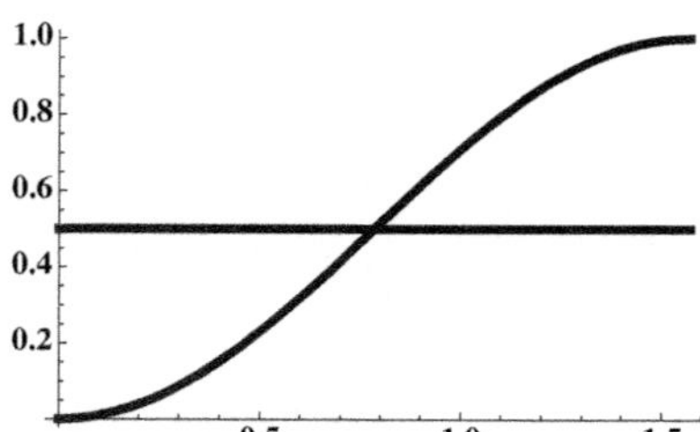

c. Using the idea from part a), the area under f over this interval must be equal to the area of the rectangle over the interval $[0, \pi/2]$ with height $1/2$. Thus the area is $\frac{\pi}{2}\cdot\frac{1}{2} = \frac{\pi}{4}$.

5.4.69

a. Note that h is continuous and differentiable on $[a,b]$, and that $h(a) = (a-b)\int_a^a f(t)\,dt + (a-a)\int_a^b g(t)\,dt = 0+0 = 0$. Also, $h(b) = (b-b)\int_a^b f(t)\,dt + (b-a)\int_b^b g(t)\,dt = 0+0 = 0$. So by Rolle's theorem, there exists c between a and b so that $h'(c)=0$. By the Product and Sum Rules, and the Fundamental Theorem of Calculus, we have $h'(x) = \int_a^x f(t)\,dt + (x-b)f(x) + \int_x^b g(t)\,dt - (x-a)g(x)$. So at the promised number c we have $h'(c) = \int_a^c f(t)\,dt + (c-b)f(c) + \int_c^b g(t)\,dt - (c-a)g(c) = 0$, so

$$\int_a^c f(t)\,dt + \int_c^b g(t)\,dt = (b-c)f(c) + (c-a)g(c).$$

b. Given f continuous on $[a,b]$, let g be the constant zero function, that is, $g(x)=0$ for all x. Applying the result of part (a), we have that there exists a c between a and b with

$$\int_a^c f(t)\,dt + 0 = f(c)(b-c) + 0,$$

so

$$\int_a^c f(t)\,dt = f(c)(b-c),$$

as desired.

c. There exists a rectangle with base from c to b and height $f(c)$ so that the area of the rectangle is equal to the value of the integral of f from a to c.

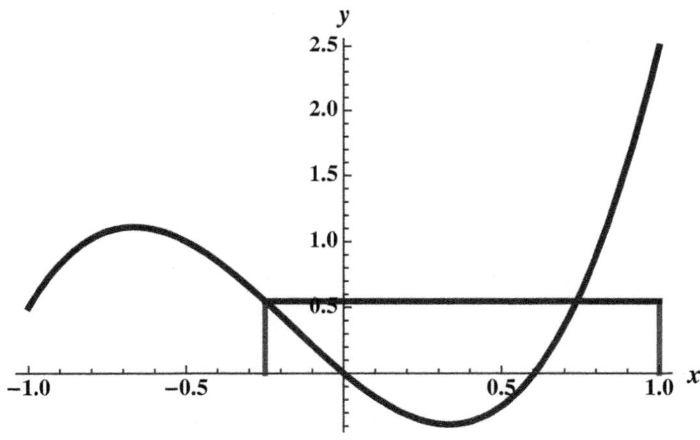

d. Given a function f continuous on $[a,b]$, let $g=f$. Then by part (a) there exists c between a and b so that

$$\int_a^c f(t)\,dt + \int_c^b f(t)\,dt = f(c)(b-c) + f(c)(c-a),$$

so

$$\int_a^b f(t)\,dt = f(c)(b-c+c-a) = f(c)(b-a),$$

so

$$\frac{1}{b-a}\int_a^b f(t)\,dt = f(c).$$

5.5 Substitution Rule

5.5.1 It is based on the Chain Rule for differentiation.

5.5.3 Typically u is substituted for the inner function, so $u = g(x)$.

5.5.5 The new integral is $\displaystyle\int_{g(a)}^{g(b)} f(u)\,du$.

5.5.7 Using the identity $\cos^2 x = \frac{1}{2} + \frac{\cos 2x}{2}$, we have $\displaystyle\int \cos^2 x\,dx = \int \left(\frac{1}{2} + \frac{\cos 2x}{2}\right) dx = \frac{x}{2} + \frac{\sin 2x}{4} + C$.

5.5.9 $\displaystyle\int (x+1)^{12}\,dx = \frac{(x+1)^{13}}{13} + C$, because $\frac{d}{dx}\left(\frac{(x+1)^{13}}{13} + C\right) = (x+1)^{12}$.

5.5.11 $\displaystyle\int \sqrt{2x+1}\,dx = \frac{(2x+1)^{3/2}}{3} + C$, because $\displaystyle\frac{d}{dx}\left(\frac{(2x+1)^{3/2}}{3} + C\right) = \frac{3}{2}\cdot\frac{1}{3}\cdot(2x+1)^{1/2}\cdot 2 = \sqrt{2x+1}$.

5.5.13 Because $u = x^2+1$, $du = 2x\,dx$. Substituting yields $\displaystyle\int u^4\,du = \frac{u^5}{5} + C = \frac{(x^2+1)^5}{5} + C$.

5.5.15 Because $u = \sin x$, $du = \cos x\,dx$. Substituting yields $\displaystyle\int u^3\,du = \frac{u^4}{4} + C = \frac{\sin^4(x)}{4} + C$.

5.5.17 Let $u = x^2 - 1$. Then $du = 2x\,dx$. Substituting yields $\displaystyle\int u^{99}\,du = \frac{u^{100}}{100} + C = \frac{(x^2-1)^{100}}{100} + C$.

5.5.19 Let $u = 1 - 4x^3$. Then $du = -12x^2\,dx$, so $\frac{-1}{6}du = 2x^2\,dx$. Substituting yields $\displaystyle\frac{-1}{6}\int \frac{1}{\sqrt{u}}\,du = \frac{-1}{3}\cdot\sqrt{u} + C = \frac{-1}{3}\cdot\sqrt{1-4x^3} + C$.

5.5.21 Let $u = x^2 + x$. Then $du = 2x + 1\,dx$. Substituting yields $\displaystyle\int u^{10}\,du = \frac{u^{11}}{11} + C = \frac{(x^2+x)^{11}}{11} + C$.

5.5.23 Let $u = x^4 + 16$. Then $du = 4x^3\,dx$, so $\frac{1}{4}du = x^3\,dx$. Substituting yields $\displaystyle\frac{1}{4}\int u^6\,du = \frac{1}{4}\cdot\frac{u^7}{7} + C = \frac{(x^4+16)^7}{28} + C$.

5.5.25 Let $u = 3x$. Then $du = 3\,dx$, so $\frac{1}{3}du = dx$. Substituting yields $\displaystyle\frac{1}{3}\int \frac{1}{\sqrt{1-u^2}}\,du = \frac{1}{3}\sin^{-1} u + C = \frac{1}{3}\sin^{-1} 3x + C$.

5.5.27 Let $u = x^6 - 3x^2$. Then $du = (6x^5 - 6x)\,dx$, so $\frac{1}{6}du = (x^5 - x)\,dx$. Substituting yields $\displaystyle\frac{1}{6}\int u^4\,du = \frac{1}{6}\cdot\frac{u^5}{5} + C = \frac{(x^6-3x^2)^5}{30} + C$.

5.5.29 Let $u = 2x$, so that $du = 2dx$. Substituting yields $\displaystyle\frac{1}{2}\int \frac{1}{1+u^2}\,du = \frac{1}{2}\tan^{-1} u + C = \frac{1}{2}\tan^{-1} 2x + C$.

5.5.31 Let $u = 2x$, so that $du = 2dx$. Substituting yields $\displaystyle 2\int \frac{1}{u\sqrt{u^2-1}}\,du = 2\sec^{-1} u + C = 2\sec^{-1} 2x + C$.

5.5.33 Let $u = x - 4$, so that $u + 4 = x$. Then $du = dx$. Substituting yields $\int \frac{u+4}{\sqrt{u}}\,du =$ $\int \left(\frac{u}{\sqrt{u}} + \frac{4}{\sqrt{u}}\right) du = \int u^{1/2} + 4u^{-1/2}\,du = \frac{2}{3}u^{3/2} + 8u^{1/2} + C = \frac{2}{3} \cdot (x-4)^{3/2} + 8\sqrt{x-4} + C.$

5.5.35 Let $u = x + 4$, so that $u - 4 = x$. Then $du = dx$. Substituting yields

$$\begin{aligned} \int \frac{u-4}{\sqrt[3]{u}}\,du = \int \left(u^{2/3} - 4u^{-1/3}\right) du &= \frac{3}{5}u^{5/3} + -6u^{2/3} + C \\ &= \frac{3}{5}(x+4)^{5/3} - 6(x+4)^{2/3} + C. \end{aligned}$$

5.5.37 Let $u = 2x + 1$. Then $du = 2dx$ and $x = \frac{u-1}{2}$. Substituting yields $\frac{1}{2}\int \frac{u-1}{2} \cdot \sqrt[3]{u}\,du = \frac{1}{4}\int (u^{4/3} -$ $u^{1/3})\,du = \frac{1}{4}\left(\frac{3}{7}u^{7/3} - \frac{3}{4}u^{4/3}\right) + C = \frac{3(2x+1)^{7/3}}{28} - \frac{3(2x+1)^{4/3}}{16} + C.$

5.5.39 Let $u = 4 - x^2$. Then $du = -2x\,dx$. Also, when $x = 0$ we have $u = 4$ and when $x = 1$ we have $u = 3$. Substituting yields $-\int_4^3 u\,du = \int_3^4 u\,du = \left(\frac{u^2}{2}\right)\Big|_3^4 = 8 - 4.5 = 3.5.$

5.5.41 Let $u = \sin\theta$. Then $du = \cos\theta\,d\theta$. Also, when $\theta = 0$ we have $u = 0$ and when $\theta = \pi/2$ we have $u = 1$. Substituting yields $\int_0^1 u^2\,du = \left(\frac{u^3}{3}\right)\Big|_0^1 = \frac{1}{3}.$

5.5.43 Let $u = x^3 + 1$. Then $du = 3x^2\,dx$. Also, when $x = -1$ we have $u = 0$ and when $x = 2$ we have $u = 9$. Substituting yields $\frac{1}{3}\int_0^9 e^u\,du = \left(\frac{e^u}{3}\right)\Big|_0^9 = \frac{e^9 - 1}{3}.$

5.5.45 Let $u = \sin x$. Then $du = \cos x\,dx$. Also, when $x = \pi/4$ we have $u = \sqrt{2}/2$ and when $x = \pi/2$ we have $u = 1$. Substituting yields $\int_{\sqrt{2}/2}^1 \frac{1}{u^2}\,du = \left(\frac{-1}{u}\right)\Big|_{\sqrt{2}/2}^1 = \left(-1 - \left(-\frac{2}{\sqrt{2}}\right)\right) = \sqrt{2} - 1.$

5.5.47 Let $u = 5x$, so that $du = 5\,dx$. Also, when $x = 2/(5\sqrt{3})$ we have $u = 2/\sqrt{3}$ and when $x = 2/5$ we have $u = 2$. Substituting yields $\int_{2/\sqrt{3}}^2 \frac{du}{u\sqrt{u^2-1}} = \sec^{-1} u \Big|_{2/\sqrt{3}}^2 = \frac{\pi}{3} - \frac{\pi}{6} = \frac{\pi}{6}.$

5.5.49 Let $u = x^2 + 1$, so that $du = 2x\,dx$. Substituting yields $\frac{1}{2}\int_1^{17} \frac{1}{u}\,du = \frac{1}{2}\ln|u|\Big|_1^{17} = \frac{\ln 17}{2}.$

5.5.51 Let $u = 3x$, so that $du = 3\,dx$. Substituting yields $\frac{4}{3}\int_1^{3/\sqrt{3}} \frac{1}{u^2+1}\,du = \frac{4}{3}\tan^{-1} u\Big|_1^{3/\sqrt{3}} =$ $\frac{4}{3}\left(\frac{\pi}{3} - \frac{\pi}{4}\right) = \frac{4}{3} \cdot \frac{\pi}{12} = \frac{\pi}{9}.$

5.5.53 $\int_{-\pi}^{\pi} \cos^2 x\,dx = 2\int_0^{\pi} \frac{1 + \cos 2x}{2}\,dx = \left(x + \frac{\sin 2x}{2}\right)\Big|_0^{\pi} = \pi.$

5.5.55 $\int \sin^2\left(\theta + \frac{\pi}{6}\right) d\theta = \frac{1}{2}\int \left(1 - \cos\left(2\theta + \frac{\pi}{3}\right)\right) d\theta = \frac{\theta}{2} - \frac{\sin\left(2\theta + \frac{\pi}{3}\right)}{4} + C.$

5.5.57 $\int_{-\pi/4}^{\pi/4} \sin^2 2\theta\,d\theta = 2\int_0^{\pi/4} \sin^2 2\theta\,d\theta = 2\int_0^{\pi/4} \frac{1 - \cos 4\theta}{2}\,d\theta = \left(\theta - \frac{\sin 4\theta}{4}\right)\Big|_0^{\pi/4} = \frac{\pi}{4}.$

5.5.59 Let $u = \sin^2 y + 2$ so that $du = 2\sin y \cos y\, dy = \sin(2y)\, dy$. Substituting yields $\int_2^{9/4} \frac{1}{u}\, du = (\ln|u|)\Big|_2^{9/4} = \ln(9/4) - \ln 2 = \ln(9/8)$.

5.5.61

a. True. This follows by substituting $u = f(x)$ to obtain the integral $\int u\, du = \frac{u^2}{2} + C = \frac{f(x)^2}{2} + C$.

b. True. Again, this follows from substituting $u = f(x)$ to obtain the integral $\int u^n\, du = \frac{u^{n+1}}{n+1} + C = \frac{(f(x))^{n+1}}{n+1} + C$ where $n \neq -1$.

c. False. If this were true, then $\sin 2x$ and $2\sin x$ would have to differ by a constant, which they do not. In fact, $\sin 2x = 2\sin x \cos x$.

d. False. The derivative of the right hand side is $(x^2+1)^9 \cdot 2x$ which is not the integrand on the left hand side.

e. False. If we let $u = f'(x)$, then $du = f''(x)\, dx$. Substituting yields $\int_{f'(a)}^{f'(b)} u\, du = \left(\frac{u^2}{2}\right)\Big|_{f'(a)}^{f'(b)} = \frac{(f'(b))^2}{2} - \frac{(f'(a))^2}{2}$.

5.5.63 Let $u = 10x$. Then $du = 10\, dw$. Substituting yields $\frac{1}{10}\int \sec^2 u\, du = \frac{1}{10}\tan u + C = \frac{1}{10}\tan 10x + C$.

5.5.65 Let $u = \cot x$. Then $du = -\csc^2 x\, dx$. Substituting yields $-\int u^{-3}\, du = \frac{1}{2u^2} + C = \frac{1}{2\cot^2 x} + C$.

5.5.67 Note that $\sin x \sec^8 x = \frac{\sin x}{\cos^8 x}$. Let $u = \cos x$, so that $du = -\sin x\, dx$. Substituting yields $-\int u^{-8}\, du = \frac{1}{7u^7} + C = \frac{1}{7\cos^7 x} + C = \frac{\sec^7 x}{7} + C$.

5.5.69 Let $u = 1 - x^2$. Then $du = -2x\, dx$. Also note that when $x = 0$ we have $u = 1$, and when $x = 1$ we have $u = 0$. Substituting yields $\frac{-1}{2}\int_1^0 \sqrt{u}\, du = \frac{1}{2}\int_0^1 \sqrt{u}\, du = \left(\frac{u^{3/2}}{3}\right)\Big|_0^1 = \frac{1}{3}$.

5.5.71 Let $u = x^2 - 1$, so that $du = 2x\, dx$. Also note that when $x = 2$ we have $u = 3$, and when $x = 3$ we have $u = 8$. Substituting yields $\frac{1}{2}\int_3^8 u^{-1/3}\, du = \frac{1}{2}\left(\frac{3u^{2/3}}{2}\right)\Big|_3^8 = \frac{3}{4}\left(4 - \sqrt[3]{9}\right)$.

5.5.73 Let $u = 16 - x^4$. Then $du = -4x^3\, dx$. Also note that when $x = 0$ we have $u = 16$, and when $x = 2$ we have $u = 0$. Substituting yields $\frac{1}{4}\int_0^{16} \sqrt{u}\, du = \frac{1}{4}\left(\frac{2u^{3/2}}{3}\right)\Big|_0^{16} = \frac{32}{3}$.

5.5.75 Let $u = 2 + \cos x$ so that $du = -\sin x\, dx$. Note that when $x = -\pi$, $u = 1$ and when $x = 0$, $u = 3$. Substituting yields $\int_1^3 \frac{-1}{u}\, du = (-\ln|u|)\Big|_1^3 = -(\ln 3 - \ln 1) = -\ln 3$.

5.5.77 Let $u = 3x + 1$ so that $du = 3\, dx$. Note that $9x^2 + 6x + 1 = (3x+1)^2 = u^2$, and also that when $x = 1$, $u = 4$ and when $x = 2$, $u = 7$. Substituting yields $\frac{4}{3}\int_4^7 \frac{1}{u^2}\, du = \frac{4}{3}\left(\frac{-1}{u}\right)\Big|_4^7 = \frac{4}{3}\left(\frac{-1}{7} - \left(-\frac{1}{4}\right)\right) = \frac{4}{3}\left(\frac{3}{28}\right) = \frac{1}{7}$.

5.5.79 $A(x) = \int_0^{\sqrt{\pi}} x \sin x^2\, dx$. Let $u = x^2$, so that $du = 2x\,dx$. Also, when $x = 0$ we have $u = 0$ and when $x = \sqrt{\pi}$ we have $u = \pi$. Substituting yields $\frac{1}{2}\int_0^{\pi} \sin u\, du = \frac{1}{2}(-\cos u)\Big|_0^{\pi} = 1$.

5.5.81 $A(x) = \int_2^6 (x-4)^4\, dx = \frac{(x-4)^5}{5}\Big|_2^6 = \frac{2^5}{5} - \left(-\frac{(2)^5}{5}\right) = \frac{64}{5}$.

5.5.83 $A(a) = \int_0^a \left(\frac{1}{a} - \frac{x^2}{a^3}\right) dx = \left(\frac{x}{a} - \frac{x^3}{3a^3}\right)\Big|_0^a = 1 - \frac{1}{3} = \frac{2}{3}$. This is a constant function.

5.5.85

a. Let $u = \sin px$, so that $du = p\cos px\, dx$. Note that when $x = 0$, $u = 0$, and when $x = \pi/2p$, $u = 1$. Substituting yields $\frac{1}{p}\int_0^1 f(u)\, du = \frac{\pi}{p}$.

b. Let $u = \sin x$ so that $du = \cos x\, dx$. Note that when $x = -\pi/2$, $u = -1$ and when $x = \pi/2$, $u = 1$. Substituting yields $\int_{-1}^1 f(u)\, du = 0$, because f is an odd function. Alternatively, we could note that when f is odd, $\cos x \cdot f(\sin x)$ is also odd, because $\sin x$ is odd and $\cos x$ is even. Thus the given integral must be zero because it is the definite integral of an odd function over a symmetric interval about 0.

5.5.87

a. $\int_0^4 \frac{200}{(t+1)^2}\, dt = \left(\frac{-200}{t+1}\right)\Big|_0^4 = -40 + 200 = 160$.

b. $\int_0^6 \frac{200}{(t+1)^3}\, dt = \left(\frac{-200}{2(t+1)^2}\right)\Big|_0^6 = \frac{-100}{49} + 100 = \frac{4800}{49}$.

c. $\Delta P = \int_0^T \frac{200}{(t+1)^r}\, dt$. This decreases as r increases, because $\frac{200}{(t+1)^r} > \frac{200}{(t+1)^{r+1}}$.

d. Suppose $\int_0^{10} \frac{200}{(t+1)^r}\, dt = 350$. Then $\left(\frac{200(t+1)^{-r+1}}{1-r}\right)\Big|_0^{10} = 350$, so $11^{1-r} - 1 = \frac{350(1-r)}{200}$, and thus $\frac{11}{11^r} = \frac{7-7r}{4} + \frac{4}{4} = \frac{11-7r}{4}$, and $11^r = \frac{44}{11-7r}$. Using trial and error to find r, we arrive at $r \approx 1.278$.

e. $\int_0^T \frac{200}{(t+1)^3}\, dt = \left(\frac{-200}{2(t+1)^2}\right)\Big|_0^T = \frac{-100}{(T+1)^2} + 100$. As $T \to \infty$, this expression $\to 100$, so in the long run, the bacteria approaches a finite limit.

5.5.89 $\frac{1}{\pi/k - 0}\int_0^{\pi/k} \sin kx\, dx = \frac{k}{\pi} \cdot \left(\frac{-\cos kx}{k}\right)\Big|_0^{\pi/k} = \frac{1}{\pi}(1 - (-1)) = \frac{2}{\pi}$.

5.5.91

a. $\int \sec x \cdot \frac{\sec x + \tan x}{\sec x + \tan x}\, dx = \int \frac{\sec^2 x + \sec x \tan x}{\sec x + \tan x}\, dx$. Let $u = \sec x + \tan x$ and note that $du = (\sec^2 x + \sec x \tan x)\, dx$. Substituting yields $\int \frac{1}{u}\, du = \ln|u| + C = \ln|\sec x + \tan x| + C$.

b. $\int \csc x \cdot \frac{\csc x + \cot x}{\csc x + \cot x}\, dx = \int \frac{\csc^2 x + \csc x \cot x}{\csc x + \cot x}\, dx$. Let $u = \csc x + \cot x$ and note that $du = -(\csc^2 x + \csc x \cot x)\, dx$. Substituting yields $-\int \frac{1}{u}\, du = -\ln|u| + C = -\ln|\csc x + \cot x| + C$.

5.5.93 The area on the left is given by $\int_4^9 \frac{(\sqrt{x}-1)^2}{2\sqrt{x}}\,dx$. If we let $u=\sqrt{x}-1$ so that $du=\frac{1}{2\sqrt{x}}\,dx$, we obtain the equivalent integral $\int_1^2 u^2\,du$ which represents the area on the right.

5.5.95 Let $u=f(x)$, so that $du=f'(x)\,dx$. Substituting yields

$$\int_4^5 (5u^3+7u^2+u)\,du = \left(\frac{5u^4}{4}+\frac{7u^3}{3}+\frac{u^2}{2}\right)\Big|_4^5 = \frac{7297}{12}.$$

5.5.97 Let $u=f^{(p)}(x)$ so that $du=f^{(p+1)}(x)\,dx$. Substituting yields

$$\int u^n\,du = \frac{u^{n+1}}{n+1}+C = \frac{1}{n+1}\left(f^{(p)}(x)\right)^{n+1}+C.$$

5.5.99 If we let $u=\sqrt{x+a}$, then $u^2=x+a$ and $2u\,du=dx$. Substituting yields $\int_{\sqrt{a}}^{\sqrt{1+a}}(u^2-a)\cdot u\cdot 2u\,du = \int_{\sqrt{a}}^{\sqrt{1+a}}(2u^4-2au^2)\,du = \left(\frac{2u^5}{5}-\frac{2au^3}{3}\right)\Big|_{\sqrt{a}}^{\sqrt{1+a}} = \frac{2(\sqrt{1+a})^5}{5}-\frac{2a(\sqrt{1+a})^3}{3}-\frac{2a^{5/2}}{5}+\frac{2a^{5/2}}{3}$.

If we let $u=x+a$, then $u-a=x$ and $du=dx$. Substituting yields $\int_a^{a+1}(u-a)\sqrt{u}\,du = \left(\frac{2u^{5/2}}{5}-\frac{2au^{3/2}}{3}\right)\Big|_a^{a+1} = \frac{2(a+1)^{5/2}}{5}-\frac{2a(a+1)^{3/2}}{3}-\frac{2a^{5/2}}{5}+\frac{2a^{5/2}}{3}$.
Note that the two results are the same.

5.5.101 If we let $u=\cos\theta$, then $du=-\sin\theta\,d\theta$. Substituting yields $\int -u^{-4}\,du = \frac{1}{3u^3}+C = \frac{1}{3\cos^3\theta}+C = \frac{\sec^3\theta}{3}+C$.

If we let $u=\sec\theta$, then $du=\sec\theta\tan\theta\,d\theta$. Substituting yields $\int u^2\,du = \frac{u^3}{3}+C = \frac{\sec^3\theta}{3}+C$. Note that the two results are the same.

5.5.103

a. Because $\sin 2x = 2\sin x\cos x$, we can write $(\sin x\cos x)^2 = \left(\frac{\sin 2x}{2}\right)^2 = \frac{\sin^2 2x}{4}$. Then we have $I = \frac{1}{4}\int \sin^2 2x\,dx = \frac{1}{4}\left(\frac{x}{2}-\frac{\sin 4x}{8}\right)+C = \frac{x}{8}-\frac{\sin 4x}{32}+C$. Note that we used the result of the previous problem during this derivation.

b. $I = \frac{1}{4}\int(1-\cos 2x)(1+\cos 2x)\,dx = \frac{1}{4}\int(1-\cos^2 2x)\,dx = \frac{1}{4}\int \sin^2 2x\,dx = \frac{1}{4}\left(\frac{x}{2}-\frac{\sin 4x}{8}\right)+C = \frac{x}{8}-\frac{\sin 4x}{32}+C$.

c. The results are consistent. The work involved is similar in each method.

5.5.105

a. Let $u=cx$. Note that $du=c\cdot dx$. Substitution yields $\int_a^b f(cx)\,dx = \frac{1}{c}\int_{ac}^{bc} f(u)\,du$.

b.

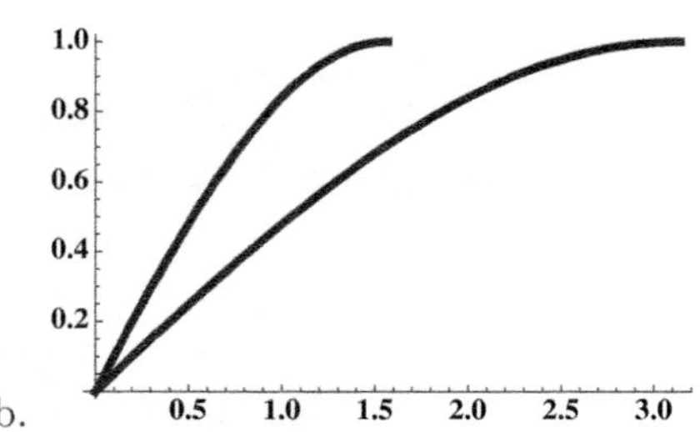

5.5.107 Let $u = \sqrt{x+1}$ so that $u^2 = x+1$. Then $2u\,du = dx$. Substituting yields $\int 2 \cdot \frac{u\,du}{\sqrt{1+u}}$. Now let $v = \sqrt{1+u}$ so that $v^2 = 1+u$ and $2v\,dv = du$. Now a substitution yields $4\int \frac{(v^2-1)v}{v}\,dv = 4\int (v^2-1)\,dv = \frac{4v^3}{3} - 4v + C = \frac{4}{3}(1+u)^{3/2} - 4\sqrt{1+u} + C = \frac{4}{3}\left(1+\sqrt{x+1}\right)^{3/2} - 4\sqrt{1+\sqrt{x+1}} + C$.

5.5.109 Let $u = 1-\sqrt{x}$. Then $x = (1-u)^2$ and $dx = 2(1-u)(-du) = -2(1-u)\cdot du$. Then we have

$$\begin{aligned}\int_0^1 \sqrt{x - x\sqrt{x}}\,dx &= \int_1^0 (1-u)\sqrt{u}\cdot(-2)(1-u)\,du \\ &= 2\int_0^1 (1-u)^2\sqrt{u}\,du = 2\int_0^1 \left(1-2u+u^2\right)\sqrt{u}\,du \\ &= 2\int_0^1 (u^{1/2} - 2u^{3/2} + u^{5/2})\,du \\ &= 2\left(\frac{2u^{3/2}}{3} - \frac{4u^{5/2}}{5} + \frac{2u^{7/2}}{7}\right)\Bigg|_0^1 \\ &= 2\left(\frac{2}{3} - \frac{4}{5} + \frac{2}{7}\right) = \frac{32}{105}.\end{aligned}$$

5.5.111 Let $u = \cos\theta$, so that $du = -\sin\theta\,d\theta$. This substitution yields $\int_0^1 \frac{u}{\sqrt{u^2+16}}\,du$. Now let $v = u^2+16$, so that $dv = 2u\,du$. Now a substitution yields $\frac{1}{2}\int_{16}^{17} v^{-1/2}\,dv = \sqrt{v}\Big|_{16}^{17} = \sqrt{17} - 4$.

Chapter Five Review

1

a. True. The antiderivative of a linear function is a quadratic function.

b. False. $A'(x) = f(x)$, not $F(x)$.

c. True, Note that f is an antiderivative of f', so this follows from the Fundamental Theorem.

d. True. Because $|f(x)| \geq 0$ for all x, this integral must be positive, unless f is constantly 0.

e. False. For example, the average value of $\sin x$ on $[0, 2\pi]$ is zero.

f. True. This is equal to $2\int_a^b f(x)\,dx - 3\int_a^b g(x)\,dx = 2\int_a^b f(x)\,dx + 3\int_b^a g(x)\,dx$.

g. True. The derivative of the right hand side is $f'(g(x))g'(x)$ by the Chain Rule.

3

a. This region can be divided up into a 4×2 rectangle and a right triangle with base and height equal to 1. Thus, the integral is equal to $8 + \frac{1}{2} = 8.5$.

b. $\int_6^4 f(x)\,dx = -\int_4^6 f(x)\,dx$. The region whose area is $\int_4^6 f(x)\,dx$ consists of a 1×3 rectangle, together with a right triangle with base 1 and height 3, so $\int_4^6 f(x)\,dx = 3 + \frac{3}{2} = 4.5$, and $\int_6^4 f(x)\,dx = -4.5$.

c. $\int_5^7 f(x)\,dx = \int_5^6 f(x)\,dx + \int_6^7 f(x)\,dx$. The region lying over $[5,6]$ is a right triangle with height 3 and base 1, so its area is $\frac{3}{2}$. The region lying under $[6,7]$ has the same area, but is below the x-axis, so $\int_6^7 f(x)\,dx = \frac{-3}{2}$. So $\int_5^7 f(x)\,dx = \frac{3}{2} + \frac{-3}{2} = 0$.

d. Note that $\int_4^5 f(x)\,dx = 3$, because the area represented is that of a 1×3 rectangle. Now by the work above, $\int_0^7 f(x)\,dx = \int_0^4 f(x)\,dx + \int_4^5 f(x)\,dx + \int_5^7 f(x)\,dx = 8.5 + 3 + 0 = 11.5$.

5 $\int_0^4 \sqrt{8x - x^2}\,dx = \int_0^4 \sqrt{16 - (x^2 - 8x + 16)}\,dx = \int_0^4 \sqrt{16 - (x-4)^2}\,dx$. This represents one quarter of the area inside the circle centered at $(4,0)$ with radius 4, so its value is $\frac{1}{4} \cdot 16\pi = 4\pi$.

7

a. The right Riemann sum is $4 \cdot 1 + 7 \cdot 1 + 10 \cdot 1 = 21$.

b. The right Riemann sum is $\sum_{k=1}^{n} \left(3\left(1 + \frac{3k}{n}\right) - 2\right) \cdot \frac{3}{n}$.

c. The sum evaluates as $\sum_{k=1}^{n} \frac{3}{n} + \sum_{k=1}^{n} \frac{27k}{n^2} = 3 + \frac{27}{n^2} \cdot \frac{n(n+1)}{2}$. As $n \to \infty$, the limit of this expression is $3 + 13.5 = 16.5$.

d.

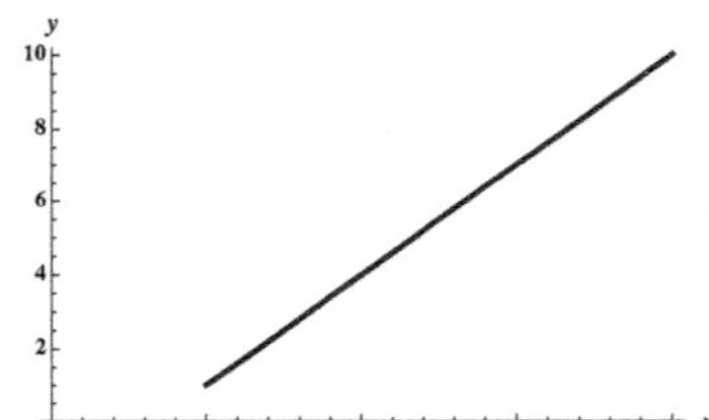

The area consists of a trapezoid with base 3 and heights 1 and 10, so the value is $(3)\left(\frac{1+10}{2}\right) = \frac{33}{2} = 16.5$. The Fundamental Theorem assures us that $\int_1^4 (3x - 2)\,dx = \left(\frac{3x^2}{2} - 2x\right)\Big|_1^4 = (24 - 8) - (3/2 - 2) = 16 + 1/2 = 16.5$.

9 Let $\Delta x = \frac{2-0}{n} = \frac{2}{n}$. Let $x_k = 0 + k\Delta x = \frac{2k}{n}$. Then $f(x_k) = \frac{4k^2}{n^2} - 4$. Thus,

$$\lim_{n\to\infty} \sum_{k=1}^{n} f(x_k)\Delta x = \lim_{n\to\infty} \sum_{k=1}^{n} \left(\frac{4k^2}{n^2} - 4\right) \cdot \frac{2}{n} = \lim_{n\to\infty} \left(\frac{8}{n^3}\sum_{k=1}^{n} k^2 - \frac{8}{n}\sum_{k=1}^{n} 1\right) =$$

$$\lim_{n\to\infty} \left(\frac{8}{n^3} \cdot \frac{n(n+1)(2n+1)}{6} - 8\right) = \frac{8}{3} - 8 = \frac{-16}{3}.$$

11 Let $\Delta x = \frac{4-0}{n} = \frac{4}{n}$. Let $x_k = 0 + k\Delta x = 0 + \frac{4k}{n}$. Then $f(x_k) = \frac{64k^3}{n^3} - \frac{4k}{n}$. Thus,

$$\lim_{n\to\infty} \sum_{k=1}^{n} f(x_k)\Delta x = \lim_{n\to\infty} \sum_{k=1}^{n} \left(\frac{64k^3}{n^3} - \frac{4k}{n}\right) \cdot \frac{4}{n} = \lim_{n\to\infty} \left(\frac{256}{n^4}\sum_{k=1}^{n} k^3 - \frac{16}{n^2}\sum_{k=1}^{n} k\right) =$$

$$\lim_{n\to\infty} \left(\frac{256}{n^4} \cdot \frac{n^2(n+1)^2}{4} - \frac{16}{n^2} \cdot \frac{n(n+1)}{2}\right) = 64 - 8 = 56.$$

13 This sum is equal to $\int_0^4 (x^5 + 1)\,dx = \left(\frac{x^6}{6} + x\right)\Big|_0^4 = \frac{4^6}{6} + 4 = \frac{2060}{3}$.

15 $\int_{-2}^{2}(3x^4-2x+1)\,dx = \left(\frac{3x^5}{5}-x^2+x\right)\Big|_{-2}^{2} = \frac{96}{5}-4+2-\left(-\frac{96}{5}-4-2\right) = \frac{192}{5}+4 = \frac{212}{5}.$

17 $\int_{0}^{2}(x+1)^3\,dx = \left(\frac{(x+1)^4}{4}\right)\Big|_{0}^{2} = \frac{81}{4}-\frac{1}{4} = 20.$

19 $\int (9x^8-7x^6)\,dx = x^9-x^7+C.$

21 $\int_{0}^{1}(x+\sqrt{x})\,dx = \left(\frac{x^2}{2}+\frac{2x^{3/2}}{3}\right)\Big|_{0}^{1} = \frac{1}{2}+\frac{2}{3} = \frac{7}{6}.$

23 $\frac{1}{2}\int_{0}^{1}\frac{dx}{\sqrt{1-(x/2)^2}} = \sin^{-1}\left(\frac{x}{2}\right)\Big|_{0}^{1} = \frac{\pi}{6}.$

25 Let $u = 25-x^2$, and note that $du = -2x\,dx$. Substituting yields $\frac{-1}{2}\int_{25}^{16}u^{-1/2}\,du = -\sqrt{u}\,\Big|_{25}^{16} = 5-4 = 1.$

27 $\int_{0}^{\pi}\sin^2 5\theta\,d\theta = \int_{0}^{\pi}\frac{1-\cos 10\theta}{2}\,d\theta = \left(\frac{\theta}{2}-\frac{\sin 10\theta}{20}\right)\Big|_{0}^{\pi} = \frac{\pi}{2}.$

29 Let $u = x^3+3x^2-6x$, and note that $du = 3x^2+6x-6\,dx = 3(x^2+2x-2)\,dx$. Substituting yields $\frac{1}{3}\int_{8}^{36}\frac{1}{u}\,du = \left(\frac{1}{3}\ln u\right)\Big|_{8}^{36} = \frac{1}{3}(\ln 36-\ln 8) = \frac{1}{3}\ln\left(\frac{9}{2}\right).$

31

The area is given by $\int_{-4}^{4}(16-x^2)\,dx = (16x-x^3/3)\Big|_{-4}^{4} = 64-64/3-(-64+64/3) = 256/3.$

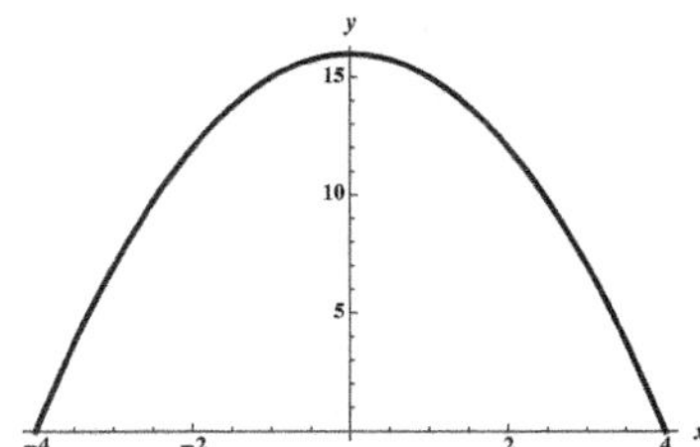

33

The area is given by $2\int_{0}^{2\pi}\sin(x/4)\,dx = 2\left(-4\cos(x/4)\right)\Big|_{0}^{2\pi} = -8(0-1) = 8.$

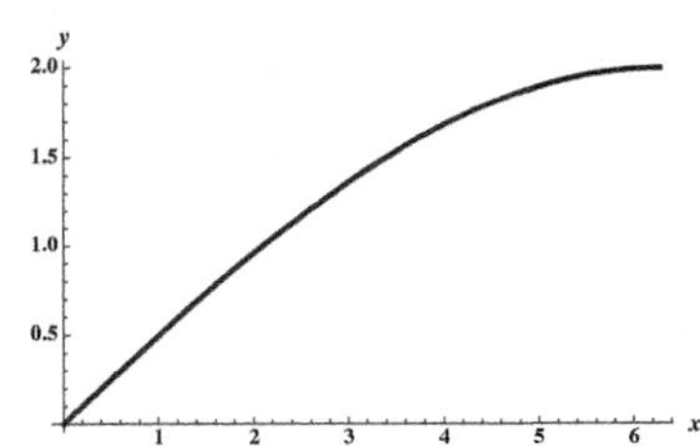

35

i. $\int_{-1}^{1} (x^4 - x^2)\,dx = (x^5/5 - x^3/3)\Big|_{-1}^{1} = (1/5 - 1/3) - (-1/5 - (-1/3)) = -4/15.$

ii. Because the region lies completely below the x-axis, the area bounded by the curve and the x-axis is $-\int_{-1}^{1} (x^4 - x^2)\,dx = 4/15$.

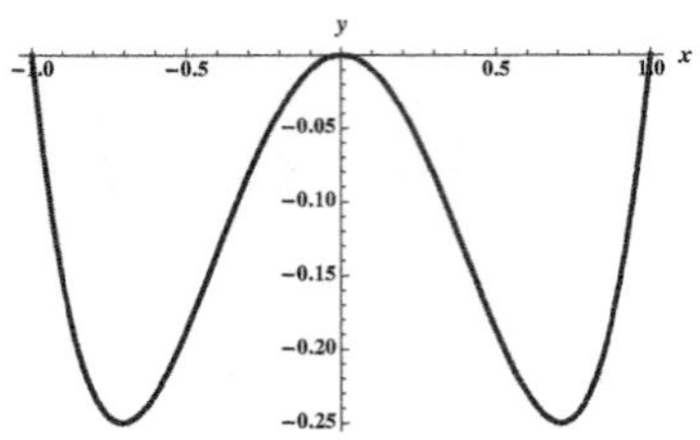

37

a. $\int_{-4}^{4} f(x)\,dx = 2\int_{0}^{4} f(x)\,dx = 2 \cdot 10 = 20.$

b. $\int_{-4}^{4} 3g(x)\,dx = 3 \cdot 0 = 0.$

c. $\int_{-4}^{4} 4f(x) - 3g(x)\,dx = 2 \cdot 4 \cdot \int_{0}^{4} f(x)\,dx - 3 \cdot 0 = 8 \cdot 10 - 0 = 80.$

d. Let $u = 4x^2$, so that $du = 8x\,dx$. Substituting yields $\int_{0}^{4} f(u)\,du = 10$.

e. Because f is an even function, $3xf(x)$ is an odd function. Thus, $\int_{-2}^{2} 3xf(x)\,dx = 0$.

39 $\int_{1}^{4} 3f(x)\,dx = 3\int_{1}^{4} f(x)\,dx = 3 \cdot 6 = 18.$

41 $\int_{1}^{4} (3f(x) - 2g(x))\,dx = 3\int_{1}^{4} f(x)\,dx - 2\int_{1}^{4} g(x)\,dx = 3 \cdot 6 - 2 \cdot 4 = 18 - 8 = 10.$

43 There is not enough information to compute this integral.

45 The displacement is $\int_{0}^{2} 5\sin \pi t\,dt = \left(\frac{-5}{\pi}\cos \pi t\right)\Big|_{0}^{2} = 0$.
The distance traveled is

$$\int_{0}^{2} 5|\sin \pi t|\,dt = 5\int_{0}^{1} \sin \pi t\,dt + 5\int_{1}^{2} (-\sin \pi t)\,dt = \left(\frac{-5}{\pi}\cos \pi t\right)\Big|_{0}^{1} + \left(\frac{5}{\pi}\cos \pi t\right)\Big|_{1}^{2} = \frac{10}{\pi} + \frac{10}{\pi} = \frac{20}{\pi}.$$

47

a. The average value is 2.5. This is because for a straight line, the average value occurs at the midpoint of the interval, which is at the point $(3.5, 2.5)$, so $c = 3.5$.

b. The average value is 3 over the interval $[2, 4]$ and 3 over the interval $[4, 6]$, so is 3 over the interval $[2, 6]$. The function takes on this value at $c = 3$ and $c = 5$.

49 Let $u = 2x$, so that $du = 2\,dx$. We have $\frac{1}{2}\int_{2}^{4} f'(u)\,du = \frac{1}{2} \cdot (f(4) - f(2)) = \frac{f(4)}{2} - 2$. Because we are given that this quantity is 10, we have $f(4) = 24$.

51

By the Fundamental Theorem, $f'(x) = \frac{1}{x}$, which is always positive for $x > 1$. Thus f is always increasing. Also, $f(1) = \int_1^1 \frac{1}{t}\,dt = 0$. Also, $f''(x) = \frac{-1}{x^2}$ which is always negative, so f is always concave down.

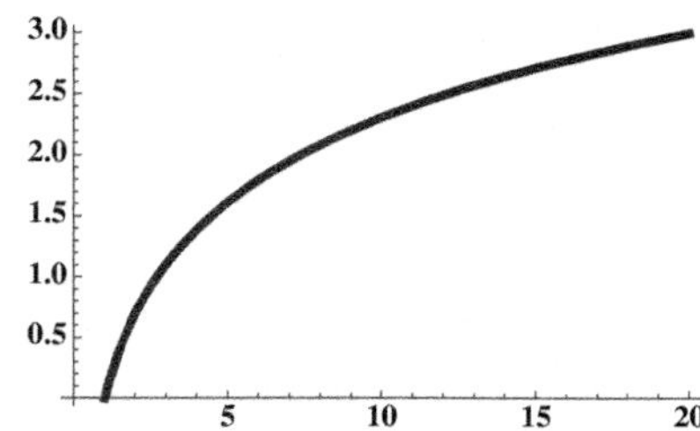

53

a.

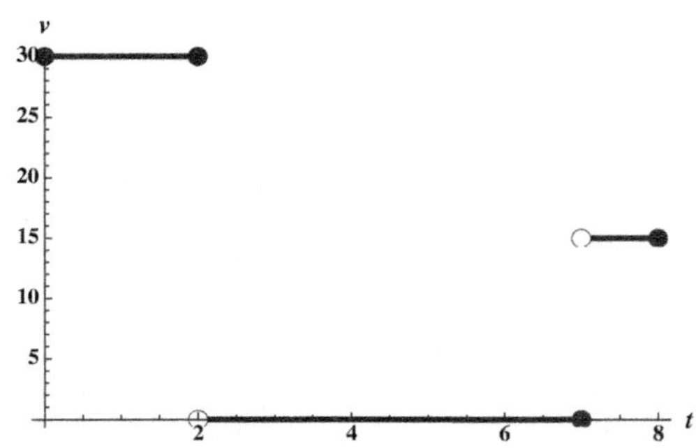

b. The area is $2 \cdot 30 + 0 + 15 \cdot 1 = 75$.

c. The area represents the distance that the diver ascends.

55

a. $F(-2) = \int_{-1}^{-2} f(t)\,dt = \int_{-1}^{-2} t\,dt = \left.\frac{t^2}{2}\right|_{-1}^{-2} = \frac{3}{2}$.

$F(2) = \int_{-1}^{2} f(t)\,dt = \int_{-1}^{0} f(t)\,dt + \int_{0}^{2} f(t)\,dt = \int_{-1}^{0} t\,dt + \int_0^2 \frac{t^2}{2}\,dt = \left.\frac{t^2}{2}\right|_{-1}^{0} + \left.\frac{t^3}{6}\right|_0^2 = \left(0 - \frac{1}{2}\right) + \left(\frac{8}{6} - 0\right) = \frac{5}{6}$.

b. By the Fundamental Theorem of Calculus, $F'(x) = f(x)$, so for $-2 \le x < 0$ we have $F''(x) = x$.

c. By the Fundamental Theorem of Calculus, $F'(x) = f(x)$, so for $0 \le x < 2$ we have $F''(x) = \frac{x^2}{2}$.

d. $F'(-1) = -1$ and $F'(1) = \frac{1}{2}$. These represent the rate of change of F at the given points. Because the graph in the exercise is the derivative of F, this is just the value of f at the given points.

e. Note that $F''(x) = \begin{cases} 1 & \text{if } -2 \le x < 0, \\ x & \text{if } 0 \le x \le 2. \end{cases}$ Thus we have $F''(-1) = 1$ and $F''(1) = 1$.

f. The difference $F(x) - G(x) = \int_{-1}^{-2} f(t)\,dt = \frac{3}{2}$, as noted in part (a).

57 By L'hôpital's rule, we have

$$\lim_{x\to 2} \frac{\int_2^x e^{t^2}\,dt}{x-2} = \lim_{x\to 2} \frac{e^{x^2}}{1} = e^4.$$

59

Because x^n and $\sqrt[n]{x}$ are inverse functions of each other, they are symmetric in the square $[0,1]\times[0,1]$ about the line $y=x$. Together, the two regions completely fill up the 1×1 square, so these two areas add to one.

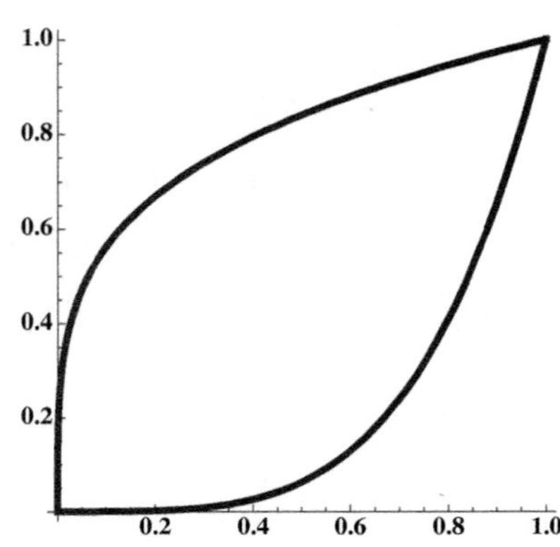

61 Factoring out $\frac{1}{b^2}$ gives $\frac{1}{b^2}\int \frac{dx}{(ax/b)^2+1}$. Now let $u=ax/b$, so that $du=\frac{a}{b}\,dx$. Substituting yields $\frac{1}{b^2}\cdot\frac{b}{a}\int\frac{du}{u^2+1}=\frac{1}{ab}\left(\tan^{-1}(u)\right)+C=\frac{1}{ab}\tan^{-1}(ax/b)+C$.

63 Let $u=\frac{1}{x}$. Then $du=\frac{-1}{x^2}\,dx$. Substituting yields $-\int \sin u\,du=\cos u+C=\cos\left(\frac{1}{x}\right)+C$.

65 Let $u=\tan^{-1}x$. Then $du=\frac{1}{1+x^2}\,dx$. Substituting yields $\int\frac{1}{u}\,du=\ln|u|+C=\ln|\tan^{-1}x|+C$.

67 Let $u=e^x+e^{-x}$. Then $du=(e^x-e^{-x})\,dx$. Substituting yields $\int\frac{1}{u}\,du=\ln|u|+C=\ln(e^x+e^{-x})+C$.

69 This follows by differentiating each side of the equation. $\frac{d}{dx}\left(u(x)+2\int_0^x u(t)\,dt\right)=u'(x)+2u(x)$, and $\frac{d}{dx}10=0$. The reverse is not true, because if $u(x)+2\int_0^x u(t)\,dt=C$ for any constant C, then it would satisfy the second equation, even if $C\neq 10$.

71 Note that $f'(x)=(x-1)^{15}(x-2)^9$, and that the zeros of f' are at $x=1$ and $x=2$.

a. f' is positive and thus f is increasing on $(-\infty,1)$ and on $(2,\infty)$, while f' is negative and f is decreasing on $(1,2)$.

b. $f''(x)=15(x-1)^{14}(x-2)^9+(x-1)^{15}\cdot 9(x-2)^8=3(x-1)^{14}(x-2)^8(8x-13)$.
f is concave up on $\left(\frac{13}{8},\infty\right)$ and concave down on $\left(-\infty,\frac{13}{8}\right)$.

c. f has a local maximum at $x=1$ and a local minimum at $x=2$.

d. f has an inflection point at $x=\frac{13}{8}$.

Chapter 7

Integration Techniques

7.1 Basic Approaches

7.1.1 Let $u = 4 - 7x$. Then $du = -7\,dx$ and we obtain $-\frac{1}{7}\int u^{-6}\,du$.

7.1.3 $\sin^2 x = \frac{1-\cos 2x}{2}$.

7.1.5 Complete the square in the denominator to get $\displaystyle\int \frac{10}{(x-2)^2+1}\,dx$. The integral now matches item 12 in Table 7.1.

7.1.7 Let $u = 3 - 5x$ so that $du = -5\,dx$. Substituting gives $\frac{-1}{5}\int u^{-4}\,du = \frac{1}{15}u^{-3} + C = \frac{1}{15(3-5x)^3} + C$.

7.1.9 Let $u = 2x - \pi/4$ so that $du = 2\,dx$. Substituting gives

$$\frac{1}{2}\int_{-\pi/4}^{\pi/2} \sin u\,du = \frac{1}{2}\left(-\cos u\right)\Big|_{-\pi/4}^{\pi/2} = \frac{1}{2}\left(0 + \sqrt{2}/2\right) = \frac{\sqrt{2}}{4}.$$

7.1.11 Let $u = \ln(2x)$ so that $du = \frac{dx}{x}$. Substituting gives $\int u\,du = u^2/2 + C = \frac{1}{2}\ln^2 2x + C$.

7.1.13 Let $u = e^x + 1$ so that $du = e^x\,dx$ Substituting gives $\int \frac{1}{u}\,du = \ln|u| + C = \ln(e^x+1) + C$.

7.1.15 We rewrite the integral by multiplying the numerator and denominator of the integrand by e^x. We have $\int \frac{e^x}{e^x - 2e^{-x}}\,dx = \int \frac{e^x}{e^x-2e^{-x}} \cdot \frac{e^x}{e^x}\,dx = \int \frac{e^{2x}}{e^{2x}-2}\,dx$. Now let $u = e^{2x} - 2$ so that $du = 2e^{2x}\,dx$. Substituting gives $\frac{1}{2}\int \frac{du}{u} = \frac{1}{2}\ln|u| + C = \frac{1}{2}\ln|e^{2x} - 2| + C$.

7.1.17 Let $u = \ln x^2 = 2\ln x$. Then $du = \frac{2}{x}\,dx$. Substituting gives $\frac{1}{2}\int_0^4 u^2\,du = \left(u^3/6\right)\Big|_0^4 = 32/3$.

7.1.19 The integral can be written as $\cot^4 x \csc^2 x\,dx$. Let $u = \cot x$ so that $du = -\csc^2 x\,dx$. Substituting gives $-\int u^4\,du = -u^5/5 + C = -(\cot^5 x)/5 + C$.

7.1.21 $\int \frac{dx}{x^{-1}+1} = \int \frac{1}{x^{-1}+1} \cdot \frac{x}{x}\,dx = \int \frac{x}{x+1}\,dx$. Using long division, we have $\frac{x}{x+1} = 1 - \frac{1}{x+1}$. Then $\int \left(1 - \frac{1}{x+1}\right)dx = x - \ln|x+1| + C$.

7.1.23 $\int \frac{x}{x^2+4}\,dx + 2\int \frac{1}{x^2+4}\,dx = \frac{1}{2}\ln(x^2+4) + \tan^{-1}(x/2) + C$.

7.1.25

$$\int \frac{\sin t}{\cos^2 t}\,dt + \int \frac{\tan t}{\cos^2 t}\,dt = \int \tan t \sec t\,dt + \int \frac{\sin t}{\cos^3 t}\,dt = \sec t + \int \frac{\sin t}{\cos^3 t}\,dt.$$

Now let $u = \cos t$ so that $du = -\sin t\,dt$. We have

$$\sec t - \int u^{-3}\,du = \sec t + u^{-2}/2 + C = \sec t + \frac{1}{2\cos^2 t} + C = \sec t + \frac{1}{2}\sec^2 t + C.$$

7.1.27

$$\int \frac{2}{\sqrt{1-x^2}}\,dx - 3\int \frac{x}{\sqrt{1-x^2}}\,dx = 2\sin^{-1}x - 3\int \frac{x}{\sqrt{1-x^2}}\,dx.$$

Let $u = 1 - x^2$ so that $du = -2x\,dx$. Substituting gives

$$2\sin^{-1}x + \frac{3}{2}\int u^{-1/2}\,du = 2\sin^{-1}x + 3\sqrt{u} + C = 2\sin^{-1}x + 3\sqrt{1-x^2} + C.$$

7.1.29 Note that long division gives $\frac{x+2}{x+4} = 1 - \frac{2}{x+4}$. Thus our integral is equal to

$$\int \left(1 - \frac{2}{x+4}\right)\,dx = x - 2\ln|x+4| + C.$$

7.1.31 Note that long division gives $\frac{t^3-2}{t+1} = t^2 - t + 1 - \frac{3}{t+1}$. Our integral is therefore

$$\int \left(t^2 - t + 1 - \frac{3}{t+1}\right)\,dt = t^3/3 - t^2/2 + t - 3\ln|t+1| + C.$$

7.1.33 Note that $x^2-2x+10 = (x^2-2x+1)+9 = (x-1)^2+9$. So we have $\int \frac{dx}{(x-1)^2+3^2} = \frac{1}{3}\tan^{-1}((x-1)/3)+C$.

7.1.35 Note that $27 - 6\theta - \theta^2 = -(\theta^2 + 6\theta + 9 - 36) = -((\theta+3)^2 - 36) = 36 - (\theta+3)^2$. Thus our integral is $\int \frac{d\theta}{\sqrt{36-(\theta+3)^2}} = \sin^{-1}((\theta+3)/6) + C$.

7.1.37 $\int \frac{1}{1+\sin\theta} \cdot \frac{1-\sin\theta}{1-\sin\theta}\,d\theta = \int \frac{1-\sin\theta}{1-\sin^2\theta}\,d\theta = \int \frac{1-\sin\theta}{\cos^2\theta}\,d\theta = \int \sec^2\theta\,d\theta - \int \frac{\sin\theta}{\cos^2\theta}\,d\theta = \tan\theta - \int \frac{\sin\theta}{\cos^2}\theta\,d\theta$. Let $u = \cos\theta$ so that $du = -\sin\theta\,d\theta$. Substituting gives $\tan\theta + \int u^{-2}\,du = \tan\theta - \frac{1}{u} + C = \tan\theta - \sec\theta + C$.

7.1.39 $\int \frac{1}{\sec x - 1} \cdot \frac{\sec x+1}{\sec x+1}\,dx = \int \frac{\sec x+1}{\sec^2 x-1}\,dx = \int \frac{\sec x+1}{\tan^2 x}\,dx = \int \frac{\sec x}{\tan^2 x}\,dx + \int \cot^2 x\,dx = \int \cot x \csc x\,dx + \int \cot^2 x\,dx = -\csc x + \int(\csc^2 x - 1)\,dx = -\csc x - \cot x - x + C$.

7.1.41

a. False. This seem to use the untrue "identity" that $\frac{a}{b+c} = \frac{a}{b} + \frac{a}{c}$.

b. False. The degree of the numerator is already less than the degree of the denominator, so long division won't help.

c. False. This is false because $\frac{d}{dx}\ln|\sin x + 1| + C \neq \frac{1}{\sin x+1}$. The substitution $u = \sin x + 1$ can't be carried out because $du = \cos x\,dx$ can't be accounted for.

d. False. In fact, $\int e^{-x}\,dx = -e^{-x} + C \neq \ln e^x + C$.

7.1.43 $\int_{-1}^{0} \frac{x}{x^2+2x+2}\,dx = \int_{-1}^{0} \frac{x}{(x+1)^2+1}\,dx$. Let $u = x + 1$ so that $du = dx$. Substituting gives $\int_0^1 \frac{u-1}{u^2+1}\,du = \int_0^1 \frac{u}{u^2+1}\,du - \int_0^1 \frac{1}{u^2+1}\,du = \left((1/2)\ln(u^2+1) - \tan^{-1}(u)\right)\Big|_0^1 = (1/2)\ln 2 - \frac{\pi}{4} = \frac{1}{4}(\ln 4 - \pi)$.

7.1.45 Using the identity $\sin 2x = 2\sin x\cos x$, we have $2\int \sin^2 x\cos x\,dx$. Let $u = \sin x$ so that $du = \cos x\,dx$. We have $2\int u^2\,du = 2u^3/3 + C = 2(\sin^3 x)/3 + C$.

7.1.47 Rewrite the integral as $\int \frac{1}{\sqrt{x}} \cdot \frac{1}{1+(\sqrt{x})^2}\,dx$ and let $u = \sqrt{x}$. Then $du = \frac{1}{2\sqrt{x}}\,dx$, and substituting gives

$$2\int \frac{1}{1+u^2}\,du = 2\tan^{-1}u + C = 2\tan^{-1}\sqrt{x} + C.$$

7.1.49 Note that $x^2+6x+13 = (x^2+6x+9)+4 = (x+3)^2+4$. Also note that we can write the numerator $x-2 = x+3-5 = \frac{1}{2}(2x+6)-5$. We have $\int \frac{\frac{1}{2}(2x+6)}{x^2+6x+13}\,dx - \int \frac{5}{(x+3)^2+4}\,dx$. For the first integral, let $u = x^2+6x+13$ so that $du = (2x+6)\,dx$. We have (for just the first integral) $\frac{1}{2}\int \frac{1}{u}\,du = \frac{1}{2}\ln|u|+C = \frac{1}{2}\ln(x^2+6x+13)+C$. The second integrand has antiderivative equal to $\frac{5}{2}\tan^{-1}((x+3)/2)$, so the original integral is equal to

$$\frac{1}{2}\ln(x^2+6x+13) - \frac{5}{2}\tan^{-1}((x+3)/2)+C.$$

7.1.51 Let $u = e^x$ so that $du = e^x\,dx$. Substituting gives $\int \frac{1}{u^2+2u+1}\,du = \int (u+1)^{-2}\,du = -\frac{1}{u+1}+C = -\frac{1}{e^x+1}+C$.

7.1.53 The denominator factors as $(x+1)^2$. $\int_1^3 \frac{2}{(x+1)^2}\,dx = -2\left(\frac{1}{x+1}\right)\Big|_1^3 = -2(1/4-1/2) = 1/2$.

7.1.55

a. If $u = \tan x$ then $du = \sec^2 x\,dx$. Substituting gives $\int u\,du = u^2/2+C = (\tan^2 x)/2+C$.

b. If $u = \sec x$, then $du = \sec x\tan x\,dx$. Substituting gives $\int u\,du = u^2/2+C = (\sec^2 x)/2+C$.

c. The seemingly different answers are the same, since $(\tan^2 x)/2$ and $(\sec^2 x)/2$ differ by a constant. In fact, $(\tan^2 x)/2 - (\sec^2 x)/2 = \frac{-1}{2}$.

7.1.57

a. Let $u = x+1$ so that $du = dx$. Note that $x = u-1$, so that $x^2 = (u-1)^2$. Substituting gives $\int \frac{u^2-2u+1}{u}\,du = \int (u-2+(1/u))\,du = u^2/2-2u+\ln|u|+C = (x+1)^2/2-2(x+1)+\ln|x+1|+C$.

b. By long division, $\frac{x^2}{x+1} = x-1+\frac{1}{x+1}$. Thus, $\int \frac{x^2}{x+1}\,dx = \int \left(x-1+\frac{1}{x+1}\right)dx = x^2/2-x+\ln|x+1|+C$.

c. The seemingly different answers are the same, because they differ by a constant. In fact, $(x+1)^2/2 - 2(x+1)+\ln|x+1| - (x^2/2-x+\ln|x+1|) = -\frac{3}{2}$.

7.1.59 $A = \int_2^4 \frac{x^2-1}{x^3-3x}\,dx$. Let $u = x^3-3x$ so that $du = 3x^2-3\,dx$. Substituting gives $A = \frac{1}{3}\int_2^{52}\frac{1}{u}\,du = \frac{1}{3}\ln u\Big|_2^{52} = \frac{1}{3}(\ln 52-\ln 2) = \ln(26)/3$.

7.1.61

a. $V = \pi\int_0^2 (x^2+1)\,dx = \pi\left(x^3/3+x\right)\Big|_0^2 = \pi(8/3+2) = 14\pi/3$.

b. $V = 2\pi\int_0^2 x\sqrt{x^2+1}\,dx$. Let $u = x^2+1$ so that $du = 2x\,dx$. Substituting gives $\pi\int_1^5 u^{1/2}\,du = \pi\left(2u^{3/2}/3\right)\Big|_1^5 = \pi(10\sqrt{5}/3-2/3)$.

7.1.63 $L = \int_0^1 \sqrt{1+\frac{25x^{1/2}}{16}}\,dx$. Let $u^2 = 1+\frac{25x^{1/2}}{16}$. Then $2u\,du = \frac{25}{32\sqrt{x}}\,dx$. Note that $\sqrt{x} = \frac{16}{25}(u^2-1)$, and that $dx = \frac{64\sqrt{x}}{25}u\,du = \frac{1024}{625}(u^3-u)\,du$. Substituting gives

$$L = \int_1^{\sqrt{41/16}} \frac{1024}{625}(u^4-u^2)\,du = \frac{1024}{625}\left(u^5/5-u^3/3\right)\Big|_1^{\sqrt{41/16}}$$

$$= \frac{1024}{625}((\sqrt{41/16})^5/5 - (\sqrt{41/16})^3/3 - (1/5-1/3)) = \frac{1024}{625}\left(\frac{2}{15}+\frac{1763\sqrt{41}}{15360}\right)$$

$$= \frac{2048+1763\sqrt{41}}{9375} \approx 1.423.$$

7.1.65 $A = 2\pi\int_0^1 \sqrt{x+1}\sqrt{1+\frac{1}{4(x+1)}}\,dx = 2\pi\int_0^1 \sqrt{x+5/4}\,dx = 2\pi\left((2/3)(x+5/4)^{3/2}\right)\Big|_0^1 = \frac{4\pi}{3}(27/8 - 5\sqrt{5}/8) = \frac{9\pi}{2} - \frac{5\sqrt{5}\pi}{6}$.

7.2 Integration by Parts

7.2.1 It is based on the product rule. In fact, the rule can be obtained by writing down the product rule, then integrating both sides and rearranging the terms in the result.

7.2.3 It is generally a good idea to let u be something easy to differentiate, keeping in mind that whatever is left for dv is something which you will need to be able to integrate. In this case, it would be prudent to let $u = x^n$ and $dv = \cos(ax)\,dx$. Note that differentiating x^n results in something simpler (lower degree,) while integrating it make it more complicated (higher degree.) However, differentiating or integrating $\cos(ax)$ yields essentially the same thing (a constant times the sine function).

7.2.5 Those for which the choice for dv is easily integrated and when the resulting new integral is no more difficult than the original.

7.2.7 Let $u = x$ and $dv = \cos x\,dx$. Then $du = dx$ and $v = \sin x$. Then $\int x\cos x\,dx = x\sin x - \int \sin x\,dx = x\sin x + \cos x + C$.

7.2.9 Let $u = t$ and $dv = e^t\,dt$. Then $du = dt$ and $v = e^t$. Then $\int te^t\,dt = te^t - \int e^t\,dt = te^t - e^t + C$.

7.2.11 Let $u = x$ and $dv = \frac{dx}{\sqrt{x+1}}$. Then $du = dx$ and $v = 2\sqrt{x+1}$. Then $\int \frac{x}{\sqrt{x+1}}\,dx = 2x\sqrt{x+1} - \int 2\sqrt{x+1}\,dx. = 2x\sqrt{x+1} - \frac{4}{3}(x+1)^{3/2} + C = \frac{2}{3}\sqrt{x+1}(x-2) + C$.

7.2.13 Let $u = \ln x^3 = 3\ln x$ and let $dv = x^2\,dx$. Then $du = \frac{3\,dx}{x}$ and $v = x^3/3$. Then $\int x^2\ln x^3\,dx = x^3\ln x - \int x^2\,dx = x^3\ln x - x^3/3 + C$.

7.2.15 Let $u = \ln x$ and $dv = x^2\,dx$. Then $du = \frac{1}{x}\,dx$ and $v = \frac{x^3}{3}$. Then $\int x^2\ln x\,dx = \frac{x^3}{3}\ln x - \frac{1}{3}\int x^2\,dx = \frac{x^3}{3}\ln x - \frac{x^3}{9} + C = \frac{x^3}{9}(3\ln x - 1) + C$.

7.2.17 Let $u = \ln x$ and $dv = x^{-10}\,dx$. Then $du = \frac{1}{x}\,dx$ and $v = -\frac{1}{9}x^{-9}$. Then $\int \frac{\ln x}{x^{10}}\,dx = -\frac{1}{9x^9}\ln x + \frac{1}{9}\int x^{-10}\,dx = -\frac{1}{9x^9}\ln x + -\frac{1}{81x^9} + C$.

7.2.19 Let $u = \tan^{-1}x$ and $dv = dx$. Then $du = \frac{1}{1+x^2}\,dx$ and $v = x$. Then $\int \tan^{-1}x\,dx = x\tan^{-1}x - \int \frac{x}{1+x^2}\,dx = x\tan^{-1}x - \frac{1}{2}\ln(1+x^2) + C$. The fact that $-\int \frac{x}{1+x^2}\,dx = -\frac{1}{2}\ln(1+x^2) + C$ follows from the ordinary substitution $u = 1 + x^2$.

7.2.21 $\int x\sin x\cos x\,dx = \frac{1}{2}\int x\cdot(2\sin x\cos x)\,dx = \frac{1}{2}\int x\sin 2x\,dx$. Now using the result of problem 8, we have

$$\int x\sin x\cos x\,dx = \frac{1}{2}\cdot\left(-\frac{1}{2}x\cos 2x + \frac{1}{4}\sin 2x\right) + C = -\frac{1}{4}x\cos 2x + \frac{1}{8}\sin 2x + C.$$

7.2.23 Let $u = t^2$ and $dv = e^{-t}\,dt$. Then $du = 2t\,dt$ and $v = -e^{-t}$. We have $\int t^2 e^{-t}\,dt = -t^2e^{-t} + 2\int te^{-t}\,dt$. To compute this last integral, we let $u = t$ and $dv = e^{-t}\,dt$. Then $\int te^{-t}\,dt = -te^{-t} + \int e^{-t}\,dt = -te^{-t} - e^{-t} + C$.

Putting these results together, we obtain

$$\int t^2e^{-t}\,dt = -t^2e^{-t} + 2(-te^{-t} - e^{-t}) + C = -e^{-t}(t^2 + 2t + 2) + C.$$

7.2.25 Let $u = \sin 4x$ and $dv = e^{-x}\,dx$. Then $du = 4\cos 4x\,dx$ and $v = -e^{-x}$. We have $\int e^{-x}\sin 4x\,dx = -e^{-x}\sin 4x + 4\int e^{-x}\cos 4x\,dx$.

Now in order to compute the integral which comprises this last term, we let $u = \cos 4x$ and $dv = e^{-x}\,dx$. Then $du = -4\sin 4x\,dx$ and $v = -e^{-x}$. Thus, $\int e^{-x}\cos 4x\,dx = -e^{-x}\cos 4x - 4\int e^{-x}\sin 4x\,dx$.

Putting these results together gives

$$\begin{aligned}\int e^{-x}\sin 4x\,dx &= -e^{-x}\sin 4x - 4e^{-x}\cos 4x - 16\int e^{-x}\sin 4x\,dx\\ 17\int e^{-x}\sin 4x\,dx &= -e^{-x}\sin 4x - 4e^{-x}\cos 4x + C\\ \int e^{-x}\sin 4x\,dx &= -\frac{e^{-x}}{17}(\sin 4x + 4\cos 4x) + C.\end{aligned}$$

7.2.27 Let $u = \cos x$ and $dv = e^x\,dx$. Then $du = -\sin x\,dx$ and $v = e^x$. We have $\int e^x\cos x\,dx = e^x\cos x + \int e^x\sin x\,dx$.

Now in order to compute the integral which comprises this last term, we let $u = \sin x$ and $dv = e^x\,dx$. Then $du = \cos x\,dx$ and $v = e^x$. Thus, $\int e^x\sin x\,dx = e^x\sin x - \int e^x\cos x\,dx$.

Putting these results together gives

$$\begin{aligned}\int e^x\cos x\,dx &= e^x\cos x + e^x\sin x - \int e^x\cos x\,dx\\ 2\int e^x\cos x\,dx &= e^x(\cos x + \sin x) + C\\ \int e^x\cos x\,dx &= \frac{e^x}{2}(\cos x + \sin x) + C.\end{aligned}$$

7.2.29 Let $u = x^2$ and $dv = \sin 2x\,dx$. Then $du = 2x\,dx$ and $v = -\frac{1}{2}\cos 2x$. Then $\int x^2\sin 2x\,dx = -\frac{1}{2}x^2\cos 2x + \int x\cos 2x\,dx$.

Now we consider computing this last term $\int x\cos 2x\,dx$ as a new problem. Let $u = x$ and $dv = \cos 2x\,dx$. Then $du = dx$ and $v = \frac{1}{2}\sin 2x$. So $\int x\cos 2x\,dx = \frac{1}{2}x\sin 2x - \frac{1}{2}\int \sin 2x\,dx = \frac{1}{2}x\sin 2x + \frac{1}{4}\cos 2x + C$.

Combining these results we have $\int x^2\sin 2x\,dx = -\frac{1}{2}x^2\cos 2x + \frac{1}{2}x\sin 2x + \frac{1}{4}\cos 2x + C$.

7.2.31 Let $u = x$ and $dv = \sin x\,dx$. Then $du = dx$ and $v = -\cos x$. Then $\int_0^\pi x\sin x\,dx = -x\cos x\Big|_0^\pi + \int_0^\pi \cos x\,dx = \pi - 0 + \sin x\Big|_0^\pi = \pi - 0 + 0 - 0 = \pi$.

7.2.33 Let $u = x$ and $dv = \cos 2x\,dx$. Then $du = dx$ and $v = \frac{1}{2}\sin 2x$. Then $\int_0^{\pi/2} x\cos 2x\,dx = \frac{1}{2}x\sin 2x\Big|_0^{\pi/2} - \frac{1}{2}\int_0^{\pi/2}\sin 2x\,dx = 0 - \left(\frac{1}{2}\cdot\frac{(-\cos 2x)}{2}\right)\Big|_0^{\pi/2} = -\frac{1}{4} - \frac{1}{4} = -\frac{1}{2}$.

7.2.35 Let $u = \ln x$ and $dv = x^2\,dx$. Then $du = \frac{1}{x}\,dx$ and $v = \frac{x^3}{3}$. Then $\int_1^{e^2} x^2\ln x\,dx = \frac{1}{3}x^3\ln x\Big|_1^{e^2} - \frac{1}{3}\int_1^{e^2} x^2\,dx = \frac{2}{3}e^6 - \frac{1}{9}x^3\Big|_1^{e^2} = \frac{2}{3}e^6 - \frac{1}{9}\left(e^6 - 1\right) = \frac{5}{9}e^6 + \frac{1}{9}$.

7.2.37 By problem 18, $\int \sin^{-1} x\,dx = x\sin^{-1} x + \sqrt{1-x^2}$. Thus,

$$\begin{aligned}\int_{1/2}^{\sqrt{3}/2} \sin^{-1} x\,dx &= \left(x\sin^{-1} x + \sqrt{1-x^2}\right)\Big|_{1/2}^{\sqrt{3}/2} \\ &= \left(\frac{\sqrt{3}}{2}\cdot\frac{\pi}{3} + \frac{1}{2}\right) - \left(\frac{1}{2}\cdot\frac{\pi}{6} + \frac{\sqrt{3}}{2}\right) \\ &= \frac{\pi}{6}\left(\sqrt{3} - \frac{1}{2}\right) + \frac{1}{2}\left(1 - \sqrt{3}\right).\end{aligned}$$

7.2.39 Using shells, we have $\frac{V}{2\pi} = \int_0^{\ln 2} xe^{-x}\,dx$. Let $u = x$ and $dv = e^{-x}\,dx$, so that $du = dx$ and $v = -e^{-x}$. Then

$$\frac{V}{2\pi} = -xe^{-x}\Big|_0^{\ln 2} + \int_0^{\ln 2} e^{-x}\,dx = -\frac{1}{2}\ln 2 - e^{-x}\Big|_0^{\ln 2} = -\frac{\ln 2}{2} - \left(\frac{1}{2} - 1\right) = \frac{1}{2}\left(1 - \ln 2\right).$$

Thus $V = \pi(1 - \ln 2)$.

7.2.41 Using disks, we have $\frac{V}{\pi} = \int_1^{e^2} x^2\ln^2 x\,dx$. By problem 26, we have $\int x^2\ln^2 x\,dx = \frac{1}{3}x^3\ln^2 x - \frac{2}{9}x^3\ln x + \frac{2}{27}x^3 + C$. Thus,

$$\frac{V}{\pi} = \left(\frac{1}{3}x^3\ln^2 x - \frac{2}{9}x^3\ln x + \frac{2}{27}x^3\right)\Big|_1^{e^2} = \left(\frac{4}{3}e^6 - \frac{4}{9}e^6 + \frac{2}{27}e^6\right) - \left(\frac{2}{27}\right) = \frac{26}{27}e^6 - \frac{2}{27}.$$

Thus, $V = \frac{\pi}{27}\left(26e^6 - 2\right)$.

7.2.43

a. False. For example, suppose $u = x$ and $dv = x\,dx$. Then $\int uv'\,dx = \int x^2\,dx = \frac{x^3}{3} + C$, but $\int u\,dx \int v'\,dx = \left(\int x\,dx\right)^2 = \left(\frac{x^2}{2} + C\right)^2$.

b. True. This is one way to write the integration by parts formula.

c. True. This is the integration by parts formula with the roles of u and v reversed.

7.2.45 Let $u = x^n$ and $dv = \cos ax\,dx$. Then $du = nx^{n-1}\,dx$ and $v = \frac{\sin ax}{a}$. Then $\int x^n\cos ax\,dx = \frac{x^n\sin ax}{a} - \frac{n}{a}\int x^{n-1}\sin ax\,dx$.

7.2.47 Let $u = \ln^n x$ and $dv = dx$. Then $du = \frac{n\ln^{n-1}(x)}{x}\,dx$ and $v = x$. Then $\int \ln^n(x)\,dx = x\ln^n x - n\int \ln^{n-1}(x)\,dx$.

7.2.49

$$\begin{aligned}\int x^2\cos 5x\,dx &= \frac{x^2\sin 5x}{5} - \frac{2}{5}\int x\sin 5x\,dx\\ &= \frac{x^2\sin 5x}{5} - \frac{2}{5}\left(-\frac{x\cos 5x}{5} + \frac{1}{5}\int \cos 5x\,dx\right)\\ &= \frac{1}{5}\left(x^2\sin 5x + \frac{2}{5}x\cos 5x - \frac{2}{25}\sin 5x\right) + C.\end{aligned}$$

7.2.51

$$\begin{aligned}\int \ln^4 x\,dx &= x\ln^4 x - 4\int \ln^3 x\,dx\\ &= x\ln^4 x - 4\left(x\ln^3 x - 3\int \ln^2 x\,dx\right)\\ &= x\ln^4 x - 4x\ln^3 x + 12\left(x\ln^2 x - 2\int \ln x\,dx\right)\\ &= x\ln^4 x - 4x\ln^3 x + 12x\ln^2 x - 24\,(x\ln x - x) + C.\end{aligned}$$

7.2.53 Let $u = \tan x + 2$, so that $du = \sec^2 x\,dx$. Then $\int \sec^2 x\ln(\tan x + 2)\,dx = \int \ln u\,du = u\ln u - u + C = (\tan x + 2)\ln(\tan x + 2) - \tan x + C$.

7.2.55 Using the change of base formula, we have $\int \log_b x\,dx = \int \frac{\ln x}{\ln b}\,dx = \frac{1}{\ln b}(x\ln x - x) + C$.

7.2.57 Let $z = \sqrt{x}$, so that $dz = \frac{1}{2\sqrt{x}}\,dx$. Substituting yields $2\int \frac{\sqrt{x}\cos\sqrt{x}}{2\sqrt{x}}\,dx = 2\int z\cos z\,dz$. Now let $u = z$ and $dv = \cos z\,dz$. then $du = dz$ and $v = \sin z$. Then by Integration by Parts, we have $2\int z\cos z\,dz = 2\left(z\sin z - \int \sin z\,dz\right) = 2z\sin z + 2\cos z + C$. Thus, the original given integral is equal to $2(\sqrt{x}\sin\sqrt{x} + \cos\sqrt{x}) + C$.

7.2.59 By the Fundamental Theorem, $f'(x) = \sqrt{\ln^2 x - 1}$. So the arc length is $\int_e^{e^3} \sqrt{1 + (f'(x))^2}\,dx = \int_e^{e^3} \ln x\,dx = (x\ln x - x)\Big|_e^{e^3} = 3e^3 - e^3 - (e - e) = 2e^3$.

7.2.61 Using shells, we have $\frac{V}{2\pi} = \int_0^{\pi/2} x\cos x\,dx$. Let $u = x$ and $dv = \cos x\,dx$, so that $du = dx$ and $v = \sin x$. We have $\frac{V}{2\pi} = x\sin x\Big|_0^{\pi/2} - \int_0^{\pi/2} \sin x\,dx = \frac{\pi}{2} - 1$.

Thus, $V = \pi(\pi - 2)$.

7.2.63 Let V_1 be the volume generated when R is revolved about the x-axis, and V_2 the volume generated when R is revolved about the y-axis.

Using disks, we have

$$\frac{V_1}{\pi} = \int_0^{\pi} \sin^2 x\,dx = \frac{1}{2}\int_0^{\pi}(1 - \cos 2x)\,dx = \frac{1}{2}\left(\pi - \frac{1}{2}\int_0^{\pi} 2\cos 2x\,dx\right) = \frac{1}{2}\left(\pi - \frac{1}{2}\int_0^{2\pi} \cos u\,du\right) = \frac{\pi}{2},$$

where the ordinary substitution $u = 2x$ was made. So $V_1 = \frac{\pi^2}{2}$.

Using shells to compute V_2, we have $\frac{V_2}{2\pi} = \int_0^\pi x \sin x\, dx$. Letting $u = x$ and $dv = \sin x\, dx$, we have $du = dx$ and $v = -\cos x$. Thus, $\frac{V_2}{2\pi} = -x\cos x \Big|_0^\pi + \int_0^\pi \cos x\, dx = \pi$. Thus, $V_2 = 2\pi^2$, and $V_2 > V_1$.

7.2.65

a. Let $u = x$ and $dv = f'(x)\, dx$. Then $du = dx$ and $v = f(x)$. So $\int x f'(x)\, dx = x f(x) - \int f(x)\, dx$.

b. Letting $f'(x) = e^{3x}$ we have $\int x e^{3x}\, dx = \frac{1}{3} x e^{3x} - \frac{1}{9} e^{3x} + C$.

7.2.67 Let $u = \sec x$ and $dv = \sec^2 x\, dx$, so that $du = \sec x \tan x\, dx$ and $v = \tan x$. Then $\int \sec^3 x\, dx = \sec x \tan x - \int \sec x \tan^2 x\, dx = \sec x \tan x - \int \sec x \left(\sec^2 x - 1\right)\, dx = \sec x \tan x - \int \sec^3 x\, dx + \int \sec x\, dx$.

Thus $2\int \sec^3 x\, dx = \sec x \tan x + \int \sec x\, dx$, so $\int \sec^3 x\, dx = \frac{1}{2} \sec x \tan x + \frac{1}{2} \int \sec x\, dx$.

7.2.69

a. We have $s(t) = 0$ when $\sin t = 0$, which occurs for $t = k\pi$, where k is an integer.

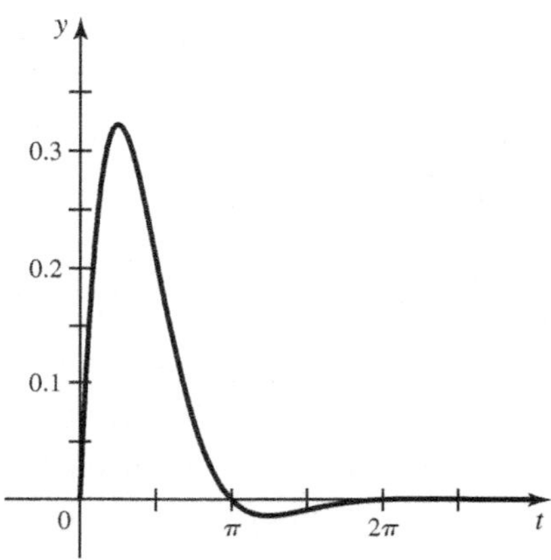

b. This is given by $\frac{1}{\pi} \int_0^\pi e^{-t} \sin t\, dt$. Using the previous problem, this is equal to

$$\frac{1}{\pi} e^{-t} \cdot \frac{-\sin t - \cos t}{2} \Big|_0^\pi = \frac{1}{2\pi}(e^{-\pi} + 1).$$

c. This is given by $\frac{1}{\pi} \int_{n\pi}^{(n+1)\pi} e^{-t} \sin t\, dt$. Using the previous problem, this is equal to

$$\frac{1}{\pi} e^{-t} \cdot \frac{-\sin t - \cos t}{2} \Big|_{n\pi}^{(n+1)\pi} = \frac{1}{2\pi} \left(e^{-(n+1)\pi} \left(-\sin(n+1)\pi - \cos(n+1)\pi\right) - e^{-n\pi} \left(-\sin n\pi - \cos n\pi\right) \right)$$

$$= \frac{1}{2\pi} \left(-e^{-(n+1)\pi} \cos(n+1)\pi + e^{-n\pi} \cos n\pi \right) = \frac{e^{-n\pi}}{2\pi} \left(\cos n\pi - e^{-\pi} \cos(n+1)\pi \right)$$

$$= \frac{e^{-n\pi}}{2\pi} \left((-1)^n - e^{-\pi}(-1)^{n+1} \right) = (-1)^n \frac{e^{-n\pi}}{2\pi} \left(1 + e^{-\pi}\right).$$

d. Each a_n is $e^{-\pi}$ times a_{n-1}.

7.2.71

a. If $u = f(x)$ then $du = f'(x)\,dx$, and if $dv = g(x)\,dx$, then $v = G_1(x)$. The integration by parts formula gives

$$\int f(x)g(x)\,dx = f(x)G_1(x) - \int f'(x)G_1(x)\,dx.$$

b. Letting $u = f'(x)$ yields $du = f''(x)\,dx$ and letting $dv = G_1(x)\,dx$ yields $v = G_2(x)$. Then continuing from part (a) we have

$$\begin{aligned}\int f(x)g(x)\,dx &= f(x)G_1(x) - \left(f'(x)G_2(x) - \int f''(x)G_2(x)\,dx\right)\\ &= f(x)G_1(x) - f'(x)G_2(x) + \int f''(x)G_2(x)\,dx.\end{aligned}$$

Note that we end up with three terms which consist of products as indicated by the arrows, with the last product inside an integral sign. The signs alternate as indicated on the chart.

c. For the trailing integral from part (b), we let $u = f''(x)$ so that $du = f'''(x)\,dx$, and let $dv = G_2(x)\,dx$ so that $v = G_3(x)$. Then we have

$$\begin{aligned}\int f(x)g(x)\,dx &= f(x)G_1(x) - f'(x)G_2(x) + \int f''(x)G_2(x)\,dx\\ &= f(x)G_1(x) - f'(x)G_2(x) + f''(x)G_3(x) - \int f'''(x)G_3(x)\,dx.\end{aligned}$$

f and its derivatives		*g* and its integrals
$f(x)$	+	$g(x)$
$f'(x)$	−	$G_1(x)$
$f''(x)$	+	$G_2(x)$
$f'''(x)$	−	$G_3(x)$

d. The table is as follows:

f and its derivatives		*g* and its integrals
x^2	+	$e^{0.5x}$
$2x$	−	$2e^{0.5x}$
2	+	$4e^{0.5x}$
0	−	$8e^{0.5x}$

So

$$\int x^2 e^{0.5x}\,dx = 2x^2e^{0.5x} - 8xe^{0.5x} + 16e^{0.5x} + C.$$

Note that the last integral is $\int 0 \cdot 8e^{0.5x}\,dx = \int 0\,dx = C$.

e. We have:

f and its derivatives		g and its integrals
x^3	+	$\cos x$
$3x^2$	−	$\sin x$
$6x$	+	$-\cos x$
6	−	$-\sin x$
0	+	$\cos x$

So $\displaystyle\int x^3 \cos x\, dx = x^3 \sin x + 3x^2 \cos x - 6x \sin x - 6 \cos x + C.$

f. $\frac{d^k}{dx^k}(p_n(x)) = 0$ for $k \geq n+1$, so the process will end.

7.2.73

a. $\int e^x \cos x\, dx = e^x \sin x + e^x \cos x - \int e^x \cos x\, dx.$

b. Adding $\int e^x \cos x\, dx$ to both sides of the previous equation gives $2\int e^x \cos x\, dx = e^x \sin x + e^x \cos x$, so

$$\int e^x \cos x\, dx = \frac{e^x \sin x + e^x \cos x}{2} + C.$$

c. The chart looks like this:

f and its derivatives	g and its integrals
e^{-2x} $+$	$\sin 3x$
$-2e^{-2x}$ $-$	$-\frac{1}{3}\cos 3x$
$4e^{-2x}$ $+$	$-\frac{1}{9}\sin 3x$

So we have

$$\int e^{-2x} \sin 3x = -\frac{1}{3}e^{-2x}\cos 3x - \frac{2}{9}e^{-2x}\sin 3x - \frac{4}{9}e^{-2x}\sin 3x.$$

Adding $\frac{4}{9}\int e^{-2x}\sin 3x\, dx$ to both sides gives

$$\frac{13}{9}\int e^{-2x}\sin 3x\, dx = -\frac{1}{3}e^{-2x}\cos 3x - \frac{2}{9}e^{-2x}\sin 3x + D,$$

where D is an arbitrary constant so

$$\int e^{-2x}\sin 3x\, dx = -\frac{3}{13}e^{-2x}\cos 3x - \frac{2}{13}e^{-2x}\sin 3x + C.$$

7.2.75 Let $u = x$ and $dv = f''(x)\, dx$. Then $du = dx$ and $v = f'(x)$. We have $\displaystyle\int_a^b xf''(x)\, dx = xf'(x)\Big|_a^b - \int_a^b f'(x)\, dx = (0-0) - f(x)\Big|_a^b = -(f(b) - f(a)) = f(a) - f(b).$

7.2.77

a. To compute I_1, we let $u = -x^2$, so that $du = -2x\, dx$. Then an ordinary substitution yields

$$-\frac{1}{2}\int e^u\, du = -\frac{1}{2}e^u + C = -\frac{1}{2}e^{-x^2} + C.$$

b. To compute I_3, we let $u = x^2$ and $dv = xe^{-x^2}\, dx$, so that $du = 2x\, dx$ and $v = -\frac{1}{2}e^{-x^2}$ (by part (a)). Then $I_3 = -\dfrac{1}{2}x^2 e^{-x^2} + \displaystyle\int xe^{-x^2}\, dx = -\frac{1}{2}x^2e^{-x^2} - \frac{1}{2}e^{-x^2} + C = -\frac{1}{2}e^{-x^2}(x^2+1) + C.$

c. To compute I_5, we let $u = x^4$ and $dv = xe^{-x^2}\, dx$. Then $du = 4x^3\, dx$ and $v = -\frac{1}{2}e^{-x^2}$. Then $I_5 = -\dfrac{1}{2}x^4e^{-x^2} + 2\displaystyle\int x^3e^{-x^2}\, dx = -\frac{1}{2}x^4e^{-x^2} + 2I_3 = -\frac{1}{2}e^{-x^2}(x^4 + 2x^2 + 2).$

d. Suppose that n is odd and that it is true that $I_n = -\frac{1}{2}e^{-x^2}p_{n-1}(x)$ where $p_{n-1}(x)$ is an even polynomial of degree $n-1$. We will show that I_{n+2} also has this property, so the result will follow by induction. Let $u = x^{n+1}$ and let $dv = xe^{-x^2}\,dx$, so that $du = (n+1)x^n\,dx$ and $v = -\frac{1}{2}e^{-x^2}$. Then $I_{n+2} = -\frac{1}{2}x^{n+1}e^{-x^2} + \frac{n+1}{2}I_n = -\frac{1}{2}e^{-x^2}(x^{n+1} + \frac{n+1}{2}p_{n-1}(x)) + C = -\frac{1}{2}e^{-x^2}p_{n+1}(x) + C$. Note that if $p_{n-1}(x)$ is an even polynomial of degree $n-1$ then $\frac{n+1}{2}p_{n-1}(x) + x^{n+1}$ is an even polynomial of degree $n+1$.

e. Note that $I_2 = -\dfrac{1}{2}xe^{-x^2} + \dfrac{1}{2}I_0$. (Using a similar technique to that above.) Now if I_2 were expressible in terms of elementary functions, then I_0 would be as well, but we are given that it isn't. Similarly, we can express I_{2k} in terms of I_{2k-2} using Integration by Parts, and if any of these were expressible in terms of elementary functions, then the even numbered one below it would be. So the inability to express I_0 that way implies the inability to express I_2 that way, which implies the inability to express I_4 that way, and so on.

7.3 Trigonometric Integrals

7.3.1 The half-angle identities for sine and cosine:

$$\sin^2 x = \frac{1-\cos 2x}{2} \quad \text{and} \quad \cos^2 x = \frac{1+\cos 2x}{2},$$

which are conjugates.

7.3.3 To integrate $\sin^3 x$, write $\sin^3 x = \sin x \sin^2 x = \sin x(1-\cos^2 x)$, and let $u = \cos x$ so that $du = -\sin x\,dx$.

7.3.5 A reduction formula is a recursive formula involving integrals. Using it, one can rewrite an integral of a certain type in a simpler form – which can then perhaps be evaluated or further reduced.

7.3.7 One would compute this integral by letting $u = \tan x$, so that $du = \sec^2 x\,dx$. This substitution leads to the integral $\displaystyle\int u^{10}\,du$, which can easily be evaluated.

7.3.9 $\displaystyle\int \sin^2 x\,dx = \frac{1}{2}\int (1-\cos 2x)\,dx = \frac{1}{2}\left(x - \frac{1}{2}\sin 2x\right) + C.$

7.3.11 $\displaystyle\int \cos^3 x\,dx = \int \cos x(1-\sin^2 x)\,dx = \int \cos x\,dx - \int \cos x \sin^2 x\,dx = \sin x - \int \cos x \sin^2 x\,dx$. Let $u = \sin x$ so that $du = \cos x\,dx$. Substituting gives $\displaystyle\sin x - \int u^2\,du = \sin x - u^3/3 + C = \sin x - (\sin^3 x)/3 + C$.

7.3.13 $\displaystyle\int \sin^5 x\,dx = \int (\sin^2 x)^2 \sin x\,dx = \int (1-\cos^2 x)^2 \sin x\,dx$. Let $u = \cos x$ so that $du = -\sin x\,dx$. Substituting yields $\displaystyle -\int (1-u^2)^2\,du = \int (-u^4 + 2u^2 - 1)\,du = \frac{-u^5}{5} + \frac{2u^3}{3} - u + C = \frac{-\cos^5 x}{5} + \frac{2\cos^3 x}{3} - \cos x + C$.

7.3.15

$$\begin{aligned}\int \sin^2 x \cos^2 x\,dx &= \int \left(\frac{1-\cos 2x}{2}\right)\left(\frac{1+\cos 2x}{2}\right)dx = \frac{1}{4}\int 1-\cos^2 2x\,dx \\ &= \frac{1}{4}\int \left(1 - \frac{1+\cos 4x}{2}\right)dx = \frac{1}{4}\int \left(\frac{1}{2} - \frac{1}{2}\cos 4x\right)dx = \frac{1}{4}\left(\frac{x}{2} - \frac{\sin 4x}{8}\right) + C.\end{aligned}$$

7.3.17 $\displaystyle\int \sin^3 x \cos^2 x\,dx = \int \sin x(1-\cos^2 x)(\cos^2 x)\,dx$. Let $u = \cos x$ so that $du = -\sin x\,dx$. Substituting gives $\displaystyle\int (u^4 - u^2)\,du = u^5/5 - u^3/3 + C = (\cos^5 x)/5 - (\cos^3 x)/3 + C$.

7.3.19 $\int \cos^3 x\sqrt{\sin x}\,dx = \int \cos x(1-\sin^2 x)\sqrt{\sin x}\,dx$. Let $u = \sin x$ so that $du = \cos x\,dx$. Substituting gives $\int (1-u^2)u^{1/2}\,du = \int (u^{1/2}-u^{5/2})\,du = 2u^{3/2}/3 - 2u^{7/2}/7 + C = 2(\sin^{3/2} x)/3 - 2(\sin^{7/2} x)/7 + C$.

7.3.21 $\int \sin^5 x\cos^{-2} x\,dx = \int (\sin x)\left(\frac{(1-\cos^2 x)^2}{\cos^2 x}\right)\,dx$. Let $u = \cos x$ so that $du = -\sin x\,dx$. Substituting yields $-\int \frac{(1-u^2)^2}{u^2}\,du = \int -u^{-2}+2-u^2\,du = \frac{1}{u}+2u-\frac{u^3}{3}+C = \sec x + 2\cos x - \frac{\cos^3 x}{3} + C$.

7.3.23 $\int \sin^2 x\cos^4 x\,dx = \int \left(\frac{1-\cos 2x}{2}\right)\left(\frac{1+\cos 2x}{2}\right)^2\,dx = \frac{1}{8}\int (1-\cos^2 2x)(1+\cos 2x)\,dx = \frac{1}{8}\int 1+\cos 2x - \cos^2 2x - \cos^3 2x\,dx = \frac{1}{8}\int 1+\cos 2x - \frac{1+\cos 4x}{2} - \cos^3 2x\,dx = \frac{1}{8}\int \frac{1}{2}+\cos 2x - \frac{1}{2}\cos 4x\,dx - \frac{1}{8}\int (1-\sin^2 2x)\cos 2x\,dx = \frac{x}{16}+\frac{\sin 2x}{16}-\frac{\sin 4x}{64}-\frac{1}{8}\int (1-\sin^2 2x)\cos 2x\,dx$. To compute this last integral, we let $u = \sin 2x$, so that $du = 2\cos 2x\,dx$. Then $\int (1-\sin^2 2x)\cos 2x\,dx = \frac{1}{2}\int (1-u^2)\,du = \frac{1}{2}\left(u-\frac{u^3}{3}\right)+C = \frac{1}{2}\left(\sin 2x - \frac{\sin^3 2x}{3}\right)+C$.

Thus, our original given integral is equal to $\frac{x}{16}+\frac{\sin 2x}{16}-\frac{\sin 4x}{64}-\frac{1}{8}\left(\frac{1}{2}\left(\sin 2x - \frac{\sin^3 2x}{3}\right)\right)+C = \frac{x}{16}-\frac{\sin 4x}{64}+\frac{\sin^3 2x}{48}+C$.

7.3.25 $\int \tan^2 x\,dx = \int (\sec^2 x - 1)\,dx = \tan x - x + C$.

7.3.27 $\int \cot^4 x\,dx = \int \cot^2 x(\csc^2 x - 1)\,dx = \int (\cot^2 x\csc^2 x - (\csc^2 x - 1))\,dx = \int \cot^2 x\csc^2 x\,dx + \cot x + x$. Let $u = \cot x$ so that $du = -\csc^2 x\,dx$. Substituting gives $-\int u^2\,du + \cot x + x = -u^3/3 + \cot x + x + C = -(\cot^3 x)/3 + \cot x + x + C$.

7.3.29

$$\begin{aligned}\int 20\tan^6 x\,dx &= 20\int (\tan^4 x)(\sec^2 x - 1)\,dx = 20\int ((\tan^4 x)\sec^2 x - (\tan^2 x)(\sec^2 x - 1))\,dx \\ &= 20\int (\tan^4 x\sec^2 x - \tan^2 x\sec^2 x + \sec^2 x - 1)\,dx.\end{aligned}$$

Let $u = \tan x$ so that $du = \sec^2 x\,dx$. We have $20\left(\int (u^4-u^2)\,du + \tan x - x\right)+C = 4u^5 - \frac{20u^3}{3} + 20\tan x - 20x + C = 4\tan^5 x - \frac{20\tan^3 x}{3} + 20\tan x - 20x + C$.

7.3.31 Let $u = \tan x$ so that $du = \sec^2 x\,dx$. Substituting gives $\int 10u^9\,du = u^{10} + C = \tan^{10} x + C$.

7.3.33 Let $u = \sec x$ so that $du = \sec x\tan x\,dx$. Substituting gives $\int u^2\,du = u^3/3 + C = (\sec^3 x)/3 + C$.

7.3.35

$$\begin{aligned}\int \tan^3 4x\,dx &= \int (\tan 4x)(\sec^2 4x - 1)\,dx = \int (\tan 4x)\sec^2 4x\,dx - \int \tan 4x\,dx \\ &= \int (\tan 4x)\sec^2 4x\,dx + \frac{\ln|\cos 4x|}{4} + C.\end{aligned}$$

Let $u = \tan 4x$ so that $du = 4\sec^2 4x\,dx$. Substituting gives

$$\frac{1}{4}\int u\,du + \frac{\ln|\cos 4x|}{4} + C = \frac{u^2}{8} + \frac{\ln|\cos 4x|}{4} + C = \frac{\tan^2 4x}{8} + \frac{\ln|\cos 4x|}{4} + C.$$

7.3.37 Let $u = \tan x$ so that $du = \sec^2 x\,dx$. Then

$$\int \sec^2 x \tan^{1/2} x\,dx = \int u^{1/2}\,du = \frac{2}{3}u^{3/2} + C = \frac{2}{3}\tan^{3/2} x + C.$$

7.3.39 $\displaystyle\int \frac{\csc^4 x}{\cot^2 x}\,dx = \int (\csc^2 x)\left(\frac{\cot^2 x + 1}{\cot^2 x}\right)dx$. Let $u = \cot x$ so that $du = -\csc^2 x\,dx$. Substituting gives $\displaystyle -\int \frac{u^2+1}{u^2}\,du = \int -1 - u^{-2}\,du = -u + \frac{1}{u} + C = -\cot x + \tan x + C$.

7.3.41 $\displaystyle\int_0^{\pi/4} \sec^4\theta\,d\theta = \int_0^{\pi/4} (\sec^2\theta)(1+\tan^2\theta)\,d\theta$. Let $u = \tan\theta$ so that $du = \sec^2\theta\,d\theta$. Note that when $\theta = 0$ we have $u = 0$ and when $\theta = \frac{\pi}{4}$ we have $u = 1$. So the original integral is equal to $\displaystyle\int_0^1 (1+u^2)\,du = \left(u + \frac{u^3}{3}\right)\Big|_0^1 = 1 + \frac{1}{3} = \frac{4}{3}$.

7.3.43 $\displaystyle\int_{\pi/6}^{\pi/3} \cot^3\theta\,d\theta = \int_{\pi/6}^{\pi/3} (\cot\theta)(\csc^2\theta - 1)\,d\theta = \int_{\pi/6}^{\pi/3} \cot\theta\csc^2\theta\,d\theta - \int_{\pi/6}^{\pi/3} \frac{\cos\theta}{\sin\theta}\,d\theta$. For the first integral, let $u = \cot\theta$ so that $du = -\csc^2\theta\,d\theta$. For the second integral, let $w = \sin\theta$ so that $dw = \cos\theta\,d\theta$. Substituting gives

$$-\int_{\sqrt{3}}^{1/\sqrt{3}} u\,du - \int_{1/2}^{\sqrt{3}/2} \frac{1}{w}\,dw = -\frac{u^2}{2}\Big|_{\sqrt{3}}^{1/\sqrt{3}} - \ln w\Big|_{1/2}^{\sqrt{3}/2}$$
$$= -\frac{1}{2}\left(\frac{1}{3} - 3\right) - \left(\ln\sqrt{3} - \ln 2 - \ln 1 + \ln 2\right) = \frac{4}{3} - \frac{\ln 3}{2}.$$

7.3.45

a. True. We have $\displaystyle\int_0^{\pi} \cos^{2m+1} x\,dx = \int_0^{\pi} (\cos^2 x)^m \cos x\,dx = \int_0^{\pi} (1-\sin^2 x)^m \cos x\,dx$. Let $u = \sin x$ so that $du = \cos x\,dx$. Substituting yields $\displaystyle\int_0^0 (1-u^2)^m\,du = 0$.

b. False. For example, suppose $m = 1$. Then $\displaystyle\int_0^{\pi} \sin x\,dx = -\cos x\Big|_0^{\pi} = -(-1-1) = 2 \neq 0$.

7.3.47 $\displaystyle\int \csc x\,dx = \int (\csc x)\left(\frac{\csc x + \cot x}{\csc x + \cot x}\right)dx = \int \frac{\csc^2 x + \csc x\cot x}{\csc x + \cot x}\,dx$. Let $u = \csc x + \cot x$ so that $du = -\csc^2 x - \csc x\cot x\,dx$. Substituting then yields $\displaystyle -\int \frac{1}{u}\,du = -\ln|u| + C = -\ln|\csc x + \cot x| + C$.

7.3.49 $\displaystyle A = \int_0^{\pi/4} \sec x - \tan x\,dx = \ln|\sec x + \tan x| + \ln|\cos x|\Big|_0^{\pi/4} = \ln\left(\sqrt{2}+1\right) + \ln\left(\frac{\sqrt{2}}{2}\right) - (0+0) = \ln\left(1 + \sqrt{2}/2\right)$.

7.3.51 Let $u = \ln\theta$ so that $du = \frac{1}{\theta}\,d\theta$. Substituting yields $\displaystyle\int \sec^4 u\,du = \int (\sec^2 u)(1+\tan^2 u)\,du$. Let $w = \tan u$ so that $dw = \sec^2 u\,du$. Substituting again gives $\displaystyle\int (1+w^2)\,dw = w + \frac{w^3}{3} + C = \tan(\ln(\theta)) + \frac{\tan^3(\ln(\theta))}{3} + C$.

7.3.53

$$\int_{-\pi/3}^{\pi/3} \sqrt{\sec^2\theta - 1}\, d\theta = 2\int_0^{\pi/3} \sqrt{\sec^2\theta - 1}\, d\theta = 2\int_0^{\pi/3} \tan\theta\, d\theta$$

$$= -2\ln|\cos\theta|\Big|_0^{\pi/3} = -2\ln(1/2) + 2\ln(1) = 2\ln 2.$$

7.3.55 $\int_0^{\pi}(1-\cos 2x)^{3/2}\,dx = \int_0^{\pi}(2\sin^2 x)^{3/2}\,dx = 2\sqrt{2}\int_0^{\pi}\sin^3 x\,dx = 2\sqrt{2}\int_0^{\pi}(\sin x)(1-\cos^2 x)\,dx$. Let $u = \cos x$ so that $du = -\sin x\,dx$. Substituting yields $-2\sqrt{2}\int_1^{-1}(1-u^2)\,du = 2\sqrt{2}\int_{-1}^{1}(1-u^2)\,du = 4\sqrt{2}\int_0^1(1-u^2)\,du = 4\sqrt{2}\left(u - \frac{u^3}{3}\right)\Big|_0^1 = \frac{8\sqrt{2}}{3}$.

7.3.57 Let $u = e^x + 1$ so that $du = e^x\,dx$. Substituting gives $\int \sec u\,du = \ln|\sec u + \tan u| + C = \ln|\sec(e^x + 1) + \tan(e^x+1)| + C$.

7.3.59 $\int_0^{\pi/2}\sqrt{1-\cos 2x}\,dx = \sqrt{2}\int_0^{\pi/2}\sin x\,dx = -\sqrt{2}\cos x\Big|_0^{\pi/2} = \sqrt{2}$.

7.3.61 $\int_0^{\pi/4}(1+\cos 4x)^{3/2}\,dx = \int_0^{\pi/4}(2\cos^2 2x)^{3/2}\,dx = 2\sqrt{2}\int_0^{\pi/4}\cos^3 2x\,dx = 2\sqrt{2}\int_0^{\pi/4}(\cos 2x)(1 - \sin^2 2x)\,dx$. Let $u = \sin 2x$ so that $du = 2\cos 2x\,dx$. Substituting gives

$$\sqrt{2}\int_0^1(1-u^2)\,du = \sqrt{2}\left(u - \frac{u^3}{3}\right)\Big|_0^1 = \frac{2\sqrt{2}}{3}.$$

7.3.63 If $y = \ln(\sec x)$ then $\frac{dy}{dx} = \tan x$. Thus, $L = \int_0^{\pi/4}\sqrt{1+\tan^2 x}\,dx = \int_0^{\pi/4}\sec x\,dx$ $= \ln|\sec x + \tan x|\Big|_0^{\pi/4} = \ln(\sqrt{2}+1)$.

7.3.65 For $n \neq 1$, $\int \tan^n x\,dx = \int(\tan^{n-2}x)(\sec^2 x - 1)\,dx = \int \tan^{n-2}x\sec^2 x\,dx - \int\tan^{n-2}x\,dx$. Let $u = \tan x$ so that $du = \sec^2 x\,dx$. Then substituting in the first of these last two integrals yields $\int u^{n-2}\,du - \int\tan^{n-2}x\,dx = \frac{u^{n-1}}{n-1} - \int\tan^{n-2}x\,dx = \frac{\tan^{n-1}x}{n-1} - \int\tan^{n-2}x\,dx$.

Thus $\int_0^{\pi/4}\tan^3 x\,dx = \frac{\tan^2 x}{2}\Big|_0^{\pi/4} - \int_0^{\pi/4}\tan x\,dx = \frac{1}{2} + \ln|\cos x|\Big|_0^{\pi/4} = \frac{1}{2} - \frac{\ln 2}{2}$.

7.3.67 $\int\sin 3x\cos 7x\,dx = \frac{1}{2}\left(\int\sin(-4x)\,dx + \int\sin 10x\,dx\right) = \frac{1}{2}\left(\frac{\cos(-4x)}{4} - \frac{\cos 10x}{10}\right) + C = \frac{\cos 4x}{8} - \frac{\cos 10x}{20} + C$.

7.3.69 $\int\sin 3x\sin 2x\,dx = \frac{1}{2}\left(\int\cos x\,dx - \int\cos 5x\,dx\right) = \frac{\sin x}{2} - \frac{\sin 5x}{10} + C$.

7.3.71

a. $\int_0^{\pi}\sin mx\sin nx\,dx = \frac{1}{2}\left(\int_0^{\pi}\cos(m-n)x\,dx - \int_0^{\pi}\cos(m+n)x\,dx\right) = \frac{1}{2}\left(\frac{1}{m-n}\int_0^{(m-n)\pi}\cos u\,du - \frac{1}{m+n}\int_0^{(m+n)\pi}\cos v\,dv\right)$ where $u = (m-n)x$ and $v = (m+n)x$. But this yields $\frac{1}{2}\left(\frac{1}{m-n}\sin u\Big|_0^{(m-n)\pi} - \frac{1}{m+n}\sin v\Big|_0^{(m+n)\pi}\right) = \frac{1}{2}(0-0) = 0$.

b. $\int_0^\pi \cos mx \cos nx\,dx = \frac{1}{2}\left(\int_0^\pi \cos(m-n)x\,dx + \int_0^\pi \cos(m+n)x\,dx\right) = 0$ by the previous part of this problem,

c. $\int_0^\pi \sin mx \cos nx\,dx = \frac{1}{2}\left(\int_0^\pi \sin(m-n)x\,dx + \int_0^\pi \sin(m+n)x\,dx\right) =$
$\frac{1}{2}\left(\frac{1}{m-n}\int_0^{(m-n)\pi} \sin u\,du + \frac{1}{m+n}\int_0^{(m+n)\pi} \sin v\,dv\right)$ where $u=(m-n)x$ and $v=(m+n)x$. This quantity is equal to $\frac{-1}{2}\left(\frac{1}{m-n}\cos u\Big|_0^{(m-n)\pi} + \frac{1}{m+n}\cos v\Big|_0^{(m+n)\pi}\right) =$
$\frac{-1}{2}\left(\frac{1}{m-n}(\cos(m-n)\pi - 1) + \frac{1}{m+n}(\cos(m+n)\pi - 1)\right) =$
$\begin{cases} 0 & \text{if } m \text{ and } n \text{ are both even or both odd;} \\ \frac{1}{m-n} + \frac{1}{m+n} = \frac{2m}{m^2-n^2} & \text{otherwise.} \end{cases}$

7.3.73

a.

$$\int_0^\pi \sin^2 x\,dx = \frac{1}{2}\int_0^\pi (1 - \cos 2x)\,dx = \frac{1}{2}\left(x - \frac{\sin 2x}{2}\right)\Big|_0^\pi = \frac{\pi}{2}.$$

$$\int_0^\pi \sin^2 2x\,dx = \frac{1}{2}\int_0^\pi (1 - \cos 4x)\,dx = \frac{1}{2}\left(x - \frac{\sin 4x}{4}\right)\Big|_0^\pi = \frac{\pi}{2}.$$

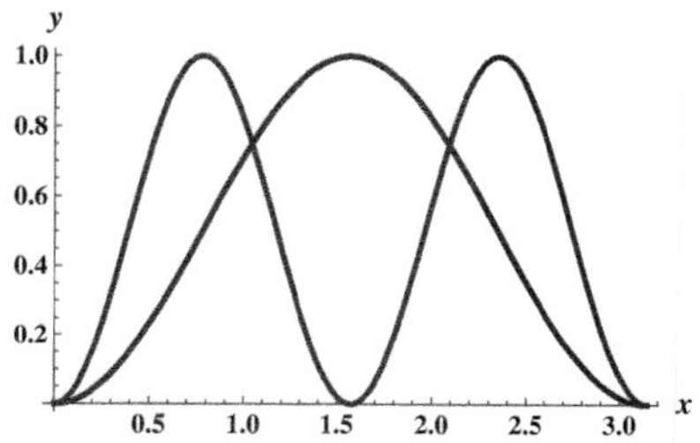

b.

$$\int_0^\pi \sin^2 3x\,dx = \frac{1}{2}\int_0^\pi (1 - \cos 6x)\,dx = \frac{1}{2}\left(x - \frac{\sin 6x}{6}\right)\Big|_0^\pi = \frac{\pi}{2}.$$

$$\int_0^\pi \sin^2 4x\,dx = \frac{1}{2}\int_0^\pi (1 - \cos 8x)\,dx = \frac{1}{2}\left(x - \frac{\sin 8x}{8}\right)\Big|_0^\pi = \frac{\pi}{2}.$$

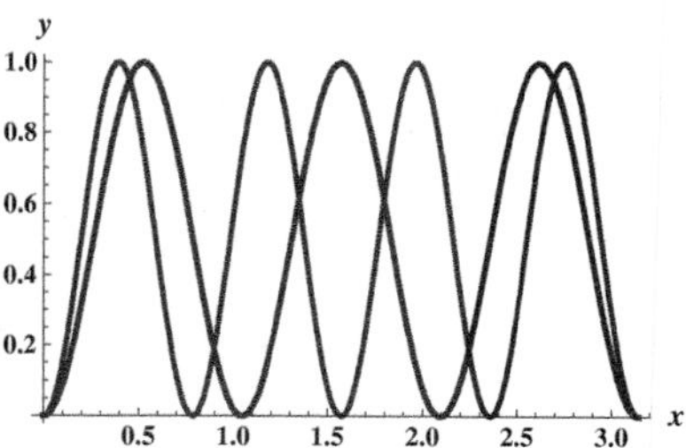

c. $\int_0^\pi \sin^2 nx\,dx = \frac{1}{2}\int_0^\pi (1 - \cos 2nx)\,dx = \frac{1}{2}\left(x - \frac{\sin 2nx}{2n}\right)\Big|_0^\pi = \frac{\pi}{2}.$

d. Yes. $\int_0^\pi \cos^2 nx\,dx = \frac{1}{2}\int_0^\pi (1 + \cos 2nx)\,dx = \frac{1}{2}\left(x + \frac{\sin 2nx}{2n}\right)\Big|_0^\pi = \frac{\pi}{2}.$

e. Claim: The corresponding integrals are all equal to $\frac{3\pi}{8}$. Proof:

$$\begin{aligned}\int_0^\pi \sin^4 nx\,dx &= \int_0^\pi \left(\frac{1-\cos 2nx}{2}\right)^2 dx \\ &= \int_0^\pi \frac{1 - 2\cos 2nx + \cos^2 2nx}{4}\,dx = \int_0^\pi \frac{1}{4}\,dx - \frac{1}{2}\int_0^\pi \cos 2nx\,dx + \frac{1}{4}\int_0^\pi \cos^2 2nx\,dx \\ &= \frac{\pi}{4} - \frac{1}{2}\left(\frac{\sin 2nx}{2n}\right)\Big|_0^\pi + \frac{1}{4}\cdot\frac{\pi}{2} = \frac{\pi}{4} - 0 + \frac{\pi}{8} = \frac{3\pi}{8}.\end{aligned}$$

f. The proof is by strong induction. The base step ($m = 1$) follows by part (a) of this problem. Now suppose the result holds for all positive integer values less than m. Now

$$\int_0^\pi \sin^{2m} x\,dx = -\frac{\sin^{2m-1} x \cos x}{2m}\Big|_0^\pi + \frac{2m-1}{2m}\int_0^\pi \sin^{2m-2} x\,dx$$
$$= \frac{2m-1}{2m}\int_0^\pi \sin^{2(m-1)} x\,dx$$
$$= \frac{2m-1}{2m}\cdot\pi\cdot\frac{1\cdot 3\cdot 5\cdots(2m-3)}{2\cdot 4\cdot 6\cdots 2(m-1)} = \pi\cdot\frac{1\cdot 3\cdot 5\cdots(2m-1)}{2\cdot 4\cdot 6\cdots 2m}.$$

Thus the result holds for all positive numbers m. Note the use of the reduction formula from problem number 64.

To see that the same result holds for $\int_0^\pi \cos^{2m} x\,dx$ first note that $\int_{\pi/2}^\pi \sin^{2m} x\,dx = -\int_{\pi/2}^0 \sin^{2m}(\pi - u)\,du = \int_0^{\pi/2} \sin^{2m} u\,du$ (using the substitution $x = \pi - u$.)

Thus, $\int_0^\pi \cos^{2m} x\,dx = -\int_{\pi/2}^{-\pi/2} \cos^{2m}(\pi/2 - u)\,du$. (Via the substitution $x = \pi/2 - u$.) This last integral can be written as $\int_{-\pi/2}^{\pi/2} \sin^{2m} u\,du = 2\int_0^{\pi/2} \sin^{2m} u\,du = \int_0^{\pi/2} \sin^{2m} u\,du + \int_{\pi/2}^{\pi} \sin^{2m} u\,du = \int_0^\pi \sin^{2m} x\,dx$.

7.4 Trigonometric Substitutions

7.4.1 This would suggest $x = 3\sec\theta$, because then $\sqrt{x^2-9} = 3\sqrt{\sec^2\theta - 1} = 3\sqrt{\tan^2\theta} = 3\tan\theta$, for $\theta \in [0, \pi/2)$.

7.4.3 This would suggest $x = 10\sin\theta$, because then $\sqrt{100 - x^2} = 10\sqrt{1-\sin^2\theta} = 10\sqrt{\cos^2\theta} = 10\cos\theta$, for $|\theta| \le \frac{\pi}{2}$.

7.4.5

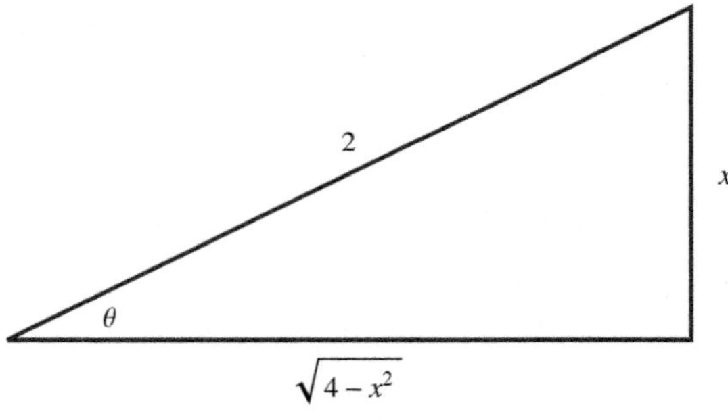

If $x = 2\sin\theta$ then $\frac{x^2}{4} = \sin^2\theta = \frac{1}{\csc^2\theta}$. Then $\cot^2\theta = \csc^2\theta - 1 = \frac{4}{x^2} - 1 = \frac{4-x^2}{x^2}$. So $\cot\theta = \frac{\sqrt{4-x^2}}{x}$ for $0 < |\theta| \le \frac{\pi}{2}$.

7.4.7 Let $x = 5\sin\theta$, so that $dx = 5\cos\theta\,d\theta$. Note that $\sqrt{25-x^2} = 5\cos\theta$. Then $\int_0^{5/2} \frac{1}{\sqrt{25-x^2}}\,dx = \int_0^{\pi/6} \frac{5\cos\theta}{5\cos\theta}\,d\theta = \frac{\pi}{6}$.

7.4.9 Let $x = 10\sin\theta$ so that $dx = 10\cos\theta\,d\theta$. Note that $\sqrt{100-x^2} = 10\cos\theta$. Then $\int_5^{10}\sqrt{100-x^2}\,dx = 100\int_{\pi/6}^{\pi/2}\cos^2\theta\,d\theta = 50\int_{\pi/6}^{\pi/2}(1+\cos 2\theta)\,d\theta = 50\left(\theta + \frac{\sin 2\theta}{2}\right)\Big|_{\pi/6}^{\pi/2} = 50\left(\frac{\pi}{2} + 0 - \left(\frac{\pi}{6} + \frac{\sqrt{3}}{4}\right)\right) = \frac{50\pi}{3} - \frac{25\sqrt{3}}{2}$.

7.4.11 Let $x = \sin\theta$ so that $dx = \cos\theta\,d\theta$. Note that $\sqrt{1-x^2} = \sqrt{1-\sin^2\theta} = \cos\theta$. Substituting gives $\int_0^{\pi/6}\sin^2\theta\,d\theta = \int_0^{\pi/6}\frac{1-\cos 2\theta}{2}\,d\theta = \frac{\theta}{2}\Big|_0^{\pi/6} - \frac{\sin 2\theta}{4}\Big|_0^{\pi/6} = \frac{\pi}{12} - \frac{\sqrt{3}}{8}$.

7.4.13 Let $x = 4\sin\theta$ so that $dx = 4\cos\theta\,d\theta$. Note that $\sqrt{16-x^2} = 4\cos\theta$. Thus, $\int\frac{1}{\sqrt{16-x^2}}\,dx = \int\frac{4\cos\theta}{4\cos\theta}\,d\theta = \theta + C = \sin^{-1}\left(\frac{x}{4}\right) + C$.

7.4.15 Let $x = 3\sin\theta$ so that $dx = 3\cos\theta\,d\theta$ and $\sqrt{9-x^2} = 3\cos\theta$. Then

$$\begin{aligned}\int\frac{\sqrt{9-x^2}}{x}\,dx &= \int\frac{3\cos\theta\cdot 3\cos\theta}{3\sin\theta}\,d\theta = 3\int\frac{1-\sin^2\theta}{\sin\theta}\,d\theta\\ &= 3\left(\int\csc\theta\,d\theta - \int\sin\theta\,d\theta\right)\,d\theta = 3\left(-\ln|\csc\theta+\cot\theta| + \cos\theta\right)\\ &= -3\ln\left|\frac{3}{x} + \frac{\sqrt{9-x^2}}{x}\right| + \sqrt{9-x^2} + C.\end{aligned}$$

7.4.17 Let $x = 8\sin\theta$ so that $dx = 8\cos\theta\,d\theta$ and $\sqrt{64-x^2} = 8\cos\theta$. Then,

$$\begin{aligned}\int\sqrt{64-x^2}\,dx &= \int 64\cos^2\theta\,d\theta = 32\int(1+\cos 2\theta)\,d\theta = 32\theta + 16\sin 2\theta + C\\ &= 32\theta + 32\sin\theta\cos\theta + C = 32\sin^{-1}\left(\frac{x}{8}\right) + \frac{x\sqrt{64-x^2}}{2} + C.\end{aligned}$$

7.4.19 Let $x = \sin\theta$ so that $dx = \cos\theta\,d\theta$. Note that $\sqrt{1-x^2} = \sqrt{1-\sin^2\theta} = \cos\theta$. Substituting gives $\int\sec^2\theta\,d\theta = \tan\theta + C = \tan(\sin^{-1}(x)) + C = \frac{x}{\sqrt{1-x^2}} + C$.

7.4.21 Let $x = 3\tan\theta$ so that $dx = 3\sec^2\theta\,d\theta$. Note that $\sqrt{x^2+9} = \sqrt{9(\tan^2\theta+1)} = 3\sec\theta$. Substituting gives $\int\frac{1}{9}\cot\theta\csc\theta\,d\theta = -\frac{1}{9}\csc\theta + C = -\frac{1}{9}\csc(\tan^{-1}(x/3)) + C = \frac{-\sqrt{x^2+9}}{9x} + C$.

7.4.23 Let $x = 6\sin\theta$ so that $dx = 6\cos\theta\,d\theta$ and $\sqrt{36-x^2} = 6\cos\theta$. Then $\int\frac{1}{\sqrt{36-x^2}}\,dx = \int\frac{6\cos\theta}{6\cos\theta}\,d\theta = \theta + C = \sin^{-1}\left(\frac{x}{6}\right) + C$.

7.4.25 Let $x = 9\sec\theta$ with $\theta \in (0,\pi/2)$. Then $dx = 9\sec\theta\tan\theta\,d\theta$ and $\sqrt{x^2-81} = 9\tan\theta$. Then $\int\frac{1}{\sqrt{x^2-81}}\,dx = \int\frac{9\sec\theta\tan\theta}{9\tan\theta}\,d\theta = \int\sec\theta\,d\theta = \ln|\sec\theta + \tan\theta| + C = \ln\left|\frac{x}{9} + \frac{\sqrt{x^2-81}}{9}\right| + C$. Note that because $x > 9$, the absolute value signs are unnecessary, and the final result can be written as $\ln(\sqrt{x^2-81} + x) + C$.

7.4.27 Let $x = \frac{\tan\theta}{2}$ so that $dx = \frac{\sec^2\theta}{2}\,d\theta$ and $\sqrt{1+4x^2} = \sec\theta$. Then $\int\frac{1}{(1+4x^2)^{3/2}}\,dx = \frac{1}{2}\int\frac{\sec^2\theta}{\sec^3\theta}\,d\theta = \frac{1}{2}\int\cos\theta\,d\theta = \frac{\sin\theta}{2} + C = \frac{x}{\sqrt{1+4x^2}} + C$.

7.4.29 Let $x = 4\sin\theta$ so that $dx = 4\cos\theta\,d\theta$. Note that $\sqrt{16-x^2} = 4\cos\theta$. Then $\int \frac{x^2}{\sqrt{16-x^2}}\,dx = \int \frac{16\sin^2\theta\cdot 4\cos\theta}{4\cos\theta}\,d\theta = 16\int \sin^2\theta\,d\theta = 8\int(1-\cos 2\theta)\,d\theta = 8\left(\theta - \frac{\sin 2\theta}{2}\right) + C = 8\theta - 8\sin\theta\cos\theta + C = 8\sin^{-1}\left(\frac{x}{4}\right) - \frac{x\sqrt{16-x^2}}{2} + C.$

7.4.31 Let $x = 3\sec\theta$ where $\theta \in (0, \pi/2)$. Then $dx = 3\sec\theta\tan\theta$ and $\sqrt{x^2-9} = 3\tan\theta$. Thus we have $\int \frac{\sqrt{x^2-9}}{x}\,dx = \int \frac{3\sec\theta\tan\theta\cdot 3\tan\theta}{3\sec\theta}\,d\theta = 3\int \tan^2\theta\,d\theta = 3\int \sec^2\theta - 1\,d\theta = 3(\tan\theta - \theta) + C = \sqrt{x^2-9} - 3\tan^{-1}\left(\frac{\sqrt{x^2-9}}{3}\right) + C = \sqrt{x^2-9} - 3\sec^{-1}(x/3) + C.$

7.4.33 Let $x = 2\tan\theta$ so that $dx = 2\sec^2\theta\,d\theta$. Note that $\sqrt{4+x^2} = 2\sec\theta$. Then $\int \frac{x^2}{\sqrt{4+x^2}}\,dx = \int \frac{4\tan^2\theta\cdot 2\sec^2\theta}{2\sec\theta}\,d\theta = 4\int \tan^2\theta\sec\theta\,d\theta = 4\int(\sec^2\theta - 1)\sec\theta\,d\theta = 4\left(\int \sec^3\theta\,d\theta - \int \sec\theta\,d\theta\right) = 4\left(\frac{1}{2}\left(\sec\theta\tan\theta + \int\sec\theta\,d\theta\right) - \int\sec\theta\,d\theta\right) = 2\sec\theta\tan\theta - 2\int\sec\theta\,d\theta = 2\sec\theta\tan\theta - 2\ln|\sec\theta + \tan\theta| + C = \frac{x\sqrt{4+x^2}}{2} - 2\ln\left|\frac{\sqrt{4+x^2}}{2} + \frac{x}{2}\right| + C$. This can be written as $\frac{x\sqrt{4+x^2}}{2} - 2\ln(x + \sqrt{4+x^2}) + C$.

7.4.35 $\int \frac{1}{\sqrt{3-2x-x^2}}\,dx = \int \frac{1}{\sqrt{4-(x+1)^2}}\,dx = \int \frac{1}{\sqrt{4-u^2}}\,du$ where $u = x+1$. Then let $u = 2\sin\theta$ so that $du = 2\cos\theta\,d\theta$. We have $\int \frac{2\cos\theta}{2\cos\theta}\,d\theta = \theta + C = \sin^{-1}\left(\frac{x+1}{2}\right) + C.$

7.4.37 Let $x = \frac{5}{3}\sec\theta$ where $\theta \in [0, \pi/2)$. Then $dx = \frac{5}{3}\sec\theta\tan\theta d\theta$ and $\sqrt{9x^2-25} = 5\tan\theta$. Thus, $\int \frac{\sqrt{9x^2-25}}{x^3}\,dx = \int \frac{5\tan\theta\cdot\frac{5}{3}\cdot\sec\theta\tan\theta}{\frac{125}{27}\sec^3\theta}\,d\theta = \frac{9}{5}\int \frac{\tan^2\theta}{\sec^2\theta}\,d\theta = \frac{9}{5}\int \frac{\sec^2\theta - 1}{\sec^2\theta}\,d\theta = \frac{9}{5}\int 1 - \cos^2\theta\,d\theta = \frac{9}{5}\int \sin^2\theta\,d\theta = \frac{9}{10}\int 1 - \cos 2\theta\,d\theta = \frac{9\theta}{10} - \frac{9\sin 2\theta}{20} + C = \frac{9\theta}{10} - \frac{9\sin\theta\cos\theta}{10} = \frac{9\cos^{-1}(5/3x)}{10} - \frac{\sqrt{9x^2-25}}{2x^2} + C.$

7.4.39 Let $x = 5\tan\theta$ so that $dx = 5\sec^2\theta\,d\theta$. Note that $25 + x^2 = 25\sec^2\theta$. Thus, $\int \frac{x^2}{(25+x^2)^2}\,dx = \int \frac{25\tan^2\theta\cdot 5\sec^2\theta}{25^2\sec^4\theta}\,d\theta = \frac{1}{5}\int \frac{\tan^2\theta}{\sec^2\theta}\,d\theta = \frac{1}{5}\int \frac{\sec^2\theta - 1}{\sec^2\theta}\,d\theta = \frac{1}{5}\int(1 - \cos^2\theta)\,d\theta = \frac{1}{5}\int \sin^2\theta\,d\theta = \frac{1}{10}\int 1 - \cos 2\theta\,d\theta = \frac{1}{10}\left(\theta - \frac{\sin 2\theta}{2}\right) + C = \frac{1}{10}(\theta - \sin\theta\cos\theta) + C = \frac{1}{10}\left(\tan^{-1}(x/5) - \frac{5x}{25+x^2}\right) + C.$

7.4.41 Let $x = 10\sin\theta$ so that $dx = 10\cos\theta\,d\theta$. Note that $\sqrt{100-x^2} = 10\cos\theta$. Thus,

$$\int \frac{x^2}{(100-x^2)^{3/2}}\,dx = \int \frac{100\sin^2\theta\cdot 10\cos\theta}{1000\cos^3\theta}\,d\theta = \int \tan^2\theta\,d\theta$$
$$= \int(\sec^2\theta - 1)\,d\theta = \tan\theta - \theta + C = \frac{x}{\sqrt{100-x^2}} - \sin^{-1}(x/10) + C.$$

7.4.43 Let $x = 9\sin\theta$ so that $dx = 9\cos\theta\,d\theta$. Note that $81 - x^2 = 81\cos^2\theta$. Thus,

$$\int \frac{x^3}{(81-x^2)^2}\,dx = \int \frac{9^3\sin^3\theta\cdot 9\cos\theta}{9^4\cos^4\theta}\,d\theta = \int \tan^3\theta\,d\theta$$
$$= \int(\tan\theta)(\sec^2\theta - 1)\,d\theta = \int \sec^2\theta\tan\theta\,d\theta - \int\tan\theta\,d\theta$$
$$= \frac{\sec^2\theta}{2} + \ln|\cos\theta| + C = \frac{81}{2(81-x^2)} + \ln\left|\frac{\sqrt{81-x^2}}{9}\right| + C.$$

This can be written as $\frac{81}{2(81-x^2)} + \ln\sqrt{81-x^2} + C$.

7.4.45 Let $x = \sec\theta$ where $\theta \in (0, \pi/2)$. Then $dx = \sec\theta\tan\theta\, d\theta$ and $\sqrt{x^2-1} = \tan\theta$. Then

$$\int \frac{1}{x(x^2-1)^{3/2}}\, dx = \int \frac{\sec\theta\tan\theta}{\sec\theta\tan^3\theta}\, d\theta = \int \cot^2\theta\, d\theta$$
$$= \int \csc^2\theta - 1\, d\theta = -\cot\theta - \theta + C = -\frac{1}{\sqrt{x^2-1}} - \sec^{-1}x + C.$$

7.4.47 Let $x = 4\tan\theta$ so that $dx = 4\sec^2\theta\, d\theta$. Note that $\sqrt{x^2+16} = 4\sec\theta$. Thus, $\int_0^1 \frac{1}{\sqrt{x^2+16}}\, dx =$ $\int_0^{\tan^{-1}(1/4)} \frac{4\sec^2\theta}{4\sec\theta}\, d\theta = \int_0^{\tan^{-1}(1/4)} \sec\theta\, d\theta = \ln|\sec\theta + \tan\theta|\Big|_0^{\tan^{-1}(1/4)} = \ln\left(\frac{\sqrt{17}+1}{4}\right)$.

7.4.49 Let $x = \tan\theta$ so that $dx = \sec^2\theta\, d\theta$ and $\sqrt{1+x^2} = \sec\theta$. Substituting gives $\int \pi/6^{\pi/4} \cot\theta\csc\theta\, d\theta =$ $(-\csc\theta)\Big|_{\pi/6}^{\pi/4} = -(\sqrt{2}-2) = 2-\sqrt{2}$.

7.4.51 Let $x = \tan\theta$ so that $dx = \sec^2\theta\, d\theta$. Note that $\sqrt{x^2+1} = \sqrt{\tan^2\theta+1} = \sqrt{\sec^2\theta} = \sec\theta$. Substituting gives $\int_0^{\pi/6} \sec^3\theta\, d\theta$. Recall from section 7.2 number 67 that $\int \sec^3\theta\, d\theta = \frac{1}{2}\sec\theta\tan\theta + \frac{1}{2}\ln|\sec\theta + \tan\theta|$. Thus the original integral is equal to $\left(\frac{1}{2}\sec\theta\tan\theta + \frac{1}{2}\ln|\sec\theta+\tan\theta|\right)\Big|_0^{\pi/6} = \frac{1\cdot 2\cdot 1}{2\cdot\sqrt{3}\cdot\sqrt{3}} + \frac{1}{2}\ln\left(\frac{2}{\sqrt{3}} + \frac{1}{\sqrt{3}}\right) =$ $\frac{1}{3} + \frac{\ln 3}{4}$.

7.4.53 Let $x = \frac{1}{3}\tan\theta$ so that $dx = \frac{1}{3}\sec^2\theta\, d\theta$. Note that $\sqrt{9x^2+1} = \sec\theta$. Thus $\int_0^{1/3} \frac{1}{(9x^2+1)^{3/2}}\, dx =$ $\int_0^{\pi/4} \frac{\frac{1}{3}\sec^2\theta}{\sec^3\theta}\, d\theta = \frac{1}{3}\int_0^{\pi/4} \cos\theta\, d\theta = \frac{1}{3}\sin\theta\Big|_0^{\pi/4} = \frac{\sqrt{2}}{6}$.

7.4.55 Let $x = 2\sec\theta$ so that $dx = 2\sec\theta\tan\theta\, d\theta$ and $x^2 - 4 = 4\tan^2\theta$. Thus, $\int_{4/\sqrt{3}}^4 \frac{1}{x^2(x^2-4)}\, dx =$ $\int_{\pi/6}^{\pi/3} \frac{2\sec\theta\tan\theta}{4\sec^2\theta\cdot 4\tan^2\theta}\, d\theta = \frac{1}{8}\int_{\pi/6}^{\pi/3} \frac{\cos^2\theta}{\sin\theta}\, d\theta = \frac{1}{8}\int_{\pi/6}^{\pi/3} \frac{1-\sin^2\theta}{\sin\theta}\, d\theta = \frac{1}{8}\int_{\pi/6}^{\pi/3} \csc\theta - \sin\theta\, d\theta =$ $\frac{1}{8}(-\ln|\csc\theta+\cot\theta| + \cos\theta)\Big|_{\pi/6}^{\pi/3} = \frac{1}{8}\left(-\ln(\sqrt{3}(2-\sqrt{3})) + \frac{1-\sqrt{3}}{2}\right) = \frac{1}{16}[1-\sqrt{3}-\ln(21-12\sqrt{3})]$.

7.4.57

a. False. In fact, we would have $\csc\theta = \frac{\sqrt{x^2+16}}{x}$.

b. True. Almost every number in the interval $[1,2]$ is not in the domain of $\sqrt{1-x^2}$, so this integral isn't defined.

c. False. It does represent a finite real number, because $\sqrt{x^2-1}$ is continuous on the interval $[1,2]$.

d. False. It can be so evaluated. The integral is equivalent to $\int \frac{1}{(x+2)^2+5}\, dx$, and this can be evaluated by the substitution $x+2 = \sqrt{5}\tan\theta$.

7.4.59 Note that the given integral can be written $\int \frac{1}{(x+3)^2+9}\, dx = \int \frac{1}{u^2+9}\, du$ where $u = x+3$. Now let $u = 3\tan\theta$ so that $du = 3\sec^2\theta\, d\theta$ and $u^2+9 = 9\sec^2\theta$. Thus we have

$$\int \frac{3\sec^2\theta}{9\sec^2\theta}\, d\theta = \frac{\theta}{3} + C = \frac{\tan^{-1}((x+3)/3)}{3} + C.$$

7.4.61 Note that the given integral can be written as $\int \frac{(x-1)^2}{\sqrt{(x-1)^2+9}}\,dx = \int \frac{u^2}{\sqrt{u^2+9}}\,du$ where $u = x-1$. Now let $u = 3\tan\theta$ so that $du = 3\sec^2\theta\,d\theta$ and $u^2+9 = 9\sec^2\theta$. Thus we have

$$\begin{aligned}\int \frac{9\tan^2\theta\cdot 3\sec^2\theta}{3\sec\theta}\,d\theta &= 9\int \tan^2\theta\sec\theta\,d\theta = 9\int(\sec^2\theta-1)(\sec\theta)\,d\theta\\ &= 9\int(\sec^3\theta-\sec\theta)\,d\theta = 9\left(\frac{1}{2}\sec\theta\tan\theta+\frac{1}{2}\int\sec\theta\,d\theta-\int\sec\theta\,d\theta\right)\\ &= \frac{9}{2}\left(\sec\theta\tan\theta-\int\sec\theta\,d\theta\right)\\ &= \frac{9}{2}\left(\sec\theta\tan\theta-\ln|\sec\theta+\tan\theta|\right)+C\\ &= \frac{9}{2}\left(\frac{(x-1)\sqrt{(x-1)^2+9}}{9}-\ln\left|\frac{\sqrt{(x-1)^2+9}}{3}+\frac{x-1}{3}\right|\right)+C.\end{aligned}$$

This can be written as $\frac{x-1}{2}\sqrt{x^2-2x+10}-\frac{9}{2}\ln(x-1+\sqrt{x^2-2x+10})+C$. Note that in the middle of this derivation we used the reduction formula for $\int \sec^3\theta\,d\theta$ given in problem 54 in the previous section.

7.4.63 Note that the given integral can be written as $\int \frac{(x-4)^2}{(25-(x-4)^2)^{3/2}}\,dx$. Let $u = x-4$, and note that we have $\int \frac{u^2}{(25-u^2)^{3/2}}\,du$. Now let $u = 5\sin\theta$ so that $du = 5\cos\theta\,d\theta$, and note that $\sqrt{25-u^2} = 5\cos\theta$. Thus we have $\int \frac{25\sin^2\theta\cdot 5\cos\theta}{5^3\cos^3\theta}\,d\theta = \int \tan^2\theta\,d\theta = \int \sec^2\theta - 1\,d\theta = \tan\theta-\theta+C = \frac{x-4}{\sqrt{25-(x-4)^2}} - \sin^{-1}\left(\frac{x-4}{5}\right)+C$.

7.4.65 $\int_{1/2}^{(\sqrt{2}+3)/2\sqrt{2}} \frac{1}{8x^2-8x+11}\,dx = \int_{1/2}^{(\sqrt{2}+3)/2\sqrt{2}} \frac{1}{8(x-1/2)^2+9}\,dx$. Let $u = x-1/2$, so that our integral becomes $\int_0^{3/2\sqrt{2}} \frac{1}{8u^2+9}\,du$. Now let $u = \frac{3}{\sqrt{8}}\tan\theta$ so that $du = \frac{3}{\sqrt{8}}\sec^2\theta\,d\theta$. Substituting gives $\int_0^{\pi/4} \frac{\frac{3}{\sqrt{8}}\sec^2\theta}{9\sec^2\theta}\,d\theta = \frac{1}{6\sqrt{2}}\int d\theta = \left.\frac{1}{6\sqrt{2}}\theta\right|_0^{\pi/4} = \frac{\pi\sqrt{2}}{48}$.

7.4.67

a. Recall that the area of a circular sector subtended by an angle θ is given by $\frac{\theta r^2}{2}$. So the area of the cap is this area minus the area of the isosceles triangle with two sides of length r and angle between them θ. So $A_{\text{cap}} = A_{\text{sector}} - A_{\text{triangle}} = \frac{\theta r^2}{2} - \frac{r^2\sin\theta}{2} = \frac{r^2}{2}(\theta-\sin\theta)$.

b. For a cap we have $0 \le \theta \le \pi$ so $0 \le \theta/2 \le \pi/2$. By symmetry, $\frac{A_{\text{cap}}}{2} = \int_{r\cos\theta/2}^{r} \sqrt{r^2-x^2}\,dx$. Let $x = r\cos\alpha/2$ so that $dx = -\frac{r}{2}\sin\alpha/2\,d\alpha$. Then we have $\frac{A_{\text{cap}}}{2} = \int_\theta^0 r\sin(\alpha/2)\cdot -\frac{r}{2}\sin(\alpha/2)\,d\alpha = \frac{r^2}{2}\int_0^\theta \sin^2(\alpha/2)\,d\alpha = \frac{r^2}{4}\int_0^\theta(1-\cos\alpha)\,d\alpha = \left.\frac{r^2}{4}(\alpha-\sin\alpha)\right|_0^\theta = \frac{r^2}{4}(\theta-\sin\theta)$.
Thus $A_{\text{cap}} = \frac{r^2}{2}(\theta-\sin\theta)$.

7.4.69

a. The area is given by $\int_0^4 \frac{1}{\sqrt{9+x^2}}\,dx$. Let $x = 3\tan\theta$, so that $dx = 3\sec^2\theta\,d\theta$. Substituting yields $\int_0^{\tan^{-1}(4/3)} \frac{3\sec^2\theta}{3\sec\theta}\,d\theta = \int_0^{\tan^{-1}(4/3)} \sec\theta\,d\theta = \ln|\sec\theta+\tan\theta|\Big|_0^{\tan^{-1}(4/3)} = \ln\left(\frac{5}{3}+\frac{4}{3}\right) = \ln 3.$

b. Using disks, we have $\frac{V}{\pi} = \int_0^4 \frac{1}{9+x^2}\,dx$. Let $x = 3\tan\theta$ so that $dx = 3\sec^2\theta\,d\theta$. Substituting yields $\int_0^{\tan^{-1}(4/3)} \frac{3\sec^2\theta}{9\sec^2\theta}\,d\theta = \frac{1}{3}\int_0^{\tan^{-1}(4/3)} 1\,d\theta = \frac{1}{3}\theta\Big|_0^{\tan^{-1}(4/3)} = \frac{1}{3}\tan^{-1}(4/3)$. Thus $V = \frac{\pi}{3}\tan^{-1}(4/3)$.

c. Using shells, we have $\frac{V}{2\pi} = \int_0^4 \frac{x}{(9+x^2)^{1/2}}\,dx$. Let $u = 9+x^2$, so that $du = 2x\,dx$. Then we have $\frac{1}{2}\int_9^{25} u^{-1/2}\,du = \sqrt{u}\Big|_9^{25} = 5-3 = 2$. So $V = 4\pi$.

7.4.71 Because $y = ax^2$, we have $1+\left(\frac{dy}{dx}\right)^2 = 1+4a^2x^2$, so the arc length is given by $\int_0^{10}\sqrt{1+4a^2x^2}\,dx$. Let $x = \frac{1}{2a}\tan\theta$ so that $dx = \frac{1}{2a}\sec^2\theta\,d\theta$. Then we have

$$\frac{1}{2a}\int_0^{\tan^{-1}(20a)} \sec^2\theta\sec\theta\,d\theta = \frac{1}{2a}\int_0^{\tan^{-1}(20a)} \sec^3\theta\,d\theta = \frac{1}{4a}\left(\sec\theta\tan\theta+\ln|\sec\theta+\tan\theta|\right)\Big|_0^{\tan^{-1}(20a)}$$
$$= \frac{1}{4a}\left(\sqrt{1+400a^2}(20a)+\ln(\sqrt{1+400a^2}+20a)\right).$$

7.4.73

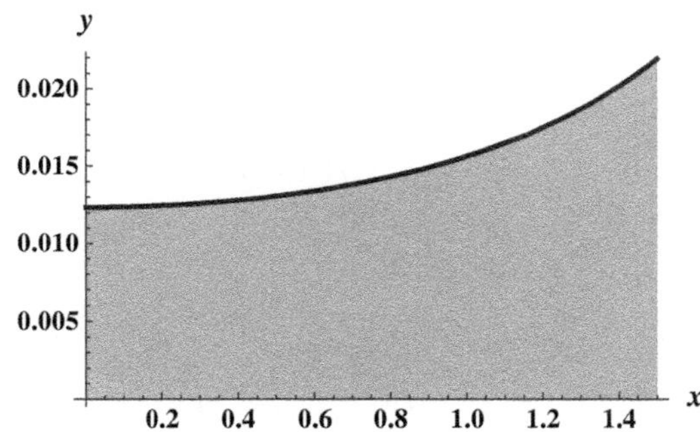

The area is given by $\int_0^{3/2} \frac{1}{(9-x^2)^2}\,dx$. Let $x = 3\sin\theta$ so that $dx = 3\cos\theta\,d\theta$. Then we have

$$\int_0^{\pi/6} \frac{3\cos\theta}{9^2\cos^4\theta}\,d\theta = \frac{1}{27}\int_0^{\pi/6} \sec^3\theta\,d\theta = \frac{1}{54}\left(\sec\theta\tan\theta+\ln|\sec\theta+\tan\theta|\right)\Big|_0^{\pi/6}$$
$$= \frac{1}{54}\left(\frac{2}{\sqrt{3}}\cdot\frac{1}{\sqrt{3}}+\ln\left(\frac{2}{\sqrt{3}}+\frac{1}{\sqrt{3}}\right)\right) = \frac{1}{81}+\frac{\ln(\sqrt{3})}{54}.$$

7.4.75

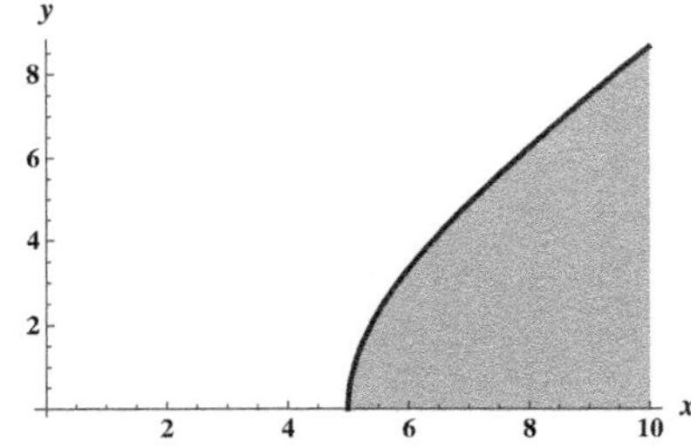

The area is given by $\int_5^{10} \sqrt{x^2-25}\,dx$. Let $x = 5\sec\theta$ so that $dx = 5\sec\theta\tan\theta\,d\theta$. Then we have

$$\begin{aligned}\int_0^{\pi/3} 5\sec\theta\tan\theta\cdot 5\tan\theta\,d\theta &= 25\int_0^{\pi/3}\sec\theta\tan^2\theta\,d\theta = 25\int_0^{\pi/3}\sec\theta(\sec^2\theta-1)\,d\theta\\ &= 25\int_0^{\pi/3}(\sec^3\theta-\sec\theta)\,d\theta = \frac{25}{2}\left(\sec\theta\tan\theta - \ln|\sec\theta+\tan\theta|\right)\Big|_0^{\pi/3}\\ &= \frac{25}{2}\left(2\sqrt{3}-\ln(2+\sqrt{3})\right) = 25\sqrt{3}-\frac{25}{2}\cdot\ln(2+\sqrt{3}).\end{aligned}$$

7.4.77 $\int_{2+\sqrt{2}}^4 \frac{1}{\sqrt{(x-1)(x-3)}}\,dx = \int_{2+\sqrt{2}}^4 \frac{1}{\sqrt{(x-2)^2-1}}\,dx = \int_{\sqrt{2}}^2 \frac{1}{\sqrt{u^2-1}}\,du$, where $u = x-2$. Now let $u = \sec\theta$, so that $du = \sec\theta\tan\theta\,d\theta$. Then $\int_{\pi/4}^{\pi/3}\frac{\sec\theta\tan\theta}{\tan\theta}\,d\theta = \int_{\pi/4}^{\pi/3}\sec\theta\,d\theta = \ln(\sec\theta+\tan\theta)\Big|_{\pi/4}^{\pi/3} = \ln(2+\sqrt{3})-\ln(\sqrt{2}+1) = \ln\left(\frac{2+\sqrt{3}}{\sqrt{2}+1}\right) = \ln((2+\sqrt{3})(\sqrt{2}-1))$.

7.4.79 Using washers, $V = \int_{-4}^4 A(x)\,dx$. Now $A(x) = \pi((f(x))^2-(g(x))^2) = \pi((6+\sqrt{16-x^2})^2 - (6-\sqrt{16-x^2})^2) = 24\pi\sqrt{16-x^2}$. Thus our integral is $\int_{-4}^4 24\pi\sqrt{16-x^2}\,dx = 48\pi\int_0^4\sqrt{16-x^2}\,dx = 48\pi\left(\frac{\pi\cdot 4^2}{4}\right) = 192\pi^2$.

7.4.81

a. $E_x(a) = \frac{kQa}{2L}\int_{-L}^L \frac{dy}{(a^2+y^2)^{3/2}}$. Let $y = a\tan\theta$ so that $dy = a\sec^2\theta\,d\theta$. Then note that

$$\begin{aligned}\int_{-L}^L \frac{dy}{(a^2+y^2)^{3/2}} &= 2\int_0^L\frac{dy}{(a^2+y^2)^{3/2}} = 2\int_0^{\tan^{-1}(L/a)}\frac{a\sec^2\theta}{a^3\sec^3\theta}\,d\theta = \frac{2}{a^2}\int_0^{\tan^{-1}(L/a)}\cos\theta\,d\theta\\ &= \frac{2}{a^2}\sin\theta\Big|_0^{\tan^{-1}(L/a)} = \frac{2}{a^2}\cdot\frac{L}{\sqrt{a^2+L^2}} = \frac{2L}{a^2\sqrt{a^2+L^2}}.\end{aligned}$$

Thus, $E_x(a) = \frac{kQ}{a\sqrt{a^2+L^2}}$.

b. Set $\rho = Q/(2L)$. Then because $\lim_{L\to\infty}\frac{2L}{a^2\sqrt{a^2+L^2}} = \frac{2}{a^2}$, we have

$$E_x(a,0) \approx \frac{kQa}{2L}\lim_{L\to\infty}\int_{-L}^L\frac{dy}{(a^2+y^2)^{3/2}} = \frac{kQa}{2L}\lim_{L\to\infty}\frac{2L}{a^2\sqrt{a^2+L^2}} = \frac{kQa}{2L}\left(\frac{2}{a^2}\right) = \frac{2kQ}{2aL} = \frac{2k\rho}{a}.$$

7.4.83

a. Because $t\in[0,\pi]$ so that $sint \ge 0$, we have

$$\int_a^b\sqrt{\frac{1-\cos t}{g(\cos a-\cos t)}}\,dt = \int_a^b\sqrt{\frac{(1-\cos t)(1+\cos t)}{g(1+\cos t)(\cos a-\cos t)}}\,dt = \int_a^b \sin t\sqrt{\frac{1}{g(1+\cos t)(\cos a-\cos t)}}\,dt.$$

Let $u = \cos t$ so that $du = -\sin t\,dt$. Then the given integral is equal to

$$-\frac{1}{\sqrt{g}}\int_{\cos a}^{\cos b}\sqrt{\frac{1}{(1+u)(\cos a-u)}}\,du.$$

Now we complete the square:

$$\begin{aligned}(1+u)(\cos a-u) &= \cos a+(\cos a-1)u-u^2\\ &= -\left(u^2-(\cos a-1)u+\left(\frac{\cos a-1}{2}\right)^2-\left(\frac{\cos a-1}{2}\right)^2\right)+\cos a\\ &= \cos a+\left(\frac{\cos a-1}{2}\right)^2-\left(u-\frac{\cos a-1}{2}\right)^2=\left(\frac{\cos a+1}{2}\right)^2-\left(u-\frac{\cos a-1}{2}\right)^2.\end{aligned}$$

Thus, setting $v=u-\frac{\cos a-1}{2}$ we have that the original integral is equal to

$-\frac{1}{\sqrt{g}}\int_{(\cos a+1)/2}^{\cos b-\frac{\cos a-1}{2}}\frac{1}{\sqrt{k^2-v^2}}\,dv$ where $k=\frac{(\cos a+1)}{2}$.

Now, $\displaystyle\int\frac{1}{\sqrt{k^2-v^2}}\,dv=\int\frac{k\cos\theta}{k\cos\theta}\,d\theta=\theta+C=\sin^{-1}(v/k)+C$ where $v=k\sin\theta$.

Therefore, the original integral is equal to

$$\begin{aligned}-\frac{1}{\sqrt{g}}\sin^{-1}\left(\frac{2v}{\cos a+1}\right)\Bigg|_{(\cos a+1)/2}^{\cos b-(\cos a-1)/2} &= \frac{1}{\sqrt{g}}\left(\sin^{-1}\left(\frac{\cos a+1}{\cos a+1}\right)-\sin^{-1}\left(\frac{2\cos b-\cos a+1}{\cos a+1}\right)\right)\\ &= \frac{1}{\sqrt{g}}\left(\frac{\pi}{2}-\sin^{-1}\left(\frac{2\cos b-\cos a+1}{\cos a+1}\right)\right).\end{aligned}$$

b. Letting $b=\pi$, we have that the integral is equal to

$$\begin{aligned}&\frac{1}{\sqrt{g}}\left(\frac{\pi}{2}-\sin^{-1}\left(\frac{-2-\cos a+1}{\cos a+1}\right)\right)\\ &=\frac{1}{\sqrt{g}}\left(\frac{\pi}{2}-\sin^{-1}(-1)\right)=\frac{1}{\sqrt{g}}\left(\frac{\pi}{2}-\left(-\frac{\pi}{2}\right)\right)=\frac{\pi}{\sqrt{g}}.\end{aligned}$$

7.4.85 If $1<x=\sec\theta$ then we need $\theta\in(0,\pi/2)$. Alternatively, if $-1>x=\sec\theta$, then we need $\theta\in(\pi/2,\pi)$. So, in the former, $\displaystyle\int\frac{1}{x\sqrt{x^2-1}}\,dx=\int\frac{\sec\theta\tan\theta}{\sec\theta\tan\theta}\,d\theta=\theta+C=\sec^{-1}x+C=\tan^{-1}\sqrt{x^2-1}+C$. In the latter case, $\displaystyle\int\frac{1}{x\sqrt{x^2-1}}\,dx=\int\frac{\sec\theta}{\sec\theta(-\tan\theta)}\,d\theta=-\theta+C=-\sec^{-1}x+C=-\tan^{-1}\sqrt{x^2-1}+C$.

7.4.87

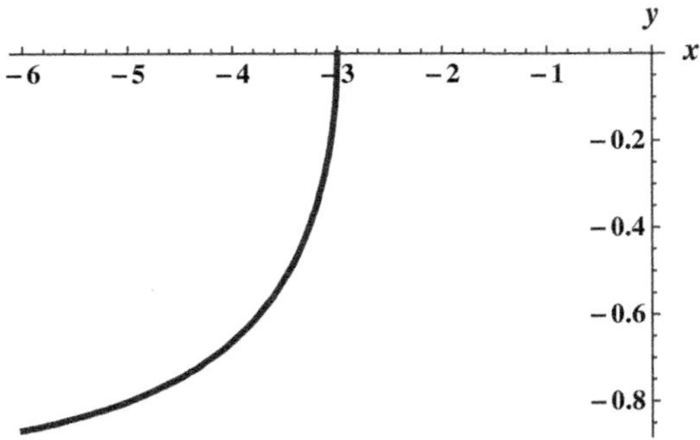

Let $x=3\sec\theta$ for $x\in(\pi/2,\pi)$. Then $dx=3\sec\theta\tan\theta\,d\theta$, and note that $|tan\theta|=-\tan\theta$. We have

$$\begin{aligned}\int_{-6}^{-3}\frac{\sqrt{x^2-9}}{x}\,dx &= \int_{2\pi/3}^{\pi}\frac{3\sec\theta\tan\theta(-3\tan\theta)}{3\sec\theta}\,d\theta=-3\int_{2\pi/3}^{\pi}\tan^2\theta\,d\theta\\ &= -3\left(\tan\theta-\theta\right)\Big|_{2\pi/3}^{\pi}=-3\left(-\pi-(-\sqrt{3}-2\pi/3)\right)=\pi-3\sqrt{3}.\end{aligned}$$

Note that this number is less than zero, as suggested by the graph.

7.4.89

a. The area of sector OAB is given by the formula $\frac{\theta}{2}a^2$ where $\sin\theta = x/a$. The area of triangle OBC is $\frac{x}{2}\sqrt{a^2-x^2}$. Thus,

$$F(x) = \frac{a^2\sin^{-1}(x/a)}{2} + \frac{x\sqrt{a^2-x^2}}{2}.$$

b. By the first fundamental theorem of calculus, $F(x)$ is an antiderivative of $\sqrt{a^2-x^2}$, because $F(x) = \int_0^x \sqrt{a^2-t^2}\,dt$. Thus, any other antiderivative differs from this by a constant, so

$$\int \sqrt{a^2-x^2}\,dx = \frac{a^2\sin^{-1}(x/a)}{2} + \frac{x\sqrt{a^2-x^2}}{2} + C.$$

7.5 Partial Fractions

7.5.1 Proper rational functions can be integrated using partial fraction decomposition.

7.5.3

a. $\dfrac{A}{x-3}$.

b. $\dfrac{A_1}{x-4}, \dfrac{A_2}{(x-4)^2}, \dfrac{A_3}{(x-4)^3}$.

c $\dfrac{Ax+B}{x^2+2x+6}$.

7.5.5 $\dfrac{2}{x^2-2x-8} = \dfrac{2}{(x-4)(x+2)} = \dfrac{A}{x-4} + \dfrac{B}{x+2}$. Thus, $2 = A(x+2) + B(x-4)$. Equating coefficients gives $A+B=0$ and $2A-4B=2$. Solving this system yields $A=1/3$ and $B=-1/3$. Thus,

$$\frac{2}{x^2-2x-8} = \frac{1/3}{x-4} - \frac{1/3}{x+2}.$$

7.5.7 $\dfrac{5x-7}{x^2-3x+2} = \dfrac{5x-7}{(x-1)(x-2)} = \dfrac{A}{x-1} + \dfrac{B}{x-2}$. Thus, $A(x-2) + B(x-1) = 5x-7$. Equating coefficients gives $A+B=5$ and $-2A-B=-7$. Solving this system yields $A=2$, $B=3$. Thus,

$$\frac{5x-7}{x^2-3x+2} = \frac{2}{x-1} + \frac{3}{x-2}.$$

7.5.9 $\dfrac{x^2}{x^3-16x} = \dfrac{x}{(x-4)(x+4)} = \dfrac{A}{x-4} + \dfrac{B}{x+4}$. Thus, $x = A(x+4) + B(x-4)$. Equating coefficients gives $A+B=1$, $4A-4B=0$. Solving this system yields $A=B=1/2$. Thus,

$$\frac{x^2}{x^3-16x} = \frac{1/2}{x-4} + \frac{1/2}{x+4}.$$

7.5.11 $\dfrac{x+2}{x^3-3x^2+2x} = \dfrac{x+2}{(x-1)\cdot x\cdot(x-2)} = \dfrac{A}{x-1} + \dfrac{B}{x} + \dfrac{C}{x-2}$. Thus $x+2 = Ax(x-2) + B(x-1)(x-2) + Cx(x-1)$. Letting $x=1$ gives $A=-3$, letting $x=0$ gives $B=1$, and letting $x=2$ gives $C=2$. Therefore,

$$\frac{x+2}{x^3-3x^2+2x} = \frac{-3}{x-1} + \frac{1}{x} + \frac{2}{x-2}.$$

7.5.13 If we write $\frac{3}{(x-1)(x+2)} = \frac{A}{x-1} + \frac{B}{x+2}$, we have $3 = A(x+2) + B(x-1)$. Letting $x = -2$ yields $B = -1$ and letting $x = 1$ yields $A = 1$. Thus, the original integral is equal to $\int \left(\frac{1}{x-1} - \frac{1}{x+2} \right) dx = \ln|x-1| - \ln|x+2| + C = \ln\left|\frac{x-1}{x+2}\right| + C.$

7.5.15 If we write $\frac{6}{x^2-1} = \frac{6}{(x-1)(x+1)} = \frac{A}{x-1} + \frac{B}{x+1}$, then we have $6 = A(x+1) + B(x-1)$. Letting $x = -1$ yields $B = -3$ and letting $x = 1$ yields $A = 3$. Thus, the original integral is equal to $\int \left(\frac{3}{x-1} - \frac{3}{x+1} \right) dx = 3\left(\ln|x-1| - \ln|x+1|\right) + C = 3\ln\left|\frac{x-1}{x+1}\right| + C.$

7.5.17 If we write $\frac{5x}{x^2-x-6} = \frac{A}{x-3} + \frac{B}{x+2}$, then we have $5x = A(x+2) + B(x-3)$. Letting $x = -2$ yields $B = 2$ and letting $x = 3$ yields $A = 3$. Thus the original integral is equal to $\int_{-1}^{2} \left(\frac{3}{x-3} + \frac{2}{x+2} \right) dx = \left(3\ln|x-3| + 2\ln|x+2|\right)\Big|_{-1}^{2} = \ln(16) - \ln(64) = -\ln 4.$

7.5.19 If we write $\frac{10x}{x^2-2x-24} = \frac{10x}{(x-6)(x+4)} = \frac{A}{x-6} + \frac{B}{x+4}$, then we have $10x = A(x+4) + B(x-6)$. Letting $x = -4$ yields $B = 4$ and letting $x = 6$ yields $A = 6$. Thus the original integral is equal to $\int \left(\frac{6}{x-6} + \frac{4}{x+4} \right) dx = \ln|(x-6)^6(x+4)^4| + C.$

7.5.21 Let $\frac{6x^2}{x^4-5x^2+4} = \frac{6x^2}{(x-2)(x+2)(x-1)(x+1)} = \frac{A}{x-2} + \frac{B}{x+2} + \frac{C}{x-1} + \frac{D}{x+1}$. Then $6x^2 = A(x+2)(x-1)(x+1) + B(x-2)(x-1)(x+1) + C(x-2)(x+2)(x+1) + D(x-2)(x+2)(x-1)$. Letting $x = 2$ gives $A = 2$, letting $x = -2$ gives $B = -2$, letting $x = 1$ gives $C = -1$, and letting $x = -1$ gives $D = 1$. Thus, the original integral is equal to $\int \left(\frac{2}{x-2} - \frac{2}{x+2} - \frac{1}{x-1} + \frac{1}{x+1} \right) dx = \ln\left|\frac{(x-2)^2(x+1)}{(x+2)^2(x-1)}\right| + C$

7.5.23 Let $\frac{x^2+12x-4}{x(x-2)(x+2)} = \frac{A}{x} + \frac{B}{x-2} + \frac{C}{x+2}$. Then $x^2+12x-4 = A(x-2)(x+2) + Bx(x+2) + Cx(x-2)$. Letting $x = 0$ gives $A = 1$, letting $x = 2$ gives $B = 3$, and letting $x = -2$ gives $C = -3$. Thus, the original integral is equal to $\int \left(\frac{1}{x} + \frac{3}{x-2} - \frac{3}{x+2} \right) dx = \ln\left|\frac{x(x-2)^3}{(x+2)^3}\right| + C.$

7.5.25 If we write $\frac{1}{x^4-10x^2+9} = \frac{1}{(x-1)(x+1)(x-3)(x+3)} = \frac{A}{x-1} + \frac{B}{x+1} + \frac{C}{x-3} + \frac{D}{x+3}$ then $1 = A(x+1)(x-3)(x+3) + B(x-1)(x-3)(x+3) + C(x-1)(x+1)(x+3) + D(x-1)(x+1)(x-3)$. Letting $x = -1$ yields $B = 1/16$. Letting $x = 3$ yields $C = 1/48$. Letting $x = -3$ yields $D = -1/48$, and letting $x = 1$ yields $A = -1/16$. Thus the original integral is equal to

$$\begin{aligned}
&\int \left(-\frac{1/16}{x-1} + \frac{1/16}{x+1} + \frac{1/48}{x-3} - \frac{1/48}{x+3} \right) dx \\
&= -\frac{1}{16}\ln|x-1| + \frac{1}{16}\ln|x+1| + \frac{1}{48}\ln|x-3| - \frac{1}{48}\ln|x+3| + C \\
&= \ln\left|\frac{(x+1)^3(x-3)}{(x-1)^3(x+3)}\right|^{1/48} + C.
\end{aligned}$$

7.5.27 If we write $\frac{81}{x^3-9x^2} = \frac{A}{x} + \frac{B}{x^2} + \frac{C}{x-9}$, then $81 = Ax(x-9) + B(x-9) + C(x^2)$. Letting $x = 0$ yields $B = -9$. Letting $x = 9$ yields $C = 1$. If we let $x = 10$, then we have $81 = 10A + B + 100C = 10A - 9 + 100$, so $A = -1$. Thus, the original integral is equal to $\int \left(-\frac{1}{x} - \frac{9}{x^2} + \frac{1}{x-9} \right) dx = \ln\left|\frac{(x-9)}{x}\right| + \frac{9}{x} + C.$

7.5.29 If we write $\frac{x}{(x+3)^2} = \frac{A}{x+3} + \frac{B}{(x+3)^2}$, then we have $x = A(x+3) + B$. Letting $x = -3$ yields $B = -3$, and then letting $x = -2$ yields $A = 1$. Thus the original integral is equal to

$$\int_{-1}^{1} \left(\frac{1}{x+3} - \frac{3}{(x+3)^2} \right) dx = \left(\ln|x+3| + \frac{3}{x+3} \right) \Big|_{-1}^{1} = \ln 4 + \frac{3}{4} - \left(\ln 2 + \frac{3}{2} \right) = \ln 2 - \frac{3}{4}.$$

7.5.31 If we write $\frac{2}{x^3+x^2} = \frac{A}{x} + \frac{B}{x^2} + \frac{C}{x+1}$, then $2 = Ax(x+1) + B(x+1) + Cx^2$. Letting $x = 0$ yields $B = 2$, and letting $x = -1$ yields $C = 2$. Then letting $x = 1$ yields $A = -2$. So the original integral is equal to

$$\int \left(-\frac{2}{x} + \frac{2}{x^2} + \frac{2}{x+1} \right) dx = 2\left(\ln|x+1| - \ln|x|\right) - \frac{2}{x} + C.$$

7.5.33 If we write $\frac{x-5}{x^2(x+1)} = \frac{A}{x} + \frac{B}{x^2} + \frac{C}{x+1}$, then we have $x - 5 = Ax(x+1) + B(x+1) + Cx^2$. Letting $x = 0$ yields $B = -5$, and letting $x = -1$ yields $C = -6$. Then letting $x = 1$ yields $-4 = 2A - 10 - 6$, so $A = 6$. The original integral is thus equal to

$$\int \left(\frac{6}{x} - \frac{5}{x^2} - \frac{6}{x+1} \right) dx = 6\left(\ln|x| - \ln|x+1|\right) + \frac{5}{x} + C.$$

7.5.35 Let $\frac{x^2-x}{(x-2)(x-3)^2} = \frac{A}{x-2} - \frac{B}{x-3} + \frac{C}{(x-3)^2}$. Then $x^2 - x = A(x-3)^2 + B(x-2)(x-3) + C(x-2)$. Letting $x = 2$ gives $A = 2$. Letting $x = 3$ gives $C = 6$. Letting $x = 0$ gives $0 = 18 + 6B - 12$, so $B = -1$. The original integral is thus

$$\int \left(\frac{2}{x-2} - \frac{1}{x-3} + \frac{6}{(x-3)^2} \right) dx = \ln\left| \frac{(x-2)^2}{x-3} \right| + \frac{-6}{x-3} + C.$$

7.5.37 Let $\frac{x^2-4}{x^3-2x^2+x} = \frac{A}{x} + \frac{B}{x-1} + \frac{C}{(x-1)^2}$. Then $x^2 - 4 = A(x-1)^2 + Bx(x-1) + Cx$. Letting $x = 0$ gives $A = -4$. Letting $x = 1$ gives $C = -3$. Letting $x = 2$ gives $0 = -4 + 2B - 6$, so $B = 5$. The given integral is thus equal to

$$\int \left(-\frac{4}{x} + \frac{5}{x-1} - \frac{3}{(x-1)^2} \right) dx = \ln\left| \frac{(x-1)^5}{x^4} \right| + \frac{3}{x-1} + C.$$

7.5.39 $\frac{20x}{(x-1)^2(x^2+1)} = \frac{A}{x-1} + \frac{B}{(x-1)^2} + \frac{Cx+D}{x^2+1}$.

7.5.41 $\frac{2x^2+3}{(x^2-8x+16)(x^2+3x+4)} = \frac{2x^2+3}{(x-4)^2(x^2+3x+4)} = \frac{A}{x-4} + \frac{B}{(x-4)^2} + \frac{Cx+D}{x^2+3x+4}$.

7.5.43 Let $\frac{x^2+x+2}{(x+1)(x^2+1)} = \frac{Ax+B}{x^2+1} + \frac{C}{x+1}$. Then $x^2 + x + 2 = (Ax+B)(x+1) + C(x^2+1)$. Letting $x = -1$ gives $C = 1$. Letting $x = 0$ gives $2 = B + 1$, so $B = 1$. Letting $x = 1$ gives $4 = 2A + 2 + 2$, so $A = 0$. The original integral is therefore equal to

$$\int \left(\frac{1}{x^2+1} + \frac{1}{x+1} \right) dx = \tan^{-1}(x) + \ln|x+1| + C.$$

7.5.45 Let $\frac{2x^2+5x+5}{(x+1)(x^2+2x+2)} = \frac{Ax+B}{x^2+2x+2} + \frac{C}{x+1}$. Then $2x^2 + 5x + 5 = (Ax+B)(x+1) + C(x^2+2x+2)$. Letting $x = -1$ gives $C = 2$. Letting $x = 0$ gives $5 = B + 4$, so $B = 1$. Letting $x = 1$ gives $12 = 2A + 2 + 2(5)$, so $A = 0$. The original integral is therefore equal to

$$\int \left(\frac{1}{x^2+2x+2} + \frac{2}{x+1} \right) dx = \int \left(\frac{1}{(x+1)^2+1} + \frac{2}{x+1} \right) dx = \tan^{-1}(x+1) + \ln((x+1)^2) + C.$$

7.5.47 If we write $\dfrac{20x}{(x-1)(x^2+4x+5)} = \dfrac{A}{x-1} + \dfrac{Bx+C}{x^2+4x+5}$, then $20x = A(x^2+4x+5)+(Bx+C)(x-1)$. Letting $x=1$ yields $A=2$. Letting $x=0$ yields $0 = 10-C$, so $C=10$. Letting $x=2$ yields $40 = 34+2B+10$, so $B=-2$. The original integral is thus $\displaystyle\int\left(\frac{2}{x-1} - \frac{2x-10}{x^2+4x+5}\right)dx = \int\left(\frac{2}{x-1} - \frac{(2x+4)-14}{x^2+4x+5}\right)dx =$ $\displaystyle\int\left(\frac{2}{x-1} - \frac{(2x+4)}{x^2+4x+5} + \frac{14}{(x+2)^2+1}\right)dx = \ln\left|\frac{(x-1)^2}{x^2+4x+5}\right| + 14\tan^{-1}(x+2)+C$

7.5.49 If we write $\dfrac{x^2}{x^3-x^2+4x-4} = \dfrac{x^2}{(x-1)(x^2+4)} = \dfrac{A}{x-1} + \dfrac{Bx+C}{x^2+4}$, then $x^2 = A(x^2+4)+(Bx+C)(x-1)$. Letting $x=1$ yields $A=1/5$. Letting $x=0$ yields $C=4/5$, and then letting $x=2$ and solving for B yields $B=4/5$. Thus the original integral is equal to $\displaystyle\int\frac{1/5}{x-1}\,dx + \frac{4}{5}\int\frac{x}{x^2+4}\,dx + \frac{4}{5}\int\frac{1}{x^2+4}\,dx$. Thus, the original integral is equal to $\frac{1}{5}\ln|x-1| + \frac{2}{5}\ln(x^2+4) + \frac{2}{5}\tan^{-1}(x/2)+C$.

7.5.51

a. False. Because the given integrand is improper, the first step would be to use long division to write the integrand as the sum of a polynomial and a proper rational function.

b. False. This is easy to evaluate via the substitution $u = 3x^2+x$.

c. False. The discriminant of the denominator is $b^2-4ac = 169-168 = 1 > 0$, so the denominator factors into linear factors of the real numbers.

d. True. The discriminant of the denominator is $b^2-4ac = 169-172 = -3 < 0$, so the given quadratic expression is irreducible.

7.5.53

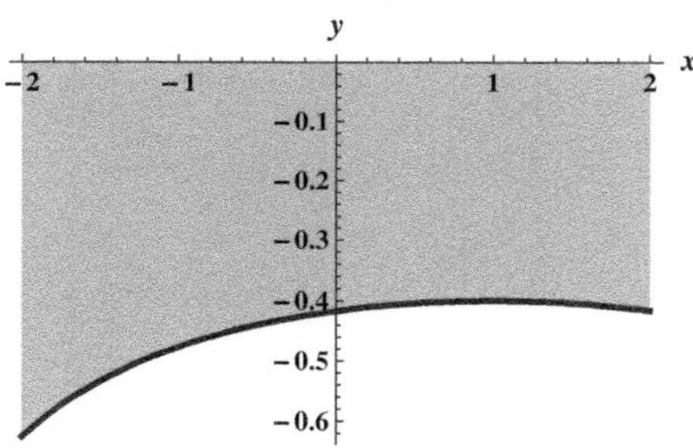

If we write $\dfrac{10}{x^2-2x-24} = \dfrac{10}{(x-6)(x+4)} = \dfrac{A}{x-6} + \dfrac{B}{x+4}$, then $10 = A(x+4)+B(x-6)$. Letting $x=-4$ gives $B=-1$ and letting $x=6$ gives $A=1$. Thus the area in question is given by

$$-\int_{-2}^{2}\left(-\frac{1}{x+4}+\frac{1}{x-6}\right)dx = (\ln(x+4) - \ln|x-6|)\Big|_{-2}^{2} = \ln 6 - \ln 4 - (\ln 2 - \ln 8) = \ln 6.$$

7.5.55

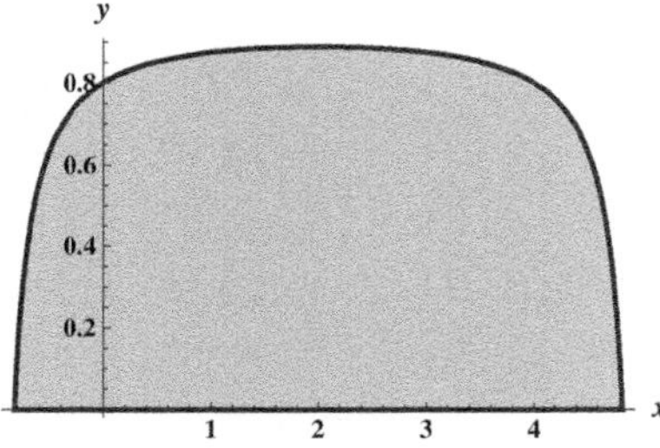

The curve intersects the x-axis at $x = 2 \pm 2\sqrt{2}$. We can write the integrand as $1 + \frac{1}{x^2-4x-5} = 1 + \frac{1}{(x-5)(x+1)}$. If we write this second term in the form $\frac{A}{x-5} + \frac{B}{x+1}$, then $1 = A(x+1) + B(x-5)$. Letting $x = -1$ yields $B = -1/6$ and letting $x = 5$ yields $A = 1/6$. Thus the area in question is given by

$$\int_{2-2\sqrt{2}}^{2+2\sqrt{2}} \left(1 + \frac{1/6}{x-5} - \frac{1/6}{x+1}\right) dx = x + \frac{1}{6}\ln|x-5| - \frac{1}{6}\ln|x+1| \Big|_{2-2\sqrt{2}}^{2+2\sqrt{2}} = 4\sqrt{2} + \frac{1}{6}\ln\left(\frac{3-2\sqrt{2}}{3+2\sqrt{2}}\right)^2.$$

7.5.57 Using disks, we have $\frac{V}{\pi} = \int_0^4 \frac{x^2}{(x+1)^2}\,dx$. Now we can perform long division to rewrite this integral as $\int_0^4 \left(1 - \frac{2x+2}{x^2+2x+1} + \frac{1}{(x+1)^2}\right) dx$. Thus we have $V = \pi\left(x - \ln|x^2+2x+1| - \frac{1}{x+1}\Big|_0^4\right) = \pi\left(4 - \ln(25) - \frac{1}{5} - (-1)\right) = \pi\left(\frac{24}{5} - \ln(25)\right)$.

7.5.59 Using disks, we have $\frac{V}{\pi} = \int_1^2 \frac{1}{x(3-x)}\,,dx$. Now if we write $\frac{1}{x(3-x)} = \frac{A}{x} + \frac{B}{3-x}$, then we have $1 = A(3-x) + Bx$. Letting $x = 0$ yields $A = 1/3$ and letting $x = 3$ yields $B = 1/3$. Thus we have $V = \frac{\pi}{3}\int_1^2 \left(\frac{1}{x} - \frac{1}{x-3}\right) dx = \frac{\pi}{3}\left(\ln x - \ln|x-3|\Big|_1^2\right) = \frac{\pi}{3}\cdot 2\ln 2$.

7.5.61 Using shells, we have $\frac{V}{2\pi} = \int_0^3 \frac{x+1}{x+2}\,dx = \int_0^3 \left(1 - \frac{1}{x+2}\right) dx = x - \ln|x+2|\Big|_0^3 = 3 + \ln(2/5)$. Thus, $V = 2\pi(3 + \ln(2/5))$.

7.5.63 Let $u = e^x$, so that $du = e^x\,dx$. Then $\int \frac{1}{1+e^x}\cdot\frac{e^x}{e^x}\,dx = \int \frac{1}{u(1+u)}\,du$. If we write $\frac{1}{u(1+u)} = \frac{A}{u} + \frac{B}{1+u}$, then $1 = A(1+u) + Bu$. Letting $u = 0$ yields $A = 1$ and letting $u = -1$ yields $B = -1$, so the original integral is equal to $\int \left(\frac{1}{u} - \frac{1}{1+u}\right) du = \ln|u| - \ln|1+u| + C = x - \ln(1+e^x) + C$.

7.5.65 After performing long division, we have that the original integrand is equal to $3 + \frac{13x-12}{(x-1)(x-2)}$, and if we write $\frac{13x-12}{(x-1)(x-2)} = \frac{A}{x-1} + \frac{B}{x-2}$, then $13x - 12 = A(x-2) + B(x-1)$. Letting $x = 1$ yields $A = -1$ and letting $x = 2$ yields $B = 14$. Thus the original integral is equal to $3x - \int \frac{1}{x-1}\,dx + 14\int \frac{1}{x-2}\,dx = 3x - \ln|x-1| + 14\ln|x-2| + C$.

7.5.67 $\int \frac{1}{2+e^t}\,dt = \int \frac{e^t}{(e^t+2)e^t}\,dt$. Let $u = e^t$, so that $du = e^t\,dt$. Then we have $\int \frac{1}{(u+2)u}\,du$. If we write $\frac{1}{(u+2)u} = \frac{A}{u} + \frac{B}{u+2}$, then $A(u+2) + Bu = 1$, and we find that $A = 1/2$ and $B = -1/2$. Then we integrate $\int \left(\frac{1/2}{u} - \frac{1/2}{u+2}\right) du = \frac{1}{2}(\ln|u| - \ln|u+2|) + C = \frac{1}{2}(t - \ln(2+e^t)) + C$.

7.5.69 This can be written as

$$\int \frac{dt}{\cos t(1+\sin t)} = \int \frac{\cos t}{\cos^2 t(1+\sin t)}\,dt = \int \frac{\cos t}{(1-\sin^2 t)(1+\sin t)}\,dt.$$

Now let $u = \sin t$ so that $du = \cos t\,dt$. Substituting gives $\int \frac{du}{(1-u^2)(1+u)} = \int \frac{du}{(1+u)^2(1-u)}$. If we write $\frac{1}{(1+u)^2(1-u)} = \frac{A}{1+u} + \frac{B}{(1+u)^2} + \frac{C}{1-u}$ then $1 = A(1+u)(1-u) + B(1-u) + C(1+u)^2$. Letting

$u = -1$ yields $B = 1/2$. Letting $u = 1$ yields $C = 1/4$. Letting $u = 0$ then yields $A = 1/4$. Then our integral is equal to

$$\int \left(\frac{1/4}{1+u} + \frac{1/2}{(1+u)^2} + \frac{1/4}{1-u} \right) du = \frac{1}{4}\left(\frac{-2}{1+u} + \ln\left|\frac{1+u}{1-u}\right| \right) + C = \frac{1}{4}\left(\frac{-2}{1+\sin t} + \ln\left(\frac{1+\sin t}{1-\sin t}\right)\right) + C.$$

7.5.71 Let $u = e^x$ so that $du = e^x\,dx$. Then the original integral is equal to $\int \frac{1}{(u-1)(u+2)}\,du$. If we write $\frac{1}{(u-1)(u+2)} = \frac{A}{u-1} + \frac{B}{u+2}$, then $1 = A(u+2) + B(u-1)$. Letting $u = -2$ yields $B = -1/3$ and letting $u = 1$ yields $A = 1/3$. Thus we have $\int \left(\frac{1/3}{u-1} - \frac{1/3}{u+2} \right) du = \frac{1}{3}\left(\ln|u-1| - \ln|u+2|\right) + C = \frac{1}{3}\ln\left|\frac{e^x-1}{e^x+2}\right| + C.$

7.5.73 $\int \frac{1}{(e^x+e^{-x})^2} \cdot \frac{(e^x)^2}{(e^x)^2}\,dx = \int \frac{e^{2x}}{(e^{2x}+1)^2}\,dx.$ Let $u = e^x$ so that $du = e^x\,dx$. Then we have $\int \frac{u}{(u^2+1)^2}\,du$. If we let $w = u^2+1$, then $dw = 2u\,du$, so we have $\frac{1}{2}\int w^{-2}\,dw = -\frac{1}{2w} + C = -\frac{1}{2u^2+2} + C = -\frac{1}{2e^{2x}+2} + C.$

7.5.75

a. $\sec x = \frac{1}{\cos x} \cdot \frac{\cos x}{\cos x} = \frac{\cos x}{\cos^2 x} = \frac{\cos x}{1-\sin^2 x}.$

b. $\int \sec x\,dx = \int \frac{\cos x}{1-\sin^2 x}\,dx.$ Let $u = \sin x$ so that $du = \cos x\,dx$. Then our integral becomes $\int \frac{du}{1-u^2}$. If we write $\frac{1}{1-u^2} = \frac{1}{(1-u)(1+u)} = \frac{A}{1-u} + \frac{B}{1+u}$, we have $1 = A(1+u) + B(1-u)$, so $A = \frac{1}{2}$ and $B = \frac{1}{2}$. We have

$$\int \frac{du}{1-u^2} = \frac{1}{2}\int \left(\frac{1}{1-u} + \frac{1}{1+u} \right) du = \frac{1}{2}(\ln|1+u| - \ln|1-u|) + C = \frac{1}{2}\ln\left|\frac{1+\sin x}{1-\sin x}\right| + C.$$

7.5.77 If we let $u^4 = x+2$, then $4u^3\,du = dx$. Substituting yields

$$\int \frac{4u^3}{u+1}\,du = \int \left(4u^2 - 4u + 4 - \frac{4}{u+1} \right) du = \frac{4}{3}u^3 - 2u^2 + 4u - 4\ln|u+1| + C$$
$$= \frac{4}{3}(x+2)^{3/4} - 2(x+2)^{1/2} + 4(x+2)^{1/4} - 4\ln((x+2)^{1/4}+1) + C.$$

7.5.79 If we let $u^6 = x$, then $6u^5\,du = dx$. Substituting yields

$$\int \frac{6u^5}{u^3+u^2}\,du = 6\int \frac{u^3}{u+1}\,du = 6\int \left(u^2 - u + 1 - \frac{1}{u+1} \right) du$$
$$= 2u^3 - 3u^2 + 6u - 6\ln|u+1| + C = 2\sqrt{x} - 3\sqrt[3]{x} + 6\sqrt[6]{x} - 6\ln(\sqrt[6]{x}+1) + C.$$

7.5.81 If we let $(u^2-1)^2 = x$, then $2(u^2-1)\cdot 2u\,du = dx$. Substituting yields $\int \frac{4u(u^2-1)}{u}\,du = 4\int (u^2-1)\,du = \frac{4u^3}{3} - 4u + C = \frac{4}{3}u(u^2-3) + C = \frac{4}{3}\sqrt{1+\sqrt{x}}(\sqrt{x}-2) + C.$

7.5.83 If we write $\frac{2}{x(x^2+1)^2} = \frac{A}{x} + \frac{Bx+C}{x^2+1} + \frac{Dx+E}{(x^2+1)^2}$, then $2 = A(x^2+1)^2 + (Bx+C)x(x^2+1) + (Dx+E)x$. Letting $x = 0$ yields $A = 2$. Expanding the right-hand side yields $2 = (2+B)x^4 + Cx^3 + (4+B+D)x^2 +$

$(C+E)x+2$. Equating coefficients gives us the equations $2+B=0$, $C=0$, $4+B+D=0$, and $C+E=0$, from which we can deduce that $B=-2$, $C=0$, $D=-2$ and $E=0$. The original integral is thus equal to $\int\left(\frac{2}{x}-\frac{2x}{x^2+1}-\frac{2x}{(x^2+1)^2}\right)dx = 2\ln|x|-\ln|x^2+1|+\frac{1}{x^2+1}+C.$

7.5.85 If we write $\frac{x}{(x-1)(x^2+2x+2)^2}=\frac{A}{x-1}+\frac{Bx+C}{x^2+2x+2}+\frac{Dx+E}{(x^2+2x+2)^2}$, then $x=A(x^2+2x+2)^2+(Bx+C)(x-1)(x^2+2x+2)+(Dx+E)(x-1)$. Letting $x=1$ yields $A=1/25$. Then expanding the polynomial on the right-hand side gives $25x=(1+25B)x^4+(4+25(B+C))x^3+(8+25D+25C)x^2+(8+25E-25D-50B)x+(4-25E-50C)$. Equating coefficients and then solving for the unknowns yields $B=-1/25$, $C=-3/25$, $D=-5/25$, and $E=10/25$. The original integral is thus equal to

$$\begin{aligned}
&\frac{1}{25}\int\left(\frac{1}{x-1}-\frac{x+3}{x^2+2x+2}-\frac{5x-10}{(x^2+2x+2)^2}\right)dx\\
&=\frac{1}{25}\int\left(\frac{1}{x-1}-\frac{x+1}{x^2+2x+2}-5\frac{x+1}{(x^2+2x+2)^2}-2\frac{1}{(x+1)^2+1}+15\frac{1}{((x+1)^2+1)^2}\right)dx\\
&=\frac{1}{25}\left(\ln|x-1|-\frac{1}{2}\ln|x^2+2x+2|+\frac{5}{2}\cdot\frac{1}{x^2+2x+2}-2\tan^{-1}(x+1)\right)+\frac{3}{5}\int\frac{1}{(v^2+1)^2}\,dv,
\end{aligned}$$

where $v=x+1$. To compute this last term, we let $v=\tan\theta$ so that $dv=\sec^2\theta\,d\theta$. Then the last term is equal to

$$\begin{aligned}
\frac{3}{5}\int\frac{\sec^2\theta}{\sec^4\theta}\,d\theta&=\frac{3}{5}\int\cos^2\theta\,d\theta=\frac{3}{10}\int(1+\cos 2\theta)\,d\theta\\
&=\frac{3}{10}\left(\theta+\frac{\sin 2\theta}{2}\right)+C=\frac{3}{10}\left(\tan^{-1}(x+1)+\frac{x+1}{(x+1)^2+1}\right)+C.
\end{aligned}$$

Putting this all together yields

$$\frac{1}{25}\left(\ln|x-1|-\frac{1}{2}\ln|x^2+2x+2|\right)+\frac{11}{50}\tan^{-1}(x+1)+\frac{1}{10}\left(\frac{3x+4}{(x+1)^2+1}\right)+C.$$

7.5.87 If we write $\frac{1}{x^2-1}=\frac{A}{x-1}+\frac{B}{x+1}$, then $1=A(x+1)+B(x-1)$, so $A=1/2$ and $B=-1/2$. Thus we have $\frac{1}{2}\int\frac{1}{x-1}-\frac{1}{x+1}\,dx=\frac{1}{2}\left(\ln|x-1|-\ln|x+1|\right)+C$.

Now let $x=\sec\theta$, so that $dx=\sec\theta\tan\theta\,d\theta$. Then the original integral is equal to $\int\csc\theta\,d\theta=-\ln|\csc\theta+\cot\theta|+C=-\ln\left|\frac{x}{\sqrt{x^2-1}}+\frac{1}{\sqrt{x^2-1}}\right|+C=-\ln\left(\frac{|x+1|}{\sqrt{x^2-1}}\right)+C=-\ln\left(\sqrt{\left|\frac{x+1}{x-1}\right|}\right)+C=\ln\left(\sqrt{\left|\frac{x-1}{x+1}\right|}\right)+C$. The two answers are equivalent.

7.5.89 Using the substitution $x=2\tan^{-1}u$ yields

$$\begin{aligned}
\int\frac{1}{1+\sin x}\,dx&=\int\frac{2}{1+u^2}\cdot\frac{1}{1+\frac{2u}{1+u^2}}\,du=\int\frac{2}{u^2+2u+1}\,du\\
&=2\int\frac{1}{(u+1)^2}\,du=-\frac{2}{u+1}+C=-\frac{2}{\tan(x/2)+1}+C.
\end{aligned}$$

7.5.91 Using the substitution $x=2\tan^{-1}u$ yields $\int\frac{1}{1-\frac{1-u^2}{1+u^2}}\cdot\frac{2}{1+u^2}\,du=\int u^{-2}\,du=-\frac{1}{u}+C=-\cot(x/2)+C$.

7.5.93 Using the substitution $\theta = 2\tan^{-1} u$ yields $\int_0^1 \frac{1}{\frac{1-u^2}{1+u^2} + \frac{2u}{1+u^2}} \cdot \frac{2}{1+u^2}\,du = \int_0^1 \frac{2}{1+2u-u^2}\,du =$ $-2\int_0^1 \frac{1}{u^2-2u+1-2}\,du = -2\int_0^1 \frac{1}{(u-1)^2-2}\,du$. If we factor the denominator as the difference of squares we have $(u-1)^2 - 2 = (u-1-\sqrt{2})(u-1+\sqrt{2})$, and using a partial fractions decomposition yields $\frac{1}{\sqrt{2}}\int_0^1 \left(\frac{1}{u+\sqrt{2}-1} - \frac{1}{u-\sqrt{2}-1}\right) du = \frac{1}{\sqrt{2}} \ln\left|\frac{u+\sqrt{2}-1}{u-\sqrt{2}-1}\right|\Big|_0^1 = \frac{1}{\sqrt{2}}\ln\left(\frac{\sqrt{2}+1}{\sqrt{2}-1}\right)$.

7.5.95 $s_A(t) = \int v_A(t)\,dt = 88\int \frac{t}{t+1}\,dt = 88\int \left(1 - \frac{1}{1+t}\right) dt = 88t - 88\ln(t+1) + C$. Because $s_A(0) = 0$, we see that $C = 0$, so $s_A(t) = 88t - 88\ln(1+t)$.

$s_B(t) = \int v_B(t)\,dt = 88\int \frac{t^2}{(t+1)^2}\,dt = 88\int \left(1 - \frac{2t+2}{t^2+2t+1} + \frac{1}{(t+1)^2}\right) dt = 88(t - \ln(t^2+2t+1) - \frac{1}{t+1}) + D$. Because $s_B(0) = 0$, we see that $D = 88$, so $s_B(t) = 88(t - \ln(t^2+2t+1) - \frac{1}{t+1} + 1)$.

$s_C(t) = \int v_C(t)\,dt = 88\int \frac{t^2}{t^2+1}\,dt = 88\int \left(1 - \frac{1}{t^2+1}\right) dt = 88(t - \tan^{-1}(t)) + E$. Because $s_C(0) = 0$, we have that $E = 0$. Thus $s_C(t) = 88t - 88\tan^{-1}(t)$.

a. $s_A(1) = 88(1 - \ln(2)) \approx 27$. $s_B(1) = 88(1 - \ln 4 - (1/2) + 1) \approx 88(3/2 - \ln 4) \approx 10$. $s_C(1) = 88(1 - \tan^{-1}(1)) \approx 18.9$. So car A travels farthest.

b. $s_A(5) = 88(5 - \ln 6) \approx 282$. $s_B(5) = 88(5 - \ln 36 - (1/6) + 1) \approx 198$. $s_C(5) = 88(5 - \tan^{-1}(5)) \approx 319$. So car C travels farthest.

c. See the development above.

d. Ultimately car C gains the lead. This can be seen by the fact that car C's velocity function is greater than that of the other cars.

7.5.97 First note that the numerator of the given integrand can be written as $x^8 - 4x^7 + 6x^6 - 4x^5 + x^4$, and this quantity when divided by x^2+1 yields $x^6 - 4x^5 + 5x^4 - 4x^2 + 4 - \frac{4}{1+x^2}$. Thus the given integral is equal to $\left(\frac{x^7}{7} - \frac{2x^6}{3} + x^5 - \frac{4x^3}{3} + 4x\right)\Big|_0^1 - (4\tan^{-1}(x))\Big|_0^1 = \frac{1}{7} - \frac{2}{3} + 1 - \frac{4}{3} + 4 - \pi = \frac{22}{7} - \pi$. Because the given integrand is positive on the interval $(0,1)$, we know that this integral is positive. Thus,

$$0 < \int_0^1 \frac{x^4(1-x)^4}{1+x^2}\,dx = \frac{22}{7} - \pi.$$

Adding π to both sides of this inequality yields $\pi < \frac{22}{7}$.

7.6 Other Integration Strategies

7.6.1 The power rule, substitution, integration by parts, and partial fraction decomposition are examples of analytical methods.

7.6.3 The computer algebra system may use a different algorithm than whoever prepared the table, so the results may look different – however, they should differ by a constant.

7.6.5 Using table entry 17, we have $\int \cos^{-1}(x)\,dx = x\cos^{-1} x - \sqrt{1-x^2} + C$.

7.6.7 Using table entry 77 for $\int \frac{1}{\sqrt{x^2+a^2}}\,dx$, we see that $\int \frac{1}{\sqrt{x^2+16}}\,dx = \ln(x + \sqrt{x^2+16}) + C$.

7.6.9 Using table entry 90 for $\int \frac{x}{ax+b}\,dx$, we see that $\int \frac{3u}{2u+7}\,du = \frac{3u}{2} - \frac{21}{4}\ln|2u+7| + C$.

7.6.11 Using table entry 47, we have $\int \frac{dx}{1-\cos 4x} = -\frac{1}{4}\cot(2x) + C$.

7.6.13 Using table entry 94 for $\int \frac{x}{\sqrt{ax+b}}\,dx$, we have that $\int \frac{x\,dx}{\sqrt{4x+1}} = \frac{1}{24}(4x-2)\sqrt{4x+1} + C = \frac{1}{12}(2x-1)\sqrt{4x+1} + C$.

7.6.15 Using table entry 69 for $\int \frac{1}{\sqrt{x^2-a^2}}\,dx$ we have $\int \frac{1}{\sqrt{9x^2-100}}\,du = \frac{1}{3}\int \frac{1}{\sqrt{u^2-100}}\,du$ where $u = 3x$. This is then equal to $\frac{1}{3}\ln|u+\sqrt{u^2-100}| + C = \frac{1}{3}\ln|3x+\sqrt{9x^2-100}| + C$. This can be written as $\frac{1}{3}\ln|x+\sqrt{x^2-(100/9)}| + C$.

7.6.17 Using table entry 84 for $\int \frac{1}{(a^2+x^2)^{3/2}}\,dx$, we have $\int \frac{1}{(16+9x^2)^{3/2}}\,dx = \frac{1}{3}\int \frac{1}{(16+u^2)^{3/2}}\,du = \frac{1}{3}\cdot\frac{3x}{16\sqrt{16+9x^2}} + C = \frac{x}{16\sqrt{16+9x^2}} + C$.

7.6.19 Using table entry 62 for $\int \frac{1}{x\sqrt{a^2-x^2}}\,dx$, we have $\int \frac{1}{x\sqrt{(12)^2-x^2}}\,dx = \frac{-1}{12}\ln\left|\frac{12+\sqrt{144-x^2}}{x}\right| + C$.

7.6.21 Using table entry 103 for $\int \ln^n x\,dx$ we have that $\int \ln^2 x\,dx = x\ln^2 x - 2\int \ln x\,dx = x\ln^2 x - 2(x\ln x - x) + C = 2x + x\ln^2 x - 2x\ln x + C$.

7.6.23 Note that $\sqrt{x^2+10x} = \sqrt{x^2+10x+25-25} = \sqrt{(x+5)^2-5^2}$. Thus, the given integral is equal to $\int \sqrt{u^2-5^2}\,du$ where $u = x+5$. Using table entry 68 we have that this is equal to $\frac{u}{2}\sqrt{u^2-25} - \frac{25}{2}\ln|u+\sqrt{u^2-25}| + C = \frac{x+5}{2}\sqrt{(x+5)^2-25} - \frac{25}{2}\ln|x+5+\sqrt{(x+5)^2-25}| + C$.

7.6.25 $\int \frac{1}{x^2+2x+10}\,dx = \int \frac{1}{(x+1)^2+9}\,dx$. Using table entry 14 this is equal to $\frac{1}{3}\tan^{-1}\left(\frac{x+1}{3}\right) + C$.

7.6.27 $\int \frac{1}{x(x^{10}+1)}\,dx = \int \frac{10x^9}{10x^{10}(x^{10}+1)}\,dx$. Let $u = x^{10}+1$ so that $du = 10x^9\,dx$. Substituting yields $\int \frac{1}{10}\cdot\frac{1}{(u-1)u}\,du$. Using table entry 96 for $\int \frac{dx}{x(ax+b)}$ we have $\frac{1}{10}\ln\left|\frac{u-1}{u}\right| + C = \frac{1}{10}\ln\left|\frac{x^{10}}{x^{10}+1}\right| + C$.

7.6.29 $\int \frac{1}{\sqrt{x^2-6x}}\,dx = \int \frac{1}{\sqrt{(x-3)^2-9}}\,dx$. Using table entry 69, this is equal to $\ln|x-3+\sqrt{(x-3)^2-9}| + C$. This can also be written as $2\ln(\sqrt{x-6}+\sqrt{x}) + C$.

7.6.31 $\int \frac{e^x}{\sqrt{e^{2x}+4}}\,dx = \int \frac{1}{\sqrt{u^2+4}}\,du$ where $u = e^x$. Then using table entry 77, we have $\ln(u+\sqrt{u^2+4}) + C = \ln(e^x+\sqrt{e^{2x}+4}) + C$.

7.6.33 $\int \frac{\cos x}{\sin^2 x + 2\sin x}\,dx = \int \frac{1}{u^2+2u}\,du = \int \frac{1}{(u+1)^2-1}\,du$ where $u = \sin x$. Then using table entry 74, we have

$$-\frac{1}{2}\ln\left|\frac{u+2}{u}\right| + C = -\frac{1}{2}\ln\left|\frac{\sin x+2}{\sin x}\right| + C.$$

7.6.35 Let $u = x^3$, so that $du = 3x^2\,dx$. Substituting yields

$$\frac{1}{3}\int \frac{\tan^{-1}(u)}{u^2}\,du = -\frac{1}{3}\left(\frac{1}{u}\tan^{-1}(u) - \int \frac{1}{u(1+u^2)}\,du\right) = -\frac{1}{3}\left(\frac{\tan^{-1}(x^3)}{x^3}\right) + \frac{1}{3}\int \frac{1}{u(1+u^2)}\,du,$$

where we used table entry 18. Now let $w = u^2+1$ so that $dw = 2u\,du$. This last integral is thus equal to $\frac{1}{3}\int \frac{2u\,du}{2u^2(1+u^2)} = \frac{1}{6}\int \frac{dw}{(w-1)w} = -\frac{1}{6}\ln\left|\frac{w}{w-1}\right| + C = -\frac{1}{6}\ln\left|\frac{u^2+1}{u^2}\right| + C = -\frac{1}{6}\ln\left|\frac{x^6+1}{x^6}\right| + C$, where we used table entry 96. Thus the original integral is equal to $-\frac{1}{3}\left(\frac{\tan^{-1}(x^3)}{x^3}\right) - \frac{1}{6}\ln\left|\frac{x^6+1}{x^6}\right| + C$. This can be written as $-\frac{\tan^{-1}(x^3)}{3x^3} + \ln\left|\frac{x}{(x^6+1)^{1/6}}\right| + C$.

7.6.37 Let $u = \ln x$, so that $du = \frac{1}{x}\,dx$. Substituting yields $\int u\sin^{-1}(u)\,du = \frac{2u^2-1}{4}\sin^{-1}(u) + \frac{u\sqrt{1-u^2}}{4} + C = \frac{2\ln^2 x - 1}{4}\sin^{-1}(\ln x) + \frac{\ln x\sqrt{1-\ln^2 x}}{4} + C$, where we used table entry 105.

7.6.39 The integral which gives the length of the curve is $\frac{1}{2}\int_0^8 \sqrt{4+x^2}\,dx$. Using table entry 76, we have $\frac{1}{2}\left(\frac{x}{2}\sqrt{4+x^2} + \frac{4}{2}\ln(x+\sqrt{4+x^2})\right)\Big|_0^8 = 4\sqrt{17} + \ln(8+2\sqrt{17}) - \ln 2 = 4\sqrt{17} + \ln(4+\sqrt{17}) \approx 18.59$.

7.6.41 The integral which gives the length of the curve is $\int_0^{\ln 2} \sqrt{1+e^{2x}}\,dx = \int_1^2 \frac{\sqrt{1+u^2}}{u}\,du$ where $u = e^x$. This is equal to $\left(\sqrt{1+u^2} - \ln\left|\frac{1+\sqrt{1+u^2}}{u}\right|\right)\Big|_1^2 = \sqrt{5} - \sqrt{2} + \ln(1+\sqrt{2}) - \ln\left(\frac{1+\sqrt{5}}{2}\right) \approx 1.22$. Note that we used table entry 83.

7.6.43 Using the method of shells, we have $\frac{V}{2\pi} = \int_0^{12} \frac{x}{\sqrt{x+4}}\,dx = \frac{2}{3}(x-8)\sqrt{x+4}\Big|_0^{12} = \frac{32}{3} + \frac{32}{3} = \frac{64}{3}$. Thus $V = \frac{128\pi}{3}$. We used table entry 94 to compute the integral.

7.6.45 Using the method of disks, we have $\frac{V}{\pi} = \int_0^{\pi/2} \sin^2 y\,dy = \frac{y}{2} - \frac{\sin 2y}{4}\Big|_0^{\pi/2} = \frac{\pi}{4}$. Thus $V = \frac{\pi^2}{4}$. We used table entry 31 to compute the antiderivative.

7.6.47 $\int \frac{x}{\sqrt{2x+3}}\,dx = \frac{1}{3}(x-3)\sqrt{3+2x} + C$.

7.6.49 $\int \tan^2 3x\,dx = \frac{1}{3}\tan 3x - x + C$.

7.6.51 $\int \frac{(x^2-a^2)^{3/2}}{x}\,dx = \frac{1}{3}(x^2-a^2)^{3/2} - a^2\sqrt{x^2-a^2} + a^3\cos^{-1}(a/x) + C$.

7.6.53 $\int (a^2-x^2)^{3/2}\,dx = \frac{-x}{8}(2x^2-5a^2)\sqrt{a^2-x^2} + \frac{3a^4}{8}\sin^{-1}(x/a) + C$.

7.6.55 $\int_{2/3}^{4/5} x^8\,dx = \frac{(4/5)^9 - (2/3)^9}{9} \approx 0.012$.

7.6.57 $\int_0^4 (9+x^2)^{3/2}\,dx = \frac{1540 + 243\ln 3}{8} \approx 225.870$.

7.6.59 $\int_0^{\pi/2} \frac{1}{1+\tan^2 t}\,dt = \frac{\pi}{4} \approx 0.785$.

7.6.61 $\int_0^1 \ln x\ln(1+x)\,dx = 2 - \frac{\pi^2}{12} - \ln 4 \approx -0.209$.

7.6.63

a. Yes, it is possible, because these are equal for $x > 1$.

b. Yes, because $\frac{1}{9} = 0.\overline{11}$.

7.6.65 The two answers differ by a constant, namely the constant one. This can be seen as follows:

$$\begin{aligned}\frac{2\sin(x/2)}{\cos(x/2)+\sin(x/2)} &= \frac{2\tan(x/2)}{1+\tan(x/2)} = 2\frac{\sin x}{1+\cos x}\cdot\frac{1}{1+\frac{\sin x}{1+\cos x}}\\ &= \frac{2\sin x}{1+\cos x+\sin x} = \frac{2\sin x}{1+\cos x+\sin x}\cdot\frac{1-\cos x-\sin x}{1-\cos x-\sin x}\\ &= \frac{2\sin x(1-\cos x-\sin x)}{-2\sin x\cos x} = \frac{\sin x+\cos x-1}{\cos x} = \frac{\sin x-1}{\cos x}+1.\end{aligned}$$

7.6.67 $\int x^3e^{2x}\,dx = \frac{1}{2}x^3e^{2x} - \frac{3}{2}\int x^2e^{2x}\,dx = \frac{1}{2}x^3e^{2x} - \frac{3}{2}\left(\frac{1}{2}x^2e^{2x} - \int xe^{2x}\,dx\right) = \frac{1}{2}x^3e^{2x} - \frac{3}{4}x^2e^{2x} + \frac{3}{2}\left(\frac{1}{2}xe^{2x} - \frac{1}{2}\int e^{2x}\,dx\right) = \frac{1}{2}x^3e^{2x} - \frac{3}{4}x^2e^{2x} + \frac{3}{4}xe^{2x} - \frac{3}{8}e^{2x} + C.$

7.6.69 Let $u = 3y$. Then $\int \tan^4 3y\,dy = \frac{1}{3}\int \tan^4 u\,du = \frac{1}{3}\left(\frac{1}{3}\tan^3 u - \int \tan^2 u\,du\right) = \frac{1}{9}\tan^3 u - \frac{1}{3}\left(\tan u - \int du\right) = \frac{1}{9}\tan^3 3y - \frac{1}{3}\tan 3y + y + C.$

7.6.71 Let $u = 2x$. Then $\int x\sin^{-1} 2x\,dx = \frac{1}{4}\int u\sin^{-1} u\,du = \frac{2u^2-1}{16}\sin^{-1} u + \frac{u\sqrt{1-u^2}}{16} + C = \frac{8x^2-1}{16}\sin^{-1} 2x + \frac{x\sqrt{1-4x^2}}{8} + C.$

7.6.73 $\int x^{-2}\tan^{-1} x\,dx = -(1/x)\tan^{-1} x + \int \frac{1}{x(1+x^2)}\,dx = \frac{-\tan^{-1} x}{x} + \ln\left(\frac{|x|}{\sqrt{1+x^2}}\right) + C.$

7.6.75

a. Note that $\int_0^b f(x)\,dx = \int_0^{b/2} f(x)\,dx + \int_{b/2}^b f(x)\,dx$. For the second integral, let $u = b - x$. Then $du = -dx$. The second integral is equal to $-\int_{b-(b/2)}^0 f(b-u)\,du = \int_0^{b/2} f(b-u)\,du$. Because this can be written as $\int_0^{b/2} f(b-x)\,dx$, we have $\int_0^b f(x)\,dx = \int_0^{b/2} (f(x)+f(b-x))\,dx$.

b.

$$\begin{aligned}\int_0^{\pi/4} \ln(1+\tan x)\,dx &= \int_0^{\pi/8} (\ln(1+\tan x) + \ln(1+\tan(\pi/4-x)))\,dx\\ &= \int_0^{\pi/8} \left(\ln(1+\tan x) + \ln\left(1+\frac{\tan\pi/4-\tan x}{1+\tan\pi/4\tan x}\right)\right)dx\\ &= \int_0^{\pi/8} \left(\ln(1+\tan x) + \ln\left(1+\frac{1-\tan x}{1+\tan x}\right)\right)dx\\ &= \int_0^{\pi/8} \left(\ln(1+\tan x) + \ln\left(\frac{2}{1+\tan x}\right)\right) = \int_0^{\pi/8} \ln(2)\,dx = \frac{\pi\ln 2}{8}.\end{aligned}$$

7.6.77

a. Using a computer algebra system, we have

θ_0	T	Relative Error
0.1	6.27927	0.000623603
0.2	6.26762	0.0024778
0.3	6.24854	0.0051388
0.4	6.22253	0.00965413
0.5	6.19021	0.0147967
0.6	6.15236	0.0208215
0.7	6.10979	0.0275963
0.8	6.06338	0.0349831
0.9	6.01399	0.0428433
1.0	5.96247	0.0510427

b. All of these values are within 10 percent of 2π.

7.6.79 Let $u = ax+b$, so that $du = a\,dx$. Then we have $\frac{1}{a}\int \frac{ax+b-b}{ax+b}\,dx = \frac{1}{a}\int\left(1-\frac{b}{ax+b}\right)dx = \frac{1}{a}\left(x - \frac{b}{a}\int\frac{1}{u}\,du\right) = \frac{1}{a}\left(x-\frac{b}{a}\ln|u|\right)+C = \frac{1}{a}\left(x-\frac{b}{a}\ln|ax+b|\right)+C.$

7.6.81 Let $u = ax+b$, so that $du = a\,dx$. Then we have $\frac{1}{a}\int \frac{u-b}{a}u^n\,du = \frac{1}{a^2}\int(u^{n+1}-bu^n)\,du = \frac{1}{a^2}\left(\frac{u^{n+2}}{n+2}-\frac{bu^{n+1}}{n+1}\right)+C = \frac{1}{a^2}\left(\frac{(ax+b)^{n+2}}{n+2}-\frac{b(ax+b)^{n+1}}{n+1}\right)+C.$

7.6.83

a. The result holds.

b. First note that $\int_0^{\pi/2}\cos^n x\,dx = -\int_{\pi/2}^{0}\cos^n(\pi/2-\theta)\,d\theta = \int_0^{\pi/2}\sin^n\theta\,d\theta$. So we only need to show the result for $\int_0^{\pi/2}\sin^{10}x\,dx$. Repeatedly using the reduction formula we have $\int_0^{\pi/2}\sin^{10}x\,dx = \frac{9}{10}\int_0^{\pi/2}\sin^8 x\,dx = \frac{9\cdot 7}{10\cdot 8}\int_0^{\pi/2}\sin^6 x\,dx = \frac{9\cdot7\cdot5}{10\cdot8\cdot6}\int_0^{\pi/2}\sin^4 x\,dx = \frac{9\cdot7\cdot5\cdot3}{10\cdot8\cdot6\cdot4}\int_0^{\pi/2}\sin^2 x\,dx = \frac{9\cdot7\cdot5\cdot3}{10\cdot8\cdot6\cdot4\cdot2}\int_0^{\pi/2}dx = \frac{63\pi}{2^9}.$

c. The values decrease as n increases.

7.7 Numerical Integration

7.7.1 $\Delta x = \frac{18-4}{28} = \frac{1}{2}$.

7.7.3 The Trapezoidal Rule approximates the definite integral by using a trapezoid over each subinterval rather than a rectangle.

7.7.5 The endpoints of the subintervals are -1, 1, 3, 5, 7, and 9. The trapezoidal rule uses the value of f at each of these endpoints.

7.7.7 The absolute error is $|\pi - 3.14| \approx 0.0015926536$. The relative error is $\frac{|\pi-3.14|}{\pi} \approx 5\times 10^{-4}$.

7.7.9 The absolute error is $|e-2.72| \approx 0.0017181715$. The relative error is $\frac{|e-2.72|}{e} \approx 6.32 \times 10^{-4}$.

7.7.11
For $n=1$, we have $f(6)\cdot 8 = 72\cdot 8 = 576$.
For $n=2$ we have $f(4)\cdot 4 + f(8)\cdot 4 = 32\cdot 4 + 128\cdot 4 = 640$.
For $n=4$, we have $f(3)\cdot 2 + f(5)\cdot 2 + f(7)\cdot 2 + f(9)\cdot 2 = 18\cdot 2 + 50\cdot 2 + 98\cdot 2 + 162\cdot 2 = 656$.

7.7.13 We have

$$\frac{1}{6}\left(\sin(\pi/12)+\sin(\pi/4)+\sin(5\pi/12)+\sin(7\pi/12)+\sin(3\pi/4)+\sin(11\pi/12)\right) \approx 0.6439505509.$$

7.7.15 For $n=2$ we have $T(2) = \frac{4}{2}(f(2)+2f(6)+f(10)) = 2(8+2(72)+200) = 704$.
Using the results of number 11: For $n=4$, note that $T(4) = \frac{T(2)+M(2)}{2} = \frac{704+640}{2} = 672$.
Using the results of number 11: For $n=8$ we have that $T(8) = \frac{T(4)+M(4)}{2} = \frac{672+656}{2} = 664$.

7.7.17 We have $T(6) = \frac{1}{12}(\sin 0 + 2\sin\pi/6 + 2\sin\pi/3 + 2\sin\pi/2 + 2\sin 2\pi/3 + 2\sin 5\pi/6 + \sin\pi) = \frac{1}{6}(\frac{1}{2} + \frac{\sqrt{3}}{2} + 1 + \frac{\sqrt{3}}{2} + \frac{1}{2}) = \frac{1}{6}(2+\sqrt{3})$.

7.7.19 The width of each subinterval is $1/25$, so $M(25) = \frac{1}{25}(\sin\pi/50 + \sin 3\pi/50 + \sin 5\pi/50 + \cdots + \sin 49\pi/50) \approx .6370388444$. Since $\int_0^1 \sin\pi x\, dx = \frac{2}{\pi}$, the absolute error is $|2/\pi - M(25)| \approx 4.19\times 10^{-4}$ and the relative error is this number divided by $2/\pi$ which is approximately 6.58×10^{-4}. The Trapezoidal Rule yields approximately .6357817937, with a relative error of ≈ 0.001316.

7.7.21

n	$M(n)$	Absolute Error	$T(n)$	Absolute Error
4	99	1	102	2
8	99.75	0.250	100.5	0.5
16	99.9375	0.0625	100.125	0.125
32	99.984375	0.0156	100.03125	0.03125

7.7.23

n	$M(n)$	Absolute Error	$T(n)$	Absolute Error
4	1.50968181	9.7×10^{-3}	1.48067370	1.9×10^{-2}
8	1.50241228	2.4×10^{-3}	1.49517776	4.8×10^{-3}
16	1.50060256	6.0×10^{-4}	1.49879502	1.2×10^{-3}
32	1.50015061	1.5×10^{-4}	1.49969879	3.0×10^{-4}

7.7.25 Because the given function has odd symmetry about the midpoint of the interval $[0,\pi]$, the midpoint rule calculates to be zero for all even values of n, as does the trapezoidal rule.

7.7.27 Answers may vary.
$\overline{T} = \frac{1}{12}\int_0^{12} T(t)\,dt \approx \frac{1}{12}\text{Trapezoid}(12) \approx \frac{1}{24}(47+2(50+46+45+48+52+54+61+62+63+63+59)+55) = 54.5$.

7.7.29 Answers may vary.
$\overline{T} = \frac{1}{12}\int_0^{12} T(t)\,dt \approx \frac{1}{12}\text{Trapezoid}(12) \approx \frac{1}{24}(35 + 2(34+34+36+36+37+37+36+35+35+34+33)+32)) \approx 35.0$.

7.7.31

a. Left Riemann sum: $\frac{1}{120}(70\cdot 20+130\cdot 25+200\cdot 15+239\cdot 30+311\cdot 20+355\cdot 10)=204.917.$
Right Riemann sum: $\frac{1}{120}(130\cdot 20+200\cdot 25+239\cdot 15+311\cdot 30+355\cdot 20+375\cdot 10)=261.375.$
Trapezoidal rule:

$$\frac{(70+130)\cdot 20}{2\cdot 120}+\frac{(130+200)\cdot 25}{2\cdot 120}+\frac{(200+239)\cdot 15}{2\cdot 120}+\frac{(239+311)\cdot 30}{2\cdot 120}+\frac{(311+355)\cdot 20}{2\cdot 120}+\frac{(355+375)\cdot 10}{2\cdot 120}=233.146$$

These are approximations to the average temperature of the curling iron on the interval $[0,120]$.

b. Because the function is increasing, the left Riemann sum is an underestimate and the right Riemann sum is an overestimate. The Trapezoidal rule appears to be a slight underestimate. The followings is a plot of the points with straight line segments connecting them. The shape suggestions that the actual function is concave down on the interval, so the trapezoidal rule will be an underestimate.

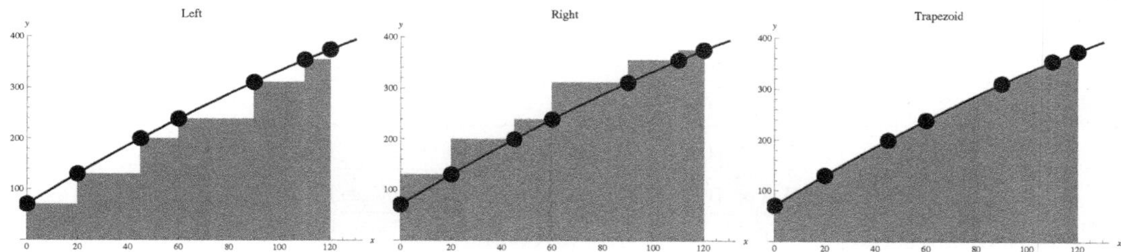

c. The change in temperature over the time interval is

$$\int_0^{120} T'(t)\,dt = T(120)-T(0)=375-70=305\,\text{degrees}.$$

7.7.33

a. The net change in elevation is $\int_0^5 v(t)\,dt$, which can be approximated by the trapezoidal rule to give

$$\frac{(0+100)\cdot 1}{2}+\frac{(100+120)\cdot 0.5}{2}+\frac{(120+150)\cdot 1.5}{2}+\frac{(150+110)\cdot 0.5}{2}+\frac{(110+90)\cdot 0.5}{2}+\frac{(90+80)\cdot 1}{2}=507.5.$$

If we add the net change to the original elevation of 5400 feet, we have an elevation of approximately 5907.5 feet.

b. The right Riemann sum is

$$100\cdot 1+120\cdot 0.5+150\cdot 1.5+110\cdot 0.5+90\cdot 0.5+80\cdot 1=565.$$

If we add the net change to the original elevation of 5400 feet, we have an elevation of approximately 5965 feet.

c. The elevation can be estimated by

$$5400+\int_0^5 g(t)\,dt = 5400+\int_0^5 (3.49t^3-43.21t^2+142.43t-1.75)\,dt \approx 5916.52,$$

so the elevation of the balloon is about 5917 feet.

7.7.35

n	$T(n)$	Absolute Error	$S(n)$	Absolute Error
25	3.19623162	—	—	—
50	3.19495398	4.3×10^{-4}	3.19452809	4.5×10^{-8}

7.7.37

n	$T(n)$	Absolute Error	$S(n)$	Absolute Error
50	1.00008509	—	—	—
100	1.00002127	2.1×10^{-5}	1.00000000	4.6×10^{-9}

7.7.39

n	$T(n)$	Absolute Error	$S(n)$	Absolute Error
4	1820	284	—	—
8	1607.75	71.8	1537	1
16	1553.9844	18	1536.0625	6.3×10^{-2}
32	1540.4990	4.5	1536.0039	3.9×10^{-3}

7.7.41

n	$T(n)$	Absolute Error	$S(n)$	Absolute Error
4	0.46911538	5.3×10^{-2}	—	—
8	0.50826998	1.3×10^{-2}	0.52132152	2.9×10^{-4}
16	0.51825968	3.4×10^{-3}	0.52158957	1.7×10^{-5}
32	0.52076933	8.4×10^{-4}	0.52160588	1.1×10^{-6}

7.7.43

a. True. In the case of a linear function, the region under the curve and over each subinterval is a trapezoid, so the trapezoidal rule gives the exact area.

b. False. Since $E_M(n) \le \frac{k(b-a)^3}{24n^2}$, we have $E_M(3n) \le \frac{k(b-a)^3}{24(9n^2)}$, so the error decreases by a factor of about 9.

c. True. Since $E_T(n) \le \frac{k(b-a)^3}{12n^2}$, we have $E_T(4n) \le \frac{k(b-a)^3}{24(16n^2)}$, so the error decreases by a factor of about 16.

7.7.45 $\displaystyle\int_0^{\pi/2} \cos^9 x\, dx = \frac{128}{315}.$

n	$M(n)$	Absolute Error	$T(n)$	Absolute Error
4	0.40635058	1.4×10^{-6}	0.40634783	1.4×10^{-6}
8	0.40634921	7.6×10^{-10}	0.40634921	7.6×10^{-9}
16	0.40634921	6.6×10^{-13}	0.40634921	6.6×10^{-13}
32	0.40634921	8.9×10^{-16}	0.40634921	7.8×10^{-16}

7.7.47 $\displaystyle\int_0^{\pi} \ln(5 + 3\cos x)x\, dx = \pi \ln(9/2).$

n	$M(n)$	Absolute Error	$T(n)$	Absolute Error
4	4.72531820	1.2×10^{-4}	4.72507878	1.2×10^{-4}
8	4.72519851	9.1×10^{-9}	4.72519849	9.1×10^{-9}
16	4.72519850	0.	4.72519850	8.9×10^{-16}
32	4.72519850	0.	4.72519850	8.9×10^{-19}

7.7.49 $\displaystyle\int_0^{\pi} \frac{\cos x}{(5/4) - \cos x}\, dx = \frac{2\pi}{3} \approx 2.094395102.$

n	$S(n)$	Absolute Error
4	1.916439963	0.178
8	2.080919302	0.0135
16	2.094341841	5.3×10^{-5}

7.7.51 $\displaystyle\int_0^{\pi} \sin 6x \cos 3x\, dx = \frac{4}{9} = 0.\bar{4}.$

n	$S(n)$	Absolute Error
8	0.0305049084	0.475
16	0.4540112289	0.0096
32	0.44487	0.00087

7.7.53 $\displaystyle\int_0^{2\pi} \sqrt{a^2\cos^2 t + b^2 \sin^2 t}\, dt,\ a = 4,\ b = 8.$

n	$S(n)$
4	41.88790205
8	39.05860599

7.7.55 We are computing $\displaystyle\frac{1}{3\sqrt{2\pi}}\int_{66}^{72} e^{-(x-69)^2/18}\, dx$. If we use Simpson's rule we obtain

n	$S(n)$
4	0.683
8	0.683

So about 68.3%.

7.7.57

a. For even n we have $S(n) = \frac{20}{n}(365)(f(a) + 4f(x_1) + 4f(x_2) + \ldots + 4f(x_{n-1}) + f(b))$. For $n = 6$ since there are 6 decades between 1940 and 2000, we have $S(6) \approx 160,000$ millions of barrels produced.

b. Following part (a) with $n = 6$ we have $S(n) \approx 68,000$ millions of barrels imported.

7.7.59

a. $T(40) = \frac{1}{80}(\sin 1 + 2\sum_{i=1}^{39} \sin e^{i/40} + \sin e) \approx .8748$.

b. $f(x) = \sin e^x$, so $f'(x) = e^x \cos e^x$. $f''(x) = -e^{2x}\sin e^x + e^x \cos e^x = e^x(\cos e^x - e^x \sin e^x)$.

c. $|f''(x)| = |e^x| \cdot |\cos e^x - e^x \sin e^x| \le |e^x|(|\cos e^x| + |e^x \sin e^x|) \le e(1+e) < 10.11$. However, the graph of the absolute value of $f''(x)$ reveals that is is actually bounded by 5.75 on the interval $[0, 1]$.

d. Since $E_T(n) \le k(b-a)^3/12n^2 = 6/(12(40^2)) = .0003125$, $T(40)$ is accurate to at least 3 decimal places.

7.7.61

a. The exact value is $\int_0^4 x^3\, dx = \left.\frac{x^4}{4}\right|_0^4 = 64$. Simpson's rule gives $S(2) = (0 + 4\cdot 8 + 64)\,\frac{2}{3} = 64$. The values match exactly.

b. $S(4) = (0 + 4\cdot 1 + 2\cdot 8 + 4\cdot 27 + 64)\,\frac{1}{3} = 64$. This also matches the exact value exactly.

c. The 4th derivative of x^3 is 0, so the value of K in the theorem can be taken to be 0, so the error is 0.

d. Any polynomial of degree 3 or less has 4th derivative equal to 0, so the value of K in the theorem can be taken to be 0, so the error is 0.

7.7.63 The trapezoidal rule will be an overestimate in this case. This is because of the fact that if the function is above the axis and concave up on the given interval, then each trapezoid on each subinterval lies over the area under the curve for that corresponding subinterval.

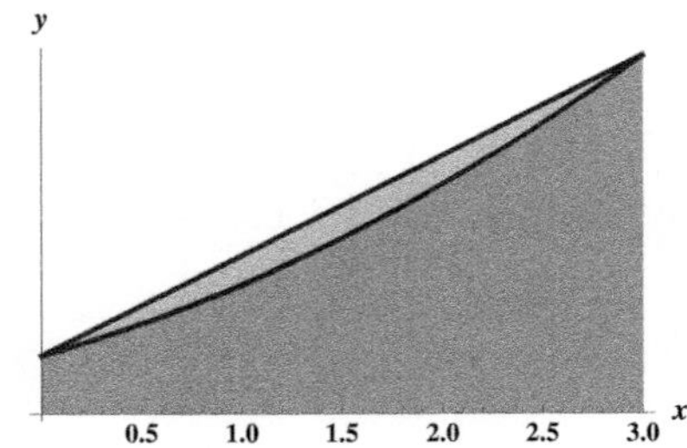

7.7.65 Using the previous results, we have

$$S(2n) = \frac{4T(2n) - T(n)}{3} = \frac{2(T(n) + M(n)) - T(n)}{3} = \frac{2M(n) + T(n)}{3}.$$

So $S(50) = \frac{1}{3}(2M(25) + T(25)) \approx .8298251909$.

7.8 Improper Integrals

7.8.1 The interval of integration is infinite or the integrand is unbounded on the interval of integration.

7.8.3 Compute $\int_0^1 \frac{1}{\sqrt{x}}\, dx = \lim_{b \to 0^+} \int_b^1 \frac{1}{\sqrt{x}}\, dx.$

7.8.5 $\int_1^\infty x^{-2}\, dx = \lim_{b \to \infty} \int_1^b x^{-2}\, dx = \lim_{b \to \infty} \left(-\frac{1}{x}\right)\Big|_1^b = \lim_{b \to \infty} \left(1 - \frac{1}{b}\right) = 1.$

7.8.7 $\int_{-\infty}^0 e^x\, dx = \lim_{b \to -\infty} \int_b^0 e^x\, dx = \lim_{b \to -\infty} e^x\Big|_b^0 = \lim_{b \to -\infty} (1 - e^b) = 1.$

7.8.9 $\int_2^\infty \frac{dx}{\sqrt{x}} = \lim_{b \to \infty} \int_2^b \frac{dx}{\sqrt{x}} = \lim_{b \to \infty} 2\sqrt{x}\big|_2^b = \lim_{b \to \infty} 2(\sqrt{b} - \sqrt{2}) = \infty$, so the integral diverges.

7.8.11 $\int_0^\infty e^{-2x}\, dx = \lim_{b \to \infty} \int_0^b e^{-2x}\, dx = \lim_{b \to \infty} \left(-\frac{1}{2}e^{-2x}\right)\Big|_0^b = \lim_{b \to \infty} \frac{1}{2}\left(1 - e^{-2b}\right) = \frac{1}{2}.$

7.8.13 $\int_0^\infty e^{-ax}\, dx = \lim_{b \to \infty} \int_0^b e^{-ax}\, dx = \lim_{b \to \infty} \left(-e^{-x}/a\right)\Big|_0^b = \lim_{b \to \infty} \left(-\frac{1}{ae^b} + \frac{1}{a}\right) = \frac{1}{a}.$

7.8.15

$$\int_{e^2}^\infty \frac{dx}{x \ln^p x} = \lim_{b \to \infty} \int_{e^2}^b \frac{dx}{x \ln^p x} = \lim_{b \to \infty} \left(\frac{1}{1-p} \ln^{1-p} x\right)\Big|_{e^2}^b = \lim_{b \to \infty} \frac{1}{p-1}\left(2^{1-p} - \ln^{1-p} b\right) = \frac{1}{(p-1)2^{p-1}}.$$

7.8.17

$$\begin{aligned}
\int_{-\infty}^\infty xe^{-x^2}\, dx &= \lim_{b \to -\infty} \int_b^0 xe^{-x^2} + \lim_{b \to \infty} \int_0^b xe^{-x^2} \\
&= \lim_{b \to -\infty} \left(-\frac{1}{2}e^{-x^2}\right)\Big|_b^0 + \lim_{b \to \infty} \left(-\frac{1}{2}e^{-x^2}\right)\Big|_0^b \\
&= \lim_{b \to -\infty} \left(-\frac{1}{2} + \frac{1}{2}e^{-b^2}\right) + \lim_{b \to \infty} \left(-\frac{1}{2}e^{-b^2} + \frac{1}{2}\right) = -\frac{1}{2} + \frac{1}{2} = 0.
\end{aligned}$$

7.8.19 $\int_2^\infty \frac{\cos(\pi/x)}{x^2}\,dx = \lim_{b\to\infty}\int_2^b \frac{\cos(\pi/x)}{x^2}\,dx = \lim_{b\to\infty}\left(-\frac{1}{\pi}\sin(\pi/x)\right)\Big|_2^b = \lim_{b\to\infty}\frac{1}{\pi}\left(1-\sin(\pi/b)\right) = \frac{1}{\pi}.$

7.8.21 $\int_0^\infty \frac{e^u}{e^{2u}+1}\,du = \lim_{b\to\infty}\int_0^b \frac{e^u}{e^{2u}+1}\,du.$ Let $u = e^u$ so that $du = e^u\,du$. After substitution we have $\lim_{b\to\infty}\int_1^{e^b}\frac{1}{u^2+1}\,du = \lim_{b\to\infty}\left(\tan^{-1}(u)\right)\Big|_1^{e^b} = \lim_{b\to\infty}(\tan^{-1}(e^b)-\tan^{-1}(1)) = \pi/2-\pi/4 = \pi/4.$

7.8.23 $\int_1^\infty \frac{1}{v(v+1)}\,dv = \lim_{b\to\infty}\int_1^b\left(\frac{1}{v}-\frac{1}{v+1}\right)dv = \lim_{b\to\infty}\ln\left|\frac{v}{v+1}\right|\,\Big|_1^b = \lim_{b\to\infty}\ln\left|\frac{b}{b+1}\right| - \ln(1/2) = 0-\ln(1/2) = \ln 2.$

7.8.25 Let $u = x^3+x$ so that $du = (3x^2+1)\,dx$ Substituting gives

$$\int_2^\infty \frac{1}{u}\,du = \lim_{b\to\infty}\int_2^b \frac{1}{u}\,du = \lim_{b\to\infty}\ln u\,\Big|_2^b = \lim_{b\to\infty}(\ln b-\ln 2) = \infty.$$

The given integral diverges.

7.8.27 $\int_2^\infty \frac{dx}{(x+2)^2} = \lim_{b\to\infty}\int_2^b\frac{dx}{(x+2)^2} = \lim_{b\to\infty}-\frac{1}{x+2}\Big|_2^b = \lim_{b\to\infty}-\frac{1}{b+2}+\frac{1}{4} = \frac{1}{4}.$

7.8.29 Using the result from Example 2, we see that the volume is given by $V = \pi\int_1^\infty x^{-4}\,dx = \frac{\pi}{4-1} = \frac{\pi}{3}.$

7.8.31 Using the result from Example 2, we see that the volume is given by

$$V = \pi\int_1^\infty\left(\frac{1}{x^2}+\frac{1}{x^3}\right)dx = \frac{\pi}{2-1}+\frac{\pi}{3-1} = \frac{3\pi}{2}.$$

7.8.33 $V = \pi\int_2^\infty\frac{dx}{x(\ln x)^2} = \pi\lim_{b\to\infty}\int_2^b\frac{dx}{x(\ln x)^2} = \pi\lim_{b\to\infty}\left(-\frac{1}{\ln x}\right)\Big|_2^b = \pi\lim_{b\to\infty}\left(\frac{1}{\ln 2}-\frac{1}{\ln b}\right) = \frac{\pi}{\ln 2}.$

7.8.35 $\int_0^8\frac{dx}{\sqrt[3]{x}} = \lim_{c\to0^+}\int_c^8 x^{-1/3}\,dx = \lim_{c\to0^+}\left(\frac{3}{2}x^{2/3}\right)\Big|_c^8 = \frac{3}{2}\lim_{c\to0^+}(4-c^{2/3}) = 6.$

7.8.37 $\lim_{c\to1^+}\int_c^2\frac{1}{\sqrt{x-1}}\,dx = \lim_{c\to1^+}\left(2\sqrt{x-1}\right)\Big|_c^2 = \lim_{c\to1^+}\left(2-2\sqrt{c-1}\right) = 2.$

7.8.39 $\lim_{b\to(\pi/2)^-}\int_0^b\sec x\tan x\,dx = \lim_{b\to(\pi/2)^-}(\sec x)\Big|_0^b = \lim_{b\to(\pi/2)^-}(\sec b-1) = \infty.$ The given integral diverges.

7.8.41 Note that $\int\frac{e^{\sqrt{x}}}{\sqrt{x}}\,dx = 2e^{\sqrt{x}}+C.$ Thus,

$$\lim_{c\to0^+}\int_c^1\frac{e^{\sqrt{x}}}{\sqrt{x}}\,dx = \lim_{c\to0^+}\left(2e^{\sqrt{x}}\right)\Big|_c^1 = \lim_{c\to0^+}\left(2e-2e^{\sqrt{c}}\right) = 2e-2.$$

7.8.43 $\int_0^1\frac{x^3}{x^4-1}\,dx = \lim_{c\to1^-}\int_0^c\frac{x^3}{x^4-1}\,dx = \lim_{c\to1^-}\left(\frac{1}{4}\ln|x^4-1|\right)\Big|_0^c = \frac{1}{4}\lim_{c\to1^-}\ln|c^4-1| = -\infty,$ so the integral diverges.

7.8.45

$$\int_0^{10} \frac{dx}{\sqrt[4]{10-x}} = \lim_{c\to 10^-} \int_0^c (10-x)^{-1/4}\, dx = \lim_{c\to 10^-} \left(-\frac{4}{3}(10-x)^{3/4} \right) \Big|_0^c$$
$$= \frac{4}{3} \lim_{c\to 10^-} \left(10^{3/4} - (10-c)^{3/4} \right) = \frac{4}{3} 10^{3/4}.$$

7.8.47 By the even symmetry of the integrand, this should be equal to $2\int_0^1 \ln y^2\, dy$. Thus we have $2\int_0^1 \ln y^2\, dy = 4 \lim_{c\to 0^+} \int_c^1 \ln y\, dx = 4 \lim_{c\to 0^+} (y \ln y - y)\Big|_c^1 = 4 \lim_{c\to 0^+} (-1 - c\ln c + c) = -4$. (The fact that $\lim_{c\to 0^+} c\ln c = 0$ can be derived using L'Hôpital's rule, or from the result $\lim_{c\to 0^+} c^c = 1$).

7.8.49 By symmetry,

$$\int_{-2}^2 \frac{dp}{\sqrt{4-p^2}} = 2\int_0^2 \frac{dp}{\sqrt{4-p^2}} = 2 \lim_{c\to 2^-} \int_0^c \frac{dp}{\sqrt{4-p^2}}$$
$$= 2 \lim_{c\to 2^-} \left(\sin^{-1}(p/2)\right)\Big|_0^c = 2 \lim_{c\to 2^-} \left(\sin^{-1}(c/2) - \sin^{-1} 0\right)$$
$$= 2(\sin^{-1} 1 - 0) = \pi.$$

7.8.51 Using disks, we have

$$V = \pi \int_1^2 (x-1)^{-1/2}\, dx = \pi \lim_{c\to 1^+} \int_c^2 (x-1)^{-1/2}\, dx = \pi \lim_{c\to 1^+} \left(2(x-1)^{1/2}\right)\Big|_c^2 = 2\pi \lim_{c\to 1^+} (1 - \sqrt{c-1}) = 2\pi.$$

7.8.53 Using shells, we have

$$V = 2\pi \int_0^4 x(4-x)^{-1/3}\, dx = 2\pi \int_0^4 (4-u)u^{-1/3}\, du = 2\pi \int_0^4 (4u^{-1/3} - u^{2/3})\, du$$

via the substitution $u = 4 - x$. Therefore

$$V = 2\pi \lim_{c\to 0+} \int_c^4 (4u^{-1/3} - u^{2/3})\, du = 2\pi \lim_{c\to 0+} \left(6u^{2/3} - \frac{3}{5}u^{5/3}\right)\Big|_c^4 = \frac{72 \cdot 2^{1/3}\pi}{5}.$$

7.8.55 $V = \pi \int_0^{\pi/2} \tan^2 x\, dx = \lim_{a\to \frac{\pi}{2}^-} \pi \int_0^a \tan^2 x\, dx = \lim_{a\to \frac{\pi}{2}^-} \pi \int_0^a (\sec^2 x - 1)\, dx = \lim_{a\to \frac{\pi}{2}^-} \pi\, (\tan x - x)\Big|_0^a = \lim_{a\to \frac{\pi}{2}^-} \pi\, (\tan a - a) = \infty$, so the volume doesn't exist.

7.8.57 As in Example 7, we have

$$\text{AUC}_i = \int_0^\infty C_i(t)\, dt = 250 \int_0^\infty e^{-0.08t}\, dt = \frac{250}{0.08} = 3125$$

and

$$\text{AUC}_o = \int_0^\infty C_0(t)\, dt = 200 \int_0^\infty (e^{-0.08t} - e^{-1.8t})\, dt = 200\left(\frac{1}{0.08} - \frac{1}{1.8}\right) = \frac{21{,}500}{9} \approx 2389,$$

(here we use the fact that $\int_0^\infty e^{-ax}\, dx = \frac{1}{a}$ for $a > 0$). Therefore the bioavailability of the drug is

$$F = \frac{\text{AUC}_o}{\text{AUC}_i} = \frac{21{,}500}{9 \cdot 3125} \approx 0.764.$$

7.8.59 The maximum distance is

$$D = 10\int_0^\infty (t+1)^{-2}\,dt = 10\lim_{b\to\infty}\int_0^b (t+1)^{-2}\,dt = 10\lim_{b\to\infty}\left(-(t+1)^{-1}\right)\Big|_0^b = 10\,\text{mi}.$$

7.8.61

a. True. The area under the curve $y = f(x)$ from 0 to ∞ is less than the area under $y = g(x)$ on this interval, which by assumption is finite.

b. False. For example, take $f(x) = 1$; then $\int_0^\infty f(x)\,dx = \infty$.

c. False. For example, take $p = 1/2$ and $q = 1$.

d. True. The area under the curve $y = x^{-q}$ from 1 to ∞ is less than the area under $y = x^{-p}$ on this interval, which by assumption is finite.

e. True. Using the result in Example 2, we see that this integral exists if and only if $3p + 2 > 1$, which is equivalent to $p > -1/3$.

7.8.63

a. The function $e^{-|x|}$ is even, so $\int_{-\infty}^\infty e^{-|x|}\,dx = 2\int_0^\infty e^{-x}\,dx = 2$. (Note that here we used the fact that $\int_0^\infty e^{-ax}\,dx = \frac{1}{a}$ for $a > 0$).

b. The function $x^3/(1+x^8)$ is odd, so $\int_{-\infty}^\infty \frac{x^3}{1+x^8}\,dx = \int_0^\infty \frac{x^3}{1+x^8}\,dx + \int_{-\infty}^0 \frac{x^3}{1+x^8}\,dx = \int_0^\infty \frac{x^3}{1+x^8}\,dx - \int_0^\infty \frac{x^3}{1+x^8}\,dx = 0$ assuming $\displaystyle\int_0^\infty \frac{x^3}{1+x^8}\,dx$ exists, which is true because $0 < \frac{x^3}{1+x^8} < \frac{1}{x^5}$ on $[1,\infty)$ and $\int_1^\infty x^{-5}\,dx$ exists.

7.8.65

n	$T_2(n)$	$T_4(n)$	$T_8(n)$
4	.880619	.886319	1.036632
8	.881704	.886227	.886319
16	.881986	.886227	.886227
32	.882058	.886227	.886227

Based on these results, we conclude that $\int_0^\infty e^{-x^2}\,dx \approx 0.886$.

7.8.67 Integration by parts gives $\displaystyle\int x\ln x\,dx = \frac{x^2}{4}(2\ln x - 1) + C$, so $\displaystyle\int_0^1 x\ln x\,dx = \lim_{c\to 0^+}\int_c^1 x\ln x\,dx = \lim_{c\to 0^+}\left(\frac{x^2}{4}(2\ln x - 1)\right)\Big|_c^1 = \frac{1}{4}\lim_{c\to 0^+}(c^2(-2\ln c + 1) - 1) = -\frac{1}{4}$. (The fact that $\displaystyle\lim_{c\to 0^+} c^2\ln c = 0$ can be derived using L'Hôpital's rule, or from the result $\lim_{c\to 0^+} c^c = 1$).

7.8.69 Let $u = x^2$ so that $2x\,dx = du$. The first integral is then equal to $\frac{1}{2}\int_0^\infty e^{-u}\,du = \frac{1}{2}$, using the fact that $\int_0^\infty e^{-ax}\,dx = \frac{1}{a}$ for $a > 0$. The second integral cannot be evaluated by finding an antiderivative for $x^2e^{-x^2}$; however using more advanced methods it can be shown that $\int_0^\infty x^2e^{-x^2}\,dx = \frac{\sqrt{\pi}}{4} \approx 0.443$.

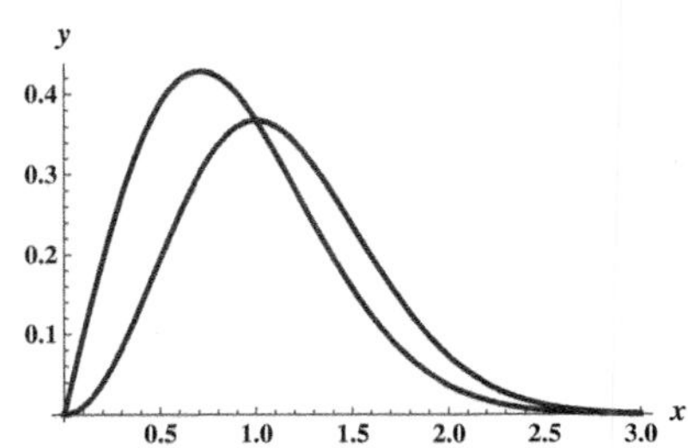

7.8.71 The region R has area $A = \displaystyle\int_0^\infty e^{-bx}\,dx - \int_0^\infty e^{-ax}\,dx = \frac{1}{b} - \frac{1}{a}$.

7.8.73

a. We have

$$A(a,b) = \int_b^\infty e^{-ax}\,dx = \lim_{c\to\infty}\int_b^c e^{-ax}\,dx = \lim_{c\to\infty}\left(-\frac{1}{a}e^{-ax}\right)\Big|_b^c = \frac{1}{a}\lim_{c\to\infty}(e^{-ab} - e^{-ac}) = \frac{e^{-ab}}{a}.$$

b. Solving $e^{-ab} = 2a$ for b gives $b = g(a) = -\frac{1}{a}\ln(2a)$.

c. The function g has $g'(x) = \frac{1}{x^2}\ln 2x - \frac{1}{x^2} = \frac{\ln 2x - 1}{x^2}$, so g has a critical point at $x = e/2$, and the first derivative test shows that g takes a minimum at this point. Hence $b^* = g(e/2) = -\frac{2}{e}$.

7.8.75

a. The solid has volume $V = \pi\int_0^1 x^{-2p}\,dx$, which by the result in problem 74 is finite if and only if $2p < 1$, or $p < 1/2$.

b. The solid has volume $V = 2\pi\int_0^1 x^{1-p}\,dx$, which by the result in problem 74 is finite if and only if $p - 1 < 1$, or $p < 2$.

7.8.77 These integrals cannot be evaluated by finding an antiderivative of their integrands. However, if we make the substitution $u = \pi/2 - x$ we find that $\displaystyle\int_0^{\pi/2} \ln\sin x\,dx = -\int_{\pi/2}^0 \ln\cos u\,du = \int_0^{\pi/2}\ln\cos x\,dx$. We also have

$$\int_{\pi/2}^{\pi} \ln\sin x\,dx = \int_0^{\pi/2}\ln\sin(x+\pi/2)\,dx = \int_0^{\pi/2}\ln\cos x\,dx,$$

and therefore

$$\int_0^{\pi/2}\ln\sin x\,dx = \frac{1}{2}\int_0^{\pi}\ln\sin x\,dx = \int_0^{\pi/2}\ln\sin 2y\,dy = \int_0^{\pi/2}(\ln\sin y + \ln\cos y + \ln 2)\,dy.$$

This implies $\displaystyle\int_0^{\pi/2}\ln\cos x\,dx = -\int_0^{\pi/2}\ln 2\,dx = -\frac{\pi\ln 2}{2}$.

7.8.79 This integral cannot be evaluated by finding an antiderivative of the integrand; however the result may be verified by numerical approximation.

7.8.81 We have the relation $B = I\int_0^\infty e^{-rt}\,dt = \frac{I}{r}$, using the result that $\int_0^\infty e^{-ax}\,dx = \frac{1}{a}$ for $a > 0$. Therefore $B = 5000/0.12 = \$41{,}666.67$.

7.8.83

a. We have $\int_0^\infty e^{-ax}\cos bx\,dx = \lim_{c\to\infty}\int_0^c e^{-ax}\cos bx\,dx = \lim_{c\to\infty}\left(\frac{e^{-ax}(b\sin bx - a\cos bx)}{a^2+b^2}\right)\Big|_0^c =$ $\lim_{c\to\infty}\frac{a + e^{-ac}(b\sin bc - a\cos bc)}{a^2+b^2} = \frac{a}{a^2+b^2}$.

b. We have $\int_0^\infty e^{-ax}\sin bx\,dx = \lim_{c\to\infty}\int_0^c e^{-ax}\sin bx\,dx = \lim_{c\to\infty}\left(-\frac{e^{-ax}(a\sin bx + b\cos bx)}{a^2+b^2}\right)\Big|_0^c =$ $\lim_{c\to\infty}\frac{b - e^{-ac}(a\sin bc + b\cos bc)}{a^2+b^2} = \frac{b}{a^2+b^2}$.

7.8.85 Evaluate the improper integral $\int_0^\infty te^{-at}\,dt = \lim_{b\to\infty}\int_0^b te^{-at}\,dt = \lim_{b\to\infty}\left(-\frac{e^{-at}(at+1)}{a^2}\right)\Big|_0^b =$ $\frac{1}{a^2}\lim_{b\to\infty}\left(1 - e^{-ab}(ab+1)\right) = \frac{1}{a^2}$, provided $a > 0$. Therefore $0.00005\int_0^\infty te^{-0.00005t}\,dt = \frac{0.00005}{0.00005^2} =$ 20,000 hrs.

7.8.87

a. We have $W = GMm\int_R^\infty x^{-2}\,dx = GMm\lim_{b\to\infty}\left(-\frac{1}{x}\right)\Big|_R^b = \frac{GMm}{R} \approx 6.279\times 10^7$ m J.

b. Solve $\frac{1}{2}v_e^2 = 6.279\times 10^7$ to obtain $v_e \approx 11.207$ km/s.

c. We need $\frac{GM}{R} \geq \frac{1}{2}c^2 \iff R \leq \frac{2GM}{c^2} \approx 9$ mm.

7.8.89

a.

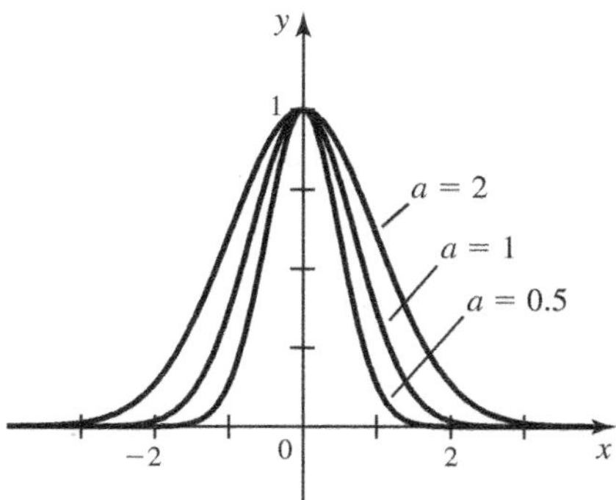

b. The areas are $\sqrt{2\pi}$, $\sqrt{\pi}$, $\sqrt{\pi/2}$ respectively.

c. Completing the square gives

$$ax^2+bx+c = a\left(x+\frac{b}{2a}\right)^2 + \frac{4ac-b^2}{4a},$$

and therefore

$$\int_{-\infty}^{\infty} e^{-(ax^2+bx+c)}\,dx = e^{(b^2-4ac)/(4a)}\int_{-\infty}^{\infty} e^{-a(x+(b/2a))^2}\,dx.$$

Make the substitution $y = x + b/(2a)$ to obtain

$$\int_{-\infty}^{\infty} e^{-(ax^2+bx+c)}\,dx = e^{(b^2-4ac)/(4a)}\int_{-\infty}^{\infty} e^{-ay^2}\,dy = e^{(b^2-4ac)/(4a)}\sqrt{\frac{\pi}{a}}.$$

7.8.91 The Laplace transform of $f(t) = e^{at}$ is given by $F(s) = \int_0^\infty e^{-st}e^{at}\,dt = \int_0^\infty e^{-(s-a)t}\,dt = \frac{1}{s-a}$, using the formula $\int_0^\infty e^{-cx}\,dx = \frac{1}{c}$ for $c>0$.

7.8.93 The Laplace transform of $f(t) = \sin at$ is given by $F(s) = \int_0^\infty e^{-st}\sin at\,dt = \frac{a}{s^2+a^2}$ (this formula is derived in the solution to problem 83 b).

7.8.95

a. Make the substitution $x = y+2$; then

$$\int_1^3 \frac{dx}{\sqrt{(x-1)(3-x)}} = \int_{-1}^{1}\frac{dy}{\sqrt{1-y^2}} = 2\int_0^1 \frac{dy}{\sqrt{1-y^2}} = 2\lim_{c\to 1^-}\left(\sin^{-1}x\right)\Big|_0^c = \pi.$$

b. The substitution $y = e^x$ gives

$$\int_1^\infty \frac{dx}{e^{x+1}+e^{3-x}} = \frac{1}{e}\int_1^\infty \frac{e^x\,dx}{e^{2x}+e^2} = \frac{1}{e}\int_e^\infty \frac{dy}{y^2+e^2} = \frac{1}{e}\lim_{b\to\infty}\left(\frac{1}{e}\tan^{-1}\left(\frac{y}{e}\right)\right)\Big|_e^b = \frac{\pi}{4e^2}.$$

7.8.97 Because $p > 0$, the functions $1/(x^p + x^{-p})$ and $1/x^p$ have the same growth rate as $x \to \infty$; therefore by the result in Example 2, we have $\int_0^\infty \frac{dx}{x^p+x^{-p}} < \infty \iff p > 1$.

7.8.99

a. Integrate by parts with $u = \sqrt{x}\ln x$ and $v = -1/(1+x)$: $\int_0^\infty \frac{\sqrt{x}\ln x}{(1+x)^2}\,dx = \frac{1}{2}\int_0^\infty \frac{\ln x+2}{\sqrt{x}(x+1)}\,dx = \frac{1}{2}\int_0^\infty \frac{\ln x}{\sqrt{x}(x+1)}\,dx + \int_0^\infty \frac{dx}{\sqrt{x}(x+1)}$ (the integration by parts is legitimate for this improper integral because the product uv has limit 0 as $x \to \infty$ and as $x \to 0^+$).

b. Let $y = 1/x$. Then $dy = -\frac{1}{x^2}\,dx$.

c. We have $\int_0^1 \frac{\ln x}{\sqrt{x}(x+1)}\,dx = \int_\infty^1 \frac{-\ln y}{\frac{1}{\sqrt{y}}\left(\frac{1}{y}+1\right)}\left(-\frac{dy}{y^2}\right) = -\int_1^\infty \frac{\ln y}{\sqrt{y}(1+y)}\,dy$, and hence $\int_0^\infty \frac{\ln x}{\sqrt{x}(x+1)}\,dx = 0$.

d. The change of variables $z = \sqrt{x}$ gives $\int_0^\infty \frac{dx}{\sqrt{x}(x+1)} = 2\int_0^\infty \frac{dz}{z^2+1} = \pi$.

7.8.101 Recall that $\frac{d}{dx}x^x = x^x(1+\ln x)$, which can be deduced from logarithmic differentiation. Thus we have $\displaystyle\int_0^a x^x(\ln x+1)\,dx = \lim_{c\to 0^+} x^x\Big|_c^a = \lim_{c\to 0^+}(a^a - c^c) = (a^a - 1)$. This last limit is deduced as follows; let $z = c^c$, then $\ln z = c\ln c = \frac{\ln c}{1/c}$, and by L'hôpital's rule, we have $\displaystyle\lim_{c\to 0^+}\frac{\ln c}{1/c} = \lim_{c\to 0^+}\frac{1/c}{-1/c^2} = \lim_{c\to 0^+} -c = 0$. Thus $\displaystyle\lim_{c\to 0^+} z = e^0 = 1$.

7.9 Introduction to Differential Equations

7.9.1 Second-order, because the highest-order derivative appearing in the equation is second order.

7.9.3 The equation is second-order, so we expect two arbitrary constants in the general solution.

7.9.5 A separable first-order differential equation is one that can be written in the form $g(y)y'(t) = h(t)$.

7.9.7 Integrate both sides with respect to t and convert the integral on the left side to an integral with respect to y.

7.9.9 $y = Ce^{-5t}$ so $y' = -5Ce^{-5t}$. Then $y' + 5y = -5Ce^{-5t} + 5Ce^{-5t} = 0$.

7.9.11 $y = C_1\sin 4t + C_2\cos 4t$ so $y' = 4C_1\cos 4t - 4C_2\sin 4t$ and then $y'' = -16C_1\sin 4t - 16C_2\cos 4t$. Then $y'' + 16y = -16C_1\sin 4t - 16C_2\cos 4t + 16C_1\sin 4t + 16C_2\cos 4t = 0$.

7.9.13 $y = 16e^{2t} - 10$, so $y' = 32e^{2t}$. So $y' - 2y = 32e^{2t} - 32e^{2t} + 20 = 20$. Also $y(0) = 16 - 10 = 6$.

7.9.15 $y = -3\cos 3t$ so $y' = 9\sin 3t$ and $y'' = 27\cos 3t$. Then $y'' + 9y = 27\cos 3t - 27\cos 3t = 0$. Also $y(0) = -3\cos 0 = -3$ and $y'(0) = 9\sin 0 = 0$.

7.9.17 Integrate both sides with respect to t: $\int y'(t)\,dt = \int(3t^2 - 4t + 10)\,dt y(t) = t^3 - 2t^2 + 10t + C$; then substitute $y(0) = 20$ to obtain $y(0) = (t^3 - 2t^2 + 10t + C)\big|_{t=0} = C = 20$, so $y(t) = t^3 - 2t^2 + 10t + 20$.

7.9.19 Integrate both sides with respect to t: $\int y'(t)\,dt = \int \frac{2t^2+4}{t}\,dt = \int\left(2t + \frac{4}{t}\right)dt y(t) = t^2 + 4\ln t + C$; then substitute $y(1) = 2$ to obtain $y(1) = (t^2 + 4\ln t + C)\big|_{t=1} = 1 + C = 2$, so $C = 1$ and thus $y(t) = t^2 + 4\ln t + 1$.

7.9.21 The general solution is $y(t) = Ce^{3t} + \frac{4}{3}$.

7.9.23 The general solution is $y(x) = Ce^{-2x} - 2$.

7.9.25 The general solution is $y(t) = Ce^{3t} + 2$; substitute $y(0) = 9$ to obtain $C + 2 = 9$, so $C = 7$; hence $y(t) = 7e^{3t} + 2$.

7.9.27 The general solution is $y(t) = Ce^{-2t} - 2$; substitute $y(0) = 0$ to obtain $C - 2 = 0$, so $C = 2$; hence $y(t) = 2e^{-2t} - 2$.

7.9.29

a. The general solution is $y(t) = Ce^{-0.02t} + 150$; substitute $y(0) = 0$ to obtain $C + 150 = 0$, so $C = -150$; hence $y(t) = 150(1 - e^{-0.02t})$.

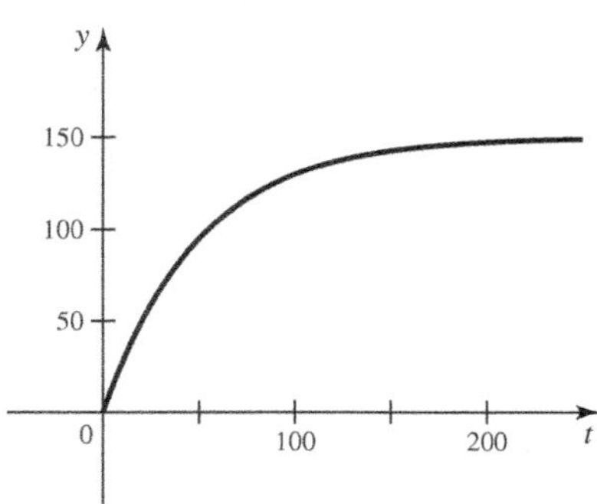

b. The steady-state level is $\lim_{t\to\infty} 150(1 - e^{-0.02t}) = 150$ mg.

c. We have $150(1 - e^{-0.02t}) = 0.9 \cdot 150$, so $e^{-0.02t} = 0.1$, and thus $t = \frac{\ln 10}{0.02} \approx 115$ hrs.

7.9.31 The equation is separable, so we have $\int y\,dy = \int 3t^2\,dt$. So $\frac{y^2}{2} = t^3 + C$, and thus $y = \pm\sqrt{2t^3 + C}$.

7.9.33 The equation is separable, so we have $\int e^{-y/2}\,dy = \int \sin t\,dt$, and so $-2e^{-y/2} = -\cos t + C$. Thus, $y = -2\ln\left(\frac{1}{2}\cos t + C\right)$.

7.9.35 This equation is not separable.

7.9.37 This equation is separable, so we have $\int 2y\,dy = \int e^t\,dt$, so $y^2 = e^t + C$, and thus $y = \pm\sqrt{e^t + C}$. Substituting $y(\ln 2) = 1$ gives $1 = 2 + C$ so $C = -1$, and the solution to this initial value problem is $y = \sqrt{e^t - 1}$.

7.9.39 This equation is separable, so we have $\int e^y\,dy = \int e^x\,dx$, and thus $e^y = e^x + C$. Therefore, $y = \ln(e^x + C)$. Substituting $y(0) = \ln 3$ gives $\ln 3 = \ln(1 + C)$, so $C = 2$ and the solution to this initial value problem is $y = \ln(e^x + 2)$.

7.9.41

a. This equation is separable, so we have $\int \frac{200}{P(200-P)}\,dP = \int 0.08\,dt$, so $\int \left(\frac{1}{P} + \frac{1}{200-P}\right) dP = 0.08t + C$. Therefore, $\ln\left|\frac{P}{200-P}\right| = 0.08t + C$. Substituting $P(0) = 50$ gives $-\ln 3 = C$, and solving for P gives $P(t) = \frac{200}{3e^{-0.08t}+1}$.

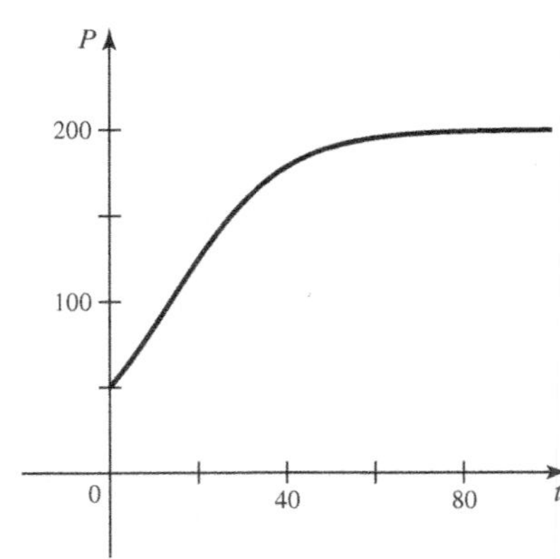

b. The steady-state population is $\lim_{t\to\infty} P(t) = 200$.

7.9.43

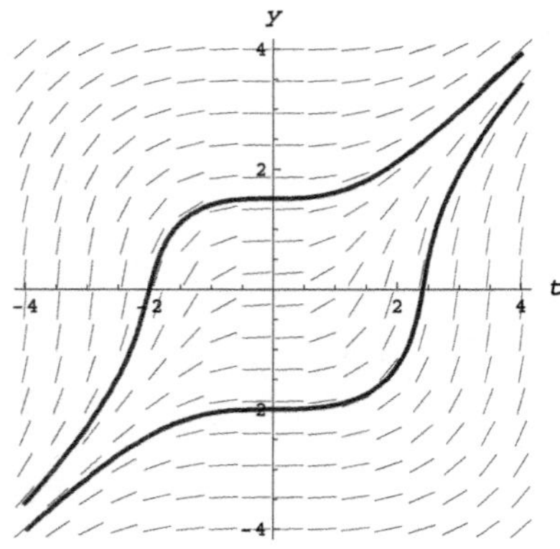

7.9.45

a. This matches with D.

b. This matches with B.

c. This matches with A.

d. This matches with C.

7.9.47

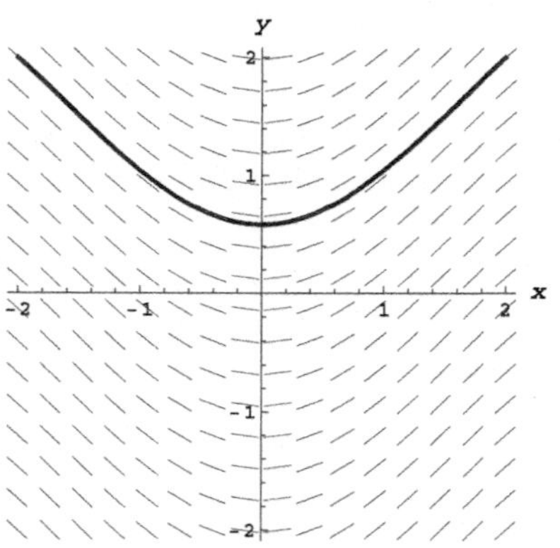

7.9.49

a. False. The general solution is $y = Ce^{20t}$.

b. False. They both do satisfy this differential equation.

c. False. Rewrite the equation as $y'(t) = (t + 2)(y + 2)$.

d. True. $y'(t) = 2(t + 1) = 2\sqrt{(t + 1)^2} = 2\sqrt{y}$.

7.9.51

a. $y = 0$ is an equilibrium solution.

b and c. 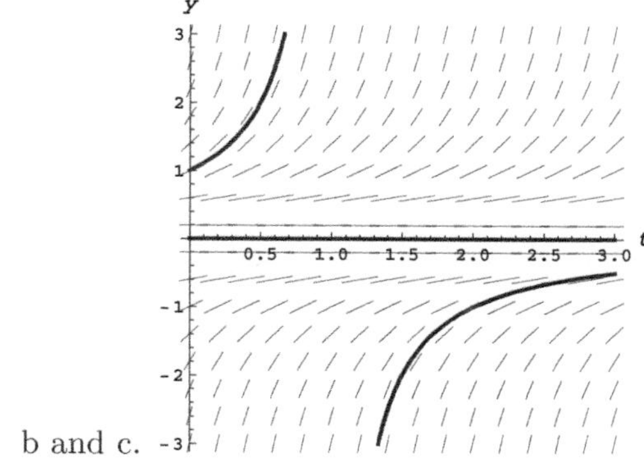

7.9.53

a. Solve $y(y-3) = 0$ to get equilibrium solutions $y = 0$ and $y = 3$.

b and c. 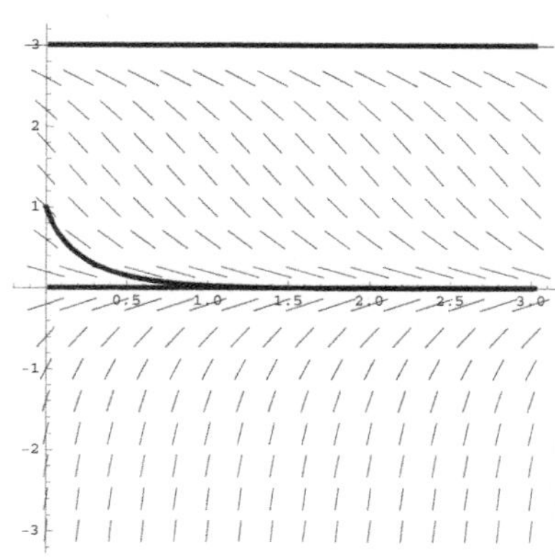

7.9.55

a. The equilibrium solutions are $y = 0$, $y = -2$ and $y = 3$.

b and c. 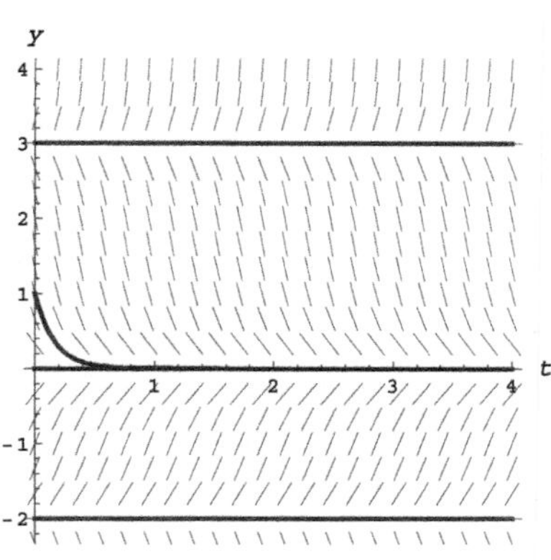

7.9.57 This equation is separable, so we have $\int \frac{dp}{p+1} = \int \frac{dt}{t^2}$, so $\ln|p+1| = -\frac{1}{t} + D$, and thus $p = Ce^{-1/t} - 1$. Substituting $p(1) = 3$ gives $3 = Ce^{-1} - 1$, so $C = 4e$ and the solution to this initial value problem is $p = 4e^{1-1/t} - 1$.

7.9.59 This equation is separable, so we have $\int \sec^2 w\, dw = \int 2t\, dt$, so $\tan w = t^2 + C$. Thus, $w = \tan^{-1}(t^2 + C)$. Substituting $w(0) = \pi/4$ gives $\pi/4 = \tan^{-1} C$, so $C = \tan(\pi/4) = 1$ and the solution to this initial value problem is $w = \tan^{-1}(t^2 + 1)$.

7.9.61

a. This equation is separable, so we have $\int \frac{1}{y(1-y)}\,dy = \int k\,dt$, so $\int \left(\frac{1}{y} + \frac{1}{1-y}\right)\,dy = kt + D$. Therefore, $\ln\left|\frac{y}{1-y}\right| = kt + D$, which is equivalent to $\frac{y}{1-y} = Ce^{kt}$. Substituting $y(0) = y_0$ gives $C = y_0/(1-y_0)$, and thus $y = \frac{y_0}{(1-y_0)e^{-kt}+y_0}$.

b.

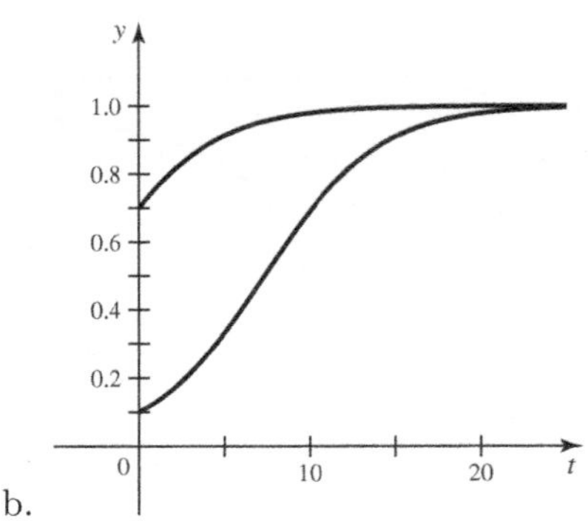

c. The denominator in $y(t)$ above is positive for all $t \geq 0$ when $0 < y_0 < 1$, so $y(t)$ is defined for all $t \geq 0$; we have $\lim_{t\to\infty} y(t) = 1$, which is the steady-state solution.

7.9.63

a. We have $mv'(t) = mg - Rv$, so $v'(t) = g - bv$ with $b = R/m$.

b. Solve $bv = g$ to obtain terminal velocity $\tilde{v} = g/b = mg/R$.

c. The equation $v' = g - bv$ is first-order linear, with general solution $v = Ce^{-bv} + \tilde{v}$. The initial condition $v(0) = 0$ gives $C = -\tilde{v}$, which gives $v = \tilde{v}(1 - e^{-bt})$.

d. We have $b = 0.1$, $\tilde{v} = 98$ m/s.

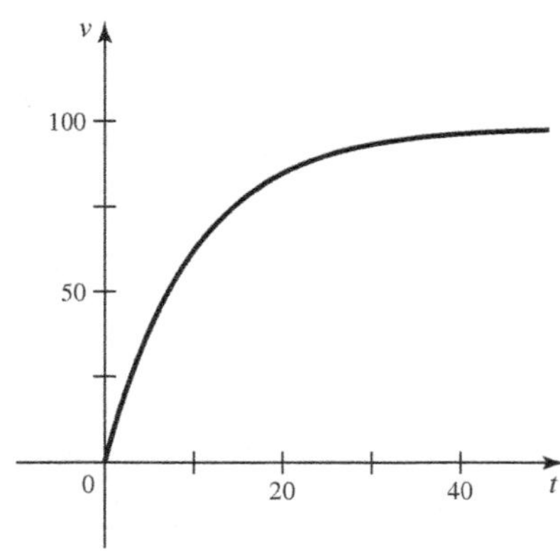

7.9.65

a. The general solution to $y' = -ky$ is $y = Ce^{-kt}$.

b. The equation $y' = -ky^2$ is separable, so we have $-\int \frac{dy}{y^2} = \int k\,dt$, so $\frac{1}{y} = kt + C$. The initial condition $y(0) = y_0$ gives $C = 1/y_0$, and solving for y gives $y = \frac{1}{kt+1/y_0} = \frac{y_0}{1+ky_0t}$.

c.

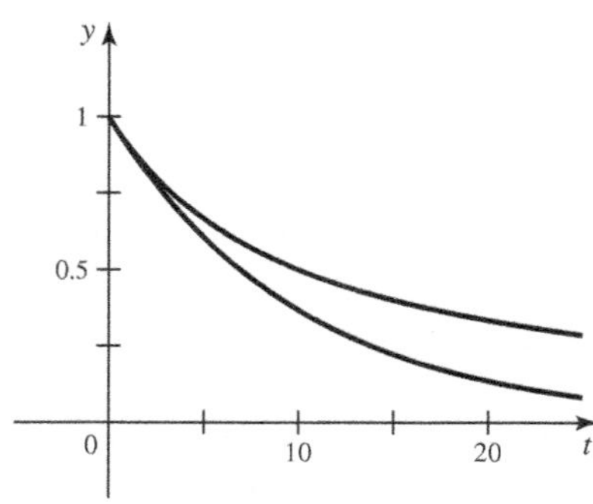

7.9.67

a. The equation $B' = aB - m$ is first-order linear, with general solution $B = Ce^{at} + m/a$; in this case $a = 0.05$, $m/a = 20{,}000$, and the initial condition $B_0 = 15{,}000$ gives $C = -5000$, so $B = 20{,}000 - 5000e^{0.05t}$. The balance decreases.

b. The steady-state (constant balance) solution is $B = m/a = \$50{,}000$, which gives $m = 0.05 \cdot 50{,}000 = \$2500$.

7.9.69

a. Solving $y' = 0$ gives the equilibrium solution $y = -b/a$, which is a horizontal line.

b. 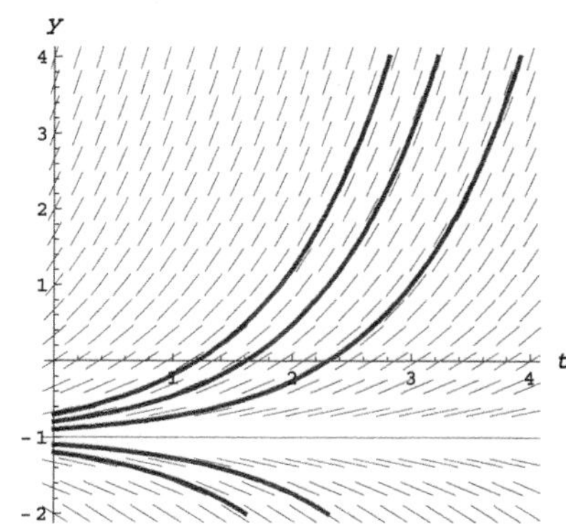

c. 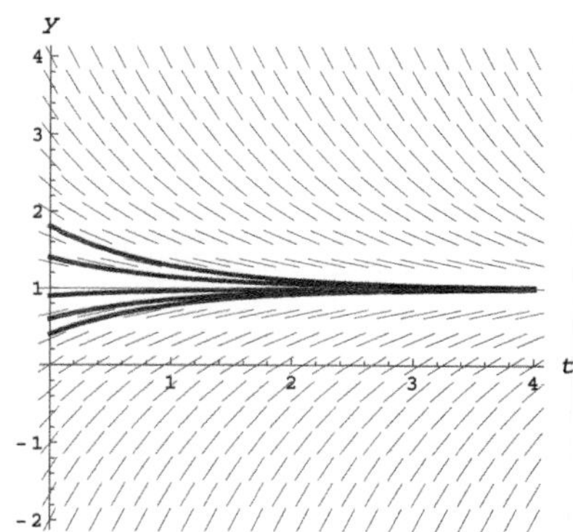

Note that the general solutions $y = (y_0 + \frac{b}{a})e^{at} - \frac{b}{a}$ increases without bound if $a > 0$ and $y_0 > \frac{-b}{a}$, and decreases without bound if $a > 0$ but $y_0 < \frac{-b}{a}$. But if $a < 0$, the general solutions have limit $\frac{-b}{a}$, but must increase to it if $y_0 < \frac{-b}{a}$ and decrease to it if $y_0 > \frac{-b}{a}$.

Chapter Seven Review

1

a. True. Two applications of integration by parts are needed to reduce to $\int x^2 e^{2x}\,dx$.

b. False. This integral can be done using a trigonometric substitution.

c. False. Both are correct, since $-\cos^2 x = \sin^2 x - 1$, so $\sin^2 x$ and $-\cos^2 x$ differ by a constant.

d. True. Recall that $2\sin x \cos x = \sin 2x$.

e. False. Use long division to write the integrand as the sum of a polynomial and a proper rational function.

3 Let $u = x + 4$ so that $du = dx$. Note that $x = u - 4$. Substituting gives

$$\int \frac{3(u-4)}{\sqrt{u}}\,du = 3\int (u^{1/2} - 4u^{-1/2})\,du = 3((2/3)u^{3/2} - 8u^{1/2}) + C$$
$$= 2(x+4)^{3/2} - 24\sqrt{x+4} + C = 2\sqrt{x+4}(x+4-12) + C = 2\sqrt{x+4}(x-8) + C.$$

5

$$\int_{-2}^{1} \frac{3}{(x+2)^2 + 9}\,dx = \left(\tan^{-1}((x+2)/3)\right)\Big|_{-2}^{1} = \pi/4 - 0 = \pi/4.$$

7 Let $u = \sqrt{t-1}$. Then $u^2+1 = t$, and $2u\,du = dt$. Substituting gives $\int \frac{u^2}{u^2+1}\,du = \int \left(1 - \frac{1}{u^2+1}\right)du = u - \tan^{-1}u + C = \sqrt{t-1} - \tan^{-1}\sqrt{t-1} + C$.

9 Let $u = x$ and $dv = (1/2)(x+2)^{-1/2}\,dx$. Then $du = dx$ and $v = (x+2)^{1/2}$. We have

$$\begin{aligned}\int \frac{x}{2\sqrt{x+2}}\,dx &= x\sqrt{x+2} - \int \sqrt{x+2}\,dx = x\sqrt{x+2} - \frac{2}{3}(x+2)^{3/2} + C\\ &= \frac{1}{3}\sqrt{x+2}(3x-2x-4) + C = \frac{1}{3}\sqrt{x+2}(x-4) + C.\end{aligned}$$

11 Let $u = x$ and $dv = \sinh x\,dx$. Then $du = dx$ and $v = \cosh x$. We have $\int x\sinh x\,dx = x\cosh x - \int \cosh x\,dx = x\cosh x - \sinh x + C$.

13 $\int_0^{\pi/4} \cos^5 2x \sin^2 2x\,dx = \int_0^{\pi/4} \cos(2x)(1-\sin^2 2x)^2 \sin^2 2x\,dx$. Let $u = \sin 2x$ so that $du = 2\cos 2x\,dx$. Substituting gives

$$\frac{1}{2}\int_0^1 (1-u^2)^2u^2\,du = \frac{1}{2}\int_0^1 (u^2-2u^4+u^6)\,du = \frac{1}{2}\left(u^3/3 - 2u^5/5 + u^7/7\right)\Big|_0^1 = \frac{1}{2}(1/3-2/5+1/7) - 0 = \frac{4}{105}.$$

15 $\int \tan^4 t\sec^2 t\,dt$. Let $u = \tan t$ so that $du = \sec^2 t\,dt$. Substituting gives

$$\int u^4\,du = u^5/5 + C = \frac{1}{5}\tan^5 t + C.$$

17 $\int \tan^2\theta\sec^2\theta(\sec\theta\tan\theta)\,d\theta = \int(\sec^2\theta - 1)\sec^2\theta(\sec\theta\tan\theta)\,d\theta$. Let $u = \sec\theta$ so that $du = \sec\theta\tan\theta\,d\theta$. Substituting gives

$$\int (u^2-1)u^2\,du = \int (u^4-u^2)\,du = u^5/5 - u^3/3 + C = \frac{1}{5}\sec^5\theta - \frac{1}{3}\sec^3\theta + C.$$

19 Let $x = \sec\theta$ so that $dx = \sec\theta\tan\theta\,d\theta$ and $\sqrt{x^2-1} = \tan\theta$. Substituting gives

$$\int_{\pi/4}^{\pi/3} \tan^2\theta\,d\theta = \int_{\pi/4}^{\pi/3} (\sec^2\theta - 1)\,d\theta = (\tan\theta - \theta)\Big|_{\pi/4}^{\pi/3} = \sqrt{3} - \pi/3 - (1-\pi/4) = \sqrt{3} - 1 - \frac{\pi}{12}.$$

21 Let $x = 2\tan\theta$ so that $dx = 2\sec^2\theta\,d\theta$ and $\sqrt{x^2+4} = 2\sec\theta$. Substituting gives

$$\int \frac{8\tan^3\theta}{2\sec\theta} 2\sec^2\theta\,d\theta = 8\int \tan\theta\sec\theta(\sec^2\theta - 1)\,d\theta.$$

Let $u = \sec\theta$ so that $du = \sec\theta\tan\theta\,d\theta$. Substituting again gives

$$\begin{aligned}8\int (u^2-1)\,du &= \frac{8}{3}u^3 - 8u + C = \frac{8}{3}\sec^3\theta - 8\sec\theta + C\\ &= \frac{8}{3}(\sec(\tan^{-1}(x/2)))^3 - 8\sec\tan^{-1}(x/2) + C = \frac{1}{3}\sqrt{x^2+4}(x^2+4) - 4\sqrt{x^2+4} + C\\ &= \frac{1}{3}\sqrt{x^2+4}(x^2+4-12) + C = \frac{1}{3}\sqrt{x^2+4}(x^2-8) + C.\end{aligned}$$

23 Write $\frac{2x^2+7x+4}{x^3+2x^2+2x} = \frac{Ax+B}{x^2+2x+2} + \frac{C}{x}$. Then $2x^2+7x+4 = Ax^2+Bx+C(x^2+2x+2)$. Letting $x=0$ gives $C = 2$. Letting $x = 1$ gives $13 = A+B+10$, so $A+B = 3$. Letting $x = -1$ gives $-1 = A-B+2$, so $A - B = -3$. Solving this system of linear equations gives $A = 0$ and $B = 3$. Thus our integral is equal to

$$\int \left(\frac{3}{x^2+2x+2} + \frac{2}{x}\right)dx = \int \left(\frac{3}{(x+1)^2+1} + \frac{2}{x}\right)dx = 3\tan^{-1}(x+1) + 2\ln|x| + C.$$

25 Write $\frac{3x^3+4x^2+6x}{(x+1)^2(x^2+4)} = \frac{Ax+B}{x^2+4} + \frac{C}{x+1} + \frac{D}{(x+1)^2}$. Then $3x^3 + 4x^2 + 6x = (Ax + B)(x + 1)^2 + C(x + 1)(x^2 + 4) + D(x^2 + 4)$. Letting $x = -1$ gives $D = -1$. Letting $x = 0$ gives $0 = B + 4C - 4$, so $B + 4C = 4$. Letting $x = 1$ gives $13 = 4A + 4B + 10C - 5$, so $9 = 2A + 2B + 5C$. Letting $x = 2$ gives $52 = 18A + 9B + 24C - 8$, so $60 = 18A + 9B + 24C$, so $20 = 6A + 3B + 8C$. Solving the system of linear equations gives $A = 2$, $B = 0$, and $C = 1$. Our integral is thus equal to

$$\int \left(\frac{2x}{x^2+4} + \frac{1}{x+1} - \frac{1}{(x+1)^2}\right) dx = \ln\left|(x^2+4)(x+1)\right| + \frac{1}{x+1} + C.$$

27 Using the table of integrals entry 77, we find that

$$\int \frac{dx}{x\sqrt{ax-b}} = \frac{2}{\sqrt{b}} \tan^{-1}\left(\sqrt{\frac{ax-b}{b}}\right) + C.$$

Therefore

$$\int \frac{dx}{x\sqrt{4x-6}} = \frac{\sqrt{6}}{3} \tan^{-1}\left(\sqrt{\frac{2x-3}{3}}\right) + C.$$

29 Using the table of integrals reduction formula (number 45) twice, we have

$$\begin{aligned}
\int \sec^5 x\,dx &= \frac{\sec^3 x \tan x}{4} + \frac{3}{4}\int \sec^3 x\,dx \\
&= \frac{\sec^3 x \tan x}{4} + \frac{3}{4}\left(\frac{\sec x \tan x}{2} + \frac{1}{2}\int \sec x\ dx\right) \\
&= \frac{\sec^3 x \tan x}{4} + \frac{3}{4}\left(\frac{\sec x \tan x}{2} + \frac{1}{2}(\ln|\sec x + \tan x|\right) + C \\
&= \frac{\sec^3 x \tan x}{4} + \frac{3 \sec x \tan x}{8} + \frac{3}{8}(\ln|\sec x + \tan x| + C.
\end{aligned}$$

31 Using a CAS, we find that

$$\int_{-1}^{1} e^{-2x^2}\,dx \approx 1.196.$$

33

a. Using a calculator program for the trapezoid and midpoint rules, we find that $T_6 = 9.125, \quad M_6 = 8.937.$

b. Similarly, $T_{12} = 9.031, \quad M_{12} = 8.984.$

35 First evaluate

$$\int_0^b xe^{-x}\,dx = -e^{-x}(x+1)\Big|_0^b = 1 - (b+1)e^{-b}.$$

Then

$$\int_0^\infty xe^{-x}\,dx = \lim_{b\to\infty}(1 - (b+1)e^{-b}) = 1.$$

37 First take $0 < c < 3$ and evaluate

$$\int_0^c \frac{dx}{\sqrt{9-x^2}} = \sin^{-1}\left(\frac{x}{3}\right)\Big|_0^c = \sin^{-1}\left(\frac{c}{3}\right).$$

Then

$$\int_0^3 \frac{dx}{\sqrt{9-x^2}} = \lim_{c\to 3^-} \sin^{-1}\left(\frac{c}{3}\right) = \frac{\pi}{2}.$$

39

$$\int \frac{1}{1+\cos\theta} \cdot \frac{1-\cos\theta}{1-\cos\theta}\,d\theta = \int \frac{1-\cos\theta}{\sin^2\theta}\,d\theta = \int (\csc^2\theta - \csc\theta\cot\theta)\,d\theta = -\cot\theta + \csc\theta + C.$$

41 Two applications of integration by parts gives

$$\int e^x \sin x\,dx = e^x \sin x - \int e^x \cos x\,dx = e^x \sin x - e^x \cos x - \int e^x \sin x\,dx.$$

Thus,

$$2\int e^x \sin x\,dx = e^x \sin x - e^x \cos x,$$

so

$$\int e^x \sin x\,dx = \frac{1}{2}(e^x \sin x - e^x \cos x) + C.$$

43 Let $u = 4\theta$, Then

$$\int \cos^2\theta\,d\theta = \frac{1}{4}\int \cos^2 u\,du = \frac{1}{4}\int \frac{1+\cos 2u}{2}\,du = \frac{u}{8} + \frac{\sin 2u}{16} + C = \frac{\theta}{2} + \frac{\sin 8\theta}{16} + C.$$

45 Let $u = \sec z$. Then $du = \sec z \tan z\,dz$ and

$$\int \sec^5 z \tan z\,dz = \int u^4\,du = \frac{u^5}{5} + C = \frac{\sec^5 z}{5} + C.$$

47 Let $u = \cos x$ so that $du = -\sin x\,dx$. Then

$$\int_0^{\pi/6} \sin^5\theta\,d\theta = \int_0^{\pi/6} \sin^4\theta \cdot \sin\theta\,d\theta = -\int_1^{\sqrt{3}/2} (1-u^2)^2\,du = \int_{\sqrt{3}/2}^1 (1-u^2)^2\,du$$
$$= \int_{\sqrt{3}/2}^1 (1-2u^2+u^4)\,du = \left(u - \frac{2}{3}u^3 + \frac{1}{5}u^5\right)\Big|_{\sqrt{3}/2}^1$$
$$= \frac{8}{15} - \frac{49\sqrt{3}}{160} = \frac{256-147\sqrt{3}}{480}.$$

49 Let $x = 2\sin\theta$ so that $dx = 2\cos\theta\,d\theta$. Then

$$\int \frac{dx}{\sqrt{4-x^2}} = \int \frac{2\cos\theta\,d\theta}{2\cos\theta} = \theta + C = \sin^{-1}(x/2) + C.$$

51 Let $y = 3\sin\theta$ so that $dy = 3\cos\theta\,d\theta$. Then

$$\int \frac{dy}{y^2\sqrt{9-y^2}} = \int \frac{3\cos\theta\,d\theta}{9\sin^2\theta \cdot 3\cos\theta} = \frac{1}{9}\int \csc^2\theta\,d\theta = -\frac{1}{9}\cot\theta + C.$$

Now use $\sin\theta = y/3$, $\cos\theta = (1/3)\sqrt{9-y^2}$ to obtain

$$\int \frac{dy}{y^2\sqrt{9-y^2}} = -\frac{1}{9y}\sqrt{9-y^2} + C.$$

53 Let $x = (3/2)\tan\theta$ so that $dx = (3/2)\sec^2\theta\,d\theta$, and note that $(3/2)\tan(\pi/6) = \sqrt{3}/2$. Then

$$\int_0^{\sqrt{3}/2} \frac{4}{9+4x^2}\,dx = \int_0^{\pi/6} \frac{4}{9\sec^2\theta} \cdot \frac{3}{2}\sec^2\theta\,d\theta = \frac{2}{3}\int_0^{\pi/6} d\theta = \frac{\pi}{9}.$$

55 Let $u = \cosh x$ so that $du = \sinh x\,dx$. Then

$$\int \frac{\sinh x}{\cosh^2 x}\,dx = \int u^{-2}\,du = \frac{-1}{u} + C = \frac{-1}{\cosh x} + C = -\operatorname{sech} x + C.$$

57 Let $u = \sinh x$ so that $du = \cosh x\,dx$. Substituting gives

$$\int_0^{\sqrt{3}} \frac{1}{\sqrt{4-u^2}}\,du = \left(\sin^{-1}(u/2)\right)\Big|_0^{\sqrt{3}} = \frac{\pi}{3}.$$

59 Using the method of partial fractions, we express $\frac{1}{x^2-2x-15} = \frac{1}{(x-5)(x+3)} = \frac{A}{x-5} + \frac{B}{x+3}$. Clearing denominators gives $1 = A(x+3) + B(x-5)$ and comparing coefficients gives $A + B = 0$, $3A - 5B = 1$ which has solution $A = 1/8$, $B = -1/8$. Hence

$$\int \frac{dx}{x^2-2x-15} = \frac{1}{8}\int\left(\frac{1}{x-5} - \frac{1}{x+3}\right)dx = \frac{1}{8}\ln\left|\frac{x-5}{x+3}\right| + C.$$

61 Using the method of partial fractions, we express $\frac{1}{(y+1)(y^2+1)} = \frac{A}{y+1} + \frac{By+C}{y^2+1}$. Clearing denominators gives $1 = A(y^2+1) + (By+C)(y+1)$ and comparing coefficients gives $A + B = 0$, $B + C = 0$ and $A + C = 1$, which has solution $A = 1/2$, $B = -1/2$, $C = 1/2$. Hence

$$\int_0^1 \frac{dy}{(y+1)(y^2+1)} = \frac{1}{2}\int_0^1\left(\frac{1}{y+1} + \frac{1-y}{y^2+1}\right)dy = \frac{1}{2}\left(\ln(y+1) + \tan^{-1}y - \frac{1}{2}\ln(y^2+1)\right)\Big|_0^1 = \frac{1}{4}\ln 2 + \frac{\pi}{8}.$$

63 First consider $\displaystyle\int_0^1 \frac{dx}{\sqrt[3]{|x-1|}} = \lim_{a\to 1^-}\int \frac{dx}{\sqrt[3]{1-x}} = \lim_{a\to 1^-} -\frac{3}{2}(1-x)^{2/3}\Big|_0^a = \lim_{a\to 1^-} -\frac{3}{2}\left((1-a)^{2/3} - 1\right) = \frac{3}{2}.$

Now consider $\displaystyle\int_1^2 \frac{dx}{\sqrt[3]{|x-1|}} = \lim_{b\to 1^+}\int_b^2 \frac{dx}{\sqrt[3]{x-1}} = \lim_{b\to 1^+} \frac{3}{2}(x-1)^{2/3}\Big|_b^2 = \lim_{b\to 1^+} \frac{3}{2}\left(1 - (b-1)^{2/3}\right) = \frac{3}{2}.$

Thus, $\displaystyle\int_0^2 \frac{dx}{\sqrt[3]{|x-1|}} = \frac{3}{2} + \frac{3}{2} = 3.$

65 Factor $x^2 - x - 2 = (x-2)(x+1)$ and use the method of partial fractions: $\frac{1}{(x-2)(x+1)} = \frac{A}{x-2} + \frac{B}{x+1}$. Clearing denominators gives $1 = A(x+1) + B(x-2)$ and equating coefficients gives $A + B = 0$, $A - 2B = 1$, so $A = 1/3$, $B = -1/3$. Therefore

$$\int \frac{dx}{x^2-x-2} = \frac{1}{3}\int\left(\frac{1}{x-2} - \frac{1}{x+1}\right)dx = \frac{1}{3}\ln\left|\frac{x-2}{x+1}\right| + C.$$

67 As a preliminary step, observe that

$$\frac{2x^2-4x}{x^2-4} = \frac{2x(x-2)}{(x-2)(x+2)} = \frac{2x}{x+2} = \frac{2(x+2-2)}{x+2} = 2 - \frac{4}{x+2}.$$

Hence

$$\int \frac{2x^2-4x}{x^2-4}\,dx = 2x - 4\ln|x+2| + C = 2(x - 2\ln|x+2|) + C.$$

69 Make the preliminary substitution $x = e^{2t}$, $dx = 2e^{2t}$. Then we have

$$\int \frac{e^{2t}}{(1+e^{4t})^{3/2}}\,dt = \frac{1}{2}\int \frac{dx}{(1+x^2)^{3/2}}.$$

Now let $x = \tan\theta$, $dx = \sec^2\theta\,d\theta$ and

$$\frac{1}{2}\int \frac{dx}{(1+x^2)^{3/2}} = \frac{1}{2}\int \frac{\sec^2\theta}{\sec^3\theta}\,d\theta = \frac{1}{2}\int \cos\theta\,d\theta = \frac{1}{2}\sin\theta + C.$$

Now

$$\sin\theta = \frac{\tan\theta}{\sec\theta} = \frac{x}{\sqrt{1+x^2}} = \frac{e^{2t}}{\sqrt{1+e^{4t}}}.$$

Therefore

$$\int \frac{e^{2t}}{(1+e^{4t})^{3/2}}\,dt = \frac{1}{2}\frac{e^{2t}}{\sqrt{1+e^{4t}}} + C.$$

71 The volume is

$$V = \pi \int_1^e (\ln x)^2\, dx = \pi x((\ln x)^2 - 2\ln x + 2)\Big|_1^e = \pi(e-2).$$

73 The volume is

$$V = 2\pi \int_1^e (x-1)\ln x\, dx = \frac{\pi}{2} x\,(2(x-2)\ln x - x + 4)\Big|_1^e = \frac{\pi}{2}\left(e^2 - 3\right).$$

75 The volume generated by revolving around the x-axis is

$$V_x = \pi \int_0^\pi \sin^2 x\, dx = \pi\left(\frac{x}{2} - \frac{\sin 2x}{4}\right)\Big|_0^\pi = \frac{\pi^2}{2},$$

and the volume generated by revolving around the y-axis is

$$V_y = 2\pi \int_0^\pi x\sin x\, dx = 2\pi(\sin x - x\cos x)\Big|_0^\pi = 2\pi^2,$$

so the greater volume is obtained by revolving around the y-axis.

77

a. Observe that

$$\int_{1/2}^b \ln x\, dx = (x\ln x - x)\Big|_{1/2}^b \approx b\ln b - b + 0.847;$$

solve $b\ln b - b + 0.847 = 0$ numerically to obtain $b \approx 1.603$.

b. Similarly, we have

$$\int_{1/3}^b \ln x\, dx = (x\ln x - x)\Big|_{1/3}^b \approx b\ln b - b + 0.700;$$

solve $b\ln b - b + 0.700 = 0$ numerically to obtain $b \approx 1.870$.

c. In general, the pair (a, b) must satisfy the equation

$$\int_a^b \ln x\, dx = (b\ln b - b) - (a\ln a - a) = 0,$$

which gives $b\ln b - b = a\ln a - a$.

d. As a increases there is less negative area to the right of $x = 1$, so $b = g(a)$ is a decreasing function of a.

79 The average velocity is

$$\bar{v} = \frac{1}{\pi}\int_0^\pi 10\sin 3t\, dt = -\frac{10}{3\pi}\cos 3t\Big|_0^\pi = \frac{20}{3\pi}.$$

81 The number of cars is given by the integral

$$\int_0^4 800te^{-t/2}\, dt = -1600(t+2)e^{-t/2}\Big|_0^4 = 3200(1 - 3e^{-2}) \approx 1901.$$

83

a. Using integration by parts, we find that

$$I(p) = \int_1^e \frac{\ln x}{x^p}\, dx = -\frac{x^{1-p}}{(p-1)^2}\left((p-1)\ln x + 1\right)\Big|_1^e = \frac{1}{(p-1)^2}(1 - pe^{1-p})$$

for $p \neq 1$, and using the substitution $u = \ln x$ gives

$$I(1) = \int_1^e \frac{\ln x}{x}\, dx = \frac{(\ln x)^2}{2}\Big|_1^e = \frac{1}{2}.$$

b. We have

$$\lim_{p\to\infty} I(p) = \lim_{p\to\infty} \frac{1}{(p-1)^2}(1 - pe^{1-p}) = \lim_{p\to\infty} \left(\frac{1}{(p-1)^2} - \frac{pe}{(p-1)^2} e^{-p} \right) = 0,$$

and

$$\lim_{p\to-\infty} I(p) = \lim_{p\to-\infty} \left(\frac{1}{(p-1)^2} - \frac{pe}{(p-1)^2} e^{-p} \right) = \infty,$$

since e^{-p} grows much faster than $(p-1)^2/p$ as $p \to -\infty$.

c. By inspection we see that $I(0) = 1$.

85 Use a calculator program for, say, Simpson's rule with $n = 100$, but replace the limits with 0.00000001 and 0.99999999 to avoid errors coming from trying to evaluate the function at $x = 0$ or $x = 1$; we obtain

$$\int_0^1 \frac{x^2 - x}{\ln x}\, dx \approx 0.4054651.$$

87 Numerically approximate the integral to obtain

$$\int_0^1 \frac{\sin^{-1} x}{x}\, dx \approx 1.0889;$$

therefore $n = \pi \ln 2/1.0889 = 2$. (When approximating the integral, replace the lower limit 0 with a small positive number like 0.00001 to avoid an error from evaluating the integrand at $x = 0$.)

89

a. Using integration by parts or a CAS, we find that the volume is $V_1(a) = \pi \int_1^a (\ln x)^2\, dx = \pi x((\ln x)^2 - 2\ln x + 2)\Big|_1^a = \pi[(a\ln^2 a - 2a\ln a + 2(a-1)]$.

b. Using integration by parts or a CAS, we find that the volume is $V_2(a) = 2\pi \int_1^a x\ln x\, dx = \frac{\pi}{2} x^2(2\ln x - 1)\Big|_1^a = \frac{\pi}{2}(2a^2 \ln a - a^2 + 1)$.

c. As shown by the graph, $V_2(a) > V_1(a)$ for all $a > 1$.

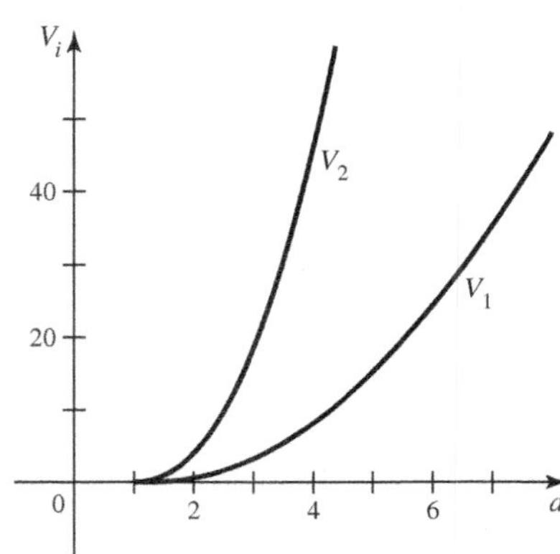

91 We have

$$V_1 = \pi \int_0^b e^{-2ax}\, dx = -\frac{\pi}{2a} e^{-2ax}\Big|_0^b = \frac{\pi}{2a}\left(1 - e^{-2ab}\right),$$

and

$$V_2 = \pi \int_b^\infty e^{-2ax}\, dx = \lim_{c\to\infty} \left(-\frac{\pi}{2a} e^{-2ax}\Big|_b^c \right) = \frac{\pi}{2a} e^{-2ab}.$$

Equating and solving gives $e^{-2ab} = 1/2$, which is equivalent to $ab = (1/2)\ln 2$.

93 This first-order linear equation has general solution $y = Ce^{2t} - 2$; the initial condition gives $C - 2 = 8$, so $C = 10$ and hence $y = 10e^{2t} - 2$.

95 This equation is separable. We have $\int 2y\,dy = \int \left(1 + \frac{1}{t}\right) dt$, so $y^2 = t + \ln t + C$. The initial condition gives $16 = 1 + C$, so $C = 15$ and solving for y gives $y = \sqrt{t + \ln t + 15}$.

97 This equation is separable. We have $\int \cos y\,dy = \int \frac{dt}{t^2}$, so $\sin y = -\frac{1}{t} + C$. The initial condition gives $0 = -1 + C$, so $C = 1$ and solving for y gives $y = \sin^{-1}\left(1 - \frac{1}{t}\right)$. Therefore $\lim_{t\to\infty} y(t) = \lim_{t\to\infty} \sin^{-1}\left(1 - \frac{1}{t}\right) = \sin^{-1} 1 = \frac{\pi}{2}$.

99

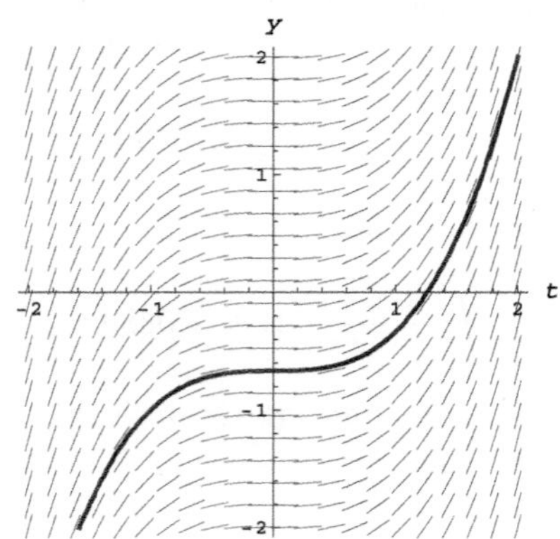

101 This equation is separable. We have

$$\int dt = -\frac{1}{10}\int \left(1 + \frac{5}{s}\right) ds \Longrightarrow t = -\frac{s + 5\ln s}{10} + C.$$

The initial condition gives $s(0) = 50$ gives $C = (50 + 5\ln 50)/10$, so the solution is given implicitly by

$$t = \frac{-s - 5\ln s + 50 + 5\ln 50}{10}.$$

As $t \to \infty$ we must have $s + 5\ln s \to -\infty$, which implies that $\lim_{t\to\infty} s(t) = 0$.

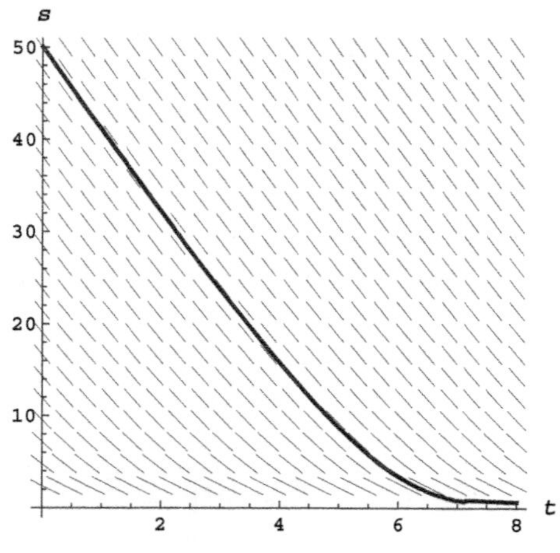

Chapter 8

Sequences and Infinite Series

8.1 An Overview

8.1.1 A *sequence* is an ordered list of numbers $a_1, a_2, a_3, \dots$, often written $\{a_1, a_2, \dots\}$ or $\{a_n\}$. For example, the natural numbers $\{1, 2, 3, ...\}$ are a sequence where $a_n = n$ for every n.

8.1.3 $a_1 = 1$ (given); $a_2 = 1 \cdot a_1 = 1$; $a_3 = 2 \cdot a_2 = 2$; $a_4 = 3 \cdot a_3 = 6$; $a_5 = 4 \cdot a_4 = 24$.

8.1.5 An *infinite series* is an infinite sum of numbers. Thus if $\{a_n\}$ is a sequence, then $a_1 + a_2 + \cdots = \sum_{k=1}^{\infty} a_k$ is an infinite series. For example, if $a_k = \frac{1}{k}$, then $\sum_{k=1}^{\infty} a_k = \sum_{k=1}^{\infty} \frac{1}{k}$ is an infinite series.

8.1.7 $S_1 = \sum_{k=1}^{1} k^2 = 1$; $S_2 = \sum_{k=1}^{2} k^2 = 1 + 4 = 5$; $S_3 = \sum_{k=1}^{3} k^2 = 1 + 4 + 9 = 14$; $S_4 = \sum_{k=1}^{4} k^2 = 1 + 4 + 9 + 16 = 30$.

8.1.9 $a_1 = \dfrac{1}{10}; a_2 = \dfrac{1}{100}; a_3 = \dfrac{1}{1000}; a_4 = \dfrac{1}{10000}.$

8.1.11 $a_1 = \frac{-1}{2}$, $a_2 = \frac{1}{2^2} = \frac{1}{4}$. $a_3 = \frac{-2}{2^3} = \frac{-1}{8}$, $a_4 = \frac{1}{2^4} = \frac{1}{16}$.

8.1.13 $a_1 = \frac{2^2}{2+1} = \frac{4}{3}$. $a_2 = \frac{2^3}{2^2+1} = \frac{8}{5}$. $a_3 = \frac{2^4}{2^3+1} = \frac{16}{9}$. $a_4 = \frac{2^5}{2^4+1} = \frac{32}{17}$.

8.1.15 $a_1 = 1 + \sin(\pi/2) = 2$; $a_2 = 1 + \sin(2\pi/2) = 1 + \sin \pi = 1$; $a_3 = 1 + \sin(3\pi/2) = 0$; $a_4 = 1 + \sin(4\pi/2) = 1 + \sin 2\pi = 1$.

8.1.17 $a_1 = 2$, $a_2 = 2 \cdot 2 = 4$, $a_3 = 2(4) = 8$, $a_4 = 2 \cdot 8 = 16$.

8.1.19 $a_1 = 10$ (given); $a_2 = 3 \cdot a_1 - 12 = 30 - 12 = 18$; $a_3 = 3 \cdot a_2 - 12 = 54 - 12 = 42$; $a_4 = 3 \cdot a_3 - 12 = 126 - 12 = 114$.

8.1.21 $a_1 = 0$ (given); $a_2 = 3 \cdot a_1^2 + 1 + 1 = 2$; $a_3 = 3 \cdot a_2^2 + 2 + 1 = 15$; $a_4 = 3 \cdot a_3^2 + 3 + 1 = 679$.

8.1.23

a. $\frac{1}{32}$, $\frac{1}{64}$.

b. $a_1 = 1$; $a_{n+1} = \frac{a_n}{2}$.

c. $a_n = \frac{1}{2^{n-1}}$.

8.1.25

a. -5, 5.

b. $a_1 = -5$, $a_{n+1} = -a_n$.

c. $a_n = (-1)^n \cdot 5$.

8.1.27

a. 32, 64.

b. $a_1 = 1$; $a_{n+1} = 2a_n$.

c. $a_n = 2^{n-1}$.

8.1.29

a. 243, 729.

b. $a_1 = 1$; $a_{n+1} = 3a_n$.

c. $a_n = 3^{n-1}$.

8.1.31 $a_1 = 9$, $a_2 = 99$, $a_3 = 999$, $a_4 = 9999$. This sequence diverges, because the terms get larger without bound.

8.1.33 $a_1 = \frac{1}{10}$, $a_2 = \frac{1}{100}$, $a_3 = \frac{1}{1000}$, $a_4 = \frac{1}{10{,}000}$. This sequence converges to zero.

8.1.35 $a_1 = -\frac{1}{2}$, $a_2 = \frac{1}{4}$, $a_3 = -\frac{1}{8}$, $a_4 = \frac{1}{16}$. This sequence converges to 0 because each term is smaller in absolute value than the preceding term and they get arbitrarily close to zero.

8.1.37 $a_1 = 1 + 1 = 2$, $a_2 = 1 + 1 = 2$, $a_3 = 2$, $a_4 = 2$. This constant sequence converges to 2.

8.1.39 $a_1 = \frac{50}{11} + 50 \approx 54.545$, $a_2 = \frac{54.545}{11} + 50 \approx 54.959$, $a_3 = \frac{54.959}{11} + 50 \approx 54.996$, $a_4 = \frac{54.996}{11} + 50 \approx 55.000$. This sequence converges to 55.

8.1.41

n	1	2	3	4	4	6	7	8	9	10
a_n	0.4636	0.2450	0.1244	0.0624	0.0312	0.0156	0.0078	0.0039	0.0020	0.0010

This sequence appears to converge to 0.

8.1.43

n	1	2	3	4	5	6	7	8	9	10
a_n	0	2	6	12	20	30	42	56	72	90

This sequence appears to diverge.

8.1.45

n	1	2	3	4	5	6	7	8	9	10
a_n	0.83333	0.96154	0.99206	0.99840	0.99968	0.99994	0.99999	1.0000	1.0000	1.0000

This sequence appears to converge to 1.

8.1.47

a. 2.5, 2.25, 2.125, 2.0625.

b. The limit is 2.

8.1.49

n	0	1	2	3	4	5	6	7	8	9	10
a_n	3	3.500	3.750	3.875	3.938	3.969	3.984	3.992	3.996	3.998	3.999

This sequence converges to 4.

8.1.51

n	0	1	2	3	4	5	6	7	8	9	10
a_n	0	1	3	7	15	31	63	127	255	511	1023

This sequence diverges.

8.1.53

n	0	1	2	3	4	5	6	7	8	9
a_n	1000	18.811	5.1686	4.1367	4.0169	4.0021	4.0003	4.0000	4.0000	4.0000

This sequence converges to 4.

8.1.55

a. 20, 10, 5, 2.5.

b. $h_n = 20(0.5)^n$.

8.1.57

a. 30, 7.5, 1.875, 0.46875.

b. $h_n = 30(0.25)^n$.

8.1.59 $S_1 = 0.3$, $S_2 = 0.33$, $S_3 = 0.333$, $S_4 = 0.3333$. It appears that the infinite series has a value of $0.3333\ldots = \frac{1}{3}$.

8.1.61 $S_1 = 4$, $S_2 = 4.9$, $S_3 = 4.99$, $S_4 = 4.999$. The infinite series has a value of $4.999\cdots = 5$.

8.1.63

a. $S_1 = \frac{2}{3}$, $S_2 = \frac{4}{5}$, $S_3 = \frac{6}{7}$, $S_4 = \frac{8}{9}$.

b. It appears that $S_n = \frac{2n}{2n+1}$.

c. The series has a value of 1 (the partial sums converge to 1).

8.1.65

a. $S_1 = \frac{1}{3}$, $S_2 = \frac{2}{5}$, $S_3 = \frac{3}{7}$, $S_4 = \frac{4}{9}$.

b. $S_n = \frac{n}{2n+1}$.

c. The partial sums converge to $\frac{1}{2}$, which is the value of the series.

8.1.67

a. True. For example, $S_2 = 1 + 2 = 3$, and $S_4 = a_1 + a_2 + a_3 + a_4 = 1 + 2 + 3 + 4 = 10$.

b. False. For example, $\frac{1}{2}, \frac{3}{4}, \frac{7}{8}, \cdots$ where $a_n = 1 - \frac{1}{2^n}$ converges to 1, but each term is greater than the previous one.

c. True. In order for the partial sums to converge, they must get closer and closer together. In order for this to happen, the difference between successive partial sums, which is just the value of a_n, must approach zero.

8.1.69 Using the work from the previous problem:

a. Here $h_0 = 20$, $r = 0.75$, so $S_1 = 40$, $S_2 = 40 + 40 \cdot 0.75 = 70$, $S_3 = S_2 + 40 \cdot (0.75)^2 = 92.5$, $S_4 = S_3 + 40 \cdot (0.75)^3 = 109.375$, $S_5 = S_4 + 40 \cdot (0.75)^4 = 122.03125$

b.

n	1	2	3	4	5	6
a_n	40	70	92.5	109.375	122.031	131.523
n	7	8	9	10	11	12
a_n	138.643	143.982	147.986	150.990	153.242	154.932
n	13	14	15	16	17	18
a_n	156.199	157.149	157.862	158.396	158.797	159.098
n	19	20	21	22	23	24
a_n	159.323	159.493	159.619	159.715	159.786	159.839

The sequence converges to 160.

8.1.71

a. 0.9, 0.99, 0.999, .9999.

b. The limit is 1.

8.1.73

a. $\frac{1}{3}, \frac{4}{9}, \frac{13}{27}, \frac{40}{81}$.

b. The limit is 1/2.

8.1.75

a. $-1, 0, -1, 0$.

b. The limit does not exist.

8.1.77

a. $\frac{3}{10} = 0.3$, $\frac{33}{100} = 0.33$, $\frac{333}{1000} = 0.333$, $\frac{3333}{10000} = 0.3333$.

b. The limit is 1/3.

8.1.79

a. $M_0 = 20$, $M_1 = 20 \cdot 0.5 = 10$, $M_2 = 20 \cdot 0.5^2 = 5$, $M_3 = 20 \cdot 0.5^3 = 2.5$, $M_4 = 20 \cdot 0.5^4 = 1.25$

b. $M_n = 20 \cdot 0.5^n$.

c. The initial mass is $M_0 = 20$. We are given that 50% of the mass is gone after each decade, so that $M_{n+1} = 0.5 \cdot M_n$, $n \geq 0$.

d. The amount of material goes to 0.

8.1.81

a. $d_0 = 200$, $d_1 = 200 \cdot .95 = 190$, $d_2 = 200 \cdot .95^2 = 180.5$, $d_3 = 200 \cdot .95^3 = 171.475$, $d_4 = 200 \cdot .95^4 = 162.90125$.

b. $d_n = 200(0.95)^n$, $n \geq 0$.

c. We are given $d_0 = 200$; because 5% of the drug is washed out every hour, that means that 95% of the preceding amount is left every hour, so that $d_{n+1} = 0.95 \cdot d_n$.

d. The sequence converges to 0.

8.2 Sequences

8.2.1 There are many examples; one is $a_n = \frac{1}{n}$. This sequence is nonincreasing (in fact, it is decreasing) and has a limit of 0.

8.2.3 There are many examples; one is $a_n = \frac{1}{n}$. This sequence is nonincreasing (in fact, it is decreasing), is bounded above by 1 and below by 0, and has a limit of 0.

8.2.5 $\{r^n\}$ converges for $-1 < r \leq 1$. It diverges for all other values of r (see Theorem 8.3).

8.2.7 $\{e^{n/100}\}$ grows faster than $\{n^{100}\}$ as $n \to \infty$.

8.2.9 Divide numerator and denominator by n^4 to get $\lim_{n\to\infty} \frac{1/n}{1+\frac{1}{n^4}} = 0$.

8.2.11 Divide numerator and denominator by n^3 to get $\lim_{n\to\infty} \frac{3-n^{-3}}{2+n^{-3}} = \frac{3}{2}$.

8.2.13 Divide numerator and denominator by 3^n to get $\lim_{n\to\infty} \frac{3+(1/3^{n-1})}{1} = 3$.

8.2.15 $\lim_{n\to\infty} \tan^{-1} n = \frac{\pi}{2}$.

8.2.17 Because $\lim_{n\to\infty} \tan^{-1} n = \frac{\pi}{2}$, $\lim_{n\to\infty} \frac{\tan^{-1} n}{n} = 0$.

8.2.19 Find the limit of the logarithm of the expression, which is $n \ln\left(1 + \frac{2}{n}\right)$. Using L'Hôpital's rule:

$$\lim_{n\to\infty} n \ln\left(1 + \frac{2}{n}\right) = \lim_{n\to\infty} \frac{\ln\left(1 + \frac{2}{n}\right)}{1/n} = \lim_{n\to\infty} \frac{\frac{1}{1+(2/n)}\left(\frac{-2}{n^2}\right)}{-1/n^2} = \lim_{n\to\infty} \frac{2}{1+(2/n)} = 2.$$

Thus the limit of the original expression is e^2.

8.2.21 Take the logarithm of the expression and use L'Hôpital's rule:

$$\lim_{n\to\infty} \frac{n}{2} \ln\left(1 + \frac{1}{2n}\right) = \lim_{n\to\infty} \frac{\ln(1+(1/2n))}{2/n} = \lim_{n\to\infty} \frac{\frac{1}{1+(1/2n)} \cdot \frac{-1}{2n^2}}{-2/n^2} = \lim_{n\to\infty} \frac{1}{4(1+(1/2n))} = \frac{1}{4}.$$

Thus the original limit is $e^{1/4}$.

8.2.23 Using L'Hôpital's rule: $\lim_{n\to\infty} \frac{n}{e^n+3n} = \lim_{n\to\infty} \frac{1}{e^n+3} = 0$.

8.2.25 Taking logs, we have $\lim_{n\to\infty} \frac{1}{n} \ln(1/n) = \lim_{n\to\infty} -\frac{\ln n}{n} = \lim_{n\to\infty} \frac{-1}{n} = 0$ by L'Hôpital's rule. Thus the original sequence has limit $e^0 = 1$.

8.2.27 Except for a finite number of terms, this sequence is just $a_n = ne^{-n}$, so it has the same limit as this sequence. Note that $\lim_{n\to\infty} \frac{n}{e^n} = \lim_{n\to\infty} \frac{1}{e^n} = 0$, by L'Hôpital's rule.

8.2.29 $\ln(\sin(1/n)) + \ln n = \ln(n \sin(1/n)) = \ln\left(\frac{\sin(1/n)}{1/n}\right)$. As $n \to \infty$, $\sin(1/n)/(1/n) \to 1$, so the limit of the original sequence is $\ln 1 = 0$.

8.2.31 $\lim_{n\to\infty} n \sin(6/n) = \lim_{n\to\infty} \frac{\sin(6/n)}{1/n} = \lim_{n\to\infty} \frac{\frac{-6\cos(6/n)}{n^2}}{(-1/n^2)} = \lim_{n\to\infty} 6\cos(6/n) = 6 \cdot \cos 0 = 6$.

8.2.33 The terms with odd-numbered subscripts have the form $-\frac{n}{n+1}$, so they approach -1, while the terms with even-numbered subscripts have the form $\frac{n}{n+1}$ so they approach 1. Thus, the sequence has no limit.

8.2.35 When n is an integer, $\sin\left(\frac{n\pi}{2}\right)$ oscillates between the values ± 1 and 0, so this sequence does not converge.

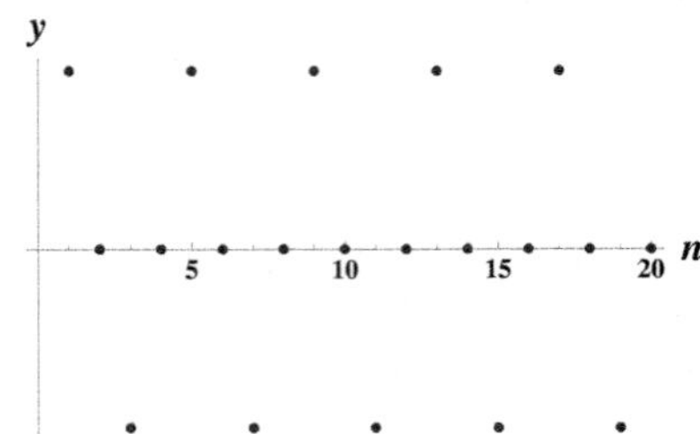

8.2.37 The numerator is bounded in absolute value by 1, while the denominator goes to ∞, so the limit of this sequence is 0.

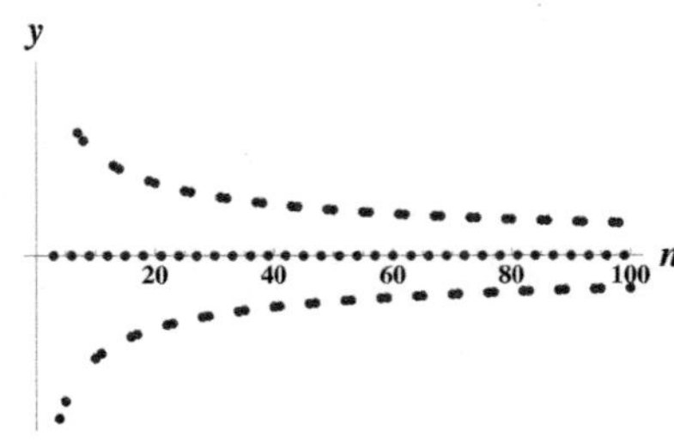

8.2.39 $\lim_{n\to\infty}(1+\cos(1/n)) = 1+\cos(0) = 2.$

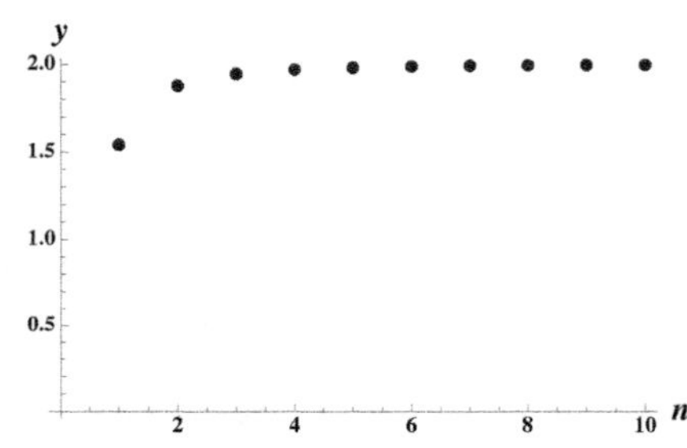

8.2.41 This is the sequence $\frac{\cos n}{e^n}$; the numerator is bounded in absolute value by 1 and the denominator increases without bound, so the limit is zero.

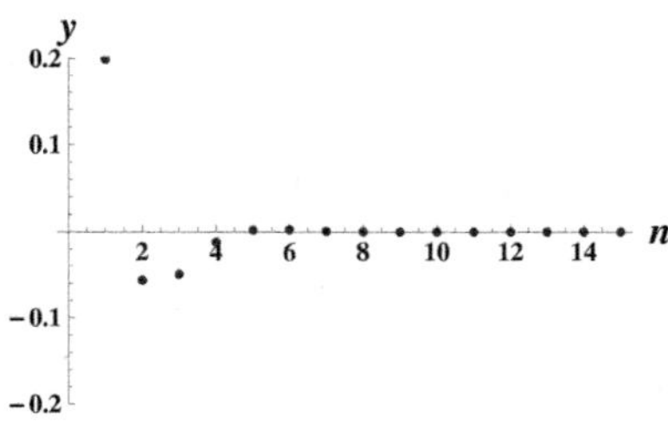

8.2.43 Ignoring the factor of $(-1)^n$ for the moment, we see, taking logs, that $\lim_{n\to\infty}\frac{\ln n}{n} = 0$, so that $\lim_{n\to\infty}\sqrt[n]{n} = e^0 = 1$. Taking the sign into account, the odd terms converge to -1 while the even terms converge to 1. Thus the sequence does not converge.

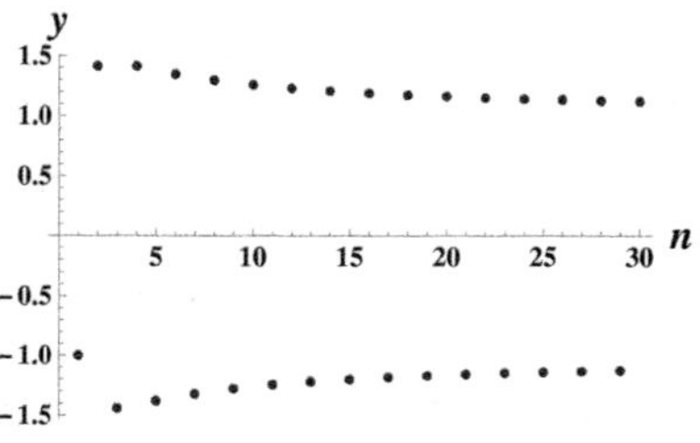

8.2.45 Because $0.2 < 1$, this sequence converges to 0. Because $0.2 > 0$, the convergence is monotone.

8.2.47 Because $|-0.7| < 1$, the sequence converges to 0; because $-0.7 < 0$, it does not do so monotonically. The sequence converges by oscillation.

8.2.49 Because $1.00001 > 1$, the sequence diverges; because $1.00001 > 0$, the divergence is monotone.

8.2.51 Because $|-2.5| > 1$, the sequence diverges; because $-2.5 < 0$, the divergence is not monotone. The sequence diverges by oscillation.

8.2.53 Because $-1 \le \cos n \le 1$, we have $\frac{-1}{n} \le \frac{\cos n}{n} \le \frac{1}{n}$. Because both $\frac{-1}{n}$ and $\frac{1}{n}$ have limit 0 as $n \to \infty$, the given sequence does as well.

8.2.55 Because $-1 \le \sin n \le 1$ for all n, the given sequence satisfies $-\frac{1}{2^n} \le \frac{\sin n}{2^n} \le \frac{1}{2^n}$, and because both $\pm\frac{1}{2^n} \to 0$ as $n \to \infty$, the given sequence converges to zero as well by the Squeeze Theorem.

8.2.57 The inverse tangent function takes values between $-\pi/2$ and $\pi/2$, so the numerator is always between $-\pi$ and π. Thus $\frac{-\pi}{n^3+4} \le \frac{2\tan^{-1} n}{n^3+4} \le \frac{\pi}{n^3+4}$, and by the Squeeze Theorem, the given sequence converges to zero.

8.2.59

a. After the nth dose is given, the amount of drug in the bloodstream is $d_n = 0.5 \cdot d_{n-1} + 80$, because the half-life is one day. The initial condition is $d_1 = 80$.

b. The limit of this sequence is 160 mg.

c. Let $L = \lim_{n\to\infty} d_n$. Then from the recurrence relation, we have $d_n = 0.5 \cdot d_{n-1} + 80$, and thus $\lim_{n\to\infty} d_n = 0.5 \cdot \lim_{n\to\infty} d_{n-1} + 80$, so $L = 0.5 \cdot L + 80$, and therefore $L = 160$.

8.2.61

a.

$$\begin{aligned}
B_0 &= 0\\
B_1 &= 1.0075 \cdot B_0 + \$100 = \$100\\
B_2 &= 1.0075 \cdot B_1 + \$100 = \$200.75\\
B_3 &= 1.0075 \cdot B_2 + \$100 = \$302.26\\
B_4 &= 1.0075 \cdot B_3 + \$100 = \$404.52\\
B_5 &= 1.0075 \cdot B_4 + \$100 = \$507.56
\end{aligned}$$

b. $B_n = 1.0075 \cdot B_{n-1} + \$100$.

c. Using a calculator or computer program, $B_n > \$5,000$ during the 43rd month.

8.2.63 Because $n! \ll n^n$ by Theorem 8.6, we have $\lim_{n\to\infty} \frac{n!}{n^n} = 0$.

8.2.65 Theorem 8.6 indicates that $\ln^q n \ll n^p$, so $\ln^{20} n \ll n^{10}$, so $\lim_{n\to\infty} \frac{n^{10}}{\ln^{20} n} = \infty$.

8.2.67 By Theorem 8.6, $n^p \ll b^n$, so $n^{1000} \ll 2^n$, and thus $\lim_{n\to\infty} \frac{n^{1000}}{2^n} = 0$.

8.2.69 Let $\varepsilon > 0$ be given and let N be an integer with $N > \frac{1}{\varepsilon}$. Then if $n > N$, we have $\left|\frac{1}{n} - 0\right| = \frac{1}{n} < \frac{1}{N} < \varepsilon$.

8.2.71 Let $\varepsilon > 0$ be given. We wish to find N such that for $n > N$, $\left|\frac{3n^2}{4n^2+1} - \frac{3}{4}\right| = \left|\frac{-3}{4(4n^2+1)}\right| = \frac{3}{4(4n^2+1)} < \varepsilon$. But this means that $3 < 4\varepsilon(4n^2+1)$, or $16\varepsilon n^2 + (4\varepsilon - 3) > 0$. Solving the quadratic, we get $n > \frac{1}{4}\sqrt{\frac{3}{\varepsilon} - 4}$, provided $\varepsilon < 3/4$. So let $N = \frac{1}{4}\sqrt{\frac{3}{\varepsilon}}$ if $\epsilon < 3/4$ and let $N = 1$ otherwise.

8.2.73 Let $\varepsilon > 0$ be given. We wish to find N such that for $n > N$, $\left|\frac{cn}{bn+1} - \frac{c}{b}\right| = \left|\frac{-c}{b(bn+1)}\right| = \frac{c}{b(bn+1)} < \varepsilon$. But this means that $\varepsilon b^2 n + (b\varepsilon - c) > 0$, so that $N > \frac{c}{b^2\varepsilon}$ will work.

8.2.75

a. True. See Theorem 8.2 part 4.

b. False. For example, if $a_n = 1/n$ and $b_n = e^n$, then $\lim_{n\to\infty} a_n b_n = \infty$.

c. True. The definition of the limit of a sequence involves only the behavior of the nth term of a sequence as n gets large (see the Definition of Limit of a Sequence). Thus suppose a_n, b_n differ in only finitely many terms, and that M is large enough so that $a_n = b_n$ for $n > M$. Suppose a_n has limit L. Then for $\varepsilon > 0$, if N is such that $|a_n - L| < \varepsilon$ for $n > N$, first increase N if required so that $N > M$ as well. Then we also have $|b_n - L| < \varepsilon$ for $n > N$. Thus a_n and b_n have the same limit. A similar argument applies if a_n has no limit.

d. True. Note that a_n converges to zero. Intuitively, the nonzero terms of b_n are those of a_n, which converge to zero. More formally, given ϵ, choose N_1 such that for $n > N_1$, $a_n < \epsilon$. Let $N = 2N_1 + 1$. Then for $n > N$, consider b_n. If n is even, then $b_n = 0$ so certainly $b_n < \epsilon$. If n is odd, then $b_n = a_{(n-1)/2}$, and $(n-1)/2 > ((2N_1+1)-1)/2 = N_1$ so that $a_{(n-1)/2} < \epsilon$. Thus b_n converges to zero as well.

e. False. If $\{a_n\}$ happens to converge to zero, the statement is true. But consider for example $a_n = 2 + \frac{1}{n}$. Then $\lim_{n\to\infty} a_n = 2$, but $(-1)^n a_n$ does not converge (it oscillates between positive and negative values increasingly close to ± 2).

f. True. Suppose $\{0.000001 a_n\}$ converged to L, and let $\epsilon > 0$ be given. Choose N such that for $n > N$, $|0.000001 a_n - L| < \epsilon \cdot 0.000001$. Dividing through by 0.000001, we get that for $n > N$, $|a_n - 1000000L| < \epsilon$, so that a_n converges as well (to $1000000L$).

8.2.77 $\{(n-2)^2 + 6(n-2) - 9\}_{n=3}^{\infty} = \{n^2 + 2n - 17\}_{n=3}^{\infty}$.

8.2.79 Evaluate the limit of each term separately: $\lim_{n\to\infty} \frac{75^{n-1}}{99^n} = \frac{1}{99} \lim_{n\to\infty} \left(\frac{75}{99}\right)^{n-1} = 0$, while $\frac{-5^n}{8^n} \le \frac{5^n \sin n}{8^n} \le \frac{5^n}{8^n}$, so by the Squeeze Theorem, this second term converges to 0 as well. Thus the sum of the terms converges to zero.

8.2.81 Because $\lim_{n\to\infty} 0.99^n = 0$, and because cosine is continuous, the first term converges to $\cos 0 = 1$. The limit of the second term is $\lim_{n\to\infty} \frac{7^n + 9^n}{63^n} = \lim_{n\to\infty} \left(\frac{7}{63}\right)^n + \lim_{n\to\infty} \left(\frac{9}{63}\right)^n = 0$. Thus the sum converges to 1.

8.2.83 Dividing the numerator and denominator by 6^n gives $a_n = \frac{1 + (1/2)^n}{1 + (n^{100}/6^n)}$. By Theorem 8.6, $n^{100} \ll 6^n$. Thus $\lim_{n\to\infty} a_n = \frac{1+0}{1+0} = 1$.

8.2.85 We can write $a_n = \frac{(7/5)^n}{n^7}$. Theorem 8.6 indicates that $n^7 \ll b^n$ for $b > 1$, so $\lim_{n\to\infty} a_n = \infty$.

8.2.87 A graph shows that the sequence appears to converge. Let its supposed limit be L, then $\lim_{n\to\infty} a_{n+1} = \lim_{n\to\infty} (2a_n(1-a_n)) = 2(\lim_{n\to\infty} a_n)(1 - \lim_{n\to\infty} a_n)$, so $L = 2L(1-L) = 2L - 2L^2$, and thus $2L^2 - L = 0$, so $L = 0, \frac{1}{2}$. Thus the limit appears to be either 0 or 1/2; with the given initial condition, doing a few iterations by hand confirms that the sequence converges to 1/2: $a_0 = 0.3$; $a_1 = 2 \cdot 0.3 \cdot 0.7 = .42$; $a_2 = 2 \cdot 0.42 \cdot 0.58 = 0.4872$.

8.2.89 Computing three terms gives $a_0 = 0.5, a_1 = 4 \cdot 0.5 \cdot 0.5 = 1, a_2 = 4 \cdot 1 \cdot (1-1) = 0$. All successive terms are obviously zero, so the sequence converges to 0.

8.2.91 For $b = 2$, $2^3 > 3!$ but $16 = 2^4 < 4! = 24$, so the crossover point is $n = 4$. For e, $e^5 \approx 148.41 > 5! = 120$ while $e^6 \approx 403.4 < 6! = 720$, so the crossover point is $n = 6$. For 10, $24! \approx 6.2 \times 10^{23} < 10^{24}$, while $25! \approx 1.55 \times 10^{25} > 10^{25}$, so the crossover point is $n = 25$.

8.2.93

a. The profits for each of the first ten days, in dollars are:

n	0	1	2	3	4	5	6	7	8	9	10
h_n	130.00	130.75	131.40	131.95	132.40	132.75	133.00	133.15	133.20	133.15	133.00

b. The profit on an item is revenue minus cost. The total cost of keeping the heifer for n days is $.45n$, and the revenue for selling the heifer on the nth day is $(200 + 5n) \cdot (.65 - .01n)$, because the heifer gains 5 pounds per day but is worth a penny less per pound each day. Thus the total profit on the nth day is $h_n = (200 + 5n) \cdot (.65 - .01n) - .45n = 130 + 0.8n - 0.05n^2$. The maximum profit occurs when $-.1n + .8 = 0$, which occurs when $n = 8$. The maximum profit is achieved by selling the heifer on the 8th day.

8.2.95 The approximate first few values of this sequence are:

n	0	1	2	3	4	5	6
c_n	.7071	.6325	.6136	.6088	.6076	.6074	.6073

The value of the constant appears to be around 0.607.

8.2.97

a. If we "cut off" the expression after n square roots, we get a_n from the recurrence given. We can thus *define* the infinite expression to be the limit of a_n as $n \to \infty$.

b. $a_0 = 1$, $a_1 = \sqrt{2}$, $a_2 = \sqrt{1 + \sqrt{2}} \approx 1.5538$, $a_3 \approx 1.5981$, $a_4 \approx 1.6118$, and $a_5 \approx 1.6161$.

c. $a_{10} \approx 1.618$, which differs from $\frac{1+\sqrt{5}}{2} \approx 1.61803394$ by less than .001.

d. Assume $\lim_{n\to\infty} a_n = L$. Then $\lim_{n\to\infty} a_{n+1} = \lim_{n\to\infty} \sqrt{1 + a_n} = \sqrt{1 + \lim_{n\to\infty} a_n}$, so $L = \sqrt{1 + L}$, and thus $L^2 = 1 + L$. Therefore we have $L^2 - L - 1 = 0$, so $L = \frac{1\pm\sqrt{5}}{2}$.

Because clearly the limit is positive, it must be the positive square root.

e. Letting $a_{n+1} = \sqrt{p + \sqrt{a_n}}$ with $a_0 = p$ and assuming a limit exists we have $\lim_{n\to\infty} a_{n+1} = \lim_{n\to\infty} \sqrt{p + a_n}$ $= \sqrt{p + \lim_{n\to\infty} a_n}$, so $L = \sqrt{p + L}$, and thus $L^2 = p + L$. Therefore, $L^2 - L - p = 0$, so $L = \frac{1\pm\sqrt{1+4p}}{2}$, and because we know that L is positive, we have $L = \frac{1+\sqrt{4p+1}}{2}$. The limit exists for all positive p.

8.2.99

a. Define a_n as given in the problem statement. Then we can *define* the value of the continued fraction to be $\lim_{n\to\infty} a_n$.

b. $a_0 = 1$, $a_1 = 1 + \frac{1}{a_0} = 2$, $a_2 = 1 + \frac{1}{a_1} = \frac{3}{2} = 1.5$, $a_3 = 1 + \frac{1}{a_2} = \frac{5}{3} \approx 1.667$, $a_4 = 1 + \frac{1}{a_3} = \frac{8}{5} = 1.6$, $a_5 = 1 + \frac{1}{a_4} = \frac{13}{8} = 1.625$.

c. From the list above, the values of the sequence alternately decrease and increase, so we would expect that the limit is somewhere between 1.6 and 1.625.

d. Assume that the limit is equal to L. Then from $a_{n+1} = 1 + \frac{1}{a_n}$, we have $\lim_{n\to\infty} a_{n+1} = 1 + \frac{1}{\lim_{n\to\infty} a_n}$, so $L = 1 + \frac{1}{L}$, and thus $L^2 - L - 1 = 0$. Therefore, $L = \frac{1\pm\sqrt{5}}{2}$, and because L is clearly positive, it must be equal to $\frac{1+\sqrt{5}}{2} \approx 1.618$.

e. Here $a_0 = a$ and $a_{n+1} = a + \frac{b}{a_n}$. Assuming that $\lim_{n\to\infty} a_n = L$ we have $L = a + \frac{b}{L}$, so $L^2 = aL + b$, and thus $L^2 - aL - b = 0$. Therefore, $L = \frac{a \pm \sqrt{a^2+4b}}{2}$, and because $L > 0$ we have $L = \frac{a+\sqrt{a^2+4b}}{2}$.

8.2.101

a. $f_0 = f_1 = 1, f_2 = 2, f_3 = 3, f_4 = 5, f_5 = 8, f_6 = 13, f_7 = 21, f_8 = 34, f_9 = 55, f_{10} = 89$.

b. The sequence is clearly not bounded.

c. $\frac{f_{10}}{f_9} \approx 1.61818$

d. We use induction. Note that $\frac{1}{\sqrt{5}}\left(\varphi + \frac{1}{\varphi}\right) = \frac{1}{\sqrt{5}}\left(\frac{1+\sqrt{5}}{2} + \frac{2}{1+\sqrt{5}}\right) = \frac{1}{\sqrt{5}}\left(\frac{1+2\sqrt{5}+5+4}{2(1+\sqrt{5})}\right) = 1 = f_1$. Also note that $\frac{1}{\sqrt{5}}\left(\varphi^2 - \frac{1}{\varphi^2}\right) = \frac{1}{\sqrt{5}}\left(\frac{3+\sqrt{5}}{2} - \frac{2}{3+\sqrt{5}}\right) = \frac{1}{\sqrt{5}}\left(\frac{9+6\sqrt{5}+5-4}{2(3+\sqrt{5})}\right) = 1 = f_2$. Now note that

$$\begin{aligned} f_{n-1} + f_{n-2} &= \frac{1}{\sqrt{5}}(\varphi^{n-1} - (-1)^{n-1}\varphi^{1-n} + \varphi^{n-2} - (-1)^{n-2}\varphi^{2-n}) \\ &= \frac{1}{\sqrt{5}}((\varphi^{n-1} + \varphi^{n-2}) - (-1)^n(\varphi^{2-n} - \varphi^{1-n})). \end{aligned}$$

Now, note that $\varphi - 1 = \frac{1}{\varphi}$, so that

$$\varphi^{n-1} + \varphi^{n-2} = \varphi^{n-1}\left(1 + \frac{1}{\varphi}\right) = \varphi^{n-1} \cdot \varphi = \varphi^n$$

and

$$\varphi^{2-n} - \varphi^{1-n} = \varphi^{-n}(\varphi^2 - \varphi) = \varphi^{-n}(\varphi(\varphi - 1)) = \varphi^{-n}.$$

Making these substitutions, we get

$$f_n = f_{n-1} + f_{n-2} = \frac{1}{\sqrt{5}}(\varphi^n - (-1)^n\varphi^{-n})$$

8.2.103

a.

2 : 1
3 : 10, 5, 16, 8, 4, 2, 1
4 : 2, 1
5 : 16, 8, 4, 2, 1
6 : 3, 10, 5, 16, 8, 4, 2, 1
7 : 22, 11, 34, 17, 52, 26, 13, 40, 20, 10, 5, 16, 8, 4, 2, 1
8 : 4, 2, 1
9 : 28, 14, 7, 22, 11, 34, 17, 52, 26, 13, 40, 20, 10, 5, 16, 8, 4, 2, 1
10 : 5, 16, 8, 4, 2, 1

b. From the above, $H_2 = 1, H_3 = 7$, and $H_4 = 2$.

c. This plot is for $1 \le n \le 100$. Like hailstones, the numbers in the sequence a_n rise and fall but eventually crash to the earth. The conjecture appears to be true.

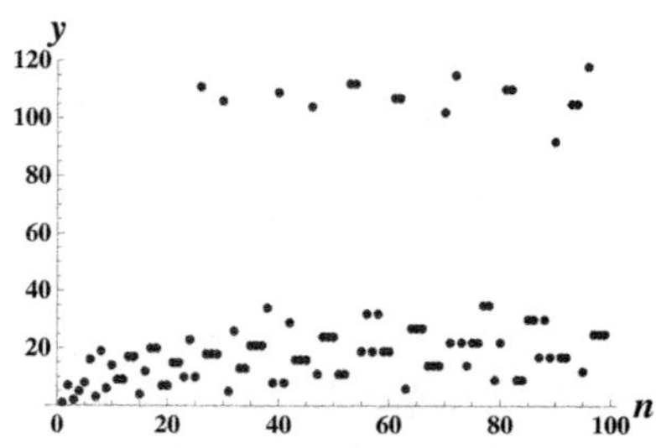

8.2.105

a. Note that $a_2 = \sqrt{3a_1} = \sqrt{3\sqrt{3}} > \sqrt{3} = a_1$. Now assume that $\sqrt{3} = a_1 < a_2 < \dots a_{k-1} < a_k$. Then

$$a_{k+1} = \sqrt{3a_k} > \sqrt{3a_{k-1}} = a_k.$$

Thus $\{a_n\}$ is increasing.

b. Clearly because $a_1 = \sqrt{3} > 0$ and $\{a_n\}$ is increasing, the sequence is bounded below by $\sqrt{3} > 0$. Further, $a_1 = \sqrt{3} < 3$; assume that $a_k < 3$. Then $a_{k+1} = \sqrt{3a_k} < \sqrt{3 \cdot 3} = 3$, so that $a_{k+1} < 3$. So by induction, $\{a_k\}$ is bounded above by 3.

c. Because $\{a_n\}$ is bounded and monotonically increasing, $\lim_{n\to\infty} a_n$ exists by Theorem 8.5.

d. Because the limit exists, we have

$$\lim_{n\to\infty} a_{n+1} = \lim_{n\to\infty} \sqrt{3a_n} = \sqrt{3} \lim_{n\to\infty} \sqrt{a_n} = \sqrt{3}\sqrt{\lim_{n\to\infty} a_n}.$$

Let $L = \lim_{n\to\infty} a_{n+1} = \lim_{n\to\infty} a_n$; then $L = \sqrt{3}\sqrt{L}$, so that $L = 3$.

8.2.107 By Theorem 8.6,

$$\lim_{n\to\infty} \frac{n^5}{e^{n/2}} = 2^5 \lim_{n\to\infty} \frac{(n/2)^5}{e^{n/2}} = 0,$$

so that $e^{n/2}$ has the larger growth rate. Using computational software we see that $e^{35/2} \approx 3.982 \times 10^7 < 35^5 \approx 5.252 \times 10^7$, while $e^{36/2} \approx 6.566 \times 10^7 > 36^5 \approx 6.047 \times 10^7$.

8.2.109 Experiment with a few widely separated values of n:

n	$n!$	$n^{0.7n}$
1	1	1
10	3.63×10^6	10^7
100	9.33×10^{157}	10^{140}
1000	4.02×10^{2567}	10^{2100}

It appears that $n^{0.7n}$ starts out larger, but is overtaken by the factorial somewhere between $n = 10$ and $n = 100$, and that the gap grows wider as n increases. Looking between $n = 10$ and $n = 100$ revels that for $n = 18$, we have $n! \approx 6.402 \times 10^{15} < n^{0.7n} \approx 6.553 \times 10^{15}$ while for $n = 19$ we have $n! \approx 1.216 \times 10^{17} > n^{0.7n} \approx 1.017 \times 10^{17}$.

8.2.111 First note that for $a = 1$ we already know that $\{n^n\}$ grows fast than $\{n!\}$. So if $a > 1$, then $n^{an} \ge n^n$, so that $\{n^{an}\}$ grows faster than $\{n!\}$ for $a > 1$ as well. To settle the case $a < 1$, recall Stirling's formula which states that for large values of n,

$$n! \sim \sqrt{2\pi n} n^n e^{-n}.$$

Thus

$$\begin{aligned}
\lim_{n\to\infty} \frac{n!}{n^{an}} &= \lim_{n\to\infty} \frac{\sqrt{2\pi n} n^n e^{-n}}{n^{an}} \\
&= \sqrt{2\pi} \lim_{n\to\infty} n^{\frac{1}{2}+(1-a)n} e^{-n} \\
&\ge \sqrt{2\pi} \lim_{n\to\infty} n^{(1-a)n} e^{-n} \\
&= \sqrt{2\pi} \lim_{n\to\infty} e^{(1-a)n \ln n} e^{-n} \\
&= \sqrt{2\pi} \lim_{n\to\infty} e^{((1-a)\ln n - 1)n}.
\end{aligned}$$

If $a < 1$ then $(1-a)\ln n - 1 > 0$ for large values of n because $1 - a > 0$, so that this limit is infinite. Hence $\{n!\}$ grows faster than $\{n^{an}\}$ exactly when $a < 1$.

8.3 Infinite Series

8.3.1 A geometric series is a series in which the ratio of successive terms in the underlying sequence is a constant. Thus a geometric series has the form $\sum ar^k$ where r is the constant. One example is $3+6+12+24+48+\cdots$ in which $a=3$ and $r=2$.

8.3.3 The ratio is the common ratio between successive terms in the sum.

8.3.5 No. For example, the geometric series with $a_n = 3\cdot 2^n$ does not have a finite sum.

8.3.7 $S = 1\cdot\dfrac{1-3^9}{1-3} = \dfrac{19682}{2} = 9841.$

8.3.9 $S = 1\cdot\dfrac{1-(4/25)^{21}}{1-4/25} = \dfrac{25^{21}-4^{21}}{25^{21}-4\cdot 25^{20}} \approx 1.1905.$

8.3.11 $S = 1\cdot\dfrac{1-(-3/4)^{10}}{1+3/4} = \dfrac{4^{10}-3^{10}}{4^{10}+3\cdot 4^9} = \dfrac{141361}{262144} \approx 0.5392.$

8.3.13 $S = 1\cdot\dfrac{1-\pi^7}{1-\pi} = \dfrac{\pi^7-1}{\pi-1} \approx 1409.84.$

8.3.15 $S = 1\cdot\dfrac{1-(-1)^{21}}{2} = 1.$

8.3.17 $\dfrac{1093}{2916}.$

8.3.19 $\dfrac{1}{1-1/4} = \dfrac{4}{3}.$

8.3.21 $\dfrac{1}{1-0.9} = 10.$

8.3.23 Divergent, because $r > 1$.

8.3.25 $\dfrac{e^{-2}}{1-e^{-2}} = \dfrac{1}{e^2-1}.$

8.3.27 $\dfrac{2^{-3}}{1-2^{-3}} = \dfrac{1}{7}.$

8.3.29 $\dfrac{1/625}{1-1/5} = \dfrac{1}{500}.$

8.3.31 $\dfrac{1}{1-e/\pi} = \dfrac{\pi}{\pi-e}.$ (Note that $e < \pi$, so $r < 1$ for this series.)

8.3.33 $\displaystyle\sum_{k=0}^{\infty}\left(\frac{1}{4}\right)^k 5^{3-k} = 5^3\sum_{k=0}^{\infty}\left(\frac{1}{20}\right)^k = 5^3\cdot\frac{1}{1-1/20} = \frac{5^3\cdot 20}{19} = \frac{2500}{19}.$

8.3.35 $\dfrac{1}{1+9/10} = \dfrac{10}{19}.$

8.3.37 $3\cdot\dfrac{1}{1+1/\pi} = \dfrac{3\pi}{\pi+1}.$

8.3.39 $\dfrac{0.15^2}{1.15} = \dfrac{9}{460} \approx 0.0196.$

8.3.41

a. $0.\overline{3} = 0.333\ldots = \sum_{k=1}^{\infty} 3(0.1)^k$.

b. The limit of the sequence of partial sums is $1/3$.

8.3.43

a. $0.\overline{1} = 0.111\ldots = \sum_{k=1}^{\infty} (0.1)^k$.

b. The limit of the sequence of partial sums is $1/9$.

8.3.45

a. $0.\overline{09} = 0.0909\ldots = \sum_{k=1}^{\infty} 9(0.01)^k$.

b. The limit of the sequence of partial sums is $1/11$.

8.3.47

a. $0.\overline{037} = 0.037037037\ldots = \sum_{k=1}^{\infty} 37(0.001)^k$.

b. The limit of the sequence of partial sums is $37/999 = 1/27$.

8.3.49 $0.\overline{12} = 0.121212\ldots = \displaystyle\sum_{k=0}^{\infty} .12 \cdot 10^{-2k} = \frac{.12}{1-1/100} = \frac{12}{99} = \frac{4}{33}$.

8.3.51 $0.\overline{456} = 0.456456456\ldots = \displaystyle\sum_{k=0}^{\infty} .456 \cdot 10^{-3k} = \frac{.456}{1-1/1000} = \frac{456}{999} = \frac{152}{333}$.

8.3.53 $0.00\overline{952} = 0.00952952\ldots = \displaystyle\sum_{k=0}^{\infty} .00952 \cdot 10^{-3k} = \frac{.00952}{1-1/1000} = \frac{9.52}{999} = \frac{952}{99900} = \frac{238}{24975}$.

8.3.55 The second part of each term cancels with the first part of the succeeding term, so $S_n = \frac{1}{1+1} - \frac{1}{n+2} = \frac{n}{2n+4}$, and $\lim_{n\to\infty} \frac{n}{2n+4} = \frac{1}{2}$.

8.3.57 $\dfrac{1}{(k+6)(k+7)} = \dfrac{1}{k+6} - \dfrac{1}{k+7}$, so the series given is the same as $\sum_{k=1}^{\infty}\left(\frac{1}{k+6} - \frac{1}{k+7}\right)$. In that series, the second part of each term cancels with the first part of the succeeding term, so $S_n = \frac{1}{1+6} - \frac{1}{n+7}$. Thus $\lim_{n\to\infty} S_n = \frac{1}{7}$.

8.3.59 Note that $\frac{4}{(4k-3)(4k+1)} = \frac{1}{4k-3} - \frac{1}{4k+1}$. Thus the given series is the same as $\displaystyle\sum_{k=3}^{\infty}\left(\frac{1}{4k-3} - \frac{1}{4k+1}\right)$. In that series, the second part of each term cancels with the first part of the succeeding term (because $4(k+1)-3 = 4k+1$), so we have $S_n = \frac{1}{9} - \frac{1}{4n+1}$, and thus $\lim_{n\to\infty} S_n = \dfrac{1}{9}$.

8.3.61 $\ln\left(\dfrac{k+1}{k}\right) = \ln(k+1) - \ln k$, so the series given is the same as $\sum_{k=1}^{\infty}(\ln(k+1) - \ln k)$, in which the first part of each term cancels with the second part of the next term, so we have $S_n = \ln(n+1) - \ln 1 = \ln(n+1)$, and thus the series diverges.

8.3.63 $\dfrac{1}{(k+p)(k+p+1)} = \dfrac{1}{k+p} - \dfrac{1}{k+p+1}$, so that $\displaystyle\sum_{k=1}^{\infty} \frac{1}{(k+p)(k+p+1)} = \sum_{k=1}^{\infty}\left(\frac{1}{k+p} - \frac{1}{k+p+1}\right)$ and this series telescopes to give $S_n = \frac{1}{p+1} - \frac{1}{n+p+1} = \frac{n}{n(p+1)+(p+1)^2}$ so that $\lim_{n\to\infty} S_n = \frac{1}{p+1}$.

8.3.65 Let $a_n = \dfrac{1}{\sqrt{n+1}} - \dfrac{1}{\sqrt{n+3}}$. Then the second term of a_n cancels with the first term of a_{n+2}, so the series telescopes and $S_n = \frac{1}{\sqrt{2}} + \frac{1}{\sqrt{3}} - \frac{1}{\sqrt{n-1+3}} - \frac{1}{\sqrt{n+3}}$ and thus the sum of the series is the limit of S_n, which is $\dfrac{1}{\sqrt{2}} + \dfrac{1}{\sqrt{3}}$.

8.3.67 $16k^2 + 8k - 3 = (4k+3)(4k-1)$, so $\frac{1}{16k^2+8k-3} = \frac{1}{(4k+3)(4k-1)} = \frac{1}{4}\left(\frac{1}{4k-1} - \frac{1}{4k+3}\right)$. Thus the series given is equal to $\dfrac{1}{4}\displaystyle\sum_{k=0}^{\infty}\left(\frac{1}{4k-1} - \frac{1}{4k+3}\right)$. This series telescopes, so $S_n = \frac{1}{4}\left(-1 - \frac{1}{4n+3}\right)$, so the sum of the series is equal to $\lim_{n\to\infty} S_n = -\frac{1}{4}$.

8.3.69

a. True. $\left(\dfrac{\pi}{e}\right)^{-k} = \left(\dfrac{e}{\pi}\right)^{k}$; because $e < \pi$, this is a geometric series with ratio less than 1.

b. True. If $\displaystyle\sum_{k=12}^{\infty} a^k = L$, then $\displaystyle\sum_{k=0}^{\infty} a^k = \left(\sum_{k=0}^{11} a^k\right) + L$.

c. False. For example, let $0 < a < 1$ and $b > 1$.

d. True. Suppose $a > \frac{1}{2}$. Then we want $a = \sum_{k=0}^{\infty} r^k = \frac{1}{1-r}$. Solving for r gives $r = 1 - \frac{1}{a}$. Because $a > 0$ we have $r < 1$; because $a > \frac{1}{2}$ we have $r > 1 - \frac{1}{1/2} = -1$. Thus $|r| < 1$ so that $\sum_{k=0}^{\infty} r^k$ converges, and it converges to a.

e. True. Suppose $a > -\frac{1}{2}$. Then we want $a = \sum_{k=1}^{\infty} r^k = \frac{r}{1-r}$. Solving for r gives $r = \frac{a}{a+1}$. For $a \ge 0$, clearly $0 \le r < 1$ so that $\sum_{k=1}^{\infty} r^k$ converges to a. For $-\frac{1}{2} < a < 0$, clearly $r < 0$, but $|a| < |a+1|$, so that $|r| < 1$. Thus in this case $\sum_{k=1}^{\infty} r^k$ also converges to a.

8.3.71 This can be written as $\dfrac{1}{3}\displaystyle\sum_{k=1}^{\infty}\left(-\frac{2}{3}\right)^k$. This is a geometric series with ratio $r = -\frac{2}{3}$ so the sum is $\frac{1}{3} \cdot \frac{-2/3}{1-(-2/3)} = \frac{1}{3} \cdot \left(-\frac{2}{5}\right) = -\frac{2}{15}$.

8.3.73 Note that

$$\frac{\ln((k+1)k^{-1})}{(\ln k)\ln(k+1)} = \frac{\ln(k+1)}{(\ln k)\ln(k+1)} - \frac{\ln k}{(\ln k)\ln(k+1)} = \frac{1}{\ln k} - \frac{1}{\ln(k+1)}.$$

In the partial sum S_n, the first part of each term cancels the second part of the preceding term, so we have $S_n = \frac{1}{\ln 2} - \frac{1}{\ln(n+1)}$. Thus we have $\lim_{n\to\infty} S_n = \dfrac{1}{\ln 2}$.

8.3.75

a. Because the first part of each term cancels the second part of the previous term, the nth partial sum telescopes to be $S_n = \frac{4}{3} - \frac{4}{3^{n+1}}$. Thus, the sum of the series is $\lim_{n\to\infty} S_n = \dfrac{4}{3}$.

b. Note that $\frac{4}{3^k} - \frac{4}{3^{k+1}} = \frac{4\cdot 3^{k+1} - 4\cdot 3^k}{3^k 3^{k+1}} = \frac{8}{3^{k+1}}$. Thus, the original series can be written as $\displaystyle\sum_{k=1}^{\infty}\frac{8}{3^{k+1}}$ which is geometric with $r = 1/3$ and $a = 8/9$, so the sum is $\frac{8/9}{1-1/3} = \frac{8}{9} \cdot \frac{3}{2} = \frac{4}{3}$.

8.3.77 At the nth stage, there are 2^{n-1} triangles of area $A_n = \frac{1}{8}A_{n-1} = \frac{1}{8^{n-1}}A_1$, so the total area of the triangles formed at the nth stage is $\dfrac{2^{n-1}}{8^{n-1}}A_1 = \left(\dfrac{1}{4}\right)^{n-1} A_1$. Thus the total area under the parabola is

$$\sum_{n=1}^{\infty}\left(\frac{1}{4}\right)^{n-1} A_1 = A_1 \sum_{n=1}^{\infty}\left(\frac{1}{4}\right)^{n-1} = A_1 \frac{1}{1-1/4} = \frac{4}{3}A_1.$$

8.3.79 It appears that the loan is paid off after about 470 months. Let B_n be the loan balance after n months. Then $B_0 = 180000$ and $B_n = 1.005 \cdot B_{n-1} - 1000$. Then $B_n = 1.005 \cdot B_{n-1} - 1000 = 1.005(1.005 \cdot B_{n-2} - 1000) - 1000 = (1.005)^2 \cdot B_{n-2} - 1000(1 + 1.005) = (1.005)^2 \cdot (1.005 \cdot B_{n-3} - 1000) - 1000(1 + 1.005) = (1.005)^3 \cdot B_{n-3} - 1000(1 + 1.005 + (1.005)^2) = \cdots = (1.005)^n B_0 - 1000(1+1.005+(1.005)^2+\cdots+(1.005)^{n-1}) = (1.005)^n \cdot 180000 - 1000\left(\frac{(1.005)^n - 1}{1.005-1}\right)$. Solving this equation for $B_n = 0$ gives $n \approx 461.667$ months, so the loan is paid off after 462 months.

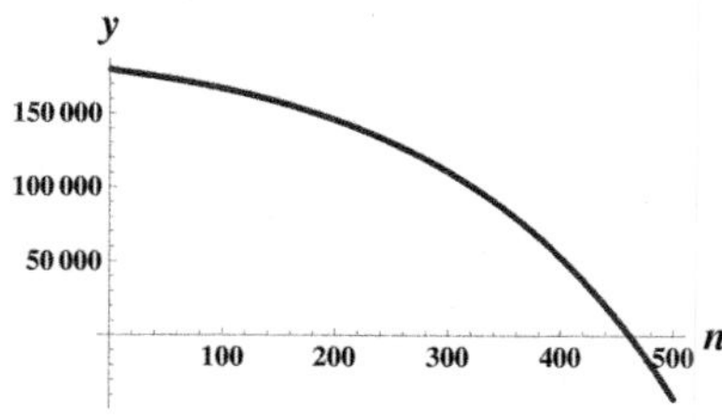

8.3.81 $F_n = (1.015)F_{n-1} - 120 = (1.015)((1.015)F_{n-2} - 120) - 120 = (1.015)((1.015)((1.015)F_{n-3} - 120) - 120) - 120 = \cdots = (1.015)^n(4000) - 120(1 + (1.015) + (1.015)^2 + \cdots + (1.015)^{n-1})$. This is equal to

$$(1.015)^n(4000) - 120\left(\frac{(1.015)^n - 1}{1.015 - 1}\right) = (-4000)(1.015)^n + 8000.$$

The long term population of the fish is 0.

8.3.83 Under the one-child policy, each couple will have one child. Under the one-son policy, we compute the expected number of children as follows: with probability $1/2$ the first child will be a son; with probability $(1/2)^2$, the first child will be a daughter and the second child will be a son; in general, with probability $(1/2)^n$, the first $n-1$ children will be girls and the nth a boy. Thus the expected number of children is the sum $\displaystyle\sum_{i=1}^{\infty} i \cdot \left(\frac{1}{2}\right)^i$. To evaluate this series, use the following "trick": Let $f(x) = \displaystyle\sum_{i=1}^{\infty} ix^i$. Then $f(x) + \displaystyle\sum_{i=1}^{\infty} x^i = \sum_{i=1}^{\infty}(i+1)x^i$. Now, let

$$g(x) = \sum_{i=1}^{\infty} x^{i+1} = -1 - x + \sum_{i=0}^{\infty} x^i = -1 - x + \frac{1}{1-x}$$

and

$$g'(x) = f(x) + \sum_{i=1}^{\infty} x^i = f(x) - 1 + \sum_{i=0}^{\infty} x^i = f(x) - 1 + \frac{1}{1-x}.$$

Evaluate $g'(x) = -1 - \frac{1}{(1-x)^2}$; then

$$f(x) = 1 - \frac{1}{1-x} - 1 - \frac{1}{(1-x)^2} = \frac{-1 + x + 1}{(1-x)^2} = \frac{x}{(1-x)^2}$$

Finally, evaluate at $x = \frac{1}{2}$ to get $f\left(\frac{1}{2}\right) = \sum_{i=1}^{\infty} i \cdot \left(\frac{1}{2}\right)^i = \frac{1/2}{(1-1/2)^2} = 2$. There will thus be twice as many children under the one-son policy as under the one-child policy.

8.3.85 Ignoring the initial drop for the moment, the height after the nth bounce is $10p^n$, so the total time spent in that bounce is $2 \cdot \sqrt{2 \cdot 10p^n/g}$ seconds. The total time before the ball comes to rest (now including the time for the initial drop) is then $\sqrt{20/g} + \sum_{i=1}^{\infty} 2 \cdot \sqrt{2 \cdot 10p^n/g} = \sqrt{\frac{20}{g}} + 2\sqrt{\frac{20}{g}} \sum_{i=1}^{\infty}(\sqrt{p})^n = \sqrt{\frac{20}{g}} + 2\sqrt{\frac{20}{g}} \frac{\sqrt{p}}{1-\sqrt{p}} = \sqrt{\frac{20}{g}}\left(1 + \frac{2\sqrt{p}}{1-\sqrt{p}}\right) = \sqrt{\frac{20}{g}}\left(\frac{1+\sqrt{p}}{1-\sqrt{p}}\right)$ seconds.

8.3.87

a. I_{n+1} is obtained by I_n by dividing each edge into three equal parts, removing the middle part, and adding two parts equal to it. Thus 3 equal parts turn into 4, so $L_{n+1} = \frac{4}{3}L_n$. This is a geometric sequence with a ratio greater than 1, so the nth term grows without bound.

b. As the result of part (a), I_n has $3 \cdot 4^n$ sides of length $\frac{1}{3^n}$; each of those sides turns into an added triangle in I_{n+1} of side length 3^{-n-1}. Thus the added area in I_{n+1} consists of $3 \cdot 4^n$ equilateral triangles with side 3^{-n-1}. The area of an equilateral triangle with side x is $\dfrac{x^2\sqrt{3}}{4}$. Thus $A_{n+1} = A_n + 3 \cdot 4^n \cdot \frac{3^{-2n-2}\sqrt{3}}{4} = A_n + \frac{\sqrt{3}}{12} \cdot \left(\frac{4}{9}\right)^n$, and $A_0 = \frac{\sqrt{3}}{4}$. Thus $A_{n+1} = A_0 + \sum_{i=0}^{n} \frac{\sqrt{3}}{12} \cdot \left(\frac{4}{9}\right)^i$, so that

$$A_\infty = A_0 + \frac{\sqrt{3}}{12}\sum_{i=0}^{\infty}\left(\frac{4}{9}\right)^i = \frac{\sqrt{3}}{4} + \frac{\sqrt{3}}{12}\frac{1}{1-4/9} = \frac{\sqrt{3}}{4}(1+\frac{3}{5}) = \frac{2}{5}\sqrt{3}.$$

8.3.89 $|S - S_n| = \left|\sum_{i=n}^{\infty} r^k\right| = \left|\dfrac{r^n}{1-r}\right|$ because the latter sum is simply a geometric series with first term r^n and ratio r.

8.3.91

a. Solve $\left|\frac{(-0.8)^n}{1.8}\right| = \frac{0.8^n}{1.8} < 10^{-6}$ for n to get $n = 60$.

b. Solve $\frac{0.2^n}{0.8} < 10^{-6}$ for n to get $n = 9$.

8.3.93

a. Solve $\frac{1/\pi^n}{1-1/\pi} < 10^{-6}$ for n to get $n = 13$.

b. Solve $\frac{1/e^n}{1-1/e} < 10^{-6}$ for n to get $n = 15$.

8.3.95

a. $f(x) = \sum_{k=0}^{\infty}(-1)^k x^k = \frac{1}{1+x}$; because f is a geometric series, $f(x)$ exists only when the ratio, $-x$, is such that $|-x| = |x| < 1$. Then $f(0) = 1$, $f(0.2) = \frac{1}{1.2} = \frac{5}{6}$, $f(0.5) = \frac{1}{1+.05} = \frac{2}{3}$. Neither $f(1)$ nor $f(1.5)$ exists.

b. The domain of f is $\{x : |x| < 1\}$.

8.3.97 $f(x)$ is a geometric series with ratio $\frac{1}{1+x}$; thus $f(x)$ converges when $\left|\frac{1}{1+x}\right| < 1$. For $x > -1$, $\left|\dfrac{1}{1+x}\right| = \dfrac{1}{1+x}$ and $\dfrac{1}{1+x} < 1$ when $1 < 1+x$, $x > 0$. For $x < -1$, $\left|\dfrac{1}{1+x}\right| = \dfrac{1}{-1-x}$, and this is less than 1 when $1 < -1-x$, i.e. $x < -2$. So $f(x)$ converges for $x > 0$ and for $x < -2$. When $f(x)$ converges, its value is $\frac{1}{1-\frac{1}{1+x}} = \frac{1+x}{x}$, so $f(x) = 3$ when $1 + x = 3x$, $x = \frac{1}{2}$.

8.3.99

a. Using Theorem 8.7 in each case except for $r = 0$ gives

r	$f(r)$
-0.9	0.526
-0.7	0.588
-0.5	0.667
-0.2	0.833
0	1
0.2	1.250
0.5	2
0.7	3.333
0.9	10

b. A plot of f is

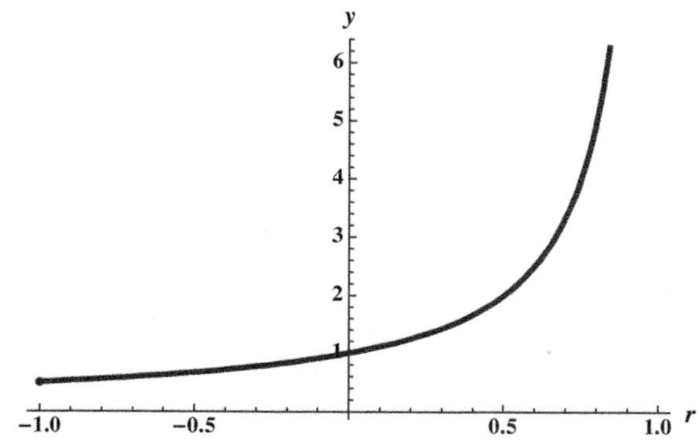

c. For $-1 < r < 1$ we have $f(r) = \frac{1}{1-r}$, so that

$$\lim_{r\to-1^+} f(r) = \lim_{r\to-1^+} \frac{1}{1-r} = \frac{1}{2}, \qquad \lim_{r\to1^-} f(r) = \lim_{r\to1^-} \frac{1}{1-r} = \infty.$$

8.4 The Divergence and Integral Tests

8.4.1 If the sequence of terms has limit 1, then the corresponding series diverges. It is necessary (but not sufficient) that the sequence of terms has limit 0 in order for the corresponding series to be convergent.

8.4.3 Yes. Either the series and the integral both converge, or both diverge, if the terms are positive and decreasing.

8.4.5 For the same values of p as in the previous problem – it converges for $p > 1$, and diverges for all other values of p.

8.4.7 The remainder of an infinite series is the error in approximating a convergent infinite series by a finite number of terms.

8.4.9 $a_k = \frac{k}{2k+1}$ and $\lim_{k\to\infty} a_k = \frac{1}{2}$, so the series diverges.

8.4.11 $a_k = \frac{k}{\ln k}$ and $\lim_{k\to\infty} a_k = \infty$, so the series diverges.

8.4.13 $a_k = \frac{1}{1000+k}$ and $\lim_{k\to\infty} a_k = 0$, so the divergence test is inconclusive.

8.4.15 $a_k = \frac{\sqrt{k}}{\ln^{10} k}$ and $\lim_{k\to\infty} a_k = \infty$, so the series diverges.

8.4.17 $a_k = k^{1/k}$. In order to compute $\lim_{k\to\infty} a_k$, we let $y_k = \ln a_k = \frac{\ln k}{k}$. By Theorem 9.6, (or by L'Hôpital's rule), $\lim_{k\to\infty} y_k = 0$, so $\lim_{k\to\infty} a_k = e^0 = 1$. The given series thus diverges.

8.4.19 Clearly $\frac{1}{e^x} = e^{-x}$ is continuous, positive, and decreasing for $x \geq 2$ (in fact, for all x), so the integral test applies. Because

$$\int_2^\infty e^{-x}\,dx = \lim_{c\to\infty} \int_2^c e^{-x}\,dx = \lim_{c\to\infty} (-e^{-x})\Big|_2^c = \lim_{c\to\infty} (e^{-2} - e^{-c}) = e^{-2},$$

the Integral Test tells us that the original series converges as well.

8.4.21 Let $f(x) = x \cdot e^{-2x^2}$. This function is continuous for $x \geq 1$. Its derivative is $e^{-2x^2}(1-4x^2) < 0$ for $x \geq 1$, so $f(x)$ is decreasing. Because $\int_1^\infty x \cdot e^{-2x^2}\,dx = \frac{1}{4e^2}$, the series converges.

8.4.23 Let $f(x) = \frac{1}{\sqrt{x+8}}$. $f(x)$ is obviously continuous and decreasing for $x \geq 1$. Because $\int_1^\infty \frac{1}{\sqrt{x+8}}\,dx = \infty$, the series diverges.

8.4.25 Let $f(x) = \frac{x}{e^x}$. $f(x)$ is clearly continuous for $x > 1$, and its derivative, $f'(x) = \frac{e^x - xe^x}{e^{2x}} = (1-x)\frac{e^x}{e^{2x}}$, is negative for $x > 1$ so that $f(x)$ is decreasing. Because $\int_1^\infty f(x)\,dx = 2e^{-1}$, the series converges.

8.4.27 The integral test does not apply, because the sequence of terms is not decreasing.

8.4.29 This is a p-series with $p = 10$, so this series converges.

8.4.31 $\sum_{k=3}^\infty \frac{1}{(k-2)^4} = \sum_{k=1}^\infty \frac{1}{k^4}$, which is a p-series with $p = 4$, thus convergent.

8.4.33 $\sum_{k=1}^\infty \frac{1}{\sqrt[3]{k}} = \sum_{k=1}^\infty \frac{1}{k^{1/3}}$ is a p-series with $p = 1/3$, thus divergent.

8.4.35

a. The remainder R_n is bounded by $\int_n^\infty \frac{1}{x^6}\,dx = \frac{1}{5n^5}$.

b. We solve $\frac{1}{5n^5} < 10^{-3}$ to get $n = 3$.

c. $L_n = S_n + \int_{n+1}^\infty \frac{1}{x^6}\,dx = S_n + \frac{1}{5(n+1)^5}$, and $U_n = S_n + \int_n^\infty \frac{1}{x^6}\,dx = S_n + \frac{1}{5n^5}$.

d. $S_{10} \approx 1.017341512$, so $L_{10} \approx 1.017341512 + \frac{1}{5\cdot 11^5} \approx 1.017342754$, and $U_{10} \approx 1.017341512 + \frac{1}{5\cdot 10^5} \approx 1.017343512$.

8.4.37

a. The remainder R_n is bounded by $\int_n^\infty \frac{1}{3^x}\,dx = \frac{1}{3^n \ln 3}$.

b. We solve $\frac{1}{3^n \ln 3} < 10^{-3}$ to obtain $n = 7$.

c. $L_n = S_n + \int_{n+1}^\infty \frac{1}{3^x}\,dx = S_n + \frac{1}{3^{n+1}\ln 3}$, and $U_n = S_n + \int_n^\infty \frac{1}{3^x}\,dx = S_n + \frac{1}{3^n \ln 3}$.

d. $S_{10} \approx 0.4999915325$, so $L_{10} \approx 0.4999915325 + \frac{1}{3^{11}\ln 3} \approx 0.4999966708$, and $U_{10} \approx 0.4999915325 + \frac{1}{3^{10}\ln 3} \approx 0.5000069475$.

8.4.39

a. The remainder R_n is bounded by $\int_n^\infty \frac{1}{x^{3/2}}\,dx = 2n^{-1/2}$.

b. We solve $2n^{-1/2} < 10^{-3}$ to get $n > 4 \times 10^6$, so let $n = 4 \times 10^6 + 1$.

c. $L_n = S_n + \int_{n+1}^\infty \frac{1}{x^{3/2}}\,dx = S_n + 2(n+1)^{-1/2}$, and $U_n = S_n + \int_n^\infty \frac{1}{x^{3/2}}\,dx = S_n + 2n^{-1/2}$.

d. $S_{10} = \sum_{k=1}^{10} \frac{1}{k^{3/2}} \approx 1.995336493$, so $L_{10} \approx 1.995336493 + 2 \cdot 11^{-1/2} \approx 2.598359182$, and $U_{10} \approx 1.995336493 + 2 \cdot 10^{-1/2} \approx 2.627792025$.

8.4.41

a. The remainder R_n is bounded by $\int_n^\infty \frac{1}{x^3}\,dx = \frac{1}{2n^2}$.

b. We solve $\frac{1}{2n^2} < 10^{-3}$ to get $n = 23$.

c. $L_n = S_n + \int_{n+1}^\infty \frac{1}{x^3}\,dx = S_n + \frac{1}{2(n+1)^2}$, and $U_n = S_n + \int_n^\infty \frac{1}{x^3}\,dx = S_n + \frac{1}{2n^2}$.

d. $S_{10} \approx 1.197531986$, so $L_{10} \approx 1.197531986 + \frac{1}{2 \cdot 11^2} \approx 1.201664217$, and $U_{10} \approx 1.197531986 + \frac{1}{2 \cdot 10^2} \approx 1.202531986$.

8.4.43 This is a geometric series with $a = \frac{1}{3}$ and $r = \frac{1}{12}$, so $\sum_{k=1}^\infty \frac{4}{12^k} = \frac{1/3}{1-1/12} = \frac{1/3}{11/12} = \frac{4}{11}$.

8.4.45 $$\sum_{k=0}^\infty \left(3\left(\frac{2}{5}\right)^k - 2\left(\frac{5}{7}\right)^k\right) = 3\sum_{k=0}^\infty \left(\frac{2}{5}\right)^k - 2\sum_{k=0}^\infty \left(\frac{5}{7}\right)^k = 3\left(\frac{1}{3/5}\right) - 2\left(\frac{1}{2/7}\right) = 5 - 7 = -2.$$

8.4.47 $$\sum_{k=1}^\infty \left(\frac{1}{3}\left(\frac{5}{6}\right)^k + \frac{3}{5}\left(\frac{7}{9}\right)^k\right) = \frac{1}{3}\sum_{k=1}^\infty \left(\frac{5}{6}\right)^k + \frac{3}{5}\sum_{k=1}^\infty \left(\frac{7}{9}\right)^k = \frac{1}{3}\left(\frac{5/6}{1/6}\right) + \frac{3}{5}\left(\frac{7/9}{2/9}\right) = \frac{5}{3} + \frac{21}{10} = \frac{113}{30}.$$

8.4.49 $$\sum_{k=1}^\infty \left(\left(\frac{1}{6}\right)^k + \left(\frac{1}{3}\right)^{k-1}\right) = \sum_{k=1}^\infty \left(\frac{1}{6}\right)^k + \sum_{k=1}^\infty \left(\frac{1}{3}\right)^{k-1} = \frac{1/6}{5/6} + \frac{1}{2/3} = \frac{17}{10}.$$

8.4.51

a. True. The two series differ by a finite amount ($\sum_{k=1}^9 a_k$), so if one converges, so does the other.

b. True. The same argument applies as in part (a).

c. False. If $\sum a_k$ converges, then $a_k \to 0$ as $k \to \infty$, so that $a_k + 0.0001 \to 0.0001$ as $k \to \infty$, so that $\sum(a_k + 0.0001)$ cannot converge.

d. False. Suppose $p = -1.0001$. Then $\sum p^k$ diverges but $p + 0.001 = -0.9991$ so that $\sum(p + .0001)^k$ converges.

e. False. Let $p = 1.0005$; then $-p + .001 = -(p - .001) = -.9995$, so that $\sum k^{-p}$ converges (p-series) but $\sum k^{-p+.001}$ diverges.

f. False. Let $a_k = \frac{1}{k}$, the harmonic series.

8.4.53 Converges by the Integral Test because $\displaystyle\int_1^\infty \frac{1}{(3x+1)(3x+4)}\,dx = \int_1^\infty \frac{1}{3(3x+1)} - \frac{1}{3(3x+4)}\,dx =$ $\displaystyle\lim_{b\to\infty} \int_1^b \left(\frac{1}{3(3x+1)} - \frac{1}{3(3x+4)}\right)dx = \lim_{b\to\infty} \frac{1}{9}\left(\ln\left(\frac{3x+1}{3x+4}\right)\right)\Big|_1^b = \lim_{b\to\infty} = -\frac{1}{9} \cdot \ln(4/7) \approx 0.06217 < \infty.$

Alternatively, this is a telescoping series with nth partial sum equal to $S_n = \frac{1}{3}\left(\frac{1}{4} - \frac{1}{3n+4}\right)$ which converges to $\frac{1}{12}$.

8.4.55 Diverges by the Divergence Test because $\displaystyle\lim_{k\to\infty} a_k = \lim_{k\to\infty} \frac{k}{\sqrt{k^2+1}} = 1 \neq 0.$

8.4.57 Converges by the Integral Test because $\displaystyle\int_2^\infty \frac{4}{x\ln^2 x}\,dx = \lim_{b\to\infty}\left(\frac{-4}{\ln x}\Big|_2^b\right) = \frac{4}{\ln 2} < \infty.$

8.4.59

a. Note that $\int \frac{1}{x \ln x (\ln \ln x)^p}\,dx = \frac{1}{1-p}(\ln \ln x)^{1-p}$, and thus the improper integral with bounds n and ∞ exists only if $p > 1$ because $\ln \ln x > 0$ for $x > e$. So this series converges for $p > 1$.

b. For large values of z, clearly $\sqrt{z} > \ln z$, so that $z > (\ln z)^2$. Write $z = \ln x$; then for large x, $\ln x > (\ln \ln x)^2$; multiplying both sides by $x \ln x$ we have that $x \ln^2 x > x \ln x (\ln \ln x)^2$, so that the first series converges faster because the terms get smaller faster.

8.4.61 Let $S_n = \sum_{k=1}^{n} \frac{1}{\sqrt{k}}$. Then this looks like a left Riemann sum for the function $y = \frac{1}{\sqrt{x}}$ on $[1, n+1]$. Because each rectangle lies above the curve itself, we see that S_n is bounded below by the integral of $\frac{1}{\sqrt{x}}$ on $[1, n+1]$. Now,

$$\int_1^{n+1} \frac{1}{\sqrt{x}}\,dx = \int_1^{n+1} x^{-1/2}\,dx = 2\sqrt{x}\Big|_1^{n+1} = 2\sqrt{n+1} - 2.$$

This integral diverges as $n \to \infty$, so the series does as well by the bound above.

8.4.63 $\sum_{k=1}^{\infty} ca_k = \lim_{n\to\infty} \sum_{k=1}^{n} ca_k = \lim_{n\to\infty} c \sum_{k=1}^{n} a_k = c \lim_{n\to\infty} \sum_{k=1}^{n} a_k$, so that one sum diverges if and only if the other one does.

8.4.65 To approximate the sequence for $\zeta(m)$, note that the remainder R_n after n terms is bounded by

$$\int_n^{\infty} \frac{1}{x^m}\,dx = \frac{1}{m-1} n^{1-m}.$$

For $m = 3$, if we wish to approximate the value to within 10^{-3}, we must solve $\frac{1}{2} n^{-2} < 10^{-3}$, so that $n = 23$, and $\displaystyle\sum_{k=1}^{23} \frac{1}{k^3} \approx 1.201151926$. The true value is ≈ 1.202056903.

For $m = 5$, if we wish to approximate the value to within 10^{-3}, we must solve $\frac{1}{4} n^{-4} < 10^{-3}$, so that $n = 4$, and $\displaystyle\sum_{k=1}^{4} \frac{1}{k^5} \approx 1.036341789$. The true value is ≈ 1.036927755.

8.4.67 $\displaystyle\sum_{k=1}^{\infty} \frac{1}{k^2} = \sum_{k=1}^{\infty} \frac{1}{(2k)^2} + \sum_{k=1}^{\infty} \frac{1}{(2k-1)^2}$, splitting the series into even and odd terms. But $\sum_{k=1}^{\infty} \frac{1}{(2k)^2} = \frac{1}{4} \sum_{k=1}^{\infty} \frac{1}{k^2}$. Thus $\frac{\pi^2}{6} = \frac{1}{4}\frac{\pi^2}{6} + \sum_{k=1}^{\infty} \frac{1}{(2k-1)^2}$, so that the sum in question is $\frac{3\pi^2}{24} = \frac{\pi^2}{8}$.

8.4.69

a. $x_1 = \sum_{k=2}^{2} \frac{1}{k} = \frac{1}{2}$, $x_2 = \sum_{k=3}^{4} \frac{1}{k} = \frac{1}{3} + \frac{1}{4} = \frac{7}{12}$, $x_3 = \sum_{k=4}^{6} \frac{1}{k} = \frac{1}{4} + \frac{1}{5} + \frac{1}{6} = \frac{37}{60}$.

b. x_n has n terms. Each term is bounded below by $\frac{1}{2n}$ and bounded above by $\frac{1}{n+1}$. Thus $x_n \ge n \cdot \frac{1}{2n} = \frac{1}{2}$, and $x_n \le n \cdot \frac{1}{n+1} < n \cdot \frac{1}{n} = 1$.

c. The right Riemann sum for $\int_1^2 \frac{dx}{x}$ using n subintervals has n rectangles of width $\frac{1}{n}$; the right edges of those rectangles are at $1 + \frac{i}{n} = \frac{n+i}{n}$ for $i = 1, 2, \ldots, n$. The height of such a rectangle is the value of $\frac{1}{x}$ at the right endpoint, which is $\frac{n}{n+i}$. Thus the area of the rectangle is $\frac{1}{n} \cdot \frac{n}{n+i} = \frac{1}{n+i}$. Adding up over all the rectangles gives x_n.

d. The limit $\lim_{n\to\infty} x_n$ is the limit of the right Riemann sum as the width of the rectangles approaches zero. This is precisely $\int_1^2 \frac{dx}{x} = \ln x\Big|_1^2 = \ln 2$.

8.4.71

a. Note that the center of gravity of any stack of dominoes is the average of the locations of their centers. Define the midpoint of the zeroth (top) domino to be $x = 0$, and stack additional dominoes down and to its right (to increasingly positive x-coordinates). Let $m(n)$ be the x-coordinate of the midpoint of the nth domino. Then in order for the stack not to fall over, the left edge of the nth domino must be placed directly under the center of gravity of dominos 0 through $n-1$, which is $\frac{1}{n}\sum_{i=0}^{n-1} m(i)$, so that $m(n) = 1 + \frac{1}{n}\sum_{i=0}^{n-1} m(i)$. We claim that in fact $m(n) = \sum_{k=1}^{n} \frac{1}{k}$. Use induction. This is certainly true for $n = 1$. Note first that $m(0) = 0$, so we can start the sum at 1 rather than at 0. Now, $m(n) = 1 + \frac{1}{n}\sum_{i=1}^{n-1} m(i) = 1 + \frac{1}{n}\sum_{i=1}^{n-1}\sum_{j=1}^{i}\frac{1}{j}$. Now, 1 appears $n-1$ times in the double sum, 2 appears $n-2$ times, and so forth, so we can rewrite this sum as $m(n) = 1 + \frac{1}{n}\sum_{i=1}^{n-1}\frac{n-i}{i} = 1 + \frac{1}{n}\sum_{i=1}^{n-1}\left(\frac{n}{i} - 1\right) = 1 + \frac{1}{n}\left(n\sum_{i=1}^{n-1}\frac{1}{i} - (n-1)\right) = \sum_{i=1}^{n-1}\frac{1}{i} + 1 - \frac{n-1}{n} = \sum_{i=1}^{n}\frac{1}{i}$, and we are done by induction (noting that the statement is clearly true for $n = 0$, $n = 1$). Thus the maximum overhang is $\sum_{k=2}^{n}\frac{1}{k}$.

b. For an infinite number of dominos, because the overhang is the harmonic series, the distance is potentially infinite.

8.4.73

a. Dividing both sides of the recurrence equation by f_n gives $\frac{f_{n+1}}{f_n} = 1 + \frac{f_{n-1}}{f_n}$. Let the limit of the ratio of successive terms be L. Taking the limit of the previous equation gives $L = 1 + \frac{1}{L}$. Thus $L^2 = L + 1$, so $L^2 - L - 1 = 0$. The quadratic formula gives $L = \frac{1 \pm \sqrt{1 - 4\cdot(-1)}}{2}$, but we know that all the terms are positive, so we must have $L = \frac{1+\sqrt{5}}{2} = \phi \approx 1.618$.

b. Write the recurrence in the form $f_{n-1} = f_{n+1} - f_n$ and divide both sides by f_{n+1}. Then we have $\frac{f_{n-1}}{f_{n+1}} = 1 - \frac{f_n}{f_{n+1}}$. Taking the limit gives $1 - \frac{1}{\phi}$ on the right-hand side.

c. Consider the harmonic series with the given groupings, and compare it with the sum of $\frac{f_{k-1}}{f_{k+1}}$ as shown. The first three terms match exactly. The sum of the next two are $\frac{1}{4} + \frac{1}{5} > \frac{1}{5} + \frac{1}{5} = \frac{2}{5}$. The sum of the next three are $\frac{1}{6} + \frac{1}{7} + \frac{1}{8} > \frac{1}{8} + \frac{1}{8} + \frac{1}{8} = \frac{3}{8}$. The sum of the next five are $\frac{1}{9} + \cdots + \frac{1}{13} > 5 \cdot \frac{1}{13} = \frac{5}{13}$. Thus the harmonic series is bounded below by the series $\sum_{k=1}^{\infty}\frac{f_{k-1}}{f_{k+1}}$.

d. The result above implies that the harmonic series diverges, because the series $\sum_{k=1}^{\infty}\frac{f_{k-1}}{f_{k+1}}$ diverges, since its general term has limit $1 - \frac{1}{\phi} \neq 0$.

8.5 The Ratio, Root, and Comparison Tests

8.5.1 Given a series $\sum a_k$ of positive terms, compute $\lim_{k\to\infty}\frac{a_{k+1}}{a_k}$ and call it r. If $0 \le r < 1$, the given series converges. If $r > 1$ (including $r = \infty$), the given series diverges. If $r = 1$, the test is inconclusive.

8.5.3 Given a series of positive terms $\sum a_k$ that you suspect converges, find a series $\sum b_k$ that you know converges, for which $\lim_{k\to\infty}\frac{a_k}{b_k} = L$ where $L \ge 0$ is a finite number. If you are successful, you will have shown that the series $\sum a_k$ converges.

Given a series of positive terms $\sum a_k$ that you suspect diverges, find a series $\sum b_k$ that you know diverges, for which $\lim_{k\to\infty}\frac{a_k}{b_k} = L$ where $L > 0$ (including the case $L = \infty$). If you are successful, you will have shown that $\sum a_k$ diverges.

8.5.5 The Ratio Test.

8.5.7 The difference between successive partial sums is a term in the sequence. Because the terms are positive, differences between successive partial sums are as well, so the sequence of partial sums is increasing.

8.5.9 The ratio between successive terms is $\frac{a_{k+1}}{a_k} = \frac{1}{(k+1)!} \cdot \frac{(k)!}{1} = \frac{1}{k+1}$, which goes to zero as $k \to \infty$, so the given series converges by the Ratio Test.

8.5.11 The ratio between successive terms is $\frac{a_{k+1}}{a_k} = \frac{(k+1)^2}{4^{(k+1)}} \cdot \frac{4^k}{(k)^2} = \frac{1}{4}\left(\frac{k+1}{k}\right)^2$. The limit is $1/4$ as $k \to \infty$, so the given series converges by the Ratio Test.

8.5.13 The ratio between successive terms is $\frac{a_{k+1}}{a_k} = \frac{(k+1)e^{-(k+1)}}{(k)e^{-(k)}} = \frac{k+1}{(k)e}$. The limit of this ratio as $k \to \infty$ is $1/e < 1$, so the given series converges by the Ratio Test.

8.5.15 The ratio between successive terms is $\frac{2^{k+1}}{(k+1)^{99}} \cdot \frac{(k)^{99}}{2^k} = 2\left(\frac{k}{k+1}\right)^{99}$; the limit as $k \to \infty$ is 2, so the given series diverges by the Ratio Test.

8.5.17 The ratio between successive terms is $\frac{((k+1)!)^2}{(2(k+1))!} \cdot \frac{(2k)!}{((k)!)^2} = \frac{(k+1)^2}{(2k+2)(2k+1)}$; the limit as $k \to \infty$ is $1/4$, so the given series converges by the Ratio Test.

8.5.19 The kth root of the kth term is $\frac{10k^3+3}{9k^3+k+1}$. The limit of this as $k \to \infty$ is $\frac{10}{9} > 1$, so the given series diverges by the Root Test.

8.5.21 The kth root of the kth term is $\frac{k^{2/k}}{2}$. The limit of this as $k \to \infty$ is $\frac{1}{2} < 1$, so the given series converges by the Root Test.

8.5.23 The kth root of the kth term is $\left(\frac{k}{k+1}\right)^{2k}$. The limit of this as $k \to \infty$ is $e^{-2} < 1$, so the given series converges by the Root Test.

8.5.25 The kth root of the kth term is$\left(\frac{1}{k^k}\right)$. The limit of this as $k \to \infty$ is 0, so the given series converges by the Root Test.

8.5.27 $\frac{1}{k^2+4} < \frac{1}{k^2}$, and $\sum_{k=1}^{\infty} \frac{1}{k^2}$ converges, so $\sum_{k=1}^{\infty} \frac{1}{k^2+4}$ converges as well, by the Comparison Test.

8.5.29 Use the Limit Comparison Test with $\{\frac{1}{k}\}$. The ratio of the terms of the two series is $\frac{k^3-k}{k^3+4}$ which has limit 1 as $k \to \infty$. Because the comparison series diverges, the given series does as well.

8.5.31 For all k, $\frac{1}{k^{3/2}+1} < \frac{1}{k^{3/2}}$. The series whose terms are $\frac{1}{k^{3/2}}$ is a p-series which converges, so the given series converges as well by the Comparison Test.

8.5.33 $\sin(1/k) > 0$ for $k \geq 1$, so we can apply the Comparison Test with $1/k^2$. $\sin(1/k) < 1$, so $\frac{\sin(1/k)}{k^2} < \frac{1}{k^2}$. Because the comparison series converges, the given series converges as well.

8.5.35 Use the Limit Comparison Test with $\{1/k\}$. The ratio of the terms of the two series is $\frac{k}{2k-\sqrt{k}} = \frac{1}{2-1/\sqrt{k}}$, which has limit $1/2$ as $k \to \infty$. Because the comparison series diverges, the given series does as well.

8.5.37 Use the Limit Comparison Test with $\frac{k^{2/3}}{k^{3/2}}$. The ratio of corresponding terms of the two series is $\frac{\sqrt[3]{k^2+1}}{\sqrt{k^3+1}} \cdot \frac{k^{3/2}}{k^{2/3}} = \frac{\sqrt[3]{k^2+1}}{\sqrt[3]{k^2}} \cdot \frac{\sqrt{k^3}}{\sqrt{k^3+1}}$, which has limit 1 as $k \to \infty$. The comparison series is the series whose terms are $k^{2/3-3/2} = k^{-5/6}$, which is a p-series with $p < 1$, so it, and the given series, both diverge.

8.5.39

a. False. For example, let $\{a_k\}$ be all zeros, and $\{b_k\}$ be all 1's.

b. True. This is a result of the Comparison Test.

c. True. Both of these statements follow from the Comparison Test.

d. True. The limit of the ratio is always 1 in the case, so the test is inconclusive.

8.5.41 Use the Divergence Test: $\lim_{k\to\infty} a_k = \lim_{k\to\infty} \left(1+\frac{2}{k}\right)^k = e^2 \neq 0$, so the given series diverges.

8.5.43 Use the Ratio Test: the ratio of successive terms is $\frac{(k+1)^{100}}{(k+2)!} \cdot \frac{(k+1)!}{k^{100}} = \left(\frac{k+1}{k}\right)^{100} \cdot \frac{1}{k+2}$. This has limit $1^{100} \cdot 0 = 0$ as $k \to \infty$, so the given series converges by the Ratio Test.

8.5.45 Use the Root Test. The kth root of the kth term is $(k^{1/k}-1)^2$, which has limit 0 as $k \to \infty$, so the given series converges by the Root Test.

8.5.47 Use the Divergence Test: $\lim_{k\to\infty} \frac{k^2+2k+1}{3k^2+1} = \frac{1}{3} \neq 0$, so the given series diverges.

8.5.49 Use the Limit Comparison Test with the harmonic series. Note that $\lim_{k\to\infty} \frac{\frac{1}{\ln k}}{\frac{1}{k}} = \lim_{k\to\infty} \frac{k}{\ln k} = \infty$, and because the harmonic series diverges, the given series does as well.

8.5.51 Use the Limit Comparison Test with the series whose kth term is $\frac{1}{k^{3/2}}$. Note that $\lim_{k\to\infty} \frac{1}{\sqrt{k^3-k+1}} \cdot \frac{\sqrt{k^3}}{1} = \lim_{k\to\infty} \sqrt{\frac{k^3}{k^3-k+1}} = \sqrt{1} = 1$, and the series $\sum_{k=1}^{\infty} \frac{1}{k^{3/2}}$ converges because it is a p-series with $p = \frac{3}{2}$. Thus, the given series also converges.

8.5.53 Use the Comparison Test. Each term $\frac{1}{k} + 2^{-k} > \frac{1}{k}$. Because the harmonic series diverges, so does this series.

8.5.55 Use the Ratio Test. $\frac{a_{k+1}}{a_k} = \frac{2^{k+1}(k+1)!}{(k+1)^{k+1}} \cdot \frac{(k)^k}{2^k(k)!} = 2\left(\frac{k}{k+1}\right)^k$, which has limit $\frac{2}{e}$ as $k \to \infty$, so the given series converges.

8.5.57 Use the Limit Comparison Test with $\{1/k^3\}$. The ratio of corresponding terms is $\frac{k^{11}}{k^{11}+3}$, which has limit 1 as $k \to \infty$. Because the comparison series converges, so does the given series.

8.5.59 This is a p-series with exponent greater than 1, so it converges.

8.5.61 $\ln\left(\frac{k+2}{k+1}\right) = \ln(k+2) - \ln(k+1)$, so this series telescopes. We get $\sum_{k=1}^{n} \ln\left(\frac{k+2}{k+1}\right) = \ln(n+2) - \ln 2$. Because $\lim_{n\to\infty} \ln(n+2) - \ln 2 = \infty$, the sequence of partial sums diverges, so the given series is divergent.

8.5.63 For $k > 7$, $\ln k > 2$ so note that $\frac{1}{k^{\ln k}} < \frac{1}{k^2}$. Because $\sum_{k=1}^{\infty} \frac{1}{k^2}$ converges, the given series converges as well.

8.5.65 Use the Limit Comparison Test with the harmonic series. $\frac{\tan(1/k)}{1/k}$ has limit 1 as $k \to \infty$ because $\lim_{x\to 0} \frac{\tan x}{x} = 1$. Thus the original series diverges.

8.5.67 Note that $\dfrac{1}{(2k+1)\cdot(2k+3)} = \dfrac{1}{2}\left(\dfrac{1}{2k+1} - \dfrac{1}{2k+3}\right)$. Thus this series telescopes.

$$\sum_{k=0}^{n} \frac{1}{(2k+1)(2k+3)} = \frac{1}{2}\sum_{k=0}^{n}\left(\frac{1}{2k+1} - \frac{1}{2k+3}\right) = \frac{1}{2}\left(-\frac{1}{2n+3}+1\right),$$

so the given series converges to $1/2$, because that is the limit of the sequence of partial sums.

8.5.69 This series is $\sum_{k=1}^{\infty} \frac{k^2}{k!}$. By the Ratio Test, $\frac{a_{k+1}}{a_k} = \frac{(k+1)^2}{(k+1)!} \cdot \frac{k!}{k^2} = \frac{1}{k+1}\left(\frac{k+1}{k}\right)^2$, which has limit 0 as $k \to \infty$, so the given series converges.

8.5.71 For $p \le 1$ and $k > e$, $\frac{\ln k}{k^p} > \frac{1}{k^p}$. The series $\sum_{k=1}^{\infty} \frac{1}{k^p}$ diverges, so the given series diverges. For $p > 1$, let $q < p - 1$; then for sufficiently large k, $\ln k < k^q$, so that by the Comparison Test, $\frac{\ln k}{k^p} < \frac{k^q}{k^p} = \frac{1}{k^{p-q}}$. But $p - q > 1$, so that $\sum_{k=1}^{\infty} \frac{1}{k^{p-q}}$ is a convergent p-series. Thus the original series is convergent precisely when $p > 1$.

8.5.73 For $p \leq 1$, $\frac{(\ln k)^p}{k^p} > \frac{1}{k^p}$ for $k \geq 3$, and $\sum_{k=1}^{\infty} \frac{1}{k^p}$ diverges for $p \leq 1$, so the original series diverges. For $p > 1$, let $q < p - 1$; then for sufficiently large k, $(\ln k)^p < k^q$. Note that $\frac{(\ln k)^p}{k^p} < \frac{k^q}{k^p} = \frac{1}{k^{p-q}}$. But $p - q > 1$, so $\sum_{k=1}^{\infty} \frac{1}{k^{p-q}}$ converges, so the given series converges. Thus, the given series converges exactly for $p > 1$.

8.5.75 Use the Ratio Test:

$$\lim_{k\to\infty} \frac{a_{k+1}}{a_k} = \lim_{k\to\infty} \frac{(k+1)p^{k+1}}{k+2} \cdot \frac{k+1}{kp^k} = p,$$

so the given series converges for $p < 1$ and diverges for $p > 1$. For $p = 1$ the given series diverges by limit comparison with the harmonic series.

8.5.77 $\lim_{k\to\infty} a_k = \lim_{k\to\infty} \left(1 - \frac{p}{k}\right)^k = e^{-p} \neq 0$, so this sequence diverges for all p by the Divergence Test.

8.5.79 These tests apply only for series with positive terms, so assume $r > 0$. Clearly the series do not converge for $r = 1$, so we assume $r \neq 1$ in what follows. Using the Integral Test, $\sum r^k$ converges if and only if $\int_1^{\infty} r^x \, dx$ converges. This improper integral has value $\lim_{b\to\infty} \left.\frac{r^x}{\ln r}\right|_1^b$, which converges only when $\lim_{b\to\infty} r^b$ exists, which occurs only for $r < 1$. Using the Ratio Test, $\frac{a_{k+1}}{a_k} = \frac{r^{k+1}}{r^k} = r$, so by the Ratio Test, the series converges if and only if $r < 1$. Using the Root Test, $\lim_{k\to\infty} \sqrt[k]{a_k} = \lim_{k\to\infty} \sqrt[k]{r^k} = \lim_{k\to\infty} r = r$, so again we have convergence if and only if $r < 1$. By the Divergence Test, we know that a geometric series diverges if $|r| \geq 1$.

8.5.81 To prove case (2), assume $L = 0$ and that $\sum b_k$ converges. Because $L = 0$, for every $\varepsilon > 0$, there is some N such that for all $n > N$, $|\frac{a_k}{b_k}| < \varepsilon$. Take $\varepsilon = 1$; this then says that there is some N such that for all $n > N$, $0 < a_k < b_k$. By the Comparison Test, because $\sum b_k$ converges, so does $\sum a_k$. To prove case (3), because $L = \infty$, then $\lim_{k\to\infty} \frac{b_k}{a_k} = 0$, so by the argument above, we have $0 < b_k < a_k$ for sufficient large k. But $\sum b_k$ diverges, so by the Comparison Test, $\sum a_k$ does as well.

8.5.83 The series clearly converges for $x = 0$. For $x \neq 0$, we have $\frac{a_{k+1}}{a_k} = \frac{x^{k+1}}{x^k} = x$. This has limit x as $k \to \infty$, so the series converges for $x < 1$. It clearly does not converge for $x = 1$. So the series converges for $x \in [0, 1)$.

8.5.85 The series clearly converges for $x = 0$. For $x \neq 0$, we have $\frac{a_{k+1}}{a_k} = \frac{x^{k+1}}{(k+1)^2} \cdot \frac{k^2}{x^k} = x\left(\frac{k}{k+1}\right)^2$, which has limit x as $k \to \infty$. Thus the series converges for $x < 1$. When $x = 1$, the series is $\frac{1}{k^2}$, which converges. Thus the original series converges for $0 \leq x \leq 1$.

8.5.87 The series clearly converges for $x = 0$. For $x \neq 0$, we have $\frac{a_{k+1}}{a_k} = \frac{x^{k+1}}{2^{k+1}} \cdot \frac{2^k}{x^k} = \frac{x}{2}$, which has limit $x/2$ as $k \to \infty$. Thus the series converges for $0 \leq x < 2$. For $x = 2$, it is obviously divergent.

8.5.89

a. $\ln \prod_{k=0}^{\infty} e^{1/2^k} = \sum_{k=0}^{\infty} \frac{1}{2^k} = 2$, so that the original product converges to e^2.

b. $\ln \prod_{k=2}^{\infty} \left(1 - \frac{1}{k}\right) = \ln \prod_{k=2}^{\infty} \frac{k-1}{k} = \sum_{k=2}^{\infty} \ln \frac{k-1}{k} = \sum_{k=2}^{\infty} (\ln(k-1) - \ln(k))$. This series telescopes to give $S_n = -\ln(n)$, so the original series has limit $\lim_{n\to\infty} P_n = \lim_{n\to\infty} e^{-\ln(n)} = 0$.

8.5.91

a. Use the Ratio Test:

$$\frac{a_{k+1}}{a_k} = \frac{1 \cdot 3 \cdot 5 \cdots (2k+1)}{p^{k+1}(k+1)!} \cdot \frac{p^k(k)!}{1 \cdot 3 \cdot 5 \cdots (2k-1)} = \frac{(2k+1)}{(k+1)p}$$

and this expression has limit $\frac{2}{p}$ as $k \to \infty$. Thus the series converges for $p > 2$.

b. Following the hint, when $p = 2$ we have $\sum_{k=1}^{\infty} \frac{(2k)!}{2^k k!(2 \cdot 4 \cdot 6 \cdots 2k)} = \sum_{k=1}^{\infty} \frac{(2k)!}{(2^k)^2(k!)^2}$. Using Stirling's formula, the numerator is asymptotic to $2\sqrt{\pi}\sqrt{k}(2k)^{2k}e^{-2k} = 2\sqrt{\pi}\sqrt{k}(2^k)^2(k^k)^2e^{-2k}$ while the denominator is asymptotic to $(2^k)^2 2\pi k(k^k)^2e^{-2k}$, so the quotient is asymptotic to $\frac{1}{\sqrt{\pi}\sqrt{k}}$. Thus the original series diverges for $p = 2$ by the Limit Comparison Test with the divergent p-series $\sum_{k=1}^{\infty} \frac{1}{k^{1/2}}$.

8.6 Alternating Series

8.6.1 Because $S_{n+1} - S_n = (-1)^n a_{n+1}$ alternates signs.

8.6.3 We have

$$S = S_{2n+1} + (a_{2n} - a_{2n+1}) + (a_{2n+2} - a_{2n+3}) + \cdots$$

and each term of the form $a_{2k} - a_{2k+1} > 0$, so that $S_{2n+1} < S$. Also

$$S = S_{2n} + (-a_{2n+1} + a_{2n+2}) + (-a_{2n+3} + a_{2n+4}) + \cdots$$

and each term of the form $-a_{2k+1} + a_{2k+2} < 0$, so that $S < S_{2n}$. Thus the sum of the series is trapped between the odd partial sums and the even partial sums.

8.6.5 The remainder is less than the first neglected term because

$$S - S_n = (-1)^{n+1}(a_{n+1} + (-a_{n+2} + a_{n+3}) + \cdots)$$

so that the sum of the series *after* the first disregarded term has the opposite sign from the first disregarded term.

8.6.7 No. If the terms are positive, then the absolute value of each term is the term itself, so convergence and absolute convergence would mean the same thing in this context.

8.6.9 Yes. For example, $\sum \frac{(-1)^k}{k^3}$ converges absolutely and thus not conditionally (see the definition).

8.6.11 The terms of the series decrease in magnitude, and $\lim_{k\to\infty} \frac{1}{2k+1} = 0$, so the given series converges.

8.6.13 $\lim_{k\to\infty} \frac{k}{3k+2} = \frac{1}{3} \neq 0$, so the given series diverges.

8.6.15 The terms of the series decrease in magnitude, and $\lim\limits_{k\to\infty} \frac{1}{k^3} = 0$, so the given series converges.

8.6.17 The terms of the series decrease in magnitude, and $\lim\limits_{k\to\infty} \frac{k^2}{k^3+1} = \lim\limits_{k\to\infty} \frac{1/k}{1+1/k^3} = 0$, so the given series converges.

8.6.19 $\lim\limits_{k\to\infty} \frac{k^2-1}{k^2+3} = 1$, so the terms of the series do not tend to zero and thus the given series diverges.

8.6.21 $\lim\limits_{k\to\infty} \left(1 + \frac{1}{k}\right) = 1$, so the given series diverges.

8.6.23 The derivative of $f(k) = \frac{k^{10}+2k^5+1}{k(k^{10}+1)}$ is $f'(k) = \frac{-(k^{20}+2k^{10}+12k^{15}-8k^5+1)}{k^2(k^{10}+1)^2}$. The numerator is negative for large enough values of k, and the denominator is always positive, so the derivative is negative for large enough k. Also, $\lim\limits_{k\to\infty} \frac{k^{10}+2k^5+1}{k(k^{10}+1)} = \lim\limits_{k\to\infty} \frac{1+2k^{-5}+k^{-10}}{k+k^{-9}} = 0$. Thus the given series converges.

8.6.25 $\lim\limits_{k\to\infty} k^{1/k} = 1$ (for example, take logs and apply L'Hôpital's rule), so the given series diverges by the Divergence Test.

8.6.27 $\frac{1}{\sqrt{k^2+4}}$ is decreasing and tends to zero as $k \to \infty$, so the given series converges.

8.6.29 We want $\frac{1}{n+1} < 10^{-4}$, or $n+1 > 10^4$, so $n = 10^4$.

8.6.31 The series starts with $k=0$, so we want $\frac{1}{2n+1} < 10^{-4}$, or $2n+1 > 10^4$, $n = 5000$.

8.6.33 We want $\frac{1}{(n+1)^4} < 10^{-4}$, or $(n+1)^4 > 10^4$, so $n = 10$.

8.6.35 The series starts with $k=0$, so we want $\frac{1}{3n+1} < 10^{-4}$, or $3n+1 > 10^4$, $n = 3334$.

8.6.37 The series starts with $k=0$, so we want $\frac{1}{4^n}\left(\frac{2}{4n+1} + \frac{2}{4n+2} + \frac{1}{4n+3}\right) < 10^{-4}$, or $\frac{4^n(4n+1)(4n+2)(4n+3)}{4(20n^2+21n+5)} >$ 10000, which occurs first for $n = 6$.

8.6.39 To figure out how many terms we need to sum, we must find n such that $\frac{1}{(n+1)^5} < 10^{-3}$, so that $(n+1)^5 > 1000$; this occurs first for $n = 3$. Thus $\frac{-1}{1} + \frac{1}{2^5} - \frac{1}{3^5} \approx -0.973$.

8.6.41 To figure out how many terms we need to sum, we must find n so that $\frac{n+1}{(n+1)^2+1} < 10^{-3}$, so that $\frac{(n+1)^2+1}{n+1} = n+1+\frac{1}{n+1} > 1000$. This occurs first for $n = 999$. We have $\sum_{k=1}^{999} \frac{(-1)^k k}{k^2+1} \approx -0.269$.

8.6.43 To figure how many terms we need to sum, we must find n such that $\frac{1}{(n+1)^{n+1}} < 10^{-3}$, or $(n+1)^{n+1} >$ 1000, so $n = 4$ ($5^5 = 3125$). Thus the approximation is $\sum_{k=1}^{4} \frac{(-1)^n}{n^n} \approx -.783$.

8.6.45 The series of absolute values is a p-series with $p = 2/3$, so it diverges. The given alternating series does converge, though, by the Alternating Series Test. Thus, the given series is conditionally convergent.

8.6.47 The series of absolute values is a p-series with $p = 3/2$, so it converges absolutely.

8.6.49 The series of absolute values is $\sum \frac{|\cos(k)|}{k^3}$, which converges by the Comparison Test because $\frac{|\cos(k)|}{k^3} \le \frac{1}{k^3}$. Thus the series converges absolutely.

8.6.51 The absolute value of the kth term of this series has limit $\pi/2$ as $k \to \infty$, so the given series is divergent by the Divergence Test.

8.6.53 The series of absolute values is $\sum \frac{k}{2k+1}$, but $\lim_{k\to\infty} \frac{k}{2k+1} = \frac{1}{2}$, so by the Divergence Test, this series diverges. The original series does not converge conditionally, either, because $\lim_{k\to\infty} a_k = \frac{1}{2} \neq 0$.

8.6.55 The series of absolute values is $\sum \frac{\tan^{-1}(k)}{k^3}$, which converges by the Comparison Test because $\frac{\tan^{-1}(k)}{k^3} < \frac{\pi}{2}\frac{1}{k^3}$, and $\sum \frac{\pi}{2}\frac{1}{k^3}$ converges because it is a constant multiple of a convergent $p-$series. So the original series converges absolutely.

8.6.57

a. False. For example, consider the alternating harmonic series.

b. True. This is part of Theorem 8.21.

c. True. This statement is simply saying that a convergent series converges.

d. True. This is part of Theorem 8.21.

e. False. Let $a_k = \frac{1}{k}$.

f. True. Use the Comparison Test: $\lim_{k\to\infty} \frac{a_k^2}{a_k} = \lim_{k\to\infty} a_k = 0$ because $\sum a_k$ converges, so $\sum a_k^2$ and $\sum a_k$ converge or diverge together. Because the latter converges, so does the former.

g. True, by definition. If $\sum |a_k|$ converged, the original series would converge absolutely, not conditionally.

8.6.59 $\sum_{k=1}^{\infty}\frac{1}{k^2}-\sum_{k=1}^{\infty}\frac{(-1)^{k+1}}{k^2}=2\sum_{k=1}^{\infty}\frac{1}{(2k)^2}=2\cdot\frac{1}{4}\sum_{k=1}^{\infty}\frac{1}{k^2}$, and thus $\sum_{k=1}^{\infty}\frac{(-1)^{k+1}}{k^2}=\frac{\pi^2}{6}-\frac{1}{2}\cdot\frac{\pi^2}{6}=\frac{\pi^2}{12}$.

8.6.61 Write $r=-s$; then $0<s<1$ and $\sum r^k=\sum(-1)^k s^k$. Because $|s|<1$, the terms s^k are nonincreasing and tend to zero, so by the Alternating Series Test, the series $\sum(-1)^k s^k=\sum r^k$ converges.

8.6.63 Let $S=1-\frac{1}{2}+\frac{1}{3}-\cdots$. Then

$$\begin{array}{rcccccccccc} S &=& (1-\frac{1}{2}) &+& (\frac{1}{3}-\frac{1}{4}) &+& (\frac{1}{5}-\frac{1}{6}) &+& (\frac{1}{7}-\frac{1}{8}) &+& \ldots \\ \frac{1}{2}S &=& \frac{1}{2} &-& \frac{1}{4} &+& \frac{1}{6} &-& \frac{1}{8} &+& \ldots \end{array}$$

Add these two series together to get

$$\frac{3}{2}S=\frac{3}{2}\ln 2=1+\frac{1}{3}-\frac{1}{2}+\frac{1}{5}+\cdots$$

To see that the results are as desired, consider a collection of four terms:

$$\begin{array}{cccccc} \cdots+ & \left(\frac{1}{4k+1}-\frac{1}{4k+2}\right) & + & \left(\frac{1}{4k+3}-\frac{1}{4k+4}\right) & + & \cdots \\ \cdots & + & \frac{1}{4k+2} & - & \frac{1}{4k+4} & + \cdots \end{array}$$

Adding these results in the desired sign pattern. This repeats for each group of four elements.

8.6.65 Both series diverge, so comparisons of their values are not meaningful.

Chapter Eight Review

1

a. False. Let $a_n=1-\frac{1}{n}$. This sequence has limit 1.

b. False. The terms of a sequence tending to zero is necessary but not sufficient for convergence of the series.

c. True. This is the definition of convergence of a series.

d. False. If a series converges absolutely, the definition says that it does not converge conditionally.

e. True. It has limit 1 as $n\to\infty$.

f. False. The subsequence of the even terms has limit 1 and the subsequence of odd terms has limit -1, so the sequence does not have a limit.

g. False. It diverges by the Divergence Test because $\lim_{k\to\infty}\frac{k^2}{k^2+1}=1\neq 0$.

h. True. The given series converges by the Limit Comparison Test with the series $\sum_{k=1}^{\infty}\frac{1}{k^2}$, and thus its sequence of partial sums converges.

3 $\lim\limits_{n\to\infty}\dfrac{8^n}{n!}=0$ because exponentials grow more slowly than factorials.

5 Take logs and compute $\lim\limits_{n\to\infty}(1/n)\ln n=\lim\limits_{n\to\infty}(\ln n)/n=\lim\limits_{n\to\infty}\frac{1}{n}=0$ by L'Hôpital's rule. Thus the original limit is $e^0=1$.

7 Take logs, and then evaluate $\lim\limits_{n\to\infty}\frac{1}{\ln n}\ln(1/n)=\lim\limits_{n\to\infty}(-1)=-1$, so the original limit is e^{-1}.

9 $a_n = (-1/0.9)^n = (-10/9)^n$. The terms grow without bound so the sequence does not converge.

11

a. $S_1 = \frac{1}{3}$, $S_2 = \frac{11}{24}$, $S_3 = \frac{21}{40}$, $S_4 = \frac{17}{30}$.

b. $S_n = \dfrac{1}{2}\left(\dfrac{1}{1} + \dfrac{1}{2} - \dfrac{1}{n+1} - \dfrac{1}{n+2}\right)$, because the series telescopes.

c. From part (b), $\lim\limits_{n\to\infty} S_n = \frac{3}{4}$, which is the sum of the series.

13 $\sum_{k=1}^{\infty} 3(1.001)^k = 3\sum_{k=1}^{\infty}(1.001)^k$. This is a geometric series with ratio greater than 1, so it diverges.

15 $\frac{1}{k(k+1)} = \frac{1}{k} - \frac{1}{k+1}$, so the series telescopes, and $S_n = 1 - \frac{1}{n+1}$. Thus $\lim\limits_{n\to\infty} S_n = 1$, which is the value of the series.

17 This series telescopes. $S_n = 3 - \frac{3}{3n+1}$, so that $\lim\limits_{n\to\infty} S_n = 3$, which is the value of the series.

19 $\displaystyle\sum_{k=1}^{\infty} \frac{2^k}{3^{k+2}} = \frac{1}{9}\sum_{k=1}^{\infty}\left(\frac{2}{3}\right)^k = \frac{1}{9}\cdot\frac{2/3}{1-2/3} = \frac{2}{9}.$

21

a. It appears that the series converges, because the sequence of partial sums appears to converge to 1.5.

b. The convergence is uncertain.

c. This series clearly appears to diverge, because the partial sums seem to be growing without bound.

23 The series can be written $\sum \frac{1}{k^{2/3}}$, which is a p-series with $p = 2/3 < 1$, so this series diverges.

25 This is a geometric series with ratio $2/e < 1$, so the series converges.

27 Applying the Ratio Test:

$$\lim_{k\to\infty} \frac{a_{k+1}}{a_k} = \lim_{k\to\infty} \frac{2^{k+1}(k+1)!}{(k+1)^{k+1}} \cdot \frac{k^k}{2^k k!} = \lim_{k\to\infty} 2\left(\frac{k}{k+1}\right)^k = \frac{2}{e} < 1,$$

so the given series converges.

29 Use the Comparison Test: $\frac{3}{2+e^k} < \frac{3}{e^k}$, but $\sum \frac{3}{e^k}$ converges because it is a geometric series with ratio $\frac{1}{e} < 1$. Thus the original series converges as well.

31 $a_k = \frac{k^{1/k}}{k^3} = \frac{1}{k^{3-1/k}}$. For $k \geq 2$, then, $a_k < \frac{1}{k^2}$. Because $\sum \frac{1}{k^2}$ converges, the given series also converges, by the Comparison Test.

33 Use the Ratio Test: $\frac{a_{k+1}}{a_k} = \frac{(k+1)^5}{e^{k+1}} \cdot \frac{e^k}{k^5} = \frac{1}{e} \cdot \left(\frac{k+1}{k}\right)^5$, which has limit $1/e < 1$ as $k \to \infty$. Thus the given series converges.

35 Use the Comparison Test. Because $\lim\limits_{k\to\infty} \dfrac{\ln k}{k^{1/2}} = 0$, we have that for sufficiently large k, $\ln k < k^{1/2}$, so that $a_k = \frac{2\ln k}{k^2} < \frac{2k^{1/2}}{k^2} = \frac{2}{k^{3/2}}$. Now $\sum \frac{2}{k^{3/2}}$ is convergent, because it is a p-series with $p = 3/2 > 1$. Thus the original series is convergent.

37 Use the Ratio Test. The ratio of successive terms is $\frac{2\cdot 4^{k+1}}{(2k+3)!} \cdot \frac{(2k+1)!}{2\cdot 4^k} = \frac{4}{(2k+3)(2k+2)}$. This has limit 0 as $k \to \infty$, so the given series converges.

39 Use the Limit Comparison Test with the harmonic series. Note that $\lim_{k\to\infty} \frac{\coth k}{k} \cdot \frac{k}{1} = \lim_{k\to\infty} \coth k = 1$. Because the harmonic series diverges, the given series does as well.

41 Use the Divergence Test. $\lim_{k\to\infty} \tanh k = \lim_{k\to\infty} \frac{e^k+e^{-k}}{e^k-e^{-k}} = 1 \neq 0$, so the given series diverges.

43 $|a_k| = \frac{1}{k^2-1}$. Use the Limit Comparison Test with the convergent series $\sum \frac{1}{k^2}$. Because $\lim_{k\to\infty} \frac{\frac{1}{k^2-1}}{\frac{1}{k^2}} = \lim_{k\to\infty} \frac{k^2}{k^2-1} = 1$, the given series converges absolutely.

45 Use the Ratio Test on the absolute values of the sequence of terms: $\lim_{k\to\infty} \left|\frac{a_{k+1}}{a_k}\right| = \lim_{k\to\infty} \frac{k+1}{e^{k+1}} \cdot \frac{e^k}{k} = \lim_{k\to\infty} \frac{1}{e} \cdot \frac{k+1}{k} = \frac{1}{e} < 1$. Thus, the original series is absolutely convergent.

47 Use the Ratio Test on the absolute values of the sequence of terms: $\lim_{k\to\infty} \left|\frac{a_{k+1}}{a_k}\right| = \lim_{k\to\infty} \frac{10}{k+1} = 0$, so the series converges absolutely.

49 Because $k^2 \ll 2^k$, $\lim_{k\to\infty} \frac{-2\cdot(-2)^k}{k^2} \neq 0$. The given series thus diverges by the Divergence Test.

51

a. For $|x| < 1$, $\lim_{k\to\infty} x^k = 0$, so this limit is zero.

b. This is a geometric series with ratio $-4/5$, so the sum is $\frac{1}{1+4/5} = \frac{5}{9}$.

53 Consider the constant sequence with $a_k = 1$ for all k. The sequence $\{a_k\}$ converges to 1, but the corresponding series $\sum a_k$ diverges by the divergence test.

55

a. This sequence converges because $\lim_{k\to\infty} \frac{k}{k+1} = \lim_{k\to\infty} \frac{1}{1+\frac{1}{k}} = \frac{1}{1+0} = 1$.

b. Because the sequence of terms has limit 1 (which means its limit isn't zero) this series diverges by the divergence test.

57 Because the series converges, we must have $\lim_{k\to\infty} a_k = 0$. Because it converges to 8, the partial sums converge to 8, so that $\lim_{k\to\infty} S_k = 8$.

59 The series converges absolutely for $p > 1$, conditionally for $0 < p \leq 1$ in which case $\{k^{-p}\}$ is decreasing to zero.

61 The sum is 0.2500000000 to ten decimal places. The maximum error is

$$\int_{20}^{\infty} \frac{1}{5^x}\, dx = \lim_{b\to\infty} \left(-\frac{1}{5^x \ln 5}\Big|_{20}^{b} \right) = \frac{1}{5^{20} \ln 5} \approx 6.5 \times 10^{-15}.$$

63 The maximum error is a_{n+1}, so we want $a_{n+1} = \frac{1}{(k+1)^4} < 10^{-8}$, or $(k+1)^4 > 10^8$, so $k = 100$.

65

a. Let T_n be the amount of additional tunnel dug during week n. Then $T_0 = 100$ and $T_n = .95 \cdot T_{n-1} = (.95)^n T_0 = 100(0.95)^n$, so the total distance dug in N weeks is

$$S_N = 100 \sum_{k=0}^{N-1} (0.95)^k = 100 \left(\frac{1-(0.95)^N}{1-0.95} \right) = 2000(1-0.95^N).$$

Then $S_{10} \approx 802.5$ meters and $S_{20} \approx 1283.03$ meters.

b. The longest possible tunnel is $S_\infty = 100\sum_{k=0}^{\infty}(0.95)^k = \frac{100}{1-.95} = 2000$ meters.

67

a. The area of a circle of radius r is πr^2. For $r = 2^{1-n}$, this is $2^{2-2n}\pi$. There are 2^{n-1} circles on the nth page, so the total area of circles on the nth page is $2^{n-1}\cdot\pi 2^{2-2n} = 2^{1-n}\pi$.

b. The sum of the areas on all pages is $\sum_{k=1}^{\infty} 2^{1-k}\pi = 2\pi\sum_{k=1}^{\infty} 2^{-k} = 2\pi\cdot\frac{1/2}{1/2} = 2\pi$.

69

a. $B_n = 1.0025B_{n-1} + 100$ and $B_0 = 100$.

b. $B_n = 100\cdot 1.0025^n + 100\cdot\frac{1-1.0025^n}{1-1.0025} = 100\cdot 1.0025^n - 40000(1-1.0025^n) = 40000(1.0025^{n+1}-1)$.

71

a. $T_1 = \frac{\sqrt{3}}{16}$ and $T_2 = \frac{7\sqrt{3}}{64}$.

b. At stage n, 3^{n-1} triangles of side length $1/2^n$ are removed. Each of those triangles has an area of $\dfrac{\sqrt{3}}{4\cdot 4^n} = \dfrac{\sqrt{3}}{4^{n+1}}$, so a total of

$$3^{n-1}\cdot\frac{\sqrt{3}}{4^{n+1}} = \frac{\sqrt{3}}{16}\cdot\left(\frac{3}{4}\right)^{n-1}$$

is removed at each stage. Thus

$$T_n = \frac{\sqrt{3}}{16}\sum_{k=1}^{n}\left(\frac{3}{4}\right)^{k-1} = \frac{\sqrt{3}}{16}\sum_{k=0}^{n-1}\left(\frac{3}{4}\right)^{k} = \frac{\sqrt{3}}{4}\left(1-\left(\frac{3}{4}\right)^{n}\right).$$

c. $\lim_{n\to\infty} T_n = \frac{\sqrt{3}}{4}$ because $\left(\frac{3}{4}\right)^n \to 0$ as $n\to\infty$.

d. The area of the triangle was originally $\frac{\sqrt{3}}{4}$, so none of the original area is left.

Chapter 9

Power Series

9.1 Approximating Functions With Polynomials

9.1.1 Let the polynomial be $p(x)$. Then $p(0) = f(0)$, $p'(0) = f'(0)$, and $p''(0) = f''(0)$.

9.1.3 The approximations are $p_0(0.1) = 1$, $p_1(0.1) = 1 + \frac{0.1}{2} = 1.05$, and $p_2(0.1) = 1 + \frac{0.1}{2} - \frac{.01}{8} = 1.04875$.

9.1.5 The remainder is the difference between the value of the Taylor polynomial at a point and the true value of the function at that point, $R_n(x) = f(x) - p_n(x)$.

9.1.7

a. Note that $f(1) = 8$, and $f'(x) = 12\sqrt{x}$, so $f'(1) = 12$. Thus, $p_1(x) = 8 + 12(x - 1)$.

b. $f''(x) = 6/\sqrt{x}$, so $f''(1) = 6$. Thus $p_2(x) = 8 + 12(x - 2) + 3(x - 1)^2$.

c. $p_1(1.1) = 12 \cdot 0.1 + 8 = 9.2$. $p_2(1.1) = 3(.1)^2 + 12 \cdot 0.1 + 8 = 9.23$.

9.1.9

a. $f'(x) = -e^{-x}$, so $p_1(x) = f(0) + f'(0)x = 1 - x$.

b. $f''(x) = e^{-x}$, so $p_2(x) = f(0) + f'(0)x + \frac{1}{2}f''(0)x^2 = 1 - x + \frac{1}{2}x^2$.

c. $p_1(0.2) = 0.8$, and $p_2(0.2) = 1 - 0.2 + \frac{1}{2}(0.04) = 0.82$.

9.1.11

a. $f'(x) = -\frac{1}{(x+1)^2}$, so $p_1(x) = f(0) + f'(0)x = 1 - x$.

b. $f''(x) = \frac{2}{(x+1)^3}$, so $p_2(x) = f(0) + f'(0)x + \frac{1}{2}f''(0)x^2 = 1 - x + x^2$.

c. $p_1(0.05) = 0.95$, and $p_2(0.05) = 1 - 0.05 + 0.0025 = 0.953$.

9.1.13

a. $f'(x) = (1/3)x^{-2/3}$, so $p_1(x) = f(8) + f'(8)(x - 8) = 2 + \frac{1}{12}(x - 8)$.

b. $f''(x) = (-2/9)x^{-5/3}$, so $p_2(x) = f(8) + f'(8)(x - 8) + \frac{1}{2}f''(8)(x - 8)^2 = 2 + \frac{1}{12}(x - 8) - \frac{1}{288}(x - 8)^2$.

c. $p_1(7.5) \approx 1.958$, $p_2(7.5) \approx 1.957$.

9.1.15 $f(0) = 1, f'(0) = -\sin 0 = 0, f''(0) = -\cos 0 = -1$, so that $p_0(x) = 1$, $p_1(x) = 1$, $p_2(x) = 1 - \frac{1}{2}x^2$.

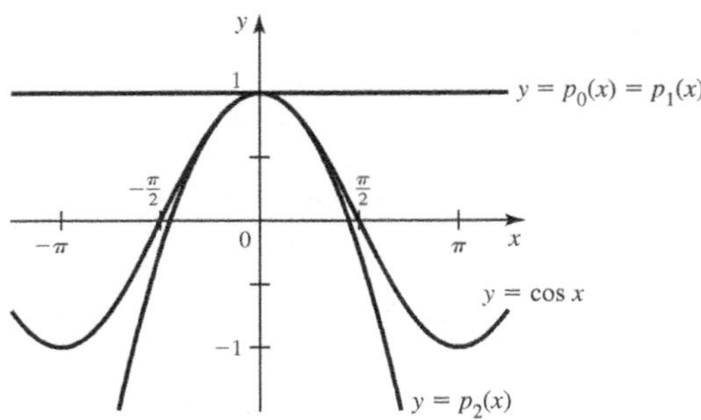

9.1.17 $f(0) = 0$, $f'(0) = -\frac{1}{1-0} = -1, f''(0) = -\frac{1}{(1-0)^2} = -1$, so that $p_0(x) = 0$, $p_1(x) = -x$, $p_2(x) = -x - \frac{1}{2}x^2$.

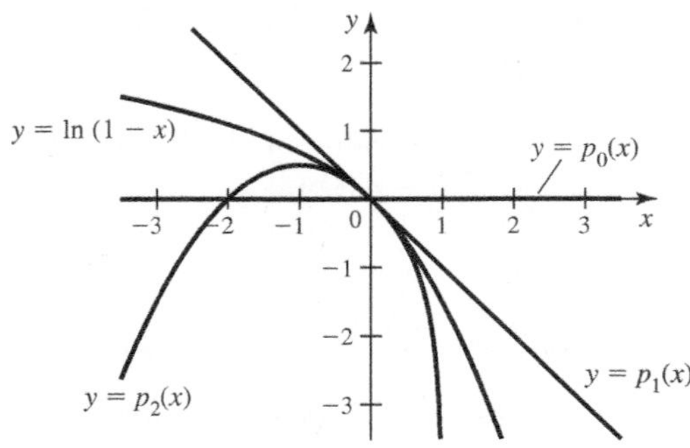

9.1.19 $f(0) = 0$. $f'(x) = \sec^2 x$, $f''(x) = 2\tan x \sec^2 x$, so that $f'(0) = 1$, $f''(0) = 0$. Thus $p_0(x) = 0$, $p_1(x) = x$, $p_2(x) = x$.

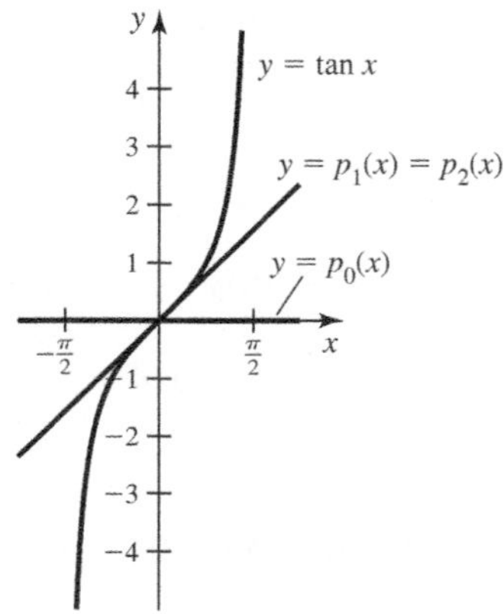

9.1.21 $f(0) = 1$, $f'(0) = -3(1+0)^{-4} = -3$, $f''(0) = 12(1+0)^{-5} = 12$, so that $p_0(x) = 1$, $p_1(x) = 1 - 3x$, $p_2(x) = 1 - 3x + 6x^2$.

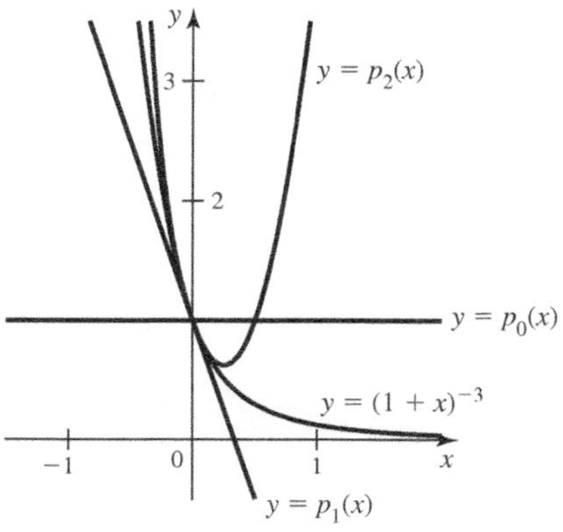

9.1.23

a. $p_2(0.05) \approx 1.025$.

b. The absolute error is $\sqrt{1.05} - p_2(0.05) \approx 7.68 \times 10^{-6}$.

9.1.25

a. $p_2(0.08) \approx 0.962$.

b. The absolute error is $p_2(0.08) - \frac{1}{\sqrt{1.08}} \approx 1.5 \times 10^{-4}$.

9.1.27

a. $p_2(0.15) \approx 0.861$.

b. The absolute error is $p_2(0.15) - e^{-0.15} \approx 5.4 \times 10^{-4}$.

9.1.29

a. Note that $f(1) = 1$, $f'(1) = 3$, and $f''(1) = 6$. Thus, $p_0(x) = 1$, $p_1(x) = 1 + 3(x-1)$, and $p_2(x) = 1 + 3(x-1) + 3(x-1)^2$.

b.

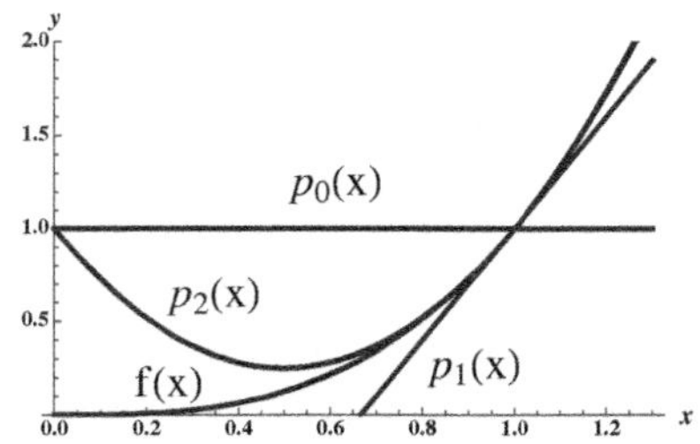

9.1.31

a. $p_0(x) = \frac{\sqrt{2}}{2}$, $p_1(x) = \frac{\sqrt{2}}{2} + \frac{\sqrt{2}}{2}(x - \frac{\pi}{4})$, $p_2(x) = \frac{\sqrt{2}}{2} + \frac{\sqrt{2}}{2}(x - \frac{\pi}{4}) - \frac{\sqrt{2}}{4}(x - \frac{\pi}{4})^2$.

b.

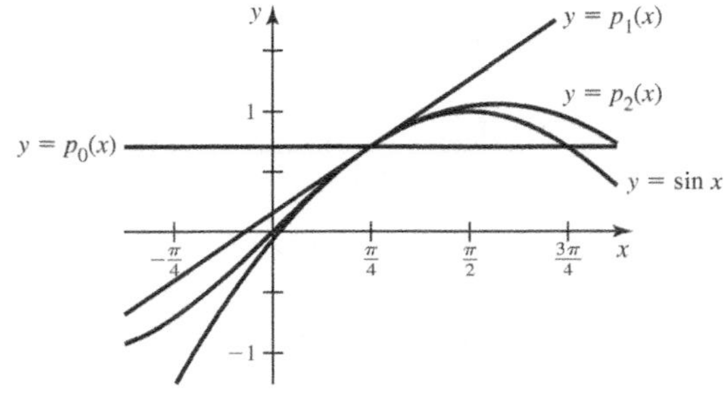

9.1.33

a. $p_0(x) = 3$, $p_1(x) = 3 + \frac{1}{6}(x-9)$, $p_2(x) = 3 + \frac{1}{6}(x-9) - \frac{1}{216}(x-9)^2$.

b.

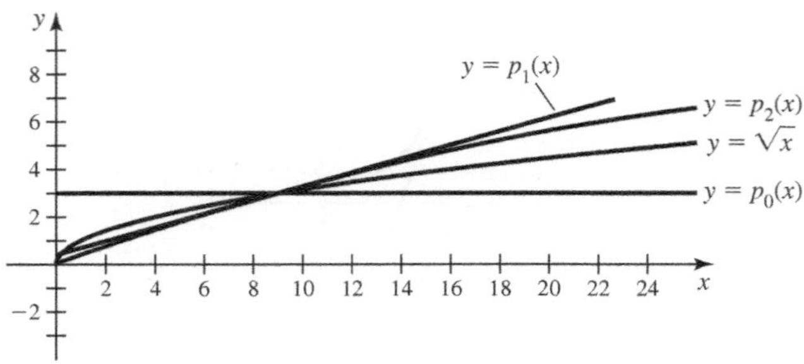

9.1.35

a. $p_0(x) = 1$, $p_1(x) = 1 + \frac{1}{e}(x-e)$, $p_2(x) = 1 + \frac{1}{e}(x-e) - \frac{1}{2e^2}(x-e)^2$.

b.

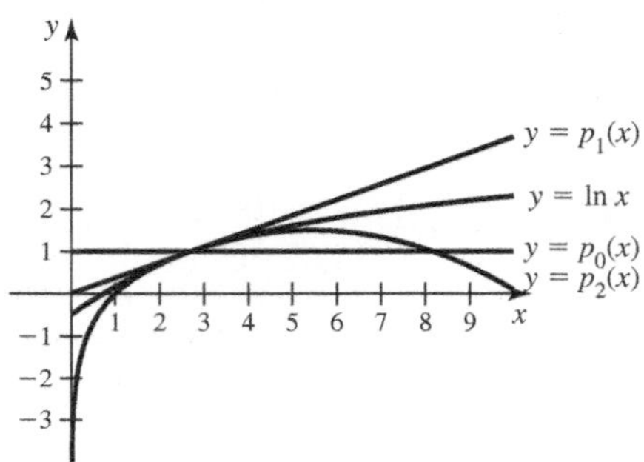

9.1.37

a. $f(1) = \frac{\pi}{4} + 2$, $f'(1) = \frac{1}{2} + 2 = \frac{5}{2}$. $f''(1) = -\frac{1}{2} + 2 = \frac{3}{2}$. $p_0(x) = 2 + \frac{\pi}{4}$, $p_1(x) = 2 + \frac{\pi}{4} + \frac{5}{2}(x-1)$, $p_2(x) = 2 + \frac{\pi}{4} + \frac{5}{2}(x-1) + \frac{3}{4}(x-1)^2$.

b.

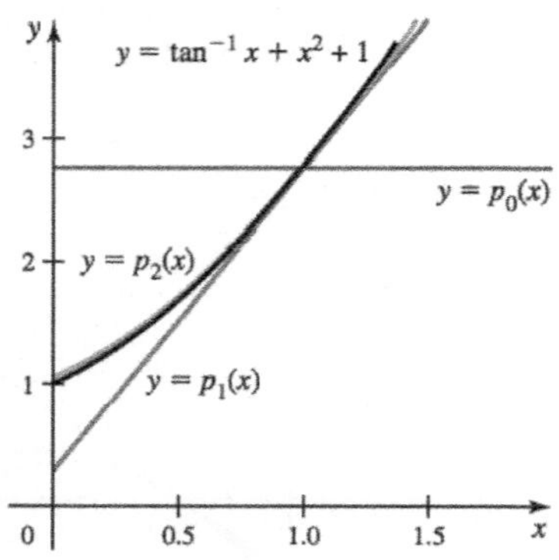

9.1.39

a. Ue the Taylor polynomial centered at 0 with $f(x) = e^x$. We have $p_3(x) = 1 + x + \frac{1}{2}x^2 + \frac{1}{6}x^3$. $p_3(0.12) \approx 1.127$.

b. $|f(0.12) - p_3(0.12)| \approx 8.9 \times 10^{-6}$.

9.1.41

a. Use the Taylor polynomial centered at 0 with $f(x) = \tan(x)$. We have $p_3(x) = x + \frac{1}{3}x^3$. $p_3(-0.1) \approx -0.100$.

b. $|p_3(-0.1) - f(-0.1)| \approx 1.3 \times 10^{-6}$.

9.1.43

a. Use the Taylor polynomial centered at 0 with $f(x) = \sqrt{1+x}$. We have $p_3(x) = 1 + \frac{1}{2}x - \frac{1}{8}x^2 + \frac{1}{16}x^3$. $p_3(0.06) \approx 1.030$.

b. $|f(0.06) - p_3(0.06)| \approx 4.9 \times 10^{-7}$.

9.1.45

a. Use the Taylor polynomial centered at 100 with $f(x) = \sqrt{x}$. We have $p_3(x) = 10 + \frac{1}{20}(x - 100) - \frac{1}{8000}(x-100)^2 + \frac{1}{1600000}(x-100)^3$. $p_3(101) \approx 10.050$.

b. $|p_3(101) - f(101)| \approx 3.9 \times 10^{-9}$.

9.1.47

a. Use the Taylor polynomial centered at 0 with $f(x) = \sinh(x)$. Note that $f(0) = 0$, $f'(0) = 1$, $f''(0) = 0$ and $f'''(0) = 1$. Then we have $p_3(x) = x + x^3/6$, so $\sinh(.5) \approx (.5)^3/6 + .5 \approx 0.521$.

b. $|p_3(.5) - \sinh(.5)| \approx 2.6 \times 10^{-4}$.

9.1.49 With $f(x) = \sin x$ we have $R_n(x) = \dfrac{f^{(n+1)}(c)}{(n+1)!}x^{n+1}$ for c between 0 and x.

9.1.51 With $f(x) = e^{-x}$ we have $f^{(n+1)}(x) = (-1)^{n+1}e^{-x}$, so that $R_n(x) = \dfrac{(-1)^{n+1}e^{-c}}{(n+1)!}x^{n+1}$ for c between 0 and x.

9.1.53 With $f(x) = \sin x$ we have $R_n(x) = \dfrac{f^{(n+1)}(c)}{(n+1)!}\left(x - \dfrac{\pi}{2}\right)^{n+1}$ for c between $\frac{\pi}{2}$ and x.

9.1.55 $f(x) = \sin x$, so $f^{(5)}(x) = \cos x$. Because $\cos x$ is bounded in magnitude by 1, the remainder is bounded by $|R_4(x)| \le \frac{0.3^5}{5!} \approx 2.0 \times 10^{-5}$.

9.1.57 $f(x) = e^x$, so $f^{(5)}(x) = e^x$. Because $e^{0.25}$ is bounded by 2, $|R_4(x)| \le 2 \cdot \frac{0.25^5}{5!} \approx 1.63 \times 10^{-5}$.

9.1.59 $f(x) = e^{-x}$, so $f^{(5)}(x) = -e^{-x}$. Because $f^{(5)}$ achieves its maximum magnitude in the range at $x = 0$, which has absolute value 1, $|R_4(x)| \le 1 \cdot \frac{0.5^5}{5!} \approx 2.6 \times 10^{-4}$.

9.1.61 Here $n = 3$ or 4, so use $n = 4$, and $M = 1$ because $f^{(5)}(x) = \cos x$, so that $R_4(x) \le \frac{(\pi/4)^5}{5!} \approx 2.49 \times 10^{-3}$.

9.1.63 $n = 2$ and $M = e^{1/2} < 2$, so $|R_2(x)| \le 2 \cdot \frac{(1/2)^3}{3!} \approx 4.2 \times 10^{-2}$.

9.1.65 $n = 2$; $f^{(3)}(x) = \frac{2}{(1+x)^3}$, which achieves its maximum at $x = -0.2$: $|f^{(3)}(x)| = \frac{2}{0.8^3} < 4$. Then $|R_2(x)| \le 4 \cdot \frac{0.2^3}{3!} \approx 5.4 \times 10^{-3}$.

9.1.67 Use the Taylor series for e^x at $x = 0$. The derivatives of e^x are e^x. On $[-0.5, 0]$, the maximum magnitude of any derivative is thus 1 at $x = 0$, so $|R_n(-0.5)| \le \frac{0.5^{n+1}}{(n+1)!}$, so for $R_n(-0.5) < 10^{-3}$ we need $n = 4$.

9.1.69 Use the Taylor series for $\cos x$ at $x = 0$. The magnitude of any derivative of $\cos x$ is bounded by 1, so $|R_n(-0.25)| \le \frac{0.25^{n+1}}{(n+1)!}$, so for $|R_n(-0.25)| < 10^{-3}$ we need $n = 3$.

9.1.71 Use the Taylor series for $f(x) = \sqrt{x}$ at $x = 1$. Then $|f^{(n+1)}(x)| = \frac{1\cdot 3\cdot \cdots \cdot(2n-1)}{2^{n+1}} x^{-(2n+1)/2}$, which achieves its maximum on $[1, 1.06]$ at $x = 1$. Then

$$|R_n(1.06)| \le \frac{1\cdot 3\cdot \cdots \cdot (2n-1)}{2^{n+1}} \cdot \frac{(1.06-1)^{n+1}}{(n+1)!},$$

and for $|R_n(0.06)| < 10^{-3}$ we need $n = 1$.

9.1.73

a. False. If $f(x) = e^{-2x}$, then $f^{(n)}(x) = (-1)^n 2^n e^{-2x}$, so that $f^{(n)}(0) \neq 0$ and all powers of x are present in the Taylor series.

b. True. The constant term of the Taylor series is $f(0) = 1$. Higher-order terms all involve derivatives of $f(x) = x^5 - 1$ evaluated at $x = 0$; clearly for $n < 5$, $f^{(n)}(0) = 0$, and for $n > 5$, the derivative itself vanishes. Only for $n = 5$, where $f^{(5)}(x) = 5!$, is the derivative nonzero, so the coefficient of x^5 in the Taylor series is $f^{(5)}(0)/5! = 1$ and the Taylor polynomial of order 10 is in fact $x^5 - 1$. Note that this statement is true of any polynomial of degree at most 10.

c. True. The odd derivatives of $\sqrt{1+x^2}$ vanish at $x = 0$, while the even ones do not.

d. True. Clearly the second-order Taylor polynomial for f at a has degree at most 2. However, the coefficient of $(x-a)^2$ is $\frac{1}{2}f''(a)$, which is zero because f has an inflection point at a.

9.1.75

a. This matches (C) because for $f(x) = (1+2x)^{1/2}$, $f''(x) = -(1+2x)^{-3/2}$ so $\frac{f''(0)}{2!} = -\frac{1}{2}$.

b. This matches (E) because for $f(x) = (1+2x)^{-1/2}$, $f''(x) = 3(1+2x)^{-5/2}$, so $\frac{f''(0)}{2!} = \frac{3}{2}$.

c. This matches (A) because $f^{(n)}(x) = 2^n e^{2x}$, so that $f^{(n)}(0) = 2^n$, which is (A)'s pattern.

d. This matches (D) because $f''(x) = 8(1+2x)^{-3}$ and $f''(0) = 8$, so that $f''(0)/2! = 4$

e. This matches (B) because $f'(x) = -6(1+2x)^{-4}$ so that $f'(0) = -6$.

f. This matches (F) because $f^{(n)}(x) = (-2)^n e^{-2x}$, so $f^{(n)}(0) = (-2)^n$, which is (F)'s pattern.

9.1.77

a. $p_2(0.1) = 0.1$. The maximum error in the approximation is $1 \cdot \frac{0.1^3}{3!} \approx 1.67 \times 10^{-4}$.

b. $p_2(0.2) = 0.2$. The maximum error in the approximation is $1 \cdot \frac{0.2^3}{3!} \approx 1.33 \times 10^{-3}$.

9.1.79

a. $p_3(0.1) = 1 - .01/2 = 0.995$. The maximum error is $1 \cdot \frac{0.1^4}{4!} \approx 4.2 \times 10^{-6}$.

b. $p_3(0.2) = 1 - .04/2 = 0.98$. The maximum error is $1 \cdot \frac{0.2^4}{4!} \approx 6.7 \times 10^{-5}$.

9.1.81

a. $p_1(0.1) = 1.05$. Because $|f''(x)| = \frac{1}{4}(1+x)^{-3/2}$ has a maximum value of $1/4$ at $x = 0$, the maximum error is $\frac{1}{4} \cdot \frac{0.1^2}{2} \approx 1.3 \times 10^{-3}$.

b. $p_1(0.2) = 1.1$. The maximum error is $\frac{1}{4} \cdot \frac{0.2^2}{2} = 5 \times 10^{-3}$.

9.1.83

a. $p_1(0.1) = 1.1$. Because $f''(x) = e^x$ is less than 2 on $[0, 0.1]$, the maximum error is less than $2 \cdot \frac{0.1^2}{2!} = 10^{-2}$.

b. $p_1(0.2) = 1.2$. The maximum error is less than $2 \cdot \frac{0.2^2}{2!} = .04 = 4 \times 10^{-2}$.

9.1.85

a.

	$\lvert\sec x - p_2(x)\rvert$	$\lvert\sec x - p_4(x)\rvert$
−0.2	3.4×10^{-4}	5.5×10^{-6}
−0.1	2.1×10^{-5}	8.5×10^{-8}
0.0	0	0
0.1	2.1×10^{-5}	8.5×10^{-8}
0.2	3.4×10^{-4}	5.5×10^{-6}

b. The errors are equal for positive and negative x. This makes sense, because $\sec(-x) = \sec x$ and $p_n(-x) = p_n(x)$ for $n = 2, 4$. The errors appear to get larger as x gets farther from zero.

9.1.87

a.

	$\lvert e^{-x} - p_1(x)\rvert$	$\lvert e^{-x} - p_2(x)\rvert$
−0.2	2.14×10^{-2}	1.40×10^{-3}
−0.1	5.17×10^{-3}	1.71×10^{-4}
0.0	0	0
0.1	4.84×10^{-3}	1.63×10^{-4}
0.2	1.87×10^{-2}	1.27×10^{-3}

b. The errors are different for positive and negative displacements from zero, and appear to get larger as x gets farther from zero.

9.1.89

a.

	$\lvert\tan x - p_1(x)\rvert$	$\lvert\tan x - p_3(x)\rvert$
−0.2	2.71×10^{-3}	4.34×10^{-5}
−0.1	3.35×10^{-4}	1.34×10^{-6}
0.0	0	0
0.1	3.35×10^{-4}	1.34×10^{-6}
0.2	2.71×10^{-3}	4.34×10^{-5}

b. The errors are equal for positive and negative x. This makes sense, because $\tan(-x) = -\tan x$ and $p_n(-x) = -p_n(x)$ for $n = 1, 3$. The errors appear to get larger as x gets farther from zero.

9.1.91 The true value of $e^{0.35} \approx 1.419067549$. The 6th-order Taylor polynomial for e^x centered at $x = 0$ is

$$p_6(x) = 1 + x + \frac{x^2}{2} + \frac{x^3}{6} + \frac{x^4}{24} + \frac{x^5}{120} + \frac{x^6}{720}.$$

Evaluating the polynomials at $x = 0.35$ produces the following table:

n	$p_n(0.35)$	$\lvert p_n(0.35) - e^{0.35}\rvert$
1	1.350000000	6.91×10^{-2}
2	1.411250000	7.82×10^{-3}
3	1.418395833	6.72×10^{-4}
4	1.419021094	4.65×10^{-5}
5	1.419064862	2.69×10^{-6}
6	1.419067415	1.33×10^{-7}

The 6th-order Taylor polynomial for e^x centered at $x = \ln 2$ is

$$p_6(x) = 2 + 2(x - \ln 2) + (x - \ln 2)^2 + \frac{1}{3}(x - \ln 2)^3 + \frac{1}{12}(x - \ln 2)^4 + \frac{1}{60}(x - \ln 2)^5 + \frac{1}{360}(x - \ln 2)^6.$$

Evaluating the polynomials at $x = 0.35$ produces the following table:

n	$p_n(0.35)$	$\lvert p_n(0.35) - e^{0.35}\rvert$
1	1.313705639	1.05×10^{-1}
2	1.431455626	1.24×10^{-2}
3	1.417987101	1.08×10^{-3}
4	1.419142523	7.50×10^{-5}
5	1.419063227	4.32×10^{-6}
6	1.419067762	2.13×10^{-7}

Comparing the tables shows that using the polynomial centered at $x = 0$ is more accurate for all n. To see why, consider the remainder. Let $f(x) = e^x$. By Theorem 9.2, the magnitude of the remainder when approximating $f(0.35)$ by the polynomial p_n centered at 0 is:

$$|R_n(0.35)| = \frac{|f^{(n+1)}(c)|}{(n+1)!}(0.35)^{n+1} = \frac{e^c}{(n+1)!}(0.35)^{n+1}$$

for some c with $0 < c < 0.35$ while the magnitude of the remainder when approximating $f(0.35)$ by the polynomial p_n centered at $\ln 2$ is:

$$|R_n(0.35)| = \frac{|f^{(n+1)}(c)|}{(n+1)!}|0.35 - \ln 2|^{n+1} = \frac{e^c}{(n+1)!}(\ln 2 - 0.35)^{n+1}$$

for some c with $0.35 < c < \ln 2$. Because $\ln 2 - 0.35 \approx 0.35$, the relative size of the magnitudes of the remainders is determined by e^c in each remainder. Because e^x is an increasing function, the remainder in using the polynomial centered at 0 will be less than the remainder in using the polynomial centered at $\ln 2$, and the former polynomial will be more accurate.

9.1.93

a. The slope of the tangent line to $f(x)$ at $x = a$ is by definition $f'(a)$; by the point-slope form for the equation of a line, we have $y - f(a) = f'(a)(x - a)$, or $y = f(a) + f'(a)(x - a)$.

b. The Taylor polynomial centered at a is $p_1(x) = f(a) + f'(a)(x - a)$, which is the tangent line at a.

9.1.95

a. We have

$$\begin{aligned} f(0) &= f^{(4)}(0) = \sin 0 = 0 & f(\pi) &= f^{(4)}(\pi) = \sin\pi = 0 \\ f'(0) &= f^{(5)}(0) = \cos 0 = 1 & f'(\pi) &= f^{(5)}(0) = \cos\pi = -1 \\ f''(0) &= -\sin 0 = 0 & f''(\pi) &= -\sin\pi = 0 \\ f'''(0) &= -\cos 0 = -1 & f'''(\pi) &= -\cos\pi = 1. \end{aligned}$$

Thus

$$\begin{aligned} p_5(x) &= x - \frac{x^3}{3!} + \frac{x^5}{5!} \\ q_5(x) &= -(x - \pi) + \frac{1}{3!}(x - \pi)^3 - \frac{1}{5!}(x - \pi)^5. \end{aligned}$$

b. A plot of the three functions, with $\sin x$ the black solid line, $p_5(x)$ the dashed line, and $q_5(x)$ the dotted line is below.

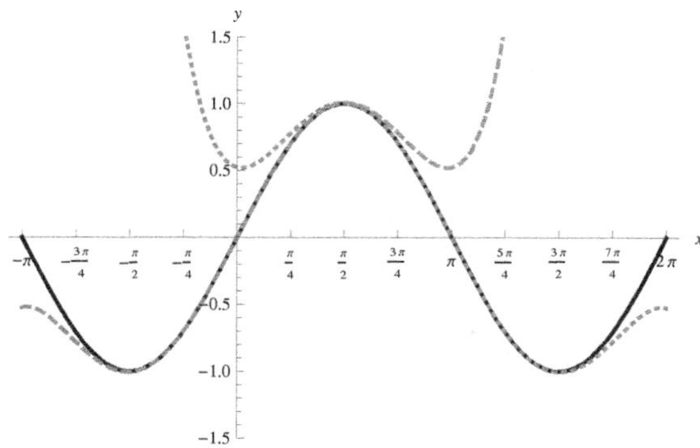

$p_5(x)$ and $\sin x$ are almost indistinguishable on $[-\pi/2, \pi/2]$, after which $p_5(x)$ diverges pretty quickly from $\sin x$. $q_5(x)$ is reasonably close to $\sin x$ over the entire range, but the two are almost indistinguishable on $[\pi/2, 3\pi/2]$. $p_5(x)$ is a better approximation than $q_5(x)$ on about $[-\pi, \pi/2)$, while $q_5(x)$ is better on about $(\pi/2, 2\pi]$.

c. Evaluating the errors gives

x	$\lvert\sin x - p_5(x)\rvert$	$\lvert\sin x - q_5(x)\rvert$
$\frac{\pi}{4}$	3.6×10^{-5}	7.4×10^{-2}
$\frac{\pi}{2}$	4.5×10^{-3}	4.5×10^{-3}
$\frac{3\pi}{4}$	7.4×10^{-2}	3.6×10^{-5}
$\frac{5\pi}{4}$	2.3	3.6×10^{-5}
$\frac{7\pi}{4}$	20.4	7.4×10^{-2}

d. $p_5(x)$ is a better approximation than $q_5(x)$ only at $x = \frac{\pi}{4}$, in accordance with part (b). The two are equal at $x = \frac{\pi}{2}$, after which $q_5(x)$ is a substantially better approximation than $p_5(x)$.

9.1.97

a. We have

$$f(36) = \sqrt{36} = 6 \qquad f(49) = \sqrt{49} = 7$$

$$f'(36) = \frac{1}{2} \cdot \frac{1}{\sqrt{36}} = \frac{1}{12} \qquad f'(49) = \frac{1}{2} \cdot \frac{1}{\sqrt{49}} = \frac{1}{14}.$$

Thus

$$p_1(x) = 6 + \frac{1}{12}(x - 36) \qquad q_1(x) = 7 + \frac{1}{14}(x - 49).$$

b. Evaluating the errors gives

x	$\lvert\sqrt{x} - p_1(x)\rvert$	$\lvert\sqrt{x} - q_1(x)\rvert$
37	5.7×10^{-4}	6.0×10^{-2}
39	5.0×10^{-3}	4.1×10^{-2}
41	1.4×10^{-2}	2.5×10^{-2}
43	2.6×10^{-2}	1.4×10^{-2}
45	4.2×10^{-2}	6.1×10^{-3}
47	6.1×10^{-2}	1.5×10^{-3}

c. $p_1(x)$ is a better approximation than $q_1(x)$ for $x \le 41$, and $q_1(x)$ is a better approximation for $x \ge 43$. To see why this is true, note that $f''(x) = -\frac{1}{4}x^{-3/2}$, so that on $[36, 49]$ it is bounded in magnitude by $\frac{1}{4} \cdot 36^{-3/2} = \frac{1}{864}$. . Thus (using P_1 for the error term for p_1 and Q_1 for the error term for q_1)

$$P_1(x) \le \frac{1}{864} \cdot \frac{|x-36|^2}{2!} = \frac{1}{1728}(x-36)^2, \qquad Q_1(x) \le \frac{1}{864} \cdot \frac{|x-49|^2}{2!} = \frac{1}{1728}(x-49)^2.$$

It follows that the relative sizes of $P_1(x)$ and $Q_1(x)$ are governed by the distance of x from 36 and 49. Looking at the different possibilities for x reveals why the results in part (b) hold.

9.2 Properties of Power Series

9.2.1 $c_0 + c_1x + c_2x^2 + c_3x^3$.

9.2.3 Generally the Ratio Test or Root Test is used.

9.2.5 The radius of convergence does not change, but the interval of convergence may change at the endpoints.

9.2.7 $|x| < \frac{1}{4}$.

9.2.9 Using the Root Test: $\lim_{k\to\infty} \sqrt[k]{|a_k|} = \lim_{k\to\infty} |2x| = |2x|$. So the radius of convergence is $\frac{1}{2}$. At $x = 1/2$ the series is $\sum 1$ which diverges, and at $x = -1/2$ the series is $\sum(-1)^k$ which also diverges. So the interval of convergence is $(-1/2, 1/2)$.

9.2.11 Using the Root Test, $\lim\limits_{k\to\infty} \sqrt[k]{|a_k|} = \lim\limits_{k\to\infty} \frac{|x-1|}{k^{1/k}} = |x-1|$. So the radius of convergence is 1. At $x = 2$, we have the harmonic series (which diverges) and at $x = 0$ we have the alternating harmonic series (which converges). Thus the interval of convergence is $[0, 2)$.

9.2.13 Using the Ratio Test: $\lim\limits_{k\to\infty} \left|\frac{a_{k+1}}{a_k}\right| = \lim\limits_{k\to\infty} \left|\frac{(k+1)^{k+1}x^{k+1}}{k^kx^k}\right| = \lim\limits_{k\to\infty} (k+1)\left(\frac{k+1}{k}\right)^k |x| = \infty$ (for $x \ne 0$) because $\lim\limits_{k\to\infty} \left(\frac{k+1}{k}\right)^k = e$. Thus, the radius of convergence is 0, the series only converges at $x = 0$.

9.2.15 Using the Root Test: $\lim\limits_{k\to\infty} \sqrt[k]{|a_k|} = \lim\limits_{k\to\infty} \sin(1/k)|x| = \sin(0)|x| = 0$. Thus, the radius of convergence is ∞ and the interval of convergence is $(-\infty, \infty)$.

9.2.17 Using the Root Test: $\lim\limits_{k\to\infty} \sqrt[k]{|a_k|} = \lim\limits_{k\to\infty} \frac{|x|}{3} = \frac{|x|}{3}$, so the radius of convergence is 3. At -3, the series is $\sum(-1)^k$, which diverges. At 3, the series is $\sum 1$, which diverges. So the interval of convergence is $(-3, 3)$.

9.2.19 Using the Root Test: $\lim\limits_{k\to\infty} \sqrt[k]{|a_k|} = \lim\limits_{k\to\infty} \frac{|x|}{k} = 0$, so the radius of convergence is infinite and the interval of convergence is $(-\infty, \infty)$.

9.2.21 Using the Ratio Test: $\lim\limits_{k\to\infty} \left|\frac{(k+1)^2x^{2k+2}}{(k+1)!} \cdot \frac{k!}{k^2x^{2k}}\right| = \lim\limits_{k\to\infty} \frac{k+1}{k^2}x^2 = 0$, so the radius of convergence is infinite, and the interval of convergence is $(-\infty, \infty)$.

9.2.23 Using the Ratio Test: $\lim\limits_{k\to\infty} \left|\frac{a_{k+1}}{a_k}\right| = \left|\frac{x^{2k+3}}{3^k} \cdot \frac{3^{k-1}}{x^{2k+1}}\right| = \frac{x^2}{3}$ so that the radius of convergence is $\sqrt{3}$. At $x = \sqrt{3}$, the series is $\sum 3\sqrt{3}$, which diverges. At $x = -\sqrt{3}$, the series is $\sum(-3\sqrt{3})$, which also diverges, so the interval of convergence is $(-\sqrt{3}, \sqrt{3})$.

9.2.25 Using the Root Test: $\lim\limits_{k\to\infty} \sqrt[k]{|a_k|} = \lim\limits_{k\to\infty} \frac{(|x-1|)k}{k+1} = |x-1|$, so the series converges when $|x-1| < 1$, so for $0 < x < 2$. The radius of convergence is 1. At $x = 2$, the series diverges by the Divergence Test. At $x = 0$, the series diverges as well by the Divergence Test. Thus the interval of convergence is $(0, 2)$.

9.2.27 Using the Ratio Test: $\lim_{k\to\infty}\left|\frac{a_{k+1}}{a_k}\right| = \left|\frac{(k+1)^{20}x^{k+1}}{(2k+3)!}\cdot\frac{(2k+1)!}{x^k k^{20}}\right| = \lim_{k\to\infty}\left(\frac{k+1}{k}\right)^{20}\frac{|x|}{(2k+2)(2k+3)} = 0$, so the radius of convergence is infinite, and the interval of convergence is $(-\infty,\infty)$.

9.2.29 $f(3x) = \frac{1}{1-3x} = \sum_{k=0}^{\infty} 3^k x^k$, which converges for $|x| < 1/3$, and diverges at the endpoints.

9.2.31 $h(x) = \frac{2x^3}{1-x} = \sum_{k=0}^{\infty} 2x^{k+3}$, which converges for $|x| < 1$ and is divergent at the endpoints.

9.2.33 $p(x) = \frac{4x^{12}}{1-x} = \sum_{k=0}^{\infty} 4x^{k+12} = 4\sum_{k=0}^{\infty} x^{k+12}$, which converges for $|x| < 1$. It is divergent at the endpoints.

9.2.35 $f(3x) = \ln(1-3x) = -\sum_{k=1}^{\infty}\frac{(3x)^k}{k} = -\sum_{k=1}^{\infty}\frac{3^k}{k}x^k$. Using the Ratio Test:

$$\lim_{k\to\infty}\left|\frac{a_{k+1}}{a_k}\right| = \lim_{k\to\infty}\frac{3k}{k+1}|x| = 3|x|,$$

so the radius of convergence is 1/3. The series diverges at 1/3 (harmonic series), and converges at $-1/3$ (alternating harmonic series).

9.2.37 $h(x) = x\ln(1-x) = -\sum_{k=1}^{\infty}\frac{x^{k+1}}{k}$. Using the Ratio Test: $\lim_{k\to\infty}\left|\frac{a_{k+1}}{a_k}\right| = \lim_{k\to\infty}\frac{k}{k+1}|x| = |x|$, so the radius of convergence is 1, and the series diverges at 1 (harmonic series) but converges at -1 (alternating harmonic series).

9.2.39 $p(x) = 2x^6\ln(1-x) = -2\sum_{k=1}^{\infty}\frac{x^{k+6}}{k}$. Using the Ratio Test: $\lim_{k\to\infty}\left|\frac{a_{k+1}}{a_k}\right| = \lim_{k\to\infty}\frac{k}{k+1}|x| = |x|$, so the radius of convergence is 1. The series diverges at 1 (harmonic series) but converges at -1 (alternating harmonic series).

9.2.41 The power series for $f(x)$ is $\sum_{k=0}^{\infty}(2x)k$, convergent for $-1 < 2x < 1$, so for $-1/2 < x < 1/2$. The power series for $g(x) = f'(x)$ is $\sum_{k=1}^{\infty} k(2x)^{k-1}\cdot 2 = 2\sum_{k=1}^{\infty} k(2x)^{k-1}$, also convergent on $|x| < 1/2$.

9.2.43 The power series for $f(x)$ is $\sum_{k=0}^{\infty} x^k$, convergent for $-1 < x < 1$, so the power series for $g(x) = \frac{1}{6}f'''(x)$ is $\frac{1}{6}\sum_{k=3}^{\infty} k(k-1)(k-2)x^{k-3} = \frac{1}{6}\sum_{k=0}^{\infty}(k+1)(k+2)(k+3)x^k$, also convergent on $|x| < 1$.

9.2.45 The power series for $\frac{1}{1-3x}$ is $\sum_{k=0}^{\infty}(3x)^k$, convergent on $|x| < 1/3$. Because $g(x) = \ln(1-3x) = -3\int\frac{1}{1-3x}\,dx$ and because $g(0) = 0$, the power series for $g(x)$ is $-3\sum_{k=0}^{\infty} 3^k\frac{1}{k+1}x^{k+1} = -\sum_{k=1}^{\infty}\frac{3^k}{k}x^k$, also convergent on $[-1/3, 1/3)$.

9.2.47 Start with $g(x) = \frac{1}{1+x}$. The power series for $g(x)$ is $\sum_{k=0}^{\infty}(-1)^k x^k$. Because $f(x) = g(x^2)$, its power series is $\sum_{k=0}^{\infty}(-1)^k x^{2k}$. The radius of convergence is still 1, and the series is divergent at both endpoints. The interval of convergence is $(-1, 1)$.

9.2.49 Note that $f(x) = \frac{3}{3+x} = \frac{1}{1+(1/3)x}$. Let $g(x) = \frac{1}{1+x}$. The power series for $g(x)$ is $\sum_{k=0}^{\infty}(-1)^k x^k$, so the power series for $f(x) = g((1/3)x)$ is $\sum_{k=0}^{\infty}(-1)^k 3^{-k}x^k = \sum_{k=0}^{\infty}\left(\frac{-x}{3}\right)^k$. Using the Ratio Test: $\lim_{k\to\infty}\left|\frac{a_{k+1}}{a_k}\right| = \lim_{k\to\infty}\left|\frac{3^{-(k+1)}x^{k+1}}{3^{-k}x^k}\right| = \frac{|x|}{3}$, so the radius of convergence is 3. The series diverges at both endpoints. The interval of convergence is $(-3, 3)$.

9.2.51 Note that $f(x) = \ln\sqrt{4-x^2} = \frac{1}{2}\ln(4-x^2) = \frac{1}{2}\left(\ln 4 + \ln\left(1-\frac{x^2}{4}\right)\right) = \ln 2 + \frac{1}{2}\ln\left(1-\frac{x^2}{4}\right)$. Now, the power series for $g(x) = \ln(1-x)$ is $-\sum_{k=1}^{\infty}\frac{1}{k}x^k$, so the power series for $f(x)$ is $\ln 2 - \frac{1}{2}\sum_{k=1}^{\infty}\frac{1}{k}\frac{x^{2k}}{4^k} = \ln 2 - \sum_{k=1}^{\infty}\frac{x^{2k}}{k2^{2k+1}}$. Now, $\lim_{k\to\infty}\left|\frac{a_{k+1}}{a_k}\right| = \lim_{k\to\infty}\left|\frac{x^{2k+2}}{(k+1)2^{2k+3}}\cdot\frac{k2^{2k+1}}{x^{2k}}\right| = \lim_{k\to\infty}\frac{k}{4(k+1)}x^2 = \frac{x^2}{4}$, so that the radius of convergence is 2. The series diverges at both endpoints, so its interval of convergence is $(-2, 2)$.

9.2.53

a. True. This power series is centered at $x = 3$, so its interval of convergence will be symmetric about 3.

b. True. Use the Root Test.

c. True. Substitute x^2 for x in the series.

d. True. Because the power series is zero on the interval, all its derivatives are as well, which implies (differentiating the power series) that all the c_k are zero.

9.2.55 Using the Ratio Test: $\lim_{k\to\infty}\left|\frac{a_{k+1}}{a_k}\right| = \lim_{k\to\infty}\left|\frac{(k+1)!\,x^{k+1}}{(k+1)^{k+1}}\cdot\frac{k^k}{k!\,x^k}\right| = \lim_{k\to\infty}\left(\frac{k}{k+1}\right)^k |x| = \frac{1}{e}|x|$. The radius of convergence is therefore e.

9.2.57 $\sum_{k=0}^{\infty}(-1)^k\frac{1}{k+1}x^k$

9.2.59 $\sum_{k=1}^{\infty}(-1)^k\frac{x^{2k}}{k!}$

9.2.61 The power series for $f(x-a)$ is $\sum c_k(x-a)^k$. Then $\sum c_k(x-a)^k$ converges if and only if $|x-a| < R$, which happens if and only if $a - R < x < a + R$, so the radius of convergence is the same.

9.2.63 This is a geometric series with ratio $\sqrt{x}-2$, so its sum is $\frac{1}{1-(\sqrt{x}-2)} = \frac{1}{3-\sqrt{x}}$. Again using the Root Test, $\lim_{k\to\infty}\sqrt[k]{|a_k|} = |\sqrt{x}-2|$, so the interval of convergence is given by $|\sqrt{x}-2| < 1$, so $1 < \sqrt{x} < 3$ and $1 < x < 9$. The series diverges at both endpoints.

9.2.65 This is a geometric series with ratio e^{-x}, so its sum is $\frac{1}{1-e^{-x}}$. By the Root Test, $\lim_{k\to\infty}\sqrt[k]{|a_k|} = e^{-x}$, so the power series converges for $x > 0$.

9.2.67 This is a geometric series with ratio $(x^2-1)/3$, so its sum is $\frac{1}{1-\frac{x^2-1}{3}} = \frac{3}{3-(x^2-1)} = \frac{3}{4-x^2}$. Using the Root Test, the series converges for $\left|x^2-1\right| < 3$, so that $-2 < x^2 < 4$ or $-2 < x < 2$. It diverges at both endpoints.

9.2.69 The power series for e^x is $\sum_{k=0}^{\infty}\frac{x^k}{k!}$. Substitute $-x$ for x to get $e^{-x} = \sum_{k=0}^{\infty}(-1)^k\frac{x^k}{k!}$. The series converges for all x.

9.2.71 Substitute $-3x$ for x in the power series for e^x to get $e^{-3x} = \sum_{k=0}^{\infty}\frac{(-3x)^k}{k!} = \sum_{k=0}^{\infty}(-1)^k\frac{3^k}{k!}x^k$. The series converges for all x.

9.2.73 The power series for $x^m f(x)$ is $\sum c_k x^{k+m}$. The radius of convergence of this power series is determined by the limit

$$\lim_{k\to\infty}\left|\frac{c_{k+1}x^{k+1+m}}{c_k x^{k+m}}\right| = \lim_{k\to\infty}\left|\frac{c_{k+1}x^{k+1}}{c_k x^k}\right|,$$

and the right-hand side is the limit used to determine the radius of convergence for the power series for $f(x)$. Thus the two have the same radius of convergence.

9.2.75

a. $f(x)g(x) = c_0d_0 + (c_0d_1 + c_1d_0)x + (c_0d_2 + c_1d_1 + c_2d_0)x^2 + \dots$

b. The coefficient of x^n in $f(x)g(x)$ is $\sum_{i=0}^{n} c_i d_{n-i}$.

9.2.77

a. For both graphs, the difference between the true value and the estimate is greatest at the two ends of the range; the difference at 0.9 is greater than that at −0.9.

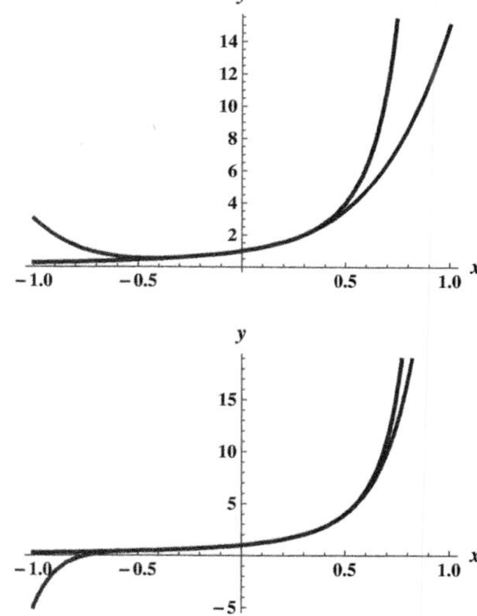

b. The difference between $f(x)$ and $S_n(x)$ is greatest for $x = 0.9$; at that point, $f(x) = \frac{1}{(1-0.9)^2} = 100$, so we want to find n such that $S_n(x)$ is within 0.01 of 100. We find that $S_{111} \approx 99.98991435$ and $S_{112} \approx 99.99084790$, so $n = 112$.

9.3 Taylor Series

9.3.1 The nth Taylor Polynomial is the nth sum of the corresponding Taylor Series.

9.3.3 The nth coefficient is $\frac{f^{(n)}(a)}{n!}$.

9.3.5 Substitute x^2 for x in the Taylor series. By theorems proved in the previous section about power series, the interval of convergence does not change except perhaps at the endpoints of the interval.

9.3.7 It means that the limit of the remainder term is zero.

9.3.9

a. Note that $f(0) = 1$, $f'(0) = -1$, $f''(0) = 1$, and $f'''(0) = -1$. So the Maclaurin series is $1 - x + x^2/2 - x^3/6 + \cdots$.

b. $\sum_{k=0}^{\infty}(-1)^k \frac{x^k}{k!}$.

c. The series converges on $(-\infty, \infty)$, as can be seen from the Ratio Test.

9.3.11

a. Because the series for $\frac{1}{1+x}$ is $1 - x + x^2 - x^3 + \cdots$, the series for $\frac{1}{1+x^2}$ is $1 - x^2 + x^4 - x^6 + \cdots$.

b. $\sum_{k=0}^{\infty}(-1)^k x^{2k}$.

c. The absolute value of the ratio of consecutive terms is x^2, so by the Ratio Test, the radius of convergence is 1. The series diverges at the endpoints by the Divergence Test, so the interval of convergence is $(-1, 1)$.

9.3.13

a. Note that $f(0) = 1$, and that $f^{(n)}(0) = 2^n$. Thus, the series is given by $1 + 2x + \frac{4x^2}{2} + \frac{8x^3}{6} + \cdots$.

b. $\sum_{k=0}^{\infty} \frac{(2x)^k}{k!}$.

c. The absolute value of the ratio of consecutive terms is $\frac{2|x|}{n}$, which has limit 0 as $n \to \infty$. So by the Ratio Test, the interval of convergence is $(-\infty, \infty)$.

9.3.15

a. By integrating the Taylor series for $\frac{1}{1+x^2}$ (which is the derivative of $\tan^{-1}(x)$), we obtain the series $x - \frac{x^3}{3} + \frac{x^5}{5} - \frac{x^7}{7} + \cdots$. Then by replacing x by $x/2$ we have $\frac{x}{2} - \frac{x^3}{3 \cdot 2^3} + \frac{x^5}{5 \cdot 2^5} - \frac{x^7}{7 \cdot 2^7} + \cdots$.

b. $\sum_{k=0}^{\infty} (-1)^k \frac{1}{(2k+1) \cdot 2^{2k+1}} x^{2k+1}$.

c. By the Ratio Test (the ratio of consecutive terms has limit $\frac{x^2}{4}$), the radius of convergence is $|x| < 2$. Also, at the endpoints we have convergence by the Alternating Series Test, so the interval of convergence is $[-2, 2]$.

9.3.17

a. Note that $f(0) = 1$, $f'(0) = \ln 3$, $f''(0) = \ln^2 3$, $f''(0) = \ln^3 3$. So the first four terms of the desired series are $1 + (\ln 3)x + \frac{\ln^2 3}{2} x^2 + \frac{\ln^3 3}{6} x^3 + \cdots$.

b. $\sum_{k=0}^{\infty} \frac{(\ln^k 3) x^k}{k!}$.

c. The ratio of successive terms is $\frac{(\ln^{k+1} 3) x^{k+1}}{(k+1)!} \cdot \frac{k!}{(\ln^k 3) x^k} = \frac{\ln 3}{k+1} x$, and the limit as $k \to \infty$ of this quantity is 0, so the interval of convergence is $(-\infty, \infty)$.

9.3.19

a. Note that $f(0) = 1$, $f'(0) = 0$, $f''(0) = 9$, $f'''(0) = 0$, etc. The first terms of the series are $1 + 9x^2/2 + 81x^4/4! + 3^6 x^6/6! + \cdots$.

b. $\sum_{k=0}^{\infty} \frac{(3x)^{2k}}{(2k)!}$.

c. The absolute value of the ratio of successive terms is $\left| \frac{(3x)^{2k+2}}{(2k+2)!} \cdot \frac{(2k)!}{(3x)^{2k}} \right| = \frac{1}{(2k+2)(2k+1)} \cdot 9x^2$, which has limit 0 as $x \to \infty$. The interval of convergence is therefore $(-\infty, \infty)$.

9.3.21

a. Note that $f(\pi/2) = 1$, $f'(\pi/2) = \cos(\pi/2) = 0$, $f''(\pi/2) = -\sin(\pi/2) = -1$, $f'''(\pi/2) = -\cos(\pi/2) = 0$, and so on. Thus the series is given by $1 - \frac{1}{2}\left(x - \frac{\pi}{2}\right)^2 + \frac{1}{24}\left(x - \frac{\pi}{2}\right)^4 - \frac{1}{720}\left(x - \frac{\pi}{2}\right)^6 + \cdots$.

b. $\sum_{k=0}^{\infty} (-1)^k \frac{1}{(2k)!} \left(x - \frac{\pi}{2}\right)^{2k}$.

9.3.23

a. Note that $f^{(k)}(1) = (-1)^k \frac{k!}{1^{k+1}} = (-1)^k \cdot k!$. Thus the series is given by $1 - (x-1) + (x-1)^2 - (x-1)^3 + \cdots$.

b. $\sum_{k=0}^{\infty} (-1)^k (x-1)^k$.

9.3.25

a. Note that $f^{(k)}(3) = (-1)^{k-1} \frac{(k-1)!}{3^k}$. Thus the series is given by $\ln(3) + \frac{x-3}{3} - \frac{1}{18}(x-3)^2 + \frac{1}{81}(x-3)^3 + \cdots$.

b. $\ln 3 + \sum_{k=1}^{\infty} (-1)^{k+1} \frac{1}{k \cdot 3^k} (x-3)^k$.

9.3.27

a. Note that $f(1) = 2$, $f'(1) = 2\ln 2$, $f''(1) = 2\ln^2 2$, $f'''(1) = 2\ln^3 2$. The first terms of the series are $2 + (2\ln 2)(x-1) + (\ln^2 2)(x-1)^2 + \frac{(\ln^3 2)(x-1)^3}{3} + \cdots$.

b. $\sum_{k=0}^{\infty} \frac{2(x-1)^k \ln^k 2}{k!}$.

9.3.29 Because the Taylor series for $\ln(1+x)$ is $x - \frac{x^2}{2} + \frac{x^3}{3} - \frac{x^4}{4} + \cdots$, the first four terms of the Taylor series for $\ln(1+x^2)$ are $x^2 - \frac{x^4}{2} + \frac{x^6}{3} - \frac{x^8}{4} + \cdots$, obtained by substituting x^2 for x.

9.3.31 Because the Taylor series for $\frac{1}{1-x} = 1 + x + x^2 + x^3 + \cdots$, the first four terms of the Taylor series for $\frac{1}{1-2x}$ are $1 + 2x + 4x^2 + 8x^3 + \cdots$ obtained by substituting $2x$ for x.

9.3.33 The Taylor series for $e^x - 1$ is the Taylor series for e^x, less the constant term of 1, so it is $x + \frac{x^2}{2} + \frac{x^3}{3!} + \frac{x^4}{4!} + \cdots$. Thus, the first four terms of the Taylor series for $\frac{e^x - 1}{x}$ are $1 + \frac{x}{2!} + \frac{x^2}{3!} + \frac{x^3}{4!} + \cdots$, obtained by dividing the terms of the first series by x.

9.3.35 Because the Taylor series for $(1+x)^{-1}$ is $1 - x + x^2 - x^3 + \cdots$, if we substitute x^4 for x, we obtain $1 - x^4 + x^8 - x^{12} + \cdots$.

9.3.37 The Taylor series for $\sinh x$ is $x + \frac{x^3}{6} + \frac{x^5}{120} + \frac{x^7}{5040} + \cdots$. Thus, the Taylor series for $\sinh x^2$ is $x^2 + \frac{x^6}{6} + \frac{x^{10}}{120} + \frac{x^{14}}{5040} + \cdots$ obtained by substituting x^2 for x.

9.3.39

a. The binomial coefficients are $\binom{-2}{0} = 1$, $\binom{-2}{1} = \frac{-2}{1!} = -2$, $\binom{-2}{2} = \frac{(-2)(-3)}{2!} = 3$, $\binom{-2}{3} = \frac{(-2)(-3)(-4)}{3!} = -4$.

Thus the first four terms of the series are $1 - 2x + 3x^2 - 4x^3 + \cdots$.

b. $1 - 2 \cdot 0.1 + 3 \cdot 0.01 - 4 \cdot 0.001 = 0.826$

9.3.41

a. The binomial coefficients are $\binom{1/4}{0} = 1$, $\binom{1/4}{1} = \frac{1/4}{1} = \frac{1}{4}$, $\binom{1/4}{2} = \frac{(1/4)(-3/4)}{2!} = -\frac{3}{32}$, $\binom{1/4}{3} = \frac{(1/4)(-3/4)(-7/4)}{3!} = \frac{7}{128}$, so the first four terms of the series are $1 + \frac{1}{4}x - \frac{3}{32}x^2 + \frac{7}{128}x^3 + \cdots$.

b. Substitute $x = 0.12$ to get approximately 1.029.

9.3.43

a. The binomial coefficients are $\binom{-2/3}{0} = 1$, $\binom{-2/3}{1} = -\frac{2}{3}$, $\binom{-2/3}{2} = \frac{(-2/3)(-5/3)}{2!} = \frac{5}{9}$, $\binom{-2/3}{3} = \frac{(-2/3)(-5/3)(-8/3)}{3!} = -\frac{40}{81}$, so the first four terms of the series are $1 - \frac{2}{3}x + \frac{5}{9}x^2 - \frac{40}{81}x^3 + \cdots$.

b. Substitute $x = 0.18$ to get 0.89512.

9.3.45 $\sqrt{1+x^2} = 1 + \frac{x^2}{2} - \frac{x^4}{8} + \frac{x^6}{16} - \cdots$. By the Ratio Test, the radius of convergence is 1. At the endpoints, the series obtained are convergent by the Alternating Series Test. Thus, the interval of convergence is $[-1, 1]$.

9.3.47 $\sqrt{9 - 9x} = 3\sqrt{1-x} = 3 - \frac{3}{2}x - \frac{3}{8}x^2 - \frac{3}{16}x^3 - \cdots$. The interval of convergence is $[-1, 1]$.

9.3.49 $\sqrt{a^2 + x^2} = a\sqrt{1 + \frac{x^2}{a^2}} = a + \frac{x^2}{2a} - \frac{x^4}{8a^3} + \frac{x^6}{16a^5} - \cdots$. The series converges when $\frac{x^2}{a^2}$ is less than 1 in magnitude, so the radius of convergence is a. The series given by the endpoints is convergent by the Alternating Series Test, so the interval of convergence is $[-a, a]$.

9.3.51 $(1+4x)^{-2} = 1 - 2(4x) + 3(4x)^2 - 4(4x)^3 + \cdots = 1 - 8x + 48x^2 - 256x^3 + \cdots$.

9.3.53 $\frac{1}{(4+x^2)^2} = (4+x^2)^{-2} = \frac{1}{16}(1+(x^2/4))^{-2} = \frac{1}{16}\left(1 - 2\cdot\frac{x^2}{4} + 3\cdot\frac{x^4}{16} - 4\cdot\frac{x^6}{64} + \cdots\right) = \frac{1}{16} - \frac{1}{32}x^2 + \frac{3}{256}x^4 - \frac{1}{256}x^6 + \cdots$

9.3.55 $(3+4x)^{-2} = \frac{1}{9}\left(1+\frac{4x}{3}\right)^{-2} = \frac{1}{9} - \frac{2}{9}\left(\frac{4x}{3}\right) + \frac{3}{9}\left(\frac{4x}{3}\right)^2 - \frac{4}{9}\left(\frac{4x}{3}\right)^3 + \cdots.$

9.3.57 The interval of convergence for the Taylor series for $f(x) = \sin x$ is $(-\infty, \infty)$. The remainder is $R_n(x) = \frac{f^{(n+1)}(c)}{(n+1)!}x^{n+1}$ for some c. Because $f^{(n+1)}(x)$ is $\pm\sin x$ or $\pm\cos x$, we have

$$\lim_{n\to\infty} |R_n(x)| \le \lim_{n\to\infty} \frac{1}{(n+1)!}\left|x^{n+1}\right| = 0$$

for any x.

9.3.59 The interval of convergence for the Taylor series for e^{-x} is $(-\infty, \infty)$. The remainder is $R_n(x) = \frac{(-1)^{n+1}e^{-c}}{(n+1)!}x^{n+1}$ for some c. Thus $\lim_{n\to\infty} |R_n(x)| = 0$ for any x.

9.3.61

a. False. Not all of its derivatives are defined at zero - in fact, none of them are.

b. True. The derivatives of $\csc x$ involve positive powers of $\csc x$ and $\cot x$, both of which are defined at $\pi/2$, so that $\csc x$ has continuous derivatives at $\pi/2$.

c. False. For example, the Taylor series for $f(x^2)$ doesn't converge at $x = 1.9$, because the Taylor series for $f(x)$ doesn't converge at $1.9^2 = 3.61$.

d. False. The Taylor series centered at 1 involves derivatives of f evaluated at 1, not at 0.

e. True. The follows because the Taylor series must itself be an even function.

9.3.63

a. The relevant Taylor series are: $e^x = 1 + x + \frac{x^2}{2!} + \frac{x^3}{3!} + \frac{x^4}{4!} + \frac{x^5}{5!} + \frac{x^6}{6!} + \cdots$ and $e^{-x} = 1 - x + \frac{x^2}{2!} - \frac{x^3}{3!} + \frac{x^4}{4!} - \frac{x^5}{5!} + \frac{x^6}{6!} + \cdots$. Thus the first four terms of the resulting series are $\frac{1}{2}\left(e^x + e^{-x}\right) = 1 + \frac{x^2}{2!} + \frac{x^4}{4!} + \frac{x^6}{6!} + \cdots$.

b. Because each series converges (absolutely) on $(-\infty, \infty)$, so does their sum. The radius of convergence is ∞.

9.3.65

a. Use the binomial theorem. The binomial coefficients are $\binom{-2/3}{0} = 1$, $\binom{-2/3}{1} = -\frac{2}{3}$, $\binom{-2/3}{2} = \frac{(-2/3)(-5/3)}{2!} = \frac{5}{9}$, $\binom{-2/3}{3} = \frac{(-2/3)(-5/3)(-8/3)}{3!} = -\frac{40}{81}$ and then, substituting x^2 for x, we obtain $1 - \frac{2}{3}x^2 + \frac{5}{9}x^4 - \frac{40}{81}x^6 + \cdots$.

b. From Theorem 9.6 the radius of convergence is determined from $\left|x^2\right| < 1$, so it is 1.

9.3.67

a. From the binomial formula, the Taylor series for $(1-x)^p$ is $\sum \binom{p}{k}(-1)^k x^k$, so the Taylor series for $(1-x^2)^p$ is $\sum \binom{p}{k}(-1)^k x^{2k}$. Here $p = 1/2$, and the binomial coefficients are $\binom{1/2}{0} = 1$, $\binom{1/2}{1} = \frac{1/2}{1!} = \frac{1}{2}$, $\binom{1/2}{2} = \frac{(1/2)(-1/2)}{2!} = -\frac{1}{8}$, $\binom{1/2}{3} = \frac{(1/2)(-1/2)(-3/2)}{3!} = \frac{1}{16}$ so that $(1-x^2)^{1/2} = 1 - \frac{1}{2}x^2 - \frac{1}{8}x^4 - \frac{1}{16}x^6 + \cdots$.

b. From Theorem 9.6 the radius of convergence is determined from $\left|x^2\right| < 1$, so it is 1.

9.3.69

a. $f(x) = (1+x^2)^{-2}$; using the binomial series and substituting x^2 for x we obtain $1 - 2x^2 + 3x^4 - 4x^6 + \cdots$.

b. From Theorem 9.6 the radius of convergence is determined from $\left|x^2\right| < 1$, so it is 1.

9.3.71 Because $f(64) = 4$, and $f'(x) = \frac{1}{3}x^{-2/3}$, $f'(64) = \frac{1}{48}$, $f''(x) = -\frac{2}{9}x^{-5/3}$, $f''(64) = -\frac{1}{4608}$, $f'''(x) = \frac{10}{27}x^{-8/3}$, and $f'''(64) = \frac{10}{1769472} = \frac{5}{884736}$, the first four terms of the Taylor series are $4 + \frac{1}{48}(x-64) - \frac{1}{4608\cdot 2!}(x-64)^2 + \frac{5}{884736\cdot 3!}(x-64)^3$. Evaluating at $x = 60$, we get 3.914870274.

9.3.73 Because $f(16) = 2$, and $f'(x) = \frac{1}{4}x^{-3/4}$, $f'(16) = \frac{1}{32}$, $f''(x) = -\frac{3}{16}x^{-7/4}$, $f''(16) = -\frac{3}{2048}$, $f'''(x) = \frac{21}{64}x^{-11/4}$, and $f'''(16) = \frac{21}{131072}$, the first four terms of the Taylor series are $2+\frac{1}{32}(x-16) - \frac{3}{2048\cdot 2!}(x-16)^2 + \frac{21}{131072\cdot 3!}(x-16)^3$. Evaluating at $x = 13$, we get 1.898937225.

9.3.75 Evaluate the binomial coefficient $\binom{1/2}{k} = \frac{(1/2)(-1/2)(-3/2)\cdots(1/2-k+1)}{k!} = \frac{(1/2)(-1/2)\cdots((3-2k)/2)}{k!} = (-1)^{k-1}2^{-k}\frac{1\cdot 3\cdots(2k-3)}{k!} = (-1)^{k-1}2^{-k}\frac{(2k-2)!}{2^{k-1}\cdot(k-1)!\cdot k!} = (-1)^{k-1}2^{1-2k}\cdot\frac{1}{k}\binom{2k-2}{k-1}$. This is the coefficient of x^k in the Taylor series for $\sqrt{1+x}$. Substituting $4x$ for x, the Taylor series becomes $\sum_{k=0}^{\infty}(-1)^{k-1}2^{1-2k}\cdot\frac{1}{k}\binom{2k-2}{k-1}(4x)^k = \sum_{k=0}^{\infty}(-1)^{k-1}\frac{2}{k}\binom{2k-2}{k-1}x^k$. If we can show that k divides $\binom{2k-2}{k-1}$, we will be done, for then the coefficient of x^k will be an integer. But $\binom{2k-2}{k-1}-\binom{2k-2}{k-2} = \frac{(2k-2)!}{(k-1)!(k-1)!} - \frac{(2k-2)!}{(k-2)!k!} = \frac{(2k-2)!}{(k-1)!(k-1)!} - \frac{(2k-2)!(k-1)}{(k-1)!(k-1)!k} = \frac{k(2k-2)!-(k-1)(2k-2)!}{k(k-1)!(k-1)!} = \frac{1}{k}\frac{(2k-2)!}{(k-1)!(k-1)!} = \frac{1}{k}\binom{2k-2}{k-1}$ and thus we have shown that k divides $\binom{2k-2}{k-1}$.

9.3.77

a. The Maclaurin series for $\sin x$ is $x - \frac{1}{3!}x^3 + \frac{1}{5!}x^5 - \frac{1}{7!}x^7 + \cdots$. Squaring the first four terms yields

$$\left(x - \frac{1}{3!}x^3 + \frac{1}{5!}x^5 - \frac{1}{7!}x^7\right)^2$$
$$= x^2 - \frac{2}{3!}x^4 + \left(\frac{2}{5!} + \frac{1}{3!3!}\right)x^6 + \left(-2\cdot\frac{1}{7!} - 2\cdot\frac{1}{3!5!}\right)x^8$$
$$= x^2 - \frac{1}{3}x^4 + \frac{2}{45}x^6 - \frac{1}{315}x^8.$$

b. The Maclaurin series for $\cos x$ is $1 - \frac{1}{2}x^2 + \frac{1}{4!}x^4 - \frac{1}{6!}x^6 + \frac{1}{8!}x^8 - \cdots$. Substituting $2x$ for x in the Maclaurin series for $\cos x$ and then computing $(1-\cos 2x)/2$, we obtain

$$(1 - (1-\frac{1}{2}(2x)^2 + \frac{1}{4!}(2x)^4 - \frac{1}{6!}(2x)^6) + \frac{1}{8!}(2x)^8)/2$$
$$= (2x^2 - \frac{2}{3}x^4 + \frac{4}{45}x^6 - \frac{2}{315}x^8)/2$$
$$= x^2 - \frac{1}{3}x^4 + \frac{2}{45}x^6 - \frac{1}{315}x^8,$$

and the two are the same.

c. If $f(x) = \sin^2 x$, then $f(0) = 0$, $f'(x) = \sin 2x$, so $f'(0) = 0$. $f''(x) = 2\cos 2x$, so $f''(x) = 2$, $f'''(x) = -4\sin 2x$, so $f'''(0) = 0$. Note that from this point $f^{(n)}(0) = 0$ if n is odd and $f^{(n)}(0) = \pm 2^{n-1}$ if n is even, with the signs alternating for every other even n. Thus, the series for $\sin^2 x$ is

$$2x^2/2 - 8x^4/4! + 32x^6/6! - 128x^8/8! + \cdots = x^2 - \frac{1}{3}x^4 + \frac{2}{45}x^6 - \frac{1}{315}x^8 + \cdots.$$

9.3.79 There are many solutions. For example, first find a series that has $(-1, 1)$ as an interval of convergence, say $\frac{1}{1-x} = \sum_{k=0}^{\infty} x^k$. Then the series $\frac{1}{1-x/2} = \sum_{k=0}^{\infty}\left(\frac{x}{2}\right)^k$ has $(-2, 2)$ as its interval of convergence. Now shift the series up so that it is centered at 4. We have $\sum_{k=0}^{\infty}\left(\frac{x-4}{2}\right)^k$, which has interval of convergence $(2, 6)$.

9.3.81 $\frac{1\cdot 3\cdot 5\cdot 7}{2\cdot 4\cdot 6\cdot 8}x^4 - \frac{1\cdot 3\cdot 5\cdot 7\cdot 9}{2\cdot 4\cdot 6\cdot 8\cdot 10}x^5$.

9.3.83 Use the Taylor series for $\cos x$ centered at $\pi/4$: $\frac{\sqrt{2}}{2}(1-(x-\pi/4)-\frac{1}{2}(x-\pi/4)^2+\frac{1}{6}(x-\pi/4)^3+\cdots)$. The remainder after n terms (because the derivatives of $\cos x$ are bounded by 1 in magnitude) is $|R_n(x)| \le \frac{1}{(n+1)!}\cdot\left(\frac{\pi}{4}-\frac{2\pi}{9}\right)^{n+1}$.

Solving for $|R_n(x)| < 10^{-4}$, we obtain $n = 3$. Evaluating the first four terms (through $n = 3$) of the series we get 0.7660427050. The true value is ≈ 0.7660444431.

9.3.85 Use the Taylor series for $f(x) = x^{1/3}$ centered at 64: $4+\frac{1}{48}(x-64)-\frac{1}{9216}(x-64)^2+\cdots$. Because we wish to evaluate this series at $x = 83$, $|R_n(x)| = \frac{|f^{(n+1)}(c)|}{(n+1)!}(83-64)^{n+1}$. We compute that $|f^{(n+1)}(c)| = \frac{2\cdot 5\cdots(3n-1)}{3^{n+1}c^{(3n+2)/3}}$, which is maximized at $c = 64$. Thus

$$|R_n(x)| \le \frac{2\cdot 5\cdots(3n-1)}{3^{n+1}64^{(3n+2)/3}(n+1)!}19^{n+1}$$

Solving for $|R_n(x)| < 10^{-4}$, we obtain $n = 5$. Evaluating the terms of the series through $n = 5$ gives 4.362122553. The true value is ≈ 4.362070671.

9.3.87

a. Use the Taylor series for $(125+x)^{1/3}$ centered at $x = 0$. Using the first four terms and evaluating at $x = 3$ gives a result (5.03968) accurate to within 10^{-4}.

b. Use the Taylor series for $x^{1/3}$ centered at $x = 125$. Note that this gives the identical Taylor series except that the exponential terms are $(x-125)^n$ rather than x^n. Thus we need terms up through $(x-125)^3$, just as before, evaluated at $x = 128$, and we obtain the identical result.

c. Because the two Taylor series are the same except for the shifting, the results are equivalent.

9.3.89 Consider the remainder after the first term of the Taylor series. Taylor's Theorem indicates that $R_1(x) = \frac{f''(c)}{2}(x-a)^2$ for some c between x and a, so that $f(x) = f(a)+f'(a)(x-a)+\frac{f''(c)}{2}(x-a)^2$. But $f'(a) = 0$, so that for every x in an interval containing a, there is a c between x and a such that $f(x) = f(a)+\frac{f''(c)}{2}(x-a)^2$.

a. If $f''(x) > 0$ on the interval containing a, then for every x in that interval, we have $f(x) = f(a)+\frac{f''(c)}{2}(x-a)^2$ for some c between x and a. But $f''(c) > 0$ and $(x-a)^2 > 0$, so that $f(x) > f(a)$ and a is a local minimum.

b. If $f''(x) < 0$ on the interval containing a, then for every x in that interval, we have $f(x) = f(a)+\frac{f''(c)}{2}(x-a)^2$ for some c between x and a. But $f''(c) < 0$ and $(x-a)^2 > 0$, so that $f(x) < f(a)$ and a is a local maximum.

9.4 Working with Taylor Series

9.4.1 Replace f and g by their Taylor series centered at a, and evaluate the limit.

9.4.3 Substitute -0.6 for x in the Taylor series for e^x centered at 0. Note that this series is an alternating series, so the error can easily be estimated by looking at the magnitude of the first neglected term.

9.4.5 The series is $f'(x) = \sum_{k=1}^{\infty} kc_k x^{k-1}$, which converges for $|x| < b$.

9.4.7 Because $e^x = 1+x+x^2/2!+x^3/3!+\cdots$, we have $\frac{e^x-1}{x} = 1+x/2!+\cdots$, so $\lim_{x\to 0}\frac{e^x-1}{x} = 1$.

9.4.9 Because $-\ln(1-x) = x+\frac{x^2}{2}+\frac{x^3}{3}+\frac{x^4}{4}+\frac{x^5}{5}+\cdots$, we have $\frac{-x-\ln(1-x)}{x^2} = \frac{1}{2}+\frac{x}{3}+\frac{x^2}{4}+\cdots$, so $\lim_{x\to 0}\frac{-x-\ln(1-x)}{x^2} = \frac{1}{2}$.

9.4.11 We compute that

$$\begin{aligned}\frac{e^x-e^{-x}}{x} &= \frac{1}{x}\left(\left(1+x+\frac{x^2}{2}+\frac{x^3}{6}+\cdots\right)-\left(1-x+\frac{x^2}{2}-\frac{x^3}{6}+\cdots\right)\right)\\ &= \frac{1}{x}\left(2x+\frac{x^3}{3}+\cdots\right)=2+\frac{x^2}{3}+\cdots\end{aligned}$$

so the limit of $\frac{e^x-e^{-x}}{x}$ as $x\to 0$ is 2.

9.4.13 We compute that

$$\begin{aligned}\frac{2\cos 2x-2+4x^2}{2x^4} &= \frac{1}{2x^4}\left(2(1-\frac{(2x)^2}{2}+\frac{(2x)^4}{24}-\frac{(2x)^6}{720}+\cdots)-2+4x^2\right)\\ &= \frac{1}{2x^4}\left(\frac{(2x)^4}{12}-\frac{(2x)^6}{360}+\cdots\right)=\frac{2}{3}-\frac{4x^2}{45}+\cdots\end{aligned}$$

so the limit of $\frac{2\cos 2x-2+4x^2}{2x^4}$ as $x\to 0$ is $\frac{2}{3}$.

9.4.15 We have $\ln(1+x)=x-\frac{1}{2}x^2+\frac{1}{3}x^3-\frac{1}{4}x^4+\cdots$, so that

$$\frac{\ln(1+x)-x+x^2/2}{x^3}=\frac{x^3/3-x^4/4+\cdots}{x^3}=\frac{1}{3}-\frac{x}{4}+\cdots$$

so that $\lim\limits_{x\to 0}\frac{\ln(1+x)-x+x^2/2}{x^3}=\frac{1}{3}$.

9.4.17 We compute that

$$\begin{aligned}\frac{3\tan^{-1}x-3x+x^3}{x^5} &= \frac{1}{x^5}\left(3\left(x-\frac{x^3}{3}+\frac{x^5}{5}-\frac{x^7}{7}+\cdots\right)-3x+x^3\right)\\ &= \frac{1}{x^5}\left(\frac{3x^5}{5}-\frac{3x^7}{7}+\cdots\right)=\frac{3}{5}-\frac{3x^2}{7}+\cdots\end{aligned}$$

so the limit of $\frac{3\tan^{-1}x-3x+x^3}{x^5}$ as $x\to 0$ is $\frac{3}{5}$.

9.4.19 The Taylor series for $\sin 2x$ centered at 0 is

$$\sin 2x=2x-\frac{1}{3!}(2x)^3+\frac{1}{5!}(2x)^5-\frac{1}{7!}(2x)^7+\cdots=2x-\frac{4}{3}x^3+\frac{4}{15}x^5-\frac{8}{315}x^7+\cdots.$$

Thus

$$\begin{aligned}\frac{12x-8x^3-6\sin 2x}{x^5} &= \frac{12-8x^3-(12x-8x^3+\frac{8}{5}x^5-\frac{16}{105}x^7+\cdots)}{x^5}\\ &= -\frac{8}{5}+\frac{16}{105}x^2-\cdots,\end{aligned}$$

so $\lim\limits_{x\to 0}\frac{12x-8x^3-6\sin 2x}{x^5}=-\frac{8}{5}$.

9.4.21 The Taylor series for $\ln(x-1)$ centered at 2 is

$$\ln(x-1)=(x-2)-\frac{1}{2}(x-2)^2+\cdots.$$

We compute that

$$\frac{x-2}{\ln(x-1)}=\frac{x-2}{(x-2)-\frac{1}{2}(x-2)^2+\cdots}=\frac{1}{1-\frac{1}{2}(x-2)+\cdots}$$

so the limit of $\frac{x-2}{\ln(x-1)}$ as $x\to 2$ is 1.

9.4.23 Computing Taylor series centers at 0 gives

$$e^{-2x} = 1 - 2x + \frac{1}{2!}(-2x)^2 + \frac{1}{3!}(-2x)^3 + \cdots = 1 - 2x + 2x^2 - \frac{4}{3}x^3 + \cdots$$

$$e^{-x/2} = 1 - \frac{x}{2} + \frac{1}{2!}\left(-\frac{x}{2}\right)^2 + \frac{1}{3!}\left(-\frac{x}{2}\right)^3 + \cdots = 1 - \frac{x}{2} + \frac{1}{8}x^2 - \frac{1}{48}x^3 + \cdots.$$

Thus

$$\begin{aligned}\frac{e^{-2x} - 4e^{-x/2} + 3}{2x^2} &= \frac{1 - 2x + 2x^2 - \frac{4}{3}x^3 + \cdots - (4 - 2x + \frac{1}{2}x^2 - \frac{1}{12}x^3 + \cdots) + 3}{2x^2} \\ &= \frac{\frac{3}{2}x^2 - \frac{5}{4}x^3 + \cdots}{2x^2} \\ &= \frac{3}{4} - \frac{5}{8}x + \cdots\end{aligned}$$

so $\displaystyle\lim_{x\to 0} \frac{e^{-2x} - 4e^{-x/2} + 3}{2x^2} = \frac{3}{4}$.

9.4.25

a. $f'(x) = \frac{d}{dx}(\sum_{k=0}^{\infty} \frac{x^k}{k!}) = \sum_{k=1}^{\infty} k\frac{x^{k-1}}{k!} = \sum_{k=0}^{\infty} \frac{x^k}{k!} = f(x)$.

b. $f'(x) = e^x$ as well.

c. The series converges on $(-\infty, \infty)$.

9.4.27

a. $f'(x) = \frac{d}{dx}(\ln(1+x)) = \frac{d}{dx}(\sum_{k=1}^{\infty}(-1)^{k+1}\frac{1}{k}x^k) = \sum_{k=1}^{\infty}(-1)^{k+1}x^{k-1} = \sum_{k=0}^{\infty}(-1)^k x^k$.

b. This is the power series for $\frac{1}{1+x}$.

c. The Taylor series for $\ln(1+x)$ converges on $(-1, 1)$, as does the Taylor series for $\frac{1}{1+x}$.

9.4.29

a.

$$f'(x) = \frac{d}{dx}(e^{-2x}) = \frac{d}{dx}(\sum_{k=0}^{\infty} \frac{(-2x)^k}{k!}) = \frac{d}{dx}(\sum_{k=0}^{\infty}(-2)^k \frac{x^k}{k!}) = -2\sum_{k=1}^{\infty}(-2)^{k-1}\frac{x^{k-1}}{(k-1)!} = -2\sum_{k=0}^{\infty}\frac{(-2x)^k}{k!}.$$

b. This is the Taylor series for $-2e^{-2x}$.

c. Because the Taylor series for e^{-2x} converges on $(-\infty, \infty)$, so does this one.

9.4.31

a. $\tan^{-1} x = x - \frac{x^3}{3} + \frac{x^5}{5} - \cdots$, so $\frac{d}{dx}\tan^{-1} x^2 = 1 - x^2 + x^4 - x^6 + \cdots$.

b. This is the series for $\frac{1}{1+x^2}$.

c. Because the series for $\tan^{-1} x$ has a radius of convergence of 1, this series does too. Checking the endpoints shows that the interval of convergence is $(-1, 1)$.

9.4.33

a. Because $y(0) = 2$, we have $0 = y'(0) - y(0) = y'(0) - 2$ so that $y'(0) = 2$. Differentiating the equation gives $y''(0) = y'(0)$, so that $y''(0) = 2$. Successive derivatives also have the value 2 at 0, so the Taylor series is $2\sum_{k=0}^{\infty} \frac{t^k}{k!}$.

b. $2\sum_{k=0}^{\infty}\frac{t^k}{k!}=2e^t$.

9.4.35

a. $y(0)=2$, so that $y'(0)=16$. Differentiating, $y''(t)-3y'(t)=0$, so that $y''(0)=48$, and in general $y^{(k)}(0)=3y^{(k-1)}(0)=3^{k-1}\cdot 16$. Thus the power series is $2+\frac{16}{3}\sum_{k=1}^{\infty}\frac{(3t)^k}{k!}=2+\sum_{k=1}^{\infty}\frac{3^{k-1}16}{k!}t^k$.

b. $2+\frac{16}{3}\sum_{k=1}^{\infty}\frac{(3t)^k}{k!}=2+\frac{16}{3}(e^{3t}-1)=\frac{16}{3}e^{3t}-\frac{10}{3}$.

9.4.37 The Taylor series for e^{-x^2} is $\sum_{k=0}^{\infty}(-1)^k\frac{x^{2k}}{k!}$. Thus, the desired integral is $\int_0^{0.25}\sum_{k=0}^{\infty}(-1)^k\frac{x^{2k}}{k!}\,dx=\sum_{k=0}^{\infty}(-1)^k\frac{x^{2k+1}}{(2k+1)k!}\Big|_0^{0.25}=\sum_{k=0}^{\infty}(-1)^k\frac{1}{(2k+1)k!4^{2k+1}}$. Because this is an alternating series, to approximate it to within 10^{-4}, we must find n such that $a_{n+1}<10^{-4}$, or $\frac{1}{(2n+3)(n+1)!\cdot 4^{2n+3}}<10^{-4}$. This occurs for $n=1$, so $\sum_{k=0}^{1}(-1)^k\frac{1}{(2k+1)\cdot k!\cdot 4^{2k+1}}=\frac{1}{4}-\frac{1}{192}\approx 0.245$.

9.4.39 The Taylor series for $\cos 2x^2$ is $\sum_{k=0}^{\infty}(-1)^k\frac{(2x^2)^{2k}}{(2k)!}=\sum_{k=0}^{\infty}(-1)^k\frac{4^kx^{4k}}{(2k)!}$. Note that $\cos x$ is an even function, so we compute the integral from 0 to 0.35 and double it:

$$2\int_0^{0.35}\sum_{k=0}^{\infty}(-1)^k\frac{4^kx^{4k}}{(2k)!}\,dx=2\left(\sum_{k=0}^{\infty}(-1)^k\frac{4^kx^{4k+1}}{(4k+1)(2k)!}\right)\Bigg|_0^{0.35}=2\left(\sum_{k=0}^{\infty}(-1)^k\frac{4^k(0.35)^{4k+1}}{(4k+1)(2k)!}\right).$$

Because this is an alternating series, to approximate it to within $\frac{1}{2}\cdot 10^{-4}$, we must find n such that $a_{n+1}<\frac{1}{2}\cdot 10^{-4}$, or $\frac{4^{n+1}(0.35)^{4n+5}}{(4n+3)(2n+2)!}<\frac{1}{2}\cdot 10^{-4}$. This occurs first for $n=1$, and we have $2\left(.35-\frac{4\cdot(0.35)^5}{5\cdot 2!}\right)\approx 0.696$.

9.4.41 $\tan^{-1}x=x-x^3/3+x^5/5-x^7/7+x^9/9-\cdots$, so $\int\tan^{-1}x\,dx=\int(x-x^3/3+x^5/5-x^7/7+x^9/9-\cdots)\,dx=C+\frac{x^2}{2}-\frac{x^4}{12}+\frac{x^6}{30}-\frac{x^8}{56}+\cdots$. Thus, $\int_0^{0.35}\tan^{-1}x\,dx=\frac{(0.35)^2}{2}-\frac{(0.35)^4}{12}+\frac{(0.35)^6}{30}-\frac{(0.35)^8}{56}+\cdots$. Note that this series is alternating, and $\frac{(0.35)^6}{30}<10^{-4}$, so we add the first two terms to approximate the integral to the desired accuracy. Calculating gives approximately 0.060.

9.4.43 The Taylor series for $(1+x^6)^{-1/2}$ is $\sum_{k=0}^{\infty}\binom{-1/2}{k}x^{6k}$, so the desired integral is $\int_0^{0.5}\sum_{k=0}^{\infty}\binom{-1/2}{k}x^{6k}\,dx=\sum_{k=0}^{\infty}\frac{1}{6k+1}\binom{-1/2}{k}x^{6k+1}\Big|_0^{0.5}=\sum_{k=0}^{\infty}\frac{1}{6k+1}\binom{-1/2}{k}(0.5)^{6k+1}$. This is an alternating series because the binomial coefficients alternate in sign, so to approximate it to within 10^{-4}, we must find n such that $a_{n+1}<10^{-4}$, or $\left|\frac{1}{6n+7}\binom{-1/2}{n+1}(0.5)^{6n+7}\right|<10^{-4}$. This occurs first for $n=1$, so we have $\binom{-1/2}{0}0.5+\frac{1}{7}\binom{-1/2}{1}(0.5)^7\approx 0.499$.

9.4.45 Use the Taylor series for e^x at 0: $1+\frac{2}{1!}+\frac{2^2}{2!}+\frac{2^3}{3!}$.

9.4.47 Use the Taylor series for $\cos x$ at 0: $1-\frac{2^2}{2!}+\frac{2^4}{4!}-\frac{2^6}{6!}$

9.4.49 Use the Taylor series for $\ln(1+x)$ evaluated at $x=1/2$: $\frac{1}{2}-\frac{1}{2}\cdot\frac{1}{4}+\frac{1}{3}\cdot\frac{1}{8}-\frac{1}{4}\cdot\frac{1}{16}$.

9.4.51 The Taylor series for f centered at 0 is $\frac{-1+\sum_{k=0}^{\infty}\frac{x^k}{k!}}{x}=\frac{\sum_{k=1}^{\infty}\frac{x^k}{k!}}{x}=\sum_{k=1}^{\infty}\frac{x^{k-1}}{k!}=\sum_{k=0}^{\infty}\frac{x^k}{(k+1)!}$. Evaluating both sides at $x=1$, we have $e-1=\sum_{k=0}^{\infty}\frac{1}{(k+1)!}$.

9.4.53 The Maclaurin series for $\ln(1+x)$ is $x-\frac{1}{2}x^2+\frac{1}{3}x^3-\frac{1}{4}x^4+\cdots=\sum_{k=1}^{\infty}(-1)^{k+1}\frac{x^k}{k}$. By the Ratio Test, $\lim_{k\to\infty}\left|\frac{a_{k+1}}{a_k}\right|=\lim_{k\to\infty}\left|\frac{x^{k+1}k}{x^k(k+1)}\right|=|x|$, so the radius of convergence is 1. The series diverges at -1 and converges at 1, so the interval of convergence is $(-1,1]$. Evaluating at 1 gives $\ln 2=\sum_{k=1}^{\infty}(-1)^{k+1}\frac{1}{k}=1-\frac{1}{2}+\frac{1}{3}-\frac{1}{4}+\cdots$.

9.4.55 $\sum_{k=0}^{\infty}\frac{x^k}{2^k}=\sum_{k=0}^{\infty}\left(\frac{x}{2}\right)^k=\frac{1}{1-\frac{x}{2}}=\frac{2}{2-x}$.

9.4.57 $\sum_{k=0}^{\infty}(-1)^k \frac{x^{2k}}{4^k} = \sum_{k=0}^{\infty}\left(\frac{-x^2}{4}\right)^k = \frac{1}{1+\frac{x^2}{4}} = \frac{4}{4+x^2}$.

9.4.59 $\ln(1+x) = -\sum_{k=1}^{\infty}(-1)^k \frac{x^k}{k}$, so $\ln(1-x) = -\sum_{k=1}^{\infty}\frac{x^k}{k}$, and finally $-\ln(1-x) = \sum_{k=1}^{\infty}\frac{x^k}{k}$.

9.4.61

$$\begin{aligned}\sum_{k=1}^{\infty}(-1)^k\frac{kx^{k+1}}{3^k} &= \sum_{k=1}^{\infty}(-1)^k\frac{k}{3^k}x^{k+1} = \sum_{k=1}^{\infty}k\left(-\frac{1}{3}\right)^k x^{k+1}\\ &= x^2\sum_{k=1}^{\infty}\left(-\frac{1}{3}\right)^k kx^{k-1} = x^2\sum_{k=1}^{\infty}\left(-\frac{1}{3}\right)^k\frac{d}{dx}(x^k)\\ &= x^2\frac{d}{dx}\left(\sum_{k=1}^{\infty}\left(-\frac{x}{3}\right)^k\right) = x^2\frac{d}{dx}\left(\frac{1}{1+\frac{x}{3}}\right) = -\frac{3x^2}{(x+3)^2}.\end{aligned}$$

9.4.63 $\sum_{k=2}^{\infty}\frac{k(k-1)x^k}{3^k} = x^2\sum_{k=2}^{\infty}\frac{k(k-1)x^{k-2}}{3^k} = x^2\frac{d^2}{dx^2}\left(\sum_{k=2}^{\infty}\frac{x^k}{3^k}\right)$
$= x^2\frac{d^2}{dx^2}\left(\sum_{k=2}^{\infty}\left(\frac{x}{3}\right)^k\right) = x^2\frac{d^2}{dx^2}\left(\frac{x^2}{9}\cdot\frac{1}{1-\frac{x}{3}}\right) = x^2\frac{d^2}{dx^2}\left(\frac{x^2}{9-3x}\right) = x^2\frac{-6}{(x-3)^3} = \frac{-6x^2}{(x-3)^3}$.

9.4.65

a. False. This is because $\frac{1}{1-x}$ is not continuous at 1, which is in the interval of integration.

b. False. The Ratio Test shows that the radius of convergence for the Taylor series for $\tan^{-1}x$ centered at 0 is 1.

c. True. $\sum_{k=0}^{\infty}\frac{x^k}{k!} = e^x$. Substitute $x = \ln 2$.

9.4.67 The Taylor series for $\sin x$ centered at 0 is

$$\sin x = x - \frac{x^3}{6} + \frac{x^5}{120} - \cdots.$$

We compute that

$$\begin{aligned}\frac{\sin ax}{\sin bx} &= \frac{ax - \frac{(ax)^3}{6} + \frac{(ax)^5}{120} - \cdots}{bx - \frac{(bx)^3}{6} + \frac{(bx)^5}{120} - \cdots}\\ &= \frac{a - \frac{a^3x^2}{6} + \frac{a^5x^4}{120} - \cdots}{b - \frac{b^3x^2}{6} + \frac{b^5x^4}{120} - \cdots}\end{aligned}$$

so the limit of $\dfrac{\sin ax}{\sin bx}$ as $x \to 0$ is $\dfrac{a}{b}$.

9.4.69 Compute instead the limit of the log of this expression, $\lim_{x\to 0}\frac{\ln(\sin x/x)}{x^2}$. If the Taylor expansion of $\ln(\sin x/x)$ is $\sum_{k=0}^{\infty}c_k x^k$, then $\lim_{x\to 0}\frac{\ln(\sin x/x)}{x^2} = \lim_{x\to 0}\sum_{k=0}^{\infty}c_k x^{k-2} = \lim_{x\to 0}c_0x^{-2} + c_1x^{-1} + c_2$, because the higher-order terms have positive powers of x and thus approach zero as x does. So compute the terms of the Taylor series of $\ln\left(\frac{\sin x}{x}\right)$ up through the quadratic term. The relevant Taylor series are: $\frac{\sin x}{x} = 1 - \frac{1}{6}x^2 + \frac{1}{120}x^4 - \cdots$, $\ln(1+x) = x - \frac{1}{2}x^2 + \frac{1}{3}x^3 - \cdots$ and we substitute the Taylor series for $\frac{\sin x}{x} - 1$ for x in the Taylor series for $\ln(1+x)$. Because the lowest power of x in the first Taylor series is 2, it follows that only the linear term in the series for $\ln(1+x)$ will give any powers of x that are at most quadratic. The only term that results is $-\frac{1}{6}x^2$. Thus $c_0 = c_1 = 0$ in the above, and $c_2 = -\frac{1}{6}$, so that $\lim_{x\to 0}\frac{\ln(\sin x/x)}{x^2} = -\frac{1}{6}$ and thus $\lim_{x\to 0}\left(\frac{\sin x}{x}\right)^{1/x^2} = e^{-1/6}$.

9.4.71 The Taylor series we need are $\cos x = 1 - \frac{1}{2}x^2 + \frac{1}{24}x^4 + \ldots$, $e^t = 1 + t + \frac{1}{2!}t^2 + \frac{1}{3!}t^3 + \frac{1}{4!}t^4 + \ldots$. We are looking for powers of x^3 and x^4 that occur when the first series is substituted for t in the second series. Clearly there will be no odd powers of x, because $\cos x$ has only even powers. Thus the coefficient of x^3 is zero, so that $f^{(3)}(0) = 0$. The coefficient of x^4 comes from the expansion of $1 - \frac{1}{2}x^2 + \frac{1}{24}x^4$ in each term of e^t. Higher powers of x clearly cannot contribute to the coefficient of x^4. Thus consider $\left(1 - \frac{1}{2}x^2 + \frac{1}{24}x^4\right)^k$. The term $-\frac{1}{2}x^2$ generates $\binom{k}{2}$ terms of value $\frac{1}{4}x^4$ for $k \geq 2$, while the other term generates k terms of value $\frac{1}{24}x^4$ for $k \geq 1$. These terms all have to be divided by the $k!$ appearing in the series for e^t. So the total coefficient of x^4 is $\frac{1}{24}\sum_{k=1}^{\infty}\frac{k}{k!} + \frac{1}{4}\sum_{k=2}^{\infty}\binom{k}{2}\frac{1}{k!}, = \frac{1}{24}\sum_{k=1}^{\infty}\frac{1}{(k-1)!} + \frac{1}{4}\sum_{k=2}^{\infty}\frac{1}{2\cdot(k-2)!}, = \frac{1}{24}\sum_{k=0}^{\infty}\frac{1}{k!} + \frac{1}{8}\sum_{k=0}^{\infty}\frac{1}{k!}, = \frac{1}{24}e + \frac{1}{8}e = \frac{e}{6}$ Thus $f^{(4)}(0) = \frac{e}{6} \cdot 4! = 4e$.

9.4.73 The Taylor series for $\sin t^2$ is $\sin t^2 = t^2 - \frac{1}{3!}t^6 + \frac{1}{5!}t^{10} - \ldots$, so that $\int_0^x \sin t^2\,dt = \frac{1}{3}t^3 - \frac{1}{7\cdot 3!}t^7 + \ldots\Big|_0^x = \frac{1}{3}x^3 - \frac{1}{7\cdot 3!}x^7 + \ldots$. Thus $f^{(3)}(0) = \frac{3!}{3} = 2$ and $f^{(4)}(0) = 0$.

9.4.75 Consider the series $\sum_{k=1}^{\infty} x^k = \frac{x}{1-x}$. Differentiating both sides gives $\frac{1}{(1-x)^2} = \sum_{k=0}^{\infty} kx^{k-1} = \frac{1}{x}\sum_{k=0}^{\infty} kx^k$ so that $\frac{x}{(1-x)^2} = \sum_{k=0}^{\infty} kx^k$. Evaluate both sides at $x = 1/2$ to see that the sum of the series is $\frac{1/2}{(1-1/2)^2} = 2$. Thus the expected number of tosses is 2.

9.4.77

a. We look first for a Taylor series for $(1 - k^2\sin^2\theta)^{-1/2}$. Because $(1 - k^2x^2)^{-1/2} = (1 - (kx)^2)^{-1/2} = \sum_{i=0}^{\infty}\binom{-1/2}{i}(kx)^{2i}$, and $\sin\theta = \theta - \frac{1}{3!}\theta^3 + \frac{1}{5!}\theta^5 - \ldots$, substituting the second series into the first gives $\frac{1}{\sqrt{1-k^2\sin^2\theta}} = 1 + \frac{1}{2}k^2\theta^2 + \left(-\frac{1}{6}k^2 + \frac{3}{8}k^4\right)\theta^4 + \left(\frac{1}{45}k^2 - \frac{1}{4}k^4 + \frac{5}{16}k^6\right)\theta^6 + \left(\frac{-1}{630}k^2 + \frac{3}{40}k^4 - \frac{5}{16}k^6 + \frac{35}{128}k^8\right)\theta^8 + \ldots$.
Integrating with respect to θ and evaluating at $\pi/2$ (the value of the antiderivative is 0 at 0) gives $\frac{1}{2}\pi + \frac{1}{48}k^2\pi^3 + \frac{1}{160}\left(-\frac{1}{6}k^2 + \frac{3}{8}k^4\right)\pi^5 + \frac{1}{896}\left(\frac{1}{45}k^2 - \frac{1}{4}k^4 + \frac{5}{16}k^6\right)\pi^7 + \frac{1}{4608}\left(-\frac{1}{630}k^2 + \frac{3}{40}k^4 - \frac{5}{16}k^6 + \frac{35}{128}k^8\right)\pi^9$. Evaluating these terms for $k = 0.1$ gives $F(0.1) \approx 1.574749680$. (The true value is approximately 1.574745562.)

b. The terms above, with coefficients of k^n converted to decimal approximations, is $1.5707 + .3918\cdot k^2 + .3597\cdot k^4 - .9682\cdot k^6 + 1.7689\cdot k^8$. The coefficients are all less than 2 and do not appear to be increasing very much if at all, so if we want the result to be accurate to within 10^{-3} we should probably take n such that $k^n < \frac{1}{2}\times 10^{-3} = .0005$, so $n = 4$ for this value of k.

c. By the above analysis, we would need a larger n because $0.2^n > 0.1^n$ for a given value of n.

9.4.79

a. By the Fundamental Theorem, $S'(x) = \sin x^2$, $C'(x) = \cos x^2$.

b. The relevant Taylor series are $\sin t^2 = t^2 - \frac{1}{3!}t^6 + \frac{1}{5!}t^{10} - \frac{1}{7!}t^{14} + \ldots$, and $\cos t^2 = 1 - \frac{1}{2!}t^4 + \frac{1}{4!}t^8 - \frac{1}{6!}t^{12} + \ldots$. Integrating, we have $S(x) = \frac{1}{3}x^3 - \frac{1}{7\cdot 3!}x^7 + \frac{1}{11\cdot 5!}x^{11} - \frac{1}{15\cdot 7!}x^{15} + \ldots$, and $C(x) = x - \frac{1}{5\cdot 2!}x^5 + \frac{1}{9\cdot 4!}x^9 - \frac{1}{13\cdot 6!}x^{13} + \ldots$.

c. $S(0.05) \approx \frac{1}{3}(0.05)^3 - \frac{1}{42}(0.05)^7 + \frac{1}{1320}(0.05)^{11} - \frac{1}{75600}(0.05)^{15} \approx 4.166664807\times 10^{-5}$. $C(-0.25) \approx (-0.25) - \frac{1}{10}(-0.25)^5 + \frac{1}{216}(-0.25)^9 - \frac{1}{9360}(-0.25)^{13} \approx -.2499023616$.

d. The series is alternating. Because $a_{n+1} = \frac{1}{(4n+7)(2n+3)!}(0.05)^{4n+7}$, and this is less than 10^{-4} for $n = 0$, only one term is required.

e. The series is alternating. Because $a_{n+1} = \frac{1}{(4n+5)(2n+2)!}(0.25)^{4n+5}$, and this is less than 10^{-6} for $n = 1$, two terms are required.

9.4.81

a. $J_0(x) = 1 - \frac{1}{4}x^2 + \frac{1}{16\cdot 2!^2}x^4 - \frac{1}{2^6\cdot 3!^2}x^6 + \ldots$.

b. Using the Ratio Test: $\left|\frac{a_{k+1}}{a_k}\right| = \frac{x^{2k+2}}{2^{2k+2}((k+1)!)^2} \cdot \frac{2^{2k}(k!)^2}{x^{2k}} = \frac{x^2}{4(k+1)^2}$, which has limit 0 as $k \to \infty$ for any x. Thus the radius of convergence is infinite and the interval of convergence is $(-\infty, \infty)$.

c. Starting only with terms up through x^8, we have $J_0(x) = 1 - \frac{1}{4}x^2 + \frac{1}{64}x^4 - \frac{1}{2304}x^6 + \frac{1}{147456}x^8 + \ldots$, $J_0'(x) = -\frac{1}{2}x + \frac{1}{16}x^3 - \frac{1}{384}x^5 + \frac{1}{18432}x^7 + \ldots$, $J_0''(x) = -\frac{1}{2} + \frac{3}{16}x^2 - \frac{5}{384}x^4 + \frac{7}{18432}x^6 + \ldots$ so that $x^2J_0(x) = x^2 - \frac{1}{4}x^4 + \frac{1}{64}x^6 - \frac{1}{2304}x^8 + \frac{1}{147456}x^{10} + \ldots$, $xJ_0'(x) = -\frac{1}{2}x^2 + \frac{1}{16}x^4 - \frac{1}{384}x^6 + \frac{1}{18432}x^8 + \ldots$, $x^2J_0''(x) = -\frac{1}{2}x^2 + \frac{3}{16}x^4 - \frac{5}{384}x^6 + \frac{7}{18432}x^8 + \ldots$, and $x^2J_0''(x) + xJ_0'(x) + x^2J_0(x) = 0$.

9.4.83

a. The power series for $\cos x$ has only even powers of x, so that the power series has the same value evaluated at $-x$ as it does at x.

b. The power series for $\sin x$ has only odd powers of x, so that evaluating it at $-x$ gives the opposite of its value at x.

9.4.85

a. Because $f(a) = g(a) = 0$, we use the Taylor series for $f(x)$ and $g(x)$ centered at a to compute that

$$\begin{aligned}\lim_{x\to a}\frac{f(x)}{g(x)} &= \lim_{x\to a}\frac{f(a)+f'(a)(x-a)+\frac{1}{2}f''(a)(x-a)^2+\cdots}{g(a)+g'(a)(x-a)+\frac{1}{2}g''(a)(x-a)^2+\cdots}\\ &= \lim_{x\to a}\frac{f'(a)(x-a)+\frac{1}{2}f''(a)(x-a)^2+\cdots}{g'(a)(x-a)+\frac{1}{2}g''(a)(x-a)^2+\cdots}\\ &= \lim_{x\to a}\frac{f'(a)+\frac{1}{2}f''(a)(x-a)+\cdots}{g'(a)+\frac{1}{2}g''(a)(x-a)+\cdots} = \frac{f'(a)}{g'(a)}.\end{aligned}$$

Because $f'(x)$ and $g'(x)$ are assumed to be continuous at a and $g'(a) \neq 0$,

$$\frac{f'(a)}{g'(a)} = \lim_{x\to a}\frac{f'(x)}{g'(x)}$$

and we have that

$$\lim_{x\to a}\frac{f(x)}{g(x)} = \lim_{x\to a}\frac{f'(x)}{g'(x)}$$

which is one form of L'Hôpital's Rule.

b. Because $f(a) = g(a) = f'(a) = g'(a) = 0$, we use the Taylor series for $f(x)$ and $g(x)$ centered at a to compute that

$$\begin{aligned}\lim_{x\to a}\frac{f(x)}{g(x)} &= \lim_{x\to a}\frac{f(a)+f'(a)(x-a)+\frac{1}{2}f''(a)(x-a)^2+\frac{1}{6}f'''(a)(x-a)^3+\cdots}{g(a)+g'(a)(x-a)+\frac{1}{2}g''(a)(x-a)^2+\frac{1}{6}g'''(a)(x-a)^3+\cdots}\\ &= \lim_{x\to a}\frac{\frac{1}{2}f''(a)(x-a)^2+\frac{1}{6}f'''(a)(x-a)^3+\cdots}{\frac{1}{2}g''(a)(x-a)^2+\frac{1}{6}g'''(a)(x-a)^3+\cdots}\\ &= \lim_{x\to a}\frac{\frac{1}{2}f''(a)+\frac{1}{6}f'''(a)(x-a)+\cdots}{\frac{1}{2}g''(a)+\frac{1}{6}g'''(a)(x-a)+\cdots} = \frac{f''(a)}{g''(a)}.\end{aligned}$$

Because $f''(x)$ and $g''(x)$ are assumed to be continuous at a and $g''(a) \neq 0$,

$$\frac{f''(a)}{g''(a)} = \lim_{x\to a}\frac{f''(x)}{g''(x)}$$

and we have that

$$\lim_{x\to a}\frac{f(x)}{g(x)} = \lim_{x\to a}\frac{f''(x)}{g''(x)}$$

which is consistent with two applications of L'Hôpital's Rule.

Chapter Nine Review

1

a. True. The approximations tend to get better as n increases in size, and also when the value being approximated is closer to the center of the series. Because 2.1 is closer to 2 than 2.2 is, and because $3 > 2$, we should have $|p_3(2.1) - f(2.1)| < |p_2(2.2) - f(2.2)|$.

b. False. The interval of convergence may or may not include the endpoints.

c. True. The interval of convergence is an interval centered at 0, and the endpoints may or may not be included.

d. True. Because $f(x)$ is a polynomial, all its derivatives vanish after a certain point (in this case, $f^{(12)}(x)$ is the last nonzero derivative).

3 $p_2(x) = 1$.

5 $p_3(x) = x - \frac{x^2}{2} + \frac{x^3}{3}$.

7 $p_2(x) = x - 1 - \frac{1}{2}(x-1)^2$.

9 $p_3(x) = \frac{5}{4} + \frac{3(x-\ln 2)}{4} + \frac{5(x-\ln 2)^2}{8} + \frac{(x-\ln 2)^3}{8}$.

11

a. $p_0(x) = 1$, $p_1(x) = 1 + x$, and $p_2(x) = 1 + x + \frac{x^2}{2}$.

b.

n	$p_n(-0.08)$	$\lvert p_n(-0.08) - e^{-0.08}\rvert$
0	1	7.7×10^{-2}
1	0.92	3.1×10^{-3}
2	0.923	8.4×10^{-5}

13

a. $p_0(x) = \frac{\sqrt{2}}{2}$, $p_1(x) = \frac{\sqrt{2}}{2}(1 + (x - \pi/4))$, and $p_2(x) = \frac{\sqrt{2}}{2}\left(1 + (x - \pi/4) - \frac{1}{2}(x - \pi/4)^2\right)$.

b.

n	$p_n(\pi/5)$	$\lvert p_n(\pi/5) - \sin(\pi/5)\rvert$
0	0.707	1.2×10^{-1}
1	0.596	8.2×10^{-3}
2	0.587	4.7×10^{-4}

15 The derivatives of $\sin x$ are bounded in magnitude by 1, so $|R_n(x)| \le M\frac{|x|^{n+1}}{(n+1)!} \le \frac{|x|^{n+1}}{(n+1)!}$. But $|x| < \pi$, so $|R_3(x)| \le \frac{\pi^4}{24}$.

17 Using the Ratio Test, $\lim_{k\to\infty}\left|\frac{a_{k+1}}{a_k}\right| = \lim_{k\to\infty}\left|\frac{(k+1)^2 x^{k+1}}{(k+1)!}\cdot\frac{k!}{k^2 x^k}\right| = \lim_{k\to\infty}\left(\frac{k+1}{k}\right)^2\frac{|x|}{k+1} = 0$, so the interval of convergence is $(-\infty, \infty)$.

19 Using the Ratio Test, $\lim_{k\to\infty}\frac{a_{k+1}}{a_k} = \lim_{k\to\infty}\left|\frac{(x+1)^{2k+2}}{(k+1)!}\cdot\frac{k!}{(x+1)^{2k}}\right| = \lim_{k\to\infty}\frac{1}{k+1}(x+1)^2 = 0$, so the interval of convergence is $(-\infty, \infty)$.

21 By the Root Test, $\lim_{k\to\infty} \sqrt[k]{|a_k|} = \lim_{k\to\infty} \left(\frac{|x|}{9}\right)^3 = \frac{|x^3|}{729}$, so the series converges for $|x| < 9$. The series given by letting $x = \pm 9$ are both divergent by the Divergence Test. Thus, $(-9, 9)$ is the interval of convergence.

23 By the Ratio Test, $\lim_{k\to\infty} \left| \frac{(x+2)^{k+1}}{2^{k+1}\ln(k+1)} \cdot \frac{2^k \ln k}{(x+2)^k} \right| = \lim_{k\to\infty} \frac{\ln k}{2\ln(k+1)} |x+2| = \frac{|x+2|}{2}$. The radius of convergence is thus 2, and a check of the endpoints gives the divergent series $\sum \frac{1}{\ln k}$ at $x = 0$ and the convergent alternating series $\sum \frac{(-1)^k}{\ln k}$ at $x = -4$. The interval of convergence is therefore $[-4, 0)$.

25 The Maclaurin series for $f(x)$ is $\sum_{k=0}^{\infty} x^{2k}$. By the Root Test, this converges for $|x^2| < 1$, so $-1 < x < 1$. It diverges at both endpoints, so the interval of convergence is $(-1, 1)$.

27 The Maclaurin series for $f(x)$ is $\sum_{k=0}^{\infty}(-5x)^k = \sum_{k=0}^{\infty}(-5)^k x^k$. By the Root Test, this has radius of convergence $1/5$. Checking the endpoints, we obtain an interval of convergence of $(-1/5, 1/5)$.

29 Note that $\frac{1}{1-10x} = \sum_{k=0}^{\infty}(10x)^k$, so $\frac{1}{10}\cdot\frac{1}{1-10x} = \frac{1}{10}\sum_{k=0}^{\infty}(10x)^k$. Taking the derivative of $\frac{1}{10}\cdot\frac{1}{1-10x}$ gives $f(x)$. Thus, the Maclaurin series for $f(x)$ is $\frac{1}{10}\sum_{k=1}^{\infty} 10k(10x)^{k-1} = \sum_{k=1}^{\infty} k(10x)^{k-1}$. Using the Ratio Test, we see that the radius of convergence is $1/10$, and checking endpoints we obtain an interval of convergence of $(-1/10, 1/10)$.

31 The first three terms are $1 + 3x + \frac{9x^2}{2}$. The series is $\sum_{k=0}^{\infty} \frac{(3x)^k}{k!}$.

33 The first three terms are $-(x - \pi/2) + \frac{1}{6}(x-\pi/2)^3 - \frac{1}{120}(x-\pi/2)^5$. The series is

$$\sum_{k=0}^{\infty}(-1)^{k+1}\frac{1}{(2k+1)!}\left(x - \frac{\pi}{2}\right)^{2k+1}.$$

35 The first three terms are $4x - \frac{1}{3}(4x)^3 + \frac{1}{5}(4x)^5$. The series is $\sum_{k=0}^{\infty}(-1)^k \frac{(4x)^{2k+1}}{2k+1}$.

37 The nth derivative of $\cosh 3x$ at $x = 0$ is 0 if n is odd and is 3^n if n is even. The first 3 terms of the series are thus $1 + \frac{9x^2}{2!} + \frac{81x^4}{4!}$. The whole series can be written as $\sum_{k=0}^{\infty} \frac{(3x)^{2k}}{(2k)!}$.

39 $f(x) = \binom{1/3}{0} + \binom{1/3}{1}x + \binom{1/3}{2}x^2 + \cdots = 1 + \frac{1}{3}x - \frac{1}{9}x^2 + \cdots$.

41 $f(x) = \binom{-3}{0} + \binom{-3}{1}\frac{x}{2} + \binom{-3}{2}\frac{x^2}{4} + \cdots = 1 - \frac{3}{2}x + \frac{3}{2}x^2 + \cdots$.

43 $R_n(x) = \frac{(-1)^{n+1}e^{-c}}{(n+1)!}x^{n+1}$ for some c between 0 and x, and $\lim_{n\to\infty}|R_n(x)| \le e^{-|x|}\lim_{n\to\infty}\frac{|x|^{n+1}}{(n+1)!} = 0$, because $n!$ grows faster than $|x|^n$ as $n \to \infty$ for all x.

45 $R_n(x) = \frac{f^{(n+1)}(c)}{(n+1)!}x^{n+1}$ for some c in $(-1/2, 1/2)$. Now, $\left|f^{(n+1)}(c)\right| = \frac{n!}{(1+c)^{n+1}}$, so $\lim_{n\to\infty}|R_n(x)| \le \lim_{n\to\infty}(2|x|)^{n+1}\cdot\frac{1}{n+1} \le \lim_{n\to\infty} 1^{n+1}\frac{1}{n+1} = 0$.

47 The Taylor series for $\cos x$ centered at 0 is

$$\cos x = 1 - \frac{x^2}{2} + \frac{x^4}{24} - \frac{x^6}{720} + \cdots.$$

We compute that

$$\begin{aligned}\frac{x^2/2 - 1 + \cos x}{x^4} &= \frac{1}{x^4}\left(x^2/2 - 1 + \left(1 - \frac{x^2}{2} + \frac{x^4}{24} - \frac{x^6}{720} + \cdots\right)\right) \\ &= \frac{1}{x^4}\left(\frac{x^4}{24} - \frac{x^6}{720} + \cdots\right) = \frac{1}{24} - \frac{x^2}{720} + \cdots\end{aligned}$$

so the limit of $\dfrac{x^2/2 - 1 + \cos x}{x^4}$ as $x \to 0$ is $\dfrac{1}{24}$.

49 The Taylor series for $\ln(x-3)$ centered at 4 is

$$\ln(x-3) = (x-4) - \frac{1}{2}(x-4)^2 + \frac{1}{3}(x-4)^3 - \cdots.$$

We compute that

$$\begin{aligned}\frac{\ln(x-3)}{x^2-16} &= \frac{1}{(x-4)(x+4)}\left((x-4) - \frac{1}{2}(x-4)^2 + \frac{1}{3}(x-4)^3 - \cdots\right)\\ &= \frac{1}{(x-4)(x+4)}\left((x-4)\left(1 - \frac{1}{2}(x-4) + \frac{1}{3}(x-4)^2 - \cdots\right)\right)\\ &= \frac{1}{x+4}\left(1 - \frac{1}{2}(x-4) + \frac{1}{3}(x-4)^2 - \cdots\right)\end{aligned}$$

so the limit of $\dfrac{\ln(x-3)}{x^2-16}$ as $x \to 4$ is $\dfrac{1}{8}$.

51 The Taylor series for $\sec x$ centered at 0 is

$$\sec x = 1 + \frac{x^2}{2} + \frac{5x^4}{24} + \frac{61x^6}{720} + \cdots$$

and the Taylor series for $\cos x$ centered at 0 is

$$\cos x = 1 - \frac{x^2}{2} + \frac{x^4}{24} - \frac{x^6}{720} + \cdots.$$

We compute that

$$\begin{aligned}&\frac{\sec x - \cos x - x^2}{x^4}\\ &= \frac{1}{x^4}\left(\left(1 + \frac{x^2}{2} + \frac{5x^4}{24} + \frac{61x^6}{720} + \cdots\right) - \left(1 - \frac{x^2}{2} + \frac{x^4}{24} - \frac{x^6}{720} + \cdots\right) - x^2\right)\\ &= \frac{1}{x^4}\left(\frac{x^4}{6} + \frac{31x^6}{360} + \cdots\right) = \frac{1}{6} + \frac{31x^2}{360} + \cdots\end{aligned}$$

so the limit of $\dfrac{\sec x - \cos x - x^2}{x^4}$ as $x \to 0$ is $\dfrac{1}{6}$.

53 We have $e^{-x^2} = 1 - x^2 + \frac{x^4}{2} - \frac{x^6}{6} + \frac{x^8}{24} - \cdots$, so $\int e^{-x^2}\,dx = \int(1 - x^2 + \frac{x^4}{2} - \frac{x^6}{6} + \frac{x^8}{24} - \cdots)\,dx = C + x - \frac{x^3}{3} + \frac{x^5}{10} - \frac{x^7}{42} + \cdots$. Thus, $\int_0^{1/2} e^{-x^2}\,dx = (0.5) - \frac{(0.5)^3}{3} + \frac{(0.5)^5}{10} - \frac{(0.5)^7}{42} + \cdots$. Because $(0.5)^7/42 < .001$, we can calculate the approximation using the first three numbers shown, arriving at approximately 0.461.

55 $x\cos x = x - \frac{x^3}{2} + \frac{x^5}{24} - \frac{x^7}{720} + \cdots$, so $\int x\cos x\,dx = \int(x - \frac{x^3}{2} + \frac{x^5}{24} - \frac{x^7}{720} + \cdots)\,dx = C + \frac{x^2}{2} - \frac{x^4}{8} + \frac{x^6}{144} - \frac{x^8}{5760} + \frac{x^{10}}{403200} - \cdots$. Thus $\int_0^1 x\cos x\,dx = \frac{1}{2} - \frac{1}{8} + \frac{1}{144} - \frac{1}{5760} + \cdots$. Because $\frac{1}{5760} < .001$, we add the first three terms to approximate to the desired accuracy. Calculating gives $\int_0^1 x\cos x\,dx \approx 0.382$.

57 The series for $f(x) = \sqrt{x}$ centered at $a = 121$ is $11 + \frac{x-121}{22} - \frac{(x-121)^2}{10648} + \frac{(x-121)^3}{2576816} + \cdots$. Letting $x = 119$ gives $\sqrt{119} \approx 11 - \frac{1}{11} - \frac{1}{2\cdot 11^3} - \frac{1}{2\cdot 11^5}$.

59 $\tan^{-1} x = x - x^3/3 + x^5/5 - x^7/7 + x^9/9 + \cdots$, so $\tan^{-1}(-1/3) \approx \frac{-1}{3} + \frac{1}{3\cdot 3^3} - \frac{1}{5\cdot 3^5} + \frac{1}{7\cdot 3^7}$.

61 Because $y(0) = 4$, we have $y'(0) - 16 + 12 = 0$, so $y'(0) = 4$. Differentiating the equation $n-1$ times and evaluating at 0 we obtain $y^{(n)}(0) = 4y^{(n-1)}(0)$, so that $y^{(n)}(0) = 4^n$. The Taylor series for $y(x)$ is thus $y(x) = 4 + 4x + \frac{4^2x^2}{2!} + \frac{4^3x^3}{3!} + \cdots$, or $y(x) = 3 + e^{4x}$.

63

a. The Taylor series for $\ln(1+x)$ is $\sum_{k=1}^{\infty}(-1)^{k+1}\frac{x^k}{k}$. Evaluating at $x=1$ gives $\ln 2 = \sum_{k=1}^{\infty}(-1)^{k+1}\frac{1}{k}$.

b. The Taylor series for $\ln(1-x)$ is $-\sum_{k=1}^{\infty}\frac{x^k}{k}$. Evaluating at $x = 1/2$ gives $\ln(1/2) = -\sum_{k=1}^{\infty}\frac{1}{k2^k}$, so that $\ln 2 = \sum_{k=1}^{\infty}\frac{1}{k2^k}$.

c. $f(x) = \ln\left(\frac{1+x}{1-x}\right) = \ln(1+x) - \ln(1-x)$. Using the two Taylor series above we have $f(x) = \sum_{k=1}^{\infty}(-1)^{k+1}\frac{x^k}{k} - \left(-\sum_{k=1}^{\infty}\frac{x^k}{k}\right) = \sum_{k=1}^{\infty}(1+(-1)^{k+1})\frac{x^k}{k} = 2\sum_{k=0}^{\infty}\frac{x^{2k+1}}{2k+1}$.

d. Because $\frac{1+x}{1-x} = 2$ when $x = \frac{1}{3}$, the resulting infinite series for $\ln 2$ is $2\sum_{k=0}^{\infty}\frac{1}{3^{2k+1}(2k+1)}$.

e. The first four terms of each series are: $1 - \frac{1}{2} + \frac{1}{3} - \frac{1}{4} \approx 0.5833333333$, $\frac{1}{2} + \frac{1}{8} + \frac{1}{24} + \frac{1}{64} \approx 0.6822916667$, $\frac{2}{3} + \frac{2}{81} + \frac{2}{1215} + \frac{2}{15309} \approx 0.6931347573$ The true value is $\ln 2 \approx 0.6931471806$. The third series converges the fastest, because it has 3^{k+1} in the denominator as opposed to 2^k, so its terms get small faster.

Chapter 11

Vectors and Vector-Valued Functions

11.1 Vectors in the Plane

11.1.1 The coordinates of a point determine its location, but a given point has no width or breadth, so it has no size or direction. A nonzero vector has size (magnitude) and direction, but it has no location in the sense that it can be translated to a different initial point and be considered the same vector.

11.1.3

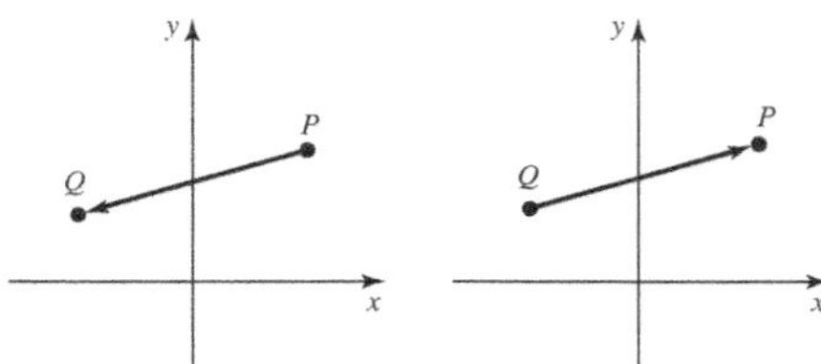

11.1.5 Two vectors are equal if they have the same magnitude and direction. Given a position vector, any translation of that vector to a different initial point yields an equivalent vector. Because there are infinitely many such translations which don't change the given vector's direction or magnitude, there are infinitely many vectors equivalent to the given one.

11.1.7 If $c > 0$ is given, the scalar multiple $c\mathbf{v}$ of the vector $\mathbf{v}$ is obtained by scaling the magnitude of $\mathbf{v}$ by a factor of c, and keeping the direction the same. If $c < 0$, then the head and tail of $\mathbf{v}$ are interchanged, and then the vector's magnitude is scaled by a factor of $|c|$.

11.1.9 $\mathbf{u}+\mathbf{v} = \langle u_1, u_2\rangle + \langle v_1, v_2\rangle = \langle u_1+v_1, u_2+v_2\rangle$.

11.1.11 $|\mathbf{v}| = |\langle v_1, v_2\rangle| = \sqrt{v_1^2+v_2^2}$.

11.1.13 If $P(p_1,p_2)$ and $Q(q_1,q_2)$ are given, then $\left|\overrightarrow{PQ}\right| = |\langle q_1-p_1, q_2-p_2\rangle| = \sqrt{(q_1-p_1)^2+(q_2-p_2)^2}$.

11.1.15 The vector $10\cdot\frac{\mathbf{v}}{|\mathbf{v}|} = 10\cdot\frac{1}{\sqrt{9+4}}\cdot\langle 3,-2\rangle = \langle\frac{30}{\sqrt{13}}, -\frac{20}{\sqrt{13}}\rangle$ has the desired properties.

11.1.17 The vectors in choices a, c, and e are all equal to $\overrightarrow{CE}$.

11.1.19

a. $3\mathbf{v}$ b. $2\mathbf{u}$ c. $-3\mathbf{u}$ d. $-2\mathbf{u}$ e. $\mathbf{v}$

11.1.21

a. $3\mathbf{u}+3\mathbf{v}$ b. $\mathbf{u}+2\mathbf{v}$ c. $2\mathbf{u}+5\mathbf{v}$ d. $-2\mathbf{u}+3\mathbf{v}$ e. $3\mathbf{u}+2\mathbf{v}$

f. $-3\mathbf{u}-2\mathbf{v}$ g. $-2\mathbf{u}-4\mathbf{v}$ h. $\mathbf{u}-4\mathbf{v}$ i. $-\mathbf{u}-6\mathbf{v}$

11.1.23

a. $\overrightarrow{OP}$

i. 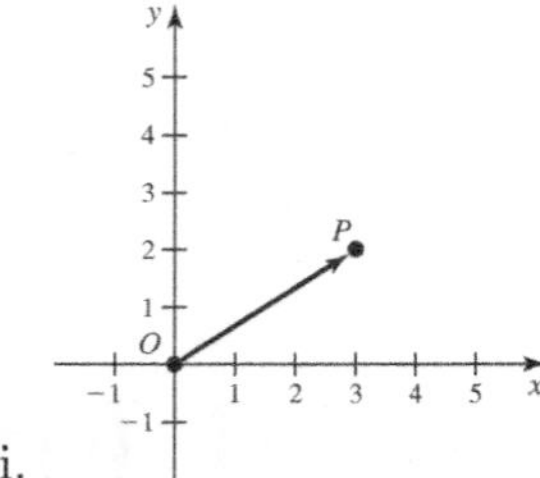

ii. $|3\mathbf{i} + 2\mathbf{j}| = \sqrt{13}$.

b. $\overrightarrow{QP}$

i. 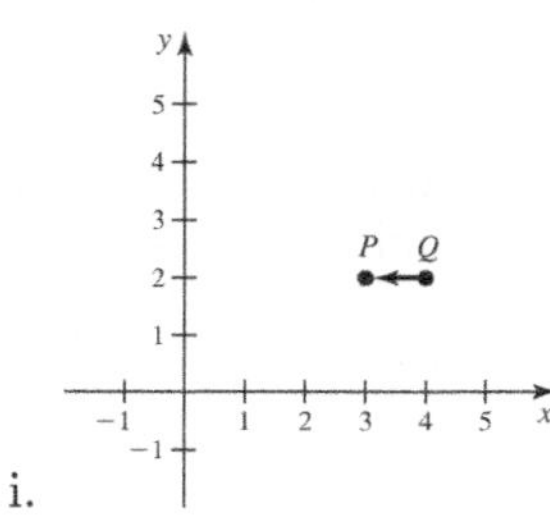

ii. $|-\mathbf{i} + 0 \cdot \mathbf{j}| = 1$.

c. $\overrightarrow{RQ}$

i. 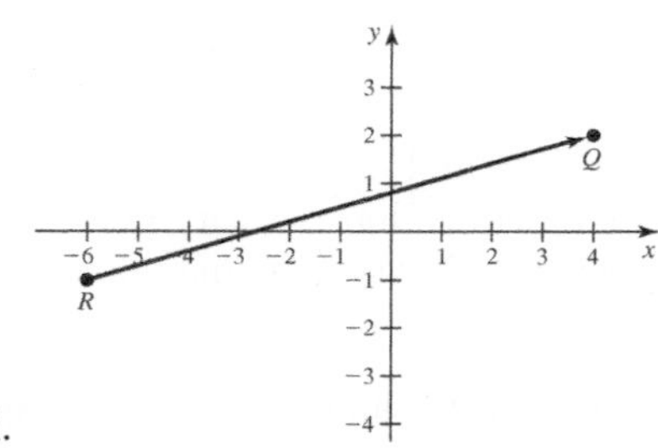

ii. $|10\mathbf{i} + 3\mathbf{j}| = \sqrt{109}$.

11.1.25 $\overrightarrow{QU} = \langle 7, 2 \rangle$, $\overrightarrow{PT} = \langle 7, 3 \rangle$, $\overrightarrow{RS} = \langle 2, 3 \rangle$.

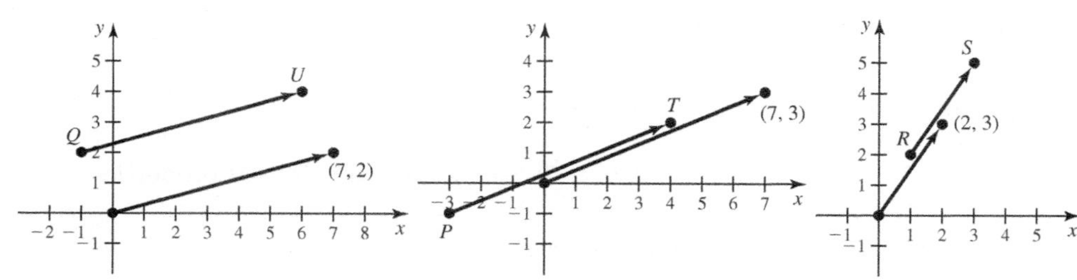

11.1.27 $\overrightarrow{QT} = \langle 5, 0 \rangle$, while $\overrightarrow{SU} = \langle 3, -1 \rangle$.

11.1.29 $\mathbf{w} - \mathbf{u} = \langle 0, 8 \rangle - \langle 4, -2 \rangle = \langle -4, 10 \rangle$.

11.1.31 $\mathbf{w} - 3\mathbf{v} = \langle 0, 8 \rangle - 3\langle -4, 6 \rangle = \langle 12, -10 \rangle$.

11.1.33 $8\mathbf{w} + \mathbf{v} - 6\mathbf{u} = 8\langle 0, 8 \rangle + \langle -4, 6 \rangle - 6\langle 4, -2 \rangle = \langle -28, 82 \rangle$.

11.1.35 $|-2\mathbf{v}| = |\langle -2,-2\rangle| = \sqrt{4+4} = 2\sqrt{2}$.

11.1.37 $|2\mathbf{u}+3\mathbf{v}-4\mathbf{w}| = |2\langle 3,-4\rangle + 3\langle 1,1\rangle - 4\langle -1,0\rangle| = |\langle 13,-5\rangle| = \sqrt{194}$.

11.1.39 The vectors we seek are $\pm 3\mathbf{v}$, so they are $\langle 3,3\rangle$ and $\langle -3,-3\rangle$.

11.1.41 $|\mathbf{u}-\mathbf{v}| = |\langle 3,-4\rangle - \langle 1,1\rangle| = |\langle 2,-5\rangle| = \sqrt{29}$. $|\mathbf{w}-\mathbf{u}| = |\langle -1,0\rangle - \langle 3,-4\rangle| = |\langle -4,4\rangle| = \sqrt{32} = 4\sqrt{2}$. $\mathbf{w}-\mathbf{u}$ has the greater magnitude.

11.1.43 $\overrightarrow{QR} = \langle 2,6\rangle - \langle 3,-4\rangle = \langle -1,10\rangle = -\mathbf{i}+10\mathbf{j}$.

11.1.45 $\mathbf{u} = \frac{\overrightarrow{PR}}{|\overrightarrow{PR}|} = \frac{\langle 2,6\rangle - \langle -4,1\rangle}{|\overrightarrow{PR}|} = \frac{\langle 6,5\rangle}{\sqrt{36+25}} = \langle 6/\sqrt{61}, 5/\sqrt{61}\rangle$ is one unit vector, while the other is $-\mathbf{u} = \langle -6/\sqrt{61}, -5/\sqrt{61}\rangle$

11.1.47 $\overrightarrow{QP} = \langle -4,1\rangle - \langle 3,-4\rangle = \langle -7,5\rangle$. A unit vector parallel to $\overrightarrow{QP}$ is $\frac{1}{\sqrt{74}}\langle -7,5\rangle$. So the desired vectors are $\frac{4}{\sqrt{74}}\langle -7,5\rangle$ and $-\frac{4}{\sqrt{74}}\langle -7,5\rangle$.

11.1.49 Let $\mathbf{w} = \langle 0,-5\rangle$ represent the water, and let $\mathbf{v_w} = \langle 40,0\rangle$ represent the boat relative to the water. Then relative to the shore we have $\mathbf{v_s} = \mathbf{w} + \mathbf{v_w} = \langle 40,-5\rangle$, which has magnitude $\sqrt{1625} \approx 40.3$ km/hr.

11.1.51 The plane's vector is given by $\mathbf{u} = -320\mathbf{i} + -20\sqrt{2}(\mathbf{i}+\mathbf{j}) = (-320-20\sqrt{2})\mathbf{i} - 20\sqrt{2}\mathbf{j}$. The magnitude of $\mathbf{u}$ is $\sqrt{(-320-20\sqrt{2})^2 + (-20\sqrt{2})^2} \approx 349.43$ miles per hour. $\theta = \tan^{-1}\left(\frac{20\sqrt{2}}{320+20\sqrt{2}}\right) \approx .0810$ radians, or about 4.64 degrees south of west.

11.1.53 Let $\mathbf{u} = \mathbf{i}$ represent the current and $\mathbf{v} = \sqrt{3}\cos(\pi/6)\mathbf{i} + \sqrt{3}\sin(\pi/6)\mathbf{j} = \frac{3}{2}\mathbf{i} + \frac{\sqrt{3}}{2}\mathbf{j}$ represent the boat relative to land. If $\mathbf{w}$ represents the wind, then $\mathbf{u}+\mathbf{w} = \mathbf{v}$, so $\mathbf{w} = \mathbf{v}-\mathbf{u} = \frac{1}{2}\mathbf{i} + \frac{\sqrt{3}}{2}\mathbf{j}$. Then $\theta = \tan^{-1}(\sqrt{3}) = \pi/3$, or 60 degrees. The speed of the wind is 1 meter per second in the direction 60 degrees north of east (or 30 degrees east of north).

11.1.55

a. $\mathbf{F} = 40\cos(\pi/3)\mathbf{i} + 40\sin(\pi/3)\mathbf{j} = 20\mathbf{i} + 20\sqrt{3}\mathbf{j}$, so the horizontal component is 20 and the vertical is $20\sqrt{3}$.

b. Yes. If it is 45 degrees, the horizontal component would be $40\cos(\pi/4) = 20\sqrt{2} > 20$.

c. No. If it is 45 degrees, the vertical component would be $40\sin(\pi/4) = 20\sqrt{2} < 20\sqrt{3}$.

11.1.57 Let the magnitude of the force on the two chains be f. Let $\mathbf{F_1} = (-\frac{\sqrt{2}}{2}\mathbf{i} + \frac{\sqrt{2}}{2}\mathbf{j})f$ and let $\mathbf{F_2} = (\frac{\sqrt{2}}{2}\mathbf{i} + \frac{\sqrt{2}}{2}\mathbf{j})f$. Then $\mathbf{F_1} + \mathbf{F_2} - 500\mathbf{j} = 0$, and solving for f yields $f = 250\sqrt{2}$ pounds.

11.1.59

a. True. This follows because $(\mathbf{u}+\mathbf{v})+\mathbf{w} = (\mathbf{w}+\mathbf{u})+\mathbf{v}$ (vector addition is commutative and associative.)

b. True. This is because $\mathbf{u} + (-\mathbf{u}) = \mathbf{0}$.

c. False. For example, if $\mathbf{u} = \langle 3,4\rangle$ and $\mathbf{v} = \langle -3,-1\rangle$, then $|\mathbf{u}+\mathbf{v}| = |\langle 0,3\rangle| = 3$, while $|\mathbf{u}| = 5$.

d. False. For example, if $\mathbf{u} = \langle 3,4\rangle$ and $\mathbf{v} = \langle -1,-4\rangle$, then $|\mathbf{u}+\mathbf{v}| = |\langle 2,0\rangle| = 2$, while $|\mathbf{u}|+|\mathbf{v}| = 5+\sqrt{17}$.

e. False. For example, if $\mathbf{u} = \langle 3,0\rangle$ and $\mathbf{v} = \langle 6,0\rangle$, then $\mathbf{u}$ and $\mathbf{v}$ are parallel, but have different lengths.

f. False. For example, given $A(0,0)$, $B(3,4)$, $C(1,1)$ and $D(4,5)$, we have $\overrightarrow{AB} = \langle 3,4\rangle$ and $\overrightarrow{CD} = \langle 3,4\rangle$, but $A \neq C$ and $B \neq D$.

g. False. For example, $\mathbf{u} = \langle 0,1\rangle$ and $\mathbf{v} = \langle -1,0\rangle$ are perpendicular, but $|\mathbf{u}+\mathbf{v}| = \sqrt{2}$, while $|\mathbf{u}|+|\mathbf{v}| = 2$.

h. True. Suppose $\mathbf{v} = k\mathbf{u}$ with $k > 0$. Then

$$|\mathbf{u}+\mathbf{v}| = |\mathbf{u}+k\mathbf{u}| = |(1+k)\mathbf{u}| = (1+k)\,|\mathbf{u}| = |\mathbf{u}| + k\,|\mathbf{u}| = |\mathbf{u}| + |k\mathbf{u}| = |\mathbf{u}| + |\mathbf{v}|\,.$$

11.1.61

a. Because the magnitude of $\mathbf{v}$ is $\sqrt{36+64} = 10$, the two desired vectors are $\langle 6/10, -8/10\rangle = \langle 3/5, -4/5\rangle$ and $\langle -3/5, 4/5\rangle$.

b. If the magnitude of $\mathbf{v}$ is 1, then $\sqrt{\frac{1}{9} + b^2} = 1$, so $b^2 = \frac{8}{9}$, so $b = \pm\frac{2\sqrt{2}}{3}$.

c. If the magnitude of $\mathbf{w}$ is 1, then $\sqrt{a^2 + \frac{a^2}{9}} = 1$, so $\frac{10a^2}{9} = 1$, so $a = \pm\frac{3}{\sqrt{10}}$.

11.1.63 $10\langle a, b\rangle = \langle 2, -3\rangle$, so $10a = 2$, and $a = 1/5$. Also, $10b = -3$, so $b = -3/10$. Thus $\mathbf{x} = \langle 1/5, -3/10\rangle$.

11.1.65 $3\langle a, b\rangle - 4\langle 2, -3\rangle = \langle -4, 1\rangle$, so $\langle a, b\rangle = \frac{1}{3}\langle 4, -11\rangle = \mathbf{x}$.

11.1.67 $\langle 4, -8\rangle = 4\mathbf{i} + -8\mathbf{j}$.

11.1.69 Let $\langle a, b\rangle = c_1\mathbf{u} + c_2\mathbf{v}$. Then $c_1 - c_2 = a$ and $c_1 + c_2 = b$. Adding these two equations to each other yields $2c_1 = a + b$, so $c_1 = \frac{a+b}{2}$. And thus $c_2 = \frac{b-a}{2}$. We have $\langle a, b\rangle = \frac{a+b}{2}\mathbf{u} + \frac{b-a}{2}\mathbf{v}$.

11.1.71 Because $2\mathbf{u} + 3\mathbf{v} = \mathbf{i}$ and $-2(\mathbf{u} - \mathbf{v}) = -2\mathbf{j}$, we can conclude that $3\mathbf{v} + 2\mathbf{v} = \mathbf{i} - 2\mathbf{j}$ (by adding), so $\mathbf{v} = \frac{1}{5}\mathbf{i} - \frac{2}{5}\mathbf{j}$. It then follows that $\mathbf{u} = \mathbf{v} + \mathbf{j} = \frac{1}{5}\mathbf{i} - \frac{2}{5}\mathbf{j} + \mathbf{j} = \frac{1}{5}\mathbf{i} + \frac{3}{5}\mathbf{j}$.

11.1.73 $\mathbf{u} = 3\frac{\langle 5, -12\rangle}{\sqrt{25+144}} = \frac{3}{13}\langle 5, -12\rangle$.

11.1.75 $\mathbf{u} = \mathbf{u_1} + \mathbf{u_2} = \langle 4, -6\rangle + \langle 5, 9\rangle = \langle 9, 3\rangle$.

11.1.77

a. The sum is $\mathbf{0}$ because each vector has exactly one additive inverse in the set among the 12 vectors.

b. The 6:00 vector, because the others cancel in pairs, but this vector remains.

c. If we remove the 1:00 through 6:00 vectors, the sum is as large as possible, because all the vectors are pointing toward the left side of the clock. Removing any 6 consecutive vectors gives a sum whose magnitude is as large as possible.

d. Let $\mathbf{w}$ be the vector that points from 12:00 toward 6:00 but which has length r equal to the radius of the clock. The sum we are seeking is $12\mathbf{w}$. The sum of the vectors pointing to 1:00 and 11:00 add up to $(2 - \sqrt{3})\mathbf{w}$, the sum of the vectors pointing to 2:00 and 10:00 is $\mathbf{w}$, the vectors pointing to 3:00 and 9:00 add up to $2\mathbf{w}$, the vectors pointing to 4:00 and 8:00 add up to $3\mathbf{w}$, and the vectors pointing to 5:00 and 7:00 add up to $(\sqrt{3} + 2)\mathbf{w}$. Finally, the single vector pointing to 6:00 is $2\mathbf{w}$. The sum of all of these is $12\mathbf{w}$.

11.1.79 The magnitude of the net force is $|\mathbf{F}| = \sqrt{40^2 + 30^2} = 50$ pounds. $\alpha = \tan^{-1}(\frac{3}{4}) \approx .6435$ radians or 36.87 degrees. The net force has magnitude 50 pounds in the direction 36.87 degrees north of east.

11.1.81 $\mathbf{u} + \mathbf{v} = \langle u_1, u_2\rangle + \langle v_1, v_2\rangle = \langle u_1 + v_1, u_2 + v_2\rangle = \langle v_1 + u_1, v_2 + u_2\rangle = \langle v_1, v_2\rangle + \langle u_1, u_2\rangle = \mathbf{v} + \mathbf{u}$.

11.1.83 $a(c\mathbf{v}) = a(c\langle v_1, v_2\rangle) = a\langle cv_1, cv_2\rangle = \langle a(cv_1), a(cv_2)\rangle = \langle (ac)v_1, (ac)v_2\rangle = (ac)\langle v_1, v_2\rangle = (ac)\mathbf{v}$.

11.1.85 $(a + c)\mathbf{v} = (a + c)\langle v_1, v_2\rangle = \langle (a + c)v_1, (a + c)v_2\rangle = \langle av_1 + cv_1, av_2 + cv_2\rangle = \langle av_1, av_2\rangle + \langle cv_1, cv_2\rangle = a\mathbf{v} + c\mathbf{v}$.

11.1.87 $|c\mathbf{v}| = |c\langle v_1, v_2\rangle| = |\langle cv_1, cv_2\rangle| = \sqrt{(cv_1)^2 + (cv_2)^2} = \sqrt{c^2}\sqrt{v_1^2 + v_2^2} = |c|\,|\mathbf{v}|$.

11.1.89

a. Note that $-6\mathbf{u} = \mathbf{v}$, so $\{\mathbf{u}, \mathbf{v}\}$ is linearly dependent. But there is no scalar c so that $c\mathbf{u} = \mathbf{w}$, nor any scalar d so that $d\mathbf{v} = \mathbf{w}$ so $\{\mathbf{u}, \mathbf{w}\}$ is linearly independent and $\{\mathbf{v}, \mathbf{w}\}$ is linearly independent.

b. Two nonzero vectors are linearly independent when they are not parallel, and are linearly dependent when they are parallel.

c. Suppose $\mathbf{u}$ and $\mathbf{v}$ are linearly independent. Consider the equation $c_1\mathbf{u} + c_2\mathbf{v} = \mathbf{w}$ for a given vector $\mathbf{w}$. We are seeking a solution for the system of linear equatons $c_1u_1 + c_2v_1 = w_1$ and $c_1u_2 + c_2v_2 = w_2$. The solution for this system is given by $c_1 = \frac{1}{u_1v_2 - u_2v_1}(v_2w_1 - v_1w_2)$ and $c_2 = \frac{1}{u_1v_2 - u_2v_1}(-u_2w_1 + u_1w_2)$, provided $u_1v_2 - u_2v_1 \neq 0$. This condition is equivalent to saying that $\mathbf{v}$ is not a multiple of $\mathbf{u}$. Thus a solution to the system of linear equations exists exactly when the vectors $\mathbf{u}$ and $\mathbf{v}$ are linearly independent.

11.1.91

a. If $\mathbf{u}$ and $\mathbf{v}$ are parallel, we must have $\frac{a}{2} = \frac{5}{6}$, so $a = \frac{5}{3}$.

b. If $\mathbf{u}$ and $\mathbf{v}$ are perpendicular, we must have $2a + 30 = 0$, so $a = -15$.

11.2 Vectors in Three Dimensions

11.2.1 Starting at the origin $(0, 0, 0)$, move 3 units in the positive x-direction, 2 units in the negative y-direction, and 1 unit in the positive z-direction, to arrive at the point $(3, -2, 1)$.

11.2.3 The plane $x = 4$ is parallel to the yz-plane, but contains all of the points with x-coordinate 4. It is perpendicular to the x-axis.

11.2.5 $\mathbf{u} + \mathbf{v} = \langle 3 + 6, 5 + (-5), -7 + 1\rangle = \langle 9, 0, -6\rangle$. $3\mathbf{u} - \mathbf{v} = \langle 9, 15, -21\rangle - \langle 6, -5, 1\rangle = \langle 3, 20, -22\rangle$.

11.2.7 Because $\sqrt{3^2 + (-1)^2 + 2^2} = \sqrt{14} < \sqrt{0^2 + 0^2 + (-4)^2} = 4$, the point $(0, 0, -4)$ is further from the origin.

11.2.9 $A(3, 0, 5)$, $B(3, 4, 0)$, $C(0, 4, 5)$.

11.2.11 $A(3, -4, 5)$, $B(0, -4, 0)$, $C(0, -4, 5)$.

11.2.13

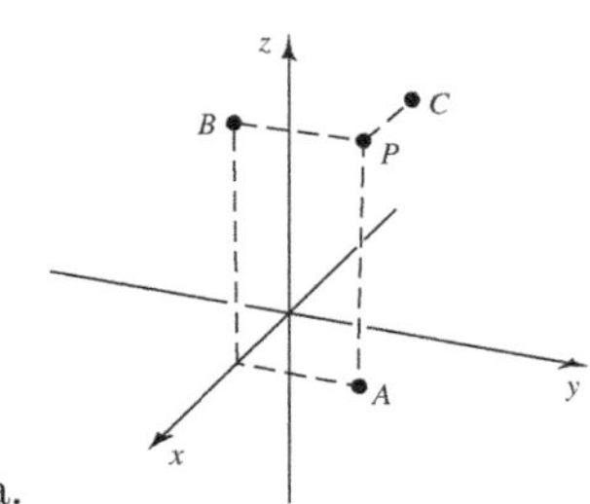

a.

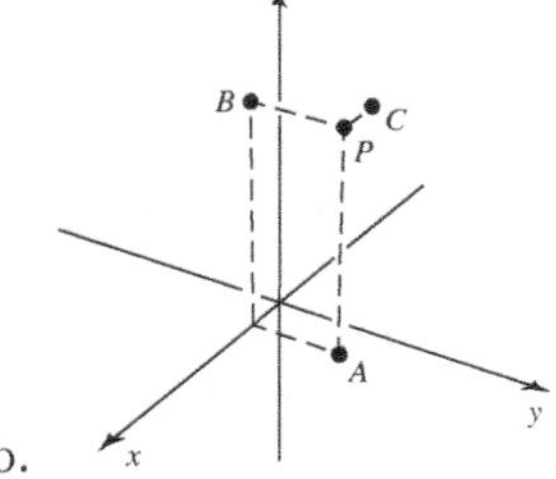

b.

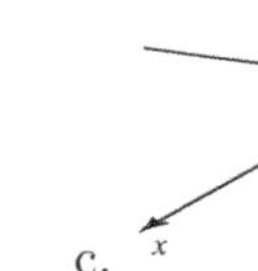

c.

11.2.15

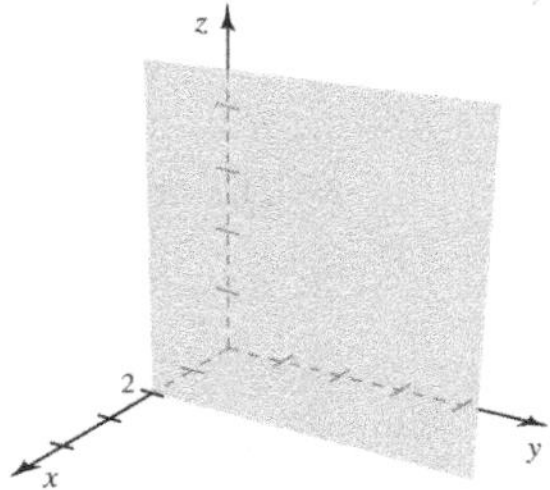

11.2.17

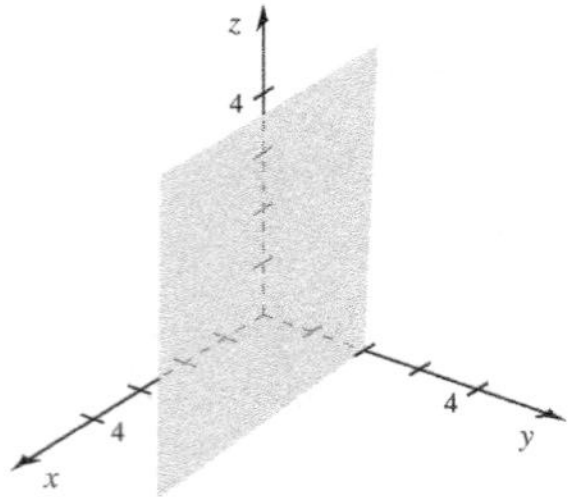

11.2.19

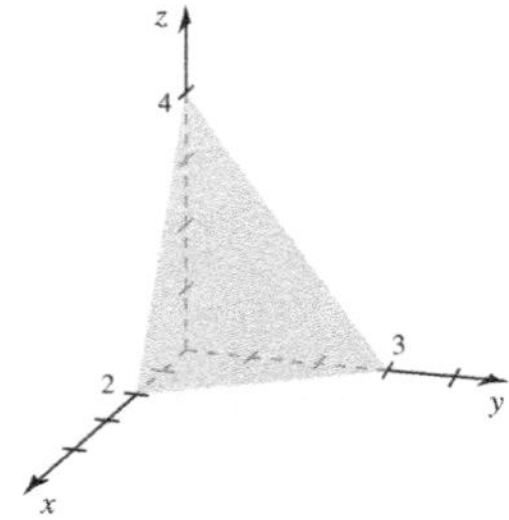

11.2.21

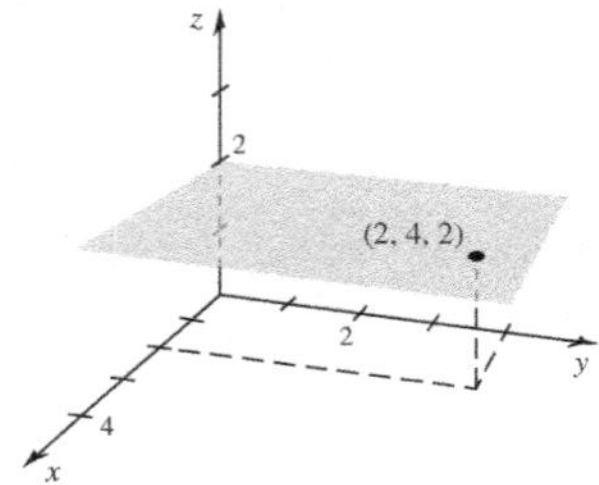

The plane $z = 2$.

11.2.23 $(x-1)^2 + (y-2)^2 + (z-3)^2 = 16$.

11.2.25 $(x+2)^2 + y^2 + (z-4)^2 \leq 1$.

11.2.27 The midpoint of the line segment $\overline{PQ}$ is $(\frac{1+2}{2}, \frac{0+3}{2}, \frac{5+9}{2}) = (3/2, 3/2, 7)$. The radius of the sphere is $r = \frac{1}{2}\sqrt{(2-1)^2 + (3-0)^2 + (9-5)^2} = \frac{\sqrt{26}}{2}$. The equation of the sphere is therefore $(x - 3/2)^2 + (y - 3/2)^2 + (z-7)^2 = \frac{13}{2}$.

11.2.29 This is a sphere centered at $(1, 0, 0)$ of radius 3.

11.2.31 Completing the squares, we have $x^2 + (y^2 - 2y + 1) + (z^2 - 4z + 4) = 4 + 5$, so we have $x^2 + (y - 1)^2 + (z-2)^2 = 3^2$, which describes a sphere of radius 3 centered at $(0, 1, 2)$.

11.2.33 Completing the square, we have $x^2 + (y^2 - 14y + 49) + z^2 \geq -13 + 49 = 36$, which can be written as $x^2 + (y-7)^2 + z^2 \geq 6^2$. This is the outside of a ball centered at $(0, 7, 0)$ with radius 6. (Including the sphere itself.)

11.2.35 Completing the squares, we have $(x^2 - 8x + 16) + (y^2 - 14y + 49) + (z^2 - 18z + 81) \leq 79 + 16 + 49 + 81 = 225$, which can be written as $(x-4)^2 + (y-7)^2 + (z-9)^2 \leq 15^2$. This is a ball centered at $(4, 7, 9)$ with radius 15.

11.2.37 Completing the squares, we have $(x^2 - 2x + 1) + (y^2 + 6y + 9) + z^2 = -10 + 1 + 9 = 0$, or $(x-1)^2 + (y+3)^2 + z^2 = 0$. This is the single point $(1, -3, 0)$.

11.2.39

a. $3\langle 4,-3,0\rangle + 2\langle 0,1,1\rangle = \langle 12,-7,2\rangle$.

b. $4\langle 4,-3,0\rangle - \langle 0,1,1\rangle = \langle 16,-13,-1\rangle$.

c. $|\langle 4,-3,0\rangle + 3\langle 0,1,1\rangle| = |\langle 4,0,3\rangle| = \sqrt{16+0+9} = 5$.

11.2.41

a. $3\langle -2,1,-2\rangle + 2\langle 1,1,1\rangle = \langle -4,5,-4\rangle$.

b. $4\langle -2,1,-2\rangle - \langle 1,1,1\rangle = \langle -9,3,-9\rangle$.

c. $|\langle -2,1,-2\rangle + 3\langle 1,1,1\rangle| = |\langle 1,4,1\rangle| = \sqrt{1+16+1} = \sqrt{18} = 3\sqrt{2}$.

11.2.43

a. $3\langle -7,11,8\rangle + 2\langle 3,-5,-1\rangle = \langle -15,23,22\rangle$.

b. $4\langle -7,11,8\rangle - \langle 3,-5,-1\rangle = \langle -31,49,33\rangle$.

c. $|\langle -7,11,8\rangle + 3\langle 3,-5,-1\rangle| = |\langle 2,-4,5\rangle| = \sqrt{4+16+25} = \sqrt{45} = 3\sqrt{5}$.

11.2.45

a. $\overrightarrow{PQ} = \langle 3-1, 11-5, 2-0\rangle = \langle 2,6,2\rangle = 2\mathbf{i} + 6\mathbf{j} + 2\mathbf{k}$.

b. $|\langle 2,6,2\rangle| = \sqrt{4+36+4} = \sqrt{44} = 2\sqrt{11}$.

c. $\langle 1/\sqrt{11}, 3/\sqrt{11}, 1/\sqrt{11}\rangle$ and $\langle -1/\sqrt{11}, -3/\sqrt{11}, -1/\sqrt{11}\rangle$.

11.2.47

a. $\overrightarrow{PQ} = \langle -3+3, -4-1, 1-0\rangle = \langle 0,-5,1\rangle = -5\mathbf{j} + 1\mathbf{k}$.

b. $|\langle 0,-5,1\rangle| = \sqrt{25+1} = \sqrt{26}$.

c. $\langle 0, -5/\sqrt{26}, 1/\sqrt{26}\rangle$ and $\langle 0, 5/\sqrt{26}, -1/\sqrt{26}\rangle$.

11.2.49

a. $\overrightarrow{PQ} = \langle -2-0, 4-0, 0-2\rangle = \langle -2,4,-2\rangle = -2\mathbf{i} + 4\mathbf{j} - 2\mathbf{k}$.

b. $|\langle -2,4,-2\rangle| = \sqrt{4+16+4} = 2\sqrt{6}$.

c. $\langle -1/\sqrt{6}, 2/\sqrt{6}, -1/\sqrt{6}\rangle$ and $\langle 1/\sqrt{6}, -2/\sqrt{6}, 1/\sqrt{6}\rangle$.

11.2.51

a. The airplane's velocity vector (without wind) is given by $\langle 0,20,0\rangle$, the wind's is given by $\langle 20,0,0\rangle$ and the downdraft's is $\langle 0,0,-10\rangle$. The sum of these is $\langle 20,20,-10\rangle$.

b. The speed is $|\langle 20,20,-10\rangle| = \sqrt{400+400+100} = 30$ mi/hr

11.2.53 The airplane's velocity is $\mathbf{v_1} = 250\mathbf{i}$. The crosswind is blowing $\mathbf{v_2} = -25\sqrt{2}\mathbf{i} - 25\sqrt{2}\mathbf{j}$. The updraft is $\mathbf{v_3} = 30\mathbf{k}$. We have $|\mathbf{v_1} + \mathbf{v_2} + \mathbf{v_3}| = |\langle 250 - 25\sqrt{2}, -25\sqrt{2}, 30\rangle| \approx 219.596$ miles per hour. The direction is sketched in the diagram—it is slightly south of east and upward.

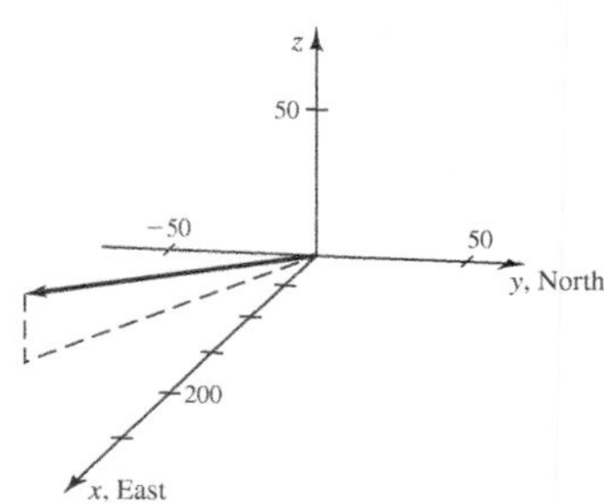

11.2.55 The component in the east direction is $(20\cos 30°)(\cos 45°) = 5\sqrt{6}$ knots. In the north direction, it is $(20\cos 30°)(\sin 45°) = 5\sqrt{6}$ knots. In the vertical direction, it is $20\sin 30° = 10$ knots.

11.2.57

a. False. For example, let $\mathbf{u} = \langle 1,0,0\rangle$, $\mathbf{v} = \langle 0,1,0\rangle$ and $\mathbf{w} = \langle 1,1,0\rangle$. Then both $\mathbf{u}$ and $\mathbf{v}$ make a 45 degree angle with $\mathbf{w}$, but $\mathbf{u}+\mathbf{v} = \mathbf{w}$ makes a zero degree angle with $\mathbf{w}$.

b. False. For example, $\mathbf{i}$ and $\mathbf{j}$ form a 90 degree angle with $\mathbf{k}$, as does $\mathbf{i}+\mathbf{j}$.

c. False. $\mathbf{i}+\mathbf{j}+\mathbf{k} = \langle 1,1,1\rangle \neq \langle 0,0,0\rangle$.

d. True. They intersect at the point $(1,1,1)$.

11.2.59

This represents all the points in 3-space, excluding the three axes.

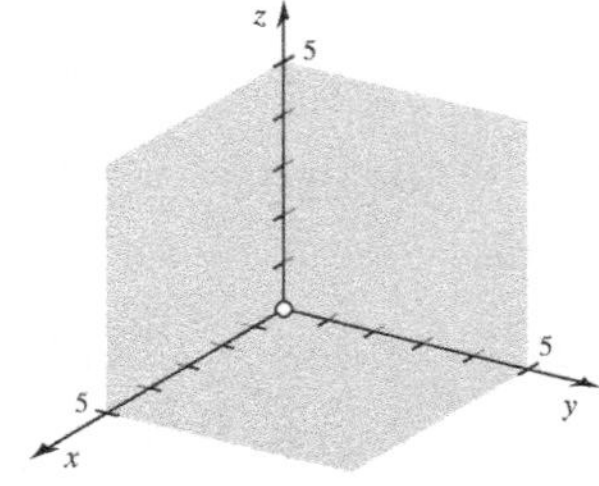

11.2.61

This represents a circle of radius 1 centered at $(0,0,0)$ in the xy-plane.

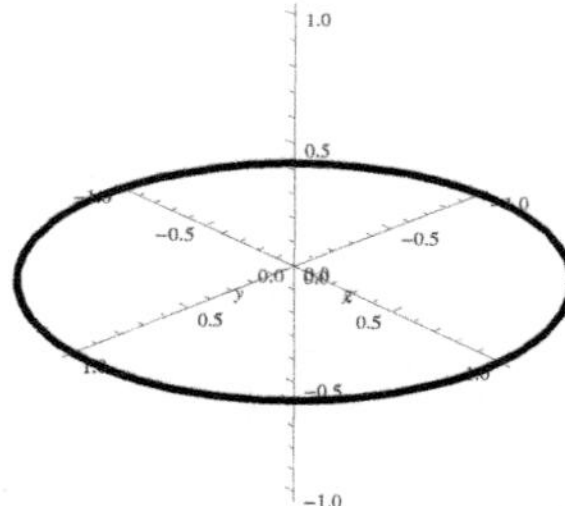

11.2.63 If $z = 1$, then $x^2 + y^2 + 1 = 5$, so $x^2 + y^2 = 4$. We have a circle of radius 2 centered at $(0,0,1)$ in the plane $z = 1$.

11.2.65 Planes parallel to the xz-plane have the form $y = c$ for a constant c, so we must have $y = 4$. Thus, we must have $(x-2)^2 + (z-1)^2 = 9$ and $y = 4$.

11.2.67 Because the magnitude of $\mathbf{v}$ is $\sqrt{36+64+0} = 10$, the desired vectors are $\pm 20\langle .6, -.8, 0\rangle = \pm\langle 12, -16, 0\rangle$.

11.2.69 Because the magnitude of $\mathbf{v}$ is $\sqrt{1+1+1} = \sqrt{3}$, the desired vectors are $\pm 3\langle -1/\sqrt{3}, -1/\sqrt{3}, 1/\sqrt{3}\rangle = \pm\langle -\sqrt{3}, -\sqrt{3}, \sqrt{3}\rangle$.

11.2.71

a. Because $\overrightarrow{PQ} = \langle 1, -1, 2\rangle$ and $\overrightarrow{PR} = \langle 3, -3, 6\rangle = 3\langle 1, -1, 2\rangle$ they are collinear. Q is between P and R.

b. Because $\overrightarrow{PQ} = \langle 4, 8, -8\rangle$ and $\overrightarrow{PR} = \langle -1, -2, 2\rangle = -\frac{1}{4}\langle 4, 8, -8\rangle$ they are collinear. P is between Q and R.

c. Because $\overrightarrow{PQ} = \langle 1, -5, 3\rangle$ and $\overrightarrow{PR} = \langle 2, -3, 6\rangle$ are not parallel, the given points are not collinear.

d. Because $\overrightarrow{PQ} = \langle 2, 13, 3\rangle$ and $\overrightarrow{PR} = \langle -3, -2, -1\rangle$ are not parallel, the given points are not collinear.

11.2.73 The diagonal of the box has magnitude $\sqrt{2^2+3^2+4^2} = \sqrt{29}$, so the longest rod that will fit in the box has length $\sqrt{29}$ feet.

11.2.75 Let $P(1, -\sqrt{3}, 0)$, $Q(1, \sqrt{3}, 0)$, $R(-2, 0, 0)$, and $S(0, 0, -2\sqrt{3})$ be the given points. Note that $\overrightarrow{PS} = \langle -1, \sqrt{3}, -2\sqrt{3}\rangle$, $\overrightarrow{QS} = \langle -1, -\sqrt{3}, -2\sqrt{3}\rangle$, $\overrightarrow{RS} = \langle 2, 0, -2\sqrt{3}\rangle$. Let $x(\overrightarrow{PS} + \overrightarrow{QS} + \overrightarrow{RS}) = -500\mathbf{k}$, then $-6\sqrt{3}x = -500$, so $x = \frac{250}{3\sqrt{3}}$. Then $x\overrightarrow{PS} = \frac{250}{3\sqrt{3}}\langle -1, \sqrt{3}, -2\sqrt{3}\rangle = \frac{250}{3}\langle -1/\sqrt{3}, 1, -2\rangle$. $x\overrightarrow{QS} = \frac{250}{3\sqrt{3}}\langle -1, -\sqrt{3}, -2\sqrt{3}\rangle = \frac{250}{3}\langle -1/\sqrt{3}, -1, -2\rangle$. $x\overrightarrow{RS} = \frac{250}{3\sqrt{3}}\langle 2, 0, -2\sqrt{3}\rangle = \frac{250}{3}\langle 2/\sqrt{3}, 0, -2\rangle$.

11.2.77 Let $R(x, y, z)$ be the fourth vertex. Then perhaps $\overrightarrow{OQ} = \overrightarrow{RP}$, so $\langle 2, 4, 3\rangle = \langle 1-x, 4-y, 6-z\rangle$, so $x = -1$, $y = 0$, and $z = 3$, so $R(-1, 0, 3)$ is one possible desired vertex. We could also have $\overrightarrow{RP} = -\overrightarrow{OQ}$, in which case $\langle -2, -4, -3\rangle = \langle 1-x, 4-y, 6-z\rangle$, so $R(3, 8, 9)$ is the other vertex. We could also have $\overrightarrow{OP} = \overrightarrow{RQ}$, so $\langle 1, 4, 6\rangle = \langle 2-x, 4-y, 3-z\rangle$ and $R(1, 0, -3)$ is the desired point.

11.2.79 Let $M(x, y, z)$ be the midpoint. Because $\overrightarrow{OM} = \overrightarrow{OP} + \frac{1}{2}\overrightarrow{PQ}$, we have $\langle x, y, z\rangle = \langle x_1, y_1, z_1\rangle + \frac{1}{2}(\langle x_2, y_2, z_2\rangle - \langle x_1, y_1, z_1\rangle) = \langle x_1, y_1, z_1\rangle + \langle \frac{1}{2}x_2, \frac{1}{2}y_2, \frac{1}{2}z_2\rangle + \langle -\frac{1}{2}x_1, -\frac{1}{2}y_1, -\frac{1}{2}z_1\rangle = \langle \frac{x_1+x_2}{2}, \frac{y_1+y_2}{2}, \frac{z_1+z_2}{2}\rangle$.

11.2.81

a. $\mathbf{u} + \mathbf{v} = -\mathbf{w}$ (by the geometric definition of vector addition), so $\mathbf{u} + \mathbf{v} + \mathbf{w} = \mathbf{0}$.

b. Let $\mathbf{M_1} = \overrightarrow{EB}$, $\mathbf{M_2} = \overrightarrow{FO}$, and $\mathbf{M_3} = \overrightarrow{GA}$. Consider triangle EAB. We have $\overrightarrow{EA} + \overrightarrow{AB} + \overrightarrow{BE} = \mathbf{0}$, so $\frac{1}{2}\mathbf{u} + \mathbf{v} = -\overrightarrow{BE} = \overrightarrow{EB} = \mathbf{M_1}$. Using similar arguments, we have $\mathbf{M_2} = \frac{1}{2}\mathbf{v} + \mathbf{w}$ and $\mathbf{M_3} = \frac{1}{2}\mathbf{w} + \mathbf{u}$.

c. Let $\mathbf{a}$, $\mathbf{b}$, and $\mathbf{c}$ be the vectors from O to the points $1/3$ of the way along $\mathbf{M_1}$, $\mathbf{M_2}$ and $\mathbf{M_3}$ respectively. Because $-\mathbf{w} = \mathbf{u} + \mathbf{v}$, we have $\frac{\mathbf{u}-\mathbf{w}}{3} = \frac{\mathbf{u}}{3} + \frac{\mathbf{u}+\mathbf{v}}{3} = \frac{2}{3}\mathbf{u} + \frac{1}{3}\mathbf{v}$. Also, $\mathbf{a} = \frac{1}{2}\mathbf{u} + \frac{1}{3}\mathbf{M_1} = \frac{1}{2}\mathbf{u} + \frac{1}{3}\left(\frac{1}{2}\mathbf{u} + \mathbf{v}\right) = \frac{1}{2}\mathbf{u} + \frac{1}{6}\mathbf{u} + \frac{1}{3}\mathbf{v} = \frac{2}{3}\mathbf{u} + \frac{1}{3}\mathbf{v}$. Thus $\mathbf{a} = \frac{\mathbf{u}-\mathbf{w}}{3}$. Also, $\mathbf{b} = -\frac{2}{3}\mathbf{M_2} = -\frac{2}{3}(\frac{1}{2}\mathbf{v} + (-\mathbf{u} - \mathbf{v})) = \frac{2}{3}\mathbf{u} + \frac{1}{3}\mathbf{v}$. We also have $\mathbf{c} = -\frac{1}{2}\mathbf{w} + \frac{1}{3}\mathbf{M_3} = -\frac{1}{2}\mathbf{w} + \frac{1}{3}(\frac{1}{2}\mathbf{w} + \mathbf{u}) = \frac{1}{3}\mathbf{u} + -\frac{1}{3}(-\mathbf{u} - \mathbf{v}) = \frac{2}{3}\mathbf{u} + \frac{1}{3}\mathbf{v}$. Thus $\mathbf{a} = \mathbf{b} = \mathbf{c}$.

d. Because $\mathbf{a} = \mathbf{b} = \mathbf{c}$, the medians all meet at a point that divides each median in a 2:1 ratio.

11.2.83

a. $\mathbf{u} + \mathbf{v} = \overrightarrow{PR}$ and $\mathbf{w} + \mathbf{x} = \mathbf{x} + \mathbf{w} = \overrightarrow{PR}$, so $\mathbf{u} + \mathbf{v} = \mathbf{w} + \mathbf{x}$.

b. $\frac{1}{2}\mathbf{u} + \frac{1}{2}\mathbf{v} = \mathbf{m} = \frac{1}{2}(\mathbf{u} + \mathbf{v})$.

c. $\frac{1}{2}\mathbf{x} + \frac{1}{2}\mathbf{w} = \mathbf{n} = \frac{1}{2}(\mathbf{x} + \mathbf{w})$.

d. We have $\mathbf{n} = \frac{1}{2}(\mathbf{x} + \mathbf{w}) = \frac{1}{2}(\mathbf{u} + \mathbf{v}) = \mathbf{m}$.

e. Because $\mathbf{m}$ and $\mathbf{n}$ are equal, they are parallel. A similar argument will show that the other two sides are parallel as well.

11.3 Dot Products

11.3.1 $\mathbf{u}\cdot\mathbf{v} = |\mathbf{u}|\,|\mathbf{v}|\cos\theta$, where θ is the angle between the two vectors.

11.3.3 $\langle 2,3,-6\rangle \cdot \langle 1,-8,3\rangle = 2\cdot 1 + 3\cdot(-8) + (-6)\cdot 3 = -40$.

11.3.5 Given non-zero vectors $\mathbf{u}$ and $\mathbf{v}$, the angle between them is $\cos^{-1}(\frac{\mathbf{u}\cdot\mathbf{v}}{|\mathbf{u}||\mathbf{v}|})$.

11.3.7 The scalar component of $\mathbf{u}$ in the direction of $\mathbf{v}$ is the number $|\mathbf{u}|\cos\theta$ where θ is the angle between the vectors. This number represents the signed length of the "shadow" that $\mathbf{u}$ casts on $\mathbf{v}$. Thus, referring to the diagram in the previous problem, the scalar projection is the length of the base of the shaded triangle.

11.3.9 $\mathbf{u}\cdot\mathbf{v} = 4\cdot 6\cdot\cos(\pi/2) = 0$.

11.3.11 The angle between these vectors is $\pi/4$. Thus, their dot product is $10\cdot 10\sqrt{2}\cdot\frac{\sqrt{2}}{2} = 100$.

11.3.13 $\mathbf{u}\cdot\mathbf{v} = |\mathbf{u}|\,|\mathbf{v}|\cos\theta = 1\cdot 1\cdot\cos(\pi/3) = 1/2$.

11.3.15 $\mathbf{u}\cdot\mathbf{v} = 1-1 = 0$, so $\theta = \cos^{-1}(0) = \pi/2$.

11.3.17 $\mathbf{u}\cdot\mathbf{v} = 1+0 = 1$, so $\theta = \cos^{-1}\left(\frac{1}{2}\right) = \pi/3$.

11.3.19 $\mathbf{u}\cdot\mathbf{v} = 4\cdot 4 + 3\cdot(-6) = -2$. The angle between the vectors is thus

$$\cos^{-1}\left(-\frac{2}{|\mathbf{u}|\,|\mathbf{v}|}\right) = \cos^{-1}\left(-\frac{2}{5\cdot 2\sqrt{13}}\right) \approx 1.627\,\text{radians}.$$

11.3.21 $\mathbf{u}\cdot\mathbf{v} = -10+0+12 = 2$. The angle between the vectors is thus

$$\cos^{-1}\left(\frac{2}{|\mathbf{u}|\,|\mathbf{v}|}\right) = \cos^{-1}\left(\frac{2}{\sqrt{116}\cdot\sqrt{14}}\right) \approx 1.521\,\text{radians}.$$

11.3.23 $\mathbf{u}\cdot\mathbf{v} = 2+0-6 = -4$. The angle between the vectors is thus

$$\cos^{-1}\left(-\frac{4}{|\mathbf{u}|\,|\mathbf{v}|}\right) = \cos^{-1}\left(-\frac{4}{\sqrt{13}\cdot\sqrt{21}}\right) \approx 1.815\,\text{radians}.$$

11.3.25 $\text{proj}_{\mathbf{v}}\mathbf{u} = 3\mathbf{i}$. $\text{scal}_{\mathbf{v}}\mathbf{u} = 3$.

11.3.27 $\text{proj}_{\mathbf{v}}\mathbf{u} = 3\mathbf{j}$. $\text{scal}_{\mathbf{v}}\mathbf{u} = 3$.

11.3.29 $\text{proj}_{\mathbf{v}}\mathbf{u} = \frac{\mathbf{u}\cdot\mathbf{v}}{\mathbf{v}\cdot\mathbf{v}}\mathbf{v} = \frac{12}{20}\langle -4,2\rangle = \langle -12/5, 6/5\rangle$. $\text{scal}_{\mathbf{v}}\mathbf{u} = \frac{\mathbf{u}\cdot\mathbf{v}}{|\mathbf{v}|} = \frac{12}{\sqrt{20}} = \frac{6}{\sqrt{5}}$.

11.3.31 $\text{proj}_{\mathbf{v}}\mathbf{u} = \frac{\mathbf{u}\cdot\mathbf{v}}{\mathbf{v}\cdot\mathbf{v}}\mathbf{v} = -\frac{6}{6}\langle 1,-1,2\rangle = \langle -1,1,2\rangle$. $\text{scal}_{\mathbf{v}}\mathbf{u} = \frac{\mathbf{u}\cdot\mathbf{v}}{|\mathbf{v}|} = -\frac{6}{\sqrt{6}} = -\sqrt{6}$.

11.3.33 $\text{proj}_{\mathbf{v}}\mathbf{u} = \frac{\mathbf{u}\cdot\mathbf{v}}{\mathbf{v}\cdot\mathbf{v}}\mathbf{v} = -\frac{14}{19}\langle 1,3,-3\rangle = \langle -14/19, -42/19, 42/19\rangle$. $\text{scal}_{\mathbf{v}}\mathbf{u} = \frac{\mathbf{u}\cdot\mathbf{v}}{|\mathbf{v}|} = -\frac{14}{\sqrt{19}}$.

11.3.35 $\text{proj}_{\mathbf{v}}\mathbf{u} = \frac{\mathbf{u}\cdot\mathbf{v}}{\mathbf{v}\cdot\mathbf{v}}\mathbf{v} = \frac{6}{6}\langle -1,1,-2\rangle = \langle -1,1,-2\rangle$. $\text{scal}_{\mathbf{v}}\mathbf{u} = \frac{\mathbf{u}\cdot\mathbf{v}}{|\mathbf{v}|} = \frac{6}{\sqrt{6}} = \sqrt{6}$.

11.3.37 $w = 30\cdot 50\cos\pi/6 = 750\sqrt{3}$ foot-pounds.

11.3.39 $w = 10\cdot 5\cdot\cos 45^\circ = 25\sqrt{2}$ J.

11.3.41 $w = (40\mathbf{i}+30\mathbf{j})\cdot 10\mathbf{i} = 400$ J.

11.3.43 Parallel to: use $\mathbf{v} = \langle\sqrt{2}/2, -\sqrt{2}/2\rangle$. $\text{proj}_{\mathbf{v}}\mathbf{F} = \frac{\mathbf{F}\cdot\mathbf{v}}{\mathbf{v}\cdot\mathbf{v}}\mathbf{v} = 5\sqrt{2}\langle\sqrt{2}/2, -\sqrt{2}/2\rangle = \langle 5,-5\rangle$.
Normal to: $\mathbf{N} = \langle 0,-10\rangle - \langle 5,-5\rangle = \langle -5,-5\rangle$.

11.3.45 Parallel to: use $\mathbf{v} = \langle 1/2, -\sqrt{3}/2\rangle$. $\text{proj}_{\mathbf{v}}\mathbf{F} = \frac{\mathbf{F}\cdot\mathbf{v}}{\mathbf{v}\cdot\mathbf{v}}\mathbf{v} = 5\sqrt{3}\langle 1/2, -\sqrt{3}/2\rangle = \langle 5\sqrt{3}/2, -15/2\rangle$.
Normal to: $\mathbf{N} = \langle 0, -10\rangle - \langle 5\sqrt{3}/2, -15/2\rangle = \langle -5\sqrt{3}/2, -5/2\rangle$.

11.3.47

a. False. One is a vector in the same direction as $\mathbf{u}$ and the other is a vector in the direction of $\mathbf{v}$, so if these vectors aren't in the same direction, they can't be equal.

b. True. This follows because $\mathbf{u}\cdot(\mathbf{u}+\mathbf{v}) = |\mathbf{u}|^2 + \mathbf{u}\cdot\mathbf{v}$ and $\mathbf{v}\cdot(\mathbf{u}+\mathbf{v}) = \mathbf{v}\cdot\mathbf{u} + |\mathbf{v}|^2$, and these are equal if $\mathbf{u}$ and $\mathbf{v}$ have the same magnitude.

c. True. Let $\mathbf{u} = \langle a, b, c\rangle$. Then $(\mathbf{u}\cdot\mathbf{i})^2 + (\mathbf{u}\cdot\mathbf{j})^2 + (\mathbf{u}\cdot\mathbf{k})^2 = a^2 + b^2 + c^2 = |\mathbf{u}|^2$.

d. False. For example, consider $\mathbf{u} = \langle 1, 0\rangle$, $\mathbf{v} = \langle 0, 1\rangle$, and $\mathbf{w} = \langle 2, 0\rangle$.

e. False. Consider $\langle 1, -1, 0\rangle$, $\langle 2, -1, -1\rangle$ and $\langle 3, -2, -1\rangle$. These are all orthogonal to $\langle 1, 1, 1\rangle$, but don't all lie in the same line.

f. True. If $\mathbf{u}$ and $\mathbf{v}$ are nonzero vectors, then $\text{proj}_{\mathbf{v}}\mathbf{u} = \frac{\mathbf{u}\cdot\mathbf{v}}{\mathbf{v}\cdot\mathbf{v}}\mathbf{v}$, and this can't be zero unless $\mathbf{u}\cdot\mathbf{v} = 0$.

11.3.49 We must have $4 - 8a + 2b = 0$, so $b = 4a - 2$. These vectors have the form $\langle 1, a, 4a - 2\rangle$ where a can be any real number.

11.3.51 Let $\mathbf{u} = \pm\langle \sqrt{2}/2, \sqrt{2}/2, 0\rangle$, $\mathbf{v} = \pm\langle -\sqrt{2}/2, \sqrt{2}/2, 0\rangle$ and $\mathbf{w} = \pm\langle 0, 0, 1\rangle$.

11.3.53

a. $\text{proj}_{\mathbf{k}}\mathbf{u} = \frac{\mathbf{u}\cdot\mathbf{k}}{\mathbf{k}\cdot\mathbf{k}}\mathbf{k} = \frac{|\mathbf{u}||\mathbf{k}|\cos\theta}{\mathbf{k}\cdot\mathbf{k}}\mathbf{k} = \frac{1}{2}\mathbf{k}$, which is independent of $\mathbf{u}$.

b. Yes, because the scalar projection is the length of the vector projection. In fact, using the above result, it is equal to $1/2$.

11.3.55 Using the idea from the last problem, any vector of the form $\langle x, y\rangle$ with $x + y = 3$ will work, so any vector of the form $\langle x, 3 - x\rangle$.

11.3.57 Note that $\text{proj}_{\mathbf{v}}\mathbf{u} = \frac{\langle 1,2,3\rangle\cdot\langle 0,0,1\rangle}{1}\langle 0, 0, 1\rangle = \langle 0, 0, 3\rangle$. We are seeking $\langle x, y, z\rangle$ so that $\frac{z}{1}\langle 0, 0, 1\rangle = \langle 0, 0, 3\rangle$, so we require $z = 3$. Any vector of the form $\langle x, y, 3\rangle$ will suffice.

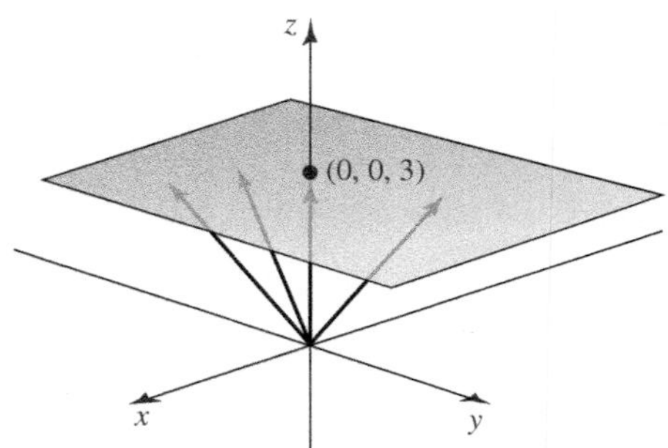

11.3.59 Let $\mathbf{p} = \text{proj}_{\mathbf{v}}\mathbf{u} = -\frac{2}{5}\langle 2, 1\rangle$. Then let $\mathbf{n} = \mathbf{u} - \mathbf{p} = \langle -2, 2\rangle - -\frac{2}{5}\langle 2, 1\rangle = \langle -6/5, 12/5\rangle$.

11.3.61 Let $\mathbf{p} = \text{proj}_{\mathbf{v}}\mathbf{u} = \frac{1}{2}\langle 2, 1, 1\rangle$. Then let $\mathbf{n} = \mathbf{u} - \mathbf{p} = \langle -1, 2, 3\rangle - \frac{1}{2}\langle 2, 1, 1\rangle = \langle -2, 3/2, 5/2\rangle$.

11.3.63

a. $\mathbf{v} = \langle 1, 2\rangle$.

b. $\mathbf{u} = \langle -12, 4\rangle$.

c. $\text{proj}_{\mathbf{v}}\mathbf{u} = -\frac{4}{5}\langle 1, 2\rangle$.

d. $\mathbf{w} = \mathbf{u} - \text{proj}_{\mathbf{v}}\mathbf{u} = \langle -12, 4\rangle - \langle -4/5, -8/5\rangle = \langle -56/5, 28/5\rangle$. Note that $\mathbf{w}\cdot\mathbf{v} = 0$, and has length equal to the distance between P and l.

e. $|\mathbf{w}| = \frac{1}{5}\sqrt{(56)^2 + (28)^2} = \frac{28\sqrt{5}}{5}$. $|\mathbf{w}|$ is the component of $\mathbf{u}$ orthogonal to $\mathbf{v}$, so it is the distance from P to l.

11.3.65

a. $\mathbf{v} = \langle -6, 8, 3\rangle$.

b. $\mathbf{u} = \langle 1, 1, -1\rangle$.

c. $\text{proj}_{\mathbf{v}}\mathbf{u} = -\frac{1}{109}\langle -6, 8, 3\rangle$.

d. $\mathbf{w} = \mathbf{u} - \text{proj}_{\mathbf{v}}\mathbf{u} = \langle 1, 1, -1\rangle - -\frac{1}{109}\langle -6, 8, 3\rangle = \langle 103/109, 117/109, -106/109\rangle$. Note that $\mathbf{w}\cdot\mathbf{v} = 0$, and has length equal to the distance between P and l.

e. $|\mathbf{w}| = \frac{1}{109}\sqrt{(103)^2 + (117)^2 + (-106)^2} = \sqrt{\frac{326}{109}}$. $|\mathbf{w}|$ is the component of $\mathbf{u}$ orthogonal to $\mathbf{v}$, so it is the distance from P to l.

11.3.67 $\mathbf{I} = \langle 1/\sqrt{2}, 1/\sqrt{2}\rangle = \frac{1}{\sqrt{2}}\mathbf{i} + \frac{1}{\sqrt{2}}\mathbf{j}$. $\mathbf{J} = \langle -1/\sqrt{2}, 1/\sqrt{2}\rangle = -\frac{1}{\sqrt{2}}\mathbf{i} + \frac{1}{\sqrt{2}}\mathbf{j}$. $\mathbf{i} = \langle 1, 0\rangle = \frac{\sqrt{2}}{2}(\mathbf{I} - \mathbf{J})$. $\mathbf{j} = \frac{\sqrt{2}}{2}(\mathbf{I} + \mathbf{J})$.

11.3.69

a. $|\mathbf{I}| = \sqrt{1/4 + 1/4 + 1/2} = 1$. $|\mathbf{J}| = \sqrt{1/2 + 1/2 + 0} = 1$. $|\mathbf{K}| = \sqrt{1/4 + 1/4 + 1/2} = 1$.

b. $\mathbf{I}\cdot\mathbf{J} = -1/2\sqrt{2} + 1/2\sqrt{2} = 0$. $\mathbf{I}\cdot\mathbf{K} = 1/4 + 1/4 - 1/2 = 0$, and $\mathbf{J}\cdot\mathbf{K} = -1/2\sqrt{2} + 1/2\sqrt{2} = 0$.

c. Let $\langle 1, 0, 0\rangle = a\mathbf{I} + b\mathbf{J} + c\mathbf{K}$. Then $\frac{1}{2}a - \frac{1}{\sqrt{2}}b + \frac{1}{2}c = 1$, $\frac{1}{2}a + \frac{1}{\sqrt{2}}b + \frac{1}{2}c = 0$, and $\frac{1}{\sqrt{2}}a - \frac{1}{\sqrt{2}}c = 0$. Solving this system of linear equations yields $a = \frac{1}{2}$, $b = -\frac{1}{\sqrt{2}}$, and $c = \frac{1}{2}$. Thus, $\langle 1, 0, 0\rangle = \frac{1}{2}\mathbf{I} + -\frac{1}{\sqrt{2}}\mathbf{J} + \frac{1}{2}\mathbf{K}$.

11.3.71 Note that $\overrightarrow{PQ} = \langle 2, 3, -2\rangle$, $\overrightarrow{QR} = \langle -4, 0, 3\rangle$, and $\overrightarrow{RP} = \langle 2, -3, -1\rangle$, and these have lengths $\sqrt{17}$, 5 and $\sqrt{14}$ respectively.

The angle at P measures $\cos^{-1}(\frac{3}{\sqrt{17}\sqrt{14}}) \approx 78.8$ degrees. The angle at Q measures $\cos^{-1}(\frac{14}{5\sqrt{17}}) \approx 47.2$ degrees, and the angle at R measures $\cos^{-1}(\frac{11}{5\sqrt{14}}) \approx 54$ degrees.

11.3.73

a. The faces on $y = 0$ and $z = 0$.

b. The faces on $y = 1$ and $z = 1$.

c. The faces on $x = 0$ and $x = 1$.

d. Because $\mathbf{Q}$ is tangential on this face, the scalar component of $\mathbf{Q}$ normal to the face is 0.

e. The scalar component of $\mathbf{Q}$ normal to $z = 1$ is 1. Note that a vector normal to $z = 1$ is $\langle 0, 0, 1\rangle$.

f. The scalar component of $\mathbf{Q}$ normal to $y = 0$ is 2. Note that a vector normal to $y = 0$ is $\langle 0, 1, 0\rangle$.

11.3.75

a. Let the coordinates of R be (x, y, z). By symmetry, we have $y = 0$. We must have $x^2 + y^2 + z^2 = (x - \sqrt{3})^2 + (y+1)^2 + z^2 = (x - \sqrt{3})^2 + (y-1)^2 + z^2 = 4$. The first equality gives $x^2 + z^2 = x^2 - 2\sqrt{3}x + 3 + 1 + z^2$, so $2\sqrt{3}x = 4$, and $x = \frac{2}{\sqrt{3}}$. It then follows that $z = \frac{2\sqrt{2}}{\sqrt{3}}$.

b. We have $\mathbf{r}_{OP} = \langle \sqrt{3}, -1, 0\rangle$, $\mathbf{r}_{OQ} = \langle \sqrt{3}, 1, 0\rangle$, $\mathbf{r}_{PQ} = \langle 0, 2, 0\rangle$, $\mathbf{r}_{OR} = \langle 2/\sqrt{3}, 0, 2\sqrt{2}/\sqrt{3}\rangle$, and $\mathbf{r}_{PR} = \langle -\sqrt{3}/3, 1, 2\sqrt{2}/\sqrt{3}\rangle$.

11.3.77 $\mathbf{u}\cdot\mathbf{v} = u_1v_1 + u_2v_2 + u_3v_3 = v_1u_1 + v_2u_2 + v_3u_3 = \mathbf{v}\cdot\mathbf{u}$.

11.3.79 $\mathbf{u}(\mathbf{v}+\mathbf{w}) = \langle u_1, u_2, u_3\rangle \cdot \langle v_1 + w_1, v_2 + w_2, v_3 + w_3\rangle = u_1(v_1 + w_1) + u_2(v_2 + w_2) + u_3(v_3 + w_3) = u_1v_1 + u_1w_1 + u_2v_2 + u_2w_2 + u_3v_3 + u_3w_3 = (u_1v_1 + u_2v_2 + u_3v_3) + (u_1w_1 + u_2w_2 + u_3w_3) = (\mathbf{u}\cdot\mathbf{v}) + (\mathbf{u}\cdot\mathbf{w})$.

11.3.81 The statement is true. We have $\text{proj}_{\langle ka,kb\rangle}\langle c, d\rangle = \frac{\langle c,d\rangle\cdot\langle ka,kb\rangle}{(ka)^2+(kb)^2}\langle ka, kb\rangle = \frac{k(\langle a,b\rangle\cdot\langle c,d\rangle)}{k^2(a^2+b^2)}\cdot k\langle a, b\rangle = \frac{\langle a,b\rangle\cdot\langle c,d\rangle}{(a^2+b^2)}\langle a, b\rangle = \text{proj}_{\langle a,b\rangle}\langle c, d\rangle$.

11.3.83

a. $\cos\alpha = \frac{a}{\sqrt{a^2+b^2+c^2}}$, $\cos\beta = \frac{b}{\sqrt{a^2+b^2+c^2}}$, and $\cos\gamma = \frac{c}{\sqrt{a^2+b^2+c^2}}$. Thus, $\cos^2\alpha + \cos^2\beta + \cos^2\gamma = \frac{a^2}{a^2+b^2+c^2} + \frac{b^2}{a^2+b^2+c^2} + \frac{c^2}{a^2+b^2+c^2} = 1$.

b. We require $\cos^2\alpha + \cos^2\beta + \cos^2\gamma = \frac{1}{2} + \frac{1}{2} + \cos^2\gamma = 1$, so $\gamma = 90°$. The vector could be $\langle 1, 1, 0\rangle$; it makes a 90 degree angle with $\mathbf{k}$.

c. We require $\cos^2\alpha + \cos^2\beta + \cos^2\gamma = \frac{1}{4} + \frac{1}{4} + \cos^2\gamma = 1$, so $\gamma = 45°$. The vector could be $\langle 1, 1, \sqrt{2}\rangle$; it makes a 45 degree angle with $\mathbf{k}$.

d. No. If so, we would have $\cos^2\alpha + \cos^2\beta + \cos^2\gamma = \frac{3}{4} + \frac{3}{4} + \cos^2\gamma = 1$, which would imply that $\cos^2\gamma = -\frac{1}{2}$, which can't occur.

e. If $\alpha = \beta = \gamma$, then $3\cos^2\alpha = 1$, and $\alpha = \cos^{-1}(\sqrt{3}/3) \approx 54.7356$ degrees. The vector could be $\langle 1, 1, 1\rangle$.

11.3.85 $\mathbf{u}\cdot\mathbf{v} = -24 - 15 + 6 = -33$. $|\mathbf{u}| = \sqrt{3^2 + (-5)^2 + 6^2} = \sqrt{70}$. $|\mathbf{v}| = \sqrt{(-8)^2 + 3^2 + 1^2} = \sqrt{74}$. Note that

$$33 < \sqrt{70}\sqrt{74},$$

so $|\mathbf{u}\cdot\mathbf{v}| < |\mathbf{u}|\,|\mathbf{v}|$.

11.3.87

a. We have $|\mathbf{u}+\mathbf{v}|^2 = (\mathbf{u}+\mathbf{v})\cdot(\mathbf{u}+\mathbf{v}) = (\mathbf{u}+\mathbf{v})\cdot\mathbf{u} + (\mathbf{u}+\mathbf{v})\cdot\mathbf{v} = \mathbf{u}\cdot(\mathbf{u}+\mathbf{v}) + \mathbf{v}\cdot(\mathbf{u}+\mathbf{v}) = \mathbf{u}\cdot\mathbf{u} + \mathbf{u}\cdot\mathbf{v} + \mathbf{v}\cdot\mathbf{u} + \mathbf{v}\cdot\mathbf{v} = |\mathbf{u}|^2 + 2(\mathbf{u}\cdot\mathbf{v}) + |\mathbf{v}|^2$

b. Note that $2(\mathbf{u}\cdot\mathbf{v}) \le 2\,|\mathbf{u}\cdot\mathbf{v}| \le 2\,|\mathbf{u}|\,|\mathbf{v}|$. Thus (using the previous part) we have,

$$|\mathbf{u}+\mathbf{v}|^2 = |\mathbf{u}|^2 + 2(\mathbf{u}\cdot\mathbf{v}) + |\mathbf{v}|^2 \le |\mathbf{u}|^2 + 2\,|\mathbf{u}|\,|\mathbf{v}| + |\mathbf{v}|^2 \le (|\mathbf{u}| + |\mathbf{v}|)^2.$$

c. Taking square roots of the previous result, and using the fact that the square root function is strictly increasing, we have $|\mathbf{u}+\mathbf{v}| \le |\mathbf{u}| + |\mathbf{v}|$.

d. Because the vectors $\mathbf{u}$, $\mathbf{v}$ and $\mathbf{u}+\mathbf{v}$ form a triangle, we can interpret this as meaning that the sum of the lengths of any two sides of a triangle is greater than or equal to the length of the other side.

11.3.89

a. One diagonal consists of the sum of one side ($\mathbf{u}$) and the side opposite the side adjacent to $\mathbf{u}$, but because it is a parallelogram, the side opposite $\mathbf{v}$ is also $\mathbf{v}$. So the diagonal is $\mathbf{u}+\mathbf{v}$. The other diagonal is the difference of two adjacent sides, so it is $\mathbf{u}-\mathbf{v}$.

b. The two diagonals are equal when $|\mathbf{u}+\mathbf{v}| = |\mathbf{u}-\mathbf{v}|$. Squaring both sides, we see that this is equivalent to requiring $|\mathbf{u}|^2 + 2(\mathbf{u}\cdot\mathbf{v}) + |\mathbf{v}|^2 = |\mathbf{u}|^2 - 2(\mathbf{u}\cdot\mathbf{v}) + |\mathbf{v}|^2$, which would imply that $2(\mathbf{u}\cdot\mathbf{v}) = -2(\mathbf{u}\cdot\mathbf{v})$, or $4(\mathbf{u}\cdot\mathbf{v}) = 0$. So if the diagonals are equal, the vectors are orthogonal. These steps are reversible, so the converse is also true.

c. $|\mathbf{u}+\mathbf{v}|^2 + |\mathbf{u}-\mathbf{v}|^2 = |\mathbf{u}|^2 + 2(\mathbf{u}\cdot\mathbf{v}) + |\mathbf{v}|^2 + |\mathbf{u}|^2 - 2(\mathbf{u}\cdot\mathbf{v}) + |\mathbf{v}|^2 = 2(|\mathbf{u}|^2 + |\mathbf{v}|^2)$.

11.4 Cross Products

11.4.1 $|\mathbf{u} \times \mathbf{v}| = |\mathbf{u}|\,|\mathbf{v}| \sin\theta$, where θ is the angle between $\mathbf{u}$ and $\mathbf{v}$.

11.4.3 Two parallel vectors have $\sin\theta = 0$ where θ is the angle between them. Thus, $|\mathbf{u} \times \mathbf{v}| = |\mathbf{u}|\,|\mathbf{v}| \sin\theta = 0$.

11.4.5 If $\mathbf{u} = \langle u_1, u_2, u_3 \rangle$ and $\mathbf{v} = \langle v_1, v_2, v_3 \rangle$, then $\mathbf{u} \times \mathbf{v}$ can be thought of as the determinant of the matrix

$$\begin{bmatrix} \mathbf{i} & \mathbf{j} & \mathbf{k} \\ u_1 & u_2 & u_3 \\ v_1 & v_2 & v_3 \end{bmatrix}.$$

11.4.7 $\mathbf{u} \times \mathbf{v} = \langle 3, 0, 0 \rangle \times \langle 0, 5, 0 \rangle = \langle 0, 0, 15 \rangle$.

11.4.9 $\mathbf{u} \times \mathbf{v} = \langle 0, 0, 0 \rangle$, so $|\mathbf{u} \times \mathbf{v}| = 0$.

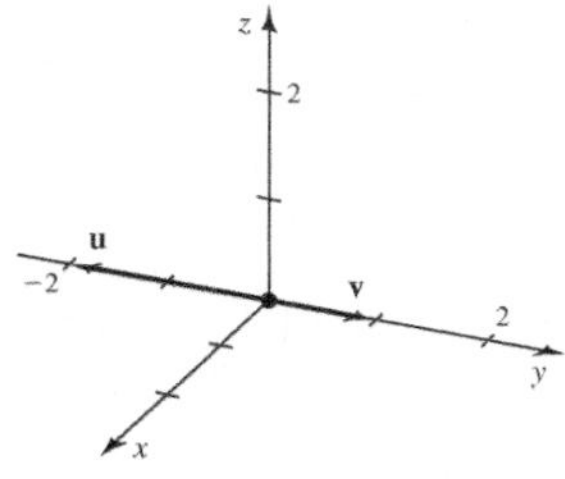

11.4.11 $\mathbf{u} \times \mathbf{v} = \langle 9\sqrt{2}, -9\sqrt{2}, 0 \rangle$, so $|\mathbf{u} \times \mathbf{v}| = 18$.

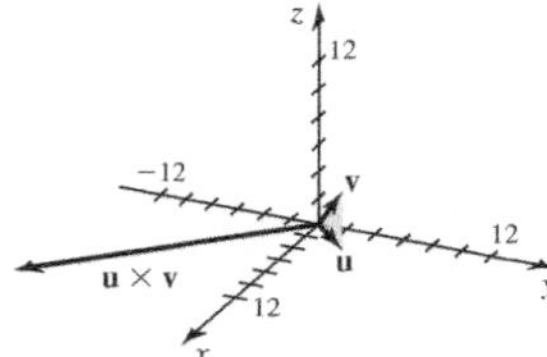

11.4.13 $|\mathbf{u} \times \mathbf{v}| = |\mathbf{u}|\,|\mathbf{v}| \sin(\pi/4) = \sqrt{2}/2$.

11.4.15 $\mathbf{j} \times \mathbf{k} = \mathbf{i}$.

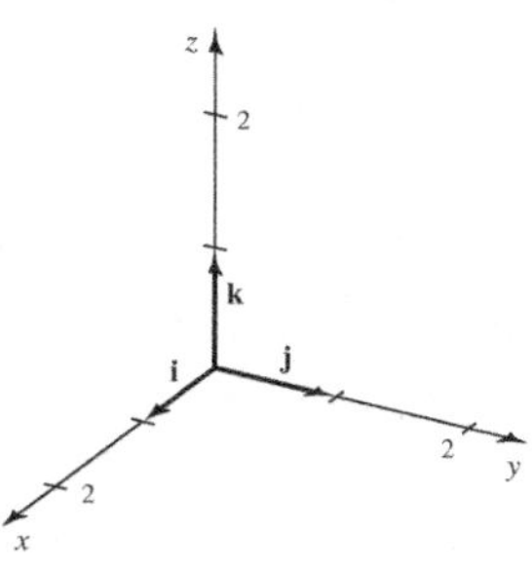

11.4.17 $-\mathbf{j} \times \mathbf{k} = -\mathbf{i}$.

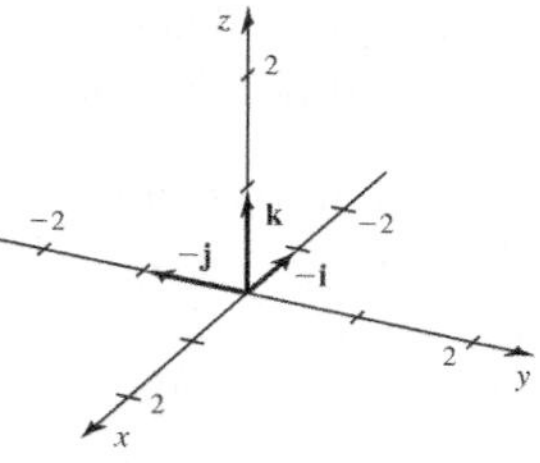

11.4.19 $-2\mathbf{i} \times 3\mathbf{k} = 6\mathbf{j}$.

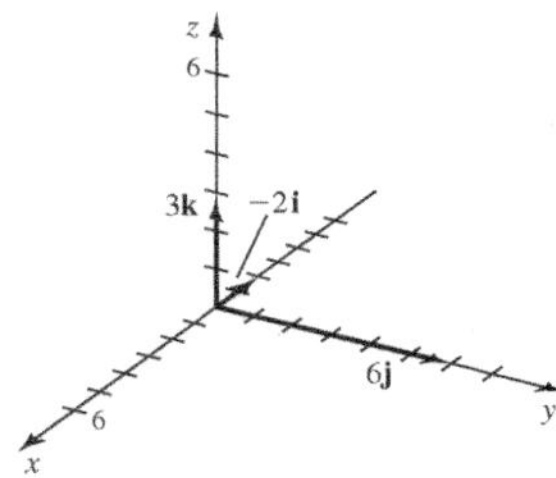

11.4.21 $|\mathbf{u} \times \mathbf{v}| = |\langle -2, -6, 9\rangle| = \sqrt{4+36+81} = 11$.

11.4.23 $|\mathbf{u} \times \mathbf{v}| = |\langle 5, -4, 7\rangle| = \sqrt{25+16+49} = 3\sqrt{10}$.

11.4.25 $\frac{1}{2} \cdot \left|\overrightarrow{AB} \times \overrightarrow{AC}\right| = \frac{1}{2} \cdot |\langle 3,0,1\rangle \times \langle 1,1,0\rangle| = \frac{1}{2} \cdot |\langle -1,1,3\rangle| = \frac{\sqrt{11}}{2}$.

11.4.27 $\frac{1}{2} \cdot \left|\overrightarrow{AB} \times \overrightarrow{AC}\right| = \frac{1}{2} \cdot |\langle 2,10,2\rangle \times \langle 1,1,1\rangle| = \frac{1}{2} \cdot |\langle 8,0,-8\rangle| = 4\sqrt{2}$.

11.4.29 $\mathbf{u} \times \mathbf{v} = \begin{vmatrix} \mathbf{i} & \mathbf{j} & \mathbf{k} \\ 3 & 5 & 0 \\ 0 & 3 & -6 \end{vmatrix} = \langle -30, 18, 9\rangle$. $\mathbf{v} \times \mathbf{u} = \langle 30, -18, -9\rangle$.

11.4.31 $\mathbf{u} \times \mathbf{v} = \begin{vmatrix} \mathbf{i} & \mathbf{j} & \mathbf{k} \\ 2 & 3 & -9 \\ -1 & 1 & -1 \end{vmatrix} = \langle 6, 11, 5\rangle$. $\mathbf{v} \times \mathbf{u} = \langle -6, -11, -5\rangle$.

11.4.33 $\mathbf{u} \times \mathbf{v} = \begin{vmatrix} \mathbf{i} & \mathbf{j} & \mathbf{k} \\ 3 & -1 & -2 \\ 1 & 3 & -2 \end{vmatrix} = \langle 8, 4, 10\rangle$. $\mathbf{v} \times \mathbf{u} = \langle -8, -4, -10\rangle$.

11.4.35 Let $\mathbf{u} = \langle 0,1,2\rangle$ and $\mathbf{v} = \langle -2,0,3\rangle$. $\mathbf{u} \times \mathbf{v} = \begin{vmatrix} \mathbf{i} & \mathbf{j} & \mathbf{k} \\ 0 & 1 & 2 \\ -2 & 0 & 3 \end{vmatrix} = \langle 3, -4, 2\rangle$ is perpendicular to both $\mathbf{u}$ and $\mathbf{v}$.

11.4.37 Let $\mathbf{u} = \langle 8,0,4\rangle$ and $\mathbf{v} = \langle -8,2,1\rangle$. $\mathbf{u} \times \mathbf{v} = \begin{vmatrix} \mathbf{i} & \mathbf{j} & \mathbf{k} \\ 8 & 0 & 4 \\ -8 & 2 & 1 \end{vmatrix} = \langle -8, -40, 16\rangle$ is perpendicular to both $\mathbf{u}$ and $\mathbf{v}$.

11.4.39 $|\tau| = |\mathbf{r} \times \mathbf{F}| = |\mathbf{r}|\,|\mathbf{F}| \sin\theta = \frac{1}{4} \cdot 20 \cdot \frac{\sqrt{2}}{2} = \frac{5\sqrt{2}}{2}\,\mathrm{N} \cdot \mathrm{m}$.

11.4.41 $\boldsymbol{\tau} = \mathbf{r} \times \mathbf{F} = \begin{vmatrix} \mathbf{i} & \mathbf{j} & \mathbf{k} \\ 1 & 1 & 1 \\ 20 & 0 & 0 \end{vmatrix} = \langle 0, 20, -20\rangle$.

11.4.43 $\boldsymbol{\tau} = \mathbf{r} \times \mathbf{F} = \begin{vmatrix} \mathbf{i} & \mathbf{j} & \mathbf{k} \\ 10 & 0 & 0 \\ 5 & 0 & -5 \end{vmatrix} = \langle 0, 50, 0\rangle$ has magntitude 50, while $\boldsymbol{\tau} = \mathbf{r} \times \mathbf{F} = \begin{vmatrix} \mathbf{i} & \mathbf{j} & \mathbf{k} \\ 10 & 0 & 0 \\ 4 & -3 & 0 \end{vmatrix} =$ $\langle 0, 0, -30\rangle$ has magnitude 30, so the first force has greater magnitude.

11.4.45
$$\mathbf{F} = 1 \cdot (\mathbf{v} \times \mathbf{B}) = \begin{vmatrix} \mathbf{i} & \mathbf{j} & \mathbf{k} \\ 0 & 0 & 20 \\ 1 & 1 & 0 \end{vmatrix} = \langle -20, 20, 0 \rangle.$$

The magnitude of $\mathbf{F}$ is $20\sqrt{2}$ and the angle of the force is 135 degrees with the positive x axis in the xy-plane.

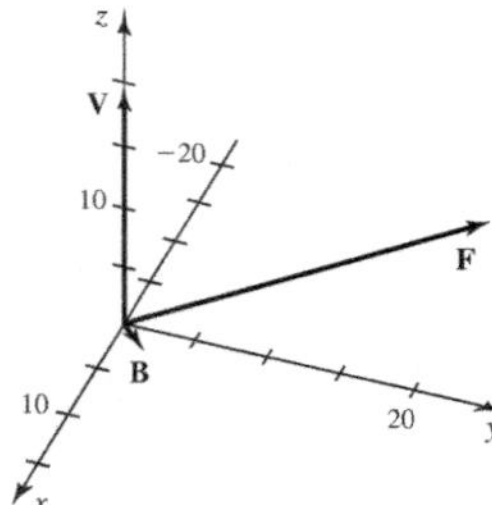

11.4.47 $|\mathbf{F}| = |q(\mathbf{v} \times \mathbf{B})| = \left|-1.6 \cdot 10^{-19}\right| \text{ C} \cdot 2 \cdot 10^5 \cdot 2 \cdot \sin 45° = 4.53 \cdot 10^{-14} \text{ kg} \cdot \text{m/s}^2$.

11.4.49

a. False. For example $\mathbf{i} \times \mathbf{i} = \langle 0, 0, 0 \rangle$, even though $\mathbf{i} \neq \langle 0, 0, 0 \rangle$.

b. False. For example, $2\mathbf{i} \times 4\mathbf{j} = 8\mathbf{k}$ has magnitude 8, while $2\mathbf{i}$ has magnitude 2 and $4\mathbf{j}$ has magnitude 4.

c. False. If the compass directions are thought to lie in a plane, $\mathbf{u} \times \mathbf{v}$ doesn't lie in that plane, so it can't be a compass direction.

d. True. If both were nonzero, the first statement implies that the vectors are parallel, and the second that they are perpendicular, which can't both occur. So at least one of the vectors must be the zero vector.

e. False. $\mathbf{i} \times 2\mathbf{i} = \langle 0, 0, 0 \rangle = \mathbf{i} \times 3\mathbf{i}$, but $2\mathbf{i} \neq 3\mathbf{i}$.

11.4.51 $\overrightarrow{AB} \times \overrightarrow{AC} = \langle 4, 6, 6 \rangle \times \langle 7, 12, 13 \rangle \neq \langle 0, 0, 0 \rangle$, so the points are not collinear.

11.4.53 Note that $\langle a, b, a \rangle \times \langle b, a, b \rangle = \langle -a^2 + b^2, 0, a^2 - b^2 \rangle$. This is the zero vector when $a = \pm b$, so the vectors are parallel when $a = \pm b$, $a, b \neq 0$.

11.4.55 The area is $\frac{1}{2}\,|\mathbf{u} \times \mathbf{v}| = \frac{1}{2} \left\| \begin{vmatrix} \mathbf{i} & \mathbf{j} & \mathbf{k} \\ 3 & 3 & 3 \\ 6 & 0 & 6 \end{vmatrix} \right\| = \frac{1}{2}\,|\langle 18, 0, -18 \rangle| = 9\sqrt{2}$.

11.4.57 Two of the sides are $\mathbf{u} = \langle 1, 2, 3 \rangle$ and $\mathbf{v} = \langle 6, 5, 4 \rangle$.

The area is $\frac{1}{2}\,|\mathbf{u} \times \mathbf{v}| = \frac{1}{2} \left\| \begin{vmatrix} \mathbf{i} & \mathbf{j} & \mathbf{k} \\ 1 & 2 & 3 \\ 6 & 5 & 4 \end{vmatrix} \right\| = \frac{1}{2}\,|\langle -7, 14, -7 \rangle| = \frac{7\sqrt{6}}{2}$.

11.4.59 Let $\mathbf{u} = \langle u_1, u_2, u_3 \rangle$. Then we have

$$\begin{vmatrix} \mathbf{i} & \mathbf{j} & \mathbf{k} \\ 1 & 1 & 1 \\ u_1 & u_2 & u_3 \end{vmatrix} = \langle -1, -1, 2 \rangle,$$

so $u_3 - u_2 = -1$, $u_1 - u_3 = -1$, and $u_2 - u_1 = 2$. The solutions to this system of linear equation can be characterized by letting u_1 be arbitrary, and by letting $u_2 = u_1 + 2$ and $u_3 = u_1 + 1$. Thus, $\mathbf{u} = \langle u_1, u_1 + 2, u_1 + 1 \rangle$ for any real number u_1.

11.4.61 Two of the sides of the triangle are $\mathbf{u} = \langle -a, b, 0 \rangle$ and $\mathbf{v} = \langle -a, 0, c \rangle$.

The area is $\frac{1}{2}\,|\mathbf{u} \times \mathbf{v}| = \frac{1}{2} \left\| \begin{vmatrix} \mathbf{i} & \mathbf{j} & \mathbf{k} \\ -a & b & 0 \\ -a & 0 & c \end{vmatrix} \right\| = \frac{1}{2}\,|\langle bc, ac, ab \rangle| = \frac{1}{2}\sqrt{b^2c^2 + a^2c^2 + a^2b^2}$.

11.4.63 $|\mathbf{u}\cdot(\mathbf{v}\times\mathbf{w})| = |\mathbf{u}|\,|\mathbf{v}\times\mathbf{w}|\,|\cos\theta|$. Because $|\mathbf{v}\times\mathbf{w}|$ represents the area of the base, we just need to see that the height of the parallelepiped is $|\mathbf{u}|\,|\cos\theta|$. Note that the height is given by the scalar projection of $\mathbf{u}$ on $\mathbf{v}\times\mathbf{w}$, which has value $|\cos\theta|\,|\mathbf{u}|$. Thus the given expression represents the volume of the parallelepiped.

11.4.65 Note that $\mathbf{r} = .66\mathbf{k}$, and $\mathbf{F} = 40\mathbf{j}$. $\boldsymbol{\tau} = \mathbf{r}\times\mathbf{F} = \begin{vmatrix} \mathbf{i} & \mathbf{j} & \mathbf{k} \\ 0 & 0 & 0.66 \\ 0 & 40 & 0 \end{vmatrix} = \langle -26.4, 0, 0\rangle$. The magnitude of the torque is 26.4 Newton-meters and the direction is on the negative x axis.

11.4.67 Because $\mathbf{F} = q(\mathbf{v}\times\mathbf{B})$, we have $|\mathbf{F}| = |q|\,|\mathbf{v}|\,|\mathbf{B}|\sin\theta$. Thus, $\frac{m|\mathbf{v}|^2}{R} = |q|\,|\mathbf{v}|\,|\mathbf{B}|\sin\pi/2$. Therefore,

$$|\mathbf{v}| = \frac{R\,|q|\,|\mathbf{B}|}{m} = \frac{0.002\cdot 1.6\cdot 10^{-19}\cdot .05}{9\cdot 10^{-31}} \approx 1.758\cdot 10^{7}\text{ m/s}.$$

11.4.69 The result is trivial if either $a = 0$ or $b = 0$, so assume $ab \neq 0$. Note that the sine of the angle between $a\mathbf{u}$ and $b\mathbf{v}$ is the same as the sine of the angle between $\mathbf{u}$ and $\mathbf{v}$, as is demonstrated in the following diagrams.

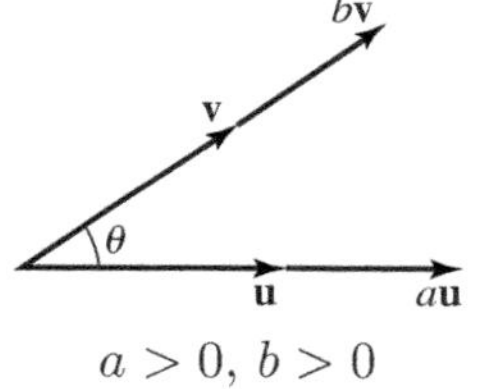

$a > 0,\ b > 0$

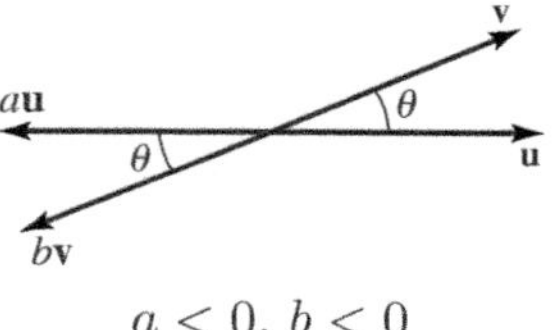

$a < 0,\ b < 0$

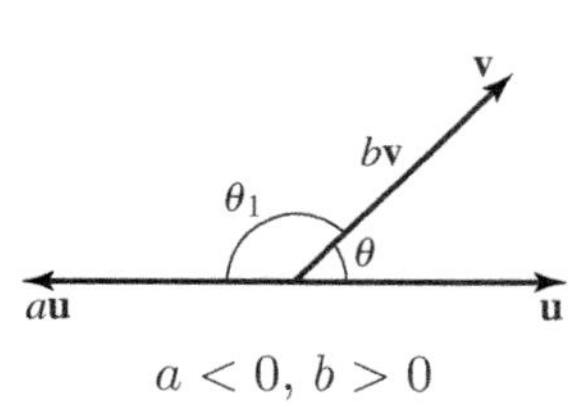

$a < 0,\ b > 0$

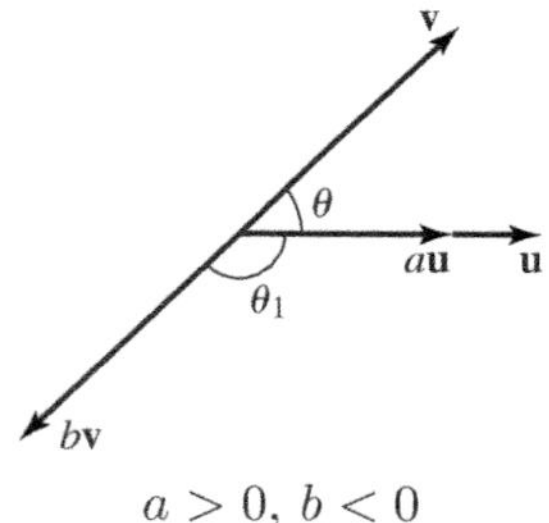

$a > 0,\ b < 0$

By the definition: $|(a\mathbf{u})\times(b\mathbf{v})| = |a\mathbf{u}|\,|b\mathbf{v}|\sin\theta$, where θ is the angle between $a\mathbf{u}$ and $b\mathbf{v}$. But this is equal to $|a|\,|\mathbf{u}|\,|b|\,|\mathbf{v}|\sin\theta = |ab|\,(|\mathbf{u}|\,|\mathbf{v}|\sin\theta) = |ab|\,(|\mathbf{u}\times\mathbf{v}|)$. When a and b have the same sign, the directions are also the same, because they are determined by the right-hand rule (see diagrams above.) When a and b have opposite signs, the directions are opposite, but then $ab < 0$.

Using the determinant formula:

$$(a\mathbf{u})\times(b\mathbf{v}) = \begin{vmatrix} \mathbf{i} & \mathbf{j} & \mathbf{k} \\ au_1 & au_2 & au_3 \\ bv_1 & bv_2 & bv_3 \end{vmatrix} = ab\begin{vmatrix} \mathbf{i} & \mathbf{j} & \mathbf{k} \\ u_1 & u_2 & u_3 \\ v_1 & v_2 & v_3 \end{vmatrix} = ab(\mathbf{u}\times\mathbf{v}).$$

11.4.71 True. $(\mathbf{u}-\mathbf{v})\times(\mathbf{u}+\mathbf{v}) = \mathbf{u}\times\mathbf{u}+\mathbf{u}\times\mathbf{v}-(\mathbf{v}\times\mathbf{u})-(\mathbf{v}\times\mathbf{v}) = 2(\mathbf{u}\times\mathbf{v}) = (2\mathbf{u}\times\mathbf{v})$.

11.4.73

$$\mathbf{u}\times(\mathbf{v}\times\mathbf{w}) = \begin{vmatrix} \mathbf{i} & \mathbf{j} & \mathbf{k} \\ u_1 & u_2 & u_3 \\ v_2w_3 - v_3w_2 & v_3w_1 - v_1w_3 & v_1w_2 - v_2w_1 \end{vmatrix}$$
$$= \langle u_2(v_1w_2 - v_2w_1) - u_3(v_3w_1 - v_1w_3), u_3(v_2w_3 - v_3w_2)$$
$$- u_1(v_1w_2 - v_2w_1), u_1(v_3w_1 - v_1w_3) - u_2(v_2w_3 - v_3w_2)\rangle$$
$$= \langle v_1(u_2w_2 + u_3w_3) - w_1(u_2v_2 + u_3v_3), v_2(u_1w_1 + u_3w_3)$$
$$- w_2(u_1v_1 + u_3v_3), v_3(u_1w_1 + u_2w_2) - w_3(u_1v_1 + u_2v_2)\rangle$$
$$= \langle v_1(\mathbf{u}\cdot\mathbf{w}) - w_1(\mathbf{u}\cdot\mathbf{v}), v_2(\mathbf{u}\cdot\mathbf{w}) - w_2(\mathbf{u}\cdot\mathbf{v}), v_3(\mathbf{u}\cdot\mathbf{w}) - w_3(\mathbf{u}\cdot\mathbf{w})\rangle$$
$$= (\mathbf{u}\cdot\mathbf{w})\mathbf{v} - (\mathbf{u}\cdot\mathbf{w})\mathbf{w}.$$

11.4.75

a. Suppose $\mathbf{u}\times\mathbf{z} = \mathbf{v}$. Then $\mathbf{v}\times(\mathbf{u}\times\mathbf{z}) = \mathbf{v}\times\mathbf{v} = \langle 0,0,0\rangle$. Now $\mathbf{v}\times(\mathbf{u}\times\mathbf{z}) = \mathbf{u}(\mathbf{v}\cdot\mathbf{z}) - \mathbf{z}(\mathbf{v}\cdot\mathbf{u})$ by exercise 65. If $\mathbf{u}\cdot\mathbf{v} = 0$, then we have $\mathbf{u}(\mathbf{v}\cdot\mathbf{z}) = \langle 0,0,0\rangle$. Any vector $\mathbf{z}$ which is perpendicular to $\mathbf{v}$ is a solution to this equation.

   Now suppose that the equation $\mathbf{u}\times\mathbf{z} = \mathbf{v}$ has a nonzero solution. Because the cross product of any two vectors is perpendicular to both of the vectors, we must have that $\mathbf{u}\times\mathbf{z}\cdot\mathbf{u} = 0$. But this means that $\mathbf{v}\cdot\mathbf{u} = 0$, as desired.

b. If there exists a vector $\mathbf{z}$ so that $\mathbf{u}\times\mathbf{z} = \mathbf{v}$, then $\mathbf{u}$ and $\mathbf{v}$ must be perpendicular. If $\mathbf{u}$ and $\mathbf{v}$ are perpendicular nonzero vectors, then there must be a plane which contains $\mathbf{u}$ and a nonzero vector $\mathbf{z}$ so that $\mathbf{u}\times\mathbf{z} = \mathbf{v}$.

11.5 Lines and Curves in Space

11.5.1 It has one, namely t.

11.5.3 For every real number t that is put into the function, the output is a vector $\mathbf{r}(t)$.

11.5.5 Let $\mathbf{d}$ be the direction vector as in the previous problem. Then $\mathbf{r}(t) = \langle x_0, y_0, z_0\rangle + t\mathbf{d}$.

11.5.7 Compute $\lim_{t\to a} f(t) = L_1$, $\lim_{t\to a} g(t) = L_2$, and $\lim_{t\to a} h(t) = L_3$. Then $\lim_{t\to a} \mathbf{r}(t) = \langle L_1, L_2, L_3\rangle$.

11.5.9 The line is $\mathbf{r}(t) = \langle 0,0,1\rangle + t\langle 4,7,0\rangle$.

11.5.11 The direction is $\langle 0,1,0\rangle$, so the line l_1 is $\mathbf{r}(t) = \langle 0,0,1\rangle + t\langle 0,1,0\rangle$.

11.5.13 The direction is $\langle 1,2,3\rangle$, so the line is $\mathbf{r}(t) = t\langle 1,2,3\rangle$.

11.5.15 The direction is $\langle 8,-5,-6\rangle$, so the line is $\mathbf{r}(t) = \langle -3,4,6\rangle + t\langle 8,-5,-6\rangle$.

11.5.17 The direction is $\langle -2,8,-4\rangle$, so the line is $\mathbf{r}(t) = t\langle -2,8,-4\rangle$.

11.5.19 The direction is $\langle 1,0,2\rangle \times \langle 0,1,1\rangle = \langle -2,-1,1\rangle$, so the line is $\mathbf{r}(t) = t\langle -2,-1,1\rangle$.

11.5.21 The direction is $\langle 1,1,2\rangle \times \langle 1,0,0\rangle = \langle 0,2,-1\rangle$, so the line is $\mathbf{r}(t) = \langle -2,5,3\rangle + t\langle 0,2,-1\rangle$.

11.5.23 The direction is $\langle -2,8,-4\rangle \times \langle -2,1,-1\rangle = \langle -4,6,14\rangle$, so the line is $\mathbf{r}(t) = \langle 1,2,3\rangle + t\langle -4,6,14\rangle$.

11.5.25 The line segment is $\mathbf{r}(t) = t\langle 1,2,3\rangle$, where $0 \le t \le 1$.

11.5.27 The line segment is $\mathbf{r}(t) = \langle 2,4,8\rangle + t\langle 5,1,-5\rangle$, where $0 \le t \le 1$.

11.5.29

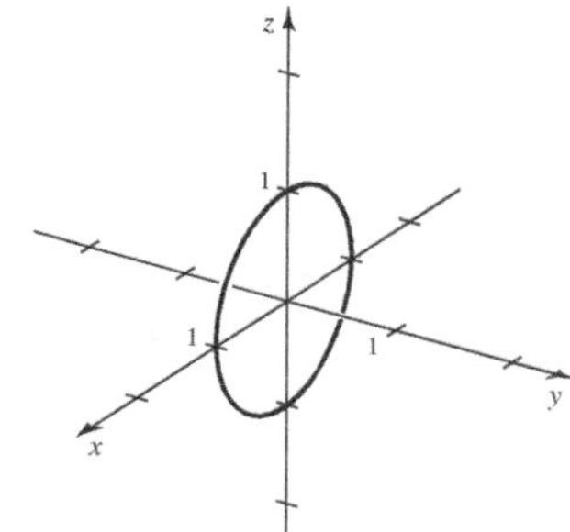

11.5.31

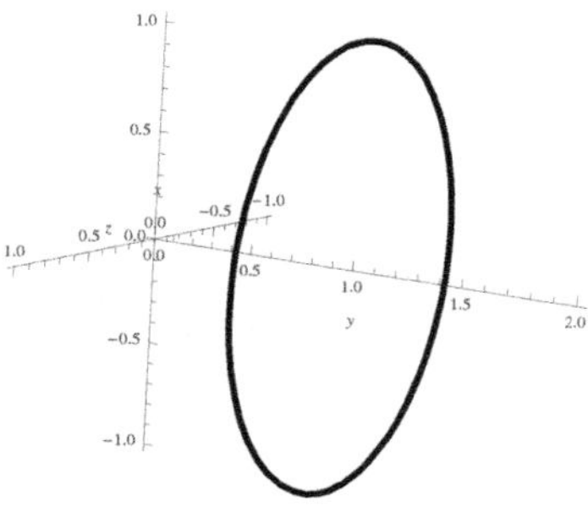

11.5.33

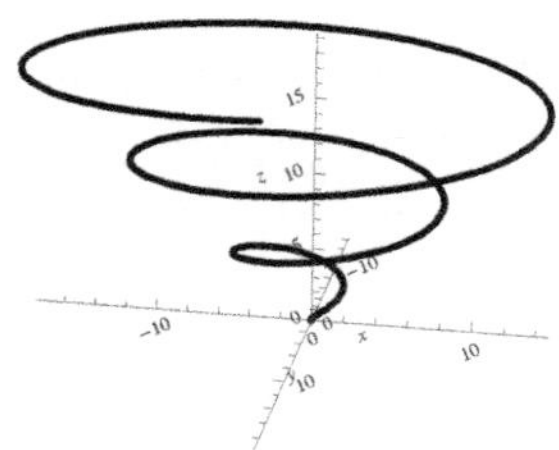

11.5.35

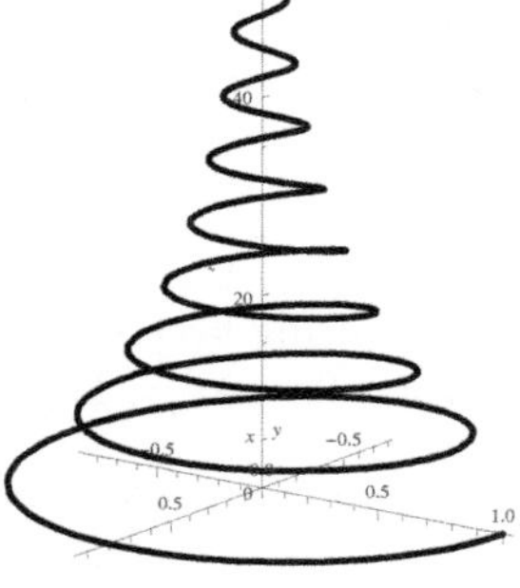

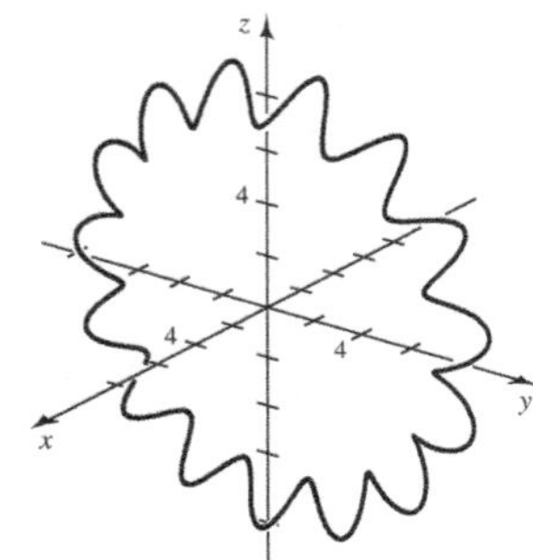

11.5.37 Note that the curve is closed (the initial point and the terminal point coincide), and is very "wavy."

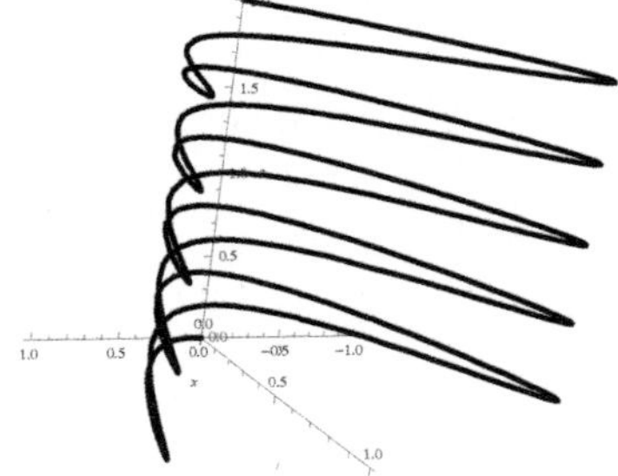

11.5.39 When viewed from the top, the curve looks parabolic.

11.5.41 $\lim_{t\to\pi/2}\langle\cos 2t, -4\sin t, \frac{2t}{\pi}\rangle = \langle\cos\pi, -4\sin\pi/2, \frac{2\cdot\pi/2}{\pi}\rangle = \langle -1, -4, 1\rangle$.

11.5.43 $\lim_{t\to\infty}\langle e^{-t}, -\frac{2t}{t+1}, \tan^{-1} t\rangle = \langle 0, -2, \pi/2\rangle$.

11.5.45 Using l'Hôpital's rule (once in the first two components, twice in the third component):
$\lim_{t\to 0}\langle\frac{\sin t}{t}, -\frac{e^t-t-1}{t}, \frac{\cos t+t^2/2-1}{t^2}\rangle = \lim_{t\to 0}\langle\cos t, 1-e^t, \frac{-\cos t+1}{2}\rangle = \langle 1,0,0\rangle = \mathbf{i}$.

11.5.47

a. True. This curve passes through the origin at $t = -1/2$.

b. False. For example, the x axis is not parallel to the line $\langle 0,0,1\rangle + t\langle 0,1,0\rangle$, but neither do they intersect.

c. True. The first component function approaches 0 as $t \to \infty$, while the others are periodic. The parametric equations $y = \sin t$ and $z = -\cos t$ form a circle in the yz-plane.

d. True. Both have limit $\langle 0,0,0\rangle$.

11.5.49 Setting $\mathbf{r}(t) = \mathbf{R}(s)$ and solving the resulting system of linear equations gives $t = 1$ and $s = 5$, so the point of intersection of the lines occurs when for $\mathbf{r}(1) = \mathbf{R}(5) = (4,3,3)$. The direction of the line perpendicular to both of these is $\langle 4,2,3\rangle \times \langle 1,2,3\rangle = \langle 0,-9,6\rangle$. The line we are seeking is therefore $\langle 4,3,3\rangle + t\langle 0,-9,6\rangle$.

11.5.51 Setting $\mathbf{r}(t) = \mathbf{R}(s)$ and solving the resulting system of linear equations gives $t = 0$ and $s = -3$, so the point of intersection of the lines occurs when for $\mathbf{r}(0) = \mathbf{R}(-3) = (1,3,2)$

11.5.53 Setting $\mathbf{r}(t) = \mathbf{R}(s)$ and attempting to solve the corresponding system of linear equations yields no solution. The lines aren't parallel since $\langle 0,-1,1\rangle$ is not a multiple of $\langle -7,4,-1\rangle$. Therefore the lines are skew.

11.5.55 These equations represent the same line. (So they are parallel and intersecting.) Note that $\mathbf{r}(3t - 5) = \langle 1 + 2(3t-5), 7 - 3(3t-5), 6 + (3t-5)\rangle = \langle -9 + 6t, 22 - 9t, 1 + 3t\rangle = \mathbf{R}(t)$.

11.5.57 The first component function has domain $[-2, \infty)$ and the second has domain $(-\infty, 2]$, so the domain of $\mathbf{r}(t)$ is $[-2, 2]$.

11.5.59 The first component function has domain $[-2, 2]$, the second has domain $[0, \infty)$, and the third has domain $(-1, \infty)$, so the domain of $\mathbf{r}(t)$ is $[0, 2]$.

11.5.61 The intersection occurs for $z = 4 = t - 6$, so for $t = 10$. The point of intesection is $(21, -6, 4)$.

11.5.63 The intersection occurs for $z = -8 = -2t + 4$, so for $t = 6$. The point of intersection is $(16, 0, -8)$.

11.5.65 The intersection occurs for $z = 16 = 4 + 3t$, so for $t = 4$. The point of intersection is $(4, 8, 16)$.

11.5.67

a. This matches graph E. (It is a straight line.)

b. This matches graph D. (It is parabolic-like.)

c. This matches graph F. (It is a circle.)

d. This matches graph C. (It is a circular helix, elongated along the x-axis.)

e. This matches graph A. (It is a closed curve which isn't a circle.)

f. This matches graph B. (It is a circular helix, elongated along the y-axis.)

11.5.69

a. $\mathbf{r}(0) = \langle 50, 0, 0\rangle$.

b. $\lim_{t\to\infty} \frac{50\cos t}{e^t} = 0$ by the squeeze theorem, and likewise $\lim_{t\to\infty} \frac{50\sin t}{e^t} = 0$. Also, $\lim_{t\to\infty}\left(5 - \frac{5}{e^t}\right) = 5$. Thus we have $\lim_{t\to\infty} \mathbf{r}(t) = \langle 0, 0, 5\rangle$.

c. 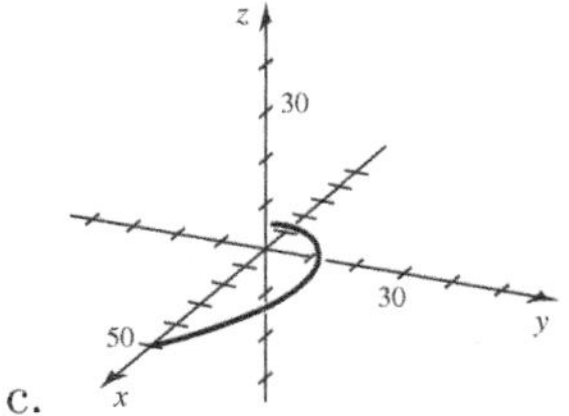

d. Let $x = 50e^{-t}\cos t$ and $y = 50e^{-t}\sin t$ and $z = 5 - 5e^{-t}$. Note that $x^2 + y^2 = 2500e^{-2t}$, so $r = 50e^{-t}$. We have $z = 5 - 5e^{-t} = 5 - \frac{r}{10}$.

11.5.71 This has the form mentioned in exercise 52, with $a = 1/\sqrt{2}$, $b = 1/\sqrt{3}$, $c = -1/\sqrt{2}$, $d = 1/\sqrt{3}$, $e = 0$, and $f = 1/\sqrt{3}$. Note that $a^2 + c^2 + e^2 = \frac{1}{2} + \frac{1}{2} + 0 = 1 = \frac{1}{3} + \frac{1}{3} + \frac{1}{3} = b^2 + d^2 + f^2$, and $ab + cd + ef = 0$. So this is a circle of radius 1 centered at the origin.

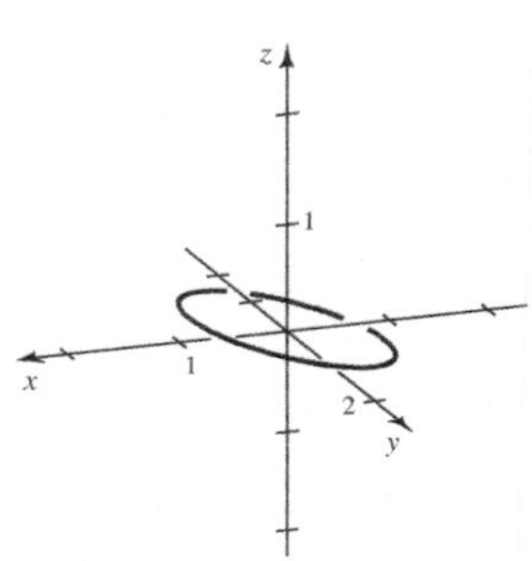

11.5.73 Note that $\mathbf{r}(0) = \langle a, c, e\rangle$ and $\mathbf{r}(\pi/2) = \langle b, d, f\rangle$, and $\mathbf{r}(\pi) = \langle -a, -c, -e\rangle$ have their terminal points on the curve. So $\langle a, c, e\rangle - \langle -a, -c, -e\rangle = \langle 2a, 2c, 2e\rangle = 2\mathbf{r}(0)$ lies in the plane containing the curve, which implies that $\mathbf{r}(0)$ lies in the plane containing the curve, and that implies that the point $(0, 0, 0)$ is in the plane containing the curve. So a normal to the curve is $\mathbf{r}(0)\times\mathbf{r}(\pi/2) = \langle a, c, e\rangle \times \langle b, d, f\rangle = \langle cf-de, be-af, ad-bc\rangle$.

11.5.75 First note that $x = \frac{1}{2}\sin 2t = \sin t\cos t$ and $y = \frac{1}{2}(1 - \cos 2t) = \sin^2 t$. Then $x^2 + y^2 + z^2 = \sin^2 t\cos^2 t + \sin^4 t + \cos^2 t = \sin^2 t(\cos^2 t + \sin^2 t) + \cos^2 t = \sin^2 t \cdot 1 + \cos^2 t = 1$. So all points on the curve are equidistant from the origin, so they lie on the sphere of radius one centered at the origin.

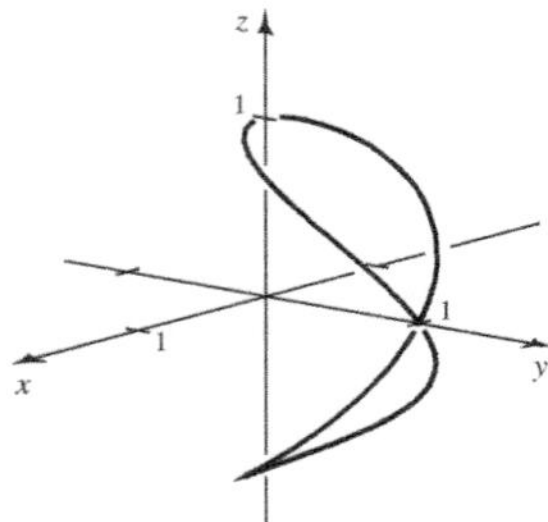

11.5.77 In order for $\sin(mt+mT)\cos(nt+nT) = \sin mt\cos nt$ and $\sin(mt+mT)\sin(nt+nT) = \sin mt\sin nt$ and $\cos(mt + mT) = \cos mt$ we would need $T = \frac{2\pi}{m}$ or a multiple of it, and then it would be necessary for $\sin(nt + nT) = \sin nt$, which would require $T = \frac{2\pi}{n}$, or a multiple of it. Thus, the smallest such T would be $\frac{2\pi}{(m,n)}$, where (m, n) represents the greatest common factor of m and n.

11.5.79 Consider the vector $\mathbf{v}$ placed geometrically so that its tail is at point P, and let the head of $\mathbf{v}$ be R so that the triangle PRQ has one side as $\mathbf{u} = \overrightarrow{PQ}$ and one side as $\mathbf{v}$. By Theorem 11.3, $\dfrac{|\mathbf{u}\times\mathbf{v}|}{|\mathbf{v}|} = |\mathbf{u}|\sin\theta$ where θ is the angle between $\mathbf{u}$ and $\mathbf{v}$. Now Let R' on $\mathbf{r}$ be the foot of the perpendicular dropped from Q as in ordinary geometry, so that the length of $\overline{R'Q}$ is the distance from Q to the line. By the trigonometry of the right triangle $PR'Q$, we have that the length of $\overline{R'Q}$ is $|\mathbf{u}|\sin\theta$ where θ is as before. Thus $R = R'$ and the distance between Q and $\mathbf{r}$ is $|\mathbf{u}|\sin\theta = \dfrac{|\mathbf{u}\times\mathbf{v}|}{|\mathbf{v}|}$.

11.5.81 Let the point on the line be $P(7, 2, 4)$, so that $\mathbf{u} = \overrightarrow{PQ} = \langle -12, 0, 5\rangle$. Then

$$d = \frac{|\langle -12, 0, 5\rangle \times \langle 5, -1, 12\rangle|}{|\langle 5, -1, 12\rangle|} = \frac{|\langle 5, 169, 12\rangle|}{|\langle 5, -1, 12\rangle|} = \frac{13\sqrt{170}}{\sqrt{170}} = 13.$$

11.6 Calculus of Vector-Valued Functions

11.6.1 It is $\mathbf{r}'(t) = \langle f'(t), g'(t), h'(t)\rangle$.

11.6.3 Divide the vector by its length, so if the vector is $\mathbf{r}'(t)$, form $\frac{\mathbf{r}'(t)}{|\mathbf{r}'(t)|}$.

11.6.5 Compute the indefinite integral of each of the component functions, and then

$$\int \mathbf{r}(t)\,dt = \langle \int f(t)\,dt, \int g(t)\,dt, \int h(t)\,dt\rangle.$$

11.6.7 $\mathbf{r}'(t) = \langle -\sin t, 2t, \cos t\rangle$.

11.6.9 $\mathbf{r}'(t) = \langle 6t, 3/\sqrt{t}, -3/t^2\rangle$.

11.6.11 $\mathbf{r}'(t) = \langle e^t, -2e^{-t}, -8e^{2t}\rangle$.

11.6.13 $\mathbf{r}'(t) = \langle e^{-t}(1 - t), 1 + \ln t, \cos t - t\sin t\rangle$.

11.6.15 $\mathbf{r}'(t) = \langle 1, 6t, 3t^2\rangle$, so $\mathbf{r}'(1) = \langle 1, 6, 3\rangle$.

11.6.17 $\mathbf{r}'(t) = \langle 1, -2\sin 2t, 2\cos t\rangle$, so $\mathbf{r}'(\pi/2) = \langle 1, 0, 0\rangle$.

11.6.19 $\mathbf{r}'(t) = \langle 8t^3, 9\sqrt{t}, -10/t^2\rangle$, so $\mathbf{r}'(1) = \langle 8, 9, -10\rangle$.

11.6.21 $\mathbf{r}'(t) = \langle 2, 2, 1\rangle$, so

$$\frac{\mathbf{r}'(t)}{|\mathbf{r}'(t)|} = \frac{1}{3}\langle 2, 2, 1\rangle = \langle 2/3, 2/3, 1/3\rangle.$$

11.6.23 $\mathbf{r}'(t) = \langle 0, -2\sin 2t, 4\cos 2t\rangle$, so

$$\frac{\mathbf{r}'(t)}{|\mathbf{r}'(t)|} = \frac{1}{\sqrt{4\sin^2 2t + 16\cos^2 2t}}\langle 0, -2\sin 2t, 4\cos 2t\rangle = \frac{1}{\sqrt{1+3\cos^2 2t}}\langle 0, -\sin 2t, 2\cos 2t\rangle.$$

11.6.25 $\mathbf{r}'(t) = \langle 1, 0, -2/t^2\rangle$, so

$$\frac{\mathbf{r}'(t)}{|\mathbf{r}'(t)|} = \frac{1}{\sqrt{1+(4/t^4)}}\langle 1, 0, -2/t^2\rangle = \frac{1}{\sqrt{t^4+4}}\langle t^2, 0, -2\rangle.$$

11.6.27 $\mathbf{r}'(t) = \langle -2\sin 2t, 0, 6\cos 2t\rangle$, so at $t = \pi/2$, we have $\mathbf{r}'(\pi/2) = \langle 0, 0, -6\rangle$. Thus, the unit tangent at $\pi/2$ is $\langle 0, 0, -1\rangle$.

11.6.29 $\mathbf{r}'(t) = \langle 6, 0, -3/t^2\rangle$, so at $t = 1$, we have $\mathbf{r}'(1) = \langle 6, 0, -3\rangle$. Thus, the unit normal at 1 is $\langle 2/\sqrt{5}, 0, -1/\sqrt{5}\rangle$.

11.6.31 $(t^{12}+3t)\mathbf{u}'(t) + \mathbf{u}(t)(12t^{11}+3) = (t^{12}+3t)\langle 6t^2, 2t, 0\rangle + \langle 2t^3, (t^2-1), -8\rangle(12t^{11}+3) = \langle 30t^{14} + 24t^3, 14t^{13} - 12t^{11} + 9t^2 - 3, -96t^{11} - 24\rangle$.

11.6.33 $\mathbf{u}'(t^4-2t)\cdot(4t^3-2) = \langle 6(t^4-2t)^2, 2(t^4-2t), 0\rangle(4t^3-2) = \langle 6(t^4-2t)^2(4t^3-2), 2(t^4-2t)(4t^3-2), 0\rangle = 4t(2t^3-1)(t^3-2)\langle 3t(t^3-2), 1, 0\rangle$.

11.6.35 $\mathbf{u}(t)\cdot\mathbf{v}'(t) + \mathbf{v}(t)\cdot\mathbf{u}'(t) = \langle 2t^3, (t^2-1), -8\rangle\cdot\langle e^t, -2e^{-t}, -2e^{2t}\rangle + \langle e^t, 2e^{-t}, -e^{2t}\rangle\cdot\langle 6t^2, 2t, 0\rangle = 2t^3e^t - 2(t^2-1)e^{-t} + 16e^{2t} + 6t^2e^t + 4te^{-t} + 0 = e^t(2t^3+6t^2) - 2e^{-t}(t^2-2t-1) + 16e^{2t}$.

11.6.37 $\langle t^2, 2t^2, -2t^3\rangle\cdot\langle e^t, 2e^t, 3e^{-t}\rangle + \langle 2t, 4t, -6t^2\rangle\cdot\langle e^t, 2e^t, -3e^{-t}\rangle = t^2e^t + 4t^2e^t - 6t^3e^{-t} + 2te^t + 8te^t + 18t^2e^{-t} = 5t^2e^t + 10te^t - 6t^3e^{-t} + 18t^2e^{-t}$.

11.6.39 $\langle 3t^2, \sqrt{t}, -2/t\rangle\cdot\langle -\sin t, 2\cos 2t, -3\rangle + \langle 6t, 1/(2\sqrt{t}), 2/t^2\rangle\cdot\langle \cos t, \sin 2t, -3t\rangle = -3t^2\sin t + 2\sqrt{t}\cos 2t + 6t\cos t + \sin(2t)/(2\sqrt{t})$.

11.6.41 $\mathbf{r}'(t) = \langle 2t, 1, 0\rangle$. $\mathbf{r}''(t) = \langle 2, 0, 0\rangle$. $\mathbf{r}'''(t) = \langle 0, 0, 0\rangle$.

11.6.43 $\mathbf{r}'(t) = \langle -3\sin 3t, 4\cos 4t, -6\sin 6t\rangle$. $\mathbf{r}''(t) = \langle -9\cos 3t, -16\sin 4t, -36\cos 6t\rangle$.
$\mathbf{r}'''(t) = \langle 27\sin 3t, -64\cos 4t, 216\sin 6t\rangle$.

11.6.45 $\mathbf{r}'(t) = \langle \frac{1}{2\sqrt{t+4}}, \frac{1}{(t+1)^2}, 2e^{-t^2}t\rangle$. $\mathbf{r}''(t) = \langle -\frac{1}{4(t+4)^{3/2}}, -\frac{2}{(t+1)^3}, e^{-t^2}(2-4t^2)\rangle$.
$\mathbf{r}'''(t) = \langle \frac{3}{8(t+4)^{5/2}}, \frac{6}{(t+1)^4}, 4e^{-t^2}t(2t^2-3)\rangle$.

11.6.47 $\displaystyle\int \langle t^4 - 3t, 2t - 1, 10\rangle\, dt = \langle t^5/5 - 3t^2/2, t^2 - t, 10t\rangle + \mathbf{C}$.

11.6.49 $\displaystyle\int \langle 2\cos t, 2\sin 3t, 4\cos 8t\rangle\, dt = \langle 2\sin t, (-2/3)\cos 3t, (1/2)\sin 8t\rangle + \mathbf{C}$.

11.6.51 $\displaystyle\int \langle e^{3t}, \frac{1}{1+t^2}, \frac{-1}{\sqrt{2t}}\rangle\, dt = \langle e^{3t}/3, \tan^{-1} t, -\sqrt{2t}\rangle + \mathbf{C}$.

11.6.53 $\int \langle e^t, \sin t, \sec^2 t\rangle\, dt = \langle e^t, -\cos t, \tan t\rangle + \mathbf{C}$. Because $\mathbf{r}(0) = \langle 2,2,2\rangle = \langle 1,-1,0\rangle + \mathbf{C}$, we have $\mathbf{C} = \langle 1,3,2\rangle$. Thus, $\mathbf{r}(t) = \langle e^t, -\cos t, \tan t\rangle + \langle 1,3,2\rangle = \langle 1+e^t, 3-\cos t, 2+\tan t\rangle$.

11.6.55 $\int \langle 1, 2t, 3t^2\rangle\, dt = \langle t, t^2, t^3\rangle + \mathbf{C}$. Because $\mathbf{r}(1) = \langle 4,3,-5\rangle$, we have $\langle 1,1,1\rangle + \mathbf{C} = \langle 4,3,-5\rangle$, so $\mathbf{C} = \langle 3,2,-6\rangle$, and $\mathbf{r}(t) = \langle t+3, t^2+2, t^3-6\rangle$.

11.6.57 $\int \langle e^{2t}, 1-2e^{-t}, 1-2e^t\rangle\, dt = \langle e^{2t}/2, t+2e^{-t}, t-2e^t\rangle + \mathbf{C}$. Because $\mathbf{r}(0) = \langle 1,1,1\rangle$, we have $\langle 1/2, 2, -2\rangle + \mathbf{C} = \langle 1,1,1\rangle$, so $\mathbf{C} = \langle 1/2, -1, 3\rangle$, and $\mathbf{r}(t) = \langle e^{2t}/2 + 1/2, t + 2e^{-t} - 1, t - 2e^t + 3\rangle$.

11.6.59 $\int_{-1}^{1} \langle 1, t, 3t^2\rangle\, dt = \langle t, t^2/2, t^3\rangle\Big|_{-1}^{1} = \langle 2,0,2\rangle$.

11.6.61 $\int_0^{\ln 2} \langle e^t, e^t\cos \pi e^t\rangle\, dt = \langle e^t, \frac{\sin \pi e^t}{\pi}\rangle\Big|_0^{\ln 2} = \langle 2,0\rangle - \langle 1,0\rangle = \langle 1,0\rangle = \mathbf{i}$.

11.6.63 $\int_{-\pi}^{\pi} \langle \sin t, \cos t, 2t\rangle\, dt = \langle -\cos t, \sin t, t^2\rangle\Big|_{-\pi}^{\pi} = \langle 0,0,0\rangle$.

11.6.65 $\int_0^2 \langle te^t, 2te^t, -te^t\rangle\, dt = \langle (t-1)e^t, 2(t-1)e^t, -(t-1)e^t\rangle\Big|_0^2 = \langle e^2+1, 2e^2+2, -e^2-1\rangle = (e^2+1)\langle 1,2,-1\rangle$.

11.6.67

a. False. For example, if $\mathbf{r}(t) = \langle \cos t, \sin t\rangle$, then $\mathbf{r}'(t) = \langle -\sin t, \cos t\rangle$ is not parallel to $\mathbf{r}(t)$, and is in fact perpendicular to it.

b. True. $\mathbf{r}'(t) = \langle 1, 2t-2, -\pi \sin \pi t\rangle \neq \langle 0,0,0\rangle$. Each component function is differentiable, and the derivative is never $\langle 0,0,0\rangle$, so the function is smooth by definition.

c. True. This follows because $\int_{-a}^{a} o(x)\, dx = 0$ for any odd function $o(x)$.

11.6.69 $\mathbf{r}'(t) = \langle -\sin t, 2\cos 2t, 1\rangle$, so $\mathbf{r}'(\pi/2) = \langle -1,-2,1\rangle$. We have $\mathbf{r}(\pi/2) = \langle 2,3,\pi/2\rangle$, so the tangent line is given by $\langle 2-t, 3-2t, \pi/2+t\rangle$.

11.6.71 $\mathbf{r}'(t) = \langle 3,7,2t\rangle$, so $\mathbf{r}'(1) = \langle 3,7,2\rangle$. We have $\mathbf{r}(1) = \langle 2,9,1\rangle$, so the tangent line is given by $\langle 2+3t, 9+7t, 1+2t\rangle$.

11.6.73 $\mathbf{v}'(e^t)\cdot e^t = e^t\langle 2e^t, -2, 0\rangle = \langle 2e^{2t}, -2e^t, 0\rangle$.

11.6.75 $\mathbf{v}'(g(t))g'(t) = \langle 4\sqrt{t}, -2, 0\rangle \left(\frac{1}{\sqrt{t}}\right) = \langle 4, -2/\sqrt{t}, 0\rangle$.

11.6.77 $\mathbf{u}(t)\times\mathbf{v}'(t) + \mathbf{u}'(t)\times\mathbf{v}(t) = \langle 1,t,t^2\rangle \times \langle 2t,-2,0\rangle + \langle 0,1,2t\rangle\times\langle t^2,-2t,1\rangle = \langle 2t^2, 2t^3, -2t^2-2\rangle + \langle 4t^2+1, 2t^3, -t^2\rangle = \langle 6t^2+1, 4t^3, -3t^2-2\rangle$

11.6.79 $\mathbf{r}'(t) = \langle 2at, 1\rangle$. We have $\mathbf{r}(t)\cdot\mathbf{r}'(t) = 0$ when $(2at)(at^2+1) + t(1) = 0$, which occurs only for $t = 0$ because $2a^2t^2 + 2a + 1 > 0$ for all t. The corresponding point on the parabola is $(1,0)$.

11.6.81 $\mathbf{r}'(t) = \langle -\sin t, \cos t, 1\rangle$. We have $\mathbf{r}(t)\cdot\mathbf{r}'(t) = 0$ when $-\sin t\cos t + \sin t \cos t + t = 0$, which occurs only for $t = 0$. So the only point on the helix where these vectors are orthogonal is at $t = 0$. This corresponds to the point $(1,0,0)$.

11.6.83 Note that $\mathbf{r}(t) = \langle a_1 t, a_2 t, a_3 t\rangle = t\langle a_1, a_2, a_3\rangle$ where the a_i's are real numbers has this property because $\mathbf{r}'(t) = \langle a_1, a_2, a_3\rangle$, and $\mathbf{r}(t)$ is a multiple of $\mathbf{r}'(t)$.

Also, $\mathbf{r}(t) = \langle a_1 e^{kt}, a_2 e^{kt}, a_3 e^{kt}\rangle$ where k is a real number has this property, as its derivative is k times itself.

11.6.85

a. $\mathbf{r}(t)\cdot\mathbf{r}'(t) = (a^2+b^2+c^2)t = |\mathbf{r}(t)|\,|\mathbf{r}'(t)|\cos\theta$, so $\cos\theta = \frac{(a^2+b^2+c^2)t}{\sqrt{a^2+b^2+c^2}t\cdot\sqrt{a^2+b^2+c^2}} = 1$, so $\theta = 0$.

b. $\mathbf{r}(t)\cdot\mathbf{r}'(t) = ax_0+by_0+cz_0+(a^2+b^2+c^2)t = |\mathbf{r}(t)|\,|\mathbf{r}'(t)|\cos\theta$, so

$$\cos\theta = \frac{ax_0+by_0+cz_0+(a^2+b^2+c^2)t}{\sqrt{(x_0+at)^2+(y_0+bt)^2+(z_0+ct)^2}\cdot\sqrt{a^2+b^2+c^2}}.$$

Because x_0, y_0, and z_0 are not all 0, $\cos\theta$ depends on t.

c. In part a, the curve is a straight line through the origin, so the position vector and the tangent vector are parallel for all t. In part b, the line is not through the origin, so the tangent vector (which is the direction vector for the line) is not parallel to the position vector.

11.6.87

$$\begin{aligned}\frac{d}{dt}(f(t)\mathbf{u}(t)) &= \frac{d}{dt}\langle f(t)u_1(t), f(t)u_2(t), f(t)u_3(t)\rangle\\ &= \langle f'(t)u_1(t)+f(t)u_1'(t)+, f'(t)u_2(t)+f(t)u_2'(t), f'(t)u_3(t)+f(t)u_3'(t)\rangle\\ &= f'(t)\mathbf{u}(t)+f(t)\mathbf{u}'(t).\end{aligned}$$

11.6.89

a. $\mathbf{r}'(t) = \langle 3t^2, 3t^2\rangle$, so $\mathbf{r}'(0) = \langle 0,0\rangle$. There is no cusp because $\lim_{t\to 0}\frac{dy}{dx} = \frac{dy/dt}{dx/dt} = \frac{3t^2}{3t^2} = 1$ exists.

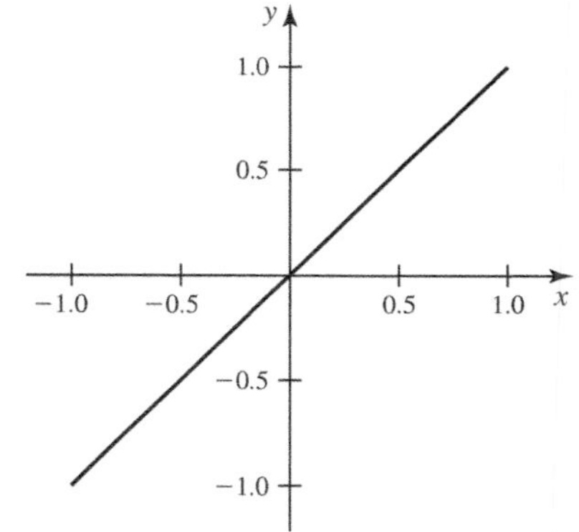

b. $\mathbf{r}'(t) = \langle 3t^2, 2t\rangle$, so $\mathbf{r}'(0) = \langle 0,0\rangle$. There is a cusp because $\lim_{t\to 0}\frac{dy}{dx} = \lim_{t\to 0}\frac{dy/dt}{dx/dt} = \lim_{t\to 0}\frac{2t}{3t^2} = \lim_{t\to 0}\frac{2}{3t}$ does not exist.

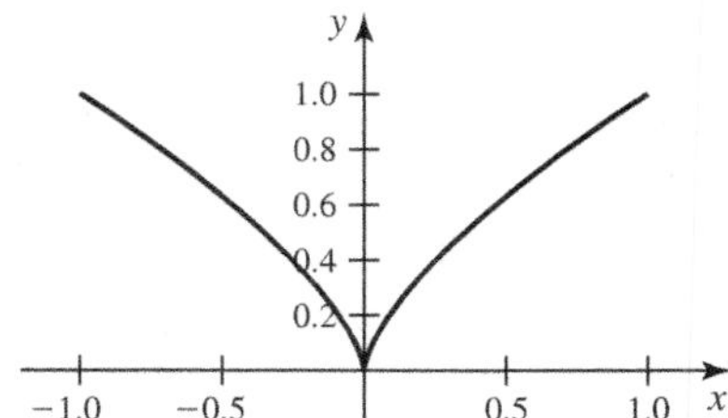

c. The curve $\mathbf{r}(t)$ for $-\infty < t < \infty$ traces out the whole curve $y = x^2$, while the curve $\mathbf{p}(t)$ only traces out the part in the first quadrant, because $x = t^2 > 0$ for all t.

d. $\mathbf{r}'(t) = \langle mt^{m-1}, nt^{n-1}\rangle$, so $\mathbf{r}'(0) = \langle 0,0\rangle$.

Assume $m > n$. There is a cusp because

$$\lim_{t\to 0}\frac{dy}{dx} = \lim_{t\to 0}\frac{dy/dt}{dx/dt} = \lim_{t\to 0}\frac{nt^{n-1}}{mt^{m-1}} = \lim_{t\to 0}(n/m)\frac{1}{t^{m-n}},$$

which does not exist.

Now assume $m < n$. There is a cusp because

$$\lim_{t\to 0}\frac{dx}{dy} = \lim_{t\to 0}\frac{dx/dt}{dy/dt} = \lim_{t\to 0}\frac{mt^{m-1}}{nt^{n-1}} = \lim_{t\to 0}(m/n)\frac{1}{t^{n-m}},$$

which does not exist.

11.7 Motion in Space

11.7.1 The velocity is the derivative of position, the speed is the magnitude of velocity, and the acceleration is the derivative of velocity.

11.7.3 $m\mathbf{a}(t) = \mathbf{F}(t)$.

11.7.5 Integrate the acceleration to find an expression for the velocity plus a constant, and then use the initial velocity condition to find the constant.

11.7.7

a. $\mathbf{v}(t) = \langle 6t, 8t\rangle$, so the speed is $\sqrt{36t^2 + 64t^2} = \sqrt{100t^2} = 10t$.

b. $\mathbf{a}(t) = \langle 6, 8\rangle$.

11.7.9

a. $\mathbf{v}(t) = \mathbf{r}'(t) = \langle 2, -4\rangle$, so the speed is $|\mathbf{r}'(t)| = \sqrt{20} = 2\sqrt{5}$.

b. $\mathbf{a}(t) = \mathbf{r}''(t) = \langle 0, 0\rangle$.

11.7.11

a. $\mathbf{v}(t) = \mathbf{r}'(t) = \langle 8\cos t, -8\sin t\rangle$, so the speed is $|\mathbf{r}'(t)| = 8$.

b. $\mathbf{a}(t) = \mathbf{r}''(t) = \langle -8\sin t, -8\cos t\rangle$.

11.7.13

a. $\mathbf{v}(t) = \langle 2t, 2t, t\rangle$, so the speed is $\sqrt{4t^2 + 4t^2 + t^2} = 3t$.

b. $\mathbf{a}(t) = \langle 2, 2, 1\rangle$.

11.7.15

a. $\mathbf{v}(t) = \mathbf{r}'(t) = \langle 1, -4, 6\rangle$, so the speed is $|\mathbf{r}'(t)| = \sqrt{1 + 16 + 36} = \sqrt{53}$.

b. $\mathbf{a}(t) = \mathbf{r}''(t) = \langle 0, 0, 0\rangle$.

11.7.17

a. $\mathbf{v}(t) = \mathbf{r}'(t) = \langle 0, 2t, -e^{-t}\rangle$, so the speed is $|\mathbf{r}'(t)| = \sqrt{4t^2 + e^{-2t}}$.

b. $\mathbf{a}(t) = \mathbf{r}''(t) = \langle 0, 2, e^{-t}\rangle$.

11.7.19

a. The interval must be shrunk by a factor of 2, so $[c, d] = [0, 1]$.

b. $\mathbf{r}'(t) = \langle 1, 2t\rangle$, and $\mathbf{R}'(t) = \langle 2, 8t\rangle$.

c. $|\mathbf{r}'(t)| = \sqrt{1+4t^2}$ and $|\mathbf{R}'(t)| = 2\sqrt{1+16t^2}$.

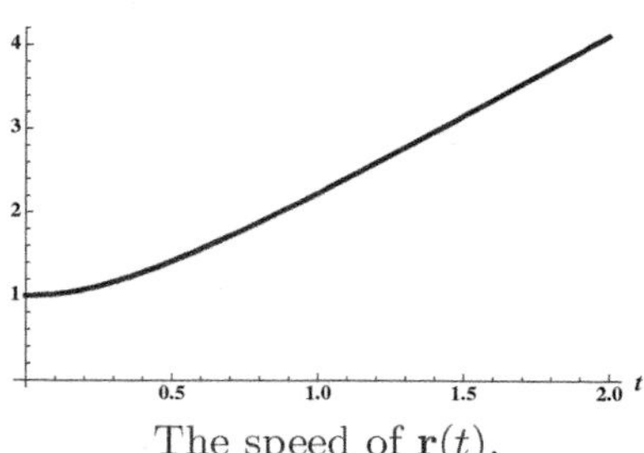

The speed of $\mathbf{r}(t)$.

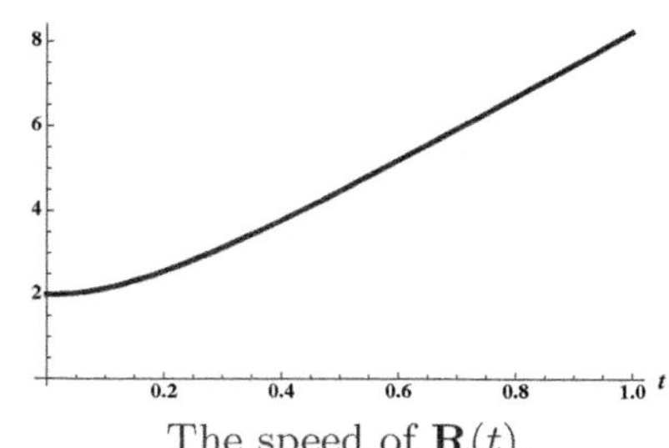

The speed of $\mathbf{R}(t)$.

11.7.21

a. The interval must be shrunk by a factor of 1/3, so $[c, d] = [0, 2\pi/3]$.

b. $\mathbf{r}'(t) = \langle -\sin t, 4\cos t\rangle$, and $\mathbf{R}'(t) = \langle -3\sin 3t, 12\cos 3t\rangle$.

c. $|\mathbf{r}'(t)| = \sqrt{\sin^2 t + 16\cos^2 t}$ and $|\mathbf{R}'(t)| = 3\sqrt{\sin^2 3t + 16\cos^2 3t}$.

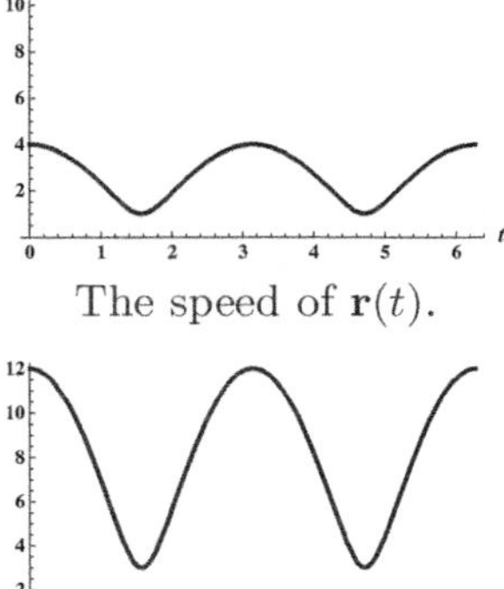

The speed of $\mathbf{r}(t)$.

The speed of $\mathbf{R}(t)$.

11.7.23

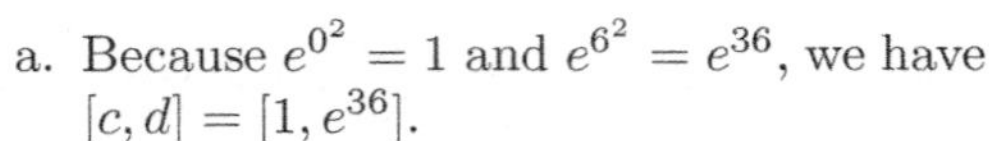

a. Because $e^{0^2} = 1$ and $e^{6^2} = e^{36}$, we have $[c, d] = [1, e^{36}]$.

b. $\mathbf{r}'(t) = \langle 2t, -8t^3, 18t^5\rangle$, and $\mathbf{R}'(t) = \langle 1/t, (-4\ln t)/t, (9\ln^2 t)/t\rangle$.

c. $|\mathbf{r}'(t)| = 2t\sqrt{1 + 16t^4 + 81t^8}$ and $|\mathbf{R}'(t)| = \frac{1}{t}\sqrt{1 + 16\ln^2 t + 81\ln^4 t}$.

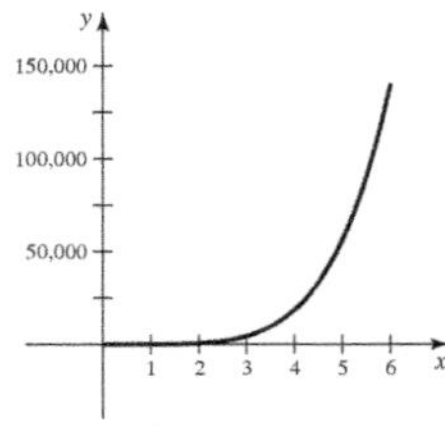

The speed of $\mathbf{r}(t)$.

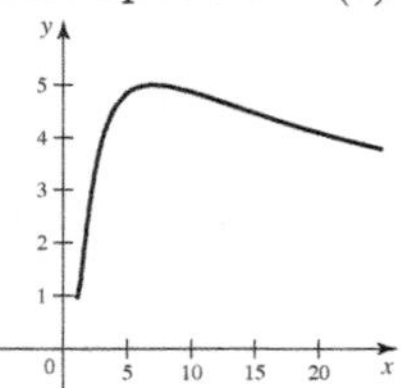

The speed of $\mathbf{R}(t)$.

11.7.25 Note that $x^2 + y^2 = 64$, so the trajectory lies on a circle centered at the origin of radius 8. $\mathbf{r}(t) \cdot \mathbf{r}'(t) = \langle 8\cos 2t, 8\sin 2t\rangle \cdot \langle -16\sin 2t, 16\cos 2t\rangle = -128\sin 2t\cos 2t + 128\sin 2t\cos 2t = 0$.

11.7.27 Note that $x^2 + y^2 = (\sin t + \sqrt{3}\cos t)^2 + (\sqrt{3}\sin t - \cos t)^2 = (\sin^2 t + 2\sin t\sqrt{3}\cos t + 3\cos^2 t) + (3\sin^2 t - 2\cos t\sqrt{3}\sin t + \cos^2 t) = 4$, so the trajectory lies on a circle centered at the origin of radius 2. $\mathbf{r}(t) \cdot \mathbf{r}'(t) = \langle \sin t + \sqrt{3}\cos t, \sqrt{3}\sin t - \cos t\rangle \cdot \langle \cos t - \sqrt{3}\sin t, \sqrt{3}\cos t + \sin t\rangle = (\sin t\cos t - \sqrt{3}\sin^2 t + \sqrt{3}\cos^2 t - 3\sin t\cos t) + (3\sin t\cos t + \sqrt{3}\sin^2 t - \sqrt{3}\cos^2 t - \sin t\cos t) = 0$.

11.7.29 $x^2 + y^2 + z^2 = \sin^2 t + \cos^2 t + \cos^2 t = 1 + \cos^2 t$, which is not a constant, so the trajectory does not lie on a sphere centered at the origin.

11.7.31 $\mathbf{v}(t) = \int \mathbf{a}(t)\,dt = \int \langle 0, 1\rangle\,dt = \langle 0, t\rangle + \mathbf{C}$. Because $\mathbf{v}(0) = \langle 2, 3\rangle$, we have $\mathbf{C} = \langle 2, 3\rangle$. Thus, $\mathbf{v}(t) = \langle 2, t + 3\rangle$.

$\mathbf{r}(t) = \int \mathbf{v}(t)\,dt = \int \langle 2, t + 3\rangle\,dt = \langle 2t, t^2/2 + 3t\rangle + \mathbf{D}$. Because $\mathbf{r}(0) = \langle 0, 0\rangle$, we have $\mathbf{D} = \langle 0, 0\rangle$. Therefore, $\mathbf{r}(t) = \langle 2t, t^2/2 + 3t\rangle$.

11.7.33 $\mathbf{v}(t) = \int \mathbf{a}(t)\,dt = \int \langle 0, 10\rangle\,dt = \langle 0, 10t\rangle + \mathbf{C}$. Because $\mathbf{v}(0) = \langle 0, 5\rangle$, we have $\mathbf{v}(t) = \langle 0, 10t + 5\rangle$.

Also, $\mathbf{r}(t) = \int \mathbf{v}(t)\,dt = \int \langle 0, 10t + 5\rangle\,dt = \langle 0, 5t^2 + 5t\rangle + \mathbf{D}$, and because $\mathbf{r}(0) = \langle 1, -1\rangle$, we have $\mathbf{r}(t) = \langle 1, 5t^2 + 5t - 1\rangle$.

11.7.35 $\mathbf{v}(t) = \int \mathbf{a}(t)\,dt = \int \langle \cos t, 2\sin t\rangle\,dt = \langle \sin t, -2\cos t\rangle + \mathbf{C}$. Because $\mathbf{v}(0) = \langle 0, 1\rangle$, we have $\mathbf{v}(t) = \langle \sin t, 3 - 2\cos t\rangle$.

Also, $\mathbf{r}(t) = \int \mathbf{v}(t)\,dt = \int \langle \sin t, 3 - 2\cos t\rangle\,dt = \langle -\cos t, 3t - 2\sin t\rangle + \mathbf{D}$, and because $\mathbf{r}(0) = \langle 1, 0\rangle$, we have $\mathbf{r}(t) = \langle 2 - \cos t, 3t - 2\sin t\rangle$.

11.7.37

a. $\mathbf{v}(t) = \int \langle 0, -9.8\rangle\,dt = \langle 0, -9.8t\rangle + \mathbf{C}$, and because $\mathbf{v}(0) = \langle 30, 6\rangle$, we have $\mathbf{v}(t) = \langle 30, 6 - 9.8t\rangle$.

Also, $\mathbf{r}(t) = \int \mathbf{v}(t)\,dt = \int \langle 30, 6 - 9.8t\rangle\,dt = \langle 30t, 6t - 4.9t^2\rangle + \mathbf{D}$, and because $\mathbf{r}(0) = \langle 0, 0\rangle$, we have $\mathbf{r}(t) = \langle 30t, 6t - 4.9t^2\rangle$.

b. 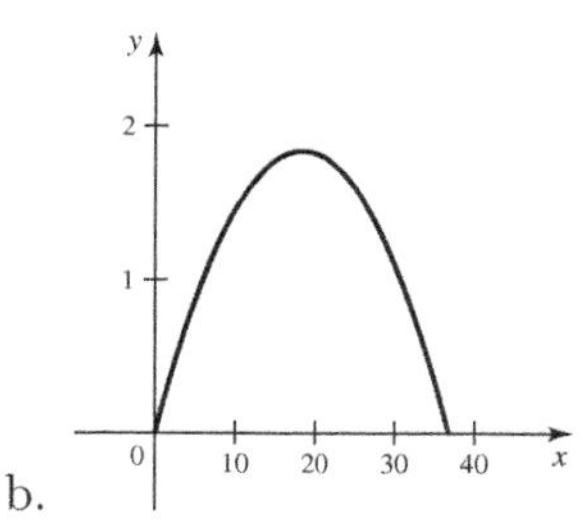

c. The ball hits the ground when $6t - 4.9t^2 = 0$, which occurs for $t = 6/4.9 \approx 1.22$ seconds. The range of the ball is approximately $30 \cdot 1.22 \approx 36.7$ meters.

d. The maximum height occurs at time $T \approx 1.22/2 = .61$ seconds, and is $6T - 4.9T^2 \approx 1.84$ meters.

11.7.39

a. $\mathbf{v}(t) = \int \langle 0, -32 \rangle \, dt = \langle 0, -32t \rangle + \mathbf{C}$, and because $\mathbf{v}(0) = \langle 80, 10 \rangle$, we have $\mathbf{v}(t) = \langle 80, 10 - 32t \rangle$.

Also, $\mathbf{r}(t) = \int \mathbf{v}(t) \, dt = \int \langle 80, 10 - 32t \rangle \, dt = \langle 80t, 10t - 16t^2 \rangle + \mathbf{D}$, and because $\mathbf{r}(0) = \langle 0, 6 \rangle$, we have $\mathbf{r}(t) = \langle 80t, 6 + 10t - 16t^2 \rangle$.

b. 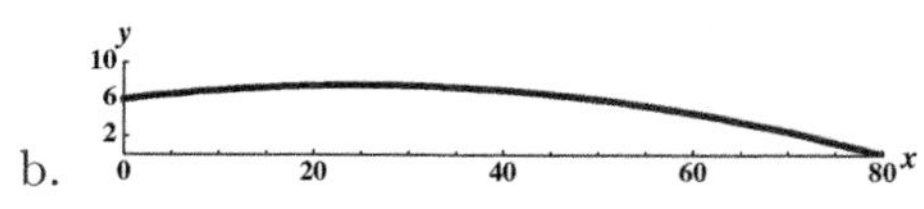

c. The ball hits the ground when $-16t^2 + 10t + 6 = -2(t-1)(8t+3) = 0$, which occurs for $t = 1$ second. The range of the ball is $80 \cdot 1 = 80$ feet.

d. The maximum height occurs at time $T \approx 10/32 \approx .3125$, and is $-16(.3125)^2 + 10(.3125) + 6 \approx 7.56$ feet.

11.7.41

a. $\mathbf{v}(t) = \int \langle 0, -32 \rangle \, dt = \langle 0, -32t \rangle + \mathbf{C}$, and because $\mathbf{v}(0) = 250\langle 1/2, \sqrt{3}/2 \rangle = \langle 125, 125\sqrt{3} \rangle$, we have $\mathbf{v}(t) = \langle 125, 125\sqrt{3} - 32t \rangle$.

Also, $\mathbf{r}(t) = \int \mathbf{v}(t) \, dt = \int \langle 125, 125\sqrt{3} - 32t \rangle \, dt = \langle 125t, 125\sqrt{3}t - 16t^2 \rangle + \mathbf{D}$, and because $\mathbf{r}(0) = \langle 0, 20 \rangle$, we have $\mathbf{r}(t) = \langle 125t, 20 + 125\sqrt{3}t - 16t^2 \rangle$.

b. 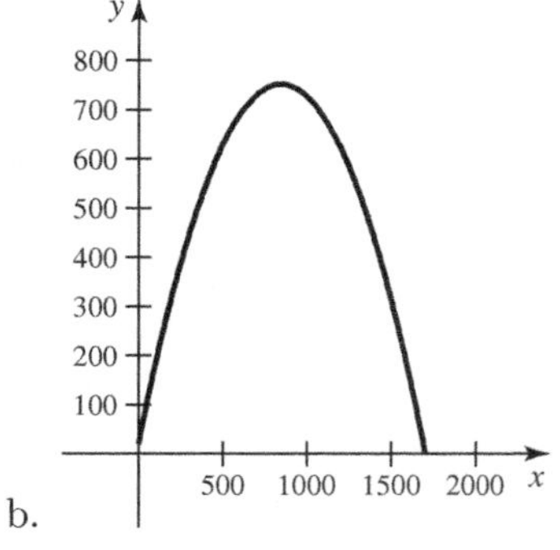

c. The ball hits the ground when $20 + 125\sqrt{3}t - 16t^2 = 0$, which occurs for $t \approx 13.62$ seconds. The range of the ball is approximately $125 \cdot 13.62 \approx 1702$ feet.

d. The maximum height occurs when $125\sqrt{3} - 32t = 0$, which is when $t \approx 6.77$ and it is about $20 + 125\sqrt{3}(6.77) - 16(6.77)^2 \approx 752.4$ feet.

11.7.43 $\mathbf{v}(t) = \int \mathbf{a}(t) \, dt = \int \langle 0, 0, 10 \rangle \, dt = \langle 0, 0, 10t \rangle + \mathbf{C}$. Because $\mathbf{v}(0) = \langle 1, 5, 0 \rangle$, we have $\mathbf{v}(t) = \langle 1, 5, 10t \rangle$.

Also, $\mathbf{r}(t) = \int \mathbf{v}(t) \, dt = \int \langle 1, 5, 10t \rangle \, dt = \langle t, 5t, 5t^2 \rangle + \mathbf{D}$, and because $\mathbf{r}(0) = \langle 0, 5, 0 \rangle$, we have $\mathbf{r}(t) = \langle t, 5t + 5, 5t^2 \rangle$.

11.7.45 $\mathbf{v}(t) = \int \mathbf{a}(t)\,dt = \int \langle \sin t, \cos t, 1\rangle\,dt = \langle -\cos t, \sin t, t\rangle + \mathbf{C}$. Because $\mathbf{v}(0) = \langle 0, 2, 0\rangle$, we have $\mathbf{v}(t) = \langle 1 - \cos t, \sin t + 2, t\rangle$.

Also, $\mathbf{r}(t) = \int \mathbf{v}(t)\,dt = \int \langle 1 - \cos t, \sin t + 2, t\rangle\,dt = \langle t - \sin t, -\cos t + 2t, t^2/2\rangle + \mathbf{D}$, and because $\mathbf{r}(0) = \langle 0, 0, 0\rangle$, we have $\mathbf{r}(t) = \langle t - \sin t, 1 - \cos t + 2t, t^2/2\rangle$.

11.7.47

a. $\mathbf{v}(t) = \int \mathbf{a}(t)\,dt = \int \langle 0, 0, -9.8\rangle\,dt = \langle 0, 0, -9.8t\rangle + \mathbf{C}$. Because $\mathbf{v}(0) = \langle 200, 200, 0\rangle$, we have $\mathbf{v}(t) = \langle 200, 200, -9.8t\rangle$.

Also, $\mathbf{r}(t) = \int \mathbf{v}(t)\,dt = \int \langle 200, 200, -9.8t\rangle\,dt = \langle 200t, 200t, -4.9t^2\rangle + \mathbf{D}$, and because $\mathbf{r}(0) = \langle 0, 0, 1\rangle$, we have $\mathbf{r}(t) = \langle 200t, 200t, -4.9t^2 + 1\rangle$.

b. 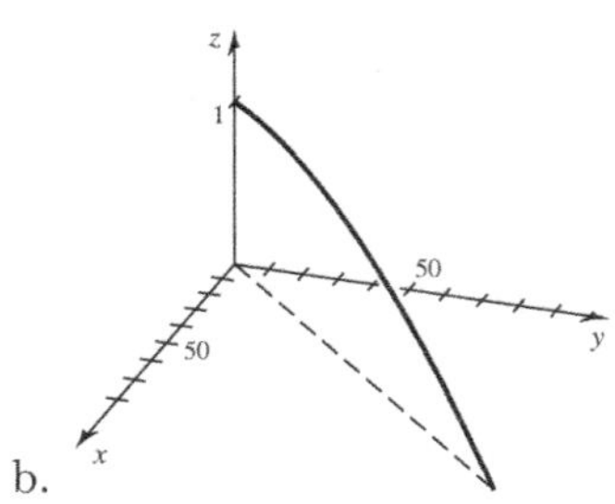

c. The bullet hits the ground when $-4.9t^2 + 1 = 0$, which occurs for $t \approx .452$ seconds. At this time, the bullet is approximately at the point $(200 \cdot 0.452, 200 \cdot 0.452, 0) \approx (90.35, 90.35, 0)$. So its range is approximately $\sqrt{90.35^2 + 90.35^2} \approx 127.8$ meters.

d. The maximum height of the bullet is its initial height of 1 meter.

11.7.49

a. $\mathbf{v}(t) = \int \mathbf{a}(t)\,dt = \int \langle 10, 0, -32\rangle\,dt = \langle 10t, 0, -32t\rangle + \mathbf{C}$. Because $\mathbf{v}(0) = \langle 60, 80, 80\rangle$, we have $\mathbf{v}(t) = \langle 10t + 60, 80, -32t + 80\rangle$.

Also, $\mathbf{r}(t) = \int \mathbf{v}(t)\,dt = \int \langle 10t + 60, 80, -32t + 80\rangle\,dt = \langle 5t^2 + 60t, 80t, -16t^2 + 80t\rangle + \mathbf{D}$, and because $\mathbf{r}(0) = \langle 0, 0, 3\rangle$, we have $\mathbf{r}(t) = \langle 5t^2 + 60t, 80t, -16t^2 + 80t + 3\rangle$.

b. 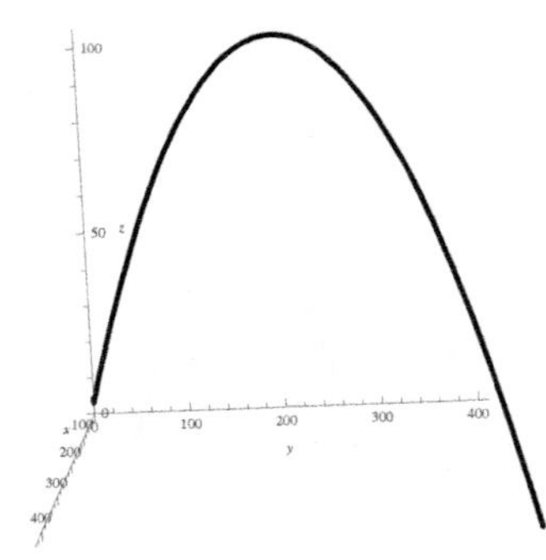

c. The ball hits the ground when $-16t^2 + 80t + 3 = 0$, which occurs for $t \approx 5.04$ seconds. At this time, the ball is at the point $(5(5.04)^2 + 60(5.04), 80(5.04), 0) \approx (429.4, 403.2, 0)$. So its range is approximately $\sqrt{429.4^2 + 403.2^2} \approx 589$ feet.

d. The maximum height of the ball occurs when $-32t + 80 = 0$, or when $t = 80/32 = 2.5$ seconds. At this time the ball's height is about $-16(2.5)^2 + 80(2.5) + 3 = 103$ feet.

11.7.51

a. $\mathbf{v}(t) = \int \mathbf{a}(t)\,dt = \int \langle 0, 2.5, -9.8\rangle\,dt = \langle 0, 2.5t, -9.8t\rangle + \mathbf{C}$. Because $\mathbf{v}(0) = \langle 300, 400, 500\rangle$, we have $\mathbf{v}(t) = \langle 300, 2.5t + 400, 500 - 9.8t\rangle$.
Also, $\mathbf{r}(t) = \int \mathbf{v}(t)\,dt = \int \langle 300, 2.5t + 400, 500 - 9.8t\rangle\,dt = \langle 300t, 1.25t^2 + 400t, 500t - 4.9t^2\rangle + \mathbf{D}$, and because $\mathbf{r}(0) = \langle 0,0,10\rangle$, we have $\mathbf{r}(t) = \langle 300t, 1.25t^2 + 400t, 10 + 500t - 4.9t^2\rangle$.

b. 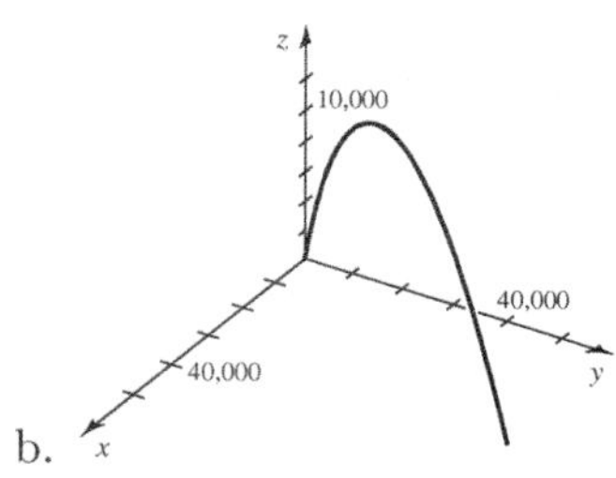

c. The rocket hits the ground when $-4.9t^2 + 500t + 10 = 0$, which occurs for $t \approx 102.1$ seconds. At this time, the rocket is at the point $(30630, 53870.5, 0)$. So its range is approximately $\sqrt{30630^2 + 53870.5^2} \approx 61969.6$ meters.

d. The maximum height of the rocket occurs when $-9.8t + 500 = 0$, or when $t = 500/9.8 \approx 51.02$ seconds. At this time the rocket's height is about $10 + 500(51.02) - 4.9(51.02)^2 \approx 12,765$ meters.

11.7.53

a. False. For example, if $\mathbf{v}(t) = \langle \cos t, \sin t\rangle$, then its speed is constantly 1 even though its components aren't constant.

b. True. They both generate $\{(x, y) \mid x^2 + y^2 = 1\}$.

c. False. For example, $\langle t, t, t\rangle$ has variable magnitude but constant direction.

d. True. If $\mathbf{a}(t) = \langle 0,0,0\rangle$, then $\mathbf{v}(t) = \langle 0,0,0\rangle + \mathbf{C}$ for a constant vector $\mathbf{C}$.

e. False. Recall that for two-dimensional motion the range is given by $\frac{|\mathbf{v}_0|^2 \sin 2\alpha}{g}$, so doubling the speed should quadruple the range.

f. True. The time of flight is given by $T = \frac{2|\mathbf{v}_0|\sin\alpha}{g}$, so doubling the speed doubles the time of flight.

g. True. For example, if $\mathbf{v}(t) = \langle e^t, e^t, e^t\rangle$, then $\mathbf{a}(t) = \langle e^t, e^t, e^t\rangle$ as well.

11.7.55 Note that $\langle u_0, v_0\rangle = 75\langle\sqrt{3}, 1\rangle$
The time of flight is $T = \frac{2|\mathbf{v}_0|\sin\alpha}{g} = \frac{2\cdot 75}{9.8} \approx 15.3$ seconds.
The range of the flight is $\frac{|\mathbf{v}_0|^2 2\sin\alpha\cos\alpha}{g} = \frac{11250\sqrt{3}}{9.8} \approx 1988.3$ meters.
The maximum height is given by $\frac{(|\mathbf{v}_0|\sin\alpha)^2}{2g} = \frac{75^2}{19.6} \approx 287$ meters.

11.7.57 Note that $\langle u_0, v_0\rangle = 200\langle 1, \sqrt{3}\rangle$ The time of flight is $T = \frac{2|\mathbf{v}_0|\sin\alpha}{g} = \frac{2\cdot 200\sqrt{3}}{32} = 21.65$ seconds.
The range of the flight is $\frac{|\mathbf{v}_0|^2 2\sin\alpha\cos\alpha}{g} = \frac{80,000\sqrt{3}}{32} = 4330.13$ feet.
The maximum height is given by $\frac{(|\mathbf{v}_0|\sin\alpha)^2}{2g} = \frac{(200\sqrt{3})^2}{64} = 1875$ feet.

11.7.59 We desire $\frac{|\mathbf{v}_0|^2 2\sin\alpha\cos\alpha}{g} = 300$ meters, so we require $\sin 2\alpha = 300 \cdot \frac{9.8}{60^2} \approx .81666$. So $2\alpha = \sin^{-1}(.81666)$, and $\alpha \approx 27.4$ degrees or $\alpha \approx 62.62$ degrees.

11.7.61

a. If $t_1 > t_0$ are two values of t, we have $\mathbf{r}(t_1) - \mathbf{r}(t_0) = (f(t_1) - f(t_0))\langle a, b, c\rangle$, which is always a vector in the same direction, regardless of the values of t_1 and t_0.

b. $\mathbf{r}'(t) = f'(t)\langle a, b, c\rangle$ is a multiple of $\langle a, b, c\rangle$, so the tangent vector is always a multiple of the vector $\langle a, b, c\rangle$, so the motion of the object doesn't vary in direction, although it might vary in speed.

11.7.63

a. The object traverses the circle once over the interval $[0, 2\pi/\omega]$.

b. The velocity is $\mathbf{v}(t) = \langle -A\omega\sin(\omega t), A\omega\cos(\omega t)\rangle$. The velocity is not constant in direction, but it is constant in speed, because the speed is $|A\omega|$.

c. The acceleration is $\mathbf{a}(t) = -A\omega^2\langle\cos\omega t, \sin\omega t\rangle$.

d. The position and velocity are orthogonal. The position and acceleration are in opposite directions.

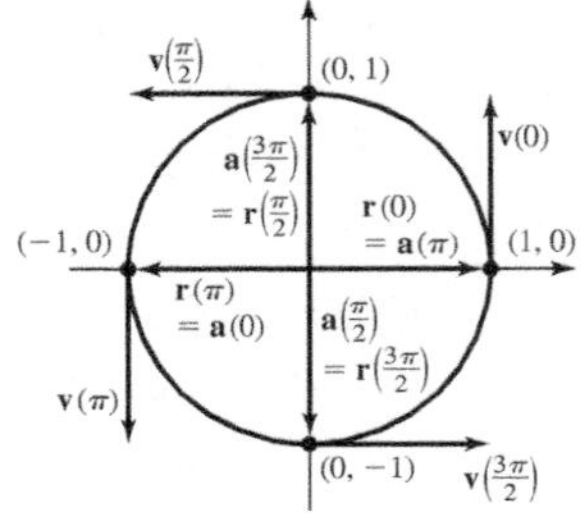

11.7.65

a. Consider $\mathbf{r}(t) = \langle 5\sin(\pi t/6), 5\cos(\pi t/6)\rangle$ for $0 \le t \le 12$. Note that the speed is the constant $5\pi/6$, and that $\mathbf{r}(0) = (0, 5) = \mathbf{r}(12)$.

b. Consider $\mathbf{r}(t) = \langle 5\sin((1-e^{-t})/5), 5\cos((1-e^{-t})/5)\rangle$ for $-\ln(10\pi+1) \le t \le 0$. Note that $\mathbf{r}(-\ln(10\pi+1)) = (0, 5) = \mathbf{r}(0)$. Also note that the speed is $|\mathbf{r}'(t)| = |e^{-t}\langle\cos((1-e^{-t})/5), -\sin((1-e^{-t})/5)\rangle| = e^{-t}$.

11.7.67

a. The velocity is $\mathbf{v}(t) = \langle -a\sin t, b\cos t\rangle$ and the speed is $\sqrt{a^2\sin^2 t + b^2\cos^2 t}$.

b. 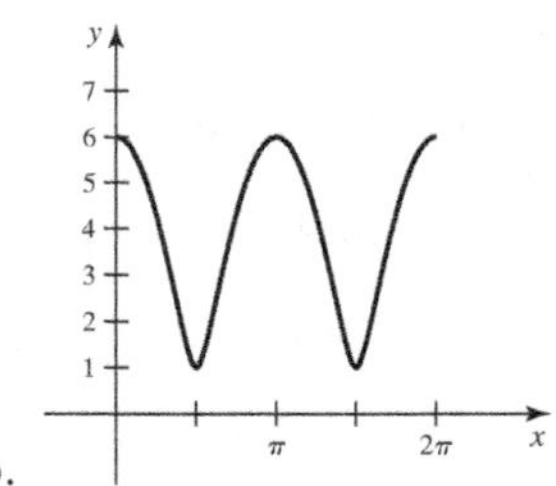

c. 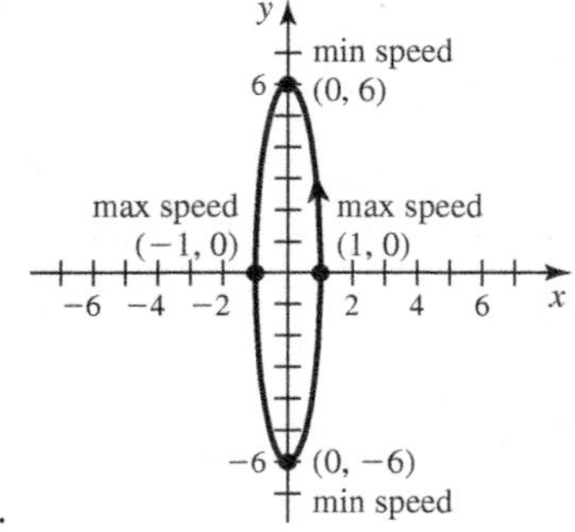

Yes, as the diagram indicates.

d. Assume $a > b > 0$. Then the maximum speed occurs at $\pi/2$ and is equal to a, while the minimum speed occurs at π and is equal to b. So the ratio is $\frac{a}{b}$. In the case $b > a > 0$, the ratio is $\frac{b}{a}$.

11.7.69

a. The initial point is $\mathbf{r}(0) = \langle 50, 0, 0\rangle$, and the "terminal" point is $\langle 0, 0, 5\rangle$ because $\lim_{t\to\infty} e^{-t} = 0$, while $\sin t$ and $\cos t$ are bounded between -1 and 1 as $t \to \infty$.

b. The speed is given by

$$5e^{-t}\left|\langle -10(\cos t + \sin t), 10(\cos t - \sin t), 1\rangle\right|,$$

which can be written as $5e^{-t}\sqrt{201}$.

c. 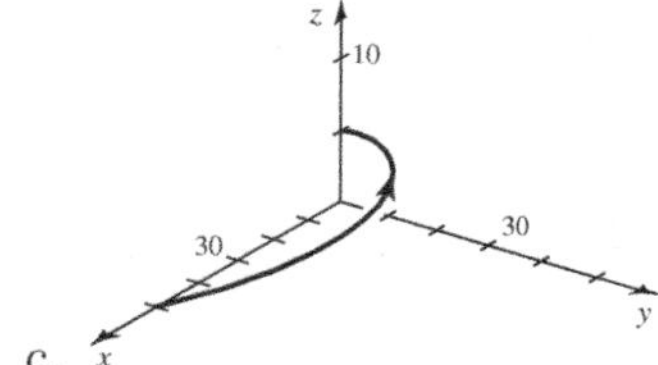

11.7.71 Let the angle be α. Then $\mathbf{v}(t) = \langle 120\cos\alpha, 120\sin\alpha - 32t\rangle$, and $\mathbf{r}(t) = \langle 120t\cos\alpha, 120t\sin\alpha - 16t^2\rangle$. Because we require the ball to land in the hole, we need the point $(420, -50)$ to be on the curve. So $120t\cos\alpha = 420$ and $120t\sin\alpha - 16t^2 = -50$. Thus $t = \frac{420}{120\cos\alpha}$, and therefore $120\cdot\frac{420\cdot\sin\alpha}{120\cos\alpha} - 16\left(\frac{420}{120\cos\alpha}\right)^2 = -50$. This can be written $420\tan\alpha - 196\sec^2\alpha + 50 = -196\tan^2\alpha + 420\tan\alpha - 146 = 0$. By the quadratic formula, we have

$$\tan\alpha = \frac{1}{14}\left(15 - \sqrt{79}\right) \text{ and } \tan\alpha = \frac{1}{14}\left(15 + \sqrt{79}\right).$$

Applying the inverse tangent and then writing the answer in degrees, we obtain $\alpha = 59.63$ degrees and $\alpha = 23.58$ degrees.

11.7.73 Let s be the initial speed of the ball. Note that $\mathbf{v}(t) = \langle s\sqrt{3}/2, s/2 - 32t\rangle$ and $\mathbf{r}(t) = \langle st\sqrt{3}/2, st/2 - 16t^2\rangle$. Because we want the second coordinate to be -50 when the first coordinate is 420, we have $st\sqrt{3}/2 = 420$ and $st/2 - 16t^2 = -50$. Solving the first equation for t yields $t = \frac{840}{\sqrt{3}s}$. Putting this value into the second equation yields $s\cdot\frac{840}{\sqrt{3}s}\cdot\frac{1}{2} - 16\left(\frac{840}{\sqrt{3}s}\right)^2 = -50$. Solving this last equation for s yields $s \approx 113.4$.

11.7.75

a. $\mathbf{v} = \langle 130, 0, -3 - 32t\rangle$ and $\mathbf{r}(t) = \langle 130t, 0, 6 - 3t - 16t^2\rangle$. When $x = 60$, $t = 6/13$, so $z = 6 - 3(6/13) - 16(6/13)^2 \approx 1.207$ feet. The flight lasts $t = 6/13$ seconds.

b. Suppose that the initial velocity is $\langle 130, 0, b\rangle$, so that $\mathbf{v}(t) = \langle 130t, 0, 6 + bt - 16t^2\rangle$. So $z = 3 = 6 + b(6/13) - 16(6/13)^2$, which when solved for b gives $b = .8846$.

c. In this scenario, we have $\mathbf{v}(t) = \langle 130, 8t, -3 - 32t\rangle$ and $\mathbf{r}(t)\langle 130t, 4t^2, 6 - 3t - 16t^2\rangle$. As before, $x = 60$ when $t = 6/13$, and at that time $y = 4(6/13)^2 \approx .8521$ feet.

d. It moves more in the second half, because of the factor of t^2. This makes life more difficult for the batter!

e. In this case $\mathbf{v}(t) = \langle 130, ct, -3 - 32t\rangle$ and $\mathbf{r}(t) = \langle 130t, -3 + ct^2/2, 6 - 3t - 16t^2\rangle$. Again, we have $t = 6/13$, and so we require $-3 + c\left(\frac{6}{13}\right)^2\cdot\frac{1}{2} = 0$, so $c \approx 28.17$.

11.7.77 We have $\mathbf{v}(t) = \langle v_0\cos\alpha, v_0\sin\alpha - gt\rangle$, and $\mathbf{r}(t) = \langle v_0t\cos\alpha, y_0 + v_0t\sin\alpha - \frac{1}{2}gt^2\rangle$. Suppose that object hits the ground at $(a, 0)$. Then $a = v_0T\cos\alpha$ and $0 = y_0 + v_0T\sin\alpha - \frac{1}{2}gT^2$ where T is the time of the flight. So by the quadratic formula, $T = \frac{v_0\sin\alpha + \sqrt{v_0^2\sin^2\alpha + 2gy_0}}{g}$. Thus $a = v_0T\cos\alpha = v_0(\cos\alpha)\left(\frac{v_0\sin\alpha + \sqrt{v_0^2\sin^2\alpha + 2gy_0}}{g}\right)$ is the range. Because the maximum height when $y_0 = 0$ is $\frac{v_0^2\sin^2\alpha}{2g}$, the maximum height in this scenario is $y_0 + \frac{v_0^2\sin^2\alpha}{2g}$.

11.7.79 Note that $x^2 + y^2 = \cos^2 t + \sin^2 t = 1$, and $z = cy$, so this curve is the intersection of the cylinder $x^2 + y^2 = 1$ with the plane $z = cy$, which results in an ellipse in that plane.

11.7.81 $\mathbf{r}(t)$ can be written $\langle R\cos\phi\cos t, R\sin\phi\cos t, R\sin t\rangle$ where R is the radius of the sphere and ϕ is a real constant. Note that

$$\mathbf{v}(t) = \langle -R\cos\phi\sin t, -R\sin\phi\sin t, R\cos t\rangle$$

and $\mathbf{a}(t) = \langle -R\cos\phi\cos t, -R\sin\phi\cos t, -R\sin t\rangle$, and that $\mathbf{r}(t)\cdot\mathbf{a}(t) = -R^2\cos^2\phi\cos^2 t - R^2\sin^2\phi\cos^2 t - R^2\sin^2 t = -R^2(\cos^2\phi + \sin^2\phi)\cos^2 t - R^2\sin^2 t = -R^2(\cos^2 t + \sin^2 t) = -R^2 = -|\mathbf{v}(t)|^2$.

11.7.83

a. Consider the vector $\mathbf{r}(0) = \langle a, c, e\rangle$. For any t so that $0 < t < 2\pi$, consider the vector $\mathbf{r}(t)$. We will show that all such vectors lie in the same plane by showing that when crossed with $\mathbf{r}(0)$, we always get a multiple of the same vector.

   Computing $\mathbf{r}(t)\times\langle a, c, e\rangle$ we obtain

$$\langle de\sin(t) - cf\sin(t), af\sin(t) - be\sin(t), bc\sin(t) - ad\sin(t)\rangle = \sin t\langle de - cf, af - be, bc - ad\rangle.$$

   So for any $t \in (0, 2\pi)$, we have that $\mathbf{r}(t)\times\langle a, c, e\rangle$ is a multiple of the constant vector $\langle de - cf, af - be, bc - ad\rangle$. This can only happen if all the vectors $\mathbf{r}(t)$ lie in the same plane.

b. $|\mathbf{r}(t)|^2 = (a\cos t + b\sin t)^2 + (c\cos t + d\sin t)^2 + (e\cos t + f\sin t)^2 = (a^2 + c^2 + e^2)\cos^2 t + (2ab + 2cd + 2ef)\sin t\cos t + (b^2 + d^2 + f^2)\sin^2 t$ In order for the path to be a circle, it would be sufficient that $a^2 + c^2 + e^2 = b^2 + d^2 + f^2$ and that $ab + cd + ef = 0$. In order for the path to be an ellipse, it would be sufficient that $ab + cd + ef = 0$.

11.8 Lengths of Curves

11.8.1 $L = \int_a^b \sqrt{x'(t)^2 + y'(t)^2}\,dt = \int_a^b \sqrt{1+4}\,dt = \sqrt{5}(b - a)$.

11.8.3 The arc length is $L = \int_a^b |\mathbf{r}'(t)|\,dt = \int_a^b |\mathbf{v}(t)|\,dt$.

11.8.5 $L = \int_0^\pi |\langle -20\sin(2t), 20\cos(2t)\rangle|\,dt = 20\pi$.

11.8.7 If the parameter t used to describe a trajectory also measures the arc length s of the curve that is generated, then we say that the curve is parametrized by its arc length. This occurs when $|\mathbf{v}(t)| = 1$.

11.8.9 $L = \int_0^1 \sqrt{36t^2 + 64t^2}\,dt = \int_0^1 10t\,dt = 5t^2\Big|_0^1 = 5$.

11.8.11 $L = \int_0^\pi \sqrt{(-3\sin t)^2 + (3\cos t)^2}\,dt = \int_0^\pi 3\,dt = 3\pi$.

11.8.13 Note that $(\cos t + t\sin t)' = -\sin t + \sin t + t\cos t = t\cos t$, and $(\sin t - t\cos t)' = \cos t - (\cos t - t\sin t) = t\sin t$. $L = \int_0^{\pi/2} \sqrt{(t\cos t)^2 + (t\sin t)^2}\,dt = \int_0^{\pi/2} t\,dt = \frac{t^2}{2}\Big|_0^{\pi/2} = \frac{\pi^2}{8}$.

11.8.15 $L = \int_1^6 \sqrt{3^2 + (-4)^2 + 3^2}\,dt = \sqrt{34}(6 - 1) = 5\sqrt{34}$.

11.8.17 $L = \int_0^{4\pi} \sqrt{1 + 64\cos^2 t + 64\sin^2 t}\,dt = \sqrt{65}(4\pi)$.

11.8.19 $L = \int_0^{\ln 2} \sqrt{4e^{4t} + 16e^{4t} + 16e^{4t}}\,dt = \int_0^{\ln 2} 6e^{2t}\,dt = 3e^{2t}\Big|_0^{\ln 2} = 12 - 3 = 9$.

11.8.21 $L = \int_0^{\pi/2} \sqrt{9\cos^4 t\sin^2 t + 9\sin^4 t\cos^2 t}\,dt = \int_0^{\pi/2} 3\sin t\cos t\,dt = \frac{3}{2}\sin^2 t\Big|_0^{\pi/2} = \frac{3}{2}$.

11.8.23 The speed is $\sqrt{36t^4 + 9t^4 + 225t^4} = \sqrt{270}\,t^2$. The length is thus $L = \int_0^4 \sqrt{270}\,t^2\,dt = \sqrt{270}\,\frac{t^3}{3}\Big|_0^4 = \sqrt{30}(64-0) = 64\sqrt{30}$.

11.8.25 The speed is $2\sqrt{(13\cos 2t)^2 + (-12\sin 2t)^2 + (-5\sin 2t)^2} = 2\cdot\sqrt{169} = 26$. The length is thus $L = \int_0^\pi 26\,dt = 26\pi$.

11.8.27 $L = \int_0^{2\pi} \sqrt{4\sin^2 t + 16\cos^2 t}\,dt = \int_0^{2\pi} \sqrt{4 + 12\cos^2 t}\,dt = 2\int_0^{2\pi} \sqrt{1 + 3\cos^2 t}\,dt \approx 19.38$.

11.8.29 $L = \int_{-2}^{2} \sqrt{1 + 64t^2}\,dt \approx 32.5$.

11.8.31 Note that the diameter of the circle is a, and that the complete circle is traversed for $0 \le t \le \pi$. $L = \int_0^\pi \sqrt{(a\sin\theta)^2 + (a\cos\theta)^2}\,d\theta = \int_0^\pi a\,d\theta = \pi a$.

11.8.33 $L = \int_0^{2\pi} \sqrt{\theta^4 + 4\theta^2}\,d\theta = \int_0^{2\pi} \theta\sqrt{\theta^2+4}\,d\theta$. Let $u = \theta^2 + 4$, so that $du = 2\theta\,d\theta$. Substituting gives $\frac{1}{2}\int_4^{4\pi^2+4} \sqrt{u}\,du = \frac{1}{2}\cdot\frac{2}{3}\left(u^{3/2}\right)\Big|_4^{4\pi^2+4} = \frac{1}{3}\left(8(\pi^2+1)^{3/2} - 8\right) = \frac{8}{3}\left((\pi^2+1)^{3/2} - 1\right)$.

11.8.35 Using symmetry, $L = 8\int_0^\pi \sqrt{(1+\cos\theta)^2 + (-\sin\theta)^2}\,d\theta = 8\int_0^\pi \sqrt{2+2\cos\theta}\,d\theta =$ $8\sqrt{2}\int_0^\pi \sqrt{1+\cos\theta}\cdot\frac{\sqrt{1-\cos\theta}}{\sqrt{1-\cos\theta}}\,d\theta = 8\sqrt{2}\int_0^\pi \frac{\sin\theta}{\sqrt{1-\cos\theta}}\,d\theta$. Let $u = 1 - \cos\theta$ so that $du = \sin\theta\,d\theta$. Then $L =$ $8\sqrt{2}\int_0^2 \frac{1}{\sqrt{u}}\,du = 16\sqrt{2}\cdot\sqrt{u}\Big|_0^2 = 32$.

11.8.37 $L = \int_0^{\ln 8} \sqrt{4e^{4\theta} + 16e^{4\theta}}\,d\theta = 2\sqrt{5}\int_0^{\ln 8} e^{2\theta}\,d\theta = \sqrt{5}\cdot e^{2\theta}\Big|_0^{\ln 8} = \sqrt{5}(64-1) = 63\sqrt{5}$.

11.8.39 $L = \int_0^{\pi/2} \sqrt{\sin^6(\theta/3) + \sin^4(\theta/3)\cos^2(\theta/3)}\,d\theta = \int_0^{\pi/2} \sin^2(\theta/3)\,d\theta = \frac{1}{2}\int_0^{\pi/2} 1 - \cos(2\theta/3)\,d\theta =$ $\frac{1}{2}\left(\theta - \frac{3}{2}\sin(2\theta/3)\right)\Big|_0^{\pi/2} = \frac{1}{2}\left(\frac{\pi}{2} - \frac{3\sqrt{3}}{4}\right) = \frac{2\pi - 3\sqrt{3}}{8}$.

11.8.41 Note that $|\mathbf{v}| = \sqrt{0 + \cos^2 t + \sin^2 t} = 1$, so it does use arc length as its parameter.

11.8.43 Note that $|\mathbf{v}| = \sqrt{1+4} \ne 1$, so it doesn't use arc length as a parameter.

Consider $\mathbf{r}(s) = \langle s/\sqrt{5}, 2s/\sqrt{5}\rangle$ for $0 \le s \le 3\sqrt{5}$. This has $|\mathbf{r}'(s)| = \frac{1}{\sqrt{5}}\sqrt{1+4} = 1$, so it does use arc length as its parameter.

11.8.45 Note that $|\mathbf{v}| = \sqrt{4\sin^2 t + 4\cos^2 t} \ne 1$, so it doesn't use arc length as a parameter.

Consider $\mathbf{r}(s) = \langle 2\cos(s/2), 2\sin(s/2)\rangle$ for $0 \le s \le 4\pi$. This has $|\mathbf{r}'(s)| = \sqrt{\sin^2(s/2) + \cos^2(s/2)} = 1$, so it does use arc length as its parameter.

11.8.47 Note that $|\mathbf{v}| = \sqrt{4t^2\sin^2(t^2) + 4t^2\cos^2(t^2)} = 2t \ne 1$, so it doesn't use arc length as a parameter.

Consider $\mathbf{r}(s) = \langle \cos s, \sin s\rangle$ for $0 \le s \le \pi$. This has $|\mathbf{r}'(s)| = \sqrt{\sin^2 s + \cos^2 s} = 1$, so it does use arc length as its parameter.

11.8.49 Note that $|\mathbf{v}| = \sqrt{e^{2t} + e^{2t} + e^{2t}} = \sqrt{3}e^t \ne 1$, so it doesn't use arc length as its parameter.

Consider $\mathbf{r}(s) = \langle \frac{s}{\sqrt{3}} + 1, \frac{s}{\sqrt{3}} + 1, \frac{s}{\sqrt{3}} + 1\rangle$ for $s \ge 0$. This has $|\mathbf{r}'(s)| = 1$, so it does use arc length as its parameter.

11.8.51

a. True. $L = \int_a^b S\,dt = S(b-a)$.

b. True. Both have length $L = \int_a^b \sqrt{f'(t)^2 + g'(t)^2}\,dt = \int_a^b \sqrt{g'(t)^2 + f'(t)^2}\,dt$.

c. True. Both have length $L = \int_a^b \sqrt{f'(t)^2 + g'(t)^2}\,dt = \int_{\sqrt{a}}^{\sqrt{b}} \sqrt{(f'(u^2)(2u))^2 + (g'(u^2)(2u))^2}\,du$. The equality can be seen via the substitution $u^2 = t$.

d. False. It is not the case that $|\mathbf{r}'(t)| = 1$ for all t, because $|\mathbf{r}'(t)| = \sqrt{1 + 40t^2}$.

11.8.53

a. Let $x = a\cos t$, $y = b\sin t$ and $z = c\sin t$. Then $x^2 + y^2 + z^2 = a^2\cos^2 t + b^2\sin^2 t + c^2\sin^2 t = a^2\cos^2 t + (b^2 + c^2)\sin^2 t = a^2$, assuming $a^2 = b^2 + c^2$. So the curve lies on a sphere, but also note that $cy = bz$, so the curve also lies in the plane $cy - bz = 0$. So the curve is a circle centered at the origin.

b. The circle has arc length $L = \int_0^{2\pi} \sqrt{a^2\sin^2 t + b^2\cos^2 t + c^2\cos^2 t}\,dt = \sqrt{a^2}\int_0^{2\pi} \sqrt{\sin^2 t + \cos^2 t}\,dt = 2a\pi$.

c. As in exercise 69a from section 11.7, the curve describes a circle when $a^2 + c^2 + e^2 = b^2 + d^2 + f^2 = R^2$ and $ab + cd + ef = 0$. Note that $|\mathbf{r}(t)|^2 = (a\cos t + b\sin t)^2 + (c\cos t + d\sin t)^2 + (e\cos t + f\sin t)^2 = (a^2 + c^2 + e^2)\cos^2 t + (2ab + 2cd + 2ef)\sin t\cos t + (b^2 + d^2 + f^2)\sin^2 t$, so if the conditions are met, then the curve describes a circle of radius R and $L = \int_0^{2\pi} \sqrt{R^2}\,dt = 2\pi R$.

11.8.55

a. $\mathbf{r}'(t) = h'(t)\langle A, B\rangle$, so $|\mathbf{r}'(t)| = |h'(t)|\sqrt{A^2 + B^2}$. Thus, $L = \sqrt{A^2 + B^2}\int_a^b |h'(t)|\,dt$

b. $L = \sqrt{2^2 + 5^2}\int_0^4 3t^2\,dt = \sqrt{29}\,t^3\Big|_0^4 = 64\sqrt{29}$.

c. $L = \sqrt{4^2 + 10^2}\int_1^8 \left|-1/t^2\right|\,dt = \sqrt{116}\,\frac{1}{t}\Big|_8^1 = \frac{7\sqrt{29}}{4}$.

11.8.57 $r'(\theta) = -ae^{-a\theta}$. Thus,

$$\begin{aligned} L &= \int_0^\infty \sqrt{e^{-2a\theta} + a^2e^{-2a\theta}}\,d\theta = \sqrt{1 + a^2}\int_0^\infty e^{-a\theta}\,d\theta \\ &= \lim_{b\to\infty} \sqrt{1 + a^2}\int_0^b e^{-a\theta}\,d\theta = \frac{\sqrt{1 + a^2}}{-a}\lim_{b\to\infty} e^{-a\theta}\Big|_0^b \\ &= \frac{\sqrt{1 + a^2}}{-a}(0 - 1) = \frac{\sqrt{1 + a^2}}{a}. \end{aligned}$$

11.8.59 Using symmetry, we are seeking 4 times the curve traversed for $0 \le \theta \le \pi/4$. Thus, $L = 4\displaystyle\int_0^{\pi/4} \sqrt{6\sin 2\theta + 6\cot 2\theta\cos 2\theta}\,d\theta = 12.85$.

11.8.61 $L = \displaystyle\int_0^{2\pi} \sqrt{(4 - 2\cos\theta)^2 + 4\sin^2\theta}\,d\theta = \int_0^{2\pi} \sqrt{20 - 16\cos\theta}\,d\theta = 26.73$.

11.8.63

a. $y = -4.9t^2 + 25t$ is 0 for $t > 0$ when $-4.9t + 25 = 0$, or $t = 25/4.9 \approx 5.102$ seconds.

b. $L \approx \int_0^{5.102} \sqrt{400 + (25 - 9.8t)^2}\,dt$.

c. Let $u = -9.8t + 25$ so that $du = -9.8dt$. Then $L \approx \frac{1}{-9.8}\int_{25}^{-24.9996} \sqrt{400 + u^2}\,du \approx 124.43$ meters.

d. $x = u_0(5.102) = 20(5.102) = 102.04$ meters.

11.8.65 Recall that a curve is parametrized by arc length exactly when $|\mathbf{v}| = 1$. We have $\mathbf{v} = \langle a, b, c\rangle$, so $|\mathbf{v}| = \sqrt{a^2+b^2+c^2}$, which is equal to one if and only if $a^2+b^2+c^2 = 1$.

11.8.67 $\int_a^b |\mathbf{r}'(t)|\,dt = \int_a^b \sqrt{(cf'(t))^2+(cg'(t))^2}\,dt = |c|\int_a^b \sqrt{f'(t)^2+g'(t)^2}\,dt = |c|\,L$.

11.8.69 The curve can be parametrized by $x = t$ and $y = f(t)$. Then $\mathbf{r}'(t) = \langle 1, f'(t)\rangle$, so

$$|\mathbf{v}(t)| = \sqrt{1+f'(t)^2}.$$

Then

$$L = \int_a^b \sqrt{1+f'(t)^2}\,dt = \int_a^b \sqrt{1+f'(x)^2}\,dx.$$

11.9 Curvature and Normal Vectors

11.9.1 A straight line has zero curvature.

11.9.3 $\kappa = \frac{1}{|\mathbf{v}|}\left|\frac{d\mathbf{T}}{dt}\right|$ or $\kappa = \frac{|\mathbf{a}\times\mathbf{v}|}{|\mathbf{v}|^3}$.

11.9.5 $\mathbf{N} = \frac{d\mathbf{T}/dt}{|d\mathbf{T}/dt|}$.

11.9.7 $\mathbf{B}$ is a length one vector mutually perpendicular to $\mathbf{T}$ and $\mathbf{N}$. The three vectors $\mathbf{T}$, $\mathbf{N}$, and $\mathbf{B}$ form a right-handed coordinate system.

11.9.9 The torsion is the rate at which the curve moves out of the osculating lane.

11.9.11 $\mathbf{r}'(t) = \langle 2, 4, 6\rangle$, so $\mathbf{T} = \frac{1}{2\sqrt{14}}\langle 2,4,6\rangle = \frac{1}{\sqrt{14}}\langle 1,2,3\rangle$.
So $\frac{d\mathbf{T}}{dt} = \langle 0,0,0\rangle$, and $\kappa = 0$.

11.9.13 $\mathbf{r}'(t) = \langle 2, 4\cos t, -4\sin t\rangle$, so $\mathbf{T}(t) = \frac{1}{\sqrt{5}}\langle 1, 2\cos t, -2\sin t\rangle$. So

$$\kappa = \frac{1}{|\mathbf{v}|}\left|\frac{d\mathbf{T}}{dt}\right| = \frac{1}{2\sqrt{5}}\left|\frac{1}{\sqrt{5}}\langle 0, -2\sin t, -2\cos t\rangle\right| = \frac{1}{5}.$$

11.9.15 $\mathbf{r}'(t) = \langle \sqrt{3}\cos t, \cos t, -2\sin t\rangle$, so $|\mathbf{v}(t)| = \sqrt{3\cos^2 t+\cos^2 t+4\sin^2 t} = 2$.
Thus, $\mathbf{T}(t) = \frac{1}{2}\langle\sqrt{3}\cos t, \cos t, -2\sin t\rangle$. So

$$\kappa = \frac{1}{|\mathbf{v}|}\left|\frac{d\mathbf{T}}{dt}\right| = \frac{1}{2}\left|\frac{1}{2}\langle -\sqrt{3}\sin t, -\sin t, -2\cos t\rangle\right| = \frac{1}{2}\cdot\frac{1}{2}\cdot 2 = \frac{1}{2}.$$

11.9.17 $\mathbf{r}'(t) = \langle 1, 4t\rangle$, so $|\mathbf{v}(t)| = \sqrt{16t^2+1}$. Thus, $\mathbf{T}(t) = \frac{1}{\sqrt{16t^2+1}}\langle 1, 4t\rangle$.

$$\kappa = \frac{|\mathbf{a}\times\mathbf{v}|}{|\mathbf{v}|^3} = \frac{1}{(16t^2+1)^{3/2}}\left|\langle 0,4,0\rangle\times\langle 1,4t,0\rangle\right| = \frac{1}{(16t^2+1)^{3/2}}\left|\langle 0,0,-4\rangle\right| = \frac{4}{(16t^2+1)^{3/2}}.$$

11.9.19 $\mathbf{r}'(t) = \langle\cos(\pi t^2/2), \sin(\pi t^2/2)\rangle$, so $|\mathbf{v}(t)| = 1$. So $\mathbf{T}(t) = \mathbf{v}(t) = \langle\cos(\pi t^2/2), \sin(\pi t^2/2)\rangle$.

$$\kappa = \frac{1}{|\mathbf{v}|}\left|\frac{d\mathbf{T}}{dt}\right| = 1\cdot\left|\langle -\pi t\sin(\pi t/^2 2), \pi t\cos(\pi t^2/2)\rangle\right| = \pi t.$$

11.9.21 $\mathbf{r}'(t) = \langle 3\sin t, 3\cos t\rangle$ and $\mathbf{r}''(t) = \langle 3\cos t, -3\sin t\rangle$. So

$$\kappa = \frac{|\mathbf{a}\times\mathbf{v}|}{|\mathbf{v}|^3} = \frac{1}{27}\left|\langle 3\cos t, -3\sin t, 0\rangle\times\langle 3\sin t, 3\cos t, 0\rangle\right| = \frac{1}{27}\left|\langle 0,0,9\rangle\right| = \frac{1}{3}.$$

11.9.23 $\mathbf{r}'(t) = \langle 2t, 1\rangle$ and $\mathbf{r}''(t) = \langle 2, 0\rangle$. So

$$\kappa = \frac{|\mathbf{a}\times\mathbf{v}|}{|\mathbf{v}|^3} = \frac{1}{(4t^2+1)^{3/2}}\,|\langle 2,0,0\rangle \times \langle 2t,1,0\rangle| = \frac{1}{(4t^2+1)^{3/2}}\,|\langle 0,0,2\rangle| = \frac{2}{(4t^2+1)^{3/2}}.$$

11.9.25 $\mathbf{r}'(t) = \langle -4\sin t, \cos t, -2\sin t\rangle$ and $\mathbf{r}''(t) = \langle -4\cos t, -\sin t, -2\cos t\rangle$.

$$\kappa = \frac{|\mathbf{a}\times\mathbf{v}|}{|\mathbf{v}|^3} = \frac{|\langle 2,0,-4\rangle|}{\left(\sqrt{20\sin^2(t)+\cos^2(t)}\right)^3} = \frac{2\sqrt{5}}{\left(20\sin^2(t)+\cos^2(t)\right)^{3/2}}.$$

11.9.27 $\mathbf{r}'(t) = \langle 2\cos t, -2\sin t\rangle$, so $\mathbf{T} = \langle \cos t, -\sin t\rangle$ and $|\mathbf{T}| = 1$. $\mathbf{N}(t) = \langle -\sin t, -\cos t\rangle$. Note that $|\mathbf{N}| = 1$ and $\mathbf{T}\cdot\mathbf{N} = -\sin t\cos t + \sin t\cos t = 0$.

11.9.29 $\mathbf{r}'(t) = \langle t, -3, 0\rangle$, and $|\mathbf{r}'(t)| = \sqrt{t^2+9}$, so $\mathbf{T} = \frac{1}{\sqrt{t^2+9}}\langle t,-3,0\rangle$ and $|\mathbf{T}| = 1$. We have $\mathbf{T}'(t) = \langle \frac{9}{(\sqrt{t^2+9})^3}, \frac{3t}{(\sqrt{t^2+9})^3}, 0\rangle$, so $\mathbf{N}(t) = \frac{1}{\sqrt{t^2+9}}\langle 3, t, 0\rangle$. Note that $|\mathbf{N}| = 1$ and $\mathbf{T}\cdot\mathbf{N} = 0$.

11.9.31 $\mathbf{r}'(t) = \langle -2t\sin t^2, 2t\cos t^2\rangle$, and $|\mathbf{r}'(t)| = 2t$, so $\mathbf{T} = \langle -\sin t^2, \cos t^2\rangle$ and $|\mathbf{T}| = 1$. $\mathbf{T}'(t) = \langle -2t\cos t^2, -2t\sin t^2\rangle$, so $\mathbf{N}(t) = \langle -\cos t^2, -\sin t^2\rangle$. Note that $|\mathbf{N}| = 1$ and $\mathbf{T}\cdot\mathbf{N} = 0$.

11.9.33 $\mathbf{r}'(t) = \langle 2t, 1\rangle$, and $|\mathbf{r}'(t)| = \sqrt{4t^2+1}$, so $\mathbf{T} = \frac{1}{\sqrt{4t^2+1}}\langle 2t, 1\rangle$ and $|\mathbf{T}| = 1$.
$\mathbf{T}'(t) = \langle \frac{2}{(\sqrt{4t^2+1})^3}, -\frac{4t}{(\sqrt{4t^2+1})^3}\rangle$, so $\mathbf{N}(t) = \frac{1}{\sqrt{4t^2+1}}\langle 1, -2t\rangle$. Note that $|\mathbf{N}| = 1$ and $\mathbf{T}\cdot\mathbf{N} = 0$.

11.9.35 $\mathbf{r}'(t) = \langle 1, 4, -6\rangle$ and $\mathbf{r}''(t) = \langle 0,0,0\rangle$. So $\kappa = 0$ and thus $a_N = 0$. Also, $a_T = 0$. We have $\mathbf{a} = 0\cdot\mathbf{T} + 0\cdot\mathbf{N} = \langle 0,0,0\rangle$.

11.9.37 In problem 26 above, we computed $|\mathbf{v}(t)| = \sqrt{3}e^t$ and $\kappa = \frac{\sqrt{2}}{3e^t}$. Also, $\mathbf{v}(t)\cdot\mathbf{a}(t) = 3e^{2t}$. Thus $a_T = \frac{3e^{2t}}{\sqrt{3}e^t} = \sqrt{3}e^t$ and $a_N = \frac{\sqrt{2}}{3e^t}\cdot 3e^{2t} = \sqrt{2}e^t$.

11.9.39 $\mathbf{r}'(t) = \langle 3t^2, 2t\rangle$ and $\mathbf{r}''(t) = \langle 6t, 2\rangle$. Note that $\mathbf{a}\cdot\mathbf{v} = 18t^3 + 4t$, so $a_T = \frac{18t^3+4t}{\sqrt{9t^4+4t^2}} = \frac{18t^2+4}{\sqrt{9t^2+4}}$. $\mathbf{a}\times\mathbf{v} = \langle 0,0,6t^2\rangle$, so $a_N = \frac{6t^2}{t\sqrt{9t^2+4}} = \frac{6t}{\sqrt{9t^2+4}}$. We have $\mathbf{a} = \langle 6t, 2\rangle = \frac{18t^2+4}{\sqrt{9t^2+4}}\cdot\mathbf{T} + \frac{6t}{\sqrt{9t^2+4}}\cdot\mathbf{N}$.

11.9.41 $\mathbf{B} = \mathbf{T}\times\mathbf{N} = \langle \cos t, -\sin t, 0\rangle \times \langle -\sin t, -\cos t, 0\rangle = \langle 0,0,-1\rangle$. Because $\mathbf{B}$ is constant, $\tau = 0$.

11.9.43 $\mathbf{B} = \mathbf{T}\times\mathbf{N} = \langle \frac{t}{\sqrt{t^2+9}}, -\frac{3}{\sqrt{t^2+9}}, 0\rangle \times \langle \frac{3}{\sqrt{t^2+9}}, \frac{t}{\sqrt{t^2+9}}, 0\rangle = \langle 0,0,1\rangle$. Because $\mathbf{B}$ is constant, $\tau = 0$.

11.9.45 $\mathbf{r}'(t) = \langle -2\sin t, 2\cos t, -1\rangle$, so $\mathbf{T} = \langle (-2/\sqrt{5})\sin t, (2/\sqrt{5})\cos t, -1/\sqrt{5}\rangle$.
$\mathbf{r}''(t) = \langle -2\cos t, -2\sin t, 0\rangle$, so $\mathbf{N} = \langle -\cos t, -\sin t, 0\rangle$. Thus, $\mathbf{B} = \mathbf{T}\times\mathbf{N} = \frac{1}{\sqrt{5}}\langle -\sin t, \cos t, 2\rangle$. Also, $\tau = \frac{-d\mathbf{B}/dt}{ds/dt}\cdot\mathbf{N} = -\frac{1}{\sqrt{5}}\cdot\frac{1}{\sqrt{5}}(\langle -\cos t, -\sin t, 0\rangle\cdot\langle -\cos t, -\sin t, 0\rangle = -\frac{1}{5}$.

11.9.47 $\mathbf{r}'(t) = \langle 12, -5\sin t, 5\cos t\rangle$, so $\mathbf{r}''(t) = \langle 0, -5\cos t, -5\sin t\rangle$. Thus, $\mathbf{T} = \langle 12/13, (-5/13)\sin t, (5/13)\cos t\rangle$ and $\mathbf{N} = \langle 0, -\cos t, -\sin t\rangle$.
So $\mathbf{B} = \mathbf{T}\times\mathbf{N} = \langle (5/13), (12/13)\sin t, (-12/13)\cos t\rangle$.
Also, $\tau = -\frac{d\mathbf{B}/dt}{ds/dt}\cdot\mathbf{N} = -\frac{1}{13}\cdot\frac{1}{13}(\langle 0, 12\cos t, 12\sin t\rangle\cdot\langle 0, -\cos t, -\sin t\rangle = -\frac{1}{169}\cdot(-12) = \frac{12}{169}$.

11.9.49

a. False. For example, consider $\mathbf{r}(t) = \langle \cos t, \sin t, 1\rangle$. Then $\mathbf{T} = \langle -\sin t, \cos t, 0\rangle$ and also $\mathbf{N} = \langle -\cos t, -\sin t, 0\rangle$. Note that $\mathbf{T}$ and $\mathbf{N}$ lie in the xy-plane, but $\mathbf{r}$ doesn't.

b. False. $\mathbf{T}$ does depend on the orientation, but $\mathbf{N}$ doesn't. Reversing the orientation changes $\mathbf{T}$ to $-\mathbf{T}$, but leaves $\mathbf{N}$ alone.

c. False. Note that $|\mathbf{T}|$ is independent of orientation, so $\left|\frac{d\mathbf{T}}{ds}\right|$ is too.

d. True. As we have already seen for the circle, $\mathbf{v}\cdot\mathbf{a}=0$. Thus $\mathbf{a}=a_T\mathbf{T}+a_N\mathbf{N}=0\cdot\mathbf{T}+\kappa|\mathbf{v}|^2\mathbf{N}=\frac{1}{R}\mathbf{N}$.

e. False. For example, if the car's motion is given by $\mathbf{r}(t)=\langle 60\cos t, 60\sin t\rangle$, then the speed is a constant 60, but $\mathbf{a}=\langle -60\cos t, -60\sin t\rangle\neq\langle 0,0\rangle$.

f. False. If it lies in the xy-plane, it will have zero torsion.

g. False. If it lies in the xy-plane, it might have very large curvature but zero torsion.

11.9.51 $f'(x)=2x$ and $f''(x)=2$, so

$$\kappa=\frac{|f''(x)|}{(1+f'(x)^2)^{3/2}}=\frac{2}{(1+4x^2)^{3/2}}$$

11.9.53 $f'(x)=1/x$ and $f''(x)=-1/x^2$, so

$$\kappa=\frac{|f''(x)|}{(1+f'(x)^2)^{3/2}}=\frac{1/x^2}{(1+(1/x)^2)^{3/2}}=\frac{x}{(x^2+1)^{3/2}}.$$

11.9.55 $\mathbf{r}'(t)=\langle f'(t),g'(t)\rangle$ and $\mathbf{r}''(t)=\langle f''(t),g''(t)\rangle$. So $\mathbf{a}\times\mathbf{v}=\langle f''(t),g''(t),0\rangle\times\langle f'(t),g'(t),0\rangle=\langle 0,0,g'(t)f''(t)-f'(t)g''(t)\rangle$. Because $|\mathbf{v}|=\sqrt{(f'(t))^2+(g'(t))^2}$, we have

$$\kappa=\frac{|\mathbf{a}\times\mathbf{v}|}{|\mathbf{v}|^3}=\frac{|f'g''-g'f''|}{((f')^2+(g')^2)^{3/2}}.$$

11.9.57 $f'(t)=a\cos t$ and $f''(t)=-a\sin t$, while $g'(t)=-b\sin t$ and $g''(t)=-b\cos t$. So

$$\kappa=\frac{|\mathbf{a}\times\mathbf{v}|}{|\mathbf{v}|^3}=\frac{|f'g''-g'f''|}{((f')^2+(g')^2)^{3/2}}=\frac{\left|-ab\cos^2 t-ab\sin^2 t\right|}{(a^2\cos^2 t+b^2\sin^2 t)^{3/2}}=\frac{|ab|}{(a^2\cos^2 t+b^2\sin^2 t)^{3/2}}.$$

11.9.59 $f'(t)=1$ and $f''(t)=0$, while $g'(t)=2at$ and $g''(t)=2a$. So

$$\kappa=\frac{|f'g''-g'f''|}{((f')^2+(g')^2)^{3/2}}=\frac{|2a-0|}{(1+4a^2t^2)^{3/2}}=\frac{2|a|}{(1+4a^2t^2)^{3/2}}.$$

11.9.61

a. 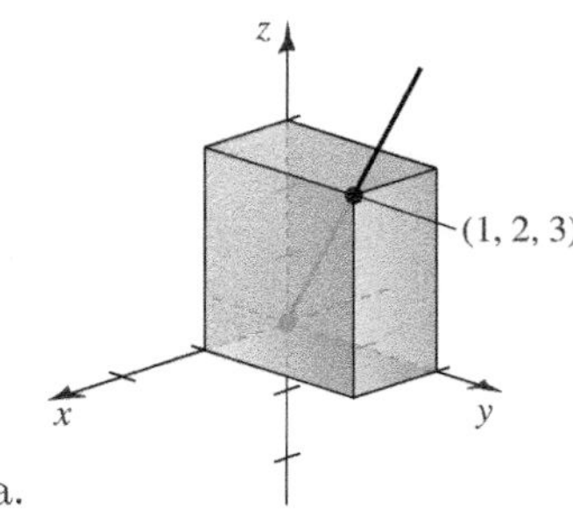

b. For line A: $\mathbf{v}(t)=\langle 1,2,3\rangle$ and $\mathbf{a}(t)=\langle 0,0,0\rangle$.
For line B: $\mathbf{v}(t)=\langle 2t,4t,6t\rangle$ and $\mathbf{a}(t)=\langle 2,4,6\rangle$.
A has constant velocity and zero acceleration, while B has linearly increasing velocity and constant acceleration.

c. For A, we have $a_T=a_N=0$. For B, we have $a_T=\frac{56t}{\sqrt{56}t}=2\sqrt{14}$ and $a_N=0$ (because $\mathbf{v}$ and $\mathbf{a}$ are in the same direction).

11.9.63

a. 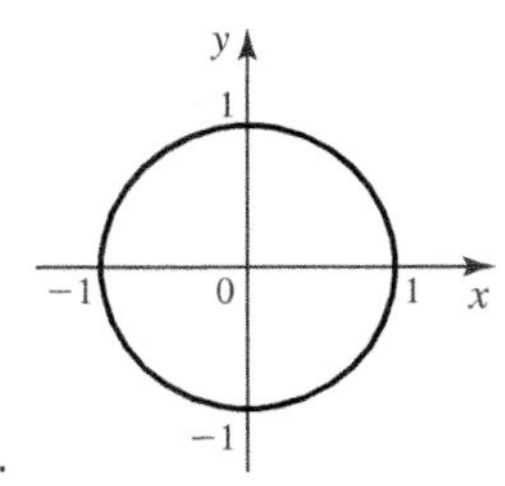

b. For curve A: $\mathbf{v}(t)=\langle -\sin t,\cos t\rangle$ and $\mathbf{a}(t)=\langle -\cos t,-\sin t\rangle$.
For curve B: $\mathbf{v}(t)=2t\langle -\sin t^2,\cos t^2\rangle$ and $\mathbf{a}(t)=\langle -4t^2\cos t^2-2\sin t^2, -4t^2\sin t^2+2\cos t^2\rangle$.
A has constant velocity 1 while B does not have constant velocity.

c. For A, we have $\mathbf{a}=\mathbf{N}$, so $a_T=0$ and $a_N=1$.
For B, we have $a_T=2$ and $a_N=4t^2$.

11.9.65

a. 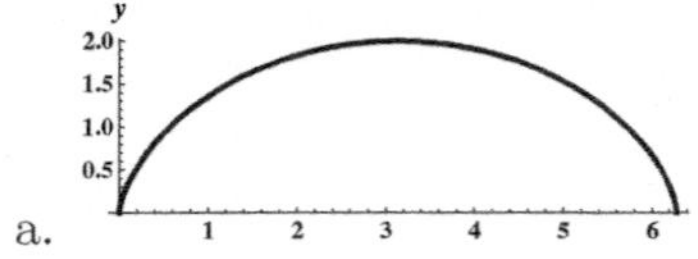

b. $\kappa = \frac{|f'g''-f''g'|}{(f'(x)^2+g'(x)^2)^{3/2}} = \frac{|(1-\cos t)\cos t - \sin t \sin t|}{((1-\cos t)^2+\sin^2 t)^{3/2}} = \frac{1-\cos t}{2\sqrt{2}(1-\cos t)^{3/2}} = \frac{1}{2\sqrt{2}\sqrt{1-\cos t}}$.

c. 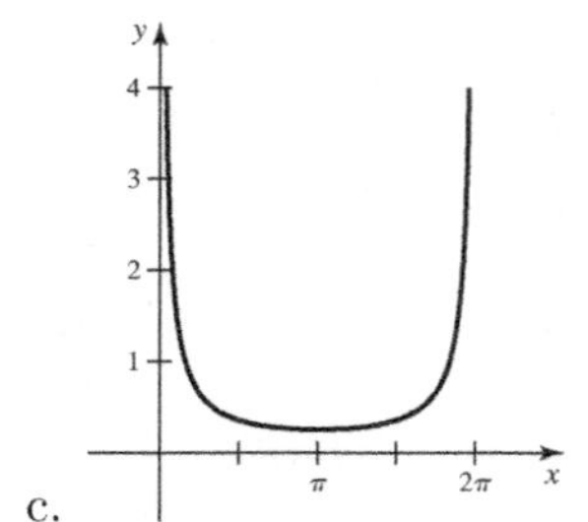

d. $\kappa'(t) = -\frac{\sin t}{4\sqrt{2}(1-\cos t)^{3/2}}$. κ has a minimum at π. $\kappa''(t) = \frac{\sin^2\left(\frac{t}{2}\right)(\cos t+3)}{4\sqrt{2}(1-\cos(t))^{5/2}}$. κ has no inflection points on the given interval.

e. Symmetry of the given curve about π (on the interval $(0, 2\pi)$ implies symmetry in κ, which does occur. The curve is flatter near π and more curved near 0 and 2π.

11.9.67

a. 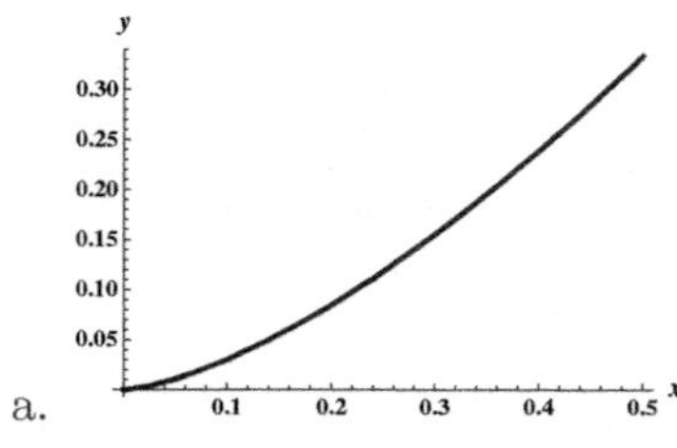

b. $\kappa = \frac{|f'g''-f''g'|}{(f'(x)^2+g'(x)^2)^{3/2}} = \frac{|t\cdot 2t - 1\cdot t^2|}{(t^2+t^4)^{3/2}} = \frac{1}{t(1+t^2)^{3/2}}$.

c. 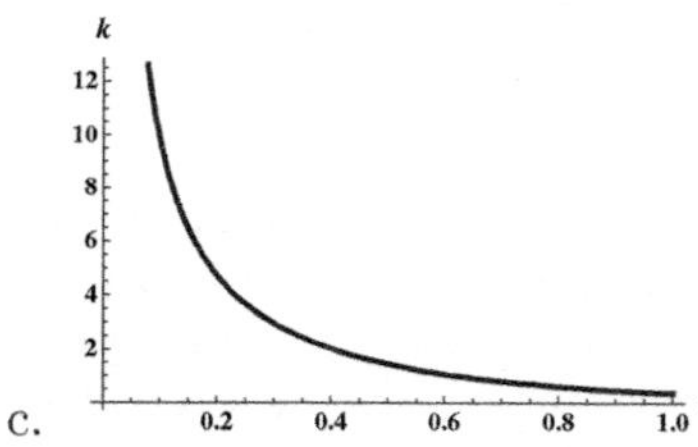

d. $\kappa'(t) = \frac{-4t^2-1}{t^2(t^2+1)^{5/2}}$. κ has no extrema. $\kappa''(t) = \frac{20t^4+7t^2+2}{t^3(t^2+1)^{7/2}}$. κ has no inflection points.

e. The curve gets flatter as $t \to \infty$.

11.9.69 $y'(x) = e^x$ and $y''(x) = e^x$. So $\kappa = \frac{|f''(x)|}{(1+f'(x)^2)^{3/2}} = \frac{e^x}{(1+(e^{2x}))^{3/2}}$. $\kappa'(x) = \frac{e^x-2e^{3x}}{(e^{2x}+1)^{5/2}}$, which is 0 for $x = -\frac{\ln 2}{2}$. The first derivative test shows that this is where the maximum curvature exists, and the value of the maximum curvature is $\kappa((-\ln 2)/2) = 2\sqrt{3}/9$.

11.9.71 $\mathbf{r}'(t) = \langle 1, 2t\rangle$ and $\mathbf{r}''(t) = \langle 0, 2\rangle$. Thus $\kappa = \frac{2}{(1+4t^2)^{3/2}}$. At $t = 0$, we have $\kappa = 2$. So we are seeking a circle of radius $1/2$. The center of the osculating circle is the point along the normal line to the curve at $(0, 0)$ which is $1/2$ unit from $(0, 0)$ and is on the inside of the curve, so it is $(0, 1/2)$. The equation is $x^2 + (y - (1/2))^2 = \frac{1}{4}$.

11.9.73 $\mathbf{r}'(t) = \langle 1-\cos t, \sin t\rangle$ and $\mathbf{r}''(t) = \langle \sin t, -\cos t\rangle$. Thus $\kappa(\pi) = \frac{(2-0)}{(2^2+0^2)^{3/2}} = \frac{2}{8} = \frac{1}{4}$, so the radius of the osculating circle is 4. The center of the osculating circle is the point along the normal line to the curve at $(\pi, 2)$ which is 4 units from $(\pi, 2)$ and is on the inside of the curve, so it is $(\pi, -2)$. The equation of the osculating circle is $(x-\pi)^2 + (y+2)^2 = 16$.

11.9.75 $y' = n\cos nx$ and $y'' = -n^2 \sin nx$, so $\kappa(\pi/2n) = \frac{|-n^2 \sin(\pi/2)|}{(1+(n^2\cos^2(\pi/2))^{3/2}} = \frac{n^2}{(1+0)^{3/2}} = n^2$. This increases as n increases.

11.9.77

a. $\mathbf{r}'(t) = \langle V_0 \cos\alpha, V_0 \sin\alpha - gt\rangle$, so the speed is

$$\sqrt{V_0^2\cos^2\alpha + V_0^2\sin^2\alpha - 2gtV_0\sin\alpha + g^2t^2},$$

which can be written

$$\sqrt{V_0^2 - 2gtV_0\sin\alpha + g^2t^2}.$$

The graph shown is for $V_0 = 1$, $g = 32$, and $\alpha = 45$ degrees.

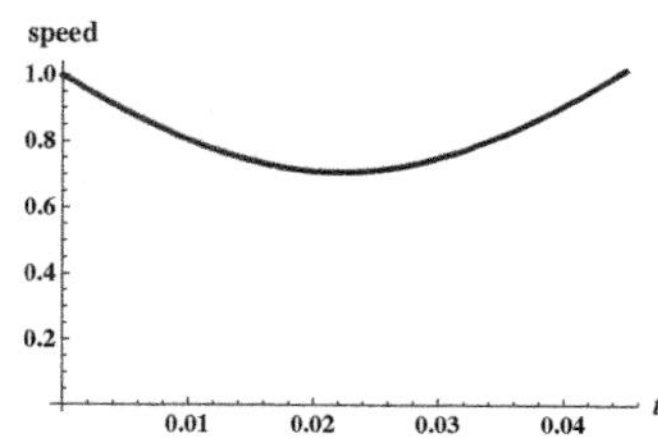

b. $\mathbf{a} = \langle 0, -g\rangle$. We have $\mathbf{a}\times\mathbf{v} = \langle 0, 0, gV_0\cos\alpha\rangle$. So $\kappa = \frac{|gV_0\cos\alpha|}{(V_0^2 - 2gtV_0\sin\alpha + g^2t^2)^{3/2}}$. The graph shown is for $V_0 = 1$, $g = 32$, and $\alpha = 45$ degrees.

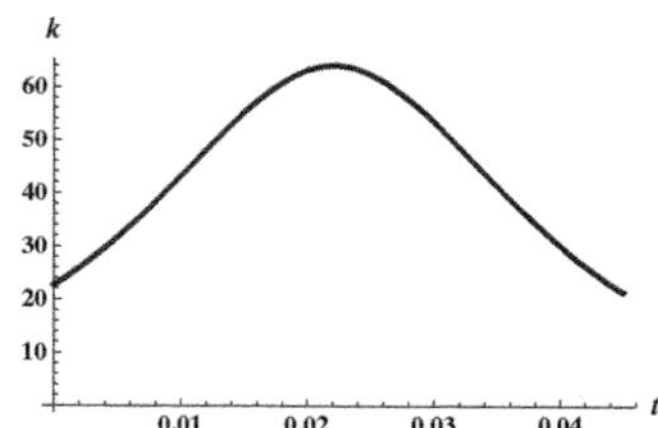

c. The speed has a minimum and the curvature has a maximum at the halfway time of the flight, namely at $\frac{V_0\sin\alpha}{g}$.

11.9.79 $\mathbf{r}'(t) = \langle pbt^{p-1}, pdt^{p-1}, pft^{p-1}\rangle = pt^{p-1}\langle b, d, f\rangle$. $\mathbf{r}''(t) = p(p-1)t^{p-2}\langle b, d, f\rangle$. Because for any t, $\mathbf{r}''(t)$ and $\mathbf{r}'(t)$ are multiples of $\langle b, d, f\rangle$, their cross product is $\langle 0, 0, 0\rangle$. Thus $\kappa = \frac{0}{|\mathbf{v}|^3} = 0$. The given curve represents a straight line, which has zero curvature.

11.9.81

a. $f_n'(x) = 2nx^{2n-1}$ and $f_n''(x) = (2n)(2n-1)x^{2n-2}$. $\kappa = \frac{|2n(2n-1)x^{2n-2}|}{(1+4n^2x^{4n-2})^{3/2}}$. So $\kappa_1(x) = \frac{2}{(1+4x^2)^{3/2}}$, $\kappa_2(x) = \frac{12x^2}{(1+16x^6)^{3/2}}$, and $\kappa_3(x) = \frac{30x^4}{(1+36x^{10})^{3/2}}$.

b.

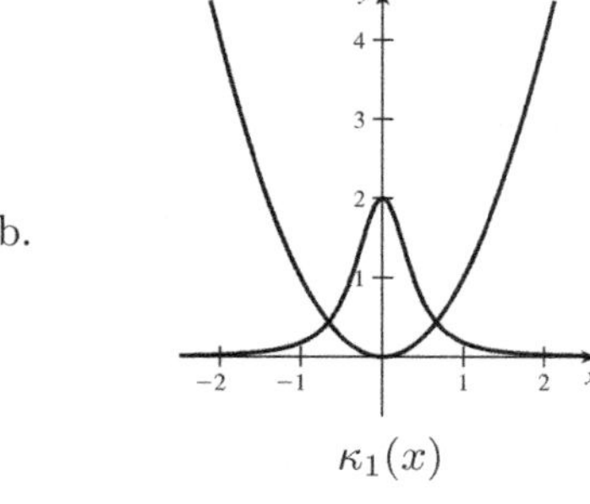

$\kappa_1(x)$

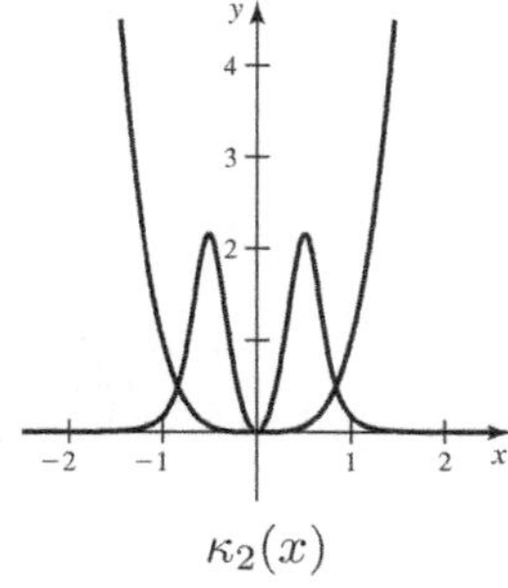

$\kappa_2(x)$

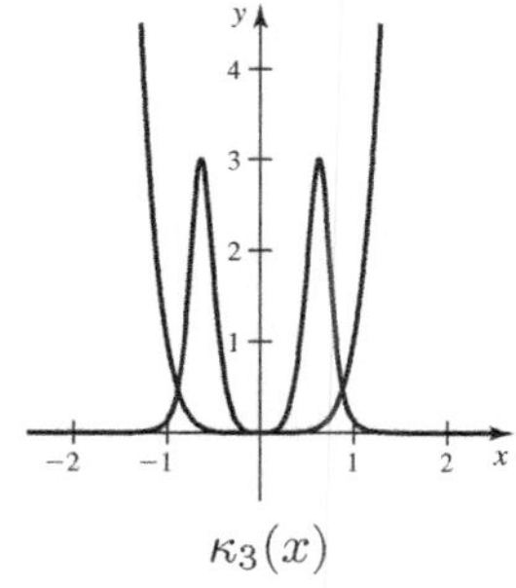

$\kappa_3(x)$

Note that the curves are symmetric about the y-axis.

c. $\kappa'(x) = -\frac{4n(2n-1)x^{2n-1}(2n^2(4n-1)x^{4n} - (n-1)x^2)}{(4n^2x^{4n}+x^2)^2\sqrt{4n^2x^{4n-2}+1}}$. By symmetry, we can concentrate on the critical points for $x > 0$. We have $\kappa'(x) = 0$ for $x > 0$ and $n > 1$, when $x = 2^{\frac{1}{2-4n}}\left(\frac{\sqrt{n^2(4n-1)}}{\sqrt{n-1}}\right)^{\frac{1}{1-2n}}$. For $n = 1$, the maximum occurs at 0. For $n = 2$, it occurs at $\frac{1}{\sqrt{2}\cdot 7^{1/6}}$. For $n = 3$, it occurs at $\frac{1}{3^{1/5}11^{1/10}}$.

d. If the maximum curvature for f_n occurs at $\pm z_n$, then $\lim_{n\to\infty} z_n = 1$.

11.9.83 We have that $\mathbf{B} = \frac{\mathbf{v}\times\mathbf{a}}{\kappa|\mathbf{v}|^3}$ and $\kappa = \frac{|\mathbf{v}\times\mathbf{a}|}{|\mathbf{v}|^3}$, so $\mathbf{B} = \frac{\mathbf{v}\times\mathbf{a}}{|\mathbf{v}\times\mathbf{a}|}$.

Chapter Eleven Review

1

a. True. Addition of vectors is commutative.

b. False. For example, the vector in the direction of $\mathbf{i}$ with the length of $\mathbf{j}$ is $\mathbf{i}$, but the vector in the direction of $\mathbf{j}$ with the length of $\mathbf{i}$ is $\mathbf{j}$, and $\mathbf{i} \neq \mathbf{j}$.

c. True, because it then follows that $\mathbf{u} = -\mathbf{v}$, so the two are parallel.

d. True. This follows because $\int \mathbf{r}'(t)\,dt = \int \langle 0,0,0\rangle\,dt = \langle 0,0,0\rangle + \mathbf{C} = \langle a,b,c\rangle$ for some real numbers a, b, and c.

e. False. Its length is $\sqrt{169\sin^2 t + 169\cos^2 t} = 13 \neq 1$.

f. False. For example, for the curve $\mathbf{r}(t) = \langle t^2, t\rangle$, we have $\mathbf{N} = \frac{1}{\sqrt{1+4t^2}}\langle 1, -2t\rangle$. So if, for example, $t = 2$, we have $\mathbf{r}(2) = \langle 4, 2\rangle$ and $\mathbf{N} = \frac{1}{\sqrt{17}}\langle 1, -4\rangle$, which aren't parallel.

3

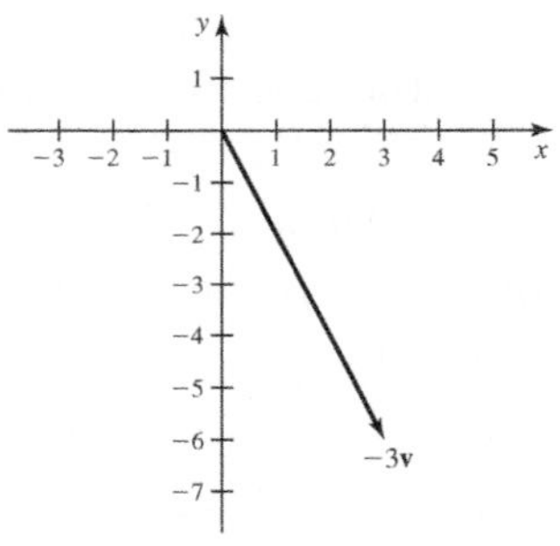

5

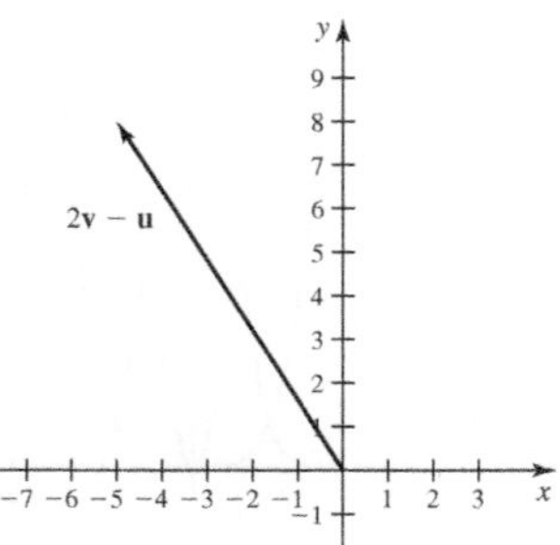

7 $|\mathbf{u}+\mathbf{v}| = |\langle -4, 14, -3\rangle| = \sqrt{16+196+9} = \sqrt{221}$.

9 $|\mathbf{v}| = \sqrt{36+100+4} = \sqrt{140}$. So the desired vector is $\frac{20}{\sqrt{140}}\langle -6, 10, 2\rangle = \frac{20}{\sqrt{35}}\langle -3, 5, 1\rangle$. The vector $-\frac{20}{\sqrt{35}}\langle -3, 5, 1\rangle$ also has the desired property.

11 $\mathbf{u}\times\mathbf{v} = \langle 2, 4, -5\rangle \times \langle -6, 10, 2\rangle = 2\langle 29, 13, 22\rangle$. Thus, $\mathbf{v}\times\mathbf{u} = -2\langle 29, 13, 22\rangle$. The area of the indicated triangle is $\frac{1}{2}\cdot 2\sqrt{29^2+13^2+22^2} \approx 38.65$.

13

a. $\mathbf{v} = 550\langle -\sqrt{2}/2, \sqrt{2}/2\rangle = \langle -275\sqrt{2}, 275\sqrt{2}\rangle$.

b. $\mathbf{v} = 550\langle -\sqrt{2}/2, \sqrt{2}/2\rangle + \langle 0, 40\rangle = \langle -275\sqrt{2}, 275\sqrt{2}+40\rangle$.

15 $\{(x,y,z) \mid (x-1)^2 + y^2 + (z+1)^2 = 16\}$.

17 $\{(x,y,z) \mid x^2 + (y-1)^2 + z^2 > 4\}$.

19 Completing the square gives $(x^2 - x + 1/4) + (y^2 + 4y + 4) + (z^2 - 6z + 9) < -11 + 1/4 + 4 + 9 = \frac{9}{4}$, or $(x-1/2)^2 + (y+2)^2 + (z-3)^2 < (3/2)^2$. This is a ball centered at $(1/2, -2, 3)$ of radius $3/2$.

21 Completing the square gives $(x^2 - 6x + 9) + y^2 + (z^2 - 20z + 100) > -9 + 9 + 100$, or $(x-3)^2 + y^2 + (z-10)^2 > 10^2$. These are the points outside of a sphere of radius 10 centered at $(3, 0, 10)$.

23 The magnitude of $\langle 0, 4, -50\rangle$ is $\sqrt{2516} \approx 50.16$ meters per second. The direction is $\cos^{-1}(4/\sqrt{2516}) \approx 85.4$ degrees below the horizontal in the northerly horizontal direction.

25 This is a circle of radius one centered at $(0, 2, 0)$ and sitting in the plane $y = 2$.

27

a. $\mathbf{u} \cdot \mathbf{v} = -3 + 12 + 12 = 21$, $|\mathbf{u}| = 3$ and $|\mathbf{v}| = 9$, so $\theta = \cos^{-1}\left(\frac{21}{27}\right) \approx .68$ radian.

b. $\text{proj}_{\mathbf{v}}\mathbf{u} = \frac{21}{81}\langle 3, 6, 6\rangle = \langle 7/9, 14/9, 14/9\rangle$, and $\text{scal}_{\mathbf{v}}\mathbf{u} = \frac{21}{9} = \frac{7}{3}$.

c. $\text{proj}_{\mathbf{u}}\mathbf{v} = \frac{21}{9}\langle -1, 2, 2\rangle = \langle -7/3, 14/3, 14/3\rangle$, and $\text{scal}_{\mathbf{u}}\mathbf{v} = \frac{21}{3} = 7$.

29 $\langle 2, -6, 9\rangle \times \langle -1, 0, 6\rangle = \langle -36, -21, -6\rangle$. The length of this vector is $3\sqrt{12^2 + 7^2 + 2^2} = 3\sqrt{197}$. Thus the unit normals are $\frac{\pm 1}{\sqrt{197}}\langle 12, 7, 2\rangle$.

31 $T(\theta) = (.4) \cdot 98 \cdot \sin\theta \approx 39.2 \sin\theta$ Newton-meters. This has a maximum of 39.2 when $\sin\theta = 1$ (at $\theta = \pi/2$) and a minimum of 0 at $\theta = 0$. The direction of the torque does not change as the knee is lifted.

33 The direction of the line segment is $\langle 2 - 0, -8 - (-3), 1 - 9\rangle = \langle 2, -5, -8\rangle$. The line segment is described by $\langle x, y, z\rangle = \langle 0, -3, 9\rangle + t\langle 2, -5, -8\rangle$, $0 \le t \le 1$.

35 The direction is given by $\langle 0, -1, 3\rangle \times \langle 2, -1, 2\rangle = \langle 1, 6, 2\rangle$. Thus the line is given by $\langle 0, 1, 1\rangle + t\langle 1, 6, 2\rangle = \langle t, 1 + 6t, 1 + 2t\rangle$.

37 Two adjacent sides of the parallelogram are given by $\langle 0, -2, 3\rangle$ and $\langle 3, 0, 1\rangle$, so the area is

$$|\langle 0, -2, 3\rangle \times \langle 3, 0, 1\rangle| = |\langle -2, 9, 6\rangle| = 11.$$

39 The curve is a circle of radius 4 with center $(0, 1, 0)$ sitting in the plane $y = 1$. It is the intersection of the plane $y = 1$ and the cylinder $x^2 + z^2 = 16$.

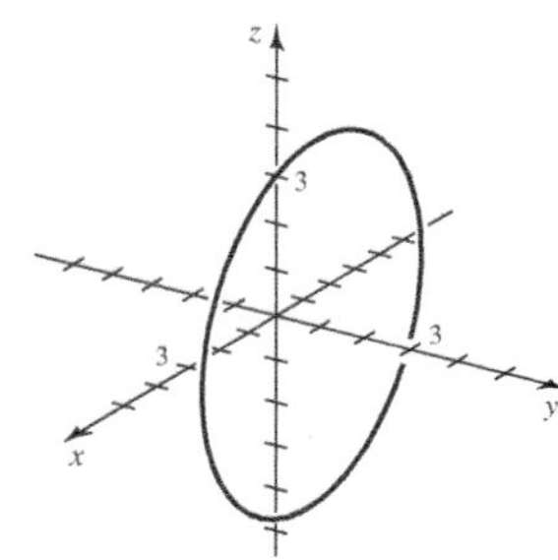

41 Note that $x^2 + y^2 + z^2 = 2$, so this curve lies on a sphere of radius 2. Also, every point satisfies $z = x$, so it is a circle centered at the origin of radius 2, sitting in the plane $z = x$.

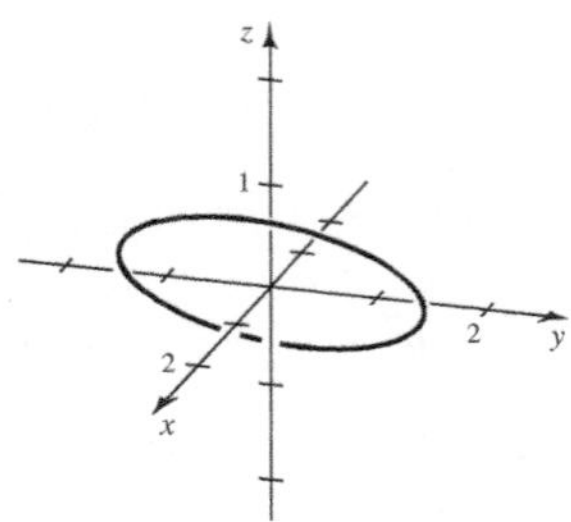

43

a. $\lim_{t\to 0} \mathbf{r}(t) = \langle 1, 0\rangle$ and $\lim_{t\to\infty} \mathbf{r}(t) = \langle 0, 1\rangle$.

b. $\mathbf{r}'(t) = \langle \frac{-2}{(2t+1)^2}, \frac{1}{(1+t)^2}\rangle$ so $\mathbf{r}'(0) = \langle -2, 1\rangle$.

c. $\mathbf{r}''(t) = \langle \frac{8}{(2t+1)^3}, \frac{-2}{(1+t)^3}\rangle$.

d. $\int \mathbf{r}(t)\,dt = \langle \frac{1}{2}\ln|2t+1|, t - \ln|t+1|\rangle + \langle C_1, C_2\rangle$.

45

a. $\lim_{t\to 0} \mathbf{r}(t) = \langle 0, 3, 0\rangle$ and $\lim_{t\to\infty} \mathbf{r}(t)$ does not exist.

b. $\mathbf{r}'(t) = \langle 2\cos 2t, -12\sin 4t, 1\rangle$ so $\mathbf{r}'(0) = \langle 2, 0, 1\rangle$.

c. $\mathbf{r}''(t) = \langle -4\sin 2t, -48\cos 4t, 0\rangle$.

d. $\int \mathbf{r}(t)\,dt = \langle -\frac{1}{2}cos2t, \frac{3}{4}\sin 4t, \frac{1}{2}t^2\rangle + \langle C_1, C_2\rangle$.

47

a. The trajectory is given by $\mathbf{r}(t) = \langle 50t, 50t - 16t^2\rangle$. The projectile is at $y = 30$ when $-16t^2+50t-30 = 0$, which occurs at $t = \frac{1}{16}\left(25 \pm \sqrt{145}\right) \approx .81 \text{ and } 2.32$. At these times, $x = 50t \approx 40.5 \text{ and } 116$. The first time represents when the projectile has not yet reached the cliff, while the second time represents when the projectile lands on the cliff, so the coordinates of the landing spot are approximately $(116, 30)$.

b. The maximum height occurs where $y' = 0$, which occurs for $50 - 32t = 0$, or $t = 25/16$. The maximum height is $50 \cdot \frac{25}{16} - 16\left(\frac{25}{16}\right)^2 = \frac{625}{16} \approx 39.06$ feet.

c. As mentioned above, the flight ends at $t \approx 2.32$ seconds.

d. The length of the trajectory is $\int_0^{2.32} \sqrt{x'(t)^2 + y'(t)^2}\,dt = \int_0^{2.32} \sqrt{2500 + (50 - 32t)^2}\,dt$.

e. $L \approx 129$ feet.

f. Suppose the launch angle is α. Then $\mathbf{r}(t) = \langle 50\sqrt{2}t\cos\alpha, 50\sqrt{2}t\sin\alpha - 16t^2\rangle$. We want $y \geq 30$ when $x = 50$. We know that $x = 50$ when $t = \frac{\sec\alpha}{\sqrt{2}}$. At this time, we have $y = 50\tan\alpha - 8\sec^2\alpha$. This expression is greater than or equal to 30 for approximately $41.5 \leq \alpha \leq 79.4$.

49 The initial velocity of the ball is given by $s\langle\sqrt{2}/2, \sqrt{2}/2\rangle$ where s is the initial speed.
We have $\mathbf{r}(t) = \langle (s\sqrt{2}/2)t, -16t^2 + (s\sqrt{2}/2)t + 6\rangle$. We know that $(s\sqrt{2}/2)t = 15$ when $-16t^2 + (s\sqrt{2}/2)t + 6 = 10$. Solving the first equation for t gives $t = 30/(s\sqrt{2})$. Putting this into the second equation gives $-16(30/(s\sqrt{2}))^2 + (s\sqrt{2}/2)(30/(s\sqrt{2})) = 4$. Solving for s gives $s \approx 25.6$ feet per second.

51 $L = \int_1^3 \sqrt{4t^2+8t+4}\,dt = 2\int_1^3 \sqrt{(t+1)^2}\,dt = 2\int_1^3 (t+1)\,dt = 2\left(t^2/2 + t\right)\Big|_1^3 = 2(9/2 + 3 - (1/2+1)) = 9 + 6 - 1 - 2 = 12$.

53

a. $\mathbf{v}(t) = \int \langle 0, \sqrt{2}, 2t\rangle\, dt = \langle 0, \sqrt{2}t, t^2\rangle + \mathbf{C}$. Because $\mathbf{v}(0) = \langle 1, 0, 0\rangle$, we have $\mathbf{C} = \langle 1, 0, 0\rangle$, so $\mathbf{v}(t) = \langle 1, \sqrt{2}t, t^2\rangle$.

b. $L = \int_0^3 \sqrt{1 + 2t^2 + t^4}\, dt = \int_0^3 (t^2 + 1)\, dt = (t^3/3 + t)\Big|_0^3 = 9 + 3 = 12.$

55 $L = \int_0^{2\pi} \sqrt{(3 - 6\cos\theta)^2 + (6\sin\theta)^2}\, d\theta = \int_0^{2\pi} 3\sqrt{5 - 4\cos(\theta)}\, d\theta \approx 40.09.$

57 $|\mathbf{r}'(t)| = \left|\langle 2t, 2\sqrt{2}t^{1/2}, 2\rangle\right| = \sqrt{4t^2 + 8t + 4} = 2\sqrt{(t+1)^2} = 2(t+1)$. Let $s = \int_0^t 2(u+1)\, du = (u^2 + 2u)\Big|_0^t = t^2 + 2t$. Then $s + 1 = (t+1)^2$, so $t = \sqrt{s+1} - 1$. Thus, $\mathbf{r}(s) = \langle (\sqrt{s+1} - 1)^2, \frac{4\sqrt{2}}{3}(\sqrt{s+1} - 1)^{3/2}, 2(\sqrt{s+1} - 1)\rangle$ for $s \geq 0$.

59

a. $\mathbf{r}'(t) = \langle -6\sin t, 3\cos t\rangle$, so $\mathbf{T} = \frac{1}{\sqrt{1+3\sin^2 t}}\langle -2\sin t, \cos t\rangle$.

b. $\kappa = \frac{|\mathbf{r}''(t)\times\mathbf{r}'(t)|}{(3\sqrt{1+3\sin^2 t})^3} = \frac{|\langle 0,0,-18\rangle|}{(3\sqrt{1+3\sin^2 t})^3} = \frac{2}{3(\sqrt{1+3\sin^2 t})^3}$.

c. Note that $\frac{1}{\sqrt{1+3\sin^2 t}}\langle -\cos t, -2\sin t\rangle$ has length one, and is perpendicular to $\mathbf{T}$ (see part [d]), and points to the inside of the curve, so it is $\mathbf{N}$.

d. $\left|\frac{1}{\sqrt{1+3\sin^2 t}}\langle -\cos t, -2\sin t\rangle\right| = \frac{\sqrt{1+3\sin^2 t}}{\sqrt{1+3\sin^2 t}} = 1$ and $\mathbf{T}\cdot\mathbf{N} = \frac{1}{\sqrt{1+3\sin^2 t}}(2\sin t\cos t - 2\sin t\cos t) = 0$.

e.

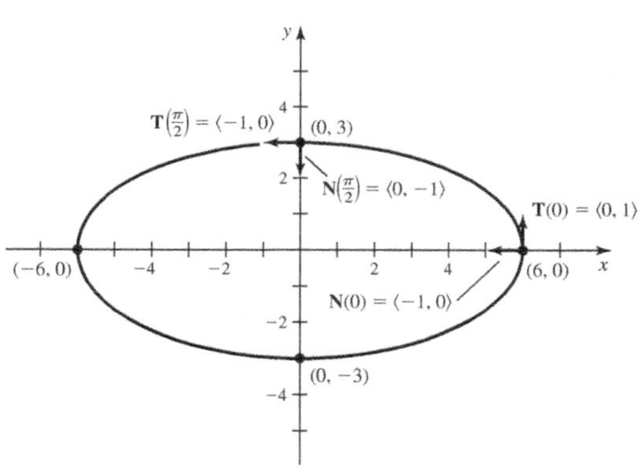

61

a. $\mathbf{r}'(t) = \langle -\sin t, -2\sin t, \sqrt{5}\cos t\rangle$, so

$$\mathbf{T} = \frac{1}{\sqrt{5}}\langle -\sin t, -2\sin t, \sqrt{5}\cos t\rangle.$$

b. $\kappa = \frac{|\mathbf{r}''(t)\times\mathbf{r}'(t)|}{(\sqrt{5})^3} = \frac{|\langle -2\sqrt{5}, \sqrt{5}, 0\rangle|}{(\sqrt{5})^3} = \frac{1}{\sqrt{5}}$.

c. $\frac{dT}{dt} = \frac{1}{\sqrt{5}}\langle -\cos t, -2\cos t, -\sqrt{5}\sin t\rangle = \mathbf{N}$.

d. $\left|\frac{1}{\sqrt{5}}\langle -\cos t, -2\cos t, -\sqrt{5}\sin t\rangle\right| = \frac{\sqrt{5}}{\sqrt{5}} = 1$ and $\mathbf{T}\cdot\mathbf{N} = \frac{1}{\sqrt{5}}(\sin t\cos t + 4\sin t\cos t - 5\sin t\cos t) = 0$.

e.

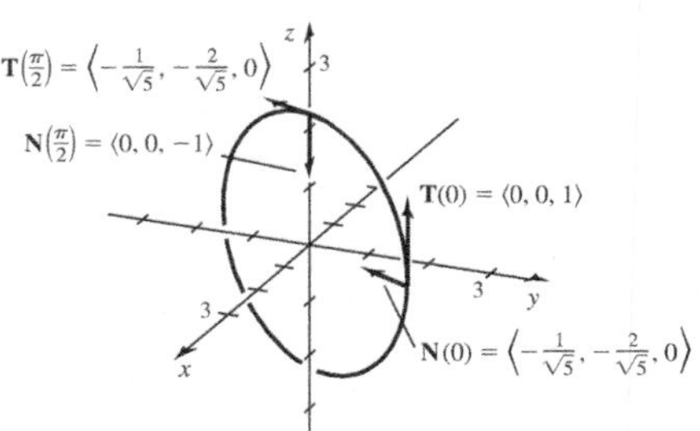

63

a. $\mathbf{v}(t) = \langle -2\sin t, 2\cos t\rangle$, and $\mathbf{a}(t) = \langle -2\cos t, -2\sin t\rangle$. Because $\mathbf{v}\cdot\mathbf{a} = 0$, we have $a_T = 0$. Note that $\mathbf{a}\times\mathbf{v} = \langle -2\cos t, -2\sin t, 0\rangle \times \langle -2\sin t, 2\cos t, 0\rangle = \langle 0,0,-4\rangle$, so $a_N = \frac{4}{2} = 2$. We have $\mathbf{a} = \langle -2\cos t, -2\sin t\rangle = 2\mathbf{N} + 0\cdot\mathbf{T}$.

b. Note that at $t = 0$ we have $\mathbf{a} = \langle -2, 0\rangle = 2\langle -1, 0\rangle = 2\mathbf{N}$, and at $t = \pi/2$ we have $\mathbf{a} = \langle 0, -2\rangle = 2\langle 0, -1\rangle = 2\mathbf{N}$.

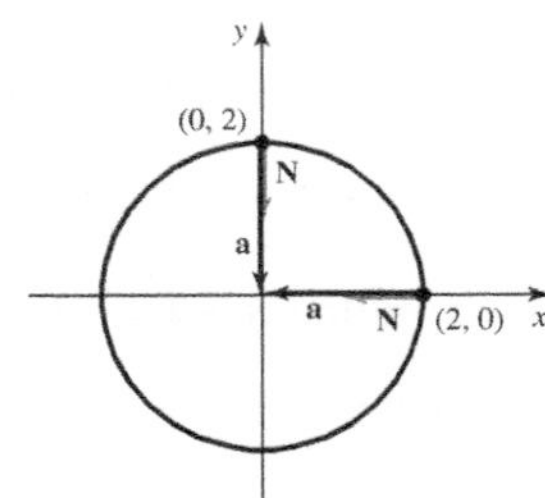

65

a. $\mathbf{v}(t) = \langle 2t, 2\rangle$, and $\mathbf{a}(t) = \langle 2, 0\rangle$. Because $\mathbf{v}\cdot\mathbf{a} = 4t$, we have $a_T = \frac{4t}{2\sqrt{t^2+1}} = \frac{2t}{\sqrt{t^2+1}}$. Note that $\mathbf{a}\times\mathbf{v} = \langle 0,0,4\rangle$, so $a_N = \frac{4}{2\sqrt{t^2+1}} = \frac{2}{\sqrt{t^2+1}}$. We have that $\mathbf{a} = \langle 2, 0\rangle = \frac{2}{\sqrt{t^2+1}}\mathbf{N} + \frac{2t}{\sqrt{t^2+1}}\mathbf{T}$.

b. At $t = 1$, we have $\mathbf{a} = \langle 2, 0\rangle = \frac{2}{\sqrt{2}}\mathbf{T} + \frac{2}{\sqrt{2}}\mathbf{N} = \frac{2}{\sqrt{2}}\langle\sqrt{2}/2, \sqrt{2}/2\rangle + \frac{2}{\sqrt{2}}\langle\sqrt{2}/2, -\sqrt{2}/2\rangle$.
At $t = 2$, we have $\mathbf{a} = \langle 2, 0\rangle = \frac{4}{\sqrt{5}}\langle 2/\sqrt{5}, 1/\sqrt{5}\rangle + \frac{2}{\sqrt{5}}\langle 1/\sqrt{5}, -2/\sqrt{5}\rangle$.

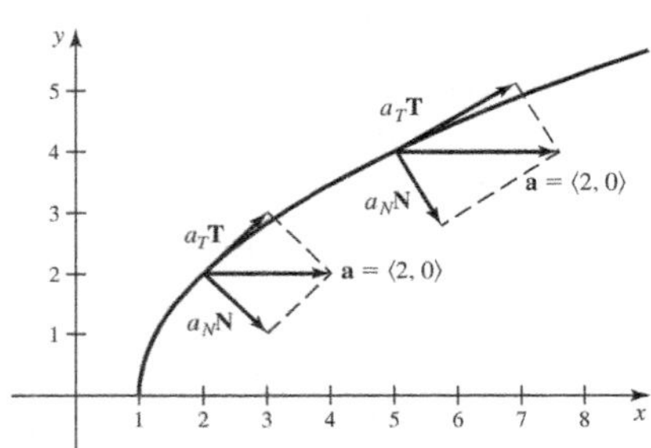

67

a. We are looking for points (x, y) so that $\langle x - x_0, y - y_0\rangle\cdot\langle a, b\rangle = 0$, so $a(x - x_0) + b(y - y_0) = 0$, or $ax + by = ax_0 + by_0$.

b. Note that $\langle a, b, 0\rangle \times \langle x - x_0, y - y_0, 0\rangle = \langle 0, 0, a(y - y_0) - b(x - x_0)\rangle$. This is equal to the zero vector when $ay - ay_0 = bx - bx_0$, or $ay - bx = ay_0 - bx_0$. So the equation of a line passing through (x_0, y_0) and parallel to $\langle a, b\rangle$ is given by $ay - bx = ay_0 - bx_0$.

69 We have $\mathbf{r}'(t) = \langle 1, 2t, 3t^2\rangle$, so $\mathbf{r}'(1) = \langle 1, 2, 3\rangle$. Thus, $\mathbf{T}(1) = \frac{1}{\sqrt{3}}\langle 1, 1, 1\rangle$.
Then $\mathbf{N}(1) = \langle -\frac{11}{\sqrt{266}}, -4\sqrt{\frac{2}{133}}, \frac{9}{\sqrt{266}}\rangle$, so $\mathbf{B} = \mathbf{T}\times\mathbf{N} = \langle \frac{3}{\sqrt{19}}, -\frac{3}{\sqrt{19}}, \frac{1}{\sqrt{19}}\rangle$. Also, $\tau = \frac{(\mathbf{r}'\times\mathbf{r}'')\cdot\mathbf{r}'''}{|\mathbf{r}'\times\mathbf{r}''|^2} = \frac{3}{19}$.

71

a. $\mathbf{r}'(t) = \langle 3\cos t, -3\sin t, 4\rangle$, and $|\mathbf{r}'(t)| = 5$, so $\mathbf{T}(t) = \frac{1}{5}\langle 3\cos t, -3\sin t, 4\rangle$.

b. $\mathbf{T}'(t) = \frac{1}{5}\langle -3\sin t, -3\cos t, 0\rangle$, so $\mathbf{N}(t) = \langle -\sin t, -\cos t, 0\rangle$.

c. At $t = 0$ we have $\mathbf{T} = \langle 3/5, 0, 4/5\rangle$ and $\mathbf{N} = \langle 0, -1, 0\rangle$. At $t = \pi/2$ we have $\mathbf{T} = \langle 0, -3/5, 4/5\rangle$ and $\mathbf{N} = \langle -1, 0, 0\rangle$.

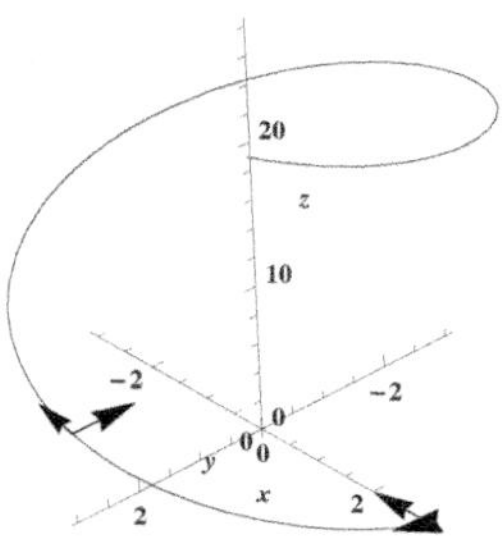

d. Yes.

e. $\mathbf{B}(t) = \mathbf{T}(t) \times \mathbf{N}(t) = \frac{1}{5}\langle 4\cos t, -4\sin t, -3\rangle$.

f.

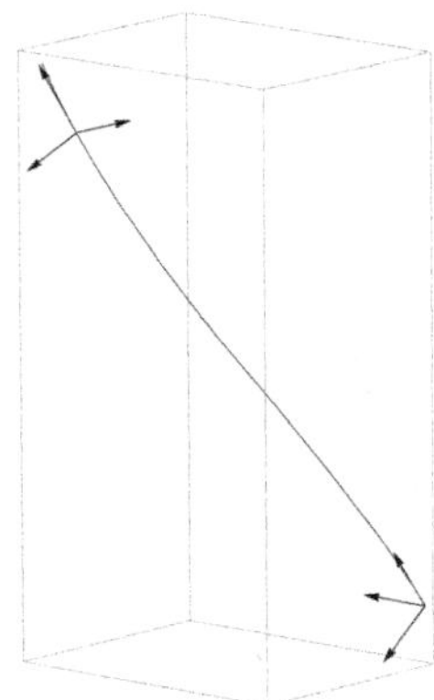

g. One should check that $\mathbf{T}$, $\mathbf{N}$, and $\mathbf{B}$ are all of unit length and are mutually orthogonal.

h. $\tau = -\frac{d\mathbf{B}/dt}{ds/dt} \cdot \mathbf{N} = \frac{1}{25}\langle -4\sin t, -4\cos t, 0\rangle \cdot \langle -\sin t, -\cos t, 0\rangle = -\frac{4}{25}$.

73

a. First consider the case where $a_3 = b_3 = c_3 = 0$. Let $t \neq s$ be in the interval I, and consider $\mathbf{r}(t) \times \mathbf{r}(s)$. We will show that this vector is always a multiple of the same constant vector. We have

$$\begin{aligned}
&\mathbf{r}(t) \times \mathbf{r}(s) \\
&= \langle a_1 f(t) + a_2 g(t), b_1 f(t) + b_2 g(t), c_1 f(t) + c_2 g(t)\rangle \times \langle a_1 f(s) + a_2 g(s), b_1 f(s) + b_2 g(s), c_1 f(s) + c_2 g(s)\rangle \\
&= (f(t)g(s) - f(s)g(t))\langle c_2 b_1 - b_2 c_1, a_2 c_1 - a_1 c_2, a_1 b_2 - a_2 b_1\rangle,
\end{aligned}$$

where this last computation admittedly requires patience. Because $\mathbf{r}(t) \times \mathbf{r}(s)$ is always orthogonal to the same vector, the vectors $\mathbf{r}(t)$ must all lie in the same plane.

Now consider the case where a_3, b_3, and c_3 are not necessarily 0, and consider $\mathbf{p}(t) = \mathbf{r}(t) - \langle a_3, b_3, c_3\rangle$. Note that $\mathbf{p}(t)$ has the form required in the argument in the previous paragraph. Using the result above, the curve $\mathbf{p}(t)$ lies in a plane, which implies that $\mathbf{r}(t) = \mathbf{p}(t) + \langle a_3, b_3, c_3\rangle$ lies in a plane as well, because we are just translating all the vectors $\mathbf{p}(t)$ by the same constant vector.

b. If the curve lies in a plane, the $\mathbf{B}$ is always normal to the plane with length 1. Hence $\mathbf{B}$ is constant, so $\tau = -\frac{d\mathbf{B}}{ds} \cdot \mathbf{N} = 0$.

Chapter 12

Functions of Several Variables

12.1 Planes and Surfaces

12.1.1 One point and a normal vector determine a plane

12.1.3 The point (x, y, z) where this plane intersects the x-axis has $y = z = 0$; substituting in the equation of the plane gives $x = -6$. Similarly, we see that the plane meets the y-axis at $y = -4$ and the z-axis at $z = 3$.

12.1.5 Since z is absent from the equation $x^2 + 2y^2 = 8$, this cylinder is parallel to the z-axis. Similarly, $z^2 + 2y^2 = 8$ is parallel to the x-axis and $x^2 + 2z^2 = 8$ is parallel to the y-axis.

12.1.7 The traces of a surface are the sets of points at which the surface intersects a plane that is parallel to one of the coordinate planes.

12.1.9 This is an ellipsoid.

12.1.11 Substituting in the general equation for a plane gives $(x - 0) + (y - 2) - (z - (-2)) = 0$, which simplifies to $x + y - z = 4$.

12.1.13 Substituting in the general equation for a plane gives $-1\,(x - 2) + 2\,(y - 3) - 3\,(z - 0) = 0$, which simplifies to $-x + 2y - 3z = 4$.

12.1.15 A vector normal to the plane is given by $\begin{vmatrix} \mathbf{i} & \mathbf{j} & \mathbf{k} \\ 1 & 0 & 1 \\ 0 & 2 & 1 \end{vmatrix} = \langle -2, -1, 2 \rangle$. Substituting in the general equation for a plane gives $-2(x - 1) - 1(y - 2) + 2(z - 3) = 0$, which simplifies to $2x + y - 2z = -2$.

12.1.17 Let $P = (1, 0, 3)$, $Q = (0, 4, 2)$ and $R = (1, 1, 1)$. Then the vectors $\overrightarrow{PQ} = \langle -1, 4, -1 \rangle$ and $\overrightarrow{PR} = \langle 0, 1, -2 \rangle$ lie in the plane, so $\mathbf{n} = \overrightarrow{PQ} \times \overrightarrow{PR} = \begin{vmatrix} \mathbf{i} & \mathbf{j} & \mathbf{k} \\ -1 & 4 & -1 \\ 0 & 1 & -2 \end{vmatrix} = -7\mathbf{i} - 2\mathbf{j} - \mathbf{k}$ is normal to the plane. The plane has equation $7\,(x - 1) + 2\,(y - 0) + 1\,(z - 3) = 0$, which simplifies to $7x + 2y + z = 10$.

12.1.19 Let $P = (2, -1, 4)$, $Q = (1, 1, -1)$ and $R = (-4, 1, 1)$. Then the vectors $\overrightarrow{PQ} = \langle -1, 2, -5 \rangle$ and $\overrightarrow{PR} = \langle -6, 2, -3 \rangle$ lie in the plane, so $\mathbf{n} = \overrightarrow{PQ} \times \overrightarrow{PR} = \begin{vmatrix} \mathbf{i} & \mathbf{j} & \mathbf{k} \\ -1 & 2 & -5 \\ -6 & 2 & -3 \end{vmatrix} = 4\mathbf{i} + 27\mathbf{j} + 10\mathbf{k}$ is normal to the plane. The plane has equation $4\,(x - 2) + 27\,(y - (-1)) + 10\,(z - 4) = 0$, which simplifies to $4x + 27y + 10z = 21$.

12.1.21 The x-intercept is found by setting $y = z = 0$ and solving $3x = 6$ to get $x = 2$. Similarly, we see that the y-intercept is -3 and the z-intercept is 6. The xy-trace is found by setting $z = 0$, which gives $3x - 2y = 6$. Similarly, the xz-trace is $3x + z = 6$ and the yz-trace is $-2y + z = 6$.

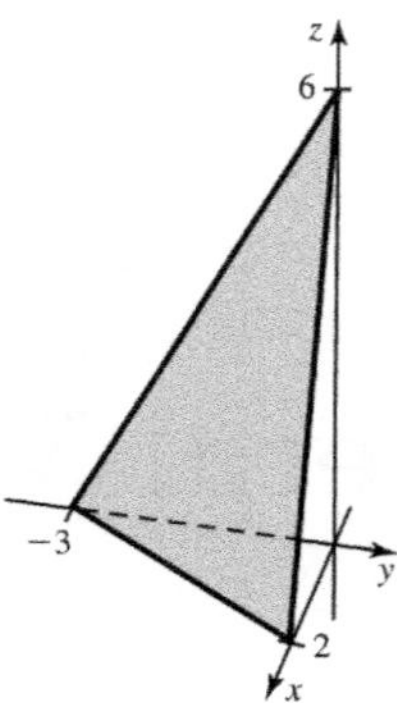

12.1.23 The x-intercept is found by setting $y = z = 0$ which gives $x = 30$. Similarly, we see that the y-intercept is 10 and the z-intercept is -6. The xy-trace is found by setting z = 0, which gives $x + 3y = 30$. Similarly, the xz-trace is $x - 5z = 30$ and the yz-trace is $3y - 5z = 30$.

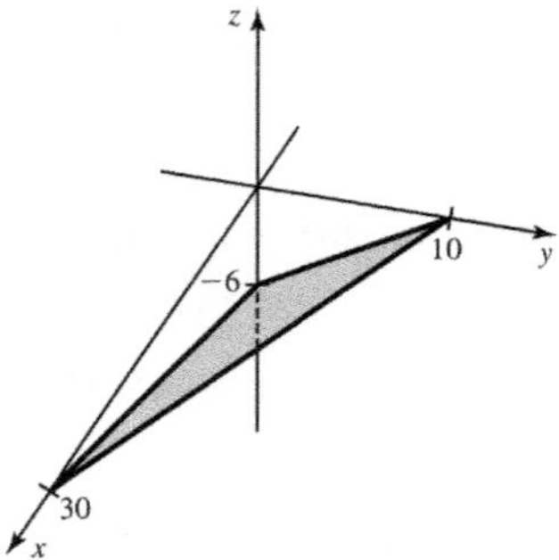

12.1.25 The normal vectors to the planes are $\langle 1, 1, 4\rangle$ and $\langle -1, -3, 1\rangle$, and the dot product of these vectors is $-1 - 3 + 4 = 0$, so the planes are orthogonal.

12.1.27 The normal vectors to the planes are $\langle 3, 2, -3\rangle$ and $\langle -6, -10, 1\rangle$. These are neither parallel nor perpendicular, because one is not a multiple of the other and because their dot product is not 0. Thus, the planes are neither parallel nor perpendicular.

12.1.29 Rewrite R and T so we have $Q : 3x - 2y + z = 12$, $R : 3x - 2y + z = 0$, $T : 3x - 2y + z = 12$. This shows that Q and T are identical, and Q, R and T are parallel. Note that $\langle 3, -2, 1\rangle \cdot \langle -1, 2, 7\rangle = 0$ so S is orthogonal to Q, R and T.

12.1.31 The plane Q has normal vector $\langle -1, 2, -4\rangle$; therefore the parallel plane passing through the point $P_0\,(1, 0, 4)$ has equation $-1\,(x - 1) + 2\,(y - 0) - 4\,(z - 4) = 0$, which simplifies to $-x + 2y - 4z = -17$.

12.1.33 The plane Q has normal vector $\langle 4, 3, -2\rangle$; therefore the parallel plane passing through the point $P_0\,(1, -1, 3)$ has equation $4\,(x - 1) + 3\,(y - (-1)) - 2\,(z - 3) = 0$, which simplifies to $4x + 3y - 2z = -5$.

12.1.35 First, note that the vectors normal to the planes, $\mathbf{n}_Q = \langle -1, 2, 1\rangle$ and $\mathbf{n}_R = \langle 1, 1, 1\rangle$, are not multiples of each other; therefore these planes are not parallel and they intersect in a line ℓ. We need to find a point on ℓ and a vector in the direction of ℓ. Setting $x = 0$ in the equations of the planes gives equations of the lines in which the planes intersect the yz-plane: $2y + z = 1$, $y + z = 0$. Solving these equations simultaneously gives $y = 1$ and $z = -1$, so $(0, 1, -1)$ is a point on ℓ. A vector in the direction of ℓ is $\mathbf{n}_Q \times \mathbf{n}_R = \begin{vmatrix} \mathbf{i} & \mathbf{j} & \mathbf{k} \\ -1 & 2 & 1 \\ 1 & 1 & 1 \end{vmatrix} = \mathbf{i} + 2\mathbf{j} - 3\mathbf{k} = \langle 1, 2, -3\rangle$. Therefore ℓ has equation $\mathrm{r}\,(t) = \langle 0, 1, -1\rangle + t\langle 1, 2, -3\rangle = \langle t, 1 + 2t, -1 - 3t\rangle$, or $x = t$, $y = 1 + 2t$, $z = -1 - 3t$.

12.1.37 First, note that the vectors normal to the planes, $\mathbf{n}_Q = \langle 2, -1, 3\rangle$ and $\mathbf{n}_R = \langle -1, 3, 1\rangle$, are not multiples of each other; therefore these planes are not parallel and they intersect in a line ℓ. We need to find a point on ℓ and a vector in the direction of ℓ. Setting $z = 0$ in the equations of the planes gives equations of the lines in which the planes intersect the xy-plane: $2x - y = 1$, $-x + 3y = 4$. Solving these equations simultaneously gives $x = \frac{7}{5}$ and $y = \frac{9}{5}$, so $\left(\frac{7}{5}, \frac{9}{5}, 0\right)$ is a point on ℓ. A vector in the direction of ℓ is $\mathbf{n}_Q \times \mathbf{n}_R = \begin{vmatrix} \mathbf{i} & \mathbf{j} & \mathbf{k} \\ 2 & -1 & 3 \\ -1 & 3 & 1 \end{vmatrix} = -10\mathbf{i} - 5\mathbf{j} + 5\mathbf{k} = -5\langle 2, 1, -1\rangle$. Therefore ℓ has equation $\mathbf{r}(t) = \langle \frac{7}{5}, \frac{9}{5}, 0\rangle + t\langle 2, 1, -1\rangle = \langle \frac{7}{5} + 2t, \frac{9}{5} + t, -t\rangle$, or $x = \frac{7}{5} + 2t$, $y = \frac{9}{5} + t$, $z = -t$.

12.1.39

a. The cylinder is parallel to the x-axis.

b. 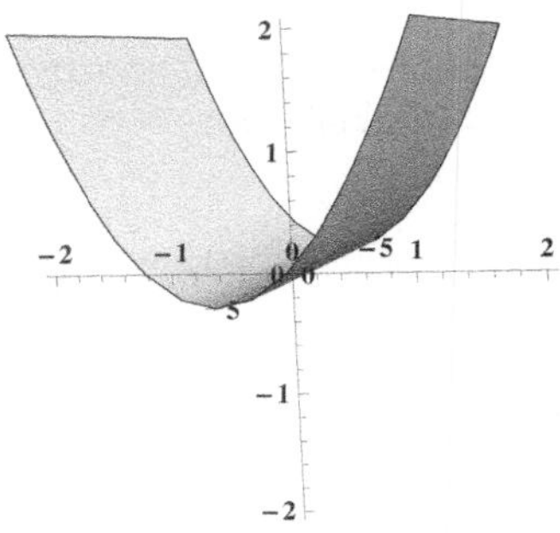

12.1.41

a. The cylinder is parallel to the y-axis.

b. 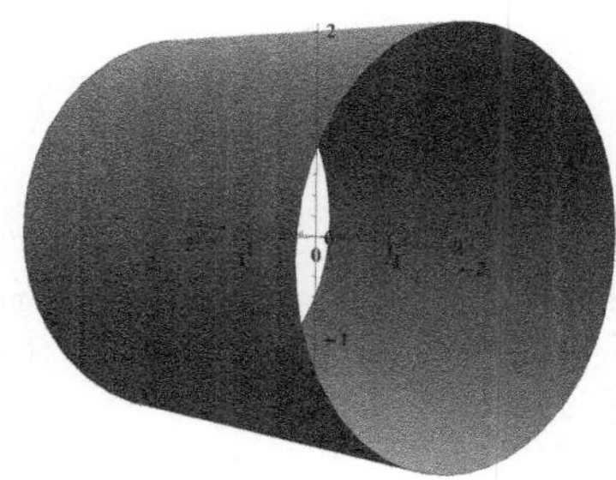

12.1.43

a. The cylinder is parallel to the z-axis.

b. 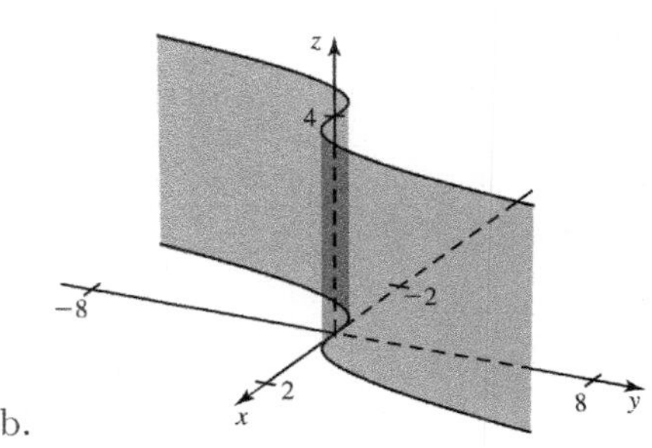

12.1.45

a. The cylinder is parallel to the x-axis.

b. 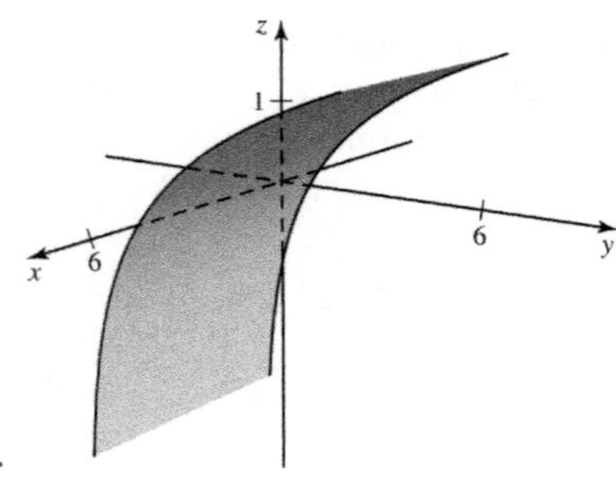

12.1.47

a. The x-intercept is found by setting $y = z = 0$ in the equation of this surface, which gives $x^2 = 1$, so the x-intercepts are $x = \pm 1$. Similarly we see that the y-intercepts are $y = \pm 2$ and the z-intercepts are $z = \pm 3$.

b. The equations for the xy-, xz- and yz-traces are found by setting $z = 0$, $y = 0$ and $x = 0$ respectively in the equation of the surface, which gives $x^2 + \frac{y^2}{4} = 1$, $x^2 + \frac{z^2}{9} = 1$, $\frac{y^2}{4} + \frac{z^2}{9} = 1$.

c.

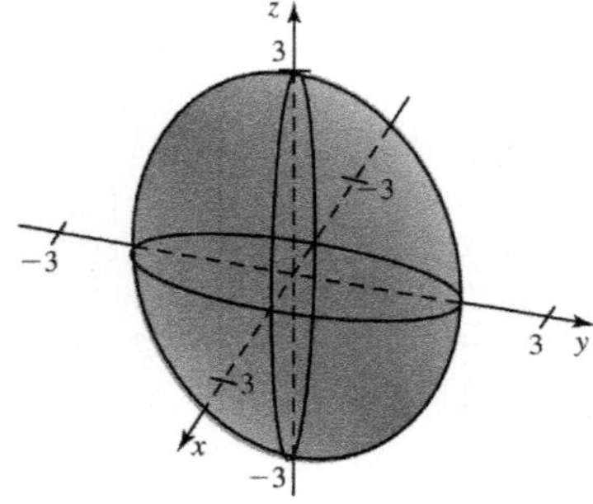

12.1.49

a. The x-intercept is found by setting $y = z = 0$ in the equation of this surface, which gives $x^2 = 9$, so the x-intercepts are $x = \pm 3$. Similarly we see that the y-intercepts are $y = \pm 1$ and the z-intercepts are $z = \pm 6$.

b. The equations for the xy-, xz- and yz-traces are found by setting $z = 0$, $y = 0$ and $x = 0$ respectively in the equation of the surface, which gives $\frac{x^2}{3} + 3y^2 = 3$,, $\frac{x^2}{3} + \frac{z^2}{12} = 3$, $3y^2 + \frac{z^2}{12} = 3$.

c.

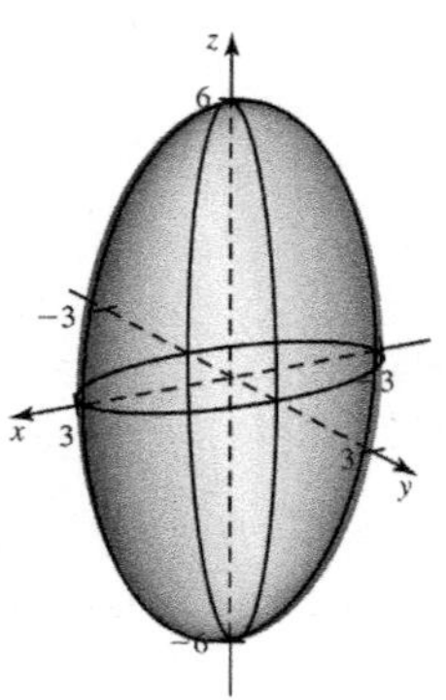

12.1.51

a. The x-intercept is found by setting $y = z = 0$ in the equation of this surface, which gives $x = 0$. Similarly we see that the y-intercept is $y = 0$ and the z-intercept is $z = 0$.

b. The equations for the xy-, xz- and yz-traces are found by setting $z = 0$, $y = 0$ and $x = 0$ respectively in the equation of the surface, which gives $x = y^2$, $x = z^2$, and $y^2 + z^2 = 0$ (which implies that $x = y = z = 0$).

c.

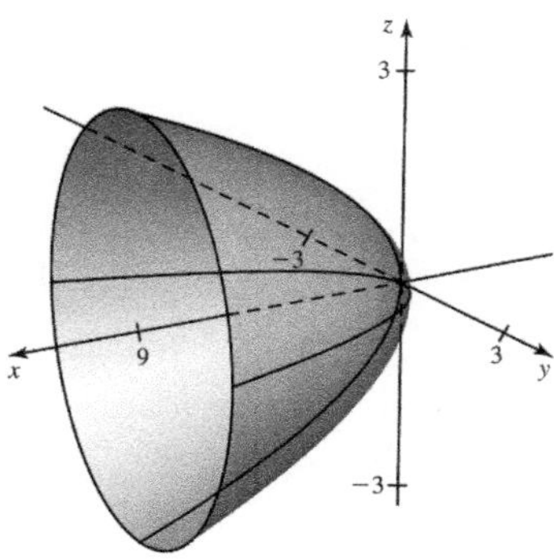

12.1.53

a. The x-intercept is found by setting $y = z = 0$ in the equation of this surface, which gives $x = 0$. Similarly we see that the y-intercept is $y = 0$ and the z-intercept is $z = 0$.

b. The equations for the xy-, xz- and yz-traces are found by setting $z = 0$, $y = 0$ and $x = 0$ respectively in the equation of the surface, which gives $x - 9y^2 = 0$, $9x - \frac{z^2}{4} = 0$, $81y^2 + \frac{z^2}{4} = 0$ (which implies that $x = y = z = 0$).

c.

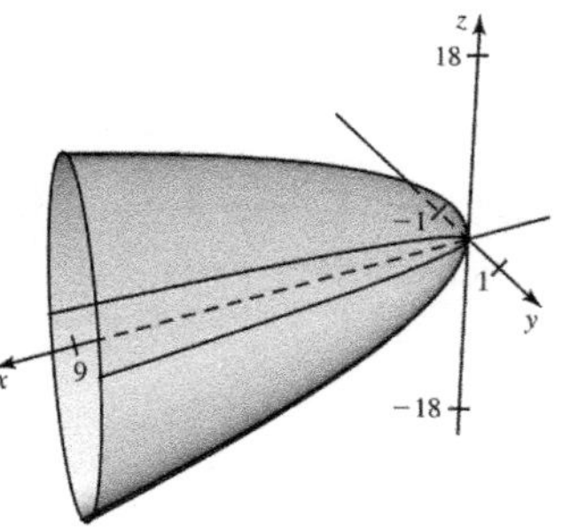

12.1.55

a. The x-intercept is found by setting $y = z = 0$ in the equation of this surface, which gives $x^2 = 25$, so the x-intercepts are $x = \pm 5$. Similarly we see that the y-intercepts are $y = \pm 3$ and there are no z-intercepts.

b. The equations for the xy-, xz- and yz-traces are found by setting $z = 0$, $y = 0$ and $x = 0$ respectively in the equation of the surface, which gives $\frac{x^2}{25} + \frac{y^2}{9} = 1$, $\frac{x^2}{25} - z^2 = 1$, $\frac{y^2}{9} - z^2 = 1$.

c.

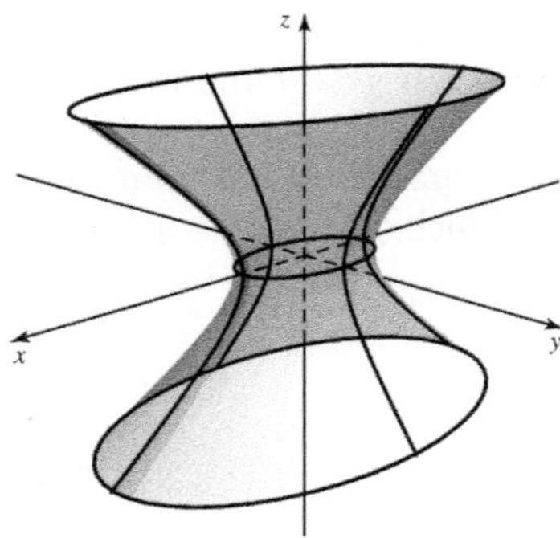

12.1.57

a. The y-intercept is found by setting $x = z = 0$ in the equation of this surface, which gives $y^2 = 144$, so the y-intercepts are $y = \pm 12$. Similarly we see that the z-intercepts are $z = \pm\frac{1}{2}$ and there are no x-intercepts.

b. The equations for the xy-, xz- and yz-traces are found by setting $z = 0$, $y = 0$ and $x = 0$ respectively in the equation of the surface, which gives $-\frac{x^2}{4} + \frac{y^2}{16} - 9 = 0$, $-\frac{x^2}{4} + 36z^2 - 9 = 0$, $\frac{y^2}{16} + 36z^2 - 9 = 0$.

c.

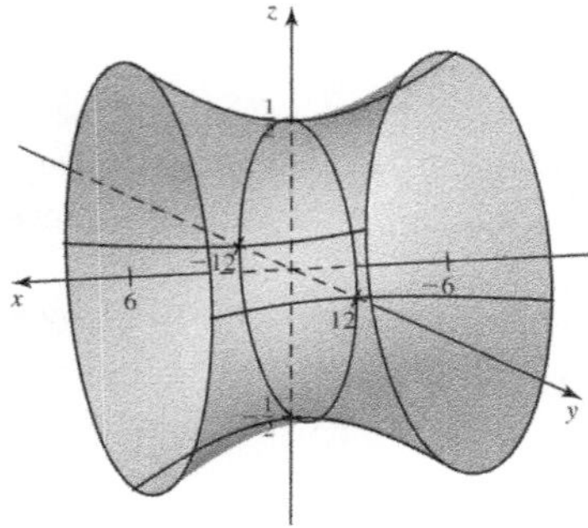

12.1.59

a. The x-intercept is found by setting $y = z = 0$ in the equation of this surface, which gives $x = 0$. Similarly we see that the y-intercept is $y = 0$ and the z-intercept is $z = 0$.

b. The equations for the xy-, xz- and yz-traces are found by setting $z = 0$, $y = 0$ and $x = 0$ respectively in the equation of the surface, which gives $\frac{x^2}{9} - y^2 = 0$, $z = \frac{x^2}{9}$, $z = -y^2$.

c.

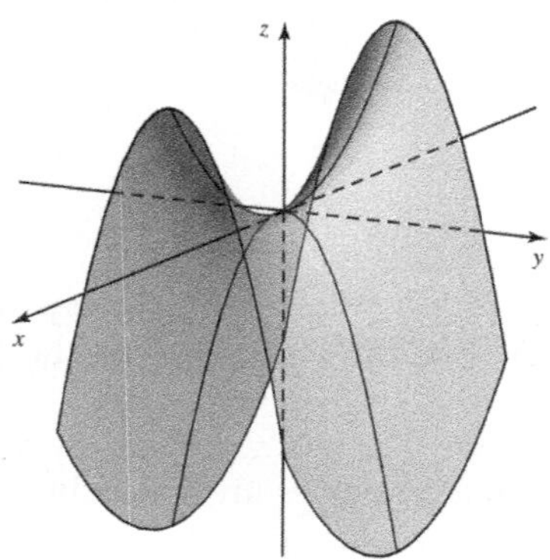

12.1.61

a. The x-intercept is found by setting $y = z = 0$ in the equation of this surface, which gives $x = 0$. Similarly we see that the y-intercept is $y = 0$ and the z-intercept is $z = 0$.

b. The equations for the xy-, xz- and yz-traces are found by setting $z = 0$, $y = 0$ and $x = 0$ respectively in the equation of the surface, which gives $5x - \frac{y^2}{5} = 0$, $5x + \frac{z^2}{20} = 0$, $-\frac{y^2}{25} + \frac{z^2}{20} = 0$.

c.

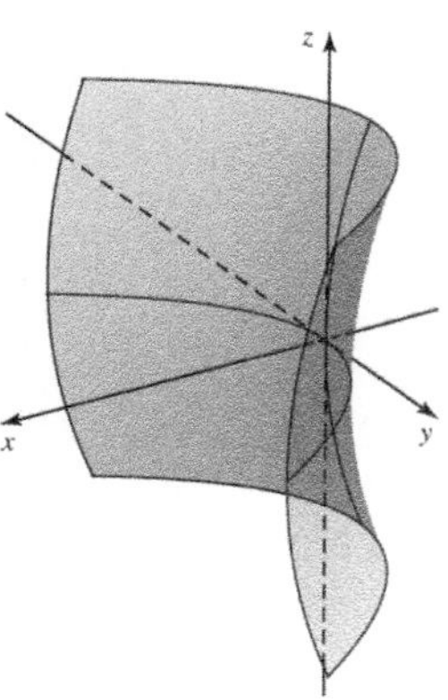

12.1.63

a. The x-intercept is found by setting $y = z = 0$ in the equation of this surface, which gives $x = 0$. Similarly we see that the y-intercept is $y = 0$ and the z-intercept is $z = 0$.

b. The equations for the xy-, xz- and yz-traces are found by setting $z = 0$, $y = 0$ and $x = 0$ respectively in the equation of the surface, which gives $x^2 + \frac{y^2}{4} = 0$ (which implies that $x = y = z = 0$), $x^2 = z^2$, $\frac{y^2}{4} = z^2$.

c.

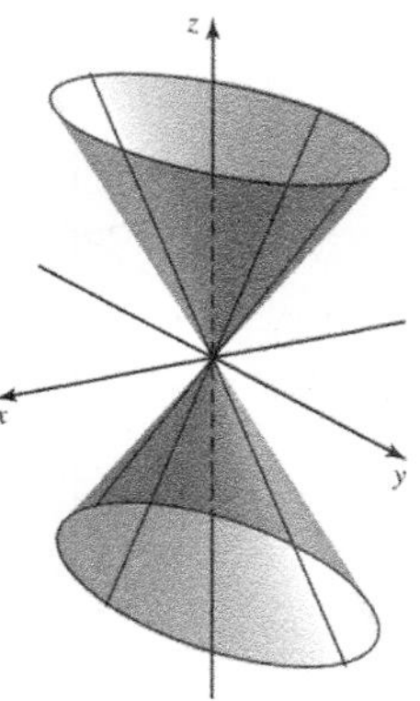

12.1.65

a. The x-intercept is found by setting $y = z = 0$ in the equation of this surface, which gives $x = 0$. Similarly we see that the y-intercept is $y = 0$ and the z-intercept is $z = 0$.

b. The equations for the xy-, xz- and yz-traces are found by setting $z = 0$, $y = 0$ and $x = 0$ respectively in the equation of the surface, which gives $\frac{y^2}{18} = 2x^2$, $\frac{z^2}{32} = 2x^2$, $\frac{z^2}{32} + \frac{y^2}{18} = 0$ (which implies that $x = y = z = 0$).

c.

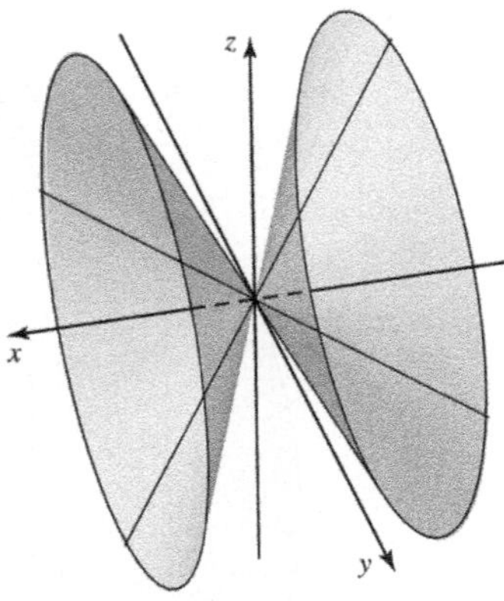

12.1.67

a. The y-intercept is found by setting $x = z = 0$ in the equation of this surface, which gives $y^2 = 4$, so the y-intercepts are $y = \pm 2$. There are no x or z-intercepts.

b. The equations for the xy-, xz- and yz-traces are found by setting $z = 0$, $y = 0$ and $x = 0$ respectively in the equation of the surface, which gives $-x^2 + \frac{y^2}{4} = 1$, $-x^2 - \frac{z^2}{9} = 1$ (no xz-trace), $\frac{y^2}{4} - \frac{z^2}{9} = 1$.

c.

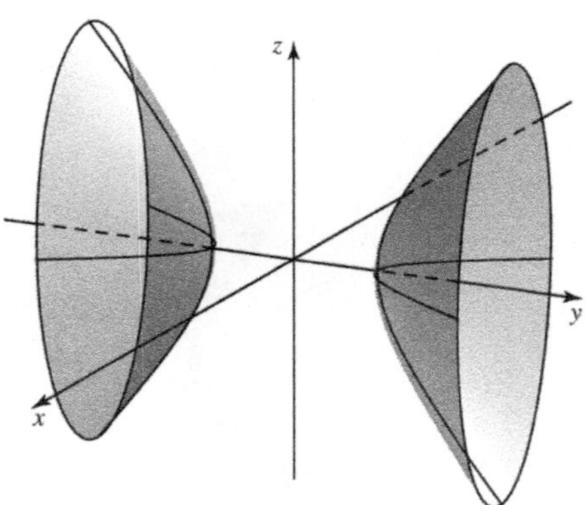

12.1.69

a. The y-intercept is found by setting $x = z = 0$ in the equation of this surface, which gives $3\ y^2 = 1$, so the y-intercepts are $y = \pm\frac{\sqrt{3}}{3}$. There are no x or z-intercepts.

b. The equations for the xy-, xz- and yz-traces are found by setting $z = 0$, $y = 0$ and $x = 0$ respectively in the equation of the surface, which gives $-\frac{x^2}{3} + 3y^2 = 1$, $-\frac{x^2}{3} - \frac{z^2}{12} = 1$ (no xz-trace), $3y^2 - \frac{z^2}{12} = 1$.

c.

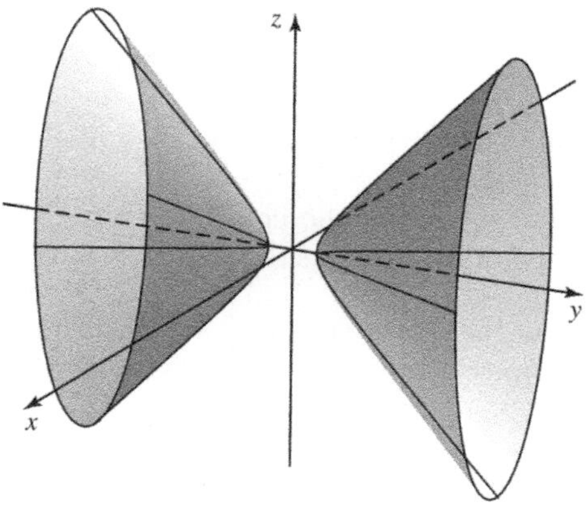

12.1.71

a. True. Observe first that these two planes are parallel since their normal vectors are parallel. The first plane has equation $1 \cdot (x-1) + 2(y-1) - 3(z-1) = 0$, which implies that $x + 2y - 3z = 0$; the point $(3, 0, 1)$ is on this plane, so the two planes are identical.

b. False. The point (1, 0, 0) is on the first plane but not the second.

c. False. There are infinite planes orthogonal to the plane Q.

d. True. Any two points on the line ℓ together with P_0 determine the same plane.

e. False. For example, the xz- and yz-coordinate planes both contain the point $(0, 0, 1)$ and are orthogonal to the xy-coordinate plane.

f. False. Two distinct lines determine a plane only if the lines are parallel or if they intersect.

g. False. Either plane S is plane P or plane S is parallel to plane P.

12.1.73 The direction of the line is $\langle 2, -4, 1\rangle$, so the line is given by $\langle 2, 1, 3\rangle + t\langle 2, -4, 1\rangle = \langle 2+2t, 1-4t, 3+t\rangle$.

12.1.75 These planes have normal $\langle 2, 3, 0\rangle \times \langle -1, -1, 2\rangle = \langle 6, -4, 1\rangle$, so the planes all have an equation of the form $6x - 4y + z = d$ for some real number d.

12.1.77 First we find the line of intersection of the first two planes. The direction of the line of intersection is $\langle 1, 0, 3\rangle \times \langle 0, 1, 4\rangle = \langle -3, -4, 1\rangle$, and by inspection, a point on both planes is $(0, 2, 1)$. Thus the line of intersection is given by $\langle -3t, 2-4t, 1+t\rangle$. This intersects the plane $x+y+6z = 9$ when $-3t+(2-4t)+6(1+t) = 9$, or $8 - t = 9$, so $t = -1$. Thus, the intersection is the single point $(3, 6, 0)$.

12.1.79

a. D. This surface is a cylinder parallel to the parabola $y = z^2$ in the yz-plane.

b. A. This surface is a plane.

c. E. This surface is an ellipsoid.

d. F. This surface is a hyperboloid of one sheet.

e. B. This surface is an elliptic cone.

f. C. This surface is a cylinder parallel to the graph $y = |x|$ in the xy-plane.

12.1.81 This surface is a hyperbolic paraboloid with saddle point at the origin.

12.1.83 This surface is an elliptic paraboloid with axis the y-axis.

12.1.85 Completing the square and rewriting the equation of the surface as $9x^2 + (y+1)^2 - 4z^2 = 1$ shows that this surface is a hyperboloid of one sheet with axis the line ℓ: $\mathbf{r} = \langle 0, -1, t \rangle$.

12.1.87 This surface is a hyperbolic cylinder (the yz-trace is a hyperbola).

12.1.89 Completing the square and rewriting the equation of the surface as $z^2 = \frac{(x-4)^2}{4} + (y-5)^2 + 12$ shows that this surface is a hyperboloid of two sheets.

12.1.91 The point $(t, t^2, 3t^2)$ lies on the plane $8x + y + z = 60$ exactly when $8t + t^2 + 3t^2 = 60$, which can be written as $t^2 + 2t - 15 = 0$, which has solutions $t = -5, 3$. Therefore the intersection points are $(-5, 25, 75)$ and $(3, 9, 27)$.

12.1.93 Suppose the point (x, y, z) lies on both the curve and the plane; then $z = \frac{x}{4}$, and substituting this in the equation $2x + 3y - 12z = 0$ gives $y = \frac{x}{3}$. We also have $x = \cos t$ and $\frac{x}{3} = 4\sin t$ for some t; therefore $\left(\frac{x}{4}\right)^2 + \left(\frac{x}{12}\right)^2 = 1$, which can be written as $10x^2 = 144$, which gives $x = \pm\frac{6\sqrt{10}}{5}$, so the intersection points are $\left(\frac{6\sqrt{10}}{5}, \frac{2\sqrt{10}}{5}, \frac{3\sqrt{10}}{10}\right)$ and $\left(-\frac{6\sqrt{10}}{5}, -\frac{2\sqrt{10}}{5}, -\frac{3\sqrt{10}}{10}\right)$.

12.1.95 The angle θ between the vectors $\mathbf{n}_1 = \langle 5, 2, -1 \rangle$ and $\mathbf{n}_2 = \langle -3, 1, 2 \rangle$ satisfies $\cos\theta = \frac{\mathbf{n}_1 \cdot \mathbf{n}_2}{|\mathbf{n}_1||\mathbf{n}_2|} = -\frac{15}{\sqrt{30}\sqrt{14}} = -\frac{\sqrt{105}}{14}$, so $\theta = \cos^{-1}\left(-\frac{\sqrt{105}}{14}\right) \approx 2.392$ rad $\approx 137°$.

12.1.97 All of the quadric surfaces in Table 12.1 except the hyperbolic paraboloid can have circular cross-sections around a coordinate axis, and so can be generated by revolving a curve in one of the coordinate planes about a coordinate axis.

12.1.99

a.

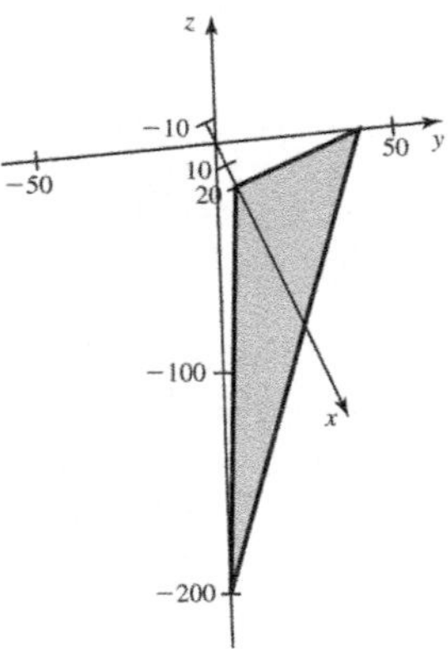

b. The profit is $z = 10 \cdot 20 + 5 \cdot 10 - 200 = \$50$ which is positive.

c. The profit is 0 when x and y lie on the line $2x + y = 40$.

12.1.101

a. Observe that any point (x, y, z) on this curve satisfies $z = cy$, so this gives the equation of the plane P.

b. Plane P has normal vector $\mathbf{n} = \langle 0, -c, 1 \rangle$, so the angle θ that P makes with the xy-plane (which has normal vector $\mathbf{k}$) satisfies $\cos\theta = \frac{\mathbf{n} \cdot \mathbf{k}}{|\mathbf{n}||\mathbf{k}|} = \frac{1}{\sqrt{1+c^2}}$; hence $\theta = \tan^{-1} c$.

c. The curve can be described as the intersection of the ellipsoid given by $x^2 + \frac{y^2}{4} + \frac{z^2}{4c^2} = 1$ with the plane P, which is an ellipse in P.

12.1.103

a. The length of the orthogonal projection of $\overrightarrow{PQ}$ onto the normal vector $\mathbf{n}$ is the magnitude of the scalar component of $\overrightarrow{PQ}$ in the direction of $\mathbf{n}$ which is $\frac{|\overrightarrow{PQ}\cdot\mathbf{n}|}{|\mathbf{n}|}$.

b. Let $P = (0, -1, 0)$ be a point on the plane. $\frac{|\overrightarrow{PQ}\cdot\mathbf{n}|}{|\mathbf{n}|} = \frac{|\langle 1,3,-4\rangle\cdot\langle 2,-1,3\rangle|}{\sqrt{4+1+9}} = \frac{|2-3-12|}{\sqrt{14}} = \frac{13}{\sqrt{14}}$.

12.2 Graphs and Level Curves

12.2.1 The independent variables are x and y and the dependent variable is z.

12.2.3 The domain of g is $\{(x, y) : x \neq 0 \text{ or } y \neq 0\}$.

12.2.5 We need three dimensions to plot points $(x, y, f(x, y))$.

12.2.7 The level curves $x^2 + y^2 = z_0$ are circles centered at $(0, 0)$ in $\mathbb{R}^2$.

12.2.9 The function f has 6 independent variables, so $n = 6$.

12.2.11 The domain of f is $\mathbb{R}^2$.

12.2.13 The domain of f is $\{(x, y) : x^2 + y^2 \leq 25\}$, which is the set of all points on or within the circle of radius 5 centered at the origin.

12.2.15 The domain of f is $\{(x, y) : y \neq 0\}$.

12.2.17 The domain of g is $\{(x, y) : y < x^2\}$.

12.2.19 The domain of g is $\{(x, y) : x\,y \geq 0, (x, y) \neq (0, 0)\}$.

12.2.21 This surface is a plane; the function's domain is $\mathbb{R}^2$ and its range is $\mathbb{R}$.

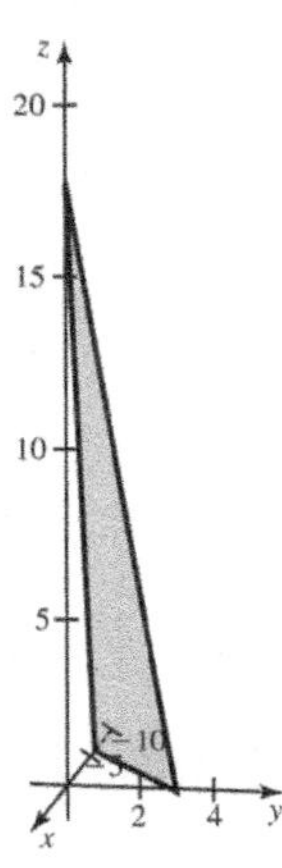

12.2.23 This surface is a hyperbolic paraboloid; the function's domain is $\mathbb{R}^2$ and its range is $\mathbb{R}$.

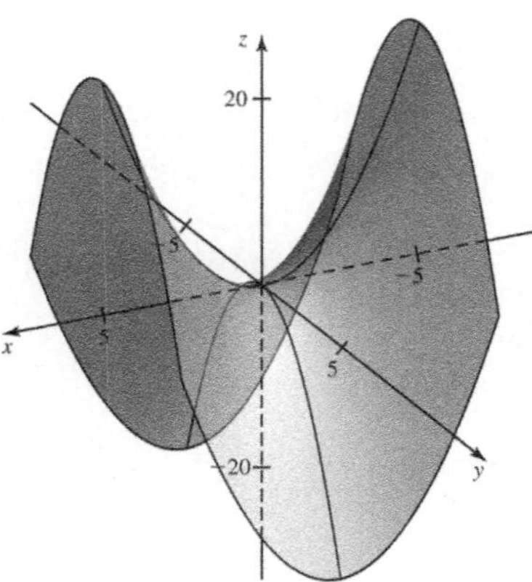

12.2.25 This surface is the lower part of a hyperboloid of two sheets; the function's domain is $\mathbb{R}^2$ and its range is the interval $(-\infty, -1]$.

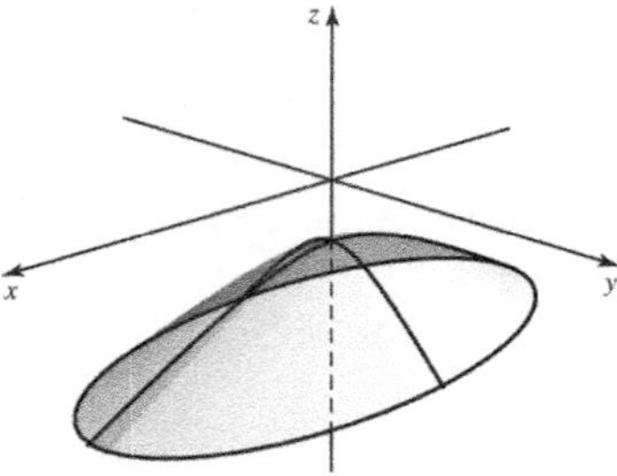

12.2.27 This surface is the upper part of a hyperboloid of one sheet; the function's domain is $\{(x, y) : x^2 + y^2 \geq 1\}$ and its range is the interval $[0, \infty)$.

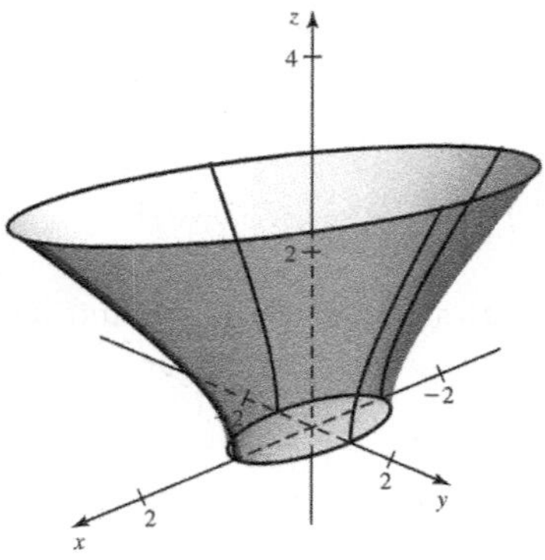

12.2.29

a. A. Notice that the range of the function in (A) is $[-1, 1]$.

b. D. Notice that the function in (D) becomes large and negative for(x, y) near $(0, 0)$.

c. B. Notice that the function in (B) becomes large as you get close to $y = x$.

d. C. Notice that the function in (C) is everywhere positive.

12.2.31

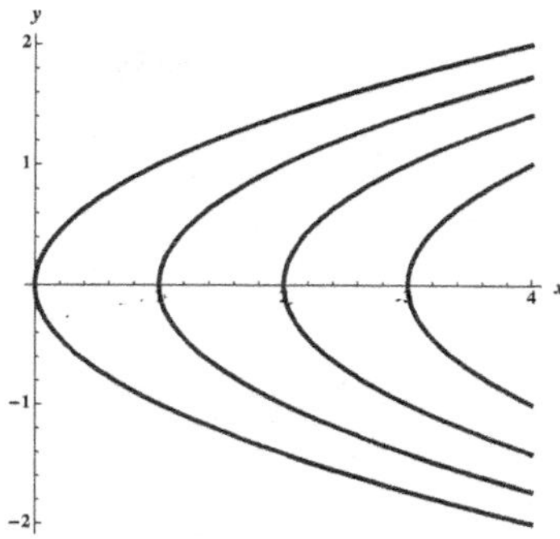

12.2.33

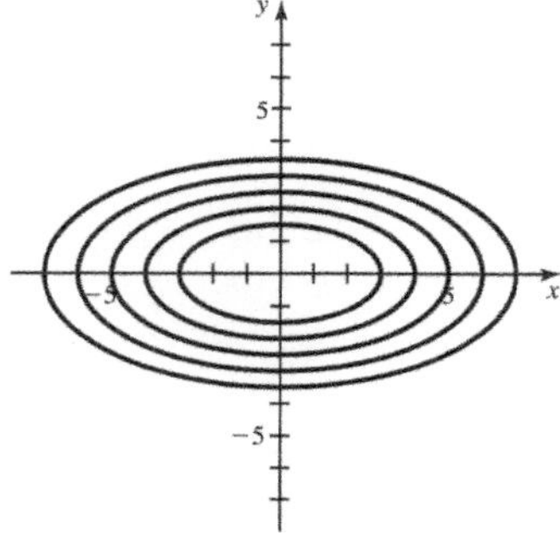

12.2.35

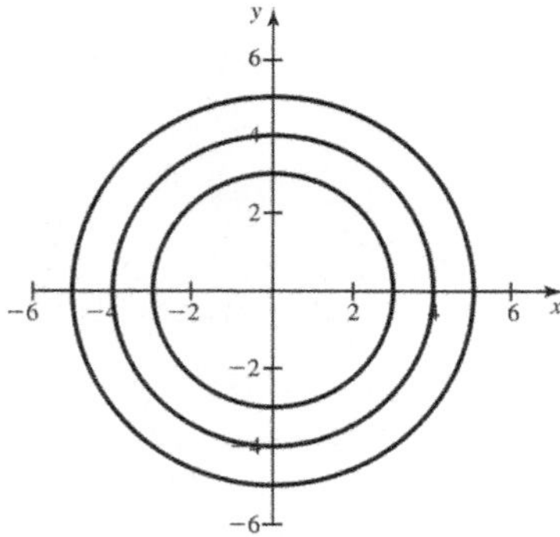

12.2.37

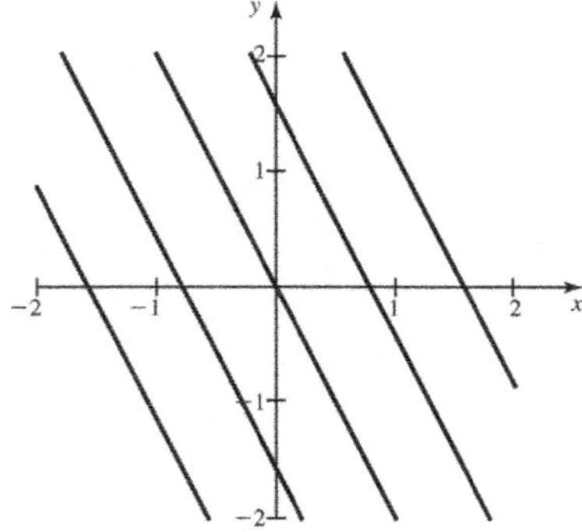

12.2.39

a.

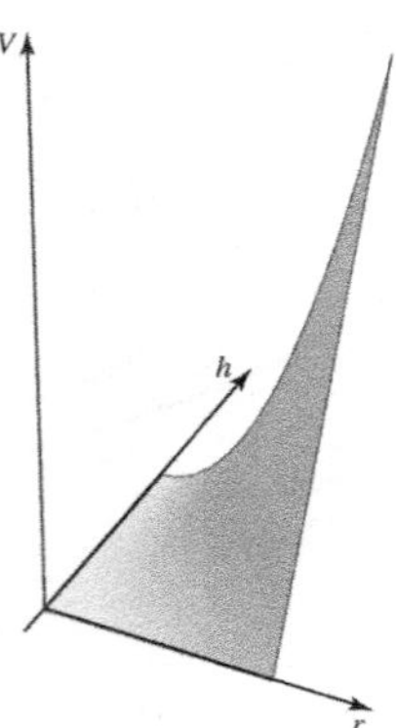

b. The domain is $D = \{(r,\, h) : r > 0,\, h > 0\}$.

c. We have $\pi r^2 h = 300$, so $h = \frac{300}{\pi r^2}$.

12.2.41

a.

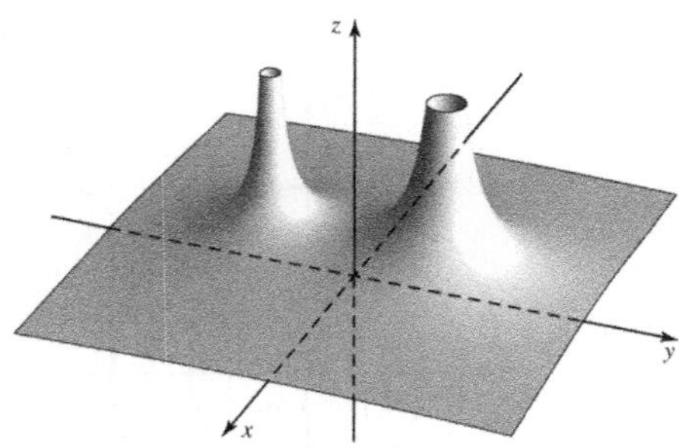

b. The potential function is defined for all $(x,\, y)$ in $\mathbb{R}^2$ except $(0,\, 1)$ and $(0,\, -1)$.

c. We have $\phi\,(2,\, 3) \approx 0.93 > \phi\,(3,\, 2) \approx 0.87$.

d.

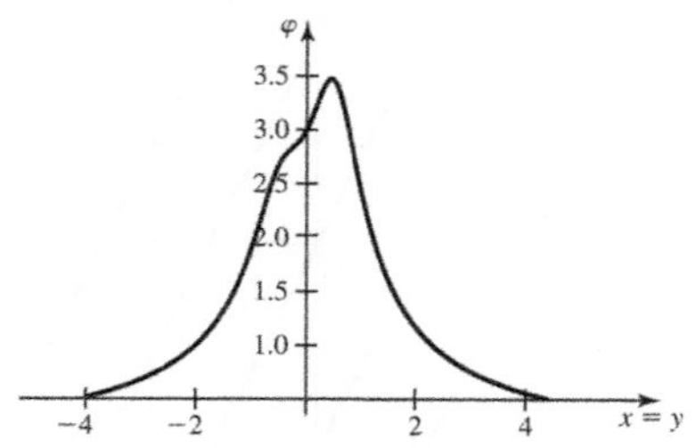

12.2.43

a.

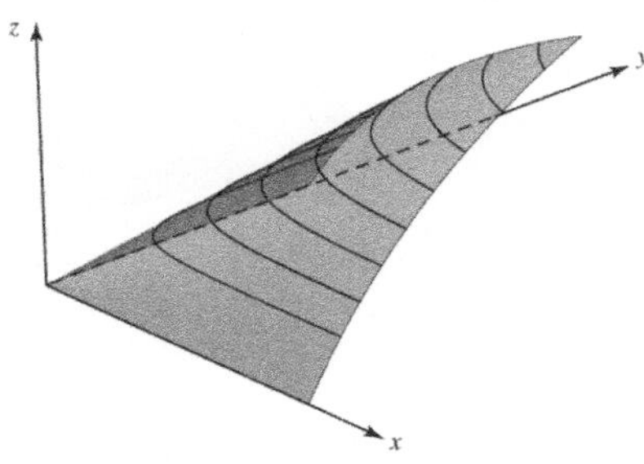

b. The maximum resistance is $R(10, 10) = 5$ ohms.

c. This means $R(x, y) = R(y, x)$.

12.2.45

a.

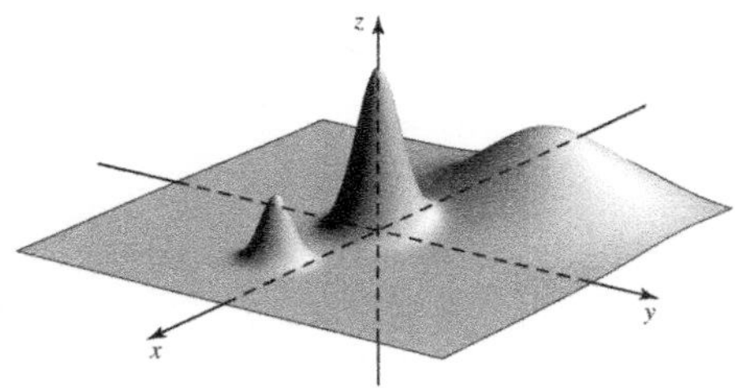

b. The peaks occur near the points $(0, 0)$, $(-5, 3)$ and $(4, -1)$.

c. We have $f(0, 0) \approx 10.17$, $f(-5, 3) \approx 5.00$, $f(4, -1) \approx 4.00$.

12.2.47 The domain of g is $\{(x, y, z) : x \neq z\}$, which is all points in $\mathbb{R}^3$ not on the plane given by $x = z$.

12.2.49 The domain of f is $\{(x, y, z) : y \geq z\}$, which is all points in $\mathbb{R}^3$ on or below the plane given by $z = y$.

12.2.51 The domain of F is $\{(x, y, z) : x^2 \leq y\}$, which is all points on the side of the vertical cylinder $y = x^2$ that contains the positive y-axis.

12.2.53

a. False. This function has domain $\mathbb{R}^2$.

b. False. The domain of a function of 4 variables is a region in $\mathbb{R}^4$.

c. True. The level curves for the function defined by $z = 2x - 3y$ are lines of the form $2x - 3y = c$ for any constant c.

12.2.55

a. The domain is $\mathbb{R}^2$ and the range is the interval $[0, \infty)$.

b.

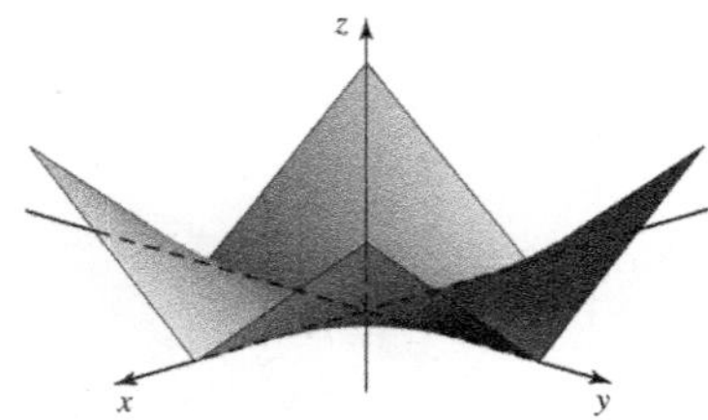

12.2.57

a. The domain is $\{(x, y) : x \neq y\}$ and the range is $\mathbb{R}$.

b.

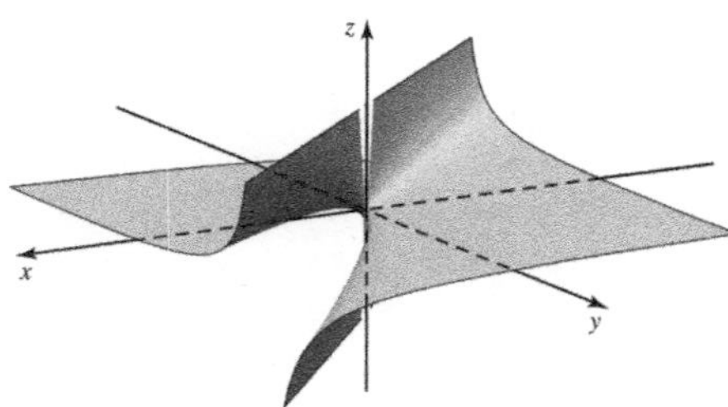

12.2.59

a. The domain is $\{(x, y) : y \neq x + \frac{\pi}{2} + n\pi$ for any integer $n\}$ and the range is the interval $[0, \infty)$.

b.

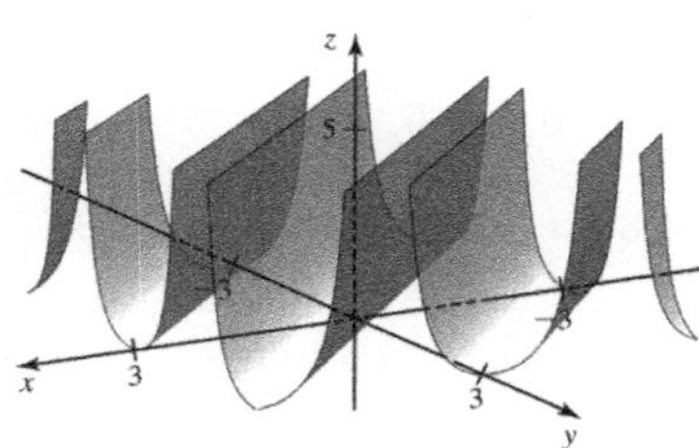

12.2.61 This function has a peak at the origin.

12.2.63 This function has a depression at the point $(1, 0)$.

12.2.65 The level curves are the lines given by $ax + by = d - cz_0$, where z_0 is a constant; these lines all have slope $-\frac{a}{b}$ (in the case $b = 0$ the lines are all vertical).

12.2.67 If $x^2+y^2-z = C$, then $z = x^2+y^2-C$, so the level surfaces are paraboloids with vertices $(0, 0, -C)$.

12.2.69 If $\sqrt{x^2 + 2z^2} = K$, then $x^2 + 2z^2 = C$ where $C = K^2$, so the level surfaces are elliptic cylinders parallel to the y-axis.

12.2.71

a. Solving for P in the equation $B(P, r, t) = 20,000$ with $t = 20$ years gives $P = \frac{20,000r}{(1+r)^{240}-1}$.

b. The level curves are given by $P = \frac{Br}{(1+r)^{240}-1}$,with $B = 5000, 10,000, 15,000$ and $25,000$.

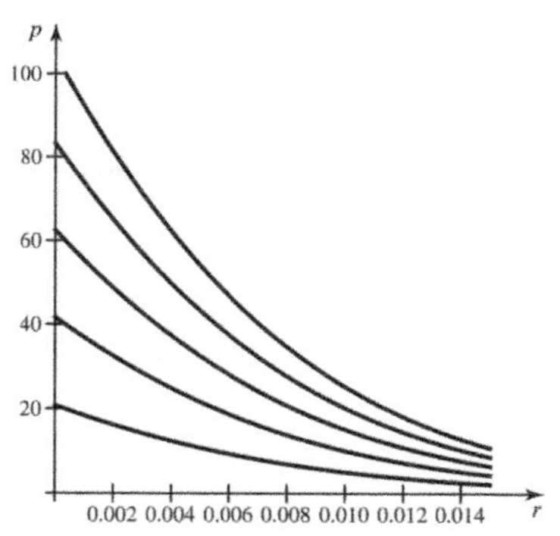

12.2.73

a. 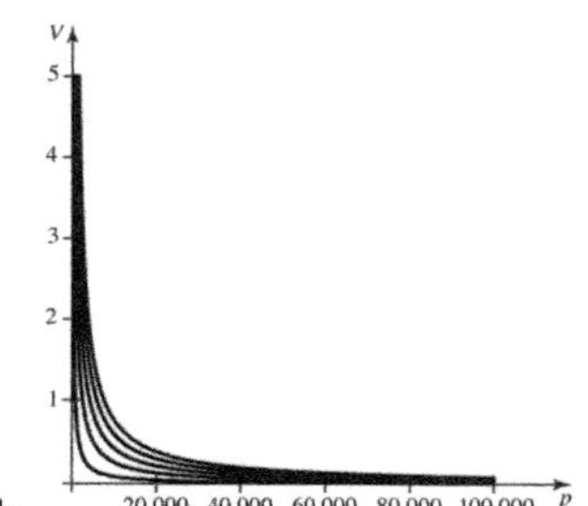

b. 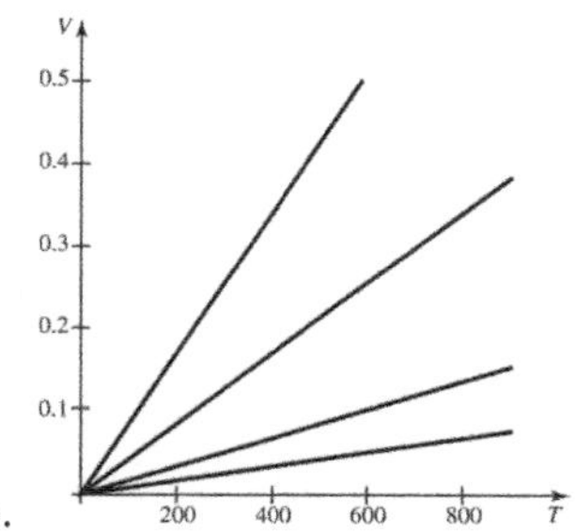

c. 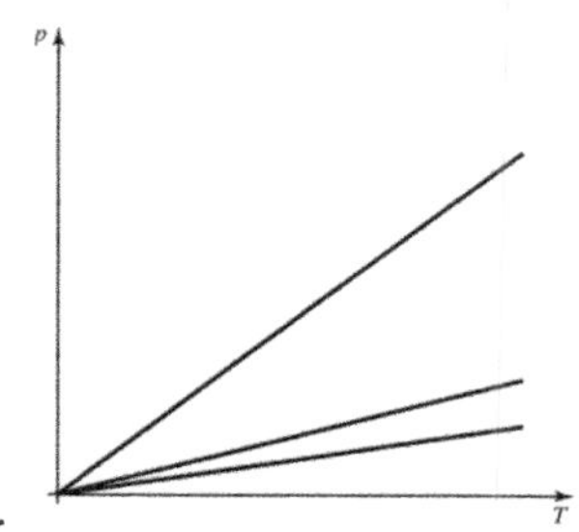

12.2.75 The domain of f is $\{(x, y) : x - 1 \leq y \leq x + 1\}$. This is the region between the two parallel lines given by $y = x - 1$ and $y = x + 1$.

12.2.77 Factor the equation $z^2 - xz + yz - xy = (z - x)(z + y)$; hence the domain of h is $\{(x, y, z) : (z - x)(z + y) \geq 0\}$, which is equivalent to $D = \{(x, y, z) : (x \leq z \text{ and } y \geq -z) \text{ or } (x \geq z \text{ and } y \leq -z)\}$. The domain consists of all points above or below both the planes given by $z = x$ and $z = -y$ as well as the points on either one of these planes.

12.3 Limits and Continuity

12.3.1 The values of $|f(x, y) - L|$ can be made arbitrarily small if (x, y) is sufficiently close to (a, b).

12.3.3 If $f(x, y)$ is a polynomial, then $\lim_{(x, y)\to(a, b)} f(x, y) = f(a, b)$; in other words, the limit can be found by plugging in $x = a$, $y = b$ in $f(x, y)$.

12.3.5 If the limits along different paths do not agree, then the limit does not exist.

12.3.7 The function f must be defined at (a, b), $\lim_{(x, y)\to(a, b)} f(x, y)$ must exist, and the limit must equal $f(a, b)$.

12.3.9 A rational function is continuous at all points where its denominator is nonzero.

12.3.11 $\lim_{(x, y)\to(2, 9)} 101 = 101$.

12.3.13 $\lim_{(x, y)\to(-3, 3)} \left(4x^2 - y^2\right) = 4 \cdot (-3)^2 - (3)^2 = 27$.

12.3.15 $\lim_{(x, y)\to(0, \pi)} \frac{\cos xy + \sin xy}{2y} = \frac{\cos 0 + \sin 0}{2\pi} = \frac{1}{2\pi}$.

12.3.17 $\lim_{(x, y)\to(2, 0)} \frac{x^2 - 3xy^2}{x + y} = \frac{2^2 - 3 \cdot 2 \cdot 0^2}{2 + 0} = 2$.

12.3.19 $\lim_{(x,\,y)\to(6,\,2)} \frac{x^2-3xy}{x-3y} = \lim_{(x,\,y)\to(6,\,2)} \frac{x(x-3y)}{x-3y} = \lim_{(x,\,y)\to(6,\,2)} x = 6.$

12.3.21 $\lim_{(x,y)\to(3,1)} \frac{x^2-7xy+12y^2}{x-3y} = \lim_{(x,y)\to(3,1)} \frac{(x-3y)(x-4y)}{x-3y} = \lim_{(x,y)\to(3,1)}(x-4y) = 3-4 = -1.$

12.3.23 $\lim_{(x,\,y)\to(2,\,2)} \frac{y^2-4}{xy-2x} = \lim_{(x,\,y)\to(2,\,2)} \frac{(y+2)(y-2)}{x(y-2)} = \lim_{(x,\,y)\to(2,\,2)} \frac{y+2}{x} = \frac{2+2}{2} = 2.$

12.3.25 $\lim_{(x,\,y)\to(1,\,2)} \frac{\sqrt{y}-\sqrt{x+1}}{y-x-1} = \lim_{(x,\,y)\to(1,\,2)} \frac{\left(\sqrt{y}-\sqrt{x+1}\right)\left(\sqrt{y}+\sqrt{x+1}\right)}{(y-x-1)\left(\sqrt{y}+\sqrt{x+1}\right)} =$
$\lim_{(x,\,y)\to(1,\,2)} \frac{y-x-1}{(y-x-1)\left(\sqrt{y}+\sqrt{x+1}\right)} = \lim_{(x,\,y)\to(1,\,2)} \frac{1}{\sqrt{y}+\sqrt{x+1}} = \frac{1}{\sqrt{2}+\sqrt{2}} = \frac{1}{2\sqrt{2}}.$

12.3.27 Observe that along the line $y=0$, $\lim_{(x,\,y)\to(0,\,0)} \frac{x+2y}{x-2y} = \lim_{x\to 0} \frac{x}{x} = 1$, whereas along the line $x=0$, $\lim_{(x,\,y)\to(0,\,0)} \frac{x+2y}{x-2y} = \lim_{y\to 0} \frac{2y}{-2y} = -1.$

12.3.29 Observe that along the line $x=0$, $\lim_{(x,\,y)\to(0,\,0)} \frac{y^4-2x^2}{y^4+x^2} = \lim_{y\to 0} \frac{y^4}{y^4} = 1$, whereas along the line $y=0$, $\lim_{(x,\,y)\to(0,\,0)} \frac{y^4-2x^2}{y^4+x^2} = \lim_{x\to 0} -\frac{2x^2}{x^2} = -2.$

12.3.31 Observe that along the line $y=x$, $\lim_{(x,\,y)\to(0,\,0)} \frac{y^3+x^3}{xy^2} = \lim_{x\to 0} \frac{2x^3}{x^3} = 2$, whereas along the line $y=-x$, $\lim_{(x,\,y)\to(0,\,0)} \frac{y^3+x^3}{xy^2} = \lim_{x\to 0} \frac{0}{-x^3} = 0.$

12.3.33 The function f is continuous on $\mathbb{R}^2$.

12.3.35 The function p is continuous at all points except the origin, where it is undefined.

12.3.37 The function f is continuous on $\mathbb{R}^2$ except where $x=0$.

12.3.39 The function f is continuous on $\mathbb{R}^2$ except the origin. Note that along the line $y=x$, $\lim_{(x,y)\to(0,0)} \frac{xy}{x^2+y^2} = \lim_{(x,y)\to(0,0)} \frac{x^2}{x^2+x^2} = \frac{1}{2} \neq 0.$

12.3.41 The function f is continuous on $\mathbb{R}^2$.

12.3.43 The function f is continuous on $\mathbb{R}^2$.

12.3.45 The function h is continuous on $\mathbb{R}^2$.

12.3.47 The function f is continuous on its domain, which is $D = \{(x,\,y) : (x,\,y) \neq (0,\,0)\}$.

12.3.49 The function g is continuous on $\mathbb{R}^2$.

12.3.51 The function f is continuous on $\mathbb{R}^2$.

12.3.53 $\lim_{(x,\,y,\,z)\to(1,\,\ln 2,\,3)} z\,e^{xy} = 3\,e^{1\cdot\ln 2} = 6.$

12.3.55 $\lim_{(x,\,y,\,z)\to(1,\,1,\,1)} \frac{yz-xy-xz-x^2}{yz+xy+xz-y^2} = \frac{1-1-1-1}{1+1+1-1} = -1.$

12.3.57 $\lim_{(x,y,z)\to(1,1,1)} \frac{x^2+xy-xz-yz}{x-z} = \lim_{(x,y,z)\to(1,1,1)} \frac{(x-z)(x+y)}{x-z} = \lim_{(x,y,z)\to(1,1,1)}(x+y) = 2.$

12.3.59

a. False. The limit may be different or not exist along other paths approaching $(0,\,0)$.

b. False. We may have $f(a,\,b)$ undefined, or $f(a,\,b) \neq L$.

c. True. The limit must exist for f to be continuous at $(a,\,b)$.

d. False. For example, take $P = (0,\,0)$ and the domain of f to be $\{(x,\,y) : (x,\,y) \neq (0,\,0)\}$.

12.3.61 $\lim_{(x,\,y)\to(0,\,1)} \frac{y\sin x}{x(y+1)} = \left(\lim_{x\to 0} \frac{\sin x}{x}\right)\left(\lim_{y\to 1} \frac{y}{y+1}\right) = 1\cdot\frac{1}{2} = \frac{1}{2}$.

12.3.63 $\lim_{(x,\,y)\to(1,\,0)} \frac{y\ln y}{x} = \left(\lim_{x\to 1} \frac{1}{x}\right)\left(\lim_{y\to 0} \ln y^y\right) = 1\cdot \ln 1 = 0$

12.3.65 Observe that along the line $y = x$, $\lim_{(x,\,y)\to(0,\,0)} \frac{|x-y|}{|x+y|} = \lim_{x\to 0} \frac{0}{2|x|} = 0$, whereas along the line $y = 2x$, $\lim_{(x,\,y)\to(0,\,0)} \frac{|x-y|}{|x+y|} = \lim_{x\to 0} \frac{|x|}{3|x|} = \frac{1}{3}$, therefore this limit does not exist.

12.3.67 Observe that $\lim_{(x,\,y)\to(2,\,0)} \frac{1-\cos y}{xy^2} = \left(\lim_{x\to 2} \frac{1}{x}\right)\left(\lim_{y\to 0} \frac{1-\cos y}{y^2}\right) = \frac{1}{2}\cdot\frac{1}{2} = \frac{1}{4}$ where the y-limit is evaluated by two applications of L'Hôpital's rule.

12.3.69 $\lim_{(x,y)\to(0,0)} \frac{x^2y}{x^2+y^2} = \lim_{r\to 0} \frac{r^3\cos^2\theta\sin\theta}{r^2} = \lim_{r\to 0} r\cos^2\theta\sin\theta = 0$.

12.3.71 $\lim_{(x,y)\to(0,0)} \frac{x^2+y^2+x^2y^2}{x^2+y^2} = \lim_{r\to 0} \frac{r^2+r^4\cos^2\theta\sin^2\theta}{r^2} = \lim_{r\to 0}(1+r^2\cos^2\theta\sin^2\theta) = 1$.

12.3.73 Let $u = x^2 + y^1 - 1$. Then as $x^2 + y^2 \to 1$, $u \to 0$. Because $\lim_{u\to 0} \frac{\sin u}{u} = 1$, we must have $b = 1$ in order for f to be continuous everywhere.

12.3.75 The limit is 0 along the lines $x = 0$ or $y = 0$. However, along the line $x = y$ we have $\lim_{(x,y)\to(0,0)} \frac{a\,x^m y^n}{b\,x^{m+n}+c\,y^{m+n}} = \lim_{x\to 0} \frac{ax^{m+n}}{bx^{n+m}+cx^{m+n}} = \frac{a}{b+c} \neq 0$ because $a \neq 0$. Therefore this limit does not exist.

12.3.77 Let $u = xy$; then $u \to 0$ as $(x,\,y) \to (1,\,0)$, so $\lim_{(x,\,y)\to(1,\,0)} \frac{\sin xy}{xy} = \lim_{u\to 0} \frac{\sin u}{u} = 1$.

12.3.79 Let $u = xy$; then $u \to 0$ as $(x,\,y) \to (0,\,2)$, so $\lim_{(x,\,y)\to(0,\,2)} (2xy)^{xy} = \lim_{u\to 0} 2^u u^u = 1$.

12.3.81 Because $\lim_{(x,\,y)\to(0,\,0)} e^{-1/(x^2+y^2)} = 0$, we should define $f\,(0,\,0) = 0$.

12.3.83 For any $\epsilon > 0$, let $\delta = \frac{\epsilon}{2}$. Then $|\,x-a\,|,\ |\,y-b\,| \le \sqrt{(x-a)^2+(y-b)^2}$, so $0 < \sqrt{(x-a)^2+(y-b)^2} < \delta$ which implies that $|x+y-(a+b)\,| \le |\,x-a\,|+|\,y-b\,| < \frac{\epsilon}{2}+\frac{\epsilon}{2} = \epsilon$.

12.3.85 Observe first that this is trivial when $c = 0$, so assume $c \neq 0$ and let $\epsilon > 0$. Then there exists $\delta > 0$ such that $0 < \sqrt{(x-a)^2+(y-b)^2} < \delta \Longrightarrow |\,f\,(x,\,y) - L\,| < \frac{\epsilon}{|c|}$. Therefore $0 < \sqrt{(x-a)^2+(y-b)^2} < \delta \Longrightarrow |\,c\,f\,(x,\,y) - c\,L\,| = |c|\,|\,f\,(x,\,y) - L\,| < |c|\cdot\frac{\epsilon}{|c|} = \epsilon$.

12.4 Partial Derivatives

12.4.1 The slope parallel to the x-axis is $f_x\,(a,b)$, and the slope parallel to the y-axis is $f_y\,(a,b)$.

12.4.3 $f_x\,(x,y) = \cos(xy) + x\,(-\sin(xy))\,y = \cos(xy) - xy\sin(xy)$, $f_y\,(x,y) = x\,(-\sin(xy))\,x = -x^2\sin(xy)$.

12.4.5 Think of x and y as being fixed, and differentiate with respect to the variable z.

12.4.7 $f_x = \lim\limits_{h\to 0} \dfrac{f(x+h,y)-f(x,y)}{h} = \lim\limits_{h\to 0} \dfrac{5(x+h)y-5xy}{h} = \lim\limits_{h\to 0} \dfrac{5hy}{h} = \lim\limits_{h\to 0} 5y = 5y.$

$$f_y = \lim_{h\to 0} \frac{f(x,y+h)-f(x,y)}{h} = \lim_{h\to 0} \frac{5x(y+h)-5xy}{h} = \lim_{h\to 0} \frac{5xh}{h} = \lim_{h\to 0} 5x = 5x.$$

12.4.9 $f_x = \lim\limits_{h\to 0} \dfrac{f(x+h,y)-f(x,y)}{h} = \lim\limits_{h\to 0} \dfrac{\frac{x+h}{y}-\frac{x}{y}}{h} = \lim\limits_{h\to 0} \dfrac{h}{hy} = \lim\limits_{h\to 0} \dfrac{1}{y} = \dfrac{1}{y}.$

$$f_y = \lim_{h\to 0} \frac{f(x,y+h)-f(x,y)}{h} = \lim_{h\to 0} \frac{\frac{x}{y+h}-\frac{x}{y}}{h} = \lim_{h\to 0} \frac{xy-x(y+h)}{y(y+h)h} = \lim_{h\to 0} \frac{-x}{y(y+h)} = -\frac{x}{y^2}.$$

12.4.11 $f_x(x, y) = 6x,\ f_y(x, y) = 12y^2$.

12.4.13 $f_x(x, y) = 6xy,\ f_y(x, y) = 3x^2$.

12.4.15 $f_x(x, y) = e^y,\ f_y(x, y) = xe^y$.

12.4.17 $g_x(x, y) = (-\sin(2xy))\,2y = -2y\sin(2xy),\ g_y(x, y) = (-\sin(2xy))\,2x = -2x\sin(2xy)$.

12.4.19 $f_x(x, y) = 2xye^{x^2y},\ f_y(x, y) = x^2e^{x^2y}$.

12.4.21 $f_w(w, z) = \frac{(w^2+z^2)\cdot 1 - w\cdot 2w}{(w^2+z^2)^2} = \frac{z^2-w^2}{(w^2+z^2)^2},\ f_z(w, z) = -w\left(w^2+z^2\right)^{-2}\cdot 2z = -\frac{2wz}{(w^2+z^2)^2}$.

12.4.23 $s_y(y, z) = z^2\left(\sec^2 yz\right)z = z^3\sec^2 yz,\ s_z(y, z) = 2z\tan yz + z^2\left(\sec^2 yz\right)y = 2z\tan yz + yz^2\sec^2 yz$

12.4.25 $G_s(s, t) = \frac{t}{2\sqrt{st}}\cdot\frac{1}{s+t} + \sqrt{st}\cdot -\frac{1}{(s+t)^2} = \frac{\sqrt{st}(s+t)-2s\sqrt{st}}{2s(s+t)^2} = \frac{\sqrt{st}(t-s)}{2s(s+t)^2},\ G_t(s, t) = \frac{s}{2\sqrt{st}}\cdot\frac{1}{s+t} + \sqrt{st}\cdot -\frac{1}{(s+t)^2} = \frac{\sqrt{st}(s+t)-2t\sqrt{st}}{2t(s+t)^2} = \frac{\sqrt{st}(s-t)}{2t(s+t)^2}$.

12.4.27 $f_x(x, y) = 2yx^{2y-1},\ f_y(x, y) = 2x^{2y}\ln x$.

12.4.29 We have $h_x(x, y) = 3x^2 + y^2,\ h_y(x, y) = 2xy$; therefore $h_{xx}(x, y) = 6x,\ h_{yy}(x, y) = 2x,\ h_{xy}(x, y) = h_{yx}(y, x) = 2y$.

12.4.31 We have $f_x(x, y) = 2xy^3,\ f_y(x, y) = 3x^2y^2$; therefore $f_{xx}(x, y) = 2y^3,\ f_{yy}(x, y) = 6x^2y,\ f_{xy}(x, y) = f_{yx}(x, y) = 6xy^2$.

12.4.33 We have $f_x(x, y) = 4y^3\cos 4x,\ f_y(x, y) = 3y^2\sin 4x$; therefore $f_{xx}(x, y) = -16y^3\sin 4x,\ f_{yy}(x, y) = 6y\sin 4x,\ f_{xy}(x, y) = f_{yx}(y, x) = 12y^2\cos 4x$.

12.4.35 We have $p_u(u, v) = \frac{2u}{u^2+v^2+4},\ p_v(u, v) = \frac{2v}{u^2+v^2+4}$; therefore $p_{uu}(u, v) = \frac{(u^2+v^2+4)\cdot 2 - 2u\cdot 2u}{(u^2+v^2+4)^2} = \frac{-2u^2+2v^2+8}{(u^2+v^2+4)^2},\ p_{vv}(u, v) = \frac{(u^2+v^2+4)\cdot 2 - 2v\cdot 2v}{(u^2+v^2+4)^2} = \frac{2u^2-2v^2+8}{(u^2+v^2+4)^2},\ p_{uv}(u, v) = p_{vu}(u, v) = -2u\left(u^2+v^2+4\right)^{-2}\cdot 2v = -\frac{4uv}{(u^2+v^2+4)^2}$.

12.4.37 We have $F_r(r, s) = e^s,\ \ F_s(r, s) = re^s$; therefore $F_{rr}(r, s) = 0,\ \ F_{ss}(r, s) = re^s,\ F_{rs}(r, s) = F_{sr}(r, s) = e^s$.

12.4.39 Observe that $f_x(x, y) = 6x^2$, so $f_{xy}(x, y) = 0$; and $f_y(x, y) = 6y$, so $f_{yx}(x, y) = 0$.

12.4.41 Observe that $f_x(x, y) = -y\sin xy$, so $f_{xy}(x, y) = -\sin xy - xy\cos xy$; and $f_y(x, y) = -x\sin xy$, so $f_{yx}(x, y) = -\sin xy - xy\cos xy$.

12.4.43 Observe that $f_x(x, y) = e^{x+y}$, so $f_{xy}(x, y) = e^{x+y}$; and $f_y(x, y) = e^{x+y}$, so $f_{yx}(x, y) = e^{x+y}$.

12.4.45 $f_x(x, y, z) = y + z;\ f_y(x, y, z) = x + z;\ f_z(x, y, z) = x + y$.

12.4.47 $h_x(x, y, z) = h_y(x, y, z) = h_z(x, y, z) = -\sin(x + y + z)$.

12.4.49 $F_u(u, v, w) = \frac{1}{v+w};\ F_v(u, v, w) = -\frac{u}{(v+w)^2};\ F_w(u, v, w) = -\frac{u}{(v+w)^2}$.

12.4.51 $f_w(w, x, y, z) = 2wxy^2;\ f_x(w, x, y, z) = w^2y^2 + y^3z^2;\ f_y(w, x, y, z) = 2w^2xy + 3xy^2z^2;\ f_z(w, x, y, z) = 2xy^3z$.

12.4.53 $h_w(w, x, y, z) = \frac{z}{xy};\ h_x(w, x, y, z) = -\frac{wz}{x^2y};\ h_y(w, x, y, z) = -\frac{wz}{xy^2};\ h_z(w, x, y, z) = \frac{w}{xy}$.

12.4.55

a. We have $V = \frac{kT}{P}$, so $\frac{\partial V}{\partial P} = -\frac{kT}{P^2}$. Because this partial derivative is negative, the volume decreases as the pressure increases at a fixed temperature.

b. We have $\frac{\partial V}{\partial T} = \frac{k}{P}$. Because this partial derivative is positive, the volume increases as the temperature increases at a fixed pressure.

c.

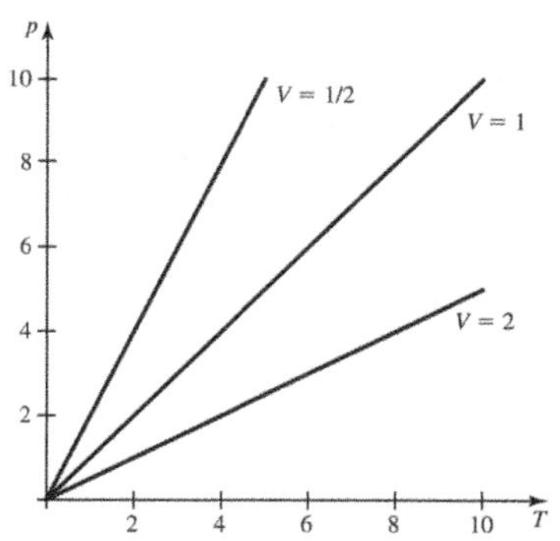

12.4.57

a. Observe that as $f(x, y) = 0$ along either coordinate axis but on the line $y = x$, $f(x, y) = -\frac{x^2}{2x^2} = -\frac{1}{2}$, so $\lim_{(x, y)\to(0, 0)} f(x, y)$ does not exist, and hence f is not continuous at $(0, 0)$.

b. By Theorem 12.6, f is not differentiable at $(0, 0)$.

c. Because f is identically 0 on the coordinate axes, $f_x(0, 0) = f_y(0, 0) = 0$.

d. We have $f_x(x, y) = -\left(\frac{(x^2+y^2)y - xy \cdot 2x}{(x^2+y^2)^2}\right) = \frac{(x^2-y^2)y}{(x^2+y^2)^2}$. Along the line $x = 2y$, $f_x(x, y) = \frac{3y^3}{25y^4} = \frac{3}{25} \cdot \frac{1}{y}$, which does not converge to 0 as $y \to 0$. Hence f_x is not continuous at $(0, 0)$. A similar argument shows that f_y is also not continuous at $(0, 0)$.

e. Theorem 12.5 does not apply because the partials f_x and f_y are not continuous at $(0, 0)$, and Theorem 12.6 does not apply because f is not differentiable at $(0, 0)$.

12.4.59

a. False. $\frac{\partial}{\partial x} y^{10} = 0$ because x and y are independent variables.

b. False. $\frac{\partial^2}{\partial x\, \partial y}(xy)^{1/2} = \frac{1}{2} \cdot x^{-1/2} \cdot \frac{1}{2} y^{-1/2} = \frac{1}{4\sqrt{xy}}$.

c. True. If f has continuous partial derivatives of all orders, then the order of differentiation for mixed partials can be exchanged.

12.4.61 $f_y(2, 3) \approx \frac{f(2,3.1) - f(2,3)}{.1} = \frac{4.384 - 4.243}{.1} = 1.41$.

12.4.63 $f_y(2.4, 3.3) =\approx \frac{f(2.4,3.4) - f(2.4,3.3)}{.1} = \frac{5.267 - 5.112}{.1} = 1.55$. Answers may vary.

12.4.65 We have $f_x(x, y) = -\frac{2x}{1+(x^2+y^2)^2}$ and $f_y(x, y) = -\frac{2y}{1+(x^2+y^2)^2}$.

12.4.67 We have $h_x(x, y, z) = z(1 + x + 2y)^{z-1}$, $h_y(x, y, z) = 2z(1 + x + 2y)^{z-1}$, and $h_z(x, y, z) = (1 + x + 2y)^z \ln(1 + x + 2y)$.

12.4.69

a. We have $z_x = \frac{1}{y^2}$ and $z_y = -\frac{2x}{y^3}$.

b.

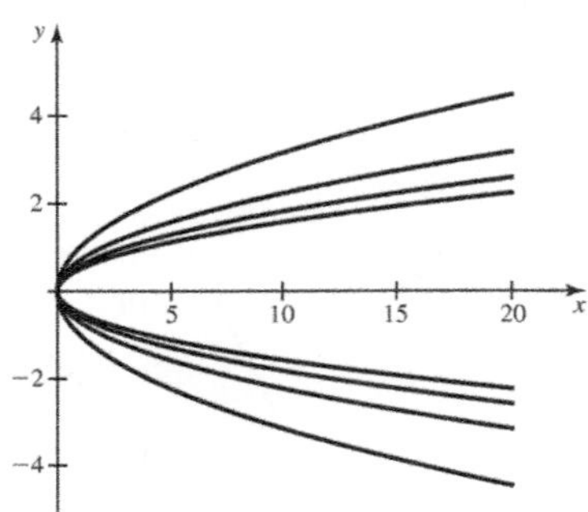

c. We observe that z increases at the same rate as x, which makes sense because $z_x = 1$ along this line.

d. We observe that z increases when $y < 0$, is undefined when $y = 0$ and decreases when $y > 0$, which is consistent with $z_y = -\frac{2}{y^3}$ along this line.

12.4.71

a. Because $\cos\left(\frac{\pi}{3}\right) = \frac{1}{2}$ we have $c = \left(a^2 + b^2 - ab\right)^{1/2}$, and therefore $\frac{\partial c}{\partial a} = \frac{2a-b}{2\sqrt{a^2+b^2-ab}}$ and $\frac{\partial c}{\partial b} = \frac{2b-a}{2\sqrt{a^2+b^2-ab}}$.

b. Implicit differentiation gives $2c\frac{\partial c}{\partial a} = 2a - b$, so $\frac{\partial c}{\partial a} = \frac{2a-b}{2c}$ and $2c\frac{\partial c}{\partial b} = 2b - a$, so $\frac{\partial c}{\partial b} = \frac{2b-a}{2c}$.

c. The necessary relationship is $2a - b > 0$ or $a > \frac{b}{2}$.

12.4.73

a. We have $\varphi_x(x, y) = -\frac{2x}{\left(x^2+(y-1)^2\right)^{3/2}} - \frac{x}{\left(x^2+(y+1)^2\right)^{3/2}}$ and $\varphi_y(x, y) = -\frac{2(y-1)}{\left(x^2+(y-1)^2\right)^{3/2}} - \frac{y+1}{\left(x^2+(y+1)^2\right)^{3/2}}$.

b. Observe that $|\varphi_x(x, y)| \le \frac{2|x|}{|x|^{3/2}} + \frac{|x|}{|x|^{3/2}} = \frac{3}{|x|^{1/2}}$ and similarly $|\varphi_y(x, y)| \le \frac{2|y-1|}{|y-1|^{3/2}} + \frac{|y+1|}{|y+1|^{3/2}} = \frac{2}{|y-1|^{1/2}} + \frac{1}{|y+1|^{1/2}}$, which both converge to 0 as $x, y \to \infty$.

c. We see that $\varphi_x(0, y) = 0$ as long as $y \ne \pm 1$. This is consistent with the observation that along horizontal lines $y = y_0$ the potential function takes its maximum at $x = 0$.

d. We see that $\varphi_y(x, 0) = \frac{1}{(x^2+1)^{3/2}}$. This implies that if we cross the x-axis at any point from below to above, the potential function is increasing.

12.4.75

a. Solving for R gives $R = \left(R_1^{-1} + R_2^{-1}\right)^{-1}$, so $\frac{\partial R}{\partial R_1} = -\left(R_1^{-1} + R_2^{-1}\right)^{-2}\left(-R_1^{-2}\right) = \frac{R_2^2}{(R_1+R_2)^2}$ and similarly $\frac{\partial R}{\partial R_2} = \frac{R_1^2}{(R_1+R_2)^2}$.

b. We have $-R^{-2}\frac{\partial R}{\partial R_1} = -R_1^{-2} \Longrightarrow \frac{\partial R}{\partial R_1} = \frac{R^2}{R_1^2}$ and similarly $\frac{\partial R}{\partial R_2} = \frac{R^2}{R_2^2}$.

c. Because $\frac{\partial R}{\partial R_1} > 0$, an increase in R_1 causes an increase in R.

d. Because $\frac{\partial R}{\partial R_2} > 0$, a decrease in R_2 causes a decrease in R.

12.4.77 Observe that $\frac{\partial^2 u}{\partial t^2} = -4c^2 \cos\left(2\left(x + ct\right)\right) = c^2\frac{\partial^2 u}{\partial x^2}$.

12.4.79 Observe that $\frac{\partial^2 u}{\partial t^2} = Ac^2 f''(x+ct) + Bc^2 g''(x-ct) = c^2 \frac{\partial^2 u}{\partial x^2}$.

12.4.81 Observe that $u_{xx} + u_{yy} = 6x - 6x = 0$.

12.4.83 Observe that $u_{xx} = \frac{2(x-1)y}{\left[(x-1)^2+y^2\right]^2} - \frac{2(x+1)y}{\left[(x+1)^2+y^2\right]^2}$, and $u_{yy} = -\frac{2(x-1)y}{\left[(x-1)^2+y^2\right]^2} + \frac{2(x+1)y}{\left[(x+1)^2+y^2\right]^2}$; so $u_{xx} + u_{yy} = 0$.

12.4.85 We see that $u_t = -16e^{-4t}\cos 2x = u_{xx}$.

12.4.87 We see that $u_t = -a^2 A e^{-a^2 t}\cos ax = u_{xx}$.

12.4.89 We have $f(0, 0) = 0$, $f_x(0, 0) = f_y(0, 0) = 0$, and $f(\triangle x, \triangle y) = \triangle x \cdot \triangle y$, so we can take $\epsilon_1 = \triangle y$, $\epsilon_2 = 0$ or $\epsilon_1 = 0$, $\epsilon_2 = \triangle x$.

12.4.91

a. Observe that $\lim_{(x,\, y)\to(0,\, 0)} \sqrt{|xy|} = 0 = f(0, 0)$, so f is continuous at $(0, 0)$.

b. Let $(a, b) = (0, 0)$, and suppose that $f(a + \triangle x, b + \triangle y) - f(a, b) = \sqrt{|\triangle x \triangle y|} = \epsilon_1 \triangle x + \epsilon_2 \triangle y$. Let $\triangle x = \triangle y$; then we obtain $\sqrt{|\triangle x|^2} = |\triangle x| = (\epsilon_1 + \epsilon_2)\triangle x$ which implies that $\epsilon_1 + \epsilon_2 = \pm 1$, and so we cannot have $\epsilon_1, \epsilon_2 \to 0$, as $\triangle x, \triangle y \to 0$. Therefore f is not differentiable at $(0, 0)$.

c. Because f is identically equal to 0 on the coordinate axes, $f_x(0, 0) = f_y(0, 0) = 0$.

d. The partial derivative $f_x(0, y)$ does not exist for $y \neq 0$ because the function $\sqrt{|x|}$ is not differentiable at $x = 0$. Similarly, the partial derivative $f_y(x, 0)$ does not exist for $x \neq 0$. Hence the partials f_x and f_y are not continuous at $(0, 0)$.

e. Theorem 12.5 does not apply because the partials f_x and f_y are not continuous at $(0, 0)$, and Theorem 12.6 does not apply because f is not differentiable at $(0, 0)$.

12.4.93

a. By the fundamental theorem of calculus, $f_x(x, y) = -\frac{\partial}{\partial x}\int_x^y h(s)\, ds = -h(x)$ and similarly $f_y(x, y) = h(y)$.

b. Let $H(s)$ be an antiderivative of $h(s)$; then $f(x, y) = H(xy) - H(1)$, so $f_x(x, y) = y\, h(xy)$, $f_y(x, y) = x\, h(xy)$.

12.4.95

a. Observe that $u_x = 2x = v_y$ and $u_y = -2y = -v_x$.

b. Observe that $u_x = 3x^2 - 3y^2 = v_y$ and $u_y = -6xy = -v_x$.

c. We have $u_{xx} = v_{yx} = v_{xy} = -u_{yy}$, so $u_{xx} + u_{yy} = 0$. The proof that $v_{xx} + v_{yy} = 0$ is similar.

12.5 The Chain Rule

12.5.1 There is one dependent variable (z), two intermediate variables (x and y) and one independent variable (t).

12.5.3 Multiply each of the partial derivatives of w by the t-derivative of the corresponding function, and add all these expressions.

12.5.5

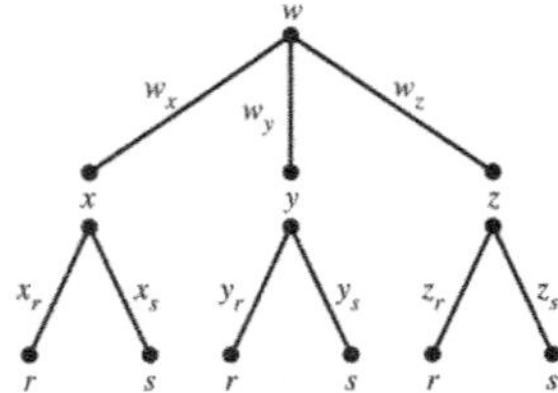

12.5.7 We have $\frac{dz}{dt} = \frac{\partial z}{\partial x}\frac{dx}{dt} + \frac{\partial z}{\partial y}\frac{dy}{dt} = 2x(2t) + 3y^2(1) = 4t^3 + 3t^2$.

12.5.9 We have $\frac{dz}{dt} = \frac{\partial z}{\partial x}\frac{dx}{dt} + \frac{\partial z}{\partial y}\frac{dy}{dt} = (\sin y)\, 2t + (x\, \cos y)\, 12t^2 = 2t\, \sin\left(4t^3\right) + 12t^4 \cos\left(4t^3\right)$.

12.5.11 We have $\frac{dw}{dt} = \frac{\partial w}{\partial x}\frac{dx}{dt} + \frac{\partial w}{\partial y}\frac{dy}{dt} = (-2\sin 2x\, \sin 3y)\left(\frac{1}{2}\right) + (3\, \cos 2x\, \cos 3y)\, 4t^3 = -\sin t\, \sin 3t^4 + 12t^3 \cos t\, \cos 3t^4$.

12.5.13 We have $\frac{dw}{dt} = \frac{\partial w}{\partial x}\frac{dx}{dt} + \frac{\partial w}{\partial y}\frac{dy}{dt} + \frac{\partial w}{\partial z}\frac{dz}{dt} = (y\sin z)\, 2t + (x \sin z)\, 12t^2 + (xy\cos z)\cdot 1 = \left(2ty + 12t^2 x\right)\sin z + xy\cos z = 20t^4 \sin(t+1) + 4t^5 \cos(t+1)$.

12.5.15 We have $\frac{dU}{dt} = \frac{\partial U}{\partial x}\frac{dx}{dt} + \frac{\partial U}{\partial y}\frac{dy}{dt} + \frac{\partial U}{\partial z}\frac{dz}{dt} = \frac{1}{x+y+z}\cdot 1 + \frac{1}{x+y+z}\cdot 2t + \frac{1}{x+y+z}\cdot 3t^2 = \frac{1+2t+3t^2}{t+t^2+t^3}$.

12.5.17

a. By the chain rule, $V'(t) = 2\pi\, r(t)\, h(t)\, r'(t) + \pi[r(t)]^2 h'(t)$.

b. Substituting $r(t) = e^t$ and $h(t) = e^{-2t}$ gives $V'(t) = 2\pi\, e^t e^{-2t} e^t + \pi\, e^{2t}\left(-2e^{-2t}\right) = 0$.

c. Because $V'(t) = 0$, the volume remains constant.

12.5.19 $z_s = \frac{\partial z}{\partial x}\frac{\partial x}{\partial s} + \frac{\partial z}{\partial y}\frac{\partial y}{\partial s} = 2x\sin y + x^2\cos y\cdot 0 = 2(s-t)\sin t^2$ and $z_t = \frac{\partial z}{\partial x}\frac{\partial x}{\partial t} + \frac{\partial z}{\partial y}\frac{\partial y}{\partial t} = (2x\sin y)(-1) + x^2\cos y(2t) = 2(t-s)\sin t^2 + 2t(s-t)^2\cos t^2$.

12.5.21 $z_s = \frac{\partial z}{\partial x}\frac{\partial x}{\partial s} + \frac{\partial z}{\partial y}\frac{\partial y}{\partial s} = (y - 2xy)\cdot 1 + \left(x - x^2\right)\cdot 1 = s - t - 2\left(s^2 - t^2\right) + (s+t) - (s+t)^2 = 2s - 3s^2 - 2st + t^2$ and $z_t = \frac{\partial z}{\partial x}\frac{\partial x}{\partial t} + \frac{\partial z}{\partial y}\frac{\partial y}{\partial t} = (y - 2xy)\cdot 1 + (x - x^2)\cdot(-1) = s - t - 2\left(s^2 - t^2\right) - (s+t) + (s+t)^2 = -s^2 - 2t + 2st + 3t^2$.

12.5.23 $z_s = \frac{\partial z}{\partial x}\frac{\partial x}{\partial s} + \frac{\partial z}{\partial y}\frac{\partial y}{\partial s} = e^{x+y}\cdot t + e^{x+y}\cdot 1 = (t+1)\, e^{st+s+t}$ and $z_t = \frac{\partial z}{\partial x}\frac{\partial x}{\partial t} + \frac{\partial z}{\partial y}\frac{\partial y}{\partial t} = e^{x+y}\cdot s + e^{x+y}\cdot 1 = (s+1)\, e^{st+s+t}$.

12.5.25 $w_s = \frac{\partial w}{\partial x}\frac{\partial x}{\partial s} + \frac{\partial w}{\partial y}\frac{\partial y}{\partial s} + \frac{\partial w}{\partial z}\frac{\partial z}{\partial s} = \frac{1}{y+z}\cdot 1 + \frac{z-x}{(y+z)^2}\cdot t - \frac{x+y}{(y+z)^2}\cdot 1 = \frac{(1+t)(z-x)}{(y+z)^2} = -\frac{2t(1+t)}{(st+s-t)^2}$ and $w_t = \frac{\partial w}{\partial x}\frac{\partial x}{\partial t} + \frac{\partial w}{\partial y}\frac{\partial y}{\partial t} + \frac{\partial w}{\partial z}\frac{\partial z}{\partial t} = \frac{1}{y+z}\cdot 1 + \frac{z-x}{(y+z)^2}\cdot s - \frac{x+y}{(y+z)^2}\cdot(-1) = \frac{(1-s)x + 2y + (1+s)z}{(y+z)^2} = \frac{2s}{(st+s-t)^2}$.

12.5.27 $\frac{dw}{dt} = \frac{dw}{dz}\left(\frac{\partial z}{\partial x}\frac{dx}{dt} + \frac{\partial z}{\partial y}\frac{dy}{dt}\right)$

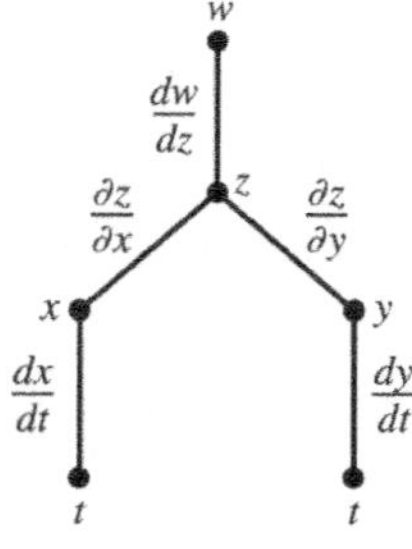

12.5.29 $\frac{\partial u}{\partial z} = \frac{du}{dv}\left(\frac{\partial v}{\partial w}\frac{dw}{dz} + \frac{\partial v}{\partial x}\frac{\partial x}{\partial z} + \frac{\partial v}{\partial y}\frac{\partial y}{\partial z}\right)$

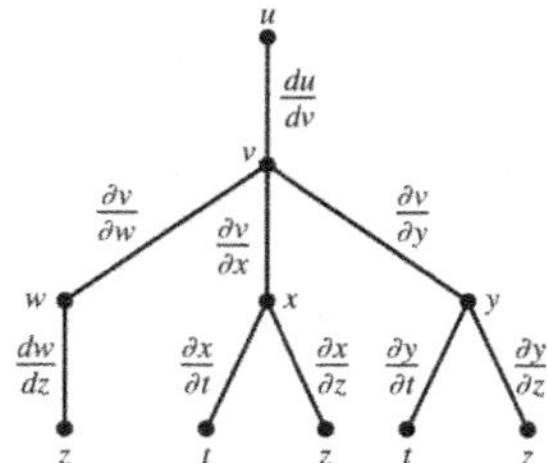

12.5.31 Let $F(x, y) = x^2 - 2y^2 - 1$; then by Theorem 12.9, we have $\frac{dy}{dx} = -\frac{F_x}{F_y} = -\frac{2x}{-4y} = \frac{x}{2y}$.

12.5.33 Let $F(x, y) = 2\sin(xy) - 1$; then by Theorem 12.9, we have $\frac{dy}{dx} = -\frac{F_x}{F_y} = -\frac{2y\cos(xy)}{2x\cos(xy)} = -\frac{y}{x}$.

12.5.35 Note that we can simplify this equation to $x^2 + 2xy + y^4 = 9$, so let $F(x, y) = x^2 + 2xy + y^4 - 9$; then by Theorem 12.9, we have $\frac{dy}{dx} = -\frac{F_x}{F_y} = -\frac{2x+2y}{2x+4y^3} = -\frac{x+y}{x+2y^3}$.

12.5.37 The chain rule gives $\frac{\partial s}{\partial x} = \frac{\partial s}{\partial u}\frac{\partial u}{\partial x} + \frac{\partial s}{\partial v}\frac{\partial v}{\partial x} = \frac{u}{\sqrt{u^2+v^2}} \cdot 0 + \frac{v}{\sqrt{u^2+v^2}} \cdot (-2) = \frac{4x}{\sqrt{4(x^2+y^2)}} = \frac{2x}{\sqrt{x^2+y^2}}$ and $\frac{\partial s}{\partial y} = \frac{\partial s}{\partial u}\frac{\partial u}{\partial y} + \frac{\partial s}{\partial v}\frac{\partial v}{\partial y} = \frac{u}{\sqrt{u^2+v^2}} \cdot 2 + \frac{v}{\sqrt{u^2+v^2}} \cdot 0 = \frac{4y}{\sqrt{4(x^2+y^2)}} = \frac{2y}{\sqrt{x^2+y^2}}$.

12.5.39

a. False. The correct equation is $\frac{\partial z}{\partial s} = \frac{\partial z}{\partial x}\frac{dx}{ds} + \frac{\partial z}{\partial y}\frac{dy}{ds}$.

b. False. w is a function of both s and t, so the rate of change of w with respect to t is the partial derivative $\frac{\partial w}{\partial t}$.

12.5.41

a. We have $z = \left(t^2 + 2t\right)^{-1} + \left(t^3 - 2\right)^{-1}$, so $z'(t) = -\frac{(2t+2)}{(t^2+2t)^2} - \frac{3t^2}{(t^3-2)^2}$.

b. Using the chain rule, $\frac{dz}{dt} = \frac{\partial z}{\partial x}\frac{dx}{dt} + \frac{\partial z}{\partial y}\frac{dy}{dt} = -\frac{(2t+2)}{x^2} - \frac{3t^2}{y^2} = -\frac{(2t+2)}{(t^2+2t)^2} - \frac{3t^2}{(t^3-2)^2}$.

12.5.43 The chain rule gives $\frac{dw}{dt} = \frac{\partial w}{\partial x}\frac{dx}{dt} + \frac{\partial w}{\partial y}\frac{dy}{dt} + \frac{\partial w}{\partial z}\frac{dz}{dt} = yz \cdot 8t^3 + xz\left(-3t^{-2}\right) + xy\left(-12t^{-4}\right) = \frac{12}{t^4} \cdot 8t^3 + 8t\left(-\frac{3}{t^2}\right) + 6t^3\left(-\frac{12}{t^4}\right) = 0$.This can also be seen by expressing w in terms of t: $w = 2t^4 3t^{-1} 4t^{-3} = 24$, so $\frac{dw}{dt} = 0$.

12.5.45 The chain rule gives $-\frac{1}{x^2} - \frac{1}{z^2}\frac{\partial z}{\partial x} = 0$, so $\frac{\partial z}{\partial x} = -\frac{z^2}{x^2}$.

12.5.47

a. The chain rule gives $w'(t) = aw_x + bw_y + cw_z$.

b. Using part (a), $w'(t) = ayz + bxz + cxy = 3abct^2$.

c. Using part (a), $w'(t) = \frac{ax}{\sqrt{x^2+y^2+z^2}} + \frac{by}{\sqrt{x^2+y^2+z^2}} + \frac{cz}{\sqrt{x^2+y^2+z^2}} = \frac{ax+by+cz}{\sqrt{x^2+y^2+z^2}} = \sqrt{a^2+b^2+c^2}\,\frac{t}{|t|}$

d. Differentiate the result from part (a) one more time:
$w''(t) = a\left(aw_{xx} + bw_{xy} + cw_{xz}\right) + b\left(aw_{yx} + bw_{yy} + cw_{yz}\right) + c\left(aw_{zx} + bw_{zy} + cw_{zz}\right)$ which simplifies to $w''(t) = a^2w_{xx} + b^2w_{yy} + c^2w_{zz} + 2abw_{xy} + 2acw_{xz} + 2bcw_{yz}$.

12.5.49 Let $F(x, y, z) = xy + xz + yz - 3$; then the result from Exercise 48 gives $\frac{\partial z}{\partial x} = -\frac{F_x}{F_z} = -\frac{y+z}{x+y}, \frac{\partial z}{\partial y} = -\frac{F_y}{F_z} = -\frac{x+z}{x+y}$.

12.5.51 Let $F(x, y, z) = xyz + x + y - z$; then the result from Exercise 48 gives $\frac{\partial z}{\partial x} = -\frac{F_x}{F_z} = -\frac{yz+1}{xy-1}$, $\frac{\partial z}{\partial y} = -\frac{F_y}{F_z} = -\frac{xz+1}{xy-1}$.

12.5.53

a. The chain rule gives $z'(t) = 2x(-\sin t) + 8y\cos t = 6\sin t\cos t = 3\sin 2t$.

b. Observe that for $0 \le t \le 2\pi$, $z'(t) = 3\sin 2t > 0$ when $0 < t < \frac{\pi}{2}$or $\pi < t < \frac{3\pi}{2}$.

12.5.55

a. The chain rule gives $z'(t) = -\frac{x}{\sqrt{1-x^2-y^2}}(-e^{-t}) + -\frac{y}{\sqrt{1-x^2-y^2}}(-e^{-t}) = \frac{2e^{-2t}}{\sqrt{1-e^{-2t}}}$.

b. Observe that $z'(t) > 0$ for all t where defined, so the function $z(t)$ is increasingfor all $t \ge \frac{1}{2}\ln 2$.

12.5.57 The chain rule gives $E'(t) = m(uu' + vv') + mgy' = m(x'x'' + y'y'' + gy') = m(u_0 \cdot 0 + y'(y'' + g)) = 0$. Therefore, the energy of the projectile remains constant during the motion.

12.5.59

a. If r and R increase at the same rate then $R - r$ is a constant C, so $V = \frac{C^2\pi^2}{4}(R + r)$ is increasing.

b. Similarly, if r and R decrease at the same rate then V is decreasing.

12.5.61

a. Consider P as a function of T and V and differentiate with respect to V: $\frac{\partial P}{\partial V}V + P \cdot 1 = 0$, so $\frac{\partial P}{\partial V} = -\frac{P}{V}$. Next, consider T as a function of P and V and differentiate with respect to P: $1 \cdot V = k\frac{\partial T}{\partial P}$, so $\frac{\partial T}{\partial P} = \frac{V}{k}$. Lastly, consider V as a function of T and P and differentiate with respect to T: $P\frac{\partial V}{\partial T} = k$, so $\frac{\partial V}{\partial T} = \frac{k}{P}$.

b. Observe that $\frac{\partial P}{\partial V}\frac{\partial T}{\partial P}\frac{\partial V}{\partial T} = -\frac{P}{V}\frac{V}{k}\frac{k}{P} = -1$.

12.5.63

a. The chain rule gives $w'(t) = \frac{yz}{z^2+1}(-\sin t) + \frac{xz}{z^2+1}(\cos t) + \frac{xy(1-z^2)}{(z^2+1)^2} \cdot 1 = -\frac{(\sin t)t}{t^2+1}\sin t + \frac{(\cos t)t}{t^2+1}\cos t + \frac{(\cos t)(\sin t)(1-t^2)}{(t^2+1)^2}$.

b. The function $w(t) = \frac{t\cos t\sin t}{1+t^2}$ takes its maximum value on $[0, \infty)$ approximately at $t = 0.838$, which gives the point $(0.669, 0.743, 0.838)$ on the spiral.

12.5.65

a. From problem 64 part (d) we have $z_x = \frac{x}{r}z_r - \frac{y}{r^2}z_\theta$, $z_y = \frac{y}{r}z_r + \frac{x}{r^2}z_\theta$

b. Differentiating the equation for z_x in part (a) with respect to x gives $z_{xx} = \frac{1}{r}z_r + x\left(-\frac{1}{r^2}\right)r_x z_r + \frac{x}{r}(z_r)_x + \frac{2y}{r^3}r_x z_\theta - \frac{y}{r^2}(z_\theta)_x = \frac{x}{r}(z_r)_x - \frac{y}{r^2}(z_\theta)_x + \left(\frac{r^2}{r^3} - \frac{x^2}{r^3}\right)z_r + \frac{2xy}{r^4}z_\theta = \frac{x}{r}\left(\frac{x}{r}z_{rr} - \frac{y}{r^2}z_{r\theta}\right) - \frac{y}{r^2}\left(\frac{x}{r}z_{\theta r} - \frac{y}{r^2}z_{\theta\theta}\right) + \frac{y^2}{r^3}z_r + \frac{2xy}{r^4}z_\theta = \frac{x^2}{r^2}z_{rr} + \frac{y^2}{r^4}z_{\theta\theta} - \frac{2xy}{r^3}z_{r\theta} + \frac{y^2}{r^3}z_r + \frac{2xy}{r^4}z_\theta$.

c. Differentiating the equation for z_y in part (a) with respect to y gives $z_{yy} = \frac{1}{r}z_r + y\left(-\frac{1}{r^2}\right)r_y z_r + \frac{y}{r}(z_r)_y - \frac{2x}{r^3}r_y z_\theta + \frac{x}{r^2}(z_\theta)_y = \frac{y}{r}(z_r)_y + \frac{x}{r^2}(z_\theta)_y + \left(\frac{r^2}{r^3} - \frac{y^2}{r^3}\right)z_r - \frac{2xy}{r^4}z_\theta = \frac{y}{r}\left(\frac{y}{r}z_{rr} + \frac{x}{r^2}z_{r\theta}\right) + \frac{x}{r^2}\left(\frac{y}{r}z_{\theta r} + \frac{x}{r^2}z_{\theta\theta}\right) + \frac{x^2}{r^3}z_r - \frac{2xy}{r^4}z_\theta = \frac{y^2}{r^2}z_{rr} + \frac{x^2}{r^4}z_{\theta\theta} + \frac{2xy}{r^3}z_{r\theta} + \frac{x^2}{r^3}z_r - \frac{2xy}{r^4}z_\theta$.

d. Adding the results from (b) and (c) gives $z_{xx} + z_{yy} = z_{rr} + \frac{1}{r}z_r + \frac{1}{r^2}z_{\theta\theta}$.

12.5.67

a. Assuming y is fixed, the chain rule gives $F_x \cdot 1 + F_y \cdot 0 + F_z \cdot \left(\frac{\partial z}{\partial x}\right)_y = 0$, so $\left(\frac{\partial z}{\partial x}\right)_y = -\frac{F_x}{F_z}$.

b. Similarly we find that $\left(\frac{\partial y}{\partial z}\right)_x = -\frac{F_z}{F_y}$ and $\left(\frac{\partial x}{\partial y}\right)_z = -\frac{F_y}{F_x}$

c. From (a) and (b) we see that $\left(\frac{\partial z}{\partial x}\right)_y \left(\frac{\partial y}{\partial z}\right)_x \left(\frac{\partial x}{\partial y}\right)_z = -1$.

d. Let $\left(\frac{\partial w}{\partial x}\right)_{y,z}$ denote the partial derivative of w with respect to x holding y and z constant, with similar notation for the other possible pairs of variables. A similar derivation as in part (a) and (b) above for $F(w, x, y, z) = 0$ shows that $\left(\frac{\partial w}{\partial x}\right)_{y,z}\left(\frac{\partial x}{\partial y}\right)_{w,z}\left(\frac{\partial y}{\partial z}\right)_{w,x}\left(\frac{\partial z}{\partial w}\right)_{x,y} = \left(-\frac{F_x}{F_w}\right)\left(-\frac{F_y}{F_x}\right)\left(-\frac{F_z}{F_y}\right)\left(-\frac{F_w}{F_z}\right) = 1$.

12.5.69

a. We have $\left(\frac{\partial w}{\partial x}\right)_y = f_x + f_z\frac{dz}{dx} = 2 + 4 \cdot 4 = 18$.

b. Rewrite $z = 4x - 2y$ as $y = 2x - \frac{z}{2}$; therefore $\left(\frac{\partial w}{\partial x}\right)_z = f_x + f_y\frac{dy}{dx} = 2 + 3 \cdot 2 = 8$.

c.

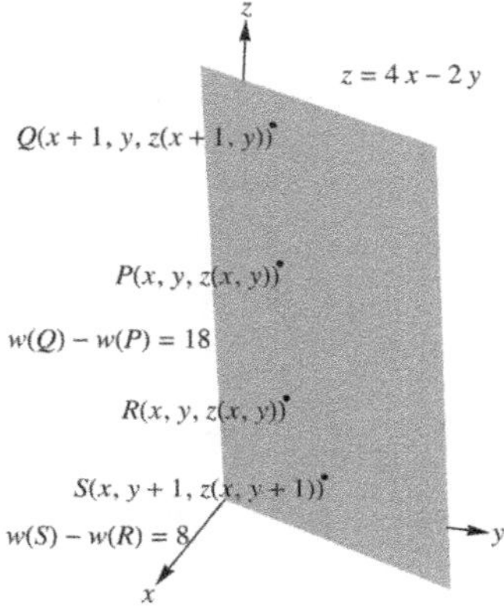

d. Hold x constant; then $\left(\frac{\partial w}{\partial y}\right)_x = f_y + f_z\frac{dz}{dy} = 3 + 4(-2) = -5$. Hold z constant; then $\left(\frac{\partial w}{\partial y}\right)_z = f_x\frac{dx}{dy} + f_y = 2 \cdot \frac{1}{2} + 3 = 4$. Hold x constant; then $\left(\frac{\partial w}{\partial z}\right)_x = f_y\frac{dy}{dz} + f_z = 3\left(-\frac{1}{2}\right) + 4 = \frac{5}{2}$. Hold y constant; then $\left(\frac{\partial w}{\partial z}\right)_y = f_x\frac{dx}{dz} + f_z = 2 \cdot \frac{1}{4} + 4 = \frac{9}{2}$.

12.6 Directional Derivatives and the Gradient

12.6.1 Take the dot product of the unit direction vector u and the gradient of the function.

12.6.3 The direction of the gradient vector is the direction in which the function is increasing the most (steepest ascent).

12.6.5 The gradient is perpendicular to the level curves.

12.6.7

a. Note that $f_x = -x$ and $f_y = -2y$. So $\nabla f(2,0) = \langle -2, 0\rangle$, $\nabla f(0,2) = \langle 0, -4\rangle$, and $\nabla f(1,1) = \langle -1, -2\rangle$.

	$(a,b) = (2,0)$	$(a,b) = (0,2)$	$(a,b) = (1,1)$
$\mathbf{u} = \langle \frac{\sqrt{2}}{2}, \frac{\sqrt{2}}{2}\rangle$	$-\sqrt{2}$	$-2\sqrt{2}$	$-3\sqrt{2}/2$
$\mathbf{v} = \langle -\frac{\sqrt{2}}{2}, \frac{\sqrt{2}}{2}\rangle$	$\sqrt{2}$	$-2\sqrt{2}$	$-\sqrt{2}/2$
$\mathbf{w} = \langle -\frac{\sqrt{2}}{2}, -\frac{\sqrt{2}}{2}\rangle$	$\sqrt{2}$	$2\sqrt{2}$	$3\sqrt{2}/2$

b. The function is decreasing at $(2,0)$ in the direction of **u** and increasing at $(2,0)$ in the direction of **v** and **w**.

12.6.9 $\nabla f(x, y) = \langle 6x, -10y\rangle$ so $\nabla f(2, -1) = \langle 12, 10\rangle$.

12.6.11 $\nabla g(x, y) = \langle 2x - 8xy - 8y^2, -4x^2 - 16xy\rangle$, so $\nabla g(-1, 2) = \langle -18, 28\rangle$.

12.6.13 $\nabla f(x, y) = \langle 2xye^{2xy} + e^{2xy}, 2x^2e^{2xy}\rangle$, so $\nabla f(1, 0) = \langle 1, 2\rangle$.

12.6.15 $\nabla F(x, y) = \langle -2xe^{-x^2-2y^2}, -4ye^{-x^2-2y^2}\rangle$, so $\nabla F(-1, 2) = 2e^{-9}\langle 1, -4\rangle$.

12.6.17 $\nabla f(x, y) = \langle 2x, -2y\rangle$, so $\nabla f(-1, -3) = \langle -2, 6\rangle$. We have $D_{\mathbf{u}}f(-1, -3) = \langle -2, 6\rangle \cdot \langle 3/5, -4/5\rangle = -6/5 - 24/5 = -30/5 = -6$.

12.6.19 $\nabla f(x, y) = \langle -6x, y^3\rangle$, so $\nabla f(2, -3) = \langle -12, -27\rangle$. We have $D_{\mathbf{u}}f(2, -3) = \langle -12, -27\rangle \cdot \langle \frac{\sqrt{3}}{2}, -\frac{1}{2}\rangle = \frac{27}{2} - 6\sqrt{3}$.

12.6.21 $\nabla f(x, y) = \langle -\frac{x}{\sqrt{4-x^2-2y}}, -\frac{1}{\sqrt{4-x^2-2y}}\rangle$, so $\nabla f(2, -2) = \langle -1, -\frac{1}{2}\rangle$. Thus, $D_{\mathbf{u}}f(2, -2) = \langle -1, -\frac{1}{2}\rangle \cdot \langle \frac{1}{\sqrt{5}}, \frac{2}{\sqrt{5}}\rangle = -\frac{2}{\sqrt{5}}$.

12.6.23 $\nabla f(x, y) = \langle 6x, 2\rangle$, so $\nabla f(1, 2) = \langle 6, 2\rangle$. A unit vector in the direction given is $\langle -3/5, 4/5\rangle$, so $D_{\mathbf{u}}f = \langle 6, 2\rangle \cdot \langle -3/5, 4/5\rangle = -2$.

12.6.25 $\nabla g(x, y) = \langle \frac{2x}{4+x^2+y^2}, \frac{2y}{4+x^2+y^2}\rangle$, so $\nabla g(-1, 2) = \langle -\frac{2}{9}, \frac{4}{9}\rangle$. A unit vector in the direction given is $\langle \frac{2}{\sqrt{5}}, \frac{1}{\sqrt{5}}\rangle$. We have $D_{\mathbf{u}}g(-1, 2) = \langle -\frac{2}{9}, \frac{4}{9}\rangle \cdot \langle \frac{2}{\sqrt{5}}, \frac{1}{\sqrt{5}}\rangle = 0$.

12.6.27

a. At the point $(1, -2)$ the value of the gradient is $\nabla f(1, -2) = \langle 2x, -8y\rangle\Big|_{(1,-2)} = \langle 2, 16\rangle$. Therefore, the direction of steepest ascent is $\mathbf{u} = \frac{1}{\sqrt{65}}\langle 1, 8\rangle$ and the direction of steepest descent is $-\mathbf{u}$.

b. Take any vector perpendicular to $\mathbf{u}$; for example, $\mathbf{v} = \frac{1}{\sqrt{65}}\langle -8, 1\rangle$.

12.6.29

a. At the point $(-1, 1)$ the value of the gradient is $\nabla f(-1, 1) = \langle 4x^3 - 2xy, -x^2 + 2y\rangle\Big|_{(-1,1)} = \langle -2, 1\rangle$. Therefore, the direction of steepest ascent is $\mathbf{u} = \frac{1}{\sqrt{5}}\langle -2, 1\rangle$ and the direction of steepest descent is $-\mathbf{u}$.

b. Take any vector perpendicular to $\mathbf{u}$; for example, $\mathbf{v} = \frac{1}{\sqrt{5}}\langle 1, 2\rangle$.

12.6.31

a. At the point $(-1, 1)$ the value of the gradient is $\nabla f(-1, 1) = \left\langle -xe^{-x^2/2-y^2/2}, -ye^{-x^2/2-y^2/2}\right\rangle\Big|_{(-1,1)} = e^{-1}\langle 1, -1\rangle$. Therefore, the direction of steepest ascent is $\mathbf{u} = \frac{1}{\sqrt{2}}\langle 1, -1\rangle$ and the direction of steepest descent is $-\mathbf{u}$.

b. Take any vector perpendicular to $\mathbf{u}$; for example, $\mathbf{v} = \frac{1}{\sqrt{2}}\langle 1, 1\rangle$.

12.6.33

a. The gradient of $f$at P is $\nabla f(3, 2) = \langle -4x, -6y\rangle\Big|_{(3,2)} = \langle -12, -12\rangle$.

b. The direction of steepest ascent is$\mathbf{u} = \frac{1}{\sqrt{2}}\langle -1, -1\rangle$ which makes angle $\theta = \frac{5\pi}{4}$ with the x-axis; therefore, the angle of maximum decrease is $\theta = \frac{\pi}{4}$ and the angles of zero change are $\frac{3\pi}{4}$ and $\frac{7\pi}{4}$.

c. We have $g(\theta) = \langle -12, -12\rangle \cdot \langle \cos\theta, \sin\theta\rangle = -12\cos\theta - 12\sin\theta$.

d. The critical points for $g(\theta)$ satisfy $g'(\theta) = 12(\sin\theta - \cos\theta) = 0$, which gives $\theta = \frac{\pi}{4}, \frac{5\pi}{4}$. By inspection we see that the maximum occurs at $\frac{5\pi}{4}$, and we have $g\left(\frac{5\pi}{4}\right) = 12\sqrt{2}$.

e. Observe that the maximum value of $g(\theta)$ occurs at the angle found in part (d), and that $|\nabla f(3,2)| = 12\sqrt{2} = g\left(\frac{5\pi}{4}\right)$.

12.6.35

a. The gradient of f at P is $\nabla f(\sqrt{3},1) = \left\langle \frac{x}{\sqrt{2+x^2+y^2}}, \frac{y}{\sqrt{2+x^2+y^2}} \right\rangle\Big|_{(\sqrt{3},1)} = \left\langle \frac{\sqrt{3}}{\sqrt{6}}, \frac{1}{\sqrt{6}} \right\rangle = \frac{\sqrt{6}}{6}\left\langle \sqrt{3}, 1\right\rangle$.

b. The direction of steepest ascent is $\mathbf{u} = \left\langle \frac{\sqrt{3}}{2}, \frac{1}{2} \right\rangle$ which makes angle $\theta = \frac{\pi}{6}$ with the x-axis; therefore, the angle of maximum decrease is $\theta = \frac{7\pi}{6}$ and the angles of zero change are $\frac{2\pi}{3}$ and $\frac{5\pi}{3}$.

c. We have $g(\theta) = \frac{\sqrt{6}}{6}\left\langle \sqrt{3}, 1\right\rangle \cdot \langle \cos\theta, \sin\theta\rangle = \frac{\sqrt{18}}{6}\cos\theta + \frac{\sqrt{6}}{6}\sin\theta$.

d. The critical points for $g(\theta)$ satisfy $g'(\theta) = \frac{\sqrt{6}}{6}\left(-\sqrt{3}\sin\theta + \cos\theta\right) = 0$, which gives $\tan\theta = \frac{1}{\sqrt{3}}$, so $\theta = \frac{\pi}{6}, \frac{7\pi}{6}$. By inspection we see that the maximum occurs at $\frac{\pi}{6}$, and we have $g\left(\frac{\pi}{6}\right) = \frac{\sqrt{6}}{3}$.

e. Observe that the maximum value of $g(\theta)$ occurs at the angle found in part (d), and that $|\nabla f(3,1)| = \frac{\sqrt{6}}{3} = g\left(\frac{\pi}{6}\right)$.

12.6.37

a. The gradient of f at P is $\nabla f(-1,0) = \left\langle -2xe^{-x^2-2y^2}, -4ye^{-x^2-2y^2} \right\rangle\Big|_{(-1,0)} = \left\langle 2e^{-1}, 0\right\rangle$.

b. The direction of steepest ascent is $\mathbf{u} = \langle 1,0\rangle$ which makes angle $\theta = 0$ with the x-axis; therefore the angle of maximum decrease is $\theta = \pi$ and the angles of zero change are $\pm\frac{\pi}{2}$.

c. We have $g(\theta) = \frac{2}{e}\langle 1,0\rangle \cdot \langle \cos\theta, \sin\theta\rangle = \frac{2}{e}\cos\theta$.

d. The maximum value of $g(\theta)$ occurs at $\theta = 0$, and we have $g(0) = \frac{2}{e}$.

e. Observe that the maximum value of $g(\theta)$ occurs at the angle found in part (d), and that $|\nabla f(-1,0)| = \frac{2}{e} = g(0)$.

12.6.39 The gradient of f at P is $\nabla f(2,-4) = \langle 8x, 4y\rangle\Big|_{(2,-4)} = \langle 16, -16\rangle$, which gives the direction of maximum increase.

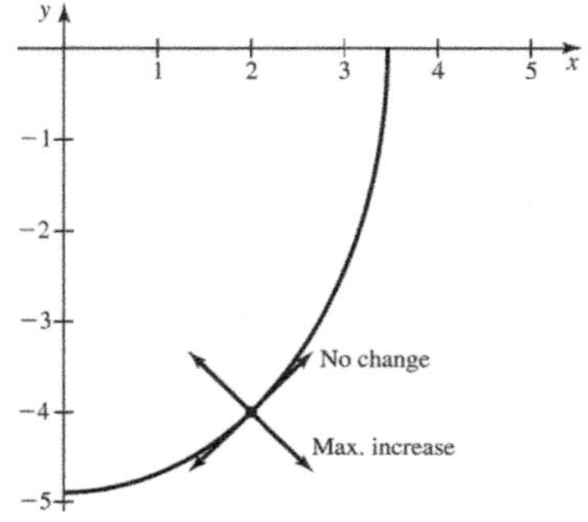

12.6.41 The gradient of f at P is $\nabla f(-3,3) = \langle 2x+y, x+2y\rangle\Big|_{(-3,3)} = \langle -3, 3\rangle$, which gives the direction of maximum increase.

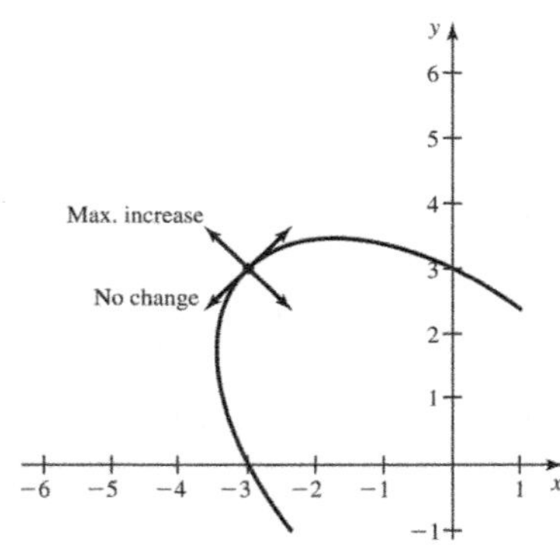

12.6.43 The slope of the level curves for $f(x,y)$ is given by $y'(x) = -\frac{f_x}{f_y} = -\frac{4x}{y}$, so the tangent line has slope 0 at $(0,16)$. The gradient of f at this point is $\nabla f(0,16) = \left\langle -\frac{x}{2}, -\frac{y}{8} \right\rangle\Big|_{(0,16)} = \langle 0,-2\rangle$, which is perpendicular to the tangent line.

12.6.45 The slope of the level curves for $f(x,y)$ is given by $y'(x) = -\frac{f_x}{f_y} = -\frac{4x}{y}$, which is undefined at $(4,0)$, so the tangent line is vertical at $(4,0)$. The gradient of f at this point is $\nabla f(4,0) = \left\langle -\frac{x}{2}, -\frac{y}{8} \right\rangle\Big|_{(4,0)} = \langle -2,0\rangle$, which is perpendicular to the tangent line.

12.6.47 Let $z = f(x,y)$. Then $z^2 = 1 - \frac{x^2}{4} - \frac{y^2}{16}$, so $2zz_x = -\frac{x}{2}$, which implies that $z_x = f_x = -\frac{x}{4z}$. Also $2zz_y = -\frac{y}{8}$, which implies that $z_y = f_y = -\frac{y}{16z}$. The slope of the level curves for $f(x,y)$ is given by $y'(x) = -\frac{f_x}{f_y} = -\frac{4x}{y}$, so the tangent line has slope $-\frac{2}{\sqrt{3}}$ at $\left(\frac{1}{2}, \sqrt{3}\right)$, and its direction is parallel to the vector $\langle 1, -\frac{2}{\sqrt{3}}\rangle$. The gradient of f at this point is $\nabla f\left(\frac{1}{2}, \sqrt{3}\right) = \left\langle -\frac{x}{4z}, -\frac{y}{16z} \right\rangle\Big|_{(1/2,\sqrt{3})} = -\frac{1}{8}\langle \frac{2}{\sqrt{3}}, 1\rangle$, which is perpendicular to the tangent direction.

12.6.49 Let $z = f(x,y)$. Then $z^2 = 1 - \frac{x^2}{4} - \frac{y^2}{16}$, so $2zz_x = -\frac{x}{2}$, which implies that $z_x = f_x = -\frac{x}{4z}$. Also, $2zz_y = -\frac{y}{8}$, which implies that $z_y = f_y = -\frac{y}{16z}$.The slope of the level curves for $f(x,y)$ is given by $y'(x) = -\frac{f_x}{f_y} = -\frac{4x}{y}$, so the tangent line is vertical at $(\sqrt{2}, 0)$, and its direction is parallel to the vector $\langle 0,1\rangle$. The gradient of f at this point is $\nabla f(\sqrt{2},0) = \left\langle -\frac{x}{4z}, -\frac{y}{16z} \right\rangle\Big|_{(\sqrt{2},0)} = \langle -\frac{1}{2}, 0\rangle$, which is perpendicular to the tangent direction.

12.6.51

a. We have $\nabla f = \langle f_x, f_y\rangle = \langle 1,0\rangle$.

b. Let $(x(t), y(t))$ be the projection into the xy-plane of the path of steepest descent starting at $(x(0), y(0)) = (4,4)$. We solve $(x'(t), y'(t)) = -\nabla f = \langle -1, 0\rangle$ which together with the initial conditions gives $x = 4 - t$, $y = 4$ for $t \geq 0$.

12.6.53

a. We have $\nabla f = \langle f_x, f_y\rangle = \langle -2x, -4y\rangle$.

b. Let $(x(t), y(t))$ be the projection into the xy-plane of the path of steepest descent starting at $(x(0), y(0)) = \left(\frac{\pi}{2}, 1\right)$. We solve $(x'(t), y'(t)) = -\nabla f = \langle 2x, 4y\rangle$ with the initial conditions $x(0) = 1$ and $y(0) = 1$. The differential equation $\frac{dx}{dt} = -2x$ is separable: we have $\int \frac{1}{x}\,dx = \int 2\,dt$ which implies that $\ln|x| = 2t + C$. The initial condition $x(0) = 1$ gives $C = 0$ so $x(t) = e^{2t}$. Similarly, $y(t) = e^{4t}$. Thus, $y = x^2$ for $x \geq 1$.

12.6.55

a. We have $\nabla f = 2x\mathbf{i} + 4y\mathbf{j} + 8z\mathbf{k}$; $\nabla f(1,0,4) = 2\mathbf{i} + 32\mathbf{k}$.

b. The vector $2\mathbf{i}+32\mathbf{k}$ has length $2\sqrt{257}$, so the unit vector in this direction is $\mathbf{u}=\frac{1}{\sqrt{257}}(\mathbf{i}+16\mathbf{k})$.

c. The rate of change of f in the direction of maximum increase at P is $|\nabla f(1,0,4)|=2\sqrt{257}$.

d. The vector $\mathbf{u}=\langle\frac{1}{\sqrt{2}},0,\frac{1}{\sqrt{2}}\rangle$ is a unit vector, so the directional derivative at P in this direction is $D_u f(1,0,4)=\langle 2,0,32\rangle\cdot\langle\frac{1}{\sqrt{2}},0,\frac{1}{\sqrt{2}}\rangle=\frac{34}{\sqrt{2}}=17\sqrt{2}$.

12.6.57

a. We have $\nabla f=4yz\mathbf{i}+4xz\mathbf{j}+4xy\mathbf{k}$; $\nabla f(1,-1,-1)=4\mathbf{i}-4\mathbf{j}-4\mathbf{k}$.

b. The vector $4\mathbf{i}-4\mathbf{j}-4\mathbf{k}$ has length $4\sqrt{3}$, so the unit vector in this direction is $\mathbf{u}=\frac{1}{\sqrt{3}}(\mathbf{i}-\mathbf{j}-\mathbf{k})$.

c. The rate of change of f in the direction of maximum increase at P is $|\nabla f(1,-1,-1)|=4\sqrt{3}$.

d. The vector $\mathbf{u}=\langle\frac{1}{\sqrt{3}},\frac{1}{\sqrt{3}},-\frac{1}{\sqrt{3}}\rangle$ is a unit vector, so the directional derivative at P in this direction is $D_u f(1,-1,-1)=\langle 4,-4,-4\rangle\cdot\langle\frac{1}{\sqrt{3}},\frac{1}{\sqrt{3}},-\frac{1}{\sqrt{3}}\rangle=\frac{4}{\sqrt{3}}$.

12.6.59

a. We have $\nabla f=\cos(x+2y-z)(\mathbf{i}+2\mathbf{j}-\mathbf{k})$; $\nabla f\left(\frac{\pi}{6},\frac{\pi}{6},-\frac{\pi}{6}\right)=\cos\left(\frac{2\pi}{3}\right)(\mathbf{i}+2\mathbf{j}-\mathbf{k})=-\frac{1}{2}\mathbf{i}-\mathbf{j}+\frac{1}{2}\mathbf{k}$.

b. The vector $-\frac{1}{2}\mathbf{i}-\mathbf{j}+\frac{1}{2}\mathbf{k}$ has length $\frac{\sqrt{3}}{\sqrt{2}}=\frac{\sqrt{6}}{2}$, so the unit vector in this direction is $\mathbf{u}=\frac{1}{\sqrt{6}}(-\mathbf{i}-2\mathbf{j}+\mathbf{k})$.

c. The rate of change of f in the direction of maximum increase at P is $\left|\nabla f\left(\frac{\pi}{6},\frac{\pi}{6},-\frac{\pi}{6}\right)\right|=\frac{\sqrt{6}}{2}$.

d. The vector $\mathbf{u}=\langle\frac{1}{3},\frac{2}{3},\frac{2}{3}\rangle$ is a unit vector, so the directional derivative at P in this direction is $D_u f\left(\frac{\pi}{6},\frac{\pi}{6},-\frac{\pi}{6}\right)=\langle\frac{1}{3},\frac{2}{3},\frac{2}{3}\rangle\cdot\langle-\frac{1}{2},-1,\frac{1}{2}\rangle=-\frac{1}{2}$.

12.6.61

a. We have $\nabla f=\frac{2}{1+x^2+y^2+z^2}(x\mathbf{i}+y\mathbf{j}+z\mathbf{k})$; $\nabla f(1,1,-1)=\frac{1}{2}\mathbf{i}+\frac{1}{2}\mathbf{j}-\frac{1}{2}\mathbf{k}$.

b. The vector $\frac{1}{2}\mathbf{i}+\frac{1}{2}\mathbf{j}-\frac{1}{2}\mathbf{k}$ has length $\frac{\sqrt{3}}{2}$, so the unit vector in this direction is $\mathbf{u}=\frac{1}{\sqrt{3}}(\mathbf{i}+\mathbf{j}-\mathbf{k})$.

c. The rate of change of f in the direction of maximum increase at$P$ is $|\nabla f(1,1,-1)|=\frac{\sqrt{3}}{2}$.

d. The vector $\mathbf{u}=\langle\frac{2}{3},\frac{2}{3},-\frac{1}{3}\rangle$ is a unit vector, so the directional derivative at P in this direction is $D_u f(1,1,-1)=\langle\frac{2}{3},\frac{2}{3},-\frac{1}{3}\rangle\cdot\langle\frac{1}{2},\frac{1}{2},-\frac{1}{2}\rangle=\frac{5}{6}$.

12.6.63

a. False. $\nabla f=2x\mathbf{i}+2y\mathbf{j}$.

b. False. The gradient is a vector, so it does not make sense to say that it is positive.

c. False. f is a function of three variables, so ∇f has three components.

d. True. This is because $f_x=f_y=f_z=0$.

12.6.65 Observe that $\nabla f(x,y)=-8x\mathbf{i}-2y\mathbf{j}$, so $\nabla f(1,2)=-8\mathbf{i}-4\mathbf{j}$. A vector perpendicular to $\nabla f(1,2)$ is $\mathbf{v}=\mathbf{i}-2\mathbf{j}$, so the unit vectors perpendicular to $\nabla f(1,2)$ are $\mathbf{u}=\pm\frac{1}{\sqrt{5}}(\mathbf{i}-2\mathbf{j})$.

12.6.67 Observe that $\nabla f(x,y)=\frac{1}{\sqrt{3+2x^2+y^2}}(2x\mathbf{i}+y\mathbf{j})$, so $\nabla f(1,-2)=\frac{2}{3}(\mathbf{i}-\mathbf{j})$. A vector perpendicular to $\nabla f(1,-2)$ is $\mathbf{v}=\mathbf{i}+\mathbf{j}$, so the unit vectors perpendicular to $\nabla f(1,-2)$ are $\mathbf{u}=\pm\frac{1}{\sqrt{2}}(\mathbf{i}+\mathbf{j})$.

12.6.69 The function $f(x,y)=ax+by+c$ has $\nabla f(x,y)=a\mathbf{i}+b\mathbf{j}$, so the path in the xy-plane corresponding to the path of steepest ascent on the plane is given by $x=x_0+at$, $y=y_0+bt$.

12.6.71

a. We have $\nabla f(x, y, z) = \langle 2x, 2y, 2z\rangle$, so $\nabla f(1,1,1) = \langle 2,2,2\rangle$.

b. Points (x, y, z) on the plane P satisfy $\langle x-1, y-1, z-1\rangle \cdot \langle 2,2,2\rangle = 0$, so $x + y + z = 3$ is an equation for P.

12.6.73

a. We have $\nabla f(x, y, z) = e^{x+y-z}\langle 1, 1, -1\rangle$, so $\nabla f(1,1,2) = \langle 1, 1, -1\rangle$.

b. Points (x, y, z) on the plane P satisfy $\langle x-1, y-1, z-2\rangle \cdot \langle 1, 1, -1\rangle = 0$, so $x + y - z = 0$ is an equation for P.

12.6.75

a.

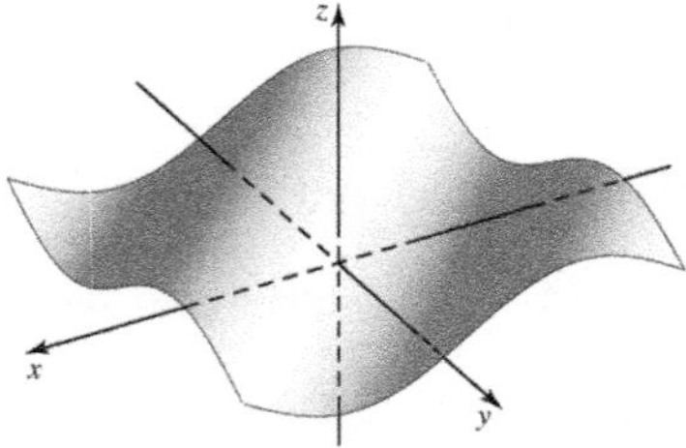

b. The height function has gradient $\nabla z = \cos(x-y)\langle 1, -1\rangle$, so the directions in which the height function has zero change are $\mathbf{v} = \pm\langle 1, 1\rangle$.

c. The direction $\mathbf{v}$ would be the opposite of the direction of ∇z, so $\mathbf{v} = \pm\langle 1, -1\rangle$.

d. These answers are consistent with the graph in part (a).

12.6.77

a. Observe that $\varphi_x = -\frac{kQ}{r^2} r_x = -\frac{kQ}{r^2} \frac{x}{\sqrt{x^2+y^2+z^2}} = -\frac{kQx}{r^3}$; similarly $\varphi_y = -\frac{kQy}{r^3}$ and $\varphi_z = -\frac{kQz}{r^3}$. Therefore $\mathrm{E}(x, y, z) = -\nabla\varphi(x, y, z) = kQ\langle \frac{x}{r^3}, \frac{y}{r^3}, \frac{z}{r^3}\rangle$.

b. We have $|\mathrm{E}| = \frac{kQ}{r^3}\,|\langle x, y, z\rangle| = \frac{kQ}{r^2}$. Therefore the magnitude of the electric field is inversely proportional to the square of the distance to the point charge.

12.6.79 We have $\langle u, v\rangle = \nabla\varphi = \langle \pi\cos\pi x \sin 2\pi y, 2\pi \sin\pi x \cos 2\pi y\rangle$.

12.6.81 We give the proofs for functions on $\mathbb{R}^2$. The proofs for functions on $\mathbb{R}^3$ are similar.

a. $\nabla(cf) = \langle (cf)_x, (cf)_y\rangle = \langle cf_x, cf_y\rangle = c\nabla f$.

b. $\nabla(f+g) = \langle (f+g)_x, (f+g)_y\rangle = \langle f_x + g_x, f_y + g_y\rangle = \nabla f + \nabla g$.

c. $\nabla(fg) = \langle (fg)_x, (fg)_y\rangle = \langle f_x g + f g_x, f_y g + f g_y\rangle = (\nabla f) g + f\nabla g$.

d. $\nabla\left(\frac{f}{g}\right) = \langle \left(\frac{f}{g}\right)_x, \left(\frac{f}{g}\right)_y\rangle = \langle \frac{gf_x - fg_x}{g^2}, \frac{gf_y - fg_y}{g^2}\rangle = \frac{g(\nabla f) - f\nabla g}{g^2}$.

e. $\nabla(f \circ g) = \langle f'(g)\, g_x, f'(g)\, g_y\rangle = f'(g)\nabla g$.

12.6.83 Using the quotient rule from Exercise 81 gives $\nabla\left(\frac{x+y}{x^2+y^2}\right) = \frac{(x^2+y^2)\nabla(x+y) - (x+y)\nabla(x^2+y^2)}{(x^2+y^2)^2} = \frac{1}{(x^2+y^2)^2}\left((x^2+y^2)\langle 1, 1\rangle - (x+y)\langle 2x, 2y\rangle\right) = \frac{1}{(x^2+y^2)^2}\langle y^2 - x^2 - 2xy, x^2 - y^2 - 2xy\rangle$.

12.6.85 Using the chain rule from Exercise 81 gives $\nabla\left(\sqrt{25-x^2-y^2-z^2}\right) = \frac{1}{2\sqrt{25-x^2-y^2-z^2}}\nabla\left(25-x^2-y^2-z^2\right) = \frac{1}{2\sqrt{25-x^2-y^2-z^2}}\langle -2x,-2y,-2z\rangle = -\frac{1}{\sqrt{25-x^2-y^2-z^2}}\langle x,y,z\rangle$.

12.6.87 Using the quotient rule from Exercise 81 gives $\nabla\left(\frac{x+yz}{y+xz}\right) = \frac{(y+xz)\nabla(x+yz)-(x+yz)\nabla(y+xz)}{(y+xz)^2} = \frac{1}{(y+xz)^2}\left((y+xz)\langle 1,z,y\rangle-(x+yz)\langle z,1,x\rangle\right) = \frac{1}{(y+xz)^2}\langle y\left(1-z^2\right),x\left(z^2-1\right),y^2-x^2\rangle$.

12.7 Tangent Planes and Linear Approximation

12.7.1 The gradient of F is a multiple of n.

12.7.3 The tangent plane has equation $F_x(a,b,c)(x-a)+F_y(a,b,c)(y-b)+F_z(a,b,c)(z-c)=0$.

12.7.5 Multiply the change in x by f_x and the change in y by f_y and add both terms to $f(a,b)$.

12.7.7 In terms of differentials, $dz = f_x(a,b)\,dx + f_y(a,b)\,dy$.

12.7.9 $\nabla F = \langle 2x,1,1\rangle$, so $\nabla F(1,1,1)=\langle 2,1,1\rangle$. The tangent plane at $(1,1,1)$ has equation $2(x-1)+(y-1)+(z-1)=0$, or $2x+y+z=4$. Also, $\nabla F(2,0,-1)=\langle 4,1,1\rangle$, so the equation of the tangent plane there is $4(x-2)+y+(z+1)=0$, or $4x+y+z=7$.

12.7.11 $\nabla F = \langle y+z,x+z,x+y\rangle$, so $\nabla F(2,2,2)=\langle 4,4,4\rangle$. The tangent plane at $(2,2,2)$ is given by $4(x-2)+4(y-2)+4(z-2)=0$, or $x+y+z=6$. At the point $(2,0,6)$ we have $\nabla F(2,0,6)=\langle 6,8,2\rangle$, so the equation of the tangent plane is $6(x-2)+8y+2(z-6)=0$, or $3x+4y+z=12$.

12.7.13 $\nabla F = \langle y\sin z, x\sin z, yz\cos z\rangle$, so $\nabla F\left(1,2,\frac{\pi}{6}\right)=\langle 1,\frac{1}{2},\sqrt{3}\rangle$ and the tangent plane at $\left(1,2,\frac{\pi}{6}\right)$ has equation $(x-1)+\frac{1}{2}(y-2)+\sqrt{3}\left(z-\frac{\pi}{6}\right)=0$, or $x+\frac{1}{2}y+\sqrt{3}z=2+\frac{\sqrt{3}\pi}{6}$. Also, $\nabla F\left(-2,-1,\frac{5\pi}{6}\right)=\langle -\frac{1}{2},-1,-\sqrt{3}\rangle$, so the tangent plane at $\left(-2,-1,\frac{5\pi}{6}\right)$ has equation $-\frac{1}{2}(x+2)-(y+1)-\sqrt{3}\left(z-\frac{5\pi}{6}\right)=0$ or $\frac{1}{2}x+y+\sqrt{3}z=\frac{5\sqrt{3}\pi}{6}-2$.

12.7.15 $\nabla F = \langle -\frac{x}{8},-\frac{2y}{9},2z\rangle$, so $\nabla F\left(4,3,-\sqrt{3}\right)=\langle -\frac{1}{2},-\frac{2}{3},-2\sqrt{3}\rangle$ and the tangent plane at $\left(4,3,-\sqrt{3}\right)$ has equation $-\frac{1}{2}(x-4)-\frac{2}{3}(y-3)-2\sqrt{3}\left(z+\sqrt{3}\right)=0$, or $\frac{1}{2}x+\frac{2}{3}y+2\sqrt{3}z=-2$. Also, $\nabla F\left(-8,9,\sqrt{14}\right)=\left\langle 1,-2,2\sqrt{14}\right\rangle$, so the tangent plane at $\left(-8,9,\sqrt{14}\right)$ has equation $(x+8)-2(y-9)+2\sqrt{14}\left(z-\sqrt{14}\right)=0$ or $x-2y+2\sqrt{14}z=2$.

12.7.17 We have $f_x=-4x$, $f_y=-2y$, so the tangent plane at $(2,2,-8)$ has equation $z=f(2,2)+f_x(2,2)(x-2)+f_y(2,2)(y-2)=-8-8(x-2)-4(y-2)$, or $z=-8x-4y+16$, and the equation of the tangent plane at $(-1,-1,1)$ is $z=f(-1,-1)+f_x(-1,-1)(x+1)+f_y(-1,-1)(y+1)=1+4(x+1)+2(y+1)$, or $z=4x+2y+7$.

12.7.19 We have $f_x=ye^{xy}$, $f_y=xe^{xy}$, so the tangent plane at $(1,0,1)$ has equation $z=f(1,0)+f_x(1,0)(x-1)+f_y(1,0)(y)=1+0+1(y)$, or $z=1+y$. The equation of the tangent plane at $(0,1,1)$ is $z=1+1(x)+0(y-1)$, or $z=1+x$.

12.7.21 We have $f_x=\left(2x+x^2\right)e^{x-y}$, $f_y=-x^2e^{x-y}$, so the tangent plane at $(2,2,4)$ has equation $z=f(2,2)+f_x(2,2)(x-2)+f_y(2,2)(y-2)=4+8(x-2)-4(y-2)$, or $z=8x-4y-4$, and the equation of the tangent plane at $(-1,-1,1)$ is $z=f(-1,-1)+f_x(-1,-1)(x+1)+f_y(-1,-1)(y+1)=1-(x+1)-(y+1)$, or $z=-x-y-1$.

12.7.23 We have $f_x=\frac{y^2+2xy-x^2}{(x^2+y^2)^2}$, $f_y=\frac{y^2-2xy-x^2}{(x^2+y^2)^2}$, so the tangent plane at $\left(1,2,-\frac{1}{5}\right)$ has equation $z=f(1,2)+f_x(1,2)(x-1)+f_y(1,2)(y-2)=-\frac{1}{5}+\frac{7}{25}(x-1)-\frac{1}{25}(y-2)$, or $z=\frac{7}{25}x-\frac{1}{25}y-\frac{2}{5}$, and the equation of the tangent plane at $\left(2,-1,\frac{3}{5}\right)$ is $z=f(2,-1)+f_x(2,-1)(x-2)+f_y(2,-1)(y+1)=\frac{3}{5}-\frac{7}{25}(x-2)+\frac{1}{25}(y+1)$, or $z=-\frac{7}{25}x+\frac{1}{25}y+\frac{6}{5}$.

12.7.25

a. We have $f_x = y+1$, $f_y = x-1$, so the linear approximation for f at $(2,3)$ is $L(x,y) = f(2,3) + f_x(2,3)(x-2) + f_y(2,3)(y-3) = 5 + 4(x-2) + (y-3)$,or $L(x,y) = 4x + y - 6$.

b. We have $L(2.1, 2.99) = 5.39$.

12.7.27

a. We have $f_x = -2x$, $f_y = 4y$, so the linear approximation for f at $(3,-1)$ is $L(x,y) = f(3,-1) + f_x(3,-1)(x-3) + f_y(3,-1)(y+1) = -7 - 6(x-3) - 4(y+1)$ or $L(x,y) = -6x - 4y + 7$.

b. We have $L(3.1, -1.04) = -7.44$.

12.7.29

a. We have $f_x = \frac{1}{1+x+y}$, $f_y = \frac{1}{1+x+y}$, so the linear approximation for f at $(0,0)$ is $L(x,y) = f(0,0) + f_x(0,0)\,x + f_y(0,0)\,y = x + y$.

b. We have $L(0.1, -0.2) = -0.1$.

12.7.31 We have $f_x = 2 - 2y$, $f_y = -3 - 2x$, and $dx = 0.1$, $dy = -0.1$, so $dz = f_x(1,4)\,dx + f_y(1,4)\,dy = -6dx - 5dy = -0.1$.

12.7.33 We have $f_x = e^{x+y}$, $f_y = e^{x+y}$, and $dx = 0.1$, $dy = -0.05$, so $dz = f_x(0,0)\,dx + f_y(0,0)\,dy = dx + dy = 0.05$.

12.7.35

a. If r increases and R decreases then $R^2 - r^2$ decreases, so S decreases.

b. If both R and r increase, then it is impossible to say whether $R^2 - r^2$ increases or decreases.

c. We have $dS = 8\pi^2(RdR - rdr) = 8\pi^2(5.50 \cdot 0.15 - 3 \cdot 0.05) = 5.4\pi^2 \approx 53.296$.

d. We have $dS = 8\pi^2(RdR - rdr) = 8\pi^2(7 \cdot 0.04 - 3 \cdot (-0.05)) = 3.44\pi^2 \approx 33.951$.

e. The surface area is approximately unchanged when $RdR = rdr$.

12.7.37 Observe that $dA = \pi(bda + adb)$ so $\frac{dA}{A} = \frac{da}{a} + \frac{db}{b}$, and hence the percentage increase in the area is approximately 2% + 1.5%= 3.5%.

12.7.39 We have $dw = \left(y^2 + 2xz\right)dx + \left(2xy + z^2\right)dy + \left(x^2 + 2yz\right)dz$.

12.7.41 We have $dw = \frac{dx}{y+z} - \frac{u+x}{(y+z)^2}dy - \frac{u+x}{(y+z)^2}dz + \frac{du}{y+z}$.

12.7.43

a. Observe that $2cdc = (2a - 2b\cos\theta)\,da + (2b - 2a\cos\theta)\,db + 2ab\sin\theta\,d\theta$ so $dc = \frac{a-b\cos\theta}{c}da + \frac{b-a\cos\theta}{c}db + \frac{ab\sin\theta}{c}d\theta$. We have $a = 2$, $b = 4$, $\theta = \frac{\pi}{3}$ which gives $c = \sqrt{12}$, and $da = 0.03$, $db = -0.04$, $d\theta = \frac{\pi}{90}$; substituting in the equation above gives $dc \approx 0.035$.

b. We have $a = 2$, $b = 4$, $da = 0.03$, $db = -0.04$, $d\theta = 0$, so $dc = -\frac{0.01+0.04\cos\theta}{c}$; comparing the cases $\theta = \frac{\pi}{20}$ and $\theta = \frac{9\pi}{20}$ we see that c is smaller and $\cos\theta$ is larger in the first case; therefore the change in c is greater when $\theta = \frac{\pi}{20}$.

12.7.45

a. True. This is because the function $F(x,y,z) = x^2 + z^2$ has $F_y = 0$.

b. True. As $z > 0$ decreases, $\frac{1}{z}$ increases.

c. False. The gradient $\nabla F(a,b,c)$ is perpendicular to the tangent plane for the surface $F(x,y,z)=0$ at (a,b,c).

12.7.47 Let $f(x,y)=\tan^{-1}(xy)$; then $f_x(x,y)=\frac{y}{1+(xy)^2}$, $f_y(x,y)=\frac{x}{1+(xy)^2}$ and the tangent plane at $\left(1,1,\frac{\pi}{4}\right)$ has equation $z=f_x(1,1)(x-1)+f_y(1,1)(y-1)+f(1,1)=\frac{1}{2}x+\frac{1}{2}y+\frac{\pi}{4}-1$.

12.7.49 The branch of the surface $\sin(xyz)=\frac{1}{2}$ at the point $\left(\pi,1,\frac{1}{6}\right)$ can be described more simply by the equation $F(x,y,z)=xyz=\frac{\pi}{6}$. We have $F_x(x,y,z)=yz$, $F_y(x,y,z)=xz$, $Fz(x,y,z)=xy$ so the tangent plane at $\left(\pi,1,\frac{1}{6}\right)$ has equation $F_x\left(\pi,1,\frac{1}{6}\right)(x-\pi)+F_y\left(\pi,1,\frac{1}{6}\right)(y-1)+Fz\left(\pi,1,\frac{1}{6}\right)\left(z-\frac{1}{6}\right)=0$, or $\frac{1}{6}(x-\pi)+\frac{\pi}{6}(y-1)+\pi\left(z-\frac{1}{6}\right)=0$.

12.7.51 Let $F(x,y,z)=x^2+2y^2+z^2-2x-2y+3$; then $F_x(x,y,z)=2x-2$, $F_y(x,y,z)=2y+2$. The tangent plane to the surface $F(x,y,z)=0$ at (a,b,c) is horizontal if and only if $F_x(a,b,c)=F_y(a,b,c)=0$, which gives $a=1$, $b=-1$. This implies $c^2=1$, so the points are $(1,-1,1)$ and $(1,-1,-1)$.

12.7.53 Let $f(x,y)=\cos 2x\sin y$; then $f_x(x,y)=-2\sin 2x\sin y$, $f_y(x,y)=\cos 2x\cos y$; so the tangent plane at $(a,b,\cos 2a\sin b)$ is horizontal at all points where $\sin 2a=\cos b=0$ or $\sin b=\cos 2a=0$. In the region $-\pi\le x\le\pi$, $-\pi\le y\le\pi$ the points are $a=0,\pm\frac{\pi}{2},\pm\pi$ and $b=\pm\frac{\pi}{2}$, or $a=\pm\frac{\pi}{4},\pm\frac{3\pi}{4}$ and $b=0,\pm\pi$.

12.7.55

a. We have $S_r=\pi\sqrt{r^2+h^2}+\frac{\pi r^2}{\sqrt{r^2+h^2}}$, $S_h=\frac{\pi rh}{\sqrt{r^2+h^2}}$; using the values $r=2.5$, $h=0.6$, $dr=0.05$, $dh=-0.02$ gives $dS=S_r dr+S_h dh=\frac{\pi}{\sqrt{r^2+h^2}}\left(\left(2r^2+h^2\right)dr+rhdh\right)\approx 0.749$.

b. If $r=100$, $h=200$ then $dS=40\sqrt{5}\pi(3dr+dh)$, so the surface area is more sensitive to small changes in r.

12.7.57

a. The differential of A is given by $dA=\frac{dx}{y}-\frac{xdy}{y^2}$; substituting $x=60$, $y=175$, $dx=2$ and $dy=5$ gives $dA=\frac{2}{1225}\approx 0.00163$.

b. If the batter fails to get a hit, the average decreases by $\frac{x}{y}-\frac{x}{y+1}=\frac{x}{y(y+1)}=\frac{A}{y+1}$, whereas if the batter gets a hit, the average increases by $\frac{x+1}{y+1}-\frac{x}{y}=\frac{y-x}{y(y+1)}=\frac{1-A}{y+1}$. If $A=0.350$ the second of these quantities is larger so the answer is no; the batting average changes more if the batter gets a hit than if he fails to get a hit.

c. The answer depends on whether A is less than or greater than 0.500.

12.7.59

a. The centerline velocity is given by $V=\frac{R^2}{L}$ so $dV=\frac{2R}{L}dR-\frac{R^2}{L^2}dL$; evaluate this with $R=3$, $dR=0.05$, $L=50$, $dL=0.5$ to obtain $dV=\frac{21}{5000}=0.0042\text{cm}^3$.

b. Rewrite the formula for dV as $\frac{dV}{V}=\frac{2dR}{R}-\frac{dL}{L}$; hence if R decreases 1% and L increases 2%, then V will decrease by approximately 4%.

c. If the radius of the cylinder increases by $p\%$, then the length of the cylinder must decrease by approximately $2p\%$ in order for the velocity to remain constant.

12.7.61

a. We have $f_r=n(1-r)^{n-1}$ and $f_n=-(1-r)^n\ln(1-r)$.

b. We have $\triangle P\approx f(20,0.1)\cdot 0.01=20\cdot(0.9)^{19}(0.01)\approx 0.027$.

c. We have $\triangle P\approx f(20,0.9)\cdot 0.01=20\cdot(0.1)^{19}(0.01)\approx 2\times 10^{-20}$.

d. Small changes in the flu rate have a greater effect on the probability of catching the flu when the flu rate is small compared to when the flu rate is large.

12.7.63 From the equation $\frac{1}{R} = \frac{1}{R_1} + \frac{1}{R_2} + \frac{1}{R_3}$ we obtain $-\frac{1}{R^2}\frac{\partial R}{\partial R_1} = -\frac{1}{R_1^2}$, which implies that $\frac{\partial R}{\partial R_1} = \frac{R^2}{R_1^2}$, with similar formulas for the other partials. Hence $dR = R^2\left(\frac{dR_1}{R_1^2} + \frac{dR_2}{R_2^2} + \frac{dR_3}{R_3^2}\right)$. Substituting the values $R_1 = 2$, $dR_1 = 0.05$, $R_2 = 3$, $dR_2 = -0.05$, $R_3 = 1.5$, $dR_3 = 0.05$ gives $R = \frac{2}{3}$ and $dR = \frac{7}{540} \approx 0.0130$ ohms.

12.7.65

a. Suppose f is a function of x and y; then $d(\ln f) = (\ln f)_x\, dx + (\ln f)_y\, dy = \frac{f_x}{f}dx + \frac{f_y}{f}dy = \frac{df}{f}$.

b. The absolute change in ln f is approximately $d(\ln f)$ and the relative change in f is approximately $\frac{df}{f}$; from part (a) these agree.

c. Observe that $df = ydx + xdy$, so $\frac{df}{f} = \frac{dx}{x} + \frac{dy}{y}$.

d. Observe that $df = \frac{ydx - xdy}{y^2}$, so $\frac{df}{f} = \frac{dx}{x} - \frac{dy}{y}$.

e. If $f = x_1 x_2 \cdots x_n$ then $\ln f = \ln x_1 + \ln x_2 + \cdots + \ln x_n$ and therefore $\frac{df}{f} = \frac{dx_1}{x_1} + \frac{dx_2}{x_2} + \cdots + \frac{dx_n}{x_n}$.

12.8 Maximum/Minimum Problems

12.8.1 It is locally the highest point on the surface; you cannot get toa higher point in any direction.

12.8.3 The partial derivatives are both zero or one or both do not exist.

12.8.5 The discriminant of f at (a,b) is the determinant given by $D(a,b) = f_{xx}(a,b)\, f_{yy}(a,b) - f_{xy}(a,b)^2$.

12.8.7 The function f has an absolute minimum value at $(a,b) \in R$ if $f(x,y) \geq f(a,b)$ for all $(x,y) \in R$.

12.8.9 We have $f_x = 2x$, $f_y = 2y$ so $(0,0)$ is the only critical point of f.

12.8.11 We have $f_x = 6(3x-2)$, $f_y = 2(y-4)$ so $\left(\frac{2}{3}, 4\right)$ is the only critical point of f.

12.8.13 We have $f_x = 4x^3 - 16y$, $f_y = 4y^3 - 16x$; solving $f_x = f_y = 0$ gives $y = \frac{x^3}{4}$ and $x = \frac{y^3}{4}$; therefore $x = \frac{x^9}{4^4}$ which gives $x = 0, \pm 2$, and the critical points are $(0,0)$, $(2,2)$ and $(-2,-2)$.

12.8.15 We have $f_x = 4x^3 - 4x$ and $f_y = 2y - 4$; solving $f_x = f_y = 0$ gives $x = 0$, ± 1 and $y = 2$; and the critical points of are $(0,2)$ and $(\pm 1, 2)$.

12.8.17 We have $f_x = 2x + 6$ and $f_y = 2y$; solving $f_x = f_y = 0$ gives $x = -3$ and $y = 0$ so $(-3,0)$ is the only critical point of f.

12.8.19 We have $f_x = 4x$, $f_y = 6y$; therefore $(0,0)$ is the only critical point. We also have $f_{xx} = 4$, $f_{yy} = 6$ and $f_{xy} = 0$; hence $D(0,0) = 4 \cdot 6 - 0^2 = 24 > 0$ and $f_{xx}(0,0) > 0$, which by the Second Derivative Test implies that f has a local minimum at $(0,0)$.

12.8.21 We have $f_x = -8x$, $f_y = 16y$; therefore, $(0,0)$ is the only critical point. We also have $f_{xx} = -8$, $f_{yy} = 16$ and $f_{xy} = 0$; hence $D(0,0) = -8 \cdot 16 < 0$, which by the Second Derivative Test implies that f has a saddle point at $(0,0)$.

12.8.23 We have $f_x = 4x^3 - 4y$, $f_y = 4y - 4x$; therefore, the critical points satisfy $y = x$ and $y = x^3$, which gives $x^3 = x$ and therefore $x = 0, \pm 1$, so the critical points are $(0,0)$, $(1,1)$ and $(-1,-1)$. We also have $f_{xx} = 12x^2$, $f_{yy} = 4$ and $f_{xy} = -4$; hence $D(x,y) = 48x^2 - 16$. Thus $D(0,0) = -16 < 0$, so f has a saddle point at $(0,0)$; and $D(1,1) = D(-1,-1) = 32 > 0$, $f_{xx}(1,1) = f_{xx}(-1,-1) = 12 > 0$ so f has a local minimum at $(1,1)$ and $(-1,-1)$.

12.8.25 Note that $f(x, y)$ has the same critical points as the simpler function

$$g(x, y) = x^2 + y^2 - 4x + 5 = (x - 2)^2 + y^2 + 1.$$

We have $g_x = 2(x - 2)$, $g_y = 2y$; therefore, $(2, 0)$ is the only critical point. We also have $g_{xx} = 2$, $g_{yy} = 2$ and $g_{xy} = 0$; hence $D(2, 0) = 4 > 0$ and $g_{xx}(2, 0) > 0$, which by the Second Derivative Test implies that g (and hence f) has a local minimum at $(2, 0)$.

12.8.27 We have $f_x = 2(1 - 2x^2)\, ye^{-x^2-y^2}$, $f_y = 2(1 - 2y^2)\, xe^{-x^2-y^2}$. Therefore, the critical points are $(0, 0)$, $\pm\left(\frac{1}{\sqrt{2}}, \frac{1}{\sqrt{2}}\right)$ and $\pm\left(\frac{1}{\sqrt{2}}, -\frac{1}{\sqrt{2}}\right)$. Also, $f_{xx} = 4(2x^2 - 3)\, xye^{-x^2-y^2}$, $f_{yy} = 4(2y^2 - 3)\, xye^{-x^2-y^2}$ and $f_{xy} = 2(1 - 2x^2)(1 - 2y^2)\, e^{-x^2-y^2}$. Hence $D(0, 0) = -4 < 0$, so f has a saddle point at $(0, 0)$ by the Second Derivative Test. We also see that $D(x, y) > 0$ at the four other critical points; also $f_{xx}\left(\pm\left(\frac{1}{\sqrt{2}}, \frac{1}{\sqrt{2}}\right)\right) < 0$ so f has a local maximum at $\pm\left(\frac{1}{\sqrt{2}}, \frac{1}{\sqrt{2}}\right)$, and $f_{xx}\left(\pm\left(\frac{1}{\sqrt{2}}, \frac{1}{\sqrt{2}}\right)\right) > 0$ so f has a local minimum at $\pm\left(\frac{1}{\sqrt{2}}, -\frac{1}{\sqrt{2}}\right)$.

12.8.29 We have $f_x = \frac{1+y^2-x^2}{(x^2+y^2+1)^2}$ and $f_y = \frac{-2xy}{(x^2+y^2+1)^2}$, so the critical points are $(\pm 1, 0)$. We have $f_{xx} = \frac{2x(x^2-3(y^2+1))}{(x^2+y^2+1)^3}$, so $f_{xx}(\pm 1, 0) = \mp\frac{1}{2}$. We have $f_{yy} = -\frac{2x(x^2-3y^2+1)}{(x^2+y^2+1)^3}$, so $f_{yy}(\pm 1, 0) = \mp\frac{1}{2}$. Also, $f_{xy} = -\frac{2y(-3x^2+y^2+1)}{(x^2+y^2+1)^3}$, so $f_{xy}(\pm 1, 0) = 0$. Thus, $D(\pm 1, 0) = \frac{1}{4}$, so there is a local maximum at $(1, 0)$ and a local minimum at $(-1, 0)$.

12.8.31 We have $f_x = 4x^3 + 8x(y - 2)$ and $f_y = 4x^2 + 16(y - 1)$. Solving $f_x = f_y = 0$ yields critical points $(0, 1)$ and $(\pm 2, 0)$. We have $f_{xx} = 12x^2 + 8(y - 2)$, $f_{yy} = 16$, and $f_{xy} = 8x$. Thus $D(0, 1) < 0$, $D(\pm 2, 0) > 0$. There is a saddle point at $(0, 1)$ and local minimums at $(\pm 2, 0)$.

12.8.33 We have $f_x = ye^x$, $f_y = e^x - e^y$; therefore, the critical points must satisfy $y = 0$ and $y = x$, so $(0, 0)$ is the only critical point. We also have $f_{xx} = ye^x$, $f_{yy} = -e^y$ and $f_{xy} = e^x$; hence $D(0, 0) = -1 < 0$ so f has a saddle point at $(0, 0)$.

12.8.35 Let x, $y \geq 0$ be the dimensions of the base of the box; then for any given x, y the maximum allowable height is given by $h = 96 - 2x - 2y$, and we must have $h \geq 0$ which implies $x + y \leq 48$. The volume of the box is given by $V = 2xy(48 - x - y)$, which we must maximize over the domain R given by x, $y \geq 0$ and $x + y \leq 48$. The critical points of V satisfy $V_x = 2(48 - 2x - y)\, y = 0$, $V_y = 2(48 - x - 2y)\, x = 0$; hence the critical points in the interior of R satisfy $2x + y = 2y + x = 48$, which gives $x = y = 16$. Furthermore $V(x, y) = 0$ on the boundary of R, so the maximum volume must occur at the point $(16, 16)$. Therefore the box with largest volume has height 32 in and base 16 in×16 in with a volume of 8192 in^3.

12.8.37 Let x, $y \geq 0$ be the dimensions of the base and $h \geq 0$ be the height of the box; then the volume of the box is $xyh = 4$, so $h = \frac{4}{xy}$. The four sides of the box plus the base have total area $A = 2xh + 2yh + xy = \frac{8}{x} + \frac{8}{y} + xy$, which we must maximize over the domain R given by x, $y \geq 0$. The critical points of A satisfy $A_x = y - \frac{8}{x^2} = 0$, $A_y = x - \frac{8}{y^2} = 0$; hence the critical points in R satisfy $x^2 y = xy^2 = 8$, which gives $x = y$ and hence $x, y = 2$; the corresponding height is 1. Furthermore $V(x, y) \to \infty$ as (x, y) approaches the boundary of R or as either $x, y \to \infty$, so the minimum area must occur at the point $(2, 2)$. Therefore the box with smallest area has dimensions 2m × 2m × 1m.

12.8.39 Observe that $f_x = 4x^3$, $f_y = 12y^3$ and $f_{xx} = 12x^2$, $f_{yy} = 36y^2$ and $f_{xy} = 0$; therefore $D(0, 0) = 0$ and the Second Derivative Test is inconclusive. Observe that both x^4 and $3y^4$ have absolute minima at 0; therefore, f has an absolute minimum at $(0, 0)$.

12.8.41 Observe that $f_x = 4x^3y^2$, $f_y = 2x^4y$ and $f_{xx} = 12x^2y^2$, $f_{yy} = 2x^4$ and $f_{xy} = 8x^3y$. Note that every point on the x-axis and on the y-axis is a critical point, and that $D = 24x^6y^2 - 64x^6y^2 = -40x^6y^2$, which has value 0 at every point on the axes, so the Second Derivative Test is inconclusive. Note that the function is always nonnegative, so the value of 0 along the coordinate axes represents the minimum value.

12.8.43 First find the values of f at all critical points in the interior of $R = \{x^2+y^2 \le 4\}$; we have $f_x = 2x$, $f_y = 2y-2$, so $(0,1)$ is the only critical point in R, and $f(0,1) = 0$. Next, find the minimum and maximum values of f on the boundary of R, which we can parameterize by $x = 2\cos\theta$, $y = 2\sin\theta$ for $0 \le \theta \le 2\pi$. Then $f(2\cos\theta, 2\sin\theta) = 5-4\sin\theta$, which has maximum value 9 at $\theta = \frac{3\pi}{2}$ and minimum value 1 at $\theta = \frac{\pi}{2}$. Therefore, the maximum value of f on R is $f(0,-2) = 9$ and the minimum value is $f(0,1) = 0$.

12.8.45 First find the values of f at all critical points in the interior of R; we have $f_x = 4x$, $f_y = 2y$, so $(0,0)$ is the only critical point in R, and $f(0,0) = 4$. Next, find the minimum and maximum values of f on the boundary of R, which is a square. On the sides $y = \pm 1$, $-1 \le x \le 1$ we have $f(x,\pm 1) = 4+2x^2+1 = 2x^2+5$, which has extreme values 5 and 7 on $[-1,1]$. On the sides $x = \pm 1$, $-1 \le y \le 1$ we have$f(\pm 1, y) = 4+2+y^2 = y^2+6$,which has extreme values 6 and 7 on $[-1,1]$. Therefore, the maximum value of f on R is 7 and the minimum value is 4.

12.8.47 First find the values of f at all critical points in the interior of R; we have $f_x = 4x-4$ and $f_y = 6y$, so the only critical point is $(1,0)$. Note that $f(1,0) = 0$. Parameterize the boundary of R by letting $x = \cos t + 1$ and $y = \sin t$ for $0 \le t \le 2\pi$. Note that $f(x,y) = (2x^2-4x+2)+3y^2 = 2(x-1)^2+3y^2$, so $f(t) = 2\cos^2 t + 3\sin^2 t = 2+\sin^2 t$, and f has a maximum of 3 on the boundary of R at $(1,\pm 1)$ and an absolute minimum of 2 on the boundary of R. Thus, the absolute maximum of f on all of R is 3 and the absolute minimum is 0.

12.8.49 First find the values of f at all critical points in the interior of R; we have $f_x = -4x+4$ and $f_y = -6y-6$, so the only critical point in the interior of R is $(1,-1)$. Note that $f(1,-1) = 4$. We parameterize the boundary of R by letting $x = 1+\cos t$ and $y = -1+\sin t$ for $0 \le t \le 2\pi$. Note that $f(x,y) = -2(x^2-2x+1) + -3(y^2+2y+1) - 1+2+3 = -2(x-1)^2 + -3(y+1)^2 + 4$. Thus $f(t) = -2\cos^2 t - 3\sin^2 t + 3\cos^2 t + 3\sin^2 t + 1 = \cos^2 t + 1$. This has a maximum of 2 at $t = 0$ and $t = \pi$ and a minimum of 1 at $t = \pi/2$ and $t = 3\pi/2$. The original function therefore has an absolute maximum of 4 at $(1,-1)$ and an absolute minimum of 1 at $(1,0)$ and at $(1,-2)$.

12.8.51 $f_x = -\frac{x(2y^4+1)}{(x^2y^2+1)^2}$, which is 0 for $x = 0$, and $f_y = \frac{(x^4+2)y}{(x^2y^2+1)^2}$, which is 0 for $y = 0$. On the boundary $y = 2$ we have $f(x,y) = \frac{8-x^2}{2+8x^2}$ which is maximized on $[1,2]$ at $x = 1$ (with value $f(1,2) = \frac{7}{9}$) and minimized at $x = 2$ (with value $f(2,2) = \frac{1}{3}$). On the boundary $y = x$ we have $f(x,y) = \frac{x^2}{2+2x^2}$ which has minimum value 0 at $(0,0)$ and maximum value $\frac{1}{4}$ at $(1,1)$. On the boundary $y = 2x$ we have $f(x,y) = \frac{7x^2}{2+8x^4}$ which has derivative $\frac{7x-28x^5}{(4x^4+1)^2}$. This is zero for $x = 0$ and for $x = \frac{1}{\sqrt{2}}$. These points lead to a minimum of 0 at $(0,0)$ and a maximum of $\frac{7}{8}$ at $\left(\frac{1}{\sqrt{2}}, \sqrt{2}\right)$. Therefore the global minimum of f on the given set is $0 = f(0,0)$ and the global maximum is $\frac{7}{8} = f\left(\frac{1}{\sqrt{2}}, \sqrt{2}\right)$.

12.8.53 Observe that $f(0,0) = -4$ and $f(x,y) \ge -4$ for all points $(x,y) \in R$; hence the absolute minimum value of f on R is -4. The function f on R takes on all values in the interval $[-4,0)$; therefore f has no absolute maximum on R.

12.8.55 Observe that $f(0,0) = 2$ and $f(x,y) \le 2$ for all points $(x,y) \in R$; hence, the absolute maximum value of f on R is 2. The function f on R takes on all values in the interval $(0,2]$; therefore, f has no absolute minimum on R.

12.8.57 The equation of the plane can be written as $z = 4-x-y$; so it suffices to minimize the square of the distance from $(x,y,4-x-y)$ to $(0,3,6)$, which is given by $w = x^2+(y-3)^2+(x+y+2)^2$. We have $w_x = 2(2x+y+2)$, $w_y = 2(x+2y-1)$, so the critical points of w satisfy $2x+y = -2$, $x+2y = 1$ which gives $(x,y,z) = \left(-\frac{5}{3}, \frac{4}{3}, \frac{13}{3}\right)$. Because we know that there is some point on the plane closest to $(0,3,6)$, this critical point must be that point.

12.8.59 Consider the square of the distance between the points (x,x^2) and $(a,a-1)$ which is $f(a,x) = (x-a)^2+(x^2-a+1)^2$. Note that $f_a = -2(x-a) - 2(x^2-a+1)$, and $f_x = 2(x-a)+4x(x^2-a+1)$. The critical points satisfy $x-a = -(x^2-a+1)$ and $x-a = -2x(x^2-a+1)$. This has a real solution only when $x = 1/2$ and $a = 7/8$, and this gives rise to the closest point on the parabola being $(1/2, 1/4)$ and the point on the line it is closest to being $(7/8, -1/8)$.

12.8.61

a. True. This is because our definition of saddle point is a critical point which is neither a local maximum or local minimum.

b. False. A necessary condition for a local maximum at (a, b) is that both $f_x = f_y = 0$ at (a, b), assuming both partials exist.

c. True. This is because f may take on its absolute maximum or minimum at a point on the boundary of its domain.

d. True. The equation of the tangent plane at a critical point (a, b) is $z = f(a, b)$.

12.8.63 This function has a local minimum near $(0.3, -0.3)$ and a saddle point at $(0, 0)$.

12.8.65 The plane has equation $z = 2 - x + y$; the distance from a point $(x, y, 2 - x + y)$ on the plane to the point $(1, 1, 1)$ is given by $d^2 = (x-1)^2 + (y-1)^2 + (x-y-1)^2$. It suffices to minimize the function $f(x, y) = (x-1)^2 + (y-1)^2 + (x-y-1)^2$ on R^2. We have $f_x = 2(x - 1 + x - y - 1) = 2(2x - y - 2)$, $f_y = 2(y - 1 + y - x + 1) = 2(-x + 2y)$, so the critical point of f satisfies $2x - y = 2$, $x - 2y = 0$ which gives $x = \frac{4}{3}$, $y = \frac{2}{3}$. The corresponding point on the plane is $\left(\frac{4}{3}, \frac{2}{3}, \frac{4}{3}\right)$. Because there is a point on the plane closest to the point $(1, 1, 1)$, this must be the point we found.

12.8.67

a. Using the relation $z = 200 - x - y$, we see that it suffices to minimize the function $f(x, y) = x^2 + y^2 + (200 - x - y)^2$ over the closed bounded region R given by $x, y \geq 0$ and $x + y \leq 200$. We have $f_x = 2(x + x + y - 200) = 2(2x + y - 200)$, $f_y = 2(y + x + y - 200) = 2(x + 2y - 200)$; therefore, the critical point of f satisfies $2x + y = 200$, $x + 2y = 200$ which gives $x = y = \frac{200}{3}$ (the corresponding value of $z = \frac{200}{3}$ as well), and we have $f\left(\frac{200}{3}, \frac{200}{3}\right) = \frac{40{,}000}{3}$. We must also find the extreme values of f on the boundary of R. Along the segment $y = 0$, $0 \leq x \leq 200$ we have $f(x, 0) = x^2 + (200 - x)^2$ which has range $[20,000, 40,000]$, and we get the same result along the other two segments that make up the boundary of R. Therefore, the minimum value of $x^2 + y^2 + z^2$ is given by $x = y = z = \frac{200}{3}$.

b. The function $\sqrt{x^2 + y^2 + z^2}$ takes its minimum at the same point that minimizes $x^2 + y^2 + z^2$, which we saw in part (a) is $x = y = z = \frac{200}{3}$.

c. Using the relation $z = 200 - x - y$, we see that it suffices to minimize the function $f(x, y) = xy(200 - x - y) = 200xy - x^2y - xy^2$ over the closed bounded region R given by $x, y \geq 0$ and $x + y \leq 200$. We have $f_x = y(200 - 2x - y)$, $f_y = x(200 - x - 2y)$; therefore, the critical points of f in the interior of R satisfy $2x + y = 200$, $x + 2y = 200$ which gives $x = y = \frac{200}{3}$ (the corresponding value of $z = \frac{200}{3}$ as well), and we have $f\left(\frac{200}{3}, \frac{200}{3}\right) = \left(\frac{200}{3}\right)^2$. We also observe that $f(x, y) = 0$ on the boundary of R; therefore, the maximum value of xyz is given by $x = y = z = \frac{200}{3}$.

d. The function $x^2y^2z^2$ takes its maximum at the same point that maximizes xyz, which we saw in part (c) is $x = y = z = \frac{200}{3}$.

12.8.69

a. The function to be minimized is $f(x, y) = x^2 + y^2 + (x-2)^2 + y^2 + (x-1)^2 + (y-1)^2 = 3x^2 - 6x + 3y^2 - 2y$; we have $f_x = 6(x - 1)$, $f_y = 2(3y - 1)$ so the optimal location is the unique critical point $\left(1, \frac{1}{3}\right)$.

b. The function to be minimized is now $f(x, y) = (x - x_1)^2 + (y - y_1)^2 + (x - x_2)^2 + (y - y_2)^2 + (x - x_3)^2 + (y - y_3)^2 = 3\left(x^2 - 2\overline{x}x + y^2 - 2\overline{y}y\right) + \text{const}$; where $\overline{x} = \frac{x_1 + x_2 + x_3}{3}$, $\overline{y} = \frac{y_1 + y_2 + y_3}{3}$. we have $f_x = 6(x - \overline{x})$, $f_y = 6(y - \overline{y})$ so the optimal location is the unique critical point $(\overline{x}, \overline{y})$.

c. The function to be minimized is now

$$f(x,y) = \sum_{i=1}^{n}(x-x_i)^2 + \sum_{i=1}^{n}(y-y_i)^2 = n\left(x^2 - 2\overline{x}x + y^2 - 2\overline{y}y\right) + \text{const}$$

where $\overline{x} = \frac{1}{n}\sum_{i=1}^{n} x_i$, $\overline{y} = \frac{1}{n}\sum_{i=1}^{n} y_i$. We have $f_x = n(x-\overline{x})$, $f_y = n(y-\overline{y})$ so the optimal location is the unique critical point $(\overline{x},\overline{y})$.

d. The actual sum of the distances is given by the function $f(x,y) = \sqrt{x^2+y^2} + \sqrt{(x-2)^2+y^2} + \sqrt{(x-1)^2+(y-1)^2}$ We can minimize this function as follows. First, fix $y = y_0$ and consider the function $g(x) = f(x,y_0)$. Each of the three terms in this function has positive second derivative, and approaches ∞ as $x \to \pm\infty$, so the same is true for their sum; therefore $g(x)$ must have a unique absolute minimum. Observe in addition that g is symmetric in the line $x = 1$, which implies that the absolute minimum must occur at $x = 1$. So to minimize $f(x,y)$, we can set $x = 1$ and reduce to minimizing the function $h(y) = f(1,y) = 2\sqrt{1+y^2} + |y-1|$, which has absolute minimum at $y = \frac{1}{\sqrt{3}}$. Therefore, the optimal location is $\left(1, \frac{1}{\sqrt{3}}\right)$, which is different from the point found in part (a).

12.8.71 Given the n data points $(x_1,y_1), \ldots, (x_n,y_n)$, we seek to minimize the function $E(m,b) = \sum_{k=1}^{n}(mx_k + b - y_k)^2 = \left(\sum x_k^2\right)m^2 + 2\left(\sum x_k\right)mb + nb^2 - 2\left(\sum x_k y_k\right)m - 2\left(\sum y_k\right)b + \sum y_k^2$. We have $E_m = 2\left(\sum x_k^2\right)m + 2\left(\sum x_k\right)b - 2\left(\sum x_k y_k\right)$, $E_b = 2\left(\sum x_k\right)m + 2nb - 2\left(\sum y_k\right)$ and solving $E_m = E_b = 0$ gives $m = \frac{(\sum x_k)(\sum y_k) - n\sum x_k y_k}{(\sum x_k)^2 - n\sum x_k^2}$, $b = \frac{1}{n}\left(\sum y_k - m\sum x_k\right)$.

12.8.73 Using the result in Exercise 69, we obtain $m = \frac{2\cdot 14 - 3\cdot 24}{2^2 - 3\cdot 10} = \frac{22}{13}$, $b = \frac{1}{3}\left(14 - \frac{22}{13}\cdot 2\right) = \frac{46}{13}$ so the line has equation $y = \frac{22}{13}x + \frac{46}{13}$.

12.8.75 Let $s = \frac{a+b+c}{2}$ be the semi-perimeter, which we assume is constant. Then we may express $c = 2s - a - b$ and therefore $A^2 = s(s-a)(s-b)(s-(2s-a-b)) = s(s-a)(s-b)(a+b-s)$, so it suffices to maximize the simpler function $f(a,b) = s(s-a)(s-b)(a+b-s)$ over the closed bounded region given by $0 \le a, b \le s$ and $a + b \ge s$. We have $f_a = s(s-b)(-(a+b-s)+s-a) = s(s-b)(2s-2a-b)$ and similarly $f_b = s(s-a)(2s-a-2b)$, so the critical points of f in the interior of R satisfy $2a + b = 2s$, $a + 2b = 2s$ which gives $a = b = \frac{2}{3}s$, and therefore $c = \frac{2}{3}s$ as well, so we get an equilateral triangle. We also observe that $f(a,b) = 0$ on the boundary of R, so this critical point must give the absolute maximum of f. We conclude that of all triangles with a given perimeter, the maximum area is obtained when all three sides are equal (in the special case of perimeter 9 units, each side length is 3 units).

12.8.77

a. We have $d_1(x,y) = \sqrt{(x-x_1)^2 + (y-y_1)^2}$, so $\nabla d_1(x,y) = \frac{x-x_1}{d_1(x,y)}\mathrm{i} + \frac{y-y_1}{d_1(x,y)}\mathrm{j}$; observe that this is a unit vector in the direction of the vector joining (x_1,y_1) to (x,y).

b. Similarly, we have $\nabla d_2(x,y) = \frac{x-x_2}{d_2(x,y)}\mathrm{i} + \frac{y-y_2}{d_2(x,y)}\mathrm{j}$ and $\nabla d_3(x,y) = \frac{x-x_3}{d_3(x,y)}\mathrm{i} + \frac{y-y_3}{d_3(x,y)}\mathrm{j}$.

c. Because $\nabla f = \nabla d_1 + \nabla d_2 + \nabla d_3$, the condition $f_x = f_y = 0$ is equivalent to $\nabla d_1 + \nabla d_2 + \nabla d_3 = 0$.

d. If three unit vectors add to 0, they must make angles of $\pm\frac{2\pi}{3}$ with each other.

e. In this case the optimal point is the vertex at the large angle.

f. Solving the equations $f_x = f_y = 0$ numerically gives $(0.255457, 0.304504)$.

12.8.79

a. We have $f(x,y) = -2x^4 + 2x^2(e^y+1) - e^{2y} - 1$; hence $f_x = -8x^3 + 4x(e^y+1)$, $f_y = 2x^2e^y - 2e^{2y}$, so the critical points must satisfy $x^2 = e^y$, and then the equation $f_x = 0$ reduces to $e^y = 1$, so the critical points are $(\pm1, 0)$. Next we compute$f_{xx} = -24x^2 + 4(1+e^y)$, $f_{yy} = 2x^2e^y - 4e^{2y}$, $f_{xy} = 4e^y$ so $f_{xx}f_{yy} - f_{xy}^2 = (-16)(-2) - (4)^2 = 16$ at both critical points; we also have $f_{xx} < 0$ at both critical points, so the critical points both yield local maxima.

b. We have $f_x = 8xe^y - 8x^3$, $f_y = 4x^2e^y - 4e^{4y}$, so the critical points must satisfy $x^2 = e^{3y}$, and then the equation $f_x = 0$ reduces to $e^y = 1$, so the critical points are $(\pm 1, 0)$. Next we compute $f_{xx} = 8e^y - 24x^2$, $f_{yy} = 4x^2e^y - 16e^{4y}$, $f_{xy} = 8xe^y$, so $f_{xx}f_{yy} - f_{xy}^2 = (-16)(-12) - (\pm 8)^2 = 128$ at both critical points; we also have $f_{xx} < 0$ at both critical points, so the critical points both yield local maxima.

12.9 Lagrange Multipliers

12.9.1 The level curves of f must be tangential to the level curves of g at the optimal point; thus, the gradients are parallel.

12.9.3 We have $\nabla f = \langle 2x, 2y, 2z \rangle$, $\nabla g = \langle 2, 3, -5 \rangle$ so the Lagrange multiplier conditions are $2x = 2\lambda$, $2y = 3\lambda$, $2z = -5\lambda$, $2x + 3y - 5z + 4 = 0$.

12.9.5 We have $\nabla f = \langle 1, 2 \rangle$, $\nabla g = \langle 2x, 2y \rangle$ so the Lagrange multiplier conditions are $1 = 2\lambda x$, $2 = 2\lambda y$, $x^2 + y^2 - 4 = 0$. Hence $\frac{1}{x} = 2\lambda = \frac{2}{y} \Longrightarrow y = 2x$; substituting this in the constraint gives $5x^2 = 4$, so $x = \pm\frac{2}{\sqrt{5}}$ and the extreme values of f on the circle $x^2 + y^2 = 4$ must occur at the points $\pm\left(\frac{2}{\sqrt{5}}, \frac{4}{\sqrt{5}}\right)$. We see that $f\left(\frac{2}{\sqrt{5}}, \frac{4}{\sqrt{5}}\right) = 2\sqrt{5}$, $f\left(-\frac{2}{\sqrt{5}}, -\frac{4}{\sqrt{5}}\right) = -2\sqrt{5}$, so these are the maximum and minimum values.

12.9.7 We have $\nabla f = \langle 1, 1 \rangle$, $\nabla g = \langle 2x - y, 2y - x \rangle$, so the Lagrange multiplier conditions are $2x - y = 1/\lambda$, $2y - x = 1/\lambda$, $x^2 - xy + y^2 = 1$. Subtracting the first two equations gives $3x - 3y = 0$, so $x = y = 1/\lambda$, which yields the points $(\pm 1, \pm 1)$. The maximum value is 2 at $(1, 1)$ and the minimum is -2 at $(-1, -1)$.

12.9.9 We have $\nabla f = \langle y, x \rangle$ and $\nabla g = \langle 2x - y, 2y - x \rangle$, so the Lagrange multiplier conditions are $y = \lambda(2x - y)$, $x = \lambda(2y - x)$, $x^2 + y^2 - xy = 9$. Multiplying the first equation by x and the second by y and subtracting leads to $\lambda(2x^2 - 2y^2) = 0$, so either $x = \pm y$ or $\lambda = 0$. If $\lambda = 0$, we have $x = y = 0$ which doesn't meet the constraint. If $x = y$, we have $x = \pm 3 = y$, if $x = -y$, we have $x = \pm\sqrt{3}$, $y = \mp\sqrt{3}$. There is a minimum value of -3 at $(\pm\sqrt{3}, \mp\sqrt{3})$ and a maximum value of 9 at $(\pm 3, \pm 3)$.

12.9.11 We have $\nabla f = \langle 2ye^{2xy}, 2xe^{2xy} \rangle$ and $\nabla g = \langle 2x, 2y \rangle$, so the Lagrange multiplier conditions are $2ye^{2xy} = 2\lambda x$, $2xe^{2xy} = 2\lambda y$, $x^2 + y^2 = 16$. If we multiply the first equation by y and the second by x and subtract, we have $(2y^2 - 2x^2)e^{2xy} = 0$, so $y = \pm x$. If $y = x$, we obtain the points $(\pm 2\sqrt{2}, \pm 2\sqrt{2})$, and if $y = -x$, we obtain $(\pm 2\sqrt{2}, \mp 2\sqrt{2})$. There is a maximum of e^{16} at $(\pm 2\sqrt{2}, \pm 2\sqrt{2})$ and a minimum of e^{-16} at $(\pm 2\sqrt{2}, \mp 2\sqrt{2})$.

12.9.13 We have $\nabla f = \langle -8x, 2y \rangle$, $\nabla g = \langle 2x, 4y \rangle$ so the Lagrange multiplier conditions are $-8x = 2\lambda x$, $2y = 4\lambda y$, $x^2 + 2y^2 - 4 = 0$. If x, $y \neq 0$ the first equation gives $\lambda = -4$, whereas the second gives $\lambda = \frac{1}{2}$ which is a contradiction; hence we must have x or $y = 0$, which gives the points $(\pm 2, 0)$ and $(0, \pm\sqrt{2})$, and $f(\pm 2, 0) = -16$, $f(0, \pm\sqrt{2}) = 2$. Hence the minimum and maximum values of f on the closed bounded set given by $x^2 + 2y^2 = 4$ are -16 and 2.

12.9.15 We have $\nabla f = \langle 1, 3, -1 \rangle$, $\nabla g = \langle 2x, 2y, 2z \rangle$ so the Lagrange multiplier conditions are $1 = 2\lambda x$, $3 = 2\lambda y$, $-1 = 2\lambda z$, $x^2 + y^2 + z^2 - 4 = 0$. These equations imply x, y, $z \neq 0$, so we can eliminate λ and obtain $y = 3x$, $z = -x$. Then the constraint gives $11x^2 = 4$, so $x = \pm\frac{2}{\sqrt{11}}$ and the solutions are the points $\pm\left(\frac{2}{\sqrt{11}}, \frac{6}{\sqrt{11}}, -\frac{2}{\sqrt{11}}\right)$. We compute $f\left(\frac{2}{\sqrt{11}}, \frac{6}{\sqrt{11}}, -\frac{2}{\sqrt{11}}\right) = 2\sqrt{11}$, $f\left(-\frac{2}{\sqrt{11}}, -\frac{6}{\sqrt{11}}, \frac{2}{\sqrt{11}}\right) = -2\sqrt{11}$, and hence the minimum and maximum values of f on the closed bounded set given by $x^2 + y^2 + z^2 = 4$ are $-2\sqrt{11}$ and $2\sqrt{11}$.

12.9.17 We have $\nabla f = \langle 1, 0, 0 \rangle$ and $\nabla g = \langle 2x, 2y, 2z - 1 \rangle$. The Lagrange multiplier conditions are $1 = 2x\lambda$, $0 = 2y\lambda$, $0 = (2z - 1)\lambda$, and $x^2 + y^2 + z^2 - z = 1$. Clearly $\lambda \neq 0$, so we must have $y = 0$ and $z = 1/2$. Solving the constraint for x gives $x = \pm\sqrt{5}/2$. There is a maximum of $\sqrt{5}/2$ at $(\sqrt{5}/2, 0, 1/2)$ and a minimum of $-\sqrt{5}/2$ at $(-\sqrt{5}/2, 0, 1/2)$.

12.9.19 We have $\nabla f = \langle 2x, 2y, 2z\rangle$ and $\nabla g = \langle 2x-4y, 2y-4x, 2z\rangle$. The Lagrange multiplier conditions are $2x = \lambda(2x-4y)$, $2y = \lambda(2y-4x)$, $2z = \lambda(2z)$, and $x^2+y^2+z^2-4xy = 1$. Suppose $z \neq 0$. Then $\lambda = 1$ and $x = y = 0$, so $z = \pm 1$. If $z = 0$, then multiplying the first equation by y and the second by x and subtract to obtain $0 = \lambda(4x^2-4y^2)$, and since we can't have $\lambda = 0$ (because then $x = y = z = 0$), we must have $x = \pm y$. When $x = y$, the constraint becomes $2x^2 - 4x^2 = 1$ which can't occur. So we must have $x = -y$, which yields $x = \pm 1/\sqrt{6}$ and $y = \mp 1/\sqrt{6}$. There is a maximum of 1 at $(0,0,\pm 1)$ and a minimum of 1/3 at $(\pm 1/\sqrt{6}, \mp 1/\sqrt{6}, 0)$.

12.9.21 $\nabla f = \langle 2, 0, 2z\rangle$ and $\nabla g = \langle 2x, 2y, 4z\rangle$. The Lagrange multiplier conditions are $2 = 2\lambda x$, $0 = 2\lambda y$, $2z = 4\lambda z$, and $x^2+y^2+2z^2 = 25$. Note that $\lambda \neq 0$ so $y = 0$ and if $z \neq 0$ then $\lambda = 1/2$ so $x = 2$ and we have the point $(2, 0, \sqrt{21/2})$. If $z = 0$, then we have $x = \pm 5$. The minimum is -10 at $(-5,0,0)$ and the maximum is 14.5 at $(2, 0, \sqrt{21/2})$.

12.9.23 We have $\nabla f = \langle 2x, 2y, 2z\rangle$, $\nabla g = \langle yz, xz, xy\rangle$, so the Lagrange multiplier conditions are $2x = \lambda yz$, $2y = \lambda xz$, $2z = \lambda xy$, $xyz - 4 = 0$. The first three equations give $\frac{\lambda xyz}{2} = x^2 = y^2 = z^2$, so $y = \pm x$, $z = \pm x$. Then using the constraint we obtain $x^3 = \pm 4$, so x, y, $z = \pm\sqrt[3]{4}$. The value of $x^2+y^2+z^2$ at any of these points is $f\left(\pm\sqrt[3]{4}, \pm\sqrt[3]{4}, \pm\sqrt[3]{4}\right) = 3 \cdot 4^{2/3} = 6\sqrt[3]{2}$. Note that $f(x,y,z)$ is the square of the distance from (x,y,z) to the origin, so this function will have an absolute minimum but no maximum on the surface given by $xyz = 4$; therefore the minimum value of f on the surface is $6\sqrt[3]{2}$.

12.9.25 Let x, y, $z \geq 0$ denote the lengths of the sides of the box, with z the longest side. Then the length plus girth of the box is $2x+2y+z$ so we must maximize the volume $f(x,y,z) = xyz$ subject to the constraint $g(x,y,z) = 2x+2y+z-108 = 0$. We have $\nabla f = \langle yz, xz, xy\rangle$, $\nabla g = \langle 2,2,1\rangle$ so the Lagrange multiplier conditions are $yz = 2\lambda$, $xz = 2\lambda$, $xy = \lambda$, $2x+2y+z-108 = 0$. Assume that x, y, $z > 0$ (otherwise the volume is 0); then the first three equations give $\frac{xyz}{2\lambda} = x = y = \frac{z}{2}$, and the constraint gives $6x = 108$, so $x = 18$ and the box has dimensions 18 in×18 in×36 in. The domain of f is the triangle with vertices $(54,0,0)$, $(0,54,0)$, $(0,0,108)$, which is closed and bounded. We also note that $f = 0$ along any of the edges of the triangle. Therefore, the maximum value of f occurs at the point we found, and the minimum value is 0.

12.9.27 It suffices to find the extreme values of the function $f(x,y) = x^2+y^2$ subject to the constraint $g(x,y) = x^2+xy+2y^2-1 = 0$. We have $\nabla f = \langle 2x, 2y\rangle$, $\nabla g = \langle 2x+y, 4y+x\rangle$, so the Lagrange multiplier conditions are $2x = \lambda(2x+y)$, $2y = \lambda(4y+x)$, $x^2+xy+2y^2-1 = 0$. The first two equations give $2x(4y+x) = \lambda(2x+y)(4y+x) = 2y(2x+y) \Longrightarrow x^2+4xy = y^2+2xy$, or $x^2+2xy-y^2$. This implies that both x, $y \neq 0$, for if, say, $x = 0$ then this condition gives $y = 0$ as well, which violates the constraint (same argument for $y = 0$). Let $r = \frac{y}{x}$, and rewrite this equation as $\frac{y^2}{x^2} - \frac{2y}{x} - 1 = r^2 - 2r - 1 = 0$, which we can solve to obtain $r = 1 \pm \sqrt{2}$. We now use the constraint and the relation $y = rx$ to obtain $x^2(1+r+2r^2) = 1$or $x^2 = \frac{1}{2r^2+r+1}$. Then the values of the function f are given by $f(x,y) = f(x,rx) = x^2(1+r^2) = \frac{1+r^2}{2r^2+r+1} = \frac{6\pm2\sqrt{2}}{7} \approx 0.4531, 1.2612$, and the corresponding minimum and maximum distances are $\sqrt{\frac{6\pm2\sqrt{2}}{7}} \approx 0.6731, 1.1230$.

12.9.29 Let (x,y) be the vertex of the rectangle in the first quadrant; then the perimeter of the rectangle is $4(x+y)$, so it suffices to maximize the function $f(x,y) = x+y$ subject to the constraint $g(x,y) = 2x^2+4y^2-3 = 0$ and x, $y \geq 0$. We have $\nabla f = \langle 1,1\rangle$, $\nabla g = \langle 4x, 8y\rangle$, so the Lagrange multiplier conditions are $1 = 4\lambda x$, $1 = 8\lambda y$, $2x^2+4y^2-3 = 0$. The first two equations give $4x = \frac{1}{\lambda} = 8y$; so $x = 2y$. Substituting in the constraint gives $8y^2+4y^2 = 3$, so $y^2 = 1/4$ and $y = 1/2$ and thus $x = 1$. Note that $f(1,1/2) = 1.5$. The domain given by the constraint and x, $y \geq 0$ is a closed and bounded arc, and we observe that at the boundary points we have $f(0,\sqrt{3}/2) = \sqrt{3}/2 \approx .87$ and $f(\sqrt{3/2},0) = \sqrt{3/2} \approx 1.25$. Thus, the dimensions of the rectangle of maximum perimeter is 2×1.

12.9.31 It suffices to minimize the function $f(x,y,z) = (x-1)^2+(y-2)^2+(z+3)^2$ subject to the constraint $4x+y-1 = 0$. We have $\nabla f = \langle 2(x-1), 2(y-2), 2(z+3)\rangle$ and $\nabla g = \langle 4,1,0\rangle$. Then the Lagrange multiplier conditions are $2x-2 = 4\lambda$, $2y-4 = \lambda$, $2z+6 = 0$, $4x+y-1 = 0$. Solving this system gives $x = -3/17$, $y = 29/17$, $z = -3$, and $\lambda = -10/17$, so the closest point on the surface to the given point is $(-3/17, 29/17, -3)$.

12.9.33 It suffices to find the extreme values the function $f(x,y,z)=(x-2)^2+(y-3)^2+(z-4)^2$ subject to the constraint $g(x,y,z)=x^2+y^2+z^2-9=0$. We have $\nabla f=\langle 2x-4,2y-6,2z-8\rangle$, $\nabla g=\langle 2x,2y,2z\rangle$ so the Lagrange multiplier conditions are $2x-4=2\lambda x$, $2y-6=2\lambda y$, $2z-8=2\lambda z$, $x^2+y^2+z^2-9=0$. We can write the first three equations in the form $(1-\lambda)\langle x,y,z\rangle=\langle 2,3,4\rangle$ so $\langle x,y,z\rangle=c\langle 2,3,4\rangle$ for some scalar c; using the constraint, we find that $c=\pm\frac{3}{\sqrt{29}}$, and hence $\langle x,y,z\rangle=\pm\frac{3}{\sqrt{29}}\langle 2,3,4\rangle$; the corresponding values of f are $f\left(\pm\left(\frac{6}{\sqrt{29}},\frac{9}{\sqrt{29}},\frac{12}{\sqrt{29}}\right)\right)=38\mp 6\sqrt{29}=\left(\sqrt{29}\mp 3\right)^2$, so the minimum distance is $\sqrt{29}-3$ and the maximum distance is $\sqrt{29}+3$.

12.9.35 Notice that the constraint is equivalent to $\ell+2g=6$. We have $\nabla U=5\langle \ell^{-1/2}g^{1/2},\ell^{1/2}g^{-1/2}\rangle$ so the Lagrange multiplier conditions are equivalent to $\ell^{-1/2}g^{1/2}=\lambda$, $\ell^{1/2}g^{-1/2}=2\lambda$, $\ell+2g=6$. Eliminating λ from the first two equations gives $\ell^{1/2}g^{-1/2}=2\ell^{-1/2}g^{1/2}$, which simplifies to $g=\frac{\ell}{2}$; substituting in the constraint then gives $\ell=3$ and $g=\frac{3}{2}$. The value of the utility function at this point is $U=15\sqrt{2}$.

12.9.37 Notice that the constraint is equivalent to $5\ell+4g=20$. We have $\nabla U=\frac{8}{5}\langle 4\ell^{-1/5}g^{1/5},\ell^{4/5}g^{-4/5}\rangle$, so the Lagrange multiplier conditions are equivalent to $4\ell^{-1/5}g^{1/5}=5\lambda$, $\ell^{4/5}g^{-4/5}=4\lambda$, $5\ell+4g=20$. Eliminating λ from the first two equations gives $16\ell^{-1/5}g^{1/5}=5\ell^{4/5}g^{-4/5}$, which simplifies to $g=\frac{5\ell}{16}$; substituting in the constraint then gives $\ell=\frac{16}{5}$, $g=1$. The value of the utility function at this point is $U=8\cdot\left(\frac{16}{5}\right)^{4/5}\approx 20.287$.

12.9.39

a. True. This is because the tangent plane to a sphere at any point has normal vector in the direction of the line joining the point to the center of the sphere.

b. False in general. In fact, the two vectors ∇f and ∇g are in the same direction, so $\nabla f\cdot\nabla g=0$ only if one of these vectors is zero.

12.9.41 Let x, $y>0$ be the dimensions of the base and $h>0$ be the height of the box; then the four sides of the box plus the base have total area $2xh+2yh+xy=2$, which is our constraint. The volume of the box is $V=xyh$, so the Lagrange multiplier conditions are $yh=\lambda(2h+y)$, $xh=\lambda(2h+x)$, $xy=2\lambda(x+y)$, $2xh+2yh+xy=2$. The first two equations give $\frac{2h+y}{yh}=\frac{2h+x}{xh}\implies\frac{2}{y}+\frac{1}{h}=\frac{2}{x}+\frac{1}{h}$, so $y=x$. The second and third equations give $\frac{2h+x}{xh}=\frac{2x+2y}{xy}\implies\frac{2}{x}+\frac{1}{h}=\frac{2}{x}+\frac{2}{y}=\frac{4}{x}$, so $h=\frac{x}{2}$. Then substituting in the constraint gives $3x^2=2$, so $x=\frac{\sqrt{6}}{3}$. Therefore, the box with largest volume has height $\frac{\sqrt{6}}{6}$ m and base $\frac{\sqrt{6}}{3}\times\frac{\sqrt{6}}{3}$ m.

12.9.43 Let x, $y\ge 0$ be the dimensions of the base and $z\ge 0$ be the height of the box; then $x+2y+3z=6$ is our constraint. The box has volume $V=xyz$, so the Lagrange multiplier conditions are $yz=\lambda$, $xz=2\lambda$, $xy=3\lambda$, $x+2y+3z=6$. The first two equations give $y=\frac{x}{2}$, the first and third equations give $z=\frac{x}{3}$, and substituting in the constraint gives $x=2$. Therefore, the box with largest volume has dimensions $x=2$, $y=1$, $z=\frac{2}{3}$.

12.9.45 The constraint is the equation of the plane $x-y+z=2$; the distance from a point (x,y,z) to the point $(1,1,1)$ is given by $d^2=(x-1)^2+(y-1)^2+(x-y-1)^2$, so it suffices to minimize the function $f(x,y,z)=(x-1)^2+(y-1)^2+(z-1)^2$ subject to the constraint $x-y+z=2$. The Lagrange multiplier conditions are $2x-2=\lambda$, $2y-2=-\lambda$, $2z-2=\lambda$, $x-y+z=2$. The first two equations give $2(x+y)=4$, so $y=2-x$, the first and third equations give $z=x$, and then substituting in the constraint gives $x=\frac{4}{3}$, so the closest point on the plane to $(1,1,1)$ is $\left(\frac{4}{3},\frac{2}{3},\frac{4}{3}\right)$.

12.9.47 We have $\nabla f=\langle 2x+y,-8y+x\rangle$; solving $2x+y=0$ and $-8y+x=0$ simultaneously gives unique solution $(0,0)$, and $f(0,0)=0$. Next we use Lagrange multipliers to find the minimum and maximum values of f on the boundary of R given by $4x^2+9y^2=36$. The Lagrange multiplier conditions are $2x+y=8\lambda x$, $-8y+x=18\lambda y$, $4x^2+9y^2=36$. The first two equations give $\lambda xy=\frac{2xy+y^2}{8}=\frac{x^2-8xy}{18}\implies 9y^2+50xy-4x^2=0$; therefore, $y=rx$ where r satisfies the quadratic $9r^2+50r-4=0$, which has roots $r=\frac{-25\pm\sqrt{661}}{9}$. Then the constraint gives $\left(4+9r^2\right)x^2=36$, so $x^2=\frac{36}{9r^2+4}=\frac{18}{8-25r}$ (using $9r^2=4-50r$) and hence $f(x,y)=\left(1-4r^2+r\right)x^2=\frac{-7+209r}{9}\cdot\frac{18}{4-25r}=\frac{418r-14}{4-25r}=\frac{-7\pm\sqrt{661}}{2}$, which gives the absolute minimum and maximum values of f on R.

12.9.49 We have $\nabla f = \langle 2(x-1), 2(y+1)\rangle$; therefore f has unique critical point $(1,-1)$ which is inside R; $f(1,-1) = 0$. Next we use Lagrange multipliers to find the minimum and maximum values of $f$on the boundary of R given by $x^2 + y^2 = 4$. The Lagrange multiplier conditions are equivalent to$x - 1 = \lambda x$, $y + 1 = \lambda y$, $x^2 + y^2 = 4$. The first two equations give $\lambda xy = xy - y = xy + x \Longrightarrow y = -x$; then the constraint gives $2x^2 = 4$, so $x = \pm\sqrt{2}$ and the solutions are $\pm\left(\sqrt{2}, -\sqrt{2}\right)$. The values of f at these points are$f\left(\sqrt{2}, -\sqrt{2}\right) = 6 - 4\sqrt{2} \approx 0.343$, $f\left(-\sqrt{2}, \sqrt{2}\right) = 6 + 4\sqrt{2} \approx 11.657$; therefore, the maximum value of f on R is $6 + 4\sqrt{2}$ and the minimum value is 0.

12.9.51 The maximum and minimum values of f along the curve $g(x,y) = 0$ occur at points where the level curves of f are tangent to the curve $g(x,y) = 0$; using this, we see that the minimum and maximum values are 1 and 8.

12.9.53 Notice that the constraint is equivalent to $2K + 3L = 30$. We have $\nabla f = \frac{1}{2}\langle K^{-1/2}L^{1/2}, K^{1/2}L^{-1/2}\rangle$, so the Lagrange multiplier conditions are equivalent to $K^{-1/2}L^{1/2} = 2\lambda$, $K^{1/2}L^{-1/2} = 3\lambda$, $2K + 3L = 30$. Eliminating λ from the first two equations gives $3K^{-1/2}L^{1/2} = 2K^{1/2}L^{-1/2}$, which simplifies to $3L = 2K$; substituting in the constraint then gives $K = 7.5$ and $L = 5$. The domain over which f is to be maximized is a closed line segment; K or L is 0 at the endpoints, and hence so is f. Therefore, the values of K and L found above must maximize f.

12.9.55 We have $\nabla f = \langle aK^{a-1}L^{1-a}, (1-a)K^aL^{-a}\rangle$, so the Lagrange multiplier conditions are equivalent to $aK^{a-1}L^{1-a} = \lambda p$, $(1-a)K^aL^{-a} = \lambda q$, $pK + qL = B$. Eliminating λ from the first two equations gives $aqK^{a-1}L^{1-a} = (1-a)pK^aL^{-a}$, which simplifies to $aqL = (1-a)pK$; substituting in the constraint then gives $K = \frac{aB}{p}$ and $L = \frac{(1-a)B}{q}$. The domain over which f is to be maximized is a closed line segment; K or L is 0 at the endpoints, and hence so is f. Therefore, the values of K and L found above must maximize f.

12.9.57 The function to be maximized is $f(x_1, x_2, x_3, x_4) = x_1 + x_2 + x_3 + x_4$, subject to the constraint $x_1^2 + x_2^2 + x_3^2 + x_4^2 = 16$. The Lagrange multiplier conditions are $1 = 2\lambda x_1$, $1 = 2\lambda x_2$, $1 = 2\lambda x_3$, $1 = 2\lambda x_4$, $x_1^2 + x_2^2 + x_3^2 + x_4^2 = 16$. The first four equations give $x_1 = x_2 = x_3 = x_4$, and then the constraint gives $4x_1^2 = 16$, so $x_1 = \pm 2$. Therefore, the maximum of f on the closed, bounded set given by $x_1^2 + x_2^2 + x_3^2 + x_4^2 = 16$ is $f(2,2,2,2) = 8$ (and the minimum is $f(-2,-2,-2,-2) = -8$).

12.9.59 The function to be maximized is $f(x_1, x_2, \ldots, x_n) = a_1x_1 + a_2x_2 + \cdots + a_nx_n$, subject to the constraint $x_1^2 + x_2^2 + \cdots + x_n^2 = 1$. The Lagrange multiplier conditions are $a_1 = 2\lambda x_1$, $a_2 = 2\lambda x_2$, ..., $a_n = 2\lambda x_n$, $x_1^2 + x_2^2 + \cdots + x_n^2 = 1$. The first n equations are equivalent to $c(x_1, x_2, \ldots, x_n) = (a_1, a_2, \ldots, a_n)$ for some c, and then the constraint gives $c^2 = a_1^2 + a_2^2 + \cdots + a_n^2$. Therefore, the maximum of f on the closed, bounded set given by $f\left(\frac{a_1}{c}, \frac{a_2}{c}, \ldots, \frac{a_n}{c}\right) = \frac{1}{c}\left(a_1^2 + a_2^2 + \cdots + a_n^2\right) = \sqrt{a_1^2 + a_2^2 + \cdots + a_n^2}$ (and the minimum is $-\sqrt{a_1^2 + a_2^2 + \cdots + a_n^2}$).

12.9.61

a. Gradients are perpendicular to level surfaces.

b. If ∇f was not in the plane spanned by ∇g and ∇h, then f could be increased or decreased by moving the point P slightly along the curve C.

c. Because ∇f is in the plane spanned by ∇g and ∇h, we can express ∇f as a linear combination of ∇g and ∇h.

d. The gradient condition from part (c), as well as the constraints, must be satisfied.

12.9.63 We wish to find the extreme values of the function $f(x,y,z) = xyz$ subject to the constraints $g(x,y,z) = x^2 + y^2 - 4 = 0$ and $h(x,y,z) = x + y + z - 1 = 0$. Using the method described in problem 61 above, we solve the equation $\nabla f = \lambda\nabla g + \mu\nabla h$, together with the constraints. This gives the conditions $yz = 2\lambda x + \mu$, $xz = 2\lambda y + \mu$, $xy = \mu$, $x^2 + y^2 = 4$, $x + y + z = 1$. The first and second equations together give $z(y - x) = 2\lambda(x - y)$, which implies either $x = y$ or $z = -2\lambda$. In the former case the first constraint gives $2x^2 = 4$, so $x = y = \pm\sqrt{2}$, solving for z gives $z = 1 \mp 2\sqrt{2}$ and $f(x,y,z) = 2 \pm 4\sqrt{2}$. In the latter case we obtain $(x+y)z = \mu = xy$ from the first and third equations, and then solving for $z = 1-x-y$ gives $(x+y)(1-x-y) - xy = 0 \iff x + y - 3xy - 4 = 0$, using the relation $x^2+y^2 = 4$. Therefore, $x - 4 = (3x-1)y(x-4)^2 = (3x-1)^2(4-x^2)x^2 - 8x + 16 = (9x^2-6x+1)(4-x^2)$ which simplifies to $9x^4 - 6x^3 - 34x^2 + 16x + 12 = 0$. This equation has roots $x \approx -0.42, -1.78, 1.96, 0.91$ in the interval $(-2, 2)$; one can check that the corresponding solutions (x, y, z) to the Lagrange conditions do not give values larger or smaller resp. than $2+4\sqrt{2}$, $2-4\sqrt{2}$, so these are in fact the maximum and minimum values of f subject to the constraints.

12.9.65 We wish to find the extreme values of the function $f(x,y,z) = x^2+y^2+z^2$ subject to the constraints $g(x,y,z) = 4x^2+4y^2-z^2 = 0$ and $h(x,y,z) = 2x+4z-5 = 0$. Using the method described in problem 61 above, we solve the equation $\nabla f = \lambda \nabla g + \mu \nabla h$, together with the constraints. This gives the conditions $2x = 8\lambda x + 2\mu$, $2y = 8\lambda y$, $2z = -2\lambda z + 4\mu$, $z^2 = 4x^2+4y^2$, $2x+4z = 5$. The second equation gives $y(1-4\lambda) = 0$, so either $y = 0$ or $\lambda = \frac{1}{4}$. Consider first the case $y = 0$; then the first constraint equation gives $z = \pm 2x$. If $z = 2x$ then the second constraint equation gives $x = \frac{1}{2}$, $z = 1$ and we obtain the point $\left(\frac{1}{2}, 0, 1\right)$; similarly if $z = -2x$ then we obtain the point $\left(-\frac{5}{6}, 0, \frac{5}{3}\right)$. In the case $\lambda = \frac{1}{4}$ the first equation gives $\mu = 0$ and then the third equation gives $z = 0$; but then the first of the constraints implies that $x = y = z = 0$, which violates the second constraint. Hence there are no solutions to the Lagrange conditions in this case, and the minimum and maximum values of the function f along this curve are $f\left(\frac{1}{2}, 0, 1\right) = \frac{5}{4}$ and $f\left(-\frac{5}{6}, 0, \frac{5}{3}\right) = \frac{125}{36}$.

Chapter Twelve Review

1

a. False. This equation describes a plane in R^3.

b. False. If $2x^2 - 6y^2 > 0$ then $z = \sqrt{2x^2-6y^2}$ or $z = -\sqrt{2x^2-6y^2}$.

c. False. For example $f(x,y) = x^2y$ has $f_{xxy} = 2$, $f_{xyy} = 0$.

d. False. ∇f lies in the xy-plane.

e. True. A normal vector for an orthogonal plane can be found by taking the cross product of normal vectors for the two intersecting planes.

3

a. Let $P = (0,0,3)$, $Q = (1,0,-6)$ and $R = (1,2,3)$. Then the vectors $\overrightarrow{PQ} = \langle 1, 0, -9\rangle$ and $\overrightarrow{PR} = \langle 1, 2, 0\rangle$ lie in the plane, so $\mathbf{n} = \overrightarrow{PQ} \times \overrightarrow{PR} = \begin{vmatrix} \mathbf{i} & \mathbf{j} & \mathbf{k} \\ 1 & 0 & -9 \\ 1 & 2 & 0 \end{vmatrix} = 18\mathbf{i} - 9\mathbf{j} + 2\mathbf{k}$ is normal to the plane. The plane has equation $18x - 9y + 2(z-3) = 0$, which simplifies to $18x - 9y + 2z = 6$.

b. The x-intercept is found by setting $y = z = 0$ and solving $18x = 6$ to obtain $x = \frac{1}{3}$. Similarly, the y and z-intercepts are $y = -\frac{2}{3}$ and $z = 3$.

c.

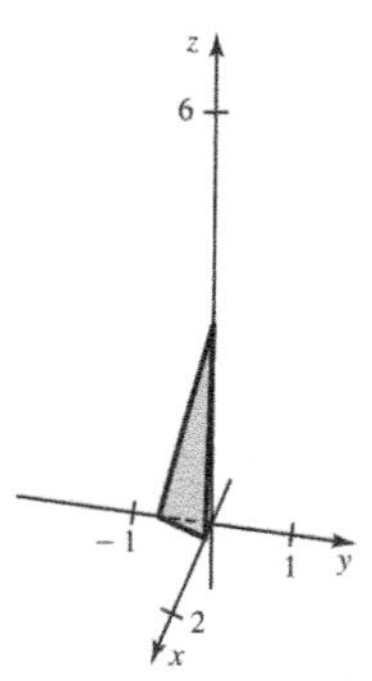

5 First, note that the vectors normal to the planes, $n_Q = \langle -3, 1, 2\rangle$ and $n_R = \langle 3, 3, 4\rangle$ are not multiples of each other; therefore, these planes are not parallel and they intersect in a line ℓ. We need to find a point on ℓ and a vector in the direction of ℓ. Setting $x = 0$ in the equations of the planes gives equations of the lines in which the planes intersect the yz plane: $y + 2z = 0$, $3y + 4z = 12$. Solving these equations simultaneously gives $y = 12$, $z = -6$, so $(0, 12, -6)$ is a point on ℓ. A vector in the direction of ℓ is $\mathbf{n}_Q \times \mathbf{n}_R = \begin{vmatrix} \mathbf{i} & \mathbf{j} & \mathbf{k} \\ -3 & 1 & 2 \\ 3 & 3 & 4 \end{vmatrix} =$ $-2\mathbf{i} + 18\mathbf{j} - 12\mathbf{k} = -2\langle 1, -9, 6\rangle$. Therefore, ℓ has equation $\mathbf{r}(t) = \langle 0, 12, -6\rangle + t\langle 1, -9, 6\rangle = \langle t, 12 - 9t, -6 + 6t\rangle$, or $x = t$, $y = 12 - 9t$, $z = -6 + 6t$.

7 Let $P = (-2, 3, 1)$, $Q = (1, 1, 0)$ and $R = (-1, 0, 1)$. Then the vectors $\overrightarrow{PQ} = \langle 3, -2, -1\rangle$ and $\overrightarrow{PR} = \langle 1, -3, 0\rangle$ lie in the plane, so $\mathbf{n} = \overrightarrow{PQ} \times \overrightarrow{PR} = \begin{vmatrix} \mathbf{i} & \mathbf{j} & \mathbf{k} \\ 3 & -2 & -1 \\ 1 & -3 & 0 \end{vmatrix} = -(3\mathbf{i} + \mathbf{j} + 7\mathbf{k})$ is normal to the plane. The plane has equation $3(x + 2) + 1(y - 3) + 7(z - 1) = 0$, which simplifies to $3x + y + 7z = 4$.

9

a. This surface is a hyperbolic paraboloid.

b. The xy-trace is found by setting $z = 0$ in the equation of the surface, which gives $y = \pm 2x$ (two lines intersecting at the origin). Similarly, we see that the xz-trace is the parabola $z = \frac{x^2}{36}$ and the yz-trace is the parabola $z = -\frac{y^2}{144}$.

c. The x-intercept is found by setting $y = z = 0$ in the equation of the surface, which gives the point $(0, 0, 0)$. Similarly, we see that the y- and z-intercepts are also $(0, 0, 0)$.

d.

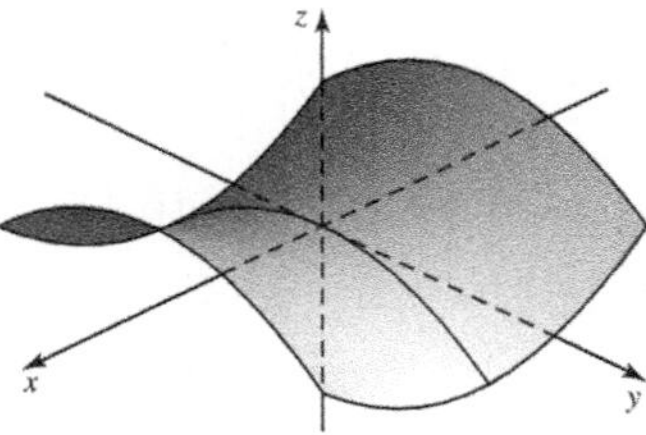

11

a. This surface is an elliptic cone.

b. The xy-trace is found by setting $z = 0$ in the equation of the surface, which gives $y = \pm 2x$ (two lines intersecting at the origin). Similarly, we see that the xz-trace is $(0, 0, 0)$ and the yz-trace is $z = \pm 5y$.

c. The x-intercept is found by setting $y = z = 0$ in the equation of the surface, which gives the point $(0, 0, 0)$. Similarly, we see that the y- and z-intercepts are also $(0, 0, 0)$.

d.

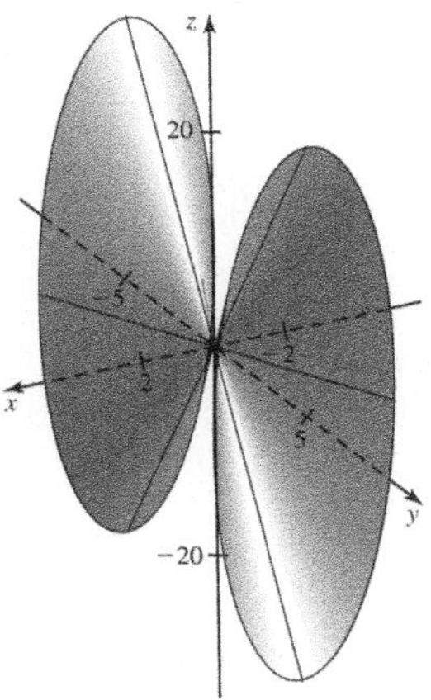

13

a. This surface is an elliptic paraboloid.

b. The xy-trace is found by setting $z = 0$ in the equation of the surface, which gives $(0, 0, 0)$. Similarly, we see that the xz-trace is the parabola $z = \frac{x^2}{16}$, and the yz-trace is the parabola $z = \frac{y^2}{36}$.

c. The x-intercept is found by setting $y = z = 0$ in the equation of the surface, which gives the point $(0, 0, 0)$. Similarly, we see that the y- and z-intercepts are also $(0, 0, 0)$.

d.

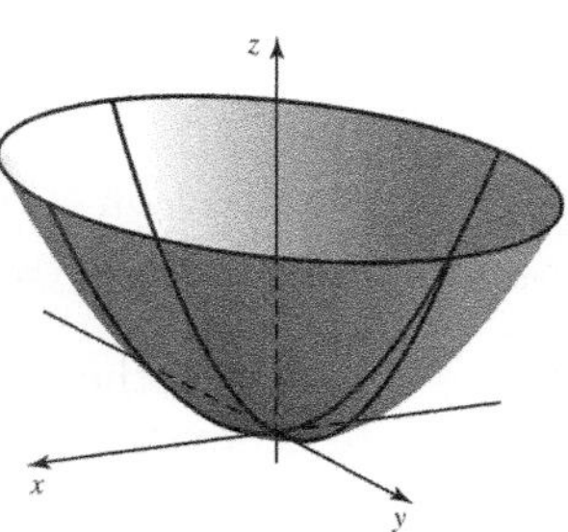

15

a. This surface is a hyperboloid of one sheet.

b. The xy-trace is found by setting $z = 0$ in the equation of the surface, which gives the hyperbola $y^2 - 2x^2 = 1$. Similarly, we see that the xz-trace is the hyperbola $4z^2 - 2x^2 = 1$, and the yz-trace is the ellipse $y^2 + 4z^2 = 1$.

c. The x-intercept is found by setting $y = z = 0$ in the equation of the surface, which gives no solutions. Similarly, we see that the y-intercepts are $(0, \pm 1, 0)$, and the z-intercepts are $\left(0, 0, \pm\frac{1}{2}\right)$.

d.

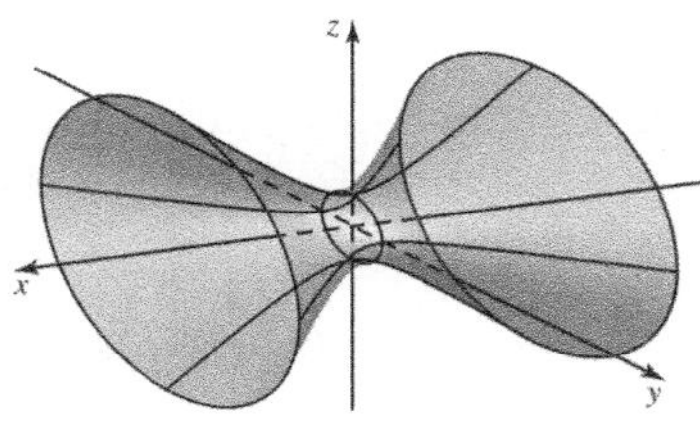

17

a. This surface is a hyperboloid of one sheet.

b. The xy-trace is found by setting $z = 0$ in the equation of the surface, which gives the ellipse $\frac{x^2}{4} + \frac{y^2}{16} = 4$. Similarly, we see that the xz-trace is the hyperbola $\frac{x^2}{4} - z^2 = 4$, and the yz-trace is the hyperbola $\frac{y^2}{16} - z^2 = 4$.

c. The x-intercept is found by setting $y = z = 0$ in the equation of the surface, which gives the points $(\pm 4, 0, 0)$. Similarly, we see that the y-intercepts are $(0, \pm 8, 0)$, and there are no z-intercepts.

d.

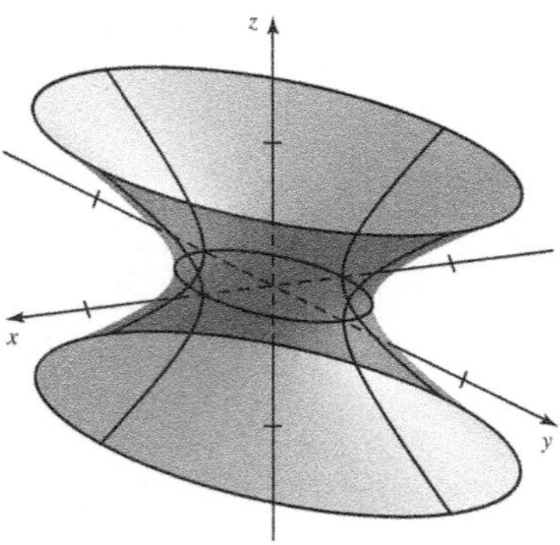

19

a. This surface is an ellipsoid.

b. The xy-trace is found by setting $z = 0$ in the equation of the surface, which gives the ellipse $\frac{x^2}{4} + \frac{y^2}{16} = 4$. Similarly, we see that the xz-trace is the ellipse$\frac{x^2}{4} + z^2 = 4$, and the yz-trace is the ellipse $\frac{y^2}{16} + z^2 = 4$.

c. The x-intercept is found by setting $y = z = 0$ in the equation of the surface, which gives the points $(\pm 4, 0, 0)$. Similarly, we see that the y-intercepts are the points $(0, \pm 8, 0)$, and the z-intercepts are the points $(0, 0, \pm 2)$.

d.

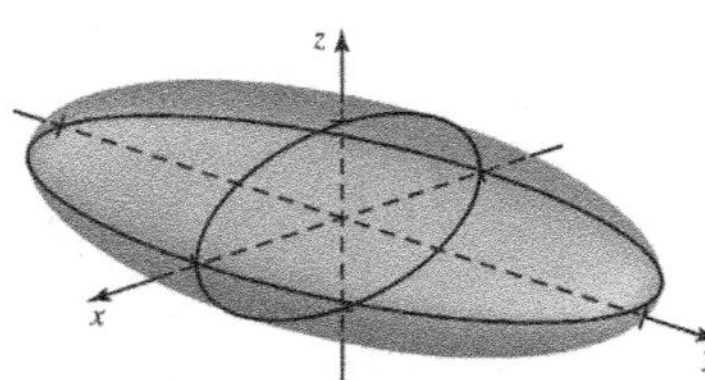

21

a. This surface is an elliptic cone.

b. The xy-trace is found by setting $z = 0$ in the equation of the surface, which gives the origin $(0, 0, 0)$. Similarly, we see that the xz-trace is $z = \pm\frac{8x}{3}$ (two lines intersecting at the origin), and the yz-trace is $y = \pm\frac{7z}{8}$.

c. The x-intercept is found by setting $y = z = 0$ in the equation of the surface, which gives the point $(0, 0, 0)$. Similarly, we see that the y and z-intercepts are also $(0, 0, 0)$.

d.

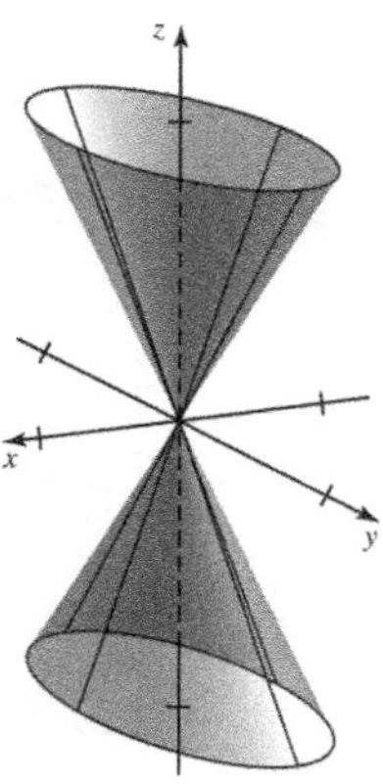

23 The domain is $D = \{(x, y) : (x, y) \neq (0, 0)\}$.

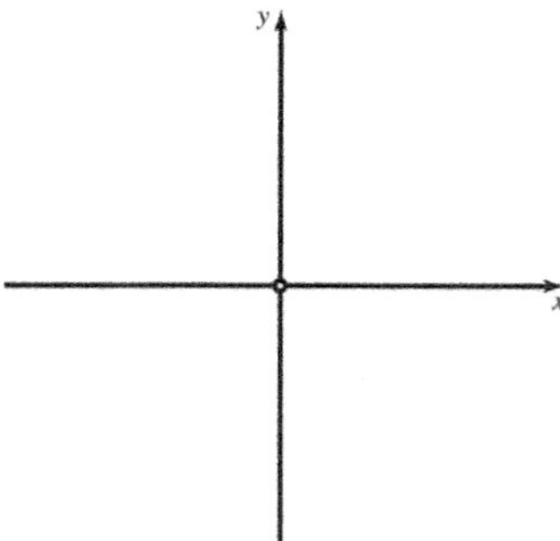

25 The domain is D=$\{(x, y) : x \geq y^2\}$.

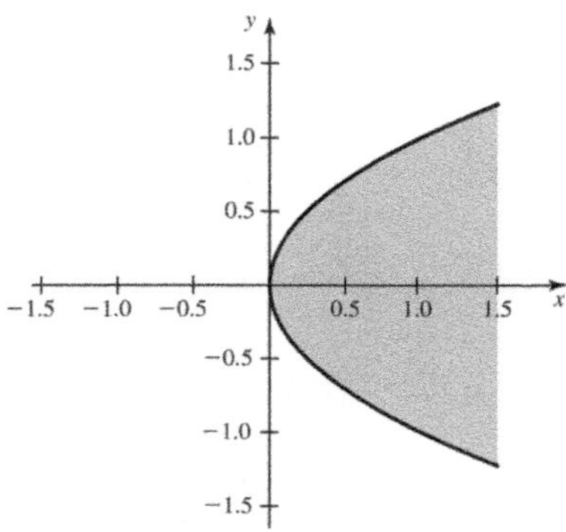

27

a. The graph of this function is part of a hyperboloid of two sheets and contains the origin, which matches A.

b. The graph of this function is a cylinder, which matches D.

c. The graph of this function is a hyperbolic paraboloid, which matches C.

d. The graph of this function is part of a hyperboloid of one sheet, which matches B.

29

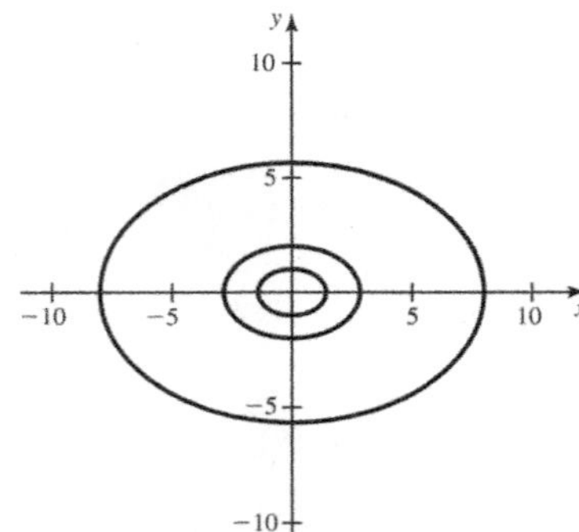

31 This limit may be evaluated directly by substitution: $\lim_{(x,y)\to(4,-2)}(10x-5y+6xy) = 10\cdot 4-5(-2)+6\cdot 4(-2) = 2$.

33 Along the path $y=-x$ we have $\lim_{(x,y)\to(0,0)} f(x,y) = \lim_{(x,y)\to(0,0)} \frac{0}{-x^2} = 0$, but along the path $y=x$ we have $\lim_{(x,y)\to(0,0)} f(x,y) = \lim_{(x,y)\to(0,0)} \frac{2x}{x^2} = \lim_{(x,y)\to(0,0)} \frac{2}{x} \neq 0$, so the limit does not exist.

35 This limit may be evaluated by factoring the numerator and denominator and canceling the common factor $x+y$: $\lim_{(x,y)\to(-1,1)} \frac{x^2-y^2}{x^2-xy-2y^2} = \lim_{(x,y)\to(-1,1)} \frac{(x-y)(x+y)}{(x-2y)(x+y)} = \lim_{(x,y)\to(-1,1)} \frac{x-y}{x-2y} = \frac{2}{3}$.

37 This limit may be evaluated directly by substitution: $\lim_{(x,y,z)\to\left(\frac{\pi}{2},0,\frac{\pi}{2}\right)} 4\cos y \sin\sqrt{xz} = 4(\cos 0)(\sin\left(\frac{\pi}{2}\right) = 4$.

39 $f_x = 6xy^5$, $f_y = 15x^2y^4$.

41 $f_x = \frac{(x^2+y^2)(2x)-x^2(2x)}{(x^2+y^2)^2} = \frac{2xy^2}{(x^2+y^2)^2}$. $f_y = \frac{0-x^2(2y)}{(x^2+y^2)^2} = \frac{-2x^2y}{(x^2+y^2)^2}$.

43 $\frac{\partial}{\partial x}\left[xye^{xy}\right] = ye^{xy}+xy^2e^{xy} = y(1+xy)e^{xy}$, $\frac{\partial}{\partial y}\left[xye^{xy}\right] = xe^{xy}+x^2ye^{xy} = x(1+xy)e^{xy}$.

45 $f_x(x,y,z) = e^{x+2y+3z}$, $f_y(x,y,z) = 2e^{x+2y+3z}$, $f_z(x,y,z) = 3e^{x+2y+3z}$.

47 $\frac{\partial^2 u}{\partial x^2} + \frac{\partial^2 u}{\partial y^2} = 6y-6y = 0$.

49

a. If r is held fixed and R increases then V increases, so $V_R > 0$, whereas, if R is held fixed and r increases then V decreases, so $V_r < 0$.

b. We have $V_R = 4\pi R^2 > 0$ and $V_r = -4\pi r^2 < 0$, consistent with the predictions in part (a).

c. If $R=3$, $r=1$ and R is increased by $\triangle R = 0.1$, then $\triangle V \approx 4\pi\cdot 3^2\cdot 0.1 = 3.6\pi$; if r is decreased by 0.1 then $\triangle V \approx -4\pi\cdot 1^2\cdot(-0.1) = 0.4\pi$. Therefore, the volume changes more if R is increased.

51 The chain rule gives $\frac{dw}{dt} = \frac{\partial w}{\partial x}\frac{dx}{dt} + \frac{\partial w}{\partial y}\frac{dy}{dt} + \frac{\partial w}{\partial z}\frac{dz}{dt} = \frac{x}{\sqrt{x^2+y^2+z^2}}\cdot\cos t + \frac{y}{\sqrt{x^2+y^2+z^2}}\cdot(-\sin t) + \frac{z}{\sqrt{x^2+y^2+z^2}}\cdot(-\sin t) = -\frac{\cos t\sin t}{\sqrt{1+\cos^2 t}}$.

53 The chain rule gives $w_r = w_xx_r + w_yy_r = \frac{1}{x}(st) + \frac{2}{y}(1) = \frac{1}{r} + \frac{2}{r+s} = \frac{3r+s}{r(r+s)}$. $w_s = w_xx_s + w_yy_s = \frac{1}{x}(rt) + \frac{2}{y}(1) = \frac{1}{s} + \frac{2}{r+s} = \frac{r+3s}{s(r+s)}$. $w_t = w_xx_t + w_yy_t = \frac{1}{x}(rs) + \frac{2}{y}\cdot 0 = \frac{1}{t}$.

55 Let $F(x,y) = y\ln(x^2+y^2)-4$; then if y is determined by $F(x,y)=0$, we have $\frac{dy}{dx} = -\frac{F_x}{F_y} = -\frac{\frac{2xy}{x^2+y^2}}{\ln(x^2+y^2)+\frac{2y^2}{x^2+y^2}} = -\frac{2xy}{2y^2+(x^2+y^2)\ln(x^2+y^2)}$.

57

a. The chain rule gives $z'(t) = 2xx'(t) - 4yy'(t) = -24\text{cos}t\text{sin}t = -12\text{sin}2t$.

b. Walking uphill corresponds to $z'(t) > 0$, which occurs when $\frac{\pi}{2} < t < \pi$ and $\frac{3\pi}{2} < t < 2\pi$.

59

a.

	$(a,b) = (0,0)$	$(a,b) = (2,0)$	$(a,b) = (1,1)$
$\mathbf{u} = \langle\sqrt{2}/2, \sqrt{2}/2\rangle$	0	$4\sqrt{2}$	$-2\sqrt{2}$
$\mathbf{v} = \langle-\sqrt{2}/2, \sqrt{2}/2\rangle$	0	$-4\sqrt{2}$	$-6\sqrt{2}$
$\mathbf{w} = \langle-\sqrt{2}/2, -\sqrt{2}/2\rangle$	0	$-4\sqrt{2}$	$2\sqrt{2}$

b. The function is increasing at $(2,0)$ in the direction of $\mathbf{u}$ and decreasing at $(2,0)$ in the directions of $\mathbf{v}$ and $\mathbf{w}$.

61 $\nabla g = \langle 2xy^3, 3x^2y^2\rangle$, so $\nabla g(-1,1) = \langle -2, 3\rangle$. $D_{\mathbf{u}}g(-1,1) = \langle -2,3\rangle \cdot \mathbf{u} = \frac{-10}{13} + \frac{36}{13} = 2$.

63 The gradient of h is given by $\nabla h(x,y) = h_x\mathbf{i} + h_y\mathbf{j} = \frac{1}{\sqrt{2+x^2+2y^2}}(x\mathbf{i} + 2y\mathbf{j})$; therefore, $\nabla h(2,1) = \frac{\sqrt{2}}{2}(\mathbf{i}+\mathbf{j})$ and the directional derivative in the direction of $\mathbf{u}$ is given by $\nabla h(2,1)\cdot\mathbf{u} = \frac{\sqrt{2}}{10}(\mathbf{i}+\mathbf{j})\cdot(3\mathbf{i}+4\mathbf{j}) = \frac{7\sqrt{2}}{10} \approx 0.9899$.

65 The gradient of f is given by $\nabla f(x,y,z) = f_x\mathbf{i} + f_y\mathbf{j} + f_z\mathbf{k} = \cos(x+2y-z)(\mathbf{i}+2\mathbf{j}-\mathbf{k})$; therefore, $\nabla f\left(\frac{\pi}{6}, \frac{\pi}{6}, -\frac{\pi}{6}\right) = -\frac{1}{2}(\mathbf{i}+2\mathbf{j}-\mathbf{k})$ and the directional derivative in the direction of $\mathbf{u}$ is given by $\nabla f\left(\frac{\pi}{6}, \frac{\pi}{6}, -\frac{\pi}{6}\right)\cdot\mathbf{u} = -\frac{1}{6}(\mathbf{i}+2\mathbf{j}-\mathbf{k})\cdot(\mathbf{i}+2\mathbf{j}+2\mathbf{k}) = -\frac{1}{2}$.

67

a. The gradient of f is given by $\nabla f(x,y) = f_x\mathbf{i} + f_y\mathbf{j} = -\frac{1}{\sqrt{4-x^2-y^2}}(x\mathbf{i}+y\mathbf{j})$, so $\nabla f(-1,1) = \frac{1}{\sqrt{2}}(\mathbf{i}-\mathbf{j})$. The direction of steepest ascent is the unit vector in this direction, $\mathbf{u} = \frac{\sqrt{2}}{2}\text{i} - \frac{\sqrt{2}}{2}\text{j}$, and the direction of steepest descent is $-\mathbf{u}$.

b. The unit vectors that point in the direction of no change are $\text{v} = \pm\left(\frac{\sqrt{2}}{2}\mathbf{i} + \frac{\sqrt{2}}{2}\mathbf{j}\right)$, because $\mathbf{u}\cdot\mathbf{v} = 0$.

69 If x is determined by $f(x,y) = C$ we have $\frac{dy}{dx} = -\frac{f_x}{f_y} = -\frac{-2y}{-4x} = \frac{y}{2x}$. Therefore, the level curve $f(x,y) = 0$ has a vertical tangent at the point $(0,0)$, so the tangent line has direction j. The gradient of f at this point is $\nabla f(2,0) = (-4x\mathbf{i} - 2y\mathbf{j})\Big|_{(2,0)} = -8\mathbf{i}$, which is perpendicular to the tangent direction.

71 Observe that $V = -\frac{k}{2}\left(\ln\left(x^2+y^2\right) - \ln R^2\right)$; therefore $\mathbf{E} = -\nabla V = \frac{k}{2}\left(\frac{2x}{x^2+y^2}\mathbf{i} + \frac{2y}{x^2+y^2}\mathbf{j}\right) = \frac{kx}{x^2+y^2}\mathbf{i} + \frac{ky}{x^2+y^2}\mathbf{j}$.

73 Let $f(x,y,z) = x^2 + y^2/4 - z^2/9$. $\nabla f = \langle 2x, y/2, -2z/9\rangle$, so $\nabla f(0,2,0) = \langle 0,1,0\rangle$. The equation of the tangent plane at $(0,2,0)$ is given by $1(y-2) = 0$, or $y = 2$. At the point $(1,1,3/2)$ we have $\nabla f = \langle 2, 1/2, -1/3\rangle$, so the equation of the tangent plane is $2(x-1) + (1/2)(y-1) + (-1/3)(z-3/2) = 0$, or $12x + 3y - 2z = 12$.

75 Let $F(x,y,z) = yze^{xz} - 8$; then $\nabla F(0,2,4) = \langle yz^2e^{xz},\ ze^{xz},\ (y+xyz)e^{xz}\rangle\Big|_{(0,2,4)} = \langle 32,4,2\rangle$, so the tangent plane at $(0,2,4)$ has equation $32x + 4(y-2) + 2(z-4) = 0$, or $16x + 2y + z - 8 = 0$. Similarly, $\nabla F(0,-8,-1) = \langle yz^2e^{xz},\ ze^{xz},\ (y+xyz)e^{xz}\rangle\Big|_{(0,-8,-1)} = \langle -8,-1,-8\rangle$, so the tangent plane at $(0,-8,-1)$ has equation $-8x - (y+8) - 8(z+1) = 0$, or $8x + y + 8z + 16 = 0$.

77 Let $f(x,y) = \ln(1+xy)$; then $f_x(x,y) = \frac{y}{1+xy}$ and $f_y(x,y) = \frac{x}{1+xy}$, so the tangent plane at $(1,2,\ln 3)$ has equation $z = f(1,2) + f_x(1,2)(x-1) + f_y(1,2)(y-2) = \ln 3 + \frac{2}{3}(x-1) + \frac{1}{3}(y-2) = \frac{2}{3}x + \frac{1}{3}y + \ln 3 - \frac{4}{3}$. Similarly, the tangent plane at $(-2,-1,\ln 3)$ has equation $z = f(-2,-1) + f_x(-2,-1)(x+2) + f_y(-2,-1)(y+1) = \ln 3 - \frac{1}{3}(x+2) - \frac{2}{3}(y+1) = -\frac{1}{3}x - \frac{2}{3}y + \ln 3 - \frac{4}{3}$.

79

a. The linear approximation is given by $L(x,y) = f(a,b) + f_x(a,b)(x-a) + f_y(a,b)(y-b) = 2 + (x-2) + 5y = x + 5y$.

b. This gives the estimate $f(1.95, 0.05) \approx 2.2$ (the actual answer is 2.205 to three decimal places).

81 We have $dV = \pi\left(2rhdr + r^2dh\right)$, so $\frac{dV}{V} = 2\frac{dr}{r} + \frac{dh}{h}$. Therefore, if the radius decreases by 3% and the height increases by 2%, the approximate change in volume is -4%.

83

a. We have $dV = \pi\left(2rh - h^2\right)dh = 2\pi(-0.05) = -0.1\pi\text{m}^3$ (notice that $r = 1.50$ m is constant, so there is no contribution from the dr term in dV).

b. The surface of the water is a disc with radius $s = \sqrt{2rh - h^2}$, so the surface area is $S = \pi\left(2rh - h^2\right)$. Therefore $dS = 2\pi(r-h)dh = -0.05\pi\text{m}^2$.

85 We have $f_x = x^2 + 2y$, $f_y = -y^2 + 2x$; therefore, the critical points satisfy the equations $y = -\frac{x^2}{2}$and $x = \frac{y^2}{2}$. Eliminating y gives $x^4 = 8x$ so $x = 0, 2$, and the critical points are $(0,0)$, $(2,-2)$. We also have $f_{xx} = 2x$, $f_{yy} = -2y$ and $f_{xy} = 2$; hence $D(x,y) = -4(1+xy)$. We see that $D(0,0) < 0$ so $(0,0)$ is a saddle. We have $D(2,-2) > 0$, $f_{xx}(2,-2) > 0$, which by the Second Derivative Test implies that f has a local minimum at $(2,-2)$.

87 We have $f_x = -3x^2 - 6x$, $f_y = -3y^2 + 6y$; therefore the critical points must have $x = 0, -2$ and $y = 0, 2$. We also have $f_{xx} = -6x - 6$, $f_{yy} = -6y + 6$ and $f_{xy} = 0$; hence $D(x,y) = 36(x+1)(y-1)$. We see that $D(0,0)$, $D(-2,2) < 0$ so $(0,0)$ and $(-2,2)$ are saddles. We have $D(0,2) > 0$, $f_{xx}(0,2) < 0$, which by the Second Derivative Test implies that f has a local maximum at $(0,2)$; $D(-2,0) > 0$, $f_{xx}(-2,0) > 0$, which by the Second Derivative Test implies that f has a local minimum at $(-2,0)$.

89 First we find the critical points of f inside the square R: we have $f_x = 4x^3 - 4y$, $f_y = 4y^3 - 4x$; the equation $f_x = 0$ gives $y = x^3$, and then substituting this in the equation $f_y = 0$ gives $x^9 = x$, or $x = 0, \pm 1$. Hence, the critical points are $(0,0)$ and $\pm(1,1)$, which are all in the interior of R. We observe that the values of f at these points are $f(0,0) = 1$, $f(1,1) = f(-1,-1) = -1$. Next we must find the maximum and minimum values of f on the boundary of R, which consists of four segments. On the segment $-2 \le x \le 2$, $y = 2$, let $g(x) = f(x,2) = x^4 - 8x + 17$: then g has a critical point at $x = \sqrt[3]{2}$, and find that g has extreme values $17 - 6\sqrt[3]{2}$ and 49 on $[0,3]$. We also note that $f(y,x) = f(-x,-y) = f(x,y)$; therefore f takes the same values on all four segments of the square. Hence, the absolute minimum and maximum values of f on R are $f(1,1) = f(-1,-1) = -1$ and $f(2,-2) = f(-2,2) = 49$.

91 First we find the critical points of f inside the semicircle. We have $f_x = y$ and $f_y = x$, so the only critical point is $(0,0)$, where the value of f is 0. On the flat part of the semicircle where $y = 0$, the value of f is also 0. Now we parametrize the circular part of the boundary by letting $x = \cos t$, $y = \sin t$ for $0 \le t \le \pi$. Then $f(x,y) = g(t) = \cos t \sin t$, and $g'(t) = -\sin^2 t + \cos^2 t$. This is zero for $t = \pi/4$ and $t = 3\pi/4$, where the value of f is $1/2$ and $-1/2$, respectively. Thus, the absolute maximum of f is $1/2$ at $(\sqrt{2}/2, \sqrt{2}/2)$ and the absolute minimum is $-1/2$ at $(-\sqrt{2}/2, \sqrt{2}/2)$.

93 We have $\nabla f = \langle 2, 1\rangle$ and $\nabla g = \langle 4(x-1), 8(y-1)\rangle$, where $g(x,y) = 2(x-1)^2 + 4(y-1)^2$. The Lagrange equations are thus $2 = 4\lambda(x-1)$, $1 = 8\lambda(y-1)$, and $2(x-1)^2 + 4(y-1)^2 = 1$. Solving gives $\lambda = 3/4$, $x = 5/3$, and $y = 7/6$, or $\lambda = -3/4$, $x = 1/3$, and $y = 5/6$. The maximum for f is $f(5/3, 7/6) = 29/2$ and the minimum for f is $f(1/3, 5/6) = 23/2$.

95 The Lagrange multiplier conditions are $1 = 2\lambda x$, $2 = 2\lambda y$, $-1 = 2\lambda z$, $x^2 + y^2 + z^2 = 1$. Hence $2\lambda = \frac{1}{x} = \frac{2}{y} = -\frac{1}{z} \Longrightarrow y = 2x$, $z = -x$; substituting these in the constraint gives $6x^2 = 1$ so $x = \pm\frac{\sqrt{6}}{6}$ and we obtain solutions $\pm\left(\frac{\sqrt{6}}{6}, \frac{\sqrt{6}}{3}, -\frac{\sqrt{6}}{6}\right)$. Therefore the extreme values of f on the closed bounded set given by $x^2 + y^2 + z^2 = 1$ are $f\left(\frac{\sqrt{6}}{6}, \frac{\sqrt{6}}{3}, -\frac{\sqrt{6}}{6}\right) = \sqrt{6}$, $f\left(-\frac{\sqrt{6}}{6}, -\frac{\sqrt{6}}{3}, \frac{\sqrt{6}}{6}\right) = -\sqrt{6}$.

97 Let (x, y) be the corner of the rectangle in the first quadrant; then the perimeter of the rectangle is $4(x + y)$, so it suffices to find the maximum value of $x + y$ subject to the constraint $\frac{x^2}{a^2} + \frac{y^2}{b^2} = 1$. The Lagrange multiplier conditions are $1 = \frac{2\lambda x}{a^2}$, $1 = \frac{2\lambda y}{b^2}$, $\frac{x^2}{a^2} + \frac{y^2}{b^2} = 1$. Hence, $2\lambda = \frac{a^2}{x} = \frac{b^2}{y} \Longrightarrow y = \frac{b^2 x}{a^2}$; substituting in the constraint gives $x^2\left(a^2 + b^2\right) = a^4$ so $x = \frac{a^2}{\sqrt{a^2+b^2}}$, $y = \frac{b^2}{\sqrt{a^2+b^2}}$, and the dimensions of the rectangle with greatest perimeter are $\frac{2a^2}{\sqrt{a^2+b^2}}$ by $\frac{2b^2}{\sqrt{a^2+b^2}}$.

99 It suffices to minimize the function $f(x, y, z) = (x-1)^2 + (y-3)^2 + (z-1)^2$ subject to the constraint $x^2 + y^2 - z^2 = 0$. The Lagrange multiplier conditions are equivalent to $x - 1 = \lambda x$, $y - 3 = \lambda y$, $z - 1 = -\lambda z$, $x^2 + y^2 - z^2 = 0$. The first two equations give $\lambda xy = (x-1)\,y = (y-3)\,x \Longrightarrow y = 3x$ and similarly, the first and third equations give $\lambda xz = (x-1)\,z = -x\,(z-1) \Longrightarrow (2x-1)\,z = x \Rightarrow z = \sqrt{10}x$. Substituting these equations in the constraint gives $(2x-1)^2 \cdot 10x^2 = x^2$, so either $x = 0$ (and hence $y = z = 0$ as well) or $10\,(2x-1)^2 = 1$, which has solutions $x = \frac{1}{2} \pm \frac{\sqrt{10}}{20}$. Therefore, there are three solutions to the Lagrange conditions: $(0,0,0)$, $\left(\frac{1}{2} \pm \frac{\sqrt{10}}{20}, \frac{3}{2} \pm \frac{3\sqrt{10}}{20}, \frac{1}{2} \pm \frac{\sqrt{10}}{2}\right)$. We see that $f(0,0,0) = 11$, $f\left(\frac{1}{2} \pm \frac{\sqrt{10}}{20}, \frac{3}{2} \pm \frac{3\sqrt{10}}{20}, \frac{1}{2} \pm \frac{\sqrt{10}}{2}\right) = \frac{11}{2} \mp \sqrt{10}$, so the closest point is $\left(\frac{1}{2} + \frac{\sqrt{10}}{20}, \frac{3}{2} + \frac{3\sqrt{10}}{20}, \frac{1}{2} + \frac{\sqrt{10}}{2}\right)$. (The function $f(x, y, z) \to \infty$ as either x, y or $z \to \infty$ on the cone; therefore, f must have minimum somewhere on the cone, which corresponds to the point we found.)

GRAPHS OF ELEMENTARY FUNCTIONS

Linear functions

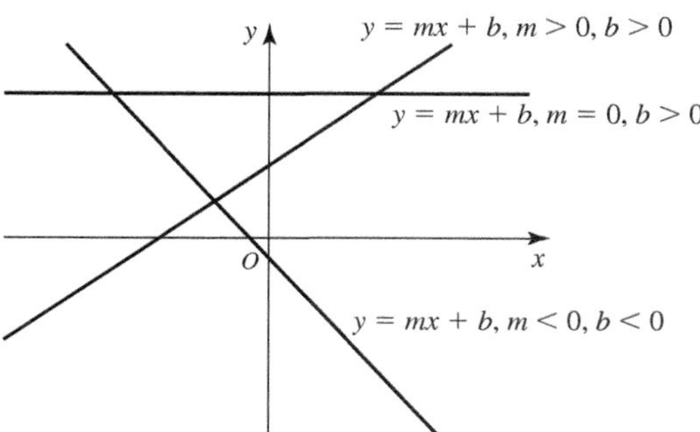

Quadratic functions

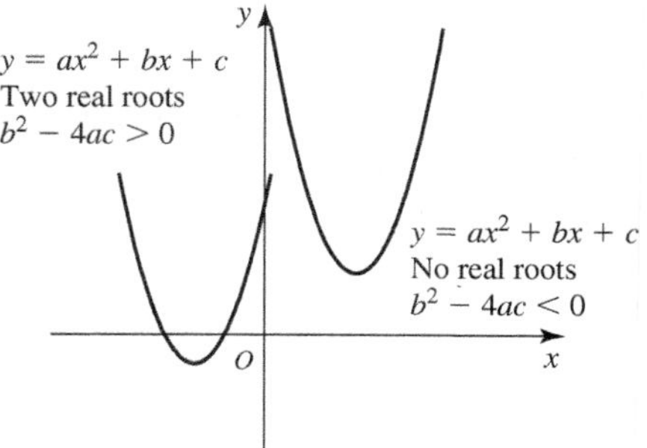

Positive even powers

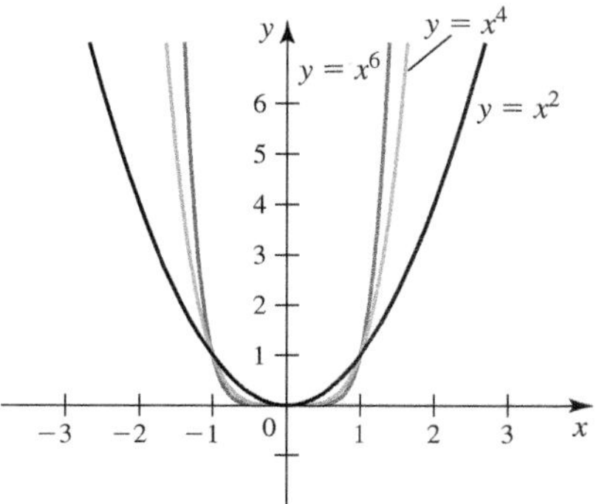

Positive odd powers

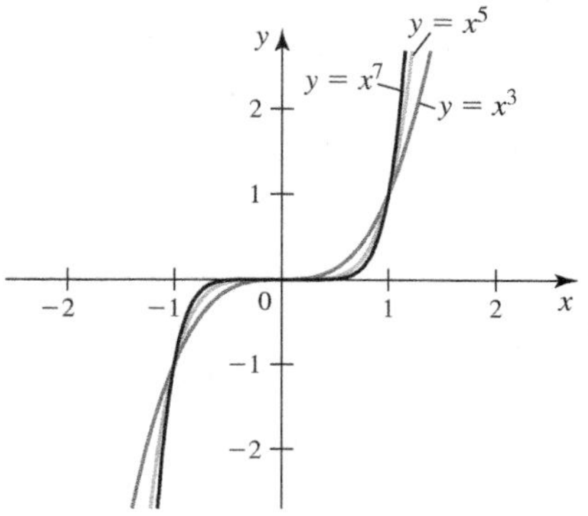

Negative even powers

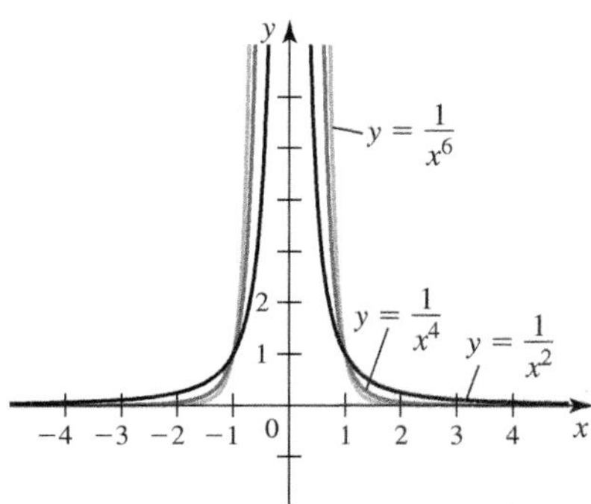

Negative odd powers

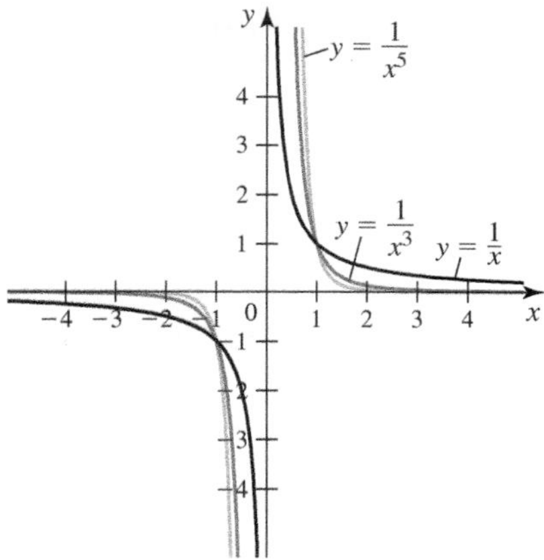

Exponential functions

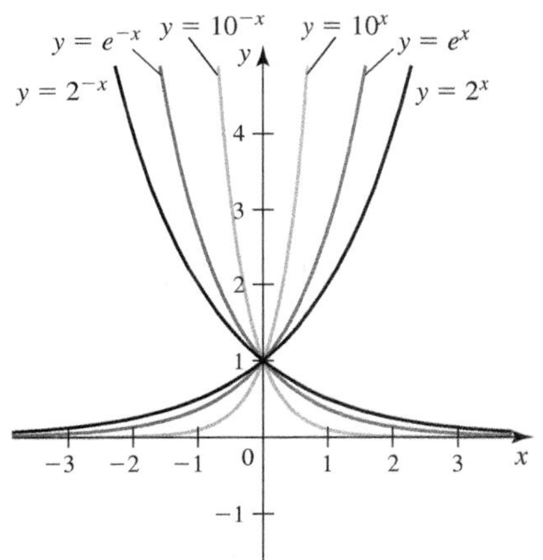

Natural logarithmic and exponential functions

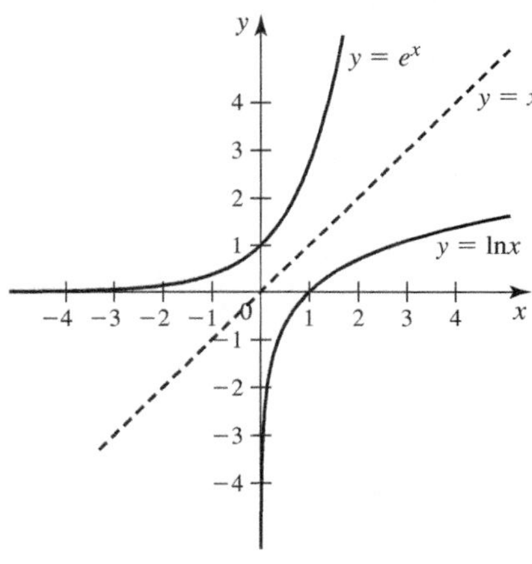

DERIVATIVES

General Formulas

$$\frac{d}{dx}(c) = 0$$
$$\frac{d}{dx}(cf(x)) = cf'(x)$$
$$\frac{d}{dx}(f(x) + g(x)) = f'(x) + g'(x)$$
$$\frac{d}{dx}(f(x) - g(x)) = f'(x) - g'(x)$$
$$\frac{d}{dx}(f(x)g(x)) = f'(x)g(x) + f(x)g'(x)$$
$$\frac{d}{dx}\left(\frac{f(x)}{g(x)}\right) = \frac{g(x)f'(x) - f(x)g'(x)}{(g(x))^2}$$
$$\frac{d}{dx}(x^n) = nx^{n-1}, \text{ for real numbers } n$$
$$\frac{d}{dx}[f(g(x))] = f'(g(x)) \cdot g'(x)$$

Trigonometric Functions

$$\frac{d}{dx}(\sin x) = \cos x$$
$$\frac{d}{dx}(\cos x) = -\sin x$$
$$\frac{d}{dx}(\tan x) = \sec^2 x$$
$$\frac{d}{dx}(\cot x) = -\csc^2 x$$
$$\frac{d}{dx}(\sec x) = \sec x \tan x$$
$$\frac{d}{dx}(\csc x) = -\csc x \cot x$$

Inverse Trigonometric Functions

$$\frac{d}{dx}(\sin^{-1} x) = \frac{1}{\sqrt{1 - x^2}}$$
$$\frac{d}{dx}(\cos^{-1} x) = -\frac{1}{\sqrt{1 - x^2}}$$
$$\frac{d}{dx}(\tan^{-1} x) = \frac{1}{1 + x^2}$$
$$\frac{d}{dx}(\cot^{-1} x) = -\frac{1}{1 + x^2}$$
$$\frac{d}{dx}(\sec^{-1} x) = \frac{1}{|x|\sqrt{x^2 - 1}}$$
$$\frac{d}{dx}(\csc^{-1} x) = -\frac{1}{|x|\sqrt{x^2 - 1}}$$

Exponential and Logarithmic Functions

$$\frac{d}{dx}(e^x) = e^x$$
$$\frac{d}{dx}(b^x) = b^x \ln b$$
$$\frac{d}{dx}(\ln |x|) = \frac{1}{x}$$
$$\frac{d}{dx}(\log_b x) = \frac{1}{x \ln b}$$

Hyperbolic Functions

$$\frac{d}{dx}(\sinh x) = \cosh x$$
$$\frac{d}{dx}(\cosh x) = \sinh x$$
$$\frac{d}{dx}(\tanh x) = \operatorname{sech}^2 x$$
$$\frac{d}{dx}(\coth x) = -\operatorname{csch}^2 x$$
$$\frac{d}{dx}(\operatorname{sech} x) = -\operatorname{sech} x \tanh x$$
$$\frac{d}{dx}(\operatorname{csch} x) = -\operatorname{csch} x \coth x$$

Inverse Hyperbolic Functions

$$\frac{d}{dx}(\sinh^{-1} x) = \frac{1}{\sqrt{x^2 + 1}}$$
$$\frac{d}{dx}(\cosh^{-1} x) = \frac{1}{\sqrt{x^2 - 1}} \quad (x > 1)$$
$$\frac{d}{dx}(\tanh^{-1} x) = \frac{1}{1 - x^2} \quad (|x| < 1)$$
$$\frac{d}{dx}(\coth^{-1} x) = \frac{1}{1 - x^2} \quad (|x| > 1)$$
$$\frac{d}{dx}(\operatorname{sech}^{-1} x) = -\frac{1}{x\sqrt{1 - x^2}} \quad (0 < x < 1)$$
$$\frac{d}{dx}(\operatorname{csch}^{-1} x) = -\frac{1}{|x|\sqrt{1 + x^2}} \quad (x \neq 0)$$